LIGHT
of the MOON

Also by Luanne Rice

LUANNE RICE

LIGHT

of the MOON

DOUBLEDAY LARGE PRINT HOME LIBRARY EDITION

Bantam Books

This Large Print Edition, prepared especially for Doubleday Large Print Home Library, contains the complete, unabridged text of the original Publisher's Edition.

LIGHT OF THE MOON
A Bantam Book / February 2008

Published by Bantam Dell
A Division of Random House, Inc.
New York, New York

Bantam Books is a registered trademark of Random House, Inc., and the colophon is a trademark of Random House, Inc.

ISBN: 978-0-7394-9202-4

Printed in the United States of America
Published simultaneously in Canada

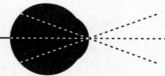

This Large Print Book carries the
Seal of Approval of N.A.V.H.

*To Karen Covert
with love*

LIGHT
of the MOON

PROLOGUE

She ran out the kitchen door into the darkness and fog, hearing her own footsteps pounding in her ears. She slipped, caught herself, kept running. Her shoulder seared—she could still feel her mother's strong hand, shoving her away, shoving her down. She tugged at the barn door; it was so heavy, and the handle was too high. When she got it open, she smelled the horses and heard them rustling in their stalls. They sensed disaster—they knew her mother was leaving, knew she had to try to stop her.

Her heart was racing. She'd heard the voices whispering. They woke her up and she'd thought it was a dream, but then she'd looked out the window and seen the bags, known in the pit of her stomach that something bad was happening. She was down the stairs in seconds and flew to her mother in the doorway, grabbing her hand.

But he was waiting in the yard, his big ugly face and bristly moustache telling her mother to hurry, they had to go. And her mother had locked furious eyes with her—as if she was angry her child loved her so much, as if she felt rage because her daughter didn't want her to go—and she'd pushed her away, sent her stumbling back into the wall.

Sari had cried out for her father, but there was no time. Her mother was running across the yard, climbing into the car. Sari had flown outside, known she had to catch up, realized Mystère was the only way.

The big white horse tossed her head. No time for a saddle or bridle; just a scramble up the rough boards, a jump onto her back. Small hands tangled in the mane. Her mother's favorite horse, so much bigger than her own pony.

Sari clucked her tongue, making Mystère

move. Out of the barn, into the blackness. Fog swirled off the marsh; it was night, pitch dark, and rain was starting to fall. She rode blindly, by instinct, toward the road, her ears straining for the sound of the car.

All she could hear were hoofbeats and the pounding of the rain. It soaked her clothes through to her skin, made her hair fall into her eyes. Her shoulder burned, and the raindrops felt like needles, and she wanted her mother to pull her off the horse and dry her with a towel and say she was so sorry for hurting her. She wanted to feel the rough towel and her mother's soft hands, and she wanted it right now.

"Mama!" she called.

She kicked Mystère once, then again, to make her move. Riding was as easy as walking—she'd grown up doing it. But now it was night, and she'd been sound asleep, and the fury in her mother's face and the thrust of her hand had shocked her into numbness. She thought she heard her mother whispering to the man, but it was just wind whispering through the reeds. Mist rising from the creeks and lagoon made it impossible to see. She knew they had reached the main road only because the horse's hoofbeats suddenly sounded sharp instead of soft.

The only sounds: hoofbeats and rain and the rustling marsh grass.

And then, up ahead: glowing monster eyes.

Red, burning through the fog, staring straight at her. But instead of being afraid, she felt her heart leap. She wasn't too late. She was awake, this wasn't a dream, she wasn't too late.

She kicked the horse, and felt her take off as if she knew, as if Mystère knew even more than she did. She'd never gone so fast—a pure gallop, hoofbeats clanging in her ears, the storm wind rising and shrieking, or was that her own voice? The rain came down hard, stinging her eyes and blurring her vision.

The red eyes winked, blinked—brake lights being tapped. Her skin drenched, hair dripping, mouth wide open and filling with tears so fast she might choke, might not be able to get the words out. Getting closer, she saw the car beginning to pull away.

She saw the beautiful face—turned half-around, looking over the back of the car seat, out the back window, arm reached out as if to touch her. She kicked Mystère faster, faster.

"Mama!" she heard herself wail, letting go of Mystère's flowing mane as she leaned forward, reaching out to her mother with all her might.

But the car pulled away, faster than any horse could gallop, its lights receding. Fog and rain and night filled the distance be-tween them, swallowing the car and making it invisible, and she was crying so hard she didn't hear the other car coming, didn't hear the wheels splashing up water. And then she was flying through the air as the big white horse suddenly dodged sideways on the glittering wet pavement.

But she had no wings, this wasn't a dream, and the whispering voices had been real, and the bags had been real, and the vi-olent shove had been real, and the red eyes had belonged to a monster that had come to destroy her family. She catapulted over the horse's head and opened her mouth to scream, but it never came out.

The scream went in instead of out, and it

was caught inside, the scream was trapped inside, and she hit the ground and broke into pieces, and she saw those glowing red eyes, and then the world turned to gray.

ONE

Air France 321, scheduled to leave Boston's Logan Airport at 7:50 that night, was full. Susannah Connolly sat in seat 22A; she had her tray table stowed, seat in the upright position, and carry-on bag tucked under the seat in front of her. She'd slipped her passport into her jacket pocket, and at this very moment, she was missing a surprise party—hers.

Her seat belt was tightly buckled. She had the window seat, and two strangers— a couple, whispering comfortably to each other—had the middle and aisle. She had a novel, a magazine, and a guidebook to read. She hoped the party guests were enjoying champagne and birthday cake. She couldn't think of many things she felt less equipped to do than pretend to be having fun at her own surprise party.

Every seat on the plane was taken. The captain's voice crackled over the loudspeaker, telling them they were third in line for takeoff. His French accent was soft, alluring, and sexy, but she barely noticed.

Staring out the window, she felt the plane begin to move, its wheels bumping slowly along the accessway. Susannah traveled a lot. Her passport had been stamped so often, the customs officials had to search for a clean page. Work had taken her away from home a hundred times in the last few years. But this was different—brand new territory: this was a journey for herself, to connect with her mother.

Her mother . . . Although she had died six months earlier, it still didn't seem real.

Susannah was a cultural anthropologist, on the fast track in a competitive field. She taught at Connecticut College, but this was a sabbatical year. Her specialty was cave paintings—specifically those with a spiritual bent—with a concentration on horse illustrations. Cave dwellers had looked to the sun, the sea, the great bear, the forest deer, the blue whale, the wild horse. They'd created saints before the birth of the church, and she'd always been impressed and moved by the inspiration they'd found in the world around them.

Susannah had traveled the world to crawl, wriggle, dive, and spelunk into the planet's deepest, most hidden crevasses— dark, usually slimy, frequently precarious holes, where other humans had gone before, to leave messages, stories, splashes of hope, despair, and beauty.

She had crawled deeper into caves than anyone else would dare to go. She'd lie on her stomach, inching forward as the rock walls closed in on her, fighting claustrophobia, knowing that if only she made it a few feet farther, she'd be rewarded with the sight of something no one had seen in thousands of years.

Ian had seemed to understand. He'd often traveled with her, but rarely entered the caves; he'd wait outside, review the data she sent back via the miracle of fiber optics. He'd had a phobia of being trapped, and no matter how hard he'd fought it, he couldn't overcome the fear—but it hadn't mattered; his analysis of the images had been without peer.

Susannah had met him when they were both grad students at Yale. They'd started out studying together; they took the same classes, had the same professors. The work was hard, so they encouraged each other. Susannah would get lost in her research, the love of her subject matter, and Ian would remind her to apply for grants, submit her work to journals.

Once they were studying in his room, and Susannah fell asleep on his bed. It was December, just before break, and an icy draft was coming through the old windows. She woke up to find him curled beside her, and she pressed against him for warmth. They lay there for a long time, and then he began to kiss her.

His arms were around her. She felt so cold and tired, and she knew she should stop him. But he stroked her hair, and whispered that he'd been feeling this way for so long. Susannah let him hold her, shivering in the cold. Her father had died not long before, and she'd buried herself in work, and she felt starved for closeness.

Susannah remembered that moment so well—the instant they'd gone from good friends and work partners to something confusing. They studied so well together, balanced each other out. She delved deeply into the raw subject matter, and he organized the material. They worked separately on their own dissertations, but coauthored several papers published in journals. Ian never missed a chance to publish. . . .

Ian gave her jade earrings for Christmas, red roses for Valentine's Day. Susannah had felt herself becoming part of a couple—almost by accident. She had so much in common with Ian. He was always there. Curious about her work, involved in her research, interested in her discoveries, sympathetic when they found her mother had lymphoma.

But was this love? He began talking about what they'd do after leaving Yale. There seemed to be an assumption that they'd be making decisions together. And since he had his mind set on Stanford, Susannah felt herself being pulled to the West Coast. She'd resisted at the time—told Ian she wanted to accept a position at Connecticut College.

He hadn't understood, but he also hadn't given up. Although they'd made their academic homes on opposite coasts, Ian kept trying to convince her they should be together. Years went by; they both advanced, working together on projects when they could. He kept up his campaign, telling her they already knew each other so well; they were passionate about the same field; and he'd spoken with the publisher of an academic press, who thought the idea of a couple visiting sites together could make a wonderful series of books.

Susannah's mother had tried not to laugh when she told her.

"Oh, darling," Susannah's mother said. "How romantic . . . he's courting you with a book deal!"

"Mom," Susannah had warned.

Margaret Connolly chuckled. She was thin and pale, her skin yellowed from the disease and treatment. But her eyes were as bright and blue as ever.

"Sweetheart, tell me your hopes and dreams . . ."

"About what, Mom?"

"About everything."

They were sitting in the oncologist's office

on Temple Street, waiting for Margaret Connolly to be seen. Her lymphoma had come
back. It had been in remission for years, but
now it had returned and spread. Susannah
sat by her side, waiting to hear the results of
the latest radiation treatments. At that moment, she wanted never to leave Connecticut again. She wanted to be with her mother
every second she had left.

"My hopes and dreams? To plant a garden, to walk on the beach, to ride again . . .
on a beautiful white horse . . ."

"Those are mine, too," her mother whispered.

"We'll do them together," Susannah said.

"Okay," her mother said, smiling. "Maybe
we'll finally take that trip together . . ."

"The Camargue!" Susannah exclaimed.
"To see Sarah! Could we? Do you really
think . . ."

Her mother just looked over, her gaze full
of love and sadness.

"No," Susannah said, answering her own
question. "No, we'll stay home instead.
We'll garden, and walk on the beach . . ."

Her mother shook her head. "No, Susannah . . . that's not how it will be."

"What do you mean?"

"I mean that you're not going to stay home and wait. . . . I want you to take that trip."

"Mom. Not without you."

"Yes, sweetheart. And others, too. Your work takes you where you need to be, and that's how I want it."

"Not now, though," Susannah said. "I should cancel everything. Lascaux, Istanbul . . ."

"Listen to me. You're the best daughter anyone's ever had. I know you'd do anything you could to make me well. You'd find a cure for cancer if you could, and I know that. But that's not your work . . ."

"Work doesn't matter now," Susannah whispered.

"Yes," her mother said, nodding. "It does. Life's work matters so much. It's the distillation of who you are, what you believe. You care about the past, because you love everything and everyone, and you want to learn all there is to know."

"You taught me to be that way."

"I tried," her mother said. "Your father and I both did. And we're so proud of who you've become. So don't hold back now, Susannah. . . . Go see Sarah."

"Maybe Ian and I should—"

"Not Ian," her mother said, her voice surprisingly sharp.

Susannah looked deeply into her mother's blue eyes.

"You think Ian is as passionate about anthropology as you are," her mother said. "But he's not. He's ambitious, darling. There's a difference."

If Susannah hadn't already known that, her mother's words might not have rung so true. The more Ian pushed, the more Susannah pulled back. And then early last fall, on a trip to Lascaux, he'd unexpectedly arrived and surprised her with a question. Susannah sat back in her seat, eyes closed, remembering it now.

He'd planned so well; he'd known how excited she'd be after exploring a new chamber, seeing cave paintings she'd never seen before. And he knew, too, how worried she was about her mother. Susannah had continued her work, her travels, because her mother insisted. But her entire spirit was pulled home, every minute. She felt ripped in half.

Susannah walked out of the cave, and Ian caught her in his arms. She was sweaty, covered with dirt, but he didn't seem to care. He held her, listening to her describe the delicate drawings, the subtle colors. She'd seen images of a mother and children, close by the fire, and tears streamed down her cheeks as she thought of her own mother.

"Those drawings," he said, "are our future."

"Our what?"

"You'll document them, I'll get everything ready for the publisher. We're a team, Susannah. You don't want to come to Stanford—fine. We'll go somewhere else, but we'll do it together. It just makes so much sense. . . ."

"Ian . . ." She wanted to ask him: *Weren't you listening to me?* But she held the words inside. He just kept talking, making his plans, and she stood there, rocked by the beautiful, ancient paintings of a mother and her family.

"What's wrong?" he asked, finally noticing her tears.

"I'm just thinking of my mother," she said.

He stood there, silent for a moment. She suddenly felt overwhelmed. She wanted him to hold her tight, understand the grief she felt—knowing her mother's illness was advancing, and there was nothing they could do.

"You're so sad," he said.

"I am," she'd whispered. Something about the cave, the earth, the almost eternal quality of the paintings, had made the idea of losing her mother all the more vivid.

"Susannah, maybe if you rethought your priorities . . . made other choices . . ."

"What are you talking about?"

"Taking time for the people you love. Relationships," Ian said, "take work. Even now, with your mother dying, it was your choice to come here . . ."

"God, stop!"

"I want us to be together," he said. "Really together. Working, traveling . . ."

She stared, in shock.

"Will you marry me, Susannah?"

"Oh, Ian . . ." She felt her eyes flood again. He knew by her non-answer what her true answer was. They stared at each other for a long moment. Susannah's face was streaked with dirt and tears. Ian looked immaculate, as always.

"You're making the wrong choice," he

said, and it sounded like a warning. "But then, I've watched you do that for years."

Sitting on the plane, Susannah thought of Ian. He was for the most part gone from her life now—she'd told him she needed a break, and although he'd made some recent overtures, they hadn't seen each other since then. But his words haunted her.

After fighting the cancer so hard for so long, her mother had died. Susannah had been in Istanbul. She'd rushed back from the Pavan Caves, but she'd been too late. And now in April, half a year later, it was Susannah's birthday, the first without her mother, and she'd known it was finally time to take that trip. . . .

"Flight attendants, prepare for takeoff," the pilot said in French.

The cabin lights dimmed. The big jet began to lumber down the runway. Slow, faster, gathering speed. The engines droned and roared. Susannah's seat shook slightly. The plane rose.

When she'd lost her mother, she'd lost her cheering section. She could hear her mother's voice; after returning home from Lascaux, Susannah had told her what he'd said, and her mother had replied, eyes flashing, "Ian doesn't know us, sweetheart. How could he even try to make you feel guilty? You don't, do you?"

"He said it was my choice . . . to go to France, instead of staying with you."

"What does he know? Besides, he's not your true love."

"What if he is?" Susannah had asked.

Her mother had smiled, taken her hand. "If he was, you'd know it by now."

"I hope you're right."

"You'll feel it—with someone else, when the time is right," her mother had said. "It will have nothing to do with your head, so stop thinking about it. You'll feel it in your heart."

As the plane gained altitude, nose pointing into the sky, Susannah's back pressed into the seat. She stared out the window, gazing down through the darkness at the beautiful yellow lights painting New England, highways straight and roads winding, neighborhoods hugging the coastline, the great black expanse of the North Atlantic stretching out beneath them in never-ending waves as the plane flew on and left the eastern seaboard of the United States—

and her surprise party back in Black Hall—
far behind.

With her mother gone, Connecticut
seemed cold and empty. Susannah had
missed the chance to say goodbye. But
there was another place, where Susannah
knew she could find her mother's spirit. . . .
They had always talked of going there together, but then it was too late. Before her
death, Margaret Connolly had made her
only child promise to make the trip herself.
Until now, that promise had never been
kept.

Flying east, Susannah thought of her
mother, and slept.

Hours later, after landing in Paris and connecting to Arles, Susannah drove out of the
rental car lot, both hands on the wheel.
Black parasol pines and olive trees, leaves
pale green and silvery, lined the sides of the
road.

Arles was a canvas by van Gogh: wild colors everywhere. Terracotta terraces, ochre
and sepia walls, houses the color of sunflowers, the shadowed black arches of the
Arènes. It was a celebratory city, light ex-

ploding from the river's surface and reflecting in bright shimmers on ancient Roman walls, markets alive with produce and flowers so beautiful they might have been painted by Vincent himself. Susannah bought a fresh almond croissant from the *boulangerie;* passing a market stall selling brightly colored silks and other fabrics, she stopped. On a whim, she bought herself a birthday present: a red hair ribbon.

Tying the ribbon around her hair, she left the city behind, pulled onward by sea. She was going to the Camargue, the starkly beautiful area of southern France where the water and the land seemed to merge in an endless expanse of silver. Helen Oakes— the head of the anthropology department, and Susannah's boss and mentor—had offered Susannah an apartment in Arles, but she'd declined and rented a place sight unseen off the Internet.

Helen had tried to insist—Susannah had promised to do a small amount of work while she was over here, to review documents at a particular library that Helen had been unable to visit herself. She'd said the apartment loan was the least she could do, but Susannah had thanked her and remained firm. She needed to be on her own.

Right now she held on to the promise she'd made her mother: to visit Sarah.

Susannah's family history included a miracle performed by a slave girl. Her parents, unable to conceive after ten years of marriage, had taken a vacation to the Camargue. While there, they had stumbled upon an ancient church in a seaside town. Inside they'd found a statue of a not-quite-official saint imbued with healing, holy powers. Susannah's mother had knelt by the statue, unbelieving but with the sort of desperation known to attract miracles.

The town itself was full of grace, named for three Marys: legend had it that in A.D. 45, a group of Christians was forced onto a small boat without sails and set adrift in the Sea of Galilee. They included Mary Magdalene; Mary Salome, mother of the apostles John and James; Mary Jacoby, sister of the Virgin; Saint Martha; Lazarus; and an Egyptian slave girl named Sarah. Swept along through storms and hundreds of miles, their small boat at last washed ashore on the coast of the Camargue.

While pilgrims from all over came to

beg the Marys for help and healing, Susannah's mother had been drawn to the statue of Sarah, the slave girl. Carved of black wood, her face was humble and sweet, her head and shoulders were draped with ribbons and tinsel, and her bare feet were surrounded by handwritten prayers and dozens of glowing votive candles—offerings left by her own devoted followers. Susannah's mother had fallen to her knees, touched by the thought of this young girl, so far from her home.

Margaret Connolly believed their daughter had been conceived that very night. Growing up, Susannah had heard the story of Sarah, almost too mystical and dangerous for a young girl to comprehend. She had loved it, especially along with the stories about the white horses.

The famous white horses of the Camargue had also been part of Susannah's family fairy tale, a mixture of story, truth, and enchanted, sacred places. Her mother had never forgotten the sight of those pure white horses running free on the endless salt grass plain, and she'd woven them into Susannah's bedtime stories. Susannah had begged for riding lessons, and her parents had obliged. Her father had taken her to the stable every Saturday morning.

Sometimes, crawling into the deepest, darkest caves, she'd calmed herself by imagining the white horses, so wild and free, unfettered and unrestrained, galloping over the marsh. When she was wedged into damp, stony chasms, or pressed by her schedule, her constant travel, her classes, the thought of those horses, and the exhilaration she herself felt in the saddle, freed her mind. They'd saved her from panicking, helped her get through the worst places.

Now Susannah was going to the Camargue to see the white horses. She wanted to hear their hoofbeats—feel them pounding the marsh beneath her feet as she stood in their midst. Her own riding, at home, at the Connecticut College stable behind the Arboretum, had ceased as she'd gotten so absorbed with work and travel. Her body and spirit felt pent up, and deep down she believed that those white horses running by the sea could somehow release them. And she had promised her mother.

Her mother had so often steered her in wonderful directions. Even her position at the college . . . after she'd graduated from

Wheaton, gotten her master's and then her doctorate at Yale, she had piles of letters ready to go out to anthropology departments all over the country. With Ian pressuring her to apply to departments on the West Coast, her mother had gently suggested Connecticut College, just a few miles away from their home in Black Hall. Susannah had sent a resumé to Professor Helen Oakes, and she'd never once regretted it.

In Arles, bright sun had streamed down from a sparkling sky, beckoning her south. But as the road wound into the marshland, silver haze first filmed and then obliterated the sun. She rolled down the car windows, letting the cool, damp air touch her skin. She knew that the Camargue was 220,000 acres of wild marsh, pastures, and dunes.

The light was mysterious, the endless marshland flat and hypnotic. No matter which way she looked, she saw only salt grass blowing in waves. Her car was alone on the road in this primeval landscape. A strong wind was kicking up from the sea, rippling the marsh. The sun faded a little more; the haze turned to fog, swirling and thickening as she drove south.

The wind was filled with energy. It didn't

feel like a storm; it just made her want to jump on a horse and ride for miles, beyond the horizon. Her eyes were peeled for the white horses; she felt they were near. She pulled the car over to the side of the road. A guidebook was open on the seat beside her; copies of pages she'd printed from the Internet lay beneath.

Stepping out of the car, Susannah breathed the salt air. Stretching her limbs, she felt as if she'd been trapped in a box. The car, the plane, her office, her mother's hospital room, the caves, her life. Every muscle ached.

Her eyes watered in the sharp wind. Facing toward the sea, she opened her arms and felt the wind against her body. Glancing down, she saw hoofprints and felt prickles on the back of her neck: the horses were nearby.

Looking around, she realized she might be lost. There were no signs, and everything was unfamiliar. Perhaps this was a dream. Or maybe she had conjured it all out of a near-forgotten bedtime story. The wind was charged, and in that moment she felt magic.

About to return to the car, she heard distant pounding and felt the ground start to

shake. Instead of fear she felt pure exhilaration: they were coming. She knew it, and
started running through the fog toward the
sound.

First the ground was dry and solid and
then it was damp. The tall green grass
brushed her ankles and calves, and her
sneakers squished in clammy mud. Graceful bone-white egrets flapped their wings
and took slow, ungainly flight to escape her,
bright blurs in the thick fog. A horse whinnied in the near distance, and Susannah
took a deep breath and listened.

The animals were coming hard and fast.
She felt their energy before she saw them.
Waiting for streaks of white, instead she
saw black. Dark shapes charging toward
her: blue-black hides, murderous curved
horns, flashing red eyes, flaring nostrils.
Thudding past her, they wheeled back in
rage, and suddenly Susannah was surrounded, not by gentle white horses, but by
twenty wild black bulls.

She wanted to drop to her knees, cover
her eyes, but she was frozen in a moment
surreal, ridiculous, and terrifying. The bulls
were exquisite, pure power, beautiful animals. But they wanted to kill her. They had

furious eyes; Susannah had invaded their territory. One bull was larger than the others, and he stood in the forefront. He sputtered and pawed the ground. And he was staring at her, straight at her head, right at the red ribbon she'd bought at the marketplace in Arles.

It was the ribbon! The red was infuriating him; she'd seen enough movies to know that. If she dropped the ribbon on the ground and backed away, he'd let her alone. She felt the entire herd inching toward her. Reaching up slowly, she started to take it off. Took hold of one end, untied the bow . . . and the red ribbon unspooled and the strong wind took it, made it stand straight out in her fingers like a red flag, and the large bull let out a deep, guttural sound and began to paw the ground harder.

And then Susannah heard the horse's whinny again, and out of the fog, out of nowhere, saw the white horse coming fast and heard a voice saying sharply, *"Donnez-moi votre main!"*

Give me your hand . . .

She reached out blindly, felt rough fingers close around her wrist, pull her onto the broad white back of the galloping horse. It happened so fast, before she could even think, and she was electrified. Suddenly she was flying across the marsh, her arms around a stranger, a French cowboy. She felt her heart beating against his backbone, and she heard the bulls charging from behind, swore she could feel their hot breath on the back of her neck.

The rider galloped them away, through the marsh, onto a sandy trail. Her sensations were intense and alive. She smelled the man's sweat and the horse's scent, and she felt the rock-hardness of his back against her chest, and the beautiful white horse beneath her. But as the adrenaline stopped rushing, and she had the chance to replay it, she felt a rush of fear and shock at what had almost just happened.

"I'm sorry," she said into his windblown hair.

"You nearly got killed," he said.

"I know."

The horse had been racing along, but now it slowed down. Susannah's arms remained locked around the man, though. Even when the horse stopped, she couldn't let go. She was trembling, and the emotions dammed up by sudden terror flooded out.

He turned half-around, looked at her over his shoulder, through a lock of gray-brown hair falling across the brightest blue eyes she'd ever seen. His skin was weather-beaten, darkly tanned.

"What were you doing back there?" he asked. His accent was American, not French.

"I was looking for white horses, and instead I found wild bulls."

"They inhabit the same places."

"I didn't realize."

"People think the Camargue is so romantic," he said. "All white horses."

"I'm not romantic," she said. "I'm academic."

He flashed such a quick, wonderful smile, for a moment she saw starbursts around his eyes, smile lines around his mouth, white teeth. He reached around, pried her fingers open, took the red ribbon she still held from her hand.

"I shouldn't have worn red," she said.

"Bulls are colorblind," he said.

"Was it the movement that angered them? The fact it was waving?"

"Smart. You *are* an academic," he said, laughing.

Then he stuck the ribbon into the pocket of his shirt, gave his horse a quick kick, and started riding back the way they'd come. Susannah tensed up, thinking they were going to encounter the herd again. He must have felt the fear in her body.

"Don't worry," he said. "They're gone now."

"How do you know?"

"I just do."

The horse carried them through the fog, straight to her car. Susannah felt confused, turned around. Jet lag had taken hold, as well as the aftermath of nearly being gored. The marsh was flat and endless. She had no idea where she was, and when the horse stopped again, the rider had to gently pry her arms from around his waist. Swinging her leg over, she let herself drop to the ground.

She stared up into his blue eyes. "Thank you," she said.

"I'm glad I was there," he said. "You're a good rider."

"Thanks. I surprised myself. It's been a while since I was on a horse."

"Well, that was some jump up."

Susannah smiled. "Maybe I should join the circus."

His eyes flickered. The easy friendliness and humor were still there, but he stared out over the marsh, and she felt him wanting to ride away.

She blinked, turning in a slow circle, trying to get her bearings. Her legs wobbled, and she realized she was feeling the effects of fear and the short, intense ride. The man glanced down again. Edging closer, she reached up and petted the horse's white neck and velvety muzzle, tangled her fingers in the white mane, long and glorious.

"You saved my life, right?" she asked the horse.

"Probably," the man answered for the animal.

"Then I need to know his name."

"Her name," he said, "is Mystère." He gazed at her without expression in his sky-blue eyes. He stared for a long time.

"What?" she asked.

But he just shook his head, gesturing at her car. "Go on, get in," he said. "I want to make sure you have a safe getaway."

"Which way . . ." she started to say, but

he just gestured left, down the road in the direction her car was already pointing.

"Six miles, straight to the sea," he said. "Stes.-Maries-de-la-Mer."

"How do you know that's where I want to go?"

He just smiled. "I'm a mind reader."

She smiled back. She walked over to her car, opened the door, climbed in. He stayed right where he was while she turned the ignition key and started the car up. Mystère's long white tail swished back and forth.

"Remember," he said, "no waving ribbons in the marsh."

"I remember," she said. "But oh, I wish . . ."

"What do you wish?"

She swallowed, gazing up at the man on the white horse. He looked tall and lean and brown, maybe forty-five, three or so years older than she was. He wore jeans and a blue cotton shirt. For the first time she noticed that there was no saddle; not only had she just executed a pretty amazing circus trick, she'd done it bareback.

"That my parents could have seen that," she said quietly. "The way you held out your hand, and I grabbed it and jumped on."

"Your parents?"

"My father used to take me to riding lessons. And my mother told me about the white horses here."

"She should have told you about the bulls, too. There's a lot of danger if you're not careful . . ."

"Then I'll be careful," she said steadily, suddenly afraid—not of the bulls, but of the cold fog enveloping the endless marsh and the town where she was heading. She feared it seeping its way into her mood. She'd come here to feel better, and stave off the dark pain of her mother's death, and her own guilt. She gazed into the man's blue eyes. She didn't want to drive away.

He hesitated, as if he understood—or as if he didn't want to leave either.

But then he made a clucking sound with his tongue, gave Mystère a little kick, and rode off into the fog. Susannah watched him disappear. Alone again, she felt a quick bolt of fear. But she chased it away. The marsh was wide and lovely, and the bulls lived here with the horses, and she had just been rescued by a blue-eyed cowboy. Quite an introduction to the Camargue. She wished she'd remembered to ask him for her red ribbon back.

She felt oddly empty, as if she'd just awakened from a dream. She realized she hadn't even asked his name. Trying to hold on to scraps—the sounds and sights and feelings of something unbelievable, otherworldly—she turned south, toward the town. She knew it was inhabited by the Rom—Romanies, known to some as Gypsies. Her mother had told her they had adopted Sarah as their honorary saint. Every year at the end of May, they held the *Pèlerinage des Gitans:* the Gypsies' Pilgrimage. Families would flock from all over, to beg Sarah for miracles and thank her for ones already granted.

In that moment, Susannah recalled the strange look in Helen Oakes's eyes when Susannah had agreed to go to Stes.-Maries-de-la-Mer, and the conversation that had followed. And now, although Helen had written a letter of introduction for Susannah to present at the library in Arles, and had written out a list of topics and questions, this was Susannah's journey and no one else's.

She put the car into gear, and drove toward the sea.

*   *   *

One hand on the wheel, the other holding the printout, Susannah drove slowly into the town, through streets lined with white houses, down to the harbor. She glimpsed the fortified Romanesque church, with its simple, pure lines, its battlements and a bell tower. She felt an instant pull toward it, but jet lag was getting the better of her. Glancing at the paper in her hand, she drove along the wharf and looked for Rue Magdalene.

A flamenco guitarist leaned against a tall stone wall, singing in a language that sounded unfamiliar. Clotheslines stretched between houses, and bright laundry and seaweed-flecked fishing nets flapped in the wind. The afternoon sun had burned a hole in the fog, and diamond patches of light sparkled on the choppy surface of the harbor, where colorful fishing boats strained at their moorings. Susannah saw Rue Magdalene, and turned right.

Number 14 stood a half block off the water, on a narrow cobbled side street. Susannah parked at the curb, pulled her bags from the back seat, and walked toward the house. It was two stories, pale pink, the color of the inside of a cockle shell; there were white shutters at the windows, and a front porch with a round table and furled white market umbrella. Like all its neighbors, the house had a red-tiled roof.

Before Susannah could climb the steps, the door opened. A woman came forward, smiling. She was darkly tanned, petite, but very strong looking—toned shoulders and bare arms under a sleeveless purple dress. She had a dragon tattoo on one bicep and one of the Virgin Mary on the other. Hoop earrings showed through tumbles of curly black hair.

"You must be Susannah Connolly," she said in thickly accented English.

"Yes," Susannah said.

"I'm Topaz Avila," the woman said, taking one of Susannah's bags. "Let me show you around the house, and then I'll be on my way. Did you have a good trip?"

"It was . . ." Susannah began. She'd been about to say "eventful," and rush into a story about the horses and bulls and the man in the marsh. But instead she just said, "It was fine."

Topaz gazed at her, as if waiting for her to say more. But when Susannah didn't continue, she smiled and led her into the house.

She showed her the kitchen and bathroom, the living room and bedroom; told her how to prime the well if the water ran out; pointed out a list of contact numbers, including her own, hanging by the phone in the kitchen. She opened the back door and gestured to the *pièce de résistance*: a small swimming pool.

"You see there's a parasol—umbrella—for sunny days. But do not put it up now, or it will blow itself out. The wind, you see."

"Yes," Susannah said. "Is there a storm coming?"

Topaz laughed. "A storm? Oh, no. This is normal for this time of year."

"The wind blows like this all the time?"

"It's the mistral," Topaz said.

Mistral. The word seemed so exotic and beautiful. Susannah felt herself grin, and Topaz returned the smile, wide and wonderful. Susannah's knees were just about buckling with exhaustion, so she just accepted the keys from Topaz, thanked her for her trouble, and saw her out. Then she walked upstairs to the bedroom, dropped her bags on the floor, stumbled over to the bed, and fell into a deep sleep.

TWO

Sari Dempsey stood in the back room of her house, sorting laundry. Everything she touched burned her skin. Her father's socks singed her fingers; her own cotton shirts seared them, too. She'd caught a fever long ago, and she couldn't be cured. That's because the malady was in her soul, not her body.

The injuries to her body had been quite terrible, at the time—a broken arm, a shattered pelvis, a hairline fracture to her skull. A bad concussion that gave her piercing headaches, that impaired her vision—bleached the world of color and, for the weeks immediately following her accident, made her see double. The double vision had abated, but the colors never came back. Sari had been colorblind ever since that night five years ago.

Ever since that night . . .

If anyone ever wrote a song about her, painted a picture of her, wrote her biography, the title would have to be *Ever Since That Night*. Nothing had been right since then. The world had turned gray, her dreams had gone dark, and all she could think of was her mother's face in a desperate knot, her mother's strong arms taut and rough as she'd pushed Sari away, running out the kitchen door to be with the man she loved—a man Sari hated.

Of course she'd hate any man her mother loved who wasn't her father. Her father was the best, even though she didn't always let him know she felt that way. Ever Since That Night, she and her father had lived in the same house, but they were a little bit like ghosts. They didn't talk much. They hardly ever laughed. And Sari often caught him watching her with such terrible sorrow, as if he blamed himself for letting Sari's mother run away. Or for not stopping Sari from climbing up onto her horse, riding after the car, and all that happened after that.

For the way she was now.

Sari didn't mind work. Now that Rosalie had left, housework kept her busy and prevented her from thinking. She liked doing chores; she knew that other girls did them with their mothers. Her mother had never really been the housework type, even before she'd left. But Sari enjoyed it, keeping her home nice for her and her father. Sometimes she imagined her mother would come back, and see how beautiful it was, and want to stay.

Her father gave her an allowance for helping with the housework, and she saved it in a jar she kept in her closet. Sometimes she imagined paying for an operation, so she could see colors again—even though the doctors had told her father there was nothing organically wrong.

That meant she was crazy. The fact she saw the world in black and white, like an old movie, was all in her head. She had stayed in the hospital for weeks after the accident. They'd kept her in traction, allowing her pelvis and arm to heal. They'd given her painkillers that kept her in a fog. They'd sent in neurologists who'd given her test after test to figure out why she'd stopped seeing colors. After that the parade of shrinks began.

Shrinks in the hospital, shrinks in Arles and Paris, even a special-expert shrink and neurologists in Providence, Rhode Island, and New York City, on a summer trip to see her grandparents. No one could really figure it out, because the truth was too simple: her mother had taken all the colors away when she left.

Missing someone so much was complicated. Especially because it had been her mother's choice to go. Sometimes Sari's shoulder still burned, from where her mother had shoved her. Slapped her. Grabbing her mother's hand, holding on to her, Sari had gotten hit. Her mother had never done that before; she'd been so despairing, so desperate to get away from Sari and her father, she'd turned violent.

Sari curved inward as she remembered. She missed her mother, but she didn't think she loved her anymore. That hurt more than anything: five years after that night, she'd stopped loving her mother. Well, sort of.

Even now, her eyes filled up with tears to think about it.

Rosalie, her mother's best friend, had been their housekeeper after that. But Sari had upset her a few weeks ago by talking about her mother, triggering Rosalie's fierce loyalty to her friend. She'd driven Rosalie away, too. Now it was just Sari and her father.

So Sari folded the clothes. She saved up her allowance for a dream so secret she could never say it out loud. Her dreams were of nature and poetry and horses and staying with the people you love forever, of colors coming back, and of something too treacherous to say. Sometimes she thought Laurent—her next-door neighbor and oldest friend—might guess. No one knew her better than Laurent. . . .

The laundry smelled like wet horses. It always did. Her father spent so much time riding, tending to the herds, his clothes were basically permeated with equine odor. It reminded Sari of happy times, before she'd stopped riding. Times riding with her parents, and with Laurent. But sometimes those memories were so happy, they made her weep.

Even though she hadn't been on a horse in five years, since she was eight—she hadn't approached Mystère in all that time—she liked the fact her father just kept riding. He treated the horses with enough love for both of them. There was comfort in the constancy. He woke up before dawn every day, hauled himself out of bed to feed the herds, rode into the marsh, took tourists on rides through the Parc.

The tourists came here to see the white horses. Sari didn't blame them: the horses were magical. Most of the tourists liked the horses because they looked pretty, not because of their rare and ancient bloodlines, dating back to the Solutre horses of the Lascaux cave paintings, many miles away.

The people flew here from New York and Florida and London and Berlin and wherever else tourists came from, to stand on the boardwalks and click pictures of the bulls and flamingos and wild white ponies. They'd pay handsomely to take trail rides in a pack, led by Sari's father and Laurent's father, Claude. Sometimes they'd ride at night, when the marsh was painted silver with moonlight. And when they'd had enough of horses, they'd all go down to

Stes.-Maries and take pictures of the Romanies.

Sari patted trail dust and mud off her
father's jeans, checked to make sure his
pockets were empty, and threw them into
the washing machine. Then she did the
same to his shirt. He was usually pretty
good about taking things out of his pockets,
but he'd missed something here—she
reached into his shirt pocket, pulled out a
ribbon.

The sight of it made her stomach hurt.

It was long, fine, made of satin: a Gypsy
ribbon. Sari stared at it, her heart skipped
a few beats—and she felt her eyes fill with
tears. What was he doing? Sari's mother
had worn ribbons like this—individually,
tied in her hair, and in the hundreds, all colors, streaming from her costume. Sari pictured her mother's favorite robe, as brilliant
and vivid as the stained glass windows at
church in Arles, flowing with fine purple,
saffron, rose, red, emerald ribbons. They'd
looked like rainbows, trailing off behind
her as she'd ridden into the arena. . . . Sari
could no longer see colors, but she could
remember them.

Had her father been talking to her mother's

people? But that was impossible—to them, he didn't exist. He was as dead to them as Sari's mother was. Had he fallen in love with another Rom woman? Or maybe, or maybe, or maybe he'd seen *her*.

Sari's heart skipped and began to pound: could her mother have come back? She must have! And the only reason her father hadn't told her was because she didn't want to see Sari.

She finished throwing the laundry into the washer, measured out soap, and turned on the machine. She heard the sound of rushing water, scalding hot, washing away all the horse smells, and all the Gypsy touch.

Walking through the house, she went to stand by the kitchen window. It was after six; her father should be home soon. She'd finished school early today, and the rest of her class had taken a trip to the museum in Nîmes. Laurent had tried to convince her to go, but she'd told him she had to go home to do chores. Gazing out at the front yard, the pastures and long fences and marsh stretching into green nothing, she tried to stay calm.

Two black cats circled around and around her ankles. Their names were Oscar and

Bruno, and Sari bent down to pick them up now. She held one in each arm, eyes closed while they licked and nuzzled her face, purring like tiny race cars. Someone had left them on her doorstep almost five years ago, in a covered basket, the lid on tight so they couldn't escape.

It was just a few months after her mother had left, right after Sari had come home from the hospital. At first she had imagined that her mother had come back, left the cats on the doorstep as a gift or coded promise. Was she trying to tell Sari she was coming back? Was she saying that if Sari took care of the kittens well, proved that she could love and respect two tiny living things, she'd return? Maybe she'd been trying to teach Sari a lesson: how hard it was to take care of things.

Sari knew how hard it had been for her mother to take care of a baby. She'd been a great beauty, a riding genius, a circus princess, born to ride white horses, her black hair flowing like her own mane. She had defied everyone to marry the American, the man everyone in Stes.-Maries-de-la-Mer saw as nothing better than a robber:

he'd stolen the most beautiful, talented, high-strung Romany for himself.

Her mother's people—all of them except Rosalie—despised her father, and they'd cut her off for marrying him and having Sari. That must have killed her—how could it not? Moving out of town, to live in the middle of the Parc, with a man who knew nothing of her traditions, nothing of her life. He had tried to turn her into a housewife. Someone who went to market, cooked, mucked out stalls, had a baby.

Sari stood at the kitchen counter. She kissed Bruno and Oscar, let them down to walk across the sink and try to drink from the faucet. She stared at their black fur, and still believed her mother had been trying to tell her something, leaving the kittens for her to take care of. Glancing down at her hands, she saw her mother's skin.

Tan, burnished with Romany blood, nothing like her father's. He was from America, and Americans were all from somewhere else. His family had roots in Ireland, England, and Canada. From what Sari had been able to see—either on her visits to Rhode Island, or when her grandparents and uncles and aunts would come here—

they had all been as different from her mother as day and night. Her mother's family, people without a territory, had settled years and years ago in Stes.-Maries. It was just down the road, but they wanted nothing to do with her.

Bruno stood on the windowsill, meowing. Sari wondered whether he still remembered those first days on the ranch, when she'd let the two kittens scoot outside and play. Everyone she knew had outdoor cats. Let them run free in the marsh, catching rats and birds, sunning themselves on the mud-flats, chasing flies, playing in the hayloft, hiding in the stables.

But after just one week, Sari had been unable to stand it. Not knowing where they were, worrying that they might not come home. She moved slowly, because her pelvis was still healing, and she'd lost sleep, worrying about her two little kittens. She'd feared monsters in the swamp, the dreaded Tarasque of the Rhone, navigating the creeks behind her house, ready to kill her boys. So she had brought them indoors and kept them there. They were house cats now, and had been for five years.

All beings had a home, and that's where they were supposed to stay.

Her father was late for dinner. Sari was almost glad, because her feelings were wild and she didn't want him to see her this way; knowing her mother had come back and didn't want to see her was like losing her mother all over again. She balled the ribbon up in her hand, pressed it into her face, and began to sob.

Astride the white mare, Grey Dempsey had taken the last kilometer slowly, giving everyone a chance to take more pictures. The fog had finally lifted, and late-day caramel light spread over the marsh, painting everything gold. He led the riders into the paddock, and everyone dismounted, thanking him. He obliged people by taking photos of them with the white horses. Several asked where he was from in the States, and how he had ended up in the Camargue, and he'd told them the basic story, that he'd grown up around horses, had come to France and made his way down here to horse country, and never gone back.

Close enough.

Once he and Claude had gotten the horses rubbed down and most of them stabled, he'd paid Claude and said he'd see him tomorrow. Claude had walked home to Anne and Laurent, leaving Grey to head over to the main paddock, where he'd left Mystère for last.

She stood there, her withers almost pure gold in the setting sun. He reached into his pocket, pulled out a carrot, fed it to her while tangling his hand in her mane, petting the side of her neck.

"You're a good girl," he said. "You worked hard today. But it wasn't like yesterday, was it?"

She ate the carrot, then he led her across the yard toward the barn. He'd ridden her since early morning, and she'd been incredible. Ever since yesterday he'd been reliving that moment in the marsh, when he'd come upon that woman standing among the bulls. He'd reacted more than thought—kicking Mystère into a dead run, stretching out his hand, pulling the woman up behind him.

She'd asked if Mystère had saved her life, and he'd said yes, and it hadn't been a lie. The bulls were wild and aggressive, and he'd never once ridden that close to them when they'd been ready to charge. The woman, fine satin ribbon waving in her hand, had been thirty seconds from being gored to death.

"But she could ride, couldn't she?" he asked now. "Couldn't she jump up? Did you see that?"

It was as if she'd had wings on her feet. Their timing had been perfect; he'd leaned over, reached down, and she'd put up her hand just in time, in the split second it took to grab her. And somehow she'd had enough momentum—nothing like a running start, because she hadn't been moving, she'd been stock-still, her instincts had told her to do that—to spring straight up, swing her leg over, and hold on tight.

Wings on her feet; that's what it had to be.

Grey had known one other woman like that. She'd been able to ride like an angel, standing tall on her horse's back, robe flowing out behind her. She'd had wings, too. And she'd spread them and flown away.

Leading Mystère into the barn, Grey opened the door to her stall. His heart ached a little, looking into her eyes. Horses felt things strongly; in that way, they were like people. She'd been missing a woman's touch for years now. Maria and Grey had bought the horse on their daughter's fourth birthday—and Sari had given her the magical name.

Maria had ridden Mystère, trained her, started teaching Sari some easy tricks. Sari had taken to riding as if she'd been born for it. But all that had ended the night Maria left. Sari had stopped riding after her fall.

And no woman had ridden Mystère until yesterday.

Was it Grey's imagination, or was she looking more alert, holding her head higher? He had his own feelings about grief and loss here in the Parc Régional de Camargue; he and Sari hadn't been the only ones affected. But petting Mystère, giving her one last carrot, heading toward the house, he knew that nothing compared to what Sari still felt.

His stomach clenched even before he walked through the kitchen door. Just knowing he'd find his daughter in there, hiding out in her own home, seeing the world in shades of gray, made him ache with the sort of dull hurt and anger he'd long stopped trying to get rid of.

"Hey there," he said, stomping his boots,

closing the door behind him. She stood at the stove, stirring something in a copper pot. *"Ça va?"*

She shrugged without turning around.

"You decided not to go to Nîmes?" he asked in English. They spoke it here at home, and during summers in Rhode Island.

"Yes," she replied. "I didn't want to."

"I thought Laurent was trying to get you to change your mind."

"I've been to the museum enough times."

"You might have seen something new this time, something you missed before. A beautiful painting, or statue."

"Paintings look dull to me," she said quietly, and he felt stabbed through the heart. He saw the tension in her shoulders as she stirred whatever she was cooking. Seeing his daughter standing at the stove, knowing paintings, landscapes, the world looked dull to her, filled him with fresh despair.

"Sari. Let me call Rosalie again, and see if she'll come back. I don't want you doing all this—you should be out, having fun, going on these trips."

"She doesn't want to be here. I just remind her of who she'd rather see."

Grey stood in the middle of the kitchen. Sari had her back to him and gave no indication of turning around any time soon. The two cats had jumped down from the windowsills and were investigating his boots. He bent down to pet them without taking his eyes off his daughter.

"What's the matter, Sari?" he asked.

She didn't reply. Instead, she reached for the pepper mill and twisted it over the pot. She was often silent and distant, but right now he saw her shoulders shaking, and her hand trembling as she cracked the pepper.

"Sari?" he asked, as he stood up from the cats and took a step closer to the stove.

"When were you going to tell me?" she asked, her voice breaking.

The look in her eyes shocked him: beseeching, filled with despair. Tears ran down her face, and her chin wobbled, as if he'd broken her heart.

"Tell you what?"

"That you saw her!"

"Sari, saw who? What are you talking about?"

Dropping the spoon back into the copper pot, she reached into the pocket of her jeans and pulled out a red ribbon. He stared at it, remembering yesterday.

"I took it from a woman in the marsh," he said.

She shook her head, dark hair flying. "No," she wailed. "You didn't. I know she's back. She's somewhere nearby, isn't she? And she doesn't want to see me?"

"No, of course not! Your mother—"

"Where did you meet her? Was it accidental? Or did she call you, and you didn't want to tell me?"

"Sari," he said.

"What color is it?" she wept. "What color ribbon was she wearing, Papa?"

He was shaking, and wanted to grab her to him. Lead her into the living room, sit her down, talk sense into her. He struggled to make his voice gentle, the way he always had, in the weeks and months after Maria had first left. He'd felt like a hypnotist, a soothsayer, trying to talk his daughter—and himself—into becoming sane. But that had stopped working some time ago. Sari had stopped listening. And he had stopped believing the lies he'd been telling all along, that her mother would be back, that she'd never forget them, never forget *her.*

"Sweetheart . . ."

"What color, Papa?" she begged.

"It's a red ribbon."

"She was wearing it, right? She's back . . . Don't lie to me, Papa. Don't make something up. Tell me the truth."

"I just did."

"You got this from a woman in the marsh?" Sari asked with disbelief, waving the ribbon. "It's a Gypsy ribbon."

"I know," he said.

"Was she Rom?"

"No," Grey said, picturing the woman's light brown hair, freckled skin, violet eyes. "No, she wasn't."

"Then what was she doing—"

"Sari, I have no idea where she got it. Maybe she bought it at a souvenir stand. Maybe she picked it up off the street. How do I know?"

"Well, how did you wind up with it? Did she give it to you?"

"Not exactly."

"What does *that* mean?" she asked, her voice inching toward hysteria.

"Whoa," Grey said, as if he were gentling a wild horse. She was very sensitive about anything concerning women. The few dates he'd had were completely secret, behind Sari's back. She lived on the tightrope of wanting her mother to come home while claiming to never want to see her again. No other woman was allowed into the picture. His grieving, wounded daughter needed him all to herself.

He knew, on some level, he was doing her a disservice. Sari wanted to believe that Grey still loved Maria, that he would forgive her for leaving, and would always keep the door open for her. It wasn't supposed to matter that her mother was with someone else now, and had been since before the night she'd left. Grey had gotten advice, telling him to be straight with Sari. But right now there was nothing to tell.

"Tell me what's going on!" she wept.

"Sari, nothing is."

"Then how'd you get the ribbon?"

"I'll tell you, sweetheart," he said. "I was out on Mystère yesterday, and we came upon a woman, a stranger, about to get trampled by twenty bulls. We rescued her, and I took the ribbon from her. She was holding it, it was blowing in the wind, and it was provoking the bulls."

"You and Mystère rescued her?" Sari asked, her lower lip trembling.

"Yes."

"Were the bulls . . ."

"They were ready to charge."

"You could have been hurt!"

He narrowed his eyes. She was right, and he could read her mind: what would she do if something ever happened to him? "We were fine."

"What kind of lady would be dumb enough to get that close to the bulls?"

"Stop that, Sari. She didn't know."

"Did she ride Mystère?"

He put his hands up, stopping her before they went down this road. Sari wouldn't ride her, but for a long time, no one else was supposed to either—not even Grey. Now Sari seemed to gain comfort from seeing her father ride her mother's favorite horse, but certainly no strange woman would be welcome to. The tension was thick between them, lightning about to strike, when suddenly he saw it drain right out of her; she thrust the ribbon at him and crouched down to pet the cats, dropping the fight for now.

"I'm just glad you're okay," she whispered, more to the cats than to her father.

"I'm fine. Everyone's fine."

"You'd better get ready for dinner."

"It smells good."

"It's *daube de boeuf*."

"I'll go change," he said. He walked up-stairs to his bedroom. Taking off his work clothes, he made a mental note to wash them himself later. Sari had talked him into letting her do the chores, but that was wrong. She needed to be a kid for as long as she could. He'd call Rosalie and beg her to come back, after Sari went to bed.

Just then he heard the screen door squeak open and softly close. He walked over to the window. It gave onto the back-yard and barn and salt plain as far as the eye could see. They lived on the edge of a world of water, the sea-silvered marsh sliced into a puzzle of islands by hundreds of dark creeks. He liked this time of night, when the colors drained away, when his daughter could see what everyone else saw.

As he watched, Sari crossed the yard. Her limp was completely gone; she walked straight and tall, then stood alone, facing the barn. The top halves of the stall doors were open, and one white horse had heard her approach, and was standing at the door.

They looked at each other, girl and horse. This was as close as Sari ever let herself get to Mystère. She never touched her, never rode her. Grey stared down at his daughter, standing there in the yard. Then he turned away from the window.

He lifted the red ribbon from his night-stand, where he'd dropped it a minute ago. Gazed at it for a few minutes, remembered how it had looked waving in the woman's hand. She had jumped up like such a champ.

He wound the ribbon into a tight coil, placed it behind a book on the shelf beside his bed, and headed downstairs for dinner.

THREE

Susannah had intended to go to the church first thing in the morning after she arrived, but she'd been unable to move. She never experienced jet lag like this when she was working, but it had tugged her down, back into bed. The fog had turned to rain, and the wind blew harder. Lying still, covers pulled up, she listened to the rain on the roof.

So far from home, she felt months' worth of grief rising to the surface. The latest issue of the *Journal of Cultural Anthropology* had just come out, her name on the cover and her article on Paleolithic art in the caves of Corsica inside. Her work in Turkey had gained attention, too, and she'd received a grant to continue there. But Susannah couldn't focus on any of that.

Eyes closed, she felt rocked by sorrow, and for the first time in all the months since she'd lost her mother, she at last gave herself over to the overwhelming guilt that haunted her. Her mother had been sick with lymphoma for so long, Susannah had gotten used to her illness as a way of life. Margaret had remained relatively stable, but Susannah wouldn't have stayed so long in Istanbul if she'd known how quickly things would change, no matter what her mother said.

Imagined images of her mother's last days had become a familiar tape: lying in the hospital, getting weaker and sicker so fast, needing higher doses of morphine, while Susannah was so far away. Had she hoped Susannah would come back on her own? Had she tried to hold on for one last goodbye?

All of that talk about "life's work" . . .

Susannah could hear her mother's voice now. She knew what Margaret believed, that a person's work and spirit were completely entwined. By encouraging Susannah to continue traveling and making discoveries, Margaret was choosing life. She never would have wanted her daughter to sit at home, waiting for her to die.

Just before Susannah left for Istanbul, there had been signs that Margaret's condition was changing; she'd felt more tired than usual. A blood test had come back with an elevated white cell count. Susannah had wanted to cancel her trip. But her mother had insisted; she'd told Susannah she felt fine, that everything would be okay.

"You have to go, sweetheart. I've never been to Istanbul, but it's always sounded so beautiful. Imagine, you'll be right there on the Bosporus. . . . You'll be seeing it for me, too," she'd said.

Three days after Susannah had arrived in Istanbul, she'd gotten word that her mother was in the hospital. She'd called Shoreline General immediately; she remembered being in her hotel room overlooking the Bosporus as they spoke together. Her mother had asked her to describe the view from her window—the city skyline, minarets, blue water—and reassured her that she was fine.

But she'd known deep inside that it was

bad; she should have trusted her instincts, not her mother's soothing words. Susannah should have been at the hospital, dealing with the doctors, holding her mother's hand. But her mother had died there alone.

Lying in a strange bed, in a rented house, Susannah wept. She'd come here, to the Camargue, to feel closer to her mother—to find a way to forgive herself. Instead, she felt the mistral seeping into her soul and wondered whether she'd ever get over what she'd done.

We die alone, the saying went. But Susannah had never believed it. Not when you come from a close family, not when you are surrounded by love. Her mother had nursed her father after his heart attack; Susannah doubted she'd ever left him for more than a few hours. And she'd been right by his side when he died.

Her mother had deserved the same from the daughter she had raised with such overflowing love. Susannah should have been there for her, not just when she died, but so many other times. She'd told herself she was making her mother proud—her parents had always encouraged her, wanted her to succeed at the college, and in her field. Her life's work . . . Susannah had told herself she was leaving Margaret with excellent health care, that she'd cancel any trip, cut it short and head right home—if things changed.

But there hadn't been time. By the time Susannah had gotten the final call, her mother was already in a coma. She'd died with no one holding her hand, while Susannah was in the air, flying home from Istanbul.

The rain beat in rhythm with her heart. The weather held its own despair. She curled into a ball under the covers, shivering and wondering why she had come.

But one day later, the sun was shining. Susannah climbed out of bed—determined to fight yesterday's darkness, the overwhelming loneliness that had swept over her in the foreign place, so distant from her home. She had traveled so often on business. The field of cultural anthropology was rich and deep, and her studies and work had taken her all over the world. She'd had moments of difficulty along the way, but she'd always stayed strong and positive, keeping the focus on her work and reveling in the exotic surroundings.

She plugged in her laptop, connected to the local phone line, and checked her email. There were birthday messages from Heather, Amy, and other friends. Reading Heather's email, Susannah smiled. *How did you do it? Slip out of town JUST in the nick of time?!?! Serves me right—I know I'd always promised never to do that, to throw you a surprise party. Helen got you off the hook in the classiest way possible. We'd invited her, and instead of coming, she sent a case of champagne with a note that she'd sent you to France on top-secret Connecticut College business. I can't quite imagine what that is, but it doesn't matter. Without going into details, you're lucky you didn't come—there was a mystery guest you'd probably just as soon have avoided. Just have a fantastic time, and don't worry about a thing.*

A mystery guest. Susannah wasn't sorry to have missed him. Seeing Ian was the last thing she needed right now. Even after their rift, he never gave up. She sent back a reply to Heather, as well as one to Amy. Then she wrote to Helen, thanking her for sending the

champagne, and for keeping her secret—
Susannah had found out about the party
and the "mystery guest" and bought the
champagne herself.

Helen had been kind enough to have the
champagne delivered; she'd understood
that Susannah just wasn't up to a surprise
party this year. Susannah closed her email
to the professor by confirming she'd contacted the library in Arles before she left,
made arrangements to research in the rare
book room later in the week, reminding
Helen to fax the library director her credentials; Susannah had a duplicate set, just in
case.

Her credentials. They fit on five 8½ × 11
pieces of paper, her whole professional
life boiled down into a curriculum vitae
of degrees, awards, publications, grants.
Wheaton. Yale. She'd started working at
Connecticut College that following summer,
after completing her doctorate.

She'd loved reading about world cultures,
and had wanted to be an anthropologist for
as long as she could remember. Her mother
had been a middle-school English teacher.
When Susannah was young, she would beg
to help correct papers. Once Margaret had

said yes, but only if Susannah read the book she'd assigned her class.

It was *Horses in the Cave: The Paintings of Lascaux,* by Anna McNeil. Susannah had gotten lost in the story about Paleolithic hunters in southwest France, the incredible, vivid paintings they had done in the caves of Lascaux. She'd been moved by the author's understanding of the people who had lived back then, and of depictions—in the color plates—of beautiful horses, some of them shot with arrows.

Susannah's mother had told her to turn to the back of the book, look at the list of source material. There, cited for quotes in chapter three, was Professor Helen Oakes of nearby Connecticut College. Susannah must have filed that information deeply away.

At Yale, she often researched in the Beinecke Library, one of the most exquisite buildings in the world, with translucent marble walls through which drifted soft, gray, diffused light. It was a cozy and romantic sanctuary, and it was there that she'd begun delving into cultures that revered horses—inspired by her early reading, and by the fact she'd always loved the animals so much.

Again, there in the library, she encountered the name of Helen Oakes; the professor had written a book called *Women, Beasts, and the Myth of True Love*. Susannah had admired the playfulness of the title and the scholarship of the work, and she'd cited the text in her own dissertation, on the cave paintings of Lascaux.

"Susannah, I'm so proud of you," her mother had said after she finished at Yale, toasting her doctorate. They were having dinner at the Renwick Inn, their favorite restaurant, right on the riverbank in Black Hall, a spot they'd always chosen for special family occasions. "Your father would be over the moon."

"I wish he were here," Susannah had said.

"I know, honey," her mother had said. "So do I. But you have him with you always; you know that."

And she did. In symbols and memories, and the big silver watch of his she always wore, and in the strength and knowledge he'd passed on to her during his lifetime—

her connection with her father would last forever.

"So, now what?" her mother had asked at that special dinner. They'd been determined to make it festive, regardless of the fact they missed him so much. "What is the next step on your amazing journey?"

"You mean, where am I going to get a job?" Susannah had laughed.

"Exactly."

"Well, I'm applying to Michigan, and I've sent letters to the departments at Harvard and Stanford. Ian's really pushing for me to apply there."

"Ian wants you where he can keep an eye on you," her mother said.

"Mom, he's not that bad . . ."

"Susannah, he lets you scramble around the caves while he sits outside, not getting dirty, taking notes on your discoveries—and sharing the credit! When I spoke to him at graduation, he made me feel as if *you* were lucky to have worked with him. It makes my blood boil."

"That's just teamwork, Mom," Susannah had said.

"Not my kind of team," her mother had said, stubbornly. "He's envious of you . . .

I watched him when you won the Fabbri Prize."

"Well, he probably should have won," Susannah said, remembering how he'd sulked. "His grades . . ."

Her mother stopped her, placing her hand over Susannah's on the table. "Don't you ever let me hear you say that again. You worked so hard for that prize. Honey, don't ever let anyone demean you—and don't you do it to yourself. You and Ian share a love of the caves . . . but you love the beauty and mystery. He loves the way your research will advance him."

"Thanks, Mom," she'd said.

"I get it," her mother said. "Time to change the subject." They sat still for a few minutes, quietly gazing out through the bright green leaves of maple and birch trees, across the long green lawn toward the golden river.

"What about," her mother asked finally, as if she'd been holding the idea inside all evening, "Connecticut College?"

"I hadn't really thought about it," Susannah said. And immediately she'd wondered why not. Its department had such an excellent reputation, partly because of its star professor.

"I read an article in the *Day,* not long ago, about an anthropologist there. Professor Helen Oakes," her mother said.

"Mom," Susannah had laughed. "Don't you remember? Her name was listed in that book you gave me to read years and years ago. The one that got me started! *Horses in the Cave: The Paintings of Lascaux,* by Anna McNeil."

"Hmm," her mother had said thoughtfully. "I do seem to remember that."

"Sure, I'll apply to Connecticut College. It's so close to home—that would be a plus."

"Well, so is Yale," her mother said. "I'm not suggesting this to keep you nearby. You know that, don't you? I want you to spread your wings. . . . Even Stanford, if that's what you want."

"Of course, Mom," Susannah had teased. "You'd much rather have me working in California, all the way across the country."

"If that's what made you happy, I absolutely would," her mother had said resolutely.

And Susannah had believed her, too. Her

parents had never tried to hold her back—
they'd done the opposite, encouraged her
to travel, explore, and do her best, wherever
that took her. But nonetheless, she'd applied for a job just ten miles from home,
been accepted by Professor Helen Oakes
herself, and—in spite of Ian's disappoint-
ment and derision—never once doubted
herself.

She'd continued working with him
through the years; because of their shared
interests, they often wound up writing about
the same sites. But as time went on, and he
kept pressing for more, she'd been very
glad they lived on opposite sides of the
country.

Now, glancing around the kitchen of her
rented house in Stes.-Maries, she knew she
was right to have traveled back to France.
The sense of her parents was everywhere.
Yet the place seemed entirely new and mysterious at the same time. Her adventure in
the marsh attested to that.

Checking the schedule of town events
hanging by the kitchen phone, she saw that
today was market day in Stes.-Maries-de-
la-Mer, and she decided to check it out.

Susannah stopped first at a café at the

foot of her street. She ordered a croissant and café au lait, and enjoyed them on the terrace, overlooking the harbor. Her thighs and shoulders ached from her wild horseback ride, and her wrist was chafed, from where the man had grabbed her. She rubbed her wrist now, looking around.

The horizon was low and limitless, and everything was scoured by light from above and reflected off the river and bay. Although the land- and seascape reminded her of Connecticut, it was also vastly different. Without trees to diffuse the sun, the light was scalding here, vivid and intense.

Wearing a sunhat and dark glasses, carrying the wicker market basket from her kitchen, Susannah headed through town to the Place des Gitanes. There were stands for charcuterie, *poulet, poisson, fromage, boulangerie,* and fresh Provence vegetables. She moved slowly through the *marché,* stopping to savor every stand, filling her basket with beautiful food, wrapped by each individual vendor in crisp white paper.

The street was bustling, as if everyone in the region had come out to enjoy the sun and do their week's shopping. One woman was selling embroidered blouses—bright flowers and symbols stitched on fine muslin—and they hung from the stall's awning, moving in the quiet breeze. Susannah bought one. Then she stopped at a stand to buy postcards to send home to Heather, Amy, and Helen.

"*Bonjour!* Mademoiselle Connolly!"

Turning, Susannah saw her landlady coming toward her—Topaz Avila, dressed today in a flowing emerald silk skirt and one of the embroidered peasant blouses. Topaz carried a string bag, a baguette wedged in among white paper packages.

"Mademoiselle Avila," she said.

"*S'il vous plaît*—call me Topaz."

"And call me Susannah."

The two women fell into step with each other as they walked along. Susannah glanced up at the old church. Once again she had planned to go inside this morning, but with the sun shining so brightly she just wanted to stay out in the streets and soak it up. Topaz caught her glance, and nodded.

"Have you been yet?"

"No, although it's one of the reasons I came here."

"That's true for many people. We have many pilgrims."

Susannah nodded, thinking of her own family story. "I can imagine."

"Do you know about the legend?"

"Some," Susannah said elusively. Although she had grown up hearing it from her mother, and despite the fact her boss had a particular academic interest in some of the details, Susannah really wanted to know the perspective of a person who lived here.

"Would you like to walk awhile? I'll tell you about it."

"That would be wonderful," Susannah said.

As the two women strolled along, Topaz told the story of the ship, drifting all the way from Galilee in the year 45, of how the three Marys, Martha, Lazarus, and Sarah made landfall right here in this ancient town, here on the edge of the marshland.

"Lazarus . . ." Susannah said.

"Yes," Topaz said. "Brought back from the dead by his best friend, Christ. But the company in this boat was so *exceptionnel,* he barely stood out. There were also Jesus's aunts—both named Mary—and Saint Martha, and, of course, Mary Magdalene. While Lazarus went on to Marseille, to found a church there, the Marys stayed. They were grateful for having landed safely, and they built a chapel right here."

"That one?" Susannah asked, gazing up at the mysterious towered structure.

"Yes, indeed."

Susannah studied the imposing Romanesque architecture. Her mind raced with thoughts regarding its historical importance, but her heart was touched by the idea that Mary Magdalene had walked this very ground, and founded this church out of pure gratitude.

"Is it a true story?" she asked softly, wanting to draw Topaz out, knowing that not all the scholarship in the world could hold a candle to a true believer.

"Of course!" Topaz said, as if there could never be any doubt.

"But how do you know?"

"The bones," Topaz said, launching into a story that Susannah already knew well. "Two female skeletons were found in the chapel crypt, beneath the Altar of Juno, during the fifteenth century. It's been determined that the women had been very old when they died; we are sure they were Mary Salome and Mary Jacoby. You see, Sarah had stayed here in this town with them, even after all the others had left."

"Sarah, the young servant girl," Susannah said, thinking of her mother's stories.

"Yes," Topaz said. "She cared for them into their old age. They were relatives of Mary Magdalene as well as Jesus Christ. Sarah stayed with them until the end."

Topaz's words pierced Susannah's heart. *Stayed with them until the end . . .*

Topaz must have seen the expression in Susannah's eyes; her own filled with compassion. "Would you like to see Sarah's statue? It's in the church . . . you really must, to understand what she means to people."

Wordlessly, Susannah nodded. She walked with Topaz across the street, up the stone walk bleached nearly white by age and the sun. Her blood was racing so fast, she could barely breathe. Was it because her parents had come here so long ago, that she was walking in their footsteps? Was it because Sarah—who had blessed Susannah's mother so many years ago—had done something Susannah herself had not—or could not—do for her mother at the end? When Topaz held open the heavy church door, Susannah stood out in the sunlight, unable to move.

"Come in," Topaz said, then smiled. "Sarah is waiting."

The sun had blinded her, and she couldn't see in the darkness in the back of the church. Topaz led her down the aisle, Susannah walking as slowly as possible. Candles burned everywhere. Her eyes became accustomed to the dim light—the church had very few windows, and those few were tiny.

"It was here, in 1449, that the former church nave was destroyed," Topaz said in a low whisper. "Right here, at L'Oreiller des Saintes . . . the skeletons were found."

Susannah bowed her head, feeling the ghosts of her beloved dead.

"There," Topaz said, pointing to the left. "Unbelievers say that in ancient times, that was a pagan altar where bulls were sacrificed in worship to Mithra." Seeing Susannah shiver, Topaz went on quickly. "But in any case, that was long ago, before the ship landed, before the Marys came. Here, past the Christian altar, is our Sarah. *Sara-la-Kali . . .*"

Gazing at the beautiful statue, ebony

wood dressed in gold leaf, the statue draped with layers of real clothes, the young girl's face so kind and loving, Susannah felt her eyes fill with tears. People had left behind crutches, canes, braces, even old bandages, evidence of every sort of hurt. They had surrounded Sarah's statue with candles, and they were burning now, so that the statue's black wood seemed to gleam from within.

Susannah knelt. She knew that her mother had been *right here.* Her parents, lovers of nature, had discovered the Camargue in their search for birds and wild horses. That they had arrived in this church at the very end of the windswept plain, perched right on the edge of the Gulf of Lions, seemed a miracle in itself. As if sensing that Susannah needed privacy, Topaz backed away.

There was something so sweet and comforting about Sarah, Susannah could instantly see why her mother had loved her. She was reminiscent of the Black Madonnas studied by colleagues of Susannah and Helen, yet not a Madonna at all. She was a young slave girl, humble for having lived an entire life of service. Yet something in her eyes—even in this statue carved centuries ago—spoke of life, curiosity, a desire to embrace everything and everyone.

And people loved her: that was obvious. She wore real clothes; her visitors dressed her in skirts, blouses, jackets, scarves. Over what appeared to Susannah to be a lovingly ragtag wardrobe was a tattered gold brocade coat with recent darns on the sleeves and pockets.

Susannah reached out, touched the cloth.

"Hello, Sarah," she whispered. "My mother loved you. You brought me to her. She asked me to come . . ."

Susannah listened. Voices carried from other parts of the church, and she swore she heard familiar whispers. She thought of the stories she'd been told as a child, and whispered her thanks to Sarah, for what she had done for her parents, for herself. She whispered the name Topaz had said earlier: *Sara-la-Kali*. And she felt her mother's presence.

After a few minutes, Susannah wiped her eyes and stood. She paused by the crypt where statues of Mary Jacoby and Mary Salome stood. As she moved away, she felt the pull of the ebony statue behind her, and she was unsure of whether it was Sarah's own power, or knowing that her parents had been here before her—or the sense that her mother was with her now. But she continued toward the door, where Topaz waited.

The dark-haired woman smiled brilliantly.

"Now that you've met her, what do you think?"

"She's wonderful. More beautiful even than I'd expected. Who dresses her that way?" Susannah asked as they walked out the door into the bright sunshine.

"The faithful," Topaz said. "We take turns. Sarah is the patron saint of the Romany people. So much so, it used to be forbidden for anyone else to enter the church. Only the Rom had that right."

"I'm glad that changed," Susannah said. "If it hadn't, I might not be here."

"What do you mean?" Topaz asked.

Susannah took a deep breath. She felt shaken by what had happened inside the church, and she wanted to preserve the feeling of her mother's presence. Talking about it helped her hold on. "My parents came here a long time ago . . . they'd been married for many years, with no children. They visited this church on a vacation to

France—it was almost by accident. They'd actually wanted to see the white horses of the Camargue, and something made them follow the road a little farther . . . down here to Stes.-Maries. My mother walked into the church, and she knelt by Sarah. My mother always said . . ."

"That Sarah blessed them with you."

"Yes," Susannah said.

"They were right," Topaz said. "Although of course it was no accident that they wound up here. It never is. Stes.-Maries calls those who need to come. Your parents were drawn to Sarah by divine inspiration." She smiled as widely as before, tilting her head. A group of Gypsy women walked past, skirts flowing; they waved at Topaz, and she back at them. Everything felt so exotic. "I shall tell . . ." Topaz began, trailing off.

"What?" Susannah asked.

Topaz hesitated, seeming to consider whether to continue. Her gaze seemed to seek out the women who'd walked past, disappearing around the back of the church. "Nothing," Topaz said. "I have friends that will be interested in your story. That is all. Now I must go. I own several houses other than the one you are renting, and they must be cleaned and readied for the next tenants."

"Well, thank you for showing me the church," Susannah said. "And Sarah. My mother and I always meant to come here together."

"You would have found her yourself," Topaz said. She flashed a smile, but it instantly disappeared. Susannah felt Topaz gazing over her shoulder toward the street, watched the woman's eyes narrow and harden.

When Susannah turned to see what had changed Topaz's mood, she saw her friend from the marsh climbing out of an old Citroën. He was tall and rangy, with that streak of silver in his brown hair, and blue eyes so bright it seemed he must never look into the sun, and the sight of him hit her like a lightning bolt. A decal of a white horse was stuck to the back window of his car; Susannah wondered how he had managed to get a sticker that looked exactly like Mystère.

"What's that man's name?" she asked Topaz.

But when she turned back to her landlady, she saw Topaz hurrying away, toward the other women, the brilliant green silk of her skirt whisking around the corner of the stone church. Susannah watched her go, then gazed back toward the man she had last seen on a white horse in the fog-shrouded marsh. She remembered her body pressed into his, riding for their lives through the mist. She smiled, waved, and ran down the steps to meet him.

Grey had come to town looking for Rosalie—never an easy proposition—and instead found the woman of the red ribbon. Here she came, beaming and looking so happy to see him that it made his heart flip. He felt the same way, and started to grin. The sunlight was white, bouncing off the sea and the stone of the church, and it made him squint and shade his eyes with his hand, and he couldn't stop smiling.

"Hello," he said, stopping beside her.

"It's you," she said. "I thought it was."

"Yep, it's me. How are you doing, since our wild ride?"

She laughed, a really wonderful, startling trill, as if the question had taken her by surprise, and just seeing her made him want to ride off with her again. He felt a physical rush that nearly knocked him over, and that put him on guard.

"It *was* a wild ride, wasn't it? Well, my legs ache, and my wrist feels like one big rope burn, but otherwise I'm fine. I'm glad the weather has cleared up. That fog was a little spooky."

"It must have been," he said, feeling spooked by a whole lot more than the fog.

"I have a question about the bulls," she said. "I just heard about how they used to be sacrificed right here, back in pagan times—is it true?"

"Supposedly," he said, gazing into her eyes. She'd been behind him on the horse, and he hadn't realized how clear, and darkly beautiful, and intelligent her eyes were. "But not all the legends around here should be believed . . ."

"But some should," she said softly.

He shrugged and said nothing.

"Those bulls," she went on, shaking her head. "They're magnificent. It's awful to think of them being sacrificed."

"I know," he said. "Even to this day."

"Bullfights?" she asked.

He nodded. "They're common here. Most

ranchers don't allow the bulls to be killed—but there are some."

"I'll avoid those ranchers," she said. "And I'll watch out for bulls in the Parc."

"Just pay attention and leave them alone. If you give them plenty of distance, and don't wave ribbons at them, they won't bother you. I'd be more worried about quicksand."

"Quicksand?" she asked.

He nodded. "It's everywhere in the Parc. It's more like sea mud, really, left behind when the tide goes out. We lose horses to it." He peered into her dark violet eyes. He wanted so much to offer to show her around; they were standing so close he could smell her hair. He remembered the feel of her—it wasn't something he'd soon forget. She seemed to be exerting a pull he hadn't encountered since Maria. It felt dangerous, so he kept his tone steady, took a half step back. "Wouldn't want to lose you. Stay on the boardwalks, and you'll be fine."

"Thanks for the warning," she said, looking down. He saw the color rising in her cheeks; he'd made her blush. Was he being too alarmist, scaring her all over again? Or was it something else? Was she feeling on edge, too? He saw sadness just behind her eyes, and wondered what had happened to cause it.

"It's not all bad in the Parc," he said. "I didn't mean that."

"I know. As a matter of fact, I was thinking about taking a trail ride," she said, looking up again, emotion even closer to the surface. He watched her wage some kind of private battle with herself. A smile emerged. "On one of those white horses I came here to see."

The bright sun beat down, paradoxically making her eyes darken. He thought of how beautifully she had made that leap, how expertly she had ridden. He imagined leading her into parts of the Parc no one else would go, where the horses could gallop through silver plains of sea grass. He'd show her himself how to avoid the quicksand. But then he thought of Sari, of the way that ribbon had set off a panic, and he knew he had to shut this down. Sari needed all his attention.

"Well, there are plenty of ranches," he said.

"I need to find a good one," she said.

"One that has a nice rancher who doesn't kill the bulls."

He nodded, and it took everything to hold himself back from offering.

"I was wondering," she said. "Since this is the second time we've met, do you think we could actually introduce ourselves?"

"Sure," he said, smiling. There couldn't be any harm in that, could there?

"I'm Susannah Connolly," she said.

"Grey Dempsey," he said, shaking her hand.

"You're American?"

He nodded. "Born and raised there," he said. "But I moved here a long time ago."

"You're an expatriate?" she asked.

He chuckled. The way she said the word, with mystery and allure, reminded him of how he'd felt when he'd first come to France in his twenties. "Yes, you can say that," he said. "I wanted to be Hemingway."

"Really? Because of the bulls?" she asked.

"I was a journalist," he said.

Something shifted in her gaze. She'd been categorizing him in a certain way—horses, bulls, the great outdoors. But suddenly her perception changed; he felt her curiosity building, and that was true for him as well. He'd felt her hand, just now, shaking it, and earlier, in the marsh; it was a little rough, surprising him. Her eyes were deep and sensitive, but also challenging; she was in charge of her own life. For some reason he'd had the feeling she worked with books.

"I'd better get going," he said.

"Oh," she said, sounding disappointed. "Okay."

"Take care," he said. "Enjoy your time here."

"Thank you. I will."

With a last look into those eyes, he turned to walk away. Sari came first, and she needed everything he had, his traumatized, colorblind child. He'd trained himself to keep from getting involved with women, but this time it hurt like hell.

Rosalie Daquin lived in the caravans on the outskirts of town, but she spent most of her days in and around the church; he needed to see her in person, to convince her to come back to work. He'd only taken a few steps when he heard Susannah call his name.

"Grey Dempsey!" she said.

He glanced back.

"That was your byline?" she asked.

"Yep," he said. "It was."

"Well, you might be a journalist, but you sure know how to ride a white horse."

"So do you, Susannah Connolly," he said.

They waved at each other once more, and then he followed the path behind the church, where he'd seen Topaz running, pretending she hadn't seen him, no doubt on her way to warn Rosalie he was coming. He tried again to put Susannah and her midnight eyes out of his mind, but he couldn't do it.

She was right there, and he knew he was in uncharted territory.

FOUR

Susannah felt exhilarated. She'd loved seeing Grey again, and she felt a little shocked by how happy it had made her. She stopped at the newsstand and picked up a local guide, listing fifteen places offering trail rides within a short drive of Stes.-Maries. The third one was called *Manade du Dempsey:* Dempsey's herd. The owner's name was listed right there: Grey Dempsey.

Her high spirits evaporated at the sight of his name. Why hadn't he told her that he owned and operated a horse ranch?

Her feelings were hurt. She had to admit it. Why had he so deliberately steered her to go somewhere else? Her recklessness in the marsh must have really appalled him—a stranger just barreling in.

She knew how that felt. When she was in the field, maneuvering into a cave, she moved very carefully, and felt intensely territorial about "her caves." One wrong move could damage everything, and she had little patience for amateurs.

Back at her little house, she put all the things she'd gotten at the market away and made herself a lunch of fresh yogurt and dark ripe figs, drizzled with lavender honey. It tasted delicious, and she found herself wondering whether Grey shopped at the market, whether he cooked for himself, whether he had someone to share meals with. She liked thinking of him as a journalist, and wondered how that and his ranch were connected. Did he still write? Or did all his effort go into caring for horses, taking visitors on rides through the Camargue?

Sitting at the kitchen table, she told herself to stop it. He'd pushed her away—that was that. She should know; she'd done the same thing to Ian. Lately when Ian wanted to attend conferences on the East Coast, and suggested they meet up or go together,

Susannah would make excuses. He'd finally gotten the message, but it had taken a while.

Reaching for her notebook, she began to record her observations about the church, Sarah, and everything Topaz had told her, retreating into the comfortable habits of her profession. Anthropology was the study of humanity. Susannah's interest lay in the way human beings related to each other and their environments at various periods of history. But at the moment, all she could think of was Grey Dempsey.

Putting down her pen, she looked around the room. This was ridiculous; she hadn't come here for this; she'd traveled to the Camargue to keep a promise and see Sarah, experience a new culture.

And she wasn't just observing Gypsy culture—she was living in it. It felt exotic, thrilling, and completely unfamiliar. Throughout Topaz's house were icons and symbols: talismans to chase the evil eye? Susannah stood, walked over to a feather hanging by the door. She knew that it was meant to repel wickedness and danger; beside it was an icon of the almost-saint Sarah.

Sara-la-Kali.

Susannah felt intrigued by the Rom, the way they'd carried their customs and beliefs into the present, woven them into everyday life, made their saint a part of their families.

Lost in thought, Susannah was startled when the phone rang. Who knew she was here? She hadn't given the house number to anyone—she didn't even know what it was. Reaching for the wall phone, she answered.

"Hello?"

"Susannah, it's Topaz."

"Oh, hi," Susannah said. "You ran off so quickly earlier, I didn't get to thank you properly for showing me the church. And Sarah."

"It was my pleasure. Listen, do you remember that I mentioned to you about some friends I have, who would be interested in the story of how Sarah blessed your family?"

"Yes, I do."

"Well, we are getting together tonight. We would love for you to join us, tell us about what happened. Would you come?"

Susannah paused. She thought of her mother, knew how much this would mean to her.

"Yes. I'd like that very much," she heard herself say. "Thank you."

"I'll pick you up at seven," Topaz said.

"You don't have to," Susannah said. "If you just give me the address, I can—"

"It's rather a long way out of town," Topaz said. "I'll be happy to drive you."

"Thank you, then. I have a question," Susannah said. "You called Sarah 'Sara-la-Kali.' I know that Sarah is from Kali's lineage, but is it commonly known? Do you think of her that way?"

"We'll explain that to you tonight," Topaz said, her voice rich and gentle, as if the very question had warmed her. *"À tout à l'heure!"*

"À tout à l'heure," Susannah said.

After she hung up the phone, she sat very still. Her eyes fell upon the page she'd been writing. It was filled with her first impressions of encountering Sarah: the dark church, the blazing votive candles, the feeling of peace that had come over her. Sarah was everywhere. It was almost as if by writing about her, Susannah had summoned Topaz's call.

As Susannah sat at the table, continuing her precise note-taking, she concentrated on her observations at the *église*. But every so often her pen wavered and she thought of those blue eyes, and knew it was futile: she had the rancher on her mind, and he wasn't going away.

Turning on her laptop, she logged on and went straight to Google. Typing in "Grey Dempsey," she found mention of the Manade du Dempsey—travel articles, or blogs by people who'd visited, glowing reviews of Grey's horses, ranch, and trail rides. It wasn't until Susannah had scrolled through four pages that she found what she'd been looking for: references to articles written by Grey Dempsey.

The most recent dateline was fourteen years old. He had written for the *International Herald Tribune,* as well as *Paris Match*. Looking further, she found reference to pieces he had published in *Harper's, The New Yorker,* and *The Atlantic Monthly*. She couldn't find any entire articles—only citations of them in other work.

But she could see from all the mentions that his subject matter had been very specific. He had written about the Rom.

Gypsies from Prague to Madrid, and especially in France. She could tell from one story that he had been based in Paris, and had come to the South of France to witness their devotion to what he referred to as "the slave saint." Sarah.

And that was the last reference she found.

How had he gone from journalist/observer of the Romany people to living right here, among them? Perhaps his desire to be Hemingway had gone deeper than he'd admitted, and the outdoors and the bulls and the horses had worked their magic on him, convinced him to put down roots in this enchanted place.

Somehow Susannah thought there was more to it than that. But since it didn't really matter anyway, she shut down the computer and pulled out the list of ranches again. She had a map of the countryside; it seemed like a good time to go exploring. She'd give the Manade du Dempsey wide berth and leave him alone—that was obviously what he wanted.

It hurt her. Susannah never felt this way. She'd always been happy to go on her way, absorbed in her work and all the discoveries the world had to offer. Now she was stunned, overwhelmed with feelings she'd never had before, and for a man who was just a stranger.

As much as she didn't want to admit it, Sari's heart jumped when she saw her father pull up with Rosalie. She was sitting at the kitchen counter, Bruno and Oscar at her feet. She'd just finished her schoolwork and had started in on dinner preparations. She'd decided to fix a gratin, and began slicing *courgettes* and tiny potatoes, grating Gruyère cheese.

Rosalie was a great cook, and she'd always put something secret in her gratins. Sari had been wracking her brain for what that ingredient might be—and here Rosalie came, through the door. The cats scattered for hiding places as they always did when non–family members entered the house.

"Bonjour, Sari," Rosalie said, preceding Sari's father into the kitchen.

"Bonjour," Sari replied, sheepishly and quite shyly, considering she'd known Rosalie since birth.

"You didn't think you'd see me again, did you?" Rosalie asked in English.

"Pas vraiment," Sari answered in French, just to be contrary.

"Not really?" Rosalie asked, eyebrows raised.

"Sari's sorry for what she said," her father said now. He was standing behind Rosalie, out of her sight. Only Sari could see the desperation in his eyes. Sari knew they needed help around the house; she wanted to do the right thing.

Rosalie stood very still. She gazed steadily, patiently, at Sari. Her dark hair was long and wavy, her eyes huge black pools. Sari's mother had had the same coloring. Sari shivered.

Her father watched her. Sari felt that buzzing feeling she sometimes got when she was afraid she'd disappoint him. She wanted to make everything right, make Rosalie want to stay; all she had to do was apologize.

"What are you making?" Rosalie asked, drifting toward the counter.

"A gratin," Sari asked. She wanted to ask Rosalie about her special touch, but she didn't dare. Her heart was aching too much, and her arm throbbed; it hardly ever hurt anymore, only when something really made her think about her mother, about that night. Seeing Rosalie was almost like looking into the eyes of her mother.

"We have things to talk about," Rosalie said, arms folded across her chest.

"I know," Sari whispered. But the rest of her thoughts, words that might make things right, were stuck in her throat.

"It hasn't been working out," Rosalie said.

"We want it to," Sari's father said. "We know you've gone out of your way to help us, and we'd like to ask you to come back. Right, Sari?"

But Sari couldn't speak, or even nod. The kitchen was silent, all except for the wall clock ticking. Outside, a rooster crowed. From the barn, someone whinnied. There had been an afternoon trail ride today, and Claude had taken the horses out, leaving just a few behind. His son, Sari's best friend, Laurent, was in the stable now, cleaning up. Sari heard the scrape of his pitchfork on the stable floor.

"You know how I feel about Maria, don't you?" Rosalie asked. "You know how hard it was for me to hear you talk about your mother the way you did?"

"I do know," Sari said quietly. "I'm very sorry."

"For what?"

Rosalie was going to make her spell it out. Sari felt heat rise in her face, making her head ache the way it had in the months after her accident.

"For what I said about my mother," Sari said.

"Were you wrong?"

"I was wrong to hurt your feelings."

"Sari," her father began.

"That's not the same thing," Rosalie said softly, her voice shaking. "Your mother is my best friend, and I love her. I know you've been through a lot, Sari. But saying you hate her was wrong. Do you understand that?"

Sari stared down at the floor. It was made of thick tiles, chalky and dotted with animal tracks from where they'd been left to dry in the sun. There were mice tracks with whispery tail marks dragging between the tiny claw prints, and chicken tracks, and even human baby footprints. Sari's own . . . The tiles were terracotta, and Sari knew—from a five-year-old memory—that they were pink.

But right now they just looked dull, the shade of mud, without any color.

"Sweetheart, say it," her father pleaded.

Sari thought back to the moment Rosalie and her father wanted her to apologize for. It had happened late last month, one of March's warmest days. The horses had had spring fever, and so had Sari.

The night before, she'd dreamed of her mother, how on one of the first warm spring days of the year she would always take Sari into Stes.-Maries to walk on the promenade, balance on the narrow white rail, pretend it was a tightrope. Sari would walk, and her mother would hold her hand. That's how Sari had learned balance, holding her mother's hand.

That memory had been so vivid. Rosalie had been standing in the yard, washing dishcloths in a tub of fresh soap suds. She'd turned, to hang the cloths to dry on a clothesline, just the way Sari's mother had used to do, and Sari had gone crazy.

Sari had upset the tub of water, soap bubbles bursting and flying into the breeze, drifting into the beautiful marsh, delicate little things breaking on every spike of tall grass. Sari had watched the bubbles, remembering how they used to look like little rainbows, and she'd started to weep.

"What's wrong?" Rosalie had asked.

"The bubbles," Sari had cried. "They're clear and empty."

"Yes . . ." Rosalie had said, not under-standing.

"They used to be so pretty," Sari had sobbed. "When my mother was here, they were like rainbows. They *shimmered*."

"Sari . . ."

"It's so ugly now," Sari had wept. "The whole world . . . it's just so ugly . . ."

"Sari, that's not true."

"You don't know what it's like," Sari said. "No blue sky, no green grass! I'm forgetting what it used to be like. Every day I forget an-other color. Today I can barely even remem-ber the color of her cheeks—they used to be so rosy! I can't remember what that color looks like!"

Rosalie had looked shocked, as if she had no idea Sari had been storing up so much pain, and that made something ex-plode inside.

Sari grabbed her hand. "She's never coming back, is she? She's gone forever. She's with that stupid man, and they have their horrible circus in the desert, and you don't care. You don't care my mother doesn't want me! I cracked my head open, and all the colors drained out with my blood! I can't see colors, and it's all because of her! How can you be her best friend—a person like that?" Sari had cried to Rosalie.

Rosalie had pulled back. Sari's mother had left over five years ago. Perhaps Rosalie thought she should be all better by now. Maybe she didn't know how awful it was, to go to bed at night and know her mother wasn't coming in to say goodnight ever again. Or how it felt to know her mother had slapped her away, pushed her down and driven away while Mystère bolted and Sari lay in pieces on the road. Didn't Rosalie care that Sari had never been put together right? Her bones worked now, and the pain in her head was mostly gone, but the world was gray, and the bubbles were clear, and Sari would never see another rainbow.

"Sari, you know your mother will always love you. She went away for a reason, too deep for you to understand. Grown-up reasons; yes, she rides in a circus, and yes, it's in the desert. But that's not why she left.

One day you'll be old enough to know why she did what she did."

"What she *did*? I'm here, and so is Papa. What she did was leave us! She's the most selfish person in the world, a terrible person. I hate her. I swear on my life that I hate her and hope she never comes back. She's not welcome here ever again. Do you hear me?"

"I hear you," Rosalie had said, backing away from Sari.

And just looking in her eyes, Sari could see that she'd wrecked something. Rosalie had been with them since Maria had left, but in that instant, it was over. And Sari broke again, knowing that Rosalie's reasons for working for them in the first place had had more to do with loyalty to her friend than with love and care for Sari and her father.

Now, her heart scratching at her throat, Sari tried to swallow and speak. She knew what she had to say. But she couldn't. The crazy thing was, she hadn't completely meant what she said: sometimes she hated her mother and sometimes she loved her. Sometimes she dreamed of flying to Las

Vegas and finding her, and sometimes she never wanted to see her again.

"Sari?" Rosalie asked.

"I was wrong to tell you," Sari whispered, scalding tears starting to flow. "Because I know she's your friend. But I can't explain the way I feel; you want me to feel only one way about her, and I don't. She shouldn't have left. Sometimes I still hate her for it."

"Sari, don't say that. Someday you'll understand."

Sari shook her head hard. "I don't *want* to understand."

Looking up finally, Sari saw her father's face fall. She saw Rosalie's expression harden. Sari's chest ached, because she was holding in a sob. She knew that the adults were trying to work things out— being around her father had never been easy for Rosalie. Rosalie was Rom, like Sari's mother, and they held her father responsible for getting Maria to marry outside the circle. The only reason Rosalie had worked here at all—and why she had come back now—had been out of sheer devotion to Maria.

Rosalie looked helpless; Sari wanted her to leave. And Rosalie did. She turned, walked back out through the door, across the yard, and climbed into the Citroën, waiting for Sari's father to drive her home.

Standing alone with him in the kitchen, Sari waited for her punishment. Her father didn't yell, but he knew how to admonish.

He'd give her a lecture. He'd tell her she'd spoiled everything, and now they were back to cooking and cleaning all on their own. No one in Stes.-Maries would work for them—because he was such a pariah in the community. Only Rosalie had ever crossed the boundary and come here.

But he didn't say a word. To Sari's shock, he walked over and hugged her so hard, it almost hurt. His arms locked around her with urgency, as if his hug could fill the world with color. His embrace felt red, yellow, blue, green, pink, violet. She felt him shaking; she wanted to say something, but she knew if she spoke she'd start to sob and never stop. Maybe he felt the same way, because he let go and walked out of the kitchen. He climbed into the car, started it up, and turned it around in the yard.

Sari watched them drive away. Rosalie stared sadly out the car window, and waved. Sari waved back. Then the car disappeared down the long road that led back to town.

Walking out into the yard, Sari stood right in the place where she'd spilled the soapy water. The ground was dry, but she swore she saw a mark, a big dark blotch permanently etched in the dirt, where most of the water had splashed. Gazing down at it, she thought she imagined a shimmer of iridescence: the ghost of one of those bubbles that had set her off.

She turned to face the barn. Her heart was pounding. She needed comfort; she needed Mystère. Even though she couldn't ride anymore—would never get up on her horse again—she needed to know she was right here.

And Mystère knew, too. Like Rosalie and all her sisters, like Sari's mother and all Rom women, Mystère had a touch of second sight as well. The wind was blowing in the other direction, so she couldn't smell Sari's scent. But nonetheless, as if Sari had called her name, Mystère came out of her stall. Sari heard her heavy footfalls on the sawdust floor, clomping out to the paddock.

They stared into each other's eyes, girl and horse. The hot tears that had been building up broke free. She didn't sob though, and the feeling stayed locked in her chest. Gazing at Mystère, Sari was rooted to the spot in the dirt. She reached out her hand, half wishing she could just walk over and pet her horse. But she knew she couldn't. She knew that if her fingers touched the white fur or soft gray muzzle, if she buried her face in that flowing mane, the rock in her chest would crack, and she would die.

She would die of grief. So she just stayed where she was, on the wet spot that would never dry, and stared at her beautiful horse.

FIVE

There were white sails in the harbor, and the water sparkled, and the sea meadow rippled endlessly. Susannah drove out of town, into the marsh plain of the Rhône estuary, leaving the sea behind. The road twisted around *étangs,* saltwater lagoons filled with hundreds of pale pink flamingos, and over narrow creeks lined with herons and egrets. The scenery was magical and vast, and from the safety of her car she could enjoy glimpses of black bulls grazing on the salt grass.

The ranches seemed to be clustered in the northwest. She crossed a graceful bridge curving over a canal, and began her search. Most of the farmhouses were white with woven straw roofs, and nearly every one bore a sign saying *Promenade Équestre.* Horseback rides.

She continued on, getting lost in her search. Just the thought of riding made her feel happy. She remembered all the times her father had taken her to her lessons, how they'd driven together through the Connecticut countryside, to the beautiful stable on the Farmington River. They hadn't had much money; her mother had been a teacher, and her father had had a lamp store on the main street of a dying industrial town. But they'd seen how much Susannah had loved horses, so they'd set money aside so she could ride.

She was lost in thoughts of her parents when she reached the crest of a narrow bridge. She stopped at the top, gazing out at the hypnotic sea of grass. Hearing a car approach, she quickly pulled over—and as the car passed, she saw that the driver was Grey Dempsey. He had a beautiful dark-haired woman beside him, and they were heading toward town.

He met Susannah's eyes as they passed.

She nodded, shocked to see him—hadn't she just left him in town, two hours earlier? In any case, he was with a woman. That made everything clearer.

She drove a zigzag north and then west. Suddenly, on the left, she saw the sign: **Manade du Dempsey**. The ranch looked like many of the others she had just passed: white house, thatched roof, large barn and paddock, trails leading into the marsh. Pausing by the side of the road, she gazed at the setting. She intended to just drive on, but then she saw the white horse.

Mystère stood in the paddock, in the shade of the salt-silvered barn. Although shadowed, her white coat gleamed like a beacon, pulling Susannah off the road. Just as she started driving in, she saw the young girl. She'd been standing as still as a post, right in Susannah's path—and with Susannah's attention on the horse, she hadn't seen her. Susannah stopped dead. They locked eyes, and Susannah had the quick impression of someone about twelve or thirteen, with long brown hair, dark green eyes, and tawny skin. One look at her, and Susannah knew the girl was part Romany.

But even though the young girl's eyes

were such a different color than Grey's blue ones, the bright life in them left no question—this was his daughter. The child stared at Susannah for another second, then turned and bolted into the farmhouse.

Feeling like an intruder, Susannah nearly turned around. But she'd stopped to see Mystère, so she drove into the dusty parking area and parked beside a group of other cars. Did they all belong to Grey, or was there a trail ride in progress? And if so, with him on his way to Stes.-Maries, who was leading it?

The questions melted away as she walked across the yard toward the white horse. Leaning on the paddock fence, she reached out her hand. Mystère came right over, nuzzled her arm, right in the crook of her elbow. Susannah leaned against her strong neck, resting her head on the horse.

"Excusez-moi, madame? Est-ce que je peux vous aider?"

Turning to look, Susannah saw a teenaged boy standing there. He was tall and lean, with sensitive eyes and a sulky mouth; he wore a dusty black shirt and blue jeans, worn cowboy boots, and work gloves.

"I was just stopping to see the horse . . ." she said in French.

"Américaine?" he asked, catching her accent.

"Yes," she said.

"A lot of Americans come to our ranch," he said in English. "Because Monsieur Dempsey is from there—from Rhode Island. I'm sorry, but the afternoon ride has already left. In fact, they should be back at any moment. Perhaps you can pick out a horse you like, and come back tomorrow. We will give you first choice."

"Oh," she said. "I—I wasn't coming to ride. Not here. I just wanted to stop and see Mystère."

"You know Mystère?"

"Very well," Susannah said. "She saved my life."

"You're the lady from the marsh!" he said, his eyes growing wide, his mouth stretching in a huge smile. "The one who was nearly trampled!"

"Ah, my secret is out," she laughed. "I guess Grey must be spreading the word."

"Yes. He couldn't stop talking about you."

"Because I was such a prize idiot?"

"No," the boy said. "Because you can

ride like someone in a dream. *'Comme un rêve.'"* Then he said, *"'Comme sur un nuage.'"*

"As if on a cloud?" she translated.

"That's what he said."

Susannah turned back to Mystère, gazing into her dark, knowing eyes. If Grey felt that way about her riding, why had he not suggested she come to his ranch? It confused her, and although she was happy to hear the praise, she felt as if perhaps she shouldn't have stopped here at all.

"Will you come with me?" the boy asked.

"Where?" Susannah asked, giving him a questioning look.

"Just for a moment. Over there, to the house . . ."

Susannah glanced at the farmhouse. She saw a checked curtain at the window move, and guessed it was the girl she'd seen in the yard before.

"Sure," she said. There'd been something about the girl—her age, or her posture, or the intensity of her gaze—that had reminded Susannah of herself as a young teenager. It was when her own passion for horses was at its peak, and she imagined how wonderful it must be for a girl that age to live on a ranch, with white horses to ride any time she felt like it.

The boy led her through the yard, up a stone sidewalk to the kitchen door. He knocked once, and then walked right in. As she followed him, Susannah wondered what his relationship to the family might be; he'd called Grey "Monsieur Dempsey." She stood just inside the doorway, looking around the room.

The kitchen was large, with windows overlooking the paddock. One black cat lay on the windowsill; another was curled up on the rush seat of a ladder-back chair. The floor was rustic sun-baked tiles, the walls were soft yellow, and all around the ceiling moldings was a hand-painted garland of laurel leaves and rose, lavender, and gold flowers. In the center of the kitchen, the scarred wooden countertop was covered with the ingredients for what looked like a gratin. Sliced potatoes and zucchini had been arranged in an oval copper pan.

"Sari," he said. "Come on, I know you're here. We just saw you looking out the window. Don't be rude."

"I'm not rude," came a soft voice. An instant later, the girl Susannah had seen outside stepped from behind a tall wooden armoire that was also painted in the style of the garland. She was small and slim, her eyes red from crying.

"This is the lady," Laurent said.

Sari didn't reply; she looked as if she wanted to run away.

"You know, didn't your father tell you? The one who went looking for ponies and found bulls instead."

"The lady who waved her ribbon?" Sari asked, turning a shy but somehow charged gaze on Susannah.

"Yep," Susannah said. "Pretty foolish, right?"

Sari just stared, as if frozen.

"Sari, she asked you a question . . ." Laurent said gently.

"Not foolish," Sari said. "But dangerous. Terrible things can happen in the marsh. The worst things of all . . ."

Susannah nodded. She heard the girl's voice shaking, saw emotion in her eyes. "What kinds of things?"

Laurent stepped closer to Sari, as if he was worried about her. The gesture seemed sweet and protective, and Susannah saw Sari look up at him.

"You're talking about the bulls, right?" Susannah asked.

"Yes, that's right," Laurent said, eyes locked with Sari's. "We grew up here, and we know to stay away from the areas where the bulls roam free. We tell the tourists the bulls are called 'black death,' just so they'll stay away from those places."

By the way Sari looked down, Susannah knew that Laurent was covering for her somehow—protecting her from something she'd been about to say? Susannah wasn't sure, but she knew from the way Laurent stood so close by that his feelings for Sari were strong.

"Why did you come back?" Sari asked after a moment.

"Me?" Susannah asked. "Well, I wanted to . . ."

"She's looking for a place that offers trail rides," Laurent said.

"That's right," Susannah said. "And when I saw Mystère—"

"You know her name?" Sari asked.

Susannah nodded. "Yes. Your father told me . . ."

Sari drew in a sharp breath. She looked around, and Susannah could feel her tension, sense her wanting to escape. Susannah knew she'd said something to upset her—was it the mention of Mystère, or her father?

"You know," Laurent said quietly, looking at Sari. "This could be such a good thing."

"What?" Sari asked.

"The best for everyone. Our visitor wants a trail ride, and she's already been on Mystère. Mystère needs to be ridden. You know that, don't you? Your father and my father both say—"

"Laurent!" Sari said.

"Sari, I think you should let her ride Mystère."

The girl lowered her eyes. Susannah saw her sway slightly, steady herself by touching the butcher-block island. Her beauty was sharp and dark, her deep golden skin sun-kissed and glowing. But as Susannah watched, the color drained out of it, and there were storms going on behind her eyes. She shut them.

"She's a great rider. Your father said so. Come on, Sari. Mystère needs contact, too, she needs to be ridden, and since this woman—Madame . . ."

"Susannah," she said. "Just call me Susannah." She watched Sari stand there with her eyes closed, as if she could shut herself in and block Laurent's words out, watched the girl growing paler by the moment, and she felt a tremor go through her body. "Thank you, Laurent, but I think Mystère is a one-girl horse."

"Pardon?" Laurent asked.

"I don't know." Susannah shook her head. "There was just something about Mystère that made me realize she's completely devoted to just one person. Horses are very loyal. What am I telling you for? You know horses better than I do. In fact, until the other day, I hadn't ridden in a very long time. Years, in fact."

Sari had opened her eyes. She didn't speak, but she was listening.

"Our horses are trained for many people to ride them," Laurent said quietly. "My father has been working for Monsieur Dempsey since before I was born. He has always made sure the horses were ready for any rider. All the horses—yes, Sari, you know this: even Mystère—"

"That might be true," Susannah said, interrupting, her eyes on Sari. "When necessary, even the most special, particular, horse can be ridden by strangers. But every horse has her own person. And I have the feeling that Mystère's person is standing right here."

"Me," Sari whispered.

Susannah nodded. "Yes. That's how it seems to me."

"That's right," Sari said.

"I could tell."

"Nobody else rides her. Except my father."

"I understand," Susannah said.

"He has to," Laurent said darkly. "Someone has to exercise her; horses need to be ridden."

Susannah opened her mouth to speak, but Sari tore from the room. She heard the girl's feet pounding upstairs. Laurent gave her an apologetic look, then went running after Sari. And Susannah was left standing alone in another family's kitchen.

Laurent had seen this happen before. No two events were ever exactly the same. But certain elements always added up for a big explosion. He walked down the hallway, pausing outside Sari's bedroom door. How many times had he been up here? Hundreds, at least. When he and Sari were little, they'd gone in and out of each others' houses, equally welcome in both.

But lately it had started feeling different. They were growing up, and although he loved her as much as ever, he'd started feeling as if they both had their own private places. He couldn't just barge through the door the way he had when they were little; but he wanted to see what was on the other side even more.

"Sari," he said, knocking.

"Go away," she wept.

"Open up."

"I don't want to talk to you."

"You're acting terrible."

"I don't care."

"Not to me," he said. "To the woman downstairs. She's a visitor, and you're being awful."

After a minute, the door opened a crack. He pushed it, saw her standing just inside. Her face was wet, but she'd stopped crying now, and he saw despair in her gaze, and all he wanted to do was make it right, make her sadness go away.

"I'm not terrible," she said, her voice

husky and choked. "How can you say that to me? Do you really think I don't care about Mystère?"

"I'm sorry," he said, wanting to touch her, wipe her tears. He held himself back. "For pushing you about Mystère."

"Don't you think I worry about her?" she asked.

"I know you do. I see you standing in the yard looking at her."

"You should do your homework instead," she whispered.

"Someone has to watch you," he said, trying to joke.

But she wouldn't smile. She just stood there shaking, as if she might break apart. He stepped closer, trying to keep his mind straight. If he focused on Mystère, maybe he could get through to her; maybe he could help.

"I know you care about Mystère. But listen, letting her loose in the paddock is just 'exercise.' She needs . . ." He couldn't make himself say "love," but that's what he'd heard his father say.

"Is that lady still here?" Sari asked.

"Of course," he said. "She looked very

worried, the way you went flying up the stairs. She's probably afraid she upset you."

"I wish she would go," Sari whispered.

"Oh, Sari. People are nice, you know? Didn't you hear her say that she understands no one rides Mystère but you?"

Sari looked at him with red, swollen eyes. She turned back toward the window in her bedroom, then walked over to look out at the ring. Laurent stood beside her; he saw her staring at the paddock, at Mystère standing by the fence. He felt the air crackling between them. It came from inside Sari—she was filled with thunder and lightning. But he knew it also came from him, from the electricity she made him feel.

"She *is* still here," Sari asked, staring at the car parked right outside.

"Well, she wants to make sure you're okay, I guess."

"Tell her I am, please?"

"Why don't you come down with me?" Laurent asked. "So she can see for herself."

Sari hesitated, then nodded.

And that surprised Laurent—it honestly did. He hadn't expected her to agree to go downstairs again. On another day, he might have taken her hand. Just as a friend, the brother he'd always been to her, showing her support for doing the right thing. But today he kept his distance, following her down the hall. He smelled her shampoo, and thinking about her taking a shower, washing her hair, made his chest tighten.

They walked down the stairs. Sure enough, Susannah was right where they'd left her, standing in the middle of the kitchen with a concerned look in her eyes.

"Is everything okay?" she asked.

"Fine," Sari said.

"I'm sorry if I upset you," Susannah said. "I didn't mean to . . ."

"You didn't," Sari said, her voice clipped. "It's just . . . you're right about my horse. No one but my father rides her right now. I . . . I had an injury, so I can't."

"Well," Susannah said, "I hope you recover soon."

Laurent was careful not to look at Sari. It wasn't that she had lied exactly; it was more that she'd given the barest hint of the true story.

"Thank you," Sari said stoically.

"Well," Susannah said. "I've gotten to see Mystère again, and I'd like to thank you, Sari—and now I should be on my way."

"Will you come back tomorrow for a trail ride?" Laurent asked. "I can hurry home from school, and help lead it. I'll make sure you get a good horse, almost as good as Mystère."

Laurent noticed the tension in Sari's jaw. He was back on thin ice with her, but he didn't care. He liked this woman, and he liked the fact Sari was talking to her.

"No," Susannah said. "I'm afraid I won't be able to." She shook Laurent's hand, said she was happy to have met him. She glanced at Sari. As she did, her gaze fell again on the counter, and all the ingredients there. "That gratin looks delicious," she said.

"Sari's a good cook," Laurent said.

"I can see that. When I went to the market in Stes.-Maries today, all the vegetables looked so good. Seeing them coming together, I'm inspired to cook one for myself tonight."

"Don't forget to add a little sage," Sari said.

"Sage? What a great idea. I'd never have thought of that," Susannah said. "I always add a tiny bit of cinnamon and nutmeg when I make gratin."

"The secret ingredients!" Sari burst out, shocking Laurent with the excitement in her voice.

Susannah smiled. "It's the way my mother taught me. There's something about the spices that works well with the cheese and cream. Sharpens them up, or something. Well, enjoy your dinner."

"You too," Sari said.

Susannah turned to go. Laurent saw her glance up at the flower garland painted on the plaster wall. He wondered what she was thinking about it. It looked so pretty. He felt like telling her those flowers were as full of poison as belladonna. Sari's mother had painted them.

Laurent knew he should follow Susannah into the yard, but he didn't. He stayed inside the kitchen with Sari. He watched Susannah walk past the paddock toward her car. Mystère stood at the fence, hazy sun glinting in her dark eyes.

The wind had kicked up again, tossing Mystère's mane and tail. Susannah paused as if she wanted to give her one last pat before she left. Laurent knew she sensed Sari watching, so she just smiled at the horse and continued to her car.

Sari followed the car with her eyes. Backing up, turning around, driving out. Laurent's stomach tensed, as if he and Sari were one and the same. Did she relive her mother's departure every time? Is that why she was frowning, brows knit, eyes flashing? Laurent knew she wouldn't relax until after the car had disappeared.

"She's gone now," he said, when it had.

"I know," Sari said. Outside, a veil of high clouds had slid in, painting a penumbra around the sun.

After a minute, she turned to the counter. She stared at the food she'd been preparing as if she'd never seen it before. Then she went to the spice cupboard and took out two small jars: nutmeg and cinnamon.

Laurent watched her season the gratin. He stared at her for a few seconds, waiting for her to say something. But she seemed lost in thought, all words locked inside, so he just walked out the kitchen door and over to the paddock to visit her horse before the rain started to fall.

SIX

Grey drove home, trying to keep his focus on the road. Rosalie had simmered the whole way back to Stes.-Maries. He'd looked over, seen her eyes welling with angry tears.

"I'm in an impossible position," she said, just as they pulled into town. "I care about Sari, yes, but Maria's my oldest and best friend. That's why I agreed to work at the Manade in the first place."

"And we appreciate it," Grey said.

"You say that," she said, shaking her head. "But you don't. I remind you of Maria—that's the real problem."

"Maria's in the past," Grey replied.

Rosalie shook her head, as if she didn't believe him. "You just want to convince yourself of that. She's in your life every minute of every day; I see the way you look at me, with such anger, and I know you're thinking of her."

"All I care about is Sari," he said harshly, wishing she'd get it. For a time, he'd thought about Maria—about confronting her in Las Vegas, forcing her to see Sari and face what she'd done to their daughter. "I need help with the house, and I don't want Sari doing it. She has schoolwork, and I want her to have time for fun. I'm worried that the more pressure she feels, the harder it will be for her to get better." He paused, giving her a hard look. "Not everything is about Maria, Rosalie."

"You blame her for everything. She made a mistake . . ."

"By marrying me, okay," he said. "But not by having Sari."

"She hates that Sari suffered."

"Suffers," Grey said through clenched teeth.

Rosalie had started to retort, but seemed to think better of it and sat deep in silent thought, until Grey stopped the car. Hand on the door handle, she gave him one last look, then shook her head and got out. She wasn't coming back to work—that was clear. He saw her friends watching from the church steps. They didn't acknowledge him in any way as he turned the car around, nor he them.

Now, approaching the kitchen door, he steeled himself. Sari would be angry and upset about what had happened with Rosalie, and he half expected to see the gratin she'd been making in the garbage. He took a deep breath and pulled the door open.

She was huddled on the window seat, shoulders hunched, arms wrapped around her knees. Staring out at the paddock, she didn't even turn around to greet him. He walked right over and stood next to her, stroking her hair.

"Rosalie hates me," Sari said. "Doesn't she?"

"Of course not."

"But she quit."

"Let that be her problem, Sari. She misses your mother. It's hard for her to be around here."

"Other people miss her, too," Sari said. "Not just Rosalie."

"I know," Grey said, still cradling her head in his hand.

She tilted her neck, looked up at him. "But you don't, do you, Papa?" she asked.

"She left a long time ago, Sari. I've gotten used to it."

"So have I," Sari said. But Grey knew that was a lie.

He dropped his hand then, turned toward the stove. If she'd ditched the gratin, he'd have to make something else for them. But there it was—golden brown and bubbling— cooling on top of the stove.

"This looks great," he said.

"Yeah," she said. "It came out well."

He washed his hands, and silently they set the table. He felt her unwinding, warming up a little. Sari put out a pitcher of water, and he filled their glasses. To his surprise, she lifted her glass and reached up to clink with his.

"Here's to . . . Mystère," she said.

Grey nodded, taken aback by the toast. "I'll drink to that," he said as they clinked glasses.

Sari served them both helpings of the

gratin, and he felt her watching him eat. She had learned to cook when she was very young. Her mother had always avoided the kitchen, preferring to be in the barn, or at a different ranch, with other riders training for the circus ring. But Grey liked to cook, and he'd taught Sari the best he could. She'd also picked things up on trips to Rhode Island, visiting his parents, from Anne, Laurent's mother, and from Rosalie.

"This is delicious," he said.

"There's a reason," she said.

"Because you made it?" he asked, smiling.

"No." She put down her fork. Suddenly the warmth in her eyes disappeared, and they were back in the deep freeze. "Someone told me the secret ingredient."

"Really? Who?"

"The lady with the ribbon."

Grey kept eating. He didn't believe her. She was testing him. Over the years, he'd discovered the danger of talking about any woman to his daughter, so he never did it. He was the father of a sweet, troubled girl who'd been abandoned by her mother, and he had learned to tread very lightly, to protect her carefully, and to not take the bait when she dangled it in front of him.

"It's true, Papa," she said.

"Sari, stop. Eat your dinner, okay?"

"She stood right here, in our kitchen."

Grey refilled his water glass, drank it down. A cool breeze blew through the open window. He smelled the marsh and the sea, and he heard the cries of distant shorebirds, and he thought of the horses in the barn. He couldn't meet his daughter's eyes.

"Can't you taste the secret ingredient?" she prodded.

"Something does taste extra good," he said, taking another bite.

"It's a combination of cinnamon and nut-meg!" she said. "Rosalie left without telling me, but that's okay, it really is. Because now I know. Because the lady with the ribbon told me."

Grey slammed his hand down, and his fork clattered onto his plate. She was push-ing him, and he felt his frustration boiling oven. There were no women in his life. No matter how much he'd have liked to invite Susannah back to the ranch, it wasn't going to happen. Now she was blaming him for it anyway. He looked up, saw Sari's eyes shining with tears.

"Why are you so mad?" she asked.

He spoke carefully. "Because I don't want you saying that about 'the lady with the ribbon.' I didn't bring her here, Sari. I don't even know her—it was an accidental meeting, just like I told you. She went her way, and I went mine. I know you don't like—"

"She might have gone her own way, but she found her way back here," Sari shot out.

"What do you mean?"

"I looked out the window, and there was this person leaning over the paddock fence. Just looking at Mystère."

Grey felt a jolt—she *had* been here. He wasn't sure why that image did the trick—but suddenly he pictured Susannah Connolly standing by the ring, greeting the horse who had rescued her. He could see it completely, and he knew Sari was telling him the truth.

"When was she here?"

"So now you believe me?" she asked.

"Yes," he said, taking a deep breath. She sounded both bitter and hurt. He saw her eyes cloud over and knew she was about to cry. "And now you believe me, too, right? I told you she was a stranger," he said.

"Yes. You didn't get the ribbon from my mother. I believe you now. Why should I have ever thought my mother would come back? What kind of idiotic idea would that be?"

"Sari . . ."

"You asked when the woman was here," Sari said. "It was while you were driving Rosalie home. She was standing right here in the kitchen, and you know what she said? That Mystère is a one-girl horse."

"She's right," Grey said.

"Most people don't get that," she said. "They think Mystère needs to be ridden more than she needs to be ridden by me. Even Laurent thinks that!"

"Mystère's doing fine," Grey said. "I make sure she gets enough exercise. You don't have to worry."

"Laurent says Susannah rides *comme un rêve*."

"Like a dream," Grey said, bowing his head as he ate, glad his daughter couldn't see the color rising in his cheeks and know that those had been his own words. *And like a cloud . . .*

"Is that true, Papa?" Sari said.

"Something like that."

"As good as my mother?"

"No one rides like your mother," Grey said.

They stared at each other across the table and their half-eaten dinners. Outside, one of the horses whinnied; Claude or Laurent must have gone into the barn. Grey thought of how Maria used to do that, visit the horses every evening. Was Sari remembering that, too?

"Exercise isn't the same as love," Sari said.

"What do you mean?"

"Mystère," she said. "Laurent says Mystère needs love."

"You love her, honey."

"But I don't ride her," Sari whispered.

Grey nodded. He'd never tried to push her. But there'd been so many times when he saw his daughter feeling the pain of missing her mother, and knew that she was also missing her horse. That night when Maria left had robbed Sari of more than just her mother.

"I could, maybe," Sari said now.

"Could what?"

"Ride again."

Grey couldn't believe his ears. Had she really said that? It was the first time in over five years that she'd even suggested riding. The doctors had told him she would heal; first her bones would knit together, then the physical pain would go away, then she'd want to live life again. And one day she'd wake up and she'd see colors.

As he watched, Sari carried her plate over to the sink and gazed out the window. He followed with his own plate and saw what she was looking at: Laurent leading one of the new ponies into the ring.

"Do you want to go out now?" Grey asked. "It's not too late, and I could get Mystère saddled up and . . ."

"Not tonight," Sari whispered.

"Okay," he said, not wanting to push.

"That lady wants to ride," Sari said softly, after a couple of minutes. The water was running, nearly drowning out her voice. "She was looking for a ranch, and Laurent asked if she wanted to come back here, but she said no."

Grey thought of their meeting on the street in Stes.-Maries, and how he hadn't told Susannah about his ranch. She'd probably thought that strange—he knew he would have. And he assumed that she'd picked up on Sari's antagonism, and not wanted anything to do with them.

"She'll find a good place," Grey said. "She said she hasn't ridden a lot lately. She probably wants to take her time finding the right horse."

"The right horse is Mystère," Sari whispered.

"She's *your* horse," Grey said.

"If that woman rides like a dream, time doesn't matter," Sari said, looking up at him with blank eyes, like a sleepwalker. "In dreams, time is nothing at all. That's how it will be for me and Mystère, too. I ride her in my sleep—I always have. I could do it right now if I wanted."

"Dreams aren't life," he said. "Sari, let me take you out, okay? We'll go easy at first, and . . ."

Sari's eyes were suddenly blazing, full of tears.

"Why did she go?" Sari whispered hotly.

Grey looked at her. They'd been over this so often in the past. Recently, he'd tried to stay away from the subject of Maria, not wanting to upset her. But something was making it all bubble back up now. "Your mother?" he asked. "I told you, sweetheart. It had nothing to do with you." He reached out to take his daughter's hand, but she turned away, her shoulders shaking with silent sobs.

"That's almost worse," she managed to say. "It's almost worse, that something so big had nothing to do with me."

"Sari . . ."

"She pushed me away from her," Sari wept, burying her face in her hands. "Right here, in the kitchen. That was worse than falling off Mystère. That was the worst of all."

"Sari," he said.

She walked out of the room. He heard her heading upstairs, listened for her door to slam. He just stood at the kitchen window, watching Laurent in the ring with the white pony. He saw the boy gaze upward and knew that Sari's light had just gone on.

Grey stared out at the paddock, thinking of Susannah Connolly standing there. Thinking of her behind him on Mystère, pressed tight against his back, her hips jammed into his, the feel of her arms locked around his waist.

The two black cats circled his feet, waiting to be fed. But he couldn't quite move.
He closed his eyes, listening to the hoofbeats in the ring outside, wondering where
Susannah was, what she was doing, why
she had really come to the ranch.

Topaz picked Susannah up right on time,
and drove through the town, past the fortified church, and into the darkening countryside. Night birds and crickets called through
the open windows as Topaz sped along
roads so narrow, reeds and rushes brushed
the car as it passed.

Purple clouds raced across stars and
moon, and Susannah felt as if a storm was
coming. Topaz had seemed distracted,
silent, since she'd picked up Susannah, but
now she shot her a quick look.

"Is the breeze too much? I could put up
the windows."

"I like it," Susannah said. It matched her
mood. She'd felt all stirred up after visiting
the Dempsey Ranch. That child, Sari, was
so lovely and seemed so lost. And who was
that woman Susannah had seen with Grey?

Susannah closed her eyes, trying to stop

thinking of Grey Dempsey, struggling to understand her feelings about him. They were
so unprecedented, such a bolt from the
blue. Obviously he had a family. But even
knowing that, she was so curious about
him, so drawn to him. After years of building
her career, worrying about her sick mother,
keeping Ian at arm's length, she felt
knocked out by the intensity of her attrac-
tion to him.

She glanced over at Topaz. She was
tempted to ask about the Dempseys, but
she'd seen how Topaz had reacted to the
sight of Grey earlier, outside the church. She
opened her mouth to speak, but Topaz
turned and spoke first.

"I am sorry for being so quiet," she said.
"I have things on my mind."

"Would you rather postpone this?" Susannah said. "I'll be here for nearly two
more weeks. We can do it another time."

"No," Topaz said, flashing her wonderful
smile. "It is when life is challenging that I
need nights like this most."

"Nights like this?"

"With the Circle," Topaz said.

She drove in silence for another few kilometers, then turned into a driveway marked with a sign that said *Mas SLK.*

"What does that mean?" Susannah asked.

"*Mas* means farmhouse," Topaz said.

"And SLK?"

Again, the wide smile. "Sara-la-Kali," Topaz said.

Topaz drove along a rutted road, into a field behind a small white house. Big boxy shapes, silhouetted by the cloud-filmed moon, were set in a wide circle around the land's perimeter. As they drove closer, Susannah thought they were cottages, many with lights glowing in their windows. But when Topaz parked the car beside one, and Susannah climbed out, she saw that the cottage had wheels.

"*Ma roulotte,*" Topaz said, gesturing with welcome.

Susannah stood looking around. The caravans were brightly painted—that was obvious, even in the shifting light. Topaz's was a warm shade of pumpkin, decorated with a painted garland of flowers over the door and windows. The flowers were bright red, cool lavender, and gold, entwined with ropes of silver-green laurel. Now, turning around, Su-

sannah looked at the other caravans—
painted in shades of brick red, dark purple,
saffron yellow, and sage green. All were
painted with flower garlands. Susannah
thought of the Dempseys' kitchen, and felt
prickles on the back of her neck.

"They're so beautiful," Susannah said.

"The flowers are familiar to you, yes?"
Topaz asked.

Susannah nodded. "I just saw some, very
similar, today . . . how did you know?"

"Rosalie saw you driving toward the Manade du Dempsey. And you asked me about
him earlier, no?"

Him; realizing she meant Grey, sent a
jolt down Susannah's spine. Feeling Topaz's
eyes on her now, Susannah felt a rush of
apprehension and didn't respond. Suddenly
she wondered why she'd been brought
here.

"Don't be afraid," Topaz said, putting her
hand on Susannah's arm. "You, of all people, should have no fear."

Susannah wanted to tell her she wasn't
afraid. She took risks in her work all the time
and reveled in exotic cultures. Visiting a
gypsy camp was nothing compared with
crawling into a skinny crack in the rock. But

her emotions were raw and unfamiliar, and right at the surface, and that was scaring her. She wished she had driven her own car, so she could leave right now. Topaz's hand closed gently around Susannah's wrist, and her gaze was calm and steady.

"Please," she said. "Everyone is so eager to meet you."

"Who painted the garlands in their kitchen?" Susannah asked. She needed to know, needed to hear that Grey was married so she could stop feeling this way.

"The Circle will tell you," Topaz said. "And they're inside right now. Please, come let me introduce you."

And Susannah swallowed her fear, allowing herself to be led up the steep, narrow stairs to the doorway of Topaz's caravan. The door opened, and Susannah stepped inside. She saw candles burning everywhere, and had the fleeting impression of Sarah's crypt—this had exactly the same feeling of candlelit devotion in a small, enclosed space.

Only instead of the lone statue of Sarah, the dark almost-saint, Topaz's caravan was filled with women. Every spot was filled— the small table and three straight-back chairs, the loveseat, the floor. Only one chair was vacant—a large comfortable-looking armchair, all the way in the back.

"Everyone," Topaz said in a thrilling voice, "this is Susannah Connolly. The person I told you about."

One by one, the women stood. Topaz conducted Susannah through the cramped, narrow interior. Susannah looked into each face, and saw that they were women of all ages, from teenaged to very old. And as Susannah went to shake each woman's hand, she was met instead with a kiss. One, clearly the oldest, had tears in her eyes.

Susannah felt overwhelmed by all the love and emotion in the room. With Topaz's arm around her shoulders, she was led to the back of the caravan, pressed down to sit in the empty armchair, the seat of honor.

"But why?" she asked. "I don't understand."

"Because your mother was blessed by Sarah," Topaz explained. "And that is why you are here."

"Here, in Stes.-Maries?" Susannah asked.

"Here on this earth," the oldest woman said. "Sarah performed a miracle, so that your mother became pregnant with you. And so you could be born."

"That's what she always said," Susannah whispered.

"To a woman who longs for a child, who prays to have a baby and can't," the old woman said, "there's no greater pain. None in the world."

"She told me she prayed all the time," Susannah said. "Every month. But never . . ."

"Until she visited Sarah," another woman said.

"And she didn't even know about Sarah," Susannah said quietly. "I mean no disrespect by this—and my mother certainly wouldn't either. But in America, in the Catholic Church, Sarah is not known. Or not talked about . . ."

"She belongs to us," a young woman said proudly. "She's *our* saint. She's of and for the Rom."

"That's right, *petite chérie*." Topaz laughed. "But Susannah is proof that Sarah looks beyond."

"I never believed such a thing," the young woman said. She had a short, spiky haircut, the tips tinged with gold.

"That is why I wanted Susannah to visit the Circle," Topaz said.

"For proof?" someone else asked.

"Yes," Topaz said. "So you could meet her, and hear her story."

SEVEN

"You . . ." Susannah said, looking around the candlelit room at all the faces turned in her direction. "All of you . . . are the 'Circle'?"

"We are," Topaz said. "The Sarah Circle. Let me introduce everyone."

Going around the room, Topaz pointed out Anaïs, Naguine, Isabel, Zuna, Eugénie, Jeanne-Marie, Zin-Zin, Florine, Ana, Étoile, and Rosalie. Susannah nodded to each woman, locking eyes with Rosalie. She had been the one in the car with Grey, and the one who had reported Susannah's trip to

the ranch to Topaz, and she regarded Susannah with suspicious eyes now.

"Pleased to meet you," Susannah said to
the room.

"And to meet you," said Zin-Zin, the old
woman, in heavily accented English.

"Tell me about the Sarah Circle," Susannah said quietly, looking at Topaz, but taking in the whole group.

"We're devoted to Sara-la-Kali," Topaz
explained. Everyone took turns talking,
while Susannah listened intently.

The women were part of a clan of
Manouche Gypsies. Their group had
branches all over northern Europe, mainly in
France and Belgium. Romanies romanced
the road, and were beset by a constant,
everlasting yearning for whatever lay beyond the next hill, the next town, the next
country.

Every woman in the room had grown
up traveling, living in caravans, helping to
support their families by basket weaving,
bracelet making, singing, and guitar playing. The single constant in their lives had
been the yearly pilgrimage here every summer, to this wild land of the Camargue, to

pay respect to Sarah. Now they had settled in town year-round.

Zin-Zin told of early days, when the fields were filled with music, and the families would congregate around the caravans. Django Reinhardt, the legendary guitarist who'd influenced B.B. King, was part of the Manouche clan, and had come here to this very spot every May 24, during the *Pèlerinage des Gitans,* to pay homage to Sarah. The room fell absolutely silent, with love and reverence, listening to the old woman talk.

"Sara-la-Kali," she said. "Black Sarah. She was like us: a girl who traveled far and wide. Her skin was dark, her spirit was pure. She served the aunts of Jesus, she arranged for their safe passage over the sea, through storms, from Palestine. She was not accepted as a saint by the Catholic Church, but that didn't matter to us."

"The Manouche has roots in India, you see," Topaz said. "We originated there, wandered through Byzantium, gained the name 'Tziganes' for our work as animal traders and trainers, moved onto Egypt. 'Gypsy' is just a corruption of 'Egyptian,' but even that wasn't right. We were enslaved and persecuted; we were called the

'Gypsy Scourge.' Louis XIV made Gypsy men his slaves."

"And he had Gypsy women flogged and deported," Zuna said.

"Yet we always had Sarah to protect us," Rosalie said, her eyes glaring at Susannah, as if she could read her mind, saw her as an interloper. "Sara-la-Kali."

"Kali," Susannah said.

"What do *you* know of her?" Rosalie asked, the question a challenge.

"Leave it!" Topaz warned.

Rosalie said something fast and harsh in a language Susannah didn't understand. But it was clear that Rosalie mistrusted and disliked her. Susannah studied the beautiful woman, with her deep brown eyes and cascading black hair, and wondered what her relationship with Grey and Sari could be.

"I just want to know," Rosalie said sharply, "what she thinks she knows about Kali."

"Don't grill her, she's our guest," Topaz said. But Susannah wanted to answer.

"I'm an anthropologist," she said.

"You're here to study us?" Rosalie asked, looking around. "Like someone else we know, eh?"

The room buzzed quietly, and Susannah thought of what she had read regarding Grey Dempsey's background as a journalist.

"I'm not here to study you," she said quietly.

"Not at all?" Rosalie challenged. "That's not why you've come?"

Susannah shook her head, trying to be as truthful as possible without saying too much. "I have work to do, it's true. The first rainy day, I'll be going to the library in Arles to do some research for a colleague . . ."

"On us?"

"Not specifically," Susannah said. "But I can't help making observations. My colleague, Helen Oakes, has taken many trips to India. One of her most important papers was on the feminine power of Sakti, and the Kali Age, on the mother-goddess and fertility cults. My understanding is that 'Sara-la-Kali' relates to that Kali. Does it also refer to your clan's origins in India?"

"Yes!" Topaz said, smiling and gleaming, as if with pride for a prize student. She gave Rosalie a quick, hard glance, then looked back at Susannah. "Kali, the essence of divine feminine spirit, of mother-love and feminine energy."

"Sakti," Susannah said. "Sanskrit for feminine energy."

Topaz nodded. "That is what Sarah means to us. She has the spirit of Kali, our connection to the divine, and to our ancient Eastern roots. For us, Sarah represents the primal, the source, the Great Mother."

"We all need her," Zuna said.

"Especially those of us who have lost our mothers," Zin-Zin said with what seemed to be secret, deeply held sorrow. "No matter how old one is, one never stops needing her mother."

The words brought tears to Susannah's eyes. She suddenly sensed her mother's spirit in the room, as strongly as she had felt it at the church earlier that day, and her chest filled with the most penetrating ache she'd ever felt. "I miss mine," she said, glancing at Rosalie. "More than I ever thought was possible. More than anything else, that's what brought me here."

"Not research," Topaz said to Rosalie, as if punctuating the point.

Zin-Zin reached over and took her hand. Susannah closed her eyes, remembered the last months of her mother's life, the times she'd sat with her, so close, just like this.

Why hadn't she done it more? Why hadn't she thrown her work aside and paid attention to what was important?

"What happened to your mother?" Zin-Zin asked.

"She died of cancer," Susannah said. "Lymphoma."

"Were you with her?"

Susannah's throat caught. "Some of the time, yes," she said. "I tried to be. Her illness lasted a long time. I . . . have to travel for my job. Grants are so hard to come by, and sometimes I'd have to keep to a schedule set by my benefactors. I'd be on-site, but I'd be thinking of my mother. . . ."

"You were torn," Topaz said.

Susannah hesitated. She'd never opened up about this before, but something about these women made the words pour out. "Completely. I love my work, and she was so proud of what I did. I'd feel I was doing it for her, as well as for myself. But I'd also be feeling such guilt, knowing she was sick at home, wanting to be with her."

"Her illness progressed?" Zin-Zin asked.

"Yes. But it didn't happen fast—we kept having hope. She would go into remission. But it always came back. At the end, it overtook her." She bowed her head, feeling all the tears and guilt and emotion come welling up. "It ran all through her body, all at once. She always handled everything with such grace, even at the end. She tried to protect me from knowing how bad it was, so I'd go to Istanbul and do my work."

"What happened?"

Susannah listened to the wind and rain outside, trying to hold herself together. "I was in Turkey, on-site. I saw such beautiful paintings . . . the most incredible of my career. I took pictures, knowing she'd love to see them. And then I got the call . . ." Remembering, she started to weep. "Her nurse said my mother wouldn't let her phone me until then. She had started to get worse, and from then on it was so fast. I called her doctor, and he told me he was putting her in hospice, and on morphine, and . . . I got on a plane, and she died while I was in the air."

Susannah cried, and she heard some of the other women crying with her.

Zin-Zin's grip on Susannah's hand tightened. "Don't blame yourself. She wouldn't want you to."

"But I do blame myself," she wept. "How can I not? I wasn't there. . . ."

"She didn't want you there," Zin-Zin whispered.

Susannah raised her eyes. "What?"

"It was her decision to have the nurses not call you. This was her journey—her own death. Perhaps she *waited* for you to travel so far away before she let herself start on it."

"What do you mean?"

Zin-Zin was old and wise, and as Susannah gazed into her eyes, she knew that she had seen many deaths. "When a mother loves her child as much as yours loved you, she might find it impossible to let go, to leave you, if you were sitting right there. She had to wait for you to go away before she could die." She paused. "You're such a smart woman—why have you not realized that?

"Listen to your own heart," she went on. "You know I'm right, don't you? I can see it in your eyes. . . ."

Susannah nodded slowly. What Zin-Zin said made such perfect sense. Susannah and her mother had been so close. It would have been impossible for them to say good-bye, for her mother to have let go.

"She's with you now," Zin-Zin said. "Right here."

Susannah looked around, just like a child who really hoped to see her mother standing right there. But all she saw were the kind, concerned faces of the Romany women.

"She brought you here," Florine said. "You know that, don't you?"

Susannah looked up, startled. She remembered her mother's words: *Visit Sarah.*

"She told me to come," Susannah said.

"To Stes.-Maries?" Naguine asked.

"To see Sarah," Topaz said gently. "Your mother knew that you needed her."

"We're blessed to have you," Ana said. "You, whose life has been such a miracle."

"It has?" Susannah asked, looking around the faces. Sometimes she felt so guarded and alone. She spent her days delving into faded wall paintings and dusty books, researching people and cultures long dead. She'd gotten tangled up in the old habit of Ian. Just because he was there, he'd kept her from looking for anything like real love.

Suddenly she heard the name *Grey*—and she swore it was her mother who'd said it. She shivered, shaking her head with disbelief. Looking around the room, she saw candlelight flickering in mirrors and the window glass, burnishing the faces around her.

"You feel something, don't you?" Topaz asked.

Susannah nodded. Her skin tingled, as if she'd just been brushed by a ghost—which, she was positive, she had.

Zin-Zin began to talk again. She told stories of Sarah and her works, and what she meant to the women of the Circle. They were the caretakers of Sarah's crypt. And they were the watchers over all the miracles she had performed.

"Topaz has brought us several like you," Zin-Zin said. "Occasionally people, women, whose lives have been touched by Sarah, have rented her house in town. But mostly they're Romany. Or with at least a connection to the clan. Some had a grandmother who was Rom, or an aunt, or a cousin. Most had grown up as devoted to Sarah as we ourselves are. They come here, crippled or ill, and when they depart town, they leave their crutches behind."

"They don't need them anymore," Susannah said, picturing Sarah's crypt, lined with offerings, its ceiling blackened with centuries' worth of soot from votive candles.

"But you," Zin-Zin continued, "you are not Rom. You're not from our lineage."

"That's what makes you so special to us right now," Topaz said. "The thing that sets you apart. Sarah has performed a miracle in your life, yet you're not a Gypsy. That is very unusual. It's why I had to introduce you to the Circle."

"Thank you," Susannah said. "I'm so glad to have met you all . . ." She trailed off, hesitating.

"What is it?" Topaz asked. "Do you have questions for us?"

"Several," Susannah said, laughing. "Do you all live here, at the Mas SLK?"

"Yes," Florine said. "These are our *roulottes* . . . many of them were driven down, over a number of years, from Flache os Courbos."

"The Pond of the Ravens," Topaz translated. "In Belgium."

"Is it just women?"

"Just women in the Circle," Ana said. "But many of us have husbands and sons.

We have families, of course—family is more important to us than anything in the world."

The women murmured their assent, smiling and nodding. Susannah felt a sharp twinge; that was true for her, too. It always had been. Yet once again, looking at Zin-Zin, she saw deep pain. The old woman closed her eyes, as if feeling private anguish. Susannah tried to catch her eye, but Zin-Zin wouldn't look up. Surrounded by these women, united by their connection to Sarah, and their devotion to her and Kali, she was struck by the fact that they also had husbands and children. How had she let herself miss out on that?

"Do you have children of your own?" Zin-Zin asked softly, suddenly raising her eyes.

The question stopped Susannah short, wondering how the old woman had read her mind. "No," she replied.

"You will," the woman said. She squeezed Susannah's hand again, then grinned, her tan and weathered face beautiful in spite of, or perhaps because of, her many wrinkles. "I feel certain of it."

Topaz had set water to boil, and when the whistle blew, she and some of the others began to pass out teacups. She'd brewed green tea that tasted of honey and lavender, and Susannah sipped it, letting it warm her hands and insides. The mistral blew, rattling the windows, shaking the caravan from side to side.

"Your caravans are very beautiful," she said after a long moment.

"Thank you," some of the women replied.

"Topaz said the Circle paints the garlands," she said. "You're all artists?"

"Creativity runs in Romany people," Zin-Zin said. "Music, poetry, painting, riding horses . . . it all comes from the same source."

"You like the garlands?" Rosalie asked sharply.

"Very much," Susannah said.

"Did you like Maria's? The one in her kitchen?"

"Stop it," Topaz warned.

"Maria's?" some of the others asked, sounding shocked.

"She was at Maria's house today!" Rosalie said. "I saw her driving there!"

"Who is Maria?" Susannah asked.

Zin-Zin dropped Susannah's hand, and a cool silence fell over the Circle. Susannah felt all eyes on her, and it took all her strength to not look away. She gazed from one face to the next, waiting for someone to answer.

"She was one of us," Florine said.

"*Is* one of us," Rosalie corrected.

Zuna let out a laugh, said something in the language Susannah couldn't understand, and Rosalie reacted as if she'd been slapped. Topaz, shrugging, said in French, "She's right. You're the only one of us who's gone to the Manade du Dempsey since Maria left. So you of all people should suspend judgment and criticism of our guest."

"It was only for the child," Rosalie said. "But that's over now."

Were they speaking of Sari? What did she mean—*that's over now*? Susannah thought of Grey; was Rosalie involved with him or not?

Just then Zin-Zin clapped her hands. "*Écoutez!*" she said sharply. "We must not fight. Not in front of an outsider." But then, turning slowly to face Susannah, she asked, in the same heavily accented English as before, "Why *were* you at the Manade?"

"The white horses," Susannah said.

"She wants to take a ride through the Parc, of course!"

"Bien sûr!"

Was it her imagination, or did the tension in the room diffuse, fly away? There was much laughing and nodding, and she heard Florine say that with their focus on Sarah, they forgot that people had other reasons for visiting the Camargue: the white horses, the black bulls, and pink clouds of flamingos—*les fleurs qui volent*, "the flowers who fly"—winging across the endless sea plain.

"There are other ranches with white horses," Rosalie said.

"True, but none are better than the Manade du Dempsey," Zin-Zin said. "Grey has the best horses in the region, and no one knows the park better. Except my father, of course, and he has been dead for fifty years."

"She asked about Maria," Rosalie said. "Perhaps we should tell her."

"Enough for tonight!" Topaz said, standing up with a quick glance at Florine that made her start to collect teacups. "I must get Susannah back home before the mistral blows trees down across the road."

Susannah stood. In spite of the hostility she felt coming from Rosalie, she realized

that she didn't want to leave. She felt so
snug in Topaz's caravan, surrounded by the
Sarah Circle. She wanted to hear about
Maria, and about Grey and Sari.

"Thank you so much," she said, gazing at
each person. "I have had a wonderful time."

"We are so glad Topaz brought you," Zin-
Zin said, clutching Susannah's hands. The
old woman's eyes gleamed, tears pooling.
"You have honored us by coming."

"I'll never forget you," Susannah said,
gazing into her eyes, kissing her cheek.
Topaz led Susannah through the caravan,
exchanging hugs and kisses with all the
other women. Only Rosalie held back, arms
folded across her chest, just watching from
the back of the *roulotte.*

Susannah walked out into the strong
wind and driving rain, heard the door close
quietly behind her. Topaz drove her out of
the *mas,* and Susannah took one last look
back at the caravan.

The curtains had been pulled, and the
glow of candlelight was no longer visible.
She closed her eyes, almost wondering
whether she had imagined everything. But
there was Topaz sitting beside her, fiercely
concentrating on the tempest-washed road-

way, and there was the small medallion of Sarah hanging from the rearview mirror.

Susannah wanted to ask about Maria, but didn't dare distract Topaz from driving. The storm raged outside the car, and Susannah imagined it was fifty percent Topaz's skill and fifty percent Sarah's grace keeping them safe on the road.

EIGHT

It was late; Sari didn't know what time, but the dream had awakened her again. A jumble of horses, and car lights, and her own scream. Had the sound actually come out of her mouth? She lay still, listening, as if she could hear it echo.

Sometimes she woke her father when she cried out in her sleep. But tonight there were no sounds coming from down the hall. No, instead, she heard them outside her window, a voice talking down below.

Heading over to the window, she peered into the darkness. The storm that had blown up earlier had broken and someone stood in the horse ring. She squinted, trying to see. It was Laurent, trying to climb onto the back of a colt, one of the new, wild ones, talking quietly, giving the yearling—or maybe himself—a pep talk.

Sari went downstairs—she moved stiffly, her bones aching, as if the dream had reminded them of how broken they'd been. She opened the kitchen door, careful not to let the cats out, and hurried barefoot into the yard. Laurent was so intent doing what he was doing, he didn't even see her.

He held the colt by a short line attached to a leather halter. Then he jumped up onto the fence, holding tight to the line, and stepped onto the colt's bare back. One careful foot, then the other . . . The colt didn't even have to rear up—he just gave a good shake, and Laurent fell off into the soft dirt.

Sari laughed.

"What's so funny?" Laurent asked, standing up and brushing himself off.

"What were you trying to do, kill yourself?"

"That would make you laugh?" he asked.

She shook her head; it would be the worst thing she could imagine. But after the bad dream she'd just had, and the upsetting events of the day, it just felt so good to laugh with her friend.

"No," she said. "It would make me cry."

He took a step closer to her. She felt his warm breath on her forehead. She wrapped her arms around herself. Her thin cotton nightgown rippled in the breeze. He was so close; squeezing her eyes tightly shut, she imagined her arms were his, that he was holding her. The thought scared and excited her so much, she stepped back and fell over flat.

"C'mere," he said, giving her his hand. "I fall off the horse, and you trip over your own feet."

"I guess I won't be joining the circus any time soon," she said, letting him help her up. "And you shouldn't either. What were you trying to do—ride standing up?"

"Yeah," he said, and suddenly they were standing close again.

Sari stared past him, at the colt in the ring. He was excited, being out so late at night in such changeable weather. The wind seemed to be coming from all directions. She shivered, and felt Laurent drape something around her shoulders—his sweater.

"I wanted to see what it was like," he said.

"Riding standing up?"

He nodded.

"What's so great about riding standing up?"

"You should know—you could do it."

"I haven't even ridden sitting down in a long, long time."

"You have circus blood in you," he said.

"Shhh."

"You do."

"Don't say that."

"It's true," he said. He paused, and she worried he was about to start talking about her mother. But to her relief, he didn't. "That woman who came here? Susannah Connolly?"

"What about her?" Sari asked. Hearing her name made her feel funny, and she wasn't sure why. There'd been something so nice about her, about the way she'd offered that suggestion about the spices, and about the way she'd said that Mystère was a one-girl horse.

"Your father said she rides like a dream, but that's nothing compared to . . ." Laurent trailed off.

Sari looked up into his deep eyes, saw

the way he was watching her. She felt herself blush.

"Nothing compared to you," Laurent finished.

"But I don't ride anymore," Sari said.

"You're going to start," he said. "I can feel
it. You want to. You're better now; your
body is healed, and you're dying to ride."

"Yes," she whispered. "But I'm still afraid."

"That's okay," he said, tugging his
sweater more tightly around her, keeping
her shoulders warm. "You won't be forever.
You'll start riding again, and once you do, I
won't be able to keep up with you."

"But you're the best rider I know!" she
said. "Our age, that is."

"I don't have what you have," he whispered, his eyes burning.

"Don't say it," she said, wanting to block
her ears.

"Gypsy blood," he said. "You'll ride the
way your mother rode. And you'll leave me
here in the ring . . ."

"Laurent," she said, "I'm not like her.
Don't say that!"

"I didn't say you were like her. I said you'll
ride . . ."

"Shhhh," she said, putting her hand over

his mouth. But he just pushed her hand away.

"Once you start, I want to make sure I'm as good as you, so we can ride together. But since you have it in you already, I have to work twice as hard."

"That's why you're out here in the middle of the night? Trying to break your neck?" she asked, touching his chest. "What would I do if you crashed down and got trampled? If I woke up in the morning and found you in a lump, with hoofprints all over your sad body? Do you think I'd be able to eat my breakfast, go to school, live my life?"

"Without even a thought," he said, grinning.

"You're an idiot," she said, and she couldn't even smile. What was wrong with him? Didn't he know what could happen to people who fooled around on horseback? She pulled his sweater from around her neck, handed it to him.

"Sari!"

"Go to sleep, Laurent. We have school in the morning."

"You want to ride, I know it," he said. "Let me get Mystère. . . ."

"No," she said, facing him. "No."

He stared at her, and she knew he saw her trembling. This time it wasn't from the chilly air. She stood still, shaking, and he reached for her. But she wouldn't let him touch her. She felt confused, her emotions wild.

"Come with me," he said, finally taking her hand. She wanted to pull back, but even more, she wanted to follow him. He led her toward the barn. Digging her heels in, she couldn't step over the threshold. "It's okay. You know who we're going to see."

"Mystère," Sari whispered, and all at once she let him pull her inside.

She never came in here anymore. Having spent just about every possible minute in this barn the first years of her life, she felt the electric memory of her last time in here: the night her mother had left. A huge shiver ran down her spine, and she felt dizzy.

But Laurent held her by the hand, and he led her over to Mystère's stall. The lights were low, and the air was cold. Mystère knew immediately that Sari was there; the horse still remembered her smell, knew her voice. Mystère turned around in the big box stall and walked over to the door, tail swish-

ing once—as if in greeting or admonish-
ment: *What took you so long?*

With Laurent holding her hand, Sari
reached toward her horse. She held her
hand out, palm up, and felt Mystère's velvety muzzle brush her fingers, and the feeling of it made her weak in the knees, made
her eyes flood with tears. She hadn't
touched her beloved horse once since her
mother had left.

"Je t'aime," she whispered, staring into
her horse's huge dark eyes, feeling as if the
last five years had just disappeared. She
wanted to throw her arms around the strong
neck, pull herself up onto the wide back.
But instead she just stood there, staring
into her horse's eyes, feeling tears on her
cheeks.

"She's missed you," Laurent said.

"I know," Sari whispered, thinking about
what he had said before about the difference between love and exercise, knowing
that he'd been right, that nothing could be
truer. Being let loose in the ring, allowed to
run around, wasn't the same as this: girl and
horse together, looking into each other's
hurt eyes.

"You know what I think?"

"What?" she asked.

"That if you ride again, something amazing will happen."

"But I *can't.*"

"You have to," he said, the words rushing out. "It will help you."

"Help me what?"

"See colors again."

"Laurent," she gasped, closing her eyes tight. She knew that he knew about her problems, but they never talked about it. Having him say it out loud made her feel so embarrassed—but also, in the strangest way—so good. To know he cared . . .

"What will make you able to ride again?" he whispered.

"I'm not sure," she whispered, feeling Mystère's warm breath on her hand, wishing she had Laurent's sweater around her shoulders again. She was icy cold, but not from the weather; from the inside out, as if her heart were a chunk of ice.

"Maybe someone could take you," he said. "So you don't have to ride alone."

"Stop," she said.

"And maybe that could happen soon," he said.

"Shhhh," she whispered, not really thinking, not wanting to do anything or be any-where but right here, standing with her horse and Laurent, just being together. She closed her eyes so she wouldn't have to see the world in black and white. With her eyes shut, feeling the warmth of Laurent and Mystère, everything was perfect. Everything was fine. . . .

Laurent had an idea of who should take Sari riding. The next morning, the storm had re-newed itself, and it was raging again, wind blowing the rain sideways. His body ached from the fall he'd taken, and pulling on his jeans, he saw that he had a big bruise on his hip. But he thought of the injuries Sari had suffered, knew that this was nothing. He ate breakfast fast, getting outside before Sari did. He caught up with Grey, standing in the barn's feed room.

"*Bonjour,*" Laurent said.

"*Ça va?*" Grey asked, hauling down a new bale of hay. Laurent went over to help him, shouldering the heavy bale out of the loft, down to the floor. "Thank you," Grey said. He looked a little surprised to see Laurent in the barn so early.

"At this hour I'm used to seeing you running out to make the school bus, with no time to stop and see the horses," Grey said.

"I didn't come to see them. I came to see you."

Again, Grey looked surprised. He was used to viewing Laurent as the little kid next door. He'd grown up playing with Sari, and if he had anything serious to talk about— well, that's what his father was for. But Grey nodded, beckoned Laurent into the stable office, gestured at the chair across the wide desk.

"What is it, Laurent?"

Maybe Grey thought he'd come to ask about more work, or a raise, or permission to ride Django, the big stallion—he had an all-business look in his eyes. So Laurent cleared his throat, feeling nervous, and said, "It's Sari."

"What about her?" Grey said in a way that let Laurent know he had his total attention— he sat up straighter, looked sharper. He always looked troubled—Laurent knew Sari gave him a lot to worry about. And right now all that concern was focused across the desk, at Laurent.

"She needs to ride."

"Well, I'd like her to," Grey said. "When she's ready. But she hasn't been . . ."

"She's ready," Laurent said. "I know her . . . better than anyone except you." He watched for Grey's reaction to that, then continued. "She stands out in the yard, looking at the horses. At night I look up and see her in her window, staring toward Mystère. And last night . . ."

"What happened last night?"

"She came into the barn."

"She did?" Grey asked, staring at him, taking that in. "By herself?"

"With me. This is the closest she's let herself come, ever since the accident," Laurent said.

"I know. Well, I'm glad to hear she went in. That's a big step."

"We have to help her ride," Laurent said, the words pouring out. "That night, Sari's heart was broken, and if we could help her in the right way, if we could make everything right for her, help her go back to the way she was before she fell, before her mother left . . ."

"Laurent—" Grey began, clearly disturbed by Laurent's direction.

"No, listen—I know I'm right! We have to help her!"

"Of course I want to help her," Grey said. "More than anything, you know that."

"She lives in the dark," Laurent said, his voice thick. "In a colorless world. I think of all the things Sari can't see, all the beautiful colors, and I try to think of ways that she could see them again."

"The doctor said that one day her ability to see colors will come back," Grey said. "It could come back gradually, or all at once." But he sounded like he was repeating long-ago words in which he'd lost hope.

Laurent already knew what the doctors had said, kept saying. He'd grown up with Sari. He'd heard his parents talking about her condition. He knew there were different kinds of colorblindness, and that hers was one of the most unusual: not only was her ability to see red and green impaired, but all colors.

"I want it to happen now," Laurent said to her father. "I want her to see colors now, and I think it will happen if she rides."

"Laurent . . ."

"I know there's a way to help her. She needs someone . . ." He trailed off, thinking of how he wished that could be him. He wished Sari would let him help her ride again; nothing mattered to him more. But somehow he knew she needed more than he could give her right now, and as he watched Grey look more intent, he knew he had to say it.

"Go ahead," Grey said. His tone had been steady and almost patronizing, as if he thought Laurent was just a kid, stupid and naive. He'd been just going along with Laurent, but suddenly he seemed to be really listening. "Tell me what you're thinking."

"You know she needs her mother," Laurent said.

Grey stared at him, hard and cold. For a minute, Laurent thought he was going to stand up and walk out of the office. But he stayed at his desk, his hands holding on to the edge. "Yes, I know," Grey said steadily. "But that's not going to happen."

Laurent nodded. "I think a woman could help her," he said.

"Like who?" Grey asked. "Sari doesn't want any women around here, doesn't want anyone to take her mother's place. Not even Rosalie."

"Not Rosalie," Laurent said. "Susannah

Connolly. The woman from the marsh, with the red ribbon . . ."

"I know who you mean," Grey said. His eyes brightened so sharply, Laurent wondered what was going on. But quickly the clouds came back. "But she's not going to ride here. For one thing, she's only visiting the area for a short time. For another, Sari wants nothing to do with her."

"I think you're wrong," Laurent said quietly, picturing the expression in Sari's eyes, standing by Mystère. She wanted to ride so badly—her longing was completely obvious. And it had been unlocked somehow by Susannah's arrival here at the ranch. That couldn't be a coincidence.

"Sari would never go for it."

"But what if she did?" Laurent pressed. "What if she did, and we let the chance pass by?"

Just then the phone rang; the Dempseys had one line that went to both the house and the barn. Grey answered while Laurent thought furiously about how he could convince him to try the plan.

When Grey hung up, the brightness was back in his eyes—along with a look of puzzlement, as if he wasn't quite sure what was going on. "Did you talk to anyone else about this?" he asked Laurent, sounding almost accusatory.

"About Sari riding? No—who would I talk to?"

Grey just stared at him; he had to know he was telling the truth. Just then the bus's horn sounded, and Laurent heard Sari's voice calling him. He grabbed his book satchel and headed for the door. "I hope you'll ask Susannah," he began.

"I'll think about it," Grey said. Frowning, he looked from Laurent back to the telephone, leaving Laurent to wonder who had called, and what was said. Then the boy pulled up his collar, ducked his head, and ran through the driving rain to the bus waiting in the road.

When Susannah woke up, she saw that rain was coming down hard. She had thought she might meander through the region, looking for another ranch that offered trail rides, but the mistral was too intense. Today would be the day she went to Arles.

Inspired by the night before, by the energy of the storm, the warmth of the caravan, and the women's stories, she felt more at peace than she had in months. Somehow last night had given her mother back to her.

Climbing out of bed, she looked out the window as she dressed, confirming that today would be a terrible day to ride. She thought of Grey, wondering what he did on days like this. She supposed ranchers had to work outside no matter what the weather was.

The drive to Arles took her right through the wildest part of the Parc, not far from where she'd encountered the bulls. The rain came sideways, blowing hard. When she passed the spot where she'd parked on that first day, gotten in trouble in the marsh, she noticed a car idling on the side of the road.

It looked like the one she had seen Grey driving—an old green Citroën. The sight of it made her heart bump; she looked over as she went past, trying to see inside the car, but the windows were slick with rain and fogged with steam. Glancing into her rearview mirror, she saw the car pull onto the road behind her.

Had she just conjured him up? Driving past this spot was completely visceral: her skin remembered the terror of the bulls, the excitement of leaping onto the horse behind Grey, of holding on to him. She needed all her concentration to drive, and lost track of the car. But when she rounded a bend, just past the wide lagoon, she saw a green blur in the rearview mirror. It might have been the mistral bending the reeds, or perhaps it was the green Citroën, on an errand all its own.

Susannah started to feel nervous. She'd already had one close call here in the Parc. There were no other cars on the road. She told herself she was being paranoid—why would Grey be following her, and how would he even know she'd be passing through? She hadn't decided, for sure, to go to the library in Arles until this morning, when she'd seen the weather.

But the heavy rain soon became a deluge, and she drove carefully along, both hands on the wheel, straight into Arles without another glance back at the road behind her. She couldn't believe how different this small city looked in the mistral from her first visit just a few days earlier; all the vibrant color had drained away, leaving gray and sepia stone. She found it even more romantic: mysterious, ancient, and haunted by ghosts.

She passed the obelisk at the Place de la République, and following the printed directions she held in one hand, drove through Old Town, into a maze of cobbled streets. Tall ochre houses lined the byways, their shutters painted in muted tones of sage, lavender, mint, and marsh rose, and Susannah couldn't help reflecting that they reminded her of the garlands on the caravans, and in Grey and Sari's kitchen.

Just past the Église St. Honorat, she parked the car, grabbed her briefcase, and ran for the alley between the medieval church and the building next door. Tucked at the very back of the narrow passage, she found a pillared enclosure with a small brass oval on the wall heralding *Bibliothèque du Cheval Blanc:* the White Horse Library.

She rang the bell, and was asked to give the password. Remembering Helen's note, she said the word *"Jardin"* into the speaker box. A buzzer sounded, then a series of quick, hard clicks as the locks were opened, and Susannah entered, shaking the water off her raincoat, wiping her shoes on the mat inside. A security guard— young, muscular, and armed—stood at the door. He searched Susannah brusquely, then sent her to another guard seated at a desk in the foyer. Susannah handed him her credentials—a letter of introduction from the professor.

The man examined the letter. *"Très bien,"* he said. Seeing that Susannah hoped to do research in the Lamartine Room, he directed her down a corridor. As she thanked him and left the desk, she heard the buzzer sound again and saw him lift the phone to ask for the password.

Susannah knew that this house had once been the rectory of the Romanesque church next door. It was now a privately funded library, containing so many rare books, manuscripts, and works of art that it required very intense security, especially since the theft by armed men, five years ago, of several priceless documents, including letters written by Saint Martha.

As Susannah approached the Lamartine Room, she noticed the heavy wooden doors, the barrel-vaulted ceilings, the solid Romanesque columns. Yet in striking contrast, the columns' capitals were decorated with bursts of lilies on one side and horses on the other, carved in high relief, an unusually decorative touch. It was a striking departure from the building's otherwise austere symmetry.

Entering through the heavy doors, Susannah settled down at a long mahogany table halfway down the room. She gave a call slip to the librarian on duty. Waiting for her request to be delivered, she noticed an unsmiling guard, machine gun held across his chest, at the entrance to the reference department. Looking up at the ceiling, Susannah saw the furrow left by a bullet five years earlier.

The robbery had been audacious. Susannah had heard all about it from Helen, who had been in Arles at the time. The thieves had entered, guns drawn, and tied up all the librarians and researchers. They'd known exactly what they were looking for: letters written by Saint Martha describing the Tarasque—the dragon that had lived in the Rhône River, attacking farmers and destroying bridges.

Saint Martha had tamed the beast with hymns and prayers.

Helen's field of interest had always been strong women. She'd studied groups influenced by powerful female figures, and one of her great passions was the study of Provence. Previously she had concentrated on Tarascon—the town on the Rhône closest to where the dragon lived.

But this trip, Susannah had promised to return to Connecticut College with material relating to the sea voyage from Galilee—for Saint Martha had been one of the group set adrift, including Lazarus and the three Marys and Sarah, who had landed in Stes.-Maries.

The librarian delivered the book to Susannah's table. Titled *Le Livre du Grand Voyage,* it was so ancient—jewel encrusted and bound by leather, with a raised cross just below the title—Susannah was required to wear special gloves so her skin oils wouldn't damage the parchment. The light overhead was dim and diffused: the parchment was so old and fragile, stronger light could harm the fibers.

Susannah made careful notes, sketching the book's cover—ruby eyes embedded in the green dragon's face, the heavy gold cross beneath the title. Gently turning the pages, she felt the thrill of touching a volume that had been created by a saint.

Time slid away. As Susannah delved into

the book, she lost track of the hours and minutes—even of the century. She was swept into a timeless story of a woman voyaging from her native land, landing in the Camargue, encountering a legendary monster along the way, taming it with love—just like Beauty and the Beast.

Susannah's mentor had told her to pay special attention to page 321. The professor had examined this book before—but back then her focus had been the Tarascon locale, not that of Stes.-Maries, located farther south in Provence. Now, reading the page, Susannah made notes on Saint Martha's gratitude to Sarah, the young slave girl. When she'd finished recording her impressions, she went back and transcribed the page, word by word.

As she wrote, Susannah thought of how deeply Sarah had affected everyone she met. She remembered last night, the emotion she'd seen in the faces of all the Circle; the fact that there was an entire clan of Manouche women who had moved to Stes.-Maries, just to be closer to Sarah; and especially the profound gratitude of her own mother.

She'd been so lost in her research, she

barely heard the heavy doors open and close. But when a slight shadow fell across the page, she flinched and looked into the dim light. She saw the outline of big shoulders and a lean torso.

"Hi," she said, shocked and happy to see Grey. She smiled, but saw the seriousness in his eyes. "What are you doing here?" she asked.

"Hi, Susannah . . . I was hoping to talk to you."

"Talk to me?" Again, she wanted to smile, but his expression didn't invite friendliness. Hands stuck into his pockets, he stood back from the table, staring down at her. "How did you find me? How did you even get in?"

"I've researched stories here," he said. "I'm in touch with the director, and he gave me the password."

"Were you researching a story in the marsh?" she asked.

"You saw me, did you?"

"Parked right in the same spot where I first met you? How could I possibly miss you?"

"I'm sorry. But I have to—"

The security guard stepped forward,

standing right beside Susannah. She glanced up at him, noticed the alarm in his eyes and the way he had his finger on the trigger of his gun. Her heart skipped so hard it hurt.

"There are strict rules about the examination of *Le Livre*," he said sternly to Grey as the librarian came forward, as if to provide backup. "I must ask you to step away."

Grey stared at Susannah. He seemed determined, intense, and suddenly she felt annoyed—what was he thinking, interrupting her research? He had had ample opportunity to approach her. She didn't know what he was trying to tell her, or why he had come, but she knew that she had to take care of this right now, and fast. He was undermining her credibility with the library staff. No one messed with her work.

She pushed her chair back, and in that instant the librarian removed the priceless book from the table. Susannah watched as she whisked it behind the counter, behind the smoked-glass enclosure where the rarest books were stored. Her blood was racing, and suddenly she felt full of fury. She peeled the white gloves off, stashed her notes in her briefcase, gestured that she would like to speak with Grey out in the hall.

They stepped outside, the heavy wooden door swinging shut behind them.

"What do you think you're doing?" she asked, her voice rising, echoing down the vaulted corridor.

"I'm sorry to interrupt your research. I really am."

"Then why are you here? What do you want?"

"It's important."

"So is my work! My colleague made special arrangements for me to look at that book. Do you know how much back-and-forth it took? She had to fax my credentials—*and* hers! They only allow it out of the vault once or twice a year!"

"I didn't realize you were here to view *Le Livre du Grand Voyage*. If I'd known, I'd have waited for you to come out. But you've been in here for a few hours already, and I started thinking maybe you'd left through the catacombs or something."

"How *could* you know what I was here to see? Or anything about me?" she asked, her temper rising further. "How could you possibly?"

"Look," he said. "I need to talk to you,

and I had to do it out of town—away from Stes.-Maries."

"Away from—" she began. "Did you really follow me here?"

"Yes," he said.

"How did you know I was coming, when I didn't even know myself?"

"I . . . was told what you do . . . that you'd be visiting the library."

She stared at him. Whom had she told? Helen had contacted the director of the library and given Susannah's name, saying that she would visit sometime during the month. And last night Susannah had mentioned to the Circle that she was doing research and planned, generally, to visit a library in Arles. But she hadn't been specific about a time—had she?

"Who told you?" she asked.

"It doesn't matter. The point is, I couldn't talk to you in town."

"But no one even knows me there! I'm only visiting. What difference—"

"They know *me,*" he said quietly, and they both fell silent.

Susannah thought of Rosalie, the hostility she had shown last night, the allusions to Maria. She gazed at his eyes, bright blue, intent on her and whatever he wanted to talk to her about. His broad shoulders filled his dark green oilskin, and she could see tremendous tension just pouring off, and his eyes were full of worry, and suddenly all her anger melted away and she knew.

"Is this about Sari?" she asked.

He nodded. "Yes, it is. I know you met my daughter at the ranch, when you stopped by yesterday."

Susannah hesitated. "I saw Mystère, and stopped. Why didn't you tell me you had a ranch?" she asked.

"For the same reason I didn't want to talk to you in Stes.-Maries. Because my daughter is very vulnerable, and I walk a fine line with her. And because the town is small, and people see everything that goes on."

"What would it matter if you talked to me?"

She watched him wage a private battle of some sort. His forehead was creased with worry, yet he was gazing at her with something veering between tenderness and concern, and it made her bones feel liquid. "It's not that I wouldn't want that," he said finally. "It's just that you've walked into a very complicated situation."

"I haven't really," she said softly. "I barely know you."

"That may be so," he said, "but I'm persona non grata to a lot of people in Stes.-Maries. They might misinterpret."

"Misinterpret what?"

"What I want from you."

"From me?"

"I want you to help my daughter."

"Sari . . ."

He nodded, then bowed his head as if he couldn't believe he was about to ask. A security guard walked by, and they exchanged nods. Grey had said he had done research here, but standing in the hallway now, he looked only like an outdoorsman. Tan, rangy, dressed in a slicker, jeans, and boots, looking as if he wanted to jump on a white horse and ride away as far and as fast as he could go.

"I would like you to . . ." He trailed off.

"Like me to what?"

"Take her riding," he said finally.

"But I'm just a tourist," she said. "I haven't ridden in such a long time."

"I know. That's what I said . . ."

"This isn't your idea? Then whose is it?"

"Laurent's. Her friend—he . . ."

"I know who you mean," she said, remembering the tall boy standing so protectively by Sari. Susannah pictured the young girl, the sadness in her supernaturally dark-green eyes, the way she'd closed those eyes as if to withdraw from the world. Susannah's heart had gone out to her.

"She has you," Susannah said quietly. "And she has Mystère . . . that's her horse, right?"

"Yes. But she hasn't ridden her in five years."

"How old is she now?"

"Thirteen."

"What happened?"

Grey hesitated. She saw him weighing his options. He didn't want to tell her at all, but he knew that he had to explain, or she might not agree to do it.

"She had a terrible fall," he said slowly. "She was eight. The mistral was blowing, and it was . . . well, very late at night. She rode off the ranch, into the marsh. It was so dark, and she took Mystère onto the main road. They . . . well, never mind. Mystère got spooked and reared up, and Sari fell."

"Was she all right?"

"Not at first," Grey said. He gazed at Susannah for a long moment, blinking slowly, holding himself together. "No, she wasn't all right at all." Susannah waited for him to go on, but it seemed he couldn't.

"Is she better now?" Susannah asked softly.

"Yes," Grey said. "But not completely." He hesitated, then told her: "The night she fell, she went colorblind."

"Oh, Grey!"

"It's lasted all this time. We've had every test possible; she's been to neurologists and psychiatrists here and in Paris, New England, New York. There's no physical reason for it. The doctors say she'll 'outgrow' it."

"How awful for her," Susannah whispered. And how awful for Grey: she looked into his face and finally understood why there was so much pain in his blue eyes.

"I just want life to be good for her," he said. "Right, and happy, and good . . . She used to love riding so much. You can't imagine how much she loved her horse. Yesterday was the first time in five years that she's set foot inside the barn."

"That's good," Susannah said.

"It was right after you'd been there—just a few hours later."

"But just a coincidence, right?" Susannah asked, both shocked and honored that he would think there was a link.

"I'm not completely sure. She doesn't trust people easily. Especially . . . not women. She doesn't like me talking to anyone, spending time with them. I'm all she's got. She tends to be . . . well, possessive. She's needed me all to herself, and I've understood that."

"Then why would you want her to ride with me?"

He stood there watching her, a hundred unspoken reasons in his eyes. "It was Laurent's idea," he said.

"He cares about her."

"Very much."

"But why me?"

"Laurent thinks it would be good if she could go riding with a woman. The more I think about it, the more that makes sense. And she—well, she really appreciated your kindness the other day." He spoke as calmly as he could, but Susannah could see the tension and worry behind his eyes.

"It was easy to be kind to her," Susannah said.

"Thank you."

"I'll ride with her," Susannah said.

"You will?"

"As soon as the rain stops—assuming it does before I have to leave, to go back home to the States," she said. "I'll come to the ranch on the first dry day."

"She gets home from school at three-thirty," Grey said.

"I'll be there," Susannah said. "I can't promise it will work—she might want nothing to do with me."

"That's possible," he admitted. "I hope that doesn't happen . . . and if it does, I hope you won't feel hurt."

"I'll try not to," she said.

Grey nodded. He said he'd let Laurent know she'd be coming, then jammed his hands into the pockets of his oilskin. He turned to walk away; as he did, his arm brushed Susannah's shoulder. He stood still, and the contact lasted a few seconds longer than it had to.

Susannah watched him go, still feeling the pressure of his arm. She heard the echo of his footsteps down the long hall. The security guard stood to greet him again, and the two men stood talking for a moment:

vestiges of his former life as a journalist? She wondered what kind of research he had done here, and how a man studying the Gypsies had wound up living on a ranch in the midst of them.

Then she turned away, to go back to Saint Martha, the woman who had entered the world of a dragon. As she let the heavy wooden doors close behind her, she thought about the beauty of jeweled books and garlanded kitchens, about the deeper truth that lay behind pretty things, and what life was like for the young girl with the burning green eyes who couldn't see colors.

NINE

It rained for days, but the atmosphere had changed, and Susannah didn't think it had much to do with barometric pressure. She made brief, solitary expeditions into the town for supplies and sat in her house writing up notes on the research she'd done at the library, and working on other articles. She couldn't concentrate. Her shoulder tingled, the spot where Grey had brushed her. Sitting at her table, she could have sworn he was standing right there, just behind her.

The telephone rang, making her jump. She picked up the receiver, but no one was there. She hung on, listening to the dial tone. Thinking of Grey so hard, she was sure it had been him. Maybe he wanted to tell her he'd changed his mind, that she shouldn't come to the ranch. Or maybe he wanted her to come sooner. . . .

When the phone rang again, she answered quickly.

"Hello?"

"Susannah . . ."

The voice made her go silent.

"It's Ian. How are you?" he asked.

"I'm fine," she said.

"You're a hard woman to track down," he said.

"I know," she said. "I had to get away . . ."

Now he was silent. She could hear the hurt pouring through the line. Their lives had been connected for so long. . . .

"Get away . . . from what?" he asked after a few moments.

"It's been rough since Mom died," she said. "I wanted to spend some time thinking about her. . . . I miss her, Ian."

"I know," he said. "Of course you do. You were close."

"That's why I came here," she said. "We'd always talked about visiting Stes.-Maries together. But somehow it never happened."

He didn't speak for a moment. She heard him breathing, felt his anger.

"I wonder why," he said after a moment, "it never happened."

"You didn't have to say that to me," she said quietly. "I say it often enough to myself."

"Susannah, what's happened to us?" he asked. "You used to tell me everything, call me all the time. You'd never take a trip like this without talking it over with me."

"I've never taken a trip like this before, ever," she said. "Everything feels new."

"You got on a plane," he said. "You flew to France. You missed a hell of a party. From what Helen told me, you're doing research. How new is any of that?" He paused, as if hearing the bitterness in his own voice. "Look, I'm sorry. But I don't understand. Why are you shutting me out?"

"Ian . . ."

"Are you going to Cosquer? Is that what you're studying?"

"Please, Ian. Stop."

He paused, catching his breath. "Look. My timing was off—it couldn't have been worse, proposing to you when you were going through so much with Margaret, when she was getting so sick. But don't hold that against me, Susannah."

"I don't hold it against you," she said.

"Then what? We have so much in common; you know how right we are for each other. No one will ever support you and your work the way I do."

"You've been . . ." she said, but stopped, hearing the past tense. He heard it, too.

"You want to tell me it's over," he said.

"Ian," she began.

"It's not, Susannah," he said. "I don't believe it, and I won't let it happen. Tell me where you're staying, and I'll fly over. I need to see you."

"No," she said. "I don't want that."

"Listen to me. You don't know what you want—you're too upset, you feel so guilty."

"I'm saying goodbye now, Ian," she said softly.

She hung up the phone and went to the window. Shaking, she stared out at the rain. The street glistened, black and gray. Raindrops bounced off the pavement. She thought of how long Ian had been part of her life, and how distant she felt from him now. Looking up at the clouds, she wondered when they would lift. She hoped it would be soon.

The phone rang again. She turned and stared. It had rung once earlier, and no one was there. She'd thought it might have been Grey, but now she knew it was Ian. So she stood where she was, feeling that spot on her shoulder where Grey had touched her, and deciding she'd said all to Ian she had to say.

Grey sat in his office in the barn, feeling like a teenager. He held the phone, listening to Susannah's number ring and ring. He'd called once, and she'd answered. Chickening out, he'd hung up. Then he'd tried again, and it was busy. Now no one was home.

What did he have to say to her anyway? His excuse for calling was to check in, make sure she was still coming to ride when the weather cleared. But the truth was, he just wanted to hear her voice. He just wanted to know she was there.

This was strange; it wasn't Grey. He was usually all business—running the ranch, taking care of Sari. He wasn't used to feeling like a kid.

Claude walked into the office, holding a saddlery catalogue. He stood across the desk, watching as Grey had to pretend he was on hold.

"Important business?" Claude asked.

"Yes," Grey said.

"Ah," Claude said. He stood there patiently, tapping the rolled-up catalogue with one leathery hand, his sweater stretched tight across his generous gut. Grey watched as Claude's gaze traveled over the desk. It came to rest on the notepad, just before Grey had the chance to cover it with his hand.

Susannah, he'd written. And not just once: *Susannah, Susannah.*

Grey watched as his stable foreman smiled. Claude lifted his eyes to meet his, and Grey felt himself redden.

"She's coming here to ride," Grey said.

"Ah," Claude said again, the smile getting bigger. "I was right, then: important business . . ."

"Laurent knows all about it," Grey said.

"Very good," Claude said. He gave the catalogue one last tap, then dropped it on Grey's desk. He left the office, leaving Grey to listen to the rain on the roof and the phone ringing endlessly in Susannah's rented house, just a few miles down the road.

Days passed, a blur of rain and fog. Laurent had said to expect a surprise on the first sunny day, and even though she wouldn't admit it to him, Sari found herself waiting for the sky to clear. She noticed that her father was being more quiet than usual—sitting in his chair at night, staring into space, as if he had serious matters on his mind. But when she asked him what was wrong, he just smiled and said, "Nothing at all. Everything's really good, Sari."

Okay . . . If he said so.

The rain was torrential. Sari tried to concentrate on her schoolwork, but lately she'd felt herself slipping. Especially when it came to writing assignments; sometimes she felt she lived in a different world than anyone else. How could she describe a scene if she couldn't really see it?

Laurent was with her when she got her paper back in history class. The teacher had asked them to write about Madame de Sévigné. They'd read her letters to Louis

XIV, describing Paris, the Court of Versailles, and especially, her time spent in the South of France with her daughter.

The passages about the palace, the costumes, the dresses, the gardens, the sea, were all so vivid. But reading about lush blue satin, about butter-yellow silk, about bright red roses, about brilliant gold crowns, about the sparkling azure sea, meant nothing to Sari; they were just words, as hard as she tried to remember how colors like that looked. So she'd written an essay so drab and unenthusiastic, her teacher had given her a barely passing grade.

"That's not like you," Laurent had said.

"The teacher thinks it is," she'd said.

"Why didn't you try harder?"

"Because I don't care," she'd whispered.

"You have to care, Sari," Laurent had said. "Don't give up."

She remembered that now, staring out at the rain. She'd come to like inclement days, when the weather turned the marsh gray. When Laurent told her something good would happen as soon as the sun came out, she'd told him she hoped it never would. He'd seemed shocked at first, but then he understood. That's why she felt so lucky to have him as a friend: he was in her corner.

Finally, the mistral stopped blowing, the clouds blew away, and right after Sari got home from school, Susannah Connolly drove into the parking area. Sari stood in the pantry, watching out the small window.

Laurent walked out of the barn, greeted Susannah. As Sari watched, Susannah took a small bag from the car, holding it under her arm as she spoke to Laurent. Sari wrapped her arms around herself, wondering what they were saying.

A minute later, he came walking toward the house. She met him at the kitchen door.

"You know that surprise I mentioned?" he asked. "Well, put your riding boots on."

Sari grabbed his hand, stared into his eyes. "What are you talking about?"

"I know you want to ride," he said. "Wanting to is the biggest part of it. Just come outside. I'm going to saddle up Mystère."

"No," Sari said.

"Sari, please . . ."

"You should know I'd never ride with a stranger," she said. "I can't, Laurent."

He stared at her as if he knew she could do it. The cats jumped down from sunny spots on the window ledges, and circled around Laurent's feet, but he ignored them.

"I think you can," he said quietly.

She shook her head.

"Then we'll have to tell her," he said, looking crestfallen.

Sari felt a twinge of doubt—she hated upsetting Laurent, and knew that he wanted the best for her. She felt like asking him to tell the woman himself, but pulled herself up straight and followed him outside.

When Sari stepped out into the yard, Susannah came to meet her. She was dressed for riding herself: dark jeans, low boots, and a denim jacket. Her face was glowing, as if the idea of riding made her so happy she couldn't hide it. Sari tried to fight her nervousness and smile back, but she found it just a little too hard.

"Hi, Sari," Susannah said.

"*Bonjour,* Susannah," Sari said shyly.

"Thank you for coming," Laurent said.

"I can't think of anything I'd rather do than ride with you," Susannah said, smiling at Sari. The words were so gentle, and Sari had the feeling she really meant them.

"It's very kind of you," Sari said, feeling stiff. "But I won't be able to ride today."

"No?" Susannah said. "Oh, I'm sorry."

"Of course, *you* can still ride," Laurent said to Susannah. "I'll go saddle up a horse for you. I'll go with you, if you'd like."

"Thank you," Susannah said. Laurent turned and walked away, leaving Sari alone with Susannah.

"I—" Sari stammered, feeling awkward, knowing she should explain a little. "I used to be a good rider, but it has been a long time."

"I'd say the same thing about myself," Susannah said.

"But," Sari said, "my father said you ride very well. *Comme un rêve.*"

Susannah laughed. She shook her head. "Hardly like a dream! I managed out of pure necessity. You remember about the bulls, right?"

Sari nodded, trying to smile. But it seemed her mouth wouldn't oblige. Her face was frozen. Her thoughts kept darting backward and forward: to the last time she'd been on a horse, that terrible night.

"I brought you something," Susannah said, handing Sari the package she had been holding.

Sari accepted it with surprise. She looked

up at Susannah, who was watching her with a patient smile. Sari opened the bag, saw the wrapped present. The paper was a pale shade, tied with a satin ribbon.

"This is for me?" she asked. "Even though I'm not going to ride?"

"Yes," Susannah said.

Sari held the package. She couldn't remember the last time she'd gotten a present just because. Her father always remembered her birthday, and there was Noël, but this . . . just for nothing . . . no special reason . . . a day like all the others on the calendar. "Why?" she asked.

"Because I wanted to," Susannah said, as if that was all the explanation that was needed.

Hands trembling, Sari untied the ribbon. She slid her finger under the paper's fold, undid the tape, tugged it open. The paper fell away, and Sari pulled out a dragon—a child's plush toy. She held it, staring down at the dragon's glittering eyes, the line of spiny scales down its curved back.

"I got it for you in Arles," Susannah said. "After your father came to ask me to ride with you."

"This was his idea?" Sari asked.

"Actually, he told me it was Laurent's."

Sari held the toy, lifted it to her face, brushed the soft fur against her cheek. She closed her eyes. The feeling carried her back a long way. She shut her eyes tighter; going inward had always been such a good way to hide. Right now she was hiding from how much she loved being given a present for no reason whatsoever, and how touched she was, that Laurent was looking after her.

"What color . . ." she heard herself whisper.

"The dragon is bright green; his eyes are red."

Sari kept her eyes closed shut.

"Your father told me about your fall," Susannah said softly. "I know what it's like to have something happen that keeps you from doing things you used to love. I've felt that way lately. And when I was at the library in Arles, doing research on Saint Martha and the Tarasque, I thought of both of us."

"You and me?" Sari asked, barely able to talk.

Susannah nodded. "Yes."

"But why?"

"Well, you know the story of Saint Martha . . . how she traveled so far, in that small boat, across the stormy sea . . . with her wonderful friends . . . how they survived all that, and landed in Stes.-Maries . . ."

"The town was named for her friends," Sari said. "The three Marys . . ."

Susannah nodded. "Yes. And from there, Martha went up the Rhône, and she settled in a town that was tormented by a dragon. A ferocious creature who destroyed boats, and attacked townspeople, and lived under bridges, keeping everyone afraid."

Sari stood still, thinking of all the stories she'd heard about the Tarasque. When she was young, her mother had told her about the beast. And once, on a trip to Tarascon, her father had shown her the riverbanks where the dragon had prowled, the curved stone bridge under which it had made its lair.

"It lived in seaweed," she said to Susannah now. "A nest of horrible, slimy weed. And it killed birds, just plucked them out of the air to eat. And it frightened children, and tried to catch them and eat them, too. Everyone in the town was terrorized. The dragon had fangs and red eyes, and it never, never slept. It just *hunted*."

Susannah nodded. "Yes," she said. "It was tormented, poor thing."

"Poor thing? *It?*" Sari asked, shocked to think of the Tarasque as an object of pity. Fear, yes. Terror . . .

"Saint Martha knew that it suffered terribly," Susannah said. "That's why it had to be so fierce and dangerous. So she went down to the river . . . not to slay it, but to make friends with it."

Sari stared at her. She heard horses' hooves clopping through the stable. A trickle of fear ran down her back.

"She calmed the dragon," Susannah said. "With hymns and prayers."

"Instead of killing it," Sari whispered, holding the dragon toy tighter.

"Yes," Susannah said.

"But I'm not scared of a dragon," Sari said, her voice not much more than a croak. Her senses were alive, alert right now. She smelled horse hair and saddle leather. Her nerves were screaming. She looked at Susannah standing so close and she remembered her mother wrestling her in the kitchen, shoving her away. That was the worst part, but she couldn't say it out loud, so she said something else instead. Her eyes brimmed with tears. "I'm afraid of my horse."

Susannah nodded. She held out her hand, and without even thinking, Sari put out hers, as tears rolled down her cheeks.

"You don't have to slay it, or chase it away, or pretend it doesn't exist," Susannah said. "As long as you know it's there, and you can help it find a way to leave, when it's ready."

"Like Saint Martha and the Tarasque?" Sari asked.

"Yes, like that," Susannah said.

Sari stared out over the marsh. She wondered why Susannah was being so nice to her—she was the girl who drove everyone away. When would Susannah discover that she was worse than a dragon? She pictured her mother speeding off, the car's taillights flashing, flashing, as it carried her away, bright as a dragon's red eyes, the last color she ever saw. And she thought of what Rosalie had told her, one time when Sari had been so badly behaved Rosalie couldn't take it anymore: that Zin-Zin said her mother must be cursed to have brought such pain on everyone, and Sari must be cursed, too.

The horses were right there. Laurent held them by their bridles; he hadn't brought Mystère because Sari had said she wasn't riding. Her father's stallion stood in the paddock, his black eyes gleaming. She remembered him riding after her that night, finding her in the road, shouting into the fog. Maybe there really was a curse: what else could explain all the terrible things that had happened to her family?

Sari felt her father standing beside her right now. She couldn't look at him. If she did, she would start to sob and never stop.

"You decided not to ride?" her father asked now. "That's okay, sweetheart."

"Papa," she said, looking up at him. She was still holding Susannah's hand and the dragon toy. She handed the dragon to her father. "Will you keep this for me?"

"What do you mean, Sari?"

"I want to ride," she said.

"You don't have to . . ."

"She wants to," Laurent said, running into the barn—she knew he was going to saddle up Mystère.

"I'll be coming with you and Susannah," her father said, his eyes gleaming.

Sari shook her head. She couldn't explain

this to him, but she had to go alone with Susannah. She couldn't have anyone there from that night. Only Mystère—because she knew that Mystère was damaged, too. That night had injured Sari's horse's spirit almost as much as it had hers.

"Are you sure?" Sari's father asked.

"I think she's sure," Susannah said softly, answering for her.

"You know to stay on the main trail?" he asked, locking eyes with Susannah. Sari watched a look pass between them that seemed too mysterious for her to begin to figure out. She was too busy trying to get her own heart under control.

"It's marked?" Susannah asked.

"Yes," he said. "You'll see blue diamonds nailed to fence posts. Just keep them to your right. They lead in a big circle through the refuge, and will get you right back here in about forty minutes."

"What about the bulls?"

Sari's father shook his head. "The bulls are far away—you won't go anywhere near them if you keep the diamonds on your right."

"The horses know the way," Laurent said.

And then, quietly, "So does Sari, from before."

"I don't want to go first," Sari said.

"You don't have to," Susannah said.

And then, Sari knew she was ready. She let go of Susannah's hand, walked over to Mystère, leaned her head against the strong white head. Forehead-to-forelock, she kissed her horse's face. Then she took the reins from Laurent. He gave her a long look, and she tried to smile, but her mouth was too dry.

She had grown a lot since she'd last ridden. She reached up to grasp Mystère's saddle, put her foot in the stirrup, and let Laurent give her a leg up. The distance from ground to horse was so much less than the last time, but it felt a thousand times as far. Her blood was racing so fast, she felt light-headed enough to topple off.

But then Susannah mounted Arabella, and she was sitting right there beside Sari on Mystère. Sari took a second to notice how calm Susannah looked, how happy. Then she glanced down at her father and Laurent. Laurent looked happy, too. Sari wondered what her father must be thinking.

"Papa, I'm riding again," she said.

"So you are," he said, the smile on his face everywhere but in his eyes. The old tragedy was there in his eyes—it had never gone away, not ever since that night—but at least his mouth was smiling.

"Are you ready?" Susannah asked.

"I think so," Sari replied.

"Then let's go for a ride," Susannah said.

And very slowly the horses began to walk, single file with Susannah and Arabella ahead, into the endless, salt-silvered cradle of sea grass that Sari knew—from an ever-so-distant memory—was soft green.

"How are you, Sari?" Susannah called back.

"I'm fine," the girl said.

The horses walked along, and Susannah heard the rhythm of their footfalls—soft in the pliant marsh ground—and the sound of tall reeds brushing their legs, and her own steady breathing. The saddle took some getting used to. She was used to riding English, but this traditional Camargue saddle was more Western. When the trail widened, she pulled up and waited for Sari to catch up, and then they rode side by side.

"Mystère looks happy," Susannah said, smiling.

"She likes having me ride her," Sari said, smiling back and—for the first time since Susannah and she had first met—her smile looking relaxed and genuine.

"As I said the other day, she's a one-girl horse."

"That's why . . ." Sari began, trailing off. Susannah didn't push her, but after a moment Sari finished her thought: "I think that's why I wanted to ride with you."

"Because I knew that about Mystère?"

Sari nodded. "Not everyone would."

"It just seemed so clear," Susannah said.

They rode along. Susannah felt Sari watching her hands.

"What is it?" she asked.

"In the Camargue, we ride with the reins in one hand," Sari said.

"I learned to ride English," Susannah said, transferring both reins into her right hand and feeling like a cowgirl in a movie. "I'm not used to this . . ."

"You're doing well," Sari reassured her.

After a few minutes, Sari gave Mystère a little kick, and she began to trot. Susannah smiled and followed. They crossed a rustic wooden bridge, flushing an entire flock of flamingos. The birds flew up in a pink cloud, but the horses seemed unperturbed. So did Sari. A blue diamond appeared up ahead, nailed to a tilting pole, and Sari kept it to her right, breaking into a canter as she guided Mystère along the well-trod path.

Susannah and Sari cantered for about half a mile, then slowed to walk again. When Susannah looked over, she saw Sari grinning. It was how Susannah felt herself: joyous to be riding. She petted her horse, feeling deep love for the animal. She'd always felt bonded with the horses she'd ridden, in touch with the mysterious communication that had nothing to do with domination and everything to do with connection.

"My father's right. You're a good rider," Sari said.

"Thank you—so are you."

"When did you start?"

"So long ago, I can barely remember! Let's see . . ." Susannah thought back. "I was in Miss Heckler's class, and that was fourth grade. So I guess I was ten."

"That's a funny way to remember. What did your school have to do with it?"

"Nothing, really. It's just that I remember

my father picking me up at school to take me to my lessons. I couldn't wait for the school day to end! I loved riding so much, I wore my riding habit all the time. Jodhpurs, boots, black velvet hat. Even to school on days when I didn't have riding lessons."

"That's so funny," Sari said.

"I dreamed horses."

At that, Sari didn't reply. Susannah glanced over, saw her gazing down at Mystère's mane with a troubled look in her eyes. Her face was a knot, just as it had been the first day Susannah met her in the kitchen. Suddenly, with that, Susannah watched the fear return to Sari's body. Her spine tensed up.

"Sari, did I say something wrong?"

"I have bad dreams," she said. "About horses."

"You're not dreaming now," Susannah said quietly, seeing the panic in Sari's face. "You're wide awake, and you're doing wonderfully."

"I'm afraid," Sari said, shutting her eyes in the way Susannah had begun to recognize as the girl's first defense against whatever was frightening her. Sari collapsed over Mystère's neck, encircling it with her arms, burying her face in the white mane.

"Remember Saint Martha," Susannah said. "The way she sang to the dragon . . . letting it know she was right there."

Sari didn't reply, but stayed hunched over as her horse walked along. Susannah watched, feeling her own panic rise, wondering what she should do. But as Laurent had said, Mystère knew the way. The beautiful white horse just stepped along, steady and calm, carrying Sari homeward.

"What would she sing?" Sari asked after a few moments, her mouth buried and her words muffled with tears. "To make the dragon not be so terrible?"

"I'm not sure," Susannah said. "What do you think?"

Sari began to sing then, her voice high and wavering. Susannah didn't recognize the song, but it sounded ineffably sweet and tender, like a lullaby one might sing a little girl beset by bad dreams. She drew up close by Sari, so she could listen better.

The strange thing was, as Sari's voice grew stronger and she felt better enough to sit up, start to guide Mystère again, turning down the last stretch toward the ranch—

just visible at the end of the trail—Susannah's heart felt heavier. She felt a huge tug inside, and she knew she didn't want this moment to end.

Not just the ride, not just being on a white horse, not just spending time with Sari: but the whole thing. The blue sky and the smell of the sea and the fact that she could see Grey waiting for them up ahead.

He had walked to the end of the road, and was watching for them. She saw his hand shoot up, giving them an exuberant wave. And they waved back—both Susannah and Sari. Then he stuck his hands in his pockets, rocking back on the heels of his well-worn boots, grinning as he watched them approach.

Susannah wondered how he did it. How had he gone from being a journalist haunting the Bibliothèque du Cheval Blanc to running a ranch? How had he switched from a life of paper and books to a life outdoors, with a beautiful daughter? How did people go from research and documents and deeply embedded sorrow to fully living their own lives? Susannah felt happier than she had in months, and she realized—for

the first time since her mother had died—
she didn't feel guilty.

"Papa!" Sari called. "I did it!"

"I see that, sweetheart," he called back.

He glanced up at Susannah, gave her a
questioning glance—had it really gone well?
She nodded that yes, it had. She saw
that he was still holding the little toy dragon
she'd bought for Sari.

And she also saw something else: a tiny
bit of hope in his eyes.

It reminded her of standing in a dark forest on a cloudy night. Looking up, through
the tangle of branches and fringe of pine,
and through layers and layers of scudding
clouds, there might be a moon. You more
knew it than saw it, but suddenly the wind
would blow, and the branches would toss,
and a scrap of cloud would clear, and there
the moon would be.

That's what Susannah saw in Grey's eyes
as he walked alongside her horse, across
the main road, into the paddock of the Manade du Dempsey. Laurent was waiting, too,
and he dashed over to Mystère, to reach up
and help Sari jump down.

"Can you see everything?" Laurent asked

in a rush. "Sari, could you see the colors out there?"

"No," she whispered.

Susannah saw Laurent's face crash. He'd wanted everything all at once. He'd hoped Sari's first ride would make her all better. Susannah looked into Grey's eyes, and saw him gazing back.

"She did okay?" he asked.

"She did a lot better than okay," she said.

Grey didn't reach up. And Susannah didn't climb down. They just stayed there, frozen. Susannah couldn't stop gazing into his eyes, searching, searching for that glint of hope. Because if she saw it again in his eyes, she might be able to believe it was reflecting something in her own.

TEN

The next morning was another brilliant, clear spring day. Many people showed up for the early trail ride, but Grey let Claude take them out, while he stayed at the stable. There were things to do, no doubt about it. A stall door that needed repair, from where one of the new, wild horses had kicked it in. And some roof tiles that needed to be replaced after blowing off in the storm.

But the truth was, he stayed because he knew she was coming back. She hadn't said a word, and he hadn't asked her, but he knew. He'd seen it in her eyes. The way she'd stared at him, returning from the ride with Sari, sitting up there on Arabella, gazing at him with those big violet eyes of hers. She'd been telling him, in everything but words, that she would be back.

So there he was, at the last stall in the stable, tool belt strapped on and one nail in his hand and another in his mouth, and the hammer swinging, and Tempest, the young and recalcitrant wild white horse bucking in the next stall and neighing like crazy, when she walked in.

"Hi," Susannah said.

"Hey," he said, grinning.

"You don't look surprised to see me," she said, smiling back.

He laughed. Tempest was really making a racket, going more than a little nuts. Susannah's gaze was calm, gentle, almost amused. He watched her take a step toward the stall, stare in at the colt.

"What's wrong?" she asked, holding out her hand.

Grey knew she was speaking to the horse, not him, but he answered anyway. "That's Tempest. Until last month, he was living wild on the plain. He's a yearling; some of his herd had a hard winter, and he was showing signs of wear. So Claude and I brought him in."

"He hates it," Susannah said.

"Yes," Grey admitted. "He did this."

Susannah looked at the wrecked stall—shattered door, splintered wood. Then she turned back to Tempest, regarded him with warm eyes.

"What is it?" she asked quietly. "Do you miss your herd?"

"Let's put him in the corral," Grey said, partly because he wanted her to talk to him instead of the angry white horse. Gesturing for Susannah to stand back, he opened the stall door, caught Tempest by the halter, and led him out the open stable door. Tempest tried to yank away, with a force that nearly pulled Grey's arm out of the socket.

Once they got outside, Susannah swung the paddock gate open, and Grey let go. The young horse ran in circles, bucking with furious energy. Grey and Susannah stood there, watching. He saw her frown, felt her sensing the horse's emotions. Her compassion was palpable. He stepped closer to her, just to feel it, like waves, pouring off her.

"Do you know a lot about horses?" he asked.

"Only that I've always loved them," she said.

"So have I," he said. "I grew up in the country, and rode almost as soon as I could walk. We had a farm across the street from Narragansett Bay, and once a year there'd be a big horse show on our land. My father was known all through the state for the horses he raised."

"That's how you wound up running a ranch here?"

"Sort of," Grey said after a pause.

She let that go. "What would your father say about Tempest?"

"That he's scared out of his mind. My father taught me that horses and people think completely differently. People have hunter mentality. We go after what we want, and don't stop until we get it. Horses think like prey, like the hunted . . ."

"Because they *were* hunted," Susannah said, watching Tempest. "The earliest cave drawings—Lascaux—right here in France, show horses with arrows piercing their sides."

He nodded. She was an anthropologist, a student of such things, but he knew she was speaking from a deeper part of herself right now—the part that loved horses.

"Horses are intrinsically wild. And they want to be free," Grey said. "Not 'owned.' As kind as a rancher might be, he's still his horses' jailer. That's what Tempest is feeling about me right now."

Susannah nodded. She watched the young horse run and buck for a few more moments, then turned to Grey. "You're a kind rancher," she said.

"Thank you." He stared down at her. "I wasn't sure you thought that—not after I followed you to Arles."

"I didn't mind that," she said. She touched his hand very lightly, sending shivers up his arm.

He had to face something: ever since he'd first met Susannah, he'd been unable to stop thinking of her. He'd made those crazy calls, and he'd had dreams about her. There was something about her that seemed as free as the white horses, and in his dreams she was pressed up against his back, as she'd been that day, her arms locked around his waist. All he wanted to do right now was turn, and kiss her, and never stop.

"Grey," she said, staring up at him as if she could read his mind. Her eyes were beautiful, her mouth just slightly open.

"I have to tell you something," he said.

"What?"

"I didn't just follow you to Arles. I called your house, too."

"What do you mean? When?"

He hesitated, embarrassed. "The other day—during the rain. You answered, and . . ."

"That was you?"

He nodded. "Then I called back, and it was . . ." He stopped himself. "Why, who did you think it was?"

Now it was her turn to look embarrassed, but she smiled through it. "Never mind," she said. "I got another call, but it doesn't really matter. You know what? I had the feeling it was you . . ."

He laughed. "Maybe we're connected. Because you know what? I knew you were going to come today."

"How did you know?"

He shrugged. "The way you looked, just before you drove away, after you and Sari came back from your ride. I felt it. . . . You stared at me, as if you wanted to say something."

"I wanted to ask you more about Sari," she said.

"She loved the ride," he said, but his heart fell a little; he was glad she was interested in Sari, but he hoped she'd been thinking about other things, too. "She hasn't talked about it much, but that's her way. She keeps things locked inside."

"I'm glad she has Laurent as a friend."

"So am I," Grey said. He waited a moment, then said, "Was there something else you wanted to say?"

She laughed lightly. "Oh, just all of it," she said.

"All of what?" he asked, stepping closer.

"I don't know," she said, looking across the salt meadow. Then, "Okay. This will sound strange, I know. But ever since I met you . . . I've felt as if I stepped out of time."

"Out of time?"

She nodded. "This place . . . it's so magical. And the way you rode out of the fog on a white horse . . ."

"I do that a lot," he said.

She laughed. "But not like that," she said.

"No," he agreed. "Never before like that . . ."

She nodded, smiling, as if she was glad to hear it.

"Would you like to take a ride?" he asked now, suddenly at a loss for words, knowing he had to move.

"I would," she said.

He saddled up Arabella for her, and took Django out of his stall, and led both horses into the yard. Giving Susannah a leg up, he held her hand for a moment and felt the connection come through his body.

He climbed up on the big stallion, and led Susannah out of the yard on the scarcely used trail that meandered down past the big lagoon. The tide came in here, flooding the plain, but he knew it was hours before that would happen, so they cantered along the silvery mud, into tall grass.

"What's your horse's name?" she asked.

"Django."

She paused for a moment, staring at him. "I heard that name just recently," she said.

He nodded, wondering who'd been talking to her.

Across the plain, they could see the long line of riders behind Claude, heading back toward the ranch. Grey steered Susannah away from them, taking the south trail, skirt-

ing the lagoon, feeling sun blast off the surface of the sparkling water. White egrets
stood in the shallows, spearing silver fish
with sharp bills.

Another mile. They rode flat out, just feeling the horses pounding across the soft
marshland, the breeze freshening as they
neared the sea, the sun warming their faces.
And then they cleared the last stretch of
green reeds, and he heard Susannah's in-
take of breath and turned to see the pleasure in her eyes as they rode out onto the
beach that ran along the sparkling Gulf of
Lions.

The Mediterranean Sea spread all the
way to Africa, as bold and azure as the
sky above. A wide pebbly beach stretched
endlessly in both directions. Climbing down
off Django, Grey held Arabella's bridle while
Susannah swung her leg over and dismounted with a jump onto the sand. The
beach was covered with black scallop
shells, small delicate fans in shades ranging
from silver to dark pewter to ebony, and he
saw her bend down to examine them.

"You're good," he said when she stood.
"You ride like a Camarguaise."

"Sari taught me to hold the reins in one hand."

"The first time I saw you ride," Grey said, "there were no reins."

"No saddle, either," she said.

He was standing right next to her. His heart was pounding from the last half mile, when the horses had really run it out. Or maybe it was her closeness, and the way her head was tilted back, and the electricity that just kept getting stronger, and the sense he had that the reality of being so near to her was merging with his dream.

He took her in his arms now, and pulled her close, and kissed her. Her lips tasted like sunlight, and her mouth was hot and cool at the same time, and he heard himself say her name right in the middle of the kiss.

He held her hand, and pulled her down— or maybe it was the other way around, because suddenly they were easing each other onto the sand. He was on fire with the way she brushed his hair back from his face, and touched his skin with such sureness, and the way her arms were around him now, as tight as the first time.

When they stopped, they just held each other, hardly able to breathe, gazing into each other's eyes. If Grey couldn't hear the horses right there, and if the sea breeze weren't blowing gently but steadily, washing over their skin, sharpening all of his senses, he might think this was another dream. He held her, afraid if he let go she'd disappea

"How did that happen?" she whispere

"I wanted it to," he said.

"So did I, I think," she said.

"You're not sure?"

"I told myself I was going to the rar to talk to you," she said. "When Sa there. And I knew you couldn't town . . ."

"Because everyone knows m

"Is that really so bad?"

"The surest way to ruin yo in Stes.-Maries is to be seen

"You have a bad reputati

"Yeah," he said, smooth brown hair back from he it. "The worst."

She was sweating f through the hot marsh icality of it all made again and again. Hi the whole thing, anu .

was a possibility he'd never get out of it alive.

"What did you do to deserve your bad reputation?" she asked when they finally broke apart, laughing.

"I don't want to tell you," he said.

"Because you think I'll disapprove?"

"Something like that." Holding her hand, he looked into her eyes. Her hand was small, fine-boned, but it felt rough, and that excited him. "Your hands don't feel as if you spend all your time at your desk."

"I don't," she said. "I'm a cave person."

"Excuse me?" he laughed.

"Half the year I'm on my hands and ees, crawling down rock tunnels into es, to study Paleolithic art."

Cave paintings?"

Mainly," she said. "Rock art of all sorts. tings, carvings . . ."

ke the horses you mentioned—at Las-
"

rses are dominant," she said, nod-
But there are many images . . . bison, eindeer, mammoths. And not just . This part of the world has many ne Dordogne, Languedoc, Roussil-rcy."

"Wow," he said, gazing at her with admiration. "That's your work. You're not just an anthropologist—you're an explorer."

She laughed. "I don't usually think of it that way, but getting into the Cosquer Cave—near Marseilles—took some doing. The entrance to the site is below our present-day sea level, so I had to learn to dive. Took lessons, went on practice dives . . ."

"Was it worth it?"

She nodded. "Yes, certainly . . . it's spectacular. The dive went down forty meters, to a small opening under the sea, then sloped back up into a tremendous chamber filled with prehistoric paintings and hand stencils; the artists traced their own hands on the rock walls. It's so moving and powerful . . . archaeologists call them 'finger tracings'— the artists used flints to etch their handprints in the soft limestone walls."

"Their way of saying 'I was here,' " Grey said.

Susannah looked at him with bright eyes. "That's it, exactly. They wanted to make their mark; all around the cave are traces of charcoal—they burned fires to illuminate the space. It's incredible."

As she spoke, he traced her hand with his fingers. "I wish I could see it," he said.

"Do you dive?" she asked.

"Yes. I grew up in Rhode Island, diving on the wreck of an old U-boat. I got certified when I was eighteen."

"Then I'll take you to Cosquer," she laughed.

"You promise?"

"Absolutely!"

"Deal," he said, knowing they were just talking. Her time here was so short, and he knew he couldn't leave the ranch just as the season was getting busy. Sari was on high alert, anyway. "Do you work with the same team all the time?" he asked. He saw her shut down; it happened all at once, like a door closing.

"I used to," she said.

He knew she was talking about a man. Did he have to do with that other call, the one she said didn't matter? He stared at her. The thought of Sari, and of someone else in her life, had brought him back to reality.

"Okay, then," she said, closing the subject. "Tell me this: why did you name your horse Django?"

He paused, holding her hand. "He's named for Django Reinhardt, who was a great guitarist. Some say the best ever. I like guitar music . . ." He trailed off, knowing it was his turn to change the subject.

"Django Reinhardt used to come to Stes.-Maries," she said. "You obviously know that . . ."

"Yes," he said.

"To the caravan circle, up the road behind the church."

So she'd been there; so she knew. He lowered his eyes, pushed himself up so he was sitting. How soon before it was all over, and what did it matter, considering it hadn't really even started yet? What was there to start? He thought of Sari, thought of every-thing, closed his eyes and wondered about this other guy in her life. Of course there would be someone. . . .

"Who's Maria?" she asked softly.

"Sari's mother," he said.

"And your . . ."

"My wife, yes."

"You're still married?"

He laughed harshly. "The marriage was annulled," he said. He didn't feel like telling her the truth, that the marriage had never been legal in the first place. Sari might find out, if he started talking about it. "How did you hear about Maria? From the same place you heard about Django?"

"Yes," she said. "The Sarah Circle."

"Oh, yes," he said, and he heard the bitterness in his own voice. "Them."

"You came to France to be Hemingway," she said. "And be a journalist. You wrote about Gypsies."

"They told you that?"

She shook her head. "No," she said. "That's what Google is for."

He looked over the sweep of blue sea, both touched and troubled that she'd looked him up. It had been a long time since he'd researched anything; what was available to find out about his life? If she typed in enough details, would the whole story show up on her computer screen?

"What did you find out?" he asked slowly.

"Not very much. Just that you wrote some pieces on the Romany people. Is that how you wound up coming to Stes.-Maries?"

"Yes," he said. He thought back; it seemed a million years ago. "I was living in Paris. I used to drink at a place on Ile St.

Louis where a bunch of writers hung out. One of them was a gypsiologist. He told us all about the Gypsy Lore Society, if you can believe that. There are some arcane fields of study, but none more than that. It's a closed, secret world. Meeting him, I got hooked."

"So you decided to write about it?"

Grey nodded. "I came down here with him. We stayed at a ranch—just a few miles from the one I own now. There was a woman there, gave trail rides, and trained horses herself, under the tutelage of one of the Gypsies' greatest horse trainers. She was a spectacular rider, rode in a circus act . . ."

"Maria?" Susannah asked.

"Yes. Maria Loisy," he said. He thought back to those first days. It was hard to believe sometimes, when he realized that his entire life had changed direction so completely, based on one chance meeting at the Brasserie de l'Ile St. Louis.

"What happened?" Susannah asked.

Grey looked into her eyes. How could he explain this to her, the way he'd felt so intoxicated by a place, and way of life, and someone who could balance on the back of a galloping white horse as though she were part of it. "Well," he said, "I fell in love with her."

"Oh," she said.

Fell in love. The words sounded like what it was, so why weren't people more afraid? Grey's father had once explained to him the difference between falling in love with someone and loving them. The old horseman had given his son the talk one day while they rode together toward Middlebridge, and he'd done it without looking him in the eye once.

"Falling in love," his father had said. "It's like taking a horse over a brush fence— you get air, rise up, take the jump. And you might land okay, or you might go flying. You want to make sure you're on solid ground. That's what loving someone is like: you land safely. You have ground under your feet."

Grey had listened to his father, but what had he wanted to land safely for? He'd been young and wild, with Hemingway as his idol, and he'd come down to the South of France to write about Gypsies, and fallen in love with the most exciting one of all.

"And are you still?" Susannah asked, bringing him back to earth. He couldn't believe how he was starting to feel about her, in such a short time. It was different from Maria, but happening just as fast, and it shocked him.

"Still?"

"In love with her?"

"No," Grey said. "I haven't been for a long time."

"But she's Sari's mother."

"She left five years ago," Grey said. "And we haven't seen her since. But she really left long before that. We fell in love fast, and Sari came, and reality set in. After Sari was born, we never turned to each other again. Not once. When the baby was big enough, she began spending most of her time at that ranch I told you about, with her horse trainer and friends. Our marriage was never accepted by them—or by any of her people— I'm the devil to them."

"It wasn't your fault!"

"Some of the older people blamed Maria as much as they did me. Supposedly, one put a curse on her, and all of her children."

"Oh, God—Sari?"

Grey shook his head impatiently. "Don't worry—I don't believe in it. Rosalie put the idea in her head one time, and I swear I nearly lost it. It's just Old World stupidity. But Maria took it to heart; she probably believes it to this day."

"Do they know where she is?"

"Of course," Grey said. "They know, I know. And so does Sari. Maria is with a circus in Nevada. She's the star—something she always wanted."

"But her daughter . . ."

Grey didn't respond. He wanted to stop talking about Maria. The waves broke gently on the shore, lulling him into a feeling of calm. His heart felt cracked open, talking to a woman who cared. He never let himself get this far. But Susannah really was different and so was all that was happening. It had to be. Grey looked at her now, touched her cheek.

"I'd started to think Sari would never ride again," he said, looking into Susannah's violet eyes.

"I'm glad she did," Susannah said. "And that I was there to see it."

"*See* it? You made it possible . . ."

"She's so good. And she obviously loves Mystère very much."

"She does. But she was badly traumatized . . . still is."

"How did she fall, Grey?" Susannah asked.

Grey paused. "She was chasing her mother. It was the night Maria left . . ."

"Oh my God!" Susannah said, closing her eyes. Grey could tell the picture was vivid in her mind, could see her imagining what it must have been like for his eight-year-old daughter.

"She fell off Mystère and just shattered," Grey said. "Completely. The physical breaks were only part of it."

Just then a group of riders from another ranch galloped out of the marsh and began riding along the beach. Grey felt them watching him and Susannah, so he gave her his hand, helped her up. He bent down and picked up a few scallop shells. Most were black, but he found two bright orange-apricot ones as well, and slipped them into his pocket.

They climbed back onto their horses and started riding home. Grey hated to leave the quiet beach. He wanted to keep talking with her, wanted to tell her everything, the whole story, but even more he wanted just to be with her.

Making their way back through the tall

reeds, he felt reality returning. As they neared the stable, he heard voices: the morning trail ride had returned, and the afternoon ride would begin shortly. He pulled back on his reins, stopping Django. Susannah glanced over her shoulder, and Arabella circled around.

As if she knew what he wanted—or wanted the same thing herself—Susannah guided Arabella to stand side by side with Django. Grey leaned across the space between the horses, wrapped his arm around Susannah, and kissed her. It was rough and hurried, compared with their time on the beach, her lips salty from the sea breeze, and her hand clutching his as if she felt the same urgency he did.

"Once we get back to the barn, there'll be people around," he said.

"I know," she said.

"I want to see you again," he said. "How long are you here for?"

"I fly home on Sunday," she said.

The words hit him with a thud; it was Thursday now. His mind raced; how could he see her every minute? Sari would be home from school soon, and tomorrow he had a vet coming from Nîmes; Saturday belonged to Sari—he knew she'd have it all planned.

"Sunday is too soon," he said.

"I know," she said.

"Look . . ." he said. "Put it off for a few days, okay? You can do that, can't you?"

"I'm not sure; I paid full fare, so it might be possible to change my ticket. . . ."

"A tour group booked a night ride for Sunday. I do that sometimes, when the moon is full, or close to it. I'd love for you to come."

"What about Sari?" Susannah asked. "Won't she mind?"

"I'm not sure," he said hoarsely, touching her face. "She and I spend Saturday together; it's always been 'our' day. I wish I could see you then, too . . . and tomorrow. But I want you to take that ride. Will you? And if you stay a few extra days, I'll figure out a way to see you after that, as well. . . ." He reached into his pocket, pulled out the scallop shells he had picked up on the beach. He handed them to Susannah.

"For me?" she asked.

"While you're thinking about staying, I want you to remember today," he said.

"Do you think I could ever forget it?" she whispered.

And he shook his head, because he knew he never could forget it either, and they turned their horses toward home, and galloped back to the stable.

ELEVEN

Susannah returned to her house after leaving the ranch, stripped off her riding clothes, got into her blue bathing suit and dived into the pool. The sun was bright, beating down on her skin, and the sensuality of it filled her with almost more longing than she could bear.

She swam more laps than she could count, just to burn off the desire that seemed to be overtaking her. Her heart pumped from the exertion, and the turquoise water split into silver sparkles as she stroked up and down the pool's length, thinking of Grey the whole time.

He had spoken of falling in love. The image of falling filled Susannah's mind as the water held her steady. The danger of teetering, losing balance, plunging into the unknown: that's how she felt right now. She'd held herself back all these years; what she'd had with Ian hadn't even come close.

Grey had asked about her "team." She'd found herself wanting to tell him about Ian. She worked so hard, all the time, and involving herself with Ian, mixing up their professional connection with something more, had kept her from being available to anything real. Even after his proposal, when she'd backed away, there had been no definite end between them. His call, as unwelcome as it had been, had at least helped her feel more clear about the fact that things were really over. If they had ever existed at all. What she felt for Grey was so different.

As she climbed out of the pool to dry herself off, she felt the towel—rough on her skin—and thought of him, and wanted him so badly she had to sit down. How had she let herself stay this alone for this long? She lay back on the terrace, letting the sun bake down, and feeling heat rise through her body from the hot blue stone beneath. She thought of how safely she had lived, how wrapped up in the cocoon of the college and the library. And she thought of Grey kissing her on the beach, and felt the world tilt beneath her.

But how could she live up to the relationship he'd had already, with Maria? When he had sat there, telling her about how fast they'd fallen in love, Susannah had had to stare down at the pebbles on the beach, just to keep herself steady, because she'd felt as if that's just what was happening to her: she was falling in love with Grey.

She took a shower in the open air, letting the warm water wash over her body, wondering how she could wait to see him again. She knew that he had ranch business tomorrow, and that Saturday belonged to Sari. It touched her, to think of him being so devoted to his daughter. . . . But she didn't know how she would make it till their next meeting. Sun streamed through the slats of the tall enclosure. She smoothed her skin with lavender wash, poured from a tall silver bottle, and knew she was already a much different woman than the one who had left Connecticut. She had to get back—she had obligations—but she had already decided to stay at least another day or two.

As she dried off and dressed, she knew that she owed a large debt to her mother, for telling her to visit Sarah. But also to Helen Oakes. The thought of coming to Stes.-Maries-de-la-Mer had been in Susannah's mind for a long time, but she'd felt so stalled after her mother's death.

Then, three days before her birthday, Susannah had been sitting at her desk. Surrounded by piles of books, papers, site maps, and photographs of findings from the Istanbul dig, she'd been lost. She heard the thump, thump of Helen's cane, just in time to look up into her mentor's patrician, austere face.

"Hello, Helen," she said.

"Susannah, may I interrupt you for a moment?" Helen asked.

"Of course," Susannah said, clearing a pile of papers from the chair beside her desk.

Helen Oakes was tall and reed thin, with white hair pulled back in an elegant French twist. She wore a hunter-green challis dress and sensible brown shoes. Her only piece of jewelry—which she always wore—was a thick gold chain from which dangled a heavy gold locket adorned by a mysterious raised cross on one side and a deeply scored monogram on the other. Heavy wool stockings hid the brace on her left leg.

"What can I do for you?" Susannah asked.

Helen had a glint in her eyes. "Well, it's rather delicate. I lay wide awake last night trying to decide what to do. I've been invited to a surprise party."

"Oh dear," Susannah said, smiling. They'd worked with each other long enough to know that neither one of them liked surprise parties.

"Yours," Helen said.

"Oh no," Susannah said, having a vision of herself walking into the party: widening her eyes, letting out a whoop of delight, pretending to be thrilled and totally surprised— she thought it over; no, that wasn't going to happen. Her eyes filled with tears.

"You've had a very hard year," Helen said.

Susannah nodded. She had a lump in her throat, and couldn't speak. She pictured all her loving, well-meaning friends planning the one thing she wouldn't be able to stand:

forced gaiety was beyond her realm right now.

"When my mother died," Helen said, "I found myself quite incapacitated. I went on a lengthy retreat."

"You did?" Susannah managed to ask.

"Yes," Helen said. "To a Buddhist monastery in northern India. The serenity I found was unparalleled. I sat in meditation for hours each day, within sight of the snow-capped Himalayas. All the feelings that had been pressed down, swirling inside, were allowed to come to the surface. And I was able to let them out."

"How did you manage that?" Susannah asked. She thought of herself sitting cross-legged on the floor of a monastery. If she did, she was quite sure that she would start crying and never stop.

"It was simply necessary," Helen said. "As I sense it is for you. We're alike, you know."

"We are," Susannah said, grateful to have such a wonderful friend and mentor.

"You are mourning your mother, my dear," Helen said, leaning closer. "But also a sense of yourself that has been lost."

"Lost?"

"Yes. You've been chasing around the world for years now. Your scholarship has been superb, but the rest of it—" She gave a thumbs-down. "Believe me, I know. In excelling at work, you sacrificed a bit of yourself. I did the same thing. I'm not saying that we've made a mistake—only that in choosing this path, we've let some of life pass us by."

"I wasn't there for my mother," Susannah said. "That's what you're saying?"

"Not at all. You made your mother so happy, doing what you love to do. I'm talking about other areas of your life. Ian Stewart, to be precise."

"What about him?"

"Susannah . . . what are you doing with him?"

"He and I are taking a break."

Helen paused, staring at her. "Are you sure he knows that?"

"You sound like my mother," Susannah said, smiling sadly.

"Well, your mother was a very wise woman. Now, does Ian knew how you feel? Or, rather, how you don't feel?"

"I'm not sure he wants to know," Susannah said. "It doesn't seem to be sinking in.

He has a talent for ignoring what he doesn't like. As you know, I've been trying to 'bond' with a group of anthropologists from Cambridge. Ian wasn't invited on my last trip with them—he just showed up."

"Well, prepare yourself," Helen said. "He's planning to 'show up' somewhere else."

"What are you talking about?"

"I made the most ridiculous mistake; I told him about your surprise party, and I believe he's insinuated himself into it. He contacted your friend Heather and asked to be invited," Helen said. "She told me when she called to invite me."

"Oh God," Susannah said. "I thought he was in Marseilles, giving a lecture about the Cosquer Cave right around now. Besides, he and I aren't together anymore."

"Well, as I said, I think maybe you need to let him know." Helen gazed at her. "He won't let go easily."

"No . . ." Susannah said. She'd already started to realize that Ian was holding on to her for all sorts of reasons.

"What are you going to do about the party?"

"I can't go, I just can't," Susannah said.

"Go to Stes.-Maries," Helen said gently.

"But my mother . . ." Susannah said. "That was going to be *our* trip."

"Let it be your trip," Helen said. "You and Margaret . . . She'll be with you every step of the way."

"Oh, Helen . . ."

"I'm not being selfless," Helen said. "I need something, and it happens to be in Arles."

"But . . ."

"There is a library there. The Bibliothèque du Cheval Blanc. It contains a magnificent work attributed to Saint Martha. There's a source of great feminine power in Stes.-Maries. I would like you to immerse yourself in that town, and make notes on what you discover."

"But my party."

"You can send them a case of champagne," Helen said. "And tell them that I've sent you to Europe on a top secret mission."

Susannah had almost laughed, but Helen suddenly looked completely serious. She gazed silently, the words "top secret" shimmering between them in a way that Susannah knew they were meant to be taken seriously.

"Are you available?"

Susannah thought of Ian. "Yes," she said. "Completely available."

Now, as she walked into the kitchen of her rented house, Susannah glanced down at the notes she had taken in Arles. The library, where Grey had found her . . . And she looked at the notes she'd made after visiting Sarah's crypt, and after attending the Sarah Circle. She wondered what Helen would think if she knew that instead of finding serenity and meditation here, Susannah was falling wildly in love.

And she had a plan; there were things she had to do, a promise she wanted to keep. She picked up the phone, called the airline, and changed her reservation. Her next calls were much more local.

That day after school, Laurent was working in the barn, and Sari joined him there. He had to put new hay down in the stalls, and she was helping him break apart the bales. It was heavy, dirty work. She never minded work—had her own chores to do around the house and farm—but this was the first time in five years, since they were little, that she'd come so close to the horses.

Almost everything had changed with that one ride. Seeing Sari coming through the marsh on Mystère, next to Susannah on Arabella, had filled Laurent with happiness . . . and pride. He had known what she needed, and he'd helped it to happen. Looking over at her now, seeing her face streaked with dirt as she threw another pitchforkful of hay into the stall, his only frustration was that she still couldn't see colors.

A few nights ago she'd caught him trying to ride one of the wild horses, and he'd told her a little of the truth—he wanted to improve his riding so he could keep up with her. But she had no idea how he felt about her. Tonight, for example; he wanted to ask her to study with him. They had the same homework, and lately he'd been concerned that her grades were falling. She could come over, and they could sit on the sofa, instead of working alone in their separate houses.

"What are you doing, leaning on your pitchfork?" she scolded. "Get to work!"

"Listen to you . . . first day back in the barn, and you start bossing me around."

"Someone has to."

"Your father's in his office—he signs my paycheck."

"Yes, well . . ."

She grinned and threw a handful of hay at him; he picked up a huge armful and dropped it on her head. She pretended to fight him off, then managed to sling her foot around his ankle and knock him down into the pile of hay. He grabbed her hand and pulled her in with him. One of the horses let out a whinny, and she laughed. It was so good to see her having fun, he hugged her. He nearly kissed her, but then their eyes met, and they pushed away.

"You're terrible," she said, "pulling me into the hay."

"Well, you knocked me down first," he said.

She was blushing, and he knew he was bright red. What was happening between them? They'd grown up practically brother and sister. Turning thirteen, the first thing that happened was that he'd started turning crazy every time Sari came near. This wasn't the first time he'd wanted to kiss her; it was just the closest they'd come.

The strangest thing was that he felt her wanting to do it, too. And he could see she felt as mixed about it as he did. Now she'd jumped up, run over to Mystère's stall. She reached for an apple from the bin, and worked off a section, holding it out toward the white mare.

Laurent walked over to stand next to her, just because if he didn't, he knew there would be weirdness between them. He'd already figured that out with other girls. But he didn't care about them; what he cared about was making sure there was no unfamiliar wall between him and Sari.

"She's so happy you're feeding her," he said, standing half behind Sari, looking down at the back of her head.

"I'm her person," Sari said.

"She always knew that, even when you stayed away."

"Of course she knew it," Sari said, turning to give Laurent the sternest, warmest, crazy-wildest look he'd ever seen. "Sometimes things are so obvious, you don't have to say it, don't have to be there, don't have to do anything at all . . ."

"Huh," Laurent said, paralyzed.

"And other times," she said, holding him still with her gaze, "you have to take drastic action."

He never saw it coming; she slid her foot behind his ankle again, and knocked him right back down. She stood there laughing, offering him a hand. He took it, and when she pulled him up, the words just came out.

"Come study with me tonight, okay? At my house?"

"That's awfully far," she teased.

Laurent felt ripples across his skin. It *was* awfully far—she had no idea what she was saying, or what he was feeling. If she had any idea that he'd long stopped thinking of her as a little sister, who knew what she'd do? So he just gave her a stupid grin, shook his head as if he thought she'd just said something ridiculous, and started forking hay into the stalls again.

"Well, how about this, too . . ." His throat was dry. Ever since he'd seen that bad grade on her history essay, he'd been thinking about how he could help. And now, Susannah had called, asked him to help *her*. He felt like part of a conspiracy—because as much as he liked her, and wanted to help, he was thrilled, because the end result meant more time with Sari. "How about studying with me at the library tomorrow?"

"Why? We can study here, can't we?"

"Yes, but it might be fun to be in town. I'll buy you some crêpes."

Sari paused, giving him a funny smile. He tried to keep a straight face, giving nothing away.

"Crêpes *sucre*?" she asked.

"Any kind you want."

"Okay, then. I'll go with you."

Laurent smiled. He glanced over at the office door. Her father was standing there, looking happy with the world. Laurent wondered whether Susannah had called him yet.

"Is there a group coming to ride tonight?" Laurent asked.

"No," Grey said. "That's scheduled for the full moon. Sunday night."

"Okay," Laurent said.

"I'm going to Laurent's to study tonight, Papa," Sari said, continuing to work. "Is that okay?"

"That's completely fine," Grey said. "Um, Sari, I wanted to talk to you about to-morrow . . ."

"Oh!" she said. "Laurent and I are going to the library after school. Is that okay, too?"

"Yes, Sari. That's great."

And Laurent could tell, by the way Grey was smiling, that it really was, that nothing could have made him happier than to know that his daughter would be busy and off on her own tomorrow evening.

Even though Susannah had told him she would change her departure to Tuesday, Grey felt time ticking away. After so many solitary years, trying to rebuild a world just for himself and Sari, he felt inseparable from a woman who would be flying across an ocean. Every minute that went by, he found himself feeling more impatient for the time to pass so he could see her. She'd called him at the barn, asked him if he could be free all the next day.

"The vet's coming, but I'll get Claude to cover for me here," he said. "Why?"

"Well, I'd need you all day," she said. "We couldn't make it there and back and do everything we'd have to do in time for Sari's school bus . . ."

"What are you talking about?" he laughed.

"I'm making good on my promise," she said.

"What promise?" he asked.

"You said you wanted to see the Cosquer Cave."

"You're kidding!"

"Get your swim trunks ready," she said. "We're going underwater."

"You don't mess around," he said.

"I hope you know the way to Marseille. Will it be a problem to pick me up early? Like . . . dawn? Will Sari worry?"

He laughed. "It's a ranch—I'm always out early. There's one thing. I'm always here when she gets home from school. But she and Laurent are going to the library tomorrow . . ."

"I thought that might work out," she'd said, laughing. "At least, I hope it does. See you at sunrise!"

Now, sitting in his office, Grey stared out into the barn. Obviously Laurent was in on it—Susannah must have called him. He and Sari were working in the stalls, laughing and fooling around. Grey watched for a few minutes, trying to remember when he'd been that young.

Grey might not be a kid anymore, but right now he felt like one. This was unexplored territory for him. Susannah was different from anyone he'd ever known. He wanted to read everything she'd ever written, see the world and the places she explored, learn all there was to know about her.

Tomorrow at dawn, he'd be with her.

Susannah was taking Grey to the sea cave. That's all she could think about. There were several more calls she had to make, to secure permits, and access, and to make sure there would be dive equipment available. But she had always been efficient, expert at making things happen, cutting through red tape. She had a BlackBerry filled with contact information, and within an hour, the plans were set.

All she had to do was wait for today to pass so tomorrow could come.

Taking her market basket for later, she headed to the church. Making her way through the dark nave, she passed several women she recognized from the caravan: Zuna, Florine, Ana, and Étoile. They had changed Sarah's clothes—removed the gold brocade coat and replaced it with a shimmering pink cloak—and arranged fresh candles all around the statue. Topaz was down the aisle, polishing the stone floor.

Waiting for the women to leave, Susannah walked into Sarah's chapel. She paused before the beautiful dark statue. Looking into Sarah's eyes, she thought of her mother, felt her right there beside her.

Zin-Zin had said she would have children. Would she really? She had just turned forty-two years old. By the time her mother had knelt here, she was only thirty-four, had been married for nine years, and had desired children for all of that time. Susannah had spent all her life studying and working, getting ahead in her field. Right now she felt overwhelmed with yearning, and it was all the more powerful because she'd never felt anything like it before.

Her eyes fell upon the base of Sarah's statue; people had left smooth stones, pieces of jewelry, handwritten notes, and scallop shells at her feet. Susannah thought of the seven shells that Grey had given her on the beach. Reaching into her pocket, she pulled them out. Five were black, but two were shades of peach. Choosing one of the palest ones, she added it to the pile of gifts for Sarah.

On her way out of the crypt, beyond the candles' light, she waved at Topaz, polishing the stone floor. Topaz waved back, and then rose to follow Susannah outside, into the sunlight.

"Good to see you," Topaz said, when they stood outside the church. "I notice you left Sarah an offering."

"A scallop shell," Susannah said.

"That is very powerful," Topaz said. "*Coquille Saint Jacques* . . . it's the symbol of pilgrims en route to the shrine of Saint James de Compostela, in northern Spain. They pass through here, and it's said the *coquilles* on our beach are black, in honor of Sarah. She will be most pleased that you left one for her."

Susannah peered at her, shielding her eyes from the sun. "Would you like to have a coffee with me? There's something I'd like to ask you about."

"Of course."

Linking arms with Susannah, Topaz began to walk her down the street. They strolled through the market, past stalls bright and vivid with fragrant flowers and ripe fruit, with squawking chickens in cages and large brown eggs piled in woven baskets, with racks of cotton dresses blowing gently in the breeze. Susannah spotted other women from the Sarah Circle: Anaïs, Naguine, Isabel, and Rosalie. They stood together talking, whispering as they saw Topaz walk by with Susannah.

Topaz waved lightly, ignoring several pointed stares, leading Susannah onto the terrace of the *café tabac*. They squeezed past a tall revolving rack of postcards, into one of the tables right in front. A faded red awning shaded them from the sun, and they both ordered double espresso from the elderly waiter. Sitting on a stone wall across the way, a young man played flamenco guitar.

"How have you enjoyed your time since we saw each other last?" Topaz asked.

"It's been wonderful," Susannah said, unable to hide a huge smile.

"We enjoyed having you join us at the caravan," Topaz said.

"I really appreciate your introducing me to the Sarah Circle," Susannah said, watching through the market stalls for Rosalie and the others.

Topaz laughed. "Not everyone is sure what to make of you. A few attitudes have shifted a bit. . . . It wasn't very long ago that we Romanies claimed Sarah all for our own. There's a certain distrust of 'outsiders.' Especially those for whom Sarah has performed miracles."

"But you seem so welcoming," Susannah said.

"I am," Topaz said. "Because I'm not one hundred percent Gypsy. My great-grandfather, on my father's side, was Spanish. It's where I get my name, Avila. He was making the pilgrimage in reverse—*from* St. Jacques—when he passed through here and met my great-grandmother. There was quite a scandal. It's taken generations for my family to really be accepted."

"Why is it so bad for a Gypsy to marry a non-Gypsy?"

Topaz laughed. "That's a good question. Have you got the next six months to listen? Because that's how long it would take for me to tell you everything I've ever heard about it. Mainly, it is because we have such a rich tradition and lineage, and because we've suffered such persecution. We're proud, and our elders want to be sure our traditions continue."

"The elders would be unhappy to see a Gypsy marry someone from outside?"

"Not just the elders, and unhappy is putting it rather mildly." Topaz turned to look Susannah in the eye. "Is this what you wanted to ask me about?"

"Yes. Maria," Susannah said.

"Ah," Topaz said. "You've found out about our Maria."

"You mentioned her the other night . . . and Rosalie . . ."

"Rosalie is very protective of Maria," Topaz said. "They were as close as sisters."

The waiter brought the two *cafés* on a small tray, and Topaz immediately added three sugar cubes to hers. Susannah sipped the strong coffee, waiting for her to go on.

"Love is miraculous, don't you agree?" Topaz asked.

"I do," Susannah said quietly.

"Well, for the Manouche—our clan—it is mysterious, magical, and always romantic. But there are certain expectations. We marry men we know, friends of the family, brothers of our girlfriends. But along came

Grey Dempsey, with his notepad and tape recorder, his fancy job as a reporter, talking of Paris and America, and Maria was swept up . . ."

Susannah listened, shocked by how painful it was to hear about Grey with another woman.

"And Maria—she could take the breath from any man. She was an exquisite beauty, with supernaturally dark eyes, and the most knowing gaze . . . she could tiptoe on the back of a horse, and the horse wouldn't even know she was there. Every Gypsy man from here to Budapest wanted her."

"But she wanted Grey . . ."

Topaz nodded. "Sometimes I think it was because it was so forbidden. Maria was always ready to take a dare."

"Did you go to their wedding?"

Topaz laughed. "No—no one did. They eloped."

"Was her family very upset?"

"Not by that," Topaz said. "The Manouche allow what's called 'runaway marriage'—the couple disappears for a day or two on their own, but then returns to feasting and celebration. There was no wedding party for Maria and Grey. They went to a judge in Arles—never telling a soul. She moved to Paris with Grey, cut off ties with all of us."

"Paris? But I thought . . ."

"The ranch came later. He had assignments from American and French magazines, and he was based in Paris. She tried to love the city, but she was horribly homesick."

"For Stes.-Maries?"

"For horses. Maria's job had always been to look after horses at her trainer's farm. That's where she'd learned to ride the way she did—truly, like an angel. Balancing on the toes of one foot, arms outstretched, a ballerina on horseback. She performed in all our festivals, from the time she could walk."

"So Grey left Paris and moved down here . . ."

"He loved horses almost as much as Maria. And I think he would have done anything to make her happy."

"Were you close to her?"

"In some ways, very," Topaz said. "I was always hopeful for her and Grey. My great-grandparents, you see. My family is proof that love doesn't always happen according to plan. In fact, I think the best kind doesn't!"

"What happened between them?"

Topaz shrugged. "They were up against such opposition. Our elders were outraged and hurt. Plus, there was Maria herself."

"What do you mean?"

"She was . . . very special. High-strung. More talented on horseback than one would believe humanly possible. Her parents died young; she was raised by Zin-Zin, who is as close to a Gypsy queen as we have. Maria was the apple of her eye! Zin-Zin was devoted to her; I think it made Maria feel so special, she always had to be the star. . . . In fact, sometimes I think that's why she married Grey. She knew such a marriage would make her stand out. It would make everyone talk. But it turned out to be wrong from the start."

"In what way?"

"A thousand ways. Maria thought she wanted love and nurturing, but she found that life with a husband was completely constricting to her. She needed complete freedom to pursue her art."

"Art?"

"Oh, yes," Topaz said. "What Maria does

on horseback is nothing less than great art. Arabesques, leaps, grande jetés . . . She needed to ride free at any hour, and to travel wherever she wanted, to train and perform."

"Is that what she's doing now?" Susannah asked. "Grey mentioned a circus."

"Yes," Topaz said simply.

"But what about Sari? How could she leave her?"

"Maria . . . is not like other people."

Susannah thought of her own mother; she could not imagine her leaving Susannah, for any reason. Nor could Susannah envision herself ever leaving a child; she pictured Sari, the hurt she'd seen in her eyes, and shook her head. "No," Susannah agreed. "She must not be."

"It's easy to judge Maria," Topaz agreed. "But you don't know her. She's truly not of this world. She's like a butterfly."

"What do you mean?"

"Maria floats like air. She appears so delicate, almost fragile. But when she rides— she's filled with as much tensile strength as the horse itself. It's magnificent. She becomes one with the horse. If you believe that we are all here for a reason, then to see

Maria you would believe God put her here to dance on horseback."

"And meanwhile, Sari suffers."

Topaz just shook her head. Then, looking Susannah straight in the eye, said, "You've gotten very attached, haven't you?"

Susannah hesitated, then nodded.

"To both of them," Topaz said. It was a statement, not a question, and it made the blood rise into Susannah's face.

"Yes," Susannah said.

Topaz nodded. A small smile touched her lips. Rosalie and the others were still watching from across the way. Susannah saw Topaz meet Rosalie's gaze; was there a hint of tension there?

"Did you manage to get to the library the other day?" Topaz asked.

"In Arles?" Susannah asked, surprised that Topaz would remember she'd mentioned it. "Yes, I did."

"And your research went well?"

"Yes. Topaz, I know I said I'm not here to study you, or any of the other women, but I have to confess, my colleague—a professor I work with—has a strong interest in Saint Martha. In particular, she asked me to study the connection with Sarah, and the women who are devoted . . ."

"Like the Sarah Circle."

"Well, yes."

Susannah glanced over, expecting to see anger on Topaz's face, but instead she saw a large, bright smile.

"That pleases me," Topaz said. "The more studies that are done, the more people will come to see Sarah. Who am I to stop the faithful? You, who've already known a miracle in your life, should know that."

Susannah laughed and nodded, sipping her coffee.

"So, tell me, Susannah: did Grey find you?"

"Excuse me?"

"At the library—in Arles?"

"Yes, but how did—" And then Susannah realized. "You told him! He said that someone had told him I was going to Arles. Was it you?"

Topaz strove to make her face blank. She stared up at the medieval church, at the blue sky behind the dark fortifications. But there was a sparkle in her eye that gave everything away: she was a Romany, but she'd been born and bred by people who believed more in love than tradition. She was the keeper of Sarah's chapel, and Sarah had already proven to be a guardian angel for Susannah and her family.

"It was you, wasn't it?" Susannah pressed.

"Perhaps I had a hand in it."

"But why?"

Topaz just shook her head, refusing to say more. Susannah paid for the espressos, and Topaz thanked her. She had to get back to the chapel, to finish cleaning before evening devotion. She hurried away and Susannah watched her disappear into the church. She was still feeling grateful and mystified, when she noticed Rosalie still staring from across the market street.

Susannah reached into her pocket; she still had six scallop shells, given to her by Grey, and her hand closed around them now. They jingled fragilely in her fingers, and reminded her that she wasn't alone.

It was a new feeling. She looked up in the sky, at the sun shining in the bright blue, and she knew she could hardly stand waiting for night to fall, and to pass, and for dawn to come, when she would see him again.

TWELVE

Dawn began as a pink shimmer in the east, blazing into a line of orange fire along the horizon, turning the sea from black to blue. Susannah had never felt so excited; at the same time, she'd never felt so calm. This morning, everything felt right with the world.

A little while later she heard tires crunching the white gravel in the driveway, and she slung her bag over her shoulder and ran outside. Grey sat in the green Citroën, grinning through the windshield. Her heart jumped just to see him. Climbing into the car, she hesitated for just a second. He didn't; he leaned over to kiss her hello.

"Good morning," she said.

"Good morning," he said, not letting go.

She leaned into his body, thinking that they could scrap the trip and just go back inside. But then he eased away, shifted into reverse to back out of her driveway and head out of town.

"Are you ready for this?" she asked.

"I am," he said. "Been looking forward to it so much, I couldn't sleep last night."

"Neither could I," she said.

They drove north to the N568, headed east onto the A55, and within an hour they were caught in Marseille commuter traffic. They skirted the bright, colorful port city, driving through dry white hills and pine-shaded olive orchards. Just beyond Cap Croisette, they angled into the Calanques— spectacular white limestone cliffs scored with fjords and sapphire bays. The massif stretched twenty kilometers along the coast road to Cassis.

"I live an hour away and hardly ever come here," Grey said, driving along the steep belvedere. "When we go to the city, it's almost always Arles or Paris. I've been to Marseille, but never driven east of the port. This is incredible."

"That's how I felt when I first came here," Susannah said, so happy she could be the one to show it to him. She explained about how the Calanques had formed at the end of the last ice age. The glacier retreated, scraping the earth's crust, leaving this spine of white mountains along the fault line. Tiny villages nestled down below, at the edge of the sea, home to fishing families.

"Where are the caves?" he asked.

"Right there," she said, pointing at Cap Morgiou. The next headland jutted boldly into the Mediterranean, the vertical drop dramatic and straight down to the sea. Following the signs on the steep switchback road, Grey turned onto a narrow one-car road that plummeted over and down the sea cliff. Several heart-stopping minutes and hairpin turns later, they'd reached the end of the road. Parking in an unpaved lot, they made the rest of the trek on foot.

They scrambled down steps carved into the rock face. Susannah reached for Grey's hand, wanting to make sure he didn't fall; she'd been here several times, and she knew how treacherous this path could be. Glancing into his eyes, she saw he had a wide smile on his face.

"What is it?" she asked.

"You," he said.

"What do you mean?"

"You're being protective; it's nice. No one ever does that for me."

She smiled back, and thought of how much she liked doing it. "Everyone needs protecting now and then," she said.

Grey just laughed, holding her hand tighter. They emerged in the tiny village at the foot of the precipice, but even on solid ground they kept holding hands. Houses painted blue, ochre, and coral lined the narrow street. They stopped in front of a dive shop: *Caratini Services Plongées.*

Inside, she greeted the owners, Felix and Jeanine Caratini. It was a wonderful reunion, involving much hugging and kissing and a steady stream of rapid French. Susannah introduced Grey; they asked him a few questions, and he told them about learning to dive off Narragansett, producing his logbook and medical certificate. They were fascinated to hear about his dives on the sunken U-boat; Susannah listened, touched by how humbly he established himself as an expert diver.

The building's plaster walls were lined

with photographs of the many divers who'd come through the door. Smiling faces, everyone dressed in wet suits and wearing air tanks—all except one person. Ian. The picture showed him standing beside Susannah, his arm around her; she looked ready to dive, in black neoprene, while he was wearing a blue button-down shirt and chinos.

"Monsieur Stewart," Jeanine said to Susannah, following her gaze as Grey stepped away to examine the tanks. "He is here, in town."

"You saw him?" Susannah asked.

"He arrived yesterday. He came here hoping to see you."

"I just spoke to him . . . How would he know I'd come to Cap Morgiou?" she asked, frowning. "I didn't even know myself . . ."

Jeanine beamed, giving Susannah a quick hug. "Because how could you resist? Staying in the South of France, so close, and not diving the Grotte Cosquer?"

"As hard as that would be to do, my real reason for coming was to show Grey . . . I want him to see the cave."

Jeanine nodded, and Susannah saw happiness in her eyes. They'd known each other for several years, and Jeanine had seen the dynamic unfold between Susannah and Ian. Susannah had always thought what a good couple the Caratinis made—how independent they each were, yet how supportive, running this business together. She had envied them, and she knew Jeanine wished Susannah could have that kind of connection with someone.

"Where is he now?" Susannah asked.

Jeanine shrugged. "That I don't know. He took a room in one of the guesthouses near the lighthouse."

"He's waiting for me?"

"Yes, I believe so," Jeanine said.

"Who is waiting?" Grey asked, walking over to meet Susannah as Jeanine turned to help some other customers.

"Ian. An old colleague."

"Your old team?" Grey asked, grinning.

"Yes," she said. "He didn't dive, though."

"Is he on this wall?" Grey asked, peering at the gallery of divers.

Susannah pointed at the photo, and watched Grey lean forward to see more closely.

"You were with him?" Grey asked. "I mean, more than just colleagues?"

"We met in grad school," Susannah said slowly. "There was so much to like about him . . . he's smart, and he loves our subject, and we worked well together. We tried . . . well, we made a stab at trying . . . for something more."

"But it didn't work out?" Grey asked.

"No," she said, shaking her head.

Grey grabbed her hand. "I'm glad it didn't work out," he said. "For whatever reason. I'd like to hear about it, if you want to tell me."

"Our breakup was a long time coming," she said slowly. "It wasn't any one thing. But once my mother got really sick . . . once I knew things were really changing—well, it made me look at everything differently."

"And you knew?"

She nodded. "I knew I couldn't be with him."

Grey took her hand, and pulled her against him. She stood there holding him, feeling a closeness she'd never felt with Ian.

Just then Felix came toward them with armloads of dive gear. Grey hugged her harder, and then they went into dressing rooms to change, came out dressed in wet suits, carrying masks, fins, and air tanks.

While Jeanine stayed at the counter to mind the shop, Felix led Susannah and Grey down the dock to his boat—*Le Chat Bleu*. Grey gave her a hand, and she stepped over the rail. The boat was captained by a friend of the Caratinis, Jean Olivier. Grey helped Jean cast off, then sat beside Susannah on the fiberglass seat as Jean started up the engine and headed into the bay.

Grey and Susannah linked fingers, feeling the sea breeze in their faces. The sun beat down, making the black wet suits feel so warm. Susannah leaned into Grey's strong body, thinking about how rough and ready and sweet and tender their brief time together had been. The horseback ride, this chance to dive. She'd never had anything like it with Ian, or with anyone. She felt so much support, connection, and trust. As the boat left the inner harbor, it gained speed, bouncing across the azure waves. Grey's arm slid around Susannah's shoulder, and he held her tight. And she grabbed his free hand, and held him right back.

* * *

The water was so clear, and Grey's breath sounded loud in his ears, and he swore he could feel both their hearts beating—his and Susannah's—as they breathed into their regulators and swam side by side, slowly down toward the sea bottom.

The undersea world felt peaceful and private, as if it belonged only to him and Susannah. She glanced over at him, through their bubbles, making sure he was okay. It touched and amused him, and he gave her a thumbs-up. No one ever looked at him like that. He was always the one taking care of business, running the ranch, caring for the horses, looking after Sari.

Diving took him back to his youth. He had learned over twenty-five years ago, long before he'd met Maria. The years melted away; the realm of the Camargue was a distant memory. He didn't feel like a kid—he hadn't lost his wisdom and battle scars—but the everyday realities of his life seemed to be dissolving with every breath he took, every meter they descended.

Brightly colored fish swam by, some covered with spines, exotic and unknown—the

clear water was itself a revelation to someone who had learned to dive in murky New
England waters. As they got closer to the
sea bottom, Susannah pointed out bright,
spiky orange coral, enormous langoustes,
red starfish, and a green eel.

She'd told him that Ian wouldn't dive
with her, and Grey almost felt sorry for
him. Who would choose to miss an experience like this? Not just the exhilaration of
diving, but also the intensity of going this
deep underwater—going anywhere—with
Susannah.

Grey swam close by her, feeling the ripple
of her leg against his. She was slim and
muscular, and the wet suit clung to every
inch of her body. He had to remind himself
to breathe steadily; that's what deep dives
were all about. But she was making it a
challenge.

As she gestured to him that they'd come
to the mouth of the cave, he held back
briefly to hold on to the moment. Up in the
boat, she'd given him some background.
The cave was a relatively recent, incredible
find: in 1991, a professional diver, Henri
Cosquer, swam into one of a hundred cav-
erns honeycombed along this stretch of the

sea bottom. At one time, before the last ice age, these caves had been several miles inland. Cosquer became the first human being in thousands of years to enter and see what was inside.

And now, because of Susannah, Grey was getting that chance. She switched on her light, and he followed. Holding on to a previously set line, she began to swim into the dark opening, Grey a few feet back behind her, his eyes getting accustomed to the blackness.

It had been a long, long time since Grey had felt anything like this. As a journalist, he'd known the thrill of making discoveries. For so many years now, he'd buried himself in the routine of his work, living the life of a rancher, catering to the tourist trade. He hadn't flexed his reporter muscles in over a decade, and right now his senses were on high alert.

The cave was completely dark; their flashlight beams provided the only illumination. Large fish darted back and forth, prompting Grey to swim closer to Susannah, wanting to keep them away from her. But she gave him a calm look through her mask; the sight of her eyes reassured him, and he kept swimming.

After a few more minutes they began to rise. Their progress was slow, in stages, taking time to decompress. Grey loved those moments—hovering in the dark with Susannah, holding hands and waiting for their blood to stabilize so they could continue their ascent. He felt light-headed, but not from nitrogen narcosis. He was intoxicated being next to Susannah.

When they reached the surface, they broke out into a rock-walled chamber. Susannah swam over to a ledge where semi-permanent staging lights had been set up by other research teams. She climbed out and flipped the switch, and the cave was filled with light.

Sliding back into the water, she swam over to Grey. They slipped off their masks. He stared around at the limestone walls rising and arching overhead, his heart hammering, his arm around her. She began pointing upward, and it took him a few moments to be able to focus on what she was seeing. But once he saw, he was awed.

"Paintings," he said. "They're everywhere."

"Yes," she said. "Over a hundred and fifty different animals are depicted."

She led him around, showing him images of horses, bulls, ibis, flamingos . . . the many species he lived beside every day, in the Parc Régional de Camargue. Then there were other, less familiar animals: mammoths, chamois, ibex, bear, even penguins. There were seals, auks, and jellyfish. The paintings were done in warm, beautiful earth tones. Some of the animals were marked with zigzags and squares. Others were pierced by spears.

The cavern was large, shaped approximately like a butterfly. She guided him through the different areas: the North Chamber, the Feline Chamber, the section nicknamed "the Beach." They swam under an arch, through a narrow passage, past the rock face anthropologists called "Chaos."

"Who did these?" he asked, gazing with amazement at the incredible images all around them.

"No one knows, exactly, but we think they were travelers," Susannah said. "We've found similar work in the Ardèche, as well as Valencia and Parpello, in Spain."

"The same artists?"

"That's my theory," she said. "I published a paper about it three years ago. We found evidence of charcoal—they built fires, and used flints. The animal paintings date back nearly nineteen thousand years. But see these?" She led him, swimming slowly, over to the large flooded shaft by the east wall, where he saw eerie images of human hands.

"You told me about these," he said, remembering when she'd first mentioned the cave.

"Hand stencils," she said. "These were done about twenty-seven thousand years ago. They're very distinctive—see how some of the fingers look incomplete?"

"Deformed, almost," he said, noticing the short, crooked digits.

"Maybe," she said. "Or perhaps the artists curled them under. It's very unusual, but I've seen the same patterns in Spain and the Ardèche . . . I found other hand stencils near Istanbul, but in those instances, the hands were more normal looking."

"What were the artists trying to communicate?" Grey asked, starting to think like a journalist for the first time in more years than he wanted to contemplate. His mind was racing, noticing how most of the hand tracings were black, with just a few done in red. Several had been scored with flints, others painted over with dots, bars, and the same zigzags he'd seen in the animal paintings.

"You already know," she said, smiling. "You told me, when we were sitting on the beach. You said they were telling us they were here."

"Making their mark?" Grey said, turning to face her.

She nodded. Their faces were inches apart. He felt her legs brushing against his, moving in rhythm, treading water. She laced her fingers with his, and he started to swim with her over to the cave wall. He scanned the surface, looking at all the hand stencils, the marks of so many who'd been there before them. Holding her hand against the rock, he gently traced her fingers with his, as he had done on the beach.

Leaning down, he kissed her. Her mouth tasted like salt, and her skin, pressing against his through two layers of neoprene, felt burning hot. He thought of their voices,

still ringing in the air, and felt the reverbera-
tions in his body.

He was shaking, wanting to hold on to her
forever. She pressed against him, pulling
back, her eyes open wide.

At first he thought she felt shocked by
the intensity of the kiss, maybe even upset.
Her eyes drank him in, as if searching for
an explanation. But then she cupped the
back of his head in her hand, softly kissed
him again, their eyes still open, as if they
couldn't bear to let go or look away. They
floated together, unanchored in the ancient
space, as though they were suspended in
time.

Finally, they broke apart. They had a long
swim back, and then they'd have to decompress. They took a last look around the
chamber, at the etched and painted animals
and sea creatures, at the hand stencils, at
the vaulted rock ceiling. Susannah extinguished the light, and Grey switched on the
flashlights.

They kissed once more in the dim light,
then plunged into the black water. Swimming through the underwater part of the
cavern, Grey felt a blanket of darkness enclose them. They were under the sea, and

that made him feel safe. No one could get to them here. No one from her college, no one from his ranch, not her one-time partner, not even, as much as he adored her, Sari. He and Susannah were moving through the underwater darkness together, and he didn't want to go up to the surface for air.

THIRTEEN

There is nothing quite like diving into a secret cave with a man with whom you're falling deeply in love. To leave the brightness of a sunny day, sift downward through the clear, clean water, and enter a new world. To swim together, holding his life in your hands, taking him into a narrow rock tunnel, deep into the earth, showing him things so few people have seen, art created in times before history.

Maybe that was the part that made it all so charged: the fact the paintings were so ancient. The hand stencils had lasted twenty-seven thousand years, in spite of the salt and damp and the fall and rise of the sea. To be swimming together, holding on to each other, bodies hot and soaking wet, legs entwined treading water, kissing under a canopy of art created millennia ago, was overwhelming.

It was primal, and intense, and beautiful, and reckless, and made them realize they were part of something huge and ever-lasting.

If only that could be true, Susannah thought. Twenty minutes after Jean had driven them back, after they had changed into their clothes and finished up at the dive shop, she sat beside Grey on the terrace of a small café overlooking the bay of Cap Morgiou. She tossed her hair, letting it dry in the late-afternoon sun; glancing over at him, she saw him peering across the cerulean water and wished that her time in France would never end, that it could last forever.

The waiter brought over a bottle of Côtes de Provence rosé, two glasses, and a small dish of niçoise olives. Grey asked if she liked shellfish, then ordered a *plateau de fruits de mer.* Lifting his glass, he looked over at her.

"To Henri Cosquer," he said. "If he hadn't

discovered that cave, I never would have gotten to see it with you."

"Here's to you, Henri," Susannah said, laughing as they clinked glasses.

The Bandol tasted delicious and dry, magical in the sea air. It quenched Susannah's thirst, made her feel as if her holiday were just beginning. The olives looked glossy in the sun, shades of green, black, and lavender; they were too pretty to eat. Grey pulled out a pen, and started tracing her hand on the table's brown paper cover. Then she did the same to his.

The *plateau* came: oysters, mussels, some periwinkles, and sea urchins arranged on seaweed. Susannah had eaten at this café before, but the food had never tasted so wonderful. She watched Grey pick up a sea urchin, spines down in his palm, maneuver the brown stuff aside with a small spoon, and find the strips of coral inside. He fed them to her, and Susannah felt as if she were tasting the inside of the sea cave.

She caught his wrist midway through the second bite, and kissed it.

"What's that for?" he asked.

"Everything," she said.

"You're the one who gave me this day,"

he said. "Every single minute of it has
been . . . I don't even have the words."

"It's been great," she said. "The best day
I've ever had."

"I was thinking something along those
lines," he said. "Do you think we can have
another one just like it?"

She laughed. "Well, you're a dive expert.
You know we can't dive two days in a row,
and it's getting awfully close to the time I
have to leave."

"Don't talk about that," he said.

"I won't," she said.

"We can't dive again, so we'll have to do
something else. Something almost as wonderful."

"Like what?" she asked, thinking that an
hour with him anywhere would be incredible.

"The moonlight ride," he said. "The night
after tomorrow."

"At the ranch?" she asked.

He nodded. His eyes were bright, but she
saw a familiar weariness settle over his
face, as if even the mention of his ranch reminded him of his real life. She slipped her
hand into his, to remind him that they didn't
have to go home yet—that the afternoon

wasn't over, they were still right here, on this sunlit terrace, surrounded by pots of beautiful flowers, the sea just beyond, the endless crystalline sky arching above.

"I'd love to," she said. "Nothing would make me happier."

He smiled. She thought of one thing: staying with him would make her happier. She wished they were on a real vacation, here in this little town, in a guesthouse overlooking the harbor. She laughed, wanting to tell him what she was thinking, when she saw his expression change.

"Here he comes," Grey said.

"Henri Cosquer?" she teased. "Or Felix or Jean?" Who else could it possibly be, who else would Grey know of here?

"I recognize him from his picture," Grey said.

Ian. Susannah knew even before she turned around. Her stomach tightened as his shadow fell across the table, and she looked up into the familiar brown eyes. He was dressed the way he always was: as if he were about to go into the classroom, not scramble around out in the field. Blue shirt, khakis, brown loafers.

"I heard you were going to be here," he

said. No hello, no introducing himself to Grey.

"Well, here I am," she said. "Grey, this is Ian Stewart. Ian, Grey Dempsey."

The men shook hands. Ian gave Grey a long, suspicious look, and Grey managed to keep his face passive.

"You missed a hell of a party back in Connecticut," Ian said.

"You mentioned that," Susannah said.

"Well, at least you're here now," he said. Susannah stared at him. Was he not realizing that she was with Grey?

"Let's not do this now," she said.

"I'd like to talk to you in private," he said, gesturing at Grey.

"There's nothing to say," Susannah said, pushing her chair back and standing up to face him.

"You're running out again?" Ian asked sharply, grabbing her arm.

"Hey." Grey jumped up, pulling Ian's hand from Susannah's wrist.

"I'm not running out," Susannah said, wanting to calm everyone, easing Grey back down. "I just . . ."

"Yes, you are," Ian said. "That's what you do—run away."

"Ian . . ."

"From the people who care about you most. Me, all your friends waiting at your party."

"This is ridiculous," Susannah said. "Stop it, now."

She sat down again, glancing at Grey. Assured that she wanted to stay, he pulled his chair closer to hers, sitting beside her. Ian remained standing, staring down.

"You let your friends down," he said. "Running out on them."

"They don't think that about me," Susannah said. "I don't do that."

"No?" Ian said. "Just ask your mother."

Susannah gasped audibly; she felt her hands cover her mouth.

"Listen to me, Susannah," Ian said, reaching for her hand. "Why do you think I came here? I knew you'd be here. I know *you*. No one knows you better than I do. We go back a long way; I've sat at your mother's bedside, haven't I?"

Susannah's eyes filled with tears. It was true. Ian had met her mother, had spent hours at her house in Black Hall, had eaten meals with her, had shared stories of many trips, and projects, and papers. "That's what makes it so terrible," Susannah said. "You *did* know my mother. She was kind to you. But she wouldn't like what you just said to me."

"But you *weren't* there," Ian went on. "When she died. You're not there when it counts, Susannah. For your mother, for me . . ."

Grey pushed his chair back. It was cast iron, one of those pretty chairs that every sidewalk café in France seems to have, and the legs scraping on the concrete made a harsh sound. Susannah saw the fire in his blue eyes, and she put her hand out to stop him, but it was too late. Grey grabbed the front of Ian's shirt, pushed him across the sidewalk, right to the water's edge. There was a six-foot drop from the walkway to the harbor, and Grey stood there with Ian leaning out.

"Take it back," Grey said.

"What are you, twelve years old?" Ian asked, his voice sounding strangled. "Let go of me."

"Take it back," Grey said, perfectly calm. "Unless you want to go swimming."

"How perfect—she studies prehistoric

art, and she's found herself a Neanderthal. I'll have you arrested," Ian said.

"He means it," Susannah said, grabbing Grey's arm. She remembered the trouble Ian had stirred up on sites, where he wanted local personnel off the job and his own people on. He knew how to manipulate situations, to involve the authorities. And she saw clearly, with no further room for denial, precisely how vindictive and small-spirited he was. "Please, Grey . . ."

Grey stared at him. Susannah could feel the energy, barely restrained, pouring off him. She stood there, knowing she should defuse the situation, make Grey stop, let Ian go. But Ian's words rang in her ears with others she had listened to for so long, and he looked so smug and superior, as if he believed Grey would never do it; she couldn't speak or act.

"Are you sorry for being rotten to Susannah?" Grey asked.

Ian managed to laugh. "What I said wasn't rotten. What she does, running off on the people who care about her, *that's*—"

Grey let go of Ian's shirt, and Ian fell into the harbor. Susannah looked down, watching Ian splash around. Grey gave her a long, serious look. "He was about to say you were rotten," Grey said.

"I know," Susannah replied, as people from the café came to stand along the sea-wall, watching Ian swim to the small curved beach by the boat launch.

"He shouldn't have said what he said about your mother."

"No, he shouldn't have," Susannah said.

Grey watched Ian stroke to shore. "Should we help him out?"

"I think he can take care of himself," Susannah said.

"Then should we leave?"

"Yes." Susannah nodded. "We should."

By the time they climbed back up to the parking area, the sun had started to set. It cast bright orange light across the white limestone cliffs, setting them afire. Susannah's heart was throbbing.

"Are you okay?" Grey asked, once they'd gotten into the car.

"I think so. Are you?"

He nodded. "What a jerk that guy was. He's a professor somewhere?"

"Stanford."

"That's hard to believe. A small-minded idiot like that. Are you sure you're all right?"

"I am, Grey," she said. She glanced over, saw him staring down the hill at the harbor, at the placid scene. She scanned the wharf, almost expecting to see police. But Ian wouldn't have called anyone, she realized; he'd be too embarrassed.

"I can't see you with him," Grey said quietly. "Not at all."

"I wasn't, really," she said.

"He was wrong about you," Grey said. "He's wrong, and he's a liar to say what he said."

"How do you know?"

"Because I know how much you care. I've seen it with Sari. I know you would have been the same with your mother . . ."

"I was," she said. Her voice broke, and her eyes filled with tears. She remembered what Zin-Zin had told her. "My mother had a journey to make, and I couldn't go with her."

Grey nodded, taking her hand. Susannah closed her eyes, wondering how she could have come so far—forgiving herself, and finding a way back to her mother—among people she had known for so brief a time.

"I feel as if you know me better than Ian ever did," she said.

He smiled, and his eyes bored into hers. "So do I," he said.

Susannah stared out the windshield as Grey drove carefully up the narrow mountain road. There were sheer drops off to the right, straight down to the sea. She trusted him completely, to get them up the hill safely. When he got to the top, he drove a few miles, then stopped at a turnoff overlooking the entire expanse of sea and sky.

They sat there in silence, but the car was full of electricity. Susannah's mind raced— with everything that had just happened, and the ticking clock that hung over them.

"There was a woman," he said after a few minutes. "She wasn't . . . we weren't serious at all, but we saw each other casually for a couple of months."

"After Maria, you mean?"

He nodded. "Yes. It was nice to have company, someone to have dinner with once in a while . . ."

"You don't have to tell me," Susannah said, shocked by how much she didn't want to hear about Grey and another woman.

"Sari couldn't deal with it," he said. "I

tried it both ways—being honest and open with her about the fact I was going out to dinner, then lying straight out, telling her I was going to a farm auction near Nîmes. Didn't matter—she picked up on the truth, fell apart."

"Fell apart?"

Grey nodded. "Yeah. Big time. Nightmares, crying, stopped eating. It scared the hell out of me."

"Why is it so bad for her?"

"She's so insecure," he said. "It's out of control. I know that. But she lost her mother in such a terrible way . . ."

"And she's afraid she'll lose you, too."

Susannah reached for his hand, wanting to comfort him. She stared into his eyes, wondering if he felt the same despair she did, about their situation.

"I'm sitting here," he said, stroking her hand, "never wanting to let you go . . ."

"I feel that way, too," she said.

"It's crazy, I know that," he said. "You just got here. We just met. You're supposed to go back to the States . . . and I can't stand it."

She stared into his face as he reached over, brushed the hair back from her eyes.

"I swear," he said, "I think she's just starting to make real progress—a lot of it thanks to you. But if you had seen what it was like—I don't want to push her . . . don't know what I can do . . ."

"Grey, I know. But I'd be lying if I said I didn't wish there were some way," she said.

"We're going to drive home tonight," he said, "and I'll already be missing you. From the minute we start back, I'll know it's just a matter of time."

"I can't be apart from you," she whispered.

He grabbed her, pulled her toward him, kissed her hard. They were desperate to be together, not even an inch of space between them; he held her on his lap, stroking her hair, holding her tightly. A cool breeze blew through the open window, making them shiver. She pressed closer against him, kissing his lips. When they stopped, they looked into each other's eyes, as they had in the cave.

"Susannah," he said, as she eased herself away, back into her seat.

"I want this to last forever," she said, thinking of Sari. "But I know we should go back . . ."

He stared out over the sea. "I keep thinking, what if you just didn't leave? What if
you did your work from here . . . what if you
stayed?"

"For a few more days?" she asked.

"No," he said. "Just as you said: forever."

His words rang in the small car, just as
their words had hung in the cavern, echoing
above the water and against the ancient animal carvings and hand prints, stenciled into
the rock walls.

There in the sea cave, Susannah had felt
as if love could last forever, as if the feelings
she had for Grey were as eternal as the
limestone, the cavern, the sea itself.

He shifted into drive, then reached across
the seat to clasp her hand. She felt him in-
terlock fingers with her, strong and steady.
The car cleared the summit, and they
headed west, into the twilight, away from
eternity and into reality. The encounter with
Ian had brought them back into the real
world very fast—and Susannah shut her
mind against him. She held Grey's hand,
closed her eyes as she felt his fingers holding hers, and pretended they were still in the
sea's warm embrace.

FOURTEEN

Susannah and Grey had kissed goodnight at her door, lingering as long as they could, and she'd watched him drive away. She moved in a daze. Her mind kept drifting back over the day, to the way he'd held her in the water, traced her hand on the cave walls. She walked into the bathroom, splashed cool water on her face. She knew she should take a bath, but she didn't want to yet; she couldn't bear to wash the salt and Grey's touch from her body.

Parked at that overlook, gazing over the Mediterranean, she had known: everything would change the minute they started back.

And it was true. With every kilometer, she'd felt them returning to their lives, back to reality, away from the place they'd somehow made in their brief time together.

Staring at her own reflection in the mirror now, she felt as if she were waking from the most incredible dream. She wanted to hold on to every feeling, every detail, and never forget any of it. She would have given anything to be able to trade her real life for the dream, but she knew that wasn't how it worked.

Things fade away. Today was already passing into memory. Maybe she could hold on to it a little longer, when what she really wanted to hold on to was Grey. She leaned on the sink, looking into her own eyes in the mirror. She barely recognized herself. She was a woman in love.

She felt thirsty, from the dive and the sun. She filled a tall glass with water and went out to sit by the pool. Somewhere down the street, a stray cat meowed. It sounded so yearning and so alone. Susannah walked over to the fence, peered into the darkness. She saw the yellow cat stalking along the alley behind her yard, crying and searching. She stared, watching it poke in and out of corners and doorways, until it stopped right in the middle of the cobblestone way.

The cat locked eyes with Susannah. It stared without fear, and Susannah reached out her hand. It held her gaze a moment longer, then darted away, continuing its search. Craning her neck, Susannah saw it disappear toward the waterfront. Even when it was out of sight, the plaintive me-owing continued, reminding Susannah of her own deep longing.

Exhausted, she crawled into bed. She didn't want the day to end, but she also wanted Sunday to get here more quickly. It was a conundrum, and she was too tired to figure anything out. Lying still, images of the day filled her mind. She saw Ian, heard him telling her she ran out on people—ran out on her mother. The words were terrible, but they didn't have any power. Being here in Stes.-Maries had brought Margaret Con-nolly back to her. And being with Grey had made her realize she wanted love, wanted it down to her bones and into her soul.

The next day, she woke up early. Sunlight streamed through the window; she closed her eyes against it, holding on to sleep and her dreams as long as she could. Fragments filled her mind: kissing Grey, the feeling of his arms around her, the cave's shimmering blue light, the intensity of emotion between them. But she couldn't stay in bed forever. . . .

After her morning coffee, she did what she always did to get herself grounded: pulled out her work. Her briefcase was filled with file folders about the sites she'd been working on most recently, so she opened the one for Cosquer Cave, to add to her notes from previous dives there.

She always left a blank section, at the bottom of every page, for new observations. It was her experience that, no matter how many times she revisited a cave, there was always something new to see, brand new discoveries to be made. It might be an image obscured by dirt, filmed by time, it could be markings that hadn't been visible before—either because of lighting, or because Susannah had been distracted by larger, more apparently significant drawings.

This time, almost her whole attention had been on Grey. Seeing his excitement and reactions, gazing up at the prehistoric art all around them, had made her feel as if she'd just bestowed the best gift she could ever give someone. He was a world-class appreciator, and his joy in discovery had been a gift right back to her.

She'd stared at him as he examined the hand stencils, noticing everything. She'd seen his intellect—so apparent in the sharpness of his gaze, the intensity of his focus. She'd sensed him wanting to record his own observations, trying to commit it all to memory. It was exciting to work alongside a person like that, who could become completely engaged by something so esoteric and obscure.

He had seemed to know that her own fascination lay with the hand stencils instead of the more beautiful, dramatic, accessible animal paintings. He had immediately understood, even without her telling him, that the artists had needed to leave their mark, that human beings needed to know they mattered. She'd been immeasurably moved by the way he'd held her hand, pressed it to the rock wall, outlined it with his own fingers. He'd made them part of the history of the cave. . . .

So as she sat there at the desk in her rented house, surrounded by documents,

by work papers, and by copies of her published work on the Cosquer Cave, all she
could do was close her eyes and picture
Grey. She wanted to hold on to every single
moment; when she returned to Connecticut,
she wanted the memory to be as distinct as
it still was right now. She wanted to be able
to feel the friction of his leg against hers, the
way it had felt treading water together, the
sublime luxury of kissing instead of studying
the Paleolithic art in the undersea cave all
around them.

By the end of the day, she needed a break
from her papers. She walked into town, had
dinner at a bistro along the harbor. Sipping
a glass of rosé, she felt memories of the
night before overtaking her. If she closed
her eyes, Grey would be right across the
table from her.

After dinner, she wandered through the
town. She felt like the yellow cat, edgy with
yearning. Every street made her wonder
whether he'd walked along it; had he come
here with Maria? Had they ever pushed Sari
in her stroller along the quay? She realized
she didn't like thinking of him with Maria any
more than he'd liked seeing her with Ian.

Finally, she realized she was too restless

to go on. If she went home, maybe he would call. What were he and Sari doing? She wished she could be with them, too; she had felt her own strong connection with the girl—when they had first met, and during their ride together.

Susannah wished things were different, so she could be more a part of their lives . . . and that made her think that maybe she could. Maybe the trail ride tomorrow would bring her and Sari closer together, let Sari begin to trust someone other than her father, and Laurent.

After half an hour back home, with the phone stubbornly silent, the swimming pool called to her. That's what she'd do: take a swim, burn off some energy. She stretched, heading into the bedroom to change, when she heard a knock at the door. Thinking it must be Topaz, she pulled it open without even checking. Grey stood there on the top step, holding a book.

She stared at him, speechless.

"I know I should have called first," he said, giving her a wicked smile.

"Really?" she asked, stepping into his arms. "You think you should have called first?"

"It would have been the polite thing to do," he said, kissing the side of her neck, sending chills all through her body.

"Polite is overrated," she said, standing on tiptoes, lips against his collarbone, wanting to do the same to him.

"I'm glad you feel that way," he said. "Because here I am." He kissed her, long and hard, arms around her back. Something sharp pressed into her spine, and even though she wanted the kiss to go on forever, she pulled back.

"What's that?" she asked.

"My excuse for coming over."

"I thought we were past needing excuses." She smiled, and took the tattered red leather-bound volume he held out to her. "What is it?"

"It's an old book I found in Paris. At one of those stalls along the Seine . . ."

"I know them well," she said. On many of her past research trips to France, she'd based herself in Paris and spent hours browsing through the used books, maps, posters, and postcards of the *bookinistes,* the secondhand booksellers whose stalls ran along the river.

"You showed me something of your

work," he said. "And I wanted to show you something of mine."

"You wrote this book?" she asked skeptically. "It looks a hundred years old."

"No," he said, laughing. "This is a biography of Django Reinhardt. There's a lot of material about Stes.-Maries, and the caravans. The writer spent time with Django himself, and really got into his early life. Lots of time spent here in the Camargue. I used the bio as background when I wrote these . . ." Tucked into the book was a sheaf of articles, published in *Harper's* and *The Atlantic;* she glanced at them, saw his byline, felt her heart turn over.

"Oh, Grey, thank you," she said, glancing through the pages. "I can't wait to read them."

"Being with you yesterday . . ." he said, trailing off. Then he looked her straight in the eye. "It really set me on fire."

"I know," she said.

"I want to research and write again. I think I told you—I wrote a series of articles about Gypsies and music. Now . . ."

"Now you're going to write a series about sea caves?"

He laughed, stepped closer, holding her

again. "Yes," he said. "And other adventures. Riding through the marsh with a beautiful woman."

Susannah smiled, to hear him say that. "Helping her escape from wild bulls, you mean?"

He shook his head. "It's pretty clear that you can take care of yourself." He kissed her, his eyes open, then pulled gently away. "I saw the way you were with Ian. You took care of it really well."

"Actually, you did," Susannah said.

"Yeah," he said, holding her. "I got carried away. But he was asking for it. I couldn't let him speak to you that way."

"I don't want it to get to me, the way he sees me," Susannah said. "But it does . . . especially when he talks about my mother."

"Don't listen to him anymore," Grey said. "You've got to realize something . . ."

"What?"

Grey stared at her long and hard. "He knows he's lost you."

"He does?"

"Yeah."

"Because he saw us together . . ."

"Partly," Grey said. "But not only that.

Guys know. They can feel when it starts to happen."

"When what does?"

"When love is over."

"If it was ever there," Susannah murmured, speaking of herself and Ian, wondering whether Grey was thinking of himself and Maria.

"You don't love him?" Grey asked, staring hard into her eyes. "You never did?"

"Not like this," she whispered. He pulled her toward him roughly, kissing her until she lost herself, until the ground tilted and she felt she was swimming in the sea.

After a few minutes, they stopped and stood there looking at each other, as if unsure what to do next. The air felt charged, and Susannah's skin tingled. "Would you like something to drink?" she asked slowly.

"Yeah," he said. "I would. But . . ."

She saw him glance at the clock.

"You have to get home?"

He nodded. "Sari was studying with Laurent, so I saw my chance to drive down here. I made an excuse . . ."

"The book?"

"Yes. She knows you went to the Cheval Blanc for work, and I let her think this was absolutely essential to your research. I lied to my daughter."

"You said you've done that before . . ." she said, thinking of what he'd told her about the woman he'd dated.

"I know. She's at Laurent's, working on a project. I didn't get the whole story, but it involved a field trip. I thought they were going to the library, but while you and I were in Marseille yesterday, Laurent took Sari to Avignon."

"That sounds wonderful for her; for both of them."

Grey nodded. "Laurent's a really good kid. He's very patient with her."

"Maybe that's because he loves her," Susannah said. She watched him, not sure how he'd take a statement like that about his daughter. He didn't reply, but just stood very still, staring at Susannah with deep thoughtfulness. After a minute, she said, "Young love, you know?"

"Young love is nothing," he said. "Compared with what can come once you know who you are."

"Do you think?"

He nodded slowly. It was dark outside. Susannah wanted him to stay on and on. She clasped his hand, led him toward the back door. The rising moon spilled white light into the small yard. She turned on the pool light, making the water glow like a blue jewel.

"Last time you turned on the lights, you lit up a whole cavern," Grey said.

"I have the power," she said, joking.

"Well, I'll try to light up the marsh for you tomorrow night," he said, gesturing toward the east, where the moon was rising. "It's almost full."

"I don't want tomorrow to come," she said, sliding her arms around his neck. "Because it's one day closer to the time I have to leave."

"Susannah," he said, pressing his forehead against hers, staring into her eyes.

"Grey," she said back.

He kissed her under the almost-full moon. The swimming pool's blue light reflected up, shimmering against the house's white plaster wall. It was no sea cave, but Susannah held Grey in her arms and made the most of it.

Sari sat across the kitchen table from Laurent as they worked on their homework together after dinner. For the first time in almost as long as she could remember, Sari was excited about something to do with school.

"Would you like a *tisane*?" Anne, Laurent's mother asked.

"Non, merci," Sari said. Anne smiled, poured hot water into the cups, making herbal tea for her and Claude.

"We're fine, Maman," Laurent said.

"You both seem very busy, writing so industriously . . ."

"Yes, working on our assignment," Laurent said.

"It must be quite ambitious, considering you didn't return from Avignon until so late last night."

"That was my fault," Sari said quickly, not wanting Laurent to get in trouble. "I was having so much fun, I made us miss the bus. We had to wait a whole hour to get the next one!"

"Sari, I'm just happy you both got home safely, and that you're so inspired by your project." Anne kissed the top of her head, then Laurent's, leaving them to their schoolwork. Sari had been writing nonstop, but she paused, gazing across the table at Laurent. She felt happy with her essay, and it was all because of him.

Usually she felt so left out. Not that she didn't have friends, or that the other kids weren't nice to her; it was more that she knew she was different. She didn't have a mother. She was half Gypsy, and sometimes that made her wonder which half of her was most real: the dark-skinned Romany half or the pale New England half. Her father loved her, no matter which she was, so she didn't worry too much about that part of things.

The real reason she felt left out was because the way she saw the world was poles apart from how others did. She was existing in a black-and-white movie while everyone else was living in bright color. It affected the way she learned; her teachers' lessons never really came alive to her. Descriptions of the court at Versailles, of the French Revolution, Madame de Sévigné in the Midi, of the bloody doings at the Conciergerie, just felt flat to Sari.

Until yesterday.

Their assignment was to write an essay about a place. It could be anywhere in the world; the only requirement was that the writer had actually visited it. Local, far away, it didn't matter as long as it was real, and as long as the student had been there. Laurent had said they were going to write at the library, but Sari didn't want to go.

"What do I care about this?" Sari had asked. "All places look alike to me. Gray, gray, gray."

"Pauvre p'tite," Laurent said, without a trace of sympathy in his voice.

"You try being colorblind!" she said. "It's not fun, I promise you."

Laurent had given her a long, even gaze. She instantly felt remorseful; she knew that he, more than anyone, felt bad for her, wanted her to be all right again. Sari was being difficult, partly because she knew her father was going out of town. He'd told her he had an errand to do in Marseille. And even though that was just a hundred kilometers away, Sari felt nervous.

"You're in a bad mood," Laurent had said.

"No," she'd said. "I'm not."

"It's because your father has things to do, isn't it?"

"You make me feel like a baby when you say that," Sari had said.

"He needs to have his life, too," Laurent

had said gently. "You should learn to let him."

Sari's eyes had filled with tears. She'd felt slapped. What a terrible thing to say, that Sari didn't let her father have his own life! She suddenly felt like a snail without its shell; everything hurt, and she felt as if Laurent, her best and oldest friend, was prodding her with a stick.

"Sari," he'd said, just standing there, not backing away, not apologizing. "I have a plan for us."

"I don't want to go to the library, I don't want to do *anything*," she'd whispered. "I don't feel very good."

"It's for the assignment . . . for the essay."

"I've been plenty of places," she'd said stubbornly, wiping tears. "I'll write about one of them."

"No," he'd said firmly, matching her stubbornness. "We're going to go somewhere new—forget the library. And we'll be evenly matched. We'll see the place exactly the same way."

"Except you'll see it in color," she'd said, unable to stop herself.

"No," he'd said. "I won't."

And he'd meant it. After school, instead

of going to the library, they'd taken the bus into Avignon. It was a very long ride, and Sari felt worried that her father would be upset with her for going. Laurent assured her that he'd cleared it with her father and his parents. That had reassured her somewhat, but it still seemed very out of the ordinary, and she'd wondered what he had in mind.

By the time they reached their destination, the sun was almost down. Avignon was a medieval city, surrounded by a crenellated wall. Getting off the bus, Sari thought it looked like a fairy-tale village, haunted and magical, with towers and castles, with Gothic slits for weapons in the walls, with the long, low fourteenth-century bridge, celebrated in the children's song, crossing the dark and mysterious Rhône River.

Laurent and she walked along the river. He teased her about the Tarasque hiding under the bridge, and she teased him back. The streets were paved with cobblestones, rounded and glinting in the twilight.

House windows glowed from within; iron grillwork looked glossy black, and the streetlamps threw long shadows onto the sidewalks and streets. Some of the busi-

est thoroughfares, still paved with cobblestones, had been paved over with asphalt.
The ancient stones peered through, tarnished silver underneath worn blacktop.

They walked down some of the narrowest
streets, lined with old wooden houses, tilting with age, paint peeling, reminiscent of
etchings and woodcuts Sari had seen in
museums, black-and-white or sepia-toned.
Laurent walked her down a crooked cobblestone alleyway, and they emerged on a wide
street, sparkling with shards of broken
glass, overlooking the Rhône River.

The rising almost-full moon played on
the water's smooth surface, illuminated the
city's Gothic towers; they stood out in sharp
silhouette against the moon's whiteness.
Laurent steered Sari toward the Palais des
Papes, built in 1335 by Pope Benedict XII;
she stood there gazing up at the half
fortress, half castle, listening to Laurent
read passages from their schoolbook.

"Here's what Petrarch said about the
Pope's Palace," he said. "*Écoute:* 'The
houses of the apostles crumble as popes
raise up their palaces of massy gold.'"

"Gold," she said. "Funny, because it
looks silver in this light."

"Yes, it does," Laurent said. "Doesn't it?"

She nodded, gazing up at the castle; it was beautiful and mysterious. Darkness cloaked the city, and the moon had bleached every last spot of color away. Every brick, stone, tile, and window was edged with foil.

The whole night looked metallic, without any color at all. She glanced around. The light and dark contrasts were so vivid that she knew that even if, during daylight, this was the most brightly colored city in the world, right now anyone would see it as a cityscape of black, white, cream, charcoal, and silver. And then Sari got it. She drew in a sharp breath, turning to Laurent.

"You did this, didn't you?" she asked.

"Did what?" he asked.

"You brought me here because you knew Avignon would be black and white."

"Not always, but it is tonight," he said.

"How did you think of this?" she whispered.

"I wanted to see like you see," he said. "I can't stand thinking of you trapped in the dark, Sari. Missing all the beautiful colors that the rest of us don't even think about.

When we got the assignment to write about a place, I didn't want to do it."

"Why not?"

"Because my places, anywhere I could think of, were all so bright. I thought about how it was for you, how different the world looks to you, and I knew—I had to make it the same for both of us."

"And you did," she said. "You made it beautiful for me."

"The moon helped," he said.

They walked under the plane trees of the Place de l'Horloge, around the massive clock tower, past all the brasseries and *bistrots.* They caught sight of their own reflection in a shop window; the light was dim here, and their faces looked back at them like two strangers. Sari reached out, touched the window's dusty surface with her fingertips, brushed the reflection of Laurent's face.

Past iron grates and steel fences, past shuttered shops and lonely alleys, they headed down to the river. Sari watched the moonlight glitter on the surface. She thought of the toy dragon Susannah had given her, wondered whether she would ever see it as bright green with red eyes, or whether it would always look gray.

"What are you thinking?" Laurent asked.

"About the toy dragon," Sari said.

"The one Susannah gave you?"

Sari nodded. She felt torn inside, liking Susannah, but feeling nervous about her. What did it mean that her father liked her so much? He did; Sari could tell. He'd told Sari he was going to Marseille on business, but she had the feeling it had something to do with Susannah.

"She's coming to the ranch tomorrow, isn't she?" Sari asked.

"I think so," Laurent said. "For the trail ride."

"I'm glad," Sari said, surprising herself.

"You really like her, don't you?" Laurent asked.

"I do," Sari said. She thought about it; she liked Susannah for being so kind, and for not pushing her, and for talking to her about dragons, and just because of the way she was. But that didn't automatically make everything easy. "She seems really nice, and I love the dragon she brought me. But she lives in America. We can't exactly see her very often, once she goes back there."

"You could visit," he said. "You and your father go to America in the summertime anyway."

"That's sort of what I've been thinking," she said slowly.

"Really?" he asked.

"It's not simple," she warned him. "It might seem that way to you, but . . ." It had been just Sari and her father for so long; that's how she'd stayed safe, how she'd healed from her fall, how she'd kept from going crazy when she thought of her mother. Her father had taken care of her.

"Believe me, I don't think it's simple. I've known you forever, remember?"

She nodded. "I want to be a good daughter; I want him to be happy. I'm thirteen, and I'm not an idiot. I know he likes her. And I . . . well, I like her, too."

"I know you do," he said, sounding proud of her for being so positive. "In fact . . ." Sari glanced over, to see what Laurent was going to say. But he fell silent, swallowing his words, as if he'd thought better of speaking them. They continued walking along the river.

When they got to the Pont St.-Bénezet, they turned onto the long, arched span, and walked out into the middle of it. Traffic went past, but Sari hardly noticed it. She stared down at the river flowing below, and couldn't help thinking of the childhood song: *Sur le pont d'Avignon, l'on y danse . . .*

"Do you think people really danced on this bridge?" she asked. "In the old days?"

"I think so," he said, staring into her eyes.

The breeze blew off the water, making her shiver. Laurent was so close she could feel his warm breath on her forehead. She tilted her head back, looked up into his face. The moon made his skin look so soft; she wanted to touch it with her hand, but she held back.

"Thank you for this," she whispered.

"For what?"

"Bringing me to Avignon," she said. "For wanting to see it with me; for waiting for a night when it would look the same to both of us."

"I wanted to," he said. "But I wish . . ."

Sari stood still, trembling, waiting for him to tell her what he wished. She saw tears in his eyes. The moon made them shine so brightly. Staring up at him, she saw him wanting something so badly he could hardly stand it.

"I wish you could see colors," he said, his voice breaking. "I thought that day you rode with Susannah, it would happen. I thought that once you got back up on Mystère, you'd be all better."

"Laurent . . ."

"Susannah seems so kind, and she wanted to help you ride," he said. "And she understood that Mystère was all yours, that she was a one-girl horse. So I thought—"

"You thought that would cure me," Sari said. He nodded, and she had to look away. Now her own eyes blurred with tears. Staring down at the river current, she wished that anything were that simple. The idea that a woman, even one as nice as Susannah, could help Sari to see right again. "It's not going to happen," she whispered to Laurent.

"What do you mean?"

"I really like her, Laurent. And I'm trying to let it be okay that my father likes her, too. I'm glad she's coming to ride Sunday night, I honestly am. And maybe I'll even try to ride with her again." She stared at him, eyes filled with tears, wanting to please him, wanting every single thing in the world to turn out right. "But just because she's gotten me back up on my horse doesn't mean I'm magically going to be fixed again."

"How can you be so sure?" he asked.

"Because she's not my mother," Sari said, her voice cracking.

"Oh, Sari," Laurent said, grabbing her hard and holding her tight. She felt him sobbing; he didn't make a sound, but she felt his chest shaking.

They held each other, pressed together, feeling the bridge shake as traffic sped past, and Sari wished she could forget all about that night so long ago, the night the world fell apart, the night her mother pushed her away and disappeared, the night she took all the colors with her.

And she knew that, for Laurent, she would try to ride Sunday night.

FIFTEEN

Sunday evening, Grey was finishing up the dinner dishes, staring out the kitchen window at twilight settling over the marsh. The sky was clear, almost iridescent purple, and the wind had dropped. The first stars were just coming out, but they'd soon be erased by moonlight. He saw people arriving, car after car. None of them was Susannah. He felt spring-loaded tension in his shoulders, wanting her to get there.

Sari sat at the table behind him, intent on her homework, an essay about her excursion to Avignon with Laurent.

"When am I going to get to read it?" he asked now, standing at the sink.

"Read what?"

"Your paper."

"I don't know. Do you want to read it?"

He laughed. "When have I ever not wanted to read one of your school papers?"

"I don't know," she said, continuing to write. "I guess you always do." She glanced up, her eyes bright. "I think this one's pretty good."

"Tell me about it," he said.

And she did: it all spilled out, the trip to Avignon, Laurent planning everything so he could see the city through Sari's eyes, how he'd waited for the moon so they could see the cobblestones, city walls, bridges, castles, everything in black and white and pewter. Grey listened, moved that someone as young as Laurent could be so perceptive, that he was so obviously in love with his daughter.

"That sounds amazing," Grey said.

"Was your time in Marseille anything like that?"

"It was really good," Grey said, holding everything in, suspecting what she was hinting at. He'd been pleased that Sari was making strides, that with everything happening so fast, she'd been accepting of Susannah. The fact that she hadn't balked at the idea of Susannah showing up for the trail ride was a feat in itself. But now, with Susannah about to leave, Grey wanted to be careful. He wanted more than anything to start a real relationship with her, and for Sari to be okay with it, so they could make plans to see each other again.

"What time is Susannah getting here?" Sari asked.

"I thought she'd be here by now," he said.

Sari nodded. She glanced down at the table. One of the cats was lying on his side, his spine pressed up against her writing arm, right beside the toy dragon Susannah had given her. Sari moved Bruno a few inches away, and he rolled onto his back, to get closer to her again.

"You're happy she's coming?" he asked.

"Yes," she said. "I want her to be able to take the moonlight ride."

Grey gazed at her. She was concentrating, not even looking up. He couldn't quite figure this out—she never liked when he left the house after dark. Lately she hadn't objected at all; this would be two nights in a row.

"You know I'm leading the ride, right?"

"I figured that."

"You used to like it when Claude took riders out at night instead of me."

"I'm not such a kid anymore," she said. "I'm trying to get used to things that used to bother me."

Grey looked down at her pad of paper. She had a stack of neatly written sheets, along with a few pages she'd doodled on. He saw the letter "L," and knew it was for "Laurent." Right now people were congregating by the paddock, and he heard Laurent asking someone if he could help adjust the stirrup length. Sari heard his voice, too, and raised her head to listen.

"I guess I should get ready," she said.

"Ready?" he asked, not getting it.

His daughter stared at him, her eyes blank. But behind their gold-green prettiness, inside their lack of expression, he knew emotions were storming. It showed in the tightness of her face, the thin line of her lips. Riding horses at night was dangerous business in their family; to Sari, that was the greatest reminder of the night that had taken her mother away, and gotten herself badly injured.

"Ready for what?" he pressed.

"The trail ride. I'm going, too. I told Laurent I'm going to ride tonight."

Grey stared at her, feeling a million things at once. "What about your essay?" he asked.

She glared at him, then drifted back to the table. "That's not what you really mean, is it?" she asked, her lower lip wobbling.

He held back, not sure how to answer her. He was shocked that she'd even consider riding at night. While he felt elated by the progress she was making, he also felt hesitant. A night ride would be huge for her. Sari had had night phobia for as long as she'd been colorblind. What if something went wrong? He had thought she'd take it slow, go out on Mystère again in the afternoons, with him, with Laurent. But she'd ridden only that one time—with Susannah.

And he had to admit that he'd been thinking that he'd have Susannah to himself tonight. He couldn't believe his own selfishness.

Sari picked up the toy dragon lying on the rustic wood table, burying her face in its green fur and spiky felt spine, and his thoughts dissolved.

"What's wrong?" he asked, going to her.

Sari held the toy to her face, shoulders shaking in quaking sobs. Grey put his arm around her, trying to soothe her, aching for her.

"You know I can't go," she sobbed. "I want to so much. For Laurent—to make him proud of me. And to spend time with Susannah . . ."

Those words killed him, they really did. His heart was sliced open—to think of Sari wanting to spend time with Susannah. Nothing had ever made him happier, yet here she was sobbing into a toy animal.

"Sari . . ." he began.

Just then, a soft knock sounded at the back door. He glanced up, saw Susannah's smiling face in the glass. But as she caught sight of Sari crying, her happiness drained away. Sari glanced over, saw it was Susannah, and tore to the door. As Grey watched, Sari yanked the door open. She stood frozen for a few seconds, and Grey steeled himself for her to explode. Instead, still clutching the dragon, she moved forward to Susannah.

She stopped short, and then Susannah reached for her and hugged her. Grey thought he was already beyond shock, but he'd never seen Sari act like this with any-one outside the family before.

"I want to go riding with you and Papa," she wept into Susannah's shoulder. "But I can't . . ."

"Oh, Sari," Susannah said, holding her tight. "I'm so sorry."

"I want to so badly," Sari said.

"Yes," Susannah said into her hair. "It's so beautiful out, such a lovely night. You want to see the moon on the water . . ."

"I want to, but I can't!" Sari cried.

"Sari, there'll be other times. You know there will . . . you don't have to rush it," Grey said.

"No, Papa," Sari said, shuddering with a long sob. "I can't *ever* ride at night. It's not even possible. No matter how much I want to!"

"Do you want your father to stay home with you?" Susannah asked.

Sari looked up with tearstained eyes. In-credibly, she shook her head.

"You sure?" Grey asked.

"Yes. You have your cell phone if I need

you," Sari said, trying to smile. She held up the toy dragon. "And I have Tarasque."

"One of these days, you'll feel ready to ride in the moonlight," Susannah said, smiling. "I know you will."

"I hope so," Sari said. "The moonlight was so beautiful last night; I'm sure it will be so pretty on the marsh. You'll have a wonderful ride. Susannah, will you come back and say goodnight to me? Promise?"

"I promise," she said.

And just then, Laurent ran over to bang on the door, letting Grey know that all the horses were saddled, that the riders were ready to go. He looked straight at Sari, and didn't even glance away.

"Only one thing," Laurent said. "Arabella has a stone in her shoe. She's a little lame tonight, not seriously, but it would be better for her to stay here—is it all right if Susannah rides a different horse?"

"Of course," Susannah said.

"Give her Mystère," Sari said instantly, the words spilling out as she stared at Laurent.

"Sari," Susannah said.

"Are you sure?" Grey asked, stunned and touched that Sari would offer, a little uneasy at the same time.

"Yes," Sari said. "Positive."

"I knew you'd say that," Laurent said, sounding proud of her.

"Thank you, Sari," Susannah said. She stepped forward to hug Sari again. Grey watched as they stood there, and as he did, he felt his heart settle down. Just one beat at a time, it went back to almost normal.

He stood still, knowing that no matter how the rest of the night went, nothing could ever be better than this, or erase the fact that it had happened. Standing in his own kitchen, seeing his daughter so happy, comforted by a woman he was pretty sure he'd fallen totally in love with.

Susannah had never seen anything as beautiful as the Parc Régional de Camargue at night. The moon rose in the east, just as Grey was leading the group through the paddock gates. It hovered, an enormous apricot-pink globe just on the horizon; then, mounting swiftly, grew smaller and whiter, until by the time they reached the first wooden bridge, it was a bright, gleaming disc.

The white horses looked luminous in the

moonlight. The glow turned the reeds glittery dark blue, and made all the creeks and lagoons look like polished onyx. There were seven tourists in the group, and Claude had also come along. Susannah and Grey rode last in line, pulling back on the reins, letting everyone else move ahead, leaving them almost alone.

When the trail widened, Grey came up alongside Susannah. He took her hand for a minute, their fingers clasped as the horses stayed side by side. Susannah glanced over, smiled at him, felt him watching her.

"I can't believe we're back here in the marsh together," he said.

"Neither can I."

"I'm not sure you understand just how big a deal this is," he said. "On a whole lot of levels."

"Like what?"

"Like Sari letting you ride Mystère. And her being okay with my going out on a night trail ride."

"She doesn't like that?"

"Not at night," he said. Then he smiled, wonderful and incandescent, making his eyes shine. "That brings me to the biggest reason of all. That I'm out here with you right now."

"Me, too," Susannah said. "That's the biggest reason of all."

She'd been looking forward to this night every minute since he'd invited her; she still had the scallop shells in her pocket, and she'd looked at them a hundred times since Grey had left the house last night. They'd helped her get to this moment, and now that it was here, she wanted to make every moment last.

"Hold on," he said to her now, gesturing for her to stay back while he rode Django past the line of riders and spoke privately to Claude. When he came back, he gazed at her as Django and Mystère stood still and the rest of the riders followed Claude down the long trail around the lagoon.

"Where are they going?" she asked.

"Away," Grey said. Django took a step closer to Mystère, and Grey leaned over to kiss Susannah. His right arm slid around her waist, sending a charge through her body, making her grab onto him with all she had.

"What did you tell Claude?"

"To go the long way around," Grey said, and laughed.

Susannah laughed, too. They began to ride in the same direction they'd gone three days ago, toward the stony beach on the Gulf of Lions.

"Are you sure Sari is okay?" she asked.

"I'm in awe of how okay she is," he said. "This is a first."

"So I gather . . ."

"Nights are hard for Sari."

"With all the time I've spent with you these last days, you still haven't told me exactly what happened—the whole story."

"I've really appreciated what you've brought to us, not having to think about it so much these past days," he said. "You don't know how great that's been for me. Some of it you know, but there's more."

"Tell me," Susannah said as they walked along.

"Her mother left at night," he said. "You know that part. But it's not just when she left, but who she left with, and how they did it . . ."

"Who took Maria away?" Susannah asked.

"Her trainer," Grey said. He didn't sound angry, or on edge at all. It was just information now; it had lost its barb. "He came to pick her up. They'd waited until after Sari was supposed to be in bed, but she sensed something going on."

"Didn't Maria say goodbye to her?"

Grey stared ahead as Django walked along. "No. She was going to just leave. Bags packed, ready to go. But Sari heard her; she'd been asleep, and she woke up and ran downstairs." He paused, and Susannah heard the horses' hooves, and the sound of animals in the marsh. "She caught her mother just before she walked out the door."

"Did Maria explain to her?"

"I don't know; she might have tried. All I know is that Sari latched onto her, wasn't going to let her out the door."

Susannah could just see it, the child trying to keep her mother from leaving.

"I was in another part of the house," Grey went on levelly. "All I heard was a big thud; I didn't realize until later that it was Maria shoving Sari away."

"Oh, no," Susannah said. She tried to imagine a scene like that between her and her mother and couldn't begin to.

"Sari chased her outside," Grey continued. "Maria was running by then, carrying her bags, out to the car waiting by the road. I guess Sari realized she wasn't going to catch up on foot, so she ran to the stable."

"Mystère . . ."

He nodded. "She opened that big barn door all by herself, climbed up on Mystère. I was downstairs by that time, and all I saw was Sari galloping by, full tilt, right past the window."

"Grey . . ."

He nodded. The horses walked on, so peacefully along the narrow sand trail, moonlight breaking apart bits of glass on the tidal creek.

"Sari rode off the ranch, onto the main road. I only know this from what I've pieced together over time, but what happened was that Adrien Ferret—'Matelo,' as he was known, Maria's trainer—had stopped the car. Maybe she was having second thoughts, maybe they were kissing, who knows? But Sari gained on them, was riding straight toward them—"

"The taillights," Susannah whispered, remembering that Sari had mentioned red lights.

"Yes," Grey said. "And the minute her mother saw her coming, she must have told

Adrien to drive off. They did—speeding away, with Maria looking out the rear window. That's Sari's last memory of her mother. She was already sobbing, hurt from where Maria had pushed her away. She kicked Mystère harder, getting her to gallop faster—a car came around the bend from the other direction, and the lights spooked Mystère."

"She reared up?"

"Or skittered away—something. Sari was thrown."

"Oh God—I'm so sorry."

"So am I. It's been bad. She was in pieces—broken pelvis, broken arm, dislocated shoulder, fractured skull. She was in intensive care for weeks—I told Rosalie to get Maria the hell back here, but supposedly she couldn't be found. Sari was just lying there in a hospital bed, crying for her mother—"

"And Maria never came . . ." Susannah murmured.

"Never came, never called. Sari was in traction, and then in casts. She went through physical therapy—it hurt so much, she'd cry nonstop. She was colorblind. At first her vision was blurred, from the skull fracture. We thought it would all improve at once; her vision would clear up, and colors would come back."

"Her vision cleared?"

"Yes, it did."

"But the colors?"

"Didn't happen."

"At all?"

"No."

"You said she's seen a lot of specialists."

"Yes, and had every test known to all of them. They've all told us the same thing. Her eyes are fine; her brain is normal. It's all in her head."

"They say that?"

"Those aren't the words, but that's the message. Makes her feel she's crazy. That if only she tried harder, didn't take everything so seriously, relaxed a little, stopped trying to control the world, she'd be fine."

"That's a lot of pressure," Susannah said. "And why wouldn't she want to control her environment, considering what she's been through?"

Grey nodded, glancing over. "That's why her riding with you was such a big deal. That was the first she's been on a horse in all those years, since the accident."

"I really wouldn't have minded if she'd wanted to come tonight," Susannah said. "But she wasn't ready."

"No. Not for riding at night."

"Someday she will be."

"Yeah," Grey said. Then he looked over at Susannah, and the way he smiled did something to her heart. "But not tonight."

"Not tonight," Susannah said.

"You can't leave," he said.

"You're right," she said, laughing softly. "I can't, but I have to."

"If we didn't have tonight," he said, taking her hand again, "I'm not sure I'd be able to stand the thought of you getting on that plane. And even with it . . ."

"I know," she whispered.

"Susannah, I'm not going to let you go."

The moon lifted higher, and a light haze rose from the lagoon. It swirled around Susannah and Grey, hiding them from anyone who might be watching. They were almost to the beach; Susannah could smell its nearness in the salt air, the sharp breeze. An owl hunted silently overhead, its silhouette dark against the moon. In the distance they heard a loon, its cry long and joyful.

At least that's how it sounded to Susannah.

Sari finished her essay. She read it over, pleased with what she'd done. Her writing brought back the beauty of the night in Avignon, the mystery of walking along the cobblestones with Laurent, the black-and-white drama of moonlight spilling over the medieval stone city.

Her father used to be a journalist; had he felt this satisfied when he'd finished a particularly fine piece of reporting? She knew that he'd been writing about Marseille, and she drifted into his study. Her intention was to leave her own essay on top of his desk, but her attention was drawn to a pile of papers.

Glancing down, she saw his handwriting and read the top page. He had written about a secret cave, underwater, filled with prehistoric drawings and etchings. Sari read something about "hand stencils," then, in big bold letters, the words LEAVE YOUR MARK, DON'T FORGET TO LIVE.

What did that mean? She wasn't sure, but the phrase sent tingles down her spine.

Don't forget to live . . . Was that what Sari had been doing? Friday night, walking with Laurent, she'd felt so amazingly, wonderfully, excitingly alive. She was so used to feeling guarded, as if everyone else was having all the fun, that she'd forgotten what it was like to just wander freely, feeling in touch with life.

Did her father feel the same way?

It disturbed and alarmed her to think that he did. Was that why he'd seemed so different ever since Susannah had come? Was she helping him to live in a different way? Sari knew she hadn't seen her father smile as often as he had recently—and if Susannah was the reason, what did that say about Sari?

She walked into the kitchen, picked up the small toy dragon, pacing back and forth by the window. The cats were sensing her excitement, weaving around her feet as if it were a game. She peered out the window, trying to see if the riders were back yet. Of course they weren't: they'd left no more than twenty minutes ago, and rides were an hour and a half long.

Bruno nearly tripped her, but she hardly noticed. She felt bad, and it was getting worse. Last night she'd stood on the bridge with Laurent, looking down at the Rhône River. She'd imagined dragons living in the shadows, but she'd felt so brave. Why was tonight different? Why did she feel her own private dragons rising up to attack her?

The dragon of fear, the dragon of horseback riding, the dragon of night, the dragon of her mother leaving, the dragon of no-colors, the dragon of her father riding in the marsh with Susannah: they all lived together in one slimy lair, deep in Sari's body and mind.

Sari stared out the kitchen window. The moon was up, and so white. It reminded Sari of when she and Laurent had walked through Avignon, up and down every dark street. She hadn't been afraid at all.

Turning from the window, she hurried upstairs. Her pelvis still ached a little—or maybe she was just focusing on it because she wasn't sure she wanted to do this. Rummaging in her bedroom closet, she found the olive jar, hidden behind her rain boots, where she kept her allowance. Just looking at the jar made her shudder with emotion.

She'd been saving for such a long time,

to be able to afford a round-trip ticket to America. She had always imagined landing in Providence, staying with her grandparents, and then putting her plan into effect.

She had saved all her money, so she could fly to Nevada to find her mother. So she could travel out West to the ranch in the desert where her mother lived, where the circus was located.

She pictured a dusty, dry yard. Deserts were filled with sand, not lovely reeds and lagoons like here. She imagined horses— not sweet, loving animals like Mystère, like the ones her father raised—but high-strung, performing circus horses that did what they were commanded for praise and applause, but never gave any love back.

Sari would knock. And when her mother answered—what would Sari do? Would she throw herself into her mother's arms? Would her mother push her away again, even harder this time, slam the door in her face? Sari crouched in the closet, thinking about her mother, starting to cry.

Everything was so wrong. She felt panic begin to bubble up, knowing her father was out in the marsh without her. The insecurity made her feel like a very little girl, and she hated that. Determined to get back the strength she'd felt last night, she dove into the closet for what she'd come up here for: her riding boots. Her old ones no longer fit, but her father had bought her this pair, for when she was ready.

Sitting on a pile of shoes, she pulled them on. She grabbed a sweater because the night was chilly. And she tore downstairs, into the kitchen, out the door. She was moving so fast, she almost let the cats out. They were circling by the kitchen door, and nearly squeaked out between her legs—but she stopped them just in time.

Running across the yard, she felt her pulse racing. She wished Laurent was here, but he had gone on the ride, she was sure. She still felt half afraid, but she was also half excited. She could do this. The moon was up, filling the Parc with white light. It illuminated the entire yard and paddock, almost as brightly as day. She told herself that this was nothing—nothing at all—like the last time she had ridden at night.

She walked over to Mystère's stall. Starting to open the door, she remembered: she had let Susannah ride Mystère. That nearly took all the wind out of her sails. No horses were left. But then, hearing a wild whinny, she turned her head and looked straight into the eyes of Tempest.

The new colt was small, stocky, very sprightly. He danced in place. She reached out her hand, and he buried his velvety nose in it. She tickled him under the chin, ran into the tack room.

Her mother's old black saddle was there, with its tarnished silver scallop shells hanging down, gathering dust—no one had used it since she'd left. The sight of the saddle made Sari shiver, but she just rushed past it to grab a bridle.

Sari hurried back to Tempest, tried to slip it over his head. He wouldn't take the bit, though. He tossed his head, pulling back with such force it nearly yanked her arm up, taking her with it.

Fine. She'd ride him with just his halter. The moonlight reminded her of last night, of Laurent, and made her feel she could do anything. She led Tempest out of his stall, through the open door, into the paddock. The breeze was blowing, and he sniffed the air. She saw his ears twitch.

Leading him over to the fence, she planned to climb up to the top rung, grab his neck for balance, and then jump on. Tempest was frisky, sidestepping as she walked him over. His muscles rippled beneath his skin, and his white coat felt hot beneath her hand. She whispered his name, and told him they were going to go for a ride.

When they got to the fence, she looked into his eye. It was dark and mischievous. She swore to herself she was ready for this; she really thought she was. But Tempest must have thought otherwise. He reared back, pulling away.

Sari let him go. She really had no choice—he had a mind of his own. She watched with alarm as he ran in a wide circle around the ring. She remembered seeing Laurent trying to ride him, getting thrown. And suddenly she saw a ghost image of her mother on his back: standing proud, connected as if she and Tempest were the same.

And then her mother disappeared, and it was just the white colt. He ran in another circle, white mane and tail flowing behind him. Sari watched him rear up again, tearing wildly at the air.

"Sari, *ça va?*" called Laurent from his front door.

"What are you doing here? I thought you went on the ride!"

"No, I . . ."

Maybe it was Laurent's voice, or maybe it was the shock of running almost free in the ring, or maybe it was the moonlight: suddenly Tempest stopped dead-still, then got a running start, and suddenly charged like a bull, straight for the gate. She thought he was going to crash it, head down, but suddenly the young horse lifted off—powerful neck up, chest forward, legs thrusting—and jumped the fence.

"He's escaped!" Laurent said, running from his house, watching Tempest gallop into the marsh.

"And it's my fault," Sari said, panicked at the idea of losing the horse.

"No, he's wild," Laurent said. "He just saw his chance to go."

"I have to tell my father," Sari said, starting to shake. She ran to the house, into the kitchen, Laurent right behind her, and began to dial her father's cell phone.

"Papa," she said, when he answered, "Tempest got away! I wanted to find you

and Susannah, and I led him into the paddock, and he ran into the marsh."

Her father said not to worry, he and Susannah would look for Tempest. And Sari
felt slightly calmed by that, because she
didn't want the half-tamed horse to go back
to the wild, especially not wearing a halter,
which could get caught on brush or wire or
fences and trap Tempest so the bulls could
gore him.

So she hung up feeling okay. Not quite
happy, but all right. Still trembling, because
she had let the horse get away, and she
couldn't stand the idea of him being lost on
the endless, lonely sea plain.

"Your father will find him," Laurent said.

"Do you think he will?" she asked, her
eyes welling.

"Of course. And my father will help. They
know more about the horses than anyone."

"I have to go look for Tempest."

"No," Laurent said, grabbing her hand.
His touch made Sari tingle, and she looked
into his eyes. Laurent had held her hand lots
of times during their lives, but lately it had
started making her feel so different. His
eyes were steady, protective. "The marsh
can be dangerous at night, Sari. It's not like

walking through Avignon with me. Stay here. They'll be home soon."

Sari stood still, frozen by the fact Laurent hadn't let go of her hand. She felt something tumble inside. His piercing eyes held her still, even as her heart was tugging her to go after Tempest.

"If we go together, it will be safe," she whispered.

"You want me to come with you?"

She nodded, but even so, she couldn't move. All she could do was look into his eyes and hold his hand and worry about the young horse being lost and think about their night in the dark, silver city, wonder why being with Laurent had started making her feel this way inside.

The waves lapped the shore, the front edge white with sea foam and moonlight. The horses grazed in the salt meadow. Grey held Susannah in his arms. He kissed her, feeling his blood surge like the sea, when his cell phone rang. The sound was startling, so out of place, and he was so lost he nearly threw the thing into the water.

But of course it was Sari. And there was a

problem: Tempest had run off. She sounded calm, pulled together, but there was an undertone of panic in her voice. And Susannah knew, the minute he hung up the phone.

"What's wrong?" she asked.

"A young horse ran off."

"Tempest?" she asked.

"That's right, you saw what he did to the stall . . ."

"He's a wild one," she said.

Grey pulled her close. They lay together on the cold sand, hearts beating together. She felt so warm in his arms, and he closed his eyes and wished the phone hadn't rung. But it had, and she was pushing back, standing up, giving him a hand to pull him to his feet. He felt wild himself, on the primitive edge of feelings he hadn't had in years.

Walking over to the horses, giving Susannah a leg up and then mounting Django himself, Grey felt almost out of control. His emotions were racing, and his blood was pounding. He only wanted to go back to the beach with Susannah. But she was in charge right now, leading him back into the marsh, on their way to save a barn-crazed colt and give Sari heartsease. Watching her, he couldn't help spinning back in time, to the last time he'd been in love. With Maria everything had been wild—their horseback rides, their lovemaking, and their fights.

His passion for Susannah was no less intense; in fact he knew it was stronger. She hadn't hesitated for an instant—her concern for Sari immediately trumped whatever she'd been feeling back on the beach.

"Where should we look?" Susannah asked, pulling him back to reality, out of his fevered thoughts.

"Maybe over where Tempest's herd used to graze," Grey said. "There's a salt field behind the Pont d'Onorato." He rode up alongside her, gave her a long kiss—probably the last in a while—and urged Django into a gallop. Susannah followed closely behind. They charged along the narrow trail, through tall rushes painted sapphire blue by the still-rising moon.

Grey knew the horses were affected by the moon's phases; he had long noticed that mares went into heat during the full moon, that stallions became more fierce, that wild horses like Tempest were more likely to escape. He felt the moon's pull himself. Even as they galloped along, intent on their purpose, he was nearly overwhelmed with desire, wanting nothing more than to pull her off Mystère, make her want to stay in France with him forever.

They rounded a bend, and he slowed down. This was not far from where the bulls were concentrated. He swore the air felt different here—hotter, as if all that aggression poured off the bulls' hides and had nowhere to go. Mist from the creeks rose and swirled. Grey and Susannah rode through this ghostly world, straight to the Pont d'Onorato. After sand and the soft earth of the trails, the horses' hooves sounded loud on the wooden slats of the curved bridge. A creek rushed down below. Somewhere in the distance a nighthawk screeched. And very close by, something screamed.

"What was that?" Susannah asked.

"A horse," Grey said.

"It sounded human."

"Horses in distress do," he replied.

They listened carefully, trying to get the direction. The wind lifted and danced, blowing the mist. It was disorienting, all the more so because Susannah was so near. Grey had to block out everything except the sound of the horse. It took a moment, but he finally had it.

When Grey realized where it was coming from, he looked straight at Susannah. His stomach dropped, knowing she'd fight him on this.

"I want you to wait here," he said.

"Why?"

He hesitated. Maybe if he didn't tell her the truth, she would just listen to him and not try to follow. But there was something about her, and about the way they'd become over this very short time together, that made him know he never wanted to lie to her.

"Because there's quicksand."

"Is . . . the horse trapped?"

"It's possible," he said, hearing the sound of the horse's panic again. "I think so."

"Where is he?"

"Over there," he said, pointing into the mist, across the narrow creek. Climbing down off Django, he turned to see Susannah jumping down from Mystère.

"Susannah," he said.

She put her hand on his arm, her eyes wide. "First," she said, "I'm afraid of being alone with the bulls. And second, I'm not letting you go into quicksand alone."

"I know this area by heart. I'm not going into quicksand."

"Good," she said, trying to smile. "That means I'm not either. You swam into the sea cave with me, I'm heading down that path with you. Come on—let's go get Tempest."

He hesitated, then nodded. The pressure of her fingers on his arm was lighter than moonlight and a hundred times more intense. It made him grab her, kiss her hard. She tasted like the beach, and he swore he heard breaking waves until he realized it was just the sound of his own blood pounding in his ears.

Grey pulled the coiled rope off Django's saddle, took Susannah by the hand, and walked headlong into a place he'd been a hundred times, yet had never been before.

SIXTEEN

Susannah barely stopped to think. She trailed Grey, ready to help. The mist enclosed them, making straight-ahead visibility almost nonexistent. Up above was another story; the fog was pinned to the rivers and lagoons, barely higher than the reeds, and through a fine layer, thin as muslin, the sky overhead was a blue field for the moon and the brightest stars.

Her feet squished in damp earth, and she flashed back to her first day in the Camargue, when she'd stepped off the path onto terrain like this, gotten caught in a stampede of wild bulls. Would they come again? Her heart beat in her throat. Moray eels in the sea cave scared her less than those bulls. Her senses were on high alert as she paid attention to every sound, and followed Grey toward the frightened horse.

They edged along a creek. The tide looked to be ebbing, with the water rushing toward the sea. Moonlight revealed ghostly creatures clinging to the banks. Susannah crouched down, staring at them.

"Those are just *favouilles*—little green crabs," he said.

"I know them well," Susannah said. She'd grown up on the Connecticut shore, spent many happy childhood hours crabbing with her dad. She stared at the tiny eyes on stalks, their oval shells—dark on top, white underneath—their small pincers raised menacingly as she and Grey passed. The bank was also lined with broken shell; the moonlight glinted on them, and she saw the unmistakable ripple of scallop shells.

Mesmerized by the sight, Susannah barely noticed the ground shift. One step later, she stepped right into a black hole—her left leg went into the muck, right up to her knee. She gasped and scrambled, feeling the mud suck her down. But Grey reached back, she grabbed his hand, and she pulled herself out. Steadying herself against him, she looked up ahead, and saw.

The horse was no more than ten yards up the path. He was veiled by mist, but even so, his terror was unmistakable. He had sunk into a hole of black swamp gunk, was nearly up to his withers in it, and was thrashing so hard he seemed in imminent danger of drowning in mud. His back was a glossy hump under slick mire. His eyes flashed with black fire. At the sight of Grey and Susannah, he let out a guttural, screaming neigh.

"Tempest," Susannah said, shocked.

"Yes," Grey said. "He's really in there."

"Can we get him out?"

Grey hesitated; she saw him scouting around the area, staying on the path, but leaning into the tall grass, rippling silver in the moonlight.

"We have to," Susannah said, determined. Inching toward Tempest, wanting to reach out her hand and calm him, she felt the wet ground pulling her feet down, and she stopped dead. "We have to get him out."

"Here," Grey said, hauling a long, weather-beaten plank out of the reeds.

"What's that?"

"People go crabbing here, and stand on it so they won't fall in."

Susannah took one end, and Grey the other. They laid it down on the ground, pointing like an arrow toward the horse. Then Grey burrowed into the wet earth on the other side of the trail, emerging with another sea-silvered board, two inches thick and at least three feet long. Using the first plank as a bridge, he laid the second one even closer to Tempest. At the sight of him, Tempest tossed his head and struggled more.

"There, boy," Grey said. "Stay still if you can. That's it. Just wait a minute now. Just another little bit . . ."

"What are we going to do?" Susannah asked, inching out along the boards. They were six inches wide. She felt as if she was walking a tightrope. The planks distributed her and Grey's weight, making it possible for them to stand on the swampy mud.

"I don't know," Grey said. "I can get the rope around his neck, but how am I going to pull him out?"

"I'll help."

He glanced at her, gave a wry smile. "You're strong, but not that strong."

"Has this ever happened before?" she asked.

Grey nodded. And his frown and the line furrowing between his brows let her know it hadn't had a good outcome.

"He's really trapped," Grey said, tense and powerless as he watched the horse thrash again, sinking another few inches.

"This is quicksand?" she asked doubtfully, looking down at what looked much more like black, tarry mud.

"It's the swamp," he said. "More silt and mud than sand. But the same thing. Tempest can't get a foothold down there. There's no purchase. The more he fights, the deeper he'll go. He weighs a ton, so I can't haul him out myself. I need to keep his head above the mud." Grey started taking off his shirt and watch. He handed them to Susannah. She noticed his hard, tan chest and shoulders, the lines of his muscles, his strong arms, gleaming in moonlight. This was life and death, but she noticed anyway. This was going to turn out right, she was sure. She had confidence in them together. They were going to save this horse, no doubt about it.

"What do we do next?" she asked.

"We're going to pull him out," he said, holding her face between his hands. His fingers felt rough, but the way he held her was so tender, as if he knew how scared she felt. He touched his forehead to hers, then kissed her. In spite of the danger, of the fact they were balancing on boards, she leaned into his body and felt the heat pouring off him, and she felt another surge of certainty. They were not going to let this horse die.

"Hang onto my stuff, okay? Throw it on that patch of tall grass if you want—it won't sink there. Then, walk down the middle of the creek bed. The tide's out, so it won't be deep. The bottom will hold you—it's silted over with pebbles and hard sand. Go to the bridge, and get Django, okay?"

"Okay," she said.

Then she stood back and watched as Grey used the boards in a sort of hopscotch over the mud, walking across one and then the other, lifting up the first to move him closer to the horse, doing it again. When he was almost on top of Tempest, the front edge of the forward plank began to tilt down into the hole. Grey inched back, shifting his weight, to keep from tipping in.

He knelt on the board. She watched him move closer, nearly eye to eye with the terrified horse. He had the rope coiled around one arm, and talking to Tempest, his voice calm and authoritative, he slipped a noose around the powerful neck. As he leaned in, his arms went up to his shoulders in silt. Tempest neighed and started to throw his head around, buck backward, but Grey spoke to him sharply. And the horse stopped.

Susannah ran down the stream. Grey had been right; the creek bed held firm, all the way to the bridge. At the sight of her, Django and Mystère danced nervously. She climbed up the bank to them, untied Django. He tossed his head, nuzzled her shoulder. Petting his neck, she tried to lead him into the water. He balked.

"It's okay, boy," she said. "It's safe . . . hurry now, we have to go get Tempest."

Django was tall for a Camarguaise horse. He towered over Susannah, and when she looked up at him and saw moonlight spilling over his lush white mane and aristocratic head, she knew that he could pull away from her in an instant. She remembered her days at River Farms, how her teacher had taught her to be strong with the horses: kind but firm. *They sense fear, and it's all over,* he'd always told her.

So she kept her hands steady, her voice low, and she told Django what she wanted him to do, and led him into the shallow creek—it came no higher than his knees— just as if she knew what she was doing. The small crabs, *favouilles,* scuttled up the muddy banks, out of their way, their claws scrabbling in the tall grass. Susannah kept an eye on Django, worried the crabs might spook him, but the stallion just walked on, and she led him along the creek, back to Grey and Tempest.

They hadn't moved, but that last fight had taken Tempest down farther. Grey knelt upright; his jeans were soaked, and his upper body was black. Tempest's mane and forelock were coated with silt, and Grey leaned over to clean mud from around his nostrils. For the first time, Susannah felt panic in her chest, wondering how long they could keep the horse from sinking.

Grey had started digging out the area immediately around him. One scoop of black mud, then another, thrown into the reeds. As if Tempest knew he was saving his life— or perhaps just frozen with terror—he stopped moving. Grey leaned closer, kept digging.

Susannah felt the wind pick up. It blew in from the sea, bringing with it fresh scents of salt air. It rippled across her skin; she felt prickles on the back of her neck. The sea breeze cleared the mist, so she could see Grey and Tempest even more clearly. But at the same time, it seemed to have brought ghosts to the scene. She felt death hovering over her shoulder.

She thought of times she'd wedged herself into caves, narrow openings; times she'd gotten stuck in one place, having to wriggle free by inches. She knew that horrible feeling of claustrophobia, knew that Tempest and Grey had to be feeling it now.

Holding on to Django, she looked around for a place to tie him; an old post had been sunk on the creek's bank—some sort of marker, the lettering long worn off the weathered old sign. She knotted his reins to the splintered post then stepped from the creek onto the squishy ground. She felt her way along the still relatively solid ground about five yards toward the swamp where Grey was with Tempest and leapt onto the first plank. It clattered under her feet, tilted momentarily, but held firm.

The moon shined down, painting everything silver—the rough wood under her feet, the tips of the tall green grass, the ripples of black mud, the glint in Tempest's eyes, the shadows around Grey's muscles. He was stretched out, tense and hard as a board, physically holding the horse's head above the surface of the mud. She reached out, touched Grey's back.

"Don't get too close," he said quietly.

"He's sinking; we have to get him out."

"He's like a greased barrel. I can't even get my arms around him."

Silence. Susannah saw Grey's back muscles straining and bunching, and she heard him trying to breathe steadily, keeping Tempest's head up.

"Django's here, waiting," she said.

"I know," he said. "But what can I do?"

"Grey," she said, "put one of the boards under Tempest's front hooves, hold the line around his neck. He'll want to run up—and you'll be on Django pulling; he'll use that force to get himself out."

"Susannah, I can't let go of him right now. If I do, he'll drown before I get to Django."

"I'll hold his head up," she said. He glanced back over his shoulder. She moved closer, gestured that he should go, that she meant it.

"I can't let—"

"You have to," she said, strong and steady. "Do it for Sari. We have to save him, Grey. You know we can . . ."

He met her eyes; he saw her confidence, and she felt him taking it in. "Okay!" he said. "We'll try. Get in here, if you can . . ." He moved aside, so she could wedge herself under his body, wrapping her arms around Tempest's thick neck. Almost instantly she pitched forward, chest-first into the mud— but she caught herself, managing to hold tight, spitting out dirt.

"Got him?" Grey asked.

"Yes," she said. And she did. Nothing was going to make her let go; she reached forward, arms braced on the board. Grey reached around her, grabbed the first plank, wedged it down into the mire at a forward-tilting slant. She saw him soothing Tempest with one hand, while feeling his way beneath his legs with the other. Susannah and

Grey were nearly chest-deep together, and he turned to give her one hard look.

"Keep his head up," Grey said. "But if you start to sink any more, let go. Got that?"

"Yes."

"I'll be just a minute. Shout to me if anything happens."

She nodded, to let him know she would. Then she handed him the rope he'd tied to Tempest, and heard him jump from the plank on which she was lying all the way to the solid ground yards away. His feet pounded across the damp marshland, then splashed into the creek. She heard Django whinny, and the slap of skin as Grey climbed up.

Tempest reacted; his ears twitched. His black eyes widened. Susannah did what she'd seen Grey do; she dug at the mud, brushed the worst of it from his nostrils so he could breathe. He sputtered; his lips sprayed her with a fine black mist.

"It's okay, darling," she said. "Don't be afraid. It'll be just a few minutes now. Stay still, Tempest. That's it . . . good boy."

"Get ready," Grey called.

She eased back, both arms around Tempest, line grasped in one hand, just in time for the rope to go taut and burn her fingers. The pain nearly made her cry out, but all her focus was on helping Tempest. She watched him start to panic—he thrashed again, legs spinning like a wheel. Only this time they found a step. He pawed at the weathered plank. Susannah threw her weight on the loose end; it was like a see-saw, with her on one side and the horse on the other.

"It's working," she called. "Pull harder!"

Tempest began to haul himself out. She heard one front leg pop free of the muck, then the other. She had just enough time to jump out of the way, watching him clear the stickiest part, moving into the creek, nearly swimming through the swamp, stepping here and there, his hooves getting caught in little mud holes.

"He's out!" she cried breathlessly.

Turning around, she saw Grey still on Django. In that instant, the rope went slack, and Grey jumped down and came running. He held the rope's end in one arm, and caught Susannah with the other. He pulled her into his arms, and they nearly fell into the mud. He held her face between his hands; they were slick all over, and his chest was slippery, covered with silt turning silver in the moonlight as it dried in the quickening breeze.

Tempest stood safely in the pebbly stream, tossing his head and dunking his face into the flowing water. Susannah glanced over at him, looked up at Grey with wide eyes, and was just about to say "We did it!" when he kissed her.

She'd been kissed before, but never like this, even by him. She felt the primal power of the wetland, and the fierce strength of the man she had fallen in love with, and his lips were hot and his chest hotter, and both of them were soaking wet and slick, and she had absolutely no idea of where she ended and he began. She thought of Sarah's latest miracle, wondered whether it was a direct result of her petition and the offering of one scallop shell . . .

A horse whinnied. It might have been Mystère or Django or even Tempest, but she was past knowing or even caring. Her hands slid across Grey's hard chest and up his muscular arms; her fingers caressed his face. The kiss went on and on, moonlight scoring shadows across their closed eyes, so that she barely noticed that they weren't alone.

Grey was the first to see. He stopped kissing her suddenly, looked over her shoulder. Laurent was walking along the trail, as if he knew the way by heart after years of horseback rides and crabbing expeditions. Right behind him, stopped dead in her tracks, one hand held over her mouth—Sari.

SEVENTEEN

Sari's eyes were bright with shock and moonlight, as if she'd just seen a ghost, as if she'd just been betrayed all over again. Grey watched the color drain out of her face, started toward her.

"Sari, Tempest's safe," Grey said. "Susannah and I saved him."

Sari didn't reply. She just stood still, staring straight into Susannah's eyes. "I didn't know it was like this," she said.

"Oh, Sari . . ."

"I thought you were my friend."

"I am your friend, Sari," Susannah said, walking toward her.

"No," Sari said, shaking her head, backing away.

"Getting Tempest out of the quicksand, I just kept thinking we had to do it for you . . ."

"No," Sari said again, shaking her head.

"Sari, don't . . ." Laurent urged.

"That's right," Grey said. "Come on now, Sari. Let's get the horses, and get everyone home."

"I don't want . . ." Sari began, her voice tiny. She closed her eyes, going inward, exactly the same way she had the first day Susannah had met her. Susannah's heart cracked, watching her retreat.

Laurent had begun rounding up Mystère and Django. Tempest stood to the side, mud dripping from his coat. Susannah and Grey flanked Sari, and Grey took a step forward, to touch her shoulder, but she seemed frozen.

"Sari?" he asked.

She just stared straight ahead, as if she had turned into a statue.

"Sari," Susannah said, moving closer, trembling with emotion at the girl's distress. She whispered that she was sorry.

Sari shut her eyes tight, retreating deep

inside, blocking out the world. She swayed, as if about to fall, and Grey caught her in his arms. Her limbs seemed useless, as if they were made of wood.

Laurent walked over with Django and Mystère, and just then Claude came galloping over the bridge. Grey looked over at Susannah. His blue eyes glinted in the moonlight, but she felt as if she was staring at him from across the sea.

They all began to walk back toward the ranch. Grey lifted Sari, almost catatonic, onto Mystère, and he climbed up behind her. Laurent gave Susannah a leg up onto Django, while he rode behind his father, leading Tempest.

Susannah just sat there on Django, watching Sari. Grey glanced over at her, filled with longing and hopelessness. *This is what it is, my life,* he wanted to tell her. *This is what we're up against.* Sari was so pretty, and looked so normal, but her psyche was a Pandora's box of what had happened that night five years ago. In her frozen silence, he knew Susannah was finally starting to understand.

When they all got back to the ranch, they went to the stable to wipe the worst of the mud off themselves and the horses. Laurent got out the hose, and he and Claude set in on Tempest. Susannah watched them talking, heard Claude admonishing the young horse for his dramatic escape. Sari stood at Grey's side, glued to him.

Grey looked over at Susannah.

"Will you come into the house?" he asked.

Susannah looked at Sari, but she seemed locked into herself, completely shut down.

"I'd better not," she said.

"Sari," Grey said, looking his daughter in the eye. "Susannah saved Tempest . . . please listen to me, will you? You know how good she's been to you."

"I can't, Papa," Sari finally choked out, her voice breaking. And Grey knew that was true—she couldn't. He could see it in his daughter's posture of defeat, the way she hung her head and started to shudder with great, heaving sobs.

"That's okay, Sari," Susannah said. "I'm going to go now."

Grey shook his head; he couldn't believe this was happening. Their days together had been like nothing he'd ever known before, a revelation. He and Susannah had a life of their own, and he'd hoped it could last, hoped they could ease Sari along until she felt ready to accept things. But Susannah was leaving.

Grey watched as Susannah walked over, stood right in front of Sari.

"Sari?" she said, and even though Sari didn't look up, Susannah went on, through her own tears. "I want you to know how much I've loved meeting you. Spending time with you . . . I'm so glad to know you're riding Mystère again; I'm sure she's happy about that, too."

"Sari, please . . ." Grey said. But she didn't even register she'd heard.

"It's okay," Susannah said. "I just want you to know I'll be thinking of you. And if you ever get to the States, I hope you'll come see me. I'd really like that."

"She visits her grandparents in Rhode Island every summer," Laurent interjected. "Every single summer."

"It's true," Grey said.

Susannah nodded at him, obviously smiling the best she could; he saw the quick sparkle in her dark violet eyes. He wanted to touch her. His arm moved, aching to pull her close. But she stayed away.

"Don't forget the Tarasque," she said, looking from Grey to Sari. She directed her words at the girl, but she was speaking to both of them, and even to herself. "Don't forget that even when there's a dragon, you're safe. You can always sing it to sleep . . ."

"Susannah," Grey said, almost pleading.

She shook her head, stepped back.

"Good night," Susannah said. She blew a kiss to Sari, but his daughter didn't open her eyes to see it. Then, to Grey, "Thank you for everything . . . this has been the most amazing time . . ."

And then she got into her car and drove down the dusty moonlit road, and he watched her, thinking of how she'd brought such unexpected beauty, such tremendous life, into his dead world. He watched her drive away from the Manade du Dempsey, and felt the weight of the last five years come crashing back down.

Hours later, Grey couldn't sleep. The full moon was all the way up now, slanting through the windows, bathing the whole house in blue light. He showered off all the black mud, watched it swirling down the drain, felt the hot water all over his sore body, remembered what it had been like to hold Susannah in his arms on the beach and by the creek.

He relived the feeling of his skin against hers, the taste of her.

Sari, his traumatized child. If she hadn't come along; or if she'd seen him kissing Susannah during the day instead of at night, when all her fears and memories were fully alive . . .

Drying off, he walked through the house. Susannah was everywhere. He faced the fact that he'd started imagining her here. He'd pictured her in the salon—he'd find a beautiful desk for her, put it by the window, a place for her books, somewhere she could do her work and study. He'd seen her in the dining room, sitting between him and Sari at the table, eating together every night. Cooking with Sari, showing her all the things she wanted to know. The three of them riding together through the marsh . . . he'd find a horse for her, the perfect one. . . .

Dreams of a home life. He'd long stopped having them. Grey Dempsey, expatriate. His brothers still thought of him as Hemingway. Maybe he didn't have the bylines anymore, but he did have the bulls and white horses, and now he had the sea cave. Even a fight by the harbor. Perfect.

What would Oscar and Ben think if they knew his wildest dreams were to have Susannah Connolly move in with him, make a life together?

He walked through the silent house. Blue shadows fell everywhere. The tile floors felt cool under his bare feet. He'd fallen in love fast before. When it came to love, he had two speeds: fast and stop.

Look how it had turned out the last time. He remembered when he had bought this place. Nearly a year into his time with her, and already they were on the rocks. He'd become a rancher just to keep his wife.

The ranch had lasted; Maria was gone.

He kept pictures of her for Sari. They stood in frames in the family room, where he hardly ever went. Walking in there now, he looked at the family they'd once been. Maria holding the baby; Maria standing on the front step; Maria standing on the back of Django.

What was he doing, keeping alive the

memory of a woman who didn't even want her daughter? Disgusted, he turned the photos facedown. He kept walking through the house, remembering how dangerous love with Maria had always felt, wondering why he had once found it so exciting. She was a circus rider now; she had adulation and cheering crowds and the adoration of the man she'd left with.

Sari was paying the price. An elusive wife was one thing; a disappearing mother was another. Grey didn't need all those doctors' diagnoses to tell him what was going on. His daughter was filled with rage—anger turned inward.

From the minute Maria had pushed her, Sari had needed to fight back. She'd watched her mother drive off, been completely powerless to stop her. She'd turned her frustration on herself.

Grey had often wondered exactly what Sari had seen, after riding Mystère up the main road, coming upon the car idling on the side, taillights glowing red in the darkness. Why had Maria and Adrien pulled over right there?

Had it really been so incredibly impossible for them to drive out of the region, away from the Parc, out of sight of Sari before making love, doing whatever they had to do?

Sari had always claimed she never saw anything. The trauma of her fall had—perhaps mercifully—blocked out any memory of her mother in Adrien's arms, whatever the two of them had been doing. But Grey had always had his suspicions, and after tonight, he thought he knew for sure.

Coming upon him and Susannah had brought it all back to her. A parent in the arms of someone else meant only one thing—they were leaving her forever. Why else would Sari have reacted the way she did? The way she shut down so violently, eyes squeezed tight, unable to let herself see . . .

Sari liked Susannah. But Grey had been deluded to think they could ever become a family. He had always thought the Gypsy's curse was complete bullshit, but right now he found himself starting to believe.

As he walked upstairs, Grey's heart felt heavy. He loved his daughter more than his own life—but sometimes he felt that that's what he had traded, to love her the way she needed to be loved, to stay here and take care of her the way she needed taking care of.

He walked along the hall, wondered how Susannah was doing. She'd seen how up-set Sari was, and she'd known. But did she know what all this was doing to Grey, how much it hurt to be without her now?

Pausing in the doorway to Sari's room, Grey checked on his daughter. She lay in bed, covered with a sheet and her duvet. The two black cats were curled up, guardians at her feet. She'd named them after his brothers, Ben and Oscar, with a French spin: Bruno and Oscar. They watched him with yellow eyes.

The moonlight, coming through Sari's window, caught something in her arms. He saw the red glints, took a step closer. There, clutched right under his daughter's chin, was the dragon toy Susannah had given her.

Don't forget the Tarasque, Susannah had said. *Don't forget that even when there's a dragon, you're safe. You can always sing it to sleep . . .*

The memory of her words was strong. It filled Grey, made him miss her so much he couldn't stand it. He pictured her lying in bed just a few miles away, her next-to-last night in the Camargue.

He wondered whether she was visited by dragons tonight, as he was. He wanted to grab Sari and shake her; he wanted to tell her she was ruining the best thing that had happened to them both in longer than he could remember.

He stood in the doorway, staring at his sleeping daughter. Then he whispered, "Good night, sweet dreams"—just as he always did—and continued down the hall to his own room.

EIGHTEEN

The next day was brilliant, full of springtime.

Susannah hadn't slept at all during the night. The full moon had poured through the window, straight into her eyes. Lying awake, she couldn't stop thinking of him, of Sari, of the evening's traumatic turn.

At first light, she went to the church to see Sarah one last time. She lit a votive candle, added it to the glow of a thousand others, letting the smoke drift up to the ceiling of Sarah's chapel, merging with the black soot of years gone by, just like the charcoal from ancient fires in the many caves she'd vis-ited. She'd bowed her head, thinking of her mother. She'd wished she could have introduced her parents to Grey and Sari. . . . She left the second apricot scallop shell Grey had given her at Sarah's feet. For thanksgiving or for hope, she wasn't sure. Maybe it didn't matter; a prayer was a prayer.

Back at her house, Susannah felt the hours drag by so slowly. She kept waiting for the phone to ring—for it to be Grey. She wanted to hear his voice, wanted to hear that Sari had come around, that the shock had worn off, that she'd felt well enough to go to school, that Susannah would have another chance to see them.

When Grey did call, mid-morning, he spoke in a low voice, as if worried that Sari might hear him.

"How are you?" he asked.

"Never mind me," she said. "How's Sari?"

"The same," he said.

"You kept her home from school?"

"I had to," he said. "It takes a while for her to come out of it . . ."

"I feel terrible," she said.

"Don't," he said. "You didn't do anything. You've come into something that was set in place long ago. She'll be okay."

"I just . . ." Susannah began. "I just hoped

I could see you. I thought maybe you both could come for dinner tonight. I wanted . . . to be with you, my last night here, and talk to Sari about what happened."

"You have no idea how much I want that," he said.

"I understand, Grey. I know you have to take care of her . . ."

"Susannah . . ." he murmured. "You know I'd be there in a minute if I could."

"What about you?" Susannah forced herself to move on. "Will you be okay?"

"Yeah," he said after a moment, as if he had to think about it. "I will. Until tomorrow."

"Tomorrow . . ."

"Until you leave . . ."

They held on for another minute, then said goodbye. Susannah hated hanging up the phone, breaking the connection.

She couldn't bear giving up the idea she'd had of cooking for him and Sari, so she left the house and walked up the street to the market. She picked out the most delicious food she could find, brought it home. She'd gotten things that were meaningful, that would connect with this magical time she'd had in the Camargue.

Coquilles St. Jacques, glistening pink

with the red roe still attached; small local crabs, just like the *favouilles* they'd seen last night; pencil-thin stalks of asparagus, as green as the fields all around the Manade; delicate squash blossoms, to be stuffed with a duxelles of mushrooms and herbs, the color bright saffron, reminiscent of the garland of flowers painted in the Dempseys' kitchen.

And then Susannah prepared the meal, just as if Grey and Sari were really coming. She filled the kitchen with the most beautiful aroma, grateful for every minute she'd spent in this enchanted place. The copper pans glinted, the olive oil poured in a cool green stream, the smells of sage and tarragon made her feel as if she were forever under Provence's romantic spell.

A knock on the door made her jump. Turning, she half expected to see them standing there. But it was Topaz instead. The setting sun shone on her burnished brown hair, dark tan arms, amber-colored silk dress. Topaz held a bag and a bouquet of dried lavender.

"I've come to say farewell," Topaz said. "And here you are, making a feast!"

"Please, come in," Susannah said.

"Who are you cooking for?"

Susannah smiled. "For my ghosts," she said. "The ones I brought with me when I came to the Camargue, and the ones I'll be leaving when I go. Since they can't very well eat all this lovely food, will you join me?"

"I'd be delighted," Topaz said. "Honestly, I smelled your cooking all the way down the street."

"I'm glad you followed it to *my* door," Susannah said. "You have the best market in the world, and I couldn't resist buying all these good things . . ."

Of course Topaz knew where everything was, so she pitched in, helping to finish cooking the meal. Susannah poured them glasses of the lovely sweet-dry rosé of Provence; it would forever remind her of being at Cap Morgiou with Grey. They clinked glasses, drank to Susannah's stay in Topaz's house.

As Susannah set the table with Provençal cotton linens, the tablecloth pale pumpkin and the napkins printed with faded red and purple flowers, her throat caught. She had wanted to make this meal so special for Sari and Grey. She set out silverware, bright crockery, a Lucite peppermill and a blue container of Fleur-de-Sel de Camargue. She still had Grey's black scallop shells and she arranged them in the center of the table, around a vase of colorful wildflowers. When she lit the tall white tapers, she felt the tears start, gritted her teeth, and turned away for a moment while she swallowed them down.

Dinner was ready. The two women dined on *soupe de favouilles,* made with stock of onions, carrots, and celery that had been simmering for hours, enriched with crème fraîche, flavored with bright threads of fragrant saffron, and thick with fresh local crabmeat.

Next came coquilles St. Jacques, served in the shell after a quick sauté in olive oil, garlic, and finely chopped tomatoes; a green salad; *fleurs de courgettes* stuffed with a duxelles of wild mushrooms; a baguette and fresh farm butter. When dinner was over, Susannah put out the last of the cheese she'd been enjoying during her stay: Crottin, creamy St. Marcellin, and one small piece of Roquefort.

Susannah did her best to eat. She wanted to savor every bite, but she barely tasted anything. She made sure Topaz had enough, and she was aware of her friend watching how much she left on her plate.

"This was delicious," Topaz proclaimed. "But it's a good thing I came."

"Yes, it is, I loved having you."

"That's not what I meant," Topaz said. "I mean that this would have been much too much food for some ghosts and a woman who barely ate a single bite . . ."

"Oh," Susannah said.

"Indeed," Topaz said.

Susannah stared into the candlelight. It flickered, and a small breeze sent columns of smoke up to the ceiling. Topaz leaned forward, catching Susannah's eyes.

"I wanted them to come for dinner tonight," Susannah said.

"Sari and Grey?"

Susannah nodded. "I wanted it very badly."

"I'm sure he did, too," Topaz said. "In fact, I know. He called me and asked me to come check on you. He didn't go into detail, but I could tell he's concerned about you. He's in deep."

Susannah gave her a direct gaze. "Why do you say that?"

"Grey Dempsey hasn't looked seriously at

a woman since Maria left," Topaz said. "He was burned by her, badly. But worse, he saw what it did to Sari."

"You should have seen her last night," Susannah said. The story started spilling out: the full-moon trail ride, the call from Sari, the lost horse, the ordeal of pulling Tempest from the quicksand. She got toward the end of the story, and Topaz guessed the rest.

"Sari saw you together?" she asked.

"Yes," Susannah said.

"That Rosalie . . ." Topaz said.

"What do you mean?"

"All the time she spent with Sari, drilling it into her head that her mother was both so special and so cursed. It's a terrible, heavy burden for Sari to carry. She thinks she drove her mother away." Topaz shook her head angrily.

"Sari thinks she drove her *away*?" Susannah asked. "Maria hit her."

"You weren't there, and neither was I," Topaz said. "But I know Maria, and she couldn't have hit her."

"Sari says she did," Susannah said. "Grey told me, and I believe them."

"You don't know Maria," Topaz said. "She

didn't hit her child." She paused a moment, and then shook her head. "If something like that *did* happen, it was a terrible, terrible accident."

Susannah watched Topaz; she seemed so secure and calm, and her statement had the confidence of conviction.

"Will you tell me about Maria leaving?" Susannah asked.

"We all adore Maria," Topaz said. "If you knew her, you would, too." She spoke steadily, defying the doubt she saw in Susannah's eyes. "It's impossible not to—her *joie de vivre* is unparalleled. Her gifts in the realms of magic, horses, and balance are truly miraculous. Sari . . . the child must remember what it was like to have a magician as a mother."

"Maria is really a magician?"

"In a manner of speaking. She can charm a horse as no one else can. Our clan reveres horses. We grow up with them, almost like members of our family. But no one, not even the elders, could ride like Maria. To see her, you would swear she's floating on air, just above the back of the animal. It's beyond description . . . and it was too great a gift for her to let go."

"Let go?" Susannah asked, suddenly filled with fury, picturing Sari standing devastated in the moonlit marsh. "So she let go of her family instead?"

"I don't expect you to understand," Topaz said quietly. "You don't know her. I'm not saying that she did it well, or did it right . . . but she had to leave."

"What about the 'curse'? Did that have something to do with it?"

"Well, perhaps," Topaz said, sighing. "Zin-Zin was furious with Maria for marrying Grey."

Topaz reached out for the wine bottle, poured them each another glass. They sat there a few moments, calming down. After another sip of Bandol, Topaz raised her eyes toward Susannah.

"She left him for another man," she said quietly.

"The trainer."

Topaz nodded. "Adrien Ferret. His Gypsy name is Matelo."

"What happened?"

"He was the son of our greatest horse trainer, a genius in his own right; he'd frequently be hired by the best horse farms, from Normandy to Belgium. He was the only trainer some people would use. Even in Ireland, for the most magnificent Irish hunters, and even for Dutch hot-bloods. He was brilliant . . ."

"And he worked with Maria?"

Again, a nod. "Yes. Everyone thought they would be married—before she met Grey. Zin-Zin decreed it."

"That's why she was so unhappy when Maria decided to marry Grey instead?"

"That's putting it mildly. As I said, Maria was feisty and independent. No one was going to tell her what to do. She made her choice to marry outside our tradition. But she paid the price. She was so terribly unhappy—and so was Grey."

"And Adrien was waiting all that time?"

Topaz nodded. "We have a festival every May. Romanies from all across Europe make the pilgrimage to see Sarah. We have dances, and parties, and there are always a lot of horses. A tent is erected on the caravan grounds, and a small circus is held. It's not for the public—just for us. Tightropes, and trapezes, and the most exquisite white horses ridden by the best riders . . . it's a show that no one else has ever seen, one that most people would believe was sheer magic."

"And Maria . . ."

"She did some of the most spectacular riding of her life there, even after she married Grey. Adrien had her lead his group, in spite of everything. You have to imagine the tent—swooping material, parachute silk, in colors from midnight blue to glowing amber, printed with gold images of stars and the moon. And the tent was lit by lanterns, a hundred of them!"

Susannah pictured the tent, glowing with light, filled with Maria's clan, watching her perform her magic. She could almost see the white horses, the avid faces, the exquisite fabric of the circus tent, Adrien watching his prize rider. But all of those images were dimmed by the sight of Grey and Sari. Were they there in the crowd? Five years ago Sari would have been eight; how proud she must have been of her mother . . .

"It was the last week of May," Topaz said. "The month of miracles was almost over. Devotions to Sarah had been made, our circus had been held, the clan was dispersing for another year. Adrien was leaving for his latest posts—this time across the Atlantic.

He had horses to train in British Columbia and Nevada."

Susannah nodded, listening.

"He went to the Manade du Dempsey; I'm not sure anyone but he and Maria, and perhaps Rosalie, know whether a plan had already been made. Rosalie has never told the truth of that. All I know is what happened next. Maria ran to his car, they drove away, and Maria never returned."

"Something else happened," Susannah said.

Topaz glanced over.

"Sari," Susannah said. The name hung in the air, reverberating. Susannah stared into the candle flame. She followed the smoke with her eyes, swirling up to the ceiling. She thought of Sarah's chapel, of the soot-blackened crypt. Her heart skipped, thinking of all Sari had gone through, from that terrible night forward. And in that instant, she felt anger at the saint.

"And now . . ." Susannah trailed off.

"Maria and Matelo run a horse facility in the desert," Topaz said. "In Nevada, just outside of Las Vegas. And they've started . . ."

"What?"

"A circus. Very similar to the magical little tented circus we have every May. It's not unlike Cirque du Soleil; they perform at one of the casinos."

"What's it called?" Susannah asked. When Topaz didn't reply, she leaned forward. "I can find out, easily enough."

"Clair de Lune," Topaz said.

"Light of the moon," Susannah whispered, thinking of the night before, picturing Grey swathed in luminous blue light. She could almost smell the sea air, feel the warmth of his arms around her.

"The show is brilliant, I've heard," Topaz said. "Friends have traveled to see it; some even work there. I'm told that one feels a spell has been cast, and—"

"What does her name mean?" Susannah asked suddenly, her head light as she thought again of the saint, and of a little girl left behind by her mother.

"Maria? She was named for the three Marys, of course," Topaz said.

"Not Maria. Sari."

"Well, it's a nickname."

"For what?"

"Sari's real name is Zinnia," Topaz said.

"She's named for Zin-Zin, in honor of all her wisdom."

"In spite of her unhappiness with Maria's marriage to Grey?"

"Perhaps because of it," Topaz said. "It was Maria's attempt to mollify Zin-Zin, win back her love."

"It didn't work?"

Topaz shook her head. "Zin-Zin is very stubborn."

Susannah pictured the face of the very old woman sitting at the Sarah Circle, her eyes kind and patient and full of love—how could someone supposedly so wise not have accepted Maria's choice? How could she think she knew better?

"What is her middle name? Sari's?" Susannah asked.

"You know already," Topaz said steadily.

"Tell me."

"It's Sarah."

Susannah stared at the candles, her eyes welling with tears. "Sarah . . . the saint hasn't taken very good care of this girl who has her name."

"Sarah takes care of everyone who asks her," Topaz said.

Susannah looked into the eyes of this

woman who had so quickly become a friend. She felt Topaz's divided loyalties: between the women she cared about; and between Sara-la-Kali, to whom she devoted so much of her life, and the young girl who'd been left behind.

"She will take care of you," Topaz said. "She already has."

"I prayed for something yesterday," Susannah said. "I almost thought . . ."

Topaz laughed gently. "And you wanted instant results?"

Susannah stared at the candle.

"My dear friend. You, who know better than any of us the miracles Sarah can perform . . . even you took nine months to be born. Miracles don't happen overnight."

"But Sari . . . she's suffering."

"She has a good father," Topaz said. "And somewhere, a mother who loves her."

"'Somewhere' isn't good enough," Susannah said.

"So you say," Topaz said. "But do you know what would happen if Maria returned? Can you say that after all this time it would be the best thing?"

"For Sari it would."

"Are you so sure that it would be better

for Sari to have a mother who longed to be somewhere else? I know how terrible that sounds to you, how much you want to judge Maria. But not everyone is like your mother. Not everyone is like you . . ."

"I'm not a mother," Susannah said.

"Remember what Zin-Zin said," Topaz said gently.

"That I will be someday."

Topaz nodded and took her hand. Then, gently, "Just not today."

"Not today," Susannah agreed, the candlelight blurring as she stared at it through tears and thought of everything she'd be leaving when she flew home tomorrow, to her wonderful life full of friends, research, classes, and colleagues. And no Grey.

NINETEEN

Tuesday the weather changed again. The sky was dark, and the wind felt spooky and cold. Grey drove into Stes.-Maries-de-la-Mer, and headed for the white house just off the harbor. Whitecaps filled the bay, and flags snapped in the wind.

He parked in the driveway, and opened the car door just as Susannah was stepping out into the drizzle. Laden down with her suitcase and briefcase, she looked shocked to see him. He felt the thudding impact of her expression and realized—she didn't want to see him.

But then he stepped out of the car, and

she dropped her bags, and she was in his arms, standing in the sharp, cold rain. He held her, rocking her, just standing there getting wet together and not caring. His mouth brushed hers, kissing her lightly and then deeply and wanting to give her everything he had. Her face was wet, only partly from the rain.

"I didn't think I'd see you again," she said.

"That could never happen," he said.

"But I'm on my way to the airport," she said. "My flight from Arles to Paris is this morning."

"I know," he said. "I'm going to drive you."

Her face fell; she pointed at the car in the driveway. "I have to return my rental car," she said.

Grey smiled. "Leave the keys; I made some calls last night, and we'll get it back to the airport for you."

"But who?" she asked.

"Topaz will drive it up, and Claude will meet her at the lot there and give her a ride back home."

She didn't need more than that. Grey lifted her bags, carried them to his car and stowed them in back. It was his battered old

Citroën; their last ride in it had been to Cap Morgiou and back. Susannah climbed in, and gave him a smile, remembering.

He was hoping the weather would cause her flight to be canceled. "Did you check with the airline?" he asked.

"Yes," she said. "No delays so far."

"Well," he said, "maybe that will change."

He backed out of the space, pulled onto the road. As he drove through town, he felt eyes on him. Grey didn't care. Let them stare all they wanted. They passed Rosalie, coming out of the post office; she stopped dead and stared coldly at the car.

Susannah waved goodbye; Rosalie didn't wave back.

"Why is she that way toward you?" Susannah asked. "So much time has passed since Maria left . . ."

"It's the way life is here," Grey said. "Everyone's very raw when it comes to Maria."

"That's why Sari was so upset at me the other night . . ."

Grey took one hand off the wheel to reach across and hold hers. He wanted to hold her and reassure her, and also reassure himself.

"Sari walks a fine line," Grey said. "A razor edge, when it comes to her mother. She got into trouble with Rosalie, for criticizing Maria to her. For saying she hates her. But she doesn't, not really. Sari has a hard time with women. If she gets too close to someone, she feels she's being disloyal to her mother. And if I do, she's afraid she's going to lose me."

"You'd told me that," Susannah said. "But seeing it was a whole other story. It was terrifying to see her that way."

Grey nodded. "I know. And she's such a wonderful girl, Susannah, she is. If only you could know her. But the line is so fine with her. She's made progress. She has. But I'm always afraid something will push her back to the way she was right after the accident. She's terrified I'll leave her, too."

"You'd never leave her."

"Of course not."

"I care about her so much," Susannah said. "I did from the moment we met. I'm not sure whether it was tied up with you or not. But I felt a bond. I wish she knew that . . ."

"Susannah, I think she does," Grey said. "And that confuses her more than anything."

When he glanced at Susannah, he saw her frowning, taking that in, as if trying to figure out what it meant, or what to do about it.

He pulled onto the road leading north, leaving Stes.-Maries behind. He watched Susannah gaze at the dark silhouette of the ancient church, the site of Sarah's chapel and so much history.

They drove through the Parc Régional de Camargue, washed with rain. The endless plain of sea grass was darkened by low clouds; white horses in the distance looked like ghosts or shadows. A herd of black bulls clustered by the road, on the other side of a fence, and Grey slowed down so she could see.

"They don't look so dangerous from in here," she said, squeezing his hand.

"If it weren't for the fence, they could do some damage to this little car," he said.

"I'll always be grateful to the bulls," she said. "When I see them in cave paintings, they'll always remind me of us. They brought us together."

He nodded. It was strange, how the most unexpected happenings could turn everything around, take life in a completely different direction. That day he'd been riding Mystère because she didn't get enough exercise. He'd crashed through the circle of bulls to rescue a stranger, who in turn had gotten Sari back up on Mystère again. Most of all, he had met Susannah . . .

"You've changed my life forever," he said.

"And you've changed mine," she said. "Let's not stop, okay? Let's keep changing our lives, until we come back together . . ."

He heard something in her tone, and when he glanced over, he felt a shiver shoot down his spine. She was on the edge of her seat.

He drove slowly away from the bulls, and checking his watch, sped toward Arles. He remembered how he had waited at the side of this road—on a rainy day just like today—and followed Susannah to the library. He'd lived here for over fifteen years, and suddenly the entire landscape was transformed. He would never again drive past these spots without thinking of Susannah, and how much he missed her.

"I want to do something," she said.

"Oh, Susannah," he said quietly, feeling another shiver. "You live in Connecticut, I live in the Camargue. But distance isn't the problem."

"I know," she said. "Talk to her, Grey."

"Do you think I haven't?" he asked.

"Maybe you haven't in a way she can hear."

"We visit the States every summer," Grey said. "My parents' house in Rhode Island isn't so far from Connecticut."

"You could visit," she said, and he felt her glance over.

"I want that more than anything," he said.

"But . . ." she began, trailing off, frowning.

He knew she meant Sari, too. Didn't she understand that wasn't going to happen? It was all over; she didn't know his daughter.

"She loves my parents," he said. "And they'd do anything for her. My brothers, too. The sun rises and sets on Sari for the whole Dempsey family. I'm thinking that maybe some day when she's out on my dad's boat, or fishing with my brothers, I can drive down to see you . . ."

"Grey," she said. And the sadness in her tone made him realize that she was backing away from him.

"I have to be with you again," he said, looking over. "It's why I had to drive you today, why I can't stand the idea of you going on that plane. Please say you'll see me when I get there this summer . . . we can meet somewhere, anywhere you say . . . I'll drive to your house, or we can go someplace else."

She glanced over, and he could see the longing in her face. He felt it, too. He wanted her now, and he'd be wanting her every minute until he saw her again.

"How long will we have?" she asked. "Will we have an hour, two?"

"Susannah, I don't know," he said, reaching for her, wanting to pull her all the way across the seat. "We'll be together as much as we can."

She stared out the window. He saw the worry lines between her brows, as if she was struggling with something.

"Of course, I want to be with you again, too," she said. "More than you can imagine. If that's all we have, then that's what it will be. But it seems so small and sad, compared to what I feel inside."

"Susannah," he said quietly. "You saw Sari in the marsh, and at the ranch afterwards. That's what I'm dealing with—no matter how much I want you, want to be with you all the time."

Susannah nodded sadly, looking over at him, not trying to talk him into something he just couldn't do.

Grey got it. Susannah wanted what they had to add up to more than just a few stolen meetings—sneaking off to the library, to the sea cave, a moonlit trail ride, this trip to the airport. He wanted that, too, and he was driving himself insane trying to think of ways to speed the process.

"She slept with your Tarasque the last two nights," he said.

"She did?"

"Yes. I looked in on her, and she was holding it tight, right under her chin."

"Grey . . ." she began, then trailed off, as if she had already said what she had to say.

And suddenly, way too soon, they were at the Nîmes-Garon airport.

Susannah checked her ticket, and he took her to the terminal. She had a Ryanair flight to Paris, connecting with Air France to Boston. She sat very still, staring straight ahead, as if she didn't want to move.

Grey sat there, his heart pounding. He had so many things he wanted to say. For the first time in years, his heart and mind were connected. They were both unlocked, and words and feelings were flowing. Everything was directed to Susannah. He only wanted to talk to her; his thoughts were for her alone. Once she got onto that plane, how would he go back to the way things had been? Locked up, locked down.

"Susannah," he said, taking her hand. "Don't go."

She looked over at him, eyes welling with tears.

"But I have to," she said. "I have work, and my house, and my life to get home to. Besides—what would happen if I stayed here? Would I hide from Sari?"

He couldn't answer that.

"I'll tell you one thing," she said, taking his hand. "I know you say she's fragile. She's your child, and you know her better than anyone. But I'll bet you anything she's stronger than you think."

He gazed at her, listening.

"You said she slept with the Tarasque; you know why, don't you?"

"Why?"

"Because she's trying to *fight*. She's thirteen, and too old for stuffed animals, but she's up against something that's scaring her so much she can't stand it. But she wants to chase it away. She does."

"What is it?"

Susannah shook her head. "I don't know, exactly. But it came out the other night, when she saw us together."

"It's just like you told her," Grey said. "She's tormented by what happened with her mother, and she has to deal with it. And she gets that! She does. Susannah, you should see her hanging on to the toy you gave her, for all she's worth . . . I know she was upset to see me with you. But . . . she likes you, Susannah. She likes you so much."

Susannah smiled, but her eyes were so sad. "Her fears really don't have to do with me," she said. "They're five years old; they've been with her ever since the night her mother drove away."

"I know," Grey said.

She nodded, gazing into his eyes as if she understood him. They were in an impossible situation, and Maria had put them there.

"Can I write you? At least let you know when we're coming to the States?" Grey asked.

"Of course," she said. "And I'll write to you, too. In fact, I'll probably write you from the plane."

He laughed. Susannah fumbled in her bag, pulled out a business card from Connecticut College, wrote down her home number, address, and email. He scribbled his address, and email address, and phone number on a scrap of paper. She reached for the paper, and he caught her hand.

She gazed into his eyes. The car was idling, and an official was standing just outside his window trying to hurry him along, but Grey couldn't move. He sat there, holding her hand, roughened from scrambling over rocks, crawling into caves. He loved her hands.

"Thank you for everything," she said.

"I didn't do anything."

"Don't get me started. There's not one thing I regret," she said.

"There is for me," he said. "I have one huge regret."

"What's that?"

"That I can't throw Ian into the harbor all over again."

She laughed. So did he, and he felt how impossible it all was. How could he meet someone like this, and feel as if he were about to lose any chance with her forever? Suddenly the security official tapped on his window, gave him a stern look. Grey indicated that he'd move right along.

"I'll park the car and walk you in," he said.

"No," Susannah said. "Please, don't . . ."

"Susannah . . ."

"This is too hard," she said.

He stared at her. He knew what she meant, but he couldn't let her go; grabbing for her hand again, he pulled her close to kiss her. Her body felt so light, and already familiar. The way his arms went around her, the weight of her hand on his shoulder, the way her mouth felt on his. When she pulled back from him, Grey saw the official approaching again.

"I already miss you," he said. "More than I can believe."

She seemed about to speak, but instead she just turned away.

And then she was out of the car, a blast of wet air coming through. She grabbed her bags. He stared after her, and she didn't look back, not even once, before running through the airport doors. The official let him watch until the last moment, then tapped his window, moving him along.

Grey put the car in gear and drove away. He could still taste Susannah's kiss and feel her small, rough hands, but she was already gone.

The plane ride from Arles had been bumpy, never quite making it above the rough weather until they crossed through central France. Then they left the mistral behind, landing at Paris in nothing much more than light drizzle.

The flight from Paris to Boston was half empty, and the cabin crew upgraded Susannah to first class. She flew Air France a lot, and this had happened before, and she'd always enjoyed the wide leather seat, the soft wool blanket, and the complimentary glass of champagne. This time she was just glad to have a little extra privacy.

She had a window seat. As the plane took off, banking around Paris, she had views of the Arc de Triomphe, the Eiffel Tower, and the Seine. She stared down at the serpentine river, twisting north toward the coast and English Channel, but she was picturing a different body of water.

The Rhône River, making its passage through the Camargue, with its estuary of marshland, endless and green, filled with black bulls and white horses. Susannah closed her eyes, trying to hold on to everything she was feeling. She brought her left hand to her face, smelled Grey: horses, leather, salt air.

Her briefcase was filled with material she'd gathered for Helen. And her suitcase was filled with some of the souvenirs she'd bought, that would always remind her of this trip: a muslin peasant shirt embroidered with flowers, a book about Sarah with a beautiful picture of her statue on the cover, a small statue of Sarah, some candles, photos of the white horses, jars of delicious things from the *marché* at Stes.-Maries-de-la-Mer.

But most of what she was bringing home she could neither pack nor carry. She felt it deep inside: a change in her heart. It was a terrible heaviness—not of grief or regret, but of wild love. It was as if during this trip her heart had shed the pain of her mother's death, opened itself up for something new and completely unexpected.

Susannah had kept herself closed off for a long time. She'd focused on work to recover from grief. She'd grown up in a home feeling completely loved and cared for. Her parents had nurtured her talents and intellect; after her father's death, she'd grown closer to her mother. They'd had a special bond—her mother the teacher, and Susannah in the department of cultural anthropology at Connecticut College.

Susannah had wanted to fall in love, get married, have a family, but it had never happened. Perhaps she'd been too spoiled by so much early love from her parents. And then Ian had come along, and they had wasted years in their halfhearted limbo, trying to hold on even after she'd realized they were completely wrong together.

Suddenly it was strange flying in first class alone. She felt the funniest ache, wishing she could share it with Grey. All the nice things: the extra attention, the warm blanket, the flight attendant coming around to refill glasses. The flight felt so special, but what did it matter?

Now that she'd been with Grey, felt what

it was like to love someone, it made being alone feel twice as hard. She'd never minded it before. She'd planned her trips solo; she'd had her books and writings for company. Right now, the seat beside her was empty, and it made her feel so hollow inside, she began to panic.

She looked out the window at the counterpane landscape of France. The coast appeared, a long jagged edge that fell into the Atlantic. She felt that once the plane flew over the water, she would lose everything: this trip had just been a vacation, a getaway, a little escape. Yes, she'd met people she liked, but what could they possibly mean to her, after all? And what could she mean to them?

Reaching into her carry-on bag, her hand was shaking. She pulled out a small silk pouch—bought only days ago, at the *marché*—just to reassure herself it had all been real. Unzipping it, she removed the black scallop shells Grey had given her on the beach. She placed them on the tray beside her seat.

And she tried to keep her heart calm, her mind from despairing, as she reminded herself it had all been real. So real, she began to cry. She hadn't asked for anything, hadn't expected to fall in love. She'd received so much more than she'd ever thought possible.

Staring down at the scallop shells, she thought of all she had left behind, on the ground in France—people she had just met and had never dreamed she could love so much—and tried to understand what it all meant, why she had fallen so deeply in love with someone she couldn't have. Why had such a thing happened?

But she couldn't answer her own question, so she just rested her head against the cold window and watched the ocean down below and remembered the peace and connection she'd felt with Grey under the sea.

TWENTY

School had never been so difficult. It was impossible to sit and think. Sari dragged herself into the building, made herself go to class, sat in her seat and pretended to listen. Her friends were all leaning forward, concentrating on what the teacher was saying.

They were all getting their *bac;* their baccalaureate certificate, necessary for continuing to college. Sari was in the A program, for arts and literature. Today's lecture had to do with themes of morality and rationality in Molière. Sari couldn't focus on a word.

Laurent met her in the hallway after

classes were over. She bumped right into him, her books went flying, she was in such another world. He gathered them up without admonishing her, even as other kids were walking past, staring.

She cringed, embarrassed. What was wrong with her? Laurent followed her into an empty classroom. She sat down at one of the pale wood desks, and he stacked her books in front of her.

"What's wrong?" he asked. "You should be happy today."

"Why?" she asked.

"Your essay," he said. "Didn't you get it back from Mademoiselle Guillaume?"

"No," she said, staring at him. "You got yours back?"

He nodded. "With a good grade; I assumed your mark would be even higher, considering your essay was better."

Sari stared down at the desk. She had enjoyed everything about that essay—the magical trip to Avignon, the way she'd felt writing about the night, the way writing seemed to unlock something inside her. The words had spilled out, describing the night Laurent had planned for her, the joy she'd felt to wander the streets with her best friend, knowing they were seeing everything the same way.

"I wonder why Mademoiselle Guillaume didn't return your paper?" he asked.

"She probably hated it," Sari said.

"Why would you say that?"

"Because of how I am," Sari said. "I never should have written the truth . . . shouldn't have told about the city being black and silver that night, and how it made me feel as if I belonged. It was too much. I never know when to stop."

"That's what made your essay stand out," Laurent said. "You told the truth."

Sari sat there shaking. She was so tired of the truth. She wanted someone else's life. She wanted to be happy and pretty, with the same color skin as everyone else—either darker or paler than her in-between medium shade. She wanted a whole family, she wanted to put on a sweater and know what color it was.

"I bet Mademoiselle Guillaume is showing your paper to the other teachers. Just wait, Sari. You'll get it back with the best grade of anyone. You could be a journalist, just like your father used to be."

Sari glanced at Laurent. How did he read

her mind the way he did? She'd had that same thought, writing the essay—maybe she could become a reporter when she finished school. But lately she'd felt too depressed to care.

"We could join the school paper," he said.

"It's almost the end of the term," she said.

"Well, there's one more issue to put out. We could write stories for it. Or help in some other way." At the look in her eyes, he stopped. He'd been sounding so enthusiastic, but she just couldn't join in.

"What's wrong?" he asked.

"Everything. I can't join the paper. Sometimes I feel as if I don't belong anywhere in the world. Here at school, on our ranch, nowhere. I'm completely different. I'm half Romany . . ."

"First of all, what does being half Romany have to do with joining the paper?"

"Nothing specifically; I just feel like an outcast," she said, struggling to explain what she felt inside.

"There are other Rom here at school," Laurent said.

"Yes, but they're all-Romany. Not mixed. My mother's people don't want me, and my father's live in America. Gypsy kids don't want anything to do with me—I can feel it, Laurent," she said when she caught the look of doubt in his eyes. "No one wants me."

"Sari, May twenty-fourth is coming—the Gypsies' Pilgrimage in Stes.-Maries. Every year you're invited to march in the parade, to carry the school banner or sing in the chorus, and every single year you refuse. *You're* the one who doesn't want anything to do with them!"

"Because of my mother! Everyone knows she just left me—it's shameful. People try to make up for it, like Susannah, but it doesn't work. I'm wrecked."

"Wrecked? You're getting better—you're so much stronger, Sari. You rode Mystère . . ."

"But I don't *want* to ride her again," Sari whispered, feeling despair. "It was just that one time. I thought I could do it. I thought I was going to be okay . . . Until that night with Susannah, when I ruined everything."

"No, you didn't," he said. "Susannah would understand, if you wanted to write to her, talk to her . . ."

"But I don't want that," Sari said, staring down at the desk. Everything was a gray blur. She'd gotten her hopes up last month; life had seemed to be changing. Her father had seemed happier, and as Laurent said, Sari had made strides. Now she felt trapped back inside the same old grainy black-and-white movie. Completely stuck, while everyone around was moving on.

"Okay, fine," he said. "Don't call her, then. Things will get better, Sari."

"I don't know . . ."

"You'll want to hold on to your paper when you get it back," he said. "Because someday you'll look back and want to remember how it was. What it's like to see through your eyes."

Laurent's words ignited something terrible in Sari. She suddenly felt her best friend didn't understand her, didn't get her at all. "What do you mean? Why would I want to remember 'what it's like to see through' my eyes? I already know!"

"I mean, once you start seeing colors again, you'll forget what it was like to see in silver."

"It's *not* silver," she said, her eyes filling with tears. "That was just how it was that night. It's gray, Laurent. Murky, muddy, colorless gray. I'm *colorblind*. I don't have to

remember anything. Why can't you understand that it will never go away? It's how it's
always going to be!"

"Sari, I didn't mean—"

She stood up to run away, but he
grabbed her.

Laurent was tall and toughly built, like
her father, and he held her away, and now
she did start to cry; big shuddering sobs
wracked her body. She had to hold the
sound inside, stifled so hard it hurt, because
her classmates were filling the halls now,
getting ready to board the buses home.
Laurent picked up her books, steered her
outside, reached into his pocket for a folded
handkerchief, handed it to her.

"I'm so sorry, Sari," he said.

"So am I," she said, wiping her eyes.

"You're very distressed, I know."

They began to walk toward the buses.
Her eyes were red and swollen; she could
feel them, puffy and stinging. That morning
she had looked in the mirror, hating herself,
and noticed dark circles beneath her eyes.
Ugly! She hadn't slept well. Not since the
night of the moonlit trail ride. The night of
Tempest. The night she'd seen her father
and Susannah . . .

As she got onto the bus, she paid close attention to all her classmates' faces—just to see if they were staring at her. They all seemed absorbed in their own conversations, except a couple of friends—Genevieve and Josephine—who smiled. Sari tried to smile back.

By the time she sat at the back of the bus, she was shaking all over again. Laurent slid in beside her. His shoulders were wide, and pressed against hers. She felt glad for his presence.

She glanced over, saw him staring down at her. He had medium-dark hair and bright eyes she remembered being hazel. He was handsome, and other girls liked him. Sometimes he rode the bus with Alice, other times with Jeanine. But for some reason, this entire year he almost always sat with Sari.

The way he was watching her felt protective. She looked up at him and wondered what he was thinking. He'd seen it all. He'd heard her screaming five years ago, the night her mother had left.

And the way she'd acted with Susannah. "I'm tired," she said, stifling a yawn.

"You must be," he said.

"What do you mean?" she asked, feeling sensitive, girding up to be teased or criticized.

"Your light was on very late last night," he said. "What were you doing?"

"Work for school," she lied. "Molière . . ."

"Sari," he said, smiling indulgently. "Tell me the truth. Were you looking on Google Earth again?"

She shrugged. That very small twitch of her shoulders was like a toggle, sending blood into her face. Her blush gave it all away.

"For Las Vegas?"

She gazed out the bus window. Despite what she'd said, Laurent knew her so well. He spent enough time at her house to know her habits. More than once he'd caught her zooming in on Las Vegas—the strip, with all the stark lights and casinos, the dancing fountains of the Bellagio. So it seemed easier to nod now—lie again—than tell him the truth.

"Since you know your mother is there, why do you not write her?" he asked. "Care of the *cirque*? Or even of the horse farm. They both have the same name, *n'est-ce pas*? Clair de Lune."

"I don't want to write her," Sari said.

"Then why do you keep looking for her online? She's not there, on your computer screen. I wish I could find her myself. I'd tell her what she's done, who she's left behind."

"She knows," Sari said, holding herself tight.

Laurent was stirred up, and so was she. She partly wanted to tell him the truth, but she couldn't quite do it. It was easier to let him think she'd been searching for her mother. Instead, Sari had aimed Google Earth, the cyber eye-in-the-sky, at an address she'd found on a card in her father's bedside table: the same place he'd hidden that ribbon just two and a half weeks ago.

11 Blue Heron Drive, Black Hall, Connecticut.

The satellite image had shown a small house, surrounded by trees, very near the wide and rippling sea of marsh grass that was the Connecticut River estuary. So, Susannah lived near marshland, just like Sari and her dad.

Zooming back, Sari saw that Connecticut was very near Rhode Island. Her grandparents lived on the farm in Narragansett, and her uncles and cousins lived in Westerly.

They were practically right next door to Susannah. At least, compared to Sari all the way in France.

"So," Laurent was saying. "What new things did you see in Las Vegas?"

"Un désert d'eau," she said without thinking. *"É'tangs, sansouire, et les îles dans le marais."*

"Really?" he asked. "Lagoons, a plane of marsh grass, and salt-marsh islands? In Nevada?"

She looked up, caught by her friend.

"You were looking up Susannah, weren't you?"

"No," she said stubbornly.

"Are you to see her?" Laurent asked, ignoring her denial. "This summer, when you and your father go to Rhode Island to see your grandparents . . . will you drive to the marsh to see Susannah in Connecticut?"

Sari gazed out the window and shook her head. "No," she said. "It's better that she's out of our lives, and we're out of hers."

"Of course, you're right," Laurent said, amusement in his eyes.

"I mean it," Sari said again, just for emphasis.

"I know, Sari. I know."

Sari stared out the school bus window at the trees and houses and marsh. Laurent thought he knew her, but this wasn't like Avignon. It was daylight, so he was seeing blue sky, green grass, colorful houses. And just like every other day for the past five years, Sari wasn't, and never would.

Life on the ranch had always had its own rhythm. Springtime meant foals being born, horses being trained and penned, tourists returning to the Camargue. Grey had always spent the spring repairing the ravages of winter, looking forward to a busy summer both here and in Rhode Island.

The young horses always went a little crazy in spring. They kicked at their stalls, pulled at the bit, tried to escape any chance they got. This year, Grey felt that way, too. His brief time with Susannah had turned him into someone new. He went through the motions of being a good father, taking care of the ranch, but all he wanted to do was be with her.

That wasn't going to happen, so he thought about her all the time instead. He found himself taking long solitary trail rides, taking Django farther and farther into the Parc. When that wasn't far enough, he'd get into the car and drive. Sometimes, if he was in the right mood, he could almost believe she was in the car with him.

She'd been right there, in the seat beside him. They'd driven east, so that's what Grey started doing. The first time, he took the N568 as far as Fos-sur-Mer. The next day, he made it onto the A55. Caught in traffic, he remembered how he and Susannah had gotten stuck in Marseille's morning rush.

One afternoon he told Claude he was taking off. Sari's history teacher had pulled her aside, told her she wanted to submit Sari's essay on Avignon to the school paper. To Grey's surprise, Sari had agreed—not only that, she had reluctantly let Laurent convince her to get involved for the paper's last issue. It would mean working after school, and meant both kids would have a shot at becoming editors next fall. Grey was so proud of her, but almost more than that, he'd been relieved because it meant he'd have more time to himself.

Being alone was his way of being with Susannah. They sent each other emails all the time. Grey checked his computer ten times a day, hoping there'd be something there from her. There usually was, and he'd write right back.

They called each other a few times when Sari was at school, but that was hard. The phone made things worse. To hear her voice and not be able to see her, to listen to the silence between words and wonder what she was thinking . . .

More than anything, Grey loved her letters. They came on fine blue stationery, embossed with a blue heron. She'd write about the marsh near her house, how it reminded her of being with him, how she'd walk through the reeds every morning just hoping he'd appear out of the mist on a white horse.

He'd hold her letters to his face, knowing the paper had been in those beautiful hands of hers, hoping for a breath of her scent. It wasn't enough, but it was all he had. He'd write back, trying to give her hope that someday everything would change, someday life would be different: Sari would grow up, get better. She wouldn't need him this much forever. And when that happened, he and Susannah could be together.

And Susannah would write back as if

she believed him. She sounded so excited about Sari's essay, about the fact she and Laurent were working on the newspaper. "Following in her father's footsteps," Susannah had written. "I can't think of anything better!"

In spite of the closeness Grey felt, reading and writing those letters and emails, his heart felt heavy. He wondered how long Susannah would wait. Years would go by, and even if she didn't fall in love with someone else in the meantime, wouldn't she drift away? His thoughts raced, trying to think of ways to make it all work.

So the afternoon he'd lined up Claude to cover for him, he drove east again. This time he didn't turn around when he got to Marseille. He kept going, along the white limestone ridge, through the pine-scented olive orchard, over the crest of the Calanques, and down the switchback road along the jagged fjord that led to Cap Morgiou.

He parked the Citroën, grabbed his backpack, and scrambled down the steep steps cut into the white cliff. Bright flowers grew out of cracks in the rock; he wished Susannah could see them. The azure bay spread out between the steep headlands, and he stared out at it, reliving each moment of their day together.

Walking into the Caratini dive shop, he felt his heart turn over. He'd stood right here, handing Felix his certificates. Susannah had been with him, excited and happy. A group of young divers stood at the counter, speaking French to a woman Grey didn't recognize. Maybe Felix, Jeanine, and Jean were out on the water, leading a dive . . .

He stood by the wall covered with photos. There must have been fifty, maybe more, all overlapping. Scanning them, he felt his pulse racing. He'd come to town to connect with Susannah. To sit at the café and write her a letter, and tell her he was here. But standing in here, knowing that the picture of her and Ian was hanging somewhere among all the other photos of happy divers, disturbed him. He looked over and over the wall, but he couldn't see it.

"May I help you?" asked the woman behind the counter.

"Uh, no," he said. "Thank you."

"Are you sure?" she asked, smiling. "Would you like to dive?"

"Not this time," he said.

"You've been before?"

"Yes," he said, backing away. "With a friend. We dove on the Cosquer Cave."

"Ah," she said. "One of the most spectacular dives in the world."

Just then the telephone rang, and Grey took the opportunity to leave the shop. He walked along the quay, wondering why he'd come. Being here without Susannah felt so empty. His chest hurt; his heart felt bruised. Taking a seat at the sidewalk café where he'd sat with her, he stared at the water.

The waiter brought him a glass of rosé. He pulled a paper and pen from his backpack, spread it out on the table, started to write.

Dear Susannah, he wrote, *I'm here in Cap Morgiou with you. You're with me everywhere, but this is our place. You showed it to me. It was brand new, just like so many things I experienced with you, and now I feel it's ours forever.*

A shadow fell across the paper, and he glanced up into a familiar face: Jeanine Caratini.

"It is you," she said. "When Amelie said a man had stopped in, speaking of the Cosquer Cave, I thought maybe it could be . . ."

"There must be many people who come here for the cave," he said, gesturing for her to take a seat. "Why would you think it was me?"

"Because Susannah said you would be back."

"Susannah?" he asked, startled and happy just to hear her name. "How would she know? I didn't tell her."

Jeanine was small and slender, with dark red hair and kind blue eyes. She stared at Grey, smiling gently. "When you love someone, you know them. You didn't have to tell her your schedule for her to know you'd be drawn back here."

The words rang in his ears. *Love someone*. He stared up at Jeanine, wanting to ask if Susannah had said she loved him.

Jeanine laughed, reading something in his eyes. "She didn't spell it out, if that's what you're wondering. Her reason for calling said it all."

"Why did she call you?"

"To ask me to take this picture down," she said, reaching into the pocket of her jacket, pulling out the photo of Susannah and Ian. She set it down on the brown paper, beside his glass of wine.

He stared into the picture. There she was, smiling into the camera, her eyes so bright and clear. Ian stood close beside her, arm around her shoulder, looking as if she belonged to him.

"She called the day after she returned home to the States," Jeanine said. "She told me that you both loved it here in Cap Morgiou, that you were certain to return, and that she didn't want you to have to see this picture hanging on our wall. I should have thrown it away, but I'd just stuck it in a folder. Susannah is one of our favorite clients, and I don't have another picture of her."

"Thank you," Grey said, unable to take his eyes off Susannah.

"You sent Monsieur Stewart for quite a swim," Jeanine said, laughter in her voice.

"I got carried away," Grey said. "I probably shouldn't have done that."

"Oh, I'm certain you should have. Susannah wouldn't love you the way she does if she felt you had acted unfairly."

"Excuse me?" Grey asked, stuck on the word "love."

"She was adamant about my taking the picture down," Jeanine said, ignoring his meaning. "She wanted you to know he doesn't matter to her."

"You knew them together?" Grey asked, looking up.

"There was no 'together.' Both my husband and I knew that from the first time we met him. Surely you could tell, just from that one meeting. They are as different as two people can be. She is sweet and kind . . . he . . ." Jeanine shrugged. "Arrogant and very full of his own importance."

"But he thought they had something . . ."

"That doesn't matter," Jeanine said. "It's what Susannah wants that we care about. Right?"

"Right," Grey said.

"Don't worry about Monsieur Stewart," she said. "I doubt very much that he will show his face in this town again."

"He managed to get out of the water okay?"

"Oh, yes. He climbed out at the boat launch ramp," she said.

Then she checked her watch, said she'd better be getting back to the shop; she'd been upstairs, doing paperwork. He thanked her very much, and she shook his hand, said that he hoped to come back and dive again.

"I'd like to," he said.

"That's what Susannah assumed, that you would," Jeanine said. "She told me that you'd had a very profound experience in the cave."

"We certainly did," Grey said. "And I'd like to do it again, but I couldn't without her."

"Then bring her back," Jeanine said, her gaze fiery.

Grey nodded. If only he could, if only it were that easy. He started to hand her back the photo.

"No," she said. "It's yours."

"But you said you don't have another of Susannah . . ."

Jeanine smiled. "As I said: bring her back here. Then we can take a picture of the two of you together." Without waiting for his response, she rose from her seat, and with a last pointed look at him, strode away.

He watched Jeanine walk along the seawall, back to the wharf. The harbor was full of boats, many more than had been here even two weeks ago. The warm weather was here, and so were the tourists. Grey looked down at the photo. He gazed at it for a long time. Susannah had wanted it destroyed, but he couldn't do that.

Instead, he ripped it down the middle. He crumpled up the half showing Ian, and he walked over to the bar to throw it in the garbage. Then he returned to his seat, lifted his glass. He remembered how he and Susannah had drunk to Henri Cosquer. But right now, feeling the warm breeze and looking at her picture, that didn't feel right.

"To you," he said to her picture.

TWENTY-ONE

Susannah tried to return to life in Connecticut, but the best part of her was back in France. She couldn't really do anything about that either, except write letters as often as she could, check email constantly, and think about Grey all the time. She felt more like a college student—young and in love—than one of their professors.

Helen was away, delivering a series of lectures at UCLA; Susannah took the opportunity to write up all the notes she'd taken on the trip: about Sarah, the *Livre du Grand Voyage,* the Cosquer Cave. In a separate journal, she poured her heart out about everything else, the things that would never be found in a scholarly paper: everything about Grey. She went out, saw friends, kept busy, but felt herself far away.

One early evening she went for a walk behind the Renwick Inn, to see the light reflected in the river. By this time of May, the air was warming up, and new leaves were on the trees. The river glistened, golden in the last rays of the setting sun. She stared out at the river, seeing the butterscotch light play on the water's surface. She thought of the Parc, of all the creeks and reeds, of how the landscapes were so similar. They were both fed by the same ocean, but they were so far apart.

She sat on a rustic bench, lost in thoughts of Grey until the waning moon lifted into the sky, through the trees. It glowed, as white as ever, but it looked as if it had been torn in half, tipped on its side.

The breeze picked up . . . a salt wind, blowing inland from Long Island Sound. Susannah felt it ripple through her hair as if it were coming straight from France. She remembered getting Tempest free of the quicksand, the way the moon had looked that night. Moonlight just pouring down . . .

She'd felt it on her skin, just as she felt the breeze now.

The moon that night had seemed to belong to her and Grey. And when she looked up now, seeing it rising higher in the sky, she realized that he had seen the same thing just hours earlier in France. And she knew that it was waning; the moon had been full, and soon it would disappear.

Sitting alone on the bench, she felt the same thing happening to her, Grey, and Sari. They'd had their moment, but it was over . . . disappearing. All she wanted was to hold on to the feelings she'd had in France. But staring up at the moon through the new leaves, she felt everything ebbing away.

In her office the next day, Susannah was surrounded by papers, transcribing notes onto her computer. Lost in work and thought, she barely heard the door open behind her.

"Hello, Susannah," came the low, elegant voice.

Susannah glanced over her shoulder and smiled, so happy to see her mentor, just back from Los Angeles, tall and thin, with her white hair pinned up in a French twist.

"Hello, Helen," she said. "It's good to see you . . ."

"The same to you, Susannah. Why don't you bring everything into my office, so we can catch up?"

Susannah gathered the material she'd brought back from France, and walked down the hall of the anthropology department. It was long and dark, with sunlight slanting in through several open office doors. Susannah entered Helen's office, and took her customary chair opposite the wide oak desk; she'd been sitting there for years, ever since their first interview, when Susannah was just out of grad school.

Helen stood in a corner of the room, waiting for the kettle to finish boiling. Their meetings always included tea and shortbread, and Helen always arranged them herself. Susannah noticed her leaning on the table, favoring her weak leg; she got up and walked over.

"Please let me get the tea today, Helen," she said.

"You know, I think I'll take you up on that,"

Helen said gratefully. "My trip was rather arduous, and I'm a bit tired."

Susannah nodded, noticing her pallor, feeling a ripple of worry. She heard the professor limping back to her desk, and finished making tea. She arranged it just as Helen always did: on a linen-cloth-covered silver tray. The cups and teapot were porcelain; the tea was loose Darjeeling, held in a silver strainer.

"So," Helen said after they were settled. "Tell me about your visit to the Bibliothèque in Arles."

"Yes, of course," Susannah said, removing from the sheaf of papers the sketch she'd made of the cover: the title, the dragon with burning red eyes, and the gold cross blessing it all.

"And page 321? Did you read it?"

"Yes, I did," Susannah said. "I was so struck by the love Saint Martha had for the dragon. It reminded me so much of 'Beauty and the Beast.'"

"It's archetypal," Helen agreed. "I've always believed the legend of Saint Martha was the genesis of that fairy tale."

"I was very moved by the idea of her singing hymns to the dragon," Susannah said, thinking of Sari, of the toy she'd given her. Lost in the thought, she looked away.

"What is it?" Helen asked.

"Oh, nothing," Susannah said, shaking her head. "I just . . . well, I met a family over there. A man and his daughter. I gave Sari a Tarasque toy . . . anyway, never mind. Back to Saint Martha . . ."

"Ah, yes," Helen said after giving Susannah a long look. "Well, as Saint Martha taught us, love is the most effective way of taming our 'enemies.' I learn it repeatedly, yet forget each time I go to war for more funding, slugging it out with boards and directors for foundation grants. Perhaps only a saint is truly capable of such gentleness . . ."

"Perhaps," Susannah said.

"Years ago, while in Tarascon, I focused my research on a work written by Vincent Phillipon in 1521: 'The Legend of the Saintes-Maries.' It was all about Sarah and her miracles. Vincent was abbot of the Franciscan monastery at San Vigilio at Bolzano . . ."

"Italy?" Susannah asked, amazed that Sarah's legend had spread so far by that time, and that it had been taken up by a member of the Catholic Church. "But Sarah isn't a real saint . . ."

"Oh, my dear," Helen said, laughing. "She absolutely is. Just ask her devotees! What you mean is, she hasn't been canonized by the Church. She was a poor girl of such humble beginnings, overshadowed by everyone else in that boat . . . Anyway, Vincent must have been a true visionary. Some archaeologist friends of mine worked on a dig at his monastery; they unearthed gardens and a greenhouse, along with notes by the master gardener—Vincent himself. So of course I had to see for myself, and spent some lovely times there, getting to know the monks. Vincent, one of them told me, was cultivating a variety of lily called 'Sara.' It was black, and named for . . ."

"Sara-la-Kali."

"Yes. Now . . . tell me more about the women you met. From what you say, many of them have actually settled in Stes.-Maries, just to be near her?"

"Yes," Susannah said. "Topaz Avila told me about several, and she took me to her caravan, so I could meet the Sarah Circle."

"How fascinating. I knew that your trip to the Camargue would bear riches! Just to think—getting such an inside look at so secret a society. Do you know, after studying women of Tarascon—which isn't so far away—most of my professional life, I've never once even heard of the Sarah Circle." She gazed across her teacup at Susannah, her eyes bright with admiration.

"Well, your focus has always been on Saint Martha and the dragon," Susannah said, feeling a pang as she thought of Sari.

"You're far too modest, my dear. You've breeched some closely guarded gates. Topaz Avila must have really trusted you, to invite you in."

"We became friendly . . ."

"Avila," Helen said. "That's a Spanish name. As in Saint Teresa of Avila?"

"Possibly. Topaz told me that some of her ancestors were Spanish. She told me about loyalty and allegiance within the group, and how her family was stigmatized by intermarriage. And . . . that seems to be an issue even now, with modern women."

"Examples please, dear. You know I live for the specific."

"Well, the story involves Grey—the father of that young girl I mentioned . . ."

"Sari?"

Susannah nodded, beginning to tell the story of Grey and Maria. She started with academic detachment, telling about his career as a journalist, the gypsiologist, his trip to the Camargue.

But once she got to his marriage to Maria, and the birth of Sari, and Maria's abandonment, the details began spilling out, and her emotions began rising. She told Helen about Grey rescuing her from the bulls in the marsh, and her first meeting with Sari, and the child's long aversion to riding, and how the night Maria left had devastated Sari so completely.

"Such pain for a young girl," Helen murmured.

As Susannah continued talking, she realized how terribly she'd been missing her mother; she'd wanted to tell her all about meeting Grey, and responding so deeply to him and Sari, and wondering what she could do to help them. Helen listened, her eyes grave as she heard about Sari's anguish.

"Sari hasn't seen her mother for five years?" Helen asked.

"No. Not since she was eight."

"Important years," the professor said. "Where is Maria now?"

"In Nevada," Susannah said. "She and Adrien, her trainer, have a stable there. They run a small circus, Clair de Lune."

"Maria remains devoted to horses," Helen said, still holding the cross medallion.

"Instead of her daughter."

Helen shook her head. "You must guard against making such assumptions," she said.

"What do you mean?" Susannah asked, shocked by Helen's statement.

"Society can be cruel to women," she said. "Many cultures force a woman to choose between motherhood and her own dreams. Even here and now, Susannah. Surely you of all people know that. It's a myth, that one can 'have it all.'"

"Plenty of people do," Susannah said stubbornly. "My mother was a teacher—work that she adored, and felt challenged by—and she also had me."

"Your mother was lucky. And you're right—many women choose to do both. Others don't, or can't." She paused. "I, for instance. With all the travel my work entails, the long periods of time I've spent in the field . . ."

Susannah sat still, listening. In spite of their closeness, she and Helen rarely talked about her personal choices.

"I'm not letting Maria off the hook," the professor said. "Sari is not an abstraction. She's a real person, and Maria left her. I'm only suggesting that there may have been powerful forces at work here."

"Internal forces?"

Helen nodded. "And perhaps the influence of a man. Adrien Ferret."

"Matelo," Susannah said. "That's his Gypsy name."

"Well, you'll have to learn the truth," Helen said.

"Excuse me?"

"When you visit the Clair de Lune, you'll have to observe their interactions."

"Visit—what do you mean?"

"I think you should go there . . ."

"Helen, I can't meet Maria!"

The panic in her tone made Helen glance over. She poured the last of the tea into their cups. Susannah's heart was pounding as she waited for her to speak.

"It will be necessary," Helen said, gazing

at Susannah. "For our further study. Now that we've learned about the Sarah Circle, and the extraordinary pull Sara-la-Kali has over her modern-day devotees, we must learn what would cause one of them to run away. Especially from a daughter named for Sarah. What an insult, what dishonor to the saint! You said Sari's middle name . . ."

"Yes, it's Sarah," Susannah said. "But Helen . . ."

"Don't you want to know?" Helen asked, leaning forward. The look in her eyes shocked Susannah with its vehemence. "Don't you want to meet this woman, who walked away from her family, and caused her daughter to live in such agony?"

"I can't be objective," Susannah said, breaking down. "I love . . . Helen, I've come to love them both—Grey and Sari."

She bowed her head, crying quietly. Helen reached over, took her hand. With her eyes closed, in the quiet of the office, Susannah could almost believe her mother was with her, sitting right here, understanding the way her heart was breaking. Silence filled the room.

"You just said you love them, Susannah,"

Helen said finally. "So you must ask your-self: what are you willing to do for them?"

Late the next night, the road was flooded. There'd been an unusually high tide, and as Grey drove south through the marsh, his tires splashed through puddles of salt water. Sitting at the café in Cap Morgiou, trying to figure out a way to Susannah, he'd come up with an idea. He felt driven, as if he had a rocket in his chest.

The diminishing moon spread sallow light across the wet pavement—it was nothing at all like the sharp, bright, ferocious white moonlight he and Susannah had had on their ride. He drove into Stes.-Maries-de-la-Mer, passing through town with barely a glance from people walking along the glassy black harbor. He turned up the wind-ing road that led behind the old church, and followed it a few miles.

When he reached the caravan park, he hesitated for a moment, staring at the sign: **Mas SLK**. Sara-la-Kali. He had a violent re-action to the sight of it; it reminded him of the closed world Maria had come from, and suddenly he thought about turning back.

What made him think he'd get anything from this? But he called up a picture of Susannah, and then one of Sari, and he drove the Citroën in through the gates, over the rutted field toward the circle of caravans.

The *roulottes* were parked in a wide circle. Even in the shadowy dark, he could see their colors: brick, amber, purple, rose. He had been here just once before—again, uninvited. Maria had never once brought him here. Five years ago he'd had to find his way himself—and for the exact same reason.

He wondered whether tonight was a Sarah Circle meeting night. Before he married Maria, she used to attend the group nearly every week. Afterwards, once she'd broken out of the clan by marrying him, she'd stopped going. Sometimes he'd see her standing by the window, looking longingly into the middle distance, and he'd always wonder whether she was seeing the Circle, seeing the faces of her family and friends, seeing a place she was no longer welcome and wishing she'd made a different choice.

Now, pulling into the grassy area where other cars were parked, he noticed someone tall coming toward him. He heard the creaking of doors, saw light pouring out of several being opened around the circle as people looked out. Music drifted across the field—guitars, violins, bells. But after a few moments, they stopped.

"Well, well," said the man's voice. "Are you back to follow up on your research?"

"Hello, Baro," he said. *Baro* meant "big," for the firstborn son. Maria's older cousin . . .

"A man comes to write an article about Romanies, but interviews weren't enough, were they? You had to marry one. Just to see, right? Just to get inside our circle, and have a bird's-eye view."

Baro got in his face. Grey stood his ground. He felt Maria's cousin spoiling for a fight, and he almost wanted to get into it himself. Baro was darkly tanned, his moustache a thick, sharp line above his mouth, his eyes narrow, bright, glowering, as if he'd been nursing hatred these last five years.

"I'm not here to see you," Grey said.

"You're not welcome here at all—no matter who you came to see."

"I'll let *her* tell me that."

"Leave now, and there'll be no trouble."

"There already is trouble, Baro. Now, let me past."

Baro shoved his face into Grey's, and Grey felt the heat pouring off him. Grey had plenty of heat of his own. This guy had never sought Sari out—not once. None of them had. She was their blood, and they'd forgotten her.

"Stop that! Both of you!" Zin-Zin stood in the doorway, on the top step of her caravan, thumping her cane.

"She's right," Topaz said, hurrying over. "Don't be idiots, acting like little boys. Baro, enough."

"I'm not turning my back on this one," he said. "Don't ask me to, Topaz."

"Why are you here?" Topaz asked, eyes nearly as fierce as Baro's, but with a tone of beseeching in her voice.

"I want to talk to Zin-Zin," Grey said.

"She won't see you," Baro snapped.

Topaz gave him a look. Then, taking Grey's arm, she turned him around, walking him away from Baro. Grey felt his heart beating overtime, pumped for a fight. Just because Topaz was leading him out of Baro's range didn't mean the clash was over. Grey knew it was just beginning.

"Wait here," Topaz said, hands on both of Grey's shoulders. She looked him long and hard in the eyes, exacting a silent promise that he wouldn't get into anything with Baro.

He nodded, and she ran up the steps to Zin-Zin. Others had started to gather—either in the windows of their *roulottes* or in the open area in the center of the circle. He glanced up, saw Rosalie hurrying over from her caravan.

She gave him a quick, harsh glance, ran up the steps to join in the talk. Grey watched the three women consulting, Rosalie obviously disagreeing, shaking her head the hardest. Zin-Zin disappeared inside her caravan, Rosalie following her. Grey's heart fell, but he knew he wasn't going home until he'd talked to the old woman. He'd force his way in if he had to.

But just then Topaz returned.

"She'll see you now," she said.

"Alone?"

"That's not possible," Topaz said.

Grey nodded. He didn't care if he had an audience or not. He climbed the steps after Topaz, walked into Zin-Zin's dusky blue caravan. Nearly every wall bore a painted swag, just like the one in his own kitchen.

Draped and swooping lengths of flowers woven into silver-green laurel leaves. His stomach churned, seeing the artwork, reminded of the symbol that united the women of Maria's clan.

"Come," Zin-Zin said. "Sit." She was stationed in a deep armchair, and she gestured at a straight-backed kitchen chair that Rosalie had drawn up alongside. The lights were dim, each lampshade covered by a rose silk scarf. Several candles burned around a makeshift shrine, a carved statue of Sarah in the center. He turned his back on the shrine.

Pulse racing out of control, he sat in the chair.

Zin-Zin sat back, regarding him with wide brown eyes. She wore her gray hair in a bun. Her face was deeply lined, reflecting a lifetime's worth of joy and pain. Grey had been so charged up outside, but right now he relaxed under her steady gaze.

"Hello, Grey," she said.

"Zin-Zin," he said, bowing his head.

"Why have you come?"

"It's about Maria."

She shrugged. "You know that I have no power over my niece. She makes her own decisions. It's been five years now since she left. Can you not make peace with her choice?"

"She has a daughter," Grey said. "Who is suffering."

"Zinnia Sarah," she said.

"Yes, Sari," Grey said.

"She misses her mother," Zin-Zin said.

"Every day."

Zin-Zin took in the words, closed her eyes. His stomach tensed, anticipating any number of reactions that might cause him to blow up. If the old woman defended Maria—or if Rosalie or Topaz did—he'd lose it.

"What would you have me do?" Zin-Zin asked.

"What do you want from Zin-Zin? You already know where Maria is," Rosalie interjected.

"I know. Nevada. I know all about Clair de Lune. I've written her letters, even tried to call. She's never responded."

"Because she's—" Rosalie started to say hotly, but Zin-Zin held up one hand.

"I know you don't understand her," Zin-Zin said. "In some ways, none of us do. She defied all of us when she married you.

Made her choice, told us we had no say in it. It angered me so terribly . . . She lived on your ranch, but it might as well have been India—she was lost to us. All of us except Rosalie . . . and Matelo."

"I could never hold anything against Maria," Rosalie said.

Grey looked at Maria's old friend, her eyes tearing up. He'd been very angry at Rosalie over the years, for many things, but he knew that her loyalty to Maria had kept her close to Sari. She'd helped out at the house and ranch, stayed even after Sari's rage at Maria had first boiled over. He saw the tension in her face, and knew that Maria's leaving had been devastating to her, too. His gaze swept back to Zin-Zin.

"Do you ever think that you're the reason she can't come back? Your 'curse'?"

"That was anger; she knows I'd never truly curse her."

"You raised her—don't you think she'd believe it was real?"

Zin-Zin just stared at him, silent.

Grey stared back at her, felt the pity in the other women's gazes. He reddened, knowing they thought he was trying to justify Maria's staying away for any reason other than the fact she couldn't stand him, and didn't want to see Sari.

"We make allowances for Maria," Topaz said gently, "because of how talented she is. Her riding is almost like flight, so we don't bind her with the same earthly rules as everyone else. Please, Grey—for your own sake, let it go. Move on with your life."

Move on with his life: that's all he wanted to do. He wanted to be with Susannah; that's what coming here was about. He knew Topaz knew that: he'd never forget that she'd called to let him know when Susannah would be at the library. But right now she was missing the point.

"Even if I could go along with that," Grey said, "her daughter can't."

"What do you mean?" Zin-Zin asked.

"Sari is hurting. She's angry. Her injuries have healed, but emotionally she's damaged. You know about her colorblindness; it hasn't gone away. Her feelings about Maria are coming out all over the place . . ."

"This is about that woman, isn't it?" Rosalie retorted. "You're upset because Sari won't accept your seeing someone."

"Rosalie, stop!" Topaz said.

"I just—" Rosalie began.

"Yes!" Grey exploded. "It's about Susannah. She's an incredible person. She was so good to Sari, and Sari responded to her. Do you know how important that is to me?"

"What would you have me do?" Zin-Zin interrupted.

"I'd like you to intervene somehow. I know that Maria respects you. Even during the years when she was separated from all of you, and even after you cut her off for marrying me, she never stopped hoping for your love, Zin-Zin. She named our daughter for you."

"I was honored by that," Zin-Zin said, voice shaking. "Maria's own mother died when she was just a baby. I raised her as if she were my own."

"That's why I'm begging you now," Grey said. "Please contact her and tell her that Sari needs to connect with her."

"And what do you think that will do?" Zin-Zin asked softly.

Grey stared into her eyes. Rosalie hadn't been all wrong; his motives very much concerned Susannah. He had the feeling that Sari needed a mother so badly, and Susannah could be that for her. The two of them had connected just as he and Susannah had—he had seen it. Every night Sari slept with that toy dragon. And although she hadn't ridden again, she'd started grooming Mystère, and walking her on a lead line. Grey knew such things were a connection to Susannah. But there was no way Sari could let herself completely trust another woman until she found a way to let go of Maria, and what she'd done to her.

"She needs to say goodbye," he said. "Sari wasn't given that chance five years ago. She's trapped in that moment when Maria drove away . . ."

"Time heals," Rosalie said.

But Grey didn't look at Rosalie. He held Zin-Zin's gaze, and saw that she understood what he was saying. Perhaps she was old enough to know that there were some things that didn't heal on their own, not without outside help.

"Not for a thirteen-year-old," he said, staring at Zin-Zin, "who still remembers that night when her mother left her lying in the road."

"Maria didn't see the accident!" Rosalie exclaimed. "That's what I keep telling Sari! Maria wouldn't have left her there if she'd known . . ."

"Sari can't hear it from you," Zin-Zin said, looking over her shoulder, patting Rosalie's hand on the back of her chair. "There's only one person who can get through . . ."

"So, will you help?"

Very slowly, resolutely, Zin-Zin nodded. "I'll do the best I can. Know that I can't promise anything."

"Are you in touch with her regularly?" Grey asked. "Do you speak to Maria? Does she ever come back here?"

But those questions were beyond what was permitted. Zin-Zin just shook her head to all in a way that let Grey know he'd crossed the line. He'd always been an outsider here. The Manouche stuck with their own; Baro and many others still vilified him for stealing Maria away in the first place.

Standing, he bowed his head in thanks and respect. "Thank you for seeing me," he said.

"Grey," Zin-Zin said. "It's an unusual name to give a little boy," she said.

"It was my mother's maiden name," he said.

"In our culture, it means 'wisdom.' For someone to be gray, to have lived life and experienced many things. I shall pray for your daughter. And also for your continued wisdom."

"Thank you," he said. "I appreciate that. Goodbye, Zin-Zin."

Then Rosalie opened the door, indicating that it was time to leave. He said goodbye to her and Topaz, walked past Baro and a group of other men standing at the foot of the stairs.

As he crossed the dark field, he looked up. There was a yellow smudge in the western sky, the last remnants of the once-full moon.

TWENTY-TWO

Laurent had been right; Sari couldn't stay off Google Earth. While her father worked in the barn—later and later each night, it seemed, as if he didn't want to spend time with her at all—Sari sat at her computer, soaring across the Atlantic.

She had three favorite locations to visit online: addresses in Narragansett, Rhode Island, where her grandparents resided, and Black Hall, Connecticut, where Susannah lived. She enjoyed getting the satellite image as clear as possible, so that she could see the roof of Susannah's small house, the trees in her yard, the car in her driveway.

The third address was just outside Las Vegas, Nevada. The satellite picture showed garish structures, a grid of streets and highway, and then nothing but desert spreading out as far as she could see. Sari knew how hot and parched the desert sands were, and that's how she felt whenever she looked at Las Vegas.

Dry, hot, as furious as the sirocco that blew through there. How could her mother raise horses in such a place? After riding here, in the beautiful green marshlands of the Camargue, how could she have flown to such a terrible, arid land? Sari's eyes sometimes filled with tears, thinking of her mother in such a place.

Every time Sari looked at Las Vegas, she'd find herself shaking so hard, she could barely see the screen. To be able to see her mother's house, right there on the computer, and not be able to reach her. So she'd click back to New England, the two southernmost states, Rhode Island and Connecticut, where her grandparents and Susannah lived almost side by side.

She wondered what Susannah was doing. Did she have any idea that Sari was spying from the sky? Possibly she would be upset to know. After the terrible way Sari had treated her at the end, Susannah probably wanted to forget she even existed. Sari wouldn't blame her. She'd thought about sending Susannah her essay about Avignon: it had been printed in the school paper.

Sari looked up, over her computer screen, out the window. The horse barn and ring were between her house and Laurent's. Summer was coming quickly. Soon she'd be traveling to the States with her father. She thought of how much Laurent did for her; if he hadn't encouraged her, she wouldn't have allowed her essay to be published.

Maybe her father would let her invite Laurent to take the trip with them. Her grandparents had such a big old farmhouse; her father and his brothers had grown up there, so there were plenty of bedrooms. They could have so much fun, surfing at the beach, riding the family's horses, maybe even visiting Susannah.

Thinking about everything, Sari just stared out the window . . . Laurent and her father were in the paddock, her father holding Tempest at the end of a longe line. She heard him talking to the feisty horse in a low voice.

Her stomach clenched, remembering that night when Tempest had gotten caught in the mud. If only Sari could do that night over again; if only she could make everything right with Susannah. But that only made her upset; she had messed it all up.

Turning away from the window, she saw her computer screen glowing. Down in the lower left corner was the icon for Las Vegas. She had minimized it. Just seeing the name gave her a start. It was like the code for a dragon, or a demon: the bad things that haunted her dreams, and, she was sure, haunted her father's.

Only her father probably dreamed in vivid color, while for Sari even the world of dreams was black and white.

Grey stood in the ring, letting the young horse run around him in circles. Tempest was stocky and muscular, and he seemed full of primal power. That night in the swamp had both broken and energized the colt, and these last few training sessions he'd seemed eager to please Grey.

Laurent helped out. Grey noticed how the boy kept looking up at Sari's window. The kids were nearly inseparable, and Grey was happy his daughter had such a good friend.

Grey forced himself to concentrate on training Tempest, because otherwise he'd go crazy missing Susannah. The colt cantered around the ring at a good, steady pace. Grey tried to stay focused on discipline, on keeping the longe line taut but not tight. The horse's hooves pounded the soft earth in gentle rhythm; Grey listened, and observed, still alert for any sign he'd been injured in the marsh. But just then, Laurent waved up at Sari's window, and Grey looked up. She waved, and his heart caught.

When she was little, and would see him exercising one of the horses, she'd come running out to watch. She'd been irrepressible, his Sari. Maria had already started fading away. She'd finish dinner, and say she had to go to town, meet Rosalie—the only one of her old friends who still welcomed her.

Looking back, Grey had realized that Maria had been meeting Adrien in the horse ring out by the caravans. He'd probably even known at the time—but he'd blocked the knowledge out, thrown himself into working with their horses, and entertaining Sari, trying to deny their family's reality.

"Papa," Sari would say, running out of the house in her nightgown, "let me help!"

"You should be in bed, asleep," he'd chide, but not very convincingly.

"I'm not tired," she'd say.

So he'd let her sit on the top rail of the fence, one arm clinging to his neck as he stood beside her, and they'd watch whichever young horse he was working with at that time. His own mind would be racing—thinking of Maria, wondering what he could do to make her happier, trying to figure out a way to help her.

"Where's Mama?" Sari would inevitably ask.

"With Rosalie," Grey would reply.

"But it's late," Sari would say.

"Yes, honey," he'd say. "But they have important things to discuss."

"Like what?"

"Secrets," he said. "They tell each other secrets."

"About what?"

"White horses," he'd always say.

"Secrets about white horses?" she'd ask.
"Oh, yes."

Sari would clutch his neck, staring at the white horse in their ring. She'd grown up here in the Camargue, knew the horses' mystical origins, running wild through the marsh and along the beach.

"She should stay here," Sari would whisper. "We have white horses here . . ."

"But Rosalie is in Stes.-Maries," Grey would say, making excuses for her. Even after he'd started to realize Maria wasn't sitting in a café with Rosalie—after he'd started noticing the smell of horse, and the bits of hay stuck in her dark hair, and the fact she always left the house wearing makeup and her brightest silk shirts—he'd cover for her with Sari.

Maria had brought home a saddle made of black leather, decorated with silver scallop shells, purposely tarnished to resemble the black coquilles St. Jacques found along the rocky strand on the Gulf of Lions. She had had it made for herself, she'd told Grey. But he'd known that was a lie, and that it had been a gift from Matelo.

And she'd been in such a hurry to leave with her lover, she'd left the saddle behind;

it still hung on a peg in the tack room, gathering dust.

Back before she left, on nights after she'd been meeting Matelo, Maria would drive in, park the car, sit in the dark with her cigarette glowing for a few moments. That time was the worst for Grey, he'd feel how much she didn't want to see him. He told himself that's all it was—she was tired of him, their marriage; he'd never let himself think she was also burdened by Sari.

"Mama!" Sari would call. Even then Maria wouldn't hurry. She'd take her time, getting herself together. And then she'd walk over to the ring.

"What are you doing up so late?" she'd scold as Sari threw herself into her arms. "What can your father possibly be thinking?"

"She wanted to see her mother," Grey invariably replied.

"It's time for bed," Maria would say.

"She's waited for you all this time."

"Yes, Mama," Sari would say, arms around Maria's neck. "Tell me secrets about white horses! Tell me!"

"Secrets about white horses?"

"Yes, I want to know!"

Maria had laughed. "Those aren't half as interesting as the horses' own secrets. You have to learn to let the horses tell you their secrets themselves."

"Horses don't talk!"

"They do, Zinnia Sarah. To people who listen to them."

"How do they do that?"

Maria's laugh held hidden sadness. Her wide almond eyes showed secret sorrow and longing. Her long dark hair flowed down her back; it sparkled with bits of bright straw. She'd been lying with Matelo, and couldn't even be bothered to clean herself up. Even before he'd let himself realize the truth, Grey would be seething inside. His body had known what his mind couldn't yet recognize.

"They do it all the time," Maria had said to Sari. "You just have to train yourself to tune in, and think like a horse."

"Train myself?" Sari had laughed, her voice spilling like water. "That's funny! Papa, you train horses, not people, right?"

"To be truly connected to the horse," Maria had said, still holding Sari, "the only training necessary is of yourself. You must listen, Sari. Let your instincts come out, and you'll hear all the secrets in the world."

"I want to," Sari had said.

And then, Grey remembered—he could see it as if it were happening right now: Maria had walked into the stable, come out leading Mystère. She had jumped up without a mounting block, without any help from Grey. And she'd pulled Sari up in front of her—Sari flying onto the horse as if she had just sprouted wings.

Grey had stood aside, watching the two dark-haired beauties, mother and daughter, ride Mystère bareback in the night. Sari had clung to the flowing white mane, her head bent as if to listen to the horse's secrets, seemingly oblivious to her mother behind her—Maria no longer sitting, but rising up on both feet, reaching up toward the night sky, graceful arms outstretched, slowly raising one leg, balancing on the toes of one pointed foot.

Tempest cantered around and around now; Grey closed his eyes and went back in time. Listening to the horse encircle him, seeing his daughter listen for horse secrets, seeing his wife stand tall on horseback, reaching for the stars, for anything that might take her away, help her escape.

From both of them: Grey and Sari.

That was the part that killed him most. Literally killed him. He loved Susannah, but he wondered what she saw in someone like him. Until she'd come, he'd felt dead inside. One legend of the Tarasque, the dragon who lived in the Rhône, was that it devoured its victims from the inside out. Grey had felt that that had happened to him. But not by some evil dragon: by the woman he'd loved. Maria had taken his guts and spirit. If she'd just left him, maybe he could have survived. But she'd left Sari, too, left her broken and blocked to the beauty all around them.

He found himself thinking back to when he'd first met Maria. He had come down here to the Camargue a brash, cocky journalist, out to file the definitive story on Gypsy women. Guys at the brasserie in Paris had teased him, told him he'd have to sleep with a Gypsy to really write the whole thing.

He'd had that in the back of his mind. He wasn't averse to the idea. He was a young jerk, a guy who'd moved to Europe to become a hotshot. He hadn't had any sisters—and certainly not yet a daughter—so he'd traveled south with certain ideas about hot sex with a beautiful Gypsy.

He'd met Maria right away, ironically at Adrien Ferret's family's horse stable; even then, Maria had been a star. While many of the other local women worked at the market, making and selling crafts, or tending to Sarah's chapel, Maria Loisy had been born to ride. Grey's first sight of her had been on the back of a white horse. She'd been wearing a short silver dress—setting off her gorgeous, strong brown legs, and just about finishing Grey off then and there.

Grey had asked permission to interview her. While Monsieur Ferret—Adrien's father—had said absolutely not, Maria had defied him and said yes. She'd climbed into Grey's car—the red Alfa Romeo he'd driven back then—and decided Stes.-Maries would be too filled with prying eyes.

They'd gone to Arles. He'd taken her to a café by the Arènes, he'd put his tape recorder on the table, and she'd started talking. Her voice was so sexy and raspy, but also, somehow, so vulnerable: she was the best rider in all the Manouche, but she'd led a completely sheltered life.

As they talked, and the hours passed, she'd flowered with confidence and trust under his rapt gaze. She told him that her parents had died in a fire when she was just a little girl; she'd had to depend on the kindness of others. But the deaths had left her feeling alone—as if she'd always be alone, no matter who else was around. She knew she had to make everyone proud of her—there were circuses in Paris, Brussels, Vienna, and she had ridden in them all, from the time she was twelve years old. And at night she would crawl into her bed and know she was all alone. It was the emptiest feeling in the world, as if she were flying through space, past the stars, with no one to hold or catch her.

At the time Grey met her, he was thirty-one and she was twenty-two. She hadn't ever fallen in love before; she knew it was expected that she marry Matelo—Adrien Ferret, son of her trainer. His nickname meant "Sailor," and that was because he rode a horse as if he were sailing the sea . . . with great beauty, grace, and majesty . . . as mystical as the boat that had carried the three Marys across the Gulf of Lions—surely Grey knew that story?

"But do you love him?" Grey had asked, focusing only on the fact she was promised to someone else.

She had shrugged, beautiful bare brown shoulders rippling under the fine silver straps of her tight dress. "How do I know?" she asked. "I have no time for love . . . only riding."

"But you're a beautiful young woman," he'd said.

"Beautiful?" she'd asked, blushing.

Hadn't anyone ever told her she was beautiful before? Was everyone in her clan too focused on her skill as a horsewoman, her potential to make money as a circus rider, to let her just be herself, figure out her feelings?

"Yes, Maria," he'd said. "So beautiful."

"I don't think of myself that way," she'd said, eyes darkly luminous, staring into his, locking in.

"How can you not?" he'd asked. "From the moment I saw you on that horse, you were the most . . ."

"You're mistaking me and the horse—*that's* beauty," she'd said. "My wonderful wild white horse . . ."

"Oh, Maria," he'd said. "You just have no idea, do you?"

"Everything I do is by the grace of Sara-la-Kali. My saint; she has blessed me with many gifts. I am nothing on my own."

"But you are, Maria. You're like no one else in the world."

She'd laughed shyly. Her eyes gleaming, hungry for his praise.

He'd known then—he wanted to take her away. He'd forgotten all about his friends at the brasserie—what did they know, anyway? He'd looked into her ebony eyes, and wanted only to be with her. He wanted to love her, so she'd know she was incredible on her own, without a horse under her, and without the hopes and dreams of her whole clan on her shoulders.

The rest was history. They'd gone to Paris; she'd cried with homesickness for horses and the marsh, so Grey had sold his Alfa, cashed in the bonds he'd inherited from his grandmother on Block Island, and bought Maria a ranch in the Camargue.

The fact that it was ramshackle, run-down, and disreputable didn't really matter. It came with five horses—including Django. Grey hired a couple to run the place: his friend Claude—whom he'd met years back, bellied up to the bar near the bullfight arena in Nîmes, when Grey was there on assignment—and his wife, Anne.

Maria got pregnant with Sari. Grey worried, because she seemed quiet, distant. It soon became obvious she was withering without her clan. As the months passed, her depression turned to anger. "I've gone against nature!" she'd screamed at Grey one terrible night just before Sari was born. "I've sinned against my family. Zin-Zin was right, I swear. I've brought shame on myself and my baby. Sarah will punish me."

"What kind of saint would punish you for who you love?" he'd asked.

"I don't love you," she'd said. "You took me away from everything I knew, everyone who knew me. Now it's all gone! And all because of you and this!" she'd tapped her big belly.

"This? You mean our *child*?"

"You've taken everything from me!" she'd screamed at him, pounding herself with closed fists.

Grey had grabbed her hands, afraid she'd hurt the baby with her violence. Those days had been nightmarish in the extreme—the way Maria would weep all the time, the way she'd go riding even late in her pregnancy. Sometimes Grey thought she purposely wanted to fall off.

The baby was born at home; she'd refused to go to the clinic in Stes.-Maries for medical care, so with Anne's help, Grey had arranged for a midwife from Arles. Maria had threatened to not feed the baby, but the minute she saw Sari, that changed: she looked into her daughter's eyes, and for the first time in months, Grey saw love in his wife's face.

Even now, holding the longe line as Tempest cooled down, he had to admit that she'd loved their child. He swore she did, even to the end. Her reasons for leaving had been about herself—not Sari. She'd named their daughter for the oldest, wisest woman in the Manouche, and for Sara-la-Kali herself. Even so, no one but Rosalie had come to see the baby. That rejection had nearly destroyed what was left of Maria's self-esteem, and turned her even more bitter.

When she and Matelo—Adrien—ran away, Grey knew that it was because she'd felt she had no real choices left to her. She couldn't live with Grey, and she couldn't return to Stes.-Maries; and Adrien didn't want anything to do with her child by another man.

Grey held the line while Tempest slowed to a walk; he thought about Susannah, wondered where she was tonight. He missed her with everything he had, but he imagined her in a peaceful place, among friends and people who loved her, far from him and the terrible, unsolvable turmoil of his life.

"Papa!" Sari called now, out the open window of her room.

"What, Sari?"

"It's late! Aren't you coming in?"

"In a few minutes. As soon as I get Tempest into his stall."

"You need sleep," she scolded. "Make him stop for the night, Laurent."

"I will," Laurent called back.

Grey chuckled despite his dark mood. The kids were ganging up on him. Walking Tempest into the barn, he stopped by Mystère's stall. He stared at her, remembering how he'd bought her for Maria and Sari. Then, a more recent memory arose: of grabbing Susannah's hand, hauling her up onto Mystère's back, feeling her arms around him. That first meeting had been as sudden and passionate, or more so, as his and Maria's. But he and Susannah had connected at a deeper level—the core place that made them who they were.

And everything that followed had felt completely real—and right. He stood in the cool, dark barn, missing this quiet, steady woman who seemed to love him and his troubled daughter without conditions or reservations. He wanted her back, he wanted her here with him right now. The feeling nearly knocked him over.

Several nights after their last meeting, Helen Oakes gazed across the table at Susannah. She had sensed a slight distance between them, ever since she had proposed that the younger woman travel to Nevada. But she cared deeply about Susannah, and she had a secret promise to keep, and she was determined to forge ahead. She had insisted on this dinner.

"Isn't this lovely, that you were able to join me tonight?" she asked, her tone formal, although inside she felt anything but. Her heart was racing. The respect and admira-

tion she felt for her protégée was mutual—
she knew Susannah returned it tenfold.
But like Helen herself, Susannah was also
extremely circumspect—guarded even—
about her private life, and Helen knew she
had to be careful to not drive her away by
pushing too hard, and with what she had
decided to reveal.

"I'm always glad to have dinner with you,"
Susannah said.

"This house has been my home base forever," Helen said, looking around. Her gaze
took in the dark mahogany furniture that
had been her parents', the oil paintings
she'd bought in Provence over the years,
the French country sideboard she'd acquired on a study trip to Tarascon, the richly
woven rugs she'd purchased on meditation
and research trips to northern India. "If
you're going to make a life in cultural anthropology, and plan to travel a great deal,
it's important that you have a home you
love—and that loves you back."

Susannah nodded, sipping mineral water.
Perhaps she was wondering when Helen
would get to the point; she'd certainly been
a guest here several times over the years.
This was hardly the first time. Helen's heart

thumped, but she held back. It wasn't yet time . . .

They dined on Provençal specialties: *soupe aux legumes,* duck with olives, and for dessert, warm apricot soufflé. They moved from the dining room into the salon, a long room with a lovely view of the mouth of the Thames River. With the days getting longer, the sun was just getting ready to set, and the two women sat by the window overlooking Ledge Light, drinking an after-dinner marc.

"Have you given any more thought to going to Nevada?" Helen asked.

"I've thought of pretty much nothing else," Susannah said.

"And have you made plans?" Helen said.

Susannah shook her head.

"Think of what you might learn from Maria," Helen said. "And how it could further our understanding of the Sarah Circle."

Susannah gave her a long look. "I think you know me well enough," she said, "to know that if I went, it wouldn't be about research."

"Even research isn't always, only, about research . . ."

"What do you mean?"

"Sometimes it's more about life . . . you already know that. It's about the way we relate very personally to our material," Helen said slowly.

"We study what matters to us," Susannah said.

"Yes," Helen said. "We're drawn to subject matter because it speaks to us, touches us . . ."

"Like you and Saint Martha . . ."

"Yes. Hers is a great love story."

Helen saw Susannah's eyes flicker at the word "love." Margaret had been her daughter's greatest supporter; Helen wished she could be here now, to see Susannah's strength and intelligence. She wished she could see how deeply Susannah had fallen in love.

"You know I was married," Helen said.

"Yes," Susannah said.

"Twice, as a matter of fact. One marriage to a man I loved deeply, but who left me for someone else. The second to a man I'd met at a symposium: handsome, brilliant, and cruel. Not unlike your Ian. Neither marriage lasted longer than five years."

"I'm sorry . . ."

"Please don't be."

"Did you ever find love again?" Susannah asked.

Helen shook her head. "I threw myself ever more deeply into my studies," she said. "But I began to focus on love as a subject. Particularly, as you know, Saint Martha and the Tarasque."

"You really think they loved each other?"

"Very much so," Helen answered.

"Metaphorically?" Susannah asked.

"Why not literally?" Helen asked, smiling. "At least on an emotional level . . . just like . . ." She paused. "I may have mentioned to you that when I traveled to that monastery in Italy, to visit the garden of black lilies—devoted to Sarah—I met a monk. We became close friends. I still remember his kindness, feel his spirit."

"Is he . . ."

"He died," Helen said, feeling her heart skip just to say the words.

"I'm sorry," Susannah said.

"We didn't even speak the same language. But our hearts spoke. We were good friends—I often think back to the first trip I took to San Vigilio—his monastery. I'd been very tied up with work, and almost hadn't gone. There were so many good reasons not to. Work deadlines, and classes to teach, and papers to grade. But something pulled me there—I had to see those black lilies . . ."

"And you went . . ."

"I had to—I can't even tell you why. A desire deeper than words. And my journey took me to a place where I met the best friend I've ever had."

Helen leaned forward, took Susannah's hand. She stared into her eyes, wanting to make this point more than she'd ever wanted to tell anything to anyone else in this world, living or dead. "Choose wisely, my dear friend," she said. "Right now."

"What do you mean?"

"I mean that you can either stay and do nothing—work in your cubicle, rise in the anthropology department at Connecticut College, watch your wonderful adventure in the Camargue fade into memory. Or . . ."

Susannah stared, nodded, as if she already knew.

"You can fight for what you love."

"Grey and Sari?"

"Yes. Grey and Sari. Go to Clair de Lune, and help Maria understand what needs to be done, so that all of you can move forward in your lives. Not just you and Grey and Sari—Maria, too. You will be doing her a great kindness."

Susannah took another sip of her drink. The sun had finally gone down, and Long Island Sound and the mouth of the Thames River were a sheet of black glass. Ferries shone their yellow lights on the water, and the beam of Ledge Light swept across the rocks. Helen Oakes savored a long, hot sip of liquor, waiting for Susannah to ask the last question.

And of course she did: Susannah was as bright a protégée as any college professor could ever hope to have.

"There's something I've been wondering," Susannah said.

"Go ahead."

"We both have such old connections to Sarah. You through your research about Martha and the monastery with the black lilies . . . and your monk. Me through my mother and her prayer at the church in Stes.-Maries. Don't you ever think about what a coincidence it is, that I wound up working with you?"

"Do you really think it's a coincidence, Susannah?"

"How else . . . ?"

"Think back," Helen said. "You'd just finished grad school at Yale, a star in your class. You could have worked at any anthropology department in the country. Stanford, Harvard, Chicago, Michigan, Yale itself—any of the top programs. Ian Stewart was pressuring you to move to California. Yet you chose my department. Why?"

"My mother suggested I apply at Connecticut College," Susannah said. Suddenly her eyes grew wide, and filled with tears. "I miss her."

"I know you do. Tell me . . . why do you think she wanted you to come to work with me?"

Susannah spoke, her voice cracking. "I've always thought it was because she hoped I'd stay close to home. But Yale was close to Black Hall as well . . . and she was so positive about my sending my application to you."

"Your mother came to me right after you were born," Helen said, holding Susannah's hand. "She'd seen a story about me in the *New London Day*—a review of my book, and an account of my research on Martha.

She thought I'd like to know about the miracle in your family."

"My birth . . ." Susannah whispered.

"I held you when you were a baby," Helen said, remembering the radiance in Margaret Connolly's eyes, the glow around the infant herself. "And I knew your mother was right—she had been blessed by Sara-la-Kali. As I've been blessed all these years to work with you."

"Oh, Helen," Susannah said, breaking down and burying her face in her hands.

"I was with her when she died, you see," Helen said softly.

Susannah raised her head, gazing through tears.

"She called you?"

Helen nodded.

"So you were there," Susannah whispered. "She didn't die alone . . ."

"She didn't die alone," Helen said, taking her hand, her throat catching as she remembered those last hours.

"Why didn't you tell me?" Susannah asked.

"Because she asked me not to. She was afraid you would be hurt, that she didn't want you to be there. She loved you so much; she knew she couldn't bear to leave if you were right there with her. Do you understand?"

"Yes," Susannah said. "It's how she always was toward me . . ."

"She made me promise that you would visit Sarah. To thank her for the life you had together . . ."

"Is this why you encouraged me to go to the Camargue after her death? The reason why you asked me to visit the library in Arles?"

"Of course, my dear," Helen said, welling up as she saw the truth dawning in Susannah's eyes. "I promised your mother I'd look after you when she was gone. I swore to her that I'd make sure you made that visit . . . and that I'd do my best to make sure your life was full of love."

TWENTY-THREE

Susannah knew she had to go. By the time she booked her flight, she realized she didn't really have a choice. Talking to Helen about her own mother made her more determined them ever to do what she could for Sari. After all she had learned in France, she wasn't at all sure or even very hopeful about what the visit to Maria would accomplish, but she had to try, for Grey and Sari.

The flight to Las Vegas was smooth, blue sky all the way. Susannah started a letter to Grey, replying to the one he'd written from Cap Morgiou. At the end, he'd mentioned

Sarah's feast day coming up at the end of May.

Come back for it, he'd written. *The procession is really something to see. Laurent has been trying to get Sari to go this year. They're on the school paper now, and he thinks it would make good material for them to cover. The truth is, I think he hopes Sari will connect with her heritage a little more. He thinks it will help to heal her. As for me, I just want to see you. Please come back.*

Susannah wrote that she wanted to be there more than anything. She started to tell him about her plan to see Maria—if all went well, maybe she could get Maria to reach out to Sari, maybe that would speed the healing along. But everything was too uncertain, so she just folded the paper, stuffed it into a book she'd bought in Stes.-Maries, with Sarah on the cover.

The sight of Sarah calmed Susannah's nerves, gave her strength, and she slid the book and letter into her briefcase. When she got to the airport, she went through the motions of renting a car, getting printed directions, and driving onto the highway toward the Clair de Lune Ranch.

The landscape was so different from the

salty blues and greens of home. As she drove off I-15 and into the Clark Mountains, she climbed into high desert. Jagged sandstone ridges threw shadows, turning the rocks red, brown, umber, and black. As unfamiliar as the terrain was for her, from coastal Connecticut, she figured it had to be the same for Maria, from the watery marshlands of the Camargue.

She passed Joshua trees, saw eagles circling overhead, jackrabbits in the scrub. The landscape was rugged and foreign; she felt farther from home than she had in the Camargue. The road ran straight for a long stretch, and she saw cattle and horses grazing in rough fields under endless blue sky.

Helen had shocked her with some of the revelations she'd offered three nights ago. Susannah held on to the part about her mother. She could imagine what it must have been like for her, driving onto the Connecticut College campus with a new baby, searching the halls for Professor Oakes's office.

Susannah's mother had always revered education. She'd been a teacher herself. But Susannah knew, from the pride and awe with which she'd tell people about her daughter working at the college, that she had held it in special regard. Susannah pictured her mother holding her, knocking on Helen Oakes's door, asking if she could tell the professor their story.

And Helen had known, the minute she saw Susannah's application, that she was that baby, all grown up. She'd always remembered Margaret Connolly and her daughter Susannah, the way Margaret had been drawn to tell her story. And later, when Margaret was dying and Susannah was so far away, Helen had sat with her until the end.

Now, just fifty minutes away from Las Vegas, Susannah turned onto White Horse Road and into another world. Eerie cactus and mesquite trees clawed the sky. The pavement ended after a mile or so, and the road became gravel, climbing higher; Susannah shivered, knowing she was near.

When she'd checked the website, she'd looked at the ranch calendar. The circus performed only one day each week—tomorrow night, in Las Vegas. All other times, the circus personnel were on location at the ranch, training for performances and offering trail rides. Accommodations were also available, and Susannah had booked a room.

The ranch came into sight. There were several rings, including one covered by a deep blue tent and set up with trapezes, tightropes, and safety nets. The rustic buildings around the property's perimeter were long and low. In the distance, purple peaks were silhouetted against the sky. Closer up, sandstone ridges, sculpted by wind and blowing grit, rose out of the hard, dry ground.

She parked in the lot, carried her bag to the door marked Reception. She walked in, expecting to be greeted by an employee, by someone hired to run the front desk, so the circus star could train or rest. But standing at the counter, going over papers, was Maria Loisy Dempsey herself.

That it was Maria, Susannah had no doubt. This was Sari's mother: cascading dark hair, wide, intelligent forehead, exquisite brown eyes, and the same shy smile. Her legs were hidden behind the counter, but Susannah saw she wore a white shirt printed with the circus's logo: a galloping silver horse leaping toward a crescent moon. Her bare arms looked tan and strong.

"Allo," she said, her French accent thick. "Welcome to Clair de Lune."

"Thank you," Susannah said. "I'm glad to be here."

"We have lovely weather today. Yesterday there was a sandstorm, not so good. The horses did not enjoy it." She dropped the "h" in "horses," and finished with a bright smile. "But today—all is fine. Your name, please?"

"Susannah Connolly," she said.

"Ah, yes. For two nights. I have you here. You are staying in the Soleil d'Or building. Golden Sun," she translated.

"There are so many French names," Susannah said. "Clair de Lune, Soleil d'Or . . ."

"Yes, my husband and I are French," she said, and smiled again. "You can tell by my accent."

Susannah nodded. So, Maria and Adrien were married.

"Are you the owners?" Susannah asked.

"Yes," she said. "I'm Maria Ferret."

Smiling, Susannah hesitated. She hadn't planned exactly how she would handle her reasons for coming. She wasn't sure whether to speak openly, jump right into the story, be honest up front about her purpose here.

"You're well known," she said. "You're the star rider in Clair de Lune."

"You know our circus?" Maria asked, pleased.

"I've read about it," Susannah said. "I hope to see tomorrow's performance. Will you be riding?"

"It's possible, although I may not be," Maria said. "I have to see."

"Honestly . . . I'm surprised to find you here, working at the desk."

"Oh, I do some of everything," she said. "We are a small operation. Mom-and-pop." She laughed at the American phrase. "Have you also come to ride?"

"Yes," Susannah said. She filled out the registration form, gave Maria her credit card to swipe, and glanced through the brochure.

"We have lovely trails," Maria said. "Our hundred acres runs right into one hundred thousand acres belonging to the Bureau of Land Management. It's almost endless, and so beautiful . . ."

Almost like the Manade du Dempsey and

its location by the Parc Régionale de Ca-margue, Susannah wanted to say, studying her face. Maria looked happy, bright, almost glowing. Her cheeks were pink, the rest of her face burnished and tan. She seemed utterly comfortable with who she was, and quite kind. Could this possibly be the woman who had abandoned her eight-year-old daughter?

"You must be tired from traveling," Maria said. "I will show you your room. Would you like some iced tea? I'll have it brought over . . ."

"Iced tea would be great."

Maria made a call to the kitchen, spoke not in French, but in the language Susannah had heard in Topaz's *roulotte,* the language of the Manouche. The sound sent prickles up Susannah's neck, and she felt the blood rising in her face. She picked up her bags, waiting for Maria to come from behind the desk, and when she did, Susannah's jaw nearly dropped.

Maria Ferret was pregnant.

The path from the main building to Soleil d'Or went directly past the stables. Several brown and white horses stood in the ring, all saddled up and ready to ride. Maria had tried to take Susannah's bags, but Susannah refused.

"I can't let you carry them," she said, glancing down at Maria's belly. Maria tapped it with her hand, and laughed.

"There's no need to coddle me," she said. "I don't believe in being an invalid during this time . . ."

"When are you due?"

"Not for another four months. At the end of September . . ."

"And you still ride?" Susannah asked, thinking of what she had said about the circus.

"Honestly, not so much. I just . . . well, I don't want people to stop going to the circus just because I'm not performing. Many people associate me so completely with the Clair de Lune. When, in fact, there are performers every bit as gifted . . ."

"Gifted," Susannah said, catching her use of the word.

"Yes. It is a great blessing to be able to ride."

"Especially the way you ride," Susannah said.

"You have heard such things?"

"Yes," Susannah said, her blood pounding. This would be the time to speak out. She could tell Maria everything. Surely, if she were expecting another child, she would be tuned in to the needs of her first-born, the daughter she'd left in France.

But just then she heard a horse's whinny, and the sound of hoofbeats, and turned to see a parade of white horses trooping out of one of the barns, toward the tented ring. Susannah's heart caught, seeing such gorgeous animals, knowing they were just like the ones in the Camargue.

"Beautiful white horses," she said.

"Yes," Maria said. "They are magnificent—we use them in our circus. When we bought this ranch, we renamed the access road White Horse Road. It is a way of honoring our beautiful horses . . . and our homeland."

"Your homeland?"

Maria nodded. "My husband and I are from the South of France. An obscure area—not well known, like Cannes and Marseille. But it is Eden, truly. A paradise filled with white horses."

"Do you miss it?" Susannah said.

Again Maria nodded, but nothing more was forthcoming. She hesitated on the path for a moment, shielding her eyes against the desert sun, watching the horses file into the tent. One horse held back, prancing in place, allowing the others to go ahead. The rider was a dark-haired man wearing a black hat. Even from so far away he looked striking and handsome, with strong features and a wide moustache, and to Susannah it was clear that he and Maria were staring at each other.

"That's my husband," Maria said.

"He's in the circus, too?"

"Adrien trains all the horses and riders," she said. "He's brilliant with horses."

Susannah nodded. *And at taking women away from their daughters,* she thought. As Maria unlocked the door to Soleil d'Or, Susannah realized that she wanted a villain. She had expected to detest Maria on sight; to her surprise, she felt the opposite. So she glanced back over her shoulder, at the man in the black hat, and felt all the anger she'd been holding inside come pouring out—at him.

The building seemed to be all one story. Maria led Susannah down the long hallway, and unlocked the door to the last room on the left. It opened into a soaring space: rustic barn-board walls rising to a cathedral ceiling.

Picture windows overlooked a landscape of cactus and sage, dry desert, and purple mountains in the distance. As Susannah stood by the window, she saw what appeared to be a trail ride returning home, four brown horses winding their way down a path from the nearest foothill.

"What a beautiful view," Susannah said.

"It's very majestic," Maria agreed. "There is something so vast about the desert."

"I agree," Susannah said. She knew they called the Camargue *un desert d'eau:* a desert of water. But she held it inside. Her heart was racing too fast, and her nerves were too much on edge to tell Maria the things she'd come to say.

"I'm sure the iced tea will arrive any moment," Maria said. "After you've refreshed yourself, if you would like to ride, just call the barn. It's marked on your phone. Someone there will assist you."

"Merci bien," Susannah said.

"You speak French!" Maria said, her smile gleaming.

"Yes," Susannah said, then, in French,

that she traveled to France as often as she could.

"It is so welcome to hear the language."

Susannah nodded, suddenly feeling exhausted, wanting to be alone. Nothing so far had gone as she'd thought it would. She had expected to arrive at the Clair de Lune and have to seek Maria out. She'd thought she would hate her on sight. Certainly, she'd never expected to find her so gentle and sympathetic—and so pregnant.

"Please call if you need anything," Maria said.

"I will," Susannah said.

Then, just as Maria was about to close the door behind her, Susannah called out. "Maria!" she said. "Just one question . . ."

"Of course," Maria said, halfway out the door, standing sideways so the silhouette of her belly was apparent.

"Why did you name your ranch and circus Clair de Lune?"

"It means 'light of the moon,' " Maria said. "Moonlight . . ."

"But what is its significance?"

Maria hesitated. For a moment Susannah thought she saw pain flicker across her eyes. Had the moon been out the night

Maria had run away with Adrien? When Susannah pictured the moment, she saw Sari riding after her mother under a moon, the car pulling ahead along the moon-white marsh road. Maria blinked, holding whatever she was thinking deep inside. Then, the smile again. "Moonlight is romantic, *non*? And it looks so beautiful on the white horses."

"Yes," Susannah said, remembering that last ride with Grey, him on Django while Susannah rode Mystère, the full moon pouring its light on the swamp while they rescued Tempest. "It does."

And then Maria left.

Susannah had started unpacking—placing her jeans and boots in the closet, setting her books and the letter she'd started to Grey on the desk by the window. She called over to the barn, told the woman who answered that she would like to ride, made an appointment to go out in an hour.

Just then a knock sounded at the door. She went to answer it, found a young woman standing there, holding a glass of iced tea on a tray. Susannah opened the door wide so she could come inside.

"Hello, madame. Shall I put your tea on

the desk?" the woman asked, and Susannah was struck by her accent—it was exactly the same as Maria's, Topaz's, Rosalie's: French mixed with something else, which Susannah knew to be Manouche.

"Yes, please," Susannah said.

"Did you have a good trip here?" she asked, pausing to give Susannah a smile. She had very curly dark hair, tumbling to her shoulders. Deep brown eyes peeked out from behind thick bangs, filled with friendly curiosity.

"Very good, thank you."

"I hope that you will enjoy the ranch," the young woman said, continuing over to the desk. Susannah had placed her books and notes there, but the woman gently moved some of them aside and lowered the tray.

"I'm sure I'll enjoy it very much," Susannah said. She went to her purse, to get some money for a tip. When she turned, to hand it to the woman, she saw her frozen in place—staring down at the desk, as if she had seen a ghost, or a rattlesnake, or something else that scared her. But when she looked over at Susannah, her eyes were suddenly wide and filled with joy.

"You know Sarah?" the woman asked.

"Excuse me?" Susannah asked.

"She is my family saint," the woman said. "We love her very much, are grateful for all she has given us, but do not hear of her here in the United States. She is very personal to my relatives, and our people."

When Susannah still looked puzzled, the woman pointed at the desk. Susannah had taken the book from her briefcase—the one in which she'd placed her letter to Grey, with the picture of the statue of Sarah on the cover.

"Sara-la-Kali," the woman said, pointing. Her voice trembled with emotion.

"Oh, yes," Susannah said. "Yes, Sarah . . ."

TWENTY-FOUR

Maria returned to the reception desk, sat down in the swivel chair. Being on her feet was getting harder. Summer was coming, the heat rising; yesterday her ankles were so swollen, Adrien had made her lie down and put her legs up. The baby had been kicking a lot. Adrien said that meant it was a boy. Maria wasn't so sure. She wasn't sure at all.

Sitting at her desk, she looked at the pile of calls she had to return. One of their top horses had had a bad hematoma and needed surgery last week, and she needed to check with the vet on how long he'd be out of commission. Several travel agents had called, wanting to arrange for special riding packages. And Rosalie had phoned twice; both times Maria had been tied up with customers, unable to settle in for a good, long talk.

Now, wanting to ensure she'd have that opportunity, she buzzed the kitchen and asked Chata to come and cover the front desk. Then she went into the inner office, just off the lobby, and closed the door behind her.

The windows gave onto the riding rings and barns. As she watched, Susannah Connolly—the new guest—walked out of Soleil d'Or, across the yard toward the barn. She wore jeans and boots, ready to ride. Her hair glinted reddish-gold in the sun. She had pale and striking purple eyes. Maria thought she was very beautiful; she also seemed very powerful, in the way that meant she had inner strength.

Checking the time, Maria realized that it was nearly nine at night in Stes.-Maries. Her blood quickened, just dialing the number of her friend's cell phone. It brought her home, hearing the foreign ring tones, and she imagined the smell of the marsh wafting through town, mingling with fog off the sea.

"Hello," Rosalie said.

"It's me."

"Finally you call back!"

"What a crazy day it's been," Maria said. "All week, as a matter of fact. I'm so tired, and it's not even summer yet. The heat . . ."

"Never mind the heat. So much time since I left those messages for you! I started to think you really have forgotten us. Life in the States is so glamorous . . ."

"Yes," Maria teased. "I'm as big as an ox, the lovely young Zuna has taken my place as star performer, and I'm soaking my feet to keep them from swelling. Okay then; surely that's not why you've called so often. What is it? Have you finally decided to come over here and see me?"

"That's not it."

"No, of course not," Maria said. "It's May, nearly time for Sarah's feast. You must be so busy. Is the town filling up?" She stopped, caught for a moment in a wave of homesickness.

On May 24 each year, all the Gypsies made a pilgrimage to Stes.-Maries. They would travel from all over to see their saint; the town would be decorated, and the statue of Sarah paraded through the streets, down to the sea in a wooden boat. It was such a beautiful ceremony, and the memory of it pierced Maria with homesick longing.

"Zin-Zin wants to talk to you," Rosalie said.

Maria thought she had misheard, lost in dreams of home. Her chest felt hot, and quickly the blood rushed up into her neck and face. "What did you say?"

"She asked me to call you for her."

"Why? After all this time?"

"Maria, you know she still loves you . . ."

"How could I know that?" Maria asked. "She sent me away . . . she spat at me. Cursed me."

"She was angry. You married him, you let him take you away from us."

"The ranch was just ten kilometers from Stes.-Maries. Now I am ten thousand kilometers away, and she wants to talk to me?"

"Yes, I told you! She had me call you," Rosalie said, sounding eager.

"Does she know about the baby?"

"I haven't told a soul—just as you asked me."

"What does she want?"

Rosalie was silent; Maria heard her tapping her fingernail on the telephone. The women had a long friendship, stretching back to when they were little girls. Maria knew all Rosalie's nervous habits.

"Come on now," Maria said. "Tell me. What does she want, Rosa?"

"Grey came to see her," Rosalie said, lowering her voice—with shame or sadness or a combination of both, Maria wasn't sure.

The sound of his name jolted Maria. It wasn't that she never thought it—she did, more often than she wished. But she had arranged her life to protect herself from unexpected mentions. She had traveled across an ocean and three-quarters of another continent to escape the dishonor of her past. Her hand was trembling; it strayed to her belly.

"What did he want?" she asked.

"You must let Zin-Zin tell you," Rosalie said.

"Rosa, no," Maria said. She cringed, thinking of Grey and Sari, shame and pain washing through her. "The past is over. Tell Zin-Zin I will not talk to her about him."

"It's not," Rosalie said, "really about him . . ."

The baby kicked. Maria bent her head down, toward her belly. She had shortness of breath—it was part of pregnancy, she'd had it the first time, too. Other similarities existed: the quality of movement, the way the baby seemed to swim inside, the quick staccato bursts of kicking.

All reminded Maria of her first pregnancy, of Sari . . . So much so that, although Adrien said this was a boy, Maria secretly called the baby Tchaj—for girl, or daughter—just as she had called her first baby when she was born.

"I do not want to hear," Maria said.

"Then you won't hear," Rosalie said. "Not from me. Zin-Zin will tell you . . ."

"No. I won't call her."

"Surely you won't ignore a request from the woman who loved you as a mother, who raised you as her own. Maria!"

"She disowned me after I married Grey," Maria said. "You're the only one who stayed loyal to me, who still loves me." Maria paused, catching her breath. "Besides, I cannot bear to hear anything she might say."

Just then Maria heard the sound of scuffling, and of muffled words, as if Rosalie had covered the receiver with her hand. Definitely—the sound of a door being closed.

"Rosa, are you walking somewhere?"

"No," Rosalie said. "I'm already here."

"What are you talking about?"

"I've just walked into Zin-Zin's *roulotte*. She is here now. I love you, my Maria . . ." and with that, before Maria could open her mouth and object, Rosalie was off the line.

"Maria." The voice was deep yet frail. It brought back worlds of memories to Maria, filled her with love, and with anger. She'd loved Zin-Zin so much, and felt so hurt when the old woman had cut her off.

"Zin-Zin," Maria said.

"I've kept track of you through Rosalie, and through Matelo's brothers. How is he?"

"He is fine."

"And you, my Tchaj?" My girl. . . . The old nickname brought tears to Maria's eyes.

"I am well, Zin-Zin. And you?"

"Old, my darling. Very old. When one reaches this age, one has crazy thoughts. Memories become weapons . . . clubs, daggers, that one uses on oneself. That is how I spend my days, Tchaj. Living with memories I wish I could undo."

Maria squeezed her eyes tight. She could hang up the phone. She could stop this conversation right now instead of going on with it. Memories she wished she could undo. Oh, Maria's heart had broken over and over again because of memories she wished she could erase. She didn't need to hear about Zin-Zin's.

"It's impossible," Maria said. "To undo memories."

"Do you think so?"

"Of course . . ."

"You, the one who can fly? Who can tip-toe across a horse's back so lightly he doesn't even know you're there? You can swing from the stars, hand-over-hand, all the way to the moon, and you can turn white horses into white doves, wings and all . . . you can do anything. Those are magical things, Maria. Supernatural."

"They are illusions," Maria said. "No more than that."

"Maria, you don't believe that."

"Of course I do. It is how I make my living; it is the premise of Clair de Lune—and of all circuses."

"I shall prove to you you're wrong," Zin-Zin said. "Prove that you are capable of performing supernatural acts."

"Such as what?"

"Taking away my regret. Erasing the terrible thing between us . . . Undoing my memory."

"How could I possibly?" Maria asked. She held the phone tightly; her tone of voice was angry. But inside her heart was racing, because she thought: what if she could do those things?

"You start with the bad night; the worst night: when you came to me, here in my *roulotte.* It was filled with pictures of you back then. On nearly every surface, photos of my darling Maria, on white horses, in costume, on the church steps. Many pictures, remember?"

"Yes," Maria said, picturing the caravan where she had once felt so loved, the wall painted with garlands of sunflowers and lavender, painted by Maria as a gift for Zin-Zin.

"Fine. You are back in time, the night when I shouted at you. When you came here to tell me about Grey Dempsey. When I told you that you were making a terrible mistake, worse than death—that I was glad, in fact, that your mother was dead, rather than see you marry such a man . . ."

Maria remembered those words. She had felt them like a knife in her heart, and the pain came back now—but Zin-Zin was wrong; that wasn't Maria's worst night.

"That night when I disowned you," Zin-Zin said. "When I cursed your marriage, and any children that might be born of your love for him. And when I told you that you would never escape your destiny, that you would leave him and destroy him and marry Matelo instead. Do you remember?"

"How could I forget?" Maria whispered, hot tears flowing from her eyes.

"Maria, that is my worst night. That is the memory I would like you to undo."

"How can I?" Maria asked, voice breaking. "It happened!"

"You can forgive me," Zin-Zin said, begging. "That is all you have to do. I pray, Maria . . . please, find the understanding to do this for me. Go deep inside your own heart, look in there and find the forgiveness. Please, oh, please . . ."

"I forgive you," Maria said. Was that it? Is

that all Zin-Zin needed? "I forgave you long ago . . ."

The phone line was filled with soft weeping. She heard Zin-Zin's lips brush the receiver, and the word *"merci"* being repeated over and over. Maria shut her eyes tight, unable to take it in, afraid of what it would dislodge. If only she could undo her own terrible memories.

"Maria," Zin-Zin said after a few moments, "was that your worst night?"

"No," she whispered. "No, it was not . . ."

"What was that?"

Maria rested her hand on the curve of her belly, almost as if she could protect the child inside the way she had failed to protect Sari. She had blocked these thoughts for so long, done whatever she could, at whatever cost, to keep them away. But Zin-Zin's question broke the dam, and they flooded in.

Packing her bags, stealing out of her house, being confronted by Sari. Sari clutching her, begging and sobbing, Maria crazed, pushing Sari away, pushing her hard. Not just a shove—she admitted that now. A slap—hard. Wanting her baby to go away, so this would be over, so Maria wouldn't have to hear her crying, so this could be over.

Those cries, her child weeping.

Climbing into the car. Telling Adrien to drive away fast—*faster!* Faster, oh, hurry. The night so dark, the road so slick. There'd been a rainstorm one hour earlier, after a season of wet weather. The road buckled; the pavement gave way; Adrien's tires stuck in the mud.

By that time, Maria weeping so hard, the sight of Sari's face seared into her eyes and brain, the terror in her daughter's eyes as Maria had shoved her, slapped her—she'd never hit her ever—the sound of Sari's helpless, confused weeping.

Maria had thrown herself into Adrien's arms, crying that she couldn't stand what they were doing, sobbing that she wanted to die. And that was the moment they'd heard hoofbeats: looking out the rearview mirror, they'd seen Sari on Mystère, bearing down on them at a gallop. Sari's last view of her mother had been in the arms of another man.

And Adrien had hit the gas just right to pull out of the rut, and they'd gone speeding up the road. Thinking of that moment, hearing her daughter's voice ringing in her ears, Maria held tight to the phone and couldn't speak. Maria hadn't stayed around to see what happened next. She'd heard about it, and that was even worse.

"It's a memory of Sari, isn't it?" Zin-Zin asked.

"Yes," Maria whispered.

"The night you left her?"

"Yes, God help me."

"Would you like to heal that memory, my darling Maria?"

"More than anything," Maria said. "But it's not possible. The hurt is too deep. When you and I fought, I was a grown woman. I left Sari when she was only eight years old. I hit her. I pushed her so violently, Zin-Zin, just to get her away from me."

"You left her because you love her," Zin-Zin said.

"How do you know that?"

"Rosalie told me. We talk of you often, Maria. Over the years, Rosa has helped me understand what you were thinking. You felt my curse was real. When I swore against your husband and any children . . . Oh, Maria."

"No, Zin-Zin," she said, shaking her head.

"It wasn't you who cursed them. I did that. By being selfish—always taking what I wanted, starting with Grey, ignoring the truths I knew. Sari . . . needed a chance without me."

"What do you mean?"

But Maria couldn't explain. She felt her heart shut down, turn into a stone. She heard the old woman speaking gently in her beloved language, but she barely registered a word. She caressed her belly, silently whispering, "Tchaj, tchaj." Girl, girl . . .

If only she could be given a second chance. A way to make up to one daughter for the pain she'd caused another. She'd named her daughter for the wisest woman in the clan, and for Sarah.

She'd always trusted Grey to care for Sari, to give her everything she needed, to shower her with more love than most children received from two parents. She'd trusted him. But even all that love and care had been unable to heal what Maria had done. Maria knew everything; she had made Rosalie tell her every last detail.

"Maria," Zin-Zin said, "Sari needs something from you now."

"What do you mean?"

"Grey came to me. The child is very troubled. The colorblindness . . "

"Hasn't gone away," Maria said. "I know. I ask Rosalie every time we speak."

"There's something else. There is a woman; someone Grey cares for very deeply."

Maria heard the words, felt her heart turn over. She was in love with Adrien, she had left Grey long ago. But still, it was hard to hear. Another woman in Sari's life?

"Even more, Sari seemed to take to her at first. But then . . ."

"Then what?"

"Sari can't let herself be happy, Maria. She feels too hopeless. Can you understand? To be thrown away by her mother . . ."

"Stop," Maria said through clenched teeth. How could Zin-Zin tell her such things?

"Think of my rejection of you—and, as you said, imagine how such a thing would feel to a child. Then you will know what you must do."

"Must do?"

"To undo the memories of that night."

"I can't!" Maria yelled. "They're in too

deep—those memories will never leave me, Zin-Zin. Never!"

"I'm speaking of Sari," Zin-Zin said quietly, with almost unimaginable tenderness. "I'm speaking of what you must do to undo those memories for her. Think this over, Tchaj. You will discover the answer . . . turn to Sarah. Pray to her for help and guidance."

"Sarah . . ."

"Even now, I hear the violins and guitars, the musicians preparing for her feast on the twenty-fourth. May, the loveliest month, Maria. Surely you remember . . . Blessings are great in May, if you open your heart to them."

Maria heard Zin-Zin say goodbye; the phone was hung up. Rosalie didn't come back on the line.

She sat in the office rocking back and forth, clutching herself, staring out the window. Matelo was in the circus ring; she could see through the panel that had been rolled up. He looked her way, grinned, blew her a kiss. She wanted to blow a kiss back, but she couldn't move.

A tap sounded at the door.

If she ignored it, the person would go away.

Two seconds later it came again, a little harder: knock, knock, knock . . .

"What is it?" she called.

"Maria!" Fayola stepped through the door. She was only twenty, already a great talent on horseback. It was a shame to use her in the kitchen, even part-time. She should be training to become a star rider, like her sister Zuna, and like Maria herself.

"Yes?" Maria asked. She felt too exhausted to even try to smile.

"That woman in Soleil d'Or? You had me bring her a glass of iced tea?"

"Yes, what about her?"

Fayola smiled wider, and her eyes gleamed. "She has a book of Sarah," she said.

"What are you talking about?"

"Sara-la-Kali. Right here, at our ranch! She has it on her desk, right now."

TWENTY-FIVE

Because she had arrived midday and the other riders were already out, Susannah found herself alone on the trail ride with a young instructor named Christiane. Christiane saddled up two horses, a pinto named Bero for Susannah, and they started into the desert. The day was spectacular, with rock formations stark against dazzling blue sky, and Susannah felt as if they were riding into a postcard.

"What does *Bero* mean?" Susannah asked.

"It means 'bear' in my language, miss," Christiane said in the same accent—French mixed with something else—as Maria and the woman who'd brought Susannah her tea.

"What language is that?" Susannah asked.

"Romany, miss."

"Oh," Susannah said. Maria and Adrien must have brought many people over with them; so far everyone Susannah had encountered had been Romany. But Christiane must have misinterpreted Susannah's tone of surprise for alarm.

"Bero is a fine horse," she said. "He is gentle, nothing like a real bear. We named him that because when he was very young one of the circus bears escaped, and this one helped find him."

"Brave horse," Susannah said, patting his neck.

"Yes," Christiane said, pleased by Susannah's compliment. "He is. . . ."

They headed along a dusty trail into the brush, flushing jackrabbits who went tearing over the dirt. Following a ridge bleached white by the sun, they wound up the foothill to a higher elevation, emerging on the side of one of those purple mountains Susannah had seen from her room.

The view gave onto a long valley running

beside a dry riverbed, deeply scored into the hard and rocky desert soil. The mountain terrain made her think of caves; she wondered about tribal art hiding in crevasses above. Susannah gazed down as Bero walked along, feeling his gentle rhythm, grateful for this chance to just ride and think. Her love of riding had flooded back to her in the Camargue, and now it brought her back to that time, and to Grey.

She stared down the mountainside at the dry creek, wondering what it must be like for Maria—coming from such a lush, verdant estuary—to be transplanted into this rough, stony land. Certainly all the people Susannah had met seemed kind, nurturing; and obviously Maria was flourishing. That in itself disturbed Susannah; how could Maria so easily make this new life for herself, have another child, while she'd left Sari in such a terrible way?

The trail widened, and Christiane fell back to ride alongside Susannah. She glanced over, making sure Susannah was fine. "You ride very well," she said.

"Thank you," Susannah said. "I rode a lot when I was young, and just took it up again recently."

Christiane nodded. "You should continue. You have a good seat, and a good rapport with your horse."

"Have you been riding long?" Susannah asked.

"All my life," Christiane said. "Like many of my people, I could ride before I could walk. My father operated a small circus outside Paris. It was very popular; many people from the fashion world would come. Our tents were very beautiful, and the models wanted to be photographed on the white horses."

"The white horses," Susannah said. "I saw some down below, at the ranch here . . ."

"Yes," Christiane said. "They are the same breed as at my father's circus."

"What breed is that?"

"Camarguaise," she said, and the word alone sent a delicate tremor down Susannah's back. "They are an ancient breed, dating back to the Paleolithic period—seventeen thousand years old! They're found only in one place in this entire world—the salt plains of southeastern France. Very beautiful place . . . There are only thirty herds of white horses in existence; they run wild through the salt water."

Susannah listened silently, holding her thoughts inside. She pictured the herds she'd seen with Grey and Sari. She could see Tempest still young and wild, trying to escape into the marsh. She thought of what Grey had said, that horses always felt hunted. Now, hiding her true reasons for being here, Susannah felt like a hunter. She was after something from Maria, that was certain.

Susannah felt that there was something so primal about riding through the mountains, with the blue sky enveloping them, that made dishonesty impossible. Susannah's gaze flicked over to Christiane.

"I've been to the Camargue," she said.

"You have? Then you know! Isn't it magnificent?"

"Yes, it truly is. You said you're from outside Paris," Susannah said. "How did you wind up here in Nevada?"

"Oh, for the chance to ride in Clair de Lune," she said, almost breathlessly. "My father reveres Matelo—that's Adrien Ferret; he and his wife are owners of this ranch, and of the circus. He is the best trainer in the world. All Gypsies want to ride with him. And Maria is famous everywhere."

"But you're so far from home," Susannah said.

Christiane smiled, a little sadly. "That is our way," she said. "Gypsies are wanderers, did you not know? We began in India, and followed the Romany Trail all the way to Byzantium, and from there to Europe. *Romany* means 'human.' We are at home in the world, wherever we go."

"That's beautiful, Christiane," Susannah said softly.

"Clair de Lune is my family now," she said. "I work in the stable, hoping for the chance to move to the circus. For now I am needed on the ranch; but I work out and practice. Matelo trains me when there is time. I am very good."

"I'm sure you are," Susannah said.

"With Maria no longer performing, others have moved up to become stars themselves. Zuna, Chata—they are both brilliant. I'm hoping to take their places in the ranks, when the time is right."

"That will happen, I bet," Susannah said. Then, "Maria no longer performs? She's expecting a baby . . ."

"Yes," Christiane said. "She stopped riding just before her pregnancy. Some women continue for at least the first few weeks, but not Maria."

"No?"

Looking uncomfortable, as if she'd said something wrong, Christiane shook her head and looked away. Susannah followed her gaze, down the long slope toward the ranch. The sun had moved behind the peak, and long shadows had begun to fall. From here, the dry riverbed looked like a hard black line through the high desert.

"She and Matelo wanted a child." Christiane paused, glancing over with excitement in her eyes. Susannah had the feeling that she didn't ordinarily gossip with guests, but that she was overflowing with the story and needed to pour it out. "They hoped for a long time, but they were under a curse."

"Really?" Susannah asked. "A real curse?"

"A spiritual sickness," Christiane said. "I don't know why, or what caused it, but Maria's soul was ailing."

"And this 'curse' was lifted?"

Again, Christiane nodded.

"How did that happen?"

"Through grace and the intercession," Christiane said. "And by Maria giving up what she loves most: riding and horses. Offering it up to God."

"Did she tell you that?"

"It is known among us," Christiane said confidently. "And now we know that she is expecting, and we are so happy for her, that soon she will have a child."

Susannah didn't reply to that. The trail took a wide, looping turn, and then began its way down the mountain—a series of switchbacks that took them back toward the ranch. The path seemed very close to the edge; Susannah's heart raced when she saw what a sheer drop there was to the bottom.

But even when they'd leveled out, walking slowly along flat even ground, her pulse refused to steady. Christiane's words stuck in her head: Maria was pregnant through grace and intercession. And in France, four thousand miles away, there was still a little girl without her mother.

Maria watched her come back. The two horses meandered down the trail, seeming to take forever to get from the last plateau of the mountainside to the barn. She stood in the hallway of Soleil d'Or, holding the book of Sarah, eyes glittering, gripped by such powerful emotion she didn't even know what to call it. Was it rage? Or sorrow? Or a word that hadn't been invented yet?

Once she was sure the horses had returned, she used her key to let herself back into the room. She was tired, and her lower back hurt. Pulling out the desk chair, she sat down—as she had two hours ago, after Fayola had run to tell her about the book.

Maria held the book now, hands shaking as she touched the single sheet of paper, folded within its pages. Her eyes had felt scalded, burning right out of her head, when she'd opened it, read the words *Dear Grey* . . .

What had inspired Maria to ransack a guest's room? She had never done such a thing before. But then, she'd never gotten a call from Zin-Zin before, followed so quickly by an employee nearly hysterical over the discovery in one of the guest rooms of a book on Sarah.

Maria had instructed Fayola to stay at the front desk, and she'd hurried here to Soleil d'Or. What had she expected to find? Looking back, it was impossible to remember or know.

Her emotions since then had been like an earthquake: rumbling, tearing, apocalyptic, destroying the familiar landscape, leaving something brand new and terrible in its place. Maria had let herself into the room, gone straight for the desk. The book was there in plain sight. The price tag—tiny white rectangle, stuck to the back cover, marked in euros—showed that the book had been sold at the gift shop in Stes.-Maries-de-la-Mer.

That's when she'd known: this wasn't an accident, wasn't a coincidence. Gypsies didn't believe in such things anyway. Maria had been taught by Zin-Zin long ago to look past the simple explanation for the deeper, darker truth. Simplicity was a myth. Gypsies knew that truth was layered, and life was complicated. Persecution had been their lot. They had been hunted and hated, and Maria knew that was why they all loved horses so much: they shared a sense of having suffered predation.

Now, here was this woman with a book on Sara-la-Kali, and a letter to Maria's ex-husband—filled with love, and aches, and promises. And Maria had a new baby kicking inside, and she hadn't been on a horse in months, almost a year, and her soul felt as if it were withering, and right now she thought she might die before Susannah Connolly returned to her room.

A buzz sounded—her walkie-talkie. Someone looking for her. She reached for it, to shut it off, heard Adrien's voice: *"Ou est tu, cherie? Ma p'tite? Viens, Maria . . ."* Her hands were shaking so hard, and she couldn't bear to speak to her beloved, so she just clicked the damn thing off.

Maria stared out the window at the Spring Mountains. She used to look at them, feel they were mocking her. *Spring* meant fresh, flowing, growing; but Maria had been as barren as the twisting, cruel, dried-up river running across their ranch.

She had gazed at those mountains, thinking of how ridiculous their name was, considering they'd spawned such a useless, dry river. Adrien had had to pipe in water for the horses. The river had gone dry the same year they'd bought the ranch; it was as if Zin-Zin's curse had spread and grown, affecting not only Maria's body, but even the land on which she and Adrien lived.

Having walked away from one child—in pursuit of riding, her miraculous "gift"—she had found the meaning of a true curse. Losing Sari, she ached for a child. She wanted a baby to love, to make up for what she'd done to Sari.

Maria had tried everything. She'd undergone in vitro fertility treatments. Adrien had brought in a Manouche healer from Bruges, and Maria had consented to many sessions that involved candles, chants, and holy water. Still, every month, she'd see those hated drops of blood, and she'd fall deeper into despair.

She would dream every night: Sari's face. That was all. Those precious eyes gazing into Maria's with such questions, such wondering. *Why?* Sari seemed to be asking. *Why did you leave me?*

I can never explain it to you, my love, Maria would try to reply. But every time she opened her mouth to let the words out, Sari would close her eyes.

That's what Sari used to do when she was little: whenever something she didn't like would happen, her big green eyes would shut tight. When Maria had tried to feed her homemade vegetable soup—eyes shut. When Grey had tried to give her medication for a bad cold—eyes shut.

Maria had felt shut down herself. She had felt her own body turning against her; she felt such shame from what she'd done to her daughter. Why should she be given a second chance to be a mother, when she'd thrown away the first one so cruelly? She'd prayed for guidance.

The dreams of Sari, the dry river, the uselessness of her body. She knew she needed to do penance, so she decided to stop riding—the greatest sacrifice she could make. Maybe if she did that, deprived herself of the thing she most loved to do, Sarah would take pity on her and let her have a baby.

Adrien had been furious. Not only because she was the greatest draw their circus had—people came from all over to see the "Gypsy princess" and her white horses—but because he knew what it would cost her spirit to stay away from horses. He had held her while she'd cried, and she had finally been able to convince him that this was something she had to do, a sacrifice she had to make.

Her last night on horseback: she and Matelo riding together in the moonlight, standing tall on the backs of their most exquisite steeds, flying through the night under a crescent moon. She had felt the horse's power moving into her bare feet, up her legs, into her body. She'd reached up, fingers stretching toward the thin moon.

Tears had fallen from her eyes, blinding her, absorbed by her horse's white coat. Even without vision, it didn't matter: she rode as if she and the horse were the same animal. Matelo—she always called her husband by his Romany nickname when they were riding—had galloped beside her, and they'd switched in midair—she jumped onto his horse, and he onto hers.

They had crisscrossed through the desert, riding blindly, switching off, back again, until finally she felt him leap up behind her. His horse whirled and fell behind while he stayed with her, holding her. She'd leaned back into his strong body, eyes wide open, taking in the field of stars and the romantic curve of moon.

His body had pressed into hers—two crescent moons becoming one. She'd been wearing her silver dress, covered with glitter like tiny stars. He'd slid his hand underneath, guided himself inside. Maria had felt him explode, and she'd known right then, that was the moment.

And she'd been right: the miracle had happened.

Adrien was careful to keep her pregnancy out of the press; he didn't want people to stop coming to Clair de Lune, and he wasn't quite ready to promote Zuna and Chata as the new stars. Maria didn't care. She just wanted to make it to full term, for the baby to be born healthy and happy.

Zin-Zin's call . . .

Forgiveness and a challenge: to "undo" the memories of that night. That night, that terrible night, Sari with her eyes open coming fast. Zin-Zin had spoken of Grey and a woman, said that Sari had taken to her—at first. Maria sat very still, holding the book and letter, thinking of her daughter taking to another woman. In spite of her own selfish grab for happiness, it hurt to think of such a thing.

The baby kicked, as she always did. Tap, tap, tap . . . memories of Sari at this stage. *Tchaj,* Maria thought. *Tchaj . . . my girl . . . my daughter.* Maria's arms encircled her growing belly, as if she could keep the child inside safe. She, more than anyone, knew how illusory safety could be.

Footsteps sounded in the hallway. The click of heels meant it was someone in riding boots, but the tread was light, so she knew it was a woman. Maria pushed herself out of the chair and rose to face the door.

The key turned in the lock; the rustic oak door swung open. Susannah Connolly stood there with a look of shock on her face. Maria felt her own mouth twitching—with nervousness and fury and words of rage. But she watched Susannah's gaze fall upon the book Maria held in her hand—watched her look at the image of Sarah—and saw Susannah's expression soften.

"Maria," Susannah said, walking toward her with an outstretched hand. "I've come here about your daughter. About Sari . . ."

TWENTY-SIX

Susannah walked forward, propelled by a force deep inside, hands outstretched to Sari's mother. Maria stood by the desk shaking, eyes red-rimmed, tears pooling, book clutched to her breast, the picture of Sarah peeking out above her hand. Susannah watched Maria flinch, withdraw, and then finally reach out her hand.

"I've come about your daughter," Susannah repeated.

"Does she know you are here?"

"No. They have no idea."

"They—Sari and Grey?"

"Yes," Susannah said. Still holding Maria's

hand, she led her to the sitting area at one end of the room. A sofa and two chairs had been grouped here, cozy and intimate, around a fireplace for chilly nights. Maria sat on the sofa, and Susannah perched on the edge of one of the armchairs. She stared down at the small book, saw the corner of the letter she'd written to Grey sticking out. Following her gaze, Maria looked her hard in the eye.

"I don't usually read guests' letters."

"But you read that one."

"Are you the woman Grey 'cares about deeply'?" Maria asked, emphasizing the phrase.

"Who told you that?" Susannah asked.

"Zin-Zin," Maria said. "The matriarch of my clan."

"I've met her," Susannah said.

"But that's not possible," Maria said. "Zin-Zin doesn't associate with outsiders."

"Maybe I'm not as much an outsider as you think. What did she say about me?"

"Nothing about you. Just that Grey went to see her. And that my daughter . . ." Maria trailed off, as if the next part was impossible to say; or maybe she just found it too difficult to discuss Sari with Susannah.

"That your daughter is in pain," Susannah said quietly.

"How dare you!" Maria said, jumping up. Her eyes were wild and fierce. She clutched her pregnant belly as if protecting the child inside from this stranger's influence and judgment.

"I spent time with her," Susannah said. "I saw . . ."

"Saw what? What can you understand of my daughter? She is mine—no one knows Sari as I do, and don't you dare judge me for what I did, for what I know to be right!"

"Right?" Susannah asked. "You pushed her away—shoved her so hard, she hit the wall. You ran out the door to be with Matelo, and you never looked back long enough to see Sari lying in the road."

Maria yanked her hand back as if to slap Susannah, but she didn't follow through. She crumbled inside, felt the world end.

"Stop," she gasped.

"It's true, isn't it?" Susannah asked. "That's why you didn't slap me just now; you know I'm just telling you what you already feel."

"You don't understand; you can't begin to imagine."

"Maria . . ."

She closed her eyes, as if she could block out Susannah's voice. But Susannah saw the torment on her face and knew that Maria was still seeing the shock and betrayal in her daughter's eyes.

"I had to get away," Maria whispered.

"Your family," Susannah said. "You defied them by marrying Grey and they cut you off. That's why you're here now, isn't it? So far from the Camargue, from the place you'd always known as home . . . it's why you and Adrien had to travel so far away. Because you were shut out of your own clan."

"You don't understand us," Maria said.

"I'm not part of you," Susannah said. "But I'm doing my best to understand. Because I care about . . ."

"About Grey? About taking over as the woman in his life, mother to my daughter?"

"About you, too, Maria," Susannah said. She felt emotion welling up, thinking of Helen Oakes and all she had said about Romany tradition, women's choices, the difficulties of being true to oneself.

"Don't waste your energy thinking of me," Maria said. "I am fine."

"I don't see how you could be, honestly,"

Susannah said. "You're pregnant again, and that is wonderful. But what did you have to give up, to get to this place? Your gift— riding the horses you love so much . . . just so you can feel you deserve to have another baby? What about the daughter you already gave up?"

"Leave me alone," Maria wept, collapsing into the desk chair. "Please, leave my ranch and let us be . . . go away and stop this talk . . ."

"Maria," Susannah said, crouching beside her, "stopping the talk won't help you. And it won't help Sari."

"Is she still suffering?" Maria made herself whisper.

"Of course. She misses her mother."

"She's still colorblind." It wasn't a question.

Susannah steeled herself. "Yes," she said.

"Zin-Zin cursed us," Maria said. "I told myself, and her, that it wasn't possible, that it's just old-world, superstitious foolishness. But maybe it's true."

"Maria, the only way a curse can work is if you let it. If your psyche is fragile, if you already feel bad about yourself, a curse can find its way in. It becomes a self-fulfilling prophecy. You believe it will work, so it does. I think you've been punishing yourself ever since you left."

"I brought it on myself, marrying an outsider."

"What happened to you was so unfair," Susannah said, thinking of Topaz and all she had said about her own family, the ancestor who had defied their culture and married a Spaniard. "You loved someone, and deserved happiness. You didn't bring *anything* on yourself. They did it to you."

"I was young," Maria said. "Zin-Zin was like a mother to me. I hated myself for hurting her. There are traditions, and she taught them to me. Her wisdom always meant so much to me—I named my daughter for her, even though I knew Zin-Zin would never approve. She was so wise . . . she even predicted my love for Adrien."

"But you had to find out for yourself," Susannah said.

Maria paused, then went on. "I left Sari to save myself, and *her*. I thought she would do better without me. Our lives, our home— they were terrible. I could never live between two worlds. . . ."

"The world with Grey and the world of Stes.-Maries?"

"Yes. I wasn't Gypsy anymore. I tried to fit into Grey's life, but it never worked. I was dying there . . . He loves Sari so much. I tell myself I wanted to do the best for her—leave her with her father, so she wouldn't have to be so divided. Matelo and I . . . we didn't know what we were going to do . . . where we'd end up . . . I knew Grey would take care of her."

"He does."

"I told myself she would be better without me. I was so unhappy. I'd ride all day, tears flowing the entire time. Sari started thinking mothers were people who cried. She looked at Anne—Laurent's mother—and wondered why she smiled so often. In my selfishness, to do what I wanted, I told myself she'd be so much better off without me."

"But she wasn't," Susannah said, touching Maria's hand.

"How do you know?"

"Because you're her only mother," Susannah said.

"How do you know so much? Do you have children?"

"No," Susannah said. "But I had a mother.

She died last winter, and I miss her every day. I miss her right now . . . I wish I could tell her about you, ask her what I could do to help you."

"Why do you want to help me?" Maria asked harshly. "When it's Grey you love? Grey and Sari?"

"Because they can't move on."

"What do you mean?"

"Sari is trapped, Maria. Trapped in the world of that night."

"She can't be," Maria whispered.

"But she is."

The words made Maria start to cry again. She bowed her head, her shoulders shook. Susannah felt tears come to her own eyes. She'd thought maybe she would try to convince Maria to return to France, just to give Sari the chance to say what she needed to say, including a proper goodbye; what she realized now was that they needed to say hello. Sari needed a life that included her mother.

Just then Susannah saw that Maria was still holding the Sarah book. Reaching over, she gently pried it from her hand. She looked down at the book, felt flooded by realizations about her own life—the time she'd spent in Stes.-Maries, the history her mother had had with Sarah.

"I told you before," Susannah said, "that I'm not as much an outsider as you think."

"Because you have that book?" Maria asked, her voice hollow.

"No. Because I've been to the Sarah Circle."

At that Maria raised her head, looked at Susannah with wet eyes. She blinked with disbelief. "No one is invited there who is not Rom."

"I was invited," Maria said. "By Topaz Avila."

"The others would never accept you."

"But they did, Maria," Susannah said. "When they heard my story."

"Which is—" She left the question in the air.

"My mother was unable to conceive," Susannah said. "My parents had tried to have children for years; they were giving up hope. My mother was in despair, and to help her, my father planned a trip. He knew she loved horses, and there was a place he'd heard about, where white horses run free . . ."

"The Camargue," Maria said.

Susannah nodded. "Yes. They explored

their way down through the park, and wound up almost by accident in Stes.-Maries. My parents were so taken by the story of the boat . . . without rudder or sails, that left Palestine . . ."

"Carrying the three Marys, and Martha, and Lazarus, and . . ."

"And Sara-la-Kali."

"You call her by her Gypsy name?"

Susannah nodded. "She's my saint, too."

"How could she be?" Maria asked.

"My mother went into the church that day. She described the statue—Sarah, so beautiful, made of ebony, dressed so lovingly by women of the village. Surrounded by candles."

"Thousands of candles, all glowing," Maria said, as if she could see it.

"My mother knelt at her side, and looked into her eyes. She prayed to Sarah, that she be blessed with a child."

"The child is you?"

Susannah nodded. She stared into Maria's face and saw something change: a shift in her gaze, in the focus of her brown eyes, in the way tension seemed to spiral right out of her.

"Sarah blessed your mother?"

"Yes," Susannah said. "And after my mother died, I kept a promise I'd made to her—to visit Sarah. I rented a house that turned out to be owned by Topaz. She was so friendly and welcoming, and when I told her the story, she insisted . . ."

"That you visit the Sarah Circle."

"Now do you understand why I was allowed to enter?" Susannah said.

"It's because Sarah caused a miracle in your family," Maria said. "And you are that miracle. They would want to meet you. You would be very holy to them . . ."

"I felt honored to meet them all. They were very kind to me. All except Rosalie."

"My best friend," Maria whispered. "The only one who stayed loyal to me after I married Grey."

"She's still loyal," Susannah said.

"She never liked to tell me about Sari; I would ask, and she would hold back. She couldn't bear to tell me my daughter was suffering. But I knew. I made her tell me everything."

Susannah paused. A group of riders was returning from the tent to the barn; she heard thundering hooves, looked up in time to see a blur of white horses going by.

Maria's shoulders tightened, and she refused to look out the window.

"I think Rosalie wanted to protect you," Susannah said.

"From what?"

"She knows you have a great gift," Susannah said. "Everyone talks about the way you ride, your love of horses. Not everyone can communicate with them the way you do. Rosalie, and in fact everyone I talked to, spoke of your leaving as a necessity for your spirit. They said you had to ride with Adrien, that to stay home would have stunted you, broken you down. Maybe that was part of the 'curse.' You didn't believe you deserved to ride, to have everything."

"Everything? What do you mean?"

Susannah thought of Helen, of their last talk, of all she believed she'd had to give up in order to rise so high in her field. Had she really had to sacrifice so much? Did any woman? Maybe that was just one version of a modern-day curse: being told you couldn't follow all your heart's desires, limiting yourself to just one.

"I mean stay in Stes.-Maries. Be with Adrien, and perform and ride, but also see Sari. Also be her mother . . ."

Maria listened. Susannah looked at her, believed that all the fight had gone out of her. She listened, really thinking about it. Her hands rested gently on her round belly. Her gaze swept from the book of Sarah to Susannah's face, the expression in her eyes thoughtful and without defiance.

"I could undo the memory . . ." Maria said.

"The memory?" Susannah asked, but Maria didn't reply.

Just then footsteps sounded in the hallway outside. Strong, powerful, running fast. Someone pounded on the door. Maria's eyes brightened; even before she answered the knock, Susannah knew who it was.

She pulled the door open, saw a man standing there. Not very tall, slightly built, he was nonetheless very strong-seeming. His eyes were black and wide-set, his cheekbones high and sharp, his mouth open to speak beneath a thick moustache.

"I'm looking for my wife," he said, looking over her shoulder.

"Mr. Ferret?" she asked, putting out her hand. "I'm Susannah Connolly. Please come in. Maria's here . . ."

He nodded, brushed past to go to Maria.

Knelt down beside her on one knee, took her right hand, brushed the dark hair back from his wife's face in a gesture so tender that Susannah felt tears spring to her own eyes. She stared at the couple, saw them whispering, heard Maria say the name "Sari" just before dissolving in another flood of weeping.

Adrien just caressed her. He listened to her speak, his ear close to her mouth. Susannah watched as Maria reached for the book on the desk, pulled it to her lap, pointed at Sarah's picture and whispered some more.

Susannah had to turn away. The moment was too intense and intimate for her to watch. And she was filled with thoughts of her own. She was picturing Grey and Sari, knew that it was the middle of the night there, hoped that they were sleeping. She remembered her last sight of Sari, being led away in the moonlight by her father; she thought of all the nights Sari had spent without her mother, knew what a toll they had taken.

Even with her back turned, she could hear Maria and Adrien talking, whispering. Their voices rasped with emotion, and she knew, even without understanding the Manouche language that they were speaking, that Maria was telling him what she needed. She had a heart's desire that needed to be fulfilled, and Susannah knew—with everything she had—that Maria was going to make sure it was.

"Tchaj," she heard Maria say in a voice full of tears. And then, in response, Adrien whispering back, "Tchaj, Maria . . ."

And Susannah stood there with her back turned, feeling someone beside her. Fingers brushed her hand. She felt the warmth, as if she were standing in a chapel filled with the light of a thousand candles. Outside the window, the rest of the white horses galloped out of the circus tent, but Susannah barely noticed. She was standing with Sarah, and they were both waiting for Maria to decide what she was going to do.

TWENTY-SEVEN

The month of May passed so slowly, Sari sometimes thought the calendar was going backward instead of forward. In nature, things happened in their own time. The marsh turned a little greener every day. The birds built nests, and eggs were hatched, and suddenly the air was filled with song. Dragonflies hovered over the ponds, iridescent wings gleaming. And the lunar cycle came around again so that soon the moon was growing full once more.

Sari looked up in the sky from her room at night, wishing time *would* go backward. She wished she could return to that last night

Susannah was on the ranch, when Sari had turned into a baby beast. She had taken the Tarasque story to heart—how could she not, sleeping with the soft dragon toy every night—and decided that *she* was the creature who needed taming.

If Sari could go back in time, she would tell Susannah she was sorry. She would ask her to go riding with her again. As time went by, she realized that her worst memory was the night her mother had driven away; now, staring up at the growing moon, Sari realized that that had happened again, with Susannah. Sari had chased her away from here. . . .

The next day at school was very busy. May 24 was coming up fast, and all the Gypsy kids were getting ready for the celebration. To honor the feast days of Stes.-Maries-de-la-Mer, the school was preparing a banner to be carried in the procession. The band would play, and the equestrian team would ride in formation.

Sari watched the team practicing from the window of her literature class, and felt an ache. She wished that she would someday be able to ride as well as those kids, and represent her school at important occasions—

just not the Gypsy procession. She wished with all her heart that these festivities would end soon. That would mean summer was here. . . . Staring into the field, she saw—or remembered—a shimmer of silver-green.

"Why are you so quiet?" Laurent asked, sitting beside her on the bus on the way home.

"I'm just thinking of summer," she said, shocked by the sight-memory of color.

"That's not for a few more weeks," he said, frowning. "Why are you hurrying through May, when there are so many exciting things we're going to do?"

" 'We're'?" she asked.

"Well, we have to go to the procession, to write an article for the paper."

"Laurent, the last issue has already come out."

"I told you. It would be for next September," he said. "The fall issue of the school paper should have some really good, strong reporting in it. All about the Pilgrimage of the Gypsies."

She just gave him a look, as if he was crazy.

"Not only that, someone has to carry the banner for the school, in the parade," he said. "I figured we could do it, and then we'd have firsthand experience. It would make the story even more powerful."

"I don't go to the procession," she said, staring at him, wondering why he was blushing. "You know that, and I keep telling you."

"You're related to so many people in town," he said. "They'd be proud of you, marching in the parade."

"Don't say that," she said, shaking her head. "You know they don't want any part of me." When she looked up, she saw Laurent staring down at her.

"You can go to the procession whether they want you or not," he said, his voice low and gravelly, "when you're with people who do want you."

"What do you mean?"

"You'll be with me," he said.

Sari felt the blood rush to her face. She had always known and loved Laurent; they had learned to walk and ride together. When the bad times started, he'd heard her crying late at night; she'd look out her window and see him standing in the yard. One night when they were nine, just a year after her mother had left, he'd climbed up the vines to lean into her window, give her a kiss. But it had been a brotherly kiss. The way he was looking at her now didn't feel like a brother.

"We'll march with the school," he said. "And our fathers will be there, and my mother."

"My father doesn't go to the procession," she said quietly.

"I think he's going this year," Laurent said. "My father told me."

Sari looked up, surprised again. Why would her father be going to the Pèlerinage des Gitans—the Pilgrimage of the Gypsies—the largest gathering of Romanies held anywhere, at any time of year? And why wouldn't he have told her? She'd noticed him being very odd and quiet lately. He'd gotten a letter in the mail two days ago. She'd seen the envelope, seen the post-mark.

Then she'd seen him reading the letter. He had taken it outside, to stand by the ring where Tempest was, to lean against the tall fence and read the pages. Watching from the kitchen window, Sari had seen there were several pages. Her father read them slowly; and when he'd finished reading the letter once, he read it through again. Of course it was from Susannah; Sari knew they wrote to each other all the time.

Her father had seemed different since that letter. Sari had stared at him just this morning, sitting at the breakfast table. He'd been so quiet, staring at the morning paper, seeming not to see the words. Sari had thought how thoughtful he seemed, just gazing into space. She had watched him, thinking he looked as black and white as the newspaper he held, and wishing she could see the color of her father's eyes.

"Will you go with me, Sari?" Laurent asked her now.

"I don't want to see those people," she said.

"Rosalie will be there," he said. "You know she loves you."

"I remind her of my mother," Sari said, shrinking. "She quit because of me."

"She still loves you."

"Everyone quits because of me," Sari whispered. "They leave."

Laurent gazed down at her. She had slunk low in the bus seat, knees drawn up almost to her chin. She wanted to disappear, but she didn't want to stop looking into Laurent's face. His eyes were filled with fire, but they had the effect of calming her down.

"I won't quit because of you," he said.

The bus drove through the Parc, crossing a bridge that rattled beneath the wheels. Out the windows, a herd of white horses grazed on the salt plain. Sari gazed out, saw a shimmer of silver-green. *Was* it? Had she just seen color? Or was she just remembering it? She thought about it now—ever since the night in Avignon with Laurent, things had looked different to her somehow, more vivid, even in black and white. Maybe that's all it was.

Laurent watched her, and Sari knew he could see every emotion she was feeling inside. Her skin was as thin as wet paper; everything showed. Laurent could see all the worry, pain, shame, fear she'd been feeling all this time, passing just under her skin. And now this shocking feeling, seeing a burst of green. She couldn't hide it from him.

"What is it?" he asked.

"I don't know," she said. "Something strange . . ."

"Tell me."

She shook her head hard. "Maybe it's just

thinking about that parade. It's crazy, my father wanting to go. What could that be about?"

"I don't know," he said. "What do you think?"

"Susannah, maybe," she said. "She and my father write to each other."

"I wonder if she's coming back to France," Laurent said after a long pause.

Sari stared out the window, wishing for another flash of green. She thought of Susannah coming back to France; it surprised her, how much she hoped that could happen.

"I'll be with you," Laurent said. "If you go to the procession."

"I'd be too afraid," Sari whispered, shutting her eyes.

She felt Laurent take her hand. His fingers slipped around hers, and he pulled her hand up to his chest. Her eyes were squeezed shut, but she felt his lips brush her knuckles. Her heart beat as if there were a dragonfly trapped inside. "I'll be with you, Sari," she heard him whisper. "The whole time."

*   *   *

The morning of May 24 dawned foggy and cool. Mist hovered over the marsh as the sun began to rise. Grey stood in the barn, brushing Mystère again, making sure her tail and mane were brilliant, flowing white.

Grey could hardly keep his feelings in. He felt as if he were trying to hold back the Atlantic Ocean—as if all the waves that had traveled across the sea were gathering force, ready to wash over him—and he had to slow them down. It was his job to stay calm, act "normal," when every cell in his body was raging to go see her.

Susannah; he felt her presence as if she were standing right here beside him. He felt her in the air, on the breeze, in the sounds of the marsh all around him. He swore Mystère sensed her, too; she pranced in place, letting out a long whinny.

"There, girl," Grey said, petting her. "Just a little longer now."

"She looks good," Claude said, poking his head into the stall. "Beautiful."

"This is her big moment," Grey said.

Claude chuckled. *"Hers?"* he asked. "Maybe you mean yours?"

"You know what I mean," Grey said.

"Indeed I do," Claude said, giving Grey a

long look before he nodded, heading into the tack room to make sure the saddle and bridle were polished and ready. He'd been careful to leave some tarnish in the grooves of the silver scallop shells, giving them the blackness of coquilles St. Jacques.

Grey saw Laurent out in the yard, pacing, waiting for Sari to wake up. Grey hurried, wanting to get Mystère ready before she did. He had asked her to lay out her best clothes before bed, to dress in the morning as if they were going to church. When she'd asked him why, he'd told her he wanted her to look pretty for the procession. She'd turned over, hidden her face so she wouldn't have to reply.

He'd stayed calm, kissed her goodnight, told her he'd see her in the morning. Now, looking back, maybe he should have told her what was going on. He felt as if he was balancing between wanting to tell her everything, so she would be prepared, and wanting to hold it all back—letting the day unfold, not getting her hopes up about something that might not turn out the way he prayed it would.

As Claude came out of the tack room, holding the gleaming bridle ready to slip over Mystère's head, Grey saw his old friend smiling. Claude knew Grey very well.

"Today will be a great day," Claude said.

"I hope so," Grey said.

"You have nothing to worry about. Anne and I will make sure Mystère gets to the parade grounds . . ."

"That's not what I'm worried about," Grey said.

"Sari? Laurent knows everything, and he'll see to it that everything goes smoothly. You can count on my son. And on me . . ."

"I know that, Claude," Grey said. "I've always been able to. You're a great friend."

"All will be well, understand?" Claude asked, hand on Grey's shoulder. "Laurent will be right there with Sari. We'll all be there together."

Grey nodded, shaking Claude's hand. Then, taking Mystère's bridle, Claude led her toward the trailer parked in the yard outside. He loaded her in, and Anne came out dressed in a light blue dress and beautiful straw hat. Waving, they drove away.

Steadying himself, Grey walked into the house. He went upstairs and shook Sari awake. She ignored him for a while, but then she climbed out of bed and turned on

the shower. He went into the kitchen for another cup of coffee, listening to her move
slowly, watching the fog burn off over the
marsh.

"Is she ready?" Laurent asked, standing
in the kitchen door.

"Not yet," Grey said. "But at least she's
moving."

"She will love the parade," Laurent said,
smiling. Oddly, the boy's words gave Grey
real hope. "I'll call up to her and see how
she's doing," Laurent continued.

Grey nodded. He watched Laurent go to
the foot of the stairs, heard him call up to
Sari and her brief reply. Then Grey walked
out into the yard. He was filled with pent-up
energy—all of it had felt almost impossible.
He stood in the dusty ranch yard, staring
across the fresh green marsh and in the direction of the road where he'd first met Susannah the day he'd rescued her from the
bulls, thinking of all that had happened
since then. . . .

A half hour later, he pulled the Citroën to
the kitchen door just as Laurent came walking out with Sari. She looked beautiful, with
her brown hair loose and flowing and wearing the black dress she reserved for special

occasions and the pearls his mother had given her for her last birthday.

"Come on, kids," Grey said, leaning over to open the door. "Hurry up, we don't want to be late."

"I don't even want to go," Sari said quietly, climbing into the back seat.

"Sit up front," Laurent said.

Sari just shook her head, arms clasped across her chest, gesturing that Laurent should sit beside Grey instead. Grey knew her so well—she was making her point: she might be complying, but she wasn't going to enjoy it. Laurent shrugged and got into the front seat. Like Grey, he knew Sari.

Grey pulled out onto the main road, into a heavy stream of traffic. Every car held a Gypsy family, coming from all over Europe. Every hotel in Stes.-Maries and the surrounding area had been booked for months.

It was the same every May—the Pilgrimage of Gypsies took place each year, and Romanies traveled from wherever they were to venerate their saint. As Grey concentrated on driving, his heart was racing. He hadn't been to this procession in so long. But all those memories faded: he could think only of what was about to happen.

Now, pulling into town, he drove to the field where the horse trailers were parked, and where the locals were staging for the procession. He knew exactly where to go, where they had arranged to meet. Passing a cluster of kids from Sari's school, he saw them wave and heard Laurent exclaim. Glancing in the rearview mirror, he caught Sari's eye. She was inching down in the seat, and her gaze seemed desperate.

"Drive me home," she said.

"Sweetheart," he said to her, "trust me."

"I can't," she said, and he watched as she did the familiar thing of closing her eyes. "I thought I could do this, but I can't."

"Sari," Laurent said. He reached into the back seat, grabbed her hand. Grey glanced over and knew with certainty—he saw something in Laurent's eyes, in the way he was being toward Sari—this wasn't just a boy comforting his childhood friend. Laurent was a young man in love, just as Susannah had said.

"Tell my father," Sari whispered, eyes shut tight now. "Tell him to take me home."

"We're carrying the banner for our school," Laurent said. "You'll be with me, and all our friends. We'll remember everything, so we can put it in the paper. You'll be fine."

"You will, Sari," Grey said. "Look—some people have come to see you."

His heart was in his throat. He parked in the appointed area in the field, saw Topaz and Rosalie coming toward the car, big smiles on their faces. Turning around, to tap Sari's hand, get her to open her eyes, he pointed out the window. "Look," he said.

And Sari did look.

The field was thronged with people. Men and women dressed in traditional Gypsy garb, prancing white horses in ornamental saddles, schoolchildren holding bright flags and banners. Grey climbed out of the car, pulled the front seat forward so Sari could climb out. Laurent came around from the other side. He and Grey flanked Sari, standing still as Topaz and Rosalie came through the crowd toward the car.

When they got closer, they stepped aside, and Grey could see who was walking behind them. His face broke into a smile; he felt he'd been holding it inside this whole month, ever since she'd left. The wave he felt was the dam breaking, the ocean flooding in, the wave knocking him over.

And then Grey didn't have to hold back anymore. He left Sari standing with Laurent and the others, and he ran through the people milling between them, his gaze locked with Susannah's. They were bumped and jostled, people kept getting in the way, car horns were blaring, horses cantered by, but Grey didn't see or hear anything.

Except her: except Susannah. She beamed to see him, her eyes were so bright, and her arms opened wide, and then he was there in front of her and he held her against his chest. They stood in the middle of the crowd; he felt his heart pounding against hers, and he heard her say his name over and over, until he leaned over, kissed her so gently, as if they were all alone, as if the rest of the world had disappeared and they were just floating together, holding on tight, never letting go.

TWENTY-EIGHT

Susannah felt Grey in her arms, and she closed her eyes and held him as long as she could. They'd been apart for so long, nearly a month, and every night she'd dreamed of this—of kissing him, her body against his, his arms around her. He felt so wonderful and familiar, as if he'd somehow become part of her those weeks last month, as if without him, she had lost part of herself.

Then, suddenly, they were surrounded by other people, reminded that they were not alone, that they had things to do. Reluctantly they broke apart. Susannah glanced over, worried that Sari might have been watching; but the crowd was so thick now, it was impossible to even see her.

"Where are they?" Susannah asked.

"There's a staging area over there," Grey said, gesturing toward the top of the street. "Laurent knows where they all have to be. We'll meet them in a minute. First, let me look at you again. Stay with me."

Susannah held his hands, and they gazed into each other's eyes. She couldn't stop smiling, just because she felt so happy to be with him.

"I've been thinking about seeing you again every day since I left," she said.

"Same with me," he said. "It's been the longest month of my life."

"So much has happened . . ."

"Thanks to you," he said.

"Don't say that yet," she said, smiling. "We still have a long way to go. There are probably a hundred things that can go wrong."

She and Grey headed for the staging area. Seeing Sari with Laurent, Susannah slowed down. Sari spotted her. Her eyes widened with happiness; she started over, then hesitated. Susannah held back, too, unsure of what Sari was feeling. But then, to her great joy, Sari rushed forward and threw her arms around her.

"I think about you a lot," Sari said shyly, stepping back a bit. "I'm so sorry about what happened."

"Oh, Sari," Susannah said, reaching for her again. "That's okay. You didn't do anything wrong. Not one thing."

"I didn't mean to drive you away."

"You didn't," Susannah said, hugging her, looking over the top of her head at Grey. "You couldn't."

"Thank you," Sari said. "I'm so glad you came back . . . did you know about the parade?"

"I absolutely did," Susannah said. "And I've even heard that you're going to be representing your school in it."

"We are," Laurent said, stepping over. "We're marching, and then we're going to write about it."

"Congratulations on your piece in the paper. . . . I was so proud of you; I told everyone at the college about it." Susannah glanced around, saw Helen right in the midst of everything, taking pictures with her digital camera. "In fact, let me introduce you to someone . . . Helen!"

Helen turned and saw them. She waved, walking over.

"Hello, everyone," Helen said, stepping forward. "Susannah has told me so much about all of you. . . ."

Susannah beamed. "Grey, Sari, Laurent . . . this is my mentor and dear friend, Professor Helen Oakes."

"It's wonderful to meet you," Helen said, shaking hands all around. She told them about how she'd first come here to study Saint Martha and the Tarasque, Sarah and the Marys, how fascinating she found the region, and how excited she was to see the procession.

Susannah looked at Grey; they'd had almost no time at all to talk. She knew that he'd set the ball rolling, and she only hoped it all worked out the way they planned. His gaze was powerful and constant, as if he couldn't look away from her. Even with people jostling, the crowd crushing in, the suspicious glances of people who knew his story, he didn't take his eyes off her.

After a few minutes, Laurent turned to Sari, reminding her their school was getting ready to line up. Sari reluctantly pulled herself away. Helen asked if the kids would mind if she accompanied them, so she could see their school organizing for the procession. They seemed excited to have her, and they all went off together.

Susannah was alone with Grey in a crowd of thousands. Now he took her hands, pulled her close again, and held her hands between them. Lowered his head to her, kissed her. She wanted to disappear into him, just feel his lips against hers and forget where they were. But there was still so much to do.

"I can't believe we're all here," she said when they pulled apart. "That it's actually happening."

"I've done the best I could," he said. "But where is—"

"Rosalie's been wonderful," Susannah said. "She and Topaz have arranged everything." The two women had already left to join the procession, and looking at her watch, Susannah realized that time was flying by.

"We'd better get to the church, I know," he said.

But he just held her hands, pulling back just slightly so he could look at her, swaying a little as the crowds rushed by. "I don't want to let you go again."

"I don't want you to, either."

"I feel as if I've been living through your letters," he said. "I can't believe you went to Nevada."

"We have Helen to thank for that. She convinced me . . ."

"You took that all on yourself . . ." he said. "I never would have asked you to."

"You didn't have to ask," she said quietly. He leaned down, kissed her again, and it lasted a long time, until the bells began to ring, letting everyone know Mass was ending and the procession was about to start.

He held her close against him as they made their way through the throngs of people. Women were dressed in embroidered blouses, full skirts, kerchiefs, adorned with gold and jewels. The men wore dark suits or dress shirts, some embroidered with colorful yarn.

Horses trotted toward the staging area, riders sitting tall and proud, on fancy tooled-leather saddles. There were all kinds of breeds and colors, but Susannah was struck most of all by the large numbers of

Camarguaise, the beautiful white horses that had drawn her here in the first place.

As she and Grey made their way into the center of town, Susannah became aware of people staring at them, whispering.

"It's not you," he said, and she felt him tensing up. "They're talking about me."

"Don't let it bother you," she urged. "Just keep walking."

A group of men jeered, and Susannah heard someone spit on the sidewalk as they passed. Her heart was racing, and she felt the crowd crushing in. She swore she heard the name "Maria" being said over and over, and she imagined people recounting the story, telling each other how Grey had stolen the beautiful Gypsy circus rider for himself. He held her tighter as they walked, as if trying to protect her from what they were saying, and she gave him a look to reassure him that she didn't care.

When they got to the main street, they joined an already excited and anticipatory crowd. She and Grey edged toward the front, wanting to have a good spot from which to watch Sari march past with her school.

The doors to the church opened, and the

faithful came pouring out. Susannah craned her neck, knowing that soon the statue of Sarah would emerge from the church—the only time of the year she was taken from her crypt, paraded down the street to the harbor, washed in the sea.

This was what everyone had come to see; Susannah looked for Helen, hoping she was taking everything in. There were bowers of black lilies, and Susannah had no doubt that the seeds had come from the monastery of Sarah's biographer, Vincent Phillipon, deep in the Italian countryside, the holy sanctuary where Helen's beloved monk had lived and prayed.

Susannah thought of her mother and father, of how they had come here to pray for a child, and she knew how lucky she had been to have had her mother as long as she did, and that when the statue of Sarah passed, she would be thanking her on behalf of her parents, too.

"Where is Maria now?" Grey asked as quietly as he could, considering the pitch of voices around them.

"She's with Zin-Zin," Susannah said. "She and Adrien spent the night in her caravan."

"This is her homecoming," Grey said. "Look at all these people. All of them . . . it seems they're waiting for her."

"Only one person really matters," Susannah said. "There's only one person here that Maria is coming home for."

"I know," Grey said, looking into her eyes. "Thank you, Susannah. This is because of you."

"Because of Sari," she said. "I just hope it all works the way we planned."

And just then, it seemed as if it wouldn't. Helen was making her way through the crowd, just ahead of Laurent, with one arm around a sobbing Sari. Head bent, long hair falling in her face, Sari was weeping into her hands.

"What happened?" Grey asked as Sari flew into his arms.

"They were lining up with their class," Helen explained, "when two old men started pointing at Sari, speaking in Manouche."

"They were making fun of me," she wept. "Saying that my mother left me, that she ran away in disgrace, that our family should be ashamed."

"Sari," he said, "don't listen to what people say."

"You didn't see them pointing and laughing!" she cried. "We shouldn't have come, Papa. I want to go home!"

"Sweetheart," he said, "we can't yet."

"I can't stay," she said, shuddering. "Please, please don't make me."

"No one will make you," Grey said. "Of course we won't."

Susannah stepped forward, toward the curb, to look up the street. She heard music playing: flamenco guitars and hauntingly beautiful violins. The procession was just starting. The priest in his black robe came down the church steps, followed by a throng of people carrying Sarah. The statue gleamed in the sunlight, and everyone stopped to watch.

Sarah was in a beautiful carved boat. Her faithful surrounded her, reaching out to touch her as she passed. Behind her came the children of local schools, including Sari and Laurent's. Susannah watched as they passed by with their homemade banner, smiling and waving at their friends. Laurent waved back, but Sari just buried her head in her father's shoulder.

Next came groups of Gypsy women— Susannah recognized so many of them from

the Sarah Circle. Her heart sped up, anticipating what was next. Zin-Zin, Topaz, Rosalie, Florine, Ana, Naguine, all dressed in
their finery, grinning with pride and overwhelming happiness. Susannah's eyes met
Zin-Zin's, and she smiled as the old woman
blew her a kiss. The sound of hoofbeats
grew louder; the horses were coming now.

"Grey," she said, catching his eye.

"Sari," Grey said softly. "Open your eyes."

"I just want to go home," she cried.

Susannah stood beside the young girl.
She thought back to their first, beautiful
ride. Sari had been so brave, climbing back
on Mystère, the animal she'd loved so much
but had been unable to ride for so long.

"Look who's coming, Sari," Susannah
said, taking her hand. "It's Mystère . . ."

"Sari, look . . ." Laurent said.

And with that, at the urging of her best
friend, Sari opened her eyes.

The horses were all in a line; it seemed to
stretch on forever. There were black horses
and gray horses, pintos and palaminos,
and, especially, stunning white horses from
the Camargue. Their riders were adorned in
embroidered cloaks, flowing capes, stud-
ded leather chaps.

Circus riders were performing: standing on their horses' backs, swaying to the music, playing guitars and mandolins and tiny silver cymbals. Susannah watched as Adrien led the entire troupe of Clair de Lune—all of them adorned in the circus colors of blue and silver, their costumes imprinted with the signature crescent moon.

The crowd gasped with delight and shock, and cried out as he passed: *Matelo, Matelo!* He obliged by waving and beaming, by standing on the back of his white stallion, doing pirouettes in the air.

If Sari recognized him, she gave no sign. Susannah watched her face. She had eyes only for Mystère, and the woman who was riding her.

The greatest rider of all, and she wasn't doing anything but sitting still in the saddle. The crowd fell silent as she passed, except to whisper her name: *Maria!*

"Mama!" Sari cried.

Maria beamed. She balanced in the gleaming black saddle, reaching her arms out. Grey stepped forward, lifted Sari off the ground. Maria held out one strong hand, swung her daughter out of Grey's arms, onto the saddle in front of her.

Susannah saw Grey and Maria lock eyes for a moment. Then she watched as Sari leaned into her mother's body, her eyes wide open, gazing straight up at the sky, with Maria's arms wrapped around her.

Maria clutched Sari, riding past. Her right hand dropped down, just long enough to brush Grey's fingers, then Susannah's. She met Susannah's eyes with a glance of gratitude. And she held Sari tight again and rode on.

Susannah turned to Grey. For once, she was the one who couldn't quite look. She pressed her face into his chest, eyes squeezed tight, feeling tears and love well up inside.

She heard Helen ask Laurent if he wanted to walk alongside Maria and Sari, heard him say yes. She heard them walk off together, heard the uneven pace as Helen walked slowly and Laurent supported her.

"Thank you," Grey whispered into her ear, holding her as tightly as he could. "Thank you, Susannah."

"Oh, Grey," she whispered back, mouth against his shirt. "I'm not the one to thank."

Susannah heard Mystère's hoofbeats clacking on the pavement, heard the jingle of silver scallops on her saddle, glistening black in the sun. She smelled the sweetness as wagons of black lilies clattered by. And then she heard Sari cry out. Grey heard it, too, and they started running down the street, behind Laurent, who was tearing as fast as he could toward Sari and her mother.

And when they got closer, they saw Sari turning, tears streaming from her eyes. Her mother's arms were around her.

"The day is so bright," Sari cried. "And I think . . . oh, I know, the sky is so blue . . . Laurent . . ."

"Sari," Laurent said, walking alongside, reaching up to touch her hand. "You mean—?"

"You have hazel eyes," Sari said, gazing at him. She'd seen that shimmer of silvery green in the marsh, and now she saw a burst of blue overhead, and looking into Laurent's eyes, they were the hazel she re-membered. Her mother held her, and Laurent was by her side, and her father had al-ways been right here. . . . She looked over at him with Susannah, and she felt such radiant joy mingling with the colors, she couldn't tell where one let off and the other began.

Susannah rocked in Grey's arms, holding on to him as the parade went on. Mystère walked proudly along, Maria holding tight to Sari. The most famous circus rider in the world wasn't standing, wasn't doing any tricks at all: was simply riding through the crowd of the people who had never stopped loving her, embracing her daughter as they moved along, past brightly colored flowers that seemed to have been set out this day just so Sari could see them, down to the sparkling blue harbor, where Sarah was being washed in the sea.

EPILOGUE

They sat on the seawall across the street from Dempsey Stables in Narragansett, Rhode Island, gazing out over the still, black water. Grey's arm was around Susannah's shoulders, and she leaned into him. The sky was perfectly clear, and midnight blue. Stars blazed overhead. Susannah wanted to ask him if the constellations looked the same as at home, in France. But she was too mesmerized, watching the horizon.

"Is that it?" Grey asked.

Susannah squinted, staring at the thin dark line where the sea met the sky. She looked for a glow, but saw only darkness.

"Not yet," she said.

As if he knew that meant they had a reprieve, he kissed her. She could have gotten completely lost in his kiss, pressed against his body, sea mist on both their faces, but she forced herself to stay present. She caressed his cheek with her hand, pulled back enough to look into his blue eyes.

"You know it's already risen in France," she said.

"But not yet here," he said. "And not yet in the desert."

"Do you think Sari will watch later?"

He laughed. "I think she wants to see everything. It's all new to her. Especially with Laurent there, and the fact they're staying at a ranch called Clair de Lune . . . and she's with her mother."

"She sounded so happy on the phone," Susannah said. She thought of the conversation, of how excited Sari had sounded, describing all the colors in the desert, and the circus, and her mother's eyes.

"I know," he said. "She's been looking forward to this visit with Maria ever since the parade."

"How is it for you?" Susannah asked.

"Me?"

"Yes," she said, stroking his face, staring into his eyes. "You've raised her alone for so long."

"Seeing her mother is good for Sari," he said. "So it's good for me, too."

Susannah nodded. She'd been with Grey when he'd driven Sari and Laurent to the airport. They'd been staying with his parents in Rhode Island, and now the kids were out in Nevada for a week, spending time with Maria. Susannah had watched Sari hug her father in the departures building, so hard it seemed she'd never let go.

But when it was time for her to go through security, she and Laurent on their way to the plane, she'd given both her father and Susannah exuberant waves, excitement in her dark green eyes.

"It's because of you," Grey said to Susannah now. "You brought them together."

"No, it wasn't me," she said, knowing she couldn't take credit for something so powerful and right. From the minute Sari had jumped up on the horse with Maria, the bond between them had started to heal. What they'd both wanted for so long, a way back to each other, had started to happen.

And it was happening in full, glorious color. . . .

Now, gazing out at the water, Susannah saw a golden line where the horizon had been. It shimmered, growing wider. The full moon began to crest, and then to rise. It had been two months since that magical trail ride, the night they'd rescued Tempest, and one month since the Gypsies' Pilgrimage, the festival of Sarah.

Susannah watched the moon rise out of the sea, wide and bright as a basket of gold. It overflowed onto the water's surface, painting a gleaming path that seemed to stretch straight to her and Grey. She felt the moonlight on her skin, stared at its trail across the sea. It looked almost solid enough to walk across.

She thought of Sari and her mother, getting to know each other all over again, and of her own mother—how much she missed her, and wished she could introduce her to these people she loved. She thought about how grateful she was to Helen, and to Zin-Zin—for helping her forgive herself for leaving her mother alone. She gazed at the moon's bright path and imagined herself walking it with Grey, taking him to meet her parents.

"If only," she said out loud.

"What?" he asked.

"If only we could all be together."

"Who do you mean?"

"Us," she said. "And all the people we love."

"I'm with you," he said, holding her.

She nodded. And she had met his parents and brothers, and Helen had given her her blessing to move to France, live on the ranch, and work on her own book, a study of Sarah's miracles in the lives of women who loved her. Sari was so happy about it, had asked Susannah to promise that they could go riding together, that they could all take a moonlight ride as soon as Sari was ready. Susannah had promised.

Right now, staring out at the moon, she felt the kind of piercing sadness that comes from so much love. She felt it so fully and completely for Grey and Sari, but she wished that she could have just one more thing, one more miracle.

"They know," Grey said.

"What do you mean?" she asked.

"Your parents," he said, holding her hand. "They know about us."

"How can they?" she asked, tears filling her eyes. "You know my mother died six months before I met you."

"Yes," he said. "But don't forget, she sent you."

Susannah stared at the sea, feeling the salt breeze in her hair, a long tingle shivering down her back.

"Sent me," she whispered.

"To thank Sarah," he said. "Do you really imagine she didn't know what would happen?"

"That I'd travel to France and meet you?"

"Exactly that," Grey said, holding her. Then, looking straight into the sky, where the moon glowed, he said in a voice almost too quiet for Susannah to hear, "Thank you—for sending Susannah to me."

Whether he was speaking to Susannah's mother, or the moon, or Sarah, Susannah didn't know. She just held Grey's hand and watched the soft white light fall on the dark and lovely sea, and they sat there together, in the light of the rising moon.

About the Author

LUANNE RICE is the author of twenty-four novels, most recently *What Matters Most, The Edge of Winter, Sandcastles, Summer of Roses, Summer's Child, Silver Bells,* and *Beach Girls*. She lives in New York City and Old Lyme, Connecticut.

GOD'S *Word*®

TRANSLATION

GREEN KEY

Holiday, Florida 34691 U.S.A.

CONTENTS

The Books of the Old Testament

The Books of the New Testament

The Books of the Old and New Testaments
(Numerical and Alphabetical Order)

Italics indicate New Testament books.

PREFACE

GOD'S WORD® Is New

The twentieth century produced more Bible translations than any other. This includes English as well as foreign language translations. GOD'S WORD®, produced by God's Word to the Nations, fills a need that has remained unmet by English Bibles: to communicate in clear, natural English to God's people today without compromising the Bible's saving, life-changing message. This translation is an exceptional literary work that consciously combines scholarly fidelity with natural English.

Traditionally, the Scriptures have been translated into English by teams of Bible scholars serving part-time. This translation employed full-time Bible scholars and full-time English editorial reviewers. GOD'S WORD® is the first English Bible in which English reviewers have been actively involved with scholars at every stage of the translation process.

Because of the involvement of English reviewers, GOD'S WORD looks and reads like contemporary English literature. It uses natural grammar, follows standard punctuation and capitalization rules, and is printed in a single column. Because of the involvement of scholars, GOD'S WORD is an accurate, trustworthy translation.

GOD'S WORD Is for Everyone

One of the goals of GOD'S WORD® is to communicate the saving, life-changing Good News about Jesus. GOD'S WORD is intended to be read by those who are well-versed in Scripture as well as first-time Bible readers, Christians as well as non-Christians, adults as well as children.

GOD'S WORD Is a Translation

Of course, the Word of God didn't originally come to us in the English language. Since many people have wanted to read the Scriptures in their own language, scholars have found it necessary to translate the Bible from the Hebrew, Aramaic, and Greek languages in which it was written. Like many Bibles published before it, GOD'S WORD® has been translated directly from those original languages. Unlike Bibles before it, however, the translation theory used to produce GOD'S WORD® is different because the theory and practice of translation has advanced through the years.

The oldest translation theory is form-equivalent translation (often inaccurately called literal translation). In this type of translation, the translator chooses one of a limited number of meanings assigned to each Hebrew, Aramaic, or Greek word. The translator fills in the words that belong in the sentence but follows the word arrangement and grammar that is characteristic of the original language. Such a translation is often viewed as accurate. However, it can result in awkward, misleading, incomprehensible, or even amusing sentences. For instance, a form-equivalent translation of 1 Samuel 9:2 could read: "From his shoulders upward Saul was taller than any of the people." In English this implies that Saul had a misshapen head and neck. Translations using this theory have made the Bible more difficult to read and understand in English than it was in the original languages.

A newer translation theory is function-equivalent translation (often inaccurately called paraphrasing). In this type of translation, the translator tries to make the English function the same way the original language functioned for the original readers. However, in trying to make the translation easy to read, the translator can omit concepts from the original text that don't seem to have corresponding modern English equivalents. Such a translation can produce a readable text, but that text can convey the wrong meaning or not enough meaning. Furthermore, function-equivalent translations attempt to make some books readable on levels at which they were not intended. For instance, Song of Songs was not written for children. Paul's letter to the Ephesians is very sophisticated and not intended for novices.

The translation theory followed by God's Word to the Nations is closest natural equivalent translation. The first consideration for the translators of GOD'S WORD® was to find equivalent English ways of expressing the meaning of the Hebrew, Aramaic, or Greek text. This procedure ensures that the translation is faithful to the meaning intended by the original writer. The next consideration was readability. The meaning is expressed in natural English by using common English punctuation, capitalization, grammar, and word choice. The third consideration was to choose the natural equivalent that most closely reflects the style of the Hebrew, Aramaic, or Greek text. This translation theory is designed to avoid the awkwardness and inaccuracy associated with form-equivalent translation, and it avoids the loss of meaning and oversimplification associated with function-equivalent translation.

Features of GOD'S WORD
Layout

The features that distinguish GOD'S WORD® from other Bible translations are designed to aid readers. The most obvious of these is the open, single-column format. This invites readers into the page. The single column takes the Bible out of the reference book category and presents it as the literary work that God intended it to be.

In prose GOD'S WORD looks like other works of literature. It contains frequent paragraphing. Whenever a different speaker's words are quoted, a new paragraph begins. Lists, genealogies, and long prayers are formatted to help readers recognize the thought pattern of the text. The prose style of GOD'S WORD favors concise, clear sentences. While avoiding very long, complicated sentences, which characterize many English Bible translations, GOD'S WORD strives to vary the word arrangement in a natural way. Doing this brings the Scriptures to life.

Poetry in GOD'S WORD is instantly recognized by its format. The single-column format enables readers to recognize parallel thoughts in parallel lines of poetry. In a single-column, across-the-page layout, a variety of indentations are possible. The mission society's translators have used indentation to indicate the relationship of one line to others in the same context. This enables a person reading the Bible in English to appreciate the Bible's poetry in much the same way a person reading the Bible in the original languages of Hebrew, Aramaic, or Greek would appreciate it.

Punctuation, Capitalization

In English, meaning is conveyed not only by words but also by punctuation. However, no punctuation existed in ancient Hebrew and Greek writing, and words were used where English grammar would prefer punctuation marks. GOD'S WORD® strives to use standard English punctuation wherever possible. At times this means that a punctuation mark or paragraph break represents the meaning that could only be expressed in words in Hebrew or Greek.

Italics are also used as they would be in other printed English texts: for foreign words or to indicate that a word is used as a word. (GOD'S WORD never uses italics to indicate emphasis.)

Wherever possible, GOD'S WORD has supplied information in headings or half-brackets to identify the speaker in quoted material. To minimize the confusion produced by quotations within quotations, quotation marks are used sparingly. For instance, they are not used after formulaic statements such as "This is what the LORD says: ..."

Contractions can fit comfortably into many English sentences. Certainly, "Don't you care that we're going to die" is less stiff than, "Do you not care that we are going to die?" GOD'S WORD achieves a warmer style by using contractions where appropriate. However, uncontracted words are used in contexts that require special emphasis.

GOD'S WORD capitalizes the first letter in proper nouns and sentences and all the letters in the word LORD when it represents Yahweh, the name of God in the Old Testament. Some religious literature chooses to capitalize pronouns that refer to the deity. As in the original languages, GOD'S WORD does not capitalize any pronouns (unless they begin sentences). In some cases scholars are uncertain whether pronouns in the ancient texts refer to God or someone else. In these cases the presence of capitalized pronouns would be misleading. However, when the Hebrew or Greek pronouns are not ambiguous, but an English pronoun would be, GOD'S WORD uses the appropriate proper noun in its place.

Gender References

The Scriptures contain many passages that apply to all people. Therefore, GOD'S WORD® strives to use gender-neutral language in these passages so that all readers will apply these passages to themselves. For example, traditionally, Psalm 1:1 has been translated, "Blessed is the man who does not follow the advice of the wicked..." As a result, many readers will understand this verse to mean that only adult males, not women or children, can receive a blessing. However, in GOD'S WORD the first Psalm begins "Blessed is the person who does not follow the advice of the wicked..."

However, if a passage focuses upon an individual, God's Word does not use plural nouns and pronouns to avoid the gender-specific pronouns *he, him, and his*. In these cases the translators considered the text's focus upon an individual more important than an artificial use of plural pronouns. In addition, gender-specific language is preserved in passages that apply specifically to men or specifically to women.

Word Choice

Many Bible translations contain theological terms that have little, if any, meaning for most nontheologically-trained readers. GOD'S WORD® avoids using these traditional terms and substitutes words that carry the same meaning in common English. In some cases traditional theological words are contained in footnotes the first time they occur in a chapter. Examples of these theological terms include *covenant, grace, justify, repent,* and *righteousness*.

While all these features make GOD'S WORD® a uniquely readable and understandable Bible, the ultimate goal of the mission society is to bring the readers of GOD'S WORD into a new or closer relationship with Jesus. The translation team and support staff of God's Word to the Nations pray that your reading of GOD'S WORD makes the words of our great God and Savior, as revealed through his prophets and apostles, come to life for you.

For more details on the translation process and the unique features that enable GOD'S WORD® to accurately and clearly communicate God's saving, life-changing message visit them at www.godsword.org or write to them at—

God's Word to the Nations
P.O. Box 400
Orange Park, Florida 32067-0400

Notes on the Text of GOD'S WORD

Brackets

Proper names or foreign words whose meaning is significant for understanding a particular Bible passage are translated in brackets ([ ]) following the name or phrase. When reading aloud a bracketed word may be treated as "that is."

Half-brackets (⌊ ⌋) enclose words that the translation team supplied because the context contains meaning that is not explicitly stated in the original language.

Footnotes

Five types of footnotes are used in GOD'S WORD:

1. Explanatory footnotes clarify historical, cultural, and geographical details from the ancient world to make the text more understandable to modern readers. These footnotes also identify word play in Hebrew or Greek that would otherwise be lost to the English reader.

2. Alternate translation footnotes offer other plausible translations. They are introduced by the word *or.*

3. Footnotes that state "English equivalent difficult" mark passages where a Hebrew or Greek expression cannot be adequately translated into modern English without resorting to a long, inappropriate paraphrase.

4. Footnotes that state "Hebrew meaning uncertain" or "Greek meaning uncertain" mark passages where scholars are not sure what a Hebrew or Greek expression means.

5. Textual footnotes are included wherever GOD'S WORD translates the meaning of some text other than the Masoretic Text printed in *Biblia Hebraica Stuttgartensia* or its footnotes (Old Testament) or the Greek text printed in the twenty-seventh edition of *Novum Testamentum Graece* (New Testament).

Terms Used In Footnotes

Aramaic	one of the languages of the Old Testament, related to Hebrew
Dead Sea Scrolls	one or more of the Qumran manuscripts
Egyptian	one or more of the ancient translations of the Bible into the ancient Egyptian or Ethiopic languages
Greek	in the Old Testament: one or more of the ancient Greek translations of the Old Testament; in the New Testament: the Greek language, the language of the New Testament
Hebrew	the primary language of the Old Testament
Latin	one or more of the ancient Latin translations of the Bible
Masoretic Text	the traditional Hebrew text of the Old Testament
manuscript	an ancient, handwritten copy of a text
Samaritan Pentateuch	Samaritan Hebrew version of the first five books of the Bible
Syriac	the ancient Syriac translation of the Bible
Targum	one of the ancient Aramaic translations of the Old Testament

THE
OLD TESTAMENT

GENESIS

The Creation

1 ¹ In the beginning God created heaven and earth.
² The earth was formless and empty, and darkness covered the deep water. The Spirit of God was hovering over the water.

³ Then God said, "Let there be light!" So there was light. ⁴ God saw the light was good. So God separated the light from the darkness. ⁵ God named the light *day,* and the darkness he named *night.* There was evening, then morning—the first day.

⁶ Then God said, "Let there be a horizon in the middle of the water in order to separate the water." ⁷ So God made the horizon and separated the water above and below the horizon. And so it was. ⁸ God named ⸢what was above⸣ the horizon *sky.* There was evening, then morning—a second day.

⁹ Then God said, "Let the water under the sky come together in one area, and let the dry land appear." And so it was. ¹⁰ God named the dry land *earth.* The water which came together he named *sea.* God saw that it was good. ¹¹ Then God said, "Let the earth produce vegetation: plants bearing seeds, each according to its own type, and fruit trees bearing fruit with seeds, each according to its own type." And so it was. ¹² The earth produced vegetation: plants bearing seeds, each according to its own type, and trees bearing fruit with seeds, each according to its own type. God saw that they were good. ¹³ There was evening, then morning—a third day.

¹⁴ Then God said, "Let there be lights in the sky to separate the day from the night. They will be signs and will mark religious festivals, days, and years. ¹⁵ They will be lights in the sky to shine on the earth." And so it was. ¹⁶ God made the two bright lights: the larger light to rule the day and the smaller light to rule the night. He also made the stars. ¹⁷ God put them in the sky to give light to the earth, ¹⁸ to dominate the day and the night, and to separate the light from the darkness. God saw that it was good. ¹⁹ There was evening, then morning—a fourth day.

²⁰ Then God said, "Let the water swarm with swimming creatures, and let birds fly through the sky over the earth." ²¹ So God created the large sea creatures, every type of creature that swims around in the water and every type of flying bird. God saw that they were good. ²² God blessed them and said, "Be fertile, increase in number, fill the sea, and let there be many birds on the earth." ²³ There was evening, then morning—a fifth day.

²⁴ Then God said, "Let the earth produce every type of living creature: every type of domestic animal, crawling animal, and wild animal." And so it was. ²⁵ God made every type of wild animal, every type of domestic animal, and every type of creature that crawls on the ground. God saw that they were good.

²⁶ Then God said, "Let us make humans in our image, in our likeness. Let them rule the fish in the sea, the birds in the sky, the domestic animals all over the earth, and all the animals that crawl on the earth."

²⁷   So God created humans in his image.
        In the image of God he created them.
        He created them male and female.

²⁸ God blessed them and said, "Be fertile, increase in number, fill the earth, and be its master. Rule the fish in the sea, the birds in the sky, and all the animals that crawl on the earth." ²⁹ God said, "I have given you every plant with seeds on the face of the earth and every tree that has fruit with seeds. This will be your food. ³⁰ I have given all green plants as food to every land animal, every bird in the sky, and every animal that crawls on the earth—every living, breathing animal." And so it was.

³¹ And God saw everything that he had made and that it was very good. There was evening, then morning—the sixth day.

2 ¹ Heaven and earth and everything in them were finished. ² By the seventh day God finished the work he had been doing. On the seventh day he stopped the work he had been doing. ³ Then God blessed the seventh day and set it apart as holy, because on that day he stopped all his work of creation.

The Creation of Man and Woman

[4] This is the account of heaven and earth when they were created, at the time when the LORD God made earth and heaven.

[5] Wild bushes and plants were not on the earth yet because the LORD God hadn't sent rain on the earth. Also, there was no one to farm the land. [6] Instead, underground water would come up from the earth and water the entire surface of the ground.

[7] Then the LORD God formed the man from the dust of the earth[a] and blew the breath of life into his nostrils. The man became a living being.

[8] The LORD God planted a garden in Eden, in the east. That's where he put the man whom he had formed. [9] The LORD God made all the trees grow out of the ground. These trees were nice to look at, and their fruit was good to eat. The tree of life and the tree of the knowledge of good and evil grew in the middle of the garden.

[10] A river flowed from Eden to water the garden. Outside the garden it divided into four rivers. [11] The name of the first river is Pishon. This is the one that winds throughout Havilah, where there is gold. [12] (The gold of that land is pure. Bdellium[b] and onyx are also ˌfoundˌ there.) [13] The name of the second river is Gihon. This is the one that winds throughout Sudan. [14] The name of the third river is Tigris. This is the one that flows east of Assyria. The fourth river is the Euphrates.

[15] Then the LORD God took the man and put him in the Garden of Eden to farm the land and to take care of it. [16] The LORD God commanded the man. He said, "You are free to eat from any tree in the garden. [17] But you must never eat from the tree of the knowledge of good and evil because when you eat from it, you will certainly die."

[18] Then the LORD God said, "It is not good for the man to be alone. I will make a helper who is right for him."

[19] The LORD God had formed all the wild animals and all the birds out of the ground. Then he brought them to the man to see what he would call them. Whatever the man called each creature became its name. [20] So the man named all the domestic animals, all the birds, and all the wild animals.

But the man found no helper who was right for him. [21] So the LORD God caused him to fall into a deep sleep. While the man was sleeping, the LORD God took out one of the man's ribs and closed up the flesh at that place. [22] Then the LORD God formed a woman from the rib that he had taken from the man. He brought her to the man.

[23] The man said,

> "This is now bone of my bones and flesh of my flesh.
> She will be named *woman*
> because she was taken from man."

[24] That is why a man will leave his father and mother and will be united with his wife, and they will become one flesh. [25] The man and his wife were both naked, but they weren't ashamed of it.

The First Sin and the First Promise

3 [1] The snake was more clever than all the wild animals the LORD God had made. He asked the woman, "Did God really say, 'You must never eat the fruit of any tree in the garden'?"

[2] The woman answered the snake, "We're allowed to eat the fruit from any tree in the garden [3] except the tree in the middle of the garden. God said, 'You must never eat it or touch it. If you do, you will die!' "

[4] "You certainly won't die!" the snake told the woman. [5] "God knows that when you eat it your eyes will be opened. You'll be like God, knowing good and evil."

[6] The woman saw that the tree had fruit that was good to eat, nice to look at, and desirable for making someone wise. So she took some of the fruit and ate it. She also gave some to her husband, who was with her, and he ate it.

[7] Then their eyes were opened, and they both realized that they were naked. They sewed fig leaves together and made clothes for themselves.

[8] In the cool of the evening, the man and his wife heard the LORD God walking around in the garden. So they hid from the LORD God among the trees in the garden. [9] The LORD God called to the man and asked him, "Where are you?"

[10] He answered, "I heard you in the garden. I was afraid because I was naked, so I hid."

[11] God asked, "Who told you that you were naked? Did you eat fruit from the tree I commanded you not to eat from?"

---

[a] 2:7 There is a play on words here between Hebrew *'adam* (man) and *'adamah* (earth).   [b] 2:12 Hebrew meaning uncertain.

¹² The man answered, "That woman, the one you gave me, gave me some fruit from the tree, and I ate it."

¹³ Then the LORD God asked the woman, "What have you done?"

"The snake deceived me, and I ate," the woman answered.

¹⁴ So the LORD God said to the snake, "Because you have done this,

> You are cursed more than all the wild or domestic animals.
> You will crawl on your belly.
> You will be the lowest of animals as long as you live.
> ¹⁵ I will make you and the woman hostile toward each other.
> I will make your descendants
>   and her descendant hostile toward each other.
> He will crush your head,
>   and you will bruise his heel."

¹⁶ He said to the woman,

> "I will increase your pain and your labor
>   when you give birth to children.
>   Yet, you will long for your husband,
>   and he will rule you."

¹⁷ Then he said to the man, "You listened to your wife and ate fruit from the tree, although I commanded you, 'You must never eat its fruit.'

> The ground is cursed because of you.
>   Through hard work you will eat ˌfood that comesˌ from it
>   every day of your life.
> ¹⁸ The ground will grow thorns and thistles for you,
>   and you will eat wild plants.
> ¹⁹ By the sweat of your brow, you will produce food to eat
>   until you return to the ground,
>   because you were taken from it.
> You are dust, and you will return to dust."

²⁰ Adam named his wife Eve [Life] because she became the mother of every living person. ²¹ The LORD God made clothes from animal skins for the man and his wife and dressed them. ²² Then the LORD God said, "The man has become like one of us, since he knows good and evil. He must not reach out and take the fruit from the tree of life and eat. Then he would live forever." ²³ So the LORD God sent the man out of the Garden of Eden to farm the ground from which the man had been formed. ²⁴ After he sent the man out, God placed angels[a] and a flaming sword that turned in all directions east of the Garden of Eden. He placed them there to guard the way to the tree of life.

Cain Murders Abel

4 ¹ Adam made love to his wife Eve. She became pregnant and gave birth to Cain. She said, "I have gotten the man that the LORD promised." ² Then she gave birth to another child, Abel, Cain's brother. Abel was a shepherd, and Cain was a farmer.

³ Later Cain brought some crops from the land as an offering to the LORD. ⁴ Abel also brought some choice parts of the firstborn animals from his flock. The LORD approved of Abel and his offering, ⁵ but he didn't approve of Cain and his offering. So Cain became very angry and was disappointed. ⁶ Then the LORD asked Cain, "Why are you angry, and why do you look disappointed? ⁷ If you do well, won't you be accepted? But if you don't do well, sin is lying outside your door ready to attack. It wants to control you, but you must master it."

⁸ Cain talked to his brother Abel. Later, when they were in the fields, Cain attacked his brother Abel and killed him.

⁹ The LORD asked Cain, "Where is your brother Abel?"

"I don't know," he answered. "Am I supposed to take care of my brother?"

¹⁰ The LORD asked, "What have you done? Your brother's blood is crying out to me from the ground. ¹¹ So now you are cursed from the ground, which has received the blood of your brother whom you killed. ¹² When you farm the ground, it will no longer yield its best for you. You will be a fugitive, a wanderer on the earth."

---

[a] 3:24 Or "cherubim."

¹³ But Cain said to the LORD, "My punishment is more than I can stand! ¹⁴ You have forced me off this land today. I have to hide from you and become a fugitive, a wanderer on the earth. Now anyone who finds me will kill me!"

¹⁵ So the LORD said to him, "Not so! Anyone who kills Cain will suffer vengeance seven times over." The LORD gave Cain a sign so that anyone meeting him would not kill him.

¹⁶ Then Cain left the LORD's presence and lived in Nod [The Land of Wandering], east of Eden.

Cain's Ten Descendants—Cain to Lamech

¹⁷ Cain made love to his wife. She became pregnant and gave birth to Enoch. Cain was building a city, and he named it Enoch after his son. ¹⁸ To Enoch was born Irad. Irad was the father of Mehujael. Mehujael was the father of Methushael. And Methushael was the father of Lamech.

¹⁹ Lamech married two women, one named Adah and the other Zillah. ²⁰ Adah gave birth to Jabal. He was the first person to live in tents and have livestock. ²¹ His brother's name was Jubal. He was the first person to play the harp and the flute. ²² Zillah also had a son, Tubalcain, who made bronze and iron tools. Tubalcain's sister was Naamah.

²³ Lamech said to his wives,

> "Adah and Zillah, listen to me!
> Wives of Lamech, hear what I say!
> I killed a man for bruising me,
>   a young man for wounding me.
> ²⁴ If Cain is avenged 7 times,
>   then Lamech, 77 times."

Adam's Godly Descendants—Adam to Enosh

²⁵ Adam made love to his wife again. She gave birth to a son and named him Seth, because ˷she said,˷ "God has given[a] me another child in place of Abel, since Cain killed him."

²⁶ A son was also born to Seth, and he named him Enosh. At that time people began to worship the LORD.

Adam's Ten Descendants—Adam to Noah—1 Chronicles 1:1–3

5 ¹ This is the written account of Adam and his descendants.

> When God created humans,
>   he made them in the likeness of God.
> ²   He created them male and female.
>   He blessed them and called them humans
> when he created them.

³ When Adam was 130 years old, he became the father ˷of a son˷ in his own likeness, in his own image. He named him Seth. ⁴ After Adam became the father of Seth, he lived 800 years and had other sons and daughters. ⁵ Adam lived a total of 930 years; then he died.

⁶ When Seth was 105 years old, he became the father of Enosh. ⁷ After he became the father of Enosh, Seth lived 807 years and had other sons and daughters. ⁸ Seth lived a total of 912 years; then he died.

⁹ When Enosh was 90 years old, he became the father of Kenan. ¹⁰ After he became the father of Kenan, Enosh lived 815 years and had other sons and daughters. ¹¹ Enosh lived a total of 905 years; then he died.

¹² When Kenan was 70 years old, he became the father of Mahalalel. ¹³ After he became the father of Mahalalel, Kenan lived 840 years and had other sons and daughters. ¹⁴ Kenan lived a total of 910 years; then he died.

¹⁵ When Mahalalel was 65 years old, he became the father of Jared. ¹⁶ After he became the father of Jared, Mahalalel lived 830 years and had other sons and daughters. ¹⁷ Mahalalel lived a total of 895 years; then he died.

¹⁸ When Jared was 162 years old, he became the father of Enoch. ¹⁹ After he became the father of Enoch, Jared lived 800 years and had other sons and daughters. ²⁰ Jared lived a total of 962 years; then he died.

²¹ When Enoch was 65 years old, he became the father of Methuselah. ²² After he became the father of Methuselah, Enoch walked with God for 300 years and had other sons and daughters. ²³ Enoch lived a total of 365 years. ²⁴ Enoch walked with God; then he was gone because God took him.

---

[a] 4:25 There is a play on words here between Hebrew *sheth* (Seth) and *shath* (given).

²⁵ When Methuselah was 187 years old, he became the father of Lamech. ²⁶ After he became the father of Lamech, Methuselah lived 782 years and had other sons and daughters. ²⁷ Methuselah lived a total of 969 years; then he died.

²⁸ When Lamech was 182 years old, he became the father of a son. ²⁹ He named him Noah [Relief], and said, "This child will bring us relief from the work and painful labor of our hands since the LORD has cursed the ground." ³⁰ After Lamech became the father of Noah, he lived 595 years and had other sons and daughters. ³¹ Lamech lived a total of 777 years; then he died.

³² When Noah was 500 years old, he became the father of Shem, Ham, and Japheth.

Evil Increases on the Earth

6 ¹ The number of people increased all over the earth, and daughters were born to them. ² The sons of God saw that the daughters of other humans were beautiful. So they married any woman they chose.

³ Then the LORD said, "My Spirit will not struggle with humans forever, because they are flesh and blood. They will live 120 years."

⁴ The Nephilim were on the earth in those days, as well as later, when the sons of God slept with the daughters of other humans and had children by them. These children were famous long ago.

⁵ The LORD saw how evil humans had become on the earth. All day long their deepest thoughts were nothing but evil. ⁶ The LORD was sorry that he had made humans on the earth, and he was heartbroken. ⁷ So he said, "I will wipe off the face of the earth these humans that I created. I will wipe out not only humans, but also domestic animals, crawling animals, and birds. I'm sorry that I made them." ⁸ But the LORD was pleased with Noah.

Noah's Family and the Ship

⁹ This is the account of Noah and his descendants.

Noah had God's approval and was a man of integrity among the people of his time. He walked with God. ¹⁰ He had three sons: Shem, Ham, and Japheth.

¹¹ The world was corrupt in God's sight and full of violence. ¹² God saw the world and how corrupt it was because all people on earth lived evil lives.

¹³ God said to Noah, "I have decided to put an end to all people because the earth is full of their violence. Now I'm going to destroy them along with the earth. ¹⁴ Make yourself a ship of cypress wood.ᵃ Make rooms in the ship and coat it inside and out with tar. ¹⁵ This is how you should build it: the ship is to be 450 feet long, 75 feet wide, and 45 feet high. ¹⁶ Make a roof for the ship, and leave an 18-inch-high opening at the top.ᵇ Put a door in the side of the ship. Build the ship with lower, middle, and upper decks. ¹⁷ I'm about to send a flood on the earth to destroy all people under the sky—every living, breathing human. Everything on earth will die.

¹⁸ "But I will make my promiseᶜ to you. You, your sons, your wife, and your sons' wives will go into the ship. ¹⁹ Bring two of every living creature into the ship in order to keep them alive with you. They must be male and female. ²⁰ Two of every type of bird, every type of domestic animal, and every type of creature that crawls on the ground will come to you to be kept alive. ²¹ Take every kind of food that can be eaten and store it. It will be food for you and the animals."

²² Noah did this. He did everything that God had commanded him.

The Flood

7 ¹ The LORD said to Noah, "Go into the ship with your whole family because I have seen that you alone are righteous among the people of today. ² Take with you seven pairs of every kind of clean animal (a male and a female of each) and one pair of every kind of uncleanᵃ animal (a male and a female). ³ Also, take seven pairs of every kind of bird (a male and a female of each) to preserve animal life all over the earth after the flood. ⁴ In seven days I will send rain to the earth for 40 days and 40 nights. I will wipe off the face of the earth every living creature that I have made."

⁵ So Noah did everything that the LORD commanded him.

⁶ Noah was 600 years old when the flood came to the earth. ⁷ Noah, his sons, his wife, and his sons' wives went into the ship to escape the floodwaters. ⁸ Clean and unclean animals, birds, and creatures that crawl on the ground ⁹ came to Noah to go into the ship in pairs (a male and female of each) as God had commanded Noah.

¹⁰ Seven days later the flood came on the earth. ¹¹ On the seventeenth day of the second month of the six hundredth year of Noah's life, all the deep springs burst open. The sky opened, ¹² and rain came pouring down on the earth for 40 days and 40 nights.

ᵃ 6:14 Or "teakwood."   ᵇ 6:16 Hebrew meaning uncertain.   ᶜ 6:18 Or "covenant."   ᵃ 7:2 "Clean" refers to anything that is presentable to God. "Unclean" refers to anything that is not presentable to God.

[13] On that same day Noah and his sons Shem, Ham, and Japheth, as well as Noah's wife and his three daughters-in-law went into the ship. [14] They had with them every type of wild animal, every type of domestic animal, every type of creature that crawls on the earth, and every type of bird (every creature with wings). [15] A pair of every living, breathing animal came to Noah to go into the ship. [16] A male and a female of every animal went in as God had commanded Noah. Then the LORD closed the door behind them.

[17] The flood continued for 40 days on the earth. The water increased and lifted the ship so that it rose high above the ground. [18] As the water rose and became very deep, the ship floated on top of the water. [19] The water rose very high above the earth. It covered all the high mountains everywhere under the sky. [20] It rose 23 feet above the mountaintops.

[21] Every creature that crawls on the earth died, including birds, domestic and wild animals, and everything that swarms over the earth, along with every human. [22] Everything on dry land (every living, breathing creature) died. [23] Every living creature on the face of the earth was wiped out. Humans, domestic animals, crawling creatures, and birds were wiped off the earth. Only Noah and those with him in the ship were left.

[24] The floodwaters were on the earth for 150 days.

God Remembers Noah

8 [1] God remembered Noah and all the wild and domestic animals with him in the ship. So God made a wind blow over the earth, and the water started to go down. [2] The deep springs and the sky had been shut, and the rain had stopped pouring. [3] The water began to recede from the land. At the end of 150 days the water had decreased. [4] On the seventeenth day of the seventh month, the ship came to rest in the mountains of Ararat. [5] The water kept decreasing until the tenth month. On the first day of the tenth month, the tops of the mountains appeared.

[6] After 40 more days Noah opened the window he had made in the ship [7] and sent out a raven. It kept flying back and forth until the water on the land had dried up. [8] Next, he sent out a dove to see if the water was gone from the surface of the ground. [9] The dove couldn't find a place to land because the water was still all over the earth. So it came back to Noah in the ship. He reached out and brought the dove back into the ship. [10] He waited seven more days and again sent the dove out of the ship. [11] The dove came to him in the evening, and in its beak was a freshly plucked olive leaf. Then Noah knew that the water was gone from the earth. [12] He waited seven more days and sent out the dove again, but it never came back to him.

[13] By the first day of the first month of Noah's six hundred and first year, the water on the land had dried up. Noah opened the top of the ship, looked out, and saw the surface of the ground. [14] By the twenty-seventh day of the second month the land was dry.

[15] Then God spoke to Noah, [16] "Come out of the ship with your wife, your sons, and your sons' wives. [17] Bring out every animal that's with you: birds, domestic animals, and every creature that crawls on the earth. Be fertile, increase in number, and spread over the earth."

[18] So Noah came out with his sons, his wife, and his sons' wives. [19] Every animal, crawling creature, and bird—everything that moves on the earth—came out of the ship, one kind after another.

[20] Noah built an altar to the LORD. On it he made a burnt offering of each type of clean[a] animal and clean bird. [21] The LORD smelled the soothing aroma. He said to himself, "I will never again curse the ground because of humans, even though from birth their hearts are set on nothing but evil. I will never again kill every living creature as I have just done.

[22]   As long as the earth exists,
             planting and harvesting,
             cold and heat,
             summer and winter,
             day and night
                 will never stop."

God Blesses Noah and His Sons

9 [1] God blessed Noah and his sons and said to them, "Be fertile, increase in number, and fill the earth. [2] All the wild animals and all the birds will fear you and be terrified of you. Every creature that crawls on the ground and all the fish in the sea have been put under your control. [3] Everything that lives and moves will be your food. I gave you green plants as food; I now give you everything else.

[4] "But you are not to eat meat with blood in it. (Blood is life.) [5] In addition, I will demand your blood for your life. I will demand it from any animal or from any person. I will demand the life of any person who kills another person.

---

[a] 8:20 "Clean" refers to anything that is presentable to God.

⁶ Whoever sheds human blood,
　　by humans his blood will be shed,
　　　　because in the image of God, God made humans.

⁷ Be fertile, and increase in number. Spread over the earth, and increase."

God's Promise—The Sign of the Rainbow

⁸ God also said to Noah and his sons, ⁹ "I am going to make my promise[a] to you, your descendants, ¹⁰ and every living being that is with you—birds, domestic animals, and all the wild animals, all those that came out of the ship—every living thing on earth. ¹¹ I am making my promise to you. Never again will all life be killed by floodwaters. Never again will there be a flood that destroys the earth."

¹² God said, "This is the sign of the promise I am giving to you and every living being that is with you for generations to come. ¹³ I will put my rainbow in the clouds to be a sign of my promise to the earth. ¹⁴ Whenever I form clouds over the earth, a rainbow will appear in the clouds. ¹⁵ Then I will remember my promise to you and every living animal. Never again will water become a flood to destroy all life. ¹⁶ Whenever the rainbow appears in the clouds, I will see it and remember my everlasting promise to every living animal on earth."

¹⁷ So God said to Noah, "This is the sign of the promise I am making to all life on earth."

Noah Curses Canaan but Blesses Shem and Japheth

¹⁸ Noah's sons, who came out of the ship, were Shem, Ham, and Japheth. ¹⁹ These were Noah's three sons. From them the whole earth was populated. Ham was the father of Canaan.[b]

²⁰ Noah, a farmer, was the first person to plant a vineyard. ²¹ He drank some wine, got drunk, and lay naked inside his tent. ²² Ham, father of Canaan, saw his father naked. So he went outside and told his two brothers.

²³ Shem and Japheth took a blanket and laid it over their shoulders. Then they walked in backwards and covered their father's naked body. They turned their faces away so that they didn't see their father naked.

²⁴ When Noah sobered up, he found out what his youngest son had done to him. ²⁵ So he said,

　　"Canaan is cursed!
　　　　He will be the lowest slave to his brothers.
²⁶ 　 Praise the LORD, the God of Shem!
　　　　Canaan will be his slave.
²⁷ 　 May God expand the territory of Japheth.[c]
　　May he live in the tents of Shem.
　　　　Canaan will be his slave."

²⁸ Noah lived 350 years after the flood. ²⁹ Noah lived a total of 950 years; then he died.

The 14 Descendants of Japheth—1 Chronicles 1:4–7

10 ¹ This is the account of Noah's sons Shem, Ham, and Japheth, and their descendants. Shem, Ham and Japheth had children after the flood.
² Japheth's descendants were
　　Gomer, Magog, Madai, Javan, Tubal, Meshech, and Tiras.
³ Gomer's descendants were
　　Ashkenaz, Riphath, and Togarmah.
⁴ Javan's descendants were
　　the people from Elishah, Tarshish, Cyprus, and Rhodes.[a]
⁵ From these descendants the people of the coastlands spread into their own countries. Each nation had its own language and families.

The 30 Descendants of Ham—1 Chronicles 1:8–16

⁶ Ham's descendants were
　　Cush, Egypt, Put, and Canaan.
⁷ Cush's descendants were
　　Seba, Havilah, Sabtah, Raamah, and Sabteca.
　Raamah's descendants were
　　Sheba and Dedan.

---

[a] 9:9 Or "covenant."　[b] 9:19 The second part of verse 18 (in Hebrew) has been placed just after verse 19 to express the complex Hebrew sentence structure more clearly in English.　[c] 9:27 There is a play on words here between the Hebrew *yapht* (May God expand) and *yepheth* (Japheth).　[a] 10:4 1 Chronicles 1:7, Samaritan Pentateuch, Greek; Masoretic Text "the Dodanim."

[8] Cush was the father of Nimrod, the first mighty warrior on the earth. [9] He was a mighty hunter whom the LORD blessed. That's why people used to say, "¸He's¸ like Nimrod, a mighty hunter whom the LORD blessed." [10] The first ¸cities¸ in his kingdom were Babylon, Erech, Accad, and Calneh in Shinar [Babylonia]. [11] He went from that land to Assyria and built Nineveh, Rehoboth Ir, Calah, [12] and Resen, the great city between Nineveh and Calah.

[13] Egypt was the ancestor of
the Ludites, Anamites, Lehabites, Naphtuhites, [14] Pathrusites, Casluhites (from whom the Philistines came), and the Caphtorites.
[15] Canaan was the father of
Sidon his firstborn, then Heth, [16] also the Jebusites, the Amorites, the Girgashites, [17] the Hivites, the Arkites, the Sinites, [18] the Arvadites, the Zemarites, and the Hamathites.
Later the Canaanite families scattered. [19] The border of the Canaanites extended from Sidon toward Gerar as far as Gaza and then toward Sodom, Gomorrah, Admah, and Zeboiim as far as Lasha.

[20] These were Ham's descendants by families and languages within their countries and nations.

The 26 Descendants of Shem—1 Chronicles 1:17–23

[21] Shem, Japheth's older brother, also had children. ¸Shem was¸ the ancestor of all the sons of Eber.
[22] Shem's descendants were
Elam, Asshur, Arpachshad, Lud, and Aram.
[23] Aram's descendants were
Uz, Hul, Gether, and Mash.
[24] Arpachshad was the father of Shelah,
and Shelah was the father of Eber.
[25] Two sons were born to Eber.
The name of the one was Peleg [Division], because in his day the earth was divided.
His brother's name was Joktan.
[26] Joktan was the father of Almodad, Sheleph, Hazarmaveth, Jerah, [27] Hadoram, Uzal, Diklah, [28] Obal, Abimael, Sheba, [29] Ophir, Havilah, and Jobab. These were Joktan's sons.
[30] The region where they lived extended from Mesha toward Sephar in the eastern mountains.

[31] These were Shem's descendants by families and languages within their countries according to their nations.
[32] These were the families of Noah's sons listed by their genealogies, nation by nation. From these ¸descendants¸ the nations spread over the earth after the flood.

The Tower of Babel

11 [1] The whole world had one language with a common vocabulary. [2] As people moved toward the east,[a] they found a plain in Shinar [Babylonia] and settled there. [3] They said to one another, "Let's make bricks and bake them thoroughly." They used bricks as stones and tar[b] as mortar. [4] Then they said, "Let's build a city for ourselves and a tower with its top in the sky. Let's make a name for ourselves so that we won't become scattered all over the face of the earth." [5] The LORD came down to see the city and the tower that the descendants of Adam were building. [6] The LORD said, "They are one people with one language. This is only the beginning of what they will do! Now nothing they plan to do will be too difficult for them. [7] Let us go down there and mix up their language so that they won't understand each other."

[8] So the LORD scattered them all over the face of the earth, and they stopped building the city. [9] This is why it was named Babel, because there the LORD turned the language of the whole earth into babble. From that place the LORD scattered them all over the face of the earth.

The Ten Descendants of Shem—Shem to Terah—1 Chronicles 1:17–23

[10] This is the account of Shem and his descendants. Two years after the flood when Shem was 100 years old, he became the father of Arpachshad. [11] After he became the father of Arpachshad, Shem lived 500 years and had other sons and daughters.

[12] Arpachshad was 35 years old when he became the father of Shelah. [13] After he became the father of Shelah, Arpachshad lived 403 years and had other sons and daughters.

[14] Shelah was 30 years old when he became the father of Eber. [15] After he became the father of Eber, Shelah lived 403 years and had other sons and daughters.

---

[a] 11:2 Or "from the east."   [b] 11:3 Or "bitumen."

¹⁶ Eber was 34 years old when he became the father of Peleg. ¹⁷ After he became the father of Peleg, Eber lived 430 years and had other sons and daughters. ¹⁸ Peleg was 30 years old when he became the father of Reu. ¹⁹ After he became the father of Reu, Peleg lived 209 years and had other sons and daughters. ²⁰ Reu was 32 years old when he became the father of Serug. ²¹ After he became the father of Serug, Reu lived 207 years and had other sons and daughters. ²² Serug was 30 years old when he became the father of Nahor. ²³ After he became the father of Nahor, Serug lived 200 years and had other sons and daughters. ²⁴ Nahor was 29 years old when he became the father of Terah. ²⁵ After he became the father of Terah, Nahor lived 119 years and had other sons and daughters. ²⁶ Terah was 70 years old when he became the father of Abram, Nahor, and Haran.

Terah Moves to Haran

²⁷ This is the account of Terah and his descendants. Terah was the father of Abram, Nahor, and Haran. Haran was the father of Lot. ²⁸ While his father Terah was still alive, Haran died in Ur of the Chaldeans, his native land. ²⁹ Both Abram and Nahor married. The name of Abram's wife was Sarai, and the name of Nahor's wife was Milcah, daughter of Haran. (Haran was the father of Milcah and Iscah.) ³⁰ Sarai was not able to have children.

³¹ Terah took his son Abram, his grandson Lot (son of Haran), and his daughter-in-law Sarai, wife of his son Abram. They set out together from Ur of the Chaldeans to go to Canaan. When they came as far as Haran, they stayed there. ³² Terah lived 205 years and died in Haran.

The LORD's First Promise to Abram

12 ¹ The LORD said to Abram,

> "Leave your land,
>   your relatives,
>   and your father's home.
>   Go to the land that I will show you.
> ² I will make you a great nation,
>   I will bless you.
>   I will make your name great,
>   and you will be a blessing.
> ³ I will bless those who bless you,
>   and whoever curses you, I will curse.
>   Through you every family on earth will be blessed."

The LORD's Second Promise to Abram

⁴ So Abram left, as the LORD had told him, and Lot went with him. Abram was 75 years old when he left Haran. ⁵ Abram set out for Canaan. He took along his wife Sarai, his nephew Lot, and all the possessions they had accumulated and the servants they had acquired in Haran.

⁶ They arrived in Canaan,ᵃ and Abram traveled through the land to the oak tree belonging to Moreh at Shechem. At that time the Canaanites were in the land. ⁷ Then the LORD appeared to Abram and said, "I'm going to give this land to your descendants." So he built an altar there to the LORD, who had appeared to him.

⁸ He moved on to the hills east of Bethel, and he put up his tent—with Bethel on the west and Ai on the east. He also built an altar to the LORD there and worshiped the LORD. ⁹ Abram kept moving toward the Negev.

Abram Deceives Pharaoh

¹⁰ There was a famine in the land. Abram went to Egypt to stay awhile because the famine was severe. ¹¹ When he was about to enter Egypt, Abram said to his wife Sarai, "I know that you're a beautiful woman. ¹² When the Egyptians see you, they'll say, 'This is his wife!' Then they'll kill me but let you live. ¹³ Please say that you're my sister. Then everything will be alright for me, and because of you I will live."

¹⁴ When Abram arrived in Egypt, the Egyptians saw how very beautiful his wife was. ¹⁵ When Pharaoh's officials saw her, they raved about her to Pharaoh, so Sarai was taken to Pharaoh's palace. ¹⁶ Everything went well for Abram because of her, and he was given sheep, cattle, donkeys, male and female slaves, and camels.

¹⁷ However, the LORD struck Pharaoh and his household with terrible plagues because of Sarai, Abram's wife. ¹⁸ Then Pharaoh called for Abram. "What have you done to me?" he asked. "Why didn't you tell me that she's your wife? ¹⁹ Why did you say, 'She's my sister' and allow me

---

ᵃ 12:6 English equivalent difficult.

to take her for my wife? Here's your wife! Take her and go!" ²⁰ Pharaoh gave his men orders concerning Abram. They sent Abram away with his wife and everything that he had.

Abram and Lot Separate

13 ¹ Abram left Egypt with his wife and everything he had and went to the Negev. Lot was with him. ² Abram was very rich because he had livestock, silver, and gold. ³ He traveled from place to place. He went from the Negev as far as Bethel, to the area between Bethel and Ai where his tent had been originally, ⁴ where he had first made an altar. There Abram worshiped the LORD.

⁵ Lot, who had been traveling with Abram, also had his own sheep, cattle, and tents. ⁶ There wasn't enough pastureland for both of them. They had so many possessions that they were unable to remain together. ⁷ Quarrels broke out between Abram's herders and Lot's herders. (Canaanites and Perizzites were also living in that area.)

⁸ Abram said to Lot, "Please, let's not have any more quarrels between us or between our herders. After all, we're relatives. ⁹ Isn't all this land yours also? Let's separate. If you go to the left, I'll go to the right, and if you go to the right, I'll go to the left." ¹⁰ Then Lot looked in the direction of Zoar as far as he could see. He saw that the whole Jordan Plain was well-watered like the LORD's garden or like Egypt. (This was before the LORD destroyed Sodom and Gomorrah.)

¹¹ Lot chose the whole Jordan Plain for himself. He moved toward the east. They each went their own way. ¹² Abram lived in Canaan, while Lot lived among the cities of the plain, moving his tents as far as Sodom. ¹³ (The people who lived in Sodom were very wicked. They committed terrible sins against the LORD.)

The LORD's Third Promise to Abram

¹⁴ After Lot left, the LORD said to Abram, "Look north, south, east, and west of where you are. ¹⁵ I will give all the land you see to you and to your descendants for an indefinite period of time. ¹⁶ I will also give you as many descendants as the dust of the earth. If anyone could count the dust of the earth, then he could also count your descendants. ¹⁷ Go! Walk back and forth across the entire land because I will give it to you." ¹⁸ So Abram moved his tents and went to live by the oak trees belonging to Mamre at Hebron. There he built an altar for the LORD.

Abram Rescues Lot

14 ¹ At that time ⸢four kings⸣—King Amraphel of Shinar, King Arioch of Ellasar, King Chedorlaomer of Elam, and King Tidal of Goiim— ² went to war against ⸢five kings⸣— King Bera of Sodom, King Birsha of Gomorrah, King Shinab of Admah, King Shemeber of Zeboiim, and the king of Bela (that is, Zoar). ³ The five kings joined forces and met in the valley of Siddim (that is, the Dead Sea). ⁴ For 12 years they had been subject to Chedorlaomer, but in the thirteenth year they rebelled. ⁵ In the fourteenth year Chedorlaomer and his allies came and defeated the Rephaim at Ashteroth Karnaim, the Zuzim at Ham, the Emim at Shaveh Kiriathaim, ⁶ and the Horites in the hill country of Seir, going as far as El Paran on the edge of the desert. ⁷ On their way back, they came to En Mishpat (that is, Kadesh), and they conquered the whole territory of the Amalekites and also the Amorites who were living at Hazazon Tamar.

⁸ Then the kings of Sodom, Gomorrah, Admah, Zeboiim, and Bela (that is, Zoar) marched out and prepared for battle in the valley of Siddim. ⁹ They fought against King Chedorlaomer of Elam, King Tidal of Goiim, King Amraphel of Shinar, and King Arioch of Ellasar—four kings against five. ¹⁰ The valley of Siddim was full of tar pits. As the kings of Sodom and Gomorrah fled, they fell because of the tar pits, but the other kings fled to the hills. ¹¹ So the four kings took all the possessions of Sodom and Gomorrah, as well as all their food, and left. ¹² They also took Abram's nephew Lot and his possessions since he was living in Sodom.

¹³ Then a soldier who had escaped came and told Abram the Hebrew what had happened. He was living next to the oak trees belonging to Mamre the Amorite, a brother of Eshcol and Aner. (These men were Abram's allies.)

¹⁴ When Abram heard that his nephew had been captured, he armedª his 318 trained men, born in his own household, and pursued the four kings all the way to Dan. ¹⁵ He split up his men to attack them at night. He defeated them, pursuing them all the way to Hobah, which is north of Damascus. ¹⁶ He brought back everything they had, including women and soldiers. He also brought back his relative Lot and his possessions.

ª 14:14 Hebrew meaning uncertain.

Melchizedek Blesses Abram

¹⁷ After Abram came back from defeating Chedorlaomer and his allies, the king of Sodom came out to meet him in the Shaveh Valley (that is, the King's Valley). ¹⁸ Then King Melchizedek of Salem brought out bread and wine. He was a priest of God Most High. ¹⁹ He blessed Abram, and said,

> "Blessed is Abram by God Most High,
> maker*ᵇ* of heaven and earth.
> ²⁰ Blessed is God Most High,
> who has handed your enemies over to you."

Then Abram gave him a tenth of everything.

²¹ The king of Sodom said to Abram, "Give me the people, and keep everything else for yourself." ²² But Abram said to the king of Sodom, "I now raise my hand and solemnly swear to the LORD God Most High, maker of heaven and earth, ²³ that I won't take a thread or a sandal strap. I won't take anything that is yours so that you will never be able to say, 'I made Abram rich.' ²⁴ I won't take one single thing except what my men have eaten. But let my allies Aner, Eshcol, and Mamre take their share."

The LORD's Fourth Promise to Abram

15 ¹ Later the LORD spoke his word to Abram in a vision. He said,

> "Abram, don't be afraid.
> I am your shield.
> Your reward will be very great."*ᵃ*

² Abram asked, "Almighty LORD, what will you give me? Since I'm going to die without children, Eliezer of Damascus will inherit*ᵇ* my household. ³ You have given me no children, so this member of my household will be my heir."

⁴ Suddenly, the LORD spoke his word to Abram again. He said, "This man will not be your heir. Your own son will be your heir." ⁵ He took Abram outside and said, "Now look up at the sky and count the stars, if you are able to count them." He also said to him, "That's how many descendants you will have!" ⁶ Then Abram believed the LORD, and the LORD regarded that faith to be his approval of Abram. ⁷ Then the LORD said to him, "I am the LORD, who brought you out of Ur of the Chaldeans to give you this land so that you will take possession of it."

⁸ Abram asked, "Almighty LORD, how can I be certain that I will take possession of it?" ⁹ He answered Abram, "Bring me a three-year-old heifer, a three-year-old female goat, a three-year-old ram, a mourning dove, and a pigeon." ¹⁰ So Abram brought all these animals to him. He cut each of them in half and laid each half opposite the other. However, he did not cut the birds in half.

¹¹ When birds of prey came down upon the carcasses, Abram drove them away. ¹² As the sun was just about to set, a deep sleep—a dreadful, deep darkness—came over Abram.

¹³ God said to Abram, "You can know for sure that your descendants will live in a land that is not their own, where they will be slaves, and they will be oppressed for 400 years. ¹⁴ But I will punish the nation they serve, and after that they will come out with many possessions. ¹⁵ But you will die in peace and be buried at a very old age. ¹⁶ In the fourth generation your descendants will come back here, because the sin of the Amorites will not have run its course until then."

¹⁷ The sun had gone down, and it was dark. Suddenly a smoking oven and a flaming torch passed between the animal pieces. ¹⁸ At that time the LORD made a promise*ᶜ* to Abram. He said, "I will give this land to your descendants. This is the land from the river of Egypt to the great river, the Euphrates. ¹⁹ It is the land of the Kenites, the Kenizzites, the Kadmonites, ²⁰ the Hittites, the Perizzites, the Rephaim, ²¹ the Amorites, the Canaanites, the Girgashites, and the Jebusites."

Abram and Hagar

16 ¹ Sarai, Abram's wife, was not able to have children. She owned an Egyptian slave named Hagar. ² So Sarai said to Abram, "The LORD has kept me from having children. Why don't you sleep with my slave? Maybe I can build a family through her." Abram agreed with Sarai.

³ After Abram had lived in Canaan for ten years, Abram's wife Sarai took her Egyptian slave Hagar and gave her to her husband Abram to be his wife. ⁴ He slept with Hagar, and she

---

ᵇ 14:19 Or "Possessor."   *ᵃ* 15:1 Or "I am your shield, your very great reward."   *ᵇ* 15:2 Hebrew meaning uncertain.
ᶜ 15:18 Or "covenant."

became pregnant. When Hagar realized that she was pregnant, she began to be disrespectful to Sarai, her owner.

⁵ So Sarai complained to Abram, "I'm being treated unfairly! And it's your fault! I know that I gave my slave to you, but now that she's pregnant, she's being disrespectful to me. May the LORD decide who is right—you or me."

⁶ Abram answered Sarai, "Here, she's your slave. Do what you like with her." Then Sarai mistreated Hagar so much that she ran away.

⁷ The Messenger of the LORD found her by a spring in the desert, the spring on the way to Shur. ⁸ He said, "Hagar, Sarai's slave, where have you come from, and where are you going?"

She answered, "I'm running away from my owner Sarai." ⁹ The Messenger of the LORD said to her, "Go back to your owner, and place yourself under her authority." ¹⁰ The Messenger of the LORD also said to her, "I will give you many descendants. No one will be able to count them because there will be so many." ¹¹ Then the Messenger of the LORD said to her,

> "You are pregnant,
>   and you will give birth to a son.
> You will name him Ishmael [God Hears],
>   because the LORD has heard your cry of distress.
> ¹²   He will be as free and wild as an untamed donkey.
> He will fight with everyone, and everyone will fight with him.
> He will have conflicts with all his relatives."ᵃ

¹³ Hagar named the LORD, who had been speaking to her, "You Are the God Who Watches Over Me." She said, "This is the place where I watched ⌐the one⌐ who watches over me." ¹⁴ This is why the well is named Beer Lahai Roi [Well of the Living One Who Watches Over Me]. It is still there between Kadesh and Bered.

¹⁵ Hagar gave birth to Abram's son. Abram named him Ishmael. ¹⁶ Abram was 86 years old when Hagar gave birth to Ishmael.

The LORD's Fifth Promise to Abraham

17 ¹ When Abram was 99 years old, the LORD appeared to him. He said to Abram, "I am God Almighty. Live in my presence with integrity. ² I will give you my promise,ᵃ and I will give you very many descendants." ³ Immediately, Abram bowed with his face touching the ground, and again God spoke to him, ⁴ "My promise is still with you. You will become the father of many nations. ⁵ So your name will no longer be Abram [Exalted Father], but Abraham [Father of Many] because I have made you a father of many nations. ⁶ I will give you many descendants. Many nations and kings will come from you. ⁷ I will make my promise to you and your descendants for generations to come as an everlasting promise. I will be your God and the God of your descendants. ⁸ I am also giving this land where you are living—all of Canaan—to you and your descendants as your permanent possession. And I will be your God."

⁹ God also said to Abraham, "You and your descendants in generations to come are to be faithful to my promise. ¹⁰ This is how you are to be faithful to my promise: Every male among you is to be circumcised. ¹¹ All of you must be circumcised. That will be the sign of the promise from me to you. ¹² For generations to come every male child who is eight days old must be circumcised, whether he is born in your household or bought with money from a foreigner who's not related to you. ¹³ Every male born in your household or bought with your money is to be circumcised without exception. So my promise will be a sign on your flesh, an everlasting promise. ¹⁴ Any uncircumcised male must be excluded from his people because he has rejected my promise."

¹⁵ God said to Abraham, "Don't call your wife by the name Sarai anymore. Instead, her name is Sarah [Princess]. ¹⁶ I will bless her, and I will also give you a son by her. I will bless her, and she will become ⌐a mother of⌐ nations, and kings will come from her." ¹⁷ Immediately, Abraham bowed with his face touching the ground. He laughed as he thought to himself, "Can a son be born to a hundred-year-old man? Can Sarah, a ninety-year-old woman, have a child?" ¹⁸ Then Abraham said to God, "Why not let Ishmael be my heir?"

¹⁹ God replied, "No! Your wife Sarah will give you a son, and you will name him Isaac [He Laughs]. I will make an everlasting promise to him and his descendants. ²⁰ I have heard your request about Ishmael. Yes, I will bless him, make him fertile, and increase the number of his descendants. He will be the father of 12 princes, and I will make him a great nation. ²¹ But I will make my promise to Isaac. Sarah will give birth to him at this time next year." ²² When God finished speaking with Abraham, he left him.

ᵃ 16:12 Hebrew meaning uncertain.   ᵃ 17:2 Or "covenant."

Abraham's Household Circumcised

²³ So Abraham took his son Ishmael, everyone born in his household, and everyone bought with money—every male in his household—and circumcised them that day, as God had told him. ²⁴ Abraham was 99 years old when he was circumcised. ²⁵ His son Ishmael was 13 years old when he was circumcised. ²⁶ That same day Abraham and his son Ishmael were circumcised. ²⁷ All the men of his household, whether born in the household or bought with money from a foreigner, were circumcised with him.

The LORD's Sixth Promise to Abraham

18 ¹ The LORD appeared to Abraham by the oak trees belonging to Mamre as he was sitting at the entrance of his tent during the hottest part of the day. ² Abraham looked up, and suddenly he saw three men standing near him. When he saw them, he ran to meet them, and he bowed with his face touching the ground.

³ "Please, sir," Abraham said, "stop by to visit me for a while. ⁴ Why don't we let someone bring a little water? After you wash your feet, you can stretch out and rest under the tree. ⁵ Let me bring some bread so that you can regain your strength. After that you can leave, since this is why you stopped by to visit me."

They answered, "That's fine. Do as you say."

⁶ So Abraham hurried into the tent to find Sarah. "Quick," he said, "get three measures of flour, knead it, and make bread."

⁷ Then Abraham ran to the herd and took one of his best calves. He gave it to his servant, who prepared it quickly. ⁸ Abraham took cheese and milk, as well as the meat, and set these in front of them. Then he stood by them under the tree as they ate.

⁹ They asked him, "Where is your wife Sarah?"

He answered, "Over there, in the tent."

¹⁰ The LORD said, "I promise I'll come back to you next year at this time, and your wife Sarah will have a son."

Sarah happened to be listening at the entrance of the tent, which was behind him. ¹¹ Abraham and Sarah were old. Sarah was past the age of childbearing. ¹² And so Sarah laughed to herself, thinking, "Now that I've become old, will I enjoy myself again? What's more, my husband is old!"

¹³ The LORD asked Abraham, "Why did Sarah laugh and say, 'Can I really have a child now that I'm old?' ¹⁴ Is anything too hard for the LORD? I will come back to you next year at this time, and Sarah will have a son."

¹⁵ Because she was afraid, Sarah denied that she had laughed.

But the LORD said, "Yes, you did laugh."

The LORD Tells Abraham About His Plan

¹⁶ Then the men got up to leave. As Abraham was walking with them to see them off, they looked toward Sodom. ¹⁷ The LORD said, "I shouldn't hide what I am going to do from Abraham. ¹⁸ After all, Abraham is going to become a great and mighty nation and through him all the nations of the earth will be blessed. ¹⁹ I have chosen him so that he will direct his children and his family after him to keep the way of the LORD by doing what is right and just. In this way I, the LORD, will do what I have promised Abraham."

²⁰ The LORD also said, "Sodom and Gomorrah have many complaints against them, and their sin is very serious. ²¹ I must go down and see whether these complaints are true. If not, I will know it."

²² From there the men turned and went on toward Sodom, but Abraham remained standing in front of the LORD. ²³ Abraham came closer and asked, "Are you really going to sweep away the innocent with the guilty? ²⁴ What if there are 50 innocent people in the city? Are you really going to sweep them away? Won't you spare that place for the sake of the 50 innocent people who are in it? ²⁵ It would be unthinkable for you to do such a thing, to treat the innocent and the guilty alike and to kill the innocent with the guilty. That would be unthinkable! Won't the judge of the whole earth do what is fair?"

²⁶ The LORD said, "If I find 50 innocent people inside the city of Sodom, I will spare the whole place for their sake."

²⁷ Abraham asked, "Consider now, if I may be so bold as to ask you, although I'm only dust and ashes, ²⁸ what if there are 45 innocent people? Will you destroy the whole city because of 5 fewer people?"

The LORD answered, "I will not destroy it if I find 45 there."

²⁹ Abraham asked him again, "What if 40 are found there?"

He answered, "For the sake of the 40 I will not do it."

³⁰ "Please don't be angry if I speak again," Abraham said. "What if 30 are found there?"

He answered, "If I find 30 there, I will not do it."

³¹ "Look now, if I may be so bold as to ask you," Abraham said. "What if 20 are found there?"

He answered, "I will not destroy it for the sake of the 20."

³² "Please don't be angry if I speak only one more time," Abraham said. "What if 10 are found there?"

He answered, "I will not destroy it for the sake of the 10." ³³ When the LORD finished speaking to Abraham, he left. Abraham returned home.

Lot's Guests Are Assaulted

19 ¹ The two angels came to Sodom in the evening as Lot was sitting in the gateway. When Lot saw them, he got up to meet them and bowed with his face touching the ground. ² He said, "Please, gentlemen, why don't you come to my home and spend the night? ⸢You can⸣ wash your feet there. Then early tomorrow morning you can continue your journey."

"No," they answered, "we'd rather spend the night in the city square."

³ But he insisted so strongly that they came with him and went into his home. He prepared a special dinner for them, baked some unleavened bread, and they ate. ⁴ Before they had gone to bed, all the young and old male citizens of Sodom surrounded the house. ⁵ They called to Lot, "Where are the men who came to ⸢stay with⸣ you tonight? Bring them out to us so that we can have sex with them."

⁶ Then Lot went outside and shut the door behind him. ⁷ "Please, my friends, don't be so wicked," he said. ⁸ "Look, I have two daughters who have never had sex. Why don't you let me bring them out to you? Do whatever you like with them. But don't do anything to these men, since I'm responsible for them."

⁹ But the men yelled, "Get out of the way! This man came here to stay awhile. Now he wants to be our judge! We're going to treat you worse than those men." They pushed hard against Lot and lunged forward to break down the door. ¹⁰ The men ⸢inside⸣ reached out, pulled Lot into the house with them, and shut the door. ¹¹ Then they struck all the men who were in the doorway of the house, young and old alike, with blindness so that they gave up trying to find the door.

Lot Leaves Sodom, and the Cities Are Destroyed

¹² Then the men asked Lot, "Do you have anyone else here—any in-laws, sons, daughters, or any other relatives in the city? Get them out of here ¹³ because we're going to destroy this place. The complaints to the LORD against its people are so loud that the LORD has sent us to destroy it."

¹⁴ So Lot went out and spoke to the men engaged to his daughters. He said, "Hurry! Get out of this place, because the LORD is going to destroy the city." But they thought he was joking.

¹⁵ As soon as it was dawn, the angels urged Lot by saying, "Quick! Take your wife and your two daughters who are here, or you'll be swept away when the city is punished." ¹⁶ When he hesitated, the men grabbed him, his wife, and his two daughters by their hands, because the LORD wanted to spare Lot. They brought them safely outside the city. ¹⁷ As soon as they were outside, one ⸢of the angels⸣ said, "Run for your lives! Don't look behind you, and don't stop on the plain. Run for the hills, or you'll be swept away!"

¹⁸ Lot answered, "Oh no! ¹⁹ Even though you've been so good to me and though you've been very kind to me by saving my life, I can't run as far as the hills. This disaster will overtake me, and I'll die. ²⁰ Look, there's a city near enough to flee to, and it's small. Why don't you let me run there? Isn't it small? Then my life will be saved."

²¹ The angel said to him, "Alright, I will grant you this request too. I will not destroy the city you're talking about. ²² Run there quickly, because I can't do anything until you get there." (The city is named Zoar [Small].)

²³ The sun had just risen over the land as Lot came to Zoar. ²⁴ Then the LORD made burning sulfur and fire rain out of heaven on Sodom and Gomorrah. ²⁵ He destroyed those cities, the whole plain, all who lived in the cities, and whatever grew on the ground. ²⁶ Lot's wife looked back and turned into a column of salt.

²⁷ Early the next morning Abraham came to the place where he had stood in front of the LORD. ²⁸ When he looked toward Sodom and Gomorrah and all the land in the plain, he saw smoke rising from the land like the thick smoke of a furnace.

²⁹ When God destroyed the cities on the plain, he remembered Abraham. Lot was allowed to escape from the destruction that came to the cities where he was living.

Lot's Daughters Have Sons by Their Father

³⁰ Lot left Zoar because he was afraid to stay there. He and his two daughters settled in the mountains where they lived in a cave. ³¹ The older daughter said to the younger one, "Our

father is old. No men are here. We can't get married as other people do. ³² Let's give our father wine to drink. Then we'll go to bed with him so that we'll be able to preserve our family line through our father." ³³ That night they gave their father wine to drink. Then the older one went to bed with her father. He didn't know when she came to bed or when she got up. ³⁴ The next day the older daughter said to the younger one, "I did it! Last night I went to bed with my father. Let's give him wine to drink again tonight. Then you go to bed with him so that we'll be able to preserve our family line through our father." ³⁵ That night they gave their father wine to drink again. Then the younger one went to bed with him. He didn't know when she came to bed or when she got up. ³⁶ So Lot's two daughters became pregnant by their father. ³⁷ The older one gave birth to a son and named him Moab. He is the ancestor of the Moabites of today. ³⁸ The younger daughter also gave birth to a son and named him Ben Ammi. He is the ancestor of the Ammonites of today.

Abraham Deceives Abimelech

20 ¹ Abraham moved to the Negev and settled between Kadesh and Shur. While he was living in Gerar, ² Abraham told everyone that his wife Sarah was his sister. So King Abimelech of Gerar sent men to take Sarah. ³ God came to Abimelech in a dream one night and said to him, "You're going to die because of the woman that you've taken! She's a married woman!" ⁴ Abimelech hadn't come near her, so he asked, "Lord, will you destroy a nation even if it's innocent? ⁵ Didn't he tell me himself, 'She's my sister,' and didn't she even say, 'He's my brother'? I did this in all innocence and with a clear conscience."

⁶ "Yes, I know that you did this with a clear conscience," God said to him in the dream. "In fact, I kept you from sinning against me. That's why I didn't let you touch her. ⁷ Give the man's wife back to him now, because he's a prophet. He will pray for you, and you will live. But if you don't give her back, you and all who belong to you are doomed to die."

⁸ Early in the morning Abimelech called together all his officials. He told them about all of this, and they were terrified. ⁹ Then Abimelech called for Abraham and asked him, "What have you done to us? How have I sinned against you that you would bring such a serious sin on me and my kingdom? You shouldn't have done this to me." ¹⁰ Abimelech also asked Abraham, "What were you thinking when you did this?"

¹¹ Abraham said, "I thought that because there are no God-fearing people in this place, I'd be killed because of my wife. ¹² Besides, she is my sister—my father's daughter but not my mother's. She is also my wife. ¹³ When God had me leave my father's home and travel around, I said to her, 'Do me a favor: Wherever we go, say that I'm your brother.' "

¹⁴ Then Abimelech took sheep, cattle, and male and female slaves and gave them to Abraham. He also gave his wife Sarah back to him. ¹⁵ Abimelech said, "Look, here's my land. Live anywhere you like." ¹⁶ He said to Sarah, "Don't forget, I've given your brother 25 pounds of silver. This is to silence any criticism against you from everyone with you. You're completely cleared."

¹⁷ Abraham prayed to God, and God healed Abimelech, his wife, and his female slaves so that they could have children. ¹⁸ (The LORD had made it impossible for any woman in Abimelech's household to have children because of Abraham's wife Sarah.)

God Provides for Hagar and Ishmael

21 ¹ The LORD came to help Sarah and did for her what he had promised. ² So she became pregnant, and at the exact time God had promised, she gave birth to a son for Abraham in his old age. ³ Abraham named his newborn son Isaac. ⁴ When Isaac was eight days old, Abraham circumcised him as God had commanded. ⁵ Abraham was 100 years old when his son Isaac was born.

⁶ Sarah said, "God has brought me laughter, and everyone who hears about this will laugh with me. ⁷ Who would have predicted to Abraham that Sarah would nurse children? Yet, I have given him a son in his old age."

⁸ The child grew and was weaned. On the day Isaac was weaned, Abraham held a big feast. ⁹ Sarah saw that Abraham's son by Hagar the Egyptian was laughing at Isaac. ¹⁰ She said to Abraham, "Get rid of this slave and her son, because this slave's son must never share the inheritance with my son Isaac." ¹¹ Abraham was upset by this because of his son Ishmael. ¹² But God said to Abraham, "Don't be upset about the boy and your slave. Listen to what Sarah says because through Isaac your descendants will carry on your name. ¹³ Besides, I will make the slave's son into a nation also, because he is your child."

¹⁴ Early the next morning Abraham took bread and a container of water and gave them to Hagar, putting them on her shoulder. He also gave her the boy and sent her on her way. So she left and wandered around in the desert near Beersheba. ¹⁵ When the water in the container was gone, she put the boy under one of the bushes. ¹⁶ Then she went about as far away as an

arrow can be shot and sat down. She said to herself, "I don't want to watch the boy die." So she sat down and sobbed loudly.

[17] God heard the boy crying, and the Messenger of God called to Hagar from heaven. "What's the matter, Hagar?" he asked her. "Don't be afraid! God has heard the boy crying from the bushes. [18] Come on, help the boy up! Take him by the hand, because I'm going to make him into a great nation."

[19] God opened her eyes. Then she saw a well. She filled the container with water and gave the boy a drink.

[20] God was with the boy as he grew up. He lived in the desert and became a skilled archer. [21] He lived in the desert of Paran, and his mother got him a wife from Egypt.

Abraham's Agreement With Abimelech

[22] At that time Abimelech, accompanied by Phicol, the commander of his army, said to Abraham, "God is with you in everything you do. [23] Now, swear an oath to me here in front of God that you will never cheat me, my children, or my descendants. Show me and the land where you've been living the same kindness that I have shown you."

[24] Abraham said, "I so swear."

[25] Then Abraham complained to Abimelech about a well which Abimelech's servants had seized. [26] Abimelech replied, "I don't know who did this. You didn't tell me, and I didn't hear about it until today."

[27] Abraham took some sheep and cattle and gave them to Abimelech, and the two of them made an agreement. [28] Then Abraham set apart seven female lambs from the flock. [29] Abimelech asked him, "What is the meaning of these seven female lambs you have set apart?"

[30] Abraham answered, "Accept these lambs from me so that they may be proof[a] that I dug this well." [31] This is why that place is called Beersheba,[b] because both of them swore an oath there.

[32] After they made the treaty at Beersheba, Abimelech and Phicol, the commander of his army, left and went back to the land of the Philistines. [33] Abraham planted a tamarisk tree at Beersheba and worshiped the LORD, the Everlasting God, there. [34] Abraham lived a long time in the land of the Philistines.

God Tests Abraham

22 [1] Later God tested Abraham and called to him, "Abraham!"

"Yes, here I am!" he answered.

[2] God said, "Take your son, your only son Isaac, whom you love, and go to Moriah. Sacrifice him there as a burnt offering on one of the mountains that I will show you."

[3] Early the next morning Abraham saddled his donkey. He took with him two of his servants and his son Isaac. When he had cut the wood for the burnt offering, he set out for the place that God had told him about. [4] Two days later Abraham saw the place in the distance. [5] Then Abraham said to his servants, "You stay here with the donkey while the boy and I go over there. We'll worship. After that we'll come back to you."

[6] Then Abraham took the wood for the burnt offering and gave it to his son Isaac. Abraham carried the burning coals and the knife. The two of them went on together.

[7] Isaac spoke up and said, "Father?"

"Yes, Son?" Abraham answered.

Isaac asked, "We have the burning coals and the wood, but where is the lamb for the burnt offering?"

[8] Abraham answered, "God will provide a lamb for the burnt offering, Son."

The two of them went on together. [9] When they came to the place that God had told him about, Abraham built the altar and arranged the wood on it. Then he tied up his son Isaac and laid him on top of the wood on the altar. [10] Next, Abraham picked up the knife and took it in his hand to sacrifice his son. [11] But the Messenger of the LORD called to him from heaven and said, "Abraham! Abraham!"

"Yes?" he answered.

[12] "Do not lay a hand on the boy," he said. "Do not do anything to him. Now I know that you fear God, because you did not refuse to give me your son, your only son."

[13] When Abraham looked around, he saw a ram behind him caught by its horns in a bush. So Abraham took the ram and sacrificed it as a burnt offering in place of his son. [14] Abraham named that place The LORD Will Provide. It is still said today, "On the mountain of the LORD it will be provided."

---

[a] 21:30 Or "a witness."   [b] 21:31 *Beersheba* can mean either "Well of the Seven" or "Well of the Oath."

The Lord's Seventh Promise to Abraham

¹⁵ Then the Messenger of the Lord called to Abraham from heaven a second time ¹⁶ and said, "I am taking an oath on my own name, declares the Lord, that because you have done this and have not refused to give me your son, your only son, ¹⁷ I will certainly bless you and make your descendants as numerous as the stars in the sky and the grains of sand on the seashore. Your descendants will take possession of their enemies' cities. ¹⁸ Through your descendant all the nations of the earth will be blessed, because you have obeyed me."

¹⁹ Then Abraham returned to his servants, and together they left for Beersheba. Abraham remained in Beersheba.

Abraham Learns of Nahor's Descendants

²⁰ Later Abraham was told, "Milcah has given birth to these children of your brother Nahor: ²¹ Uz (the firstborn), Buz (his brother), Kemuel (father of Aram), ²² Kesed, Hazo, Pildash, Jidlaph, and Bethuel. ²³ Bethuel is the father of Rebekah. Milcah had these eight sons by Abraham's brother Nahor. ²⁴ Nahor's concubine,ᵃ whose name was Reumah, had the following children: Tebah, Gaham, Tahash, and Maacah."

Sarah's Death

23 ¹ Sarah lived to be 127 years old. This was the length of her life. ² She died in Kiriath Arba (that is, Hebron) in Canaan. Abraham went to mourn for Sarah and to cry about her death.

³ Then Abraham left the side of his dead wife and spoke to the Hittites, ⁴ "I'm a stranger with no permanent home. Let me have some of your property for a tomb so that I can bury my dead wife."

⁵ The Hittites answered Abraham, ⁶ "Listen to us, sir. You are a mighty leader among us. Bury your dead in one of our best tombs. Not one of us will withhold from you his tomb for burying your dead."

⁷ Abraham got up in front of the Hittites, the people of that region, and bowed with his face touching the ground. ⁸ He said to them, "If you are willing to let me bury my wife, listen to me. Encourage Ephron, son of Zohar, ⁹ to let me have the cave of Machpelah that he owns at the end of his field. He should sell it to me for its full price as my property to be used as a tomb among you."

¹⁰ Ephron was sitting among the Hittites. He answered Abraham so that everyone who was entering the city gate could hear him. He said, ¹¹ "No, sir, listen to me. I'm giving you the field together with the cave that is in it. My people are witnesses that I'm giving it to you. Bury your wife!"

¹² Abraham bowed down again in front of the people of that region. ¹³ He spoke to Ephron so that the people of that region could hear him. He said, "If you would only listen to me. I will pay you the price of the field. Take it from me so that I can bury my wife there."

¹⁴ Ephron answered Abraham, ¹⁵ "Sir, listen to me. The land is worth ten pounds of silver. What is that between us? Bury your wife!"

¹⁶ Abraham agreed to Ephron's terms. So he weighed out for Ephron the amount stated in front of the Hittites: ten pounds of silver at the current merchants' exchange rate.

¹⁷ So Ephron's field at Machpelah, east of Mamre, was sold ¹⁸ to Abraham. His property included the field with the cave in it as well as all the trees inside the boundaries of the field.ᵃ The Hittites together with all who had entered the city gate were the official witnesses for the agreement.

¹⁹ After this, Abraham buried his wife Sarah in the cave in the field of Machpelah, east of Mamre (that is, Hebron). ²⁰ So the field and its cave were sold by the Hittites to Abraham as his property to be used as a tomb.

Abraham Instructs His Servant

24 ¹ By now Abraham was old, and the Lord had blessed him in every way. ² So Abraham said to the senior servant of his household who was in charge of all that he owned, "Take a solemn oath. ³ I want you to swear by the Lord God of heaven and earth that you will not get my son a wife from the daughters of the Canaanites among whom I'm living. ⁴ Instead, you will go to the land of my relatives and get a wife for my son Isaac."

⁵ The servant asked him, "What if the woman doesn't want to come back to this land with me? Should I take your son all the way back to the land you came from?"

ᵃ 22:24 A concubine is considered a wife except she has fewer rights under the law.   ᵃ 23:18 The last part of verse 17 (in Hebrew) has been placed in verse 18 to express the complex Hebrew sentence structure more clearly in English.

⁶"Make sure that you do not take my son back there," Abraham said to him. ⁷"The LORD God of heaven took me from my father's home and the land of my family. He spoke to me and swore this oath: 'I will give this land to your descendants.'

"God will send his angel ahead of you, and you will get my son a wife from there. ⁸If the woman doesn't want to come back with you, then you'll be free from this oath that you swear to me. But don't take my son back there." ⁹So the servant did as his master Abraham commanded and swore the oath to him concerning this.

¹⁰Then the servant took ten of his master's camels and left, taking with him all of his master's best things. He traveled to Aram Naharaim, Nahor's city.

Abraham's Servant Finds a Wife for Isaac

¹¹The servant had the camels kneel down outside the city by the well. It was evening, when the women would go out to draw water. ¹²Then he prayed, "LORD, God of my master Abraham, make me successful today. Show your kindness to Abraham. ¹³Here I am standing by the spring, and the girls of the city are coming out to draw water. ¹⁴I will ask a girl, 'May I please have a drink from your jar?' If she answers, 'Have a drink, and I'll also water your camels,' let her be the one you have chosen for your servant Isaac. This way I'll know that you've shown your kindness to my master."

¹⁵Before he had finished praying, Rebekah came with her jar on her shoulder. She was the daughter of Bethuel, son of Milcah, who was the wife of Abraham's brother Nahor. ¹⁶The girl was a very attractive virgin. No man had ever had sexual intercourse with her. She went down to the spring, filled her jar, and came back.

¹⁷The servant ran to meet her and said, "Please give me a drink of water."

¹⁸"Drink, sir," she said. She quickly lowered her jar to her hand and gave him a drink. ¹⁹When she had finished giving him a drink, she said, "I'll also keep drawing water for your camels until they've had enough to drink." ²⁰So she quickly emptied her jar into the water trough, ran back to the well to draw more water, and drew enough for all his camels. ²¹The man was silently watching her to see whether or not the LORD had made his trip successful.

²²When the camels had finished drinking, the man took out a gold nose ring weighing a fifth of an ounce and two gold bracelets weighing four ounces. ²³He asked, "Whose daughter are you? Please tell me whether there is room in your father's house for us to spend the night."

²⁴She answered him, "I'm the daughter of Bethuel, son of Milcah and Nahor. ²⁵We have plenty of straw and feed for your camels, and room for you to spend the night."

²⁶The man knelt, bowing to the LORD with his face touching the ground. ²⁷He said, "Praise the LORD, the God of my master Abraham. The LORD hasn't failed to be kind and faithful to my master. The LORD has led me on this trip to the home of my master's relatives."

²⁸The girl ran and told her mother's household about these things. ²⁹Rebekah had a brother whose name was Laban. ³⁰He saw the nose ring and the bracelets on his sister's wrists and heard her tell what the man had said to her. Immediately, Laban ran out to the man by the spring.ᵃ He came to the man, who was standing with the camels by the spring. ³¹He said, "Come in, you whom the LORD has blessed. Why are you standing out here? I have straightened up the house and made a place for the camels."

³²So the man went into the house. The camels were unloaded and given straw and feed. Then water was brought for him and his men to wash their feet. ³³When the food was put in front of him, he said, "I won't eat until I've said what I have to say."

"Speak up," Laban said.

³⁴"I am Abraham's servant," he said. ³⁵"The LORD has blessed my master, and he has become wealthy. The LORD has given him sheep and cattle, silver and gold, male and female slaves, camels and donkeys. ³⁶My master's wife Sarah gave him a son in her old age, and my master has given that son everything he has. ³⁷My master made me swear this oath: 'Don't get a wife for my son from the daughters of the Canaanites, in whose land I'm living. ³⁸Instead, go to my father's home and to my relatives, and get my son a wife.'

³⁹"I asked my master, 'What if the woman won't come back with me?'

⁴⁰"He answered me, 'I have been living the way the LORD wants me to. The LORD will send his angel with you to make your trip successful. You will get my son a wife from my relatives and from my father's family. ⁴¹Then you will be free from your oath to me. You will also be free of your oath to me if my relatives are not willing to do this when you go to them.'

⁴²"When I came to the spring today, I prayed, 'LORD God of my master Abraham, please make my trip successful. ⁴³I'm standing by the spring. I'll say to the young woman who comes out to draw water, "Please give me a drink of water." ⁴⁴If she says to me, "Not only may you

---

ᵃ 24:30 The last part of verse 29 (in Hebrew) has been placed in verse 30 to express the complex Hebrew sentence structure more clearly in English.

have a drink, but I will also draw water for your camels," let her be the woman the LORD has chosen for my master's son.'

⁴⁵ "Before I had finished praying, Rebekah came with her jar on her shoulder. She went down to the spring and drew water.

"So I asked her, 'May I have a drink?' ⁴⁶ She quickly lowered her jar and said, 'Have a drink, and I'll water your camels too.' So I drank, and she also watered the camels.

⁴⁷ "Then I asked her, 'Whose daughter are you?'

"She answered, 'The daughter of Bethuel, son of Nahor and Milcah.'

"I put the ring in her nose and the bracelets on her wrists. ⁴⁸ I knelt, bowing down to the LORD. I praised the LORD, the God of my master Abraham. The LORD led me in the right direction to get the daughter of my master's relative for his son. ⁴⁹ Tell me whether or not you're going to show my master true kindness so that I will know what to do."

⁵⁰ Laban and Bethuel answered, "This is from the LORD. We can't say anything to you one way or another. ⁵¹ Here's Rebekah! Take her and go! She will become the wife of your master's son, as the LORD has said."

⁵² When Abraham's servant heard their answer, he bowed down to the LORD. ⁵³ The servant took out gold and silver jewelry and clothes and gave them to Rebekah. He also gave expensive presents to her brother and mother. ⁵⁴ Then he and the men who were with him ate and drank and spent the night. When they got up in the morning, he said, "Let me go back to my master."

⁵⁵ Her brother and mother replied, "Let the girl stay with us ten days or so. After that she may go."

⁵⁶ He said to them, "Don't delay me now that the LORD has made my trip successful. Let me go back to my master."

⁵⁷ So they said, "We'll call the girl and ask her."

⁵⁸ They called for Rebekah and asked her, "Will you go with this man?"

She said, "Yes, I'll go."

⁵⁹ So they let their sister Rebekah and her nurse go with Abraham's servant and his men. ⁶⁰ They gave Rebekah a blessing:

> "May you, our sister, become the mother of many thousands of children.
> May your descendants take possession of their enemies' cities."

⁶¹ Then Rebekah and her maids left. Riding on camels, they followed the man. The servant took Rebekah and left.

Isaac and Rebekah Are Married

⁶² Isaac had just come back from Beer Lahai Roi, since he was living in the Negev. ⁶³ Toward evening Isaac went out into the field to meditate.[b] When he looked up, he saw camels coming. ⁶⁴ When Rebekah saw Isaac, she got down from her camel. ⁶⁵ She asked the servant, "Who is that man over there coming through the field to meet us?"

"That is my master," the servant answered. Then she took her veil and covered herself. ⁶⁶ The servant reported to Isaac everything he had done. ⁶⁷ Isaac took her into his mother Sarah's tent. He married Rebekah. She became his wife, and he loved her. So Isaac was comforted after his mother's death.

Abraham's Second Marriage and His Death—1 Chronicles 1:32–33

25 ¹ Abraham married again, and his wife's name was Keturah. ² Keturah gave birth to these sons of Abraham: Zimran, Jokshan, Medan, Midian, Ishbak, and Shuah. ³ Jokshan was the father of Sheba and Dedan. Dedan's descendants were the Assyrians, the Letushites, and the Leummites. ⁴ The sons of Midian were Ephah, Epher, Hanoch, Abida, and Eldaah. These were the descendants of Keturah.

⁵ Abraham left everything he had to Isaac. ⁶ But while he was still living, Abraham had given gifts to the sons of his concubines.[a] He sent them away from his son Isaac to a land in the east.

⁷ Abraham lived 175 years. ⁸ Then he took his last breath, and died at a very old age. After a long and full life, he joined his ancestors in death. ⁹ His sons Isaac and Ishmael buried him in the cave of Machpelah in the field of Ephron, son of Zohar the Hittite. The cave is east of Mamre. ¹⁰ This was the field that Abraham had bought from the Hittites. There Abraham was buried with his wife Sarah. ¹¹ After Abraham died, God blessed his son Isaac, who settled near Beer Lahai Roi.

---

[b] 24:63 Greek; Hebrew meaning uncertain.   [a] 25:6 A concubine is considered a wife except she has fewer rights under the law.

The 12 Tribes of Ishmael—1 Chronicles 1:29–31

[12] This is the account of the descendants of Abraham's son Ishmael. He was the son of Sarah's Egyptian slave Hagar and Abraham. [13] These are the names of the sons of Ishmael listed in the order of their birth: Nebaioth (Ishmael's firstborn), Kedar, Adbeel, Mibsam, [14] Mishma, Dumah, Massa, [15] Hadad, Tema, Jetur, Naphish, and Kedemah. [16] These are the sons of Ishmael and their names listed by their settlements and camps—12 leaders of their tribes.

[17] Ishmael lived 137 years. Then he took his last breath and died. He joined his ancestors in death. [18] His descendants lived as nomads from the region of Havilah to Shur, which is near Egypt, in the direction of Assyria. They all fought with each other.

Esau and Jacob

[19] This is the account of Abraham's son Isaac and his descendants. Abraham was the father of Isaac. [20] Isaac was 40 years old when he married Rebekah, daughter of Bethuel the Aramean from Paddan Aram and sister of Laban the Aramean. [21] Isaac prayed to the Lord for his wife because she was childless. The Lord answered his prayer, and his wife Rebekah became pregnant. [22] When the children inside her were struggling with each other, she said, "If it's like this now, what will become of me?"[b] So she went to ask the Lord.

[23] The Lord said to her,

> "Two countries are in your womb.
> Two nations will go their separate ways from birth.
> One nation will be stronger than the other,
>   and the older will serve the younger."

[24] When the time came for her to give birth, she had twins. [25] The first one born was red. His whole body was covered with hair, so they named him Esau [Hairy]. [26] Afterwards, his brother was born with his hand holding on to Esau's heel, and so he was named Jacob [Heel]. Isaac was 60 years old when they were born.

[27] They grew up. Esau became an expert hunter, an outdoorsman. Jacob remained a quiet man, staying around the tents. [28] Because Isaac liked to eat the meat of wild animals, he loved Esau. However, Rebekah loved Jacob.

[29] Once, Jacob was preparing a meal when Esau, exhausted, came in from outdoors. [30] So Esau said to Jacob, "Let me have the whole pot of red stuff to eat—that red stuff—I'm exhausted." This is why he was called Edom.[c]

[31] Jacob responded, "First, sell me your rights as firstborn."

[32] "I'm about to die." Esau said. "What good is my inheritance to me?"

[33] "First, swear an oath," Jacob said. So Esau swore an oath to him and sold him his rights as firstborn, [34] Then Jacob gave Esau a meal of bread and lentils. He ate and drank, and then he got up and left.

This is how Esau showed his contempt for his rights as firstborn.

The Lord's First Promise to Isaac

26 [1] There was a famine in the land in addition to the earlier one during Abraham's time. So Isaac went to King Abimelech of the Philistines in Gerar.

[2] The Lord appeared to Isaac and said, "Don't go to Egypt. Stay where I tell you. [3] Live here in this land for a while, and I will be with you and bless you. I will give all these lands to you and your descendants. I will keep the oath that I swore to your father Abraham. [4] I will make your descendants as numerous as the stars in the sky and give all these lands to your descendants. Through your descendant all the nations of the earth will be blessed. [5] I will bless you because Abraham obeyed me and completed the duties, commands, laws, and instructions I gave him." [6] So Isaac lived in Gerar.

Isaac and Rebekah at Gerar

[7] When the men of that place asked about his wife, Isaac answered, "She's my sister." He was afraid to say "my wife." He thought that the men of that place would kill him to get Rebekah, because she was an attractive woman. [8] When he had been there a long time, King Abimelech of the Philistines looked out of his window and saw Isaac caressing his wife Rebekah.

[9] Abimelech called for Isaac and said, "So she's really your wife! How could you say, 'She's my sister'?"

---

[b] 25:22 Hebrew meaning of this sentence uncertain.   [c] 25:30 There is a play on words here between Hebrew 'adom (red stuff) and Edom.

Isaac answered him, "I thought I would be killed because of her."

[10] Then Abimelech said, "What have you done to us! One of the people might have easily gone to bed with your wife, and then you would have made us guilty of sin." [11] So Abimelech ordered his people, "Anyone who touches this man or his wife will be put to death."

[12] Isaac planted ˎcropsˏ in that land. In that same year he harvested a hundred times as much as he had planted because the LORD had blessed him. [13] He continued to be successful, becoming very rich. [14] Because he owned so many flocks, herds, and servants, the Philistines became jealous of him. [15] So the Philistines filled in all the wells that his father's servants had dug during his father Abraham's lifetime.

[16] Finally, Abimelech said to Isaac, "Go away from us! You've become more powerful than we are."

[17] So Isaac moved away. He set up his tents in the Gerar Valley and lived there. [18] He dug out the wells that had been dug during his father Abraham's lifetime. The Philistines had filled them in after Abraham's death. He gave them the same names that his father had given them.

[19] Isaac's servants dug in the valley and found a spring-fed well. [20] The herders from Gerar quarreled with Isaac's herders, claiming, "This water is ours!" So Isaac named the well Esek [Argument], because they had argued with him. [21] Then they dug another well, and they quarreled over that one too. So Isaac named it Sitnah [Accusation]. [22] He moved on from there and dug another well. They didn't quarrel over this one. So he named it Rehoboth [Roomy] and said, "Now the LORD has made room for us, and we will prosper in this land."

The LORD's Second Promise to Isaac

[23] He went from there to Beersheba. [24] That night the LORD appeared to Isaac, and said, "I am the God of your father Abraham. Don't be afraid, because I am with you. I will bless you and increase the number of your descendants for my servant Abraham's sake." [25] So Isaac built an altar there and worshiped the LORD. He also pitched his tent in that place, and his servants dug a well there.

Isaac's Agreement With Abimelech

[26] Abimelech, his friend Ahuzzath, and Phicol, the commander of his army, came from Gerar to see Isaac. [27] Isaac asked them, "Why have you come to me, since you hate me and sent me away from you?"

[28] They answered, "We have seen that the LORD is with you. So we thought, 'There should be a solemn agreement between us.' We'd like to make an agreement with you [29] that you will not harm us, since we have not touched you. We have done only good to you and let you go in peace. Now you are blessed by the LORD."

[30] Isaac prepared a special dinner for them, and they ate and drank. [31] Early the next morning they exchanged oaths. Then Isaac sent them on their way, and they left peacefully.

[32] That same day Isaac's servants came and told him about a well they had dug. They said to him, "We've found water." [33] So he named it Shibah [Oath]. That is why the name of the city is still Beersheba today.

Esau's Marriages

[34] When Esau was 40 years old, he married Judith, daughter of Beeri the Hittite. He also married Basemath, daughter of Elon the Hittite. [35] These women brought Isaac and Rebekah a lot of grief.

Jacob Gets Isaac's Blessing

27 [1] When Isaac was old and going blind, he called his older son Esau and said to him, "Son!"

Esau answered, "Here I am."

[2] Isaac said, "I'm old. I don't know when I'm going to die. [3] Now take your hunting equipment, your quiver and bow, and go out into the open country and hunt some wild game for me. [4] Prepare a good-tasting meal for me, just the way I like it. Bring it to me to eat so that I will bless you before I die."

[5] Rebekah was listening while Isaac was speaking to his son Esau. When Esau went into the open country to hunt for some wild game to bring back, [6] Rebekah said to her son Jacob, "I've just heard your father speaking to your brother Esau. [7] He said, 'Bring me some wild game, and prepare a good-tasting meal for me to eat so that I will bless you in the presence of the LORD before I die.' [8] Now listen to me, Son, and do what I tell you. [9] Go to the flock, and get me two good young goats. I'll prepare them as a good-tasting meal for your father, just the way he likes it. [10] Then take it to your father to eat so that he will bless you before he dies."

¹¹ Jacob said to his mother Rebekah, "My brother Esau is a hairy man, and my skin is smooth.ᵃ ¹² My father will feel ˌmy skinˌ and think I'm mocking him. Then I'll bring a curse on myself instead of a blessing."

¹³ His mother responded, "Let any curse on you fall on me, Son. Just obey me and go! Get me ˌthe young goatsˌ."

¹⁴ He went and got them and brought them to his mother. She prepared a good-tasting meal, just the way his father liked it. ¹⁵ Then Rebekah took her older son Esau's good clothes, which she had in the house, and put them on her younger son Jacob. ¹⁶ She put the skins from the young goats on his hands and on the back of his neck. ¹⁷ Then she gave her son Jacob the good-tasting meal and the bread she had prepared.

¹⁸ He went to his father and said, "Father?"

"Yes?" he answered. "Who are you, Son?"

¹⁹ Jacob answered his father, "I'm Esau, your firstborn. I've done what you told me. Sit up and eat this meat I've hunted for you so that you may bless me."

²⁰ Isaac asked his son, "How did you find it so quickly, Son?"

"The LORD your God brought it to me," he answered.

²¹ Then Isaac said to Jacob, "Come over here so that I can feel your skin, Son, ˌto find outˌ whether or not you really are my son Esau." ²² So Jacob went over to his father. Isaac felt ˌhis skinˌ. "The voice is Jacob's," he said, "but the hands are Esau's." ²³ He didn't recognize Jacob, because his hands were hairy like his brother Esau's hands. So he blessed him. ²⁴ "Are you really my son Esau?" he asked him.

"I am," Jacob answered.

²⁵ Isaac said, "Bring me some of the game, and I will eat it, Son, so that I will bless you." Jacob brought it to Isaac, and he ate it. Jacob also brought him wine, and he drank it.

²⁶ Then his father Isaac said to him, "Come here and give me a kiss, Son." ²⁷ He went over and gave him a kiss. When Isaac smelled his clothes, he blessed him and said,

> "The smell of my son
>   is like the smell of open country
>   that the LORD has blessed.
> ²⁸ May God give you dew from the sky,
>   fertile fields on the earth,
>   and plenty of fresh grain and new wine.
> ²⁹ May nations serve you.
> May people bow down to you.
>   Be the master of your brothers,
>   and may the sons of your mother bow down to you.
> May those who curse you be cursed.
> May those who bless you be blessed."

³⁰ Isaac finished blessing Jacob. Jacob had barely left when his brother Esau came in from hunting. ³¹ He, too, prepared a good-tasting meal and brought it to his father. Then he said to his father, "Please, Father, eat some of the meat I've hunted for you so that you will bless me."

³² "Who are you?" his father Isaac asked him.

"I'm your firstborn son Esau," he answered.

³³ Trembling violently all over, Isaac asked, "Who hunted game and brought it to me? I ate it before you came in. I blessed him, and he will stay blessed."

³⁴ When Esau heard these words from his father, he shouted out a very loud and bitter cry and said to his father, "Bless me too, Father!"

³⁵ Isaac said, "Your brother came and deceived me and has taken away your blessing."

³⁶ Esau said, "Isn't that why he's named Jacob? He's cheated me twice already: He took my rights as firstborn, and now he's taken my blessing." So he asked, "Haven't you saved a blessing for me?"

³⁷ Isaac answered Esau, "I have made him your master, and I have made all his brothers serve him. I've provided fresh grain and new wine for him. What is left for me to do for you, Son?"

³⁸ Esau asked, "Do you have only one blessing, Father? Bless me too, Father!" And Esau sobbed loudly.

³⁹ His father Isaac answered him,

> "The place where you live will lack the fertile fields of the earth
>   and the dew from the sky above.

ᵃ 27:11 Or "but I am a smooth man."

⁴⁰ You will use your sword to live,
    and you will serve your brother.
      But eventually you will gain your freedom*ᵇ*
        and break his yoke*ᶜ* off your neck."

⁴¹ So Esau hated Jacob because of the blessing that his father had given him. Esau said to himself, "The time to mourn for my father is near. Then I'll kill my brother Jacob." **⁴²** When Rebekah was told what her older son Esau had said, she sent for her younger son Jacob and said to him, "Watch out! Your brother Esau is comforting himself by planning to kill you.*ᵈ* **⁴³** So now, Son, obey me. Quick! Run away to my brother Laban in Haran. **⁴⁴** Stay with him awhile, until your brother's anger cools down. **⁴⁵** When your brother's anger is gone and he has forgotten what you did to him, I'll send for you and get you back. Why should I lose both of you in one day?"

⁴⁶ Rebekah said to Isaac, "I can't stand Hittite women! If Jacob marries a Hittite woman like one of those from around here, I might as well die."

Isaac Sends Jacob Away

28 **¹** Isaac called for Jacob and blessed him. Then he commanded him, "You are not to marry any of the Canaanite women. **²** Quick! Go to Paddan Aram. Go to the home of Bethuel, your mother's father, and get yourself a wife from there from the daughters of your uncle Laban. **³** May God Almighty bless you, make you fertile, and increase the number of your descendants so that you will become a community of people. **⁴** May he give to you and your descendants the blessing of Abraham so that you may take possession of the land where you are now living, the land that God gave to Abraham."

⁵ Isaac sent Jacob to Paddan Aram. Jacob went to live with Laban, son of Bethuel the Aramean and brother of Rebekah. She was the mother of Jacob and Esau.

⁶ Esau learned that Isaac had blessed Jacob and had sent him away to Paddan Aram to get a wife from there. He learned that Isaac had blessed Jacob and had commanded him not to marry any of the Canaanite women. **⁷** He also learned that Jacob had obeyed his father and mother and had left for Paddan Aram. **⁸** Esau realized that his father Isaac disapproved of Canaanite women. **⁹** So he went to Ishmael and married Mahalath, daughter of Abraham's son Ishmael and sister of Nebaioth, in addition to the wives he had.

Jacob's First Encounter With God

¹⁰ Jacob left Beersheba and traveled toward Haran. **¹¹** When he came to a certain place, he stopped for the night because the sun had gone down. He took one of the stones from that place, put it under his head, and lay down there. **¹²** He had a dream in which he saw a stairway set up on the earth with its top reaching up to heaven. He saw the angels of God going up and coming down on it. **¹³** The LORD was standing above it, saying, "I am the LORD, the God of your grandfather Abraham and the God of Isaac. I will give the land on which you are lying to you and your descendants. **¹⁴** Your descendants will be like the dust on the earth. You will spread out to the west and to the east, to the north and to the south. Through you and through your descendant every family on earth will be blessed. **¹⁵** Remember, I am with you and will watch over you wherever you go. I will also bring you back to this land because I will not leave you until I do what I've promised you."

¹⁶ Then Jacob woke up from his sleep and exclaimed, "Certainly, the LORD is in this place, and I didn't know it!" **¹⁷** Filled with awe, he said, "How awe-inspiring this place is! Certainly, this is the house of God and the gateway to heaven!"

¹⁸ Early the next morning Jacob took the stone he had put under his head. He set it up as a marker and poured olive oil on top of it. **¹⁹** He named that place Bethel [House of God]. Previously, the name of the city was Luz.

²⁰ Then Jacob made a vow: "If God will be with me and will watch over me on my trip and give me food to eat and clothes to wear, **²¹** and if I return safely to my father's home, then the LORD will be my God. **²²** This stone that I have set up as a marker will be the house of God, and I will surely give you a tenth of everything you give me."

Jacob's Arrival in Haran

29 **¹** Jacob continued on his trip and came to the land in the east. **²** He looked around, and out in a field he saw a well with a large stone over the opening. Three flocks of sheep were lying down near it, because the flocks were watered from that well. **³** When all the flocks were

---

ᵇ 27:40 Hebrew meaning uncertain.   *ᶜ* 27:40 A yoke is a wooden bar placed over the necks of work animals so that they can pull plows or carts.   *ᵈ* 27:42 English equivalent difficult.

gathered there, the stone would be rolled off the opening of the well so that the sheep could be watered. Then the stone would be put back in place over the opening of the well.

[4] Jacob asked some people, "My friends, where are you from?"

"We're from Haran," they replied.

[5] He asked them, "Do you know Laban, Nahor's grandson?"

They answered, "We do."

[6] "How is he doing?" Jacob asked them.

"He's fine," they answered. "Here comes his daughter Rachel with the sheep."

[7] "It's still the middle of the day," he said. "It isn't time yet to gather the livestock. Water the sheep. Then let them graze."

[8] They replied, "We can't until all the flocks are gathered. When the stone is rolled off the opening of the well, we can water the sheep."

[9] While he was still talking to them, Rachel arrived with her father's sheep, because she was a shepherd. [10] Jacob saw Rachel, daughter of his uncle Laban, with his uncle Laban's sheep. He came forward and rolled the stone off the opening of the well and watered his uncle Laban's sheep. [11] Then Jacob kissed Rachel and sobbed loudly. [12] When Jacob told Rachel that he was her father's nephew and that he was Rebekah's son, she ran and told her father.

[13] As soon as Laban heard the news about his sister's son Jacob, he ran to meet him. He hugged and kissed him and brought him into his home. Then Jacob told Laban all that had happened. [14] Laban said to him, "You are my own flesh and blood."

Jacob Obtains Wives

Jacob stayed with him for a whole month. [15] Then Laban said to him, "Just because you're my relative doesn't mean that you should work for nothing. Tell me what your wages should be."

[16] Laban had two daughters. The name of the older one was Leah, and the name of the younger one was Rachel. [17] Leah had attractive eyes,[a] but Rachel had a beautiful figure and beautiful features. [18] Jacob loved Rachel. So he offered, "I'll work seven years in return for your younger daughter Rachel."

[19] Laban responded, "It's better that I give her to you than to any other man. Stay with me." [20] Jacob worked seven years in return for Rachel, but the years seemed like only a few days to him because he loved her.

[21] At the end of the seven years, Jacob said to Laban, "The time is up; give me my wife! I want to sleep with her." [22] So Laban invited all the people of that place and gave a wedding feast. [23] In the evening he took his daughter Leah and brought her to Jacob. Jacob slept with her. When morning came, he realized it was Leah.[b] [24] (Laban had given his slave Zilpah to his daughter Leah as her slave.)

[25] "What have you done to me?" Jacob asked Laban. "Didn't I work for you in return for Rachel? Why did you cheat me?"

[26] Laban answered, "It's not our custom to give the younger daughter ¸in marriage¸ before the older one. [27] Finish the week of wedding festivities with this daughter. Then we will give you the other one too. But you'll have to work for me another seven years."

[28] That's what Jacob did. He finished the week with Leah. Then Laban gave his daughter Rachel to him as his wife. [29] (Laban had given his slave Bilhah to his daughter Rachel as her slave.) [30] Jacob slept with Rachel too. He loved Rachel more than Leah. So he worked for Laban another seven years.

Leah and Rachel Compete for Jacob's Love

[31] When the LORD saw Leah was unloved, he made it possible for her to have children, but Rachel had none. [32] Leah became pregnant and gave birth to a son. She named him Reuben [Here's My Son], because she said, "Certainly, the LORD has seen my misery; now my husband will love me!" [33] She became pregnant again and gave birth to another son. She said, "Certainly, the LORD has heard that I'm unloved, and he also has given me this son." So she named him Simeon [Hearing]. [34] She became pregnant again and gave birth to another son. She said, "Now at last my husband will become attached to me because I've given him three sons." So she named him Levi [Attached]. [35] She became pregnant again and gave birth to another son. She said, "This time I will praise the LORD." So she named him Judah [Praise]. Then she stopped having children.

30 [1] Rachel saw that she could not have children for Jacob, and she became jealous of her sister. She said to Jacob, "Give me children, or I'll die!"

[2] Jacob became angry with Rachel and asked, "Can I take the place of God, who has kept you from having children?"

---

[a] 29:17 Or "had no sparkle in her eyes."   [b] 29:23 The first part of verse 25 (in Hebrew) has been placed in verse 23 to express the complex Hebrew paragraph structure more clearly in English.

³ She said, "Here's my servant Bilhah. Sleep with her. She can have children for me, and I can build a family for myself through her." ⁴ So she gave him her slave Bilhah as his wife, and Jacob slept with her. ⁵ Bilhah became pregnant, and she gave birth to a son for Jacob. ⁶ Rachel said, "Now God has judged in my favor. He has heard my prayer and has given me a son." So she named him Dan [He Judges].

⁷ Rachel's slave Bilhah became pregnant again and gave birth to a second son for Jacob. ⁸ Rachel said, "I have had a great struggle* with my sister, and I have won!" So she named him Naphtali [My Struggle].

⁹ When Leah saw that she had stopped having children, she took her slave Zilpah and gave her to Jacob as his wife. ¹⁰ Leah's slave Zilpah gave birth to a son for Jacob. ¹¹ Leah said, "I've been lucky!" So she called him Gad [Luck].

¹² Leah's slave Zilpah gave birth to her second son for Jacob. ¹³ Leah said, "I've been blessed! Women will call me blessed." So she named him Asher [Blessing].

¹⁴ During the wheat harvest Reuben went out into the fields and found some mandrakes.ᵇ He brought them to his mother Leah. Rachel said to Leah, "Please give me some of your son's mandrakes."

¹⁵ Leah replied, "Isn't it enough that you took my husband? Are you also going to take my son's mandrakes?"

Rachel said, "Very well, Jacob can go to bed with you tonight in return for your son's mandrakes."

¹⁶ As Jacob was coming in from the fields that evening, Leah went out to meet him. "You are to sleep with me," she said. "You are my reward for my son's mandrakes." So he went to bed with her that night. ¹⁷ God answered Leah's prayer. She became pregnant and gave birth to her fifth son for Jacob. ¹⁸ Leah said, "God has given me my reward because I gave my slave to my husband." So she named him Issachar [Reward].

¹⁹ She became pregnant again and gave birth to her sixth son for Jacob. ²⁰ Leah said, "God has presented me with a beautiful present. This time my husband will honor me because I have given him six sons." So she named him Zebulun [Honor].

²¹ Later she gave birth to a daughter and named her Dinah.

²² Then God remembered Rachel. God answered her prayer and made it possible for her to have children. ²³ So she became pregnant and gave birth to a son. Then she said, "God has taken away my disgrace." ²⁴ She named him Joseph [May He Give Another] and said, "May the LORD give me another son."

Jacob's Flocks Prosper

²⁵ After Rachel gave birth to Joseph, Jacob said to Laban, "Let me go home to my own country. ²⁶ Give me my wives and my children for whom I've worked, and let me go. You know how much work I've done for you."

²⁷ Laban replied, "Listen to me. I've learned from the signs I've seen that the LORD has blessed me because of you." ²⁸ So he offered, "Name your wages, and I'll pay them."

²⁹ Jacob responded, "You know how much work I've done for you and what has happened to your livestock under my care. ³⁰ The little that you had before I came has grown to a large amount. The LORD has blessed you wherever I've been. When can I do something for my own family?"

³¹ Laban asked, "What should I give you?"

"Don't give me anything," Jacob answered. "Instead, do something for me, then I'll go back to taking care of and watching your flocks again. ³² Let me go through all of your flocks today and take every speckled or spotted sheep, every black lamb, and every spotted or speckled goat. They will be my wages. ³³ My honesty will speak for itself whenever you come to check on my wages. Any goat I have that isn't speckled or spotted or any lamb that isn't black will be considered stolen."

³⁴ Laban answered, "Agreed. We'll do as you've said." ³⁵ However, that same day Laban took out the striped and spotted male goats, all the speckled and spotted female goats (every one with white on it), and every black lamb. He had his sons take charge of them. ³⁶ He traveled three days away from Jacob. Jacob continued to take care of the rest of Laban's flocks.

³⁷ Then Jacob took fresh-cut branches of poplar, almond, and plane trees and peeled the bark on them in strips of white, uncovering the white which was on the branches.ᶜ ³⁸ He placed the peeled branches in the troughs directly in front of the flocks, at the watering places where the flocks came to drink. When they were in heat and came to drink, ³⁹ they mated in front of the branches. Then they gave birth to young that were striped, speckled, or spotted.

ᵃ 30:8 Or "I have struggled the struggles of God."   ᵇ 30:14 Mandrakes were considered a source of fertility for women.
ᶜ 30:37 English equivalent difficult.

⁴⁰ Jacob separated the rams from the flock and made the rest of the sheep face any that were striped or black in Laban's flocks. So he made separate herds for himself and did not add them to Laban's flocks. ⁴¹ Whenever the stronger of the flocks were in heat, Jacob would lay the branches in the troughs in front of them so that they would mate by the branches. ⁴² But when the flocks in heat were weak, he didn't lay down the branches. So the weaker ones belonged to Laban and the stronger ones to Jacob. ⁴³ As a result, Jacob became very wealthy. He had large flocks, male and female slaves, camels, and donkeys.

Jacob's Second and Third Encounters With God

31 ¹ Jacob heard that Laban's sons were saying, "Jacob has taken everything that belonged to our father and has gained all his wealth from him." ² He also noticed that Laban did not appear as friendly to him as before.

³ Then the LORD said to Jacob, "Go back to the land of your ancestors and to your relatives, and I will be with you."

⁴ So Jacob sent a message to Rachel and Leah to come out to the open country where his flocks were. ⁵ He said to them, "I have seen that your father isn't as friendly to me as he was before, but the God of my father has been with me. ⁶ You know that I have worked as hard as I could for your father. ⁷ Your father has cheated me. He has changed my wages ten times. But God hasn't let him harm me. ⁸ Whenever he said, 'The speckled ones will be your wages,' all the flocks gave birth to speckled young. And whenever he said, 'The striped ones will be your wages,' all the flocks gave birth to striped young. ⁹ So God has taken away your father's livestock and has given them to me.

¹⁰ "During the mating season I had a dream: I looked up and saw that the male goats which were mating were striped, speckled, or spotted. ¹¹ In the dream the Messenger of God called to me, 'Jacob!' And I answered, 'Yes, here I am.' ¹² He said, 'Look up and see that all the male goats which are mating are striped, speckled, or spotted, because I have seen everything that Laban is doing to you. ¹³ I am the God who appeared to you at Bethel,ᵃ where you poured olive oil on a stone marker for a holy purpose and where you made a vow to me. Now leave this land, and go back to the land of your relatives.' "

¹⁴ Rachel and Leah answered him, "Is there anything left in our father's household for us to inherit? ¹⁵ Doesn't he think of us as foreigners? Not only did he sell us, but he has used up the money that was paid for us. ¹⁶ Certainly, all the wealth that God took away from our father belongs to us and our children. Now do whatever God has told you."

Laban and Jacob Make Peace

¹⁷ Then Jacob put his children and his wives on camels. ¹⁸ He drove all his livestock ahead of him and took all the possessions that he had accumulated. He took his own livestock that he had accumulated in Paddan Aram and went back to his father Isaac in Canaan.

¹⁹ When Laban went to shear his sheep, Rachel stole her father's idols. ²⁰ Jacob also tricked Laban the Aramean by not telling him he was leaving. ²¹ So he left in a hurry with all that belonged to him. He crossed the Euphrates River and went toward the mountains of Gilead.

²² Two days later Laban was told that Jacob had left in a hurry. ²³ He and his relatives pursued Jacob for seven days. Laban caught up with him in the mountains of Gilead.

²⁴ God came to Laban the Aramean in a dream at night and said to him, "Be careful not to say anything at all to Jacob."

²⁵ When Laban finally caught up with Jacob, Jacob had put up his tents in the mountains. So Laban and his relatives put up their tents in the mountains of Gilead. ²⁶ Then Laban asked Jacob, "What have you done by tricking me? You've carried off my daughters like prisoners of war. ²⁷ Why did you leave secretly and trick me? You didn't even tell me you were leaving. I would have sent you on your way rejoicing, with songs accompanied by tambourines and lyres. ²⁸ You didn't even let me kiss my grandchildren and my daughters. You've done a foolish thing. ²⁹ I have the power to harm you. Last night the God of your father said to me, 'Be careful not to say anything at all to Jacob.' ³⁰ Now you have left for your father's home because you were so homesick. But why did you steal my gods?"

³¹ Jacob answered Laban, "I left because I was afraid. I thought you would take your daughters away from me by force. ³² If you find your gods, the one who has them will not be allowed to live. In the presence of our relatives, search as much as you want through what I have, and take what is yours." (Jacob didn't know that Rachel had stolen the gods.)

³³ So Laban went into Jacob's tent, into Leah's tent, and into the tent of the two slaves. But he found nothing. He came out of Leah's tent and went into Rachel's tent. ³⁴ Rachel had taken

---

ᵃ 31:13 Greek; Masoretic Text "the God at Bethel."

the idols and had put them in her camel's saddle-bag and was sitting on them. Laban rummaged through the whole tent but found nothing. ³⁵ Rachel said to her father, "Don't be angry, Father, but I can't get up to greet you; I'm having my period." So even though Laban had made a thorough search, he didn't find the idols.

³⁶ Then Jacob became angry and confronted Laban. "What is my crime?" Jacob demanded of Laban. "What is my offense that you have come chasing after me? ³⁷ Now that you've rummaged through all my things, did you find anything from your house? Put it here in front of all our relatives. Let them decide which one of us is right.

³⁸ "I've been with you for 20 years. Your sheep and goats never miscarried, and I never ate any rams from your flocks. ³⁹ I never brought you any of the flock that was killed by wild animals. I paid for the loss myself. That's what you demanded of me when any of the flock was stolen during the day or at night. ⁴⁰ The scorching heat during the day and the cold at night wore me down, and I lost a lot of sleep. ⁴¹ I've been with your household 20 years now. I worked for you 14 years for your two daughters and 6 years for your flocks, and you changed my wages ten times. ⁴² If the God of my father, the God of Abraham and the Fear of Isaac,ᵇ had not been with me, you would have sent me away empty-handed by now. God has seen my misery and hard work, and last night he made it right."

⁴³ Then Laban answered Jacob, "These are my daughters, my grandchildren, and my flocks. Everything you see is mine! Yet, what can I do today for my daughters or for their children? ⁴⁴ Now, let's make an agreement and let it stand as a witness between you and me."

⁴⁵ Jacob took a stone and set it up as a marker. ⁴⁶ Then Jacob said to his relatives, "Gather some stones." They took stones, put them into a pile, and ate there by the pile of stones. ⁴⁷ In his language‚ Laban called it Jegar Sahadutha [Witness Pile], but Jacob called it Galeed.ᶜ ⁴⁸ Laban said, "This pile of stones stands as a witness between you and me today." This is why it was named Galeed ⁴⁹ and also Mizpah [Watchtower], because he said, "May the LORD watch between you and me when we're unable to see each other. ⁵⁰ If you mistreat my daughters or marry other women behind my back, remember that God stands as a witness between you and me."

⁵¹ Laban said to Jacob, "Here is the pile of stones, and here is the marker that I have set up between you and me. ⁵² This pile of stones and this marker stand as witnesses that I will not go past the pile of stones to harm you, and that you will not go past the pile of stones or marker to harm me. ⁵³ May the God of Abraham and Nahor—the God of their father—judge between us."

So Jacob swore this oath by the Fear of his father Isaac ⁵⁴ and offered a sacrifice on the mountain. He invited his relatives to eat the meal with him. They ate with him and spent the night on the mountain.ᵈ

⁵⁵ Early the next morning Laban kissed his grandchildren and his daughters and blessed them. Then Laban left and went back home.

Jacob Sends Messages and Gifts to Esau

32ᵃ ¹ As Jacob went on his way, God's angels met him. ² When he saw them, Jacob said, "This is God's camp!" He named that place Mahanaim [Two Camps].

³ Jacob sent messengers ahead of him to his brother Esau in Seir, the country of Edom. ⁴ He commanded them to give this message to Esau, "Sir, this is what Jacob has to say, 'I've been living with Laban and have stayed until now. ⁵ I have cattle and donkeys, sheep and goats, and male and female slaves. I've sent ‚these messengers‚ to tell you ‚this news‚ in order to win your favor.' "

⁶ When the messengers came back to Jacob, they said, "We went to your brother Esau. He is coming to meet you with 400 men."

⁷ Jacob was terrified and distressed. So he divided the people, the sheep and goats, the cattle, and the camels into two camps. ⁸ He thought, "If Esau attacks the one camp, then the other camp will be able to escape."

⁹ Then Jacob prayed, "God of my grandfather Abraham and God of my father Isaac! LORD, you said to me, 'Go back to your land and to your relatives, and I will make you prosperous.' ¹⁰ I'm not worthy of all the love and faithfulness you have shown me. I only had a shepherd's staff when I crossed the Jordan River, but now I have two camps. ¹¹ Please save me from my brother Esau, because I'm afraid of him. I'm afraid that he'll come and attack me and the mothers and children too. ¹² But you did say, 'I will make sure that you are prosperous and that your descendants will be as many as the grains of sand on the seashore. No one will be able to count them because there are so many.' "

ᵇ 31:42 Or "Protection of Isaac."   ᶜ 31:47 *Galeed* is the Hebrew equivalent of the Aramaic words *Jegar Sahadutha*.   ᵈ 31:54 Genesis 31:55 in English Bibles is Genesis 32:1 in the Hebrew Bible.   ᵃ 32:1 Genesis 32:1–32 in English Bibles is Genesis 32:2–33 in the Hebrew Bible.

[13] He stayed there that night. Then he prepared a gift for his brother Esau from what he had brought with him: [14] 200 female goats and 20 male goats, 200 female sheep and 20 male sheep, [15] 30 female camels with their young, 40 cows and 10 bulls, 20 female donkeys and 10 male donkeys.

[16] He placed servants in charge of each herd. Then he said to his servants, "Go ahead of me, and keep a distance between the herds." [17] He commanded the first servant, "When my brother Esau meets you and asks you, 'To whom do you belong, and where are you going, and whose animals are these ahead of you?' [18] then say, 'Sir, they belong to your servant Jacob. This is a gift sent to you. Jacob is right behind us.' " [19] He also commanded the second servant, the third, and all the others who followed the herds. He said, "Say the same thing to Esau when you find him. [20] And be sure to add, 'Jacob is right behind us, sir.' " He thought, "I'll make peace with him by giving him this gift that I'm sending ahead of me. After that I will see him, and he'll welcome me back." [21] So Jacob sent the gift ahead of him while he stayed in the camp that night.

Jacob's Fourth Encounter With God—He Wrestles With God

[22] During that night he got up and gathered his two wives, his two slaves and his eleven children and crossed at the shallow part of the Jabbok River. [23] After he sent them across the stream, he sent everything else across. [24] So Jacob was left alone. Then a man wrestled with him until dawn. [25] When the man saw that he could not win against Jacob, he touched the socket of Jacob's hip so that it was dislocated as they wrestled. [26] Then the man said, "Let me go; it's almost dawn."

But Jacob answered, "I won't let you go until you bless me."

[27] So the man asked him, "What's your name?"

"Jacob," he answered.

[28] The man said, "Your name will no longer be Jacob but Israel [He Struggles With God], because you have struggled with God and with men—and you have won."

[29] Jacob said, "Please tell me your name."

The man answered, "Why do you ask for my name?" Then he blessed Jacob there. [30] So Jacob named that place Peniel [Face of God], because he said, "I have seen God face to face, but my life was saved." [31] The sun rose as he passed Penuel.[b] He was limping because of his hip. [32] (Therefore, even today the people of Israel do not eat the muscle of the thigh attached to the hip socket because God touched the socket of Jacob's hip at the muscle of the thigh.)

Jacob Meets Esau

33 [1] Jacob saw Esau coming with 400 men. So he divided the children among Leah, Rachel, and the two slaves. [2] He put the slaves and their children in front, Leah and her children after them, and Rachel and Joseph last. [3] He went on ahead of them and bowed seven times with his face touching the ground as he came near his brother.

[4] Then Esau ran to meet Jacob. Esau hugged him, threw his arms around him, and kissed him. They both cried. [5] When he saw the women and children, Esau asked, "Who are these people here with you?"

"The children God has graciously given me, sir," Jacob answered.

[6] Then the slaves and their children came forward and bowed down. [7] Likewise, Leah and her children came forward and bowed down. Finally, Joseph and Rachel came forward and bowed down.

[8] Then Esau asked, "Why did you send this whole group ⸤of people and animals⸥ I met?"

He answered, "To win your favor, sir."

[9] Esau said, "I have enough. Keep what you have, Brother."

[10] Jacob said, "No, please take the gift I'm giving you, because I've seen your face as if I were seeing the face of God, and yet you welcomed me so warmly. [11] Please take the present I've brought you, because God has been gracious to me and has given me all that I need." So Esau took it because Jacob insisted.

[12] Then Esau said, "Let's get ready to go, and I'll go with you."

[13] Jacob said to him, "Sir, you know that the children are frail and that I have to take care of the flocks and cattle that are nursing their young. If they're driven too hard for even one day, all the flocks will die. [14] Go ahead of me, sir. I will slowly and gently guide the herds that are in front of me at their pace and at the children's pace until I come to you in Seir."

[15] Esau said, "Then let me leave some of my men with you."

"Why do that?" Jacob asked. "I only want to win your favor, sir."

[16] That day Esau started back to Seir. [17] But Jacob moved on to Succoth, where he built a house for himself and made shelters for his livestock. That is why the place is named Succoth [Shelters].

---

[b] 32:31 Another name for Peniel.

¹⁸ So having come from Paddan Aram, Jacob came safely to the city of Shechem in Canaan. He camped within sight of the city. ¹⁹ Then he bought the piece of land on which he had put up his tents. He bought it from the sons of Hamor, father of Shechem, for 100 pieces of silver. ²⁰ He set up an altar there and named it God Is the God of Israel.

Dinah Is Raped

34 ¹ Dinah, daughter of Leah and Jacob, went out to visit some of the Canaanite women. ² When Shechem, son of the local ruler Hamor the Hivite, saw her, he took her and raped her. ³ He became very fond of Jacob's daughter Dinah. He loved the girl and spoke tenderly to her.

⁴ So Shechem said to his father Hamor, "Get me this girl for my wife."

⁵ Jacob heard that Shechem had dishonored his daughter Dinah. His sons were with his livestock out in the open country, so Jacob kept quiet until they came home.

⁶ So Shechem's father Hamor came to Jacob to speak with him. ⁷ Jacob's sons came in from the open country as soon as they heard the news. The men felt outraged and very angry because Shechem had committed such a godless act against Israel's family by raping Jacob's daughter. This shouldn't have happened.

⁸ Hamor told them. "My son Shechem has his heart set on your daughter. Please let her marry him. ⁹ Intermarry with us; give your daughters to us, and take ours for yourselves. ¹⁰ You can live with us, and the land will be yours. Live here, move about freely in this area, and acquire property here."

¹¹ Then Shechem said to Dinah's father and her brothers, "Do me this favor. I'll give you whatever you ask. ¹² Set the price I must pay for the bride and the gift I must give her as high as you want. I'll pay exactly what you tell me. Give me the girl as my wife."

¹³ Then Jacob's sons gave Shechem and his father Hamor a misleading answer because he had dishonored their sister Dinah. ¹⁴ They said, "We can't do this. We can't give our sister to a man who is uncircumcised. That would be a disgrace to us! ¹⁵ We will give our consent to you only on one condition: Every male must be circumcised as we are. ¹⁶ Then we'll give our daughters to you and take yours for ourselves, and we'll live with you and become one people. ¹⁷ If you won't agree to be circumcised, we'll take our daughter and go."

¹⁸ Their proposal seemed good to Hamor and his son Shechem. ¹⁹ The young man didn't waste any time in doing what they said because he took such pleasure in Jacob's daughter. He was the most honored person in all his father's family.

²⁰ So Hamor and his son Shechem went to their city gate to speak to the men of their city. They said, ²¹ "These people are friendly toward us, so let them live in our land and move about freely in the area. Look, there's plenty of room in this land for them. We can marry their daughters and let them marry ours. ²² These people will consent to live with us and become one nation on one condition: Every male must be circumcised as they are. ²³ Won't their livestock, their personal property, and all their animals be ours? We only need to agree to do this for them. Then they'll live with us."

²⁴ All the men who had come out to the city gate agreed with Hamor and his son Shechem. So they were all circumcised at the city gate.

²⁵ Two days later, while the men were still in pain, two of Jacob's sons, Simeon and Levi, Dinah's brothers, took their swords and boldly attacked the city. They killed every man ²⁶ including Hamor and his son Shechem. They took Dinah from Shechem's home and left. ²⁷ Then Jacob's sons stripped the corpses and looted the city where their sister had been dishonored. ²⁸ They took the sheep and goats, cattle, donkeys, and whatever else was in the city or out in the fields. ²⁹ They carried off all the wealth and all the women and children and looted everything in the houses.

³⁰ Then Jacob said to Simeon and Levi, "You have caused me a lot of trouble! You've made the people living in the area, the Canaanites and the Perizzites, hate me. There are only a few of us. If they join forces against me and attack me, my family and I will be wiped out."

³¹ Simeon and Levi asked, "Should Shechem have been allowed to treat our sister like a prostitute?"

Jacob's Fifth Encounter With God

35 ¹ Then God said to Jacob, "Go to Bethel and live there. Make an altar there. I am the God who appeared to you when you were fleeing from your brother Esau."

² So Jacob said to his family and those who were with him, "Get rid of the foreign gods which you have, wash yourselves until you are ritually clean,ᵃ and change your clothes. ³ Then let's go to Bethel. I will make an altar there to God, who answered me when I was trou-

---

ᵃ 35:2 "Clean" refers to anything that is presentable to God.

bled and who has been with me wherever I've gone." [4] So they gave Jacob all the foreign gods that they had in their possession as well as the earrings that they had on. Jacob buried these things under the oak tree near Shechem.

[5] As they moved on, God made the people of the cities that were all around them terrified so that no one pursued them. [6] Jacob and all the people who were with him came to Luz (that is, Bethel) in the land of Canaan. [7] He built an altar there and called that place El Bethel [God of the House of God]. That's where God had revealed himself to Jacob when he was fleeing from his brother. [8] Rebekah's nurse Deborah died and was buried under the oak tree outside Bethel. So Jacob called it the Tree of Crying.

Jacob's Sixth Encounter With God—His Name Changed to Israel

[9] Then God appeared once more to Jacob after he came back from Paddan Aram, and he blessed him. [10] God said to him, "Your name is Jacob. You will no longer be called Jacob, but your name will be Israel." So he named him Israel.

[11] God also said to him, "I am God Almighty. Be fertile, and increase in number. A nation and a community of nations will come from you, and kings will come from you. [12] I will give you the land that I gave to Abraham and Isaac. I will also give this land to your descendants." [13] Then God went up from him at the place where he had spoken with him. [14] So Jacob set up a memorial, a stone marker, to mark the place where God had spoken with him. He poured a wine offering and olive oil on it. [15] Jacob named the place where God had spoken with him Bethel [House of God].

Jacob's [Israel's] Sons—1 Chronicles 2:1–2

[16] Then they moved on from Bethel. When they were still some distance from Ephrath, Rachel went into labor and was having severe labor pains. [17] During one of her pains, the midwife said to her, "Don't be afraid! You're having another son!" [18] Rachel was dying. As she took her last breath, she named her son Benoni [Son of My Sorrow], but his father named him Benjamin [Son of My Right Hand].

[19] Rachel died and was buried on the way to Ephrath (that is, Bethlehem). [20] Then Jacob set up a stone as a marker for her grave. The same marker is at Rachel's grave today.

[21] Israel moved on again and put up his tent beyond Migdal Eder. [22] While Israel was living in that region, Reuben went to bed with his father's concubine[b] Bilhah, and Israel heard about it.

Jacob had 12 sons.

[23] The sons of **Leah** were

Jacob's firstborn Reuben, then Simeon, Levi, Judah, Issachar, and Zebulun.

[24] The sons of **Rachel** were

Joseph and Benjamin.

[25] The sons of Rachel's slave **Bilhah** were

Dan and Naphtali.

[26] The sons of Leah's slave **Zilpah** were

Gad and Asher.

These were Jacob's sons, who were born in Paddan Aram.

[27] Jacob came home to his father Isaac to Mamre's city, Kiriath Arba (that is, Hebron). Abraham and Isaac had lived there for a while. [28] Isaac was 180 years old [29] when he took his last breath and died. He joined his ancestors in death at a very old age. His sons Esau and Jacob buried him.

The Origin of Edom—1 Chronicles 1:35–54

36 [1] This is the account of Esau (that is, Edom) and his descendants. [2] Esau chose his wives from the women of Canaan: Adah, daughter of Elon the Hittite; Oholibamah, daughter of Anah and granddaughter of Zibeon the Hivite; [3] also Basemath, daughter of Ishmael and sister of Nebaioth. [4] Adah gave birth to Eliphaz for Esau, and Basemath gave birth to Reuel. [5] Oholibamah gave birth to Jeush, Jalam, and Korah. These were the sons of Esau who were born in Canaan.

[6] Esau took his wives, his sons, his daughters, all the members of his household, his possessions, all his cattle, and everything he had accumulated in Canaan and went to another land away from his brother Jacob. [7] He did this because they had too many possessions to live together. There wasn't enough pastureland for all of their livestock. [8] So Esau, who was also known as Edom, lived in the mountains of Seir.

---

[b] 35:22 A concubine is considered a wife except she has fewer rights under the law.

[9] This is the account of Esau and his descendants. He was the father of the people of Edom in the mountains of Seir.
[10] These were the names of Esau's sons:
Eliphaz, son of Esau's wife Adah, and Reuel, son of Esau's wife Basemath.
[11] The sons of Eliphaz were
Teman, Omar, Zepho, Gatam, and Kenaz. [12] Timna was a concubine[a] of Esau's son Eliphaz. She gave birth to Amalek for Eliphaz. These were the grandsons of Esau's wife Adah.
[13] These were Reuel's sons:
Nahath, Zerah, Shammah, and Mizzah. These were the grandsons of Esau's wife Basemath.
[14] These were the sons of Esau's wife Oholibamah, daughter of Anah and granddaughter of Zibeon. She gave birth to Jeush, Jalam, and Korah for Esau.

[15] These were the tribal leaders among Esau's descendants:
The sons of Eliphaz, Esau's firstborn, were
Teman, Omar, Zepho, Kenaz, [16] Korah, Gatam, and Amalek. These were the tribal leaders descended from Eliphaz in Edom. They were the grandsons of Adah.
[17] These were the tribal leaders among the descendants of Esau's son Reuel:
Nahath, Zerah, Shammah, and Mizzah. These were the tribal leaders descended from Reuel in Edom. They were the grandsons of Esau's wife Basemath.
[18] These were the tribal leaders among the descendants of Esau's wife Oholibamah:
Jeush, Jalam, and Korah. These were the tribal leaders descended from Esau's wife Oholibamah, Anah's daughter.
[19] These were the descendants of Esau (that is, Edom), who were tribal leaders.

[20] These were the sons of Seir the Horite, the people living in that land:
Lotan, Shobal, Zibeon, Anah, [21] Dishon, Ezer, and Dishan. These Horite tribal leaders were the sons of Seir in Edom.
[22] The sons of Lotan were
Hori and Hemam. Lotan's sister was Timna.
[23] These were the sons of Shobal:
Alvan, Manahath, Ebal, Shepho, and Onam.
[24] These were the sons of Zibeon:
Aiah and Anah. (Anah found the hot springs[b] in the desert while he was taking care of the donkeys that belonged to his father Zibeon.)
[25] These were the children of Anah:
Dishon and Oholibamah, daughter of Anah.
[26] These were the sons of Dishon:
Hemdan, Eshban, Ithran, and Cheran.
[27] These were the sons of Ezer:
Bilhan, Zaavan, and Akan.
[28] These were the sons of Dishan:
Uz and Aran.
[29] These were the Horite tribal leaders:
Lotan, Shobal, Zibeon, Anah, [30] Dishon, Ezer, and Dishan. These were the Horite tribal leaders in the land of Seir.

[31] These were the kings who ruled Edom before any king ruled the people of Israel:
[32] Bela, son of Beor, ruled Edom. The name of his ˻capital˼ city was Dinhabah.
[33] After Bela died, Jobab, son of Zerah from Bozrah, succeeded him as king.
[34] After Jobab died, Husham from the land of the Temanites succeeded him as king.
[35] After Husham died, Hadad, son of Bedad succeeded him as king. Hadad defeated the Midianites in the country of Moab. The name of his capital city was Avith.
[36] After Hadad died, Samlah from Masrekah succeeded him as king.
[37] After Samlah died, Shaul from Rehoboth on the river succeeded him as king.
[38] After Shaul died, Baal Hanan, son of Achbor, succeeded him as king.
[39] After Baal Hanan, son of Achbor, died, Hadar succeeded him as king, and the name of his capital city was Pau. His wife's name was Mehetabel, daughter of Matred and granddaughter of Mezahab.

[40] These were the names of the tribal leaders descended from Esau, by family, place, and name:
Timna, Alvah, Jetheth, [41] Oholibamah, Elah, Pinon, [42] Kenaz, Teman, Mibzar, [43] Magdiel, and Iram.

---

[a] 36:12 A concubine is considered a wife except she has fewer rights under the law.   [b] 36:24 Latin; Hebrew meaning uncertain.

These were the tribal leaders of Edom listed by the places where they lived and the property they owned.

Esau was the father of the people of Edom.

Joseph's Brothers Sell Him Into Slavery

37 ¹ Jacob continued to live in the land of Canaan, where his father had lived. ² This is the account of Jacob and his descendants.

Joseph was a seventeen-year-old young man. He took care of the flocks with the sons of Bilhah and Zilpah, his father's wives. Joseph told his father about the bad things his brothers were doing.

³ Israel loved Joseph more than all his sons because Joseph had been born in Israel's old age. So he made Joseph a special robe with long sleeves. ⁴ Joseph's brothers saw that their father loved him more than any of them. They hated Joseph and couldn't speak to him on friendly terms.

⁵ Joseph had a dream and when he told his brothers, they hated him even more. ⁶ He said to them, "Please listen to the dream I had. ⁷ We were tying grain into bundles out in the field, and suddenly mine stood up. It remained standing while your bundles gathered around my bundle and bowed down to it."

⁸ Then his brothers asked him, "Are you going to be our king or rule us?" They hated him even more for his dreams and his words.

⁹ Then he had another dream, and he told it to his brothers. "Listen," he said, "I had another dream: I saw the sun, the moon, and 11 stars bowing down to me."

¹⁰ When he told his father and his brothers, his father criticized him by asking, "What's this dream you had? Will your mother and I and your brothers come and bow down in front of you?" ¹¹ So his brothers were jealous of him, but his father kept thinking about these things.

¹² His brothers had gone to take care of their father's flocks at Shechem. ¹³ Israel then said to Joseph, "Your brothers are taking care of the flocks at Shechem. I'm going to send you to them."

Joseph responded, "I'll go."

¹⁴ So Israel said, "See how your brothers and the flocks are doing, and bring some news back to me." Then he sent Joseph away from the Hebron Valley.

When Joseph came to Shechem, ¹⁵ a man found him wandering around in the open country. "What are you looking for?" the man asked.

¹⁶ Joseph replied, "I'm looking for my brothers. Please tell me where they're taking care of their flocks."

¹⁷ The man said, "They moved on from here. I heard them say, 'Let's go to Dothan.' " So Joseph went after his brothers and found them at Dothan.

¹⁸ They saw him from a distance. Before he reached them, they plotted to kill him. ¹⁹ They said to each other, "Look, here comes that master dreamer! ²⁰ Let's kill him, throw him into one of the cisterns, and say that a wild animal has eaten him. Then we'll see what happens to his dreams."

²¹ When Reuben heard this, he tried to save Joseph from their plot. "Let's not kill him," he said. ²² "Let's not have any bloodshed. Put him into that cistern that's out in the desert, but don't hurt him." Reuben wanted to rescue Joseph from them and bring him back to his father.

²³ So when Joseph reached his brothers, they stripped him of his special robe with long sleeves. ²⁴ Then they took him and put him into an empty cistern. It had no water in it.

²⁵ As they sat down to eat, they saw a caravan of Ishmaelites coming from Gilead. Their camels were carrying the materials for cosmetics, medicine, and embalming. They were on their way to take them to Egypt.

²⁶ Judah asked his brothers, "What will we gain by killing our brother and covering up his death? ²⁷ Let's sell him to the Ishmaelites. Let's not hurt him, because he is our brother, our own flesh and blood." His brothers agreed.

²⁸ As the Midianite merchants were passing by, the brothers pulled Joseph out of the cistern. They sold him to the Ishmaelites for eight ounces of silver. The Ishmaelites took him to Egypt.

²⁹ When Reuben came back to the cistern and saw that Joseph was no longer there, he tore his clothes in grief. ³⁰ He went back to his brothers and said, "The boy isn't there! What am I going to do?"

³¹ So they took Joseph's robe, killed a goat, and dipped the robe in the blood. ³² Then they brought the special robe with long sleeves to their father and said, "We found this. You better examine it to see whether it's your son's robe or not."

[33] He recognized it and said, "It is my son's robe! A wild animal has eaten him! Joseph must have been torn to pieces!" [34] Then, to show his grief, Jacob tore his clothes, put sackcloth around his waist, and mourned for his son a long time. [35] All his other sons and daughters came to comfort him, but he refused to be comforted. He said, "No, I will mourn for my son until I die." This is how Joseph's father cried over him.

[36] Meanwhile, in Egypt the Midianites sold Joseph to Potiphar, one of Pharaoh's officials and captain of the guard.

Judah's Sin With Tamar

38 [1] About that time Judah left his brothers and went to stay with a man from Adullam whose name was Hirah. [2] There Judah met the daughter of a Canaanite man whose name was Shua. He married her and slept with her. [3] She became pregnant and gave birth to a son named[a] Er. [4] She became pregnant again and gave birth to another son, whom she named Onan. [5] Then she became pregnant again and gave birth to another son, whom she named Shelah. He was born at Kezib.

[6] Judah chose a wife for his firstborn son Er. Her name was Tamar. [7] Er angered the LORD. So the LORD took away his life. [8] Then Judah said to Onan, "Go sleep with your brother's widow. Do your duty for her as a brother-in-law, and produce a descendant for your brother." [9] But Onan knew that the descendant wouldn't belong to him, so whenever he slept with his brother's widow, he wasted his semen on the ground to avoid giving his brother a descendant. [10] What Onan did angered the LORD so much that the LORD took away Onan's life too.

[11] Then Judah said to his daughter-in-law Tamar, "Return to your father's home. Live as a widow until my son Shelah grows up." He thought that this son, too, might die like his brothers. So Tamar went to live in her father's home.

[12] After a long time Judah's wife, the daughter of Shua, died. When Judah had finished mourning, he and his friend Hirah from Adullam went to Timnah where the men were shearing Judah's sheep. [13] As soon as Tamar was told that her father-in-law was on his way to Timnah to shear his sheep, [14] she took off her widow's clothes, covered her face with a veil, and disguised herself. Then she sat down at the entrance to Enaim, which is on the road to Timnah. (She did this because she realized that Shelah was grown up now, and she hadn't been given to him in marriage.)

[15] When Judah saw her, he thought she was a prostitute because she had covered her face. [16] Since he didn't know she was his daughter-in-law, he approached her by the roadside and said, "Come on, let's sleep together!"

She asked, "What will you pay to sleep with me?"

[17] "I'll send you a young goat from the flock," he answered.

She said, "First give me something as a deposit until you send it."

[18] "What should I give you as a deposit?" he asked.

"Your signet ring, its cord, and the shepherd's staff that's in your hand," she answered.

So he gave them to her. Then he slept with her, and she became pregnant. [19] After she got up and left, she took off her veil and put her widow's clothes back on.

[20] Judah sent his friend Hirah to deliver the young goat so that he could get back his deposit from the woman, but his friend couldn't find her. [21] He asked the men of that area, "Where's that prostitute who was beside the road at Enaim?"

"There's no prostitute here," they answered.

[22] So he went back to Judah and said, "I couldn't find her. Even the men of that area said, 'There's no prostitute here.' "

[23] Then Judah said, "Let her keep what I gave her, or we'll become a laughingstock. After all, I did send her this young goat, but you couldn't find her."

[24] About three months later Judah was told, "Your daughter-in-law Tamar has been acting like a prostitute. What's more, because of it she's pregnant."

Judah ordered, "Bring her out to be burned."

[25] As she was brought out, she sent a message to her father-in-law, "I'm pregnant by the man who owns these things. See if you recognize whose signet ring, cord, and shepherd's staff these are."

[26] Judah recognized them and said, "She's not guilty. I am! She did this because I haven't given her my son Shelah." Judah never made love to her again.

[27] The time came for Tamar to give birth, and she had twin boys. [28] When she was giving birth, one of them put out his hand. The midwife took a piece of red yarn, tied it on his wrist, and said, "This one came out first." [29] As he pulled back his hand, his brother was born. So she

---

[a] 38:3 Some Hebrew manuscripts "son, whom he named"; other Hebrew manuscripts, Samaritan Pentateuch, and Targum "son, whom she named."

said, "Is this how you burst into the world!" He was named Perez [Bursting Into]. [30] After that his brother was born with the red yarn on his hand. He was named Zerah [Sunrise].

Joseph in Potiphar's House

39 [1] Joseph had been taken to Egypt. Potiphar, one of Pharaoh's Egyptian officials and captain of the guard, bought him from the Ishmaelites who had taken him there. [2] The LORD was with Joseph, so he became a successful man. He worked in the house of his Egyptian master. [3] Joseph's master saw that the LORD was with him and that the LORD made everything he did successful. [4] Potiphar liked Joseph so much that he made him his trusted servant. He put him in charge of his household and everything he owned. [5] From that time on the LORD blessed the Egyptian's household because of Joseph. Therefore, the LORD's blessing was on everything Potiphar owned in his house and in his fields. [6] So he left all that he owned in Joseph's care. He wasn't concerned about anything except the food he ate.

Joseph was well-built and handsome. [7] After a while his master's wife began to desire Joseph, so she said, "Come to bed with me."

[8] But Joseph refused and said to her, "My master doesn't concern himself with anything in the house. He trusts me with everything he owns. [9] No one in this house is greater than I. He's kept nothing back from me except you, because you're his wife. How could I do such a wicked thing and sin against God?" [10] Although she kept asking Joseph day after day, he refused to go to bed with her or be with her.

[11] One day he went into the house to do his work, and none of the household servants were there. [12] She grabbed him by his clothes and said, "Come to bed with me!" But he ran outside and left his clothes in her hand. [13] When she realized that he had gone but had left his clothes behind, [14] she called her household servants and said to them, "Look! My husband brought this Hebrew here to fool around with us. He came in and tried to go to bed with me, but I screamed as loud as I could. [15] As soon as he heard me scream, he ran outside and left his clothes with me." [16] She kept Joseph's clothes with her until his master came home. [17] Then she told him the same story: "The Hebrew slave you brought here came in and tried to fool around with me. [18] But when I screamed, he ran outside and left his clothes with me."

[19] When Potiphar heard his wife's story, especially when she said, "This is what your slave did to me," he became very angry. [20] So Joseph's master arrested him and put him in the same prison where the king's prisoners were kept.

While Joseph was in prison, [21] the LORD was with him. The LORD reached out to him with his unchanging love and gave him protection. The LORD also put Joseph on good terms with the warden. [22] So the warden placed Joseph in charge of all the prisoners who were in that prison. Joseph became responsible for everything that they were doing. [23] The warden paid no attention to anything under Joseph's care because the LORD was with Joseph and made whatever he did successful.

Joseph in Prison

40 [1] Later the king's cupbearer[a] and his baker offended their master, the king of Egypt. [2] Pharaoh was angry with his chief cupbearer and his chief baker. [3] He put them in the prison of the captain of the guard, the same place where Joseph was a prisoner. [4] The captain of the guard assigned them to Joseph, and he took care of them.

After they had been confined for some time, [5] both prisoners—the cupbearer and the baker for the king of Egypt—had dreams one night. Each man had a dream with its own special meaning.

[6] When Joseph came to them in the morning, he saw that they were upset. [7] So he asked these officials of Pharaoh who were with him in his master's prison, "Why do you look so unhappy today?"

[8] "We both had dreams," they answered him, "but there's no one to tell us what they mean."

"Isn't God the only one who can tell what they mean?" Joseph asked them. "Why don't you tell me all about them."

[9] So the chief cupbearer told Joseph his dream. He said "In my dream a grapevine with three branches appeared in front of me. [10] Soon after it sprouted it blossomed. Then its clusters ripened into grapes. [11] Pharaoh's cup was in my hand, so I took the grapes and squeezed them into it. I put the cup in Pharaoh's hand."

[12] "This is what it means," Joseph said to him. "The three branches are three days. [13] In the next three days Pharaoh will release you and restore you to your position. You will put Pharaoh's cup in his hand as you used to do when you were his cupbearer. [14] Remember me

---

[a] 40:1 A cupbearer was a trusted royal official who ensured that the king's drink was not poisoned.

when things go well for you, and please do me a favor. Mention me to Pharaoh, and get me out of this prison. [15] I was kidnapped from the land of the Hebrews, and even here I've done nothing to deserve being put in this prison."

[16] The chief baker saw that the meaning Joseph had given to the cupbearer's dream was good. So he said to Joseph, "I had a dream too. In my dream three baskets of white baked goods were on my head. [17] The top basket contained all kinds of baked goods for Pharaoh, but the birds were eating them out of the basket on my head."

[18] "This is what it means," Joseph replied. "The three baskets are three days. [19] In the next three days Pharaoh will cut off your head and hang your dead body on a pole. The birds will eat the flesh from your bones."

[20] Two days later, on his birthday, Pharaoh had a special dinner prepared for all his servants. Of all his servants he gave special attention to the chief cupbearer and the chief baker. [21] He restored the chief cupbearer to his position. So the cupbearer put the cup in Pharaoh's hand. [22] But he hung the chief baker just as Joseph had said in his interpretation.

[23] Nevertheless, the chief cupbearer didn't remember Joseph. He forgot all about him.

Joseph Interprets Pharaoh's Dreams

41 [1] After two full years Pharaoh had a dream. He dreamed he was standing by the Nile River. [2] Suddenly, seven nice-looking, well-fed cows came up from the river and began to graze among the reeds. [3] Seven other cows came up from the river behind them. These cows were sickly and skinny. They stood behind the first seven cows on the riverbank. [4] The cows that were sickly and skinny ate the seven nice-looking, well-fed cows. Then Pharaoh woke up.

[5] He fell asleep again and had a second dream. Seven good, healthy heads of grain were growing on a single stalk. [6] Seven other heads of grain, thin and scorched by the east wind, sprouted behind them. [7] The thin heads of grain swallowed the seven full, healthy heads. Then Pharaoh woke up. It was only a dream.

[8] In the morning he was so upset that he sent for all the magicians and wise men of Egypt. Pharaoh told them his dreams, but no one could tell him what they meant.

[9] Then the chief cupbearer[a] spoke to Pharaoh, "I remember a promise I failed to keep.[b] [10] Some time ago when Pharaoh was angry with his servants, he confined me and the chief baker to the captain of the guard's prison. [11] We both had dreams the same night. Each dream had its own meaning. [12] A young Hebrew, a slave of the captain of the guard, was with us. We told him our dreams, and he told each of us what they meant. [13] What he told us happened: Pharaoh restored me to my position, but he hung the baker on a pole."

[14] Then Pharaoh sent for Joseph, and immediately he was brought from the prison. After he had shaved and changed his clothes, he came in front of Pharaoh.

[15] Pharaoh said to Joseph, "I had a dream, and no one can tell me what it means. I heard that when you are told a dream, you can say what it means."

[16] Joseph answered Pharaoh, "I can't, but God can give Pharaoh the answer that he needs."

[17] Then Pharaoh said to Joseph, "In my dream I was standing on the bank of the Nile. [18] Suddenly, seven nice-looking, well-fed cows came up from the river and began to graze among the reeds. [19] Seven other cows came up behind them. These cows were scrawny, very sick, and thin. I've never seen such sickly cows in all of Egypt! [20] The thin, sickly cows ate up the seven well-fed ones. [21] Even though they had eaten them, no one could tell they had eaten them. They looked just as sick as before. Then I woke up.

[22] "In my second dream I saw seven good, full heads of grain growing on a single stalk. [23] Seven other heads of grain, withered, thin, and scorched by the east wind, sprouted behind them. [24] The thin heads of grain swallowed the seven good heads. I told this to the magicians, but no one could tell me what it meant."

[25] Then Joseph said to Pharaoh, "Pharaoh had the same dream twice. God has told Pharaoh what he's going to do. [26] The seven good cows are seven years, and the seven good heads of grain are seven years. It's all the same dream. [27] The seven thin, sickly cows that came up behind them are seven years. The seven empty heads of grain scorched by the east wind are also seven years of famine are coming.

[28] "It's just as I said to Pharaoh. God has shown Pharaoh what he's going to do. [29] Seven years are coming when there will be plenty of food in Egypt. [30] After them will come seven years of famine. People will forget that there was plenty of food in Egypt, and the famine will ruin the land. [31] People won't remember that there once was plenty of food in the land, because the coming famine will be so severe. [32] The reason Pharaoh has had a recurring dream is because the matter has been definitely decided by God, and he will do it very soon.

---

[a] 41:9 A cupbearer was a trusted royal official who ensured that the king's drink was not poisoned.
[b] 41:9 English equivalent difficult.

Joseph Advises Pharaoh

[33] "Pharaoh should look for a wise and intelligent man and put him in charge of Egypt. [34] Make arrangements to appoint supervisors over the land to take a fifth of Egypt's harvest during the seven good years. [35] Have them collect all the food during these good years and store up grain under Pharaoh's control, to be kept for food in the cities. [36] This food will be a reserve supply for our country during the seven years of famine that will happen in Egypt. Then the land will not be ruined by the famine."

[37] Pharaoh and all his servants liked the idea. [38] So Pharaoh asked his servants, "Can we find anyone like this—a man who has God's Spirit in him?"

[39] Then Pharaoh said to Joseph, "Because God has let you know all this, there is no one as wise and intelligent as you. [40] You will be in charge of my palace, and all my people will do[c] what you say. I will be more important than you, only because I'm Pharaoh."

[41] Then Pharaoh said to Joseph, "I now put you in charge of Egypt." [42] Then Pharaoh took off his signet ring and put it on Joseph's finger. He had Joseph dressed in robes of fine linen and put a gold chain around his neck. [43] He had him ride in the chariot of the second-in-command. Men ran ahead of him and shouted, "Make way!"[d] Pharaoh put Joseph in charge of Egypt.

[44] He also said to Joseph, "Even though I am Pharaoh, no one anywhere in Egypt will do anything without your permission." [45] Pharaoh named Joseph Zaphenathpaneah and gave him Asenath as his wife. She was the daughter of Potiphera, priest from the city of On. Joseph traveled around Egypt.

Joseph Serves Pharaoh

[46] Joseph was 30 years old when he entered the service of Pharaoh (the king of Egypt). He left Pharaoh and traveled all around Egypt. [47] During the seven good years the land produced large harvests. [48] Joseph collected all the food grown in Egypt during those seven years and put this food in the cities. In each city he put the food from the fields around it. [49] Joseph stored up grain in huge quantities like the sand on the seashore. He had so much that he finally gave up keeping any records because he couldn't measure it all.

[50] Before the years of famine came, Joseph had two sons by Asenath, daughter of Potiphera, priest from the city of On. [51] Joseph named his firstborn son Manasseh [He Helps Me Forget], because God helped him forget all his troubles and all about his father's family. [52] He named the second son Ephraim [Blessed Twice With Children], because God gave him children in the land where he had suffered.

[53] The seven years when there was plenty of food in Egypt came to an end. [54] Then the seven years of famine began as Joseph had said they would. All the other countries were experiencing famine. Yet, there was food in Egypt. [55] When everyone in Egypt began to feel the effects of the famine, the people cried to Pharaoh for food. But Pharaoh said to all the Egyptians, "Go to Joseph! Do what he tells you!"

[56] When the famine had spread all over the country, Joseph opened all the storehouses[e] and sold grain to the Egyptians. He did this because the famine was severe in Egypt. [57] The whole world came to Joseph in Egypt to buy grain, since the famine was so severe all over the world.

Jacob [Israel] Sends Ten Sons to Egypt

42 [1] When Jacob found out that grain was for sale in Egypt, he said to his sons, "Why do you keep looking at each other? [2] I've heard there's grain for sale in Egypt. Go there and buy some for us so that we won't starve to death."

[3] Ten of Joseph's brothers went to buy grain in Egypt. [4] Jacob wouldn't send Joseph's brother Benjamin with the other brothers, because he was afraid that something would happen to him. [5] Israel's sons left with the others who were going to buy grain, because there was also famine in Canaan.

Joseph Sends Nine of His Brothers Back to Canaan

[6] As governor of the country, Joseph was selling grain to everyone. So when Joseph's brothers arrived, they bowed in front of him with their faces touching the ground. [7] As soon as Joseph saw his brothers, he recognized them. But he acted as if he didn't know them and spoke harshly to them. "Where did you come from?" he asked them.

"From Canaan, to buy food," they answered.

[8] Even though Joseph recognized his brothers, they didn't recognize him. [9] Then he remembered the dreams he once had about them. "You're spies!" he said to them, "And you've come to find out where our country is unprotected."

---

[c] 41:40 Greek; Hebrew meaning uncertain.   [d] 41:43 Hebrew meaning uncertain.   [e] 41:56 Greek, Syriac; Masoretic Text "all that was in them."

¹⁰ "No, sir!" they answered him. "We've come to buy food. ¹¹ We're all sons of one man. We're honest men, not spies."

¹² He said to them, "No! You've come to find out where our country is unprotected."

¹³ They answered him, "We were 12 brothers, sons of one man in Canaan. The youngest brother stayed with our father, and the other one is no longer with us."

¹⁴ "It's just as I told you," Joseph said to them. "You're spies! ¹⁵ This is how you'll be tested: I solemnly swear, as surely as Pharaoh lives, that you won't leave this place unless your youngest brother comes here. ¹⁶ One of you must be sent to get your brother while the rest of you stay in prison. We'll see if you're telling the truth. If not, I solemnly swear, as surely as Pharaoh lives, you are spies!" ¹⁷ Then he put them in jail for three days.

¹⁸ On the third day Joseph said to them, "Do this, and you will live. I, too, fear God. ¹⁹ If you are honest men, you will let one of your brothers stay here in prison. The rest of you will go and take grain back to your starving families. ²⁰ But you must bring me your youngest brother. This will show that you've been telling the truth. Then you won't die." So they agreed.

²¹ They said to each other, "We're surely being punished for what we did to our brother. We saw how troubled he was when he pleaded with us for mercy, but we wouldn't listen. That's why we're in trouble now."

²² Reuben said to them, "Didn't I tell you not to sin against the boy? But you wouldn't listen. Now we must pay for this bloodshed."

²³ They didn't know that Joseph could understand them, because he was speaking through an interpreter. ²⁴ He stepped away from them to cry. When he could speak to them again, he came back. Then he picked Simeon and had him arrested right in front of their eyes.

²⁵ Joseph gave orders to fill their bags with grain. He put each man's money back into his sack and gave them supplies for their trip. After their bags were filled, ²⁶ they loaded their grain on their donkeys and left.

²⁷ At the place where they stopped for the night, one of them opened his sack to feed his donkey. His money was right inside his sack. ²⁸ He said to his brothers, "My money has been put back! It's right here in my sack!"

They wanted to die. They trembled and turned to each other and asked, "What has God done to us?"

Jacob's [Israel's] Sons Report to Him

²⁹ When they came to their father Jacob in Canaan, they told him all that had happened to them. They said, ³⁰ "The governor of that land spoke harshly to us and treated us like spies. ³¹ But we said to him, 'We're honest men, not spies. ³² We were 12 brothers, sons of the same father. One is no longer with us. The youngest brother stayed with our father in Canaan.'

³³ "Then the governor of that land said to us, 'This is how I'll know that you're honest men: Leave one of your brothers with me. Take food for your starving families and go. ³⁴ But bring me your youngest brother. Then I'll know that you're not spies but honest men. I'll give your brother back to you, and you'll be able to move about freely in this country.' "

³⁵ As they were emptying their sacks, each man found his bag of money in his sack. When they and their father saw the bags of money, they were frightened. ³⁶ Their father Jacob said to them, "You're going to make me lose all my children! Joseph is no longer with us, Simeon is no longer with us, and now you want to take Benjamin. Everything's against me!"

³⁷ So Reuben said to his father, "You may put my two sons to death if I don't bring him back to you. Let me take care of him, and I'll bring him back to you."

³⁸ Jacob replied, "My son will not go with you. His brother is dead, and he's the only one left. If any harm comes to him on the trip you're taking, the grief would drive this gray-haired old man to his grave!"

Jacob [Israel] Sends Ten Sons Back to Egypt

43 ¹ The famine was severe in the land. ² When they finished eating the grain they had brought from Egypt, Israel said to his sons, "Go back and buy us a little more food."

³ Judah said to him, "The man gave us a severe warning: 'You won't be allowed to see me again unless your brother is with you.' ⁴ If you let our brother go with us, we'll go and buy food for you. ⁵ If you won't let him go, we won't go. The man said to us, 'You won't be allowed to see me again unless your brother is with you.' "

⁶ Israel asked, "Why have you made trouble for me by telling the man you had another brother?"

⁷ They answered, "The man kept asking about us and our family: 'Is your father still alive? Do you have another brother?' We simply answered his questions. How could we possibly know he would say, 'Bring your brother here'?"

⁸ Then Judah said to his father Israel, "Send the boy along with me. Let's get going so that we won't starve to death. ⁹ I guarantee that he will come back. You can hold me responsible for him. If I don't bring him back to you and place him here in front of you, you can blame me the rest of my life. ¹⁰ If we hadn't waited so long, we could have made this trip twice by now."

¹¹ Then their father Israel said to them, "If that's the way it has to be, then take the man a gift. Put some of the best products of the land in your bags. Take a little balm, a little honey, gum, myrrh, pistachio nuts, and almonds. ¹² Take twice as much money with you. You must return the money that was put back in your sacks. Maybe it was a mistake. ¹³ Take your brother, and go back to the man. ¹⁴ May God Almighty make him merciful to you so that he will send your other brother and Benjamin ˍhomeˍ with you. If I lose my children, I lose my children."

¹⁵ The men took the gifts, twice as much money, and Benjamin. They went to Egypt, where they presented themselves to Joseph.

The Banquet at Joseph's House

¹⁶ When Joseph saw Benjamin with them, he said to the man in charge of his house, "Take these men to my house. Butcher an animal, and prepare a meal, because they are going to eat with me at noon."

¹⁷ So the man did as Joseph said and took them to Joseph's house. ¹⁸ The men were frightened, because they had been brought to Joseph's house. They thought, "We've been brought here because of the money that was put back into our sacks the first time. They're going to attack us, overpower us, take our donkeys, and make us slaves."

¹⁹ So they came to the man in charge of Joseph's house and spoke to him at the door. ²⁰ "Please, sir," they said, "we came here to buy food once before. ²¹ When we stopped for the night, we opened our sacks, and each man found all of his money inside. So we brought it back with us. ²² We also brought more money to buy food. We have no idea who put our money back in our sacks."

²³ "It's alright," he said. "Don't be afraid! Your God, the God of your father, must have given you treasure in your sacks. I received your money." Then he brought Simeon out to them.

²⁴ The man took the brothers into Joseph's house. He gave them water to wash their feet and feed for their donkeys. ²⁵ They got their gifts ready for Joseph's return at noon, because they had heard they were going to eat there.

²⁶ When Joseph came home, they gave him the gifts they had brought to the house. Then they bowed to him with their faces touching the ground. ²⁷ He asked them how they were. Then he said, "You told me about your elderly father. How is he? Is he still alive?"

²⁸ They answered, "Yes, sir. Our father is alive and well." Then they knelt, bowing down.

²⁹ As Joseph looked around, he saw his brother Benjamin, his mother's son. "Is this your youngest brother, the one you told me about?" he asked. "God be gracious to you, my son," he said. ³⁰ Deeply moved at the sight of his brother, he hurried away, looking for a place to cry. He went into his private room and cried there.

³¹ Then he washed his face and came out. He was in control of his emotions when he said, "Serve the food."

³² He was served separately from his brothers. The Egyptians who were there with him were also served separately, because they found it offensive to eat with Hebrews. ³³ The brothers were seated facing him according to their ages—from the oldest to the youngest. They looked at each other in amazement.

³⁴ Joseph had portions of food brought to them from his table, but Benjamin's portion was five times more than any of the others. So they ate and drank with Joseph until they were drunk.

Joseph's Plan to Trap His Brothers

44 ¹ Joseph commanded the man in charge of his house, "Fill the men's sacks with as much food as they can carry. Put each man's money in his sack. ² Then put my silver cup in the youngest brother's sack along with the money for his grain." He did what Joseph told him.

³ At dawn the men were sent on their way with their donkeys. ⁴ They had not gone far from the city when Joseph said to the man in charge of his house, "Go after those men at once, and when you catch up with them, say to them, 'Why have you paid me back with evil when I was good to you? ⁵ Isn't this the cup that my master drinks from and that he uses for telling the future? What you have done is evil!' "

⁶ When he caught up with them, he repeated these words to them. ⁷ They answered him, "Sir, how can you say such things? We would never think of doing anything like that! ⁸ We brought the money we found in our sacks back from Canaan. So why would we steal any sil-

ver or gold from your master's house? ⁹ If one of us has it, he will die, and the rest of us will become your slaves."

¹⁰ "I agree," he said. "We'll do what you've said. The man who has the cup will be my slave, and the rest of you can go free."

¹¹ Each one quickly lowered his sack to the ground and opened it. ¹² Then the man made a thorough search. He began with the oldest and ended with the youngest. The cup was found in Benjamin's sack. ¹³ When they saw this, they tore their clothes in grief. Then each one loaded his donkey and went back into the city.

¹⁴ Judah and his brothers arrived at Joseph's house while Joseph was still there. Immediately, they bowed with their faces touching the ground. ¹⁵ Joseph asked them, "What have you done? Don't you know that a man like me can find things out because he knows the future?"

¹⁶ "Sir, what can we say to you?" Judah asked. "How else can we explain it? How can we prove we're innocent? God has uncovered our guilt. Now all of us are your slaves, including the one who had the cup."

¹⁷ But Joseph said, "I would never think of doing that! Only the man who had the cup will be my slave. The rest of you can go back to your father in peace."

Judah Defends Benjamin

¹⁸ Then Judah went up to Joseph and said, "Please, sir, let me speak openly with you. Don't be angry with me, although you are equal to Pharaoh. ¹⁹ Sir, you asked us, 'Do you have a father or a brother?' ²⁰ We answered, 'We have a father who is old and a younger brother born to him when he was already old. The boy's brother is dead, so he's the only one of his mother's sons left, and his father loves him.'

²¹ "Then you said to us, 'Bring him here to me so that I can see him myself.' ²² We replied, 'The boy can't leave his father. If the boy leaves him, his father will die.' ²³ Then you told us, 'If your youngest brother doesn't come here with you, you will never be allowed to see me again.' ²⁴ When we went back to our father, we told him what you had said.

²⁵ "Then our father said, 'Go back and buy us a little more food.' ²⁶ We answered, 'We can't go back. We can only go back if our youngest brother is with us. The man won't see us unless our youngest brother is with us.'

²⁷ "Then our father said to us, 'You know that my wife ˌRachelˌ gave me two sons. ²⁸ One is gone, and I said, "He must have been torn to pieces!" I haven't seen him since. ²⁹ If you take this one away from me too and anything happens to him, you'll drive this gray-haired old man to his grave.'

³⁰ "Our father's life is wrapped up with the boy's life. If I come ˌhomeˌ without the boy ³¹ and he sees that the boy isn't ˌwith meˌ, he'll die. The grief would drive our gray-haired old father to his grave.

³² "I guaranteed my father that the boy would come back. I said, 'If I don't bring him back to you, then you can blame me the rest of my life, Father.' ³³ Sir, please let me stay and be your slave in the boy's place, and let the boy go back with his brothers. ³⁴ How could I go back to my father if the boy isn't with me? I couldn't bear to see my father's misery!"

Joseph Reveals His Identity

45 ¹ Joseph could no longer control his emotions in front of everyone who was standing around him, so he cried out, "Have everyone leave me!" No one else was there when Joseph told his brothers who he was. ² He cried so loudly that the Egyptians heard him, and Pharaoh's household heard about it.

³ Joseph said to his brothers, "I am Joseph! Is my father still alive?" His brothers could not answer him because they were afraid of him.

⁴ "Please come closer to me," Joseph said to his brothers. When they did so, he said, "I am Joseph, the brother you sold into slavery in Egypt! ⁵ Now, don't be sad or angry with yourselves that you sold me. God sent me ahead of you to save lives. ⁶ The famine has been in the land for two years. There will be five more years without plowing or harvesting. ⁷ God sent me ahead of you to make sure that you would have descendants on the earth and to save your lives in an amazing way. ⁸ It wasn't you who sent me here, but God. He has made me ˌlikeˌ a father to Pharaoh, lord over his entire household, and ruler of Egypt.

⁹ "Hurry back to my father, and say to him, 'This is what your son Joseph says, "God has made me lord of Egypt. Come here to me right away! ¹⁰ Live in the land of Goshen, where you will be near me. Live there with your children and your grandchildren, as well as your flocks, your herds, and everything you have. ¹¹ I will provide for you in Egypt, since there will be five more years of famine. Then you, your family, and all who belong to you won't lose everything.'"

¹² "You and my brother Benjamin can see for yourselves that I am the one who is speaking to you. ¹³ Tell my father how greatly honored I am in Egypt and about everything you have seen. Hurry and bring my father here!"

14 He threw his arms around his brother Benjamin and cried with Benjamin, who was crying on his shoulder. **15** He kissed all his brothers and cried with them. After that his brothers talked with him.

Pharaoh Invites Jacob's [Israel's] Family to Live in Egypt

16 When Pharaoh's household heard the news that Joseph's brothers had come, Pharaoh and his officials were pleased. **17** So Pharaoh said to Joseph, "Say to your brothers, 'Load up your animals, and go back to Canaan. **18** Take your father and your families, and come to me. I will give you the best land in Egypt. Then you can enjoy the best food in the land.'

19 "Give them this order: 'Take wagons with you from Egypt for your children and your wives. Bring your father, and come back. **20** Don't worry about your belongings because the best of everything in Egypt is yours.'"

21 Israel's sons did as they were told. Joseph gave them wagons and supplies for their trip as Pharaoh had ordered. **22** He gave each of them a change of clothes, but he gave Benjamin three hundred pieces of silver and five changes of clothes. **23** He sent his father ten male donkeys carrying Egypt's best products and ten female donkeys carrying grain, bread, and food for his father's trip. **24** So Joseph sent his brothers on their way. As they were leaving, he said to them, "Don't quarrel on your way back!"

25 So they left Egypt and came to their father Jacob in Canaan. **26** They told him, "Joseph is still alive! Yes, he is ruler of Egypt." Jacob was stunned and didn't believe them. **27** Yet, when they told their father everything Joseph had said to them and he saw the wagons Joseph had sent to bring him back, his spirits were lifted.

28 "You have convinced me!" Israel said. "My son Joseph is still alive. I will go and see him before I die."

Jacob's [Israel's] Seventh Encounter With God

46 **1** Israel moved with all he had. When he came to Beersheba, he offered sacrifices to the God of his father Isaac.

2 God spoke to Israel in a vision that night and said, "Jacob, Jacob!"

"Here I am," he answered.

3 "I am God, the God of your father," he said. "Don't be afraid to go to Egypt, because I will make you a great nation there. **4** I will go with you to Egypt, and I will make sure you come back again. Joseph will close your eyes ˌwhen you dieˌ."

5 So Jacob left Beersheba. Israel's sons put their father Jacob, their children, and their wives in the wagons Pharaoh had sent to bring him back. **6** They also took their livestock and the possessions they had accumulated in Canaan.

Jacob and all his family arrived in Egypt. **7** He had brought his sons, his grandsons, his daughters, and his granddaughters—his entire family.

Jacob's [Israel's] Descendants—Exodus 6:14–16; 1 Chronicles 2:3–5

8 These are the names of Israel's descendants (Jacob and his descendants) who arrived in Egypt.

Reuben was Jacob's firstborn.
9 The sons of **Reuben** were
Hanoch, Pallu, Hezron, and Carmi.
10 The sons of **Simeon** were
Jemuel, Jamin, Ohad, Jakin, Zohar, and Shaul, the son of a Canaanite woman.
11 The sons of **Levi** were
Gershon, Kohath, and Merari.
12 The sons of **Judah** were
Er, Onan, Shelah, Perez, and Zerah. (Er and Onan had died in Canaan.)
The sons of Perez were
Hezron and Hamul.
13 The sons of **Issachar** were
Tola, Puvah, Iob, and Shimron.
14 The sons of **Zebulun** were
Sered, Elon, and Jahleel.
15 These were the descendants of the sons Leah gave to Jacob in Paddan Aram, in addition to his daughter Dinah. The total number of these sons and daughters was 33.

16 The sons of **Gad** were
Ziphion, Haggi, Shuni, Ezbon, Eri, Arodi, and Areli.

¹⁷ The sons of **Asher** were
    Imnah, Ishvah, Ishvi, and Beriah. Their sister was Serah.
    The sons of Beriah were
      Heber and Malchiel.
¹⁸ These were the descendants of Zilpah, whom Laban gave to his daughter Leah. She gave birth to these children for Jacob. The total was 16.

¹⁹ The sons of Jacob's wife Rachel were
    Joseph and Benjamin.
²⁰   In Egypt, Manasseh and Ephraim were born to **Joseph** by Asenath, daughter of Potiphera, priest from the city of On.
²¹   The sons of **Benjamin** were
      Bela, Beker, Ashbel, Gera, Naaman, Ehi, Rosh, Muppim, Huppim, and Ard.
²² These were the descendants of Rachel who were born to Jacob. The total was 14.

²³ The son of **Dan** was
    Hushim.
²⁴ The sons of **Naphtali** were
    Jahzeel, Guni, Jezer, and Shillem.
²⁵ These were the descendants of Bilhah, whom Laban gave to his daughter Rachel. She gave birth to these sons for Jacob. The total was 7.

²⁶ The total number of Jacob's direct descendants who went with him to Egypt was 66. This didn't include the wives of Jacob's sons. ²⁷ Joseph had two sons who were born in Egypt. The grand total of people in Jacob's household who went to Egypt was 70.

Joseph and Jacob [Israel] Reunited

²⁸ Israel sent Judah ahead of him to Joseph to get directions to Goshen. When Israel's family arrived in the region of Goshen, ²⁹ Joseph prepared his chariot and went to meet his father Israel. As soon as he saw his father, he threw his arms around him and cried on his shoulder a long time.

³⁰ Israel said to Joseph, "Now that I've seen for myself that you're still alive, I'm ready to die."

³¹ Then Joseph said to his brothers and his father's family, "I'm going to Pharaoh to tell him, 'My brothers and my father's family, who were in Canaan, have come to me. ³² The men are shepherds. They take care of livestock. They've brought their flocks and herds and everything they own.' ³³ Now, when Pharaoh calls for you and asks, 'What kind of work do you do?' ³⁴ you must answer, 'We have taken care of herds all our lives, as our ancestors have done.' You must say this, so that you may live in the region of Goshen, because all shepherds are disgusting to Egyptians."

Jacob [Israel] Meets Pharaoh

47 ¹ Joseph went and told Pharaoh, "My father and my brothers have arrived from Canaan with their flocks, herds, and everything they have. Now they are in Goshen." ² Since he had taken five of his brothers with him, he presented them to Pharaoh.

³ Pharaoh asked the brothers, "What kind of work do you do?"

They answered Pharaoh, "We are shepherds, as were our ancestors. ⁴ We have come to live in this land for a while. The famine is so severe in Canaan that there's no pasture for our flocks. So please let us live in Goshen."

⁵ Then Pharaoh said to Joseph, "Your father and your brothers have come to you. ⁶ All of Egypt is available to you. Have your father and your brothers live in the best part of the land. Let them live in Goshen. If they are qualified, put them in charge of my livestock."

⁷ Then Joseph brought his father Jacob and had him stand in front of Pharaoh. Jacob blessed Pharaoh. ⁸ Pharaoh asked him, "How old are you?"

⁹ Jacob answered Pharaoh, "The length of my stay on earth has been 130 years. The years of my life have been few and difficult, fewer than my ancestors' years." ¹⁰ Then Jacob blessed Pharaoh and left.

¹¹ As Pharaoh had ordered, Joseph had his father and his brothers live in the best part of Egypt, the region of Rameses. He gave them property there. ¹² Joseph also provided his father, his brothers, and all his father's family with food based on the number of children they had.

Joseph Acquires All the Land in Egypt for Pharaoh

¹³ The famine was so severe that there was no food anywhere. Neither Egypt nor Canaan were producing crops because of the famine. ¹⁴ Joseph collected all the money that could be

found in Egypt and in Canaan as payment for the grain people bought. Then he took it to Pharaoh's palace. **15** When the money in Egypt and Canaan was gone, all the Egyptians came to Joseph. "Give us food," they said. "Do you want us to die right in front of you? We don't have any more money!"

16 Joseph replied, "If you don't have any more money, give me your livestock, and I'll give you food*a* in exchange." **17** So they brought their livestock to Joseph, and he gave them food in exchange for their horses, sheep, goats, cattle, and donkeys. During that year he supplied them with food in exchange for all their livestock.

18 When that year was over, they came to him the next year. "Sir," they said to him, "you know that our money is gone, and you have all our livestock. There's nothing left to bring you except our bodies and our land. **19** Do you want us to die right in front of you? Do you want the land to be ruined? Take us and our land in exchange for food. Then we will be Pharaoh's slaves and our land will be his property. But give us seed so that we won't starve to death and the ground won't become a desert."

20 Joseph bought all the land in Egypt for Pharaoh. Every Egyptian sold his fields because the famine was so severe. The land became Pharaoh's. **21** All over Egypt Joseph moved the people to the cities. **22** But he didn't buy the priests' land because the priests received an income from Pharaoh, and they lived on that income. That's why they didn't sell their land.

23 Joseph said to the people, "Now that I have bought you and your land for Pharaoh, here is seed for you. Plant crops in the land. **24** Every time you harvest, give one-fifth of the produce to Pharaoh. Four-fifths will be yours to use as seed for your fields and as food for your households."

25 "You have saved our lives," they said. "Please, sir, we are willing to be Pharaoh's slaves."

26 Joseph made a law concerning the land in Egypt which is still in force today: One-fifth of the produce belongs to Pharaoh. Only the land of the priests didn't belong to Pharaoh.

Jacob's [Israel's] Last Days in Egypt

27 So the Israelites settled in Egypt in the region of Goshen. They acquired property there and had many children.

28 Jacob lived in Egypt 17 years, so he lived a total of 147 years. **29** Israel was about to die. He called for his son Joseph and said to him, "I want you to swear that you love me and are faithful to me. Please don't bury me here. **30** I want to rest with my ancestors. Take me out of Egypt, and bury me in their tomb."

"I will do as you say," Joseph answered.

31 "Swear to me," he said. So Joseph swore to him. Then Israel bowed down in prayer with his face at the head of his bed.

Jacob [Israel] Blesses Joseph's Two Sons

48 **1** Later Joseph was told, "Your father is ill." So he took his two sons Manasseh and Ephraim to see Jacob. **2** When Jacob was told, "Your son Joseph is here to see you," Israel gathered his strength and sat up in bed.

3 Jacob said to Joseph, "God Almighty appeared to me at Luz in Canaan and blessed me. **4** He said to me, 'I will make you fertile and increase the number of your descendants so that you will become a community of people. I will give this land to your descendants as a permanent possession.'

5 "So your two sons, who were born in Egypt before I came here, are my sons. Ephraim and Manasseh will be mine just as Reuben and Simeon are. **6** Any other children you have after them will be yours. They will inherit the land listed under their brothers' names. **7** As I was coming back from Paddan, Rachel died in Canaan when we were still some distance from Ephrath. So I buried her there on the way to Ephrath" (that is, Bethlehem).

8 When Israel saw Joseph's sons, he asked, "Who are they?"

9 "They are my sons, whom God has given me here in Egypt," Joseph answered his father. Then Israel said, "Please bring them to me so that I may bless them."

10 Israel's eyesight was failing because of old age, and he could hardly see. So Joseph brought his sons close to his father, and Israel hugged them and kissed them.

11 Israel said to Joseph, "I never expected to see you again, and now God has even let me see your sons."

12 Joseph took them off his father's lap and bowed with his face touching the ground. **13** Then Joseph took both of them, Ephraim on his right, facing Israel's left, and Manasseh on his left, facing Israel's right, and brought them close to him. **14** But Israel crossed his hands and

---

a 47:16 Samaritan Pentateuch, Greek, Targum; Masoretic Text "I'll give to you."

reached out. He put his right hand on Ephraim's head, although Ephraim was the younger son. He put his left hand on Manasseh's head, although Manasseh was older.
¹⁵ Then Jacob blessed Joseph,

> "May God, in whose presence my grandfather Abraham
> and my father Isaac walked,
> may God, who has been my shepherd all my life to this very day,
> ¹⁶ may the Messenger, who has rescued me from all evil,
> bless these boys.
> May they be called by my name
> and by the names of my grandfather Abraham and my father Isaac.
> May they have many children on the earth."

¹⁷ When Joseph saw that his father had put his right hand on Ephraim's head, he didn't like it. So he took his father's hand in order to move it from Ephraim's head to Manasseh's. ¹⁸ Then he said to his father, "That's not right, Father! This is the firstborn. Put your right hand on his head." ¹⁹ His father refused and said, "I know, Son, I know! Manasseh, too, will become a nation, and he, too, will be important. Nevertheless, his younger brother will be more important than he, and his descendants will become many nations." ²⁰ That day he blessed them. He said,

> "Because of you, Israel will speak this blessing,
> 'May God make you like Ephraim and Manasseh!' "

In this way Israel put Ephraim ahead of Manasseh.
²¹ Then Israel said to Joseph, "Now I'm about to die, but God will be with you. He will bring you back to the land of your fathers. ²² I'm giving you one more mountain ridge than your brothers. I took it from the Amorites with my own sword and bow."

Jacob [Israel] Blesses His 12 Sons

49 ¹ Jacob called for his sons and said, "Come here, and let me tell you what will happen to you in the days to come.

² "Gather around and listen, sons of Jacob.
Listen to your father Israel.

³ **"Reuben,** you are my firstborn,
my strength, the very first son I had,
first in majesty and first in power.
⁴ You will no longer be first
because you were out of control like a flood
and you climbed into your father's bed.
Then you dishonored it.
He climbed up on my couch.

⁵ **"Simeon** and **Levi** are brothers.
Their swordsᵃ are weapons of violence.
⁶ Do not let me attend their secret meetings.
Do not let me join their assembly.
In their anger they murdered men.
At their whim they crippled cattle.
⁷ May their anger be cursed because it's so fierce.
May their fury be cursed because it's so cruel.
I will divide them among ˌthe sons ofˌ Jacob
and scatter them among ˌthe tribes ofˌ Israel.

⁸ **"Judah,** your brothers will praise you.
Your hand will be on the neck of your enemies.
Your father's sons will bow down to you.
⁹ Judah, you are a lion cub.
You have come back from the kill, my son.
He lies down and rests like a lion.
He is like a lioness. Who dares to disturb him?
¹⁰ A scepter will never depart from Judah
nor a ruler's staff from between his feet

ᵃ 49:5 Hebrew meaning uncertain.

until Shiloh comes
and the people obey him.
11 He will tie his donkey to a grapevine,
his colt to the best vine.
He will wash his clothes in wine,
his garments in the blood of grapes.
12 His eyes are darker than wine.
His teeth are whiter than milk.

13 "**Zebulun** will live by the coast.
He will have ships by the coast.
His border will go as far as Sidon.

14 "**Issachar** is a strong donkey,
lying down between the saddlebags.
15 When he sees that his resting place is good
and that the land is pleasant,
he will bend his back to the burden
and will become a slave laborer.

16 "**Dan** will hand down decisions[b] for his people
as one of the tribes of Israel.
17 Dan will be a snake on a road,
a viper on a path,
that bites a horse's heels
so that its rider falls off backwards.

18 "I wait with hope for you to rescue me, O LORD.

19 "**Gad** will be attacked by a band of raiders,
but he will strike back at their heels.

20 "**Asher's** food will be rich.
He will provide delicacies fit for a king.

21 "**Naphtali** is a doe set free
that has beautiful fawns.

22 "**Joseph** is a fruitful tree,
a fruitful tree by a spring,
with branches climbing over a wall.
23 Archers provoked him,
shot at him,
and attacked him.
24 But his bow stayed steady, and his arms remained limber
because of the help of the Mighty One of Jacob,
because of the name of the Shepherd, the Rock of Israel,
25 because of the God of your father who helps you,
because of the Almighty who gives you
blessings from the heavens above,
blessings from the deep springs below the ground,
blessings from breasts and womb.
26 The blessings of your father are greater than
the blessings of the oldest mountains
and the riches of the ancient hills.
May these blessings rest on the head of Joseph,
on the crown of the prince among his brothers.

27 "**Benjamin** is a ravenous wolf.
In the morning he devours his prey.
In the evening he divides the plunder."

28 These are the 12 tribes of Israel and what their father said to them when he gave each of them his special blessing.

---

b 49:16 There is a play on words here between *Dan* and *yadin* (he will hand down decisions).

²⁹ Then he gave them these instructions, "I am about to join my ancestors in death. Bury me with my ancestors in the cave in the field of Ephron the Hittite. ³⁰ Abraham bought the cave that is in the field of Machpelah, east of Mamre in Canaan, from Ephron the Hittite to use as a tomb. ³¹ Abraham and his wife Sarah are buried there. Isaac and his wife Rebekah are buried there. I also buried Leah there. ³² The field and the cave in it were bought from the Hittites."

³³ When Jacob finished giving these instructions to his sons, he pulled his feet into his bed. He took his last breath and joined his ancestors in death.

Joseph Buries His Father

50 ¹ Joseph threw himself on his father, cried over him, and kissed him. ² Then Joseph ordered the doctors in his service to embalm his father. So the doctors embalmed Israel. ³ The embalming was completed in the usual time—40 days. The Egyptians mourned for him 70 days.

⁴ When the time of mourning for Jacob was over, Joseph spoke to Pharaoh's palace staff. He said, "Please speak directly to Pharaoh. Tell him, ⁵ 'My father made me swear an oath. He said, "I'm about to die. Bury me in the tomb I bought for myself in Canaan." Please let me go there and bury my father; then I'll come back.' "

⁶ Pharaoh replied, "Go and bury your father, as you have promised him."

⁷ So Joseph left to bury his father. All Pharaoh's officials, the leaders in his palace staff, and all the leaders of Egypt went with him. ⁸ Joseph's household, his brothers, and his father's household also went with him. (Only their children, their flocks, and their cattle were left in Goshen.) ⁹ Chariots and horsemen went with him. It was a very large group.

¹⁰ When they came to the threshing floorᵃ of Atad, which is on the east side of the Jordan River, they began a great and solemn ceremony to mourn Jacob's death. Joseph took seven days to mourn his father's death. ¹¹ When the Canaanites living there saw the funeral ceremonies at the threshing floor of Atad, they said, "These funeral ceremonies are taken very seriously by the Egyptians." That's why that place on the east side of the Jordan was named Abel Mizraim [Egyptian Funeral Ceremonies].

¹² Jacob's sons did for him what he had told them to do. ¹³ They carried him back to Canaan and buried him in the cave in the field of Machpelah, east of Mamre. Abraham had bought this tomb from Ephron the Hittite.

¹⁴ After Joseph had buried his father, he went back to Egypt along with his brothers and everyone who had gone there with him to bury his father.

Joseph Forgives His Brothers

¹⁵ Joseph's brothers realized what their father's death could mean. So they thought, "What if Joseph holds a grudge against us? What if he decides to pay us back for all the evil we did to him?" ¹⁶ They sent a messenger to Joseph to say, "Before your father died, he commanded us, ¹⁷ 'This is what you should say to Joseph, "I'm begging you to forgive the crime and the sin your brothers committed against you. What they did to you was very evil.' " So now, please forgive our crime, because we are servants of your father's God." Joseph cried when he got their message.

¹⁸ Then his brothers also came and immediately bowed down in front of him. "We are your slaves!" they said.

¹⁹ Joseph said to them, "Don't be afraid! I can't take God's place. ²⁰ Even though you planned evil against me, God planned good to come out of it. This was to keep many people alive, as he is doing now. ²¹ Don't be afraid! I will provide for you and your children." In this way he reassured them, setting their minds at ease.

²² Joseph and his father's family stayed in Egypt. Joseph lived to be 110 years old. ²³ He saw his grandchildren, Ephraim's children. Even the children of Machir, son of Manasseh, were adopted by Joseph at birth.

²⁴ At last Joseph said to his brothers, "I'm about to die. God will definitely take care of you and take you out of this land to the land he swore with an oath to give to Abraham, Isaac, and Jacob." ²⁵ Joseph made Israel's sons swear an oath. He said, "God will definitely take care of you. So be sure to carry my bones back with you."

²⁶ Joseph died when he was 110 years old. His body was embalmed and placed in a coffin in Egypt.

ᵃ 50:10 A threshing floor is an outdoor area where grain is separated from its husks.

EXODUS

Israel Comes to Egypt

1 ¹ These are the names of the sons of Israel (that is, Jacob) who came with him to Egypt with their families: ² Reuben, Simeon, Levi, and Judah; ³ Issachar, Zebulun, and Benjamin; ⁴ Dan and Naphtali; Gad and Asher. ⁵ Joseph was already in Egypt. The total number of Jacob's descendants was 70.

⁶ Eventually, Joseph, all his brothers, and that entire generation died. ⁷ But the descendants of Israel had many children. They became so numerous and strong that the land was filled with them.

The Israelites Become Slaves

⁸ Then a new king, who knew nothing about Joseph, began to rule in Egypt. ⁹ He said to his people, "There are too many Israelites, and they are stronger than we are. ¹⁰ We have to outsmart them, or they'll increase in number. Then, if war breaks out, they will join our enemies, fight against us, and leave the country."

¹¹ So the Egyptians put slave drivers in charge of them in order to oppress them through forced labor. They built Pithom and Rameses as supply cities for Pharaoh. ¹² But the more the Israelites were oppressed, the more they increased in number and spread out. The Egyptians couldn't stand them ˌany longerˌ. ¹³ So they forced the Israelites to work hard as slaves. ¹⁴ They made their lives bitter with back-breaking work in mortar and bricks and every kind of work in the fields. All the jobs the Egyptians gave them were brutally hard.

Pharaoh Tells the Midwives to Kill All Hebrew Baby Boys

¹⁵ Then the king of Egypt told the Hebrew midwives, whose names were Shiphrah and Puah, ¹⁶ "When you help the Hebrew women in childbirth, look at the child when you deliver it. If it's a boy, kill it, but if it's a girl, let it live."

¹⁷ However, the midwives feared God and didn't obey the king of Egypt's orders. They let the boys live. ¹⁸ So the king of Egypt called for the midwives. He asked them, "Why have you done this? Why have you let the boys live?"

¹⁹ The midwives answered Pharaoh, "Hebrew women are not like Egyptian women. They are so healthy that they have their babies before a midwife arrives."

²⁰ God was good to the midwives. So the people increased in number and became very strong. ²¹ Because the midwives feared God, he gave them families of their own.

²² Then Pharaoh commanded all his people to throw into the Nile every ˌHebrewˌ boy that was born, but to let every girl live.

Pharaoh's Daughter Adopts Moses

2 ¹ A man from Levi's family married a Levite woman. ² The woman became pregnant and had a son. She saw how beautiful he was and hid him for three months. ³ When she couldn't hide him any longer, she took a basket made of papyrus plants and coated it with tar and pitch. She put the baby in it and set it among the papyrus plants near the bank of the Nile River. ⁴ The baby's sister stood at a distance to see what would happen to him.

⁵ While Pharaoh's daughter came to the Nile to take a bath, her servants walked along the bank of the river. She saw the basket among the papyrus plants and sent her slave girl to get it. ⁶ Pharaoh's daughter opened the basket, looked at the baby, and saw it was a boy. He was crying, and she felt sorry for him. She said, "This is one of the Hebrew children."

⁷ Then the baby's sister asked Pharaoh's daughter, "Should I go and get one of the Hebrew women to nurse the baby for you?"

⁸ She answered, "Yes!" So the girl brought the baby's mother.

⁹ Pharaoh's daughter said to the woman, "Take this child, nurse him for me, and I will pay you."

She took the child and nursed him. ¹⁰ When the child was old enough, she brought him to Pharaoh's daughter, and he became her son. Pharaoh's daughter named him Moses [Pulled Out] and said, "I pulled him out of the water."

Moses Commits Murder and Flees to Midian

¹¹ In the course of time Moses grew up. Then he went to ˻see˼ his own people and watched them suffering under forced labor. He saw a Hebrew, one of his own people, being beaten by an Egyptian. ¹² He looked all around, and when he didn't see anyone, he beat the Egyptian to death and hid the body in the sand.

¹³ When Moses went there the next day, he saw two Hebrew men fighting. He asked the one who started the fight, "Why are you beating another Hebrew?"

¹⁴ The man asked, "Who made you our ruler and judge? Are you going to kill me as you killed the Egyptian?" Then Moses was afraid and thought that everyone knew what he had done.

¹⁵ When Pharaoh heard what Moses had done, he tried to have him killed. But Moses fled from Pharaoh and settled in the land of Midian.

Moses Marries Zipporah

One day, while Moses was sitting by a well, ¹⁶ seven daughters of the priest of Midian came. They drew water and filled the troughs to water their father's sheep. ¹⁷ But some shepherds came and chased them away. So Moses got up, came to their defense, and then watered their sheep.

¹⁸ When they came back to their father Reuel, he asked them, "Why have you come home so early today?"

¹⁹ They answered, "An Egyptian rescued us from some shepherds. He even drew water for us and watered the sheep."

²⁰ Reuel asked his daughters, "Where is he? Why did you leave the man there? Go, invite him to supper."

²¹ Moses decided to stay with the man. So Reuel gave his daughter Zipporah to Moses as his wife. ²² She gave birth to a son. Moses named him Gershom [Foreigner], because he said, "I was a foreigner living in another country."

The Israelites Pray to God During Their Suffering

²³ After a long time passed, the king of Egypt died. The Israelites still groaned because they were slaves. So they cried out, and their cries for help went up to God. ²⁴ God heard their groaning, and he remembered his promise[a] to Abraham, Isaac, and Jacob. ²⁵ God saw the Israelites ˻being oppressed˼ and was concerned about them.

Moses at the Burning Bush

3 ¹ Moses was taking care of the sheep of his father-in-law Jethro, the priest of Midian. As he led the sheep to the far side of the desert, he came to Horeb, the mountain of God.

² The Messenger of the LORD appeared to him there as flames of fire coming out of a bush. Moses looked, and although the bush was on fire, it was not burning up. ³ So he thought, "Why isn't this bush burning up? I must go over there and see this strange sight."

⁴ When the LORD saw that Moses had come over to see it, God called to him from the bush, "Moses, Moses!"

Moses answered, "Here I am!"

⁵ God said, "Don't come any closer! Take off your sandals because this place where you are standing is holy ground. ⁶ I am the God of your ancestors,[a] the God of Abraham, Isaac, and Jacob." Moses hid his face because he was afraid to look at God.

⁷ The LORD said, "I have seen the misery of my people in Egypt, and I have heard them crying out because of the slave drivers. I know how much they're suffering. ⁸ I have come to rescue them from the power of the Egyptians and to bring them from that land to a good land with plenty of room ˻for everyone˼. It is a land flowing with milk and honey where the Canaanites, Hittites, Amorites, Perizzites, Hivites, and Jebusites live. ⁹ I have heard the cry of the people of Israel. I have seen how the Egyptians are oppressing them. ¹⁰ Now, go! I am sending you to Pharaoh so that you can bring my people Israel out of Egypt."

¹¹ But Moses said to God, "Who am I that I should go to Pharaoh and bring the people of Israel out of Egypt?"

¹² God answered, "I will be with you. And this will be the proof that I sent you: When you bring the people out of Egypt, all of you will worship God on this mountain."

¹³ Then Moses replied to God, "Suppose I go to the people of Israel and say to them, 'The God of your ancestors has sent me to you,' and they ask me, 'What is his name?' What should I tell them?"

ᵃ 2:24 Or "covenant."   ᵃ 3:6 Samaritan Pentateuch, Greek, Acts 7:32; Masoretic Text "ancestor."

¹⁴ God answered Moses, "I Am Who I Am. This is what you must say to the people of Israel: 'I Am has sent me to you.' "

¹⁵ Again God said to Moses, "This is what you must say to the people of Israel: The LORD God of your ancestors, the God of Abraham, Isaac, and Jacob, has sent me to you. This is my name forever. This is my title throughout every generation.

¹⁶ "Go, assemble the leaders of Israel. Say to them, 'The LORD God of your ancestors, the God of Abraham, Isaac, and Jacob, appeared to me. He said, "I have paid close attention to you and have seen what has been done to you in Egypt. ¹⁷ I promise I will take you away from your misery in Egypt to the land of the Canaanites, Hittites, Amorites, Perizzites, Hivites, and Jebusites, a land flowing with milk and honey." '

¹⁸ "The leaders of Israel will listen to you. Then you and the leaders must go to the king of Egypt and say to him, 'The LORD God of the Hebrews has met with us. Please let us travel three days into the desert to offer sacrifices to the LORD our God.' ¹⁹ I know that the king of Egypt will not let you go, even if he is forced to. ²⁰ So I will use my power to strike Egypt. After all the miracles that I will do there, he will let you go. ²¹ I will make the Egyptians kind to the people of Israel so that, when you leave, you will not leave empty-handed.

²² "Every Hebrew woman should ask her Egyptian neighbor and any woman living in her home for silver and gold jewelry and for clothes. Put them on your sons and daughters. This way you will strip Egypt of its wealth."

4 ¹ "They will never believe me or listen to me!" Moses protested. "They will say, 'The LORD didn't appear to you.' "

² Then the LORD asked him, "What's that in your hand?"

He answered, "A shepherd's staff."

³ The LORD said, "Throw it on the ground."

When Moses threw it on the ground, it became a snake, and he ran away from it.

⁴ Then the LORD said to Moses, "Reach out and grab the snake by its tail." He reached out and grabbed it, and it turned back into a staff as he held it. ⁵ ͺThe LORD explained,ͺ "This is to convince the people that the LORD God of their ancestors, the God of Abraham, Isaac, and Jacob, appeared to you."

⁶ The LORD said to him, "Put your hand inside your shirt." So Moses did this, and when he took his hand out, it had a skin disease. It looked as ͺflaky asͺ snow. ⁷ "Now put your hand back inside your shirt," the LORD said. Moses put it back, and when he took it out this time, it was healthy again like the rest of his body.

⁸ ͺThen the LORD said,ͺ "If they won't believe you or pay attention to the first miraculous sign, they may believe the second. ⁹ But if they won't believe these two miraculous signs or listen to you, take some water from the Nile River and pour it on the ground. The water you take from the Nile will turn into blood on the ground."

¹⁰ Moses said to the LORD, "Please, Lord, I'm not a good speaker. I've never been a good speaker, and I'm not now, even though you've spoken to me. I speak slowly, and I become tongue-tied easily."

¹¹ The LORD asked him, "Who gave humans their mouths? Who makes humans unable to talk or hear? Who gives them sight or makes them blind? It is I, the LORD! ¹² Now go, and I will help you speak and will teach you what to say."

¹³ But Moses said, "Please, Lord, send someone else."

¹⁴ Then the LORD became angry with Moses and asked, "What about your brother Aaron the Levite? I know he can speak well. He's already on his way to meet you, and he will be very glad to see you. ¹⁵ You will speak to him and tell him what to say. I will help both of you speak, and I will teach you both what to do. ¹⁶ Aaron will speak to the people for you. He will be your spokesman, and you will be like God. ¹⁷ Take that shepherd's staff with you, and use it to do the miraculous signs."

Moses Returns to Egypt

¹⁸ Then Moses went back to his father-in-law Jethro. Moses said to him, "Please let me go back to my own people in Egypt. I would like to see if they're still alive."

Jethro said to Moses, "You may go."

¹⁹ Now, the LORD had said to Moses in Midian, "Go back to Egypt, because all the men who wanted to kill you are dead."

²⁰ So Moses took his wife and sons, put them on a donkey, and started out for Egypt. He also brought with him the staff God had told him to take.

²¹ The LORD said to Moses, "When you get back to Egypt, see that you show Pharaoh all the amazing things that I have given you the power to do. But I will make him stubborn so that he will not let the people go. ²² Then tell Pharaoh, 'This is what the LORD says: Israel is my first-

born son. ²³ I told you to let my son go so that he may worship me. But you refused to let him go. So now I'm going to kill your firstborn son.' "

²⁴ Along the way they stopped for the night. The LORD met Moses and tried to kill him. ²⁵ Then Zipporah took a flint knife, cut off her son's foreskin, and touched Moses' feet ⌐with it⌐. She said, "You are a bridegroom of blood to me!" ²⁶ So the LORD let him alone. It was because of the circumcision that she said at that time, "You are a bridegroom of blood!"

Moses and Aaron Tell the People What the LORD Said

²⁷ Meanwhile, the LORD had told Aaron to meet Moses in the desert.

When Aaron met Moses at the mountain of God, he kissed him. ²⁸ Moses told Aaron everything the LORD had sent him to say and all the miraculous signs the LORD had commanded him to do.

²⁹ Then Moses and Aaron went ⌐to Egypt⌐ and assembled all the leaders of the people of Israel. ³⁰ Aaron told them everything the LORD had said to Moses. He also did the miraculous signs for the people, ³¹ and the people believed them. When they heard that the LORD was concerned about the people of Israel and that he had seen their misery, they knelt, bowing with their faces touching the ground.

Moses and Aaron Confront Pharaoh

5 ¹ Later Moses and Aaron went to Pharaoh and said, "This is what the LORD God of Israel says: Let my people go into the desert to celebrate a festival in my honor."

² Pharaoh asked, "Who is the LORD? Why should I obey him and let Israel go? I don't know the LORD, and I won't let Israel go."

³ They replied, "The God of the Hebrews has met with us. Please let us travel three days into the desert to offer sacrifices to the LORD our God. If we don't go, he may kill us with a plague or a war."

⁴ The king of Egypt said to them, "Moses and Aaron, why are you distracting the people from their work? Get back to work!" ⁵ Then Pharaoh added, "Look how many people there are in the land! Do you want them to quit working?"

Pharaoh Increases the Israelites' Labor

⁶ That same day Pharaoh gave these orders to the slave drivers and foremen: ⁷ "Don't give the people any more straw to make bricks as you have been doing. Let them gather their own straw, ⁸ but insist that they make the same number of bricks they were making before. Making fewer bricks will not be acceptable. They're lazy! That's why they're crying, 'Let us go offer sacrifices to our God.' ⁹ Make the work harder for these people so that they will be too busy to listen to lies."

¹⁰ The slave drivers and foreman went out and said to them, "This is what Pharaoh says: I'm no longer giving you straw. ¹¹ Get your own straw wherever you can find it, but your work load will not be reduced one bit."

¹² So the people scattered all over Egypt to gather stubble for straw. ¹³ The slave drivers kept hurrying them. They said, "Finish the same amount of work each day, just as when you had straw."

¹⁴ Pharaoh's slave drivers had placed Israelite foremen in charge of the people. The slave drivers beat the foremen and said, "You didn't finish all the bricks you were ordered to make yesterday or today. Why didn't you make as many as you used to?"

¹⁵ Then the Israelite foremen complained to Pharaoh. They asked, "Why are you treating us this way? ¹⁶ We're given no straw, and yet we're told to make bricks. We're being beaten, but your men are at fault."

¹⁷ "You're lazy! ⌐Just plain⌐ lazy!" Pharaoh answered. "That's why you keep saying, 'Let us go offer sacrifices to the LORD.' ¹⁸ Now get back to work! You won't be given any straw, but you must still make the same number of bricks."

¹⁹ The Israelite foremen realized they were in trouble when they were told, "Don't make fewer bricks each day than you're supposed to."

²⁰ As they left Pharaoh, they found Moses and Aaron waiting for them. ²¹ So they said, "May the LORD see what you have done and judge you! You have made Pharaoh and his officials hate us. You have given them an excuse to kill us."

²² Moses went back to the LORD and asked, "Why have you brought this trouble on your people? Why did you send me? ²³ Ever since I went to Pharaoh to speak for you, he has treated your people cruelly, and you have done nothing at all to rescue your people."

6 ¹ Then the LORD said to Moses, "Now you will see what I will do to Pharaoh. I will show him my power, and he will let my people go. I will show him my power, and he will throw them out of his country."

The LORD Tells Moses to Speak to Pharaoh Again

[2] God spoke to Moses, "I am the LORD. [3] I appeared to Abraham, Isaac, and Jacob as God Almighty, but I didn't make myself known to them by my name, the LORD. [4] I even made a promise[a] to give them Canaan, the land where they lived as foreigners. [5] Now I have heard the groaning of the Israelites, whom the Egyptians hold in slavery, and I have remembered my promise.

[6] "Tell the Israelites, 'I am the LORD. I will bring you out from under the oppression of the Egyptians, and I will free you from slavery. I will rescue you with my powerful arm and with mighty acts of judgment. [7] Then I will make you my people, and I will be your God. You will know that I am the LORD your God, who brought you out from under the forced labor of the Egyptians. [8] I will bring you to the land I solemnly swore to give to Abraham, Isaac, and Jacob. I will give it to you as your own possession. I am the LORD.'"

[9] Moses reported this to the Israelites. But they would not listen to him because they were so discouraged by their back-breaking work.

[10] Then the LORD spoke to Moses, [11] "Go tell Pharaoh (the king of Egypt) to let the Israelites leave his country."

[12] But Moses protested to the LORD, "The Israelites wouldn't listen to me. Why would Pharaoh listen to me? I'm such a poor speaker."

[13] The LORD spoke to Moses and Aaron about the Israelites and Pharaoh (the king of Egypt). He commanded them to bring the Israelites out of Egypt.

Aaron and Moses' Ancestry—Genesis 46:9–11

[14] These were the heads of the families:

The sons of **Reuben,** Israel's firstborn, were Hanoch, Pallu, Hezron, and Carmi. These were the families descended from Reuben.

[15] The sons of **Simeon** were Jemuel, Jamin, Ohad, Jachin, Zohar, and Shaul, the son of a Canaanite woman. These were the families descended from Simeon.

[16] These are the names of the sons of **Levi** listed in birth order: Gershon, Kohath, and Merari. Levi lived 137 years.

[17] The sons of Gershon listed by their families were Libni and Shimei.

[18] The sons of Kohath were Amram, Izhar, Hebron, and Uzziel. Kohath lived 133 years.

[19] The sons of Merari were Mahli and Mushi.

These were the families descended from Levi listed in birth order.

[20] Amram married his father's sister Jochebed. She gave birth to Aaron and Moses. Amram lived 137 years.

[21] The sons of Izhar were Korah, Nepheg, and Zichri.

[22] The sons of Uzziel were Mishael, Elzaphan, and Sithri.

[23] Aaron married Elisheba, daughter of Amminadab and sister of Nahshon. She gave birth to Nadab, Abihu, Eleazar, and Ithamar.

[24] The sons of Korah were Assir, Elkanah, and Abiasaph.

These were the families descended from Korah.

[25] Eleazar, son of Aaron, married one of the daughters of Putiel. She gave birth to Phinehas. These were the heads of Levite households listed by their families.

[26] This was the same Aaron and Moses to whom the LORD said, "Bring the Israelites out of Egypt in organized family groups." [27] They—this same Moses and Aaron—told Pharaoh (the king of Egypt) to let the Israelites leave Egypt.

Aaron's Staff Becomes a Snake

[28] At that time the LORD spoke to Moses in Egypt. [29] He said to Moses, "I am the LORD. Tell Pharaoh (the king of Egypt) everything I tell you."

[30] But Moses said to the LORD, "Why would Pharaoh listen to me?"

7 [1] The LORD answered Moses, "I have made you a god to Pharaoh, and your brother Aaron is your prophet. [2] Tell your brother Aaron everything I command you, and he must tell Pharaoh to let the Israelites leave the country. [3] But I will make Pharaoh stubborn. Even though I will do many miraculous signs and amazing things in Egypt, [4] Pharaoh will not listen to you. Then I will use my power to punish Egypt severely, and I will bring my people, the Israelites, out of Egypt in organized family groups. [5] The Egyptians will know that I am the LORD when I use my power against Egypt and bring the Israelites out of there."

[6] Moses and Aaron did as the LORD had commanded them. [7] Moses was 80 years old and Aaron was 83 when they talked to Pharaoh.

---

[a] 6:4 Or "covenant."

⁸ The LORD said to Moses and Aaron, ⁹ "When Pharaoh says to you, 'Give me a sign to prove that God has sent you,' tell Aaron, 'Take your shepherd's staff and throw it down in front of Pharaoh,' and it will become a large snake."

¹⁰ Moses and Aaron went to Pharaoh and did as the LORD had commanded. Aaron threw his staff down in front of Pharaoh and his officials, and it became a large snake. ¹¹ Then Pharaoh sent for his wise men and sorcerers. These Egyptian magicians did the same thing using their magic spells. ¹² Each of them threw his staff down, and they all became large snakes. But Aaron's staff swallowed theirs. ¹³ Yet, Pharaoh continued to be stubborn and would not listen to them, as the LORD had predicted.

The First Plague—The Nile River Turns Into Blood

¹⁴ Then the LORD said to Moses, "Pharaoh is being stubborn. He refuses to let my people go. ¹⁵ In the morning meet Pharaoh when he's on his way to the Nile. Wait for him on the bank of the river. Take along the staff that turned into a snake. ¹⁶ Say to him, 'The LORD God of the Hebrews sent me to tell you, "Let my people go to worship me in the desert." So far you have not listened. ¹⁷ Here is what the LORD says: This is the way you will recognize that I am the LORD: With this staff in my hand, I'm going to strike the Nile, and the water will turn into blood. ¹⁸ The fish in the Nile will die, and the river will stink. The Egyptians will not be able to drink any water from the Nile.' "

¹⁹ The LORD said to Moses, "Tell Aaron, 'Take your staff and stretch out your hand over the waters of Egypt—its rivers, canals, ponds, and all its reservoirs—so that they turn into blood. There will be blood everywhere in Egypt, even in the wooden and stone containers.' "

²⁰ Moses and Aaron did as the LORD had commanded. In front of Pharaoh and his officials, Aaron raised his staff and struck the Nile. All the water in the river turned into blood. ²¹ The fish in the Nile died, and it smelled so bad that the Egyptians couldn't drink any water from the river. There was blood everywhere in Egypt.

²² But the Egyptian magicians did the same thing using their magic spells. So Pharaoh continued to be stubborn and would not listen to Moses and Aaron, as the LORD had predicted. ²³ Pharaoh turned and went back to his palace. He dismissed the entire matter from his mind.

²⁴ All the Egyptians dug along the Nile for water to drink because they couldn't drink any of the water from the river.

²⁵ Seven days passed after the LORD struck the Nile.

The Second Plague—Frogs

8ᵃ ¹ Then the LORD said to Moses, "Go to Pharaoh, and tell him, 'This is what the LORD says: Let my people go to worship me. ² If you refuse to let them go, I will bring a plague of frogs on your whole country. ³ The Nile River will swarm with frogs. They will come into your palace, into your bedroom, on your bed, into the houses of your officials, on your people, into your ovens and into your mixing bowls. ⁴ The frogs will jump on you, on your people, and on all your officials.' "

⁵ Then the LORD said to Moses, "Tell Aaron, 'Hold your staff over the rivers, canals, and ponds. This will bring frogs onto the land.' "

⁶ So Aaron held his staff over the waters of Egypt. The frogs came up and covered the land of Egypt. ⁷ But the magicians did the same thing using their magic spells and brought frogs onto the land.

⁸ Pharaoh sent for Moses and Aaron and said, "Pray that the LORD will take the frogs away from me and my people. Then I will let your people go to offer sacrifices to the LORD."

⁹ Moses answered Pharaoh, "You may have the honor of choosing when I should pray for you, your officials, and your people. Then the frogs will leave you and your homes. The only ones left will be those in the Nile."

¹⁰ "Pray for me tomorrow," Pharaoh said.

Moses replied, "It will be as you say so that you will know that there is no one like the LORD our God. ¹¹ The frogs will leave you, your homes, your officials, and your people. The only frogs left will be those in the Nile."

¹² After Moses and Aaron left Pharaoh, Moses prayed to the LORD about the frogs he had brought on Pharaoh. ¹³ The LORD did what Moses asked. The frogs died in the houses, in the yards, and in the fields. ¹⁴ They were piled into countless heaps, and the land began to stink because of them.

¹⁵ When Pharaoh saw that the plague was over, he became stubborn and would not listen to Moses and Aaron, as the LORD had predicted.

ᵃ 8:1 Exodus 8:1–32 in English Bibles is Exodus 7:26–8:28 in the Hebrew Bible.

The Third Plague—Gnats

¹⁶ Then the LORD said to Moses, "Tell Aaron, 'Hold out your staff and strike the dust on the ground. All over Egypt the dust will turn into gnats.' "
¹⁷ When Moses told him, Aaron held out the staff in his hand and struck the dust on the ground. It turned into gnats that bit people and animals. All the dust on the ground everywhere in Egypt turned into gnats.
¹⁸ The magicians also tried to produce gnats using their magic spells, but they couldn't do it. The gnats bit people and animals. ¹⁹ So the magicians said to Pharaoh, "This is the hand of God!"

Yet, Pharaoh continued to be stubborn and would not listen to Moses and Aaron, as the LORD had predicted.

The Fourth Plague—Flies

²⁰ Then the LORD said to Moses, "Early in the morning, stand in Pharaoh's way when he's going to the Nile. Say to him, 'This is what the LORD says: Let my people go to worship me. ²¹ If you will not let my people go, I will send swarms of flies on you, your officials, your people, and your houses. The homes of the Egyptians will be filled with flies, and even the ground outside will be covered with them. ²² But on that day I will treat the region of Goshen differently. That is where my people live. There won't be any flies there. This way you will know that I, the LORD, am here in this land. ²³ I will distinguish between my people and yours. This miraculous sign will happen tomorrow.' "
²⁴ The LORD did what he said. Dense swarms of flies came into Pharaoh's palace and into the houses of his officials. All over Egypt the flies were ruining everything. ²⁵ Pharaoh called for Moses and Aaron and said, "Go, sacrifice to your God here in this country."
²⁶ Moses replied, "It wouldn't be right to do that. The sacrifices we offer to the LORD our God are disgusting to Egyptians. If they see us offer sacrifices that they consider disgusting, won't they stone us to death? ²⁷ We need to travel three days into the desert to offer sacrifices to the LORD our God, as he told us to do."
²⁸ Pharaoh said, "I will let you go, but don't go very far. You may offer sacrifices to the LORD your God in the desert and pray for me."
²⁹ Moses answered, "As soon as I leave you, I will pray to the LORD. Tomorrow the swarms of flies will go away from you, your officials, and your people. But you must stop tricking us by not letting the people go to offer sacrifices to the LORD."
³⁰ Moses left Pharaoh and prayed to the LORD. ³¹ The LORD did what Moses asked. The swarms of flies left Pharaoh, his officials, and his people. Not one fly was left. ³² Yet, this time, too, Pharaoh was stubborn and did not let the people go.

The Fifth Plague—Death of Livestock

9 ¹ Then the LORD said to Moses, "Go to Pharaoh, and tell him, 'This is what the LORD God of the Hebrews says: Let my people go to worship me. ² If you refuse to let them go and continue to hold them ⸤in slavery⸥, ³ the LORD will bring a terrible plague on your livestock, including your horses, donkeys, camels, cattle, sheep, and goats. ⁴ But the LORD will distinguish between Israel's livestock and the livestock of the Egyptians. No animals belonging to the Israelites will die.' " ⁵ The LORD set a definite time. He said, "Tomorrow I will do this."
⁶ The next day the LORD did as he said. All the livestock of the Egyptians died, but none of the Israelites' animals died. ⁷ Pharaoh found out that not one of the Israelites' animals had died. Yet, Pharaoh continued to be stubborn and would not let the people go.

The Sixth Plague—Boils

⁸ Then the LORD said to Moses and Aaron, "Take a handful of ashes from a kiln, and have Moses throw them up in the air as Pharaoh watches. ⁹ They will become a fine dust throughout Egypt. The dust will cause boils to break into open sores on people and animals throughout Egypt."
¹⁰ They took ashes from a kiln and stood in front of Pharaoh. Moses threw the ashes up in the air, and they caused boils to break into open sores on people and animals. ¹¹ The magicians couldn't compete with Moses because they had boils like all the other Egyptians.
¹² But the LORD made Pharaoh stubborn, so he wouldn't listen to Moses and Aaron, as the LORD had predicted to Moses.

The Seventh Plague—Hail

¹³ Then the LORD said to Moses, "Early in the morning, go to Pharaoh and say to him, 'This is what the LORD God of the Hebrews says: Let my people go to worship me. ¹⁴ Now I will send plagues that will affect you personally as well as your officials and people. This is how you will know that there is no one like me anywhere on earth. ¹⁵ By now I could have used my power

to kill you and your people with a plague that would have wiped you off the earth. [16] But I have spared you for this reason. I want to show you my power and make my name famous throughout the earth. [17] You are still blocking my people from leaving. [18] So, at this time tomorrow I will send the worst hailstorm that has ever happened in Egypt since the beginning of its history. [19] Now, send servants, to bring your livestock and everything else you have indoors. All people and animals still outside and not brought in will die when the hail falls on them.' "

[20] Those members of Pharaoh's court who listened to the LORD'S warning brought their servants and cattle indoors quickly. [21] But those who didn't take the LORD'S warning seriously left their servants and animals out in the open.

[22] Then the LORD said to Moses, "Lift your hand toward the sky, and hail will fall on people, animals, and every plant in the fields of Egypt."

[23] When Moses lifted his staff toward the sky, the LORD sent thunder and hail, and lightning struck the earth. So the LORD made it hail on Egypt. [24] It hailed, and lightning flashed while it hailed. This was the worst storm in all the land of Egypt since it had become a nation. [25] All over Egypt the hail knocked down everything that was out in the open. It struck down people, animals, and every plant in the fields and destroyed every tree in the fields. [26] The only place it didn't hail was the region of Goshen, where the Israelites lived.

[27] Then Pharaoh sent for Moses and Aaron. "This time I have sinned," he told them. "The LORD is right, and my people and I are wrong. [28] Pray to the LORD. We've had enough of God's thunder and hail. I'll let you go; you don't have to stay here any longer."

[29] Moses replied, "As soon as I'm out of the city, I'll spread out my hands to the LORD in prayer. The thunder will stop, and there will be no more hail. This is how you will know that the earth belongs to the LORD. [30] But I know that you and your officials still don't fear the LORD God."

[31] (The flax and the barley were ruined, because the barley had formed heads and the flax was in bloom. [32] Neither the wheat nor the wild grain was damaged, because they ripen later.)

[33] As soon as he left Pharaoh and went out of the city, Moses spread out his hands to the LORD in prayer. The thunder and the hail stopped, and no more rain came pouring down on the ground.

[34] When Pharaoh saw that the rain, the hail, and the thunder had stopped, he sinned again. He and his officials continued to be stubborn. [35] Pharaoh was stubborn and would not let the Israelites go, as the LORD had predicted through Moses.

The Eighth Plague—Locusts

10 [1] Then the LORD said to Moses, "Go to Pharaoh. I have made him and his officials stubborn so that I can do these miraculous signs among them. [2] You will be able to tell your children and grandchildren exactly how I treated the Egyptians and what miraculous signs I did among them. This is how you will all know that I am the LORD."

[3] So Moses and Aaron went to Pharaoh and said to him, "This is what the LORD God of the Hebrews says: How long will you refuse to humble yourself in my presence? Let my people go to worship me. [4] If you refuse to let my people go, tomorrow I will bring locusts into your country. [5] They will cover the land so that the ground can't be seen. They will eat everything left by the hail, including every tree still standing in the fields. [6] They will fill your houses and the houses of all your officials and those of all the Egyptians. Your parents and ancestors never saw anything like this from the time they first came here until now." Moses turned and left Pharaoh.

[7] Then Pharaoh's officials asked him, "How long will this man hold us in his grip? Let the Israelite men go to worship the LORD their God. When will you realize that Egypt is ruined?"

[8] So Moses and Aaron were brought back to Pharaoh. "Go, worship the LORD your God," he said to them. "But exactly who will be going?"

[9] Moses answered, "Everyone! We'll be taking our young and old, our sons and daughters, our flocks and herds with us. For us it's a pilgrimage festival in the LORD'S honor."

[10] Pharaoh said to them, "The LORD would have to be with you if I would ever let you take your women and children along. I know you're up to no good! [11] No! Only the men may go to worship the LORD, since that's what you've been asking for." Then Moses and Aaron were thrown out of Pharaoh's palace.

[12] The LORD said to Moses, "Stretch out your hand over Egypt to bring locusts. They will invade Egypt and eat up every plant in the land—everything left by the hail."

[13] Moses held his staff over the land of Egypt, and the LORD made a wind from the east blow over the land all that day and all that night. By morning the east wind had brought the locusts. [14] They invaded all of Egypt and landed all over the country in great swarms. Never before had there been so many locusts like this, nor would there ever be that many again. [15] They covered all the ground until it was black with them. They ate all the plants and all the fruit on the trees that the hail had left. Nothing green was left on any tree or plant anywhere in Egypt.

¹⁶ Then Pharaoh quickly called for Moses and Aaron and said, "I have sinned against the LORD your God and against you. ¹⁷ Please forgive my sin one more time. Pray to the LORD your God to take this deadly plague away from me."

¹⁸ Moses left Pharaoh and prayed to the LORD. ¹⁹ Then the LORD changed the wind to a very strong west wind. It picked up the locusts and blew them into the Red Sea. Not one locust was left anywhere in Egypt.

²⁰ But the LORD made Pharaoh stubborn, so he did not let the Israelites go.

The Ninth Plague—Darkness

²¹ Then the LORD said to Moses, "Lift your hand toward the sky, and a darkness ˌso thickˌ that it can be felt will come over Egypt." ²² Moses lifted his hand toward the sky, and throughout Egypt there was total darkness for three days. ²³ People couldn't see each other, and no one went anywhere for three days. But all the Israelites had light where they were living.

²⁴ Then Pharaoh called for Moses and said, "Go, worship the LORD! Even your women and children may go with you, but your flocks and herds must stay behind."

²⁵ But Moses said, "You must allow us to take ˌour animalsˌ for the sacrifices and burnt offerings we have to make to the LORD our God. ²⁶ All our livestock must go with us. Not one animal must be left behind. We'll have to use some of them for worshiping the LORD our God, and we won't know what we'll need until we get there."

²⁷ But the LORD made Pharaoh stubborn, so he refused to let them go. ²⁸ Pharaoh said to Moses, "Get out of my sight! Don't ever let me see your face again. The day I do, you will die."

²⁹ "You're right!" Moses answered. "You'll never see my face again."

The Tenth Plague—The Death of the Firstborn

11 ¹ Then the LORD said to Moses, "I will bring one more plague on Pharaoh and Egypt. After that he will let you go. When he does, he will be certain to force all of you out of here. ² Now announce to the people ˌof Israelˌ that each man and woman must ask the Egyptians for silver and gold jewelry."

³ The LORD made the Egyptians kind to the people. And Moses was highly respected by Pharaoh's officials and all the Egyptians.

⁴ Moses said, "This is what the LORD says: About midnight I will go out among the Egyptians. ⁵ Every firstborn son in Egypt will die, from the firstborn of Pharaoh who rules the land, to the firstborn children of female slaves who use their handmills, including every firstborn domestic animal. ⁶ There will be loud crying throughout Egypt, such as there has never been or ever will be again. ⁷ But where the Israelites are, not even a dog will be startled by any person or animal. This is how you will see that the LORD shows the distinction between Egypt and Israel. ⁸ Then all these officials of yours will come, bow down to me, and say, 'You and all the people who follow you, get out!' After that I will leave." Burning with anger, Moses left Pharaoh.

⁹ The LORD had said to Moses, "Pharaoh will not listen to you. This is why I will do more amazing things in Egypt." ¹⁰ Moses and Aaron showed Pharaoh all these amazing things. Yet, the LORD made Pharaoh stubborn, so he wouldn't let the Israelites leave his country.

Passover

12 ¹ The LORD said to Moses and Aaron in Egypt, ² "This month will be the very first month of the year for you. ³ Tell the whole community of Israel: On the tenth ˌdayˌ of this month each man must take a lamb or a young goat for his family—one animal per household. ⁴ A household may be too small to eat a whole animal. That household and the one next door can share one animal. Choose your animal based on the number of people and what each person can eat. ⁵ Your animal must be a one-year-old male that has no defects. You may choose a lamb or a young goat. ⁶ Take care of it until the fourteenth ˌdayˌ of this month.

"Then at dusk, all the assembled people from the community of Israel must slaughter their animals. ⁷ They must take some of the blood and put it on the sides and tops of the doorframes of the houses where they will eat the animals. ⁸ The meat must be eaten that same night. It must be roasted over a fire and eaten with bitter herbs and unleavened bread. ⁹ Don't eat any of it raw or boiled but roast the whole animal over a fire. ¹⁰ Don't leave any of it until morning. Anything left over in the morning must be burned up. ¹¹ This is how ˌyou should be dressed whenˌ you eat it: with your belt on, your sandals on your feet, and your shepherd's staff in your hand. You must eat it in a hurry. It is the LORD's Passover.

¹² "On that same night I will go throughout Egypt and kill every firstborn male, both human and animal. I will severely punish all the gods of Egypt, ˌbecauseˌ I am the LORD. ¹³ But the blood on your houses will be a sign for your protection. When I see the blood, I will pass over you. Nothing will touch or destroy you when I strike Egypt.

¹⁴ "This day will be one for you to remember. This is a permanent law for generations to come: You will celebrate this day as a pilgrimage festival in the LORD's honor. ¹⁵ For seven days you must eat unleavened bread. On the very first day you must remove any yeast that you have in your houses. Whoever eats anything with yeast in it from the first day through the seventh day must be excluded from Israel. ¹⁶ You must have a holy assembly on the first day and another one on the seventh. You must not work on these days except to prepare your own meals. That's all you may do.

¹⁷ You must celebrate the Festival of Unleavened Bread because it was on this very day that I brought you out of Egypt in organized family groups. This is a permanent law for future generations: You must celebrate this day. ¹⁸ From the evening of the fourteenth day of the first month until the evening of the twenty-first day you must eat unleavened bread. ¹⁹ There should be no yeast in your houses for seven days. Whoever eats anything with yeast in it must be excluded from the community of Israel, whether he is an Israelite or not. ²⁰ Eat nothing made with yeast. Wherever you live, you must eat ⌊only⌋ unleavened bread."

²¹ Then Moses called for all the leaders of Israel. He said to them, "Pick out a lamb or a young goat for your families, and kill the Passover animal. ²² Take the branch of a hyssop plant, dip it in the blood which is in a bowl, and put some of the blood on the top and sides of the doorframes ⌊of your houses⌋. No one may leave the house until morning. ²³ The LORD will go throughout Egypt to kill the Egyptians. When he sees the blood on the top and sides of the doorframe, he will pass over that doorway, and he will not let the destroyer come into your home to kill you.

²⁴ "You must follow these instructions. They are a permanent law for you and your children. ²⁵ When you enter the land that the LORD will give you as he promised, observe this ceremony. ²⁶ When your children ask you what this ceremony means to you, ²⁷ you must answer, 'It's the Passover sacrifice in the LORD's honor. The LORD passed over the houses of the Israelites in Egypt and spared our homes when he killed the Egyptians.' "

Then the people knelt, bowing with their faces touching the ground. ²⁸ The Israelites did as the LORD had commanded Moses and Aaron.

²⁹ At midnight the LORD killed every firstborn male in Egypt from the firstborn son of Pharaoh who ruled the land to the firstborn son of the prisoner in jail, and also every firstborn animal. ³⁰ Pharaoh, all his officials, and all the ⌊other⌋ Egyptians got up during the night. There was loud crying throughout Egypt because in every house someone had died.

Pharaoh Allows the Israelites to Leave Egypt

³¹ Pharaoh called for Moses and Aaron during the night. He said, "You and the Israelites must leave my people at once. Go, worship the LORD as you asked. ³² Take your flocks and herds, too, as you asked. Just go! And bless me, too!"

³³ The Egyptians begged the people to leave the country quickly. They said, "Soon we'll all be dead!" ³⁴ So the people picked up their bread dough before it had risen and carried it on their shoulders in bowls, wrapped up in their clothes.

³⁵ The Israelites did what Moses had told them and asked the Egyptians for gold and silver jewelry and for clothes. ³⁶ The LORD made the Egyptians generous to the people, and they gave them what they asked for. So the Israelites stripped Egypt of its wealth.

The Israelites Leave Egypt

³⁷ The Israelites left Rameses to go to Succoth. There were about six hundred thousand men on foot, plus all the women and children. ³⁸ Many other people also went with them, along with large numbers of sheep, goats, and cattle.

³⁹ With the dough they had brought from Egypt, they baked round, flat bread. The dough hadn't risen because they'd been thrown out of Egypt and had no time to prepare food for the trip.

⁴⁰ The Israelites had been living in Egypt for 430 years. ⁴¹ After exactly 430 years all the LORD's people left Egypt in organized family groups. ⁴² That night the LORD kept watch to take them out of Egypt. (All Israelites in future generations must keep watch on this night, since it is dedicated to the LORD.)

Rules for the Passover

⁴³ The LORD said to Moses and Aaron, "These are the rules for the Passover:

"No foreigner may eat the Passover meal.

⁴⁴ "Any male slave you have bought may eat it after you have circumcised him.

⁴⁵ "No foreigner visiting you may eat it.

"No hired worker may eat it.

⁴⁶ "The meal must be eaten inside one house. Never take any of the meat outside the house. "Never break any of the bones.

47 "The whole community of Israel must celebrate the Passover.

48 "Foreigners may want to celebrate the LORD's Passover. First, every male in the household must be circumcised. Then they may celebrate the Passover like native-born Israelites. But no uncircumcised males may ever eat the Passover meal. **49** The same instructions apply to native-born Israelites as well as foreigners."

50 All the Israelites did as the LORD had commanded Moses and Aaron. **51** That very day the LORD brought all the Israelites out of Egypt in organized family groups.

13 **1** The LORD spoke to Moses, **2** "Set apart every firstborn male for me. Every firstborn male offspring among the Israelites is mine, whether human or animal."

3 Then Moses said to the people, "Remember this day—the day when you left Egypt, the land of slavery. The LORD used his mighty hand to bring you out of there. Don't eat anything made with yeast. **4** Today, in the month of Abib, you are leaving Egypt. **5** The LORD swore to your ancestors that he would give you the land of the Canaanites, Hittites, Amorites, Hivites, and Jebusites. When he brings you into that land flowing with milk and honey, you must observe this ceremony in this month.

6 "For seven days you must eat unleavened bread. The seventh day will be a pilgrimage festival in the LORD's honor. **7** Only unleavened bread should be eaten during these seven days. No sourdough or yeast should be seen anywhere in your territory. **8** On that day tell your children, 'We do this because of what the LORD did for us when we left Egypt.' **9** This ˎfestivalˏ will be ˎlikeˏ a mark on your hand or a reminder on your forehead that the teachings of the LORD are ˎalwaysˏ to be a part of your conversation. Because the LORD used his mighty hand to bring you out of Egypt, **10** you must follow these rules every year at this time.

Rules Concerning the Firstborn Child

11 "When the LORD brings you to the land of the Canaanites and gives it to you, as he swore to you and your ancestors, **12** sacrifice every firstborn male offspring to the LORD. The firstborn male offspring of each of your animals belongs to the LORD. **13** It will cost you a sheep or a goat to buy any firstborn donkey back from the LORD. If you don't buy it back, then you must break the donkey's neck. You must also buy every firstborn son back from the LORD.

14 "In the future when your children ask you what this means, tell them, 'The LORD used his mighty hand to bring us out of slavery in Egypt. **15** When Pharaoh was too stubborn to let us go, the LORD killed every firstborn male in Egypt—human and animal. This is why we sacrifice every firstborn male to the LORD and buy every firstborn son back from the LORD.' **16** So this ˎfestivalˏ will be ˎlikeˏ a mark on your hand and ˎlikeˏ a band on your forehead, because the LORD used his mighty hand to bring us out of Egypt."

God Leads the People out of Egypt

17 When Pharaoh let the people go, God didn't lead them on the road through Philistine territory, although that was the shortest route. God said, "If they see that they have to fight a war, they may change their minds and go back to Egypt." **18** So God led the people around the other way, on the road through the desert toward the Red Sea. The Israelites were ready for battle when they left Egypt.

19 Moses took the bones of Joseph with him, because Joseph had made the Israelites solemnly swear to do this. Joseph had said, "God will definitely come to help you. When he does, take my bones with you."

20 They moved from Succoth and camped at Etham, on the edge of the desert. **21** By day the LORD went ahead of them in a column of smoke to lead them on their way. By night he went ahead of them in a column of fire to give them light so that they could travel by day or by night. **22** The column of smoke was always in front of the people during the day. The column of fire was always there at night.

Pharaoh Pursues Israel

14 **1** Then the LORD said to Moses, **2** "Tell the Israelites to go back and set up their camp facing Pi Hahiroth, between Migdol and the sea. Set up your camp facing north—by the sea. **3** Pharaoh will think, 'The Israelites are ˎjustˏ wandering around. The desert is blocking their escape.' **4** I will make Pharaoh so stubborn that he will pursue them. Then, because of what I do to Pharaoh and his entire army, I will receive honor, and the Egyptians will know that I am the LORD." So that is what the Israelites did.

5 When Pharaoh (the king of Egypt) was told that the people had fled, he and his officials changed their minds about them. They said, "What have we done? We've lost our slaves because we've let Israel go." **6** So Pharaoh prepared his chariot and took his army with him. **7** He took 600 of his best chariots as well as all the other chariots in Egypt, placing an officer in each of them. **8** The LORD made Pharaoh (the king of Egypt) so stubborn that he pursued the Israelites, who were boldly leaving Egypt. [9] The Egyptians pursued the Israelites. Pharaoh's army, including all his horse-drawn chariots and cavalry, caught up with them as they were setting up their camp by the sea at Pi Hahiroth facing north.

[10] As Pharaoh approached, the Israelites looked up and saw that the Egyptians were coming after them. Terrified, the Israelites cried out to the LORD. [11] They said to Moses, "Did you bring us out into the desert to die because there were no graves in Egypt? Look what you've done by bringing us out of Egypt! [12] Didn't we tell you in Egypt, 'Leave us alone! Let us go on serving the Egyptians'? It would have been better for us to serve the Egyptians than to die in the desert!"

The LORD Divides the Red Sea

[13] Moses answered the people, "Don't be afraid! Stand still, and see what the LORD will do to save you today. You will never see these Egyptians again. [14] The LORD is fighting for you! So be still!"

[15] Then the LORD said to Moses, "Why are you crying out to me? Tell the Israelites to start moving. [16] Raise your staff, stretch out your hand over the sea, and divide the water. Then the Israelites will go through the sea on dry ground. [17] I am making the Egyptians so stubborn that they will follow the Israelites. I will receive honor because of what I will do to Pharaoh, his entire army, his chariots, and cavalry. [18] The Egyptians will know that I am the LORD when I am honored for what I did to Pharaoh, his chariots, and his cavalry."

[19] The Messenger of God, who had been in front of the Israelites, moved behind them. So the column of smoke moved from in front of the Israelites and stood behind them [20] between the Egyptian camp and the Israelite camp. The ˌcolumn ofˌ smoke was there when darkness came, and it lit up the night. Neither side came near the other all night long.

[21] Then Moses stretched out his hand over the sea. All that night the LORD pushed back the sea with a strong east wind and turned the sea into dry ground. The water divided, [22] and the Israelites went through the middle of the sea on dry ground. The water stood like a wall on their right and on their left.

[23] The Egyptians pursued them, and all Pharaoh's horses, chariots, and cavalry followed them into the sea. [24] Just before dawn, the LORD looked down from the column of fire and smoke and threw the Egyptian camp into a panic. [25] He made the wheels of their chariots come off so that they could hardly move. Then the Egyptians shouted, "Let's get out of here! The LORD is fighting for Israel! He's against us!"

[26] Then the LORD said to Moses, "Stretch out your hand over the sea so that the water will flow back over the Egyptians, their chariots, and their cavalry."

[27] Moses stretched his hand over the sea, and at daybreak the water returned to its usual place. The Egyptians tried to escape, but the LORD swept them into the sea. [28] The water flowed back and covered Pharaoh's entire army, as well as the chariots and the cavalry that had followed Israel into the sea. Not one of them survived.

[29] Meanwhile, the Israelites had gone through the sea on dry ground while the water stood like a wall on their right and on their left. [30] That day the LORD saved Israel from the Egyptians, and Israel saw the Egyptians lying dead on the seashore. [31] When the Israelites saw the great power the LORD had used against the Egyptians, they feared the LORD and believed in him and in his servant Moses.

The Song of Moses

15 [1] Then Moses and the Israelites sang this song to the LORD:

"I will sing to the LORD.
   He has won a glorious victory.
   He has thrown horses and their riders into the sea.
[2]   The LORD is my strength and my song.
   He is my Savior.
     This is my God, and I will praise him,
       my father's God, and I will honor him.
[3]   The LORD is a warrior!
   The LORD is his name.
[4]   He has thrown Pharaoh's chariots and army into the sea.
   Pharaoh's best officers were drowned in the Red Sea.
[5]   The deep water covered them.
     They sank to the bottom like a rock.
[6]   Your right hand, O LORD, wins glory because it is strong.
   Your right hand, O LORD, smashes your enemies.

7   With your unlimited majesty, you destroyed those who attacked you.
        You sent out your burning anger.
            It burned them up like straw.
8   With a blast from your nostrils, the water piled up.
        The waves stood up like a dam.
            The deep water thickened in the middle of the sea.

9   "The enemy said, 'I'll pursue them!
        I'll catch up with them!
            I'll divide the loot!
                I'll take all I want!
                    I'll use my sword!
                        I'll take all they have!'
10 Your breath blew the sea over them.
        They sank like lead in the raging water.

11 "Who is like you among the gods, O Lord?
    Who is like you?
        You are glorious because of your holiness
            and awe-inspiring because of your splendor.
        You perform miracles.
12 You stretched out your right hand.
    The earth swallowed them.

13 "Lovingly, you will lead the people you have saved.
    Powerfully, you will guide them to your holy dwelling.
14   People will hear of it and tremble.
            The people of Philistia will be in anguish.
15   The tribal leaders of Edom will be terrified.
            The powerful men of Moab will tremble.
            The people of Canaan will be deathly afraid.
16   Terror and dread will fall on them.
    Because of the power of your arm, they will be petrified
        until your people pass by, O Lord,
        until the people you purchased pass by.
17 You will bring them and plant them on your own mountain,
        the place where you live, O Lord,
        the holy place that you built with your own hands, O Lord.
18 The Lord will rule as king forever and ever."

¹⁹ When Pharaoh's horses, chariots, and cavalry went into the sea, the Lord made the water of the sea flow back over them. However, the Israelites had gone through the sea on dry ground.

The Song of Miriam

²⁰ Then the prophet Miriam, Aaron's sister, took a tambourine in her hand. All the women, dancing with tambourines, followed her. ²¹ Miriam sang to them:

    "Sing to the Lord.
        He has won a glorious victory.
        He has thrown horses and their riders into the sea."

God Provides Water for the Israelites

²² Moses led Israel away from the Red Sea into the desert of Shur. For three days they traveled in the desert without finding water. ²³ When they came to Marah, they couldn't drink the water because it tasted bitter. That's why the place was called Marah [Bitter Place]. ²⁴ The people complained about Moses by asking, "What are we supposed to drink?"

²⁵ Moses cried out to the Lord, and the Lord showed[a] him a piece of wood. He threw it into the water, and the water became sweet.

There the Lord set down laws and rules for them to live by, and there he tested them. ²⁶ He said, "If you will listen carefully to the Lord your God and do what he considers right, if you pay attention to his commands and obey all his laws, I will never make you suffer any of the diseases I made the Egyptians suffer, because I am the Lord, who heals you."

---

a 15:25 Samaritan Pentateuch, Syriac, Targum, Latin; Masoretic Text "taught."

²⁷ Next, they went to Elim, where there were 12 springs and 70 palm trees. They camped there by the water.

The Lord Provides Manna and Quails for the Israelites to Eat

16 ¹ The whole community of Israelites moved from Elim and came to the desert of Sin, which is between Elim and Sinai. This was on the fifteenth day of the second month after they had left Egypt. ² In the desert the whole community complained about Moses and Aaron. ³ The Israelites said to them, "If only the Lord had let us die in Egypt! There we sat by our pots of meat and ate all the food we wanted! You brought us out into this desert to let us all starve to death!"

⁴ The Lord said to Moses, "I'm going to send you food from heaven like rain. Each day the people should go out and gather only what they need for that day. In this way I will test them to see whether or not they will follow my instructions. ⁵ But on the sixth day when they prepare what they bring home, it should be twice as much as they gather on other days."

⁶ So Moses and Aaron said to all the Israelites, "In the evening you will know that it was the Lord who brought you out of Egypt. ⁷ In the morning you will see the glory of the Lord, because he has heard you complaining about him. Why are you complaining about us?" ⁸ Moses also said, "The Lord will give you meat to eat in the evening and all the food you want in the morning. The Lord has heard you complaining about him. Who are we? You're not complaining about us but about the Lord."

⁹ Moses said to Aaron, "Tell the whole community of Israelites, 'Come into the Lord's presence. He has heard you complaining.' "

¹⁰ While Aaron was speaking to the whole community of Israelites, they looked toward the desert. Suddenly, they saw the glory of the Lord in the column of smoke.

¹¹ The Lord said to Moses, ¹² "I've heard the Israelites complaining. Tell them, 'At dusk you will eat meat, and in the morning you will eat all the food you want. Then you will know that I am the Lord your God.' "

¹³ That evening quails came and covered the camp, and in the morning there was a layer of dew around the camp. ¹⁴ When the dew was gone, the ground was covered with a thin layer of flakes like frost on the ground. ¹⁵ When the Israelites saw it, they asked each other, "What is this?" because they didn't know what it was.

Moses said to them, "It's the food the Lord has given you to eat. ¹⁶ This is what the Lord has commanded: Each of you should gather as much as you can eat. Take two quarts for each person in your tent."

¹⁷ So that is what the Israelites did. Some gathered more, some less. ¹⁸ They measured it into two-quart containers. Those who had gathered more didn't have too much. Those who had gathered less didn't have too little. They gathered as much as they could eat.

¹⁹ Then Moses said to them, "No one may keep any of it until morning."

²⁰ But some of them didn't listen to Moses. They kept part of it until morning, and it was full of worms and smelled bad. So Moses was angry with them.

²¹ Each morning they gathered as much food as they could eat. When the sun was hot, it melted away. ²² But on the sixth day they gathered twice as much food, four quarts per person. All the leaders of the community came to Moses and told him about it.

²³ He said to them, "This is what the Lord said: Tomorrow is a day of worship, a holy day of worship dedicated to the Lord. Bake what you want to bake, and boil what you want to boil. Save all that's left over, and keep it until tomorrow morning."

²⁴ So they saved it until the next morning as Moses had commanded, but it didn't smell or have worms in it. ²⁵ "Eat it today," Moses said, "because today is a day of worship dedicated to the Lord. You won't find anything on the ground today. ²⁶ You can gather food on six days, but on the seventh day, the day of worship, you won't find any."

²⁷ On the seventh day some people went out to gather food, but they didn't find any. ²⁸ The Lord said to Moses, "How long will you refuse to do what I have commanded and instructed you to do? ²⁹ Remember: The Lord has given you this day of worship. That's why he gives you enough food on the sixth day for two days. On the seventh day you may not leave. Everyone, stay where you are." ³⁰ So the people never worked on the seventh day of the week.

³¹ The Israelites called the food *manna*. It was like coriander seeds. It was white and tasted like wafers made with honey.

³² Moses said, "This is what the Lord has commanded: Take two quarts of manna to be kept for your descendants. This way they will see the food that I gave you to eat in the desert when I brought you out of Egypt."

³³ Moses said to Aaron, "Take a jar, put two quarts of manna in it, and put it in the Lord's presence to be kept for your descendants." ³⁴ Aaron put the jar of manna in front of the words of God's promise to be kept there, as the Lord commanded Moses.

³⁵ The Israelites ate manna for 40 years until they came to a place to settle. They ate manna until they came to the border of Canaan. ³⁶ (Now, the standard dry measure at that time held 20 quarts.)

The LORD Provides Water for the Israelites From a Rock

17 ¹ The whole community of Israelites left the desert of Sin and traveled from place to place as the LORD commanded them. They camped at Rephidim, but there was no water for the people to drink. ² So they complained to Moses by saying, "Give us water to drink!"

Moses said to them, "Why are you complaining to me? Why are you testing the LORD?"

³ But the people were thirsty for water there. They complained to Moses and asked, "Why did you bring us out of Egypt? Was it to make us, our children, and our livestock die of thirst?"

⁴ So Moses cried out to the LORD, "What should I do with these people? They're almost ready to stone me!"

⁵ The LORD answered Moses, "Bring some of the leaders of Israel with you, and go to where the people can see you. Take the staff you used to strike the Nile River. ⁶ I'll be standing in front of you there by a rock at Mount Horeb. Strike the rock, and water will come out of it for the people to drink."

Moses did this while the leaders of Israel watched him.

⁷ He named that place Massah [Testing] and Meribah [Complaining] because the Israelites complained and because they tested the LORD, asking, "Is the LORD with us or not?"

God Defeats the Amalekites

⁸ The Amalekites fought Israel at Rephidim. ⁹ Moses said to Joshua, "Choose some of our men. Then fight the Amalekites. Tomorrow I will stand on top of the hill. I will hold in my hand the staff God told me to take along."

¹⁰ Joshua did as Moses told him and fought the Amalekites, while Moses, Aaron, and Hur went to the top of the hill. ¹¹ As long as Moses held up his hands, Israel would win, but as soon as he put his hands down, the Amalekites would start to win. ¹² Eventually, Moses' hands felt heavy. So Aaron and Hur took a rock, put it under him, and he sat on it. Aaron held up one hand, and Hur held up the other. His hands remained steady until sunset. ¹³ So Joshua defeated the Amalekite army in battle.

¹⁴ The LORD said to Moses, "Write this reminder on a scroll, and make sure that Joshua hears it, too: I will completely erase any memory of the Amalekites from the earth."

¹⁵ Moses built an altar and called it The LORD Is My Banner. ¹⁶ He said, "Because a hand was lifted against the LORD's throne,ᵃ he will be at war against the Amalekites from one generation to the next."

Moses' Father-in-law Visits Israel's Camp

18 ¹ Moses' father-in-law Jethro, the priest of Midian, heard about everything God had done for Moses and his people Israel and how the LORD had brought Israel out of Egypt. ² When Moses had sent away his wife Zipporah, his father-in-law Jethro had taken her in, ³ along with her two sons. The one son was named Gershom [Foreigner], because Moses said, "I was a foreigner living in another country." ⁴ The name of the other was Eliezer [My God Is a Helper], because he said, "My father's God was my helper. He saved me from Pharaoh's death sentence."

⁵ Moses' father-in-law Jethro brought Moses' sons and wife to Moses in the desert where he was camped near the mountain of God. ⁶ Jethro had sent word to Moses, "I'm coming to ˻visit˼ you, ˻and I'm bringing˼ your wife and her two sons."

⁷ So Moses went out to meet his father-in-law. Moses bowed with his face touching the ground and kissed Jethro. After they asked each other how they were, they went into the tent. ⁸ Moses told his father-in-law everything the LORD had done to Pharaoh and the Egyptians for Israel, all the hardships they had had on the way, and how the LORD had saved them.

⁹ Jethro was delighted ˻to hear˼ about all the good things the LORD had done for Israel in rescuing them from the Egyptians. ¹⁰ He said, "Thank the LORD! He rescued you from the Egyptians and their Pharaoh and rescued these people from the control of the Egyptians, ¹¹ who treated Israel with contempt. Now I know that the LORD is greater than all other gods."

¹² Then Jethro, Moses' father-in-law, brought a burnt offering and other sacrifices to God. Aaron and all the leaders of Israel came to eat the meal with Moses' father-in-law in God's presence.

¹³ The next day Moses was settling disagreements among the people. The people stood around Moses from morning until evening. ¹⁴ When Moses' father-in-law saw everything

---

ᵃ 17:16 Hebrew meaning uncertain.

Moses was doing for the people, he asked, "Why are you doing this for the people? Why do you sit here alone, while all the people stand around you from morning until evening?"

¹⁵ Moses answered his father-in-law, "Because the people come to me to find out God's will. ¹⁶ Whenever they have a disagreement and bring it to me, I decide which person is right, and I tell them God's laws and instructions."

¹⁷ Moses' father-in-law replied, "What you're doing is not good. ¹⁸ You and your people will wear yourselves out. This is too much work for you. You can't do it alone! ¹⁹ Now listen to me, and I'll give you some advice. May God be with you! You must be the people's representative to God and bring their disagreements to him. ²⁰ You must instruct them in the laws and the teachings, show them how to live, and tell them what to do.

²¹ "But choose capable men from all the people, men who fear God, men you can trust, men who hate corruption. Put them in charge of groups of 1,000, or 100, or 50, or 10 people. ²² Let them be the ones who usually settle disagreements among the people. They should bring all important cases to you, but they should settle all minor cases themselves. Make it easier for yourself by letting them help you. ²³ If God commands you, and you do this, you will be able to continue your work, and all these people will have their disagreements settled so that they can go home."

²⁴ Moses listened to his father-in-law and did everything he said. ²⁵ Moses chose capable men from all the Israelites and put them in charge of groups of 1,000, or 100, or 50, or 10 people. ²⁶ These men were the ones who usually settled disagreements among the people. They would bring difficult cases to Moses, but they settled all minor ones themselves.

²⁷ Moses sent his father-in-law on his way. So Jethro went back to his own country.

Israel at Mount Sinai

19 ¹ Two months after the Israelites left Egypt, they came to the desert of Sinai. ² Israel had moved from Rephidim and had come into the desert of Sinai. They had set up camp there in front of the mountain.

³ Then Moses went up the mountain to God, and the LORD called to him from the mountain, "This is what you must say to the descendants of Jacob. Tell the Israelites, ⁴ 'You have seen for yourselves what I did to Egypt and how I carried you on eagles' wings and brought you to my mountain. ⁵ If you carefully obey me and are faithful to the terms of my promise,ᵃ then out of all the nations you will be my own special possession, even though the whole world is mine. ⁶ You will be my kingdom of priests and my holy nation.' These are the words you must speak to the Israelites."

⁷ So Moses went down and called for the leaders of the people. He repeated to them all the words that the LORD had commanded him. ⁸ All the people answered together, "We will do everything the LORD has said." So Moses brought their answer back to the LORD.

⁹ The LORD said to Moses, "I am coming to you in a storm cloud so that the people will hear me speaking with you and will always believe you." Moses told the LORD what the people had said.

¹⁰ So the LORD said to Moses, "Go to the people, and tell them they have two days to get ready. They must set themselves apart as holy. Have them wash their clothes ¹¹ and be ready by the day after tomorrow. On that day the LORD will come down on Mount Sinai as all the people watch. ¹² Mark off a boundary around the mountain for the people, and tell them not to go up the mountain or even touch it. Those who touch the mountain must be put to death. ¹³ No one should touch them. They must be stoned or shot with arrows. No matter whether it's an animal or a person, it must not live. The people may go up the mountain ˪only˩ when the ram's horn sounds a long blast."

¹⁴ After Moses went down the mountain to the people, he had them get ready, and they washed their clothes. ¹⁵ Then Moses said to the people, "Be ready two days from now. Don't disqualify yourselves by having sexual intercourse."

¹⁶ On the morning of the second day, there was thunder and lightning with a heavy cloud over the mountain, and a very loud blast from a ram's horn ˪was heard˩. All the people in the camp shook with fear. ¹⁷ Then Moses led the people out of the camp to meet with God, and they stood at the foot of the mountain. ¹⁸ All of Mount Sinai was covered with smoke because the LORD had come down on it in fire. Smoke rose from the mountain like the smoke from a kiln, and the whole mountain shook violently. ¹⁹ As the sound of the horn grew louder and louder, Moses was speaking, and the voice of God answered him.

²⁰ The LORD came down on top of Mount Sinai and called Moses to the top of the mountain. So Moses went up. ²¹ The LORD said to him, "Go down and warn the people not to force their way through ˪the boundary˩ to see the LORD, or many of them will die. ²² Even the priests who

---

ᵃ 19:5 Or "terms of my covenant."

are allowed to come near the LORD must set themselves apart as holy, or the LORD will violently kill them."

²³ Moses said to the LORD, "The people can't come up Mount Sinai, because you warned us yourself to mark off a boundary around the mountain and consider it holy."

²⁴ The LORD said to him, "Go down, and bring Aaron back with you. But the priests and the people must not force their way through the boundary to come up to the LORD, or he will violently kill them."

²⁵ So Moses went down to the people and told them.

The Ten Commandments—Deuteronomy 5:6–21

20 ¹ Then God spoke all these words:
² "I am the LORD your God, who brought you out of slavery in Egypt.

³ "Never have any other god. ⁴ Never make your own carved idols or statues that represent any creature in the sky, on the earth, or in the water. ⁵ Never worship them or serve them, because I, the LORD your God, am a God who does not tolerate rivals. I punish children for their parents' sins to the third and fourth generation of those who hate me. ⁶ But I show mercy to thousands of generations of those who love me and obey my commandments.

⁷ "Never use the name of the LORD your God carelessly. The LORD will make sure that anyone who carelessly uses his name will be punished.

⁸ "Remember the day of worship by observing it as a holy day. ⁹ You have six days to do all your work. ¹⁰ The seventh day is the day of worship dedicated to the LORD your God. You, your sons, your daughters, your male and female slaves, your cattle, and the foreigners living in your city must never do any work ˌon that dayˌ. ¹¹ In six days the LORD made heaven, earth, and the sea, along with everything in them. He didn't work on the seventh day. That's why the LORD blessed the day he stopped his work and set this day apart as holy.

¹² "Honor your father and your mother, so that you may live for a long time in the land the LORD your God is giving you.

¹³ "Never murder.

¹⁴ "Never commit adultery.

¹⁵ "Never steal.

¹⁶ "Never lie when you testify about your neighbor.

¹⁷ "Never desire to take your neighbor's household away from him.

"Never desire to take your neighbor's wife, his male or female slave, his ox, his donkey, or anything else that belongs to him."

The People's Reaction

¹⁸ All the people heard the thunder and saw the lightning. They heard the blast of the ram's horn and saw the mountain covered with smoke. So they shook with fear and stood at a distance. ¹⁹ Then they said to Moses, "You speak to us, and we'll listen. But don't let God speak to us, or we'll die!"

²⁰ Moses answered the people, "Don't be afraid! God has come only to test you, so that you will be in awe of him and won't sin."

²¹ The people kept their distance while Moses went closer to the dark cloud where God was.

General Rules for Worship

²² The LORD said to Moses, "This is what you must say to the Israelites: You've seen for yourselves that I have spoken to you from heaven. ²³ Never make any gods of silver or gold for yourselves. Never worship them.

²⁴ "You must build an altar for me made out of dirt. Sacrifice your burnt offerings and your fellowship offerings, your sheep, goats, and cattle on it. Wherever I choose to have my name remembered, I will come to you and bless you. ²⁵ If you build an altar for me made out of stones, never make it with cut stone blocks. If you use a chisel on it, you will make it unacceptable to me. ²⁶ Never use stairs to go up to my altar. Otherwise, people will be able to see under your clothes."

Laws Concerning the Treatment of Slaves

21 ¹ ˌThe LORD continued,ˌ "Here are the legal decisions to be used by the Israelites:
² "Whenever you buy a Hebrew slave, he will be your slave for six years. In the seventh year he may leave as a free man, without paying for his freedom. ³ If he comes to you by himself, he must leave by himself. If he comes as a married man, his wife may leave with him. ⁴ If his master gives him a wife and she gives birth to sons or daughters, the wife and her children belong to the master, and the slave must leave by himself. ⁵ But if he makes this statement: 'I hereby declare my love for my master, my wife, and my children. I don't want to leave as a free

man,' ⁶ then his master must bring him to God. The master must bring him to the door or the doorframe and pierce his ear with an awl. Then he will be his slave for life.

⁷ "Whenever a man sells his daughter into slavery, she will not go free the way male slaves do. ⁸ If she doesn't please the master who has chosen her as a wife,ᵃ he must let her be bought back by one of her close relatives. He has no right to sell her to foreigners, since he has treated her unfairly. ⁹ But if he has chosen her for his son, he must treat her like a daughter. ¹⁰ If that son marries another woman, he must not deprive the first wife of food, clothes, or sex.

¹¹ If he doesn't give her these three things, she can go free, without paying any money for her freedom.

Laws Concerning Injury to People

¹² "Whoever strikes someone and kills him must be put to death. ¹³ If it wasn't done intentionally, but God let it happen, the killer should flee to a place I will set aside for you. ¹⁴ But whenever someone becomes so angry that he plans to kill his neighbor, you must take him away from my altar and put him to death.

¹⁵ "Whoever hits his father or mother must be put to death.

¹⁶ "Whoever kidnaps another person must be put to death, whether he has sold the kidnapped person or still has him.

¹⁷ "Whoever curses his father or mother must be put to death.

¹⁸ "This is what you must do whenever men quarrel and one hits the other with a rock or with his fist and injures him so that he has to stay in bed. ¹⁹ If the injured man can get up again and walk around outside with a cane, the one who hit him must not be punished. He must pay the injured man for the loss of his time and for all his medical expenses.

²⁰ "Whenever an owner hits his male or female slave with a stick so that the slave dies from the beating, the owner must be punished. ²¹ But if the slave gets up in a day or two, the owner must not be punished. The slave is his property.

²² "This is what you must do whenever men fight and injure a pregnant woman so that she gives birth prematurely. If there are no other injuries, the offender must pay whatever fine the court allows the woman's husband to demand. ²³ If anyone is injured, the offender must pay a life for a life, ²⁴ an eye for an eye, a tooth for a tooth, a hand for a hand, a foot for a foot, ²⁵ a burn for a burn, a bruise for a bruise, a wound for a wound.

²⁶ "Whenever an owner hits his male or female slave in the eye and the slave is blinded, he must let the slave go free to make up for the loss of the eye. ²⁷ If the owner knocks out the tooth of his male or female slave, he must let the slave go free to make up for the loss of the tooth.

²⁸ "Whenever a bull gores a man or a woman to death, the bull must be stoned to death, and its meat may not be eaten. The bull's owner is free from any liability. ²⁹ But if the bull has had the habit of goring, and the owner has been warned but has not kept it confined, and it kills a man or a woman, then the bull must be stoned and its owner must be put to death, too. ³⁰ However, if only a cash settlement is demanded from the owner, the bull's owner may save his life by paying whatever price is demanded of him. ³¹ If the bull gores someone's son or daughter, this same ruling applies. ³² If the bull gores a male or female slave, its owner must pay 12 ounces of silver to the slave's master, and the bull must be stoned.

Laws Concerning Property

³³ "Whenever someone opens up a cistern or digs a new one and doesn't cover it and a bull or a donkey falls into it, ³⁴ the owner of the cistern must make up for the loss. He must pay money to the animal's owner, and then the dead animal will be his.

³⁵ "Whenever one person's bull kills another person's bull, they must sell the live bull and divide the money between them. They must divide the dead bull, too. ³⁶ However, if it was known that the bull had the habit of goring, and its owner didn't keep it confined, the owner must make up for the loss—bull for bull—and then the dead bull will be his."

22ᵃ ¹ ⸢The Lord continued,⸣ "Whenever someone steals a bull or a sheep and butchers it or sells it, he must make up for the loss with five head of cattle to replace the bull or four sheep to replace the sheep.

² "If anyone catches a thief breaking in and hits him so that he dies, he is not guilty of murder. ³ But if it happens after sunrise, he is guilty of murder.

"A thief must make up for what he has stolen. If he is unable to do so, he must be sold ⸢as a slave⸣ to pay for what he stole. ⁴ But if the stolen animal is found alive in his possession, whether it's a bull, donkey, or a sheep, he must make up for the loss with double the amount.

ᵃ 21:8 Or "master so that he does not choose her as a wife."   ᵃ 22:1 Exodus 22:1–31 in English Bibles is Exodus 21:37–22:30 in the Hebrew Bible.

⁵ "Whenever someone lets his livestock graze in a field or a vineyard, and they stray and graze in another person's field, he must make up for what the damaged field was expected to produce. But if he lets them ruin the whole field with their grazing,ᵇ he must make up from his own field for the loss with the best from his field and vineyard.

⁶ "Whenever a fire starts and spreads into the underbrush so that it burns up stacked or standing grain or ruins a field, the person who started the fire must make up for the loss.

⁷ "This is what you must do whenever someone gives his neighbor silver or ˌotherˌ valuables to keep for him, and they are stolen from that person's house: If the thief is caught, he must make up for the loss with double the amount. ⁸ If the thief is not caught, the owner of the house must be brought to God to find out whether or not he took his neighbor's valuables. ⁹ If there is a dispute over the ownership of a bull, a donkey, a sheep, an article of clothing, or any ˌotherˌ lost property which two people claim as their own, both people must bring their case to God. The one whom God declares guilty must make up for his neighbor's loss with double the amount.

¹⁰ "This is what you must do whenever someone gives his neighbor a donkey, a bull, a sheep, or any other kind of animal to keep for him, and it dies, is injured, or is captured in war, and there are no witnesses. ¹¹ The case between them must be settled by swearing an oath to the Lord that the neighbor did not take the other person's animal. The owner must accept the oath. The neighbor doesn't have to make up for the loss. ¹² But if the animal was stolen from the neighbor, he must make up for the owner's loss. ¹³ If it was killed by a wild animal, he must bring in the dead body as evidence. He doesn't have to make up for an animal that has been killed.

¹⁴ "Whenever someone borrows an animal from his neighbor, and it is injured or dies while the owner is not present, the borrower must make up for the loss. ¹⁵ If the owner is with the animal, the borrower doesn't have to make up for the loss. If it is rented, the rental fee covers the loss.

Laws for Living as God's Holy People

¹⁶ "Whenever a man seduces a virgin who is not engaged to anyone and has sexual intercourse with her, he must pay the bride-price and marry her. ¹⁷ If her father absolutely refuses to give her to him, he must pay an amount of money equal to the bride-price for virgins.

¹⁸ "Never let a witch live.

¹⁹ "Whoever has sexual intercourse with an animal must be put to death.

²⁰ "Whoever sacrifices to any god except the Lord must be condemned and destroyed.

²¹ "Never mistreat or oppress foreigners, because you were foreigners living in Egypt.

²² "Never take advantage of any widow or orphan. ²³ If you do and they cry out to me, you can be sure that I will hear their cry. ²⁴ I will become angry and have you killed in combat. Then your wives and children will become widows and orphans.

²⁵ "If you lend money to my people—to any poor person among you—never act like a moneylender. Charge no interest. ²⁶ If you take any of your neighbor's clothes as collateral, give it back to him by sunset. ²⁷ It may be the only clothes he has to cover his body. What else will he sleep in? When he cries out to me, I will listen because I am compassionate.

²⁸ "Never show disrespect for God or curse a leader of your people.

²⁹ "Never withhold your best wineᶜ from me.

"You must give me your firstborn son. ³⁰ You must do the same with your cattle and your sheep. They will stay with their mothers seven days, but on the eighth day you must give them to me.

³¹ "You must be my holy people. Never eat the meat of an animal that has been killed by wild animals out in the countryside. Throw it to the dogs."

23 ¹ ˌThe Lord continued,ˌ "Never spread false rumors. Don't join forces with wicked people by giving false testimony. ² Never follow a crowd in doing wrong. When you testify in court, don't side with the majority to pervert justice. ³ Never give special favors to poor people in court.

⁴ "Whenever you come across your enemy's ox or donkey wandering loose, be sure to take it back to him. ⁵ Whenever you see that the donkey of someone who hates you has collapsed under its load, don't leave it there. Be sure to help him with his animal.

⁶ "Never deny justice to poor people in court. ⁷ Avoid telling lies. Don't kill innocent or honest people, because I will never declare guilty people innocent. ⁸ Never take a bribe, because bribes blind those who can see and deny justice to those who are in the right.

⁹ "Never oppress foreigners. You know what it's like to be foreigners because you were foreigners living in Egypt.

ᵇ 22:5 "he must make . . . grazing" Greek, Samaritan Pentateuch, Dead Sea Scrolls; Masoretic Text omits these words.
ᶜ 22:29 Hebrew meaning of "your best wine" uncertain.

[10] "For six years you may plant crops in your fields and harvest them, [11] but in the seventh year you must leave the land unplowed and unused. In that way the poor among your people will have food to eat, and wild animals may eat what the poor people leave. You must do the same with your vineyards and olive groves.

[12] "For six days you will do your work, but on the seventh day you must not work. Then your ox and donkey can rest. The slaves born in your household and foreigners will also be refreshed.

[13] "Be careful ˌto doˌ everything I told you.

"Never mention the names of other gods or let them be heard on your lips.

Laws for Three Festivals

[14] "Three times a year you must celebrate a pilgrimage festival in my honor.

[15] "Celebrate the Festival of Unleavened Bread: For seven days you must eat unleavened bread, as I commanded you. Do this at the appointed time in the month of Abib, because that was when you left Egypt. No one may come into my presence without an offering.

[16] "Celebrate the Festival of the Harvest with the first produce harvested from whatever you plant in your fields.

"Celebrate the Festival of the Final Harvest at the end of the year when you harvest your crops from the fields.

[17] "These are the three times each year that all your men must come into the presence of the Master, the LORD.

[18] "Never offer the blood of a sacrifice to me at the same time you offer anything containing yeast. The fat sacrificed at my festivals should never be left over in the morning.

[19] "You must bring the best of the first produce harvested from your soil to the house of the LORD your God.

"Never cook a young goat in its mother's milk.

Laws About God's Messenger, Who Will Bring Israel to the Promised Land

[20] "I'm going to send a Messenger in front of you to protect you on your trip and bring you to the place I have prepared. [21] Pay attention to him, and listen to him. Don't defy him, because he will not forgive your disobedience. He is acting on my authority. [22] But if you will listen to him and do everything I say, then I will be an enemy to your enemies and an opponent to your opponents.

[23] "My Messenger will go ahead of you and will bring you to ˌthe land ofˌ the Amorites, Hittites, Perizzites, Canaanites, Hivites, and Jebusites. I will wipe them out. [24] Never worship or serve their gods or follow their practices. Instead, you must destroy their gods and crush their sacred stones. [25] You must serve the LORD your God, and he will bless your food and water. I will take away all sickness from among you. [26] No woman in your land will miscarry or be unable to have children. I will let you live a normal life span.

[27] "I will send my terror ahead of you and throw any nation you meet into a panic. I will make all your enemies flee from you. [28] I will spread panic ahead of you to force the Hivites, Canaanites, and Hittites out of your way. [29] I will not force them out of your way in one year. Otherwise, the land would be deserted, and wild animals would take over. [30] Little by little I will force them out of your way until you have increased enough in number to take possession of the land.

[31] "I will establish your borders from the Red Sea to the Mediterranean Sea and from the Sinai Desert to the Euphrates River. I will put the people living in the land under your control, and you will force them out of your way. [32] Never make a treaty with them and their gods. [33] Never let them live in your land, or they will make you sin against me and trap you into serving their gods."

The Promise Sealed With Blood

24 [1] The LORD said to Moses, "You and Aaron, Nadab, Abihu, and 70 of Israel's leaders come up the mountain to me and worship at a distance. [2] Moses may come near the LORD, but the others may not. The people must not come along with Moses."

[3] Moses went and told the people all the LORD's words and legal decisions. Then all the people answered with one voice, "We will do everything the LORD has told us to do." [4] So Moses wrote down all the LORD's words.

Early the next morning he built an altar at the foot of the mountain and ˌset upˌ 12 sacred stones for the 12 tribes of Israel. [5] Then he sent young Israelite men, and they sacrificed bulls as burnt offerings and fellowship offerings to the LORD. [6] Moses took half of the blood and put it into bowls, and he threw the other half against the altar. [7] Then he took the Book of the

LORD's Promise[a] and read it while the people listened. They said, "We will obey and do everything the LORD has said."

[8] Moses took the blood and sprinkled it on the people and said, "Here is the blood which seals the promise that the LORD has made to you based on everything you have just heard."

[9] Moses went up with Aaron, Nadab, Abihu, and 70 of Israel's leaders. [10] They saw the God of Israel. Under his feet was something like a pavement made out of sapphire as clear and blue as the sky itself. [11] God didn't harm these leaders of the Israelites. So they saw God, and then they ate and drank.

Moses Goes up the Mountain to Receive God's Words Written on Stone

[12] The LORD said to Moses, "Come up to me on the mountain. Stay there, and I will give you the stone tablets with the teachings and the commandments I have written for the people's instruction."

[13] Moses set out with his assistant Joshua, and Moses went up on the mountain of God. [14] He said to the leaders, "Wait here for us until we come back to you. Aaron and Hur are here with you. Take all your disagreements to them."

[15] So Moses went up on the mountain, and the cloud covered it. [16] The glory of the LORD settled on Mount Sinai. For six days the cloud covered it, and on the seventh day the LORD called to Moses from inside the cloud. [17] To the Israelites, the glory of the LORD looked like a raging fire on top of the mountain. [18] Moses entered the cloud as he went up the mountain. He stayed on the mountain 40 days and 40 nights.

Gifts for Use in the Tent of Meeting—Exodus 35:4–9

25 [1] The LORD said to Moses, [2] "Tell the Israelites to choose something to give me as a special contribution. You must accept whatever contribution each person freely gives. [3] This is the kind of contribution you will accept from them: gold, silver, and bronze, [4] violet, purple, and bright red yarn, fine linen, goats' hair, [5] rams' skins dyed red, fine leather,[a] acacia wood, [6] olive oil for the lamps, spices for the anointing oil and for the sweet-smelling incense, [7] onyx stones, and other precious stones to be set in the ⌊chief priest's⌋ ephod[b] and his breastplate.

[8] "Then have them make a holy place for me, and I will live among them. [9] Make the tent and all its furnishings exactly like the plans I am showing you.

The Ark—Exodus 37:1–9

[10] "Make an ark of acacia wood 45 inches long, 27 inches wide, and 27 inches high. [11] Cover it with pure gold inside and out, and put a gold molding around it. [12] Cast four gold rings for it, and fasten them to its four feet, two rings on each side. [13] Make poles of acacia wood, and cover them with gold. [14] Put the poles through the rings on the sides of the ark in order to carry it. [15] The poles must stay in the rings of the ark. Never remove them. [16] Then you will put into the ark the words of my promise which I will give you.

[17] "Make a throne of mercy to cover the ark out of pure gold 45 inches long and 27 inches wide. [18] Make two angels[c] out of hammered gold for the two ends of the throne of mercy, [19] one on each end. Form the angels and the throne of mercy out of one piece of gold. [20] The angels should have their wings spread above the throne of mercy, overshadowing it. They should face each other, looking at the throne of mercy. [21] After you put into the ark the words of my promise which I will give you, place the throne of mercy on top. [22] I will be above the throne of mercy between the angels whenever I meet with you and give you all my commands for the Israelites.

The Table—Exodus 37:10–16

[23] "Make a table of acacia wood 36 inches long, 18 inches wide, and 27 inches high. [24] Cover it with pure gold, and put a gold molding around it. [25] Make a rim three inches wide around it, and put a gold molding around the rim. [26] Make four gold rings for it, and fasten them to the four corners, where the four legs are. [27] The rings are to be close to the rim. They are to hold the poles for carrying the table. [28] Make the poles out of acacia wood, cover them with gold, and use them to carry the table. [29] Make plates and dishes for the table out of pure gold, as well as pitchers and bowls to be used for pouring wine offerings. [30] Put the bread of the presence on this table so that it will be in front of me all the time.

The Lamp Stand—Exodus 37:17–24

[31] "Make a lamp stand out of pure gold. The lamp stand, its base, and its shaft, as well as the flower cups, buds, and petals must be hammered out of one piece of gold. [32] Six branches are to come out of the sides, three branches on one side and three on the other. [33] Each of the six

---

[a] 24:7 Or "Covenant."   [a] 25:5 Hebrew meaning uncertain.   [b] 25:7 *Ephod* is a technical term for a part of the priest's clothes. Its exact usage and shape are unknown.   [c] 25:18 Or "cherubim."

branches coming out of the lamp stand is to have three flower cups shaped like almond blossoms, with buds and petals. [34] The lamp stand itself is to have four flower cups shaped like almond blossoms, with buds and petals. [35] There should be a bud under each of the three pairs of branches coming out of the lamp stand. [36] The buds and branches should also be hammered out of the same piece of pure gold as the lamp stand.

[37] "Make seven lamps, and set them on the lamp stand so that they light up ˌthe areaˌ in front of it. [38] The tongs and incense burners must be made of pure gold. [39] Use 75 pounds of pure gold to make the lamp stand and all the utensils. [40] Be sure to make them according to the plans you were shown on the mountain."

The Tent—Exodus 36:8–38

26 [1] ˌThe LORD continued,ˌ "Make the inner tent with ten sheets made from fine linen yarn. Take violet, purple, and bright red yarn, and creatively work an angel[a] design into the fabric. [2] Each sheet will be 42 feet long and 6 feet wide—all the same size. [3] Five of the sheets must be sewn together, and the other five must also be sewn together. [4] Make 50 violet loops along the edge of the end sheet in each set, [5] placing the loops opposite each other. [6] Make 50 gold fasteners. Use them to link the ˌtwo sets ofˌ sheets together so that the tent is a single unit.

[7] "Make 11 sheets of goats' hair to form an outer tent over the inner tent. [8] Each of the 11 sheets will be 45 feet long and 6 feet wide. [9] Sew five of the sheets together into one set and the remaining six into another set. Fold the sixth sheet in half ˌto hangˌ in front of the tent. [10] Make 50 loops along the edge of the end sheet in each set. [11] Make 50 bronze fasteners, and put them through the loops to link the inner tent together as a single unit. [12] The remaining half-sheet should hang over the back of the inner tent. [13] There will be 18 inches left over on each side because of the length of the outer tent's sheets. That part should hang over each side in order to cover the inner tent. [14] Make a cover of rams' skins that have been dyed red for the outer tent. Over that put a cover made of fine leather.[b]

[15] "Make a framework out of acacia wood for the inner tent. [16] Each frame is to be 15 feet long and 27 inches wide, [17] with two identical pegs. Make all the frames for the inner tent the same way. [18] Make 20 frames for the south side of the inner tent. [19] Then make 40 silver sockets at the bottom of the 20 frames, two sockets at the bottom of each frame for the two pegs. [20] For the north side of the inner tent ˌmakeˌ 20 frames [21] and 40 silver sockets, two at the bottom of each frame. [22] Make six frames for the far end, the west side. [23] Make two frames for ˌeach ofˌ the corners at the far end of the inner tent. [24] These will be held together at the bottom and held tightly at the top by a single ring.[c] Both corner frames will be made this way. [25] There will be eight frames with 16 silver sockets, two at the bottom of each frame.

[26] "Make crossbars out of acacia wood: five for the frames on one side of the inner tent, [27] five for those on the other side, and five for the frames on the far end of the inner tent, the west side. [28] The middle crossbar will run from one end to the other, halfway up the frames. [29] Cover the frames with gold, make gold rings to hold the crossbars, and cover the crossbars with gold.

[30] "Set up the inner tent according to the plans you were shown on the mountain.

[31] "Make a canopy of violet, purple, and bright red yarn. Creatively work an angel design into fine linen yarn. [32] Use gold hooks to hang it on four posts of acacia wood covered with gold, standing in four silver sockets. [33] Hang the canopy from the fasteners in the ceiling, and put the ark containing the words of my promise under it. The canopy will mark off the most holy place from the holy place. [34] Put the throne of mercy that is on the ark in the most holy place.

[35] "Place the table outside the canopy on the north side of the inner tent, and put the lamp stand opposite the table on the south side.

[36] "For the entrance of the outer tent, make a screen out of fine linen yarn, embroidered with violet, purple, and bright red yarn. [37] Make five posts of acacia wood for the screen and cover them with gold. Make gold hooks for this screen. Cast five bronze bases for the posts."

The Altar—Exodus 38:1–7

27 [1] ˌThe LORD continued,ˌ "Make an altar out of acacia wood. It should be 7½ feet square, and 4½ feet high. [2] Make a horn at each of its four corners. The four horns and the altar must be made out of one piece ˌof woodˌ covered with bronze.

[3] "Make all the utensils for it out of bronze: pots for taking away the altar's ashes, also shovels, bowls, forks, and incense burners.

---

[a] 26:1 Or "a cherubim."   [b] 26:14 Hebrew meaning uncertain.   [c] 26:24 Or "These are to be separated at the bottom but held together at the top by a single ring."

⁴ "Make a grate for it out of bronze mesh, and make a bronze ring for ˍeach ofˍ the four corners of the grate. ⁵ Put the grate under the ledge of the altar so that it comes halfway up the altar.

⁶ "Make poles out of acacia wood for the altar, and cover them with bronze. ⁷ The poles should be put through the rings on both sides of the altar to carry it.

⁸ "Make the altar out of boards so that it's hollow inside. It must be made just as you were shown on the mountain.

The Courtyard—Exodus 38:9–20

⁹ "Make a courtyard for the tent. The south side of the courtyard should be 150 feet long and have curtains made out of fine linen yarn, ¹⁰ ˍhungˍ on 20 posts ˍset inˍ 20 bronze bases. The hooks and bands on the posts should be made of silver. ¹¹ The north side should be the same: 150 feet long, with curtains on 20 posts set in 20 bronze bases. The hooks and bands on the posts should be made of silver.

¹² "The courtyard on the west end should be 75 feet wide and have curtains ˍhungˍ on ten posts ˍset inˍ ten bases. ¹³ On the east end, facing the rising sun, the courtyard should also be 75 feet wide.

¹⁴⁻¹⁵ Each side ˍof the entranceˍ will be 22½ feet wide with curtains ˍhung onˍ three posts ˍset inˍ three bases.

¹⁶ "The entrance to the courtyard must have a 30-foot screen made from fine linen yarn, embroidered with violet, purple, and bright red yarn, ˍhungˍ on four posts ˍset inˍ four bases. ¹⁷ All the posts around the courtyard should have silver bands, silver hooks, and bronze bases. ¹⁸ The courtyard should be 150 feet long, 75 feet wide, and 7½ feet high, with ˍcurtainsˍ made of fine linen yarn and with bronze bases.

¹⁹ "All the things for the tent, no matter how they're used, including all the pegs for the tent and the courtyard, must be made of bronze.

Lamps in the Tent—Leviticus 24:1–4

²⁰ "For the lighting, you must command the Israelites to bring you pure, virgin olive oil so that the lamps won't go out. ²¹ In the tent of meeting outside the canopy where the words of my promise are, Aaron and his descendants must keep the lamps lit in the LORD'S presence from evening until morning. This is a permanent law among the Israelites for generations to come."

The Holy Clothes—Exodus 39:1

28 ¹ ˍThe LORD continued,ˍ "Out of all the Israelites, bring your brother Aaron and his sons Nadab, Abihu, Eleazar, and Ithamar to you. They will serve me as priests. ² Make holy clothes for your brother Aaron to give him dignity and honor.

³ "Tell all those who have the skill—those to whom I have given this ability—to make Aaron's clothes. These clothes will set him apart as holy when he serves me as priest. ⁴ These are the clothes they will make: a breastplate, an ephod and the robe that is worn with it, another specially woven linen robe, the chief priest's turban, and a cloth belt. They will make these holy clothes for your brother Aaron and his sons so that they can serve me as priests. ⁵ They must use gold, violet, purple, and bright red yarn, and fine linen.

The Ephod—Exodus 39:2–7

⁶ "Make the ephod out of fine linen yarn. Creatively work gold, violet, purple, and bright red yarn into the fabric. ⁷ It will have two shoulder straps attached at the ˍtopˍ corners so that it can be fastened. ⁸ Make the belt that is attached to the ephod out of the same fabric. ⁹ Take two onyx stones, and engrave on them the names of the sons of Israel ¹⁰ in birth order—six of their names on one stone and the remaining six on the other. ¹¹ Engrave the names of the sons of Israel on the two stones the same way a jeweler engraves a signet ring. Mount them in gold settings, ¹² and fasten them on the shoulder straps of the ephod as reminders of who the Israelites are. In this way Aaron will carry their names on his shoulders as a reminder in the LORD'S presence. ¹³ Make gold settings ¹⁴ and two chains of pure gold, twisted like ropes, and fasten these chains to the settings.

The Breastplate—Exodus 39:8–21

¹⁵ "Make the breastplate for decision-making as creatively as you make the ephod. Make it out of gold, violet, purple, and bright red yarn and out of fine linen yarn. ¹⁶ Fold it in half so that it's 9 inches square. ¹⁷ Fasten four rows of precious stones on it. In the first row put red quartz, topaz, and emerald. ¹⁸ In the second row put turquoise, sapphire, and crystal. ¹⁹ In the third row put jacinth, agate, and amethyst. ²⁰ In the fourth row put beryl, onyx, and gray quartz. Mount

them in gold settings. ²¹ The stones correspond to the 12 sons of Israel, by name, each stone engraved (like a signet ring) with the name of one of the 12 tribes.

²² "For the breastplate make chains out of pure gold, twisted like ropes. ²³ Make two gold rings for the breastplate. Attach them to the two ˎtopˎ corners of the breastplate. ²⁴ Then fasten the two gold ropes to the rings at the ˎtopˎ corners of the breastplate. ²⁵ Fasten the other ends of the ropes to the two settings on the shoulder straps of the ephod ˎso that the breastplate hangsˎ in front of it. ²⁶ Make two gold rings, and fasten them to the other two corners of the breastplate on the inside edge next to the ephod. ²⁷ Make two ˎmoreˎ gold rings, and fasten them to the bottom of the shoulder straps on the front of the ephod. This will be close to the seam just above the belt of the ephod. ²⁸ Then the breastplate should be fastened by its rings to the rings of the ephod with a violet cord. This will attach it just above the belt of the ephod and will hold the breastplate in place.

²⁹ "Whenever Aaron goes into the holy place, he will be carrying the names of the sons of Israel over his heart as a constant reminder in the LORD's presence. He must do this by wearing the breastplate for decision-making. ³⁰ Put the Urim and Thummim*ᵃ* into the breastplate for decision-making. They, too, will be over Aaron's heart when he comes into the LORD's presence. In this way whenever he's in the LORD's presence, Aaron will always be carrying over his heart the ˎmeans for determining the LORD'Sˎ decisions for the Israelites.

Other Clothes for Aaron and His Sons—Exodus 39:22–31

³¹ "Make the robe that is worn with the ephod entirely of violet material. ³² Make an opening for the head in the center with a reinforced edge (like a leather collar*ᵇ*) all around it to keep it from tearing. ³³ All around the hem of the robe make pomegranates of violet, purple, and bright red yarn with gold bells in between— ³⁴ a gold bell alternating with a pomegranate all around the hem of the robe. ³⁵ Aaron must wear it when he serves as priest. The sound of the bells must be heard when he comes into and goes out of the LORD's presence in the holy place so that he won't die.

³⁶ "Make a flower-shaped medallion out of pure gold, and engrave on it (as on a signet ring): Holy to the LORD. ³⁷ Fasten a violet cord to it, and tie it so that it's on the front of the turban. ³⁸ It will be on Aaron's forehead. He's the one to be blamed for anything done wrong when the Israelites bring their holy offerings—whatever their gifts may be. The medallion must always be on Aaron's forehead so that the LORD will accept their offerings.

³⁹ "Make the specially woven inner robe of fine linen. Make the turban of fine linen, but the belt should be embroidered with colored yarn.

⁴⁰ "Also make linen robes, belts, and turbans for Aaron's sons. These clothes will give them dignity and honor. ⁴¹ Put these clothes on your brother Aaron and his sons, anoint them, ordain them, and set them apart to serve me as priests.

⁴² "Make linen undergarments to cover them down to their thighs. ⁴³ Aaron and his sons must wear them when they go into the tent of meeting or when they come near the altar to serve as priests in the holy place. Then they will be blameless and won't die.

"This is a permanent law for him and his descendants."

Make Aaron and His Sons Priests—Leviticus 8:1–36

29 ¹ ˎThe LORD continued,ˎ "Now, this is what you must do in order to set Aaron and his sons apart to serve me as priests:

"Take a young bull that has no defects and two rams that have no defects. ² Use the finest wheat flour, but no yeast, and bake some loaves of bread, some rings of bread made with olive oil, and some wafers brushed with olive oil. ³ Put the bread in a basket, and bring the basket along with the young bull and the two rams.

⁴ "Then bring Aaron and his sons to the entrance of the tent of meeting, and wash them. ⁵ Take the clothes, and put them on Aaron—the linen robe, the ephod and the robe that is worn with it, and the breastplate. Use the belt to tie it on him tightly. ⁶ Put his turban on him, and fasten the holy crown to it. ⁷ Take the anointing oil, pour it on his head, and anoint him.

⁸ "Have his sons come forward. Dress them in their linen robes, ⁹ and put turbans on them. Tie belts around the waists of Aaron and his sons. They alone are to be priests; this is a permanent law. In this way you will ordain Aaron and his sons.

¹⁰ "Then bring the young bull to the front of the tent of meeting. Aaron and his sons will place their hands on its head. ¹¹ Slaughter the bull in the LORD's presence at the entrance to the tent of meeting. ¹² Take some of the bull's blood, and put it on the horns of the altar with your finger. Pour the rest of it out at the bottom of the altar.

ᵃ 28:30 The Urim and Thummim were used by the chief priest to determine God's answer to questions.
ᵇ 28:32 Hebrew meaning of "a leather collar" uncertain.

¹³ "Then take all the fat that covers the internal organs, the lobe of the liver, and the two kidneys with the fat on them, and burn them on the altar. ¹⁴ But burn the bull's meat, skin, and excrement outside the camp. It is an offering for sin.

¹⁵ "Take one of the rams. Then Aaron and his sons will place their hands on its head. ¹⁶ Slaughter it, take the blood, and throw it against the altar on all sides. ¹⁷ Cut the ram into pieces, wash the internal organs and legs, and put them with the other pieces and the head. ¹⁸ Then burn the whole ram on the altar. It's a burnt offering, a soothing aroma, an offering by fire to the LORD.

¹⁹ "Take the other ram. Then Aaron and his sons will place their hands on its head. ²⁰ Slaughter it, take some of the blood, and put it on the right ear lobes of Aaron and his sons, on their right thumbs, and on the big toes of their right feet. Throw the ˌrest of theˌ blood against the altar on all sides. ²¹ Take some of the blood that is on the altar and some of the anointing oil, and sprinkle it on Aaron and his clothes and on his sons and their clothes. In this way Aaron, his sons, and their clothes will be holy.

²² "From this ˌsameˌ ram take the fat, the fat from the tail, the fat that covers the internal organs, the lobe of the liver, the two kidneys with the fat on them, and the right thigh. (This is the ram for the ordination.) ²³ From the basket of unleavened bread which is in the LORD'S presence, take a round loaf of bread, a ring of bread made with olive oil, and a wafer. ²⁴ Put all of these in the hands of Aaron and his sons, who will offer them to the LORD. ²⁵ Then take them from their hands, and burn them on the altar on top of the burnt offering. It's a soothing aroma in the LORD'S presence, an offering by fire to the LORD.

²⁶ "Take the breast from the ram used for Aaron's ordination, and present it to the LORD. This will be your share. ²⁷ Set apart as holy the breast that is offered to the LORD and the thigh that is the contribution. Both will come from the ram used for the ordination. They both belong to Aaron and his sons. ²⁸ It is a permanent law that the Israelites give this portion to Aaron and his sons as a contribution. This will also be their contribution to the LORD from the fellowship offerings.

²⁹ "Aaron's holy clothes will belong to his descendants so that they can be anointed and ordained in them. ³⁰ The son who succeeds him as priest—the one who goes into the tent of meeting to serve in the holy place—will wear them for seven days.

³¹ "Take the ram used for the ordination, and boil its meat in a holy place. ³² At the entrance to the tent of meeting, Aaron and his sons will eat the meat of the ram and the bread ˌleftˌ in the basket. ³³ They will eat those offerings through which they made peace with the LORD at their ordination and installation. No one else may eat them because the offerings are holy. ³⁴ If any meat or bread from the ordination is left over until morning, burn it up. It must not be eaten because it is holy.

³⁵ "Do this with Aaron and his sons exactly as I have commanded you. Take seven days to ordain them. ³⁶ Each day sacrifice a young bull as an offering to make peace with the LORD. Sacrifice this offering for sin on the altar in order to pay for its sins. Then anoint it ˌwith olive oilˌ in order to dedicate it. ³⁷ For seven days at the altar make peace with the LORD and set the altar apart for its holy purpose. Then the altar will be most holy. Anything that touches the altar will become holy.

³⁸ "This is what you are to offer on the altar regularly every day: two one-year-old lambs. ³⁹ Offer one in the morning and the other at dusk. ⁴⁰ With the first lamb make an offering of eight cups of flour mixed with one quart of virgin olive oil. Make a wine offering of one quart of wine. ⁴¹ Offer the other lamb at dusk, and with it make the same grain offering and wine offering as in the morning. This is a soothing aroma, an offering by fire to the LORD.

⁴² "For generations to come this will be the daily burnt offering ˌmadeˌ in the LORD'S presence at the entrance to the tent of meeting. There I will meet with you to speak to you. ⁴³ I will also meet with the Israelites there, and my glory will make this place holy. ⁴⁴ I will dedicate the tent of meeting and the altar for their holy purposes. I will set Aaron and his sons apart for their holy duties of serving me as priests.

⁴⁵ "Then I will live among the Israelites and be their God. ⁴⁶ They will know that I am the LORD their God. I brought them out of Egypt so that I might live among them. I am the LORD their God."

The Altar for Incense—*Exodus 37:25–29*

30 ¹ ˌThe LORD continued,ˌ "Build an altar out of acacia wood for burning incense. ² Make it 18 inches square and 36 inches high. The horns and altar must be made out of one piece ˌof woodˌ. ³ Cover all of it with pure gold—the top, the sides, and the horns. Put a gold molding around it. ⁴ Make two gold rings, and put them below the molding on opposite sides to hold the poles for carrying it. ⁵ Make the poles out of acacia wood, and cover them with gold. [6] Put the altar in front of the canopy which ˏhangsˏ over the ark containing the words of my promise. I will meet with you there in front of the throne of mercy that is on the ark.

[7] "Aaron must burn sweet-smelling incense on this altar every morning when he takes care of the lamps. [8] Also, when Aaron lights the lamps at dusk, he must burn incense. For generations to come an incense offering must burn constantly in the LORD's presence.

[9] "Never burn any unauthorized incense on this altar or any burnt offerings or grain offerings. Never pour a wine offering on it. [10] Once a year Aaron must make peace with the LORD by putting blood on its horns. Once a year—for generations to come—blood from the offering must be placed on the altar to make peace with the LORD. It is most holy to the LORD."

Counting the Israelites

[11] Then the LORD said to Moses, [12] "When you take a census of the Israelites, each person must pay the LORD a ransom for his life when he is counted. Then no plague will happen to them when they are counted. [13] As each person is counted, he must give one-fifth of an ounce of silver using the standard weight of the holy place.[a] This one-fifth of an ounce of silver is a contribution to the LORD. [14] Everyone counted who is at least 20 years old must give this contribution to the LORD. [15] The rich must not give more than one-fifth of an ounce of silver, and the poor must not give less. This contribution is given to make peace with the LORD and make your lives acceptable to the LORD. [16] Take the money the Israelites give to make peace with the LORD, and use it to pay the expenses of the tent of meeting. It will be a reminder for the Israelites in the LORD's presence that the sins in their lives are removed."

The Bronze Basin—Exodus 38:8

[17] The LORD said to Moses, [18] "Make a bronze basin with a bronze stand for washing. Put it between the tent of meeting and the altar, and fill it with water. [19] Aaron and his sons will use it for washing their hands and feet. [20] Before they go into the tent of meeting, they must wash so that they will not die. Before they come near the altar to serve as priests and burn an offering by fire to the LORD, [21] they will wash their hands and feet so that they will not die. This will be a permanent law for him and his descendants for generations to come."

The Oil for Anointing

[22] The LORD said to Moses, [23] "Take the finest spices: 12½ pounds of powdered[b] myrrh; half as much, that is, 6¼ pounds of fragrant cinnamon; 6¼ pounds of fragrant cane; [24] 12½ pounds of cassia-all weighed using the standard weight of the holy place—and 4 quarts of olive oil. [25] Have a perfumer make these into a holy oil, a fragrant mixture, used only for anointing. This will be the holy oil used for anointing.

[26] "Use it to anoint the tent of meeting, the ark containing the words of my promise, [27] the table and all the dishes, the lamp stand and all the utensils, the altar for incense, [28] the altar for burnt offerings and all its accessories, and the basin with its stand. [29] In this way you will dedicate them for their holy purpose. Then they will be most holy, and anything that touches them will become holy. [30] Anoint Aaron and his sons as well. In this way you will set them apart for their holy duties of serving me as priests.

[31] "Say to the Israelites, 'For generations to come, this will be my holy oil used only for anointing. [32] It must never be poured on the bodies of other people. Never make any perfumed oil using this formula. It is holy, and you must treat it as holy. [33] Whoever prepares a perfume like this or puts it on anyone who is not a priest must be excluded from the people.' "

The Incense for Use in the Tent

[34] The LORD said to Moses, "Take one part fragrant spices (two kinds of gum resin and aromatic mollusk shells), and mix them with one part pure frankincense. [35] Have a perfumer make it into fragrant incense, seasoned with salt, pure and holy. [36] Grind some of it into a fine powder, and put it in front of ˏthe ark containingˏ the words of my promise in the tent of meeting, where I will meet with you. You must treat it as most holy. [37] Never make any incense for yourselves using this formula. Treat it as holy to the LORD. [38] Whoever prepares anything like it for his own enjoyment must be excluded from his people."

The Craftsmen for the Tent—Exodus 35:30–35

31 [1] The LORD said to Moses, [2] "I have chosen Bezalel, son of Uri and grandson of Hur, from the tribe of Judah. [3] I have filled Bezalel with the Spirit of God, making him highly skilled, resourceful, and knowledgeable in all trades. [4] He's a master artist familiar with gold, silver, and bronze. [5] He knows how to cut and set stones and how to work with wood. He's an expert in all trades. [6] Also, I have appointed Oholiab, son of Ahisamach, from the tribe of Dan,

---

[a] 30:13 Hebrew adds, "There are 20 gerahs to the standard shekel."   [b] 30:23 Or "liquid."

to help him. I have given every craftsman the skill necessary to make everything I have commanded you: [7] the tent of meeting, the ark containing the words of my promise with the throne of mercy on it, and all the ˌotherˌ furnishings for the tent, [8] the table and the dishes, the pure ˌgoldˌ lamp stand and all its utensils, the altar for incense, [9] the altar for burnt offerings and all its accessories, the basin with its stand, [10] the special[a] clothes—the holy clothes for the priest Aaron and the clothes for his sons when they serve as priests, [11] the anointing oil, and the sweet-smelling incense for the holy place. They will make all these things as I commanded you."

The Sign Between the LORD and His People

[12] The LORD said to Moses, [13] "Say to the Israelites, 'Be sure to observe my days of worship. This will be a sign between me and you for generations to come so that you will know that I am the LORD who makes you holy.

[14] " 'Observe the day of worship because it is holy to you. Whoever treats it like any other day must be put to death. Whoever works on that day must be excluded from the people. [15] You may work for six days, but the seventh day is a day of worship, a day when you don't work. It is holy to the LORD. Whoever works on that day must be put to death. [16] The Israelites must observe this day of worship, celebrating it for generations to come as a permanent reminder of my promise.[b] [17] It will be a permanent sign between me and the Israelites, because the LORD made heaven and earth in six days, and on the seventh day he stopped working and was refreshed.' "

[18] The LORD finished speaking to Moses on Mount Sinai. Then he gave him the two tablets with his words on them, stone tablets inscribed by God himself.

The Gold Calf

32 [1] When the people saw that Moses delayed coming down from the mountain, they gathered around Aaron. They said to him, "We don't know what has happened to this Moses, who led us out of Egypt. Make gods who will lead us."

[2] Aaron said to them, "Have your wives, sons, and daughters take off the gold earrings they are wearing, and bring them to me."

[3] So all the people took off their gold earrings and handed them to Aaron. [4] After he had worked on the gold with a tool,[a] he made it into a statue of a calf.

Then they said, "Israel, here are your gods who brought you out of Egypt."

[5] When Aaron saw this, he built an altar in front of it and announced, "Tomorrow there will be a festival in the LORD's honor."

[6] Early the next day the people sacrificed burnt offerings and brought fellowship offerings. Afterward, they sat down to a feast, which turned into an orgy.

[7] The LORD said to Moses, "Go back down there. Your people whom you brought out of Egypt have ruined ˌeverythingˌ. [8] They've already turned from the way I commanded them to live. They've made a statue of a calf for themselves. They've bowed down to it and offered sacrifices to it. They've said, 'Israel, here are your gods who brought you out of Egypt.' "

[9] The LORD added, "I've seen these people, and they are impossible to deal with. [10] Now leave me alone. I'm so angry with them I am going to destroy them. Then I'll make you into a great nation."

[11] But Moses pleaded with the LORD his God. "LORD," he said, "why are you so angry with your people whom you brought out of Egypt using your great power and mighty hand? [12] Don't let the Egyptians say, 'He was planning all along to kill them in the mountains and wipe them off the face of the earth. That's why he brought them out ˌof our landˌ.' Don't be so angry. Reconsider your decision to bring this disaster on your people. [13] Remember your servants Abraham, Isaac, and Israel. You took an oath, swearing on yourself. You told them, 'I will make your descendants as numerous as the stars in the sky. I will give to your descendants all the land I spoke of. It will be their permanent possession.' "

[14] So the LORD reconsidered his threat to destroy his people.

[15] Moses turned and went down the mountain carrying the two tablets with God's words. They were written on both sides, front and back. [16] The tablets were the work of God, and the writing was God's writing inscribed on the tablets.

[17] Then Joshua heard the noise of the people shouting. He said to Moses, "It's the sound of war in the camp!"

[18] Moses replied,

"It's not the sound of winners shouting.
　　It's not the sound of losers crying.
　　　　It's the sound of a wild celebration[b] that I hear."

---

[a] 31:10 Greek, Syriac, Targum; Hebrew meaning uncertain.　　[b] 31:16 Or "covenant."　　[a] 32:4 Hebrew meaning uncertain.
[b] 32:18 Hebrew meaning of "wild celebration" uncertain.

[19] When he came near the camp, he saw the calf and the dancing. In a burst of anger Moses threw down the tablets and smashed them at the foot of the mountain. [20] Then he took the calf they had made, burned it, ground it into powder, scattered it on the water, and made the Israelites drink it.

[21] Moses asked Aaron, "What did these people do to you that you encouraged them to commit such a serious sin?"

[22] "Don't be angry, sir," Aaron answered. "You know that these people are evil. [23] They said to me, 'We don't know what's happened to this Moses who brought us out of Egypt. Make gods for us. They will lead us.' [24] So I told them to take off any gold they were wearing. They gave it to me. I threw it into the fire, and out came this calf!"

[25] Aaron had let the people get out of control, and they became an object of ridicule to their enemies. When Moses saw this, [26] he stood at the entrance to the camp and said, "If you're on the LORD's side, come over here to me!" Then all the Levites gathered around him.

[27] He said to them, "This is what the LORD God of Israel says: Each of you put on your sword. Go back and forth from one end of the camp to the other, and kill your relatives, friends, and neighbors."

[28] The Levites did what Moses told them, and that day about 3,000 people died.

[29] Moses said, "Today you are ordained as the LORD's priests. God gave you a blessing today because each of you fought with your own sons and brothers."[c]

Moses Begs the LORD to Spare the People

[30] The next day Moses said to the people, "You have committed a serious sin. Now I will go up the mountain to the LORD. Maybe I will be able to make a payment for your sin and make peace with the LORD for your sin."

[31] So Moses went back to the LORD and said, "These people have committed such a serious sin! They made gods out of gold for themselves. [32] But will you forgive their sin? If not, please wipe me out of the book you have written."

[33] The LORD answered Moses, "I will wipe out of my book whoever sins against me. [34] Now, go! Lead the people to the place I told you about. My Messenger will go ahead of you. But when I punish, I will punish them for their sin."

[35] So the LORD killed people because they had Aaron make the calf.

The LORD Assures Moses That He Will Have Mercy on Israel

33 [1] Then the LORD said to Moses, "You and the people you brought out of Egypt must leave this place. Go to the land I promised to Abraham, Isaac, and Jacob with an oath, saying, 'I will give it to your descendants.' [2] I will send a Messenger ahead of you, and I will force out the Canaanites, Amorites, Hittites, Perizzites, Hivites, and Jebusites. [3] Go to that land flowing with milk and honey. But I will not be with you, because you are impossible to deal with, and I would destroy you on the way."

[4] When the people heard this bad news, they acted as if someone had died. No one wore any jewelry. [5] The LORD had said to Moses, "Tell the Israelites, 'You are impossible to deal with. If I were with you, I might destroy you at any time. Now take off your jewelry, and I'll decide what to do with you.' " [6] After they left Mount Horeb, the Israelites no longer wore their jewelry.

[7] Now, Moses used to take a tent and set it up far outside the camp. He called it the tent of meeting. Anyone who was seeking the LORD's will used to go outside the camp to the tent of meeting. [8] Whenever Moses went out to the tent, all the people would rise and stand at the entrances to their tents and watch Moses until he went in. [9] As soon as Moses went into the tent, the column of smoke would come down and stay at the entrance to the tent while the LORD spoke with Moses. [10] When all the people saw the column of smoke standing at the entrance to the tent, they would all bow with their faces touching the ground at the entrance to their own tents. [11] The LORD would speak to Moses personally, as a man speaks to his friend. Then Moses would come back to the camp, but his assistant, Joshua, son of Nun, stayed inside the tent.

[12] Moses said to the LORD, "You've been telling me to lead these people, but you haven't let me know whom you're sending with me. You've also said, 'I know you by name, and I'm pleased with you.' [13] If you really are pleased with me, show me your ways so that I can know you and so that you will continue to be pleased with me. Remember: This nation is your people."

[14] The LORD answered, "My presence will go ˻with you,˼ and I will give you peace."

---

[c] 32:29 Or "God gave you a blessing today at the cost of your own sons and brothers."

¹⁵ Then Moses said to him, "If your presence is not going ˛with us˛, don't make us leave this place. ¹⁶ How will anyone ever know you're pleased with your people and me unless you go with us? Then we will be different from all other people on the face of the earth."

¹⁷ The LORD answered Moses, "I will do what you have asked, because I am pleased with you, and I know you by name."

¹⁸ Then Moses said, "Please let me see your glory."

¹⁹ The LORD said, "I will let all my goodness pass in front of you, and there I will call out my name 'the LORD.' I will be kind to anyone I want to. I will be merciful to anyone I want to. ²⁰ But you can't see my face, because no one may see me and live."

²¹ Then the LORD said, "Look, there's a place near me. Stand by this rocky cliff. ²² When my glory passes by, I will put you in a crevice in the cliff and cover you with my hand until I have passed by. ²³ Then I will take my hand away, and you'll see my back, but my face must not be seen."

The LORD Meets With Moses on the Mountain

34 ¹ The LORD said to Moses, "Cut two ˛more˛ stone tablets like the first ones, and I will write on them the words that were on the first tablets which you smashed. ² Be ready in the morning. Then come up on Mount Sinai, and stand in my presence on the top of the mountain. ³ No one may come with you or even be seen anywhere on the mountain. Even the flocks and herds may not graze in front of this mountain."

⁴ So Moses cut two ˛more˛ stone tablets like the first ones. Early the next morning he went up on Mount Sinai, as the LORD had commanded him, carrying the two stone tablets.

⁵ The LORD came down in a cloud and stood there with him and called out his name "the LORD."

⁶ Then he passed in front of Moses, calling out, "The LORD, the LORD, a compassionate and merciful God, patient, always faithful and ready to forgive. ⁷ He continues to show his love to thousands of generations, forgiving wrongdoing, disobedience, and sin. He never lets the guilty go unpunished, punishing children and grandchildren for their parents' sins to the third and fourth generation."

⁸ Immediately, Moses knelt, bowing with his face touching the ground. ⁹ Then he said, "Lord, please go with us! Even though we are impossible to deal with, forgive our sin and the wrong we have done, and accept us as your own people."

The LORD Makes His Promise With Israel Again

¹⁰ The LORD said, "I'm making my promise[a] again. In front of all your people I will perform miracles that have never been done in any other nation in all the world. All the people around you will see how awesome these miracles are that I will perform for you. ¹¹ Do everything that I command today. Then I will force the Amorites, Canaanites, Hittites, Perizzites, Hivites, and Jebusites out of your way. ¹² Be careful not to make a treaty with those who live in the land where you're going. This will prove to be a trap to you. ¹³ But tear down their altars, crush their sacred stones, and cut down their poles dedicated to the goddess Asherah. ¹⁴ (Never worship any other god, because the LORD is a God who does not tolerate rivals. In fact, he is known for not tolerating rivals.) ¹⁵ Be careful not to make a treaty with those who live in that land. When they chase after their gods as though they were prostitutes and sacrifice to them, they may invite you to eat the meat from their sacrifices with them. ¹⁶ Then your sons will end up marrying their daughters. When their daughters chase after their gods as though they were prostitutes, they'll lead your sons to do the same thing.

¹⁷ "Never make an idol.

¹⁸ "You must celebrate the Festival of Unleavened Bread. As I commanded you, you must eat unleavened bread for seven days at the appointed time in the month of Abib, because in that month you came out of Egypt.

¹⁹ "Every first male offspring is mine, even the firstborn males[b] of all your livestock, whether cattle, sheep, or goats. ²⁰ It will cost you a sheep or a goat to buy back the firstborn donkey. If you don't buy it back, then you must break the donkey's neck. You must buy back every firstborn of your sons.

"No one may come into my presence without an offering.

²¹ "You may work six days, but on the seventh day you must not work. Even during the time of plowing or harvesting you must not work ˛on this day˛.

²² "You must celebrate the Festival of Weeks with the first grain from your wheat harvest, and the Festival of the Final Harvest at the end of the season.

²³ "Three times a year all your men must come into the presence of the Master, the LORD God of Israel. ²⁴ I will force nations out of your way and will expand ˛your country's˛ borders. No one will want to take away your land while you're gone three times a year to the LORD's festivals.

---

[a] 34:10 Or "covenant."   [b] 34:19 Greek, Latin; Hebrew meaning of the Masoretic Text uncertain.

²⁵ "Never offer the blood of a sacrifice to me at the same time you offer anything containing yeast. No part of the sacrifice at the Passover festival should be left over in the morning. ²⁶ "You must bring the first and best of the produce harvested from your soil to the house of the LORD your God.

"Never cook a young goat in its mother's milk."

²⁷ Then the LORD said to Moses, "Write down these words, because on the basis of these words I'm making a promise to Israel and to you." ²⁸ Moses was there with the LORD 40 days and 40 nights without food or water. He wrote on the tablets the words of the promise, the ten commandments.

Moses Returns to the People

²⁹ Moses came down from Mount Sinai, carrying the two tablets with God's words on them. His face was shining from speaking with the LORD, but he didn't know it.

³⁰ When Aaron and all the Israelites looked at Moses and saw his face shining, they were afraid to come near him. ³¹ Moses called to them, so Aaron and all the leaders of the community came back to him. Then Moses spoke to them. ³² After that, all the other Israelites came near him, and he commanded them to do everything the LORD told him on Mount Sinai. ³³ When Moses finished speaking to them, he put a veil over his face. ³⁴ But whenever Moses went into the LORD'S presence to speak with him, he took off the veil until he came out. Whenever he came out and told the Israelites what he had been commanded, ³⁵ they would see that Moses' face was shining. Then Moses would put the veil back on until he went in again to speak with the LORD.

Rules About the Day of Worship

35 ¹ Moses assembled the whole Israelite community and said to them, "These are the things the LORD has commanded you to do: ² You may work for six days, but the seventh day is a holy day of worship, a day when you don't work. It is dedicated to the LORD. Whoever does any work on this day should be put to death. ³ Never light a fire in any of your homes on this day of worship."

The People Contribute Their Wealth—Exodus 25:1–7

⁴ Then Moses said to the whole Israelite community, "This is what the LORD has commanded: ⁵ Choose something of your own to give as a special contribution to the LORD. Let everyone who is willing bring this kind of contribution to the LORD: gold, silver, and bronze, ⁶ violet, purple, and bright red yarn, fine linen, goats' hair, ⁷ rams' skins dyed red, fine leather,ᵃ acacia wood, ⁸ olive oil for the lamps, spices for the anointing oil and for the sweet-smelling incense, ⁹ onyx stones, and other precious stones to be set in the ˌchief priest'sˌ ephodᵇ and breastplate.

The Craftsmen for the Tent—Exodus 31:2–6

¹⁰ "Have all the skilled craftsmen among you come and make everything the LORD has commanded: ¹¹ the inner tent, the outer tent, and cover, along with the fasteners, frames, crossbars, posts, and sockets, ¹² the ark with its poles, the throne of mercy and the canopy over it, ¹³ the table with its poles, all the dishes, the bread of the presence, ¹⁴ the lamp stand used for the light with its utensils, its lamps and the olive oil for the lamps, ¹⁵ the altar for incense with its poles, the anointing oil, the sweet-smelling incense, the screen for the entrance to the tent, ¹⁶ the altar for burnt offerings with its bronze grate, its poles, and all its accessories, the basin with its stand, ¹⁷ the curtains for the courtyard, the posts, bases, and the screen for the entrance to the courtyard, ¹⁸ the pegs for the tent and the courtyard with their ropes, ¹⁹ the special clothesᵃ worn for official duties in the holy place—both the holy clothes for Aaron the priest and the clothes for his sons when they serve as priests."

²⁰ Then the whole Israelite community left Moses. ²¹ Those who were willing and whose hearts moved them came and brought their contributions to the LORD. The gifts were used to construct the tent of meeting, to pay other expenses, and to make the holy clothes. ²² All who were willing—men and women alike—came and brought all kinds of gold jewelry: pins,ᵃ earrings, signet rings, and pendants. They took these gifts of gold and offered them to the LORD. ²³ Those who had violet, purple, or bright red yarn, fine linen, goats' hair, rams' skins dyed red, or fine leather brought them. ²⁴ Those who could give silver or bronze brought it as their contribution to the LORD. Those who had acacia wood that could be used in the construction brought it. ²⁵ All the women who were skilled in spinning yarn brought violet, purple, and bright red yarn, and fine linen, which they had made by hand. ²⁶ All the women who were willing and

---

ᵃ 35:7, 19, 22 Hebrew meaning uncertain.   ᵇ 35:9 Ephod is a technical term for a part of the priest's clothes. Its exact usage and shape are unknown.

had the skill spun the goats' hair. [27] The leaders brought onyx stones and other precious stones to be set in the ˌchief priest'sˌ ephod and breastplate. [28] They also brought the spices and the olive oil for the lamps, the anointing oil, and the sweet-smelling incense. [29] Every Israelite man and woman who was willing brought all these items to the LORD as a freewill offering. They brought these items to be used to make everything the LORD had commanded through Moses.

[30] Then Moses said to the Israelites, "The LORD has chosen Bezalel, son of Uri and grandson of Hur, from the tribe of Judah. [31] The LORD has filled Bezalel with the Spirit of God, making him highly skilled, resourceful, and knowledgeable in all trades. [32] He's a master artist familiar with gold, silver, and bronze. [33] He knows how to cut and set stones and how to work with wood. He's an expert in all trades. [34] Also, the LORD has given Bezalel and Oholiab, son of Ahisamach, from the tribe of Dan the ability to teach others. [35] The LORD has made these men highly skilled in all trades. They can do the work of jewelers, carpenters, and designers. They know how to embroider violet, purple and bright red yarn on fine linen. They know how to weave yarn on a loom. They can do all kinds of trades. They are master artists."

36 [1] ˌMoses continued,ˌ "So Bezalel and Oholiab will do the work as the LORD has commanded. They will do this with the help of every other craftsman to whom the LORD has given the necessary skills and talents. They will know how to do all the work for constructing the holy place."

[2] Moses called Bezalel and Oholiab and every other craftsman to whom the LORD had given these skills and who was willing to come and do the work.

Excess Contributions

[3] Moses turned over to them all the contributions the Israelites had brought for the work of constructing the holy place. But the people still kept bringing him freewill offerings every morning. [4] Finally, all the skilled craftsmen who were working on the holy place stopped what they were doing. They all came to Moses. [5] They said, "The people are bringing much more than we need for doing the work the LORD commanded us to do."

[6] So Moses gave instructions to have the following message announced all over camp: "No man or woman needs to make anything more to give as their special contribution to the holy place." Then the people stopped bringing gifts. [7] The material they had was more than enough to do the job.

The Tent—*Exodus 26:1–37*

[8] All the skilled craftsmen among the workers made the inner tent with ten sheets made from fine linen yarn and violet, purple, and bright red yarn. An angel[a] design was creatively worked into the fabric. [9] Each sheet was 42 feet long and 6 feet wide—all the same size. [10] Five of the sheets were sewn together, and the other five were also sewn together. [11] Then they made 50 violet loops along the edge of the end sheet in each set, [12] placing the loops opposite each other. [13] They also made 50 gold fasteners. They used them to link the ˌtwo sets ofˌ sheets together so that the inner tent was a single unit.

[14] They made 11 sheets of goats' hair to form an outer tent over the inner tent. [15] Each of the 11 sheets was 45 feet long and 6 feet wide. [16] Five of the sheets were sewn together into one set, and the remaining six into another set. [17] Then they made 50 loops along the edge of the end sheet in each set. [18] They also made 50 bronze fasteners to link the inner tent together as a single unit. [19] They made a cover out of rams' skins that had been dyed red for the outer tent, and over that they put a cover made of fine leather.[b]

[20] They made a framework out of acacia wood for the inner tent. [21] Each frame was 15 feet long and 27 inches wide, [22] with two identical pegs. They made all the frames for the inner tent this same way. [23] They made 20 frames for the south side of the inner tent. [24] Then they made 40 silver sockets at the bottom of the 20 frames, two sockets at the bottom of each frame for the two pegs. [25] For the north side of the inner tent ˌthey made,ˌ 20 frames [26] and 40 silver sockets, two at the bottom of each frame. [27] They made six frames for the far end, the west side. [28] They made two frames for ˌeach ofˌ the corners at the far end of the inner tent. [29] They were held together at the bottom and held tightly at the top by a single ring.[c] Both corner frames were made this way. [30] There were eight frames with 16 silver sockets, two at the bottom of each frame.

[31] They also made crossbars out of acacia wood. Five were for the frames on one side of the inner tent, [32] five were for those on the other side, and five were for the frames on the far side of the inner tent, the west side. [33] They made the middle crossbar so that it ran from one end to the other, halfway up the frames. [34] They covered the frames with gold and made gold rings to hold the crossbars. They also covered the crossbars with gold.

---

[a] 36:8 Or "A cherubim."   [b] 36:19 Hebrew meaning uncertain.   [c] 36:29 Or "These were separated at the bottom but held together at the top by a single ring."

[35] They made the canopy out of violet, purple, and bright red yarn and fine linen yarn. An angel design was creatively worked into the fabric. [36] They made four posts of acacia wood for it and covered them with gold. They made gold hooks for the posts, and they cast four silver bases for them. [37] They made a screen out of fine linen yarn for the entrance to the outer tent. It was embroidered with violet, purple, and bright red yarn. [38] They also made five posts with hooks for hanging the screen. They covered the tops of the posts and the bands with gold, but the five bases for the posts were made of bronze.

The Ark—*Exodus 25:10–20*

37 [1] Bezalel made the ark out of acacia wood 45 inches long, 27 inches wide, and 27 inches high. [2] He covered it with pure gold inside and out and put a gold molding around it. [3] He cast four gold rings for its four feet, two rings on each side. [4] Then he made poles out of acacia wood and covered them with gold. [5] He put them through the rings on the sides of the ark in order to carry it.

[6] He made the throne of mercy out of pure gold 45 inches long and 27 inches wide. [7] Then he made two angels[a] out of hammered gold for the two ends of the throne of mercy, [8] one on each end. He formed the angels and the throne of mercy out of one piece of gold. [9] The angels had their wings spread above the throne of mercy, overshadowing it. They faced each other, looking at the throne of mercy.

The Table—*Exodus 25:23–30*

[10] He made the table out of acacia wood 36 inches long, 18 inches wide, and 27 inches high. [11] He covered it with pure gold and put a gold molding around it. [12] He made a rim 3 inches wide around it and put a gold molding around the rim. [13] He cast four gold rings for it and fastened the rings to the four corners, where the four legs were. [14] The rings were put close to the rim to hold the poles for carrying the table. [15] These poles were made out of acacia wood and were covered with gold. [16] For the table he made plates, dishes, bowls, and pitchers to be used for pouring wine offerings. All of them were made out of pure gold.

The Lamp Stand—*Exodus 25:31–39*

[17] He made the lamp stand out of pure gold. The lamp stand, its base, and its shaft, as well as the flower cups, buds, and petals were hammered out of one piece of gold. [18] Six branches came out of its sides, three branches on one side and three on the other. [19] Each of the six branches coming out of the lamp stand had three flower cups shaped like almond blossoms, with buds and petals. [20] The lamp stand itself had four flower cups shaped like almond blossoms, each with a bud and petals. [21] There was a bud under each of the three pairs of branches coming out of the lamp stand. [22] The buds and branches were hammered out of the same piece of pure gold as the lamp stand.

[23] He made the seven lamps, the tongs, and the incense burners out of pure gold. [24] The lamp stand and all the utensils were made out of 75 pounds of pure gold.

The Altar for Incense—*Exodus 30:1–5*

[25] He made an altar out of acacia wood for burning incense. It was 18 inches square and 36 inches high. The horns and altar were made out of one piece of wood. [26] He covered all of it with pure gold—the top, the sides, and the horns—and he put a gold molding around it. [27] He made two gold rings and put them below the molding on opposite sides to hold the poles for carrying it. [28] He made the poles out of acacia wood and covered them with gold.

[29] He also had a perfumer make the holy oil to be used for anointing and for the pure, sweet-smelling incense.

The Altar for Burnt Offerings—*Exodus 27:1–8*

38 [1] He made the altar for burnt offerings out of acacia wood 7½ feet square and 4½ feet high. [2] He made a horn at each of its four corners. He made the four horns and the altar out of one piece of wood covered with bronze. [3] He made all the utensils out of bronze: pots, shovels, forks, and incense burners. [4] He made a grate for the altar out of bronze mesh, and put it under the ledge, halfway up the altar. [5] He cast four rings to hold the poles (one for each of the four corners of the bronze grate). [6] He made the poles out of acacia wood and covered them with bronze. [7] He put the poles through the rings on the sides of the altar to carry it. He made the altar out of boards so that it was hollow inside.

---

[a] 37:7 Or "cherubim."

The Bronze Basin—Exodus 30:17–21

⁸ He made the basin and stand out of the bronze mirrors given by the women who served at the entrance to the tent of meeting.

The Courtyard—Exodus 27:9–19

⁹ He also made the courtyard. The south side of the courtyard was 150 feet long and had curtains made out of fine linen yarn, ¹⁰ ‚hung‚ on 20 posts ‚set in‚ 20 bronze bases. The hooks and bands on the posts were made of silver. ¹¹ The north side was also 150 feet long with 20 posts and 20 bronze bases. The hooks and bands on the posts were made of silver. ¹² The west side was 75 feet long and had curtains ‚hung‚ on 10 posts ‚set in‚ 10 bases. The hooks and bands on the posts were made of silver. ¹³ The east side, facing the rising sun, was 75 feet ‚wide‚.

¹⁴⁻¹⁵ Each side of the entrance to the courtyard was 22½ feet wide with curtains ‚hung‚ on three posts ‚set in‚ three bases. ¹⁶ All the curtains around the courtyard were made out of fine linen yarn. ¹⁷ The bases for the posts were made of bronze. The hooks and bands on the posts were made of silver. The tops of the posts were covered with silver. And the bands on all the posts of the courtyard were made of silver.

¹⁸ The screen for the entrance to the courtyard was made of violet, purple, and bright red yarn embroidered on ‚fabric made from‚ fine linen yarn. It was 30 feet long and 7½ feet high, just like the curtains of the courtyard. ¹⁹ It was hung on four posts ‚set in‚ four bronze bases. The hooks and bands on the posts were made of silver. The tops of the posts were covered with silver.

²⁰ All the pegs for the tent and the surrounding courtyard were made of bronze.

The Amount of Gold, Silver, and Bronze Used

²¹ This is the amount of material that was used for the tent (the tent of the words of God's promise). An inventory was ordered by Moses and carried out by the Levites under the direction of Ithamar, son of the priest Aaron.

²² Now Bezalel, son of Uri and grandson of Hur, from the tribe of Judah, made everything the LORD had commanded Moses. ²³ He was a jeweler, carpenter, designer, and he knew how to embroider violet, purple, and bright red yarn on fine linen. His assistant was Oholiab, son of Ahisamach, from the tribe of Dan.

²⁴ The total amount of gold from the offerings presented to the LORD used in building the holy place weighed over 2,193 pounds, using the standard weight of the holy place.

²⁵ The silver collected when the census of the community was taken weighed 7,544 pounds using the standard weight of the holy place. ²⁶ This came to one-fifth of an ounce per person, for everyone counted who was at least 20 years old: 603,550 people. ²⁷ He used 7,500 pounds of silver to cast the 100 bases for the holy place and the canopy. This was 75 pounds per base. ²⁸ He used 44 pounds of silver to make the hooks and bands for the posts and the coverings for the tops of the posts.

²⁹ The bronze from the offerings presented to the LORD weighed 5,310 pounds. ³⁰ With this he made the bases for the entrance to the tent of meeting, the bronze altar with its bronze grate and all its accessories, ³¹ the bases all around the courtyard, the bases for the entrance to the courtyard, all the pegs for the tent, and all the pegs for the surrounding courtyard.

The Holy Clothes—Exodus 28:1–5

39 ¹ From the violet, purple, and bright red yarn they made special clothes worn for official duties in the holy place. They also made the holy clothes for Aaron. They followed the LORD's instructions to Moses.

The Ephod—Exodus 28:6–14

² They made the ephod out of fine linen yarn and gold, violet, purple, and bright red yarn. ³ They hammered the gold into thin sheets and cut them up. They twisted the gold into threads, which they creatively worked into each strand of the violet, purple, and bright red yarn, and throughout the fine linen. ⁴ They made two shoulder straps attached at the ‚top‚ corners so that the ephod could be fastened. ⁵ They made the belt that is attached to the ephod out of the same fabric. They followed the LORD'S instructions to Moses. ⁶ They mounted the onyx stones in gold settings, and engraved on them the names of the sons of Israel. ⁷ Then they fastened them on the shoulder straps of the ephod as a reminder of who the Israelites are. They followed the LORD'S instructions to Moses.

The Breastplate—Exodus 28:15–28

⁸ They made the breastplate as creatively as they made the ephod. It was made out of gold, violet, purple, and bright red yarn, and of fine linen yarn. ⁹ It was folded in half and was 9

inches square. [10] They fastened four rows of precious stones on it. In the first row they put red quartz, topaz, and emerald. [11] In the second row they put turquoise, sapphire, and crystal. [12] In the third row they put jacinth, agate, and amethyst. [13] In the fourth row they put beryl, onyx, and gray quartz. The stones were mounted in gold settings. [14] They corresponded to the 12 sons of Israel, by name, each stone engraved (like a signet ring) with the name of one of the 12 tribes.

[15] For the breastplate they made chains out of pure gold, twisted like ropes. [16] They made two gold settings and two gold rings and attached the two rings to the ˌtopˌ two corners of the breastplate. [17] They fastened the two gold ropes to the rings at the ˌtopˌ corners of the breastplate. [18] They fastened the other ends of the ropes to the two settings on the shoulder straps of the ephod ˌso that the breastplate hungˌ in front of it. [19] They made two gold rings and fastened them to the other two corners of the breastplate on the inside edge next to the ephod. [20] They made two ˌmoreˌ gold rings and fastened them to the bottom of the shoulder straps on the front of the ephod. This was close to the seam just above the belt of the ephod. [21] Then they fastened the breastplate by its rings to the rings of the ephod with a violet cord. So the breastplate was attached just above the belt of the ephod and was held in place. They followed the LORD's instructions to Moses.

Other Clothes for Aaron and His Sons—*Exodus 28:31–43*

[22] They made the robe that is worn with the ephod, woven entirely of violet yarn. [23] The opening in the center of the robe had a finished edge (like a leather collar[a]) all around it to keep it from tearing. [24] On the hem of the robe they made pomegranates of violet, purple, and bright red yarn, and fine yarn. [25] They made bells out of pure gold and fastened them in between the pomegranates all around the hem of the robe. [26] A gold bell alternated with a pomegranate all around the hem of the robe that is worn by Aaron when he serves as priest. They followed the LORD's instructions to Moses.

[27] They wove inner robes out of fine linen for Aaron and his sons. [28] They also made the chief priest's turban and the other beautiful turbans out of fine linen. They made the undergarments and belt out of fine linen yarn. [29] The belt was embroidered with violet, purple, and bright red yarn. They followed the LORD's instructions to Moses.

[30] They made the flower-shaped medallion (the holy crown) out of pure gold and engraved on it (as on a signet ring): Holy to the LORD. [31] They fastened a violet cord to it and tied it on top of the turban. They followed the LORD's instructions to Moses.

The Tent Is Brought to Moses

[32] So all the work on the inner tent (the tent of meeting) was now done. The Israelites followed all the LORD's instructions to Moses. [33] Then they brought everything to Moses—the inner tent, the outer tent and all its furnishings, the fasteners, frames, crossbars, posts, sockets, [34] the cover made of rams' skins dyed red, the cover made of fine leather,[b] the canopy over ˌthe arkˌ, [35] the ark containing the words of God's promise with its poles and the throne of mercy, [36] the table with all the dishes, the bread of the presence, [37] the pure ˌgoldˌ lamp stand with its lamps in a row and all its utensils, the olive oil for the lamps, [38] the gold altar, the anointing oil, the sweet-smelling incense, the screen for the entrance to the tent, [39] the bronze altar with its bronze grate, its poles, and all its accessories, the basin with its stand, [40] the curtains for the courtyard, the posts, bases, and screen for the entrance to the courtyard, the ropes and pegs—all the equipment needed for the service of the inner tent (the tent of meeting)— [41] the special clothes worn when serving as priests in the holy place—both the holy clothes for the priest Aaron and the clothes for his sons when serving as priests. [42] The Israelites had done all the work following the LORD's instructions to Moses.

[43] Moses inspected all the work and saw that they had followed the LORD's instructions. So Moses blessed them.

Instructions for Setting Up the Tent

40 [1] Then the LORD said to Moses, [2] "Set up the tent (the tent of meeting) on the first day of the first month of the year. [3] Place the ark containing the words of my promise inside it, and hang the canopy over the ark. [4] Bring in the table, and arrange everything on it. Bring in the lamp stand, and set up the lamps. [5] Put the gold altar for incense in front of the ark. Put up the screen at the entrance to the tent.

[6] "Put the altar for burnt offerings in front of the entrance to the tent of meeting. [7] Put the basin between the tent of meeting and the altar, and put water in it. [8] Set up the surrounding courtyard, and put up the screen at the entrance to the courtyard. [9] Take the anointing oil, and anoint the tent and everything in it. In this way you will dedicate it and all its furnishings. Then

---

[a] 39:23 Hebrew meaning of "a leather collar" uncertain.   [b] 39:34 Hebrew meaning uncertain.

it will be holy. [10] Anoint the altar for burnt offerings and all the utensils. In this way you will dedicate the altar, and it will be most holy. [11] Anoint the basin and stand, and they will be dedicated.

[12] "Bring Aaron and his sons to the entrance of the tent of meeting, and wash them. [13] Then dress Aaron in the holy clothes, and anoint him. In this way you will dedicate him to serve me as priest. [14] Have his sons come forward, and dress them in their linen robes. [15] Anoint them to serve me as priests, as you anointed their father. Their anointing will begin a permanent priesthood for them for generations to come."

Moses Sets Up the Tent

[16] Moses did everything as the LORD commanded him. [17] So the tent was set up on the first day of the first month of the second year ⸢after the Israelites had left Egypt⸥. [18] When Moses set up the tent, he put the sockets in place, put up the frames, inserted the crossbars, and set up the posts. [19] He spread the outer tent over the inner tent and put the cover on top. Moses followed the LORD'S instructions.

[20] He took the words of God's promise and put them in the ark. He put the poles on the ark and placed the throne of mercy on top of the ark. [21] Then he brought the ark into the tent and hung the canopy over it to mark off where the ark was. Moses followed the LORD'S instructions.

[22] Moses put the table in the tent of meeting on the north side of the tent outside the canopy. [23] He arranged the bread on the table in the LORD'S presence, following the LORD'S instructions. [24] He placed the lamp stand in the tent of meeting opposite the table, on the south side of the tent. [25] He set up the lamps in the LORD'S presence, following the LORD'S instructions.

[26] Moses put the gold altar in the tent of meeting in front of the canopy. [27] He burned sweet-smelling incense on it, following the LORD'S instructions. [28] Then he put up the screen at the entrance to the tent.

[29] He put the altar for burnt offerings at the entrance to the tent (the tent of meeting). He sacrificed burnt offerings and grain offerings on it. Moses followed the LORD'S instructions.

[30] He put the basin between the tent of meeting and the altar and put water in it for washing. [31] Moses, Aaron, and his sons used this water to wash their hands and feet. [32] They would wash whenever they went into the tent of meeting or whenever they approached the altar. Moses followed the LORD'S instructions.

[33] He set up the courtyard around the tent and the altar and put up the screen at the entrance to the courtyard. Finally, Moses finished the work.

The LORD Comes to the Tent

[34] Then the ⸢column of⸥ smoke covered the tent of meeting, and the glory of the LORD filled the tent. [35] Moses couldn't go into the tent of meeting, because the smoke settled on it and the glory of the LORD filled the tent.

[36] In all their travels, whenever the ⸢column of⸥ smoke moved from the tent, the Israelites would break camp. [37] But if the column didn't move, they wouldn't break camp. [38] So the LORD'S column stayed over the tent during the day, and there was fire in the smoke at night. In this way all the Israelites could see the column throughout their travels.

LEVITICUS

1 ¹The LORD called Moses and spoke to him from the tent of meeting. He said, ²"Tell the Israelites: If any of you bring a sacrifice to the LORD, you must offer an animal from your cattle, sheep, or goats.

Burnt Offerings of Cattle

³"If you bring a burnt offering from your cattle, you must offer a male that has no defects. Offer it at the entrance to the tent of meeting so that the LORD will accept you. ⁴Place your hand on the animal's head. The burnt offering will be accepted to make peace with the LORD. ⁵Then slaughter the bull in the LORD's presence. Aaron's sons, the priests, will offer the blood. They will throw it against all sides of the altar that is at the entrance to the tent of meeting. ⁶Skin the burnt offering, and cut it into pieces. ⁷Then the sons of the priest Aaron will start a fire on the altar and lay the wood on the fire. ⁸Aaron's sons, the priests, will also lay the pieces, the head, and the fat on top of the wood burning on the altar. ⁹Wash the internal organs and legs. Then the priest will burn all of it on the altar. It is a burnt offering, an offering by fire, a soothing aroma to the LORD.

Burnt Offerings of Sheep or Goats

¹⁰"If your offering is a sheep or goat, you must bring a male that has no defects. ¹¹Slaughter it in the LORD's presence on the north side of the altar. Aaron's sons, the priests, will throw the blood against the altar on all sides. ¹²Then cut it into pieces. The priest will lay the head and the fat on the wood burning on the altar. ¹³Wash the internal organs and legs. Then the priest will burn all of it on the altar. It is a burnt offering, an offering by fire, a soothing aroma to the LORD.

Burnt Offerings of Birds

¹⁴"If your offering to the LORD is a bird, you must sacrifice a mourning dove or pigeon. ¹⁵The priest must bring it to the altar. He will break its neck and burn the bird on the altar. First, he will drain the blood against the side of the altar. ¹⁶Remove the gizzard with its filth and throw it on the east side of the altar on the place for the ashes. ¹⁷Then pull on the bird's wings to tear the bird open, but don't pull the wings off. Then the priest will lay the bird on the wood burning on the altar. It is a burnt offering, an offering by fire, a soothing aroma to the LORD."

Uncooked Grain Offerings

2 ¹The LORD continued, "Now, if any of you bring a grain offering to the LORD, your offering must be flour. Pour olive oil on it, and put incense on it. ²Then bring it to Aaron's sons, the priests. Take from this a handful of flour with olive oil, and all the incense. The priest will burn it on the altar as a reminder. It is an offering by fire, a soothing aroma to the LORD. ³The rest of the grain offering will belong to Aaron and his sons. It is very holy, set apart from the LORD's offering by fire.

Cooked Grain Offerings

⁴"If you bring a grain offering which has been baked in an oven, it must be rings of unleavened bread made of flour mixed with olive oil or wafers of unleavened bread brushed with olive oil. ⁵If your grain offering is prepared in a frying pan, it, too, will be unleavened bread made of flour mixed with olive oil. ⁶Break it into pieces and pour olive oil over it. It is a grain offering. ⁷If your grain offering is prepared in a skillet, it will be made of flour with olive oil. ⁸"Bring the LORD the grain offering prepared in any of these ways. Offer it to the priest who will bring it to the altar. ⁹The priest will remove part of the grain offering and burn it as a reminder on the altar. It is an offering by fire, a soothing aroma to the LORD. ¹⁰The rest of the grain offering belongs to Aaron and his sons. It is very holy, set apart from the LORD's offering by fire.

Other Ingredients

¹¹"Every grain offering that you bring to the LORD must be prepared without yeast. Never burn yeast or honey as an offering to the LORD. ¹²You may bring them to the LORD as offerings of your first products. But they must never be placed on the altar to make a soothing aroma.

¹³ Also put salt on each of your grain offerings. The salt of God's promise[a] must never be left out of your grain offerings. Put salt on all your offerings.

Offering the First Grain Harvested

¹⁴ "If you bring a grain offering to the LORD from the first grain you harvest, roast the cracked grain over fire. ¹⁵ Put olive oil on it, and place incense on it. It is a grain offering. ¹⁶ The priest will burn the flour, olive oil, and all the incense as a reminder. It is an offering by fire to the LORD."

Fellowship Offerings of Cattle

3 ¹ The LORD continued, "If your sacrifice is a fellowship offering of cattle in the LORD's presence, it must be a male or female animal that has no defects. ² Place your hand on the animal's head. Then slaughter it at the entrance to the tent of meeting. Then Aaron's sons, the priests, will throw the blood against the altar on all sides. ³ From your offering remove the fat that covers the internal organs ⁴ and the two kidneys with the fat on them and offer them by fire to the LORD. Also cut off the lobe of the liver along with the kidneys. ⁵ Then Aaron's sons will lay them on top of the burnt offering on the burning wood. It is an offering by fire, a soothing aroma to the LORD.

Fellowship Offerings of Sheep

⁶ "If your sacrifice is a fellowship offering of sheep to the LORD, you must bring a male or female animal that has no defects. ⁷ If your offering is a lamb, you must bring it to the LORD. ⁸ Place your hand on the animal's head. Slaughter it in front of the tent of meeting. Then Aaron's sons will throw the blood against the altar on all sides. ⁹ Then take the fat from the fellowship offering and offer it by fire to the LORD. Remove all the fat from the tail and the fat that covers the internal organs. ¹⁰ Also remove the two kidneys with the fat on them along with the lobe of the liver. ¹¹ Then the priest will burn the fellowship offering on the altar. It is food, an offering by fire to the LORD.

Fellowship Offerings of Goats

¹² "If your offering is a goat, you must bring it to the LORD. ¹³ Place your hand on its head. Slaughter it in front of the tent of meeting. Then Aaron's sons will throw the blood against the altar on all sides. ¹⁴ Then bring the fat that covers the internal organs ¹⁵ and the two kidneys with the fat on them as an offering by fire to the LORD. Also remove the lobe of the liver along with the kidneys. ¹⁶ Then the priest will burn them on the altar. It is food, an offering by fire to the LORD. It is a soothing aroma. All the fat belongs to the LORD. ¹⁷ This is a permanent law for generations to come wherever you live: Never eat any fat or blood."

Offerings for Unintentional Wrongdoing

4 ¹ The LORD spoke to Moses, ² "Tell the Israelites: If a person unintentionally does something wrong—even one thing that is forbidden by any of the LORD's commands—this is what he must do.

Offerings for Wrongdoing by the Chief Priest

³ "If the anointed priest does something wrong and brings guilt on the people, he must bring a bull that has no defects as an offering for sin to the LORD. ⁴ He must bring the bull into the LORD's presence at the entrance to the tent of meeting. He will place his hand on the bull's head. He will then slaughter the bull in the LORD's presence. ⁵ Then the anointed priest will take some of the bull's blood and bring it into the tent of meeting. ⁶ The priest will dip his finger in it and sprinkle some of the blood seven times in the LORD's presence facing the canopy in the holy place. ⁷ Then the priest will put some of the blood on the horns of the altar for sweet-smelling incense in the LORD's presence in the tent of meeting. He will pour the rest of the bull's blood at the bottom of the altar for burnt offerings at the entrance to the tent of meeting. ⁸ He will remove all of the fat from the bull that is the offering for sin, the fat that covers the internal organs, ⁹ and the two kidneys with the fat on them. He will also remove the lobe of the liver and the kidneys ¹⁰ the same way they were removed from the bull used for the fellowship offering. The priest will lay them on the altar for burnt offerings. ¹¹ Then he will take the entire bull (the skin, meat, head, legs, internal organs, and excrement) ¹² to a clean[a] place outside the camp where the ashes are dumped. He will burn it there on a wood fire.

Offerings for Wrongdoing by the Whole Congregation

¹³ "If the whole congregation of Israel unintentionally does something wrong, without the assembly being aware of it, if they do even one thing that is forbidden by any of the LORD's com-

---

mands, they will be guilty. ¹⁴ When the wrong they have done becomes known, the congregation must sacrifice a bull as an offering for sin. They must bring it in front of the tent of meeting. ¹⁵ The leaders of the congregation will place their hands on the bull's head in the LORD's presence. One of them will slaughter it in the LORD's presence. ¹⁶ Then the anointed priest will bring some of the bull's blood into the tent of meeting. ¹⁷ The priest will dip his finger in some of the blood and sprinkle it seven times in the LORD's presence facing the canopy. ¹⁸ He will also put some blood on the horns of the altar in the LORD's presence in the tent of meeting. He will pour the rest of the blood at the bottom of the altar for burnt offerings at the entrance to the tent of meeting. ¹⁹ He will remove all the fat and burn it on the altar. ²⁰ He will do the same thing with this bull that he did with the bull used as the offering for sin. So the priest will make peace with the LORD for the people, and they will be forgiven. ²¹ Then he will take the bull outside the camp and will burn it the same way he burned the first bull. It is an offering for sin for the community.

Offerings for Wrongdoing by a Leader

²² "When a leader unintentionally does something wrong—even one thing that is forbidden by any of the commands of the LORD his God—he will be guilty. ²³ When he is told about what he has done wrong, he must bring a male goat that has no defects as his offering. ²⁴ He will place his hand on the goat's head and slaughter it in the LORD's presence where he slaughters animals for burnt offerings. It is an offering for sin. ²⁵ Then the priest will take some of the blood of the offering for sin with his finger and put it on the horns of the altar for burnt offerings. He will pour the rest of the blood at the bottom of the altar for burnt offerings. ²⁶ He will burn all the fat on the altar the same way the fat of the fellowship offering is burned. So the priest will make peace with the LORD for what the leader did wrong, and the leader will be forgiven.

Offerings for Wrongdoing by a Common Person—Goats

²⁷ "If a common person unintentionally does something wrong—even one thing forbidden by the LORD's commands—he will be guilty. ²⁸ When he is told about what he has done wrong, he must bring a female goat that has no defects as his offering for what he has done wrong. ²⁹ He will place his hand on the animal's head and slaughter it where animals for burnt offerings are slaughtered. ³⁰ The priest will take some of the blood with his finger and put it on the horns of the altar for burnt offerings. He will pour the rest of the blood at the bottom of the altar. ³¹ He will remove all the fat the same way it is removed from the fellowship offering. The priest will burn it on the altar for a soothing aroma to the LORD. So the priest will make peace with the LORD for that person, and that person will be forgiven.

Offerings for Wrongdoing by a Common Person—Lambs

³² "If someone brings a lamb as his offering for sin, he must bring a female that has no defects. ³³ He will place his hand on the animal's head and slaughter it where he slaughters animals for burnt offerings. ³⁴ Then the priest will take some of the blood from the offering for sin with his finger and put it on the horns of the altar for burnt offerings. He will pour the rest of the blood at the bottom of the altar. ³⁵ He will remove all the fat the same way the fat of the lamb is removed from the fellowship offerings. Then the priest will burn it on the altar with the offering by fire to the LORD. So the priest will make peace with the LORD for what that person did wrong, and that person will be forgiven."

Sins Which Require an Offering for Sin

5 ¹ The LORD continued, "Now, if you are a witness under oath and won't tell what you saw or what you know, you are sinning and will be punished.

² "If you touch anything unclean*—the unclean dead body of a wild or tame animal or the body of an unclean, swarming creature—and then ignore what you did, you are unclean and will be guilty.

³ "If you become unclean by touching human uncleanness of any kind and then ignore it (although you know what you did), you will be guilty.

⁴ "If you hastily take a vow about what you will or will not do (as some people do) and then ignore it (although you know what you said), you will be guilty.

⁵ "So if you are guilty of any of these sins, you must confess it. ⁶ Bring your guilt offering to the LORD for the sin you committed. It must be a female sheep or goat as an offering for sin. Then the priest will make peace with the LORD for what you did wrong.

If You Cannot Afford a Sheep

⁷ "Now, if you cannot afford a sheep, you must bring to the LORD two mourning doves or two pigeons as a guilt offering for the sin you committed. One will be an offering for sin, the

---

* 5:2 "Unclean" refers to anything that is not presentable to God.

other a burnt offering. [8] Bring them to the priest, and he will sacrifice the offering for sin first. He will break the bird's neck without pulling its head off. [9] He will sprinkle some of the blood from the offering for sin on the side of the altar, and the rest of the blood will be drained at the bottom of the altar. It is an offering for sin. [10] Then, following the proper procedures, he will sacrifice the second bird as a burnt offering. So the priest will make peace with the LORD for what you did wrong.

If You Cannot Afford Two Mourning Doves

[11] "But if you cannot afford two mourning doves or two pigeons, then bring eight cups of flour as an offering for the sin you committed. Never put olive oil on it or add incense to it, because it is an offering for sin. [12] Bring it to the priest. The priest will take a handful of it. He will burn it as a reminder on top of the offering by fire to the LORD on the altar. It is an offering for sin. [13] So the priest will make peace with the LORD for what you did wrong, and you will be forgiven. The offering will belong to the priest like the grain offering."

For Unintentional Wrongdoing Against the LORD's Property

[14] The LORD spoke to Moses, [15] "If any of you fail to do your duty by unintentionally doing something wrong with any of the LORD's holy things, bring a guilt offering to the LORD. It must be a ram that has no defects or its value in silver weighed according to the official standards of the holy place. [16] Pay for whatever holy things you used plus one-fifth more. Give it to the priest. So the priest will use the ram sacrificed for the guilt offering to make peace with the LORD for what you did wrong, and you will be forgiven.

For Unintentionally Disobeying the LORD's Commands

[17] "If any of you do wrong—even one thing forbidden by any of the LORD's commands, but you didn't know it—when you realize your guilt, you must be punished. [18] You must bring the priest a ram that has no defects from the flock or its value in money for a guilt offering. The priest will make peace with the LORD for the wrong you did unintentionally (although you didn't know what you did), and you will be forgiven. [19] It is a guilt offering because you are certainly guilty as far as the LORD is concerned."

For Sins Against the LORD's People

6[a] [1] The LORD spoke to Moses, [2] "If any of you sin against the LORD by failing to do your duty, if you lie to your neighbor about something you were supposed to take care of or if you lie about something stolen or seized from your neighbor, you are sinning and will be guilty. [3] If you find something that someone lost and lie about it under oath, or commit any other sin like this, [4] you are sinning and will be guilty. Return what you stole or seized, what you were supposed to take care of, the lost item you found, [5] or whatever it was that you swore falsely about. Pay it back in full plus one-fifth more. Give it back to its owner on the day you bring your guilt offering. [6] Then bring the LORD your guilt offering, a ram that has no defects or its value in money. Bring it to the priest. [7] So the priest will make peace with the LORD. Then you will be forgiven for whatever you did that made you guilty."

Instructions for Taking Care of the Fire

[8] The LORD spoke to Moses, [9] "Command Aaron and his sons: These are the instructions for the burnt offering that stays on the altar overnight while the altar fire is kept burning.

[10] "The priest must put on his linen clothes, including his linen undergarments. Then he will remove the ashes left on the altar from the fire that consumed the burnt offering and will put them next to the altar. [11] Then he will take off these clothes and put on some others. He will take the ashes to a clean place outside the camp. [12] The fire must always be burning on the altar. It must never go out. The priest will burn wood on it every morning. He will lay the burnt offering on the fire and burn the fat of the fellowship offering. [13] The fire must always be burning on the altar. It must never go out.

The Grain Offering From the People

[14] "These are the instructions for the grain offering. Aaron's sons must bring it into the LORD's presence in front of the altar. [15] One of them will remove a handful of flour from the grain offering, together with the olive oil and all the incense. He will burn it on the altar as a reminder. It is a soothing aroma to the LORD. [16] Aaron and his sons will eat the rest of it. They will eat unleavened bread in a holy place, in the courtyard of the tent of meeting. [17] Don't use yeast in baking the bread. I have given it to them as their share from the offerings by fire made to me. It is very holy like the offering for sin and the guilt offering. [18] Every male

---

[a] 6:1 Leviticus 6:1–30 in English Bibles is Leviticus 5:20–6:23 in the Hebrew Bible.

descendant of Aaron may eat it. It is a permanent law for generations to come regarding the offering by fire to the LORD. Everyone who touches it will become holy."

Special Grain Offerings From the Priests

[19] The LORD spoke to Moses, [20] "This is the offering that Aaron and his sons must bring to the LORD on the day he is anointed—eight cups of flour. They must do this every day. He must offer half of it in the morning and half in the evening. [21] Prepare it in a frying pan with olive oil, mixing it well. Offer baked pieces of the grain offering as a soothing aroma to the LORD. [22] Aaron's son who is anointed to take his place as priest will prepare it. This is a permanent law of the LORD: It must be completely burned. [23] Every grain offering made by a priest must be completely burned. It must not be eaten."

Instructions for the Offering for Sin

[24] The LORD spoke to Moses, [25] "Tell Aaron and his sons: These are the instructions for the offering for sin. The offering for sin must be slaughtered in the LORD's presence in the same place where the burnt offering is slaughtered. It is very holy. [26] The priest who makes the offering for sin will eat it in a holy place, in the courtyard of the tent of meeting. [27] Anything that touches its meat will be holy. If blood gets on someone's clothes, he must wash them in a holy place. [28] Any piece of pottery in which the offering for sin is cooked must be broken into pieces. Any copper kettle in which the offering for sin is cooked must be scoured and rinsed with water. [29] Any male among the priests may eat the offering for sin. It is very holy. [30] Any offering for sin must not be eaten if some of the blood was brought into the holy place in the tent of meeting to make peace with the LORD. It must be burned."

Instructions for the Guilt Offering

7 [1] The LORD continued, "These are the instructions for the guilt offering. It is very holy. [2] It must be slaughtered in the same place where the burnt offering is slaughtered. A priest will throw the blood against the altar on all sides. [3] He will offer all the fat, the fat from the tail, the fat covering the internal organs, [4] and the two kidneys with the fat on them. He will also remove the lobe of the liver along with the kidneys. [5] The priest will burn them on the altar. It is a guilt offering by fire to the LORD. [6] Any male among the priests may eat it. It will be eaten in a holy place. It is very holy.

[7] "The same instructions apply to the offering for sin and the guilt offering. Both offerings belong to the priest to make peace with the LORD. [8] The skin of the burnt offering belongs to the priest who sacrifices it. [9] Every grain offering, whether baked in an oven or prepared in a skillet or a frying pan, belongs to the priest who offers it. [10] Every grain offering, whether mixed with olive oil or dry, will be shared equally by all of Aaron's sons.

Instructions for the Fellowship Offering of Thanksgiving

[11] "These are the instructions for the fellowship offering that you must bring to the LORD. [12] If you offer it as a thank offering, you must also bring rings of unleavened bread mixed with olive oil, wafers of unleavened bread brushed with olive oil, and loaves made from flour mixed well with olive oil. [13] In addition to these rings of bread, you must bring bread with yeast along with your fellowship offering of thanksgiving. [14] From every offering you must bring one loaf to the LORD as a special contribution. It will belong to the priest who throws the blood of the fellowship offering.

[15] "The meat from your fellowship offering of thanksgiving must be eaten on the day it is offered. Never leave any of it until morning.

Instructions for Other Fellowship Offerings

[16] "If your sacrificial offering is something you vowed or a freewill offering, it must be eaten the day you offer it or the next day. [17] However, on the third day any meat left over from the sacrifice must be burned. [18] You will not be accepted if any meat from the fellowship offering is eaten on the third day. You will not receive credit for it. It is repulsive to God. The person who eats any of it must be punished.

[19] "Meat that touches anything unclean must not be eaten. It must be burned. Anyone who is clean may eat from these sacrifices. [20] Those who eat meat from the LORD's fellowship offering while unclean must be excluded from the people. [21] Those who touch anything unclean, human or animal, or any other disgusting uncleanness and still eat the LORD's fellowship offering must be excluded from the people."

No Fat or Blood May Be Eaten

[22] The LORD spoke to Moses, [23] "Tell the Israelites: Never eat any fat from bulls, sheep, or goats. [24] The fat from an animal that dies naturally or is killed by wild animals you may use for

any other purpose, but you must never eat it. ²⁵Those who eat the fat from an animal which they sacrificed by fire to the LORD must be excluded from the people.

²⁶ "Never eat the blood of any bird or animal no matter where you live. ²⁷Those who eat any blood must be excluded from the people."

Dividing the Fellowship Offering Between the People and the Priests

²⁸ The LORD spoke to Moses, ²⁹ "Tell the Israelites: Anyone who offers the LORD a fellowship offering must bring a part of that sacrifice as a gift to the LORD. ³⁰Bring the sacrifices by fire made to the LORD yourself. Bring the fat with the breast. Take the breast and present it to the LORD.

³¹ "The priest will burn the fat on the altar. However, the breast will belong to Aaron and his sons. ³²You will also give the priest the right thigh as a contribution. ³³When any of Aaron's sons offer the blood and fat of the fellowship offering, the right thigh will belong to him as his share. ³⁴From the fellowship offerings of the Israelites, I have taken the breast that was presented to me, and the thigh from the contribution offering. I have given them to the priest Aaron and his sons. This is a permanent law for generations to come.

³⁵ "This is the share for Aaron and his sons from the sacrifices by fire made to the LORD. It was given to them on the day Moses ordained them to serve the LORD as priests. ³⁶The LORD commanded the Israelites to give it to them on the day he anointed them. This is a permanent law for generations to come."

Summary of Offerings

³⁷ These are the instructions for the burnt offering, the grain offering, the offering for sin, the guilt offering, the ordination offering, and the fellowship offering. ³⁸On Mount Sinai the LORD gave Moses commands about these offerings at the same time that he commanded the Israelites to bring their offerings to him in the Sinai Desert.

Aaron and His Sons Made Priests—Exodus 29:1–45

8 ¹The LORD spoke to Moses, ² "Take Aaron and his sons, the priests' clothes, the anointing oil, the bull that will be the offering for sin, the two rams, and the basket of unleavened bread. ³Gather the whole congregation at the entrance to the tent of meeting."

⁴ Moses did as the LORD commanded him, and the congregation gathered at the entrance to the tent of meeting. ⁵Moses told the congregation, "The LORD has commanded that this is what you must do."

⁶ Moses had Aaron and his sons come forward, and he washed them. ⁷He put the linen robe on Aaron and fastened the belt around him. He also dressed him in the robe that is worn with the ephod.^a He fastened the ephod to it. ⁸Then he put the breastplate on him, and into it he placed the Urim and Thummim.^b ⁹He put the turban on him and fastened the gold medallion (the holy crown) to the front of the turban as the LORD had commanded Moses.

¹⁰ Moses took the anointing oil to anoint the tent and everything in it and dedicate them. ¹¹He sprinkled some of the oil on the altar seven times and anointed the altar, all the utensils, and the basin with its stand to dedicate them.

¹² He also poured some of the anointing oil on Aaron's head and anointed him to set him apart for his holy duties.

¹³ Moses had Aaron's sons come forward. He put linen robes on them, fastened their belts around them, and put turbans on them as the LORD had commanded Moses.

¹⁴ He brought the bull that was the offering for sin. Aaron and his sons placed their hands on its head. ¹⁵When it was slaughtered, Moses took the blood and put it on the horns of the altar all around with his finger and cleansed the altar from sins. He poured the rest of the blood at the bottom of the altar and declared it holy so that priests could use it to make peace with the LORD. ¹⁶Moses took all the fat that was on the internal organs, the lobe of the liver, and the two kidneys with their fat, and he burned them on the altar. ¹⁷He burned the rest of the bull, its skin, meat, and excrement outside the camp, as the LORD commanded him.

¹⁸ He brought forward the ram for the burnt offering. Aaron and his sons placed their hands on the ram's head. ¹⁹Moses slaughtered it and threw the blood against the altar on all sides. ²⁰When the ram was cut into pieces, Moses burned the head with the other pieces and the fat. ²¹He washed the internal organs and the legs. Then Moses burned the whole ram on the altar as the LORD commanded him. It was a burnt offering, a soothing aroma, an offering by fire to the LORD.

²² He brought forward the second ram for the ordination offering. Aaron and his sons placed their hands on the ram's head. ²³Moses slaughtered it, took some of the blood, and put it on Aaron's right ear lobe, on his right thumb, and on the big toe of his right foot. ²⁴Moses also brought Aaron's sons forward. He put some of the blood on their right ear lobes,

---

^a 8:7 *Ephod* is a technical term for part of the priest's clothes. Its exact usage and shape are unknown.
^b 8:8 The Urim and Thummim were used by the chief priest to determine God's answer to questions.

on their right thumbs, and on the big toes of their right feet. Moses threw the rest of the blood against all the sides of the altar. [25] He took the fat, the fat from the tail, all the fat on the internal organs, the lobe of the liver, the two kidneys with their fat, and the right thigh. [26] He took a loaf of unleavened bread, a ring of bread made with olive oil, and a wafer from the basket of unleavened bread which was in the Lord's presence. He put them on the fat and the right thigh. [27] Then he placed all these things in the hands of Aaron and his sons. Moses presented all these things to the Lord as an offering. [28] Then he took them from their hands and burned them on top of the burnt offering on the altar. These were ordination offerings, offerings by fire, a soothing aroma to the Lord. [29] Moses also took the breast from the ram of the ordination offering and presented it to the Lord. It was Moses' share, as the Lord had commanded.

[30] Moses took some of the anointing oil and some of the blood that was on the altar, sprinkled it on Aaron and his clothes and on his sons and their clothes. In this way he dedicated Aaron, his clothes, his sons, and their clothes.

[31] Moses told Aaron and his sons: "Cook the meat at the entrance to the tent of meeting. Take the meat and the bread in the basket of the ordination offering. Eat them there as I commanded when I said, 'Aaron and his sons will eat it.' [32] You must burn any meat or bread that is left over. [33] You will not leave the entrance to the tent of meeting for seven days, not until the last day of your ordination is over. It will take seven days to ordain you. [34] I did today what the Lord commanded me to make peace with the Lord for you. [35] You will stay at the entrance to the tent of meeting day and night for seven days and serve as the Lord tells you. Then you will not die. This is what I was commanded."

[36] So Aaron and his sons did everything the Lord commanded through Moses.

Aaron's First Sacrifices

9 [1] On the eighth day Moses summoned Aaron and his sons and the leaders of Israel. [2] He told Aaron, "Take a calf that has no defects for yourself as an offering for sin and a ram that has no defects as a burnt offering. Sacrifice them in the Lord's presence. [3] Also tell the Israelites: 'Take a male goat as an offering for sin, a calf and a lamb (each one year old and without defects) as a burnt offering, [4] a bull and a ram as a fellowship offering, and a grain offering mixed with olive oil to sacrifice in the Lord's presence. The Lord will appear to you today.' "

[5] So they took the things Moses commanded and brought them in front of the tent of meeting. The whole congregation came and stood in the Lord's presence.

[6] Moses said, "The Lord has commanded you to offer these sacrifices so that you may see the Lord's glory."

[7] Moses told Aaron, "Come to the altar and sacrifice an offering for sin and a burnt offering to make peace with the Lord for your sins and the sins of the people. Also make an offering for the people, to make peace with the Lord for them as the Lord commanded."

[8] Aaron came to the altar and slaughtered the calf as his own offering for sin. [9] Aaron's sons brought him the blood. He dipped his finger in the blood and put it on the horns of the altar. Then he poured out the blood at the bottom of the altar. [10] On the altar he burned the fat, kidneys, and lobe of the liver from the offering for sin as the Lord had commanded Moses. [11] He burned the meat and the skin outside the camp.

[12] He slaughtered the animal for the burnt offering. Aaron's sons gave him the blood, and he threw it against the altar on all sides. [13] They also gave him the burnt offering, which was cut in pieces and included the head. He burned it on the altar. [14] He washed the internal organs and the legs and laid them on top of the burnt offering on the altar.

[15] He brought the people's offerings. He took the male goat for the people's offering for sin and slaughtered it. He sacrificed it to take away sins as he had done before. [16] Following the proper procedures, he brought forward the burnt offering and sacrificed it. [17] He also brought the grain offering. He took a handful of grain and burned it on the altar in addition to the morning burnt offering. [18] He slaughtered the bull and the ram for the people's fellowship offering. Aaron's sons gave him the blood, which he threw against the altar on all sides. [19] However, the fat from the bull and the ram (the fat from the tail, the layer of fat, the kidneys, and the lobe of the liver) [20] they placed on the breasts. Aaron burned them all on the altar. [21] However, he first took the breasts and the right thighs and presented them to the Lord as Moses commanded.

[22] Then Aaron raised his hands toward the people and blessed them. He sacrificed the offering for sin, the burnt offering, and the fellowship offering. Then he came down from the altar. [23] Moses and Aaron went into the tent of meeting. When they came out, they blessed the people. Then the Lord's glory appeared to all the people. [24] Fire came out from the Lord's presence and consumed the burnt offering and the pieces of fat on the altar. When all the people saw this, they shouted and bowed with their faces touching the ground.

Improper Conduct for Priests

10 [1] Aaron's sons Nadab and Abihu each took an incense burner and put burning coals and incense in it. Then in the LORD's presence they offered this unauthorized fire. [2] A fire flashed from the LORD and burned them, and they died in the presence of the LORD. [3] Moses said to Aaron, "This is exactly what the LORD said:

'I will show my holiness among those who come to me.
I will show my glory to all the people.'"

Aaron was speechless.
[4] Moses called Mishael and Elzaphan, the sons of Aaron's uncle, Uzziel. He told them, "Come and take your relatives away from in front of the holy place. Take them outside the camp." [5] So they came and took them away to a place outside the camp, as Moses told them. The dead men were still in their linen robes.
[6] Moses told Aaron and his sons Eleazar and Ithamar: "Do not mourn by leaving your hair uncombed or tearing your clothes. If you do, you will die and the LORD will become angry with the whole congregation. All the other Israelites may cry over the fire the LORD sent, but you may not. [7] You must not leave the entrance to the tent of meeting or else you, too, will die, because the LORD has anointed you with his oil." They obeyed Moses.

Proper Conduct for Priests

[8] The LORD spoke to Aaron, [9] "You and your sons must not drink any wine or liquor when you go into the tent of meeting, or you will die. This is a permanent law for generations to come. [10] Teach them the difference between what is holy and what is unholy, what is clean and what is unclean.[a] [11] Also teach the Israelites all the laws that I gave them through Moses."
[12] Moses told Aaron and his surviving sons Eleazar and Ithamar, "Take the grain offering left over from the offering by fire to the LORD. Make unleavened bread, and eat it next to the altar because it is very holy. [13] Eat it in a holy place because it is the part of the offering by fire to the LORD that belongs to you and your children. That is the command I received. [14] Also eat the breast presented ˌto the LORDˌ, and the thigh that was given as a contribution. You and your sons and daughters may eat them in a clean place because they are your part of the fellowship offerings from the Israelites. [15] They will bring the thigh given as a contribution, the breast presented ˌto the LORDˌ, and the fat that is to be burned and present them to the LORD. These parts will belong to you and your children. This will be a permanent law, as the LORD has commanded."

Eleazar and Ithamar Sacrifice the Offering for Sin

[16] Moses tried to find out what had happened to the male goat that was supposed to be the offering for sin. To his surprise, it had already been burned. So he became angry with Eleazar and Ithamar, Aaron's surviving sons. [17] He asked them, "Why didn't you eat the offering for sin in the holy place? It is very holy and was given to you to take away the sins of the congregation and to make peace with the LORD for them. [18] Since its blood was not brought inside the holy place, you certainly should have eaten it there, as I commanded."
[19] Aaron answered Moses, "Today they sacrificed their offering for sin and their burnt offering in the LORD's presence, and look what happened to me. If I had eaten the offering for sin today, would the LORD have approved?"
[20] When Moses heard this, he was satisfied.

Laws About Animals the Israelites May and May Not Eat—*Deuteronomy 14:3–20*

11 [1] The LORD spoke to Moses and Aaron, [2] "Tell the Israelites: Here are the kinds of land animals you may eat: [3] all animals that have completely divided hoofs and that also chew their cud. [4] However, from those that either chew their cud or have divided hoofs, these are the kinds you must never eat: You must never eat camels. (Camels are unclean because they chew their cud but do not have divided hoofs.) [5] You must never eat rock badgers. (Rock badgers are unclean because they chew their cud but do not have divided hoofs.) [6] You must never eat rabbits. (Rabbits are unclean because they chew their cud but do not have divided hoofs.) [7] You must never eat pigs. (Because pigs have completely divided hoofs but do not chew their cud, they are also unclean.) [8] Never eat the meat of these animals or touch their dead bodies. They are unclean for you.
[9] "Here are the kinds of creatures that live in the water which you may eat—anything in the seas and streams that has fins and scales. [10] However, you must consider all swarming creatures living in the seas or the streams that have no fins or scales disgusting. [11] They must

---

[a] 10:10 "Clean" refers to anything that is presentable to God. "Unclean" refers to anything that is not presentable to God.

remain disgusting to you. Never eat their meat. Consider their dead bodies disgusting. [12] Every creature in the water without fins or scales is disgusting to you.

[13] "Here are the kinds of birds you must consider disgusting and must not eat. They are eagles, bearded vultures, black vultures, [14] kites, all types of buzzards, [15] all types of crows, [16] ostriches, nighthawks, seagulls, all types of falcons, [17] little owls, cormorants, great owls, [18] barn owls, pelicans, ospreys, [19] storks, all types of herons, hoopoes, and bats.

[20] "Every swarming, winged insect that walks across the ground like a four-legged animal is disgusting to you. [21] However, you may eat winged insects that swarm if they use their legs to hop on the ground. [22] You may eat any kind of locust, cricket, katydid, or grasshopper. [23] Every kind of winged insect that walks across the ground like a four-legged animal is disgusting to you.

[24] "Regarding the creatures mentioned above, this is how you would become unclean: Whoever touches their dead bodies will be unclean until evening. [25] Whoever carries any part of their dead bodies must wash his clothes. He will be unclean until evening. [26] All animals whose hoofs are not completely divided or that don't chew their cud are unclean for you. Whoever touches them is unclean. [27] All four-legged animals that walk on their paws are unclean for you. Whoever touches their dead bodies will be unclean until evening. [28] Those who carry the dead body of any of these animals must wash their clothes and will be unclean until evening. These animals are unclean for you.

[29] "The following swarming creatures that move on the ground are unclean for you—moles, mice, and all types of lizards: [30] geckos, monitors, lizards, skinks, and chameleons. [31] Among all the swarming creatures that move on the ground, these are unclean for you. Whoever touches their dead bodies will be unclean until evening. [32] When the dead body of one of these creatures falls on something, that thing will be unclean. It may be a wooden article, clothing, leather, a sack, or anything used for any purpose. It should be put in water and will be unclean until evening. Then it will be clean ˌagainˌ.

[33] "If any of these creatures falls into a piece of pottery, break the pottery because everything in it is unclean. [34] If water ˌfrom that potteryˌ touches any food, the food is unclean. Any liquid that you drink from that pottery is unclean. [35] Anything on which their dead bodies fall is unclean. If it is an oven or a stove, smash it. It is unclean and will remain unclean for you. [36] However, a spring or a cistern holding water will remain clean. But anyone who touches their dead bodies will be unclean. [37] If their dead bodies fall on seed that is to be planted, the seed is clean. [38] But if water is poured on the seed and their dead bodies fall on it, the seed is unclean for you.

[39] "When any animal that you are allowed to eat dies, whoever touches its dead body will be unclean until evening. [40] Those who eat any of its dead body must wash their clothes and will be unclean until evening. Those who carry its dead body away will wash their clothes and will be unclean until evening.

[41] "Any creature that swarms on the ground is disgusting and must not be eaten. [42] Don't eat any creature with many legs that goes on its belly or on the ground like a four-legged animal, or any creature that swarms on the ground. Consider them disgusting. [43] Don't become disgusting by eating anything that swarms on the ground. Never allow yourselves to become unclean because of them.

[44] "Here is the reason: I am the LORD your God. You must live holy lives. Be holy because I am holy. Never become unclean by touching anything that swarms or crawls on the ground. [45] Here is the reason ˌagainˌ: I am the LORD. I brought you out of Egypt to be your God. Be holy because I am holy.

[46] "These are the instructions about animals, birds, and every living creature that swims in the water and every creature that swarms on the ground. [47] These instructions help you distinguish between clean and unclean, the animals you may eat and those you may not eat."

Instructions for Women After Childbirth

12 [1] The LORD spoke to Moses, [2] "Tell the Israelites: When a woman gives birth to a boy, she will be unclean for seven days. This is the same number of days she is unclean for her monthly period. [3] The boy must be circumcised when he is eight days old. [4] Then she must stay at home for 33 days in order to be made clean from her bleeding. She must not touch anything holy or go into the holy place until the days needed to make her clean are over.

[5] "When a woman gives birth to a girl, she will be unclean as in her monthly period. However, she will be unclean for two weeks. Then she must stay at home for 66 days in order to be made clean from her bleeding.

[6] "When the days needed to make her clean are over, she must bring a one-year-old lamb for a burnt offering and a pigeon or a mourning dove as an offering for sin. She must bring them to the priest at the entrance to the tent of meeting. [7] The priest will offer them in the LORD's presence to make peace with the LORD for her. Then she will be clean from her flow of blood.

"These are the instructions for the woman who gives birth to a boy or a girl. [8] If she cannot afford a lamb, she must use two mourning doves or two pigeons. One will be the burnt offering and the other the offering for sin. So the priest will make peace with the LORD for her, and she will be clean."

Skin Diseases

13 [1] The LORD spoke to Moses and Aaron, [2] "If anyone has a sore, a rash, or an irritated area on his skin that turns into an infectious skin disease, he must be taken to the priest Aaron or to one of his sons who are also priests. [3] The priest will examine the disease. If the hair in the diseased area has turned white, and the diseased area looks deeper than the rest of his skin, it is an infectious skin disease. When the priest has examined him, he must declare him unclean. [4] But if the irritated area is white and does not look deeper than the rest of the skin, and the hair has not turned white, the priest must put him in isolation for seven days. [5] On the seventh day the priest will examine him again. If the disease looks the same and has not spread, the priest must put him in isolation for another seven days. [6] On the seventh day the priest will examine him again. If the diseased area has faded and not spread, the priest must declare him clean. It is only a rash. The person must wash his clothes and will be clean. [7] But if the rash has spread after he has shown himself to the priest to be declared clean, he must show himself to the priest again. [8] The priest will examine him one more time, and if the rash has spread, the priest must declare him unclean. It is an infectious skin disease.

[9] "If anyone has an infectious skin disease, he must be taken to the priest. [10] The priest will examine him. If there is a white sore that has turned the hair white, and if there is raw flesh in the sore, [11] he has a chronic skin disease. Without putting him in isolation, the priest must declare him unclean because he is unclean. [12] If skin disease develops and covers the whole person from head to foot (so far as the priest can see), [13] the priest will examine him. If the disease does cover his whole body, the priest must declare the diseased person clean. His body has turned white. The person is clean. [14] But if raw flesh appears, he will be unclean. [15] The priest will examine the raw flesh and declare him unclean. The raw flesh is unclean. It is an infectious skin disease. [16] But if the raw flesh turns white again, he must go to the priest. [17] The priest will examine him again, and if the diseased area has turned white, the priest must declare the diseased person clean. He is clean.

[18] "If a boil on the skin has healed [19] and in its place there is a white sore or a pink area, it must be shown to the priest. [20] The priest will examine it. If it looks deeper than the rest of the skin and its hair has turned white, the priest must declare the person unclean. An infectious skin disease has developed in the boil. [21] But if the priest examines the affected area and the hair in it is not white or the affected area is not deeper than the rest of the skin but has faded, the priest must put him in isolation for seven days. [22] If the area has spread, the priest must declare him unclean. It is a skin disease. [23] But if the irritated area has not spread, it is a scar caused by the boil. The priest must declare him clean.

[24] "If anyone has a burn on his skin and the raw flesh of the burn turns into a pink or bright white area, [25] the priest will examine it. If the hair on the affected area has turned white and the affected area looks deeper than the rest of the skin, an infectious skin disease has developed in the burn. The priest must declare him unclean. It is an infectious skin disease. [26] But if the priest examines it and the hair in it is not white and the affected area is not deeper than the rest of the skin but has faded, the priest must put him in isolation for seven days. [27] On the seventh day the priest will examine him again. If the area has spread, the priest must declare him unclean. It is an infectious skin disease. [28] If the irritated area does not spread but has faded, it is only a sore caused by the burn. The priest must declare him clean, because it is a scar caused by the burn.

[29] "If a man or a woman has some disease on the head or chin, [30] the priest will examine the disease. If it looks deeper than the rest of the skin and there is thin yellow hair on it, the priest must declare the person unclean. It is a scab, a disease on the head or the chin. [31] But if the priest examines the scabby disease and it does not look deeper than the rest of the skin and there is no black hair in it, the priest must put the person with the scabby disease in isolation for seven days. [32] On the seventh day the priest will examine the disease. If the scab has not spread, there is no yellow hair on it, and the scab does not look deeper than the rest of the skin, [33] the person will shave everything except the scab. The priest will put the person with the scab in isolation for another seven days. [34] On the seventh day the priest will examine the scab again. If the scab has not spread on the skin and does not look deeper than the rest of the skin, the priest must declare him clean. When he has washed his clothes, he will be clean. [35] But if the scab spreads after the person has been declared clean, [36] the priest will make another examination. If the scab has spread on the skin, the priest does not have to look for yellow hair. The person is unclean. [37] But if he sees that the scab hasn't spread and black hair grows on it, the scab is healed. The person is clean, so the priest must declare him clean.

38 "If a man or a woman has white irritated areas of skin, **39** the priest will make an examination. If the irritated areas on the skin are pale white, a rash has developed on the skin. The person is clean.

40 "If a man loses his hair, he is clean, even though he is bald. **41** If he loses the hair on the front of his head, he is clean, even though he is bald on the forehead. **42** But if there is a pink patch on the bald places in back or in front, a skin disease is developing in those places. **43** The priest will examine him. If the sore from the disease in the bald places in back or in front is pink like a skin disease somewhere else on the body, **44** the man has come down with an infectious skin disease. He is unclean. The priest must declare him unclean because of the skin disease on his head.

45 "People who come down with a skin disease must wear torn clothes and leave their hair uncombed. They must cover their upper lips and call out, 'Unclean, unclean!' **46** As long as they have the skin disease, they are unclean. They must live outside the camp.

Mildew in Clothing or Leather Articles

47 "Now about clothing—if there is a green or red area on a piece of clothing **48** that is woven or knitted from linen or wool or on any leather article, **49** it is mildew. It must be shown to the priest. **50** The priest will examine the mildew and will put the clothing in a separate place for seven days. **51** On the seventh day he will examine the area again. If the spot is spreading, it is unclean. **52** He must burn the piece of clothing or the leather article because the mildew is growing. **53** But if the priest sees that the area has not spread, **54** he must order the area to be washed and put the clothing in a separate place for seven more days. **55** The priest will examine the area again after it is washed. If it doesn't look any different and the mildew has not spread, it is still unclean. It must be burned, whether the area is on the outside or the inside. **56** If the priest sees that the area is pale after washing, he will tear it out of the clothing or the leather. **57** However, if it shows up again, you must burn the clothing or the leather article. **58** But if the area disappears from the woven or knitted clothing or any leather article when it is washed, wash it again, and it will be clean.

59 "These are the instructions for deciding whether mildew in clothing that is woven or knitted from linen or wool or in any leather article is clean or unclean."

Cleansing After Skin Diseases

14 **1** The LORD spoke to Moses, **2** "These are the instructions for making a person clean after a skin disease. He must be taken to the priest. **3** The priest will go outside the camp and examine him. If the person is healed, **4** the priest will order someone to get two living, clean birds, some cedar wood, red yarn, and a hyssop sprig to use for the cleansing. **5** Then the priest will order someone to kill one bird over a clay bowl containing fresh water. **6** The priest will take the living bird, the cedar wood, the red yarn, and the hyssop sprig and dip them and the living bird in the blood of the bird that was killed over the fresh water. **7** He will sprinkle the blood seven times on the one to be cleansed and will declare that person clean. Then he will let the living bird fly away into the open country.

8 "The one to be cleansed must wash his clothes, shave off all his hair, and wash. Then he will be clean. After that he may go into the camp. However, for seven days he will live outside his tent. **9** On the seventh day he must shave off all the hair on his head, his beard, and his eyebrows, and he must wash his clothes and body. Then he will be clean.

10 "On the eighth day he must take two male lambs that have no defects and a one-year-old female lamb that has no defects. He must also take eight cups of flour mixed with olive oil for a grain offering along with a quart of olive oil. **11** The priest who will declare him clean must bring the person and his offerings into the LORD's presence at the entrance to the tent of meeting. **12** The priest will take one of the male lambs and the quart of olive oil and present them to the LORD as a guilt offering. **13** He will slaughter the lamb in the holy place where he slaughters the offering for sin and the burnt offering. He will do this because the guilt offering, like the offering for sin, belongs to the priest. It is very holy. **14** Then the priest will take some of the blood from the guilt offering and put it on the right ear lobe, on the right thumb, and on the big toe of the right foot of the one to be cleansed. **15** The priest will also take some of the olive oil and pour it into his own left hand. **16** He will dip his right finger in the oil in his left hand, and with his finger sprinkle some of the oil seven times in the LORD's presence. **17** The priest will put some of the oil that is still in his hand on the right ear lobe, on the right thumb, and on the big toe of the right foot of the one to be cleansed. These are the same places he had put the blood of the guilt offering. **18** The priest will put the rest of the oil in his hand on the head of the one to be cleansed. So he will make peace with the LORD for that person in the LORD's presence. **19** The priest will also sacrifice the offering for sin to make peace with the LORD for the one who is being cleansed from his impurity. After that, he will slaughter the burnt offering. **20** The priest will sacrifice the burnt offering and the grain offering on the altar. So the priest will make peace with the LORD for that person, and the person who had the skin disease will be clean.

Cleansing for a Poor Person After a Skin Disease

²¹ "But if the one to be cleansed is poor and cannot afford that much, he must take one male lamb, present it to make peace with the LORD for himself, and use it for his guilt offering. He will take only eight cups of flour mixed with olive oil as a grain offering, a quart of olive oil, ²² and two mourning doves or two pigeons (whatever he can afford). The one will be an offering for sin and the other a burnt offering. ²³ On the eighth day he will take them to the priest for his cleansing at the entrance to the tent of meeting in the LORD's presence. ²⁴ The priest will take the lamb for the guilt offering and the quart of olive oil and present them to the LORD. ²⁵ He will slaughter the lamb as a guilt offering. Then the priest will take some of the blood of the guilt offering and put it on the right ear lobe, on the right thumb, and on the big toe of the right foot of the one to be cleansed. ²⁶ The priest will pour some of the olive oil into his own left hand. ²⁷ With his right finger he will sprinkle some of the oil seven times in the LORD's presence. ²⁸ The priest will put some of the oil that is in his hand on the right ear lobe, on the right thumb, and on the big toe of the right foot of the one to be cleansed. These are the same places he had put the blood of the guilt offering. ²⁹ In the LORD's presence, the priest will pour the rest of the oil in his hand on the head of the one to be cleansed in order to make a payment for him. ³⁰ Then the one to be cleansed must take one of the mourning doves or pigeons (whichever he can afford),ᵃ ³¹ and sacrifice it as an offering for sin. He will take the other and sacrifice it as a burnt offering together with the grain offering. So in the LORD's presence the priest will make peace with the LORD for the one who is being cleansed. ³² These are the instructions for one who has an infectious skin disease but cannot afford what is needed for his cleansing."

Mildew in Houses

³³ The LORD spoke to Moses and Aaron, ³⁴ "When you come to Canaan that I am going to give to you, mildew may appear in a house. ³⁵ The owner of that house must come and tell the priest that there is something that looks like mildew in his house.

³⁶ "Before the priest examines the house, he will order everything taken out of it so that nothing in the house will become unclean. Then the priest will go inside to examine the house. ³⁷ He will examine the mildew area on the walls. If it is green and red in sunken areas that are deeper than the rest of the wall, ³⁸ the priest will go out to the door of the house and close up the house for seven days. ³⁹ On the seventh day the priest will go back and examine it again. If the mildew in the walls of the house has spread, ⁴⁰ the priest must order the stones that have the mildew to be torn out and thrown outside the city in an unclean place. ⁴¹ He must have the entire inside of the house scraped. The plaster dust scraped off the walls must be dumped in an unclean place outside the city. ⁴² The stones must be replaced, and the house must be plastered again. ⁴³ If the mildew develops again in the house after all this, ⁴⁴ the priest will examine it one more time. If it is a spreading type of mildew, the house is unclean. ⁴⁵ The house—stones, wood, and all the plaster—must be torn down and taken to an unclean place outside the city. ⁴⁶ Whoever goes into the house any time it is closed up will be unclean until evening. ⁴⁷ Whoever sleeps or eats in the house must wash his clothes. ⁴⁸ But if the priest comes and makes an examination and the mildew has not spread in the house after it is plastered again, the priest must declare the house clean. The mildew is gone.

⁴⁹ "The priest must take two birds, cedar wood, red yarn, and a hyssop sprig and use them to make the house clean. ⁵⁰ He must kill the one bird over a clay bowl containing fresh water. ⁵¹ He must take the cedar wood, the hyssop sprig, the red yarn, and the living bird and dip them in the fresh water containing the blood of the bird that was killed. He must sprinkle the house seven times. ⁵² So he must use the bird's blood, the fresh water, the living bird, the cedar wood, the hyssop, and the red yarn to make the house clean. ⁵³ Then he will let the living bird fly from the city into the open country. He will make peace with the LORD for the house, and it will be clean.

⁵⁴ "These are the instructions for any kind of mildew or fungus ⁵⁵ that infects clothing or houses ⁵⁶ and for skin diseases where there is a sore, a rash, or an irritated area. ⁵⁷ These instructions for skin diseases and mildew help you distinguish between what is clean and what is unclean."

Bodily Discharges From Men

15 ¹ The LORD spoke to Moses and Aaron, ² "Tell the Israelites: If a man has a discharge from his penis, his discharge is unclean. ³ He is unclean because of the discharge from his penis. Whether it is chronic or not makes no difference; he is still unclean.

⁴ "The man who has a discharge makes everything he lies on or sits on unclean. ⁵ Those who touch his bed must wash their clothes and their bodies. They will be unclean until

---

ᵃ 14:30 Greek, Syriac; Masoretic Text repeats "whichever he can afford."

evening. [6] Those who sit on anything he sat on must wash their clothes and their bodies. They will be unclean until evening. [7] Those who touch a man who has a discharge must wash their clothes and their bodies. They will be unclean until evening. [8] If a man who has a discharge spits on anyone who is clean, the person he spits on must wash his clothes and his body. He will be unclean until evening. [9] When a man who has a discharge sits on a saddle, it becomes unclean. [10] Those who carry such things must wash their clothes and their bodies. They will be unclean until evening. [11] If a man who has a discharge touches anyone without first rinsing his hands, the person he touched must wash his clothes and his body. He will be unclean until evening. [12] When a man who has a discharge touches pottery, it must be broken, and any wooden bucket he touches must be rinsed.

[13] "When a man's discharge stops, he must wait seven days to be cleansed. He must wash his clothes and his body in fresh water. Then he will be clean. [14] On the eighth day he must take two mourning doves or two pigeons and come into the LORD's presence at the entrance to the tent of meeting. He will give these birds to the priest. [15] The priest will sacrifice one as an offering for sin and the other as a burnt offering. So in the LORD's presence, the priest will make peace with the LORD for the man who had a discharge.

[16] "If a man has an emission of semen, he must bathe his whole body. He will be unclean until evening. [17] Any clothes or any leather with semen on it must be washed. It will be unclean until evening.

[18] "When a man has sexual intercourse with a woman and has an emission of semen, they must wash themselves. They will be unclean until evening.

Bodily Discharges From Women

[19] "When a woman has her monthly period, she will be unclean for seven days. Those who touch her will be unclean until evening. [20] Everything she lies on or sits on during her period will be unclean. [21] Those who touch her bed must wash their clothes and their bodies. They will be unclean until evening. [22] Those who touch anything she sits on must wash their clothes and their bodies. They will be unclean until evening. [23] If her blood touches anything on the bed or anything she sits on, it will be unclean until evening. [24] If a man has sexual intercourse with her while she has her period, he will be unclean for seven days. Any bed he lies on will become unclean.

[25] "If a woman has a discharge of blood for many days other than her monthly period, she is unclean. If her period lasts longer than usual, she will be unclean as long as she has a discharge. It is like her period. [26] As long as she has a discharge, any bed she lies on or anything she sits on is unclean. It is like her period. [27] Those who touch these things are unclean and must wash their clothes and their bodies. They will be unclean until evening.

[28] "When her discharge stops, she must wait seven days. After that, she will be clean. [29] On the eighth day she must take two mourning doves or two pigeons and bring them to the priest at the entrance to the tent of meeting. [30] The priest will offer one as an offering for sin and the other as a burnt offering. So in the LORD's presence the priest will make peace with the LORD for the woman who had an unclean discharge.

[31] "You must separate the Israelites from anything that keeps them from being presentable to me. Otherwise, they will die because they make my tent, which is among them, unclean.

[32] "These are the instructions for any man who has a discharge or an emission of semen that makes him unclean, [33] for any woman who has her period, for any man or woman who has a discharge, or for any man who has sexual intercourse with a woman when she is unclean."

The Day for Making Peace With the LORD

16 [1] The LORD spoke to Moses after Aaron's two sons had come into the LORD's presence and died. [2] The LORD said, "Tell your brother Aaron that he cannot go into the holy place whenever he wants to. If he goes up to the canopy and stands in front of the throne of mercy on the ark, he will die, because I appear in the smoke above the throne of mercy.

[3] "This is what Aaron must do in order to come into the holy place: He must take a bull as an offering for sin and a ram as a burnt offering. [4] He must put on a holy linen robe and wear linen undergarments. He must wear a linen belt and turban. These are holy clothes. He must wash his body and put them on. [5] He will take two male goats from the congregation of Israel as an offering for sin and a ram as a burnt offering.

[6] "Aaron must sacrifice the bull as his own offering for sin. By doing this, he will make peace with the LORD for himself and his family. [7] He must take the two male goats and bring them into the LORD's presence at the entrance to the tent of meeting. [8] Then Aaron must throw lots for the two goats. One lot will be for the LORD and the other for Azazel.[a] [9] Aaron must sacrifice the goat chosen by lot for the LORD as an offering for sin. [10] But he must bring the goat

---

[a] 16:8 Unknown Hebrew term.

chosen by lot for Azazel into the LORD's presence. He will release it in the desert to Azazel in order to make peace with the LORD for himself and his family.

[11] "Aaron will bring the bull. He will then slaughter it as his own offering for sin. By doing this he will make peace with the LORD for himself and his family. [12] He will take an incense burner full of burning coals from the altar, which is in the LORD's presence, and two handfuls of finely ground, sweet-smelling incense. He will bring them up to the canopy. [13] Then he will put the incense on the fire in the LORD's presence. The cloud of incense will cover the throne of mercy, which is over the words of God's promise, so that he will not die. [14] He will take some of the bull's blood and sprinkle it with his finger on the east side of the throne of mercy. Then he will sprinkle some of the blood with his finger seven times in front of the throne of mercy.

[15] "Next, Aaron will slaughter the goat for the people's offering for sin. He will take the blood inside, go up to the canopy, and sprinkle it on the throne of mercy and in front of it, as he did with the bull's blood. [16] So he will make peace with the LORD for all the sins the Israelites committed against the holy place. These sins happened because the Israelites were unclean and because they committed rebellious acts. He will do the same for the tent of meeting which is among an unclean people. [17] No one may be in the tent of meeting from the time Aaron enters the holy place to do this until he comes out. Aaron will make peace with the LORD for his own sins, his family's sins, and the sins of the entire assembly of Israel. [18] Then he will go out to the altar that is in the LORD's presence and make peace with the LORD there for the sins committed. He will take some of the blood from the bull and some of the goat's blood and put it all around the horns of the altar. [19] With his finger he will sprinkle some of the blood on it seven times. Because the Israelites made it unclean, he will cleanse it and declare it holy.

[20] "When he finishes making peace with the LORD at the holy place, the tent of meeting, and the altar, he will bring the living goat forward. [21] Aaron will place both hands on its head. He will confess over it all the sins, all the rebellious acts, and all the things the Israelites did wrong. He will transfer them to the goat's head. A man will be appointed to release the goat in the desert. [22] The goat will take all their sins away to a deserted place. The man must release the goat in the desert.

[23] "Then Aaron will go to the tent of meeting, take off the linen clothes he had put on to go into the holy place, and leave them there. [24] He will wash his body in the holy place and put on his other clothes. Then he will come out and sacrifice the burnt offering for himself and for the people to make peace with the LORD for his own sins and the sins of the people. [25] He will burn the fat of the offering for sin on the altar.

[26] "The man who released the goat to Azazel must wash his clothes and his body. Then he may return to the camp. [27] He must take the bull and the goat outside the camp. These animals were the offering for sin whose blood was brought into the holy place to make peace with the LORD for sins. The skin, meat, and excrement from the animals must be burned. [28] Whoever burns them must wash his clothes and his body. Then he may return to the camp.

[29] "This will be a permanent law for you: On the tenth day of the seventh month both native Israelites and foreigners must humble themselves. They must do no work. [30] On this day Aaron will make peace with the LORD to make you clean. Then you will be clean from all your sins in the LORD's presence. [31] This is the most important worship festival there is for you. You will humble yourselves. It is a permanent law. [32] The priest who is anointed and ordained to serve as chief priest in his father's place will pay for sins. He will put on the holy linen clothes [33] and will make peace with the LORD at the holy place, the tent of meeting, and the altar. He will make peace with the LORD for the priests and all the worshipers.

[34] "This permanent law tells you how to make peace with the LORD once a year for all the sins the Israelites committed."

Aaron did as the LORD had commanded Moses.

Eating Sacrifices

17 [1] The LORD spoke to Moses, [2] "Tell Aaron, his sons, and all the Israelites that this is what the LORD has commanded: [3] Any Israelite who slaughters a bull, sheep, or goat inside or outside the camp [4] is guilty of bloodshed. He has shed blood and must be excluded from the people. Bring the animal to the entrance of the tent of meeting. Offer it to the LORD in front of the LORD's tent. [5] This means, that the people of Israel must take the sacrifices they have been making in the open fields and bring them to the LORD. They must bring them to the priest at the entrance to the tent of meeting. The people will sacrifice them as fellowship offerings to the LORD. [6] The priest will pour the blood against the LORD's altar at the entrance to the tent of meeting. He will burn the fat as a soothing aroma to the LORD. [7] The people must stop sacrificing to goat idols and chasing after them as though they were prostitutes. This is a permanent law for the people and for future generations.

[8] "Tell them: If Israelites or foreigners make burnt offerings or sacrifices [9] but do not bring them to the entrance of the tent of meeting to offer them to the LORD, they must be excluded from the people.

Eating Blood

[10] "If Israelites or foreigners eat any blood, I will condemn them and exclude them from the people, [11] because blood contains life. I have given this blood to you to make peace with me on the altar. Blood is needed to make peace with me. [12] That is why I have said to the people of Israel: Neither you nor foreigners should ever eat blood.

[13] "If Israelites or foreigners hunt any animal or bird that may be eaten, they must pour out the animal's blood and cover it with dirt. [14] This is because the life of any creature is in its blood. So I have said to the people of Israel: Never eat any blood, because the life of any creature is in its blood. Whoever eats blood must be excluded from the people.

[15] "Native Israelites or foreigners who eat the body of an animal that dies naturally or is killed by another animal must wash their clothes and their bodies. They will be unclean until evening. Then they will be clean. [16] If they don't wash their clothes and their bodies, they will be guilty of sin."

Forbidden Sexual Practices

18 [1] The LORD spoke to Moses, [2] "Tell the Israelites: I am the LORD your God. [3] You used to live in Egypt. Don't live the way the Egyptians do. I am bringing you to Canaan. Don't live the way the Canaanites do. Never live by their standards. [4] Follow my rules, and live by my standards. I am the LORD your God. [5] Live by my standards, and obey my rules. You will have life through them. I am the LORD.

[6] "Never have sexual intercourse with anyone related to you by blood. I am the LORD.

[7] "Never have sexual intercourse with your mother. She is your own mother. Never have sexual intercourse with her. [8] Never have sexual intercourse with your stepmother. She is related to you through your father. [9] Never have sexual intercourse with your stepsister, whether she is your father's daughter or your mother's daughter. It makes no difference whether or not she was born in your house. [10] Never have sexual intercourse with your granddaughter, whether she is your son's daughter or your daughter's daughter, because she is related to you. [11] Never have sexual intercourse with a daughter of your father and his wife. She is your own sister. [12] Never have sexual intercourse with your father's sister. She is your paternal aunt. [13] Never have sexual intercourse with your mother's sister. She is your maternal aunt. [14] Never have sexual intercourse with the wife of your father's brother. She, too, is your aunt. [15] Never have sexual intercourse with your daughter-in-law. She is your son's wife. Never have sexual intercourse with her. [16] Never have sexual intercourse with your sister-in-law. She is your brother's wife. [17] Never have sexual intercourse with a woman and her daughter or a woman and her granddaughter. They are related. Doing this is perverted. [18] While your wife is living, never marry her sister as a rival wife and have sexual intercourse with her.

[19] "Never have sexual intercourse with a woman while she is unclean during her monthly period. [20] Never have sexual intercourse with your neighbor's wife and become unclean with her. [21] Never give your children as sacrifices to the god Molech by burning them alive. If you do, you are dishonoring the name of your God. I am the LORD. [22] Never have sexual intercourse with a man as with a woman. It is disgusting. [23] Never have sexual intercourse with any animal and become unclean with it. A woman must never offer herself to an animal for sexual intercourse. It is unnatural.

Punishment for Sexual Sins

[24] "Do not become unclean in any of these ways. By these practices all the nations which I am forcing out of your way have become unclean. [25] The land has become unclean. I will punish it for its sins. The land will vomit out those who live in it. [26] Live by my standards, and obey my rules. Neither you nor any foreigner should ever do any of these disgusting things. [27] The people of the land who were there before you did all these disgusting things. As a result, the land has become unclean. [28] If you make the land unclean, it will vomit you out as it has vomited out the people who were there before you. [29] Whoever does any of these disgusting things must be excluded from the people. [30] So you must follow my instructions. Don't live by the standards of the people who lived there before you. What they do is disgusting. Never become unclean that way. I am the LORD your God."

Duties of the People Toward God

19 [1] The LORD spoke to Moses, [2] "Tell the whole congregation of Israel: Be holy because I, the LORD your God, am holy.

³ "Respect your mother and father. Observe my days of worship. I am the LORD your God. **⁴** "Don't turn to worthless gods or cast metal idols. Never make any gods for yourselves. I am the LORD your God. **⁵** "When you bring a fellowship offering to the LORD, sacrifice it ˌproperlyˌ so that you will be accepted. **⁶** Eat your sacrifice on the day you bring it and on the next day. On the third day burn whatever is left over. **⁷** If you eat any of it on the third day, it is repulsive and will not be accepted. **⁸** Those who eat it will be punished because they have dishonored what is holy to the LORD. They must be excluded from the people.

Duties of the People Toward Each Other

⁹ "When you harvest the grain in your land, don't harvest the grain in the corners of your fields or gather what is left after you're finished. **¹⁰** Don't harvest your vineyard a second time or pick up fallen grapes. Leave them for poor people and foreigners. I am the LORD your God. **¹¹** "Never steal, lie, or deceive your neighbor. **¹²** "Never swear by my name in order to deceive anyone. This dishonors the name of your God. I am the LORD. **¹³** "Never oppress or rob your neighbor. Never keep the pay you owe a hired worker overnight. **¹⁴** Never curse deaf people or put anything in the way of blind people to make them stumble. Instead, fear your God. I am the LORD. **¹⁵** "Don't be corrupt when administering justice. Never give special favors to poor people, and never show preference to important people. Judge your neighbor fairly. **¹⁶** Never gossip. Never endanger your neighbor's life. I am the LORD. **¹⁷** "Never hate another Israelite. Be sure to correct your neighbor so that you will not be guilty of sinning along with him. **¹⁸** Never get revenge. Never hold a grudge against any of your people. Instead, love your neighbor as you love yourself. I am the LORD.

Other Duties

¹⁹ "Obey my laws. Never crossbreed different kinds of animals. Never plant two kinds of crops in your field. Never wear clothes made from two kinds of material. **²⁰** "If a man has sexual intercourse with a female slave who is engaged to another man and if her freedom was never bought or given to her, they should not be put to death. He will only pay a fine because she is a slave. **²¹** He must bring a ram for his guilt offering to the LORD at the entrance to the tent of meeting. **²²** In the LORD's presence the priest will use them to make peace with the LORD for this sin. The man will be forgiven for this sin. **²³** "When you come into the land and plant all kinds of fruit trees, you must not eat the fruit for ˌthe firstˌ three years. **²⁴** In the fourth year all the fruit will be a holy offering of praise to the LORD. **²⁵** In the fifth year you may eat the fruit. Do this to make the trees produce more for you. I am the LORD your God. **²⁶** "Never eat any meat with blood still in it.

"Never cast evil spells, and never consult fortunetellers. **²⁷** "Never shave the hair on your foreheads, and never cut the edges of your beard. **²⁸** Never slash your body to mourn the dead, and never get a tattoo. I am the LORD. **²⁹** "Never dishonor your daughter by making her a prostitute, or the country will turn to prostitution and be filled with people who are perverted. **³⁰** "Observe my days of worship and respect my holy tent. I am the LORD. **³¹** "Don't turn to psychics or mediums to get help. That will make you unclean. I am the LORD your God. **³²** "Show respect to the elderly, and honor older people. In this way you show respect for your God. I am the LORD. **³³** "Never mistreat a foreigner living in your land. **³⁴** Foreigners living among you will be like your own people. Love them as you love yourself, because you were foreigners living in Egypt. I am the LORD your God. **³⁵** "Don't be corrupt when administering justice concerning length, weight, or measuring liquid. **³⁶** Use honest scales, honest weights, and honest measures. I am the LORD your God who brought you out of Egypt. **³⁷** "Obey all my laws and all my rules, and live by them. I am the LORD."

Punishment for Serious Crimes

20 **¹** The LORD spoke to Moses, **²** "Tell the Israelites: If Israelites or foreigners living among you give one of their children as a sacrifice to ˌthe godˌ Molech, they must be put to death. The common people must stone them to death. **³** I will condemn them and exclude them from the people. They gave one of their children to Molech, made my holy tent unclean, and dishonored my holy name. **⁴** If the common people ignore those who give their children to Molech and do not put them to death, ⁵ I will condemn them and their families. I will exclude them from the people. I will exclude from the people everyone who chases after Molech as if he were a prostitute.

⁶ "I will condemn people who turn to mediums and psychics and chase after them as though they were prostitutes. I will exclude them from the people.

⁷ "Live holy lives. Be holy because I am the LORD your God. ⁸ Obey my laws, and live by them. I am the LORD who sets you apart as holy.

⁹ "Whoever curses his father or mother must be put to death. He has cursed his father or mother and deserves to die.

¹⁰ "If a man commits adultery with another man's wife or with his neighbor's wife, both he and the woman must be put to death for their adultery. ¹¹ Whoever has sexual intercourse with his father's wife has violated his father's marriage. Both he and his father's wife must be put to death. They deserve to die. ¹² If a man has sexual intercourse with his daughter-in-law, both of them must be put to death. They have done a disgusting thing and deserve to die. ¹³ When a man has sexual intercourse with another man as with a woman, both men are doing something disgusting and must be put to death. They deserve to die. ¹⁴ When a man marries a woman and her mother, they have done a perverted thing. The man and the two women must be burned. Never do this perverted thing. ¹⁵ A man who has sexual intercourse with an animal must be put to death. You must kill the animal, too. ¹⁶ When a woman offers herself sexually to any animal, you must kill both the woman and the animal. They must be put to death. They deserve to die. ¹⁷ Whoever takes his sister, his father's daughter or his mother's daughter and has sexual intercourse does a shameful thing. They both must be publicly excluded from the people. He has had sexual intercourse with his sister and must be punished. ¹⁸ If a man has sexual intercourse with a woman while she has her monthly period, both of them have had sexual intercourse in blood. They must be excluded from the people. ¹⁹ Never have sexual intercourse with your mother's sister or your father's sister. Whoever has sexual intercourse with a close relative must be punished. ²⁰ Whoever has sexual intercourse with his uncle's wife violates his uncle's marriage. That man and woman are guilty of sin. They will die without children. ²¹ Whoever marries his brother's wife violates his brother's marriage and does an unclean thing. That man and woman will have no children.

²² "If you carefully obey all my laws and my rules, the land I am bringing you to live in will not vomit you out. ²³ Never follow the practices of the people I am forcing out of your way. I cannot stand them because they did all these things. ²⁴ I have told you that you will take their land. I will give it to you as your own. It is a land flowing with milk and honey. I am the LORD your God who separated you from other people. ²⁵ Separate clean and unclean* animals and birds. Never become disgusting by eating any animal or bird or anything that crawls on the ground. I have separated you from every unclean thing. ²⁶ Be my holy people because I, the LORD, am holy. I have separated you from other people to be my very own.

²⁷ "Every man or woman who is a medium or a psychic must be put to death. They must be stoned to death because they deserve to die."

Holiness for All the Priests

21 ¹ The LORD spoke to Moses, "Tell the priests, Aaron's sons: None of you should become unclean by touching one of your relatives who has died. ² However, you are allowed to become unclean when one of your nearest relatives dies. These relatives include your mother, father, son, daughter, or brother, ³ and especially an unmarried virgin sister who is still close to you. ⁴ As the head of your people, you should never become unclean. That would make you unholy.

⁵ "You should never mourn by shaving bald spots on your heads, shaving the edges of your beards, or slashing your bodies.

⁶ "Be God's holy men, and don't dishonor the name of your God. Be holy because you bring sacrifices by fire to the LORD. It is the food of your God. ⁷ You should never marry prostitutes, those who have lost their virginity, or divorced women because a priest is God's holy man. ⁸ Be holy because you offer the food of your God. Be holy because I, the LORD, am holy. I set you apart as holy. ⁹ When a priest's daughter dishonors herself by becoming a prostitute, she dishonors her father. She must be burned.

Holiness for the Chief Priest

¹⁰ "The priest who is anointed with oil and wears the chief priest's clothes is chief over his brothers. He must never mourn by leaving his hair uncombed or by tearing his clothes. ¹¹ He must never go near any dead bodies or become unclean, even for his father or mother. ¹² He must not leave the holy tent of his God. If he does, he will be dishonoring it, because he is dedicated with the anointing oil of his God. I am the LORD.

ª 20:25 "Clean" refers to anything that is presentable to God. "Unclean" refers to anything that is not presentable to God.

¹³ "The anointed priest must marry a virgin. ¹⁴ He must never marry a widow, a divorced woman, a woman who has lost her virginity, or a prostitute. He may only marry a virgin from his own people. ¹⁵ He must not dishonor his children among his people because I, the LORD, set him apart as holy."

¹⁶ The LORD spoke to Moses, ¹⁷ "Tell Aaron: If any of your descendants (now or in future generations) has a physical defect, he must never bring food to offer to God. ¹⁸ Indeed, no one who has a physical defect may ever come near ˌthe altarˌ. That means anyone who is blind or lame, who has a disfigured face, a deformity, ¹⁹ or a crippled hand or foot, ²⁰ who is a hunchback or dwarf, who has defective sight, skin diseases, or crushed testicles. ²¹ If a descendant of the priest Aaron has a physical defect, he must never bring sacrifices by fire to the LORD. He has a defect. He must never bring food to offer to God. ²² He may eat the food of his God—what is holy and what is very holy. ²³ However, he must never come up to the canopy or to the altar, since he has a physical defect. He must never dishonor the holy places because I, the LORD, set them apart as holy."

²⁴ So Moses spoke to Aaron and his sons and to all the Israelites.

Eating the Priests' Share of the Sacrifice

22 ¹ The LORD spoke to Moses, ² "Tell Aaron and his sons that they must respect the holy offerings which the Israelites set apart for me. In this way they will not dishonor my holy name. I am the LORD.

³ "Tell them: In future generations if any of your descendants, while unclean, comes near the holy offerings the Israelites set apart for the LORD, that person must be excluded from my presence. I am the LORD.

⁴ "No descendant of Aaron who has a skin disease or a discharge may eat any of the holy offerings until he is clean. Any person who has an emission of semen or touches a dead body, ⁵ an unclean swarming creature, or an unclean person ⁶ will be unclean until evening. He must not eat any of the holy offerings unless he has washed himself. ⁷ When the sun has set, he will be clean. Then he may eat the holy offerings because they are his food. ⁸ He must never eat the meat of an animal that dies naturally or is killed by wild animals. It will make him unclean. I am the LORD. ⁹ The priests must do what I order, or their sin will bring them death because they dishonored a holy offering. I am the LORD, who sets them apart as holy.

¹⁰ "Laypeople must never eat any holy offering, even if they are visiting a priest or are working for him. ¹¹ But if a priest buys a slave, the slave and anyone born in his household may eat the priest's food. ¹² However, if a priest's daughter marries a layman, she must never eat the food taken from the holy contributions. ¹³ If a priest's daughter is widowed or divorced, doesn't have any children, and comes back to live in her father's home, she may eat her father's food. But a layperson must never eat it.

¹⁴ "Those who eat a holy offering by mistake must give another holy offering to the priest and add one-fifth more to it. ¹⁵ Priests must not dishonor the holy offerings that the Israelites contribute to the LORD. ¹⁶ They must make those people pay the penalty for their guilt because they have eaten the priests' holy offerings. I am the LORD, who sets them apart as holy."

Animals Accepted for Sacrifice

¹⁷ The LORD spoke to Moses, ¹⁸ "Tell Aaron, his sons, and all the Israelites: Israelites or foreigners may bring burnt offerings to the LORD for anything they vowed or as freewill offerings. ¹⁹ The offering must be a male that has no defects from your cattle, sheep, or goats in order to be accepted. ²⁰ Never bring any animal with a physical defect, because it will not be accepted on your behalf. ²¹ A person may bring the LORD a fellowship offering to fulfill a vow or for a freewill offering. Whether it is from the cattle, sheep, or goats, it must be an animal that has no defects in order to be accepted. It must never be an animal that has defects. ²² Never bring the LORD an animal that is blind, has broken bones, cuts, warts, scabs, or ringworm. Never give the LORD any of these in a sacrifice by fire on the altar. ²³ You may use a bull or a sheep with a deformity or one that is stunted in growth as a freewill offering. However, it will not be accepted for a vow. ²⁴ Never bring the LORD an animal that has bruised, crushed, torn out, or cut out testicles. Never do any of these things to an animal in your land. ²⁵ Never bring any kind of castrated animal received from a foreigner as a food offering for your God. A castrated animal will not be accepted on your behalf because castration is a physical defect."

²⁶ The LORD spoke to Moses, ²⁷ "When a calf, a lamb, or a goat is born, it must stay with its mother for seven days. From the eighth day on it may be accepted as a sacrifice by fire to the LORD. ²⁸ Never slaughter a cow or a sheep and its young the same day.

²⁹ "When you sacrifice a thank offering to the LORD, do it in the proper way. ³⁰ Eat it the same day. Never leave any of it until morning. I am the LORD.

[31] "Carefully obey my commands. I am the LORD. [32] Never dishonor my holy name. I will show my holiness among the Israelites. I am the LORD, who sets you apart as holy. [33] I brought you out of Egypt to be your God. I am the LORD."

The Day of Worship

23 [1] The LORD spoke to Moses, [2] "Tell the Israelites: These are the appointed festivals with the LORD, which you must announce as holy assemblies. [3] You may work for six days. But the seventh day is a day of worship, a day when you don't work, a holy assembly. Don't do any work. It is the LORD's day of worship wherever you live.

[4] "The following are the LORD's appointed festivals with holy assemblies, which you must announce at their appointed times.

The Spring Festivals

[5] "The fourteenth day of the first month, in the evening, is the LORD's Passover. [6] The fifteenth day of this same month is the LORD's Festival of Unleavened Bread. For seven days you must eat unleavened bread. [7] On the first day there will be a holy assembly. Don't do any regular work. [8] Bring the LORD a sacrifice by fire for seven days. On the seventh day there will be a holy assembly. Don't do any regular work."

[9] The LORD spoke to Moses, [10] "Tell the Israelites: When you come to the land I am going to give you and you harvest grain, bring the priest a bundle of the first grain you harvest. [11] He will present it to the LORD so that you will be accepted. He will present it on the day after Passover. [12] On the day you present the bundle, you must sacrifice a one-year-old male lamb that has no defects as a burnt offering to the LORD. [13] Bring a grain offering of four quarts of flour mixed with olive oil with it. This will be a sacrifice by fire made to the LORD, a soothing aroma. Use one quart of wine for the wine offering. [14] Don't eat bread, roasted grain, or fresh grain until this same day, when you bring the offering to your God. It is a permanent law for generations to come wherever you live.

[15] "Count seven full weeks from the day after Passover (the day you bring the bundle of grain as an offering presented to the LORD) [16] until the day after the seventh week. This is a total of fifty days. Then bring a new grain offering to the LORD. [17] Bring two loaves of bread from your homes to present to the LORD. Bake them with four quarts of flour. They are the first harvested grain for the LORD. [18] With the bread bring seven one-year-old lambs that have no defects, one bull, and two rams. They will be a burnt offering to the LORD. With these offerings also bring grain and wine offerings. They will be a sacrifice by fire, a soothing aroma to the LORD. [19] Also sacrifice one male goat as an offering for sin and two one-year-old lambs as a fellowship offering. [20] The priest must present them along with the bread of the first harvested grain as an offering to the LORD. All this, along with the two lambs, will be holy and will belong to the LORD's priests. [21] Make an announcement that there will be a holy assembly on that same day. Don't do any regular work. It is a permanent law for generations to come wherever you live.

[22] "When you harvest the grain in your land, don't harvest the grain in the corners of your fields or gather what is left after you're finished. Leave it for poor people and foreigners. I am the LORD your God."

The Fall Festivals

[23] The LORD spoke to Moses, [24] "Tell the Israelites: On the first day of the seventh month hold a worship festival. It will be a memorial day, a holy assembly announced by the blowing of rams' horns. [25] Don't do any regular work. Bring a sacrifice by fire to the LORD."

[26] The LORD spoke to Moses, [27] "In addition, the tenth day of this seventh month is a special day for the payment for sins. There will be a holy assembly. Humble yourselves, and bring the LORD a sacrifice by fire. [28] Don't do any work that day. It is a special day for the payment for sins. It is a time when you make peace with the LORD your God. [29] Those who do not humble themselves on that day will be excluded from the people. [30] I will kill those who do any work on that day. [31] Don't do any work. It is a permanent law for generations to come wherever you live. [32] It is a day of worship, a day when you don't work. Humble yourselves starting on the evening of the ninth day of the month. From that evening to the next, observe the day of worship."

[33] The LORD spoke to Moses, [34] "Tell the Israelites: The fifteenth day of this seventh month is the Festival of Booths to the LORD. It will last seven days. [35] On the first day there will be a holy assembly. Don't do any regular work. [36] For seven consecutive days bring a sacrifice by fire to the LORD. On the eighth day there will be a holy assembly. Bring the LORD a sacrifice by fire. This is the last festival of the year. Don't do any regular work.

[37] "These are the LORD's appointed festivals. Announce them as holy assemblies for bringing sacrifices by fire to the LORD. Bring burnt offerings, grain offerings, other sacrifices, and wine offerings—each one on its special day. [38] This is in addition to the LORD's days of worship, your gifts, all your vows, and your freewill offerings to the LORD.

[39] "However, on the fifteenth day of the seventh month, when you have gathered what the land produces, celebrate the LORD's festival for seven days. The first and the eighth days will be worship festivals. [40] On the first day take the best fruits, palm branches, the branches of leafy trees and poplars, and celebrate in the presence of the LORD your God for seven days. [41] It is the LORD's festival. Celebrate it for seven days each year. This is a permanent law for generations to come. Celebrate this festival in the seventh month. [42] Live in booths for seven days. Everyone born in Israel must live in booths [43] so that generations to come may learn how I made the people of Israel live in booths when I brought them out of Egypt. I am the LORD your God."

[44] So Moses told the Israelites about the LORD's appointed festivals.

Duties in the Tent of Meeting—*Exodus 27:20–21*

24 [1] The LORD spoke to Moses, [2] "Command the Israelites to bring you pure, virgin olive oil for the lamp stand so that the lamps won't go out. [3] In the tent of meeting, outside the canopy where the words of my promise are, Aaron must keep the lamps lit in the LORD's presence from evening until morning. It is a permanent law for generations to come. [4] Aaron must keep the lamps on the pure gold lamp stand lit in the LORD's presence.

[5] "Also take flour and bake twelve rings of bread. Each ring will contain four quarts of flour. [6] Put them in two stacks of six each on the gold table in the LORD's presence. [7] Lay pure incense on top of each stack. The incense on the bread will be a reminder, an offering by fire to the LORD. [8] Every day of worship ˻a priest˼ must arrange the bread in the LORD's presence. It is a continual reminder of my promise*a* to the Israelites. [9] The bread will belong to Aaron and his sons. They will eat ˻it in a holy place. It is very holy, set apart from the LORD's offering by fire. This is a permanent law."

The Man Who Cursed the LORD's Name

[10] A man, whose mother was Shelomith (daughter of Dibri, from the tribe of Dan in Israel) and whose father was from Egypt, got into a quarrel with an Israelite in the camp. [11] The Israelite woman's son began cursing the LORD's name and treating it with contempt. So they brought him to Moses.*b* [12] They kept him in custody until the LORD told them what to do.

[13] The LORD spoke to Moses, [14] "The man who cursed ˻my name˼ must be taken outside the camp. All who heard him curse ˻my name˼ must lay their hands on his head. Then the whole congregation must stone him to death.

[15] "Also tell the Israelites: Those who treat their God with contempt will be punished for their sin. [16] But those who curse the LORD's name must be put to death. The whole congregation must stone them to death. It makes no difference whether they are Israelites or foreigners. Whoever curses the LORD's name must die.

[17] "Whoever kills another person must be put to death. [18] Whoever kills an animal must replace it, life for life. [19] Whoever injures a neighbor must receive the same injury in return— [20] a broken bone for a broken bone, an eye for an eye, a tooth for a tooth. Whoever injures another person must receive the same injury in return. [21] Whoever kills an animal must replace it. Whoever kills a person must be put to death. [22] The same rule applies to every one of you. It makes no difference whether you are a foreigner or an Israelite, because I am the LORD your God."

[23] Moses spoke to the people of Israel. So the man who had cursed the LORD's name was taken outside the camp. There they stoned him to death as the LORD commanded Moses. The Israelites did as the LORD commanded Moses.

The Year to Honor the LORD

25 [1] The LORD spoke to Moses on Mount Sinai, [2] "Tell the Israelites: When you come into the land I'm giving you, the land will celebrate a year to honor the LORD. [3] Then, for six years you may plant crops in your fields, prune your vineyards, and gather what they produce. [4] However, the seventh year will be a festival year for the land. It will be a year to honor the LORD. Don't plant crops in your fields or prune your vineyards. [5] Don't harvest what grows by itself or harvest grapes from your vines. That year will be a festival for the land. [6] Whatever the land produces during that year is for all of you to eat—for you, your male and female slaves, your hired workers, foreigners among you, [7] your animals, and the wild animals in your land. Everything the land produces will be yours to eat.

The Jubilee for the Land

[8] "Count seven of these years seven times for a total of 49 years. [9] On the tenth day of the seventh month, the special day for the payment for sin, sound rams' horns throughout the

---

a 24:8 Or "covenant."   *b* 24:11 Part of verse 11 (in Hebrew) has been placed in verse 10 to express the complex Hebrew paragraph structure more clearly in English.

country. ¹⁰ Set apart the fiftieth year as holy, and proclaim liberty to everyone living in the land. This is your jubilee year. Every slave will be freed in order to return to his property and to his family. ¹¹ That fiftieth year will be your jubilee year. Don't plant or harvest what grows by itself or pick grapes from the vines in the land. ¹² The jubilee ˻year˼ will be holy to you. You will eat what the field itself produces.

¹³ "In this jubilee year every slave will be freed in order to return to his property. ¹⁴ If you sell anything to your neighbor or buy anything from him, don't take advantage of him. ¹⁵ When you buy property from your neighbor, take into account the number of years since the jubilee. Your neighbor must sell it to you taking into account the number of crops ˻until the next jubilee˼. ¹⁶ If there are still many years ˻until the jubilee˼, you will pay more for it. If there are only a few years ˻until the jubilee˼, you will pay less for it because he is selling you only the number of crops. ¹⁷ Never take advantage of each other. Fear your God, because I am the LORD your God.

¹⁸ "Obey my laws, and carefully follow my rules. Then you will live securely in the land. ¹⁹ The land will give you its products, and you will eat all you want and live there securely. ²⁰ You may ask, 'What will we eat in the seventh year if we do not plant or bring in our crops?' ²¹ I will give you my blessing in the sixth year so that the land will produce enough for three years. ²² You will plant ˻again˼ in the eighth year but live on what the land already produced. You will eat it, even in the ninth year, until the land produces more.

²³ "Land must never be sold permanently, because the land is mine. To me you are strangers without permanent homes. ²⁴ People must always have the right to buy their property back. ²⁵ If your brother becomes poor and sells some of his property, then the one who can assume responsibility, his nearest relative, must buy back what he sold. ²⁶ If a man doesn't have anyone to buy it back for him, but if he prospers and earns enough to buy it back himself, ²⁷ he must count the years from its sale. Then he will pay what is left to the man to whom he sold it, and it will be his property again. ²⁸ However, if he cannot earn enough to buy it back, what he sold stays in the hands of the buyer until the year of jubilee. In the jubilee it will be released, and he will own it again.

²⁹ "If anyone sells a home in a walled city, for one year after selling it he has the right to buy it back. He may buy it back only within that time. ³⁰ If he does not buy it back during that year, the house in the city belongs to the buyer for generations to come. It will not be released in the jubilee. ³¹ However, houses in villages without walls are regarded as belonging to the fields of the land. They can be bought back. They will be released in the jubilee.

³² "The Levites always have the right to buy back their property in the cities they own. ³³ If any Levite buys back ˻a house˼, in the jubilee the purchased house in the city will be released, because the houses in the Levite cities are their property among the Israelites. ³⁴ But a field that belongs to their cities must not be sold, because it is their permanent property.

The Jubilee for the People

³⁵ "If an Israelite becomes poor and cannot support himself, help him. He must live with you as a stranger without a permanent home. ³⁶ Don't collect interest or make any profit from him. Fear your God by respecting other Israelites' lives. ³⁷ Never collect any kind of interest on your money or on the food you give them. ³⁸ I am the LORD your God, who brought you out of Egypt to give you Canaan and to be your God.

³⁹ "If an Israelite becomes poor and sells himself to you, don't work him like a slave. ⁴⁰ He will be like a hired worker or a visitor to you. He may work with you until the year of jubilee. ⁴¹ Then you will release him and his children to go back to their family and the property of their ancestors. ⁴² They are my servants. I brought them out of Egypt. They must never be sold as slaves. ⁴³ Do not treat them harshly. Fear your God.

⁴⁴ "You may have male and female slaves, but buy them from the nations around you. ⁴⁵ You may also buy them from the foreigners living among you and from their families born in your country. They will be your property. ⁴⁶ You may acquire them for yourselves and for your descendants as permanent property. You may work them as slaves. However, do not treat the Israelites harshly. They are your relatives.

⁴⁷ "Someone who is a foreigner without a permanent home among you may become rich, and your relative living with him may be poor. The poor Israelite may sell himself to that foreigner or a member of his family. ⁴⁸ After he has sold himself, he has the right to be bought back. One of his brothers may buy him back. ⁴⁹ His uncle, his cousin, or some other relative could also buy him back. If he becomes rich, he could buy his own freedom. ⁵⁰ Then he and his buyer must take into account the number of years from the year he was bought until the year of jubilee. His sale price will be adjusted based on the number of years he was with his buyer, like the wages of a hired worker. ⁵¹ If there are many years left, he must refund from his purchase price an amount equal ˻to those years˼. ⁵² If there are only a few years left until the year of jubilee, he must take them into account. He must refund from his purchase price an

amount equal to those years. ⁵³ During those years he should serve his buyer as a hired worker. His buyer should not treat him harshly. ⁵⁴ If he cannot buy his freedom in these ways, he and his children will be released in the year of jubilee.

⁵⁵ "The Israelites belong to me as servants. They are my servants. I brought them out of Egypt. I am the LORD your God."

God's Promises for Those Who Keep His Laws

26 ¹ The LORD continued, "Never make worthless idols or set up a carved statue or a sacred stone for yourselves. Never cut figures in stone to worship them in your country, because I am the LORD your God. ² Observe my days of worship and respect my holy tent. I am the LORD.

³ "This is what I will do if you will live by my laws and carefully obey my commands:

⁴ "I will give you rain at the right time. The land will produce its crops, and the trees in the field will produce their fruit. ⁵ Threshing*ᵃ* time will last until grape gathering, and grape gathering will last until planting. You will eat all you want and live securely in your land.

⁶ "I will bring peace to your land. You will lie down with no one to scare you. I will remove dangerous animals, and there will be no war in your land. ⁷ You will chase your enemies, and you will defeat them. ⁸ Five of you will chase a hundred of them, and a hundred of you will chase ten thousand of them. You will defeat your enemies, ⁹ and I will be pleased with you. Your families will be large, and I will keep my promise*ᵇ* to you. ¹⁰ You will clear out old food supplies to make room for new ones.

¹¹ "I will put my tent among you, and I will never look at you with disgust. ¹² So I will live among you and be your God, and you will be my people. ¹³ I am the LORD your God. I brought you out of Egypt so that you are no longer slaves of the Egyptians. I have broken their power over you and made you live as a free people.

God's Curses for Those Who Break His Laws

¹⁴ "If you will not listen to me and obey all these commands, ¹⁵ if you reject my laws and look at my rules with disgust, if you reject my promise by disobeying my commands, ¹⁶ then this is what I will do to you: I will terrorize you with disease and fever. You will suffer from eye problems and depression. You will plant your crops and get nothing because your enemies will eat them. ¹⁷ I will condemn you so that you will go down in defeat in front of your enemies. Those who hate you will be your rulers. You will run away even when no one is chasing you.

¹⁸ "If you still will not listen to me, I will discipline you seven times for your sins. ¹⁹ I will crush your arrogance. You will have no rain, and your land will be as hard as cement. ²⁰ You will work hard for nothing because your land will produce no crops and the trees will produce no fruit.

²¹ "If you resist and don't listen to me, I will increase the punishment for your sins seven times. ²² I will send wild animals among you. They will rob you of your children, destroy your cattle, and make you so few that your roads will be deserted.

²³ "If this discipline does not help and you still resist, ²⁴ then I, too, will resist you. I will punish you seven times for your sins. ²⁵ I will bring war on you to get revenge for my promise that you rejected. When you gather in your cities, I will send plagues on you and you will fall under the control of your enemy. ²⁶ I will destroy your food supply. Ten women will need only one oven to prepare your food. You will eat and go away hungry.

²⁷ "If in spite of this you do not listen to me and still resist me, ²⁸ I will fiercely resist you. I will discipline you seven times for your sins. ²⁹ You will eat the bodies of your sons and daughters. ³⁰ I will destroy your worship sites, cut down your incense altars, and pile your dead bodies on top of your dead idols. I will look at you with disgust. ³¹ I will make your cities deserted and ruin your sacred places. I will no longer accept the soothing aroma from your sacrifices. ³² I will make your land so deserted that your enemies will be shocked as they settle in it. ³³ I will scatter you among the nations. War will follow you. Your country will be in ruins. Your cities will be deserted.

³⁴ "Then the land will enjoy its time to honor the LORD while it lies deserted and you are in your enemies' land. Then the land will joyfully celebrate its time to honor the LORD. ³⁵ All the days it lies deserted, it will celebrate the time to honor the LORD it never celebrated while you lived there. ³⁶ I will fill with despair those who are left in the land of their enemies. The sound of a windblown leaf will make them run. They will run away and fall, but no one will be chasing them. ³⁷ They will stumble over each other, but no one will be after them. They will not be able to stand up to their enemies. ³⁸ They will be destroyed among the nations. The land of their enemies will devour them. ³⁹ Those who are left will waste away in the lands of their enemies because of their sins and the sins of their ancestors.

ᵃ 26:5 Threshing is the process of beating stalks to separate them from the grain.   *ᵇ* 26:9 Or "covenant."

God Will Remember His Promise

[40] "But if they confess their sins and the sins of their ancestors—the treacherous things they did to oppose me— [41] I will oppose them and bring them into the lands of their enemies. Then, if they humble their uncircumcised hearts and accept their guilt, [42] I will remember my promise to Jacob, Isaac, and Abraham. I will also remember the land. [43] The land, abandoned by them, will enjoy its time to honor the LORD while it lies deserted without them. They must accept their guilt because they rejected my rules and looked at my laws with disgust. [44] Even when they are in the land of their enemies, I will not reject them or look at them with disgust. I will not reject or cancel my promise to them, because I am the LORD their God. [45] But for their sake, I will remember the promise to their ancestors. I brought them out of Egypt to be their God while nations looked on. I am the LORD."

[46] These are the laws, rules, and instructions that the LORD gave to the Israelites through Moses on Mount Sinai.

Special Vows

27 [1] The LORD spoke to Moses, [2] "Tell the Israelites: If any of you makes a special vow ⸗to give a person⸗ to the LORD, you may give money instead of the person. [3] The amount you must give for a man from 20 to 60 years old is 20 ounces of silver. Use the standard weight of the holy place. [4] If it is a woman, give 12 ounces. [5] For a boy from 5 to 20 years old, give 8 ounces and for a girl give 4 ounces. [6] For a boy from one month to five years old, give 2 ounces of silver and for a girl give about one ounce. [7] For a man 60 years or over, give 6 ounces and for a woman give 4 ounces. [8] But the person who is too poor to pay the required amount must stand in front of the priest. The priest will determine the amount based on what the person can afford.

[9] "If ⸗the vow⸗ is to give the kind of animal that people offer to the LORD, it will be considered holy. [10] Don't exchange or substitute animals, a good one for a bad one or a bad one for a good one. If you do exchange one animal for another, then both animals will be holy. [11] If it is an unclean animal that cannot be brought to the LORD as an offering, bring it in front of the priest. [12] The priest will determine what its value is. The value will be whatever the priest decides. [13] If you want to buy it back, you must pay its full value plus one-fifth more.

[14] "If you give your house to the LORD as something holy, the priest will determine what its value is. The value will be whatever the priest decides. [15] If you want to buy it back, you must pay its full value plus one-fifth more.

[16] "If a person gives part of a field to the LORD as something holy, its value will be based on the seed planted on it. Ground planted with 2 quarts of barley will be worth 20 ounces of silver. [17] If you give your field in the jubilee year, it will have its full value. [18] But if you give the field after the jubilee year, the priest will estimate its value based on the number of years left until the next jubilee year. [19] If you want to buy it back, you must pay its full value plus one-fifth more. [20] But if you don't buy it back and it is sold to someone else, you cannot buy it back. [21] When the field is released in the jubilee year, it will be holy like a field claimed by the LORD. It will become the property of the priest. [22] You may give a field you bought (not one that was a part of your family property) to the LORD as something holy. [23] The priest must figure out the field's value until the jubilee year. You will pay its value on that day as something holy, belonging to the LORD. [24] In the jubilee year the field will go back to the person from whom it was bought, to whom it belongs as family property.

[25] "All values will be set using the standard weight of the holy place.[a]

[26] "A firstborn animal already belongs to the LORD because it was born first. Therefore, it cannot be set apart as holy. Whether it is a bull or a sheep, it belongs to the LORD. [27] But if it is an unclean animal, it must be bought back. The payment will be its full value plus one-fifth more. If it is not bought back, it must be sold at the value given it.

[28] "However, everything dedicated to the LORD for destruction—a person, an animal, or a field that belongs to you—must not be sold or bought back. Everything dedicated in that way is very holy. It belongs to the LORD. [29] People dedicated this way cannot be bought back. They must be put to death.

[30] "One-tenth of what comes from the land, whether grain or fruit, is holy and belongs to the LORD. [31] If you buy back any part of it, you must add one-fifth more to it. [32] Every tenth head of cattle or sheep that you counted is holy and belongs to the LORD. [33] You must not look to see if it is good or bad or exchange it. But if you do exchange it, both the first animal and its substitute will be holy. They cannot be bought back."

[34] These are the commands the LORD gave Moses on Mount Sinai for the Israelites.

---

[a] 27:25 Hebrew adds "There are 20 gerahs to the standard shekel."

NUMBERS

Moses Takes a Census of Israel

1 ¹The LORD spoke to Moses in the tent of meeting in the Desert of Sinai. It was the first day of the second month in the second year after leaving Egypt. He said, ² "Take a census of the whole community of Israel by families and households. List every man by name ³ who is at least 20 years old. You and Aaron must register everyone in Israel who is eligible for military duty. List them by divisions. ⁴ One man from each tribe will help you. Each of these men must be the head of a household.

⁵ "Here are the names of the men who will help you:
Elizur, son of Shedeur, from the tribe of Reuben;
⁶ Shelumiel, son of Zurishaddai, from the tribe of Simeon;
⁷ Nahshon, son of Amminadab, from the tribe of Judah;
⁸ Nethanel, son of Zuar, from the tribe of Issachar;
⁹ Eliab, son of Helon, from the tribe of Zebulun;
¹⁰ Elishama, son of Ammihud, from the tribe of Ephraim;
Gamaliel, son of Pedahzur, from the tribe of Manasseh;
(Ephraim and Manasseh are Joseph's descendants.)
¹¹ Abidan, son of Gideoni, from the tribe of Benjamin;
¹² Ahiezer, son of Ammishaddai, from the tribe of Dan;
¹³ Pagiel, son of Ochran, from the tribe of Asher;
¹⁴ Eliasaph, son of Deuel, from the tribe of Gad;
¹⁵ Ahira, son of Enan, from the tribe of Naphtali."

¹⁶ These were the men chosen from the community, the leaders of their ancestors' tribes, and heads of the divisions of Israel.

¹⁷ Moses and Aaron took the men who had been named ¹⁸ and assembled the whole community on the first day of the second month. Each man at least 20 years old provided his genealogy by family and household. Then his name was listed. ¹⁹ So Moses registered the men of Israel in the Desert of Sinai as the LORD had commanded him.

²⁰ The roster of families and households for the descendants of **Reuben,** Israel's firstborn son, listed every man by name who was at least 20 years old and eligible for military duty. ²¹ The total for the tribe of Reuben was 46,500.

²² The roster of families and households for the descendants of **Simeon** registered and listed every man by name who was at least 20 years old and eligible for military duty. ²³ The total for the tribe of Simeon was 59,300.

²⁴ The roster of families and households for the descendants of **Gad** listed the men by name who were at least 20 years old and eligible for military duty. ²⁵ The total for the tribe of Gad was 45,650.

²⁶ The roster of families and households for the descendants of **Judah** listed the men by name who were at least 20 years old and eligible for military duty. ²⁷ The total for the tribe of Judah was 74,600.

²⁸ The roster of families and households for the descendants of **Issachar** listed the men by name who were at least 20 years old and eligible for military duty. ²⁹ The total for the tribe of Issachar was 54,400.

³⁰ The roster of families and households for the descendants of **Zebulun** listed the men by name who were at least 20 years old and eligible for military duty. ³¹ The total for the tribe of Zebulun was 57,400.

³² The roster of families and households for the descendants of **Joseph**—those from **Ephraim**—listed the men by name who were at least 20 years old and eligible for military duty. ³³ The total for the tribe of Ephraim was 40,500.

³⁴ The roster of families and households for the descendants of **Manasseh** listed the men by name who were at least 20 years old and eligible for military duty. ³⁵ The total for the tribe of Manasseh was 32,200.

³⁶ The roster of families and households for the descendants of **Benjamin** listed the men by name who were at least 20 years old and eligible for military duty. ³⁷ The total for the tribe of Benjamin was 35,400.

³⁸ The roster of families and households for the descendants of **Dan** listed the men by name who were at least 20 years old and eligible for military duty. ³⁹ The total for the tribe of Dan was 62,700.

⁴⁰ The roster of families and households for the descendants of **Asher** listed the men by name who were at least 20 years old and eligible for military duty. ⁴¹ The total for the tribe of Asher was 41,500.

⁴² The roster of families and households for the descendants of **Naphtali** listed the men by name who were at least 20 years old and eligible for military duty. ⁴³ The total for the tribe of Naphtali was 53,400.

⁴⁴ Moses, Aaron, and the 12 leaders of Israel, each representing his own family, added up these totals. ⁴⁵ So the Israelites were registered by households. The grand total of men who were at least 20 years old and eligible for military duty ⁴⁶ was 603,550.

⁴⁷ But the households from the tribe of **Levi** were not registered along with the other Israelites. ⁴⁸ The LORD had said to Moses, ⁴⁹ "Don't register the tribe of Levi or include them in the census with the other Israelites. ⁵⁰ Put the Levites in charge of the tent of God's words, including the equipment for the tent and everything else having to do with the tent. The Levites will carry the tent and all its equipment. They will take care of the tent and camp around it. ⁵¹ When the tent has to be moved, the Levites will take it down. When we camp, they will set it up. Anyone else who comes near the tent will be put to death.

⁵² "The other Israelites will camp with each family in its own area under its own flag. ⁵³ The Levites will camp all around the tent of God's words. In this way ˌthe LORDˌ won't be angry with the community of Israel. So the Levites will be in charge of the tent of God's words."

⁵⁴ The Israelites did everything as the LORD commanded Moses.

The Arrangement of Israel's Camp

2 ¹ The LORD spoke to Moses and Aaron, ² "The Israelites will put up their tents with each family under the flag that symbolizes its household. They will put their tents around the tent of meeting, facing it.

³ "On the east side, facing the rising sun, the armies led by **Judah** will camp under their flag. The leader for the people of Judah is Nahshon, son of Amminadab. ⁴ The total number of men in his army is 74,600.

⁵ "Next to them will be the tribe of **Issachar**. The leader for the people of Issachar is Nethanel, son of Zuar. ⁶ The total number of men in his army is 54,400.

⁷ "Then ˌwill beˌ the tribe of **Zebulun**. The leader for the people of Zebulun is Eliab, son of Helon. ⁸ The total number of men in his army is 57,400.

⁹ "The grand total of all the troops in Judah's camp is 186,400. They will be the first group to move out.

¹⁰ "On the south side the armies led by **Reuben** will camp under their flag. The leader for the people of Reuben is Elizur, son of Shedeur. ¹¹ The total number of men in his army is 46,500.

¹² "Next to them will be the tribe of **Simeon**. The leader for the people of Simeon is Shelumiel, son of Zurishaddai. ¹³ The total number of men in his army is 59,300.

¹⁴ "Then ˌwill beˌ the tribe of **Gad**. The leader for the people of Gad is Eliasaph, son of Deuel. ¹⁵ The total number of men in his army is 45,650.

¹⁶ "The grand total of all the troops in Reuben's camp is 151,450. They will be the second group to move out.

¹⁷ "When the tent of meeting is moved, the **Levites** will stay in the middle of the groups. The tribes will move out in the same order as they are in the camp, everyone in place under his own flag.

¹⁸ "On the west side the armies led by **Ephraim** will camp under their flag. The leader for the people of Ephraim is Elishama, son of Ammihud. ¹⁹ The total number of men in his army is 40,500.

²⁰ "Next to them will be the tribe of **Manasseh**. The leader for the people of Manasseh is Gamaliel, son of Pedahzur. ²¹ The total number of men in his army is 32,200.

²² "Then ˌwill beˌ the tribe of **Benjamin**. The leader for the people of Benjamin is Abidan, son of Gideoni. ²³ The total number of men in his army is 35,400.

²⁴ "The grand total of all the troops in Ephraim's camp is 108,100. They will be the third group to move out.

²⁵ "On the north side the armies led by **Dan** will camp under their flag. The leader for the people of Dan is Ahiezer, son of Ammishaddai. ²⁶ The total number of men in his army is 62,700.

²⁷ "Next to them will be the tribe of **Asher**. The leader for the people of Asher is Pagiel, son of Ochran. ²⁸ The total number of men in his army is 41,500.

²⁹ "Then will be the tribe of **Naphtali**. The leader for the people of Naphtali is Ahira, son of Enan. ³⁰ The total number of men in his army is 53,400.

³¹ "The grand total of all the men in Dan's camp is 157,600. They will be the last group to move out. They will travel under their own flag."

³² This is the total number of Israelites, counted by households. The grand total of all the troops in the camps was 603,550. ³³ As the LORD had commanded Moses, the Levites were not registered along with the other Israelites.

³⁴ So the Israelites did everything as the LORD had commanded Moses. They set up camp under their flags, and each person traveled with his own family and household.

The Tribe of Levi Is Registered and Assigned Duties

3 ¹ This is the list of Aaron and Moses' descendants at the time when the LORD spoke to Moses on Mount Sinai.

² The names of Aaron's sons are Nadab (the firstborn), Abihu, Eleazar, and Ithamar. ³ These are the names of Aaron's sons, the anointed priests, who were ordained to serve as priests. ⁴ Nadab and Abihu died in the LORD's presence because they offered unauthorized fire in his presence in the Desert of Sinai. They had no children. So only Eleazar and Ithamar served as priests during the lifetime of their father Aaron.

⁵ The LORD said to Moses, ⁶ "Bring the tribe of Levi, and have them stand in front of the priest Aaron to assist him. ⁷ They will work for him and the whole community in front of the tent of meeting, doing what needs to be done for the inner tent. ⁸ They will take care of all the furnishings in the tent of meeting and work for the Israelites, doing what needs to be done for the inner tent. ⁹ Give the Levites to Aaron and his sons. The Levites will be the only Israelites given to them. ¹⁰ Appoint Aaron and his sons to serve as priests. Anyone else who tries to do the priests' duties must be put to death."

¹¹ The LORD said to Moses, ¹² "Out of all the Israelites, I have taken the Levites to be substitutes for every firstborn male offspring among them. The Levites are mine, ¹³ because every firstborn is mine. The day I killed every firstborn male in Egypt, I set apart as holy every firstborn in Israel, whether human or animal. They will be mine. I am the LORD."

¹⁴ The LORD said to Moses in the Desert of Sinai, ¹⁵ "Count the Levites by households and families. Count every male who is at least one month old." ¹⁶ So Moses did what the LORD said and registered them as he had been commanded.

¹⁷ Gershon, Kohath, and Merari were the sons of Levi.

¹⁸ Libni and Shimei were the sons of Gershon. Their families were named after them.

¹⁹ Amram, Izhar, Hebron, and Uzziel were the sons of Kohath. Their families were named after them.

²⁰ Mahli and Mushi were the sons of Merari. Their families were named after them.

These were the households of Levite families.

²¹ To Gershon belonged the families descended from Libni and Shimei. These were the families descended from **Gershon**. ²² The total number of all the males at least one month old was 7,500. ²³ The families descended from Gershon put up their tents on the west side behind the tent of meeting. ²⁴ The leader of the Gershonite households was Eliasaph, son of Lael. ²⁵ At the tent of meeting the Gershonites were in charge of the inner tent, the outer tent and cover, the screen for the entrance to the tent of meeting, ²⁶ the curtains for the courtyard, the screen for the entrance to the courtyard that surrounds the inner tent and the altar, and the ropes. They took care of all these things.

²⁷ To **Kohath** belonged the families descended from Amram, Izhar, Hebron, and Uzziel. These were the families descended from Kohath. ²⁸ The number of all the males at least one month old was 8,600. They were in charge of the holy place. ²⁹ The families descended from Kohath put up their tents on the south side of the tent of meeting. ³⁰ The leader of the Kohathite families and households was Elizaphan, son of Uzziel. ³¹ They were in charge of the ark, the table, the lamp stand, the altars, the utensils used in the holy place, and the screen. They took care of all these things.

³² The chief leader of the Levites was Eleazar, son of the priest Aaron. It was Eleazar's duty to supervise those who were in charge of the holy place.

³³ To **Merari** belonged the families descended from Mahli and Mushi. These were the families descended from Merari. ³⁴ The total number of all the males at least one month old was 6,200. ³⁵ The leader of the Merarite families and households was Zuriel, son of Abihail. They put up their tents on the north side of the tent of meeting. ³⁶ It was the duty of the Merarites to be in charge of the framework of the inner tent, the crossbars, posts, sockets, and all the equipment. They took care of all these things. ³⁷ They also took care of the posts for the surrounding courtyard, the bases, pegs, and ropes.

³⁸ Moses, Aaron, and his sons put up their tents on the east side in front of the tent of meeting. They were in charge of the holy place on behalf of the Israelites. Anyone else who tried to do the Levites' duties had to be put to death.

³⁹ The grand total of Levites that Moses and Aaron counted at the LORD's command, by families, every male who was at least one month old, was 22,000.

⁴⁰ The LORD said to Moses, "Register every firstborn male of the Israelites who is at least one month old, and make a list of their names. ⁴¹ I am the LORD. Take the Levites for me to be substitutes for all firstborn Israelites. Also take the animals of the Levites to be substitutes for all firstborn animals of the Israelites."

⁴² So Moses registered all the firstborn Israelites as the LORD commanded him. ⁴³ The total of all the firstborn males at least one month old was 22,273. They were listed by name.

⁴⁴ The LORD said to Moses, ⁴⁵ "Take the Levites to be substitutes for all the firstborn Israelites and the animals of the Levites to be substitutes for their animals. The Levites will be mine. I am the LORD. ⁴⁶ There are 273 more firstborn male Israelites than there are Levites. ⁴⁷ It will cost you two ounces of silver per person (using the standard weight of the holy place) to buy them back. ⁴⁸ Give the silver to Aaron and his sons. It will buy back those Israelites who outnumber the Levites."

⁴⁹ So Moses took this ransom money from the Israelites who outnumbered the Levites. ⁵⁰ The silver Moses collected for the firstborn Israelites weighed 34 pounds using the standard weight of the holy place. ⁵¹ Then Moses did what the LORD said and gave Aaron and his sons this ransom money as he had been commanded.

The Duties of the Families Descended From Levi's Sons

4 ¹ The LORD said to Moses and Aaron, ² "Take a census of the Levites who are descended from Kohath. List them by families and households. ³ Register all the men between the ages of 30 and 50 who are qualified to work at the tent of meeting.

⁴ "This is the work the Kohathites will do in the tent of meeting: They will take care of the most holy things. ⁵ When the camp is supposed to move, Aaron and his sons will go in and take down the canopy that hangs over the ark containing the words of God's promise. First they will cover the ark with the canopy. ⁶ Over this they will put a covering of fine leather.ᵃ On top of that they will spread a cloth made entirely of violet material. Then they will put the poles in place.

⁷ "They will spread a violet cloth over the table of the presence and put on it the plates, dishes, bowls, and pitchers for the wine offerings. The bread that is always in the LORD's presence will also be on it. ⁸ They will spread a bright red cloth over everything on the table. They will cover all this with fine leather. Then they will put the poles in place.

⁹ "They will take a violet cloth and cover the lamp stand, as well as the lamps, tongs, trays, and all the containers for the olive oil used in the lamps. ¹⁰ Then they will put the lamp stand and all its utensils under a covering of fine leather and put them on a frame to carry them.

¹¹ "They will spread a violet cloth over the gold altar and cover the cloth with fine leather. Then they will put the poles in place.

¹² "They will take all the articles that are used in the holy place, put them in a violet cloth, cover that with fine leather, and put them on a frame to carry them.

¹³ "After they take the ashes away, they will spread a purple cloth over the altar. ¹⁴ Next, they will put all the accessories used at the altar on it. These are the trays, forks, shovels, and bowls—all the altar's accessories. They will spread a covering of fine leather over all this. Then they will put the poles in place.

¹⁵ "When Aaron and his sons have finished covering the holy things and the camp is ready to move, the Kohathites will come to carry all the holy articles. They must never touch the holy things, or they will die. The Kohathites will carry all the things from the tent of meeting.

¹⁶ "Eleazar, son of the priest Aaron, will be in charge of the oil for the lamps, the sweet-smelling incense, the daily grain offering, and the anointing oil. He is in charge of the whole tent and everything in it, the holy place and its contents."

¹⁷ The LORD said to Moses and Aaron, ¹⁸ "Don't let the Kohathite families from Levi's tribe be destroyed. ¹⁹ This is what you must do so that they won't die when they come near the most holy things: Aaron and his sons will go into the holy place and tell each man what he will do and what he will carry. ²⁰ But the Kohathites must not go in to look at the holy things, even for a moment, or they will die."

²¹ The LORD said to Moses, ²² "Also take a census of the Gershonites. List them by households and families. ²³ Register all the men between the ages of 30 and 50 who are qualified to serve at the tent of meeting.

ᵃ 4:6 Hebrew meaning uncertain.

²⁴ "This is what the Gershonite families will do and what they will carry: ²⁵ They will carry the sheets that are part of the inner tent and the tent of meeting. They will also carry the inner cover for the tent of meeting, the outer cover of fine leather that goes over it, the screen for the entrance to the tent of meeting, ²⁶ the curtains for the courtyard around the tent and the altar, the screen for the entrance to the courtyard, the ropes, and all the equipment used to set up the curtains. The Gershonites will do everything that needs to be done with these things. ²⁷ All their work, whatever they carry and all their duties, will be done under the direction of Aaron and his sons. You are in charge of telling them everything they're supposed to carry. ²⁸ This is the work of the Gershonite families in the tent of meeting. Ithamar, son of the priest Aaron, will be in charge of them.

²⁹ "Register the Merarites by families and households. ³⁰ Register all the men between the ages of 30 and 50 who are qualified to serve at the tent of meeting. ³¹ These are their duties as they work at the tent of meeting: They will carry the framework for the inner tent, the cross-bars, posts, and sockets, ³² the posts for the surrounding courtyard, the bases, pegs, and ropes. They must take care of all this equipment. Tell each man by name the things he will carry. ³³ This is what the Merarite families will do as they work at the tent of meeting. Ithamar, son of the priest Aaron, will be in charge of them."

³⁴ Moses, Aaron, and the leaders of the community registered the Kohathites by their families and households. ³⁵ They registered all the men between the ages of 30 and 50 who were qualified to work at the tent of meeting. ³⁶ The total of those who were registered was 2,750. They were listed by families. ³⁷ This was the total of all those in the Kohathite families who served at the tent of meeting. Moses and Aaron did as the LORD had commanded Moses and registered the Kohathites.

³⁸ The Gershonites were registered by families and households. ³⁹ All the men between the ages of 30 and 50 who were qualified to serve at the tent of meeting were registered. ⁴⁰ The total of those who were registered was 2,630. They were listed by families and households. ⁴¹ This was the total of all those in the Gershonite families who worked at the tent of meeting. Moses and Aaron did as the LORD had commanded Moses and registered the Gershonites.

⁴² The Merarites were registered by families and households. ⁴³ All the men between the ages of 30 and 50 who were qualified to serve at the tent of meeting were registered. ⁴⁴ The total of all those who were registered was 3,200. They were listed by families. ⁴⁵ This was the total of those registered in the Merarite families. Moses and Aaron did as the LORD had commanded Moses and registered the Merarites.

⁴⁶ The grand total of all the Levites whom Moses, Aaron, and the leaders of Israel registered was 8,580. They were listed by families and households. ⁴⁷ These were the men between the ages of 30 and 50 who were qualified to do the work of serving and who carried the tent of meeting.ᵇ ⁴⁹ At the LORD's command through Moses each man was registered and told what to do and what to carry.

So they were registered as the LORD commanded Moses.

Removing Unclean People From the Camp

5 ¹ The LORD said to Moses, ² "Command the Israelites to send outside the camp anyone who has a serious skin disease or a discharge or anyone who is uncleanᵃ from touching a dead body. ³ Send all of these unclean men and women outside the camp. They must not make this camp where I live among you unclean." ⁴ So the Israelites did as the LORD had told Moses. They sent these unclean people outside the camp.

Confessing and Paying for Sins

⁵ The LORD said to Moses, ⁶ "Tell the Israelites: If you do something wrong to another person, you have been unfaithful to the LORD. When you realize your guilt, ⁷ you must confess your sin, pay in full for what you did wrong, add one-fifth to it, and give it to the person who was wronged. ⁸ But there may be no heir to whom the payment can be made. In that case, the payment for what you did wrong must be given to the LORD for the priest ⌞to use⌟. This payment is in addition to the ram which makes peace with the LORD.

⁹ "Any contribution over and above the holy offerings that the Israelites bring to the priest will belong to the priest. ¹⁰ Each person's holy offerings will belong to that person, but whatever is given to the priest will belong to the priest."

When a Husband Suspects That His Wife Has Been Unfaithful

¹¹ The LORD said to Moses: ¹² "Speak to the Israelites and tell them: A man's wife may have been unfaithful to him ¹³ and may have had sexual intercourse with another man without her

---

ᵇ 4:47 Verse 48 (in Hebrew) has been placed in verse 46 to express the complex Hebrew sentence structure more clearly in English.   ᵃ 5:2 "Unclean" refers to anything that is not presentable to God.

husband's knowledge. She may have kept it secret if there were no witnesses to accuse her and she wasn't caught in the act.

14 "A husband may have a fit of jealousy and suspect his wife, whether she was actually unfaithful or not. **15** He must then take his wife to the priest along with eight cups of barley flour as an offering for her. He must not pour olive oil on the flour or put frankincense on it, since it is a grain offering brought because of the husband's jealousy, an offering used for a confession—to remind someone of a sin that was committed.

16 "The husband will have the woman come forward and stand in the LORD's presence. **17** Then the priest will take holy water in a piece of pottery and put some dust from the floor of the tent into the water. **18** The priest will bring the woman into the LORD's presence and loosen her hair. In her hands he will put the offering used for a confession (that is, the grain offering brought because of the husband's jealousy). The priest will hold in his hands the bitter water that can bring a curse.*ᵇ*

19 "Then the priest will say to her, 'If no other man has had sexual intercourse with you and you haven't been unfaithful to your husband, you're not guilty. This bitter water that can bring a curse will not harm you. **20** If, in fact, you have been unfaithful and have had sexual intercourse with another man, **21** may the LORD make you an example for your people to see what happens when the curse of this oath comes true: The LORD will make your uterus drop and your stomach swell.'*ᶜ*

"Then the priest will administer the oath and the curse by saying: **22** 'May this water that can bring a curse go into your body and make your stomach swell and your uterus drop!'

"Then the woman will say, 'Amen, amen!'

23 "The priest will write these curses on a scroll and wash them off into the bitter water. **24** Then he will have the woman drink the bitter water that can bring the curse. This water will go into her ⌊and⌋ become bitter. **25** The priest will take the grain offering she was holding, present it to the LORD, and bring it to the altar. **26** The priest will take a handful of the grain offering as a memorial portion and burn it on the altar. Then he will have the woman drink the water. **27** If she has become unclean by being unfaithful to her husband, the water that can bring the curse will go into her and become bitter. Her stomach will swell, her uterus will drop, and she will become cursed among her people. **28** But if the woman is not unclean and is pure, she is not guilty and will be able to have children.

29 "These are the instructions for how to deal with jealousy. They tell you what to do when a woman is unfaithful to her husband and becomes unclean. **30** They also tell you what to do when a husband has a fit of jealousy and is suspicious of his wife. He will make his wife stand in the LORD's presence, and the priest will do everything these instructions tell him to do. **31** The husband isn't guilty of doing anything wrong, but the woman will suffer the consequences of her sin."

Taking a Special Vow

6 **1** The LORD said to Moses, **2** "Speak to the Israelites and tell them: A man or a woman may make a special vow to live as a Nazirite dedicated to the LORD. **3** Nazirites must never drink wine, liquor, vinegar made from wine or liquor, or any kind of grape juice, and they must never eat fresh grapes or raisins. **4** As long as they are Nazirites, they must never eat anything that comes from a grapevine, not even grape seeds or skins.

5 "As long as they are under the Nazirite vow, no razor may touch their heads. During the entire time that they are dedicated to the LORD as Nazirites, they will be holy. They must let their hair grow long. **6** While they are dedicated to the LORD as Nazirites, they must never go near a dead body. **7** Even if their own father, mother, brother, or sister dies, they must not make themselves unclean*ᵃ* by going near them. Nazarites show their vow to God with their long hair. **8** As long as they are Nazirites, they will be holy to the LORD.

9 "Someone might suddenly drop dead next to a Nazirite and make the Nazirite's hair unclean. Seven days later he must shave his head in order to be declared clean.*ᵇ* **10** On the eighth day he must bring two mourning doves or two young pigeons to the priest at the entrance to the tent of meeting. **11** The priest will sacrifice one as an offering for sin and the other one as a burnt offering. The priest will make peace with the LORD for the person who touched the dead body. That same day the person must dedicate his head again. **12** Once again he will dedicate himself to the LORD as a Nazirite for the same length of time as before. He must bring a one-year-old male lamb as an offering for guilt. The first time period won't count. He has to start over from when he became unclean.

ᵇ 5:18 In this verse and the following verses there is a play on words between the Hebrew words *hammarîm* (bitter) and *hame 'araîm* (that can bring a curse). *ᶜ* 5:21 Or "make you have miscarriages and become sterile." *ᵃ* 6:7 "Unclean" refers to anything that is not presentable to God. *ᵇ* 6:9 "Clean" refers to anything that is presentable to God.

¹³ "These are the instructions for Nazirites who complete their vows: They must come to the entrance of the tent of meeting. ¹⁴ They must bring these offerings to the LORD: a one-year-old male lamb as a burnt offering, a one-year-old female lamb as an offering for sin, and a ram as a fellowship offering. All of these animals must have no defects. ¹⁵ They must also bring a basket of unleavened bread containing some rings of bread made with olive oil and wafers of unleavened bread brushed with olive oil, along with other grain offerings and wine offerings.

¹⁶ "The priest will bring these offerings to the LORD and make the offering for sin and the burnt offering. ¹⁷ He will sacrifice the ram as a fellowship offering to the LORD, offer the basket of unleavened bread along with it, and make the grain offerings and wine offerings.

¹⁸ "Then the Nazirites will shave their heads at the entrance to the tent of meeting, take the hair as proof that they had made this vow, and put it on the fire under the fellowship offering.

¹⁹ "Then the priest will take one of the shoulders from a boiled ram, one ring of unleavened bread from the basket, and one wafer of unleavened bread and hand them to the Nazirites after they have shaved off their hair. ²⁰ The priest will present them as an offering to the LORD. They are holy and belong to the priest, along with the ram's breast that is presented and the thigh that is given. After that, the Nazirites may drink wine.

²¹ "These are the instructions for those who have vowed to bring their offerings to the LORD because they were Nazirites. They must bring these offerings in addition to anything else they can afford. They must fulfill the requirements of these instructions for Nazirites and finish whatever they vowed to do."

How Aaron and His Sons Will Bless the Israelites

²² The LORD said to Moses, ²³ "Tell Aaron and his sons, 'This is how you will bless the Israelites. Say to them:

²⁴   The LORD will bless you and watch over you.
²⁵   The LORD will smile on you and be kind to you.
²⁶   The LORD will look on you with favor and give you peace.'

²⁷ "So whenever they use my name to bless the Israelites, I will bless them."

Offerings for the Dedication of the Altar

7 ¹ When Moses finished setting up the tent, he anointed it and dedicated it and all the furnishings. He also anointed and dedicated the altar and all the utensils. ² Then the leaders of Israel, the heads of the households—those tribal leaders who helped in the census—came to give their offerings. ³ They brought these gifts to the LORD: six freight wagons and twelve oxen, one wagon from every two leaders and one ox from each leader. They brought them in front of the tent.

⁴ The LORD said to Moses, ⁵ "Accept these gifts from them to use in the work done for the tent of meeting. Give them to the Levites to use wherever they need these gifts for their work." ⁶ Moses took the wagons and the oxen and gave them to the Levites. ⁷ He gave two wagons and four oxen to the Gershonites for the work they had to do. ⁸ He gave four wagons and eight oxen to the Merarites for the work they had to do under the direction of Ithamar, son of the priest Aaron. ⁹ But Moses gave none of these gifts to the Kohathites, because they took care of the holy things. They had to carry the holy things on their own shoulders.

¹⁰ The leaders also brought offerings for the dedication of the altar when it was anointed. They presented their gifts in front of the altar. ¹¹ The LORD said to Moses, "Each day a different leader will bring his gift for the dedication of the altar."

¹² The one who brought his gifts on the first day was Nahshon, son of Amminadab, from the tribe of **Judah.** ¹³ He brought a silver plate that weighed 3¼ pounds and a silver bowl that weighed 1¾ pounds using the standard weight of the holy place. Each dish was filled with flour mixed with olive oil as a grain offering. ¹⁴ He also brought a gold dish that weighed 4 ounces, filled with incense; ¹⁵ a young bull, a ram, and a one-year-old male lamb as a burnt offering; ¹⁶ a male goat as an offering for sin; ¹⁷ and two bulls, five rams, five male goats, and five one-year-old male lambs as a fellowship offering. These were the gifts from Nahshon, son of Amminadab.

¹⁸ On the second day Nethanel, son of Zuar, the leader from the tribe of **Issachar,** brought his gifts. ¹⁹ He brought a silver plate that weighed 3¼ pounds and a silver bowl that weighed 1¾ pounds using the standard weight of the holy place. Each dish was filled with flour mixed with olive oil as a grain offering. ²⁰ He also brought a gold dish that weighed 4 ounces, filled with incense; ²¹ a young bull, a ram, and a one-year-old male lamb as a burnt offering; ²² a male goat as an offering for sin; ²³ and two bulls, five rams, five male goats, and five one-year-old male lambs as a fellowship offering. These were the gifts from Nethanel, son of Zuar.

²⁴ On the third day the leader of the descendants of **Zebulun,** Eliab, son of Helon, ²⁵ brought his gifts: a silver plate that weighed 3¼ pounds and a silver bowl that weighed 1¾ pounds

using the standard weight of the holy place. Each dish was filled with flour mixed with olive oil as a grain offering. [26] He also brought a gold dish that weighed 4 ounces, filled with incense; [27] a young bull, a ram, and a one-year-old male lamb as a burnt offering; [28] a male goat as an offering for sin; [29] and two bulls, five rams, five male goats, and five one-year-old male lambs as a fellowship offering. These were the gifts from Eliab, son of Helon.

[30] On the fourth day the leader of the descendants of **Reuben,** Elizur, son of Shedeur, [31] brought his gifts: a silver plate that weighed 3¼ pounds and a silver bowl that weighed 1¾ pounds using the standard weight of the holy place. Each dish was filled with flour mixed with olive oil as a grain offering. [32] He also brought a gold dish that weighed 4 ounces, filled with incense; [33] a young bull, a ram, and a one-year-old male lamb as a burnt offering; [34] a male goat as an offering for sin; [35] and two bulls, five rams, five male goats, and five one-year-old male lambs as a fellowship offering. These were the gifts from Elizur, son of Shedeur.

[36] On the fifth day the leader of the descendants of **Simeon,** Shelumiel, son of Zurishaddai, [37] brought his gifts: a silver plate that weighed 3¼ pounds and a silver bowl that weighed 1¾ pounds using the standard weight of the holy place. Each dish was filled with flour mixed with olive oil as a grain offering. [38] He also brought a gold dish that weighed 4 ounces, filled with incense; [39] a young bull, a ram, and a one-year-old male lamb as a burnt offering; [40] a male goat as an offering for sin; [41] and two bulls, five rams, five male goats, and five one-year-old male lambs as a fellowship offering. These were the gifts from Shelumiel, son of Zurishaddai.

[42] On the sixth day the leader of the descendants of **Gad,** Eliasaph, son of Deuel, [43] brought his gifts: a silver plate that weighed 3¼ pounds and a silver bowl that weighed 1¾ pounds using the standard weight of the holy place. Each dish was filled with flour mixed with olive oil as a grain offering. [44] He also brought a gold dish that weighed 4 ounces, filled with incense; [45] a young bull, a ram, and a one-year-old male lamb as a burnt offering; [46] a male goat as an offering for sin; [47] and two bulls, five rams, five male goats, and five one-year-old male lambs as a fellowship offering. These were the gifts from Eliasaph, son of Deuel.

[48] On the seventh day the leader of the descendants of **Ephraim,** Elishama, son of Ammihud, [49] brought his gifts: a silver plate that weighed 3¼ pounds and a silver bowl that weighed 1¾ pounds using the standard weight of the holy place. Each dish was filled with flour mixed with olive oil as a grain offering. [50] He also brought a gold dish that weighed 4 ounces, filled with incense; [51] a young bull, a ram, and a one-year-old male lamb as a burnt offering; [52] a male goat as an offering for sin; [53] and two bulls, five rams, five male goats, and five one-year-old male lambs as a fellowship offering. These were the gifts from Elishama, son of Ammihud.

[54] On the eighth day the leader of the descendants of **Manasseh,** Gamaliel, son of Pedahzur, [55] brought his gifts: a silver plate that weighed 3¼ pounds and a silver bowl that weighed 1¾ pounds using the standard weight of the holy place. Each dish was filled with flour mixed with olive oil as a grain offering. [56] He also brought a gold dish that weighed 4 ounces, filled with incense; [57] a young bull, a ram, and a one-year-old male lamb as a burnt offering; [58] a male goat as an offering for sin; [59] and two bulls, five rams, five male goats, and five one-year-old male lambs as a fellowship offering. These were the gifts from Gamaliel, son of Pedahzur.

[60] On the ninth day the leader of the descendants of **Benjamin,** Abidan, son of Gideoni, [61] brought his gifts: a silver plate that weighed 3¼ pounds and a silver bowl that weighed 1¾ pounds using the standard weight of the holy place. Each dish was filled with flour mixed with olive oil as a grain offering. [62] He also brought a gold dish that weighed 4 ounces, filled with incense; [63] a young bull, a ram, and a one-year-old male lamb as a burnt offering; [64] a male goat as an offering for sin; [65] and two bulls, five rams, five male goats, and five one-year-old male lambs as a fellowship offering. These were the gifts from Abidan, son of Gideoni.

[66] On the tenth day the leader of the descendants of **Dan,** Ahiezer, son of Amishaddai, [67] brought his gifts: a silver plate that weighed 3¼ pounds and a silver bowl that weighed 1¾ pounds using the standard weight of the holy place. Each dish was filled with flour mixed with olive oil as a grain offering. [68] He also brought a gold dish that weighed 4 ounces, filled with incense; [69] a young bull, a ram, and a one-year-old male lamb as a burnt offering; [70] a male goat as an offering for sin; [71] and two bulls, five rams, five male goats, and five one-year-old male lambs as a fellowship offering. These were the gifts from Ahiezer, son of Amishaddai.

[72] On the eleventh day the leader of the descendants of **Asher,** Pagiel, son of Ochran, [73] brought his gifts: a silver plate that weighed 3¼ pounds and a silver bowl that weighed 1¾ pounds using the standard weight of the holy place. Each dish was filled with flour mixed with olive oil as a grain offering. [74] He also brought a gold dish that weighed 4 ounces, filled with incense; [75] a young bull, a ram, and a one-year-old male lamb as a burnt offering; [76] a male goat as an offering for sin; [77] and two bulls, five rams, five male goats, and five one-year-old male lambs as a fellowship offering. These were the gifts from Pagiel, son of Ochran.

[78] On the twelfth day the leader of the descendants of **Naphtali,** Ahira, son of Enan, [79] brought his gifts: a silver plate that weighed 3¼ pounds and a silver bowl that weighed 1¾

pounds using the standard weight of the holy place. Each dish was filled with flour mixed with olive oil as a grain offering. [80] He also brought a gold dish that weighed 4 ounces, filled with incense; [81] a young bull, a ram, and a one-year-old male lamb as a burnt offering; [82] a male goat as an offering for sin; [83] and two bulls, five rams, five male goats, and five one-year-old male lambs as a fellowship offering. These were the gifts from Ahira, son of Enan.

[84] These were the gifts from the leaders of Israel for the dedication of the altar when it was anointed: 12 silver plates, 12 silver bowls, and 12 gold dishes. [85] Each silver plate weighed 3¼ pounds, and each bowl weighed 1¾ pounds. Together all the silver dishes weighed 60 pounds using the standard weight of the holy place. [86] The 12 gold dishes filled with incense weighed 4 ounces each using the standard weight of the holy place. Together all the gold dishes weighed about 3 pounds. [87] The total number of animals for the burnt offerings was 12 young bulls, 12 rams, 12 one-year-old male lambs, along with their grain offerings. Twelve male goats were used as offerings for sin. [88] The total number of animals for fellowship offerings was 24 bulls, 60 rams, 60 male goats, and 60 one-year-old male lambs. These were the gifts for the dedication of the altar after it was anointed.

[89] Whenever Moses went into the tent of meeting to speak with the LORD, he heard the voice speaking to him from above the throne of mercy on the ark containing the words of God's promise, from between the two angels.[a] This is how the LORD spoke with Moses.

The Lamp Stand in the Tent

8 [1] The LORD said to Moses, [2] "Speak to Aaron and tell him: When you set up the seven lamps on the lamp stand, they should light up the area in front of it."

[3] So Aaron set up the lamps on the lamp stand to light up the area in front of it, as the LORD commanded Moses.

[4] This is how the lamp stand was made: The whole lamp stand, from top to bottom, was hammered out of gold. It was made exactly like the one the LORD had shown Moses.

The Levites Are Made Ready to Do the LORD's Work

[5] The LORD said to Moses, [6] "Separate the Levites from the rest of the Israelites, and make them clean.[a] [7] This is what you must do to make them clean: Sprinkle them with water to take away their sins. Make them shave their whole bodies and wash their clothes. Then they will be clean. [8] Next, they must take a young bull and the grain offering of flour mixed with olive oil that is offered with it. You must take a second young bull as an offering for sin. [9] Bring the Levites to the front of the tent of meeting, and assemble the whole community of Israel. [10] Then bring the Levites into the LORD's presence, and the Israelites will place their hands on them. [11] Aaron will present the Levites to the LORD as an offering from the Israelites. Then they will be ready to do the LORD's work.

[12] "The Levites will place their hands on the heads of the young bulls. Sacrifice one of them as an offering for sin and the other one as a burnt offering to the LORD. These sacrifices will make peace with the LORD for the Levites. [13] Make the Levites stand in front of Aaron and his sons, and present them as an offering to the LORD. [14] In this way you will separate the Levites from the other Israelites, and the Levites will be mine.

[15] "Once you have made them clean and presented them as an offering, the Levites may come and do their work at the tent of meeting. [16] They will be the only Israelites given to me. I have taken them to be mine as substitutes for every firstborn male offspring of the Israelites. [17] Every firstborn in Israel, whether human or animal, is mine. The day I killed every firstborn male in Egypt, I set them apart as holy to me. [18] So I have taken the Levites as substitutes for all the firstborn sons of the Israelites. [19] The Levites will be the only Israelites I give to Aaron and his sons. They will work for the Israelites at the tent of meeting. They will make peace with the LORD for the Israelites. Then no plague will strike the Israelites when they come near the holy place."

[20] Moses, Aaron, and the whole community of Israel did what the LORD commanded Moses to do to the Levites. [21] The Levites performed the ceremonies to take away their sins and washed their clothes. Aaron presented them as an offering to the LORD and made peace with the LORD for them in order to make them clean. [22] After that, the Levites came and did their work at the tent of meeting in the presence of Aaron and his sons. They did as the LORD had commanded Moses.

[23] The LORD said to Moses, [24] "These are the instructions for the Levites: Men 25 years old or older are eligible to serve at the tent of meeting. [25] But when they're 50 years old, they must retire from active service and not work anymore. [26] They may assist the other Levites in their duties at the tent of meeting, but they may not do any regular work. This is how you will handle the Levites' duties."

---

[a] 7:89 Or "cherubim."   [a] 8:6 "Clean" refers to anything that is presentable to God.

The Second Passover

9 [1] In the first month of the second year after the Israelites left Egypt, the LORD spoke to Moses in the Desert of Sinai. He said, [2] "The Israelites must celebrate the Passover at the same time every year. [3] You must celebrate it on the fourteenth day of this month at dusk. Follow all the rules and regulations for the celebration of the Passover."

[4] So Moses told the Israelites to celebrate the Passover, [5] and they celebrated it on the fourteenth day of the first month at dusk while they were in the Desert of Sinai. The Israelites did everything as the LORD had commanded Moses.

[6] But there were some men who had become unclean[a] from touching a dead body, and they couldn't celebrate the Passover that day. They came to Moses and Aaron [7] and said, "We are unclean because we touched a dead body. Why won't you let us bring our offerings to the LORD at the same time the rest of the Israelites bring their offerings?"

[8] Moses answered them, "Wait here until I find out what the LORD commands you to do."

[9] Then the LORD said to Moses, "Tell the Israelites: [10] Suppose you or any of your descendants is unclean from touching a dead body or is away on a long trip. You may still celebrate the Passover. [11] You will celebrate it on the fourteenth day of the second month at dusk. You must eat the Passover animal along with unleavened bread and bitter herbs. [12] You must never leave any of the meat until morning or break any of the animal's bones. You must follow all the rules for the Passover when you celebrate it. [13] But if you are clean[b] and not on a trip and yet don't bother to celebrate the Passover, you must be excluded from the people. You didn't bring your offering to the LORD at the right time. You must suffer the consequences for your sin.

[14] "Foreigners living with you may want to celebrate the LORD's Passover. They must follow these same rules and regulations. The same rules will apply to foreigners and native-born Israelites."

The Column of Smoke Leads Israel Through the Desert

[15] On the day the tent of the words of God's promise was set up, the ˌcolumn ofˌ smoke covered it. From evening until morning, the smoke over the tent glowed like fire. [16] The smoke always glowed this way. At night the smoke covering the tent glowed like fire. [17] Whenever the smoke moved from the tent, the Israelites would break camp, and wherever it stopped, the Israelites would set up camp. [18] At the LORD's command the Israelites would break camp, and at his command they would set up camp. As long as the ˌcolumn ofˌ smoke stayed over the tent, they would stay in the same place. [19] When the smoke stayed over the tent for a long time, the Israelites obeyed the LORD's command and wouldn't break camp. [20] The same thing happened when the smoke stayed only a few days over the tent: At the LORD's command they would set up camp, and at his command they would break camp. [21] Sometimes the ˌcolumn ofˌ smoke stayed only from evening until morning. When the smoke moved in the morning, they broke camp. Day or night, when the smoke moved, they broke camp. [22] Whether it was two days, a month, or a year, as long as the ˌcolumn ofˌ smoke stayed over the tent, the Israelites would stay in the same place and not break camp. But when the smoke moved, they would break camp. [23] At the LORD's command they set up camp, and at his command they broke camp. They obeyed the command that the LORD had given through Moses.

Two Silver Signal Trumpets

10 [1] The LORD said to Moses, [2] "Make two trumpets out of hammered silver. Use them to call the community together and as a signal to break camp. [3] When you blow both trumpets, the whole community will meet with you at the entrance to the tent of meeting. [4] If only one trumpet blows, the leaders, the heads of the divisions of Israel, will meet with you. [5] When they hear the trumpet fanfare, the tribes that are camped on the east side will break camp first. [6] When the trumpets sound a second fanfare, the tribes that are camped on the south will break camp. The fanfare is the signal to break camp. [7] But when you gather the assembly, the trumpets will blow without sounding a fanfare. [8] The sons of Aaron, the priests, will blow the trumpets. This will be a permanent law for you and your descendants.

[9] "When you go to war in your own country against an enemy who is oppressing you, the trumpets will sound a fanfare. Then the LORD your God will remember you and rescue you from your enemies. [10] Also, on your festival days and on the first day of the month, blow the trumpets when you sacrifice your burnt offerings and fellowship offerings. The trumpets will be a reminder for you in God's presence. I am the LORD your God."

---

[a] 9:6 "Unclean" refers to anything that is not presentable to God.   [b] 9:13 "Clean" refers to anything that is presentable to God.

Israel Leaves Mount Sinai

[11] On the twentieth day of the second month of the second year, the ˎcolumn ofˏ smoke left the tent of the words of God's promise. [12] So the Israelites moved from the Desert of Sinai and traveled from place to place until the ˎcolumn ofˏ smoke stopped in the Desert of Paran. [13] This was the first time they moved, following the command that the LORD had given through Moses. [14] With their flag in front, the armies led by Judah's descendants broke camp first. Nahshon, son of Amminadab, was in command. [15] Nethanel, son of Zuar, commanded the army of Issachar. [16] Eliab, son of Helon, commanded the army of Zebulun. [17] Then the tent ˎofˏ meetingˏ was taken down, and the Gershonites and Merarites, who carried it, broke camp. [18] With their flag in front, the armies led by Reuben's descendants broke camp next. Elizur, son of Shedeur, was in command. [19] Shelumiel, son of Zurishaddai, commanded the army of Simeon. [20] Eliasaph, son of Deuel, commanded the army of Gad. [21] Then the Kohathites, who carried the holy things, broke camp. By the time they arrived, the tent ˎof meetingˏ would already be set up. [22] With their flag in front, the armies led by Ephraim's descendants broke camp next. Elisha, son of Ammihud, was in command. [23] Gamaliel, son of Pedahzur, commanded the army of Manasseh. [24] Abidan, son of Gideoni, commanded the army of Benjamin. [25] As a rear guard for the whole camp, the armies led by Dan's descendants broke camp last with their flag in front. Ahiezer, son of Ammishaddai, was in command. [26] Pagiel, son of Ochran, commanded the army of Asher. [27] Ahira, son of Enan, commanded the army of Naphtali. [28] This was the order in which the Israelite armies broke camp when they went from place to place.

[29] Moses said to his brother-in-law Hobab, son of Reuel the Midianite, "We are going to the place the LORD promised to give us. Come with us. We will be good to you, because the LORD has promised good things to Israel." [30] Hobab answered, "No, I won't go. I want to go back to my own country where my relatives are." [31] But Moses said, "Please don't leave us. You know where we can set up camp in the desert, and you could be our guide. [32] If you come with us, we will share with you all the good things the LORD gives us."

[33] So they left the mountain of the LORD and traveled for three days. The ark of the LORD's promise went ahead of them a distance of three days' journey to find them a place to rest. [34] The LORD's ˎcolumn ofˏ smoke was over them by day when they moved the camp. [35] Whenever the ark started to move, Moses would say,

> "Arise, O LORD!
>   Scatter your enemies!
>   Make those who hate you run away from you!"

[36] And whenever it stopped, he would say,

> "Return, O LORD, to the countless thousands of Israel!"

The People of Israel Demand Meat to Eat

11 [1] The people began complaining out loud to the LORD about their troubles. When the LORD heard them, he became angry, and fire from the LORD began to burn among them. It destroyed some people on the outskirts of the camp. [2] The people cried out to Moses, Moses prayed to the LORD, and the fire died down. [3] That place was called Taberah [Fire] because fire from the LORD burned among them there.

[4] Some foreigners among the Israelites had a strong craving for ˎother kinds ofˏ food. Even the Israelites started crying again and said, "If only we had meat to eat! [5] Remember all the free fish we ate in Egypt and the cucumbers, watermelons, leeks, onions, and garlic we had? [6] But now we've lost our appetite! Everywhere we look there's nothing but manna!" [7] (Manna was ˎsmallˏ like coriander seeds and looked like resin. [8] The people would go around and gather it, then grind it in a handmill or crush it in a mortar. They would cook it in a pot or make round loaves of bread out of it. It tasted like rich pastry made with olive oil. [9] When dew fell on the camp at night, manna fell with it.)

[10] Moses heard people from every family crying at the entrance to their tents. The LORD became very angry, and Moses didn't like it either. [11] So he asked, "LORD, why have you brought me this trouble? How have I displeased you that you put the burden of all these people on me? [12] Am I their mother? Did I give birth to them? Are you really asking me to carry them in my arms—as a nurse carries a baby—all the way to the land you promised their ancestors with an oath? [13] Where can I get meat for all these people? They keep crying for me to give

them meat to eat. [14] I can't take care of all these people by myself. This is too much work for me! [15] If this is how you're going to treat me, why don't you just kill me? I can't face this trouble anymore."

[16] The LORD answered Moses, "Bring me 70 Israelite men who you know are leaders and officers of the people. Take them to the tent of meeting, and have them stand with you. [17] I'll come down and speak with you there. I'll take some of the Spirit that is on you and put it on them. They will help you take care of the people. You won't have to take care of the people alone. [18] Tell the people to get ready for tomorrow. They must be set apart as holy. Then they will eat meat. I, the LORD, heard them crying and saying, 'If only we had meat to eat! We were better off in Egypt!' So I will give them meat. [19] They won't eat it just for one or two days, or five, or ten, or twenty days, [20] but for a whole month, until it comes out of their ears and they're sick of it. This is because they rejected the LORD who is here among them and cried in front of him, asking, 'Why did we ever leave Egypt?' "

[21] But Moses said, "Here I am with 600,000 foot soldiers around me. Yet, you say, 'I will give them meat to eat for a whole month!' [22] Would they have enough if all the flocks and herds were butchered for them? Would they have enough if all the fish in the sea were caught for them?"

[23] The LORD asked Moses, "Is there a limit to the LORD's power? Now you will see whether or not my words come true."

[24] Moses went out and told the people what the LORD said. He gathered 70 of the leaders of the people and had them stand around the tent. [25] Then the LORD came down in the ˎcolumn ofˎ smoke and spoke with him. He took some of the Spirit that was on Moses and put it on the 70 leaders. When the Spirit came to rest on them, they prophesied, but they never prophesied again.

[26] Two men, named Eldad and Medad, had stayed in the camp. They were on the list with the other leaders but hadn't gone with them to the tent. The Spirit came to rest on them, too, and they prophesied in the camp.

[27] Then a young man ran and told Moses, "Eldad and Medad are prophesying in the camp." [28] So Joshua, son of Nun, who had been Moses' assistant ever since he was a young man, spoke up and said, "Stop them, sir!"

[29] But Moses asked him, "Do you think you need to stand up for me? I wish all the LORD's people were prophets and that the LORD would put his Spirit on them."

[30] Then Moses and the leaders went back to the camp.

[31] The LORD sent a wind from the sea that brought quails and dropped them all around the camp. There were quails on the ground about three feet deep as far as you could walk in a day in any direction.

[32] All that day and night and all the next day the people went out and gathered the quails. No one gathered less than 60 bushels. Then they spread the quails out all around the camp.

[33] While the meat was still in their mouths—before they had even had a chance to chew it—the LORD became angry with the people and struck them with a severe plague. [34] That place was called Kibroth Hattaavah [Graves of Those Who Craved ˎMeatˎ] because there they buried the people who had a strong craving ˎfor meatˎ.

[35] From Kibroth Hattaavah the people moved to Hazeroth, and they stayed there.

Miriam and Aaron Oppose Moses

12 [1] Miriam and Aaron began to criticize Moses because he was married to a woman from Sudan. [2] They asked, "Did the LORD speak only through Moses? Didn't he also speak through us?" The LORD heard their complaint.

[3] (Moses was a very humble man, more humble than anyone else on earth.)

[4] Suddenly, the LORD said to Moses, Aaron, and Miriam, "All three of you come to the tent of meeting." So all three of them came. [5] Then the LORD came down in the column of smoke and stood at the entrance to the tent. He called to Aaron and Miriam, and they both came forward.

[6] He said, "Listen to my words: When there are prophets of the LORD among you, I make myself known to them in visions or speak to them in dreams. [7] But this is not the way I treat my servant Moses. He is the most faithful person in my household.[a] [8] I speak with him face to face, plainly and not in riddles. He even sees the form of the LORD. Why weren't you afraid to criticize my servant Moses?"

[9] The LORD was angry with them, so he left.

[10] When the smoke left the tent, Miriam was covered with an infectious skin disease. She was as white as snow. Aaron turned to her and saw she was covered with the disease. [11] So he said to Moses, "Please, sir, don't punish us for this foolish sin we committed. [12] Don't let her be like a stillborn baby that's not completely developed."

---

[a] 12:7 Or "He is in charge of my entire household."

¹³ So Moses cried to the LORD, "Please, God, heal her!"

¹⁴ The LORD replied to Moses, "If her own father had spit in her face, wouldn't she be excluded from the community for seven days? She must be put in isolation outside the camp for seven days. Then she can be brought back." ¹⁵ So Miriam was put in isolation outside the camp for seven days. The people didn't break camp until she was brought back.

¹⁶ After that, the people moved from Hazeroth and set up camp in the Desert of Paran.

Moses Sends Out 12 Spies

13 ¹ The LORD said to Moses, ² "Send men to explore Canaan, which I'm giving to the Israelites. Send one leader from each of their ancestors' tribes."

³ So at the LORD's command, Moses sent these men from the Desert of Paran. All of them were leaders of the Israelites.

⁴ These are their names:
Shammua, son of Zaccur, from the tribe of Reuben;
⁵ Shaphat, son of Hori, from the tribe of Simeon;
⁶ Caleb, son of Jephunneh, from the tribe of Judah;
⁷ Igal, son of Joseph, from the tribe of Issachar;
⁸ Hoshea, son of Nun, from the tribe of Ephraim;
⁹ Palti, son of Raphu, from the tribe of Benjamin;
¹⁰ Gaddiel, son of Sodi, from the tribe of Zebulun;
¹¹ Gaddi, son of Susi, from the tribe of Joseph (that is, the tribe of Manasseh);
¹² Ammiel, son of Gemalli, from the tribe of Dan;
¹³ Sethur, son of Michael, from the tribe of Asher;
¹⁴ Nahbi, son of Vophsi, from the tribe of Naphtali;
¹⁵ Geuel, son of Machi, from the tribe of Gad.
¹⁶ These are the names of the men Moses sent to explore the land. But Moses gave Hoshea, son of Nun, the name Joshua.

¹⁷ When Moses sent them to explore Canaan, he told them, "Go through the Negev and then into the mountain region. ¹⁸ See what the land is like and whether the people living there are strong or weak, few or many. ¹⁹ Is the land they live in good or bad? Do their cities have walls around them or not? ²⁰ Is the soil rich or poor? Does the land have trees or not? Do your best to bring back some fruit from the land." (It was the season when grapes were beginning to ripen.)

²¹ So the men explored the land from the Desert of Zin to the border of Hamath. ²² They went through the Negev and came to Hebron, where Ahiman, Sheshai, and Talmai lived. They are descendants of Anak. (Hebron was built seven years before Zoan in Egypt.) ²³ When they came to the Eshcol Valley, they cut off a branch with only one bunch of grapes on it. They carried it on a pole between two of them. They also brought some pomegranates and figs. ²⁴ So they called that valley Eshcol [Bunch of Grapes] because of the bunch of grapes the Israelites cut off there.

²⁵ Forty days later, they came back from exploring the land. ²⁶ They came back to Moses, Aaron, and the whole community of Israel at Kadesh in the Desert of Paran. They gave their report and showed them the fruit from the land.

²⁷ This is what they reported to Moses: "We went to the land where you sent us. It really is a land flowing with milk and honey. Here's some of its fruit. ²⁸ But the people who live there are strong, and the cities have walls and are very large. We even saw the descendants of Anak there. ²⁹ The Amalekites live in the Negev. The Hittites, Jebusites, and Amorites live in the mountain region. And the Canaanites live along the coast of the Mediterranean Sea and all along the Jordan River."

³⁰ Caleb told the people to be quiet and listen to Moses. Caleb said, "Let's go now and take possession of the land. We should be more than able to conquer it."

³¹ But the men who had gone with him said, "We can't attack those people! They're too strong for us!" ³² So they began to spread lies among the Israelites about the land they had explored. They said, "The land we explored is one that devours those who live there. All the people we saw there are very tall. ³³ We saw Nephilim there. (The descendants of Anak are Nephilim.) We felt as small as grasshoppers, and that's how we must have looked to them."

The People Rebel Against the LORD

14 ¹ Then all the people in the Israelite community raised their voices and cried out loud all that night. ² They complained to Moses and Aaron, "If only we had died in Egypt or this desert! ³ Why is the LORD bringing us to this land—just to have us die in battle? Our wives and children will be taken as prisoners of war! Wouldn't it be better for us to go back to Egypt?" ⁴ They said to each other, "Let's choose a leader and go back to Egypt."

[5] Immediately, Moses and Aaron bowed with their faces touching the ground in front of the whole community of Israel assembled there. [6] At the same time, two of those who had explored the land, Joshua (son of Nun) and Caleb (son of Jephunneh), tore their clothes in despair. [7] They said to the whole community of Israel, "The land we explored is very good. [8] If the LORD is pleased with us, he will bring us into this land and give it to us. This is a land flowing with milk and honey! [9] Don't rebel against the LORD, and don't be afraid of the people of the land. We will devour them like bread. They have no protection, and the LORD is with us. So don't be afraid of them."

[10] But when the whole community of Israel talked about stoning Moses and Aaron to death, they all saw the glory of the LORD ˻shining˼ at the tent of meeting. [11] The LORD said to Moses, "How long will these people treat me with contempt? How long will they refuse to trust me in spite of all the miraculous signs I have done among them? [12] I'll strike them with a plague, I'll destroy them,[a] and I'll make you into a nation larger and stronger than they are."

[13] But Moses said to the LORD, "What if the Egyptians hear about it? (You used your power to take these people away from them.) [14] What if the Egyptians tell the people who live in this land? LORD, they have already heard that you are with these people, that they have seen you with their own eyes, that your column of smoke stays over them, and that you go ahead of them in a column of smoke by day and in a column of fire by night. [15] But if you kill all these people at the same time, then the nations who have heard these reports about you will say, [16] 'The LORD wasn't able to bring these people into the land he promised them, so he slaughtered them in the desert.'

[17] "Lord, let your power be as great as when you said, [18] 'The LORD. . .patient, forever loving. . . . He forgives wrongdoing and disobedience. . . . He never lets the guilty go unpunished, punishing children. . . for their parents' sins to the third and fourth generation. . . .' [19] By your great love, please forgive these people's sins, as you have been forgiving them from the time they left Egypt until now."

[20] The LORD said, "I forgive them, as you have asked. [21] But as I live and as the glory of the LORD fills the whole earth, I solemnly swear that [22] none of the people who saw my glory and the miraculous signs I did in Egypt and in the desert will see the land which I promised their ancestors. They have tested me now ten times and refused to obey me.[b] [23] None of those who treat me with contempt will see it! [24] But because my servant Caleb has a different attitude and has wholeheartedly followed me, I'll bring him to the land he already explored. His descendants will possess it. [25] (The Amalekites and Canaanites are living in the valleys.) Tomorrow you must turn around, go back into the desert, and follow the road that goes to the Red Sea."

[26] Then the LORD said to Moses and Aaron, [27] "How long must I put up with this wicked community that keeps complaining about me? I've heard the complaints the Israelites are making about me. [28] So tell them, 'As I live, declares the LORD, I solemnly swear I will do everything to you that you said I would do. [29] Your bodies will drop dead in this desert. All of you who are at least 20 years old, who were registered and listed, and who complained about me will die. [30] I raised my hand and swore an oath to give you this land to live in. But none of you will enter it except Caleb (son of Jephunneh) and Joshua (son of Nun). [31] You said your children would be taken as prisoners of war. Instead, I will bring them into the land you rejected, and they will enjoy it. [32] However, your bodies will drop dead in this desert. [33] Your children will be shepherds in the desert for 40 years. They will suffer for your unfaithfulness until the last of your bodies lies dead in the desert. [34] For 40 days you explored the land. So for 40 years—one year for each day—you will suffer for your sins and know what it means for me to be against you.' [35] I, the LORD, have spoken. I swear I will do these things to all the people in this whole wicked community who have joined forces against me. They will meet their end in this desert. Here they will die!"

[36] So the men Moses sent to explore the land died in front of the LORD from a plague. [37] They died because they had returned and made the whole community complain about Moses by spreading lies about the land.[c] [38] Of all the men who went to explore the land, only Joshua (son of Nun) and Caleb (son of Jephunneh) survived.

The Amalekites and Canaanites Defeat Israel

[39] When Moses told these things to all the Israelites, the people mourned bitterly, as if someone had died. [40] Early the next morning they headed into the mountain region. They said, "We have sinned. Now we'll go to the place the LORD promised."

[41] But Moses asked, "Why are you disobeying the LORD's command? Your plan won't work! [42] Don't go! You will be defeated by your enemies because the LORD is not with you. [43] The

---

[a] 14:12 Or "I'll take away the land I promised them."   [b] 14:22 Part of verse 23 (in Hebrew) has been placed in verse 22 to express the complex Hebrew sentence structure more clearly in English.   [c] 14:37 Part of verse 37 (in Hebrew) has been placed at the end of verse 36 to express the complex Hebrew sentence structure more clearly in English.

Amalekites and Canaanites are there, and you will die in battle. Now that you have turned away from the LORD, the LORD will not be with you."

44 But they headed into the mountain region anyway, even though the ark of the LORD's promise and Moses stayed in the camp. **45** The Amalekites and Canaanites who lived there came down from those mountains, attacked the Israelites, and defeated them at Hormah.*ᵈ*

Grain and Wine Made Part of the Sacrifices to the LORD

15 **1** The LORD said to Moses, **2** "Speak to the Israelites and tell them: Once you're settled in the land I'm giving you, **3** you may bring offerings by fire to the LORD. They may be burnt offerings or any other kind of sacrifice. They may be offered to fulfill a vow, as a freewill offering, or as one of your festival offerings. They may be cattle, sheep, or goats—offerings that are a soothing aroma to the LORD. **4** Whoever brings the offering must also give the LORD a grain offering of eight cups of flour mixed with one quart of olive oil. **5** With each sheep or goat for the burnt offering or any other sacrifice, also give an offering of one quart of wine.

6 "With a ram, give a grain offering of 16 cups of flour mixed with 1¼ quarts of oil **7** and an offering of 1¼ quarts of wine. Offer them as a soothing aroma to the LORD.

8 "Suppose you sacrifice a young bull as a burnt offering to the LORD or make any other kind of sacrifice—to keep a vow or as a fellowship offering. **9** Offer with the young bull a grain offering of 24 cups of flour mixed with two quarts of olive oil. **10** Also give an offering of two quarts of wine. It is an offering by fire, a soothing aroma to the LORD. **11** Do this for each bull, each ram, and each sheep or goat. **12** Do it for each animal, however many you sacrifice. **13** All native-born Israelites must do it this way when they bring an offering by fire, a soothing aroma to the LORD.

14 "Suppose foreigners are visiting you or living among you in future generations. If they bring an offering by fire, a soothing aroma to the LORD, they must do as you do. **15** There is one law for the whole assembly: for you and foreigners who are living with you. It is a permanent law for future generations. As far as the LORD is concerned, you and foreigners are the same. **16** The instructions and rules are the same for you as well as foreigners who are living with you."

Offering the First Bread Dough to the LORD

17 The LORD said to Moses, **18** "Speak to the Israelites and tell them: When you enter the land where I'm taking you **19** and eat any of the food from the land, give some of it as a contribution to the LORD. **20** Shape one part of your dough into a ring the same way you do with the contribution you make from the threshing floor.*ᵃ* **21** For generations to come, you must give one part of your dough as a contribution to the LORD.

What Is to Be Done About Unintentional and Intentional Wrongdoings

22 "Suppose you unintentionally do something wrong by not obeying all these commands the LORD gave Moses. **23** (Everything the LORD commanded you through Moses holds as true for generations to come as it did the day the LORD gave the commands.) **24** If it was unintentional and no one else knows about it, the whole community must sacrifice a young bull as a burnt offering, a soothing aroma to the LORD, along with the proper grain and wine offerings, and a male goat as an offering for sin. **25** The priest will make peace with the LORD for the whole community of Israel. Then they will be forgiven because the wrongdoing was unintentional and they brought these two offerings to the LORD for their sin: an offering by fire and an offering for sin. **26** So the whole community of Israel will be forgiven, including foreigners who are living among them, since all the people were involved in the unintentional wrongdoing.

27 "If one person unintentionally does something wrong, a one-year-old female goat must be sacrificed as an offering for sin. **28** The priest will offer the sacrifice to make peace with the LORD for that person, and that person will be forgiven. **29** You must give the same instructions to everyone who does something wrong unintentionally, whether they are native-born Israelites or not.

30 "But any native-born Israelite or foreigner who deliberately does something wrong insults the LORD and must be excluded from the people. **31** That person has despised the word of the LORD and broken the LORD's command. He must be excluded completely. He remains guilty."

A Man Breaks the Rules for the Day of Worship

32 While the Israelites were in the desert, they found a man gathering wood on the day of worship. **33** Those who found him gathering wood brought him to Moses and Aaron and the whole community. **34** They kept him in custody until they decided what to do with him.

ᵈ 14:45 Or "and defeated them, chasing them all the way to Hormah."   *ᵃ* 15:20 A threshing floor is an outdoor area where grain is separated from its husks.

³⁵ Then the LORD said to Moses, "This man must be put to death. The whole community must take him outside the camp and stone him." ³⁶ So the whole community took him outside the camp and stoned him to death, as the LORD commanded Moses.

The Israelites Are Commanded to Wear Tassels

³⁷ The LORD said to Moses, ³⁸ "Speak to the Israelites and tell them: For generations to come they must wear tassels on the corners of their clothes with violet threads in each tassel. ³⁹ Whenever you look at the threads in the tassel, you will remember all the LORD's commands and obey them. Then you won't do whatever you want and go after whatever you see, as if you were chasing after prostitutes. ⁴⁰ You will remember to obey all my commands, and you will be holy to your God. ⁴¹ I am the LORD your God, who brought you out of Egypt to be your God. I am the LORD your God."

Korah's Rebellion

16 ¹ Korah (son of Izhar), Dathan and Abiram (sons of Eliab), and On (son of Peleth) dared to challenge Moses.ᵃ (Korah was a descendant of Kohath and Levi. Dathan, Abiram, and On were descendants of Reuben.) ² These four men were joined by 250 Israelite men, well-known leaders of the community, chosen by the assembly. ³ They came together to confront Moses and Aaron and said to them, "You've gone far enough! Everyone in the whole community is holy, and the LORD is among them. Why do you set yourselves above the LORD's assembly?"

⁴ As soon as Moses heard this, he bowed with his face touching the ground. ⁵ Then he said to Korah and all his followers, "In the morning the LORD will show who belongs to him, who is holy, and who it is that he will allow to come near him. Only the person the LORD chooses will be allowed to come near him. ⁶ Korah, you and all your followers must do this tomorrow: Take incense burners, ⁷ and put burning coals and incense in them in the LORD's presence. Then the LORD will choose the man who is holy. You've gone far enough!"

⁸ Moses also said to Korah, "Listen, you Levites! ⁹ Isn't it enough for you that the God of Israel has separated you from the rest of the community of Israel? The LORD has brought you near himself to do the work for his tent and stand in front of the community to serve them. ¹⁰ He has brought you and all the other Levites near himself, but now you demand to be priests. ¹¹ So you and all your followers have joined forces against the LORD! Who is Aaron that you should complain about him?"

¹² Then Moses sent for Dathan and Abiram, sons of Eliab. But they said, "We won't come! ¹³ Isn't it enough that you brought us out of a land flowing with milk and honey only to kill us in the desert? Do you also have to order us around? ¹⁴ Certainly you haven't brought us into a land flowing with milk and honey or given us any fields and vineyards to own. Do you think you can still pull the wool over our eyes? We won't come."

¹⁵ Moses became angry and said to the LORD, "Don't accept their offering. I haven't taken anything from them, not even a donkey. And I haven't mistreated any of them."

¹⁶ Moses said to Korah, "Tomorrow you and all your followers must come into the LORD's presence. Aaron will also be there with you. ¹⁷ Each man will take his incense burner and put incense in it. They will offer all 250 incense burners to the LORD. Then you and Aaron offer your incense burners."

¹⁸ So each man took his incense burner, put burning coals and incense in it, and stood with Moses and Aaron at the entrance to the tent of meeting. ¹⁹ When Korah had gathered all his followers—those who opposed Moses and Aaron—at the entrance to the tent of meeting, the glory of the LORD appeared to the whole group.

²⁰ The LORD said to Moses and Aaron, ²¹ "Move away from these men, and I'll destroy them in an instant." ²² Immediately, they bowed with their faces touching the ground and said, "O God, you are the God who gives the breath of life to everyone! If one man sins, will you be angry with the whole community?"

²³ Then the LORD said to Moses, ²⁴ "Tell the community: Move away from the tents of Korah, Dathan, and Abiram."

²⁵ Moses got up and went to Dathan and Abiram, and the leaders of Israel followed him. ²⁶ He said to the community, "Move away from the tents of these wicked men. Don't touch anything that belongs to them, or you'll be swept away because of all their sins." ²⁷ So they moved away from the tents of Korah, Dathan, and Abiram. Dathan and Abiram had come out and were standing at the entrances to their tents with their wives and children.

²⁸ Moses said, "This is how you will know that the LORD sent me to do all these things and that it wasn't my idea: ²⁹ If these men die like all other people—if they die a natural death—

ᵃ 16:1 The beginning of verse 2 (in Hebrew) has been placed in verse 1 to express the complex Hebrew sentence structure more clearly in English.

then the LORD hasn't sent me. [30] But if the LORD does something totally new—if the ground opens up, swallows them and everything that belongs to them, and they go down alive to their graves—then you'll know that these men have treated the LORD with contempt."

[31] As soon as he had finished saying all this, the ground under them split, [32] and the earth opened up to swallow them, their families, the followers of Korah, and all their property. [33] They went down alive to their graves with everything that belonged to them. The ground covered them, and so they disappeared from the assembly. [34] All the Israelites around them ran away when they heard their screams. They thought the ground would swallow them, too.

[35] Fire came from the LORD and consumed the 250 men who were offering incense.[b]

[36] Then the LORD said to Moses, [37] "Tell Eleazar, son of the priest Aaron, to take the incense burners out of the fire and scatter the coals and incense somewhere else, because the incense burners have become holy. [38] The incense burners of these men who sinned and lost their lives are holy, because they were offered to the LORD. Hammer them into thin metal sheets to cover the altar. This will be a sign to the Israelites."

[39] So the priest Eleazar took the bronze incense burners which had been brought by those who had been burned to death. The incense burners were then hammered into thin metal sheets to cover the altar, [40] following the command that the LORD had given through Moses. The bronze-covered altar will remind Israel that no one but a descendant of Aaron can come near to burn incense to the LORD. Everyone else will die like Korah and his followers.

[41] The next day the whole community of Israel complained to Moses and Aaron. They said, "You have killed the LORD's people." [42] The community came together to confront Moses and Aaron. When they turned toward the tent of meeting, they saw the smoke covering it, and the glory of the LORD appeared.

[43] Then Moses and Aaron went to the front of the tent of meeting. [44] The LORD said to Moses, [45] "Get away from these people, and let me destroy them in an instant!" Immediately, they bowed with their faces touching the ground.

[46] Moses said to Aaron, "Take your incense burner, put burning coals from the altar and incense in it, and go quickly into the community to make peace with the LORD for the people. The LORD is showing his anger; a plague has started."

[47] Aaron took his incense burner, as Moses told him, and ran into the middle of the assembly, because the plague had already begun among the people. He put incense on the incense burner to make peace with the LORD for the people. [48] He stood between those who had died and those who were still alive, and the plague stopped. [49] Still, 14,700 died from the plague in addition to those who had died because of Korah. [50] By the time Aaron came back to Moses at the entrance to the tent of meeting, the plague had stopped.

Aaron's Staff Grows

17[a] [1] The LORD said to Moses, [2] "Speak to the Israelites, and get 12 staffs from them, one from the leader of each of their tribes.[b] Write each man's name on his staff. [3] Write Aaron's name on the staff for Levi because there must be one staff for the head of each tribe. [4] Put them in the tent of meeting where I meet with you, in front of the words of my promise. [5] The staff from the man I choose will begin to grow. In this way I will silence the frequent complaints the Israelites make against you and Aaron."

[6] So Moses spoke to the Israelites. Their leaders gave him 12 staffs, one from the leader of each of their tribes. Aaron's staff was among them. [7] Moses put the staffs in the LORD's presence in the tent of the words of God's promise.

[8] The next day Moses went into the tent. He found that Aaron's staff for the tribe of Levi had not only begun to grow, but it had also blossomed and produced ripe almonds. [9] Moses brought out the staffs from the LORD's presence and showed them to all the Israelites. They looked at them, and each man took his staff.

[10] The LORD said to Moses, "Put Aaron's staff back in front of the words of my promise, and keep it there as a sign to warn any other rebels. Then you will stop their complaints about me, and they won't die."

[11] Moses did exactly what the LORD commanded him to do.

[12] The Israelites said to Moses, "Now we're going to die! We're lost! We're all lost! [13] Anyone who comes near the LORD's tent will die! Are we all going to die?"

The Duties of the Levites and Priests

18 [1] The LORD said to Aaron, "You, your sons, and your family will be responsible for any sins against the holy place. You and your sons will also be responsible for any sins you

---

[b] 16:35 Numbers 16:36–50 in English Bibles is Numbers 17:1–15 in the Hebrew Bible.   [a] 17:1 Numbers 17:1–13 in English Bibles is Numbers 17:16–28 in the Hebrew Bible.   [b] 17:2 There is a play on words here. Hebrew *matteh* can mean "staff" or "tribe."

commit when you work as priests. ²Bring the other Levites from your ancestor's tribe to join you and help you and your sons serve in front of the tent of the words of my promise. ³They will work for you, doing whatever work is necessary for the whole tent. But they must not come near the altar or the furnishings in the holy place, or they will die, and you will die, too. ⁴They will join you and do whatever work is necessary for the tent of meeting, including all the maintenance work for the tent. But no one else may come near you.

⁵"You must be in charge of the work done at the holy place and at the altar. Then I won't show my anger against the Israelites again. ⁶I have chosen the other Levites from among the Israelites to help you. They are a gift given to the LORD to do whatever work is necessary at the tent of meeting. ⁷Only you and your sons may do the work of priests—everything done at the altar and under the canopy. This is my gift to you: You may serve me as priests. Anyone else who comes near the holy place to do this work must die."

Contributions for the Levites and Priests

⁸The LORD said to Aaron, "I am putting you in charge of all the contributions given to me. I am giving you and your descendants all the holy gifts from the Israelites as your share. These contributions will always be yours. ⁹That part of the most holy offerings which is not burned belongs to you. It may come from a grain offering, an offering for sin, or a guilt offering. Whatever is brought to me as a most holy offering will belong to you and your sons. ¹⁰Eat it in a most holy place. Any male may eat it. You must consider it holy.

¹¹"The contributions that come as gifts taken from the offerings presented by the Israelites are also yours. I am giving these to you, your sons, and your daughters. They will always be yours. Anyone in your household who is clean*ᵃ* may eat them.

¹²"I am also giving you the first of the produce they give the LORD: the best of all the olive oil and the best of the new wine and fresh grain. ¹³The first of all produce harvested in their land that they bring to the LORD is yours. Anyone in your household who is clean may eat it.

¹⁴"Anything in Israel that is claimed by the LORD is yours. ¹⁵Every firstborn male, human or animal, that is brought to the LORD is yours. But you must buy back every firstborn son and the firstborn male of any unclean animal. ¹⁶When they are one month old, you must buy them back at the fixed price of two ounces of silver using the standard weight of the holy place.

¹⁷"But you must never buy back a firstborn ox, sheep, or goat. They are holy. Throw the blood from these animals against the altar, and burn the fat as an offering by fire, a soothing aroma to the LORD. ¹⁸But the meat is yours, like the breast and the right thigh that are presented. ¹⁹I am giving you, your sons, and your daughters all the holy contributions the Israelites bring to the LORD. These contributions will always be yours. It is an everlasting promise of salt in the LORD's presence for you and your descendants."

²⁰The LORD said to Aaron, "You will have no land or property of your own as the other Israelites will have. I am your possession and your property among the Israelites.

²¹"I am giving the Levites one-tenth of every Israelite's income. This is in return for the work they do at the tent of meeting. ²²The other Israelites must never again come near the tent of meeting. Otherwise, they'll suffer the consequences of their sin and die. ²³Only the Levites will do the work at the tent of meeting. They will be responsible for their own sins. This is a permanent law for future generations. They will own no property as the other Israelites will. ²⁴Instead, I will give the Levites what the Israelites contribute to the LORD—one-tenth of the Israelites' income. This is why I said about them, 'They will own no property as the other Israelites do.'"

²⁵The LORD said to Moses, ²⁶"Speak to the Levites and say to them: You will take one-tenth of the Israelites' income which I'm giving you as your property. When you do, you must contribute one-tenth of that income as your contribution to the LORD. ²⁷Your contribution will be considered to be grain from the threshing floor*ᵇ* or juice from the winepress. ²⁸So you, too, will contribute one-tenth of your income to the LORD out of all that you receive from the Israelites' income. You will give the LORD's contribution to the priest Aaron. ²⁹Out of all the gifts you receive, you must contribute the best and holiest parts to the LORD.

³⁰"Also tell them: When you contribute the best part, your contribution will be considered to be produce from the threshing floor or winepress. ³¹So you and your households may eat it anywhere, because it's the wages you receive for your work at the tent of meeting. ³²When you contribute the best part, you won't suffer the consequences of any sin. You won't be dishonoring the holy offerings given by the Israelites, and you won't die."

ᵃ 18:11 "Clean" refers to anything that is presentable to God.   *ᵇ* 18:27 A threshing floor is an outdoor area where grain is separated from its husks.

Water That Makes Israel Clean After Someone Dies

19 ¹ The LORD said to Moses and Aaron, ² "This is what the LORD's teachings have commanded: Tell the Israelites to bring you a red cow that is perfect, with no defects. Also, it must never have worn a yoke.ᵃ ³ Give it to the priest Eleazar. It must be taken outside the camp and slaughtered in his presence. ⁴ The priest Eleazar will take some of the blood with his finger and sprinkle it seven times toward the front of the tent of meeting. ⁵ Then the entire cow (the skin, meat, blood, and excrement) will be burned while he watches. ⁶ The priest will take some cedar wood, a hyssop sprig, and some red yarn and throw them onto the burning cow. ⁷ The priest must then wash his clothes and his body. After that, he may go into the camp. But he will be uncleanᵇ until evening. ⁸ The person who burned the calf must also wash his clothes and his body. He, too, will be unclean until evening.

⁹ "A man who is cleanᶜ will collect the ashes from the cow and put them in a clean place outside the camp. They will be kept by the community of Israel and used in the water that takes away uncleanness. The cow is an offering for sin. ¹⁰ The person who collected the ashes from the cow must also wash his clothes. He will be unclean until evening. This will be a permanent law for the Israelites and for the foreigners who live with them.

¹¹ "Whoever touches the dead body of any human being will be unclean for seven days. ¹² The unclean person must use this water on the third day and the seventh day to take away his sin. Then he will be clean. But if he doesn't use this water on the third day and the seventh day, he will not be clean. ¹³ Whoever touches the dead body of a human being and doesn't use this water to take away his sin makes the LORD's tent unclean. That person must be excluded from Israel, because the water that takes away uncleanness wasn't sprinkled on him. He is unclean; his uncleanness stays with him.

¹⁴ "These are your instructions for when a person dies in a tent: Everyone who goes into the tent and everyone who is in the tent will be unclean for seven days. ¹⁵ Every container without a lid fastened on it is unclean.

¹⁶ "Whoever is outdoors and touches someone who was killed or has died naturally or anyone who touches a human bone or a grave will be unclean for seven days.

¹⁷ " ˌThis is what you do˩ for people who become unclean from touching a dead body. Put some of the ashes from the red cow that was burned as an offering for sin into a container. Then pour fresh water on them. ¹⁸ A person who is clean will take a sprig of hyssop, dip it in the water, and sprinkle the tent, all the furnishings, and all the people who were in the tent ˌwith the dead bodyˌ. He must also sprinkle any person who has touched a human bone or a grave and any person who has touched someone who has been killed or who has died naturally. ¹⁹ A person who is clean will sprinkle these types of unclean people on the third day and the seventh day. On the seventh day the clean person will finish taking away their sins. Then they must wash their clothes and bodies, and in the evening they will be clean. ²⁰ But if the person who becomes unclean doesn't have his sin taken away, that person must be excluded from the assembly. He has made the holy place of the LORD unclean. The water to take away uncleanness wasn't sprinkled on him. He is unclean. ²¹ This will be a permanent law for them.

"Whoever sprinkles the water to take away uncleanness must wash his clothes. And whoever touches this water will be unclean until evening. ²² Anything that an unclean person touches becomes unclean, and the person who touches it will be unclean until evening."

Water From the Rock

20 ¹ In the first month the whole community of Israel came into the Desert of Zin, and they stayed at Kadesh. Miriam died and was buried there.

² Since the community was without water, they came together to confront Moses and Aaron. ³ The people complained to Moses and said, "If only we had died when the other Israelites died in the LORD's presence! ⁴ Did you bring the LORD's assembly into this desert just to have us and our animals die here? ⁵ Why did you make us leave Egypt and bring us into this terrible place? This is no place to plant crops. Even figs, grapes, and pomegranates won't grow here. And there's no water to drink!"

⁶ Moses and Aaron went from the assembly to the entrance of the tent of meeting. Immediately, they bowed with their faces touching the ground, and the glory of the LORD appeared to them.

⁷ The LORD said to Moses, ⁸ "Take your staff, then you and your brother Aaron gather the community. Right before their eyes, tell the rock to give up its water. In this way you will give the community water from the rock for them and their animals to drink."

ᵃ 19:2 A yoke is a wooden bar placed over the necks of work animals so that they can pull plows or carts.   ᵇ 19:7 "Unclean" refers to anything that is not presentable to God.   ᶜ 19:9 "Clean" refers to anything that is presentable to God.

⁹ Moses took his staff out of ˌthe tent inˌ the LORD's presence as he had been commanded. ¹⁰ Then Moses and Aaron assembled the community in front of the rock and said to them, "Listen, you rebels, must we bring water out of this rock for you?" ¹¹ Moses raised his hand and hit the rock twice with the staff. Water came pouring out, and all the people and their animals drank.

¹² But the LORD said to Moses and Aaron, "You didn't trust me! You didn't show the Israelites how holy I am! So you will not bring this congregation into the land I'm giving them." ¹³ This was the oasis of Meribah [Complaining], where the Israelites complained about the LORD and where he showed them he was holy.

Edom Refuses to Allow Israel to Pass Through Its Territory

¹⁴ Moses sent messengers from Kadesh to the king of Edom. He said, "This is what your brother Israel says: You know all the hardships we've had. ¹⁵ Our ancestors went to Egypt, and we lived there for many years. The Egyptians mistreated us and our ancestors. ¹⁶ When we cried out to the LORD, he heard us, sent a messenger, and brought us out of Egypt.

"Now we're here in Kadesh, a city on the edge of your territory. ¹⁷ Please let us go through your country. We won't go through any of your fields or vineyards, or drink any of the water from your wells. We'll stay on the king's highway and never leave it until we've passed through your territory."

¹⁸ But the Edomites answered, "You may not pass through our country. If you try, we'll come out and attack you."

¹⁹ The Israelites replied, "We'll stay on the main road, and if we or our livestock drink any of your water, we'll pay for it. We want to pass through on foot. That's all."

²⁰ But the Edomites said, "You may not pass through." Then they came out and attacked with many well-armed troops. ²¹ Since the Edomites refused to let Israel go through their territory, the Israelites turned around and went a different way.

Aaron's Death

²² The whole community of Israel left Kadesh and came to Mount Hor. ²³ At Mount Hor, near the border of Edom, the LORD said to Moses and Aaron, ²⁴ "Aaron must now join his ancestors ˌin deathˌ, since he cannot enter the land I'm giving the Israelites. This is because you both rebelled against my command at the oasis of Meribah. ²⁵ Bring Aaron and his son Eleazar up on Mount Hor. ²⁶ Take off Aaron's priestly clothes, and put them on his son Eleazar. Then Aaron will die there and join ˌhis ancestorsˌ."

²⁷ Moses did as the LORD commanded. The whole community saw them go up on Mount Hor. ²⁸ Moses took off Aaron's priestly clothes and put them on his son Eleazar. Aaron died there on top of the mountain. Then Moses and Eleazar came down from the mountain. ²⁹ The whole community saw that Aaron had died, and all the Israelites mourned for Aaron 30 days.

The King of Arad Is Defeated

21 ¹ When the Canaanite king of Arad, who lived in the Negev, heard that the Israelites were coming on the road to Atharim, he fought them and took some of them as prisoners. ² Then the Israelites made this vow to the LORD: "If you will hand these people over to us, we'll destroy their cities because you've claimed them." ³ The LORD listened to the Israelites and handed the Canaanites over to them. They destroyed the Canaanites and their cities. So they called the place Hormah [Claimed for Destruction].

The Bronze Snake

⁴ Then they moved from Mount Hor, following the road that goes to the Red Sea, in order to get around Edom. The people became impatient on the trip ⁵ and criticized God and Moses. They said, "Why did you make us leave Egypt—just to let us die in the desert? There's no bread or water, and we can't stand this awful food!"

⁶ So the LORD sent poisonous snakes among the people. They bit the people, and many of the Israelites died. ⁷ The people came to Moses and said, "We sinned when we criticized the LORD and you. Pray to the LORD so that he will take the snakes away from us." So Moses prayed for the people.

⁸ The LORD said to Moses, "Make a snake, and put it on a pole. Anyone who is bitten can look at it and live." ⁹ So Moses made a bronze snake and put it on a pole. People looked at the bronze snake after they were bitten, and they lived.ᵃ

ᵃ 21:9 There is a play on words here between Hebrew *nachash* (snake) and *nechosheth* (bronze).

Israel Travels Past Edom to Moab

¹⁰ The Israelites moved and set up camp at Oboth. ¹¹ Next they moved from Oboth and set up camp at Iye Abarim in the desert west of Moab. ¹² From there they moved and set up camp at the Zered River. ¹³ They moved from there and set up camp on the other side of the Arnon Valley in the desert that extends into Amorite territory. (The Arnon Valley is the border between Moab and the Amorites.) ¹⁴ This is how it's described in the Book of the Wars of the LORD:

> ". . . Waheb in Suphah and the valleys,
> ¹⁵   Arnon and the slopes of the valleys
>   that go down to the site of Ar
>   and lie along the border of Moab. . . ."

¹⁶ From there they went to Beer [Well]. This is the well where the LORD said to Moses, "Gather the people, and I will give them water." ¹⁷ Then Israel sang this song about the well:

> "Make your water spring up!
>   Sing to the well,
> ¹⁸   the well dug by princes,
>   dug out by the nobles of the people
>   with their scepters and staffs."

From the desert they went to Mattanah, ¹⁹ and from Mattanah to Nahaliel, and from Nahaliel to Bamoth, ²⁰ and from Bamoth to the valley in Moab where Mount Pisgah overlooks Jeshimon.

Sihon and Og Defeated

²¹ Then Israel sent messengers to say to King Sihon of the Amorites, ²² "Let us go through your country. We won't go through any of your fields or vineyards or drink any of the water from your wells. We'll stay on the king's highway until we've passed through your territory."
²³ Sihon wouldn't let Israel pass through his territory. Sihon gathered all his troops and came out into the desert to attack Israel. When Sihon's troops came to Jahaz, they fought against Israel. ²⁴ But Israel defeated them in battle and took possession of their land from the Arnon Valley to the Jabbok River. They stopped at the border of the Ammon because it was fortified. ²⁵ Israel took all those Amorite cities, including Heshbon and all its villages, and lived in them. ²⁶ Heshbon was the city of King Sihon of the Amorites. He had fought the former king of Moab and had taken all his land up to the Arnon Valley.
²⁷ This is why the poets say:

> "Come to Heshbon! Rebuild it!
>   Restore Sihon's city!
> ²⁸   Fire came out of Heshbon,
>   flames from Sihon's city.
>   They destroyed Ar of Moab,
>   the rulers of Arnon's worship sites.^b
> ²⁹   How horrible it is for you, Moab!
>   You are destroyed, you people of the god Chemosh.
>   Chemosh let his sons become refugees
>   and he let his daughters become prisoners
>   of King Sihon of the Amorites.
> ³⁰   But we shot the Amorites full of arrows.
>   From Heshbon to Dibon they all died.
>   We destroyed everyone and everything
>   between Nophah and Medeba."

³¹ So Israel settled in the land of the Amorites. ³² After Moses sent spies to Jazer, the Israelites captured its cities and villages and forced out the Amorites who were there. ³³ Then they turned and followed the road that goes to Bashan. King Og of Bashan and all his troops came out to fight the Israelites at Edrei.
³⁴ The LORD said to Moses, "Don't be afraid of him. I'll hand him, all his troops, and his land over to you. Do to him what you did to King Sihon of the Amorites, who ruled in Heshbon."
³⁵ The Israelites defeated him, his sons, and all his troops, leaving no survivors. And they took possession of his land.

---

^b 21:28 Masoretic Text; Greek "it consumed Arnon's worship sites."

Balaam Is Hired to Curse Israel

22 ¹ Then the Israelites moved and set up camp across from Jericho, on the plains of Moab east of the Jordan River.

² Balak, son of Zippor, saw all that Israel had done to the Amorites. ³ The Moabites were very afraid because there were so many Israelites. Besides, the Moabites couldn't stand these people.

⁴ So the Moabites said to the leaders of Midian, "All those people will eventually eat up everything around us the same way an ox eats up the grass in a field."

At that time Balak, son of Zippor, was king of Moab. ⁵ He sent messengers to summon Balaam, son of Beor, who was at Pethor, on the Euphrates River, in the land where his people lived. Balak's message was, "A nation has just come here from Egypt. They've spread out all over the countryside and are setting up their camp here in front of me. ⁶ Please come and curse these people for me, because they are too strong for me. Maybe then I'll be able to defeat them and force them out of the country. I know that whomever you bless is blessed and whomever you curse is cursed."

⁷ The leaders of Moab and Midian left, taking money with them to pay for Balaam's services. They came to Balaam and told him what Balak had said.

⁸ "Spend the night here," Balaam said to them, "and I'll report to you what the LORD tells me." So the princes of Moab stayed with Balaam.

⁹ God came to Balaam and asked, "Who are these men with you?"

¹⁰ Balaam answered, "Balak, son of King Zippor of Moab, sent them with this message: ¹¹ 'Some people have just come from Egypt and are spreading out all over the countryside. Now come and curse them for me. Maybe I'll be able to fight them and force them out.' "

¹² But God said to Balaam, "Don't go with them! Don't curse these people, because they are blessed."

¹³ When Balaam got up in the morning, he said to Balak's princes, "Go back to your own country, because the LORD has refused to let me go with you."

¹⁴ So the Moabite princes went back to Balak and said, "Balaam refused to come with us."

¹⁵ Balak sent a larger group of more highly respected princes. ¹⁶ When they came to Balaam, they said to him, "This is what Balak, son of Zippor, says: Don't let anything keep you from coming to me. ¹⁷ I will make sure that you are richly rewarded, and I will do whatever you ask. Please, come and curse these people for me."

¹⁸ But Balaam answered Balak's servants, "Even if Balak gave me his palace filled with silver and gold, I couldn't disobey the command of the LORD my God no matter whether the request was important or not. ¹⁹ Now, why don't you stay here tonight, as the others did, and I'll find out what else the LORD may have to tell me."

²⁰ That night God came to Balaam and said, "If these men have come to summon you, go with them, but do only what I tell you."

Balaam's Journey to Moab

²¹ When Balaam got up in the morning, he saddled his donkey and left with the Moabite princes.

²² God became angry that he was going. So the Messenger of the LORD stood in the road to stop him. Balaam was riding on his donkey, accompanied by his two servants. ²³ When the donkey saw the Messenger of the LORD standing in the road with his sword drawn, the donkey turned off the road into a field. Balaam hit the donkey to get it back on the road.

²⁴ Where the road went through the vineyards, it was narrow, with stone walls on both sides. Now the Messenger of the LORD stood there. ²⁵ When the donkey saw the Messenger of the LORD, it moved over and pinned Balaam's foot against the wall. So Balaam hit the donkey again.

²⁶ Then the Messenger of the LORD moved ahead and stood in a narrower place where there was no room to turn to the right or the left. ²⁷ When the donkey saw the Messenger of the LORD, it lay down under Balaam. Balaam became so angry he hit the donkey with his stick. ²⁸ Then the LORD made the donkey speak, and it asked Balaam, "What have I done to make you hit me three times?"

²⁹ Balaam answered, "You've made a fool of me! If I had a sword in my hand, I'd kill you right now."

³⁰ The donkey said to Balaam, "I'm your own donkey. You've always ridden me. Have I ever done this to you before?"

"No," he answered.

³¹ Then the LORD let Balaam see the Messenger of the LORD who was standing in the road with his sword drawn. So Balaam knelt, bowing with his face touching the ground.

³² The Messenger of the Lord asked him, "Why have you hit your donkey three times like this? I've come here to stop you because the trip you're taking is evil.ᵃ ³³ The donkey saw me and turned away from me these three times. If it had not turned away from me, I would certainly have killed you by now but spared the donkey."

³⁴ Balaam said to the Messenger of the Lord, "I've sinned. I didn't know you were standing there in the road to stop me. If you still think this trip is evil, I'll go back."

³⁵ The Messenger of the Lord said to Balaam, "Go with the men, but say only what I tell you." So Balaam went with Balak's princes.

³⁶ When Balak heard that Balaam had come, he went out to meet him at Ir Moab, in the region of the Arnon Valley, right on the border of Moab. ³⁷ Balak said to Balaam, "Why didn't you come when I summoned you? You knew I'd be able to reward you."

³⁸ Balaam replied, "Well, I've come to you now. But I can't say whatever I want to. I can only say what God tells me to say."

³⁹ Balaam went with Balak to Kiriath Huzoth. ⁴⁰ Balak sacrificed cattle, sheep, and goats, and sent some of the meat to Balaam and the princes who were with him.

⁴¹ The next morning Balak took Balaam up to Bamoth Baal. From there he could see the outskirts of the Israelites' camp.

Balaam's First Prophecy

23 ¹ Balaam said to Balak, "Build seven altars here, and prepare seven bulls and seven rams for me." ² Balak did what Balaam told him, and the two of them offered a bull and a ram on each altar.

³ Balaam said to Balak, "Stay here beside your burnt offering while I'm gone. Maybe the Lord will come and meet with me. I will tell you whatever he reveals to me." Then Balaam went off to a higher place where there were no trees.

⁴ God came to him, and Balaam said, "I have set up seven altars, and I offered a bull and a ram on each altar."

⁵ The Lord told Balaam, "Go back to Balak, and give him my message."

⁶ So he went back to Balak and found him standing beside his burnt offering with all the princes of Moab. ⁷ Then Balaam delivered this message:

"Balak brought me from Aram.
The king of Moab summoned me from the eastern mountains.
'Come, curse Jacob for me,' he said.
'Come, condemn Israel.'
⁸ How can I curse those whom God hasn't cursed?
How can I condemn those whom the Lord hasn't condemned?
⁹ I see them from the top of rocky cliffs,
I look at them from the hills.
I see a nation that lives by itself,
people who do not consider themselves
to be like other nations.
¹⁰ The descendants of Jacob are like specks of dust.
Who can count them
or number even one-fourth of the people of Israel?
Let me die the death of innocent people.
Let my end be like theirs."

¹¹ Balak said to Balaam, "What have you done to me? I brought you here to curse my enemies, but all you've done is bless them!"

¹² Balaam answered, "I must say what the Lord tells me to say."

Balaam's Second Prophecy

¹³ Then Balak said to him, "Please come with me to another place, where you can see the Israelites. You will see only some of them, not all of them. Curse them for me from there."

¹⁴ So he took him to the Field of Zophimᵃ on top of Mount Pisgah, where he built seven altars. He offered a bull and a ram on each altar. ¹⁵ Then Balaam said to Balak, "Stay here beside your burnt offering while I meet with God over there."

¹⁶ The Lord came to Balaam and told him, "Go back to Balak, and give him my message."

¹⁷ He came to Balak and found him standing beside his burnt offering with the princes of Moab. Balak asked him, "What did the Lord say?" ¹⁸ Then Balaam delivered this message:

ᵃ 22:32 Greek; Hebrew meaning of "because. . . evil" uncertain.   ᵃ 23:14 Or "to a lookout point."

"Stand up, Balak, and listen!
Hear me, son of Zippor!
¹⁹ God is not like people. He tells no lies.
He is not like humans. He doesn't change his mind.
When he says something, he does it.
When he makes a promise, he keeps it.
²⁰ I have received a command to bless.
He has blessed, and I can't change it.
²¹ He doesn't want any trouble for the descendants of Jacob.
He sees no misfortune for the people of Israel.
The LORD their God is with them,
praised as their king.
²² The God who brought them out of Egypt
has the strength of a wild bull.
²³ No spell can curse the descendants of Jacob.
No magic can harm the people of Israel.
Now it will be said of Jacob and Israel:
'See what God has done!'
²⁴ Here is a nation that attacks like a lioness
and is as ferocious as a lion.
It doesn't lie down until it eats its prey
and drinks the blood of its victim."

²⁵ Balak said to Balaam, "If you won't curse them, then at least don't bless them!"

²⁶ Balaam answered, "Didn't I tell you that I must do whatever the LORD says?"

²⁷ Balak said to Balaam, "Come, let me take you to another place. Maybe God wants you to curse them for me from there." ²⁸ So Balak took Balaam to the top of Mount Peor, which overlooks Jeshimon.

²⁹ Balaam said to Balak, "Build seven altars here, and prepare seven bulls and seven rams for me." ³⁰ Balak did what Balaam told him, and he offered a bull and a ram on each altar.

Balaam's Third Prophecy

24 ¹ When Balaam saw that the LORD wanted to bless Israel, he didn't look for omens as he had done before. He turned toward the desert, ² looked up, and saw Israel's camp grouped by tribes. The Spirit of God entered him, ³ and he delivered this message:

"This is the message of Balaam, son of Beor.
This is the message of the man whose eyesight is clear.[a]
⁴ This is the message of the one who hears the words of God,
has a vision from the Almighty,
and falls ͵ into a trance ͵ with his eyes open:
⁵ How beautiful are your tents, Jacob,
and the places where you live, Israel.
⁶ Your tents spread out like rivers,
like gardens by a river,
like aloes planted by the LORD,
like cedars by the water.
^{7.} Water will flow from their buckets,
and their crops will have plenty of water.
Their king will be greater than Agag,
and their kingdom will be considered the best.
⁸ The God who brought them out of Egypt
has the strength of a wild bull.
He will devour nations that are his enemies,
crush their bones,
and pierce them with arrows.
⁹ His people lie down ͵ and ͵ rest like a lion.
They are like a lioness. Who dares to disturb them?
Those who bless you will be blessed!
Those who curse you will be cursed!"

---

[a] 24:3 Greek, Targum; Hebrew meaning uncertain.

Balaam's Fourth Prophecy

10 Balak became angry with Balaam. He clapped his hands and said, "I summoned you to curse my enemies, and now you have blessed them three times. **11** Get out of here! Go home! I said I'd reward you richly, but the LORD has made you lose your reward."

12 Balaam answered Balak, "I told the messengers you sent me, **13** 'Even if Balak would give me his palace filled with silver and gold, I couldn't disobey the LORD's command no matter how good or bad the request might seem to me. I must say only what the LORD says.' **14** Even though I'm going back to my people, I'll give you some advice. I'll tell you what these people will do to your people in the days to come."

15 Then Balaam delivered this message:

"This is the message of Balaam, son of Beor.
This is the message of the man whose eyesight is clear.
16   This is the message of the one who hears the words of God,
        receives knowledge from the Most High,
            has a vision from the Almighty,
                and falls ˌinto a tranceˌ with his eyes open:
17   I see someone who is not here now.
        I look at someone who is not nearby.
            A star will come from Jacob.
            A scepter will rise from Israel.
                He will crush the heads of the Moabites
                    and destroy all the people of Sheth.*b*
18   Edom will be conquered,
            and Seir, his enemy, will be conquered.
                So Israel will become wealthy.
19   He will rule from Jacob
            and destroy whoever is left in their cities."

20 Then Balaam saw the Amalekites and delivered this message:

"Amalek was first among the nations,
    but in the end it will be destroyed."

21 Then he saw the Kenites and delivered this message:

"You have a permanent place to live.
Your nest is built in a rock.
22   But it is destined to be burned, you ˌdescendants ofˌ Cain,
            when Assyria takes you as prisoners of war."*c*

23 He delivered this message:

"Oh no! Who will live when God decides to do this?
24   Ships will come from the shores of Cyprus.
        They will conquer Assyria and Eber.
            But they, too, will be totally destroyed."

25 Then Balaam got up and went back home, and Balak also went on his way.

Israel Commits Idolatry

25 **1** While Israel was staying at Shittim, the men began to have sex with Moabite women **2** who invited the people to the sacrifices offered to their gods. The people ate the meat from the sacrifices and worshiped these gods. **3** Since the Israelites joined in worshiping the god Baal of Peor, the LORD became angry with Israel.

4 The LORD said to Moses, "Take all the leaders of the people, and execute them in broad daylight in the LORD's presence. This will turn the LORD's anger away from Israel."

5 So Moses said to the judges of Israel, "Each of you must kill the men who have joined in worshiping the god Baal of Peor."

6 One of the Israelite men brought a Midianite woman to his brothers. He did this right in front of Moses and the whole community of Israel while they were crying at the entrance to the tent of meeting. **7** Phinehas, son of Eleazar and grandson of the priest Aaron, saw this. So he left the assembly, took a spear in his hand, **8** and went into the tent after the Israelite man.

---

b 24:17 Or "all the descendants of Seth."   *c* 24:21–22 There is a play on words here among Hebrew *qeyniy* (Kenite), *qinneka* (your nest), and *qayin* (Cain).

He drove the spear through the man and into the woman's body. Because of this, the plague that the Israelites were experiencing stopped. [9] However, 24,000 people died from that plague.

[10] Then the LORD said to Moses, [11] "Phinehas, son of Eleazar and grandson of the priest Aaron, turned my fury away from the Israelites. Since he stood up for me, I didn't have to stand up for myself and destroy them. [12] So tell Phinehas that I'm making a promise of peace to him. [13] My promise is that he and his descendants will be priests permanently because he stood up for his God and he made peace with the LORD for the Israelites."

[14] The name of the Israelite man who was killed with the Midianite woman was Zimri, son of Salu. (Salu was the leader of a family from Simeon.) [15] The name of the Midianite woman who was killed was Cozbi, daughter of Zur. (Zur was the head of a family from the Midianite tribes.)

[16] The LORD said to Moses, [17] "Treat the Midianites as your enemies, and kill them [18] because they treated you as enemies. They plotted to trick you in the incident that took place at Peor. They used their sister Cozbi, daughter of a Midianite leader, who was killed on the day of the plague caused by the incident at Peor."

Moses Takes Another Census of Israel

26 [1] After the plague the LORD said to Moses and Eleazar, son of the priest Aaron, [2] "Take a census of the whole community of Israel by households. List those who are at least 20 years old and eligible for military duty."

[3] So Moses and the priest Eleazar spoke to the Israelites on the plains of Moab near the Jordan River across from Jericho. They said, [4] "Take a census of those at least 20 years old, as the LORD commanded Moses."

These are the Israelites who came from Egypt:

[5] **Reuben** was Israel's firstborn. The descendants of Reuben were the family of Hanoch, the family of Pallu, [6] the family of Hezron, and the family of Carmi. [7] These were the families of Reuben. The total number of men was 43,730.

[8] Eliab was the son[a] of Pallu, [9] and Nemuel, Dathan, and Abiram were the sons of Eliab. (It was Dathan and Abiram, men chosen by the community, who defied Moses and Aaron's authority. They joined Korah's followers when they defied the LORD's authority. [10] The ground opened up and swallowed them along with Korah. They and their followers died when the fire consumed the 250 men. This was a warning. [11] But the descendants of Korah didn't die.)

[12] The families descended from **Simeon** were the family of Nemuel, the family of Jamin, the family of Jakin, [13] the family of Zerah, and the family of Shaul. [14] These were the families of Simeon. The total number of men was 22,200.

[15] The families descended from **Gad** were the family of Zephon, the family of Haggi, the family of Shuni, [16] the family of Ozni, the family of Eri, [17] the family of Arodi,[b] and the family of Areli. [18] These were the families of Gad's descendants. The total number of men was 40,500.

[19] Er and Onan were sons of **Judah,** but they died in Canaan. [20] The families descended from Judah were the family of Shelah, the family of Perez, and the family of Zerah. [21] The descendants of Perez were the family of Hezron and the family of Hamul. [22] These were the families of Judah. The total number of men was 76,500.

[23] The families descended from **Issachar** were the family of Tola, the family of Puah,[c] [24] the family of Jashub, and the family of Shimron. [25] These were the families of Issachar. The total number of men was 64,300.

[26] The families descended from **Zebulun** were the family of Sered, the family of Elon, and the family of Jahleel. [27] These were the families of Zebulun. The total number of men was 60,500.

[28] The families descended from **Joseph** ˌthroughˌ Manasseh and Ephraim were [29] (from Manasseh) the family of Machir (Machir was the father of Gilead) and the family of Gilead. [30] The descendants of Gilead were the family of Iezer, the family of Helek, [31] the family of Asriel, the family of Shechem, [32] the family of Shemida, and the family of Hepher. [33] (Zelophehad, son of Hepher, had no sons—only daughters. Their names were Mahlah, Noah, Hoglah, Milcah, and Tirzah.) [34] These were the families of Manasseh. The total number of men was 52,700.

---

[a] 26:8 Ancient scribal tradition; Masoretic Text "sons."   [b] 26:17 Genesis 46:16, Samaritan Pentateuch, Greek, Syriac; Masoretic Text "Arod."   [c] 26:23 Samaritan Pentateuch, Greek, Syriac, Latin; Masoretic Text "Puvah."

[35] The families descended from Ephraim were the family of Shuthelah, the family of Beker, and the family of Tahan.
[36] The descendants of Shuthelah were the family of Eran.
[37] These were the families of Ephraim's descendants. The total number of men was 32,500. These were the families descended from Joseph.

[38] The families descended from **Benjamin** were the family of Bela, the family of Ashbel, the family of Ahiram, [39] the family of Shupham,[d] and the family of Hupham.
[40] The descendants of Bela (through Ard and Naaman) were the family of Ard and the family of Naaman.
[41] These were the families descended from Benjamin. The total number of men was 45,600.

[42] The family descended from **Dan** was the family of Shuham.
This was the family descended from Dan. [43] The total number of men in all the family of Shuham was 64,400.

[44] The families descended from **Asher** were the family of Imnah, the family of Ishvi, and the family of Beriah.
[45] The descendants of Beriah were the family of Heber and the family of Malchiel.
[46] (Asher had a daughter named Serah.)
[47] These were the families of Asher's descendants. The total number of men was 53,400.

[48] The families descended from **Naphtali** were the family of Jahzeel, the family of Guni, [49] the family of Jezer, and the family of Shillem.
[50] These were the families of Naphtali. The total number of men was 45,400.
[51] The total number of Israelite men was 601,730.

[52] Then the LORD said to Moses, [53] "The land these people will possess must be divided using the list of names from the census. [54] Give more land to larger tribes and less land to smaller ones. Use the totals from the census in giving land to each tribe. [55] But the land must be divided by drawing lots. The tribes will receive their land based on the names of their ancestors. [56] Whether the tribes are large or small, the land must be divided by drawing lots."
[57] The families descended from **Levi** were listed as the family of Gershon, the family of Kohath, and the family of Merari.
[58] These were the families of Levi: the Libnite family, the Hebronite family, the Mahlite family, the Mushite family, and the Korahite family.
Kohath was the ancestor of Amram. [59] The name of Amram's wife was Jochebed, a descendant of Levi, who was born in Egypt. She gave birth to Amram's children: Aaron, Moses, and their sister Miriam. [60] Aaron was the father of Nadab, Abihu, Eleazar, and Ithamar. [61] But Nadab and Abihu had died because they offered unauthorized fire in the LORD's presence.
[62] The total number of all the Levite males at least one month old was 23,000. They were not counted along with the other Israelites, because they were given no land of their own.
[63] Moses and the priest Eleazar added up the total number of Israelites on the plains of Moab near the Jordan River across from Jericho. [64] Among them there wasn't a single one of the Israelites Moses and the priest Aaron had counted in the Desert of Sinai. [65] The LORD had said, "They must all die in the desert." The only ones left were Caleb (son of Jephunneh) and Joshua (son of Nun).

A Request From Zelophehad's Daughters

27 [1] The daughters of Zelophehad, son of Hepher, grandson of Gilead, descendant of Machir, whose father was Manasseh, belonged to the families of Manasseh, son of Joseph. Their names were Mahlah, Noah, Hoglah, Milcah, and Tirzah. They came [2] to Moses and stood in front of him, the priest Eleazar, the leaders, and the whole community at the entrance to the tent of meeting. They said, [3] "Our father died in the desert. He was not a part of Korah's followers who joined forces against the LORD. He died for his own sin and left no sons. [4] Why should our father's name be allowed to die out in his family because he had no son? Give us property among our father's relatives."
[5] So Moses brought their case to the LORD, [6] and the LORD said to him, [7] "Zelophehad's daughters are right. You must give them property of their own among their father's relatives. Turn their father's property over to them.
[8] "Tell the Israelites: If a man dies and leaves no sons, turn his property over to his daughters. [9] If he has no daughters, give his property to his brothers. [10] If he has no brothers, give his property to his uncles on his father's side of the family. [11] If he has no uncles, give his prop-

---

[d] 26:39 A few Hebrew manuscripts, Samaritan Pentateuch, Greek, Syriac, Targum, Latin; Masoretic Text "Shephupham."

erty to the nearest relative in his family, and that relative will take possession of it. This will be a rule for the Israelites, as the LORD commanded Moses."

The LORD Appoints Joshua to Succeed Moses

¹² The LORD said to Moses, "Go up into the Abarim Mountains, and take a look at the land I will give the Israelites. ¹³ After you see it, you, too, will join your ancestors ˌin deathˌ, as your brother Aaron did. ¹⁴ You both rebelled against my command in the Desert of Zin. You didn't show the people how holy I am when they were complaining at the oasis." (This was the oasis of Meribah at Kadesh in the Desert of Zin.)

¹⁵ Moses said to the LORD, ¹⁶ "LORD, you are the God who gives the breath of life to everyone. Please appoint someone over the community ¹⁷ who will lead them in and out ˌof battleˌ so that the LORD's community will not be like sheep without a shepherd."

¹⁸ So the LORD said to Moses, "Take Joshua, son of Nun, a man who has the Spirit, and place your hand on him. ¹⁹ Make him stand in front of the priest Eleazar and the whole community, and give him his instructions in their presence. ²⁰ Give him some of your authority so that the whole community of Israel will obey him. ²¹ He will stand in front of the priest Eleazar, who will use the Urimᵃ to make decisions in the LORD's presence. At his command Joshua and the whole community of Israel will go into battle. And at his command they will return."

²² Moses did as the LORD commanded him. He took Joshua and made him stand in front of the priest Eleazar and the whole community. ²³ Moses placed his hands on Joshua and gave him his instructions as the LORD had told him.

Daily Sacrifices

28 ¹ The LORD said to Moses, ² "Give this command to the Israelites: Be sure to bring me my offerings at the right times. They are my food. They are offerings by fire, a soothing aroma. ³ These are the offerings by fire that you must bring to the LORD. Every day you must bring as a daily burnt offering two one-year-old lambs that have no defects. ⁴ Offer one in the morning and the other at dusk. ⁵ ˌWith each of themˌ also bring a grain offering of eight cups of flour mixed with one quart of virgin olive oil. ⁶ This is the daily burnt offering which was established on Mount Sinai. This offering is a soothing aroma, an offering by fire to the LORD. ⁷ Also bring a wine offering of one quart of wine for each lamb. Pour it out to the LORD in a holy place. ⁸ Offer the other lamb at dusk along with the same grain offering and wine offering as you brought in the morning. This is an offering by fire, a soothing aroma to the LORD.

Weekly Sacrifices

⁹ "On the day of worship offer two one-year-old lambs that have no defects, a grain offering of 16 cups of flour mixed with olive oil, and the wine offering that goes with it. ¹⁰ This burnt offering is for every day of worship in addition to the daily burnt offerings and the wine offerings that go with them.

Monthly Sacrifices

¹¹ "On the first of every month bring the LORD a burnt offering of two young bulls, one ram, and seven one-year-old lambs that have no defects. ¹² With each bull there will be a grain offering of 24 cups of flour mixed with olive oil, with each ram a grain offering of 16 cups of flour mixed with olive oil, ¹³ and with each one-year-old lamb a grain offering of 8 cups of flour mixed with olive oil. This is a burnt offering, a soothing aroma, an offering by fire to the LORD. ¹⁴ The wine offering that goes with each bull will be 2 quarts of wine, with each ram 1½ quarts of wine, and with each lamb 1 quart of wine. This will be the monthly burnt offering for every month of the year. ¹⁵ In addition to the daily burnt offering with its wine offering, one male goat must be offered to the LORD as an offering for sin.

Annual Sacrifices

¹⁶ "The fourteenth day of the first month is the LORD's Passover. ¹⁷ The fifteenth of this same month is a pilgrimage festival. For seven days you must eat only unleavened bread. ¹⁸ On the first day there will be a holy assembly. Don't do any regular work. ¹⁹ Instead, bring the LORD an offering by fire, a burnt offering of two young bulls, one ram, and seven one-year-old lambs, all of them without defects. ²⁰ Along with them bring grain offerings of flour mixed with olive oil. Bring 24 cups for each bull, 16 cups for each ram, ²¹ and 8 cups for each of the seven lambs. ²² Also bring one male goat as an offering for sin to make peace with the LORD. ²³ Offer these in addition to the morning burnt offering. ²⁴ Bring all these offerings on each of the seven days. They are food. They are offerings by fire, a soothing aroma to the LORD. They will be offered

---

ᵃ 27:21 The Urim and Thummim were used by the chief priest to determine God's answer to questions.

in addition to the daily burnt offering and the wine offering that goes with it. [25] On the seventh day you must have a holy assembly. You must not do any regular work.

[26] "During the Festival of Weeks, you must have a holy assembly. On that day you must not do any regular work. Bring the LORD your new grain offering, the first produce harvested from your fields. [27] Bring a burnt offering as a soothing aroma to the LORD—two young bulls, one ram, and seven one-year-old lambs. [28] Along with them bring grain offerings of flour mixed with olive oil. Bring 24 cups for each bull, 16 cups for each ram, [29] and 8 cups for each of the seven lambs. [30] Also bring one male goat to make peace with the LORD. [31] Offer these animals that have no defects along with their wine offerings, in addition to the daily burnt offerings and their grain offerings."

29 [1] ⌊The LORD continued,⌋ "On the first day of the seventh month you must have a holy assembly. You must not do any regular work. It is a day for ⌊the trumpets to sound⌋ a fanfare. [2] As a burnt offering, a soothing aroma to the LORD, bring one young bull, one ram, and seven one-year-old lambs that have no defects. [3] Along with them bring grain offerings of flour mixed with olive oil. Bring 24 cups for each bull, 16 cups for each ram, [4] and 8 cups for each of the seven lambs. [5] Also bring one male goat as an offering for sin to make peace with the LORD. [6] Offer these in addition to the monthly burnt offering with its grain offering, and the daily burnt offerings with their proper grain offerings and wine offerings. They are a soothing aroma, an offering by fire to the LORD.

[7] "On the tenth day of the seventh month you must have a holy assembly. You must humble yourselves. You must not do any work. [8] As a burnt offering, a soothing aroma, bring one young bull, one ram, and seven one-year-old lambs, all of them without defects. [9] Along with them bring grain offerings of flour mixed with olive oil. Bring 24 cups for each bull, 16 cups for each ram, [10] and 8 cups for each of the seven lambs. [11] Also bring one male goat as an offering for sin (in addition to the ⌊other⌋ offering for sin to make peace with the LORD) and the daily burnt offerings with their grain offerings and wine offerings.

[12] "On the fifteenth day of the seventh month you must have a holy assembly. You must not do any regular work. Instead, celebrate a festival to the LORD for seven days. [13] As a burnt offering, an offering by fire, a soothing aroma to the LORD, bring 13 young bulls, 2 rams, and 14 one-year-old lambs, all of them without defects. [14] Along with them bring grain offerings of flour mixed with olive oil. Bring 24 cups for each of the 13 bulls, 16 cups for each of the 2 rams, [15] and 8 cups for each of the 14 one-year-old lambs. [16] Also bring one male goat as an offering for sin in addition to the daily burnt offerings with their grain offerings and wine offerings.

[17] "On the second day bring 12 young bulls, 2 rams, and 14 one-year-old lambs that have no defects. [18] Along with them bring the proper amount of grain offerings and wine offerings for each of the bulls, rams, and lambs. [19] Also bring one male goat as an offering for sin in addition to the daily burnt offerings with their grain offerings and wine offerings.

[20] "On the third day bring 11 bulls, 2 rams, and 14 one-year-old lambs that have no defects. [21] Along with them bring the proper amount of grain offerings and wine offerings for each of the bulls, rams, and lambs. [22] Also bring one male goat as an offering for sin in addition to the daily burnt offerings with their grain offerings and wine offerings.

[23] "On the fourth day bring 10 bulls, 2 rams, and 14 one-year-old lambs that have no defects. [24] Along with them bring the proper amount of grain offerings and wine offerings for each of the bulls, rams, and lambs. [25] Also bring one male goat as an offering for sin in addition to the daily burnt offerings with their grain offerings and wine offerings.

[26] "On the fifth day bring 9 bulls, 2 rams, and 14 one-year-old lambs that have no defects. [27] Along with them bring the proper amount of grain offerings and wine offerings for each of the bulls, rams, and lambs. [28] Also bring one male goat as an offering for sin in addition to the daily burnt offerings with their grain offerings and wine offerings.

[29] "On the sixth day bring 8 bulls, 2 rams, and 14 one-year-old lambs that have no defects. [30] Along with them bring the proper amount of grain offerings and wine offerings for each of the bulls, rams, and lambs. [31] Also bring one male goat as an offering for sin in addition to the daily burnt offerings with their grain offerings and wine offerings.

[32] "On the seventh day bring 7 bulls, 2 rams, and 14 one-year-old lambs that have no defects. [33] Along with them bring the proper amount of grain offerings and wine offerings for each of the bulls, rams, and lambs. [34] Also bring one male goat as an offering for sin in addition to the daily burnt offerings with their grain offerings and wine offerings.

[35] "On the eighth day you must hold a religious assembly. You must not do any daily work. [36] As a burnt offering, an offering by fire, a soothing aroma to the LORD, bring one bull, one ram, and seven one-year-old lambs that have no defects. [37] Along with them bring the proper amount of grain offerings and wine offerings for the bull, the ram, and the lambs. [38] Also bring one male goat as an offering for sin in addition to the daily burnt offerings with their grain offerings and wine offerings.

³⁹ "These are the offerings you must bring to the LORD at your festivals. They are the offerings you must bring in addition to the offerings for anything you vowed to give to the LORD, your freewill offerings, your burnt offerings, your grain offerings, your wine offerings, and your fellowship offerings."ᵃ

⁴⁰ Moses told the Israelites everything the LORD had commanded him.

Teachings About Vows

30 ᵃ ¹ Moses said to the heads of the tribes of Israel, "This is what the LORD has commanded ₗabout vows₎: ² If a man makes a vow to the LORD that he will do something or swears an oath that he won't do something, he must not break his word. He must do everything he said he would do.

³ "A young girl, who still lives in her father's house, might make a vow to the LORD that she will do something or swear an oath that she won't do something. ⁴ If her father says nothing to her when he hears about it, her vow or oath must be kept. ⁵ But if her father objects when he hears about it, her vow or oath doesn't have to be kept. The LORD will free her ₗfrom this vow or oath₎ because her father objected.

⁶ "An unmarried woman might make a vow that she will do something or carelessly promise that she won't do something. When she marries, ⁷ her husband may hear about it but say nothing to her. Then her vow or oath must be kept. ⁸ But if her husband objects when he hears about it, he can cancel the vow or promise she made. The LORD will free her ₗfrom this vow or promise₎.

⁹ "But a widow or a divorced woman must keep her vow or her promise.

¹⁰ "A married woman might make a vow that she will do something or swear an oath that she won't do something. ¹¹ Her husband may hear about it but may say nothing and not object. Then her vow or oath must be kept. ¹² But if her husband cancels it when he hears about it, nothing she said in her vow or oath has to be kept. Her husband has canceled it, and the LORD will free her ₗfrom this vow or oath₎.

¹³ "A husband decides whether or not his wife has to keep any vow to do something or any oath to do without something. ¹⁴ If he says nothing to her about it day after day, this means he's decided that she must keep her vow or oath. She must keep it because he said nothing to her when he heard about it. ¹⁵ But if he cancels it later, he will suffer the consequences."

¹⁶ These are the laws the LORD gave Moses for husbands and wives, and for fathers with young daughters still living at home.

The LORD Commands Israel to Defeat Midian

31 ¹ The LORD said to Moses, ² "Get even with the Midianites for what they did to the Israelites. After that you will join your ancestors ₗin death₎."

³ Moses said to the people, "Some of your men must get ready to go to war against the Midianites. The LORD will use them to get even with Midian. ⁴ Send 1,000 men from each of the tribes of Israel."

⁵ So 1,000 men from each tribe were supplied from the divisions of Israel—12,000 men ready for war. ⁶ Then Moses sent them off to war, 1,000 men from each tribe along with Phinehas, son of the priest Eleazar. Phinehas took with him the holy articles and the trumpets for the fanfare.

⁷ They went to war against Midian, as the LORD commanded Moses, and killed every man. ⁸ Among those killed were the five kings of Midian—Evi, Rekem, Zur, Hur, and Reba. They also killed Balaam, son of Beor, in battle. ⁹ The Israelites took the Midianite women and children as prisoners of war. They also took all their animals, their livestock, and their valuables as loot. ¹⁰ They burned all the cities where the Midianites lived and all their settlements. ¹¹ Then they took everything as loot, including all the people and animals, ¹² and brought the prisoners of war, the loot, and everything to Moses, the priest Eleazar, and the community of Israel at the camp on the plains of Moab near the Jordan River across from Jericho.

¹³ Moses, the priest Eleazar, and all the leaders of the community went outside the camp to meet them. ¹⁴ Moses was angry with the officers of the army, the commanders of the companies and battalions, who were returning from battle.

¹⁵ "Why did you let all the women live?" he asked them. ¹⁶ "Remember, they were the ones who followed Balaam's advice and causedᵃ the Israelites to be unfaithful to the LORD in the incident that took place at Peor. The LORD's community experienced a plague at that time. ¹⁷ So kill all the Midianite boys and every Midianite woman who has gone to bed with a man. ¹⁸ But save for yourselves every girl who has never gone to bed with a man.

ᵃ 29:39 Numbers 29:40 in English Bibles is Numbers 30:1 in the Hebrew Bible.   ᵃ 30:1 Numbers 30:1–16 in English Bibles is Numbers 30:2–17 in the Hebrew Bible.   ᵃ 31:16 Targum; Hebrew meaning of "caused" uncertain.

¹⁹ "Everyone who killed a person or touched a dead body must stay outside the camp seven days. You and your prisoners of war must use the ritual water on the third and seventh days in order to take away your sin. ²⁰ Do the same for all the clothes and everything made of leather, goats' hair, or wood."

²¹ Then the priest Eleazar said to the soldiers who had gone into battle, "This is what the LORD's teachings told Moses to do: ²² Any gold, silver, bronze, iron, tin, or lead— ²³ anything that won't burn—must be put through fire in order to make it clean.ᵇ Then it must also be put through the ritual water in order to take away its sin. Whatever might burn must ⌐only⌐ be put through the ritual water. ²⁴ On the seventh day wash your clothes, and you will be clean. Then you may come into the camp."

²⁵ The LORD said to Moses, ²⁶ "You, the priest Eleazar, and the heads of the families of the community need to count all the loot, including the people and animals you captured. ²⁷ Divide the loot between the soldiers who served in the war and the rest of the community. ²⁸ Collect a tax for the LORD. From the soldiers who served in the war collect one out of every 500 things. This includes people, cattle, donkeys, sheep, and goats. ²⁹ Collect all these things from the soldiers' half of the loot, and give them to the priest Eleazar as a contribution to the LORD. ³⁰ From the Israelites' half of the loot, collect one out of every 50 things. This includes people, cattle, donkeys, sheep, goats, and every other kind of animal. Give them to the Levites who are in charge of the work done at the LORD's tent." ³¹ Moses and the priest Eleazar did as the LORD commanded Moses.

³² This is the loot that was left from everything that the troops took: 675,000 sheep and goats, ³³ 72,000 cattle, ³⁴ 61,000 donkeys, and ³⁵ 32,000 women who had never gone to bed with a man.

³⁶ Half of it went to the soldiers who served in the war. Of the 337,500 sheep and goats they received, ³⁷ 675 went to the LORD as taxes. ³⁸ Of the 36,000 cattle they received, 72 went to the LORD as taxes. ³⁹ Of the 30,500 donkeys they received, 61 went to the LORD as taxes. ⁴⁰ Of the 16,000 people they received, 32 went to the LORD as taxes.

⁴¹ Moses gave the LORD's taxes to the priest Eleazar, as the LORD had commanded him.

⁴² Moses took the Israelites' half of the loot from the soldiers. ⁴³ The community received 337,500 sheep and goats, ⁴⁴ 36,000 cattle, ⁴⁵ 30,500 donkeys, ⁴⁶ and 16,000 people.

⁴⁷ From the Israelites' half Moses collected one out of every 50 things, including people and animals, as the LORD commanded him. Then he gave all this to the Levites who were in charge of the work done at the LORD's tent.

⁴⁸ Then the officers from the military divisions, the commanders of the companies and battalions of men, came to Moses. ⁴⁹ They said to him, "Sir, we have counted all the soldiers under our command, and not one of them is missing. ⁵⁰ So we have brought as gifts to the LORD the gold jewelry that each of us found—arm bands, bracelets, signet rings, earrings, and pendants. We offer them to make peace with the LORD."

⁵¹ Moses and the priest Eleazar took all the hand-crafted gold articles from them. ⁵² All the gold contributed to the LORD by the commanders weighed about 420 pounds. ⁵³ Each soldier kept his own loot. ⁵⁴ Moses and the priest Eleazar took the gold from the commanders and brought it into the LORD's presence at the tent of meeting as a reminder to the Israelites.

The Tribes of Reuben and Gad Request Land East of the Jordan River

32 ¹ The tribes of Reuben and Gad had a large number of livestock. They saw that the regions of Jazer and Gilead were a good place for livestock. ² So they came to Moses, the priest Eleazar, and the leaders of the community, and said to them, ³ "Ataroth, Dibon, Jazer, Nimrah, Heshbon, Elealeh, Sebam, Nebo, and Beon, ⁴ the land that the LORD won for the community of Israel, is a good place for livestock. Gentlemen, we have livestock. ⁵ Please give us this land as our property. Don't make us cross the Jordan River."

⁶ Moses asked the tribes of Gad and Reuben, "Are you going to stay here while the rest of the Israelites go to war? ⁷ That might discourage them from entering the land the LORD has given them. ⁸ That's what your ancestors did when I sent them from Kadesh Barnea to take a look at the land. ⁹ They went as far as the Eshcol Valley and saw the land. But then they discouraged the rest of the Israelites from entering the land that the LORD had given them. ¹⁰ That day the LORD became angry and swore this oath, ¹¹ 'None of the people 20 years old or older, who came from Egypt, will see the land I promised Abraham, Isaac, and Jacob with an oath. This is because they didn't wholeheartedly follow me.' ¹² Only Caleb (son of Jephunneh the Kenizzite) and Joshua (son of Nun) will get to see the land. This is because they wholeheartedly followed the LORD. ¹³ Since the LORD was angry with the Israelites, he made them wander

---

ᵇ 31:23 "Clean" refers to anything that is presentable to God.

in the desert for 40 years until the whole generation of those who had done evil in the LORD's presence was gone.

¹⁴ "You're just like your parents! You're a bunch of sinners trying to make the LORD angry with Israel again. ¹⁵ If you turn away from him, he will abandon all these people in the desert. You would be responsible for their destruction."

¹⁶ Then the tribes of Gad and Reuben came up to Moses and said, "Allow us to build stone fences for our livestock and cities for our families here. ¹⁷ Then we'll be ready ⸤to march⸥ in battle formationᵃ ahead of the other Israelites until we have brought them to their land. Meanwhile our families will live in walled cities, safe from the other people who live here. ¹⁸ We will not return to our homes until every Israelite has received his own land. ¹⁹ We won't take possession of any land on the other side of the Jordan River, to the west and beyond. We already have our land here, east of the Jordan."

²⁰ Moses answered, "Do what you have said. In the LORD's presence have all your armed men get ready for battle. ²¹ Have them cross the Jordan, and fight until the LORD forces out his enemies ²² and the land is conquered. Then you may come back. You will have fulfilled your military duty to the LORD and Israel. This land will be your own property in the LORD's presence.

²³ "If you don't do all these things, you will be sinning against the LORD. You can be sure that you will be punished for your sin. ²⁴ Build cities for your families and stone fences for your flocks, but do what you have promised."

²⁵ Then the tribes of Gad and Reuben said to Moses, "Sir, we will do as you command. ²⁶ Our children, our wives, our livestock, and all our other animals will stay here in the cities of Gilead. ²⁷ But in the LORD's presence we will all get ready for battle and go with you, as you have said."

²⁸ So Moses gave orders about them to the priest Eleazar, Joshua (son of Nun), and the family heads of the tribes of Israel. ²⁹ Moses told them, "If the tribes of Gad and Reuben get ready for battle in the LORD's presence and cross the Jordan River with you and you conquer the land, give them Gilead as their own property. ³⁰ If they don't get ready for battle and go with you, the land they will take possession of must be in Canaan with yours."

³¹ The tribes of Gad and Reuben answered, "Sir, we will do as the LORD has said. ³² We will enter Canaan as armed troops in the LORD's presence, but the land we will take possession of is here, east of the Jordan."

³³ So Moses gave the tribes of Gad, Reuben, and half of the tribe of Manasseh, son of Joseph, the kingdoms of King Sihon of the Amorites and King Og of Bashan—the whole land with its cities and its surrounding territory.

³⁴ The tribe of Gad rebuilt the cities of Dibon, Ataroth, Aroer, ³⁵ Atroth Shophan, Jazer, Jogbehah, ³⁶ Beth Nimrah, and Beth Haran as walled cities. They also built stone fences for their flocks.

³⁷ The tribe of Reuben rebuilt the cities of Heshbon, Elealeh, Kiriathaim, ³⁸ Nebo, Baal Meon (whose names were changed), and Sibmah. These are the names they gave the cities they rebuilt.

³⁹ The descendants of Machir, son of Manasseh, went to Gilead, captured it, and forced out the Amorites who were there. ⁴⁰ So Moses gave Gilead to the people of Machir (the descendants of Manasseh), and they lived there. ⁴¹ Then Jair, a descendant of Manasseh, captured the settlements in Gilead. He called them Havvoth Jair [Settlements of Jair]. ⁴² Nobah captured Kenath and its villages. He named it Nobah after himself.

A Summary of Israel's Journeys After Leaving Egypt

33 ¹ This is a list of all the places where the Israelites set up camp after they left Egypt in organized groups under the leadership of Moses and Aaron. ² At the LORD's command Moses wrote down the places where they went as they traveled. This is the list:

³ They moved from Rameses on the fifteenth day of the first month, the day after the Passover. The Israelites boldly left in full view of all the Egyptians. ⁴ The Egyptians were burying all their firstborn sons, whom the LORD had killed in a mighty act of judgment on their gods.

⁵ The Israelites moved from Rameses and set up camp at Succoth.

⁶ They moved from Succoth and set up camp at Etham, on the edge of the desert.

⁷ They moved from Etham and turned back to Pi Hahiroth, east of Baal Zephon, and set up camp near Migdol.

⁸ They moved from Pi Hahirothᵃ and went through the middle of the sea into the desert. After they traveled for three days in the Desert of Etham, they set up camp at Marah.

ᵃ 32:17 Greek, Latin; Masoretic Text "ready ⸤to march⸥ ahead quickly."   ᵃ 33:8 Most Hebrew manuscripts, Samaritan Pentateuch, Syriac, Latin; some Hebrew manuscripts "moved from in front of Hahiroth."

[9] They moved from Marah and came to Elim. Elim had 12 springs and 70 palm trees, so they set up camp there.

[10] They moved from Elim and set up camp by the Red Sea.

[11] They moved from the Red Sea and set up camp in the Desert of Sin.

[12] They moved from the Desert of Sin and set up camp at Dophkah.

[13] They moved from Dophkah and set up camp at Alush.

[14] They moved from Alush and set up camp at Rephidim, where there was no water for the people to drink.

[15] They moved from Rephidim and set up camp in the Desert of Sinai.

[16] They moved from the Desert of Sinai and set up camp at Kibroth Hattaavah.

[17] They moved from Kibroth Hattaavah and set up camp at Hazeroth.

[18] They moved from Hazeroth and set up camp at Rithmah.

[19] They moved from Rithmah and set up camp at Rimmon Perez.

[20] They moved from Rimmon Perez and set up camp at Libnah.

[21] They moved from Libnah and set up camp at Rissah.

[22] They moved from Rissah and set up camp at Kehelathah.

[23] They moved from Kehelathah and set up camp at Mount Shepher.

[24] They moved from Mount Shepher and set up camp at Haradah.

[25] They moved from Haradah and set up camp at Makheloth.

[26] They moved from Makheloth and set up camp at Tahath.

[27] They moved from Tahath and set up camp at Terah.

[28] They moved from Terah and set up camp at Mithcah.

[29] They moved from Mithcah and set up camp at Hashmonah.

[30] They moved from Hashmonah and set up camp at Moseroth.

[31] They moved from Moseroth and set up camp at Bene Jaakan.

[32] They moved from Bene Jaakan and set up camp at Hor Haggidgad.

[33] They moved from Hor Haggidgad and set up camp at Jotbathah.

[34] They moved from Jotbathah and set up camp at Abronah.

[35] They moved from Abronah and set up camp at Ezion Geber.

[36] They moved from Ezion Geber and set up camp at Kadesh in the Desert of Zin.

[37] They moved from Kadesh and set up camp at Mount Hor on the border of Edom. [38] At the LORD's command the priest Aaron went up on Mount Hor. He died there on the first day of the fifth month in the fortieth year after the Israelites had left Egypt. [39] Aaron was 123 years old when he died on Mount Hor.

[40] (The Canaanite king of Arad, who lived in the Negev, which was in Canaan, heard that the Israelites were coming.)

[41] They moved from Mount Hor and set up camp at Zalmonah.

[42] They moved from Zalmonah and set up camp at Punon.

[43] They moved from Punon and set up camp at Oboth.

[44] They moved from Oboth and set up camp at Iye Abarim on the border of Moab.

[45] They moved from Iyim[b] and set up camp at Dibon Gad.

[46] They moved from Dibon Gad and set up camp at Almon Diblathaim.

[47] They moved from Almon Diblathaim and set up camp in the Abarim Mountains east of Nebo.

[48] They moved from the Abarim Mountains and set up camp on the plains of Moab near the Jordan River across from Jericho. [49] They set up camp on the plains of Moab along the Jordan. Their camp extended from Beth Jeshimoth to Abel Shittim.

The Canaanites Must Be Forced Out

[50] The LORD said to Moses on the plains of Moab near the Jordan River across from Jericho, [51] "Tell the Israelites, 'You will be crossing the Jordan River and entering Canaan. [52] As you advance, force out all the people who live there. Get rid of all their stone and metal idols, and destroy all their places of worship. [53] Take possession of the land and live there, because I will give it to you for your own. [54] Divide the land among your families by drawing lots. Give more land to larger families and less land to smaller ones. The land must be given to each family by drawing lots. Divide it among your ancestors' tribes.

[55] " 'But if you do not force out those who live in the land, they will be like splinters in your eyes and thorns in your sides. They will constantly fight with you over the land you live in. [56] Then I will do to you what I planned to do to them.' "

---

[b] 33:45 Or "Iye Abarim."

The Boundaries of Israel's Land

34 [1] The LORD said to Moses, [2] "Give the Israelites these instructions. When you enter Canaan, the land that will be given to you as your inheritance has these borders:

[3] "The southern side includes part of the Desert of Zin along the border of Edom. In the east the southern border starts from the end of the Dead Sea [4] and turns south of the Akrabbim Pass. It then goes past Zin and ends at Kadesh Barnea. From there it goes to Hazar Addar and on to Azmon. [5] From Azmon it turns toward the River of Egypt so that the border ends at the Mediterranean Sea.

[6] "The western border is the coastline of the Mediterranean Sea.

[7] "The northern border extends from the Mediterranean Sea to Mount Hor, [8] and from Mount Hor to the border of Hamath so that it ends at Zedad. [9] From there the border goes to Ziphron and ends at Hazar Enan.

[10] "The eastern border extends from Hazar Enan to Shepham. [11] From Shepham the border goes down to Riblah, east of Ain, and continues along the eastern slope of the Sea of Galilee. [12] Then the border goes along the Jordan River so that it ends at the Dead Sea.

"This will be your land and the borders around it."

[13] Moses commanded the Israelites, "This is the land you will divide by drawing lots. The LORD has commanded that this land will be given to the nine-and-a-half tribes. [14] The households from the tribes of Reuben, Gad, and half of the tribe of Manasseh have already received their land. [15] Those two-and-a-half tribes received land east of the Jordan River across from Jericho."

Men Are Appointed to Divide the Land

[16] The LORD said to Moses, [17] "These are the names of the men who will divide the land for you: the priest Eleazar and Joshua, son of Nun. [18] You must also take one leader from each tribe to divide the land. [19] These are their names:

Caleb, son of Jephunneh, from the tribe of Judah;
[20] Shemuel, son of Ammihud, from the tribe of Simeon;
[21] Elidad, son of Kislon, from the tribe of Benjamin;
[22] Bukki, son of Jogli, the leader of the tribe of Dan;
[23] Hanniel, son of Ephod, the leader of the tribe of Manasseh;
[24] Kemuel, son of Shiphtan, the leader of the tribe of Ephraim;
    (Manasseh and Ephraim are Joseph's descendants.)[a]
[25] Elizaphan, son of Parnach, the leader of the tribe of Zebulun;
[26] Paltiel, son of Azzan, the leader of the tribe of Issachar;
[27] Ahihud, son of Shelomi, the leader of the tribe of Asher;
[28] Pedahel, son of Ammihud, the leader of the tribe of Naphtali."
[29] These are the men the LORD commanded to divide Canaan for the Israelites.

Cities for the Levites

35 [1] The LORD spoke to Moses on the plains of Moab near the Jordan River across from Jericho. He said, [2] "Tell the Israelites to give the Levites some cities from their own property. They must also give the Levites the pastureland around those cities. [3] Then the Levites will have cities to live in and pastureland for their cattle, the flocks they own, and any other animals they have.

[4] "The land around the cities that you give the Levites will extend 1,500 feet from the city wall. [5] Outside the city measure off 3,000 feet on the east side, 3,000 feet on the south side, 3,000 feet on the west side, and 3,000 feet on the north side, with the city in the center. This will be their pastureland around the city.

[6] "Six of the cities you give the Levites will be cities of refuge. You must allow murderers to escape to these cities. In addition, you must also give the Levites 42 other cities. [7] So you will give a total of 48 cities with pastureland to the Levites. [8] The cities you give the Levites from the property of the other Israelites must be given based on the amount of land each tribe owns. Take more cities from larger tribes and fewer from smaller tribes."

Cities of Refuge

[9] The LORD said to Moses, [10] "Tell the Israelites: When you cross the Jordan River and enter Canaan, [11] select certain cities to be places of refuge. Anyone who unintentionally kills another person may run to them. [12] These cities will be places of refuge from any relative who can avenge the death. So anyone accused of murder will not have to die until he has had a trial in front of the community. [13] There will be six cities you select as places of refuge, [14] three on the

---

[a] 34:24 This sentence has been moved from verse 23 in order to express the complex Hebrew sentence structure more clearly in English.

east side of the Jordan River and three in Canaan. [15] These six cities will be places of refuge for Israelites, foreigners, and strangers among you. Anyone who unintentionally kills another person may flee to these cities.

[16] "But if any of you uses an iron weapon to kill another person, you are a murderer. Murderers must be put to death. [17] If any of you picks up a stone as a weapon and uses it to kill another person, you are a murderer. Murderers must be put to death. [18] Or if any of you picks up a piece of wood as a weapon and uses it to kill another person, you are a murderer. Murderers must be put to death. [19] The relative who can avenge the death must make sure a murderer is put to death. When he catches up with the murderer, he must kill him. [20] If any of you kills someone you hate by shoving him or by deliberately throwing something at him, [21] or if you beat your enemy to death with your bare hands, you must be put to death. You are a murderer. The relative who can avenge the death must kill you when he catches up with you, because you are a murderer.

[22] "But suppose you accidentally kill someone who wasn't your enemy. Maybe you shoved him or threw something at him but didn't mean to kill him. [23] Or suppose you drop a big stone, and someone is killed. However, you didn't know the person was there, he wasn't your enemy, and you weren't trying to harm him. [24] Then the community must use these rules in order to decide if you ˌare innocentˌ or if the dead person's relative can avenge the death. [25] ˌIf you are innocent,ˌ the community must protect you from that relative. They must take you back to the city of refuge you fled to. You must live there until the death of the chief priest who was anointed with the holy oil.

[26] "But don't go outside the city of refuge you fled to. [27] If the relative who can avenge the death finds you outside the city of refuge and kills you, the relative is not guilty of murder. [28] Accused murderers must stay in their city of refuge until the death of the chief priest. They may go back to their own property only after his death.

[29] "These will be the rules for future generations wherever you live.

[30] "Whoever kills another person will be put to death as a murderer only on the testimony of more than one witness. No one can be put to death on the testimony of only one witness.

[31] "Never accept a cash payment in exchange for the life of a convicted murderer who has been given the death penalty. Murderers must be put to death.

[32] "An accused murderer who has fled to a city of refuge must never go back and live on his own land before the death of the chief priest. Don't accept a cash payment to allow him to do this.

[33] "You must not pollute the land where you live. Murder is what pollutes the land. The land where a murder was committed can never make peace with the LORD except through the death of the murderer. [34] Never make the land where you and I live unclean.[a] I, the LORD, live among the Israelites."

The Rights of Women to Inherit Land

36 [1] The heads of the households whose families were descended from Gilead, son of Machir and grandson of Manasseh (families of Joseph's descendants), came and spoke to Moses and the leaders of the other Israelite households. [2] They said, "Sir, the LORD commanded you to give the Israelites their land by drawing lots. The LORD also commanded you to give the land of our relative Zelophehad to his daughters. [3] Suppose they marry men from the other tribes of Israel. Their land will be taken away from that of our ancestors and added to the land of the tribe they marry into. Then we will have lost part of our land. [4] When the Israelites' jubilee year comes, their land will be added to that of the tribe they married into. Then part of the land of our ancestor's tribe will be gone."

[5] So Moses gave the Israelites a command from the LORD. "The tribe of Joseph's descendants is right. [6] This is what the LORD commands for Zelophehad's daughters: They may marry anyone they want to, but only within a family of their ancestor's tribe. [7] In this way no land of the Israelites will pass from one tribe to another. Every Israelite must keep the tribal land inherited from his ancestors. [8] A woman who inherits land in any of the tribes of Israel may marry a man from any family in her ancestor's tribe. In this way every Israelite keeps the land inherited from his ancestors. [9] No land may pass from one tribe to another. Each Israelite tribe must keep the land it inherits."

[10] Zelophehad's daughters did as the LORD commanded Moses. [11] Mahlah, Tirzah, Hoglah, Milcah, and Noah married their cousins on their father's side of the family. [12] They married within the families of the descendants of Manasseh, son of Joseph. So their land stayed in the tribe of their father's family.

[13] These are the commands and rules the LORD gave the Israelites through Moses on the plains of Moab near the Jordan River across from Jericho.

---

[a] 35:34 "Unclean" refers to anything that is not presentable to God.

DEUTERONOMY

Moses Speaks to the People 40 Years After Leaving Egypt

1 ¹ This is the speech Moses gave in the desert east of the Jordan River, on the plains, near Suph, between Paran and Tophel, and near Laban, Hazeroth, and Di Zahab. He spoke to all the Israelites. ² (It takes 11 days to go from Mount Horeb to Kadesh Barnea by way of Mount Seir.) ³ On the first day of the eleventh month in the fortieth year ˌafter they had left Egyptˌ, Moses told the Israelites everything the LORD had commanded him to tell them. ⁴ This was after he had defeated King Sihon of the Amorites, who ruled in Heshbon, and King Og of Bashan, who ruled in Ashtaroth andᵃ in Edrei. ⁵ The Israelites were east of the Jordan River in Moab when Moses began to review God's teachings.

Moses Reminds Israel of the Events at Mount Horeb

This is what he said:

⁶ At Mount Horeb the LORD our God said to us, "You have stayed at this mountain long enough. ⁷ Break camp, and get ready! Go to the mountain region of the Amorites, and go to everyone living on the plains, in the mountains, in the foothills, in the Negev, on the whole Mediterranean coast (the land of the Canaanites), and into Lebanon as far as the Euphrates River. ⁸ I'm giving you this land. Enter, and take possession of the land the LORD swore to give to your ancestors Abraham, Isaac, and Jacob, and to you, their descendants."

⁹ At that time I said to you, "I'm not able to take care of you by myself. ¹⁰ The LORD your God has made your population increase so that you are now as numerous as the stars in the sky. ¹¹ May the LORD God of your ancestors make you a thousand times more numerous, and may he bless you as he has promised. ¹² How can I take care of your problems, your troubles, and your disagreements all by myself? ¹³ From each of your tribes, choose some men who are wise, intelligent, and experienced, and I'll appoint them to be your leaders."

¹⁴ You agreed that this was a good idea.

¹⁵ So I took the heads of your tribes who were wise and experienced men and made them officers for each of your tribes. I put them in charge of groups of 1,000, or 100, or 50, or 10 people. ¹⁶ Also at that time I gave these instructions to your judges: "Hear the cases that your people bring. Judge each case fairly, no matter whether it is ˌa disputeˌ between two Israelites or ˌa disputeˌ between an Israelite and a non-Israelite. ¹⁷ Be impartial in your decisions. Listen to the least important people the same way you listen to the most important people. Never be afraid of anyone, since your decisions come from God. You may bring me any case that's too hard for you, and I will hear it." ¹⁸ So I told you how to handle these situations.

Moses Reminds Israel of the Events at Kadesh Barnea

¹⁹ So we left Mount Horeb, as the LORD our God had commanded. We traveled through all that vast and dangerous desert you saw on the way to the mountain region of the Amorites. At last we came to Kadesh Barnea. ²⁰ Then I said to you, "We have come to the mountain region of the Amorites, which the LORD our God is giving us. ²¹ The LORD your God is giving you this land. Go ahead! Take possession of it, as the LORD God of your ancestors told you. Don't be afraid or terrified."

²² All of you came to me and said, "Let's send men ahead of us to gather information about the land for us. Have them report to us about the route we should take and the cities we'll come to."

²³ It seemed like a good idea to me. So I chose 12 of your men, one from each tribe. ²⁴ They left and went into the mountains. When they came to the Eshcol Valley, they explored it. ²⁵ They took some of the region's fruit with them and brought it back to us. They reported, "The land that the LORD our God is giving us is good."

²⁶ But you rebelled against the command of the LORD your God and refused to go. ²⁷ You complained in your tents and said, "The LORD hates us! That's why he brought us out of Egypt. He wanted to hand us over to the Amorites so that they could destroy us! ²⁸ Where are we going anyway? Our own men have discouraged us by saying, 'The people there are taller and stronger than we are. The cities are big with sky-high walls! We even saw the people of Anak there.' "

ᵃ 1:4 One Hebrew manuscript, Greek, Syriac, Latin; Masoretic Text omits "and."

²⁹ Then I said to you, "Don't tremble. Don't be afraid of them. ³⁰ The LORD your God, who is going ahead of you, will fight for you as you saw him fight for you in Egypt ³¹ and in the desert." There you saw how the LORD your God carried you, as parents carry their children. He carried you wherever you went until you came to this place.

³² In spite of this, you didn't trust the LORD your God, ³³ who went ahead of you to find places for you to camp. He appeared in a column of fire at night and in a column of smoke during the day to show you which route to take.

³⁴ When the LORD heard what you said, he was angry and took this oath: ³⁵ "Not one of these evil people will ever see the good land that I swore to give to your ancestors, ³⁶ except Caleb, son of Jephunneh. He will see it, and I will give the land that he set his feet on to him and his descendants, because he wholeheartedly followed the LORD."

³⁷ The LORD became angry with me because of you. He said, "You won't go there either. ³⁸ But your assistant Joshua, son of Nun, will go there. Encourage him, because he will help Israel take possession of the land. ³⁹ Although you thought the little children would be captured in war, your children, who are still too young to know the difference between good and evil, will enter that land. I will give it to them, and they will take possession of it. ⁴⁰ Turn around, go back into the desert, and follow the road that goes to the Red Sea."

⁴¹ You responded, "We have sinned against the LORD. We'll go and fight, as the LORD our God commanded us to do." Each of you armed yourself for war, thinking you could easily invade the mountain region.

⁴² But the LORD said to me, "Tell them, 'Don't go and fight, because I won't be with you. You will be defeated by your enemies.' "

⁴³ I told you, but you wouldn't listen. You defied the LORD's command and invaded the mountain region. ⁴⁴ The Amorites who lived there came out and attacked you and chased you like a swarm of bees. They defeated you, chasing you from Seir all the way to Hormah. ⁴⁵ When you came back, you cried to the LORD, but the LORD didn't listen to you or hear you. ⁴⁶ That's why you stayed in Kadesh as long as you did.

Moses Reminds Israel of the Events at Mount Seir

2 ¹ We went back into the desert, following the road that goes to the Red Sea as the LORD had told me. For a long time we traveled around the region of Mount Seir.

² The LORD said to me, ³ "You've traveled around this region long enough. Now go north. ⁴ Give the people these instructions: 'You're going to pass through the territory of your relatives, the descendants of Esau, who live in Seir. They'll be afraid of you, but be very careful. ⁵ Don't start a fight with them, because I'm not giving you any of their land—not even enough to stand on. I've given Esau's descendants the region of Mount Seir as their property. ⁶ You must pay them in silver for the food you eat and the water you drink.' "

⁷ The LORD your God has blessed you in everything you have done. He has watched over you as you traveled through this vast desert. For 40 years now the LORD your God has been with you, and you haven't needed a thing.

⁸ So we passed by our relatives, the descendants of Esau, who lived in Seir. We turned off the road that goes through the plains to Elath and Ezion Geber and took the road that goes through the desert of Moab.

⁹ The LORD said to me, "Don't bother the people of Moab or start a war with them. I'm not giving you any of Ar as your property. I have given it to the descendants of Lot."

¹⁰ The Emites used to live there. These people were as strong, as numerous, and as tall as the people of Anak. ¹¹ They were thought to be Rephaim, like the people of Anak, but the Moabites called them Emites. ¹² The Horites used to live in Seir, but the descendants of Esau claimed their land, wiped them out, and took their place, as Israel did in the land that the LORD gave them.

¹³ Then the LORD said, "Now cross the Zered River."

So we crossed the Zered River. ¹⁴ Thirty-eight years passed from the time we left Kadesh Barnea until we crossed the Zered River. During that time all our soldiers from that generation died, as the LORD had sworn they would. ¹⁵ In fact, it was the LORD himself who got rid of all of them until none were left in the camp.

Moses Reminds Israel About Ammon

¹⁶ When the last of these soldiers had died, ¹⁷ the LORD said to me, ¹⁸ "Today you are going to pass by the border of Moab at Ar. ¹⁹ When you come near the Ammonites, don't bother them or start a fight with them. I'm not giving you any of the land that I have already given to the descendants of Lot as their property."

²⁰ This land was thought of as the land of the Rephaim who used to live there, but the Ammonites called them Zamzummim. ²¹ These people were as strong, as numerous, and as tall as the people of Anak. But the LORD wiped them out before the Ammonites came so that the

Ammonites claimed their land and took their place. ²² The LORD did the same thing for the descendants of Esau, who lived in Seir. Before the descendants of Esau came, he wiped out the Horites so that Esau's descendants claimed their land and took their place. Esau's descendants are still there today. ²³ The same thing happened to the Avvites who lived in villages as far away as Gaza. The Caphtorites, who came from Crete, wiped them out and took their place.

Moses Reminds Israel About King Og and King Sihon

²⁴ ͵The LORD continued,͵ "Now break camp. Cross the Arnon Valley. I'm going to hand King Sihon of Heshbon, the Amorite, over to you. Fight him, and take possession of his country. ²⁵ Today I will start to make all the people under heaven terrified of you. When they hear about you, they will tremble and shake because of you."

²⁶ From the desert of Kedemoth, I sent messengers to King Sihon of Heshbon with the following offer of peace: ²⁷ "If you allow us to travel through your country, we'll go straight through and won't ever leave the road. ²⁸ We'll pay you in silver for the food we eat and the water we drink. Please let us go through, ²⁹ as the descendants of Esau, who live in Seir, and the Moabites, who live in Ar, did for us. We'll keep going until we cross the Jordan River into the land the LORD our God is giving us."

³⁰ But King Sihon of Heshbon wouldn't allow us to pass through. The LORD your God made him stubborn and overconfident in order to hand him over to you, as he has now done. ³¹ The LORD said to me, "I have begun to give you Sihon and his country. Go ahead! Take possession of his land."

³² Sihon and all his troops came out to meet us in battle at Jahaz. ³³ The LORD our God gave Sihon to us, and we defeated him, his sons, and all his troops. ³⁴ At that time we captured all his cities and claimed them for God by destroying men, women, and children. There were no survivors. ³⁵ However, we did loot the cities that we captured, taking the cattle and goods. ³⁶ From Aroer on the edge of the Arnon Valley and the city in that valley as far as Gilead, no city had walls that could keep us out. The LORD our God gave us all of them. ³⁷ But the LORD our God had forbidden you to go anywhere near the land of the Ammonites. So you didn't enter the land along the bank of the Jabbok River or capture the cities in the mountains.

Moses Reminds Israel of How They Defeated King Og of Bashan

3 ¹ Next we turned and followed the road that goes to Bashan. King Og of Bashan and all his troops came to fight us at Edrei. ² The LORD said to me, "Don't be afraid of him. I'll hand him, all his troops, and his land over to you. Do to him what you did to King Sihon of the Amorites, who ruled in Heshbon."

³ So the LORD our God also handed King Og of Bashan and all his troops over to us. We defeated him, leaving no survivors. ⁴ At that time we captured all of his cities. There wasn't a city we didn't take. We captured a total of 60 cities—the whole territory of Argob, the kingdom of Og in Bashan. ⁵ All of these cities were fortified with high walls and double-door gates with bars across the gates. We also captured a large number of unwalled villages. ⁶ We claimed them all for God, destroying every city, including men, women, and children—as we did to King Sihon of Heshbon. ⁷ However, we did loot the cities, taking all of the cattle and goods.

⁸ We took the land of the two Amorite kings east of the Jordan River, from the Arnon Valley to Mount Hermon. ⁹ (The Sidonians call Mount Hermon by the name Sirion, and the Amorites call it Senir.) ¹⁰ We took all of the cities of the plateau, all of Gilead, and all of Bashan as far as Salcah and Edrei, cities of Og's kingdom in Bashan. ¹¹ (Of the Rephaim only King Og of Bashan was left. His bed was made of iron and was more than 13 feet long and 6 feet wide. It is still in the Ammonite city of Rabbah.)

¹² At that time we took possession of this land. I gave the tribes of Reuben and Gad the land north of Aroer near the Arnon Valley and half of the mountain region of Gilead with its cities. ¹³ I gave the rest of Gilead and all of Bashan ruled by Og to half of the tribe of Manasseh. (The whole territory of Argob in Bashan used to be called the land of the Rephaim. ¹⁴ Jair, a descendant of Manasseh, took the whole territory of Argob as far as the border of the Geshurites and the Maacathites. The settlements in Bashan he named Havvoth Jair after himself. This is still their name today.) ¹⁵ I gave Gilead to Machir. ¹⁶ I gave the tribes of Reuben and Gad some of Gilead from the Arnon Valley (the middle of the valley is the border) to the Jabbok River, which is the border of Ammon. ¹⁷ Their land included the plains around the Jordan River. The western border was the river, from the Sea of Galilee to the Sea of the Plains (the Dead Sea), which is near Mount Pisgah on the east.

¹⁸ I gave the tribes of Reuben and Gad and half of the tribe of Manasseh this command: "The LORD your God has given you this land so that you can take possession of it. All your soldiers must be ready for battle when they cross ͵the Jordan River͵ ahead of the other Israelites. ¹⁹ I know you have a lot of livestock. Your wives, children, and livestock must stay here in the cities that I gave you. ²⁰ Your soldiers will go with the other Israelites until they take possession of

the land the LORD your God is giving them on the other side of the Jordan River. Then they will have a place to rest as you have. After that each of you may go back to the land I gave you." ²¹ I also gave Joshua this command: "You have seen with your own eyes everything that the LORD your God has done to these two kings. The LORD will do the same to all of the kingdoms on the other side ˌof the Jordan Riverˌ where you're going. ²² Don't be afraid of them, because the LORD your God himself will fight for you."

Moses Reminds Israel Why He Will Not Enter Canaan

²³ Then I pleaded with the LORD: ²⁴ "Almighty LORD, you have ˌonlyˌ begun to show me how great and powerful you are. What kind of god is there in heaven or on earth who can do the deeds and the mighty acts you have done? ²⁵ Please let me go over and see the beautiful land on the other side of the Jordan River—those beautiful mountains in Lebanon."

²⁶ The LORD was angry with me because of you, so he wouldn't listen to me. He said, "That's enough out of you! Don't talk to me anymore about this. ²⁷ Go to the top of Mount Pisgah, and look west, north, south, and east. You may look at the land, but you will never cross the Jordan River. ²⁸ Give instructions to Joshua. Encourage and strengthen him, because he will lead these people across ˌthe Jordan Riverˌ, and he will help them take possession of the land you see."

²⁹ So we stayed in the valley near Beth Peor.

Moses Reminds Israel to Be Loyal to the LORD

4 ¹ Israel, listen to the laws and rules I am about to teach you. Obey them so that you will live and be able to enter and take possession of the land that the LORD God of your ancestors is giving you. ² Never add anything to what I command you, or take anything away from it. Then you will be able to obey the commands of the LORD your God that I give you.

³ With your own eyes you saw what the LORD did at Baal Peor. The LORD your God destroyed everyone among you who worshiped the god Baal while you were at Peor. ⁴ But you were loyal to the LORD your God and are still alive today.

⁵ I have taught you laws and rules as the LORD my God commanded me. You must obey them when you've entered the land and taken possession of it. ⁶ Faithfully obey these laws. This will show the people of the world your wisdom and insight. When they hear about all these laws, they will say, "What wise and insightful people there are in this great nation!" ⁷ What great nation ever had their gods as near to them as the LORD our God is near to us whenever we pray to him? ⁸ Or what other great nation has such fair laws and rules as all these teachings I am giving you today?

⁹ However, be careful, and watch yourselves closely so that you don't forget the things which you have seen with your own eyes. Don't let them fade from your memory as long as you live. Teach them to your children and grandchildren. ¹⁰ Never forget the day you stood in front of the LORD your God at Mount Horeb. The LORD had said to me, "Assemble the people in front of me, and I will let them hear my words. Then they will learn to fear me as long as they live on earth, and they will teach their children the same thing."

¹¹ So you came and stood at the foot of the mountain, which was on fire with flames shooting into the sky. It was dark, cloudy, and gloomy. ¹² The LORD spoke to you from the fire. You heard a voice speaking but saw no one. There was only a voice. ¹³ The LORD told you about the terms of his promise, the ten commandments, which he commanded you to do. Then he wrote them on two stone tablets. ¹⁴ The LORD also commanded me to teach you the laws and rules you must obey after you cross ˌthe Jordan Riverˌ and take possession of the land.

¹⁵ You didn't see the LORD the day he spoke to you from the fire at Mount Horeb. So be very careful ¹⁶ that you don't become corrupt and make your own carved idols. Don't make statues that represent men or women, ¹⁷ any animal on earth, any creature with wings that flies, ¹⁸ any creature that crawls on the ground, or any fish in the water. ¹⁹ Don't let yourselves be tempted to worship and serve what you see in the sky—the sun, the moon, the stars, or anything else. The LORD your God has given them to all people everywhere. ²⁰ But you are the people the LORD brought out of Egypt, the iron smelter, in order to make you his own people as you still are today.

²¹ The LORD was angry with me because of you. So the LORD your God took an oath that I wouldn't cross the Jordan River and enter the good land he is giving you as your property. ²² I'm going to die in this land and not cross the Jordan River, but you're going to go across and take possession of that good land. ²³ Be careful that you don't forget the promise[a] that the LORD your God made to you. Don't make your own carved idols or statues that represent anything the LORD your God has forbidden. ²⁴ The LORD your God is a raging fire, a God who does not tolerate rivals.

²⁵ Even when you have children and grandchildren and have grown old in that land, don't become corrupt and make carved idols or statues that represent anything. I call heaven and

---

ᵃ 4:23 Or "covenant."

earth as witnesses against you today:[b] If you do this thing that the LORD your God considers evil, making him furious, [26] you will quickly disappear from the land you're going to possess on the other side of the Jordan River. You won't live very long there. You'll be completely wiped out. [27] The LORD will scatter you among the people of the world, and only a few of you will be left among the nations where the LORD will force you to live. [28] There you will worship wooden and stone gods made by human hands. These gods can't see, hear, eat, or smell.

[29] But if you look for the LORD your God when you are among those nations, you will find him whenever you search for him with all your heart and with all your soul. [30] When you're in distress and all these things happen to you, then you will finally come back to the LORD your God and obey him. [31] The LORD your God is a merciful God. He will not abandon you, destroy you, or forget the promise to your ancestors that he swore he would keep.

[32] Search the distant past, long before your time. Start from the very day God created people on earth. Search from one end of heaven to the other. Has anything as great as this ever happened before, or has anything like it ever been heard of? [33] Have any ˻other˼ people ever heard God speak from a fire and lived? You did! [34] Or has any god ever tried to come and take one nation away from another for himself? The LORD your God used his mighty hand and powerful arm to do this for you in Egypt. He did this using plagues, miraculous signs, amazing things, and war. He did his great and awe-inspiring deeds in front of you.

[35] You were shown these things so that you would know that the LORD is God. There is no other god. [36] He let you hear his voice from heaven so that he could instruct you. He showed you his great fire on earth, and you heard him speak from the column of fire. [37] Because he loved your ancestors and chose their descendants, he was with you as he brought you out of Egypt by his great power. [38] He forced nations greater and stronger than you out of your way to bring you into their land and give it to you. This land is your own possession today.

[39] Remember today, and never forget that the LORD is God in heaven above and here on earth. There is no other god. [40] Obey his laws and commands which I'm giving you today. Then things will go well for you and your descendants. You will live for a long time in the land. The LORD your God is giving you the land for as long as you live.

Three Cities of Refuge East of the Jordan River

[41] Then Moses set aside three cities on the east side of the Jordan River. [42] Those who unintentionally killed someone whom they had never hated could flee to one of these cities and save their lives. [43] The cities were Bezer on the desert plateau for the tribe of Reuben, Ramoth in Gilead for the tribe of Gad, and Golan in Bashan for the tribe of Manasseh.

Introduction to Moses' Teachings

[44] This is what Moses taught the people of Israel. [45] These are the commandments, laws, and rules Moses gave the Israelites after they had left Egypt. [46] He gave these to the people when they were east of the Jordan River in the valley near Beth Peor, in the land of King Sihon of the Amorites, who ruled in Heshbon. Moses and Israel defeated him after they left Egypt. [47] They took possession of his land and the land of King Og of Bashan, the two kings of the Amorites who were east of the Jordan River. [48] This land went from Aroer on the edge of the Arnon Valley to Mount Siyon (that is, Mount Hermon). [49] It included all the plains on the east side of the Jordan River as far as the Dead Sea at the foot of the slopes of Mount Pisgah.

The Ten Commandments—Exodus 20:1–21

5 [1] Moses summoned all Israel and said to them: Israel, listen to the laws and rules I'm telling you today. Learn them and faithfully obey them.

[2] The LORD our God made a promise[a] to us at Mount Horeb. [3] He didn't make this promise to our ancestors, but to all of us who are alive here today. [4] The LORD spoke to you face to face from the fire on the mountain. [5] I stood between the LORD and you to tell you the word of the LORD, because you were afraid of the fire and didn't go up on the mountain. The LORD said:

[6] "I am the LORD your God, who brought you out of slavery in Egypt.

[7] "Never have any other gods. [8] Never make your own carved idols or statues that represent any creature in the sky, on the earth, or in the water. [9] Never worship them or serve them, because I, the LORD your God, am a God who does not tolerate rivals. I punish children for their parents' sins to the third and fourth generation of those who hate me. [10] But I show mercy to thousands of generations of those who love me and obey my commandments.

[11] "Never use the name of the LORD your God carelessly. The LORD will make sure that anyone who uses his name carelessly will be punished.

---

[b] 4:25 The first part of verse 26 (in Hebrew) has been placed in verse 25 to express the complex Hebrew sentence structure more clearly in English.   [a] 5:2 Or "covenant."

¹² "Observe the day of worship as a holy day. This is what the LORD your God has commanded you. ¹³ You have six days to do all your work. ¹⁴ The seventh day is the day of worship dedicated to the LORD your God. You, your sons, your daughters, your male and female slaves, your oxen, your donkeys—all of your animals—even the foreigners living in your city must never do any work ˌon that dayˌ. In this way your male and female slaves can rest as you do. ¹⁵ Remember that you were slaves in Egypt and that the LORD your God used his mighty hand and powerful arm to bring you out of there. This is why the LORD your God has commanded you to observe the day of worship.

¹⁶ "Honor your father and your mother as the LORD your God has commanded you. Then you will live for a long time, and things will go well for you in the land the LORD your God is giving you.

¹⁷ "Never murder.

¹⁸ "Never commit adultery.

¹⁹ "Never steal.

²⁰ "Never avoid the truth when you testify about your neighbor.ᵇ

²¹ "Never desire to take your neighbor's wife away from him.

"Never long for your neighbor's household, his field, his male or female slave, his ox, his donkey, or anything else that belongs to him."

²² These are the commandments the LORD spoke to your whole assembly on the mountain. He spoke in a loud voice from the fire, the cloud, and the gloomy darkness. Then he stopped speaking. He wrote the commandments on two stone tablets and gave them to me.

²³ But when you heard the voice coming from the darkness and saw the mountain blazing with fire, all the leaders and heads of your tribes came to me. ²⁴ You said, "The LORD our God has let us see how great and glorious he is. We've heard his voice come from the fire. Today we've seen that people can live even if God speaks to them. ²⁵ Why should we die? This great fire will consume us! If we continue to hear the voice of the LORD our God, we'll die! ²⁶ Who has ever heard the voice of the living God speak from a fire, as we did, and lived? ²⁷ ˌMoses,ˌ go and listen to everything that the LORD our God says. Then tell us whatever the LORD our God tells you. We'll listen and obey."

²⁸ When the LORD heard the words that you spoke to me, he said, "I have heard what these people said to you. Everything they said was good. ²⁹ If only they would fear me and obey all my commandments as long as they live! Then things would go well for them and their children forever.

³⁰ "Tell the people to go back to their tents. ³¹ But you stay here with me. I will give you all the commands, laws, and rules that you must teach them to obey in the land which I'm giving them to possess."

³² So be careful to do what the LORD your God has commanded you. Never stop living this way. ³³ Follow all the directions the LORD your God has given you. Then you will continue to live, life will go well for you, and you will live for a long time in the land that you are going to possess.

Love the LORD

6 ¹ These are the commands, laws, and rules the LORD your God commanded me to teach you. Obey them after you enter the land and take possession of it. ² As long as you live, you, your children, and your grandchildren must fear the LORD your God. All of you must obey all his laws and commands that I'm giving you, and you will live a long time. ³ Listen, Israel, and be careful to obey these laws. Then things will go well for you and your population will increase in a land flowing with milk and honey, as the LORD God of your ancestors promised you.

⁴ Listen, Israel: The LORD is our God. The LORD is the only God. ⁵ Love the LORD your God with all your heart, with all your soul, and with all your strength. ⁶ Take to heart these words that I give you today. ⁷ Repeat them to your children. Talk about them when you're at home or away, when you lie down or get up. ⁸ ˌWrite them down, andˌ tie them around your wrist, and wear them as headbands as a reminder. ⁹ Write them on the doorframes of your houses and on your gates.

¹⁰ The LORD your God will bring you into the land and give it to you, as he swore to your ancestors Abraham, Isaac, and Jacob. This land will have large, prosperous cities that you didn't build. ¹¹ Your houses will be filled with all kinds of things that you didn't put there. You will have cisterns that you didn't dig and vineyards and olive trees that you didn't plant. After you have eaten all that you want, ¹² be careful that you don't forget the LORD, who brought you out of slavery in Egypt. ¹³ You must fear the LORD your God, serve him, and take your oaths only in his name. ¹⁴ Never worship any of the gods worshiped by the people around you. ¹⁵ If you do, the LORD your God will become very angry with you and will wipe you off the face of the earth, because the LORD your God, who is with you, is a God who does not tolerate rivals.

¹⁶ Never test the LORD your God as you did at Massah. ¹⁷ Be sure to obey the commands of the LORD your God and the regulations and laws he has given you. ¹⁸ Do what the LORD con-

---

ᵇ 5:20 Deuteronomy 5:21–33 in English Bibles is Deuteronomy 5:17–30 in some Hebrew Bibles.

siders right and good. Then things will go well for you, and you will enter and take possession of that good land which the LORD promised to your ancestors with an oath. [19] You will see the LORD expel your enemies as he said he would.

[20] In the future your children will ask you, "What do these regulations, laws, and rules which the LORD our God commanded you mean to you?" [21] Tell them, "We were Pharaoh's slaves in Egypt, but the LORD used his mighty hand to bring us out of there. [22] Right before our eyes the LORD did miraculous signs and amazing things that were spectacular but terrible for Egypt, Pharaoh, and his whole family. [23] The LORD led us out of there to bring us here and give us this land he promised to our ancestors with an oath. [24] The LORD our God commanded us to obey all these laws and to fear him. These laws are for our own good as long as we live so that he will preserve our lives. It's still true today. [25] This is how we'll have the LORD's approval: If we faithfully obey all these laws in the presence of the LORD our God, as he has commanded us."

Israel Is Commanded to Destroy the Canaanites and Their Idols

7 [1] The LORD your God will bring you to the land you're about to enter and take possession of. He will force many nations out of your way: the Hittites, Girgashites, Amorites, Canaanites, Perizzites, Hivites, and Jebusites—seven nations larger and more powerful than you. [2] When the LORD your God gives them to you and you defeat them, destroy every one of them because they have been claimed by the LORD. Don't make any treaties with them or show them any mercy. [3] Never marry any of them. Never let your daughters marry their sons or your sons marry their daughters. [4] These people will turn your children away from me to worship other gods. Then the LORD will get very angry with you and will quickly destroy you.

[5] But this is what you must do to these people: Tear down their altars, smash their sacred stones, cut down their poles dedicated to the goddess Asherah, and burn their idols. [6] You are a holy people, who belong to the LORD your God. He chose you to be his own special possession out of all the nations on earth.

[7] The LORD set his heart on you and chose you, even though you didn't outnumber all the other people. You were the smallest of all nations. [8] You were chosen because the LORD loved you and kept the oath he swore to your ancestors. So he used his mighty hand to bring you out. He freed you from slavery under Pharaoh (the king of Egypt). [9] Keep in mind that the LORD your God is ‚the only‚ God. He is a faithful God, who keeps his promise[a] and is merciful to thousands of generations of those who love him and obey his commands. [10] But he sends destruction to pay back everyone who hates him. He never takes long to pay back anyone who hates him.

[11] So obey the commands, laws, and rules I'm giving you today.

[12] If you listen to these rules and faithfully obey them, the LORD your God will keep his promise to you and be merciful to you, as he swore to your ancestors. [13] He will love you, bless you, and increase the number of your descendants. He will bless you with children. He will bless your land with produce: grain, new wine, and olive oil. He will bless your herds with calves, and your flocks with lambs and kids. This will all happen in the land the LORD will give you, as he swore to your ancestors. [14] You will be blessed more than any other people. Your men and women will be able to have children, and your animals will be able to have offspring. [15] The LORD will keep you from having any kind of illness. He will not strike you with any of the terrible diseases you experienced in Egypt. Instead, he will strike all those who hate you. [16] You must destroy all the people the LORD your God hands over to you. Have no pity on them, and never worship their gods, because they will be a trap for you.

[17] You may say to yourselves, "These nations outnumber us. How can we force them out?" [18] Don't be afraid of them. Remember what the LORD your God did to Pharaoh and all of Egypt. [19] You saw with your own eyes the terrible plagues, the miraculous signs, and the amazing things the LORD did. He used his mighty hand and powerful arm to bring you out. He will do the same thing to all the people you're afraid of. [20] The LORD your God will spread panic among them until they all die. There will be no one left—not even those who were hiding from you. [21] Don't be afraid of them, because the LORD your God is with you. He is a great and awe-inspiring God. [22] Little by little he will force these nations out of your way. You won't be able to wipe them out quickly. Otherwise, you would be overrun with wild animals. [23] The LORD your God will hand these people over to you and will throw them into a great panic until they're destroyed. [24] He will hand their kings over to you, and no one on earth will even remember their names. No one will be able to stop you. You will destroy them all. [25] Burn their idols. Don't ever long for the silver and gold on these idols or take any of it for yourselves. It might be a trap for you. Besides, these idols are disgusting to the LORD your God. [26] Never bring a disgusting idol into your house. If you do, you and the idol will be destroyed. Consider it detestable and disgusting. It must be destroyed."

---

[a] 7:9 Or "covenant."

Israel Told Never to Forget God

8 [1] Be careful to obey every command I give you today. Then you will live, and your population will increase. You will enter and take possession of the land that the LORD promised to your ancestors with an oath.

[2] Remember that for 40 years the LORD your God led you on your journey in the desert. He did this in order to humble you and test you. He wanted to know whether or not you would wholeheartedly obey his commands. [3] So he made you suffer from hunger and then fed you with manna, which neither you nor your ancestors had seen before. He did this to teach you that a person cannot live on bread alone but on every word that the LORD speaks. [4] Your clothes didn't wear out, and your feet didn't swell these past 40 years. [5] Learn this lesson by heart: The LORD your God was disciplining you as parents discipline their children. [6] Obey the commands of the LORD your God. Follow his directions, and fear him.

[7] The LORD your God is bringing you into a good land. It is a land with rivers that don't dry up. There are springs and underground streams flowing through the valleys and hills. [8] The land has wheat and barley, grapevines, fig trees, and pomegranates. The land has honey and olive trees for olive oil. [9] The land will have enough food for you, and you will have everything you need. The land has rocks with iron ore, and you will be able to mine copper ore in the hills. [10] When you have eaten all you want, thank the LORD your God for the good land he has given you.

[11] Be careful that you don't forget the LORD your God. Don't fail to obey his commands, rules, and laws that I'm giving you today. [12] You will eat all you want. You will build nice houses and live in them. [13] Your herds and flocks, silver and gold, and everything else you have will increase. [14] When this happens, be careful that you don't become arrogant and forget the LORD your God, who brought you out of slavery in Egypt. [15] He was the one who led you through that vast and dangerous desert—a thirsty and arid land, with poisonous snakes and scorpions. He was the one who made water come out of solid rock for you. [16] He was the one who fed you in the desert with manna, which your ancestors had never seen. He did this in order to humble you and test you. But he also did this so that things would go well for you in the end. [17] You may say to yourselves, "I became wealthy because of my own ability and strength." [18] But remember the LORD your God is the one who makes you wealthy. He's confirming the promise[a] which he swore to your ancestors. It's still in effect today.

[19] I warn you today that if you forget the LORD your God and follow other gods, and if you serve them and bow down to them, you will certainly be destroyed. [20] The LORD is going to destroy other nations as you enter the land. You will be destroyed like them if you don't obey the LORD your God.

Israel Has Been Given Canaan Because of God's Mercy

9 [1] Listen, Israel, you're about to cross the Jordan River. You'll be forcing out nations that are larger and stronger than you, with big cities that have sky-high walls. [2] Their people are tall and strong. They're descendants of Anak. You know all about them. You've also heard it said, "Who can oppose the descendants of Anak?" [3] Realize today that the LORD your God is the one who is going ahead of you like a raging fire. He will wipe them out and will use you to crush their power. You will take possession of their land and will quickly destroy them as the LORD promised you.

[4] When the LORD your God expels these people in front of you, don't say to yourselves, "Because we've been living right, the LORD brought us here to take possession of this land." No, it's because these nations are so wicked that the LORD is forcing them out of your way. [5] It's not because you've been living right or because you're so honest that you're entering to take possession of their land. It's because these people are so wicked that the LORD your God is forcing them out of your way. It's also because the LORD wants to confirm the promise he swore to your ancestors Abraham, Isaac, and Jacob. [6] So understand this: It's not because you've been living right that the LORD your God is giving you this good land to possess. You are impossible to deal with!

[7] Never forget how you made the LORD your God angry in the desert. You've rebelled against the LORD from the day you left Egypt until you came here. [8] Even at Mount Horeb you made the LORD so angry that he wanted to destroy you. [9] When I went up on the mountain to get the stone tablets, the tablets of the promise that the LORD made to you, I stayed on the mountain 40 days and 40 nights without food or water. [10] Then the LORD gave me the two stone tablets inscribed by God himself. On them were written all the words that the LORD spoke to you from the fire on the mountain on the day of the assembly.

[11] At the end of the 40 days and 40 nights, the LORD gave me the two stone tablets with his promise on them. [12] He told me, "Leave right away. Your people whom you brought out of

---

[a] 8:18 Or "covenant."

Egypt have ruined ˌeverythingˌ. They've quickly turned from the way I commanded them to live. They've made an idol for themselves."

[13] The LORD also said to me, "I've seen these people, and they are impossible to deal with. [14] Leave me alone! I'll destroy them and wipe their name off the earth. Then I'll make you into a nation larger and stronger than they are."

[15] So I turned and went down the mountain while it was still burning with fire. I was carrying the two tablets with the promise on them. [16] Then I saw that you had sinned against the LORD your God. You had made a statue of a calf for yourselves. You had quickly turned from the way the LORD commanded you to live. [17] I took the two tablets, threw them down, and smashed them in front of you.

[18] Once again I threw myself down in front of the LORD. I went without food and water for 40 days and 40 nights because of the sin you committed. You did what the LORD considered evil and made him furious. [19] I was terrified of the LORD's anger and fury. He was so angry he wanted to destroy you. But once more the LORD listened to me.

[20] The LORD also became very angry with Aaron and wanted to destroy him. But at that time I prayed for Aaron, too.

[21] I took that sinful calf you made and burned it. I crushed it, grinding it thoroughly until it was as fine as powder. Then I threw the powder into the river that flowed down the mountain.

[22] You also made the LORD angry at Taberah, Massah, and Kibroth Hattaavah.

[23] When the LORD sent you from Kadesh Barnea, he said, "Go and take possession of the land I'm giving you." But you rebelled against the word of the LORD your God. You didn't believe him or obey him. [24] You've rebelled against the LORD as long as I've known you.

[25] I threw myself down in front of the LORD for 40 days and 40 nights because the LORD said he would destroy you. [26] I prayed to the LORD and said, "Almighty LORD, don't destroy your people. They belong to you. You saved them by your great power and used your mighty hand to bring them out of Egypt. [27] Remember your servants Abraham, Isaac, and Jacob. Disregard the stubbornness, wickedness, and sin of these people. [28] Otherwise, the country we left will say, "The LORD wasn't able to bring them to the land he promised them. He hated them. That's why he brought them out—to let them die in the desert." [29] They are your people. They belong to you. You used your great strength and powerful arm to bring them out ˌof Egyptˌ.

10 [1] At that time the LORD said to me, "Cut two ˌmoreˌ stone tablets like the first ones, and come up to me on the mountain. Also make an ark out of wood. [2] I will write on the tablets the same words that were on the first tablets, which you smashed. Then you will put them in the ark."

[3] I made an ark out of acacia wood. I cut two ˌmoreˌ stone tablets like the first ones. I carried the two tablets up the mountain. [4] The LORD wrote on these tablets the same words as before, the ten commandments. He had spoken these words to you from the fire on the mountain on the day of the assembly. Then the LORD gave them to me. [5] I came back down the mountain and put the tablets in the ark I had made. They are still there, where the LORD commanded me to put them.

[6] The Israelites moved from the wells of the Jaakanites to Moserah. Aaron died there and was buried, and his son Eleazar succeeded him as priest. [7] They moved from there to Gudgodah, and from Gudgodah to Jotbathah, a land with rivers that don't dry up. [8] At that time the LORD set apart the tribe of Levi to carry the ark of the LORD's promise, to stand in the LORD's presence when they serve him as priests, and to praise his name, as they still do today. [9] This is why the tribe of Levi has no land of their own as the other tribes have. The LORD your God is their only possession, as he promised them.

[10] I stayed on the mountain 40 days and 40 nights as I did the first time. Once again the LORD listened to me and agreed not to destroy you. [11] The LORD said to me, "Lead the people on their journey. They will enter and take possession of the land I will give them, as I swore to their ancestors."

Israel Encouraged to Follow God's Guidance

[12] Israel, what does the LORD your God want you to do? He wants you to fear him, follow all his directions, love him, and worship him with all your heart and with all your soul. [13] The LORD wants you to obey his commands and laws that I'm giving you today for your own good. [14] Remember that the sky, the highest heaven, the earth and everything it contains belong to the LORD your God. [15] The LORD set his heart on your ancestors and loved them. Because of this, today he chooses you, their descendants, out of all the people of the world.

[16] So circumcise your uncircumcised hearts, and don't be impossible to deal with any longer. [17] The LORD your God is God of gods and Lord of lords, the great, powerful, and awe-inspiring God. He never plays favorites and never takes a bribe. [18] He makes sure orphans and widows receive justice. He loves foreigners and gives them food and clothes. [19] So you should love foreigners, because you were foreigners living in Egypt. [20] Fear the LORD your God, wor-

ship him, be loyal to him, and take your oaths in his name. ²¹ He is your glory. He is your God, who did for you these spectacular and awe-inspiring deeds you saw with your own eyes. ²² When your ancestors went to Egypt, there were 70 of them. Now the LORD your God has made you as numerous as the stars in the sky.

11 ¹ Love the LORD your God, and do what he wants you to do. Always obey his laws, rules, and commands. ² Remember today the discipline you learned from the LORD your God. (¸I'm not talking¸ to your children. They didn't see or experience any of this.) You saw and experienced his great power—his mighty hand and powerful arm. ³ You saw the miraculous signs and deeds he did in Egypt to Pharaoh (the king of Egypt) and to his whole country. ⁴ You saw what he did to the Egyptian army, its horses and chariots. He drowned them in the Red Sea when they pursued you. So the LORD destroyed them forever. ⁵ You saw what he did for you in the desert until you came here. ⁶ You also saw what he did to Dathan and Abiram, the sons of Eliab, from the tribe of Reuben. In the middle of all the Israelites the ground opened up and swallowed them, their families, their tents, and every living creature with them. ⁷ You saw with your own eyes all these spectacular things that the LORD did.

⁸ Obey all the commands I'm giving you today. Then you will have the strength to enter and take possession of the land once you've crossed ¸the Jordan River¸. ⁹ Then you will also live for a long time in the land the LORD swore to give your ancestors and their descendants—a land flowing with milk and honey.

¹⁰ The land you're about to enter and take possession of isn't like the land you left in Egypt. There you used to plant your seed, and you had to water it like a vegetable garden. ¹¹ The land you're about to enter is a land with hills and valleys, watered by rain from the sky. ¹² It is a land the LORD your God cares about. He watches over it all year long.

¹³ If you faithfully obey the commands that I'm giving you today, love the LORD your God, and serve him with all your heart and with all your soul, ¹⁴ I will send rain on your land at the right time, both in the fall and in the spring. Then you will gather your own grain, new wine, and olive oil. ¹⁵ I will provide grass in the fields for your animals, and you will be able to eat all you want.

¹⁶ Be careful, or you'll be tempted to turn away and worship other gods and bow down to them. ¹⁷ The LORD will become angry with you. He'll shut the sky so that there'll be no rain. Then the ground won't grow any crops, and you'll quickly disappear from this good land the LORD is giving you.

¹⁸ Take these words of mine to heart and keep them in mind. ¸Write them down,¸ tie them around your wrist, and wear them as headbands as a reminder. ¹⁹ Teach them to your children, and talk about them when you're at home or away, when you lie down or get up. ²⁰ Write them on the doorframes of your houses and on your gates. ²¹ Then you and your children will live for a long time in this land that the LORD swore to give to your ancestors—as long as there's a sky above the earth.

²² Faithfully obey all these commands I'm giving you. Love the LORD your God, follow all his directions, and be loyal to him. ²³ Then the LORD will force all these people out of your way. Then you will take possession of ¸the land belonging to¸ people taller and stronger than you. ²⁴ I will give you every place on which you set foot. Your borders will be from the desert to Lebanon, from the Euphrates River to the Mediterranean Sea. ²⁵ No one will be able to stop you. As the LORD your God promised, he will make people terrified of you wherever you go in this land.

Choose the Blessing or the Curse

²⁶ Today I'm giving you the choice of a blessing or a curse. ²⁷ You'll be blessed if you obey the commands of the LORD your God that I'm giving you today. ²⁸ You'll be cursed if you disobey the commands of the LORD your God, if you turn from the way I'm commanding you to live today, and if you worship other gods you never knew. ²⁹ When the LORD your God brings you into the land you're about to enter, recite the blessing from Mount Gerizim and the curse from Mount Ebal. ³⁰ (These mountains are on the west side of the Jordan, beyond the road that goes west, in the region of the Canaanites who live on the plains facing Gilgal, next to the oak trees of Moreh.) ³¹ You're about to cross the Jordan River to enter and take possession of the land the LORD your God is giving you. When you take possession of it and live there, ³² be careful to obey all the laws and rules I'm giving you today.

The Proper Place to Worship

12 ¹ Here are the laws and rules you must faithfully obey in the land that the LORD God of your ancestors is giving you as your own. You must obey them as long as you live in the land.

² Completely destroy all the worship sites on the high mountains, on the hills, and under every large tree. The people you're forcing out worship their gods in these places. ³ Tear down their altars, crush their sacred stones, burn their poles dedicated to the goddess Asherah, cut down their idols, and wipe out the names of their gods from those places.

⁴ Never worship the LORD your God in the way they worship their gods. ⁵ The LORD your God will choose a place out of all your tribes to live and put his name. Go there and worship him. ⁶ Bring him your burnt offerings, your sacrifices, one-tenth of your income, your contributions, the offerings you vow to bring, your freewill offerings, and the firstborn of your cattle, sheep, and goats. ⁷ There, in the presence of the LORD your God, you and your families will eat and enjoy everything you've worked for, because the LORD your God has blessed you.

⁸ Never worship in the way that it's being done here today, where everyone does whatever he considers right. ⁹ Up until now you haven't come to your place of rest, the property the LORD your God is giving you. ¹⁰ But you will cross the Jordan River and settle in the land the LORD your God is giving you as your own property. He will give you peace from all your enemies around you so that you will live securely. ¹¹ Then the LORD your God will choose a place where his name will live. You must bring everything I command you to that place. Bring your burnt offerings, your sacrifices, one-tenth of your income, your contributions, and all the best offerings you vow to bring to the LORD. ¹² Enjoy yourselves in the presence of the LORD your God along with your sons, daughters, male and female slaves, and the Levites. (The Levites live in your cities because they have no land of their own as you have.) ¹³ Be careful that you don't sacrifice your burnt offerings wherever you want. ¹⁴ Instead, sacrifice them ˌonlyˌ at the place that the LORD will choose in one of your tribes. There you must do everything I command you.

¹⁵ In whatever city you live, you may slaughter and eat as much meat as you want from what the LORD your God has blessed you with. Clean and unclean*ᵃ* people may eat it as if they were eating a gazelle or a deer. ¹⁶ But never eat the blood. Pour it on the ground like water. ¹⁷ You may not eat ˌthe LORD's offeringsˌ in your cities. Those offerings are: one-tenth of your grain, new wine, and olive oil; the firstborn of your cattle, sheep, or goats; the offerings you vow to bring; your freewill offerings; and your contributions. ¹⁸ Instead, you, your sons and daughters, male and female slaves, and the Levites who live in your cities must eat these in the presence of the LORD your God at the place he will choose. There in the presence of the LORD your God enjoy everything you've worked for. ¹⁹ Don't forget to take care of the Levites as long as you live in your land.

²⁰ The LORD your God will expand your ˌcountry'sˌ borders as he promised. You will say, "I'm hungry for meat." Then eat as much meat as you want. ²¹ If the place the LORD your God chooses to put his name is too far away from you, you may slaughter an animal from the herds or flocks that the LORD has given you. Eat as much as you want in your city. I have commanded you to do this. ²² Eat it as you would eat a gazelle or a deer: Clean and unclean people may eat it together. ²³ However, be sure you never eat blood, because blood contains life. Never eat the life with the meat. ²⁴ Never eat blood. Pour it on the ground like water. ²⁵ If you don't eat blood, things will go well for you and your descendants. You will be doing what the LORD considers right.

²⁶ Take the holy things and the offerings you have vowed to bring, and go to the place the LORD will choose. ²⁷ Sacrifice the meat and the blood of your burnt offerings on the altar of the LORD your God. The blood of your sacrifices is to be poured out beside the altar of the LORD your God, but you may eat the meat. ²⁸ Be sure you obey all these instructions I'm giving you. Then things will always go well for you and your descendants because you will be doing what the LORD your God considers good and right.

²⁹ The LORD your God will destroy the nations where you're going and force them out of your way. You will take possession of their land and live there. ³⁰ After they've been destroyed, be careful you aren't tempted to follow their customs. Don't even ask about their gods and say, "How did these people worship their gods? We want to do what they did." ³¹ Never worship the LORD your God in the way they worship their gods, because everything they do for their gods is disgusting to the LORD. He hates it! They even burn their sons and daughters as sacrifices to their gods.*ᵇ*

³² Be sure to do everything I command you. Never add anything to it or take anything away from it.

How Israel Is to Deal With False Prophets

13 *ᵃ* ¹ One of your people, claiming to be a prophet or to have prophetic dreams, may predict a miraculous sign or an amazing thing. ² What he predicts may even take place. But don't listen to that prophet or dreamer*ᵇ* if he says, "Let's worship and serve other gods." (Those gods may be gods you've never heard of.) ³ The LORD your God is testing you to find out if you really love him with all your heart and with all your soul. ⁴ Worship the LORD your God, fear him, obey his commands, listen to what he says, serve him, and be loyal to him. ⁵ That prophet or dreamer must be put to death because he preached rebellion against the

---

ᵃ 12:15 "Clean" refers to anything that is presentable to God. "Unclean" refers to anything that is not presentable to God.
ᵇ 12:31 Deuteronomy 12:32 in English Bibles is Deuteronomy 13:1 in the Hebrew Bible.   *ᵃ* 13:1 Deuteronomy 13:1–18 in English Bibles is Deuteronomy 13:2–19 in the Hebrew Bible.   *ᵇ* 13:2 The first part of verse 3 (in Hebrew) has been placed in verse 2 to express the complex Hebrew paragraph structure more clearly in English.

LORD your God, who brought you out of Egypt and freed you from slavery. He was trying to lead you away from following the directions the LORD your God gave you. You must get rid of this evil.

⁶ Your own brother, son, or daughter, the wife you love, or your best friend may secretly tempt you, saying, "Let's go worship other gods." (Those gods may be gods that you and your ancestors never knew. ⁷ They may be the gods of the people around you, who live near or far, from one end of the land to the other.) ⁸ Don't be influenced by any of these people or listen to them. Have no pity on them. Don't feel sorry for them or protect them. ⁹ You must put them to death. You must start the execution. Then all the other people will join you in putting them to death. ¹⁰ Stone them to death because they were trying to lead you away from the LORD your God, who brought you out of slavery in Egypt. ¹¹ All Israel will hear about it and be afraid. Then no one among you will ever do such a wicked thing again.

¹² You may hear that the residents in one of the cities which the LORD your God is giving you to live in ¹³ have been led away from the LORD your God by worthless people. You may hear that these people have been saying, "Let's worship other gods." (Those gods may be gods you've never heard of.) ¹⁴ Then make a thorough investigation. If it is true, and you can prove that this disgusting thing has been done among you, ¹⁵ you must kill the residents of that city with swords and destroy that city and everyone in it, including the animals, because they are claimed by God. ¹⁶ Gather their goods into the middle of the city square. Then burn their city and all their goods as a burnt offering to the LORD your God. It must remain a mound of ruins and never be rebuilt. ¹⁷ Don't ever take any of the things claimed for destruction. Then the LORD will stop being angry and will show you mercy. In his mercy he will make your population increase, as he swore to your ancestors. ¹⁸ The LORD your God will do this if you listen to him, obey all the commands that I'm giving you today, and do what he considers right.

Religious Practices—Leviticus 11:1–23

14 ¹ You are the children of the LORD your God. So when someone dies, don't ˌmournˌ by cutting yourselves or shaving bald spots on your head. ² You are people who are holy to the LORD your God. Out of all the people who live on earth, the LORD has chosen you to be his own special possession.

³ Never eat anything that is disgusting to the LORD. ⁴ Here are the ˌkinds ofˌ animals you may eat: oxen, sheep, goats, ⁵ deer, gazelles, fallow deer,ᵃ wild goats, mountain goats, antelope, and mountain sheep. ⁶ You may eat all animals that have completely divided hoofs and that also chew their cud. ⁷ But some animals chew their cud, while others have completely divided hoofs. You may not eat these ˌkinds ofˌ animals. They include camels, rabbits, and rock badgers. (Although they chew their cud, they don't have divided hoofs. They are uncleanᵇ for you.) ⁸ Also, you may not eat pigs. (Although their hoofs are divided, they don't chew their cud.) Never eat their meat or touch their dead bodies.

⁹ Here's what you may eat of every creature that lives in the water: You may eat any creature that has fins and scales. ¹⁰ But never eat anything that doesn't have fins and scales. It is unclean for you.

¹¹ You may eat any clean bird. ¹² But here are the birds that you should never eat: eagles, bearded vultures, black vultures, ¹³ buzzards, all types of kites, ¹⁴ all types of crows, ¹⁵ ostriches, nighthawks, seagulls, all types of falcons, ¹⁶ little owls, great owls, barn owls, ¹⁷ pelicans, ospreys, cormorants, ¹⁸ storks, all types of herons, hoopoes, and bats.

¹⁹ Every swarming, winged insect is also unclean for you. They must never be eaten. ²⁰ However, you may eat any ˌother kind ofˌ flying creature that is clean.

²¹ Never eat any creature that dies naturally. You may give it to the foreigners who live in your cities, and they may eat it. You may also sell it to foreigners who are visiting. But you are people who are holy to the LORD your God.

Never cook a young goat in its mother's milk.

Giving God One-Tenth of Everything

²² Every year be sure to save a tenth of the crops harvested from whatever you plant in your fields. ²³ Eat the tenth of your grain, new wine, and olive oil, and eat the firstborn of your cattle, sheep, and goats in the presence of the LORD your God in the place he will choose to put his name. Then you will learn to fear the LORD your God as long as you live.

²⁴ But the place the LORD your God will choose to put his name may be too far away. He may bless you with so much that you can't carry a tenth of your income that far. ²⁵ If so, exchange the tenth part of your income for silver. Take the silver with you, and go to the place the LORD your God will choose. ²⁶ Use the silver to buy whatever you want: cattle, sheep, goats, wine,

---

ᵃ 14:5 A specific species of deer.   ᵇ 14:7 "Unclean" refers to anything that is not presentable to God.

liquor—whatever you choose. Then you and your family will eat and enjoy yourselves there in the presence of the LORD your God. [27] Never forget to take care of the Levites who live in your cities. They have no land of their own as you have.

[28] At the end of every third year bring a tenth of that year's crop, and store it in your cities. [29] Foreigners, orphans, and widows who live in your cities may come to eat all they want. The Levites may also come because they have no land of their own as you have. Then the LORD your God will bless you in whatever work you do.

The Seventh-Year Celebration

15 [1] At the end of every seven years, you must cancel debts. [2] This is what you will do: If you've made a loan, don't collect payment on the debt your neighbor still owes you. Don't demand that your neighbor or relative pay you, because the ˌtimeˌ for suspending payments on debts has been proclaimed in the LORD's honor. [3] You may demand that a foreigner pay, but don't collect payment on the debt another Israelite still owes you. [4] In any case, there shouldn't be any poor people among you, because the LORD your God will certainly bless you in the land he is giving you as your own possession. [5] He will bless you only if you listen carefully to the LORD your God and faithfully obey all these commands I'm giving you today. [6] The LORD your God will bless you, as he promised. You will make loans to many nations, but you will not have to borrow from any of them. You will rule many nations, but no nation will ever rule you.

[7] This is what you must do whenever there are poor Israelites in one of your cities in the land that the LORD your God is giving you. [8] Be generous to these poor people, and freely lend them as much as they need. Never be hard-hearted and tight-fisted with them.[a]

[9] When the seventh year—the year when payments on debts are canceled—is near, you might be stingy toward poor Israelites and give them nothing. Be careful not to think these worthless thoughts. The poor will complain to the LORD about you, and you will be condemned for your sin. [10] Be sure to give to them without any hesitation. When you do this, the LORD your God will bless you in everything you work for and set out to do. [11] There will always be poor people in the land. That's why I command you to be generous to other Israelites who are poor and needy.

[12] Whenever Hebrew men or women are sold to you as slaves, they will be your slaves for six years. In the seventh year you must let them go free. [13] But when you let them go, don't send them away empty-handed. [14] Generously give them provisions—sheep from your flocks, grain from your threshing floor,[b] and wine from your winepress. Be as generous to them as the LORD your God has been to you. [15] Remember that you were slaves in Egypt and the LORD your God freed you. That's why I'm giving you this command today.

[16] But suppose a male slave says to you, "I don't want to leave you," because he loves you and your family and is happy with you. [17] Then take an awl and pierce it through his ear lobe into a door, and he will be your slave for life. Do the same to a female slave ˌif she doesn't want to leaveˌ.

[18] If you have to let your slave go free, it won't be a hardship for you. It would have cost you twice as much to hire someone to do the same work for those six years. Besides, the LORD your God will bless you in everything you do.

Setting Aside Firstborn Males for God

[19] You must dedicate every firstborn male from your herds and flocks to the LORD your God. Never use a firstborn ox for work, and never shear a firstborn sheep. [20] Every year you and your family must eat these animals in the presence of the LORD your God in the place the LORD will choose. [21] But if an animal is lame or blind or has any other serious defect—never sacrifice it to the LORD your God. [22] Eat it in your city. Clean and unclean[c] people may eat them together as if they were eating a gazelle or a deer. [23] But never eat the blood. Pour it on the ground like water.

Three Major Festivals

16 [1] Honor the LORD your God by celebrating Passover in the month of Abib. In the month of Abib the LORD your God brought you out of Egypt at night. [2] Slaughter an animal from your flock or herd as the Passover sacrifice to the LORD your God. Do this at the place where the LORD will choose for his name to live. [3] Never eat leavened bread with the meat from this sacrifice. Instead, for seven days you must eat unleavened bread at this festival. (It is the bread of misery because you left Egypt in a hurry.) Eat this bread so that, as long as you live, you will remember the day you left Egypt. [4] There should be no yeast anywhere in your land for seven days. Never leave until morning any of the meat you slaughter on the evening of the first day.

---

[a] 15:8 This sentence has been moved from verse 7 to express the complex Hebrew sentence structure more clearly in English.
[b] 15:14 A threshing floor is an outdoor area where grain is separated from its husks.   [c] 15:22 "Clean" refers to anything that is presentable to God. "Unclean" refers to anything that is not presentable to God.

⁵ You're not allowed to slaughter the animals for Passover in any of the cities the LORD your God is giving you. ⁶ Instead, slaughter your animals for Passover in the place where the LORD your God will choose for his name to live. Do this in the evening as the sun goes down. This is the same time you did it when you left Egypt. ⁷ Cook the meat, and eat it at the place the LORD your God will choose. In the morning you may go back to your tents. ⁸ For six days eat unleavened bread, and on the seventh day hold a religious assembly dedicated to the LORD your God. Don't do any work that day.

⁹ Count seven weeks from the time you start harvesting grain. ¹⁰ Then celebrate the Festival of Weeks to the LORD your God. Bring a freewill offering in proportion to the blessings the LORD your God has given you. ¹¹ Enjoy yourselves in the presence of the LORD your God along with your sons, daughters, male and female slaves, the Levites who live in your cities, the foreigners, orphans, and widows who live among you. Enjoy yourselves at the place the LORD your God will choose for his name to live. ¹² Remember that you were slaves in Egypt, and obey these laws carefully.

¹³ After you have gathered the grain from your threshing floor[a] and made your wine, celebrate the Festival of Booths for seven days. ¹⁴ Enjoy yourselves at the festival along with your sons, daughters, male and female slaves, the Levites, foreigners, orphans, and widows who live in your cities. ¹⁵ For seven days you will celebrate this festival dedicated to the LORD your God in the place he will choose. You will enjoy yourselves, because the LORD your God will bless all your harvest and all your work.

¹⁶ Three times a year all your men must come into the presence of the LORD your God at the place he will choose: at the Festival of Unleavened Bread, the Festival of Weeks, and the Festival of Booths. But no one may come into the presence of the LORD without an offering. ¹⁷ Each man must bring a gift in proportion to the blessings the LORD your God has given him.

Administering Justice

¹⁸ Appoint judges and officers for your tribes in every city that the LORD your God is giving you. They are to judge the people fairly. ¹⁹ Never pervert justice. Instead, be impartial. Never take a bribe, because bribes blind wise people and deny justice to those who are in the right. ²⁰ Strive for nothing but justice so that you will live and take possession of the land that the LORD your God is giving you.

²¹ When you build the altar for the LORD your God, never plant beside it any tree dedicated to the goddess Asherah. ²² Never set up a sacred stone. These are things the LORD your God hates.

17 ¹ Never offer an ox or a sheep that has a defect or anything seriously wrong with it as a sacrifice to the LORD your God. That would be disgusting to him.

² In one of the cities the LORD your God is giving you, there may be a man or woman among you who is doing what the LORD considers evil. This person may be disregarding the conditions of the LORD's promise[a] ³ by worshiping and bowing down to other gods, the sun, the moon, or the whole army of heaven. I have forbidden this. ⁴ When you are told about it, investigate it thoroughly. If it's true and it can be proven that this disgusting thing has been done in Israel, ⁵ then bring the man or woman who did this evil thing to the gates of your city, and stone that person to death. ⁶ The person can only be sentenced to death on the testimony of two or three witnesses, but no one should ever be sentenced to death on the testimony of only one witness. ⁷ The witnesses must start the execution, then all the other people will join them in putting the person to death. You must get rid of this evil.

⁸ There may be a case that is too hard for you to decide. It may involve murder, assault, or a dispute—any case which may be brought to court in your cities. Take this case to the place that the LORD your God will choose. ⁹ Go to the Levitical priests and the judge who is serving at that time. Ask for their opinion, and they will give you their verdict ¹⁰ at the place that the LORD will choose. Do what they tell you. Follow all their instructions carefully, ¹¹ and do what they tell you to do in their verdict. Do exactly what they tell you to do in their decision. ¹² If anyone deliberately disobeys the priest (who serves the LORD your God) or the judge, that person must die. You must get rid of this evil in Israel. ¹³ When all the people hear about it, they will be afraid and will never defy ‚God's law‚ again.

¹⁴ You will enter the land that the LORD your God is giving you. You will take possession of it and live there. You will say, "Let's have our own king like all the other nations around us." ¹⁵ Be sure to appoint the king the LORD your God will choose. He must be one of your own people. Never let a foreigner be king, because he's not one of your own people.

¹⁶ The king must never own a large number of horses or make the people return to Egypt to get more horses. The LORD has told you, "You will never go back there again." ¹⁷ The king

---

[a] 16:13 A threshing floor is an outdoor area where grain is separated from its husks.   [a] 17:2 Or "covenant."

must never have a large number of wives, or he will turn away ⸢from God⸣. And he must never own a lot of gold and silver. [18] When he becomes king, he should have the Levitical priests make him a copy of these teachings on a scroll. [19] He must keep it with him and read it his entire life. He will learn to fear the LORD his God and faithfully obey everything found in these teachings and laws. [20] Then he won't think he's better than the rest of his people, and he won't disobey these commands in any way. So he and his sons will rule for a long time in Israel.

Laws for the Levites

18 [1] The Levitical priests—in fact, the whole tribe of Levi—will receive no land or property of their own like the rest of the Israelites. They will eat what has been sacrificed to the LORD. These sacrifices will be what they receive.[a] [2] So the Levites will have no land of their own like the other Israelites. The LORD will be their inheritance, as he promised them.

[3] This is what the people owe the priests whenever they sacrifice an ox, a sheep, or a goat: the shoulder, jaws, and stomach. [4] Also, give them the first produce harvested: grain, new wine, olive oil, and the first wool you shear from your sheep. [5] Out of all your tribes, the LORD your God has chosen the Levites and their descendants to do the work of serving in the name of the LORD forever.

[6] A Levite from any of your cities in Israel may come from where he has been living to the place the LORD will choose. He may come as often as he wants [7] and may serve in the name of the LORD his God like all the other Levites who do their work in the LORD's presence. [8] If he does, he'll get the same amount of food as they do, in addition to what he gets from selling his family's goods.[b]

Laws About Prophets

[9] When you come to the land that the LORD your God is giving you, never learn the disgusting practices of those nations. [10] You must never sacrifice your sons or daughters by burning them alive, practice black magic, be a fortuneteller, witch, or sorcerer, [11] cast spells, ask ghosts or spirits for help, or consult the dead. [12] Whoever does these things is disgusting to the LORD. The LORD your God is forcing these nations out of your way because of their disgusting practices. [13] You must have integrity ⸢in dealing⸣ with the LORD your God. [14] These nations you are forcing out listen to fortunetellers and to those who practice black magic. But the LORD your God won't let you do anything like that.

[15] The LORD your God will send you a prophet, an Israelite like me. You must listen to him. [16] This is what you asked the LORD your God to give you on the day of the assembly at Mount Horeb. You said, "We never want to hear the voice of the LORD our God or see this raging fire again. If we do, we'll die!" [17] The LORD told me, "What they've said is good. [18] So I will send them a prophet, an Israelite like you. I will put my words in his mouth. He will tell them everything I command him. [19] Whoever refuses to listen to the words that prophet speaks in my name will answer to me. [20] But any prophet who dares to say something in my name that I didn't command him to say or who speaks in the name of other gods must die."

[21] You may be wondering, "How can we recognize that the LORD didn't speak this message?" [22] If a prophet speaks in the LORD's name and what he says doesn't happen or come true, then it didn't come from the LORD. That prophet has spoken on his own authority. Never be afraid of him.

Criminal Laws

19 [1] The LORD your God will destroy all the nations that are living in the land that he's giving you. You will force them out and live in their cities and houses. [2] When all this is done, set aside three cities in the land that the LORD your God is giving you. [3] Provide a route to each of these cities and divide the land that the LORD your God is giving you into three regions. Whoever kills someone may run to one of these cities.

[4] A person who unintentionally kills someone he never hated in the past may run to one of these cities to save his life. [5] Suppose two people go into the woods to cut wood. As one of them swings the ax to cut down a tree, the head flies off the handle, hits, and kills the other person. The one who accidentally killed the other person may run to one of these cities and save his life. [6] Otherwise, in a rage the relative who has the authority to avenge the death will pursue him. If the place is too far away, the relative may catch up with him and take his life even though he didn't deserve the death penalty, because in the past he never hated the person he killed. [7] This is why I'm commanding you to set aside three cities for yourselves.

---

[a] 18:1 Or "They are to eat the sacrifices offered by fire to the Lord or any of the other sacrifices to the Lord."
[b] 18:8 Hebrew meaning of "what he gets from selling his family's goods" uncertain.

⁸ The LORD your God may expand your country's borders as he promised your ancestors with an oath. He may give you the whole land he promised to give them. ⁹ He may do this because you faithfully obey all these commands I am now giving you—to love the LORD your God and follow his directions as long as you live. If this happens, you may add three more cities of refuge to these three. ¹⁰ That way, innocent people won't be killed in the land that the LORD your God is giving you, and you won't be guilty of murder.

¹¹ Suppose someone hates another person, waits in ambush for him, attacks him, takes his life, and runs to one of these cities. ¹² If someone does this, the leaders of your city must send for that person. They must take him from that city and hand him over to the relative who has the authority to avenge the death. He must die. ¹³ They must have no pity on him. The guilt of murdering an innocent person must be removed from Israel. Then things will go well for Israel.

¹⁴ Never move your neighbor's original boundary marker on any property in the land that the LORD your God is giving you.

¹⁵ One witness is never enough to convict someone of a crime, offense, or sin he may have committed. Cases must be settled based on the testimony of two or three witnesses.

¹⁶ This is what you must do whenever a witness takes the stand to accuse a person falsely of a crime. ¹⁷ The two people involved must stand in the LORD's presence, in front of the priests and judges who are serving at that time. ¹⁸ The judges must make a thorough investigation. If it is found that the witness lied when he testified against the other Israelite, ¹⁹ then do to him what he planned to do to the other person. You must get rid of this evil. ²⁰ When the rest of the people hear about this, they will be afraid. Never again will such an evil thing be done among you. ²¹ Have no pity on him: ˌTakeˌ a life for a life, an eye for an eye, a tooth for a tooth, a hand for a hand, and a foot for a foot.

Laws for Warfare

20 ¹ When you go to war against your enemies, you may see horses, chariots, and armies larger than yours. Don't be afraid of them, because the LORD your God, who brought you out of Egypt, will be with you. ² Before the battle starts, a priest must come and speak to the troops. ³ He should tell them, "Listen, Israel, today you're going into battle against your enemies. Don't lose your courage! Don't be afraid or alarmed or tremble because of them. ⁴ The LORD your God is going with you. He will fight for you against your enemies and give you victory."

⁵ The officers should tell the troops, "If you have built a new house but not dedicated it, you may go home. Otherwise, you might die in battle, and someone else will dedicate it. ⁶ If you have planted a vineyard and not enjoyed the grapes, you may go home. Otherwise, you might die in battle, and someone else will enjoy the grapes. ⁷ If you are engaged to a woman but have not married her, you may go home. Otherwise, you might die in battle, and someone else will marry her."

⁸ The officers should also tell the troops, "If you are afraid or have lost your courage, you may go home. Then you won't ruin the morale of the other Israelites." ⁹ When the officers finish speaking to the troops, they should appoint commanders to lead them.

¹⁰ When you approach a city to attack it, offer its people a peaceful way to surrender. ¹¹ If they accept it and open ˌtheir gatesˌ to you, then all the people there will be made to do forced labor and serve you. ¹² If they won't accept your offer of peace but declare war on you, set up a blockade around the city. ¹³ When the LORD your God hands the city over to you, kill every man in that city with your swords. ¹⁴ But take the women and children, the cattle and everything else in the city, including all its goods, as your loot. You may enjoy your enemies' goods that the LORD your God has given you. ¹⁵ This is what you must do to all the cities that are far away which don't belong to the nations nearby.

¹⁶ However, you must not spare anyone's life in the cities of these nations that the LORD your God is giving you as your property. ¹⁷ You must claim the Hittites, Amorites, Canaanites, Perizzites, Hivites, and Jebusites for the LORD and completely destroy them, as the LORD your God has commanded you. ¹⁸ Otherwise, they will teach you to do all the disgusting things they do for their gods, and you will sin against the LORD your God.

¹⁹ This is what you must do whenever you blockade a city for a long time in order to capture it in war. Don't harm any of its fruit trees with an ax. You can eat the fruit. Never cut those trees down, because the trees of the field are not people you have come to blockade. ²⁰ You may destroy trees that you know are not fruit trees. You may cut them down and use them in your blockade until you capture the city.

When a Murder Is Committed, but the Murderer Can't Be Found

21 ¹ This is what you must do if you find a murder victim lying in a field in the land that the LORD your God is giving you. If no one knows who committed the murder, ² your leaders and judges must go and measure the distance from the body to each of the neighboring cities. ³ When it has been determined which city is nearest the body, the leaders from that

city must choose a heifer that has never been put to work and never worn a yoke.[a] [4] The leaders of that city will bring the heifer down to a river, to a location where the land hasn't been plowed or planted. At the river they must break the heifer's neck. [5] The priests, the descendants of Levi, must come forward. The LORD your God has chosen them to serve him as priests and to bless people in the LORD's name. Their decision is final in all cases involving a disagreement or an assault. [6] All the leaders from the city which was nearest the murder victim must wash their hands over the dead heifer. [7] Then they must make this formal statement: "We didn't commit this murder, and we didn't witness it. [8] LORD, make peace with your people Israel, whom you freed. Don't let the guilt of this unsolved murder remain among your people Israel." Then there will be peace with the LORD despite the murder. [9] This is how you will get rid of the guilt of an unsolved murder by doing what the LORD considers right.

Laws About Marriage and Family

[10] When you go to war with your enemies and the LORD your God hands them over to you, you may take them captive. [11] If you see a beautiful woman among the captives and have your heart set on her, you may marry her. [12] Bring her into your home. She must shave her head, cut her nails, [13] and no longer wear the clothes she was wearing when you captured her. Then she may live in your house and mourn the loss of her father and mother for one month. After that, you may sleep with her. Then you will become husband and wife.

[14] But if it happens that you are no longer pleased with her, let her go wherever she wants. You must never sell her or mistreat her as if she were a slave,[b] since you've already had sex with her.

[15] A man might have two wives and love one but not the other. Both wives might have children, and the firstborn son might belong to the wife that the man doesn't love. [16] When the day comes for the father to give his sons their inheritance, he can't treat the son of the wife he loves as if that son were the firstborn. This would show a total disregard for the real firstborn (the son of the wife he doesn't love). [17] Instead, he must recognize the son of the wife he doesn't love as the firstborn. He must give that son a double portion of whatever he owns. That son is the very first son he had. The rights of the firstborn son are his.

[18] Parents might have a stubborn and rebellious son who doesn't obey them. Even though they punish him, he still won't listen to them. [19] His father and mother must take him to the leaders of the city at the city gate. [20] They will say to the leaders of the city, "This son of ours is stubborn and rebellious. He won't obey us. He eats too much and is a drunk." [21] All the men of the city should stone him to death. You must get rid of this evil. When all Israel hears about it, they will be afraid.

Various Laws

[22] When a convicted person is put to death, [23] never leave his dead body hung on a pole overnight. Be sure to bury him that same day, because anyone whose body is hung on a pole is cursed by God. The land that the LORD your God is giving you must never become unclean.[c]

22 [1] If you see another Israelite's ox or sheep out where it doesn't belong, don't pretend that you don't see it. Make sure you take it back. [2] If the owner doesn't live near you or you don't know who owns it, take the animal home with you. Keep it until the owner comes looking for it. Then give it back. [3] Do the same if you find a donkey, some clothes, or anything else that another Israelite may have lost. Don't pretend that you don't know what to do.

[4] If you see another Israelite's donkey or ox lying on the road, don't pretend that you don't see it. Make sure you help him get it back on its feet.

[5] A woman must never wear anything men would wear, and a man must never wear women's clothes. Whoever does this is disgusting to the LORD your God.

[6] Whenever you're traveling and find a nest containing chicks or eggs, this is what you must do. If the mother bird is sitting on the nest, never take her with the chicks. [7] You may take the chicks, but make sure you let the mother go. Then things will go well for you, and you will live for a long time.

[8] Whenever you build a new house, put a railing around the edge of the roof. Then you won't be responsible for a death at your home if someone falls off the roof.

[9] Never plant anything between the rows in your vineyard. Otherwise, you will have to give everything that grows there to the holy place. This includes the crop you planted and the grapes from the vineyard.

[10] Never plow with an ox and a donkey harnessed together.

[11] Never wear clothes made of wool and linen woven together.

[12] Make tassels on the four corners of the shawl you wear over your clothes.

---

[a] 21:3 A yoke is a wooden bar placed over the necks of work animals so that they can pull plows or carts.   [b] 21:14 Hebrew meaning of "mistreat her as if she were a slave" uncertain.   [c] 21:23 "Unclean" refers to anything that is not presentable to God.

Laws About Sex and Marriage

13 A man might marry a woman, sleep with her, and decide he doesn't like her. **14** Then he might make up charges against her and ruin her reputation by saying, "I married this woman. But when I slept with her, I found out she wasn't a virgin." **15** The girl's father and mother must go to the city gate where the leaders of the city are and submit the evidence that their daughter was a virgin. **16** The girl's father will tell the leaders, "I gave my daughter in marriage to this man, but he doesn't like her. **17** Now he has made up charges against her. He says he found out that my daughter wasn't a virgin. But here's the evidence!" Then the girl's parents must spread out the cloth in front of the leaders of the city. **18** The leaders of that city must take the man and punish him. **19** They will fine him 2¼ pounds of silver and give it to the girl's father. The husband ruined the reputation of an Israelite virgin. She will continue to be his wife, and he can never divorce her as long as he lives.

20 But if the charge is true, and no evidence that the girl was a virgin can be found, **21** they must take the girl to the entrance of her father's house. The men of her city must stone her to death because she has committed such a godless act in Israel: She had sex before marriage, while she was still living in her father's house. You must get rid of this evil.

22 If a man is caught having sexual intercourse with a married woman, both that man and the woman must die. You must get rid of this evil in Israel.

23 This is what you must do when a man has sexual intercourse with a virgin who is engaged to another man. If this happens in a city, **24** take them to the gate of the city and stone them to death. The girl must die because she was in a city and didn't scream for help. The man must die because he had sex with another man's wife. You must get rid of this evil.

25 But if a man rapes an engaged girl out in the country, then only the man must die. **26** Don't do anything to the girl. She has not committed a sin for which she deserves to die. This is like the case of someone who attacks and murders another person. **27** The man found the girl out in the country. She may have screamed for help, but no one was there to rescue her.

28 This is what you must do when a man rapes a virgin who isn't engaged. When the crime is discovered, **29** the man who had sexual intercourse with her must give the girl's father 1¼ pounds of silver, and she will become his wife. Since he raped her, he can never divorce her as long as he lives.[a]

30 A man must never marry his father's wife because this would disgrace his father.

Various Laws

23 [a] **1** A man whose testicles are crushed or whose penis is cut off may never join the assembly of the LORD.

2 A man born from an illicit union may not join the assembly of the LORD. No descendant of his may join the assembly of the LORD for ten generations.

3 Ammonites or Moabites may not join the assembly of the LORD. Not one descendant of theirs may join the assembly of the LORD for ten generations. **4** They cannot join because they didn't greet you with food and water on your trip from Egypt. They even hired Balaam, son of Beor, from Pethor in Aram Naharaim, to curse you. **5** But the LORD your God refused to listen to Balaam. Instead, he turned Balaam's curse into a blessing for you because the LORD your God loves you. **6** Never offer them peace or friendship as long as you live.

7 Never consider the Edomites disgusting. They're your relatives. Never consider the Egyptians disgusting. You once were foreigners living in their country. **8** Their grandchildren may join the assembly of the LORD.

9 When you're at war and have set up camp to fight your enemies, stay away from anything that will make you unclean.[b] **10** If one of your men becomes unclean from a nocturnal emission, he must go outside the camp and stay there. **11** Toward evening he must wash, and at sunset he may come back to camp.

12 Choose a place outside the camp where you can go ˌto relieve yourselfˌ. **13** You must carry a pointed stick as part of your equipment. When you go outside to squat, dig a hole with it. When you're done, cover up your excrement. **14** The LORD your God moves around in your camp to protect you and hand your enemies over to you. So your camp must always be holy. This way, the LORD will never see anything offensive among you and turn away from you.

15 If a slave escapes from his master and comes to you, don't return him to his master. **16** Let him stay with you ˌand liveˌ among your people wherever he chooses, in any of your cities that seems best to him. Never mistreat him.

---

[a] 22:29 Deuteronomy 22:30 in English Bibles is Deuteronomy 23:1 in the Hebrew Bible.   [a] 23:1 Deuteronomy 23:1–25 in English Bibles is Deuteronomy 23:2–26 in the Hebrew Bible.   [b] 23:9 "Unclean" refers to anything that is not presentable to God.

¹⁷ No Israelite man or woman should ever become a temple prostitute. ¹⁸ Never bring gifts or money earned by prostitution into the house of the LORD your God as an offering you vowed to give. These earnings are disgusting to the LORD your God.

¹⁹ Never charge another Israelite any interest on money, food, or anything else that is borrowed. ²⁰ You may charge a foreigner interest, but not an Israelite. Then the LORD your God will bless you in everything you do once you've entered the land and taken possession of it.

²¹ If you make a vow to the LORD your God, don't avoid keeping it. The LORD your God expects you to keep it. You would be guilty of a sin if you didn't. ²² If you didn't make a vow, you would not be guilty. ²³ Make sure you do what you said you would do ˌin your vowˌ. You freely chose to make your vow to the LORD your God.

²⁴ If you go into your neighbor's vineyard, you may eat as many grapes as you like until you're full. But never put any in your basket. ²⁵ If you go into your neighbor's grain field, you may pick grain by hand. But never use a sickle to cut your neighbor's grain.

Various Laws

24 ¹ This is what you must do if a husband writes out a certificate of divorce, gives it to his wife, and makes her leave his house. (He divorced her because he found out something indecent about her and she no longer pleased him.) ² She might marry another man after she leaves his house. ³ If her second husband doesn't love her and divorces her, or if he dies, ⁴ her first husband is not allowed to marry her again. She has become unclean.ᵃ This would be disgusting in the LORD's presence. Don't pollute with sin the land that the LORD your God is giving you as your property.

⁵ A man who has recently been married will be free from military duty or any other public service. For one year he is free to stay at home and make his new wife happy.

⁶ Never let a family's handmill for grinding flour—or even part of a handmill—be taken to guarantee a loan. The family wouldn't be able to prepare food in order to stay alive.

⁷ Whoever kidnaps another Israelite must die. The kidnapper must die, whether he treated the other person like a slaveᵇ or sold him. You must get rid of this evil.

⁸ Guard against outbreaks of serious skin diseases. Be very careful to do exactly as the Levitical priests instruct you. Make sure you do what I commanded them. ⁹ Remember what the LORD your God did to Miriam on your trip from Egypt.

¹⁰ When you make a loan to your neighbor, don't go into his house to take a security deposit. ¹¹ Wait outside, and the person to whom you're making the loan will bring the deposit out to you. ¹² If the person is poor, don't keep the coat you took as a deposit overnight. ¹³ Make sure you bring it back to him at sunset. When he wears his coat to bed ˌthat nightˌ, he'll bless you. You will have done the right thing in the presence of the LORD your God.

¹⁴ Don't withhold pay from hired workers who are poor and needy, whether they are Israelites or foreigners living in one of your cities. ¹⁵ Pay them each day before sunset because they are poor and need their pay. Otherwise, they will complain to the LORD about you, and you will be condemned for your sin.

¹⁶ Parents must never be put to death for the crimes of their children, and children must never be put to death for the crimes of their parents. Each person must be put to death for his own crime.

¹⁷ Never deprive foreigners and orphans of justice. And never take widows' clothes to guarantee a loan. ¹⁸ Remember that you were slaves in Egypt and the LORD your God freed you from slavery. So I'm commanding you to do this.

¹⁹ This is what you must do when you're harvesting wheat in your field. If you forget to bring in one of the bundles of wheat, don't go back to get it. Leave it there for foreigners, orphans, and widows. Then the LORD your God will bless you in everything you do.

²⁰ When you harvest olives from your trees, never knock down all of them. Leave some for foreigners, orphans, and widows.

²¹ When you pick the grapes in your vineyard, don't pick all of them. Leave some for foreigners, orphans, and widows. ²² Remember that you were slaves in Egypt. So I'm commanding you to do this.

Various Laws

25 ¹ This is what you must do whenever ˌtwoˌ people have a disagreement that is brought into court. The judges will hear the case and decide who's right and who's wrong. ² If the person who's in the wrong deserves to be beaten, the judge will order him to lie down. Then the judge will have him beaten with as many lashes as the crime deserves. ³ Forty lashes may be given, but no more. If an Israelite were given more than that, he would be publicly humiliated.

ᵃ 24:4 "Unclean" refers to anything that is not presentable to God.   ᵇ 24:7 Hebrew meaning of "treated like a slave" uncertain.

[4] Never muzzle an ox when it's threshing[a] grain.

[5] When brothers live together and one of them dies without having a son, his widow must not marry outside the family. Her husband's brother must marry her and sleep with her. He must do his duty as her brother-in-law. [6] Then the first son she has will carry the dead brother's name so that his name won't die out in Israel.

[7] But if the man doesn't want to marry his brother's widow, she must go to the leaders of the city at the city gate. She must say, "My brother-in-law refuses to let his brother's name continue in Israel. He doesn't want to do his duty as my brother-in-law." [8] Then the leaders of the city must summon him and talk to him. If he persists in saying that he doesn't want to marry her, [9] his brother's widow must go up to him in the presence of the leaders. She must take off one of his sandals and spit in his face. She must make this formal statement: "This is what happens to a man who refuses to continue his brother's family line." [10] Then in Israel his family will be called the Family of the Man Without a Sandal.

[11] This is what you must do when two men are fighting and the wife of one of them comes to rescue her husband from the man who is beating him. If she tries to stop the fight by grabbing the other man's genitals, [12] cut off her hand. Have no pity on her.

[13] Never carry two sets of weights, a heavier one and a lighter one. [14] Never have two kinds of measures in your house, a larger one and a smaller one. [15] Use accurate and honest weights and measures. Then you will live for a long time in the land that the LORD your God is giving you. [16] Everyone who uses dishonest weights and measures is disgusting to the LORD.

[17] Remember what the Amalekites did to you on your trip from Egypt. [18] They attacked you when you were tired and exhausted and killed all those who were lagging behind. They weren't afraid of God. [19] So when the LORD your God gives you peace from all your enemies around you in the land that he is giving you as your own property, don't forget to erase every memory of the Amalekites from the earth.

A Reminder to Keep God's Laws

26 [1] Soon you will enter and take possession of the land that the LORD your God is giving you as your property. When you have settled there, [2] take some of the first produce harvested from the fields in the land that the LORD your God is giving you, and put it in a basket. Then go to the place where the LORD your God will choose for his name to live. [3] Go to the priest who is serving at that time, and tell him, "I declare today to the LORD your God that I have come to the land that the LORD is giving us, as he swore to our ancestors." [4] Then the priest will take the basket from you and set it down in front of the altar of the LORD your God. [5] You will make this formal statement in the presence of the LORD your God: "My ancestors were wandering Arameans. There were only a few of them when they went to Egypt and lived as foreigners. But then they became a great, powerful, and large nation. [6] So the Egyptians treated us cruelly, oppressed us, and made us do back-breaking work for them. [7] We cried out to the LORD God of our ancestors, and he heard us. He saw our misery, suffering, and oppression. [8] Then the LORD used his mighty hand and powerful arm to bring us out of Egypt. He used spectacular and awe-inspiring deeds, miraculous signs, and amazing things. [9] He brought us to this place and gave us this land flowing with milk and honey. [10] So now I've brought the first produce harvested from the fields you gave me, LORD."

You will place the basket in the presence of the LORD your God and bow down in front of him. [11] Then you, the Levites, and the foreigners who live among you can enjoy all the good things which the LORD your God has given you and your family.

[12] Every third year is the year when you will store a tenth of that year's crops in your houses. During that year distribute what you have stored to the Levites, foreigners, orphans, and widows in your cities, and they may eat all they want. [13] When you have distributed all that was stored, say to the LORD your God, "Nothing is left of the holy offering stored in my house. I distributed it to the Levites, foreigners, orphans, and widows as you commanded me. I disobeyed none of your commands, and I didn't forget to do what you commanded. [14] I didn't eat any of this holy offering while I was in mourning. I didn't distribute any of it while I was unclean.[a] I didn't offer any of it to the dead. I have obeyed the LORD my God. I have done everything you commanded me. [15] Look down from your holy place in heaven. Bless your people Israel and the land flowing with milk and honey that you have given us, as you promised with an oath to our ancestors."

[16] Today the LORD your God is commanding you to obey these laws and rules. You must faithfully obey them with all your heart and with all your soul. [17] Today you have declared that the LORD is your God and that you will follow his directions, obey his laws, commands, and

---

[a] 25:4 Threshing is the process of beating stalks to separate them from the grain.   [a] 26:14 "Unclean" refers to anything that is not presentable to God.

rules, and listen to him. ¹⁸ Today the LORD has declared that you are his people, his own special possession, as he told you. But you must be sure to obey his commands. ¹⁹ Then he will place you high above all the other nations he has made. He will give you praise, fame, and honor, and you will be a people holy to the LORD your God, as he promised.

Write the Law on Stones

27 ¹ Moses and the leaders of Israel told the people, "Obey every command I'm giving you today.

² "The day you cross the Jordan River and enter the land that the LORD your God is giving you, set up some large stones and cover them with plaster. ³ The LORD God of your ancestors is giving you a land flowing with milk and honey, as he promised you. After you're in that land, write all the words of these teachings on the stones. ⁴ After you cross the Jordan River, set up these stones on Mount Ebal, and cover them with plaster, following the command I'm giving you today. ⁵ Build an altar of stones there dedicated to the LORD your God. Don't use an iron chisel on the stones. ⁶ You must use uncut stones to build the altar of the LORD your God. Sacrifice burnt offerings on it to the LORD your God. ⁷ Sacrifice fellowship offerings, eat them there, and enjoy yourselves in the presence of the LORD your God. ⁸ Write clearly and carefully all the words of these teachings on the stones you set up."

⁹ Then Moses and the Levitical priests said to all Israel, "Be quiet and listen, Israel. Today you have become the people of the LORD your God. ¹⁰ Obey the LORD your God and follow his commands and laws which I'm giving you today."

Curses Which Are to Be Recited

¹¹ That same day Moses gave the people this command: ¹² After you cross the Jordan River, these are the tribes that will stand on Mount Gerizim to bless the people: Simeon, Levi, Judah, Issachar, Joseph, and Benjamin. ¹³ These are the tribes that will stand on Mount Ebal to announce the curses: Reuben, Gad, Asher, Zebulun, Dan, and Naphtali.

¹⁴ The Levites will declare to all the people of Israel in a loud voice:

¹⁵ "Whoever has a carved or metal statue, anything disgusting to the LORD that was made by a craftsman, and sets it up in secret will be cursed." Then all the people will say amen.

¹⁶ "Whoever curses his father or mother will himself be cursed." Then all the people will say amen.

¹⁷ "Whoever moves his neighbor's boundary marker will be cursed." Then all the people will say amen.

¹⁸ "Whoever leads blind people in the wrong direction will be cursed." Then all the people will say amen.

¹⁹ "Whoever deprives foreigners, orphans, or widows of justice will be cursed." Then all the people will say amen.

²⁰ "Whoever has sexual intercourse with his father's wife will be cursed. He has disgraced his father." Then all the people will say amen.

²¹ "Whoever has sexual intercourse with any animal will be cursed." Then all the people will say amen.

²² "Whoever has sexual intercourse with his sister, his father's daughter, or his mother's daughter will be cursed." Then all the people will say amen.

²³ "Whoever has sexual intercourse with his mother-in-law will be cursed." Then all the people will say amen.

²⁴ "Whoever kills another person secretly will be cursed." Then all the people will say amen.

²⁵ "Whoever accepts money to kill an innocent person will be cursed." Then all the people will say amen.

²⁶ "Whoever doesn't obey every word of these teachings will be cursed." Then all the people will say amen.

Blessings From the LORD

28 ¹ Carefully obey the LORD your God, and faithfully follow all his commands that I'm giving you today. If you do, the LORD your God will place you high above all the other nations in the world. ² These are all the blessings that will come to you and stay close to you because you obey the LORD your God:

³ You will be blessed in the city and blessed in the country.

⁴ You will be blessed. You will have children. Your land will have crops. Your animals will have offspring. Your cattle will have calves, and your flocks will have lambs and kids.

⁵ The grain you harvest and the bread you bake will be blessed.

⁶ You will be blessed when you come and blessed when you go.

[7] The LORD will defeat your enemies when they attack you. They will attack you from one direction but run away from you in seven directions. [8] The LORD will bless your barns and everything you do. The LORD your God will bless you in the land that he is giving you.

[9] You will be the LORD's holy people, as he promised you with an oath. He will do this if you obey the commands of the LORD your God and follow his directions. [10] Then all the people in the world will see that you are the LORD's people, and they will be afraid of you. [11] The LORD will give you plenty of blessings: You will have many children. Your animals will have many offspring. Your soil will produce many crops in the land the LORD will give you, as he swore to your ancestors.

[12] The LORD will open the heavens, his rich storehouse, for you. He will send rain on your land at the right time and bless everything you do. You will be able to make loans to many nations but won't need to borrow from any. [13] The LORD will make you the head, not the tail. You will always be at the top, never at the bottom, if you faithfully obey the commands of the LORD your God that I am giving you today. [14] Do everything I'm commanding you today. Never worship other gods or serve them.

Curses From the LORD

[15] Obey the LORD your God, and faithfully follow all his commands and laws that I am giving you today. If you don't, all these curses will come to you and stay close to you:

[16] You will be cursed in the city and cursed in the country. [17] The grain you harvest and the bread you bake will be cursed. [18] You will be cursed. You will have few children. Your land will have few crops. Your cattle will be cursed with few calves, and your flocks will have few lambs and kids. [19] You will be cursed when you come and cursed when you go.

[20] The LORD will send you curses, panic, and frustration in everything you do until you're destroyed and quickly disappear for the evil you will do by abandoning the LORD. [21] The LORD will send one plague after another on you until he wipes you out of the land you're about to enter and take possession of. [22] The LORD will strike you with disease, fever, and inflammation; heat waves,[a] drought,[b] scorching winds,[c] and ruined crops. They will pursue you until you die. [23] The sky above will look like bronze, and the ground below will be as hard as iron. [24] The LORD will send dust storms and sandstorms on you from the sky until you're destroyed.

[25] The LORD will let your enemies defeat you. You will attack them from one direction but run away from them in seven directions. You will become a thing of horror to all the kingdoms in the world. [26] Your dead bodies will be food for all the birds and wild animals. There will be no one to scare them away. [27] The LORD will strike you with the same boils that plagued the Egyptians. He will strike you with hemorrhoids,[d] sores,[e] and itching[f] that won't go away. [28] The LORD will strike you with madness, blindness, and panic. [29] You will grope in broad daylight as blind people grope in their blindness. You won't be successful in anything you do.[g] As long as you live, you will be oppressed and robbed with no one to rescue you.

[30] You will be engaged to a woman, but another man will have sex with her. You will build a house, but you won't live in it. You will plant a vineyard, but you won't enjoy the grapes. [31] Your ox will be butchered as you watch, but you won't eat any of its meat. You will watch as your donkey is stolen from you, but you'll never get it back. Your flock will be given to your enemies, and no one will rescue it. [32] You will watch with your own eyes as your sons and daughters are given to another nation. You will strain your eyes looking for them all day long, but there will be nothing you can do. [33] People you never knew will eat what your land and your hard work have produced. As long as you live, you will know nothing but oppression and abuse. [34] The things you see will drive you mad. [35] The LORD will afflict your knees and legs with severe boils that can't be cured. The boils will cover your whole body from the soles of your feet to the top of your head.

[36] The LORD will lead you and the king you choose to a nation that you and your ancestors never knew. There you will worship gods made of wood and stone. [37] You will become a thing of horror. All the nations where the LORD will send you will make an example of you and ridicule you.

[38] You will plant many crops in your fields, but harvest little because locusts will destroy your crops. [39] You will plant vineyards and take care of them, but you won't drink any wine or gather any grapes, because worms will eat them. [40] You will have olive trees everywhere in your country but no olive oil to rub on your skin, because the olives will fall off the trees.

---

[a] 28:22 Or "uncontrolled fever."   [b] 28:22 Latin; Masoretic Text "warfare."   [c] 28:22 Or "blight."   [d] 28:27 Or "boils."
[e] 28:27 Or "scurvy."   [f] 28:27 Hebrew meaning uncertain.   [g] 28:29 Or "darkness, but you won't be able to find your way."

[41] You will have sons and daughters, but you won't be able to keep them because they will be taken as prisoners of war. [42] Crickets will swarm all over your trees and the crops in your fields.

[43] The ˌstandard of living for the˩ foreigners who live among you will rise higher and higher, while your ˌstandard of living˩ will sink lower and lower. [44] They will be able to make loans to you, but you won't be able to make loans to them. They will be the head, and you will be the tail.

[45] All these curses will come to you. They will pursue you and stay close to you until you're destroyed, because you didn't obey the LORD your God or follow his commands and laws, which I'm giving you. [46] These curses will be a sign and an amazing thing to warn you and your descendants forever. [47] You didn't serve the LORD your God with a joyful and happy heart when you had so much. [48] So you will serve your enemies, whom the LORD will send against you. You will serve them even though you are already hungry, thirsty, naked, and in need of everything. The LORD will put a heavy burden of hard work on you until he destroys you.

[49] The LORD will bring against you a nation from far away, from the ends of the earth. The nation will swoop down on you like an eagle. It will be a nation whose language you won't understand. [50] Its people will be fierce-looking. They will show no respect for the old and no pity for the young. [51] They'll eat the offspring of your animals and the crops from your fields until you're destroyed. They'll leave you no grain, no new wine, no olive oil, no calves from your herds, and no lambs or kids from your flocks. They'll continue to do this until they've completely ruined you. [52] They will blockade all your cities until the high, fortified walls in which you trust come down everywhere in your land. They'll blockade all the cities everywhere in the land that the LORD your God is giving you.

[53] Because of the hardships your enemies will make you suffer during the blockade, you will eat the flesh of your own children, the sons and daughters, whom the LORD your God has given you. [54] Even the most tender and sensitive man among you will become stingy toward his brother, the wife he loves, and the children he still has left. [55] He will give none of them any of the flesh of his children that he is eating. It will be all that he has left, because of the hardships your enemies will make you suffer during the blockade of all your cities. [56] The most tender and sensitive woman among you—so sensitive and tender that she wouldn't even step on an ant—will become stingy toward the husband she loves or toward her own son or daughter. [57] She won't share with them the afterbirth from her body and the children she gives birth to. She will secretly eat them out of dire necessity, because of the hardships your enemies will make you suffer during the blockade of your cities.

[58] You might not faithfully obey every word of the teachings that are written in this book. You might not fear this glorious and awe-inspiring name: the LORD your God. [59] If so, the LORD will strike you and your descendants with unimaginable plagues. They will be terrible and continuing plagues and severe and lingering diseases. [60] He will again bring all the diseases of Egypt that you dreaded, and they will cling to you. [61] The LORD will also bring you every kind of sickness and plague not written in this Book of Teachings. They will continue until you're dead. [62] At one time you were as numerous as the stars in the sky. But only a few of you will be left, because you didn't obey the LORD your God. [63] At one time the LORD was more than glad to make you prosperous and numerous. Now the LORD will be more than glad to destroy you and wipe you out. You will be torn out of the land you're about to enter and take possession of.

[64] Then the LORD will scatter you among all the people of the world, from one end of the earth to the other. There you will serve gods made of wood and stone that neither you nor your ancestors ever knew. [65] Among those nations you will find no peace, no place to call your own. There the LORD will give you an unsettled mind, failing eyesight, and despair. [66] Your life will always be hanging by a thread. You will live in terror day and night. You will never feel sure of your life. [67] In the morning you'll say, "If only it were evening!" And in the evening you'll say, "If only it were morning!" You'll talk this way because of the things that will terrify you and because of the things you'll see. [68] The LORD will bring you back to Egypt in ships[h] on a journey that I said you would never take again. There you will try to sell yourselves as slaves to your enemies, but no one will buy you.

Israel's Past, Present, and Future

29[a] [1] These are the terms of the promise[b] that the LORD commanded Moses to give to the Israelites in Moab. This was in addition to the promise the LORD gave them at Mount Horeb.

[2] Moses summoned all the people of Israel and said to them:

You've seen with your own eyes everything that the LORD did in Egypt to Pharaoh, to all his officials, and to his whole country. [3] You also saw those terrible plagues, those miraculous

---

[h] 28:68 Or "in sorrow.   [a] 29:1 Deuteronomy 29:1–29 in English Bibles is Deuteronomy 28:69–29:28 in the Hebrew Bible.
[b] 29:1 Or "covenant."

signs, and those spectacular, amazing things. [4] But to this day the LORD hasn't given you a mind that understands, eyes that see, or ears that hear. [5] For 40 years I led you through the desert. During that time your clothes and shoes never wore out. [6] You ate no bread and drank no wine or liquor. I did this so that you would know that I am the LORD your God.

[7] When you came to this place, King Sihon of Heshbon and King Og of Bashan came out to fight us, but we defeated them. [8] We took their land and gave it to the tribes of Reuben, Gad, and half of the tribe of Manasseh as their property. [9] Faithfully obey the terms of this promise. Then you will be successful in everything you do.

[10] All of you are standing here today in the presence of the LORD your God. The heads of your tribes,[c] your leaders, your officers, and all the men of Israel are here. [11] Your children, your wives, and the foreigners who cut wood and carry water in your camp are also here. [12] You are ready to accept the terms and conditions of the promise that the LORD your God is giving you today. [13] With this promise the LORD will confirm today that you are his people and that he is your God. This is what he told you, and this is what he promised your ancestors Abraham, Isaac, and Jacob with an oath. [14] You aren't the only people to receive this promise and its conditions. [15] It is for those of you who are standing here with us today in the presence of the LORD our God and also for those who are not here today.

[16] You know how we lived in Egypt and how we passed through other countries on our way here. [17] You saw their disgusting gods and idols made of wood, stone, silver, and gold. [18] Make sure there is no man, woman, family, or tribe among you today who turns from the LORD our God to worship the gods of those nations. Make sure that no one among you is the source of this kind of bitter poison.

[19] Someone may hear the conditions of this promise. He may think that he is so blessed that he can say, "I'll be safe even if I go my own stubborn way. After all, ⸤the LORD would never⸥ sweep away well-watered ground along with dry[d] ground." [20] The LORD will never be willing to forgive that person, because the LORD's burning anger will smolder against him. All the curses described in this book will happen to him. The LORD will erase ⸤every memory of⸥ that person's name from the earth. [21] And the LORD will single him out from all the tribes of Israel for disaster based on all the conditions of the promise written in this Book of the Teachings.

[22] Then the next generation of your children and foreigners who come from distant countries will see the plagues that have happened in this land and the diseases the LORD sent here. [23] They will see all the soil poisoned with sulfur and salt. Nothing will be planted. Nothing will be growing. There will be no plants in sight. It will be as desolate as Sodom, Gomorrah, Admah, and Zeboiim, cities the LORD destroyed in fierce anger. [24] Then all the other nations in the world will ask, "Why has the LORD done this to their land? Why is he so angry?"

[25] The answer will be, "Because they abandoned the promise of the LORD God of their ancestors. He made this promise to them when he brought them out of Egypt. [26] They worshiped other gods and bowed down to them. These were gods they never heard of, gods the LORD didn't permit them to have. [27] So the LORD became angry with this land and brought on it all the curses described in this book. [28] In his fierce anger and fury the LORD uprooted these people from their land and deported them to another country, where they still are today."

[29] Some things are hidden. They belong to the LORD our God. But the things that have been revealed in these teachings belong to us and to our children forever. We must obey every word of these teachings.

30 [1] All these blessings and curses I have spoken about will happen to you. Take them to heart when you are among all the nations where the LORD your God will scatter you. [2] If you and your children return to the LORD your God and obey him with all your heart and with all your soul, doing everything I command you today, [3] he will restore your fortunes. He will have mercy on you and gather you from all the nations of the world where he will scatter you. [4] Even if you are scattered to the most distant country in the world, the LORD your God will gather you and bring you back from there. [5] The LORD your God will bring you to the land your ancestors owned. You will take possession of it, and the LORD will make you more prosperous and numerous than your ancestors were.

[6] The LORD your God will circumcise your hearts and the hearts of your descendants. You will love the LORD your God with all your heart and with all your soul, and you will live. [7] Then the LORD your God will put all these curses on your enemies, those who hate you and persecute you. [8] You will again obey the LORD and follow all his commands that I'm giving you today. [9] The LORD your God will give you many blessings in everything you do: You will have many children. Your animals will have many offspring. Your soil will produce many crops. The LORD will again delight in making you as prosperous as he made your ancestors. [10] He will do this if

---

[c] 29:10 Syriac, Greek, Targum; Masoretic Text "your heads, your tribes."   [d] 29:19 Hebrew meaning of "After all. . . dry" uncertain.

you obey him and follow his commands and laws that are written in this Book of Teachings and return to the LORD your God with all your heart and with all your soul.

¹¹ This command I'm giving you today isn't too hard for you or beyond your reach. ¹² It's not in heaven. You don't have to ask, "Who will go to heaven to get this command for us so that we can hear it and obey it?" ¹³ This command isn't on the other side of the sea. You don't have to ask, "Who will cross the sea to get it for us so that we can hear it and obey it?" ¹⁴ No, these words are very near you. They're in your mouth and in your heart so that you will obey them.

Choose Between Life and Death

¹⁵ Today I offer you life and prosperity or death and destruction. ¹⁶ This is what I'm commanding you today: Love the LORD your God, follow his directions, and obey his commands, laws, and rules. Then you will live, your population will increase, and the LORD your God will bless you in the land that you're about to enter and take possession of.

¹⁷ But your hearts might turn away, and you might not listen. You might be tempted to bow down to other gods and worship them. ¹⁸ If you do, I tell you today that you will certainly be destroyed. You will not live for a long time in the land that you're going to take possession of when you cross the Jordan River.

¹⁹ I call on heaven and earth as witnesses today that I have offered you life or death, blessings or curses. Choose life so that you and your descendants will live. ²⁰ Love the LORD your God, obey him, and be loyal to him. This will be your way of life, and it will mean a long life for you[a] in the land that the LORD swore to give to your ancestors Abraham, Isaac, and Jacob.

Joshua Becomes Israel's Leader to Replace Moses

31 ¹ Moses continued to speak to all the Israelites:

² "I'm 120 years old now, and I'm not able to lead you anymore. Besides, the LORD has told me that I cannot cross the Jordan River. ³ The LORD your God is the one who will cross the river ahead of you. He will destroy those nations as you arrive, and you will take possession of their land. Joshua will also cross the river ahead of you, as the LORD told you. ⁴ The LORD will do to those nations what he did to King Sihon and King Og of the Amorites and to their lands when he destroyed them. ⁵ The Lord will hand them over to you, and you must do to them everything that I commanded you. ⁶ Be strong and courageous. Don't tremble! Don't be afraid of them! The LORD your God is the one who is going with you. He won't abandon you or leave you."

⁷ Then Moses called for Joshua and said to him in the presence of all Israel, "Be strong and courageous. You will go with these people into the land that the LORD will give them, as he swore to their ancestors. You will help them take possession of the land.[a] ⁸ The LORD is the one who is going ahead of you. He will be with you. He won't abandon you or leave you. So don't be afraid or terrified."

⁹ Moses wrote down these teachings and gave them to the Levitical priests who carried the ark of the LORD's promise and to all the leaders of Israel. ¹⁰ Then Moses commanded them, "At the end of every seventh year you must cancel debts. At that time, during the Festival of Booths, ¹¹ all the Israelites will come into the presence of the LORD your God at the place he will choose. Read these teachings so that they can hear them. ¹² Assemble the men, women, and children, as well as the foreigners who live in your cities. Have them listen and learn to fear the LORD your God and faithfully obey every word of these teachings. ¹³ Their children, who don't know these teachings, must hear them and learn to fear the LORD your God as long as you live in the land that you are going to take possession of when you cross the Jordan River."

¹⁴ The LORD said to Moses, "The time of your death is coming soon. Call for Joshua. Both of you come to the tent of meeting, and I will give him his instructions." Moses and Joshua came to the tent of meeting. ¹⁵ Then the LORD appeared in a column of smoke at the entrance to the tent.

¹⁶ The LORD said to Moses, "Soon you are going to lie down in death with your ancestors. When these people enter the land and are living among the foreigners there, they will chase after foreign gods as though they were prostitutes. They will abandon me and reject the promise[b] I made to them. ¹⁷ On that day I will become angry with them. I will abandon them and turn away from them. They will be destroyed, and many terrible disasters will happen to them. On that day they will ask, 'Haven't these disasters happened to us because our God isn't with us?' ¹⁸ On that day I will certainly turn away from them because of all the evil they've done in turning to other gods.

¹⁹ "Write down this song, teach it to the Israelites, and have them sing it. This song will be a witness for me against the Israelites. ²⁰ I will bring them into the land that I swore to give to

---

[a] 30:20 Or "He is your life, and he will let you live for a long time."   [a] 31:7 Or "And you will distribute the land to them."
[b] 31:16 Or "covenant."

their ancestors, a land flowing with milk and honey. When they have eaten all they want and have become fat,*c* they will turn to other gods and worship them. They will despise me and reject my promise. **21** When many terrible disasters happen to them, this song will testify against them, because it will never be forgotten by their descendants. I know what their hearts are set on doing, even now before I bring them into the land that I swore to give them." **22** That day Moses wrote down this song and taught it to the Israelites.

23 The LORD gave this command to Joshua, son of Nun: "Be strong and courageous, because you will bring the Israelites into the land that I swore to give them, and I will be with you."

24 Finally, Moses finished writing all the words of these teachings in a book. **25** He gave this command to the Levites who carried the ark of the LORD's promise: **26** "Take this Book of Teachings, and put it next to the ark of the promise of the LORD your God, where it will be a witness against you. **27** I know how rebellious you are. You are impossible to deal with. While I am alive and still with you, you are rebelling against the LORD. How much more rebellious will you be after I die? **28** Assemble all the leaders of your tribes and your officers in front of me. As they listen, I will speak these words and call on heaven and earth to testify against them. **29** I know that after I die you will become thoroughly corrupt and turn from the way I have commanded you to live. In the days to come disasters will happen to you because you will make the LORD furious by doing what he considers evil."

The Song of Moses

30 Then, as the whole congregation of Israel listened, Moses recited all the words of this song:

32 **1** Listen, heaven, and I will speak.
Earth, hear the words from my mouth.

2 Let my teachings come down like raindrops.
Let my words drip like dew,
like gentle rain on grass,
like showers on green plants.
3 I will proclaim the name of the LORD.
Give our God the greatness he deserves!
4 He is a rock.
What he does is perfect.
All his ways are fair.
He is a faithful God, who does no wrong.
He is honorable and reliable.

5 He recognizes that his people are corrupt.
To their shame they are no longer his children.
They are devious and scheming.
6 Is this how you repay the LORD,
you foolish and silly people?
Isn't he your Father and Owner,
who made you and formed you?

7 Remember a time long ago.
Think about all the past generations.
Ask your fathers to remind you,
and your leaders to tell you.
8 When the Most High gave nations their land,
when he divided the descendants of Adam,
he set up borders for the tribes
corresponding to the number of the sons of Israel.

9 But the LORD's people were his property.
Jacob was his own possession.
10 He found his people in a desert land,
in a barren place where animals howl.
He guarded them, took care of them,
and protected them because they were helpless.
11 Like an eagle that stirs up its nest,
hovers over its young,
spreads its wings to catch them,
and carries them on its feathers,

---

c 31:20 Or "prosperous."

12 so the LORD alone led his people.
    No foreign god was with him.
13   He made them ride on the heights of the earth
        and fed them with the produce of the fields.
      He gave them honey from rocks
        and olive oil from solid rock.
14   They ate cheese from cows
        and drank milk from sheep and goats.
      He gave them fat from lambs,
        rams from the stock of Bashan,
          male goats, and the best wheat.
      They drank the blood-red wine of grapes.

15 Jeshurun[a] got fat and disrespectful.
      (You got fat! You were stuffed! You were gorged!)
      They abandoned the God who made them
        and treated the rock of their salvation like a fool.
16   They made him furious because they worshiped foreign gods
        and angered him because they worshiped worthless idols.
17   They sacrificed to demons that are not God,
        to gods they never heard of.
          These were new gods, who came from nearby,
            gods your ancestors never worshiped.
18 (You ignored the rock who fathered you
    and forgot the God who gave you life.)

19 The LORD saw this and rejected them,
      because his own sons and daughters had made him angry.
20   He said, "I will turn away from them
        and find out what will happen to them.
      They are devious people,
        children who can't be trusted.
21   They made him furious because they worshiped foreign gods
        and angered him because they worshiped worthless idols.
    So I will use those who are not my people to make them jealous
      and a nation of godless fools to make them angry.
22 My anger has started a fire
      that will burn to the depths of hell.
        It will consume the earth and its crops
          and set the foundations of the mountains on fire.
23 I will bring one disaster after another on them.
    I will use up all my arrows on them.
24   They will be starved by famines
        and ravaged by pestilence and deadly epidemics.
    I will send vicious animals against them
      along with poisonous animals that crawl on the ground.
25 Foreign wars will kill off their children,
      and even at home there will be horrors.
        Young men and young women alike will die
          as well as nursing babies and gray-haired men.
26 I said that I would cut them in pieces[b]
      and erase everyone's memory of them.
27 But I didn't want their enemies to make me angry.
      I didn't want their opponents to misunderstand and say,
        'We won this victory!
          It wasn't the LORD who did all this!' "

28 My people have lost their good sense.
    They are not able to understand.
29 If only they were wise enough to understand this
      and realize what will happen to them!

---

[a] 32:15 "Jeshurun" is another name for Israel.   [b] 32:26 Hebrew meaning of "cut them in pieces" uncertain.

30 How could one person chase a thousand
      or two people make ten thousand flee?
   Their rock used these people to defeat them
      and the LORD gave them no help.
31 Their rock isn't like our rock.
      Even our enemies will agree with this.
32 Their grapevines come from the vineyards of Sodom
      and from the fields of Gomorrah.
   Their grapes are poisonous,
      and their clusters are bitter.
33 Their wine is snake venom,
      the deadly poison of cobras.

34 Isn't this what I've stored
      under lock and key in my storehouses?
35 I will take revenge and be satisfied.
   In due time their foot will slip,
      because their day of disaster is near.
         Their doom is coming quickly.
36 The LORD will judge his people
      and have compassion on his servants
   when he sees that their strength is gone
      and that no one is left, neither slaves nor free people.
37 Then he will ask, "Where are their gods?
   Where is the rock they took refuge in?
38   Where are the gods who ate the fat from their sacrifices
      and drank the wine from their wine offerings?
         Let them come to help you!
         Let them be your refuge!"

39 See, I am the only God.
      There are no others.
   I kill, and I make alive.
      I wound, and I heal,
      and no one can rescue you from my power.
40 I raise my hand toward heaven and solemnly swear:
      As surely as I live forever,
41   I will sharpen my flashing sword
         and take justice into my own hands.
      Then I will take revenge on my enemies
         and pay back those who hate me.
42   My arrows will drip with blood
         from those who were killed and taken captive.
      My sword will cut off the heads
         of the enemy who vowed to fight.

43 Joyfully sing with the LORD's people, you nations,
      because he will take revenge for the death of his servants.
   He will get even with his enemies
      and make peace for his people's land.[c]

Moses Is Allowed to See Canaan

44 Moses came with Hoshea,[d] son of Nun, and recited all the words of this song as the people listened. 45 When Moses had finished reciting all these words to Israel, 46 he said to them, "Pay attention to all these warnings I've given you today. Then you will command your children to faithfully obey every word of these teachings. 47 Don't think these words are idle talk. They are your life! By these words you will be able to live for a long time in the land that you are going to take possession of when you cross the Jordan River."

48 That same day the LORD said to Moses, 49 "Go into the Abarim Mountains, to Mount Nebo in Moab, across from Jericho. Take a look at the land of Canaan that I'm giving the Israelites as their own property. 50 On this mountain where you're going, you will die and join your ances-

---

[c] 32:43 Dead Sea Scrolls, Samaritan Pentateuch, Greek, Latin; Masoretic Text "his land [and] his people."
[d] 32:44 "Hoshea" is another name for Joshua.

tors in death, as your brother Aaron died on Mount Hor. **51** This is because both of you were unfaithful to me at the oasis of Meribah at Kadesh in the Desert of Zin. You didn't show the Israelites how holy I am. **52** You may see the land from a distance, but you may not enter the land I'm giving the Israelites."

Moses Blesses the Twelve Tribes

33 **1** Moses, the man of God, blessed the Israelites with this blessing before he died. **2** He said,

"The LORD came from Sinai.
    For his people he rose from Seir ⌐like the sun⌐.
      He appeared like sunshine from Mount Paran.
He came with tens of thousands of holy ones.
    On his right was a raging fire for them.*a*
3 You certainly love your people.
    All your holy ones are in your hands.
      They bow at your feet
        to receive your instructions.*b*
4   Moses gave us these teachings.
          They belong to the assembly of Jacob.
5 The LORD was king of Jeshurun*c*
    when the leaders of the people assembled
      together with all the tribes of Israel.

6   "May the tribe of **Reuben** live and not die out,
    though their people are few in number."

7 This is what he said about the tribe of **Judah**:

"Hear the cry of Judah, O LORD,
    and bring them to their people.
They must defend themselves.
    Help them against their enemies."

8 About the tribe of **Levi** he said,

"Your Thummim and Urim*d* belong to your faithful people.
You tested your people at Massah.
You quarreled with them at the oasis of Meribah.
9 They said that they didn't know their father and mother.
They didn't recognize their own brothers.
They didn't acknowledge their own children.
    But they obeyed your word
      and were faithful to the terms of your promise.*e*
10 They teach Jacob your rules
    and give Israel your teachings.
They burn incense for you to smell
    and sacrifice burnt offerings on your altar.
11 LORD, bless them with strength
    and be pleased with the work they do.
Break the backs of those who attack them and hate them
    so that they can never get up again."

12 About the tribe of **Benjamin** he said,

"The LORD's beloved people will live securely with him.
    The LORD will shelter them all day long,
      since he, too, lives on the mountain slopes."

13 About the tribes of **Joseph** he said,

"May the LORD bless their land with ⌐water,⌐
    the best gift heaven can send,
      with dew and deep springs below the ground.

---

a 33:2 Hebrew meaning of "a raging fire" uncertain.   *b* 33:3 Hebrew meaning of "They bow . . . your instructions" uncertain.   *c* 33:5 "Jeshurun" is another name for Israel.   *d* 33:8 The Urim and Thummim were used by the chief priest to determine God's answer to questions.   *e* 33:9 Or "covenant."

¹⁴ May the LORD bless their land with crops,
the best gift the sun can give,
the best produce of each month,
¹⁵ the finest fruits from the oldest mountains,
the best from the ancient hills,
¹⁶ and the most plentiful crops of the earth.
May the LORD bless their land with the favor
of the one who was in the burning bush.
May these blessings come to the tribes of Joseph.
May they crown the people who are like princes in Israel.
¹⁷ They will be as majestic as a firstborn bull.
Their horns will be like the horns of a wild ox.
They will use them to push away nations
including those at the ends of the earth.
The tens of thousands from the tribe of Ephraim
and the thousands from the tribe of Manasseh will be like this."

¹⁸ About the tribe of **Zebulun** he said,

"People of Zebulun, enjoy yourselves when you go to war,
and you people of **Issachar,** enjoy yourselves when you stay at home.
¹⁹ They will invite nations to their mountain,
and there they will offer the proper sacrifices.
They will be nourished by the abundance from the seas
and the treasures hidden in the sand."

²⁰ About the tribe of **Gad** he said,

"Blessed is the one who gives the people of Gad more land.
They wait there like a lion.
They can tear off an arm or a head.
²¹ They chose the best land for themselves.
Indeed, a commander's piece of land was reserved for them.
They were leaders of the people
and did for Israel what the LORD considers fair and honorable."[f]

²² About the tribe of **Dan** he said,

"The people of Dan are a lion cub.
Out of Bashan they pounce ˻on their enemies˼."

²³ About the tribe of **Naphtali** he said,

"The people of Naphtali enjoy the LORD's favor
and are filled with the LORD's blessings.
They will take possession of the lake and the land south of it."

²⁴ About the tribe of **Asher** he said,

"The people of Asher are the most blessed of the sons of Israel.
May they be the Israelites' favorite tribe
and wash their feet in olive oil.
²⁵ May the locks and bolts of your gates be made of iron and copper.
May your strength last as long as you live.

²⁶ "There's no one like your God, Jeshurun!
He rides through the heavens to help you.
In majesty he rides through the clouds.
²⁷ The eternal God is your shelter,
and his everlasting arms support you.
He will force your enemies out of your way
and tell you to destroy them.
²⁸ So Israel will live securely.
Jacob's spring will be ˻left˼ alone
in a land of grain and new wine.
Dew will drip from Israel's skies.

---

^f 33:21 Hebrew meaning of this sentence uncertain.

29 You are blessed, Israel!
   Who is like you,
      a nation saved by the LORD?
   He is a shield that helps you
      and a sword that wins your victories.
   Your enemies will come crawling to you,
      and you will stomp on their backs."

Moses' Death and Burial

34 ¹ Then Moses went up on Mount Nebo from the plains of Moab. He went to the top of Pisgah, across from Jericho. The LORD showed him the whole land. He could see Gilead as far as Dan, ² all of Naphtali, the territory of Ephraim and Manasseh, all the territory of Judah as far as the Mediterranean Sea, ³ the Negev, and the Jordan Plain—the valley of Jericho (the City of Palms)—as far as Zoar.

⁴ Then the LORD said to him, "This is the land I promised with an oath to Abraham, Isaac, and Jacob. I said I would give it to their descendants. I have let you see it with your own eyes, but you may not go there."

⁵ As the LORD had predicted, the LORD's servant Moses died in Moab. ⁶ He was buried in a valley in Moab, near Beth Peor. Even today no one knows where his grave is.

⁷ Moses was 120 years old when he died. His eyesight never became poor, and he never lost his physical strength. ⁸ The Israelites mourned for Moses in the plains of Moab for 30 days. Then the time of mourning for him was over.

⁹ Joshua, son of Nun, was filled with the Spirit of wisdom, because Moses had laid his hands on him. The Israelites obeyed him and did what the LORD had commanded through Moses.

¹⁰ There has never been another prophet in Israel like Moses, whom the LORD dealt with face to face. ¹¹ He was the one the LORD sent to do all the miraculous signs and amazing things in Egypt to Pharaoh, to all his officials, and to his whole country. ¹² Moses used his mighty hand to do all the spectacular and awe-inspiring deeds that were seen by all the Israelites.

JOSHUA

The LORD Instructs Joshua

1 ¹ After the death of the LORD's servant Moses, the LORD said to Moses' assistant Joshua, son of Nun, ² "My servant Moses is dead. Now you and all these people must cross the Jordan River into the land that I am going to give the people of Israel. ³ I will give you every place on which you set foot, as I promised Moses. ⁴ Your borders will be the desert [on the south], nearby Lebanon to the Euphrates River (the country of the Hittites) [on the north], and the Mediterranean Sea on the west. ⁵ No one will be able to oppose you successfully as long as you live. I will be with you as I was with Moses. I will never neglect you or abandon you. ⁶ Be strong and courageous, because you will help these people take possession of the land I swore to give their ancestors.

⁷ "Only be strong and very courageous, faithfully doing everything in the teachings that my servant Moses commanded you. Don't turn away from them. Then you will succeed wherever you go. ⁸ Never stop reciting these teachings. You must think about them night and day so that you will faithfully do everything written in them. Only then will you prosper and succeed.

⁹ "I have commanded you, 'Be strong and courageous! Don't tremble or be terrified, because the LORD your God is with you wherever you go.' "

The People Promise to Obey Joshua

¹⁰ Then Joshua ordered the officers of the people, ¹¹ "Go through the camp. Tell the people, 'Get your supplies ready. In three days you will cross the Jordan River to take possession of the land the LORD your God is going to give you.' "

¹² Next, Joshua said to the tribes of Reuben and Gad and half of the tribe of Manasseh, ¹³ "Remember what the LORD's servant Moses commanded you. Moses said, 'The LORD your God will give you this land—a place to rest.' ¹⁴ Your wives, children, and livestock may stay in the land that Moses gave you east of the Jordan River. However, all your best soldiers must march in battle formation ahead of your relatives. You must help your relatives ¹⁵ take possession of the land the LORD your God is going to give them. Then they will have a place to rest like you do. After that, you may go back and take possession of the land east of the Jordan River which the LORD's servant Moses gave you."

¹⁶ The people responded to Joshua, "We'll do everything you tell us and go wherever you send us. ¹⁷ We will obey you as we obeyed Moses. May the LORD your God be with you as he was with Moses. ¹⁸ Whoever rebels against your authority or does not obey your orders will be put to death. Just be strong and courageous!"

Joshua Sends Spies to Jericho

2 ¹ From Shittim Joshua, son of Nun, secretly sent out two men as spies. He told them, "Go, look at that country, especially the city of Jericho." So they went to Jericho and entered the house of a prostitute named Rahab to spend the night there.

² The king of Jericho was told, "Some Israelites have entered the city tonight. They came to gather information about our land." ³ So the king of Jericho sent messengers to Rahab, who told her, "Bring out the men who came to your house. They came here to gather information about the entire land."

⁴ But the woman had already taken the two men inside and hidden them. So she said, "Yes, the men did come here. But I didn't know where they had come from. ⁵ When it was dark and the gate was just about to close, they left. I don't know where they went. If you hurry, you'll catch up with them." ⁶ (She had taken them up to the roof and covered them with the flax which she had laid up there.)

⁷ The king's men pursued them on the road leading to a shallow place to cross the Jordan River. As soon as the king's men had left, the gate was closed.

⁸ Before the spies fell asleep, Rahab went up to them on the roof. ⁹ She said to them, "I know the LORD will give you this land. Your presence terrifies us. All the people in this country are deathly afraid of you. ¹⁰ We've heard how the LORD dried up the water of the Red Sea in front of you when you left Egypt. We've also heard what you did to Sihon and Og, the two kings of the Amorites, who ruled east of the Jordan River. We've heard how you destroyed them for the LORD.

[11] When we heard about it, we lost heart. There was no courage left in any of us because of you. The LORD your God is the God of heaven and earth. [12] Please swear by the LORD that you'll be as kind to my father's family as I've been to you. Also give me some proof [13] that you'll protect my father, mother, brothers, sisters, and their households, and that you'll save us from death."

[14] The men promised her, "We pledge our lives for your lives. If you don't tell anyone what we're doing here, we'll treat you kindly and honestly when the LORD gives us this land."

[15] So she let them down by a rope from her window since her house was built into the city wall. (She lived in the city wall.) [16] She told them, "Go to the mountains so that the men who are pursuing you will not find you. Hide there for three days until they return to Jericho. Then you can go on your way."

[17] The men told her, "We will be free from the oath which you made us swear, [if you tell anyone what we're doing here]. [18] When we invade your land, tie this red cord in the window through which you let us down. Also, gather your father, mother, brothers, and all your father's family into your house. [19] Whoever leaves your house will be responsible for his own life. We will be free from that responsibility. But we will take responsibility if anyone inside your house is harmed. [20] If you tell anyone what we're doing here, we will be free from the oath which you made us swear."

[21] "I agree," she said. So she let them go and tied the red cord in the window.

[22] The men went to the mountains and stayed there for three days until the king's men returned to Jericho. The king's men had searched for them all along the road but had not found them. [23] Then the two spies came down out of the mountains, crossed the Jordan River, and returned to Joshua, son of Nun. They told him everything that had happened to them. [24] They told Joshua, "The LORD has given us the whole country. The people who live there are deathly afraid of us."

Crossing the Jordan River

3 [1] Joshua got up early the next morning. He and all the Israelites left Shittim. They came to the Jordan River, where they camped before crossing.

[2] Three days later the officers went through the camp. [3] They told the people, "As soon as you see the ark of the promise of the LORD your God and the Levitical priests who carry it, break camp and follow them. [4] However, stay about half a mile behind them. Don't come any closer to them so that you will know which way to go because you have not gone this way before."

[5] Joshua told the people, "Perform the ceremonies to make yourselves holy because tomorrow the LORD will do miracles among you."

[6] Joshua also told the priests, "Take the ark of the promise, and go ahead of the people." They did as they were told.

[7] Then the LORD said to Joshua, "Today I will begin to honor you in front of all the people of Israel. I will do this to let them know that I am with you just as I was with Moses. [8] Order the priests who carry the ark of the promise, 'When you step into the water of the Jordan River, stand there.'"

[9] So Joshua said to the people of Israel, "Come here, and listen to the words of the LORD your God." [10] Joshua continued, "This is how you will know that the living God is among you and that he will certainly force the Canaanites, Hittites, Hivites, Perizzites, Girgashites, Amorites, and Jebusites out of your way. [11] Watch the ark of the promise of the Lord of the whole earth as it goes ahead of you into the Jordan River. [12] Choose one man from each of the 12 tribes of Israel. [13] The priests who carry the ark of the LORD, the Lord of the whole earth, will stand in the water of the Jordan. Then the water flowing from upstream will stop and stand up like a dam."

[14] So they broke camp to cross the Jordan River. The priests who carried the ark of the promise went ahead of the people. [15] (The Jordan overflows all its banks during the harvest season.)[a] When the priests who were carrying the ark came to the edge of the Jordan River and set foot in [16] the water, the water stopped flowing from upstream. The water rose up like a dam as far away as the city of Adam near Zarethan. The water flowing down toward the Sea of the Plains (the Dead Sea) was completely cut off. Then the people crossed from the east side [of the Jordan River] directly opposite Jericho. [17] The priests who carried the ark of the LORD's promise stood firmly on dry ground in the middle of the Jordan until the whole nation of Israel had crossed the Jordan River on dry ground.

A Reminder of the Crossing

4 [1] The whole nation finished crossing the Jordan River. The LORD had told Joshua, [2] "Choose one man from each of the 12 tribes. [3] Order them to pick up 12 stones from the

---

[a] 3:15 This sentence has been moved from verse 16 to express the complex Hebrew paragraph structure more clearly in English.

middle of the Jordan, where the priests' feet stood firmly. Take the stones along with you, and set them down where you will camp tonight."

⁴Joshua called the 12 men whom he had selected (one from each tribe). ⁵He said to them, "Go to the middle of the Jordan River in front of the ark of the Lord your God. Each man must take a stone on his shoulder, one for each tribe of Israel. ⁶This will be a sign for you. In the future your children will ask, 'What do these stones mean to you?' ⁷You should answer, 'The water of the Jordan River was cut off in front of the ark of the Lord's promise. When the ark crossed the Jordan, the river stopped flowing. These stones are a permanent reminder for the people of Israel.' "

⁸The people of Israel did as Joshua had ordered. They took 12 stones, one for each of the tribes of Israel. They took them from the middle of the Jordan as the Lord had told Joshua. They carried them to the camp and set them down there.

⁹Joshua also set 12 stones in the middle of the Jordan River, where the priests who carried the ark of the promise had stood. The stones are still there today.

¹⁰The priests who carried the ark remained standing in the middle of the Jordan. They stood there until everything the Lord had ordered Joshua to tell the people had been carried out. This was as Moses had told Joshua. The people hurried to the other side. ¹¹As soon as everyone had crossed, the priests with the Lord's ark crossed and went ahead of them.

¹²The men of Reuben, Gad, and half of the tribe of Manasseh did as Moses had told them. They marched across in battle formation ahead of the people of Israel. ¹³About 40,000 armed men crossed the river in front of the Lord to the plains of Jericho for battle.

¹⁴On that day the Lord honored Joshua in the presence of all the Israelites. As long as Joshua lived, the Israelites respected him in the same way they had respected Moses.

¹⁵The Lord said to Joshua, ¹⁶"Order the priests who carry the ark of the testimony to come out of the Jordan River."

¹⁷So Joshua ordered the priests, "Come out of the Jordan."

¹⁸The priests who carried the ark of the Lord's promise came out of the middle of the Jordan. When their feet stepped onto dry land, the water of the Jordan returned to its seasonal flood level.

¹⁹On the tenth day of the first month, the people came out of the Jordan River. They made their camp at Gilgal, just east of Jericho. ²⁰At Gilgal Joshua set up the 12 stones they had taken from the Jordan. ²¹He said to the people of Israel, "In the future when children ask their parents, 'What do these stones mean?' ²²the children should be told that Israel crossed the Jordan River on dry ground. ²³The Lord your God dried up the Jordan ahead of you until you had crossed, as he did to the Red Sea until we had crossed. ²⁴The Lord did this so that everyone in the world would know his mighty power and that you would fear the Lord your God every day of your life."

Preparations for the First Passover in Canaan

5 ¹All the Amorite kings west of the Jordan River and all the Canaanite kings along the Mediterranean Sea heard that the Lord had dried up the Jordan River so that the Israelites could cross. So they lost heart and had no courage left to face the people of Israel.

²At that time the Lord spoke to Joshua, "Make flint knives, and circumcise the men of Israel." ³So Joshua made flint knives and circumcised the men of Israel at the Hill of Circumcision.ᵃ

⁴This is the reason Joshua circumcised them: All the soldiers had died on the way through the desert after they left Egypt. ⁵The men who left Egypt had been circumcised. However, the men born later, on the way through the desert, were not circumcised. ⁶For 40 years the Israelites wandered through the desert until all their soldiers who left Egypt died. They died because they disobeyed the Lord. The Lord swore that he would not let them see this land flowing with milk and honey which he had sworn to give our ancestors.

⁷The sons who took their place had not been circumcised on the way. So Joshua circumcised them. ⁸When all the men had been circumcised, they remained in the camp until they recovered.

⁹The Lord said to Joshua, "Today I have removed the disgrace of Egypt from you." So Joshua named the place Gilgal,ᵇ the name it still has today.

¹⁰The people of Israel camped at Gilgal in the Jericho plain. There they celebrated the Passover on the evening of the fourteenth day of the month. ¹¹On the day after the Passover, they ate some of the produce of the land, unleavened bread and roasted grain. ¹²The day after that, the manna stopped. The people of Israel never had manna again. That year they began to eat the crops that grew in Canaan.

The Commander of the Lord's Army Speaks With Joshua

¹³When Joshua was near Jericho, he looked up and saw a man standing in front of him with a sword in his hand. Joshua went up to him and asked, "Are you one of us or one of our ene-

---

ᵃ 5:3 Or "Hill of Foreskins."   ᵇ 5:9 There is a play on words here between Hebrew *gilgal* (rolled) and *gallothi* (roll away/remove).

mies?" **14** He answered, "Neither one! I am here as the commander of the LORD's army." Immediately, Joshua bowed with his face touching the ground and worshiped. He asked, "Sir, what do you want to tell me?" **15** The commander of the LORD's army said to Joshua, "Take off your sandals because this place where you are standing is holy." So Joshua did as he was told.

Jericho Is Destroyed

6 **1** Jericho was bolted and barred shut because the people were afraid of the Israelites. No one could enter or leave.

2 The LORD said to Joshua, "I am about to hand Jericho, its king, and its warriors over to you. **3** All the soldiers will march around the city once a day for six days. **4** Seven priests will carry rams' horns ahead of the ark. But on the seventh day you must march around the city seven times while the priests blow their horns. **5** When you hear a long blast on the horn, all the troops must shout very loudly. The wall around the city will collapse. Then the troops must charge straight ahead into the city."

6 Joshua, son of Nun, summoned the priests. He said to them, "Pick up the ark of the promise, and have seven priests carry seven rams' horns ahead of the LORD's ark."

7 He told the troops, "March around the city. Let the armed men march ahead of the LORD's ark."

8 After Joshua had given orders to the troops, the seven priests carrying the seven rams' horns ahead of the LORD marched off as they blew their horns. The ark of the LORD's promise followed them. **9** The armed men went ahead of the priests, who blew their horns. The rear guard followed the ark while the priests continued to blow their horns.

10 Joshua ordered the troops, "Don't shout, make any noise, or let one word come out of your mouth until I tell you to shout. Then shout!" **11** So the LORD's ark went around the city once. Then they went back to the camp and stayed there for the night.

12 Joshua got up early in the morning. The priests carried the LORD's ark. **13** The seven priests carrying the seven rams' horns were ahead of it. The priests blew their horns as they went. The armed men were ahead of them, and the rear guard followed the LORD's ark while the horns blew continually. **14** They went around the city once on the second day and returned to the camp. They did this for six days.

15 On the seventh day they got up at dawn. They marched around the city seven times the same way they had done it before. That was the only day they marched around it seven times. **16** When they went around the seventh time, the priests blew their rams' horns.

Joshua said to the troops, "Shout, because the LORD has given you the city! **17** The city has been claimed by the LORD. Everything in it belongs to the LORD. Only the prostitute Rahab and all who are in the house with her will live because she hid the messengers we sent. **18** But stay away from what has been claimed by the LORD for destruction, or you, too, will be destroyed by the LORD. If you take anything that is claimed by the LORD, you will bring destruction and disaster on the camp of Israel. **19** All the silver and gold and everything made of bronze and iron are holy and belong to the LORD. They must go into the LORD's treasury."

20 So the troops shouted very loudly when they heard the blast of the rams' horns, and the wall collapsed. The troops charged straight ahead and captured the city. **21** They claimed everything in it for the LORD. With their swords they killed men and women, young and old, as well as cattle, sheep, and donkeys.

22 But Joshua said to the two spies, "Go to the prostitute's house. Bring the woman out, along with everything she has, as you swore you would do for her."

23 The spies went and brought out Rahab, her father, mother, brothers, everything she had, and even all of her relatives. They gave them a place outside the camp of Israel. **24** Then Israel burned the city and everything in it. But they put the silver and gold and everything made of bronze and iron into the LORD's treasury. **25** Joshua spared the prostitute Rahab, her father's family, and everything she had. She still lives in Israel today because she hid the messengers Joshua had sent to look at Jericho.

26 At that time Joshua pronounced this curse:

"The LORD will curse
   whoever comes to rebuild the city of Jericho.
      It will cost him his firstborn son
         to lay the foundation.
      It will cost him his youngest son
         to set up the city doors."

27 So the LORD was with Joshua, and his fame spread throughout the land.

Achan's Sin and Its Consequences

7 [1] The people of Israel proved to be disloyal about the things claimed by the LORD. Achan, son of Carmi, grandson of Zabdi, great-grandson of Zerah, and a member of the tribe of Judah, took something that had been claimed by the LORD. So the LORD became angry with the people of Israel.

[2] Joshua sent men from Jericho to Ai. Ai is near Beth Aven, east of Bethel. He said to them, "Go, look at that country." So the men went and looked at Ai. [3] They came back to Joshua and told him, "You don't need to send all the troops. Only about two or three thousand men are needed to destroy Ai. Don't tire the troops out by sending all of them. There are only a few troops in Ai." [4] So about three thousand men were sent. However, they fled from the men of Ai. [5] The men of Ai killed about thirty-six of them, chasing them from the city gate to the slope of the stone quarries. Israel's troops lost heart and were scared stiff.

[6] Joshua and the leaders of Israel tore their clothes in grief. They put dust on their heads and bowed down to the ground in front of the LORD's ark. They stayed there until evening. [7] Joshua said, "Almighty LORD, why did you bring these people across the Jordan River? Was it to hand us over to the Amorites so that they could destroy us? I wish we had been content to live on the other side of the Jordan! [8] Lord, what else can I say after Israel ran away from its enemy? [9] When the Canaanites and everyone who lives in the land hears about it, they will surround us and remove every memory of us from the earth. What will you do then so that your great name [will be remembered]?"

[10] The LORD said to Joshua, "Get up! What are you doing bowing on the ground? [11] Israel has sinned. They have ignored the requirements[a] that I have placed on them. They have taken what I claimed for myself and put it among their own goods. They have not only stolen, but they have also lied.

[12] "The people of Israel will not be able to defend themselves against their enemies. They will run away from their enemies because the people of Israel are now claimed for destruction. I will not be with you anymore unless you destroy what I have claimed for myself.

[13] "Get up! Tell the people, 'Get ready for tomorrow by performing the ceremonies to make yourselves holy. This is what the LORD God of Israel says: You have what I claimed for myself, Israel. You will not be able to defend yourselves against your enemies until you get rid of what I have claimed. [14] In the morning come forward by tribes [to the tent of meeting]. The tribe the LORD selects will come forward by families. Then the family the LORD selects will come forward by households, and the household the LORD selects will come forward man by man. [15] The man who is selected, along with everything he has, must be burned because he has [stolen] what the LORD has claimed. He has ignored the LORD's requirements and done a godless thing in Israel.' "

[16] Joshua got up early in the morning. He had Israel come forward by tribes. The tribe of Judah was selected. [17] Then he had the families of Judah come forward, and the family of Zerah was selected. Then he had the family of Zerah come forward man by man, and Zabdi was selected. [18] Then he had Zabdi's household come forward man by man, and Achan was selected. Achan from the tribe of Judah was the son of Carmi, grandson of Zabdi, and great-grandson of Zerah.

[19] Joshua said to Achan, "Son, give honor and praise to the LORD God of Israel! Tell me what you have done. Don't hide anything from me."

[20] Then Achan answered Joshua, "It's true. I have sinned against the LORD God of Israel. This is what I did: [21] I saw a fine robe from Babylonia, five pounds of silver, and a bar of gold weighing about one pound among the loot. I wanted them, so I took them. You will find them buried inside my tent with the silver beneath them."

[22] Joshua sent messengers, and they ran to the tent. The loot was buried inside with the silver beneath it. [23] They took the loot from the tent and brought it to Joshua and all the people of Israel. Then they laid it out in the presence of the LORD.

[24] Joshua and all Israel took Achan (son of Zerah), the silver, the robe, the bar of gold, his sons and daughters, his cattle, his donkeys, his sheep, and his tent—everything he had—and brought them to the valley of Achor [Disaster]. [25] Then Joshua said, "Why did you bring this disaster on us? The LORD will bring disaster on you today!" And all Israel stoned Achan and his family to death. Then they burned the bodies and piled stones over them. [26] They made such a large pile of stones over Achan that it is still there today. Then the LORD withdrew his burning anger. For this reason that place is still called the valley of Achor today.

---

[a] 7:11 Or "covenant."

Israel's Victory at Ai

8 ¹ The LORD said to Joshua, "Don't be terrified or afraid. Take all the troops with you, and march against Ai. I am about to hand the king of Ai, his people, city, and land over to you. ² You will do the same thing to Ai and its king that you did to Jericho and its king. However, you may take its loot and livestock for yourselves. Set an ambush behind the city."

³ So Joshua and all the soldiers started to march against Ai. Joshua picked 30,000 of his best soldiers and sent them out at night ⁴ with these orders: "Set an ambush behind the city. Don't go very far away from the city. Everyone must be ready. ⁵ I'll approach the city with the rest of the troops. When they come out to attack us as they did the first time, we will run away from them. ⁶ They'll come out after us, and we will lure them away from the city. They'll say, 'They're running away from us just like the first time.' As we run away from them, ⁷ you come out of hiding and capture the city. The LORD your God will hand it over to you. ⁸ When you have captured the city, set it on fire. Do what the LORD says. These are your orders."

⁹ So Joshua sent them out, and they hid. They took their position west of Ai, between Bethel and Ai. Joshua spent the night with the troops.

¹⁰ Joshua got up early in the morning and assembled the troops. Then he and the leaders of Israel led the army to Ai. ¹¹ All the troops with him marched until they were near the city. They camped north of Ai with the ravine between them and Ai.

¹² Joshua had taken about five thousand men and had them hide between Bethel and Ai, west of the city. ¹³ All the troops were positioned. The main camp was north of the city, and the other troops were hiding west of the city. That night Joshua went down into the middle of the valley.

¹⁴ When the king of Ai saw the main camp, he and all his troops got up early in the morning. They rushed out toward the plains to meet Israel for battle, just where [Joshua] expected. However, the king didn't know there were troops behind the city waiting to attack him.

¹⁵ Joshua and all Israel pretended to be defeated. They ran away toward the desert. ¹⁶ All the troops in the city were called out to chase them. As they chased Joshua, they were lured away from the city. ¹⁷ Not one man was left in Ai or Bethel; they all went after Israel. So the city was left unprotected as they chased Israel.

¹⁸ Then the LORD said to Joshua, "Hold out the spear in your hand toward the city, because I am handing Ai over to you." So Joshua held out his spear. ¹⁹ The men who were hiding got up as soon as he stretched out his hand. They entered the city, captured it, and quickly set it on fire. ²⁰ When the men of Ai looked back, they could see the city going up in smoke. They had no place to go, since the Israelites, who had been running toward the desert, had now turned back on them. ²¹ When Joshua and all Israel saw that the men who had been hiding had captured the city and that it was going up in smoke, they turned and attacked the men of Ai. ²² The men who had captured the city also came out and attacked them. The men of Ai were caught between the battle lines of Israel. So Israel attacked them on both sides. None of them survived or escaped. ²³ But they captured the king of Ai alive and brought him to Joshua.

²⁴ Israel had finished killing all the inhabitants of Ai in the fields and in the desert where they had been pursued. They put them all to death; not one person survived. Then the Israelites went back to Ai and killed everyone left there. ²⁵ Twelve thousand men and women from Ai died that day. ²⁶ Joshua did not lower his hand holding the spear until he had completely destroyed all the inhabitants of Ai. ²⁷ Israel took the loot and the livestock of that city for themselves, as the LORD had commanded Joshua. ²⁸ So Joshua burned Ai and made it a deserted mound of ruins.ᵃ It is still in ruins today.

²⁹ Joshua hung the king of Ai's [dead body] on a pole and left him there until evening. When the sun went down, Joshua gave the order to take his body down. They threw it in the entrance of the city and made a large pile of stones over it. That pile is still there today.

The LORD Renews His Promise With Israel

³⁰ At that time Joshua built an altar on Mount Ebal to the LORD God of Israel. ³¹ He built an altar with uncut stones on which no iron chisels had been used. This was as the LORD's servant Moses had commanded the people of Israel in the Book of Moses' Teachings. They made burnt offerings to the LORD and sacrificed fellowship offerings on the altar. ³² There in front of the people of Israel he wrote on stone slabs a copy of the Teachings which Moses had written down.

³³ All the people of Israel, whether foreigners or native Israelites, the leaders, officers, and judges were standing on opposite sides of the ark. They faced the Levitical priests who carried the ark of the LORD's promise. Half of the people were in front of Mount Gerizim and the other half in front of Mount Ebal. Right from the beginning, the LORD's servant Moses had commanded the priests to bless the people of Israel this way. ³⁴ Afterwards, Joshua read all the Teachings—the blessings and curses—as they had all been written down by Moses. ³⁵ Joshua read [Moses'

ᵃ 8:28 Ai means "ruins."

Teachings] in front of the whole assembly of Israel, including women, children, and foreigners living among them. He did not leave out one word from everything Moses had commanded.

The People From Gibeon Deceive Joshua

9 ¹ When all the kings west of the Jordan River heard about these events, ² they joined together to fight Joshua and Israel. (They were the kings in the mountains, the foothills, and along the whole Mediterranean coast as far as Lebanon, the kings of the Hittites, Amorites, Canaanites, Perizzites, Hivites, and Jebusites.)ᵃ

³ When the people living in Gibeon heard what Joshua had done to Jericho and Ai, ⁴ they devised a scheme. They posed as messengers. They took worn-out sacks on their donkeys. Their wineskins were old, split, and patched. ⁵ Their sandals were worn-out and repaired, and their clothes were tattered. All their bread was dried out and crumbling. ⁶ They came to Joshua in the camp at Gilgal. They told Joshua and the men of Israel, "We have come from a distant country. Make a treaty with us right now."

⁷ The men of Israel said to the Hivites, "What if you're living in this area? We wouldn't be able to make a treaty with you."

⁸ They responded to Joshua, "We're at your mercy."

Joshua asked them, "Who are you, and where did you come from?"

⁹ They answered him, "We came from a country very far away because the LORD your God has become famous. We heard stories about him and everything he did in Egypt. ¹⁰ We also heard everything he did to the two kings of the Amorites east of the Jordan, King Sihon of Heshbon and King Og of Bashan in Ashtaroth. ¹¹ Our leaders and everyone who lives in our country told us, 'Take what you need for the trip, and go meet them. Tell them, "We're at your mercy. Make a treaty with us right now." ' ¹² Our bread was warm when we left home to meet with you. Look at it now! It's dry and crumbling. ¹³ These were new wineskins when we filled them. Look at them now! See how they are splitting! Our clothes and sandals are also worn-out because we have come such a long way."

¹⁴ The men believed the evidence they were shown, but they did not ask the LORD about it. ¹⁵ So Joshua made peace with them by making a treaty which allowed them to live. The leaders of the congregation swore to it with an oath.

¹⁶ But three days after the treaty was made, the Israelites heard that these people were their neighbors and lived with them. ¹⁷ The Israelites broke camp. They came to the cities of Gibeon, Chephirah, Beeroth, and Kiriath Jearim two days later. ¹⁸ The Israelites didn't destroy these other people, because the leaders of the congregation had sworn an oath about them to the LORD God of Israel. The whole congregation complained about the leaders. ¹⁹ But all the leaders said to them, "We have sworn an oath about them to the LORD God of Israel, so we cannot touch them now. ²⁰ We must let them live to avoid [the LORD's] anger because of the oath we swore." ²¹ The leaders said that they should be allowed to live. So they became woodcutters and water carriers for the whole congregation, as the leaders had said.

²² Joshua sent for the people of Gibeon and asked, "Why did you deceive us by saying, 'We live very far away from you,' when you live here with us? ²³ You are under a curse now. You will always be servants. You will be woodcutters and water carriers for the house of my God."

²⁴ They answered Joshua, "We were told that the LORD your God commanded his servant Moses to give you the whole land and destroy all who live there. We deceived you because we feared for our lives. ²⁵ Now we're at your mercy. Do to us what you think is good and right."

²⁶ So Joshua rescued them and did not let the people of Israel kill them. ²⁷ But that day Joshua made them woodcutters and water carriers for the congregation. They served the LORD's altar, wherever he chose to put it. They still serve today.

The Day the Sun Stood Still

10 ¹ King Adoni Zedek of Jerusalem heard that Joshua had captured Ai and claimed it for the LORD the same way he had destroyed Jericho and its king. He also heard that the people of Gibeon had made peace with the people of Israel and were living with them. ² He and his people were terribly afraid because Gibeon was a large city. It was like one of the royal cities, larger than Ai. All its men were warriors. ³ So King Adoni Zedek of Jerusalem sent [this message] to King Hoham of Hebron, King Piram of Jarmuth, King Japhia of Lachish, and King Debir of Eglon: ⁴ "Come, help me destroy Gibeon because it has made peace with Joshua and the people of Israel." ⁵ So the five Amorite kings of Jerusalem, Hebron, Jarmuth, Lachish, and Eglon combined their armies. They marched to Gibeon, camped there, and attacked it.

ᵃ 9:2 Part of verse 1 (in Hebrew) has been placed in verse 2 to express the complex Hebrew paragraph structure more clearly in English.

⁶ The men of Gibeon sent this message to Joshua at the camp in Gilgal: "Don't abandon us! Come quickly, and save us. Help us because all the Amorite kings who live in the mountains have united against us."

⁷ So Joshua, with all his soldiers and best warriors, set out from Gilgal. ⁸ The LORD told Joshua, "Don't be afraid of them. I have handed them over to you. None of them can stand up to you." ⁹ So Joshua marched all night from Gilgal and took them by surprise. ¹⁰ The LORD threw the enemy into disorder in front of Israel and defeated them decisively at Gibeon. He chased them along the road that goes to the slope of Beth Horon and continued to defeat them all the way to Azekah and Makkedah.

¹¹ As they fled from the Israelites down the slope of Beth Horon toward Azekah, the LORD threw huge hailstones on them. More died from the hailstones than from Israelite swords.

¹² The day the LORD handed the Amorites over to the people of Israel, Joshua spoke to the LORD while Israel was watching,

> "Sun, stand still over Gibeon,
>   and moon, stand still over the valley of Aijalon!"
> ¹³ The sun stood still,
>   and the moon stopped
>   until a nation got revenge on its enemies.

Isn't this recorded in the Book of Jashar? The sun stopped in the middle of the sky, and for nearly a day the sun was in no hurry to set. ¹⁴ Never before or after this day was there anything like it. The LORD did what a man told him to do, because the LORD fought for Israel.

¹⁵ Then Joshua and all Israel returned to the camp at Gilgal.

¹⁶ The five kings ran away and hid in the cave at Makkedah. ¹⁷ Someone told Joshua, "The five kings have been found. They are hiding in the cave at Makkedah."

¹⁸ Joshua replied, "Roll large stones against the mouth of the cave, and post a guard there. ¹⁹ But don't stop. Chase your enemies! Cut off their rear guard. Don't let them get back into their own cities, because the LORD your God has handed them over to you."

²⁰ Joshua and the Israelites defeated them decisively, almost destroying them. But some who survived got back into the fortified cities. ²¹ Then the whole army returned safely to Joshua in the camp at Makkedah. Not a single person dared to speak against any of the Israelites.

²² Joshua said, "Open the cave, and bring me the five kings!" ²³ So they brought him the kings of Jerusalem, Hebron, Jarmuth, Lachish, and Eglon.

²⁴ When they brought them to Joshua, he called for all the men of Israel. He told the officers who had gone with him, "Come forward and put your feet on the necks of these kings." So that's what they did. ²⁵ Joshua told them, "Don't be afraid or terrified! Be strong and courageous, because this is what the LORD will do to all the enemies you're fighting against."

²⁶ After this, Joshua put them to death and hung their bodies on five poles until evening. ²⁷ When the sun went down, Joshua gave the order to take them down from the poles. Then they threw them into the cave where they had been hiding and put large stones over the mouth of the cave. These stones are still there today.

Joshua Defeats the Southern Kings

²⁸ That same day Joshua captured Makkedah, and the Israelites killed its people and king with swords. He claimed them for the LORD by destroying them. There were no survivors. He did the same thing to the king of Makkedah that he had done to the king of Jericho.

²⁹ Joshua and all Israel marched from Makkedah to Libnah and attacked it. ³⁰ The LORD also handed Libnah and its king over to Israel. He killed all the people. There were no survivors. He did the same thing to the king of Libnah that he had done to the king of Jericho.

³¹ Joshua and all Israel marched from Libnah to Lachish, camped there, and attacked it. ³² The LORD handed Lachish over to Israel. He captured it on the next day and killed all the people, the same way he had captured Libnah. ³³ At that time King Horam of Gezer had come to help Lachish. But Joshua killed him and his troops. There were no survivors.

³⁴ Joshua and all Israel marched from Lachish to Eglon, camped there, and attacked it. ³⁵ They captured it that day and killed everyone in it. He claimed it for the LORD by destroying it the same way he had destroyed Lachish.

³⁶ Then Joshua and all Israel marched from Eglon to Hebron and attacked it. ³⁷ They captured it and its neighboring villages and killed its king and all the people. There were no survivors, the same as at Eglon. He claimed the city and all its people for the LORD by destroying them.

³⁸ Then Joshua and all Israel went back to Debir and attacked it. ³⁹ He captured it and its king and all its neighboring villages and killed everyone. So they claimed them all for the LORD by destroying them. There were no survivors. He did the same thing to Debir and its king that he had done to Hebron and Libnah and their kings.

⁴⁰ So Joshua captured the whole land—the mountains, the Negev, the foothills, and the slopes. There were no survivors. He claimed every living creature for the LORD by destroying it, as the LORD God of Israel had commanded. ⁴¹ So Joshua defeated the people from Kadesh Barnea to Gaza and from all the country of Goshen as far as Gibeon. ⁴² Joshua captured all these kings and their territories in one campaign because the LORD God of Israel fought for Israel. ⁴³ Then Joshua and all Israel returned to the camp at Gilgal.

Joshua Defeats the Northern Kings

11 ¹ King Jabin of Hazor heard [what had happened]. So he sent messengers to King Jobab of Madon and to the kings of Shimron and Achshaph. ² He also sent messengers to the northern kings in the mountains, the plains south of Chinneroth, the foothills, and Naphoth Dor in the west, ³ the Canaanites from east and west, the Amorites, Hittites, Perizzites, the Jebusites in the mountains, and the Hivites at the foot of Mount Hermon in Mizpah. ⁴ They came out with all their armies. Their troops were as numerous as the grains of sand on the seashore. They also had horses and chariots. ⁵ All these kings camped together by the Springs of Merom in order to fight Israel.

⁶ The LORD told Joshua, "Don't be afraid of them because I am going to give them to Israel. About this time tomorrow they will all be dead. You must disable their horses so that they cannot be used in battle. You must burn their chariots." ⁷ Joshua and all his troops arrived suddenly at the Springs of Merom and attacked the Canaanite armies. ⁸ The LORD handed them over to Israel, and the Israelites defeated them. The Israelites chased them as far as Great Sidon, Misrephoth Maim, and the valley of Mizpah in the east. There were no survivors. ⁹ Joshua disabled their horses and burned their chariots, as the LORD had told him.

¹⁰ Then Joshua turned back and captured Hazor. He killed its king with a sword. (Hazor was formerly the head of all these kingdoms.) ¹¹ They claimed everyone for the LORD by destroying them with swords. Not one person survived. Joshua also burned Hazor.

¹² So Joshua captured all these cities and their kings. He claimed them for the LORD by destroying them, as the LORD's servant Moses had commanded him. ¹³ Israel did not burn cities built on mounds. However, Joshua made an exception and burned Hazor. ¹⁴ The people of Israel took all the loot and livestock from these cities. But they put everyone to death until they were all destroyed. Not one person survived. ¹⁵ So Joshua carried out what the LORD had commanded his servant Moses and what Moses had commanded him. He did not leave out anything the LORD had commanded Moses.

¹⁶ Joshua took all this land, the mountains, all the Negev, all the land of Goshen, the foothills, the plains, and the mountains and foothills of Israel. ¹⁷ The land extended from Mount Halak which ascends to Seir as far as Baal Gad in the Lebanon Valley at the foot of Mount Hermon. He captured all their kings and killed them. ¹⁸ Joshua waged war with all these kings for a long time. ¹⁹ Not one city had made a peace treaty with the people of Israel except Gibeon, where the Hivites lived. Israel captured everything in battle. ²⁰ The LORD made their enemies stubborn enough to continue fighting against Israel so that he could claim them all for destruction without mercy, as he had commanded Moses.

²¹ At that time Joshua also wiped out the people of Anak in the mountains, in Hebron, Debir, and Anab, and in all the hills of Judah and Israel. Joshua claimed them for the LORD by destroying them and their cities. ²² None of the people of Anak remained in Israel. Some of them were left in Gaza, Gath, and Ashdod. ²³ Joshua captured the whole land as the LORD had promised Moses. He gave it to Israel as a possession, dividing it among the tribes. So the land had peace.

Kings East of the Jordan River Defeated by Moses

12 ¹ These are the kings of the land east of the Jordan River that the people of Israel defeated. Israel also took possession of their lands from the Arnon Valley to Mount Hermon, and all the eastern plains.

² Sihon was the Amorite king who lived in Heshbon. His rule extended from Aroer on the edge of the Arnon Valley to the Jabbok River, which is the border of Ammon. This included the middle of the valley and half of Gilead. ³ It included the eastern plains from the Sea of Galilee to the Sea of the Plains (the Dead Sea) and the road that goes south from Beth Jeshimoth to the foot of the slopes of Pisgah.

⁴ The territory of King Og of Bashan who lived in Ashtaroth and Edrei was captured. He was the last of the Rephaim. ⁵ He ruled Mount Hermon, Salecah, all of Bashan to the border of Geshur and Maacath, and half of Gilead to the border of King Sihon of Heshbon.

⁶ The LORD's servant Moses and the people of Israel defeated them. Then he gave their land as a possession to the tribes of Reuben and Gad and half of the tribe of Manasseh.

Kings West of the Jordan River Defeated by Joshua

[7] These are the kings of the land west of the Jordan River that Joshua and the people of Israel defeated. [Their lands extended] from Baal Gad in the valley of Lebanon to Mount Halak which rises toward Seir. Joshua gave it as a possession to Israel, dividing it among the tribes. [8] It included the mountains, foothills, plains, slopes, desert, and the Negev [that the] Hittites, Amorites, Canaanites, Perizzites, Hivites, and Jebusites [had possessed].

The kings were

[9] the king of Jericho, the king of Ai (near Bethel),
[10] the king of Jerusalem, the king of Hebron,
[11] the king of Jarmuth, the king of Lachish,
[12] the king of Eglon, the king of Gezer,
[13] the king of Debir, the king of Geder,
[14] the king of Hormah, the king of Arad,
[15] the king of Libnah, the king of Adullam,
[16] the king of Makkedah, the king of Bethel,
[17] the king of Tappuah, the king of Hepher,
[18] the king of Aphek, the king of Sharon,[a]
[19] the king of Madon, the king of Hazor,
[20] the king of Shimron Meron, the king of Achshaph,
[21] the king of Taanach, the king of Megiddo,
[22] the king of Kedesh, the king of Jokneam in Carmel,
[23] the king of Dor in Naphoth Dor, the king of Goiim in Gilgal,[b]
[24] the king of Tirzah.
The total was 31 kings.

Land Yet to Be Conquered

13 [1] Joshua was old, near the end of his life. So the LORD said to him, "You are old, near the end of your life, and there is a lot of land left to be conquered. [2] The land that is left includes all the districts that belong to the Philistines and Geshur. [3] It extends from the Shihor River, east of Egypt, northward as far as the border of Ekron. This is considered to be Canaanite territory, even though there are five Philistine rulers over Gaza, Ashdod, Ashkelon, Gath, and Ekron, as well as the Avvim people [4] in the south. This territory includes all the land of the Canaanites as well as Mearah which belongs to Sidon as far as Aphek, the Amorite border. [5] It also includes the land of the people of Gebal, all Lebanon eastward from Baal Gad at the foot of Mount Hermon to the border of Hamath. [6] I will force out of the way of the people of Israel everyone who lives in the mountains from Lebanon to Misrephoth Maim and all the people of Sidon. However, you must distribute the land as an inheritance to Israel by drawing lots, as I commanded you. [7] So divide this land. It will be an inheritance for the nine tribes and half of the tribe of Manasseh."

Tribes That Received Land East of the Jordan River

[8] The tribes of Reuben and Gad with half of the tribe of Manasseh had received their inheritance east of the Jordan River, since the LORD's servant Moses had already given it to them. [9] The border extended from Aroer on the edge of the Arnon Valley, including the city in the middle of the valley, and the whole plateau from Medeba to Dibon. [10] It included all the cities of King Sihon of the Amorites up to the border of Ammon. Sihon's capital was Heshbon. [11] It also included Gilead, the territory of the people of Geshur and Maacath, all of Mount Hermon, and all of Bashan as far as Salecah [12] (the whole kingdom of Og in Bashan). Og ruled in Ashtaroth and Edrei. He was the last of the Rephaim. Moses had defeated them and forced them out. [13] But the Israelites did not force out the people of Geshur and Maacath. So they still live in Israel today.

[14] Moses did not give any land as an inheritance to the tribe of Levi. The sacrifices offered to the LORD God of Israel are what the Levites inherited, as the LORD had promised them.

[15] Moses gave some land as an inheritance to the tribe of Reuben for their families. [16] Their territory extended from Aroer on the edge of the Arnon Valley, including the city in the middle of the valley and the whole plateau near Medeba. [17] It included Heshbon and all its cities on the plateau, Dibon, Bamoth Baal, Beth Baal Meon, [18] Jahaz, Kedemoth, Mephaath, [19] Kiriathaim, Sibmah, Zereth Shahar on the mountain in the valley, [20] Beth Peor, the slopes of Pisgah, and Beth Jeshimoth. [21] It also included all the cities of the plateau, the whole kingdom of King Sihon of the Amorites, who ruled in Heshbon. Moses defeated him and Midian's leaders—Evi, Rekem, Zur, Hur, and Reba. They were princes of Sihon, who lived in that country. [22] Along with

---

[a] 12:18 Or "Lasharon." [b] 12:23 Or "Galilee."

these leaders, the people of Israel also killed Balaam, son of Beor, who used black magic. ²³ The border of Reuben's territory was the Jordan River. This was Reuben's inheritance for its families. It included cities with their villages.

²⁴ Moses gave some land as an inheritance to the tribe of Gad for its families. ²⁵ Their territory included Jazer, all the cities of Gilead, and half of Ammon as far as Aroer, which is by Rabbah. ²⁶ It extended from Heshbon to Ramath Mizpeh and Betonim, and from Mahanaim as far as the border of Lidbir. ²⁷ In the Jordan Valley it included Beth Haram, Beth Nimrah, Succoth, and Zaphon, the rest of the kingdom of King Sihon of Heshbon. The Jordan River served as its western border, extending to the end of the Sea of Galilee. ²⁸ This was Gad's inheritance for its families. It included cities with their villages.

²⁹ Moses gave some land as an inheritance to half of the tribe of Manasseh. It was only for the families of that half of the tribe. ³⁰ Their territory extended from Mahanaim and included all of Bashan (the whole kingdom of King Og of Bashan) and all 60 settlements of Jair that were in Bashan. ³¹ It also included half of Gilead with Ashtaroth and Edrei, the royal cities of Og in Bashan. They were given to half the families of Machir, son of Manasseh, for their inheritance].

³² This is the land that Moses distributed on Moab's plains, east of the Jordan River near Jericho. ³³ Moses did not give any land as an inheritance to the tribe of Levi. The LORD God of Israel is what they inherited, as he had promised them.

The First Stage in Dividing the Land

14 ¹ This is the land that the people of Israel inherited in Canaan. The priest Eleazar, Joshua (son of Nun), and the heads of Israel's tribes distributed it to the people. ² The land inherited by the nine-and-a-half tribes was determined by drawing lots as the LORD had commanded through Moses. ³ Moses had given the two-and-a-half tribes their inheritance east of the Jordan River. He did not give any land as an inheritance to Levi's tribe, ⁴ because Joseph's descendants, Manasseh and Ephraim, formed two tribes. The Levites were not given a share of the land. Joseph's descendants gave the Levites cities to live in with pasturelands for their cattle and everything they had. ⁵ So the people of Israel divided the land as the LORD had commanded Moses.

Special Land for Caleb

⁶ Then the people of Judah came to Joshua at Gilgal. Caleb, son of Jephunneh and grandson of Kenaz, said to him, "You know what the LORD said to Moses, the man of God, at Kadesh Barnea about you and me. ⁷ I was 40 years old when the LORD's servant Moses sent me from Kadesh Barnea to explore the land. I reported to him exactly what I thought. ⁸ But my companions discouraged the people. However, I was completely loyal to the LORD my God. ⁹ On that day Moses swore this oath: 'The land your feet walked on will be a permanent inheritance for you and your descendants because you were completely loyal to the LORD my God.'

¹⁰ "So look at me. The LORD has kept me alive as he promised. It's been 45 years since Israel wandered in the desert when the LORD made this promise to Moses. So now look at me today. I'm 85 years old. ¹¹ I'm still as fit to go to war now as I was when Moses sent me out. ¹² Now give me this mountain region which the LORD spoke of that day. You heard that the people of Anak are still there and that they have large, fortified cities. If the LORD is with me, I can force them out, as he promised."

¹³ So Joshua blessed Caleb, son of Jephunneh, and gave him Hebron as his inheritance. ¹⁴ Hebron is still the inheritance of Caleb, son of Jephunneh and grandson of Kenaz, because Caleb was completely loyal to the LORD God of Israel. ¹⁵ In the past Hebron was called Kiriath Arba. Arba was the greatest man among the people of Anak. So the land had peace.

Judah's Land

15 ¹ The lot was drawn for the families of the tribe of Judah. Their territory extends as far south as the territory of Edom and the desert of Zin. ² The southern border starts from the south end of the Dead Sea ³ and goes south of the Akrabbim Pass. It then passes Zin and goes up south of Kadesh Barnea. From there it goes to Hezron, up to Addar, around to Karka, ⁴ and on to Azmon. It comes out at the River of Egypt so that the border ends at the Mediterranean Sea. This is the southern border.

⁵ The eastern border is the Dead Sea as far north as the mouth of the Jordan River.

The northern border starts from the north end of the Dead Sea at the mouth of the Jordan ⁶ and goes up to Beth Hoglah. It then passes north to Beth Arabah and goes up to the Rock of Bohan, son of Reuben. ⁷ From the valley of Achor, the border goes up to Debir and turns north to the region that faces the Adummim Pass, south of the valley. Then the border passes the Springs of En Shemesh and ends at En Rogel. ⁸ It continues up the valley of Ben Hinnom to the south slope of the Jebusite city Jerusalem. It then goes to the top of the mountain that overlooks the valley of Hinnom to the west at the north end of the valley of Rephaim. [9] From the top of that mountain the border goes around to the spring of Nephtoah. From there it goes to the cities of Mount Ephron and around to Baalah (now called Kiriath Jearim). [10] From Baalah the border turns west to Mount Seir and over to the north slope of Mount Jearim (now called Chesalon). Then it goes down to Beth Shemesh and on to Timnah. [11] From there the border goes on the north side of Ekron and turns to Shikkeron, on to Mount Baalah, and comes out at Jabneel. The border ends at the Mediterranean Sea.

[12] The western border is the coastline of the Mediterranean Sea. These are the borders around Judah that belong to their families.

[13] Joshua gave Caleb, son of Jephunneh, a share of land among the people of Judah as the LORD had told them. It was Kiriath Arba (now called Hebron). Arba was the father of Anak. [14] Caleb forced out Sheshai, Ahiman, and Talmai, three descendants of Anak from Hebron. [15] From there he marched against the people living in Debir. (In the past Debir was called Kiriath Sepher.)

[16] Caleb said, "I will give my daughter Achsah as a wife to anyone who attacks Kiriath Sepher and captures it." [17] Then Othniel, son of Caleb's brother Kenaz, captured it. So Caleb gave him his daughter Achsah as a wife. [18] When she came to Othniel, she persuaded him to ask her father for a field. When she got down from her donkey, Caleb asked her, "What do you want?" [19] She answered, "Give me a blessing. Since you've given me some dry land, also give me some springs." So Caleb gave her the upper and lower springs.

[20] This is the land inherited by the families of the tribe of Judah.

[21] On the farthest edge of the Negev, on the border of Edom, they gave the tribe of Judah 29 cities with their villages: Kabzeel, Eder, Jagur, [22] Kinah, Dimonah, Adadah, [23] Kedesh, Hazor, Ithnan, [24] Ziph, Telem, Bealoth, [25] Hazor Hadattah, Kerioth Hezron (now called Hazor), [26] Amam, Shema, Moladah, [27] Hazar Gaddah, Heshmon, Beth Pelet, [28] Hazar Shual, Beersheba, Biziothiah, [29] Baalah, Iim, Ezem, [30] Eltolad, Chesil, Hormah, [31] Ziklag, Madmannah, Sansannah, [32] Lebaoth, Shilhim, Ain, and Rimmon.

[33] In the foothills they gave Judah 14 cities with their villages: Eshtaol, Zorah, Ashnah, [34] Zanoah, En Gannim, Tappuah, Enam, [35] Jarmuth, Adullam, Socoh, Azekah, [36] Shaaraim, Adithaim, Gederah, and Gederothaim.

[37] They also gave Judah 16 other cities with their villages: Zenan, Hadashah, Migdalgad, [38] Dilean, Mizpah, Joktheel, [39] Lachish, Bozkath, Eglon, [40] Cabbon, Lahmas, Chitlish, [41] Gederoth, Beth Dagon, Naamah, and Makkedah.

[42] An additional nine cities with their villages were given to Judah: Libnah, Ether, Ashan, [43] Iphtah, Ashnah, Nezib, [44] Keilah, Achzib, and Mareshah.

[45] Judah also received Ekron with its cities and villages. [46] This included all the cities with their villages between Ekron and the Mediterranean Sea and alongside Ashdod. [47] Added to this were Ashdod and Gaza with their cities and villages as far as the River of Egypt and the coast of the Mediterranean Sea.

[48] In the mountains they gave Judah 11 cities with their villages: Shamir, Jattir, Socoh, [49] Dannah, Kiriath Sannah (now called Debir), [50] Anab, Eshtemoh, Anim, [51] Goshen, Holon, and Giloh.

[52] They also gave Judah nine other cities with their villages: Arab, Dumah, Eshan, [53] Janim, Beth Tappuah, Aphekah, [54] Humtah, Kiriath Arba (now called Hebron), and Zior.

[55] They also received another ten cities with their villages: Maon, Carmel, Ziph, Juttah, [56] Jezreel, Jokdeam, Zanoah, [57] Kain, Gibeah, and Timnah.

[58] Halhul, Bethzur, Gedor, [59] Maarath, Bethanoth, and Eltekon were six other cities with their villages that were given to Judah.[a]

[60] The two cities of Kiriath Baal (now called Kiriath Jearim) and Rabbah with their villages [were given to Judah].

[61] In the desert Judah was given six cities with their villages: Beth Arabah, Middin, Secacah, [62] Nibshan, Ir Hamelah, and En Gedi.

[63] However, Judah was not able to force out the people of Jebus who lived in Jerusalem. So they still live with Judah in Jerusalem today.

Land for Joseph's Sons

16 [1] The lot was drawn for Joseph. The border of Joseph's territory goes from the Jordan River at Jericho to the springs of Jericho on the east, through the desert that goes up from Jericho, and through the mountains to Bethel. [2] From Bethel the border goes to Luz and over to Ataroth at the border of the Archites. [3] Then it descends west to the border of Japhlet and Lower Beth Horon, on to Gezer, and ends at the Mediterranean Sea. [4] So Joseph's sons, Manasseh and Ephraim, received this land as their inheritance.

---

[a] 15:59 Greek adds, "They also gave them 11 cities with their villages: Tekoa, Ephrathah (now called Bethlehem), Peor, Etam, Dulon, Tatam, Sores, Carem, Gallim, Bether, and Manach."

Ephraim's Land

⁵ This is the territory for the families descended from Ephraim. The eastern border of the land they inherited is from Ataroth Addar to Upper Beth Horon. ⁶ From there the border goes west, with Michmethath on the north. The border then turns east to Taanath Shiloh and passes east to Janoah. ⁷ From Janoah it descends to Ataroth and Naarah, touches Jericho, and ends at the Jordan River. ⁸ At Tappuah the border goes west along the Kanah River and ends at the Mediterranean Sea. This is the land given as an inheritance to the families of the tribe of Ephraim ⁹ with all the cities and their villages selected for Ephraim in Manasseh's territory. ¹⁰ However, they did not force out the Canaanites who lived in Gezer. So the Canaanites still live in Ephraim today, but they are required to do forced labor.

Manasseh's Land

17 ¹ The lot was drawn for the tribe of Manasseh, because Manasseh was Joseph's first born. Machir, Manasseh's firstborn, the ancestor of the people living in Gilead, had received Gilead and Bashan because he was a soldier. ² The land was given to the rest of the families descended from Manasseh, to the descendants of Abiezer, Helek, Asriel, Shechem, Hepher, and Shemida. These were the male descendants of Joseph's son Manasseh listed by their families.

³ Zelophehad, son of Hepher, grandson of Gilead, and great-grandson of Machir, whose father was Manasseh, had no sons—only daughters. Their names were Mahlah, Noah, Hoglah, Milcah, and Tirzah. ⁴ They came to the priest Eleazar, Joshua (son of Nun), and the leaders. They said, "The LORD commanded Moses to give us some land as an inheritance among our male relatives." So they gave them an inheritance among their father's relatives as the LORD had required. ⁵ Ten portions of land went to Manasseh, besides the land of Gilead and Bashan east of the Jordan River. ⁶ These portions were distributed because Manasseh's daughters were given an inheritance along with his sons, while Gilead belonged to Manasseh's other descendants.

⁷ Manasseh's border extends from Asher to Michmethath, which faces Shechem. Then the border goes south toward the people who live in En Tappuah. ⁸ (The land of Tappuah belongs to Manasseh, but Tappuah itself, on the border of Manasseh, belongs to Ephraim.) ⁹ The border then descends southward to the Kanah River. These cities belong to Ephraim, although they are among Manasseh's cities. Manasseh's [southern] border is the river, which ends at the Mediterranean Sea. ¹⁰ What is south [of the river] belongs to Ephraim, and what is north [of it] belongs to Manasseh. So the Mediterranean Sea [is its western border], Asher its northern border, and Issachar its eastern border. ¹¹ In Issachar and Asher, Manasseh possessed Beth Shean and Ibleam with their villages and the people living in Dor, En Dor, Taanach, and Megiddo and their villages. The last three are on mountain ridges.[a]

¹² But Manasseh was not able to take possession of these cities since the Canaanites were determined to stay in this land. ¹³ When the Israelites became strong enough, they made the Canaanites do forced labor, since they didn't force all of them out.

¹⁴ Joseph's descendants asked Joshua, "Why did you give us only one region for an inheritance? We have a lot of people because the LORD has blessed us."

¹⁵ Joshua replied, "If there are so many of you, go into the forest! Clear ground for yourselves there in the land of the Perizzites and Rephaim if the mountains of Ephraim are too confining for you."

¹⁶ Joseph's descendants responded, "The mountains are not enough for us either. Besides, all the Canaanites living in the valley, in Beth Shean and its villages, and in the valley of Jezreel have chariots made of iron."

¹⁷ Then Joshua said to the descendants of Joseph, [the tribes of] Ephraim and Manasseh, "You are an important and very powerful people. One region is really not enough for you. ¹⁸ The mountain region will be yours as well. It is a forest, so you will have to clear it. All of it will be yours. But you must force out the Canaanites, even though they are strong and have chariots made of iron."

The Second Stage in Dividing the Land

18 ¹ The whole congregation of Israel gathered at Shiloh and set up the tent of meeting there. The land was under their control.

² There were still seven tribes in Israel who had not yet received any land as their inheritance. ³ So Joshua asked the Israelites, "How long are you going to waste time conquering the land which the LORD God of your ancestors has given you? ⁴ Choose three men from each tribe, and I will send them out. They will survey the land and write a description of it which shows [the borders of] their inheritance. Then they will come back to me. ⁵ They will divide the land

---

ᵃ 17:11 Hebrew meaning uncertain.

into seven parts. Judah will stay within its territory in the south, and Joseph's descendants will stay within their territory in the north. ⁶ You must describe the seven parts of the land and report to me here. I will draw lots for you here in the presence of the LORD our God. ⁷ Levi's tribe has no separate region among you, because their inheritance is to serve the LORD as priests. The tribes of Gad and Reuben and half of the tribe of Manasseh have received the inheritance that the LORD's servant Moses gave them on the east side of the Jordan River."

⁸ As the men got ready to go, Joshua ordered them to write a description of the land. He said, "Go survey the land. Write a description of it, and return to me. Then I will draw lots for you in the presence of the LORD here in Shiloh."

⁹ The men surveyed the land. They described it in a book. The land was divided into seven parts according to its cities. Then they returned to Joshua at the camp at Shiloh. ¹⁰ So Joshua drew lots for them in the presence of the LORD in Shiloh. There Joshua divided the land among the tribes of Israel.

Benjamin's Land

¹¹ The lot was drawn for the families of the tribe of Benjamin. Their territory lies between Judah's and Joseph's. ¹² Their northern border starts at the Jordan, goes up the slope north of Jericho, west through the mountains, and ends at the desert of Beth Aven. ¹³ From there the border goes to the south slope of Luz (now called Bethel). Then the border goes down to Ataroth Addar over the mountains south of Lower Beth Horon. ¹⁴ The border turns and goes around on the west side, south of the mountain that faces Beth Horon, and ends at Kiriath Baal (now called Kiriath Jearim), a city of Judah. ¹⁵ The southern border begins just outside Kiriath Jearim and goes west, to the springs of Nephtoah. ¹⁶ Then the border descends to the foot of the mountain that overlooks the valley of Ben Hinnom, in the north end of the valley of Rephaim. It descends to the valley of Hinnom, to the south slope of the city of Jebus, and down to En Rogel. ¹⁷ Then it turns north and goes to En Shemesh and from there to the region opposite the Adummim Pass. It descends to the Rock of Bohan, son of Reuben. ¹⁸ Then it continues on to the north side of the slope facing the plains and down into the plains. ¹⁹ The border continues to the north slope of Beth Hoglah and ends at the northern bay of the Dead Sea at the south end of the Jordan River. This is its southern border. ²⁰ The Jordan River is its eastern border. These are the borders surrounding the inheritance given to Benjamin for its families.

²¹ These are the 12 cities with their villages that belong to the tribe of Benjamin for its families: Jericho, Beth Hoglah, Emek Keziz, ²² Beth Arabah, Zemaraim, Bethel, ²³ Avvim, Parah, Ophrah, ²⁴ Chephar Ammoni, Ophni, and Geba. ²⁵ There were 14 other cities with their villages: Gibeon, Ramah, Beeroth, ²⁶ Mizpeh, Chephirah, Mozah, ²⁷ Rekem, Ir Peel, Taralah, ²⁸ Zela, Eleph, Jebus (now called Jerusalem), Gibeath, and Kiriath. This is Benjamin's inheritance for its families.

Simeon's Land

19 ¹ The second lot was drawn for the families of the tribe of Simeon. Their inheritance was within Judah. ² In their inheritance they received 13 cities and their villages: Beersheba (Sheba), Moladah, ³ Hazar Shual, Balah, Ezem, ⁴ Eltolad, Bethul, Hormah, ⁵ Ziklag, Beth Marcaboth, Hazar Susah, ⁶ Beth Lebaoth, and Sharuhen. ⁷ There were four other cities with their villages: Ain, Rimmon, Ether, and Ashan. ⁸ All the villages around these cities as far as Baalath Beer and Ramath Negev were also included. This is the inheritance of the tribe of Simeon for its families. ⁹ Simeon's inheritance was a part of Judah's because Judah had more land than it needed. So Simeon received its inheritance inside Judah's borders.

Zebulun's Land

¹⁰ The third lot was drawn for the families descended from Zebulun. The border of their inheritance goes as far as Sarid. ¹¹ Toward the west the border ascends to Maralah and touches Dabbesheth and the river near Jokneam. ¹² But from Sarid it turns directly east toward the border of Chisloth Tabor, on to Daberath, and then ascends toward Japhia. ¹³ From there it goes directly east to Gath Hepher, Eth Kazin, and Rimmon, where it turns to Neah. ¹⁴ There the border turns north to Hannathon and ends at the valley of Iphtah El. ¹⁵ This also includes Kattath, Nahalal, Shimron, Idalah, and Bethlehem. There were 12 cities with their villages. ¹⁶ These cities with their villages are the inheritance given to the families descended from Zebulun.

Issachar's Land

¹⁷ The fourth lot was drawn for the families descended from Issachar. ¹⁸ Their territory included Jezreel, Chesulloth, Shunem, ¹⁹ Hapharaim, Shion, Anaharath, ²⁰ Rabbith, Kishion, Ebez, ²¹ Remeth, En Gannim, En Haddah, and Beth Pazzez. ²² The border touches Tabor, Shahazimah, and Beth Shemesh and ends at the Jordan River. There were 16 cities with their villages. ²³ These cities with their villages are the inheritance for the families of the tribe of Issachar.

Asher's Land

24 The fifth lot was drawn for the families of the tribe of Asher. **25** Their territory included Helkath, Hali, Beten, Achshaph, **26** Allammelech, Amad, and Mishal. The border touches Carmel and Shihor Libnath in the west. **27** Then it turns east to Beth Dagon and touches Zebulun and the valley of Iphtah El in the north and goes to Beth Emek and Neiel. From there it goes northward to Cabul, **28** Abdon,[a] Rehob, Hammon, Kanah, and as far as Great Sidon. **29** Then it turns at Ramah and goes on to the fortified city of Tyre. The border then turns to Hosah and ends at the Mediterranean Sea. The territory includes Meheleb, Achzib, **30** Umma, Acco, Aphek, and Rehob. There were 22 cities with their villages. **31** These cities with their villages are the inheritance for the families of the tribe of Asher.

Naphtali's Land

32 The sixth lot was drawn for the families descended from the tribe of Naphtali. **33** Their border starts from Heleph at the oak tree at Zaanannim. It continues to Adami Nekeb, Jabneel, to Lakkum, and ends at the Jordan River. **34** The border turns west to Aznoth Tabor, and from there to Hukok. It touches Zebulun in the south, Asher in the west, and Judah in the east at the Jordan. **35** The fortified cities were Ziddim, Zer, Hammath, Rakkath, Chinnereth, **36** Adamah, Ramah, Hazor, **37** Kedesh, Edrei, En Hazor, **38** Yiron, Migdal El, Horem, Beth Anath, and Beth Shemeth. There were 19 cities with their villages. **39** These cities with their villages are the inheritance for the families of the tribe of Naphtali.

Dan's Land

40 The seventh lot was drawn for the families of the tribe of Dan. **41** The territory of their inheritance included Zorah, Eshtaol, Ir Shemesh, **42** Shaalabbin, Aijalon, Ithlah, **43** Elon, Timnah, Ekron, **44** Eltekeh, Gibbethon, Baalath, **45** Jehud, Bene Berak, Gath Rimmon, **46** Me Jarkon, and Rakkon, with the border passing in front of Joppa. **47** The border of Dan extended beyond them. Dan's descendants went up and attacked Leshem, captured it, and killed everyone there. They took it, settled there, and renamed the city Dan after their ancestor Dan. **48** These cities with their villages are the inheritance for the families of the tribe of Dan.

Special Land for Joshua

49 When they all had finally received the land they were to inherit, the people of Israel also gave land within their territory as an inheritance to Joshua, son of Nun. **50** They gave him the city he asked for, as the LORD had instructed them to do. It was Timnath Serah in the mountains of Ephraim. He rebuilt the city and lived there.

51 This is the land that the tribes of Israel drew by lot. The priest Eleazar, Joshua son of Nun, and the leaders of the families divided the land by drawing lots. They did this in Shiloh in the presence of the LORD at the entrance of the tent of meeting. So they finished dividing the land.

Six Cities of Refuge

20 **1** The LORD said to Joshua, **2** "Tell the people of Israel, 'Now choose for yourselves the cities of refuge about which I spoke to you through Moses. **3** Choose them so that anyone who unintentionally kills someone may run to them. They will be a place of refuge from any relative who can avenge the death.

4 " 'A person who kills someone accidentally can run to one of these cities. There he will stand at the entrance to the city, where court is held, and present his case to the leaders of that city. Then they will take him into their city and give him a place to live with them.

5 " 'If the relative who can avenge the death pursues him, the leaders must not hand him over to the relative because he didn't intend to kill the other person. He didn't even hate the person he killed. **6** The accused person may remain in that city until he can stand trial in front of the congregation or until whoever is chief priest at that time dies. Then he may go back to his home in the city from which he ran away.' "

7 Kedesh in Galilee in the mountains of Naphtali, Shechem in the mountains of Ephraim, and Kiriath Arba (now called Hebron) in the mountains of Judah were chosen as cities of refuge. **8** Bezer on the desert plateau from the tribe of Reuben, Ramoth in Gilead from the tribe of Gad, and Golan in Bashan from the tribe of Manasseh were chosen as cities of refuge on the east side of the Jordan River, east of Jericho.

9 These are the cities chosen as cities of refuge for all Israelites, including the foreigners living among them. Anyone who accidentally kills someone may escape to these cities. Then he will not be handed over to the relative who can avenge a death before he stands trial in front of the congregation.

---

[a] 19:28 Some Hebrew manuscripts, Joshua 21:30, 1 Chronicles 6:59; other Hebrew manuscripts "Ebron."

Cities for the Tribe of Levi

21 [1] Then the leaders of the families of Levi came to the priest Eleazar, to Joshua (son of Nun), and to the leaders of the families of the other Israelite tribes [2] at Shiloh in Canaan. They said to them, "The LORD commanded through Moses that we should receive cities to live in and pasturelands for our livestock." [3] So, as the LORD had instructed, Levi's descendants were given the following cities with pasturelands from the Israelites' inheritance.

[4] These are the cities for the families of Kohath that were chosen by drawing lots. These descendants of the priest Aaron the Levite received 13 cities from the tribes of Judah, Simeon, and Benjamin. [5] The rest of Kohath's descendants received 10 cities from the families of the tribes of Ephraim and Dan and half of the tribe of Manasseh.

[6] Gershon's descendants received 13 cities from the families of the tribes of Issachar, Asher, Naphtali, and half of the tribe of Manasseh in Bashan.

[7] Merari's descendants received 12 cities for their families from the tribes of Reuben, Gad, and Zebulun. [8] The Israelites gave these cities with pasturelands to Levi's descendants by drawing lots, as the LORD had commanded through Moses.

Cities for Kohath's Descendants

[9] These are the names of the cities from the tribes of Judah and Simeon [10] that they gave Aaron's descendants who were from the families of Kohath in the tribe of Levi. Their lot was the first one drawn. [11] They gave them Kiriath Arba (Arba was Anak's father) and the pastureland around it. This is the city of Hebron located in the mountains of Judah. [12] But they gave its fields and villages to Caleb, son of Jephunneh, as his possession. [13] So they gave the following cities with pasturelands to the descendants of Aaron, the priest. The nine cities from those two tribes were Hebron (a city of refuge for murderers), Libnah, [14] Jattir, Eshtemoa, [15] Holon, Debir, [16] Ain, Juttah, and Beth Shemesh. [17] The tribe of Benjamin also gave them four cities: Gibeon, Geba, [18] Anathoth, and Almon. [19] In all, 13 cities with pasturelands were given to the priests, the descendants of Aaron.

[20] Cities were chosen by lot from the tribe of Ephraim to give to the rest of Levi's descendants who were from the families of Kohath. [21] These four cities with pasturelands were Shechem (a city of refuge for murderers) in the mountains of Ephraim, Gezer, [22] Kibzaim, and Beth Horon. [23] The tribe of Dan gave them four cities: Eltekeh, Gibbethon, [24] Aijalon, and Gath Rimmon. [25] Half of the tribe of Manasseh gave them two cities with pasturelands: Taanach and Gath Rimmon. [26] In all, ten cities with pasturelands were given to the rest of the families of Kohath.

Cities for Gershon's Descendants

[27] They gave the families of Gershon's descendants, who were in the tribe of Levi, two cities with pasturelands from half of the tribe of Manasseh: Golan in Bashan (a city of refuge for murderers) and Ashtaroth. [28] Four cities with pasturelands were also given to them from the tribe of Issachar: Kishion, Daberath, [29] Jarmuth, and En Gannim. [30] Another four cities with pasturelands were given to them from the tribe of Asher: Mishal, Abdon, [31] Helkath, and Rehob. [32] Also three cities with pasturelands were given to them from the tribe of Naphtali: Kedesh in Galilee (a city of refuge for murderers), Hammoth Dor, and Kartan. [33] In all, 13 cities with pasturelands were given to Gershon's families.

Cities for Merari's Descendants

[34] To the families of Merari, who were from the tribe of Levi, the tribe of Zebulun gave four cities with pasturelands: Jokneam, Kartah, [35] Dimnah, and Nahalal. [36] The tribe of Reuben also gave them four cities with pasturelands: Bezer, Jahaz, [37] Kedemoth, and Mephaath. [38] The tribe of Gad also gave them four cities with pasturelands: Ramoth in Gilead (a city of refuge for murderers), Mahanaim, [39] Heshbon, and Jazer. [40] All these cities belonged to the families of Merari. They were the last of the families of Levi. These 12 cities were chosen by lot.

[41] Within the territory owned by the Israelites there were 48 cities in all for Levi's descendants. [42] Each of these cities had its own pastureland around it.

[43] So the LORD gave Israel the whole land he had sworn to give their ancestors. They took possession of it and settled there. [44] The LORD allowed them to have peace on every side, as he had sworn with an oath to their ancestors. Not one of their enemies stood up to them. The LORD handed all their enemies over to them. [45] Every single good promise that the LORD had given the nation of Israel came true.

Joshua Blesses the Tribes That Live East of the Jordan River

22 [1] Joshua summoned the tribes of Reuben and Gad and half of the tribe of Manasseh. [2] He said to them, "You have done everything the LORD's servant Moses commanded you. You have also obeyed me in everything I commanded you. [3] All this time, to this day, you have never deserted your relatives. You have carefully kept the commands of the LORD your God.

⁴ "Now the LORD your God has given your relatives peace, as he promised them. So return home, to the land that is your own possession. It is the land that the LORD's servant Moses gave you east of the Jordan River. ⁵ Carefully follow the commands and teachings that the LORD's servant Moses gave you. Love the LORD your God, follow his directions, and keep his commands. Be loyal to him, and serve him with all your heart and soul." ⁶ Then Joshua blessed them. He sent them on their way, and they went to their homes.

⁷ Moses had given land in Bashan as an inheritance to half of Manasseh, and Joshua had given the other half of the tribe their land with their relatives west of the Jordan. When Joshua sent them home, he blessed them. ⁸ He also said to them, "Return to your homes with your vast wealth, large herds of livestock, silver, gold, bronze, iron, and loads of clothing. Divide the loot from your enemies with your relatives."

An Altar for the LORD Is Built East of the Jordan River

⁹ So the tribes of Reuben and Gad and half of the tribe of Manasseh left the rest of the Israelites at Shiloh in Canaan. They returned to Gilead. This was their own possession which they had captured as the LORD had instructed them through Moses. ¹⁰ Reuben, Gad, and half of the tribe of Manasseh came to the region of the Jordan that was still in Canaan. They built an altar by the Jordan River. The altar was very large and highly visible. ¹¹ The rest of the Israelites heard about it and said, "See there! Reuben, Gad, and half of the tribe of Manasseh have built an altar at the border of Canaan. It's in the region near the Jordan River on Israel's side." ¹² When the people of Israel heard about it, the whole congregation of Israel gathered at Shiloh. They intended to wage war against them.

¹³ The Israelites sent Phinehas, son of the priest Eleazar, to the tribes of Reuben and Gad and half of the tribe of Manasseh in Gilead. ¹⁴ Ten leaders, one from each tribe in Israel, went with him. Each man was a leader of a household and head of a family division in Israel. ¹⁵ When they arrived these leaders said to the people of Gilead, ¹⁶ "All of the LORD's congregation is asking, 'What is this faithless act you have committed against the God of Israel?' Today you have turned away from following the LORD by building an altar for yourselves. Today you have rebelled against the LORD! ¹⁷ Does the sin we committed at Peor mean nothing to us anymore? Didn't we cleanse ourselves from it? Because of that sin there was a plague on the LORD's congregation! ¹⁸ You have turned away from following the LORD! Today you rebel against the LORD, and tomorrow he will be angry with the whole congregation of Israel. ¹⁹ If your land is unclean,ᵃ come over here to the LORD's land. The LORD's tent is standing here. Take some property for yourselves among us. Don't rebel against the LORD or against us by building an altar for yourselves in addition to the altar of the LORD our God. ²⁰ Didn't Achan, son of Zerah, act faithlessly with the things claimed by the LORD? Didn't the LORD become angry with the whole congregation of Israel? Achan wasn't the only one who died because of his sin."

²¹ Then the tribes of Reuben and Gad and half of the tribe of Manasseh answered the heads of the divisions of Israel. ²² They said, "The LORD is [the only true] God! The LORD is [the only true] God! He knows, so let Israel know! If our act is rebellious or unfaithful to the LORD, ²³ don't spare us today. If we built an altar with the intention of no longer following him, and if we built it for making burnt offerings, grain offerings, or fellowship offerings, let the LORD punish us.

²⁴ "We were worried because of the situation we're in. We thought sometime in the future your children might say to our children, 'What relationship do you have with the LORD God of Israel? ²⁵ The LORD has made the Jordan River a dividing line between us and you, the descendants of Reuben and Gad. You have no connection with the LORD!' So your descendants would stop our descendants from worshiping the LORD. ²⁶ Then we said, 'Let's build an altar for ourselves. It will not be for burnt offerings or sacrifices, ²⁷ but it will stand as a witness between us for generations to come. It will stand as a witness that we may worship in the presence of the LORD with our burnt offerings, sacrifices, and fellowship offerings.' Then your descendants cannot say to our descendants, 'You have no connection with the LORD!' ²⁸ So we thought, if this statement is made to us or to our descendants in the future, we will answer, 'Look at the model of the LORD's altar our ancestors made. They didn't make it for burnt offerings or sacrifices but to stand as a witness between us.' ²⁹ It would be unthinkable for us to rebel against the LORD or to turn back today from following the LORD by building an altar for burnt offerings, grain offerings, or sacrifices in addition to the altar of the LORD our God that is in front of his tent."

³⁰ When the priest Phinehas, the leaders of the congregation, and the heads of the divisions of Israel heard what the tribes of Reuben, Gad, and Manasseh said, they were satisfied. ³¹ Then Phinehas, son of the priest Eleazar, said to the tribes of Reuben, Gad, and Manasseh, "Today we know the LORD is among us, because you did not commit an unfaithful act against the LORD. Now you have rescued the people of Israel from the LORD's punishment."

ᵃ 22:19 "Unclean" refers to anything that Moses' Teachings say is not presentable to God.

³²Then Phinehas (son of the priest Eleazar) and the leaders returned from Reuben and Gad in Gilead to Israel in Canaan and gave them the report. ³³The people of Israel were satisfied with the report. So they praised God and didn't talk anymore about going to war against Reuben and Gad and destroying the land where they were living.

³⁴The tribes of Reuben and Gad gave the altar a name: Witness Between Us That the LORD Is [the Only True] God.

A Reminder to Follow Moses' Teachings

23 ¹A long time afterward, the LORD gave the Israelites peace with all their enemies around them. Joshua was old, near the end of his life. ²So he called all the leaders, chiefs, judges, and officers of Israel together. He said to them, "I am old, near the end of my life. ³You have seen for yourselves everything the LORD your God did to all those nations. The LORD your God fought for you! ⁴I have given you the territory of the nations that still remain as an inheritance for your tribes. This includes the territory of all the nations I have already destroyed from the Jordan River westward to the Mediterranean Sea. ⁵The LORD your God will expel them right in front of your eyes and force them out of your way. You will take their land as the LORD your God told you. ⁶Now you must be very strong to keep and to do everything written in the Book of Moses' Teachings. Don't turn away from them. ⁷Don't get mixed up with the nations left in your territory. Don't ever mention the names of their gods or swear an oath to them. Don't ever serve their gods or bow down to them. ⁸But you must be loyal to the LORD your God, as you have been until now. ⁹The LORD has forced important and powerful nations out of your way. Not one person has ever been able to stand up to you. ¹⁰One of you used to chase a thousand. That was because the LORD your God was fighting for you, as he had promised you. ¹¹Be very careful to love the LORD your God.

¹²"But if you turn away and go along with the other nations within your [borders], if you intermarry with them or associate with them, ¹³then you should know that the LORD your God will never again force these people out of your way. Instead, they will be a snare and a trap for you, a whip laid to your sides, and thorns in your eyes until none of you are left in this good land that the LORD your God has given you.

¹⁴"Pay attention, because I will soon die like everyone else. You know with all your heart and soul that not one single promise which the LORD your God has given you has ever failed to come true. Every single word has come true.

¹⁵"Every good word the LORD your God has promised you has come true for you. In the same way the LORD will bring about every evil curse until he has destroyed you from this good land that he has given you. ¹⁶When you ignore the conditions[a] placed on you by the LORD your God and follow other gods, serve them and bow down to them, the LORD will be angry with you. Then you will quickly disappear from the good land he has given you."

Joshua Adds an Agreement to the Book of God's Teachings

24 ¹Joshua gathered all the tribes of Israel together at Shechem. He called together Israel's leaders, chiefs, judges, and officers, and they presented themselves to God.

²Joshua said to all the people, "This is what the LORD God of Israel says: Long ago your ancestors, Terah and his sons Abraham and Nahor, lived on the other side of the Euphrates River and served other gods. ³But I took your ancestor Abraham from the other side of the Euphrates River. I led him through all of Canaan and gave him many descendants. I also gave him Isaac. ⁴To Isaac I gave Jacob and Esau. I gave Esau the mountains in Seir as his own. However, Jacob and his sons went to Egypt.

⁵"Then I sent Moses and Aaron, and I struck Egypt with plagues. Later I led you out. ⁶When I led your ancestors out of Egypt, you came to the sea. The Egyptians with their chariots and horsemen chased your ancestors to the Red Sea. ⁷When your ancestors cried out to the LORD, he put darkness between you and the Egyptians. He made the sea flow back and cover them. You saw for yourselves what I did to Egypt. Then you lived in the desert for a long time.

⁸"After that I brought you to the land of the Amorites who lived on the east side of the Jordan River. They fought you. However, I handed them over to you. So you took their land, and I destroyed them in front of you. ⁹Then Balak, son of King Zippor of Moab, fought Israel. He summoned Balaam, son of Beor, to curse you. ¹⁰But I refused to listen to Balaam. All he could do was bless you. So I saved you from his power.

¹¹"Then you crossed the Jordan River and came to Jericho. The citizens of Jericho, the Amorites, Perizzites, Canaanites, Hittites, Girgashites, Hivites, and Jebusites fought you. But I handed them over to you. ¹²I sent hornets ahead of you to force out the two kings of the Amorites ahead of you. These things didn't happen because of your battle skills or fighting

---

[a] 23:16 Or "covenant."

ability. ¹³ So I gave you a land that you hadn't farmed, cities to live in that you hadn't built, vineyards and olive groves that you hadn't planted. So you ate all you wanted!

¹⁴ "Fear the LORD, and serve him with integrity and faithfulness. Get rid of the gods your ancestors served on the other side of the Euphrates River and in Egypt, and serve only the LORD. ¹⁵ But if you don't want to serve the LORD, then choose today whom you will serve. Even if you choose the gods your ancestors served on the other side of the Euphrates or the gods of the Amorites in whose land you live, my family and I will still serve the LORD."

¹⁶ The people responded, "It would be unthinkable for us to abandon the LORD to serve other gods. ¹⁷ The LORD our God brought us and our ancestors out of slavery in Egypt. He did these spectacular signs right before our eyes. He guarded us wherever we went, especially as we passed through other nations. ¹⁸ The LORD forced out all the people ahead of us, including the Amorites who lived in this land. We, too, will serve the LORD, because he is our God."

¹⁹ But Joshua answered the people, "Since the LORD is a holy God, you can't possibly serve him. He is a God who does not tolerate rivals. He will not forgive your rebellious acts and sins. ²⁰ If you abandon the LORD and serve foreign gods, he will turn and bring disaster on you. He will destroy you, although he has been so good to you."

²¹ The people answered Joshua, "No! We will [only] serve the LORD!"

²² Joshua said to the people, "You have testified that you have chosen to serve the LORD." They answered, "Yes, we have!"

²³ "Get rid of the foreign gods that are among you. Turn yourselves entirely over to the LORD God of Israel."

²⁴ The people replied to Joshua, "We will serve the LORD our God and obey him."

²⁵ That day Joshua made an agreement for the people and set up laws and rules for them at Shechem. ²⁶ Joshua wrote these things in the Book of God's Teachings. Then he took a large stone and set it up under the oak tree at the LORD's holy place. ²⁷ Joshua told all the people, "This stone will stand as a witness for us. It has heard all the words which the LORD spoke to us. It will stand as a witness for you. You cannot deceive your God." ²⁸ Then Joshua sent the people away, each to his own property.

The Deaths of Joshua and Eleazar

²⁹ After these events, the LORD's servant Joshua, son of Nun, died. He was 110 years old. ³⁰ He was buried on his own land at Timnath Serah in the mountains of Ephraim north of Mount Gaash.

³¹ Israel served the LORD as long as Joshua and the older leaders, who outlived him and who knew everything the LORD had done for Israel, were alive.

³² Joseph's bones, which the people of Israel had brought from Egypt, were buried at Shechem. They were placed in the plot of ground Jacob had bought from the sons of Hamor, father of Shechem, for 100 pieces of silver. The plot was inherited by Joseph's descendants.

³³ Aaron's son Eleazar also died. He was buried on the hill that had been given to his son Phinehas in the mountains of Ephraim.

JUDGES

Israel Fails to Force Out the Canaanites

1 ¹ After Joshua's death the Israelites asked the Lord, "Who will go first to fight the Canaanites for us?"

² The Lord answered, "Judah's troops will go first. I am about to hand the Canaanites over to you."

³ The tribe of Judah said to the tribe of Simeon, "Come with us into the territory given to us when we drew lots, and together we will fight the people of Canaan. Then we'll go with you into your territory." So the tribe of Simeon went along with Judah.

Judah Attempts to Force Out the Canaanites

⁴ Judah's troops went into battle, and the Lord handed the Canaanites and Perizzites over to them. They defeated 10,000 men at Bezek. ⁵ At Bezek they also caught up with Adoni Bezek. They fought him and defeated the Canaanites and Perizzites. ⁶ Adoni Bezek fled. Judah's troops chased him, caught him, and cut off his thumbs and big toes. ⁷ Adoni Bezek said, "Seventy kings who had their thumbs and big toes cut off used to pick up food under my table. God has paid me back for what I did to them." Judah's troops brought Adoni Bezek to Jerusalem, where he died.

⁸ The men of Judah attacked Jerusalem and captured it. They killed everyone there and set the city on fire. ⁹ After that, the men of Judah went to fight the Canaanites who lived in the mountains, the Negev, and the foothills. ¹⁰ Then they went to fight the Canaanites who lived at Hebron. (In the past Hebron was called Kiriath Arba.) There they killed Sheshai, Ahiman, and Talmai.

¹¹ From there Judah's troops went to fight the people living at Debir. (In the past Debir was called Kiriath Sepher.) ¹² Caleb said, "I will give my daughter Achsah as a wife to whoever defeats Kiriath Sepher and captures it." ¹³ Then Othniel, son of Caleb's younger brother Kenaz, captured it. So Caleb gave him his daughter Achsah as a wife. ¹⁴ When she came to Othniel, she persuaded him to ask her father for a field. When she got down from her donkey, Caleb asked her, "What do you want?"

¹⁵ She answered, "Give me a blessing. Since you've given me some dry land, also give me some springs." So Caleb gave her the upper and lower springs.

¹⁶ The descendants of Moses' father-in-law, the Kenite, went with the people of Judah from the City of Palms into the desert of Judah. There they lived with the people of Judah in the Negev near Arad.

¹⁷ The tribe of Judah went to fight along with the tribe of Simeon, their close relatives. They defeated the Canaanites who lived in Zephath and claimed it for the Lord by destroying it. So the city was called Hormah [Claimed for Destruction]. ¹⁸ Judah also captured Gaza, Ashkelon, and Ekron with their territories. ¹⁹ The Lord was with the men of Judah so that they were able to take possession of the mountains. But they could not force out the people living in the valley who had chariots made of iron. ²⁰ As Moses had promised, Hebron was given to Caleb, who forced out the three sons of Anak.

²¹ The men of Benjamin did not force out the Jebusites who lived in Jerusalem. The Jebusites still live with the tribe of Benjamin in Jerusalem today.

²² The descendants of Joseph also went into battle against Bethel, and the Lord was with them. ²³ They sent men to spy on Bethel. (In the past the city was called Luz.) ²⁴ The spies saw a man coming out of the city. They told him, "Show us how we can get into the city, and we'll treat you kindly." ²⁵ He showed them. So they got into the city and killed everyone there. But they let that man and his whole family go free. ²⁶ The man went to the land of the Hittites. There he built a city and called it Luz. The city still has that name today.

²⁷ Now, the tribe of Manasseh did not force out the people of Beth Shean, Taanach, Dor, Ibleam, and Megiddo or their villages. The Canaanites were determined to live in this land. ²⁸ When the Israelites were strong enough, they made the Canaanites do forced labor. But they did not force all of them out.

²⁹ The tribe of Ephraim did not force out the Canaanites who lived in Gezer. So the Canaanites continued to live with them in Gezer.

[30] The tribe of Zebulun did not force out those who lived at Kitron or Nahalol. So the Canaanites continued to live with them and were made to do forced labor.

[31] The tribe of Asher did not force out those who lived at Acco or Sidon, Ahlab, Achzib, Helbah, Aphek, or Rehob. [32] So the tribe of Asher continued to live with the Canaanites because they did not force them out.

[33] The tribe of Naphtali did not force out those who lived at Beth Shemesh or Beth Anath. So they continued to live with the Canaanites. But the people of Beth Shemesh and Beth Anath were made to do forced labor.

[34] The Amorites forced the tribe of Dan into the mountains and would not let them come down into the valley.

[35] The Amorites were determined to live at Har Heres, Aijalon, and Shaalbim. But when the tribes of Joseph became stronger, they made the Amorites do forced labor. [36] The territory of the Amorites extended from the Akrabbim Pass—from Selah northward.

The Messenger of the LORD Reacts to Israel's Failure

2 [1] The Messenger of the LORD went from Gilgal to Bochim. He said, "I brought you out of Egypt into the land that I swore to give to your ancestors. I said, 'I will never break my promise[a] to you. [2] You must never make a treaty with the people who live in this land. You must tear down their altars.' But you didn't obey me. What do you think you're doing? [3] So I have this to say, 'I will not force them out of your way. They will be like thorns in your sides, and their gods will become a trap for you.' "

[4] While the Messenger of the LORD was saying this to all the people of Israel, they began to cry loudly. [5] So they called that place Bochim [Those Who Cry]. They offered sacrifices there to the LORD.

The Death of Joshua

[6] Now, Joshua sent the people of Israel home. So each family went to take possession of the territory they had inherited. [7] The people served the LORD throughout Joshua's lifetime and throughout the lifetimes of the leaders who had outlived him and who had seen all the spectacular works the LORD had done for Israel. [8] The LORD's servant Joshua, son of Nun, died at the age of 110. [9] He was buried at Timnath Heres within the territory he had inherited. This was in the mountains of Ephraim north of Mount Gaash. [10] That whole generation had joined their ancestors in death. So another generation grew up after them. They had no personal experience with the LORD or with what he had done for Israel.

The Sin of the Next Generation

[11] The people of Israel did what the LORD considered evil. They began to serve other gods— the Baals. [12] The Israelites abandoned the LORD God of their ancestors, the God who brought them out of Egypt. They followed the other gods of the people around them. They worshiped these gods, and that made the LORD angry. [13] They abandoned the LORD to serve the god Baal and the goddess Astarte. [14] So the LORD became angry with the people of Israel. He handed them over to people who robbed them. He also used their enemies around them to defeat them. They could no longer stand up against their enemies. [15] Whenever the Israelites went to war, the power of the LORD brought disaster on them. This was what the LORD said he would do in an oath. So he made them suffer a great deal.

[16] Then the LORD would send judges[b] to rescue them from those who robbed them. [17] But the people wouldn't listen to the judges. The Israelites chased after other gods as though they were prostitutes and worshiped them. They quickly turned from the ways of their ancestors who had obeyed the LORD's commands. They refused to be like their ancestors. [18] But when the LORD appointed judges for the Israelites, he was with each judge. The LORD rescued them from their enemies as long as that judge was alive. The LORD was moved by the groaning of those who were tormented and oppressed. [19] But after each judge died, the people went back to their old ways and acted more corruptly than their parents. They followed, served, and worshiped other gods. They never gave up their evil practices and stubborn ways.

The LORD Allows the Nations to Stay in Order to Test His People

[20] The LORD became angry with Israel. He said, "Because the people of this nation have rejected the promise I gave their ancestors and have not obeyed me, [21] I will no longer force out the nations Joshua left behind when he died. [22] I will test the people of Israel with these nations to see whether or not they will carefully follow the LORD's ways as their ancestors did."

---

[a] 2:1 Or "covenant."   [b] 2:16 The judges served as God-appointed political/religious leaders of Israel.

[23] So the LORD let these nations stay. He had not handed them over to Joshua or forced them out quickly.

3 [1] These are the nations the LORD left behind to test all the Israelites who had not experienced any war in Canaan. [2] The LORD left them to teach Israel's descendants about war, at least those who had known nothing about it in the past. [3] He left the five rulers of the Philistines, all the Canaanites, the Sidonians, and the Hivites who lived on Mount Lebanon from Mount Baal Hermon to the border of Hamath. [4] These nations were left to test the Israelites, to find out if they would obey the commands the LORD had given their ancestors through Moses.

The People Fail the Test

[5] So the people of Israel lived among the Canaanites, Hittites, Amorites, Perizzites, Hivites, and Jebusites. [6] The Israelites allowed their sons and daughters to marry these people. Israel also served their gods.

Othniel Defeats Cushan Rishathaim

[7] The people of Israel did what the LORD considered evil. They forgot the LORD their God and served other gods and goddesses—the Baals and the Asherahs. [8] The LORD became angry with the people of Israel. He used King Cushan Rishathaim of Aram Naharaim to defeat them. So Israel served Cushan Rishathaim for eight years.

[9] Then the people of Israel cried out to the LORD for help. The LORD sent a savior to rescue them. It was Othniel, son of Caleb's younger brother Kenaz. [10] When the LORD's Spirit came over him, he became the judge of Israel. He went out to war. The LORD handed King Cushan Rishathaim of Aram Naharaim over to him, and Othniel overpowered him. [11] So there was finally peace in the land for 40 years. Then Othniel, son of Kenaz, died.

Ehud Defeats Moab

[12] Once again, the people of Israel did what the LORD considered evil. So the LORD made King Eglon of Moab stronger than Israel, because Israel did what the LORD considered evil. [13] Eglon got the Ammonites and the Amalekites to help him, and they defeated the Israelites and occupied the City of Palms. [14] The Israelites served King Eglon of Moab for 18 years.

[15] Then the people of Israel cried out to the LORD for help. The LORD sent a savior to rescue them. It was Ehud, a left-handed man from the tribe of Benjamin. (Ehud was the son of Gera.)

The people sent him with their tax payment to King Eglon of Moab. [16] Ehud made a two-edged dagger for himself. He fastened it to his right side under his clothes. [17] Then he brought the tax payment to King Eglon. (Eglon was a very fat man.) [18] When Ehud had finished delivering the payment, he sent back the men who had carried it. [19] However, Ehud turned around at the stone idols near Gilgal ˎand returned to Eglonˏ. He said, "Your Majesty, I have a secret message for you."

The king replied, "Keep quiet!" Then all his advisers left the room.

[20] Ehud came up to him as he sat alone in his room on the roof. He said to the king, "I have a message from God for you." As the king rose from his throne, [21] Ehud reached with his left hand, took the dagger from his right side, and plunged it into Eglon's belly. [22] Even the handle went in after the blade. Eglon's fat covered the blade because Ehud didn't pull the dagger out. The blade stuck out in back.[a] [23] Ehud left the room.[a] (He had closed and locked the doors of the room before he left.)

[24] After Ehud went out, Eglon's advisers came in. They were surprised that the doors were locked. "He must be using the toilet," they said. [25] They waited and waited, but Eglon didn't open the doors. So they took the key and opened the door. They were shocked to see their ruler lying on the floor, dead.

[26] While they had been waiting, Ehud escaped. He went past the stone idols and escaped to Seirah. [27] When he arrived there, he blew a ram's horn in the mountains of Ephraim ˎto summon the troopsˏ. So the troops of Israel came down from the mountains with him, and he led them. [28] He told them, "Follow me! The LORD will hand your enemy Moab over to you."

They followed him and captured the shallow crossings of the Jordan River that led to Moab and refused to let anyone cross. [29] At that time they killed about ten thousand of Moab's best fighting men. Not one of them escaped. [30] The power of Moab was crushed by Israel that day. So there was finally peace in the land for 80 years.

Shamgar Defeats the Philistines

[31] After Ehud came Shamgar, son of Anath. He killed 600 Philistines with a sharp stick used for herding oxen. So he, too, rescued Israel.

---

[a] 3:22, 23 Hebrew meaning uncertain.

The LORD Calls Barak Through Deborah

4 [1] After Ehud died, the people of Israel again did what the LORD considered evil. [2] So the LORD used King Jabin of Canaan, who ruled at Hazor, to defeat them. The commander of King Jabin's army was Sisera, who lived at Harosheth Haggoyim. [3] The people of Israel cried out to the LORD for help. King Jabin had 900 chariots made of iron and had cruelly oppressed Israel for 20 years.

[4] Deborah, wife of Lappidoth, was a prophet. She was the judge in Israel at that time. [5] She used to sit under the Palm Tree of Deborah between Ramah and Bethel in the mountains of Ephraim. The people of Israel would come to her for legal decisions.

[6] Deborah summoned Barak, son of Abinoam, from Kedesh in Naphtali. She told him, "The LORD God of Israel has given you this order: 'Gather troops on Mount Tabor. Take 10,000 men from Naphtali and Zebulun with you. [7] I will lead Sisera (the commander of Jabin's army), his chariots, and troops to you at the Kishon River. I will hand him over to you.'"

[8] Barak said to her, "If you go with me, I'll go. But if you don't go with me, I won't go." [9] Deborah replied, "Certainly, I'll go with you. But you won't win any honors for the way you're going about this, because the LORD will use a woman to defeat Sisera."

Barak Defeats Jabin

So Deborah started out for Kedesh with Barak. [10] Barak called the tribes of Zebulun and Naphtali together at Kedesh. Ten thousand men went to fight under his command. Deborah also went along with him.

[11] Heber the Kenite had separated from the other Kenites (the descendants of Hobab, Moses' father-in-law). Heber went as far away as the oak tree at Zaanannim near Kedesh and set up his tent.

[12] The report reached Sisera that Barak, son of Abinoam, had come to fight at Mount Tabor. [13] So Sisera summoned all his chariots (900 chariots made of iron) and all his troops from Harosheth Haggoyim to come to the Kishon River.

[14] Then Deborah said to Barak, "Attack! This is the day the LORD will hand Sisera over to you. The LORD will go ahead of you."

So Barak came down from Mount Tabor with 10,000 men behind him. [15] The LORD threw Sisera, all his chariots, and his whole army into a panic in front of Barak's deadly assault. Sisera got down from his chariot and fled on foot. [16] Barak pursued the chariots and the army to Harosheth Haggoyim. So Sisera's whole army was killed in combat. Not one man survived.

[17] Meanwhile, Sisera fled on foot toward the tent of Jael, the wife of Heber the Kenite. Sisera did this because King Jabin of Hazor and Heber's family were on peaceful terms. [18] When Jael came out ˌof her tentˌ, she met Sisera. She told him, "Sir, come in here! Come into my tent. Don't be afraid." So he went into her tent, and she hid him under a tent curtain.

[19] Sisera said to her, "Please give me a little water to drink. I'm thirsty." But instead she gave him milk to drink and covered him up again.

[20] He said to her, "Stand at the door of the tent. If anyone comes and asks if there has been a man around here, tell them no."

[21] When Sisera had fallen sound asleep from exhaustion, Jael, Heber's wife, took a tent peg and walked quietly toward him with a hammer in her hand. She hammered the tent peg through his temples into the ground. So Sisera died.

[22] Barak was still pursuing Sisera. When Jael came out ˌof her tentˌ, she met him. She said to him, "Come in! I have something to show you—the man you've been looking for." So Barak went into her tent. He saw Sisera lying there dead with the tent peg through his temples.

[23] So on that day, God used the people of Israel to crush the power of King Jabin of Canaan. [24] The Israelites became stronger and stronger until they destroyed him.

The Victory Song of Deborah and Barak

5 [1] On that day Deborah and Barak, son of Abinoam, sang this song:

[2]   Praise the LORD!
      Men in Israel vowed to fight,
         and people volunteered for service.

[3]   Listen, you kings!
      Open your ears, you princes!
         I will sing a song to the LORD.
         I will make music to the LORD God of Israel.

[4]   O LORD,
      when you went out from Seir,
      when you marched from the country of Edom,

the earth quaked,
the sky poured,
the clouds burst,

5   and the mountains shook
in the presence of the LORD God of Sinai,
in the presence of the LORD God of Israel.

6 In the days of Shamgar, son of Anath,
in the days of Jael,
roads were deserted.
Those who traveled took back roads.

7 Villages in Israel were deserted—
deserted until I, Deborah, took a stand—
took a stand as a mother of Israel.

8 When the people chose new gods,
war broke out inside the city gates.
Not a weapon was seen among 40,000 in Israel.

9 My heart goes out to Israel's commanders,
to those people who volunteered.
Praise the LORD!

10 You people who ride on brown donkeys,
who sit on saddle blankets,
and who walk on the road—think.

11 Listen to the voices of those singing at the wells.[a]
Over and over again they repeat
the victories of the LORD,
the victories for his villages in Israel.
Then the LORD's people went down to the city gates.

12 Get up! Get up, Deborah!
Get up! Get up and create a song!

Barak, attack! Take your prisoners, son of Abinoam.

13 Then those mighty men who were left came down.
The LORD's people went into battle for me against the mighty soldiers.

14   Those who had settled in Amalek's country
came down from Ephraim.
Benjamin came with its troops
after Ephraim.
Commanders from Machir went into battle.
The officers from Zebulun also went.

15 Issachar's commanders were with Deborah.
They were also with Barak,
sent into the valley under his command.

Among Reuben's divisions important men had second thoughts.

16 Why did you sit between the saddlebags?
Was it to listen to the shepherds playing their flutes?
Reuben's divisions of important men had second thoughts.

17 Gilead remained east of the Jordan River.
And Dan . . . Why did he stay by the ships?
Asher sat on the seashore and remained along the inlets.

18   But Zebulun mocked death,
and Naphtali risked his life on the battlefield.

19 Kings came and fought.
Then the kings of Canaan fought.
They fought at Taanach by the waters of Megiddo.
But they didn't carry off any rich loot.

20 The stars fought from heaven.
They fought against Sisera from their heavenly paths.

21 The Kishon River swept them away—
that old river, the Kishon.

---

[a] 5:11 Hebrew meaning of this line uncertain.

I must march on with strength!

22 Then the horses' hoofs pounded.
    The mighty war horses galloped on and on.
23 "Curse Meroz!" said the Messenger of the LORD.
    "Bitterly curse those who live there!
        They did not come to help the LORD,
            to help the LORD and his heroes."
24 Jael, wife of Heber the Kenite,
    should be the most blessed woman,
    the most blessed woman living in a tent.
25 Sisera asked for water.
    She gave him milk.
    She offered him buttermilk in a royal bowl.
26 She reached for a tent peg with one hand,
    for a workman's hammer with the other.
    She struck Sisera.
        She crushed his head.
            She shattered and pierced his temples.
27 He sank.
    He fell.
        He lay between her feet!
    He sank.
    He fell between her feet.
        Where he sank, he fell dead.

28 Sisera's mother looked through her window
    and cried as she peered through the lattice.
    "Why is his chariot taking so long?
    Why don't I hear the clatter of his chariots?"
29 Her wisest servants gave her an answer.
    But she kept repeating to herself,
30   "They're really finding and dividing the loot:
        A girl or two for each soldier,
            colorful clothes for Sisera,
                colorful, embroidered clothes,
                    and two pieces of colorful, embroidered cloth
                        for the neck of the looter."

31 May all your enemies die like that, O LORD.
    But may those who love the LORD
        be like the sun when it rises in all its brightness.

So the land had peace for 40 years.

Israel Sins Again

6 ¹ The people of Israel did what the LORD considered evil. So the LORD handed them over to Midian for seven years. ² Midian's power was too strong for Israel. The Israelites made hiding places in the mountains, caves, and mountain strongholds to protect themselves from Midian. ³ Whenever Israel planted crops, Midian, Amalek, and Kedem came and damaged the crops. ⁴ The enemy used to camp on the land and destroy the crops all the way to Gaza. They left nothing for Israel to live on—not one sheep, cow, or donkey. ⁵ Like swarms of locusts, they came with their livestock and their tents. They and their camels could not be counted. They came into the land only to ruin it. ⁶ So the Israelites became very poor because of Midian and cried out to the LORD for help.

⁷ When the people of Israel cried out to the LORD for help because of what the Midianites had done to them, ⁸ the LORD sent a prophet to them. He said, "This is what the LORD God of Israel says:

I brought you out of Egypt.
I took you away from slavery.
9   I rescued you from the power of the Egyptians
        and from the power of those who oppressed you.
    I forced people out of your way.
    I gave you their land.
10   I said to you, 'I am the LORD your God.
        You must never fear the gods of the Amorites

in whose land you will live.'
But you have not obeyed me."

Gideon Is Chosen to Be a Judge

[11] The Messenger of the LORD came and sat under the oak tree in Ophrah that belonged to Joash from Abiezer's family. Joash's son Gideon was beating out wheat in a winepress to hide it from the Midianites. [12] The Messenger of the LORD appeared to Gideon and said, "The LORD is with you, brave man."

[13] Gideon responded, "Excuse me, sir! But if the LORD is with us, why has all this happened to us? Where are all the miracles our ancestors have told us about? Didn't they say, 'The LORD brought us out of Egypt?' But now the LORD has abandoned us and has handed us over to Midian."

[14] The LORD turned to him and said, "You will rescue Israel from Midian with the strength you have. I am sending you."

[15] Gideon said to him, "Excuse me, sir! How can I rescue Israel? Look at my whole family. It's the weakest one in Manasseh. And me? I'm the least important member of my family."

[16] The LORD replied, "I will be with you. You will defeat Midian as if it were ˻only˼ one man."

[17] Gideon said to him, "If you find me acceptable, give me a sign that it is really you speaking to me. [18] Don't leave until I come back. I want to bring my gift and set it in front of you."

"I will stay until you come back," he said.

[19] Then Gideon went into ˻his house˼ and prepared a young goat and unleavened bread made with 18 quarts of flour. He put the meat in a basket and the broth in a pot. then he went out and presented them to the messenger of the LORD under the oak tree.

[20] The Messenger of the LORD told him, "Take the meat and the unleavened bread, put them on this rock, and pour the broth over them." Gideon did so. [21] Then the Messenger of the LORD touched the meat and the bread with the tip of the staff that was in his hand. Fire flared up from the rock and burned the meat and the bread. Then the Messenger of the LORD disappeared. [22] That's when Gideon realized that this had been the Messenger of the LORD. So he said, "LORD God! I have seen the Messenger of the LORD face to face."

[23] The LORD said to him, "Calm down! Don't be afraid. You will not die." [24] So Gideon built an altar there to the LORD. He called it The LORD Calms. To this day it is still in Ophrah, which belongs to Abiezer's family.

Gideon Destroys an Altar Dedicated to Baal

[25] That same night the LORD said to Gideon, "Take a bull from your father's herd, a bull that is seven years old. Tear down your father's altar dedicated to the god Baal and cut down the pole dedicated to the goddess Asherah that is next to it. [26] Then, in the proper way, build an altar to the LORD your God on top of this fortified place. Take this second bull and sacrifice it as a burnt offering on the wood from the Asherah pole that you have cut down."

[27] Gideon took ten of his servants and did what the LORD had told him to do. However, he didn't do anything during the day. He was too afraid of his father's family and the men of the city, so he did it at night. [28] When the men of the city got up early in the morning, they saw that the Baal altar had been torn down. The Asherah pole next to it had also been cut down. They saw that the second bull had been sacrificed as a burnt offering on the altar that had been built. [29] They asked each other, "Who did this?" While they were investigating the matter, someone said, "Gideon, son of Joash, did this."

[30] Then the men of the city told Joash, "Bring your son out. He must die. He has torn down the Baal altar and cut down the Asherah pole that was beside it."

[31] But Joash said to everyone standing around him, "You're not going to defend Baal, are you? Do you think you should save him? Whoever defends him will be put to death in the morning. If he's a god, let him defend himself when someone tears down his altar." [32] So that day they nicknamed Gideon "Jerubbaal" [Let Baal Defend Himself], because they said, "When someone tears down Baal's altar, let Baal defend himself."

Gideon Summons an Army

[33] All of Midian, Amalek, and Kedem combined their armies, crossed ˻the Jordan River˼, and camped in the valley of Jezreel. [34] Then the LORD's Spirit gave Gideon strength. So Gideon blew the ram's horn to summon Abiezer's family to follow him. [35] He also sent messengers throughout Manasseh to summon the people to follow him. The tribes of Asher, Zebulun, and Naphtali were also summoned to follow him, and they went to meet the enemy in battle.

[36] Then Gideon said to God, "You said that you would rescue Israel through me. [37] I'll place some wool on the threshing floor.[a] If there is dew on the wool while all the ground is dry, then

---

[a] 6:37 A threshing floor is an outdoor area where grain is separated from its husks.

I'll know that you will rescue Israel through me, as you said." **38** And that is what happened. The next morning Gideon got up early. He squeezed out a bowl full of water from the wool.

39 Then Gideon said to God, "Don't be angry with me. But let me ask one more thing. Let me make one more test with the wool. Let the wool be dry while all the ground is covered with dew." **40** During the night, God did what Gideon asked. The wool was dry, but all the ground was covered with dew.

Gideon Defeats Midian

7 **1** Jerubbaal (that is, Gideon) and all the troops with him got up early and camped above En Harod. Midian's camp was north of him at the hill of Moreh in the valley.

2 The LORD said to Gideon, "You have too many men with you for me to hand Midian over to you. Israel might brag and say, 'We saved ourselves.' **3** Announce to the troops, 'Whoever is scared or frightened should leave Mount Gilead and go back home.'" So 22,000 men went back home, and 10,000 were left.

4 The LORD said to Gideon, "There are still too many men. Bring them down to the water, and I will test them for you there. If I say to you, 'This one will go with you,' he must go with you. And if I say to you, 'This one won't go with you,' he must not go."

5 So Gideon took the men down to the water. The LORD said to him, "Separate those who lap water with their tongues like dogs from those who kneel down to drink." **6** Three hundred men lapped water with their hands to their mouths. All the rest of the men knelt down to drink water. **7** Then the LORD said to Gideon, "With the 300 men who lapped water I will save you and hand Midian over to you. All the other men should go home." **8** So Gideon sent the other men of Israel home, but the 300 men who stayed kept all the supplies and rams' horns.

The camp of Midian was below him in the valley.

9 That night the LORD said to Gideon, "Attack! Go into the camp! I will hand it over to you. **10** But if you're afraid to go, take your servant Purah to the camp with you. **11** Listen to what people are saying. After that, you will have the courage to go into the camp and attack it."

So Gideon and his servant Purah went to the edge of the camp. **12** Midian, Amalek, and all of Kedem were spread out in the valley like a swarm of locusts. There were so many camels that they could not be counted. They were as numerous as the grains of sand on the seashore.

13 When Gideon got there, he heard a man telling his friend a dream. The man said, "I had a strange dream. There was a loaf of barley bread rolling around in the camp of Midian. When it got to the command post, the loaf of bread hit that tent so hard that the tent collapsed, turned upside down, and fell flat."

14 His friend replied, "That can only be the sword of Gideon, son of Joash, from Israel. God is going to hand Midian and the whole camp over to him."

15 When Gideon heard the dream and its interpretation, he worshiped the LORD. Then he went back to the camp of Israel and said, "Attack! The LORD will hand Midian's camp over to you."

16 Gideon divided the 300 men into three companies. He gave them each rams' horns and jars with torches inside. **17** He said to them, "Watch me, and do what I do. When I come to the edge of the camp, do exactly as I do. **18** When I and those with me blow our rams' horns, then the rest of you around the camp do the same and shout, 'For the LORD and for Gideon!'"

19 Gideon and his 100 men came to the edge of the camp. It was the beginning of the midnight watch just at the change of the guards. They blew their rams' horns and smashed the jars they were holding in their hands. **20** The three companies also blew their rams' horns and broke their jars. They held the torches in their left hands and the rams' horns in their right hands so that they could blow them. They shouted, "A sword for the LORD and for Gideon!" **21** While each man kept his position around the camp, everyone in the Midianite camp began to run away, screaming as they fled. **22** The 300 men kept on blowing their rams' horns, and the LORD caused the whole camp of Midian to fight among themselves. They fled as far as Beth Shittah, toward Zererah, and as far as the bank of the stream at Abel Meholah near Tabbath.

23 The men of Israel were summoned from Naphtali, Asher, and all Manasseh to help pursue the troops of Midian. **24** Gideon also sent messengers to the whole mountain region of Ephraim with this message, "Go into battle against Midian. Capture the watering holes as far as Beth Barah and the Jordan River." All the men of Ephraim were also summoned to help. They captured the watering holes as far as Beth Barah and the Jordan River. **25** They also captured Oreb and Zeeb, the two Midianite commanders. They killed Oreb at the Rock of Oreb and Zeeb at the Winepress of Zeeb and kept on pursuing Midian. Then they brought the severed heads of Oreb and Zeeb to Gideon on the other side of the Jordan River.

8 **1** The men from Ephraim strongly protested Gideon's actions. They said, "Why did you do this to us? You didn't invite us to go fight Midian with you."

2 Gideon replied, "I haven't done anything compared with what you have done. Aren't the grapes that Ephraim picked after the harvest better than all the grapes in Abiezer's entire harvest? [3] God handed Oreb and Zeeb, Midian's commanders, over to you. What have I done compared with that?" When they heard what Gideon said, they weren't angry with him anymore.

[4] Gideon and his 300 men headed toward the Jordan River. They were exhausted when they crossed it, but they kept pursuing the enemy. [5] So Gideon said to the men of Succoth, "Please give me some food for the men under my command. They're exhausted, and I'm pursuing King Zebah and King Zalmunna of Midian."

[6] The generals at Succoth replied, "We shouldn't give your army food. You haven't captured Zebah and Zalmunna yet."

[7] Gideon responded, "Alright, then. When the LORD hands Zebah and Zalmunna over to me, I'll whip your bodies with thorns and thistles from the desert."

[8] Then Gideon went to Penuel and asked the people there for the same help. But they gave him the same reply that the men of Succoth gave. [9] So he told them, "When I come back after my victory, I'll tear down this tower."

[10] Zebah and Zalmunna were in Karkor with an army of about 15,000 men. This was all that was left of Kedem's entire army. In the battle, 120,000 soldiers died. [11] So Gideon went up Tent Dwellers Road, east of Nobah and Jogbehah, and defeated the unsuspecting Midianite army. [12] Zebah and Zalmunna fled as Gideon pursued them. He captured King Zebah and King Zalmunna of Midian, and the whole Midianite army panicked.

[13] Gideon, son of Joash, returned from the battle through the Heres Pass [14] and captured a young man from Succoth. He questioned him, and the young man wrote down for him the names of the 77 officials and leaders of Succoth. [15] Gideon went to the men of Succoth and said, "Here are Zebah and Zalmunna! You insulted me when you said, 'We shouldn't give your exhausted men food before you've captured Zebah and Zalmunna.'" [16] So Gideon took the leaders of the city and taught them a lesson using thorns and thistles from the desert. [17] Then he tore down the tower of Penuel and killed the men of that city.

[18] He asked Zebah and Zalmunna, "What kind of men did you kill at Tabor?"

They answered, "They were like you. Each one looked like a king's son."

[19] Gideon replied, "They were my brothers, my mother's sons. I solemnly swear, as the LORD lives, if you had let them live, I would not have to kill you now." [20] Then he told Jether, his firstborn son, "Get up and kill them!" But Jether didn't draw his sword. He was afraid because he was only a young man.

[21] Zebah and Zalmunna said, "Get up and do it yourself! It's a man's job!" So Gideon got up and killed them. Then he took the half-moon ornaments that were on their camels' necks.

Gideon Makes a Gold Idol

[22] The men of Israel said to Gideon, "You, then your son, and then your grandson, must rule us. You rescued us from Midian."

[23] Gideon replied, "I will not rule you nor will my son. The LORD will rule you." [24] Then Gideon said to them, "Do me a favor. Each of you give me the earrings from your loot." (Their enemies, the Ishmaelites, wore gold earrings.)

[25] The men of Israel answered, "Yes, we'll give them to you." So they spread out a coat. Each man took the earrings from his loot and dropped them on it. [26] The gold earrings Gideon had asked for weighed 40 pounds. This did not include the half-moon ornaments, the earrings, the purple clothes worn by the kings of Midian, and the chains from their camels' necks. [27] Then Gideon used the gold to make an idol[a] and placed it in his hometown, Ophrah. All Israel chased after it there as though it were a prostitute. It became a trap for Gideon and his family.

[28] The power of Midian was crushed by the people of Israel, and Midian never again became a threat. So the land had peace for 40 years during Gideon's life.

[29] Jerubbaal, son of Joash, went home to live. [30] Gideon had 70 sons because he had many wives. [31] His concubine[b] at Shechem also gave birth to a son. That son was named Abimelech.

[32] Gideon, son of Joash, died at a very old age. He was buried in the tomb of his father Joash at Ophrah, the city belonging to Abiezer's family.

[33] As soon as Gideon died, the people of Israel chased after other gods—the Baals—as though they were prostitutes. They made Baal Berith their god. [34] The Israelites did not remember the LORD their God, who had rescued them from all the enemies around them. [35] And they were not kind to the family of Jerubbaal (that is, Gideon) despite all the good he had done for Israel.

---

[a] 8:27 Or "ephod," a technical term for a part of the priest's clothes. Its exact usage and shape are unknown.
[b] 8:31 A concubine is considered a wife except she has fewer rights under the law.

Abimelech Kills His Brothers

9 [1] Abimelech, son of Jerubbaal [Gideon], went to Shechem to see the uncles on his mother's side of the family. He spoke to them and his mother's whole family. [2] He said, "Please ask all citizens of Shechem, 'What seems best to you? Do you really want all of Jerubbaal's 70 sons to rule you or just one man? Remember, I'm your own flesh and blood.'"

[3] His uncles repeated everything he said to all citizens of Shechem. They were persuaded to follow Abimelech because he was their relative. [4] So they gave him 70 pieces of silver from the temple of Baal Berith. With the silver, Abimelech hired worthless and reckless men to follow him. [5] Then he went to his father's home in Ophrah. There he executed his 70 brothers, Jerubbaal's sons. But Jotham, Jerubbaal's youngest son, survived because he hid. [6] All the citizens from Shechem and Beth Millo united. They went to the oak tree that was still standing in Shechem and proclaimed Abimelech king.

Jotham's Story

[7] When Jotham was told about this, he went to a high spot on Mount Gerizim. He shouted to them, "Listen to me, you citizens of Shechem, so that God might listen to you.

[8]   "The trees went to anoint someone to be king over them.
        They said to the olive tree,
            'Be our king!'
[9]   But the olive tree responded,
            'Should I stop producing oil,
            which people use to honor gods and humans,
                in order to rule the trees?'
[10]   Then the trees said to the fig tree,
            'You come and be our king!'
[11]   But the fig tree responded,
            'Should I stop producing my good, sweet fruit
                in order to rule the trees?'
[12]   Then the trees said to the grapevine,
            'You come and be our king!'
[13]   But the grapevine responded,
            'Should I stop producing my wine,
            which makes gods and humans happy,
                in order to rule the trees?'
[14]   Then all the trees said to the thornbush,
            'You come and be our king!'
[15]   But the thornbush responded to the trees,
            'If you really want to anoint me to be your king,
                then come and take shelter in my shade.
            But if not, fire will come out of the thornbush
                and burn up the cedars of Lebanon.'

[16] "If you acted with sincerity and integrity when you made Abimelech king, ˌbe happy.ˌ If you treated Jerubbaal and his family well, if you treated him as he deserved, be happy. [17] My father fought for you. He risked his life and rescued you from Midian. [18] But today you have attacked my father's family. You have executed his 70 sons. You have made Abimelech, who is the son of my father's slave girl, king over the citizens of Shechem just because he's your brother. [19] So if you are now acting with sincerity and integrity toward Jerubbaal and his family, then be happy with Abimelech and let Abimelech be happy with you. [20] But if that's not the case, let fire come out of Abimelech and burn up citizens of Shechem and Beth Millo. Also let fire come out of citizens of Shechem and Beth Millo and burn up Abimelech."

[21] Then Jotham ran away quickly. He went to Beerah and lived there ˌto avoidˌ his brother Abimelech.

Abimelech's Battles

[22] Abimelech ruled Israel for three years. [23] Then God sent an evil spirit to cause problems between Abimelech and citizens of Shechem. So citizens of Shechem turned against Abimelech. [24] God did this so that the bloody violence committed against Jerubbaal's 70 sons would happen to Abimelech and citizens of Shechem. Citizens of Shechem had helped Abimelech execute his brothers.

[25] So citizens of Shechem set ambushes for Abimelech on top of the mountains. They also robbed everyone who passed by them on the road. This was reported to Abimelech.

²⁶ Then Gaal (son of Ebed) and his brothers moved into Shechem. Citizens of Shechem trusted him. ²⁷ They went into the country and harvested grapes in the vineyards to make wine. Then they made an offering of praise in the temple of their gods. They ate, drank, and cursed Abimelech. ²⁸ Gaal (son of Ebed) said, "Who's Abimelech, and who are we, the people of Shechem, that we should serve him? Isn't he Jerubbaal's son, and isn't Zebul his officer? Serve the descendants of Hamor, Shechem's father! Why should we serve Abimelech? ²⁹ How I wish I controlled these people! Then I'd get rid of Abimelech. I would tell him,ᵃ 'Get yourself a big army and come out.' "

³⁰ Zebul, Shechem's ruler, heard what Gaal (son of Ebed) had said, and he became angry. ³¹ He secretly sent messengers to Abimelech. "Watch out! Gaal (son of Ebed) and his brothers have come to Shechem. They have turned the city against you. ³² You and your men must start out tonight. Set an ambush ˌfor themˌ in the fields ˌaround Shechemˌ. ³³ In the morning, when the sun rises, get up quickly and raid the city. When Gaal and his men come out to attack you, do whatever you want to him."

³⁴ Abimelech and all his troops started out at night. He used four companies to set ambushes around Shechem. ³⁵ Gaal (son of Ebed) went out and stood at the entrance to the city. Then Abimelech and his troops rose from their ambush. ³⁶ When Gaal saw the troops, he said to Zebul, "Look, troops are coming down from the mountaintops!"

Zebul replied, "The shadows of the mountains look like men to you."

³⁷ Gaal spoke again, "No, there are troops coming down from Tabbur Haares. One company is coming along the road by the Fortunetellers' Tree."

³⁸ Then Zebul said to him, "Where is your big mouth now? You were the one who said, 'Who's Abimelech that we should serve him?' Aren't these the troops ˌwhose rulerˌ you despised? Now go out and fight him."

³⁹ Then Gaal led citizens of Shechem out to fight Abimelech. ⁴⁰ Abimelech chased Gaal so that he ran away from him. Many were killed at the entrance of the city. ⁴¹ Abimelech continued to live at Arumah. Zebul threw Gaal and his brothers out and would not let them live in Shechem.

⁴² The next day the people ˌof Shechemˌ went into the fields. Abimelech was told about it. ⁴³ So he took his troops, divided them into three companies, and set an ambush in the fields. He watched and saw the people coming out of the city. Then he began to attack them. ⁴⁴ Abimelech and his company charged the city and captured its entrance. The other two companies charged at everyone in the fields and attacked them. ⁴⁵ Abimelech attacked the city all day long. He captured the city and killed the people in it. He also tore down the city and scattered salt all over the land.

⁴⁶ All the citizens of Shechem's Tower heard about it and went into the basement of the temple of El Berith. ⁴⁷ When Abimelech was told that they had gathered there, ⁴⁸ he and all his men went to Mount Zalmon. Abimelech took an ax, cut some brushwood, and carried it on his shoulder. He told his men, "Hurry and do what you've seen me do!" ⁴⁹ So all his troops also cut brushwood and followed Abimelech. They piled the brushwood on top of the basement and set it on fire with the people inside. So all the people in Shechem's Tower died too. There were about a thousand men and women.

⁵⁰ Then Abimelech went to Thebez, camped there, and captured it. ⁵¹ Now, there was a strong tower inside the town. All the men, women, and leaders of the town fled to it. They locked the door behind them and went up on the roof of the tower. ⁵² Abimelech came to the tower. He began to fight against it and went near the entrance of the tower to burn it down. ⁵³ Then a woman threw a small millstone that hit Abimelech on the head and cracked his skull. ⁵⁴ He quickly called his armorbearer. He told him, "Take your sword and kill me! I don't want anyone to say, 'A woman killed Abimelech.' " His armorbearer did as he said, so Abimelech died. ⁵⁵ When the people of Israel saw that Abimelech was dead, they all went home.

⁵⁶ So God paid back Abimelech for the evil he had done to his father when he killed his 70 brothers. ⁵⁷ God also paid back the men of Shechem for all their evil. So the curse of Jotham, son of Jerubbaal, came true.

Tola Serves as Judge

10 ¹ After Abimelech, Tola, who was the son of Puah and grandson of Dodo, came to rescue Israel. Tola was from Issachar and lived in Shamir in the mountains of Ephraim. ² He judged Israel for 23 years. Tola died and was buried in Shamir.

Jair Serves as Judge

³ After Tola, Jair from Gilead became a judge. He judged Israel for 22 years. ⁴ Jair had 30 sons who rode on 30 donkeys. He also had 30 towns that are still called Havvoth Jair to this day. They are in the region of Gilead. ⁵ Jair died and was buried in Kamon.

ᵃ 9:29 Greek; Masoretic Text "So he said to Abimelech."

Israel Sins Again

⁶ The people of Israel again did what the LORD considered evil. They began to serve other gods and goddesses—the Baals and the Astartes—and the gods of Aram, Sidon, Moab, Ammon, and the gods of the Philistines. They abandoned the LORD and did not serve him.

⁷ The LORD became angry with the people of Israel. So he used the Philistines and Ammonites to defeat them. ⁸ They oppressed and crushed the people of Israel that year. For 18 years they oppressed all who lived east of the Jordan River in the land of the Amorites in Gilead. ⁹ Ammon also crossed the Jordan River to fight the tribes of Judah, Benjamin, and Ephraim. So Israel suffered a great deal.

¹⁰ Then the people of Israel cried out to the LORD for help. They said, "We have sinned against you. We have abandoned our God and served other gods—the Baals."

¹¹ The LORD said to the people of Israel, "When the Egyptians, the Amorites, the Ammonites, the Philistines, ¹² the Sidonians, the Amalekites, and the Maonites oppressed you, you cried out to me for help. Didn't I rescue you from them? ¹³ But you still abandoned me and served other gods. That's why I won't rescue you again. ¹⁴ Cry out for help to the gods you chose. Let them rescue you when you're in trouble."

¹⁵ The people of Israel said to the LORD, "We have sinned. Do to us whatever you think is right. But please rescue us today!" ¹⁶ Then they got rid of the foreign gods they had and served the LORD. So the LORD could not bear to have Israel suffer any longer.

¹⁷ The troops of Ammon were summoned to fight, and they camped at Gilead. The people of Israel also gathered together and camped at Mizpah. ¹⁸ The leaders of the people of Gilead said to each other, "Whoever starts the fight against Ammon will rule everyone who lives in Gilead."

Jephthah Called to Be Judge

11 ¹ Jephthah was a soldier from the region of Gilead. Jephthah's father was named Gilead. His mother was a prostitute. ² Gilead's wife also gave birth to sons. When his wife's sons grew up, they threw Jephthah out. They told him, "You'll get no inheritance from our father. You're the son of that other woman." ³ Jephthah fled from his brothers. He went to live in the land of Tob. Worthless men gathered around Jephthah and went out ˎon raidsˎ with him.

⁴ Later, Ammon waged war with Israel. ⁵ When the Ammonites attacked Israel, Gilead's leaders went to get Jephthah from the land of Tob. ⁶ They said to Jephthah, "Come and be our commander so that we can wage war against Ammon."

⁷ But Jephthah replied to Gilead's leaders, "Don't you hate me? Didn't you throw me out of my father's house? So why are you coming to me now when you're in trouble?"

⁸ Gilead's leaders answered Jephthah, "The reason we've turned to you now is that we want you to go with us and wage war against Ammon. You will be the ruler of everyone who lives in Gilead."

⁹ Jephthah told them, "If you take me back to fight against Ammonites and the LORD gives them to me, I will be your leader."

¹⁰ Gilead's leaders said to Jephthah, "The LORD is a witness between us. We will certainly do what you say." ¹¹ Jephthah went with them, and the people made him their leader and commander. So Jephthah went to Mizpah and repeated all these things in the presence of the LORD.

The King of Ammon Refuses to Deal With Jephthah

¹² Jephthah sent messengers to the king of Ammon. They asked the king, "Why did you invade my land and wage war against me?"

¹³ The king of Ammon answered Jephthah's messengers, "When the people of Israel left Egypt, they took my land. It stretched from the Arnon River to the Jabbok River and the Jordan River. Now give it back peacefully."

¹⁴ Jephthah again sent messengers to the king of Ammon. ¹⁵ They said, "This is what Jephthah says: The people of Israel didn't take away the land belonging to Moab or Ammon. ¹⁶ When the people of Israel left Egypt, they went through the desert to the Red Sea and came to Kadesh. ¹⁷ The people of Israel sent messengers to the king of Edom. They said, 'Please let us go through your country.' But the king of Edom wouldn't listen to them. They also sent messengers to the king of Moab. But he wouldn't allow it, either. So the people of Israel remained at Kadesh.

¹⁸ "Then they went through the desert, by-passing Edom and Moab. They camped east of Moab—east of the Arnon River. They did not cross the Arnon River because it was Moab's border.

¹⁹ "Then the people of Israel sent messengers to King Sihon of the Amorites. Sihon ruled from Heshbon. The people of Israel said to him, 'Please let us go through your land to our own.' ²⁰ But Sihon did not trust the Israelites enough to let them go through his territory. Sihon assembled all his troops. He camped at Jahaz and attacked Israel. ²¹ But the LORD God

of Israel handed Sihon and all his people over to Israel. Israel defeated them and took possession of all the land of the Amorites who lived there. ²² Israel took all the Amorite territory from the Arnon River to the Jabbok River and from the desert to the Jordan River.

²³ "The LORD God of Israel forced the Amorites out of the way of his people Israel. So what right do you have to take it back? ²⁴ Shouldn't you take possession of what your god Chemosh took for you? Shouldn't we take everything the LORD our God took for us? ²⁵ You're not any better than Balak, son of King Zippor of Moab, are you? Did he ever have a case against Israel? Or did he ever fight against Israel? ²⁶ Israel has now lived in Heshbon, Aroer, all their villages, and in all the cities along the Arnon River for 300 years. Why didn't you recapture these cities during that time? ²⁷ I haven't sinned against you. But you have done wrong by waging war against me. The LORD is the judge who will decide today whether Israel or Ammon is right."

²⁸ But the king of Ammon didn't listen to the message Jephthah sent him.

Jephthah's Vow

²⁹ Then the LORD's Spirit came over Jephthah. Jephthah went through Gilead, Manasseh, and Mizpah in Gilead ˌto gather an armyˌ. From Mizpah in Gilead Jephthah went to attack Ammon. ³⁰ Jephthah made a vow to the LORD. He said, "If you will really hand Ammon over to me, ³¹ then whatever comes out of the doors of my house to meet me when I return safely from Ammon will belong to the LORD. I will sacrifice it as a burnt offering."

³² So Jephthah went to fight against Ammon. The LORD handed the people of Ammon over to him. ³³ He defeated them from Aroer to Minnith and on to Abel Keramim, 20 cities in all. It was a decisive defeat. So the Ammonites were crushed by the people of Israel.

³⁴ When Jephthah went to his home in Mizpah, he saw his daughter coming out to meet him. She was dancing with tambourines in her hands. She was his only child. Jephthah had no other sons or daughters. ³⁵ When he saw her, he tore his clothes in grief and said, "Oh no, Daughter! You've brought me to my knees! What disaster you've brought me! I made a foolish promise to the LORD. Now I can't break it."

³⁶ She said to him, "Father, you made a promise to the LORD. Do to me whatever you promised since the LORD has punished your enemy Ammon." ³⁷ Then she said to her father, "Do me a favor. Give me two months for my friends and me to walk in the mountains and mourn that I will never have an opportunity to get married."

³⁸ "Go!" he said, and he sent her off for two months. She and her friends went to the mountains, and she cried about never being able to get married. ³⁹ At the end of those two months she came back to her father. He did to her what he had vowed, and she never had a husband. So the custom began in Israel ⁴⁰ that for four days every year the girls in Israel would go out to sing the praises of the daughter of Jephthah, the man from Gilead.

Ephraim's Jealousy

12 ¹ The men of Ephraim were summoned to fight. They crossed ˌthe Jordan Riverˌ to Zaphon. They said to Jephthah, "Why did you fight against Ammon without inviting us to go with you? Now we're going to burn your house down with you in it."

² Jephthah answered, "My people and I were involved in a legal dispute with Ammon. I asked you for help, but you didn't rescue me from them. ³ When I saw that you would not rescue me, I risked my life and went to fight the people of Ammon. The LORD handed them over to me. So why did you come to fight against me today?"

⁴ Then Jephthah gathered all the men of Gilead and fought Ephraim. The men of Gilead defeated Ephraim. ˌThey did this becauseˌ Ephraim had said, "You people from Gilead are nothing but fugitives from Ephraim and Manasseh."

⁵ The men of Gilead captured the shallow crossings of the Jordan River leading back to Ephraim. Whenever a fugitive from Ephraim said, "Let me cross," the men of Gilead would ask, "Are you from Ephraim?" If he answered, "No," ⁶ they would tell him, "Say the word *shibboleth*." If the fugitive would say *sibboleth,* because he couldn't pronounce the word correctly, they would grab him and kill him at the shallow crossings of the Jordan River. At that time 42,000 men from Ephraim died.

⁷ Jephthah judged Israel for six years. Then Jephthah of Gilead died and was buried in one of the cities of Gilead.

Ibzan Serves as Judge

⁸ After Jephthah, Ibzan from Bethlehem judged Israel. ⁹ He had 30 sons and 30 daughters. His sons and daughters married people from outside their own families. He judged Israel for seven years. ¹⁰ When Ibzan died, he was buried in Bethlehem.

Elon Serves as Judge

[11] After Ibzan, Elon from the tribe of Zebulun judged Israel. He judged Israel for ten years. [12] When Elon died, he was buried in Aijalon in the territory of Zebulun.

Abdon Serves as Judge

[13] After Elon, Abdon, son of Hillel, from Pirathon judged Israel. [14] He had 40 sons and 30 grandsons who rode on 70 donkeys. He judged Israel for eight years. [15] When Abdon died, he was buried in Pirathon, in the territory of Ephraim, in the mountains of Amalek.

The Messenger of the LORD Appears to Samson's Parents

13 [1] The people of Israel again did what the LORD considered evil. So the LORD handed them over to the Philistines for 40 years.

[2] There was a man from Zorah named Manoah. Manoah was from the family of Dan. His wife was not able to have children. [3] The Messenger of the LORD appeared to her and said, "You've never been able to have a child, but now you will become pregnant and have a son. [4] Now you must be careful. Don't drink any wine or liquor or eat any unclean[a] food. [5] You're going to become pregnant and have a son. You must never cut his hair because the boy will be a Nazirite dedicated to God from birth. He will begin to rescue Israel from the power of the Philistines."

[6] The woman went to tell her husband. She said, "A man of God came to me. He had a very frightening appearance like the Messenger of God. So I didn't ask him where he came from, and he didn't tell me his name. [7] He told me, 'You're going to become pregnant and have a son. So don't drink any wine or liquor or eat any unclean food because the boy will be a Nazirite dedicated to God from the time he is born until he dies.' "

[8] Then Manoah pleaded with the LORD, "Please, Lord, let the man of God you sent come back to us. Let him teach us what we must do for the boy who will be born."

[9] God did what Manoah asked. The Messenger of God came back to his wife while she was sitting out in the fields. But her husband Manoah was not with her. [10] The woman ran quickly to tell her husband. She said, "The man who came to me the other day has just appeared to me ˌagainˌ."

[11] Manoah immediately followed his wife. When he came to the man, he asked him, "Are you the man who spoke to my wife?"

"Yes," he answered.

[12] Then Manoah asked, "When your words come true, how should the boy live and what should he do?"

[13] The Messenger of the LORD answered Manoah, "Your wife must be careful to do everything I told her to do. [14] She must not eat anything that comes from the grapevines, drink any wine or liquor, or eat any unclean food. She must be careful to do everything I commanded."

[15] Manoah said to the Messenger of the LORD, "Please stay while we prepare a young goat for you to eat."

[16] But the Messenger of the LORD responded, "If I stay here, I will not eat any of your food. But if you make a burnt offering, sacrifice it to the LORD." (Manoah did not realize that it was the Messenger of the LORD.)

[17] Then Manoah asked the Messenger of the LORD, "What is your name? When your words come true, we will honor you."

[18] The Messenger of the LORD asked him, "Why do you ask for my name? It's a name that works miracles."

[19] So Manoah took a young goat and a grain offering and sacrificed them to the LORD on a rock he used as an altar. While Manoah and his wife watched, the LORD did something miraculous. [20] As the flame went up toward heaven from the altar, the Messenger of the LORD went up in the flame. When Manoah and his wife saw this, they immediately bowed down with their faces touching the ground.

[21] The Messenger of the LORD didn't appear again to Manoah and his wife. Then Manoah knew that this had been the Messenger of the LORD. [22] So Manoah said to his wife, "We will certainly die because we have seen God."

[23] But Manoah's wife replied, "If the LORD wanted to kill us, he would not have accepted our burnt offering and grain offering. He would not have let us see or hear all these things just now."

[24] So the woman had a son and named him Samson. The boy grew up, and the LORD blessed him. [25] The LORD's Spirit began to stir in him while he was at Mahaneh Dan, between Zorah and Eshtaol.

---

[a] 13:4 "Unclean" refers to anything that Moses' Teachings say is not presentable to God.

Samson Marries a Philistine

14 ¹ When Samson went to Timnah, he saw a young Philistine woman. ² He went ˌhomeˌ and told his father and mother, "I've seen a Philistine woman at Timnah. Now get her for me so that I can marry her."

³ His father and mother asked him, "Aren't there any women among our relatives or all our people? Do you have to marry a woman from those godless Philistines?"

But Samson told his father, "Get her for me! She's the one I want!" ⁴ His father and mother didn't know that the LORD was behind this. The LORD was looking for an opportunity to do something to the Philistines. (At that time the Philistines were ruling Israel.)

⁵ Samson went with his father and mother to Timnah. When they were coming to the vineyards of Timnah, a young roaring lion met Samson. ⁶ The LORD's Spirit came over him. With his bare hands, he tore the lion apart as if it were a young goat. He didn't tell his parents what he had done.

⁷ Then he went to talk to the young woman. She was the one he wanted. ⁸ Later he went back to marry her. ˌOn his wayˌ he left the road to look at the lion he had killed. He saw a swarm of bees and some honey in the lion's dead body. ⁹ He scraped ˌthe honeyˌ into his hands and ate it as he walked along. When he came to his father and mother, he gave them some of the honey to eat. He didn't tell them he had scraped it out of the lion's dead body.

¹⁰ After his father went to see the woman, Samson threw a party. (This is what young men used to do.) ¹¹ When ˌher familyˌ saw him, they chose 30 of their friends to be with him.

¹² Then Samson said to them, "Let me tell you a riddle. If you solve it during the seven days of the party, I'll give you 30 linen shirts and 30 changes of clothes. ¹³ But if you can't solve it, you will give me the same things."

They responded, "Tell us your riddle! Let's hear it!"

¹⁴ So Samson said to them,

> "From the eater
>   came something to eat.
> From the strong one
>   came something sweet."

For three days they couldn't solve the riddle. ¹⁵ On the fourth day they said to Samson's wife, "Trick your husband into solving the riddle for us. If you don't, we'll burn you and your family to death. Did the two of you invite us ˌjust to make us poorˌ?"

¹⁶ So Samson's wife cried on his shoulder. She said, "You hate me! You don't really love me! You gave my friends a riddle and didn't tell me the answer."

Samson replied, "I haven't even told my father and mother, so why should I tell you?"

¹⁷ But she cried on his shoulder for the rest of the seven days of the party. Finally, on the seventh day he told her the answer because she made his life miserable. Then she told her friends the answer to the riddle.

¹⁸ So before sundown on the seventh day, the men of the city said to him,

> "What is sweeter than honey?
> What is stronger than a lion?"

Samson replied,

> "If you hadn't used my cow to plow,
>   you wouldn't know my riddle now."

¹⁹ When the LORD's Spirit came over him, he went to Ashkelon and killed 30 men there. He took their clothes and gave them to the men who solved the riddle. He was angry, and he went to his father's house. ²⁰ Samson's wife was given to his best man.

Samson Serves as Judge

15 ¹ Later, during the wheat harvest, Samson went to visit his wife. He took a young goat along for her. He said, "I'm going to sleep with my wife in her bedroom."

But her father would not let him go in. ² Her father said, "I thought you hated her. So I gave her to your best man. Isn't her younger sister better looking? Marry her instead!"

³ Samson said to him, "This time I won't be guilty when I get even with the Philistines, even though I'm going to do something terrible to them." ⁴ So Samson caught 300 foxes. He tied them together in pairs by their tails. Then he fastened a torch between their tails. ⁵ He set the torches on fire and released the foxes in the Philistines' grain fields. So he set fire to all their grain, whether it was stacked or in the fields. Their olive orchards also caught on fire.

⁶ Some Philistines asked, "Who did this?"

They were told, "Samson! He's the son-in-law of the man at Timnah. Samson did it because the man at Timnah took Samson's wife and gave her to his best man." So the Philistines burned Samson's wife and her father to death.

⁷ Samson said to them, "If that's how you're going to act, I'll get even with you before I stop." ⁸ So he attacked them violently and slaughtered them. Then he went to live in a cave in the cliff at Etam.

⁹ The Philistines came, camped in Judah, and overran Lehi. ¹⁰ The men of Judah asked, "Why did you come to fight us?"

The Philistines answered, "We've come to tie up Samson and do to him what he did to us."

¹¹ So 3,000 men from Judah went to the cave in the cliff at Etam. They said to Samson, "Don't you know that the Philistines rule us? Why have you done this to us?"

Samson replied, "I did to them what they did to me."

¹² So the men from Judah told him, "We've come to tie you up and hand you over to the Philistines."

Samson said to them, "Swear to me that you won't harm me yourselves."

¹³ They told him, "We promise we'll only tie you up and hand you over to them. We certainly won't kill you." So they tied him up with two new ropes and brought him back from the cliff.

¹⁴ When he came to Lehi, the Philistines met him with shouts ˏof triumphˏ. But the LORD's Spirit came over him. The ropes on his arms became like strings burned in a fire, and those on his hands snapped.

¹⁵ Samson found the jawbone from a donkey that had just died. He picked it up and killed 1,000 men with it. ¹⁶ Then Samson said,

"With a jawbone from a donkey,
I've made two piles of them.
With a jawbone from a donkey,
I've killed a thousand men."

¹⁷ When he finished saying this, he threw the jawbone away. He called that place Ramath Lehi [Jawbone Hill].

¹⁸ Samson was very thirsty. So he called out to the LORD and said, "You have given me this great victory. But now I'll die from thirst and fall into the power of godless men."

¹⁹ So God split open the hollow place at Lehi, and water gushed out. Samson drank some water. Then he was refreshed and revived. So he called the place En Hakkore [Spring of the One Who Calls Out]. It is still there at Lehi today.

²⁰ Samson judged Israel for 20 years during the time of the Philistines.

16 ¹ Samson went to Gaza. There he saw a prostitute and slept with her. ² The people of Gaza were told, "Samson's here!" So they surrounded the place and waited all night at the city gate to ambush him. They were quiet all night. They thought, "We'll kill him at dawn."

³ But Samson was in bed ˏwith the prostituteˏ only until midnight. Then he got up, took hold of the doors, door posts, and bar of the city gate and pulled them out. He carried them on his shoulders to the top of the hill facing Hebron.

Samson and Delilah

⁴ After ˏleaving Gazaˏ, he fell in love with a woman in the Sorek Valley. Her name was Delilah. ⁵ The Philistine rulers came to her and said, "Trick him, and find out what makes him so strong. Find out how we can overpower him. We want to tie him up in order to torture him. Each of us will give you 1,100 pieces of silver."

⁶ So Delilah said to Samson, "Please tell me what makes you so strong. How can you be tied up so that someone could torture you?"

⁷ Samson told her, "If someone ties me up with seven new bowstrings that are not dried out, I will be like any other man."

⁸ The Philistine rulers brought her seven new bowstrings that were not dried out. She tied Samson up with them. ⁹ Some men were hiding in the bedroom waiting for her ˏto tie him upˏ. Then she said to him, "Samson, the Philistines are attacking!" Samson snapped the bowstrings as a thread snaps when it touches fire. So no one found out why he was so strong.

¹⁰ Delilah told Samson, "Look, you're making fun of me by telling me lies. Now, tell me how you can be tied up."

¹¹ Samson told her, "If someone ties me up tightly with new ropes that have never been used, I will be like any other man."

¹² So Delilah took some new ropes and tied him up with them. Then she said to him, "Samson, the Philistines are attacking!" Some men were in her bedroom waiting to ambush him. But Samson tore the ropes off his arms as though they were strings.

¹³ Delilah told Samson, "You're still making fun of me by telling me lies. Tell me how you can be tied up."

Samson replied, "Just weave the seven braids of my hair with the other threads in the loom."

¹⁴ So Delilah tied his braids to the loom shuttle. Then she said to him, "Samson, the Philistines are attacking!" But Samson woke up and tore his braids and the threads out of the loom shuttle.

¹⁵ Delilah said to Samson, "How can you say that you love me when your heart isn't mine? You've made fun of me three times now, but you still haven't told me what makes you so strong."

¹⁶ Every day she made his life miserable with her questions. She pestered him until he wished he were dead. ¹⁷ Finally, he told her the truth. He told her, "Because I'm a Nazirite, no one has ever cut the hair on my head. I was dedicated to God before I was born. If my hair is ever shaved off, my strength will leave me. Then I'll be like any other man."

¹⁸ When Delilah realized that he had told her everything, she sent a message to the Philistine rulers, "Come here once more." (She did this because Samson had told her everything.) So the Philistine rulers arrived with the money in their hands.

¹⁹ Delilah put Samson to sleep on her lap. She called for a man to shave off his seven braids. Then she began to torture him because his strength had left him. ²⁰ She said, "Samson, the Philistines are attacking!" Samson woke up. He thought, "I'll get out of this as usual and shake myself free." (He didn't realize that the LORD had left him.) ²¹ The Philistines grabbed him. They poked out his eyes and took him to the prison in Gaza. They tied him up with double chains and made him grind grain in the mill there.

²² But his hair started to grow back as soon as it was shaved off.

²³ Now, the Philistine rulers gathered together to offer a great sacrifice to their god Dagon and to celebrate. They said, "Our god handed Samson, our enemy, over to us." ²⁴ When the people saw him, they praised their god. They said,

> "Our god gave our enemy,
>   destroyer of our land
>   and killer of so many,
>   into our very hand!"

²⁵ When all the Philistines were enjoying themselves, they said, "Call Samson in to entertain us."

Samson was called from the prison, and he made them laugh. They made him stand between two columns. ²⁶ Samson told the young man who was leading him by the hand, "Let me rest. Let me touch the columns on which the building stands so that I can lean against them." ²⁷ The building was filled with people. All the Philistine rulers were there. On the roof there were about three thousand men and women who watched Samson entertain them.

²⁸ Then Samson called to the LORD, "Almighty LORD, please remember me! God, give me strength just one more time! Let me get even with the Philistines for at least one of my two eyes." ²⁹ Samson felt the two middle columns on which the building stood. With his right hand on one column and his left on the other, he pushed hard against them. ³⁰ "Let me die with the Philistines," he said. With that, he pushed with all his might, and the building fell on the rulers and everyone in it. So he killed more Philistines when he died than he had when he was alive.

³¹ Then his relatives and his father's whole family went to Gaza. They took Samson and buried him between Zorah and Eshtaol in the tomb of his father Manoah.

Samson had judged Israel for 20 years.

Micah's Idolatry

17 ¹ There was a man named Micah from the mountain region of Ephraim. ² He told his mother, "You were upset about the 1,100 pieces of silver that were taken from you. I even heard you put a curse on them. Here's the silver. I took it!"

His mother said, "The LORD bless you, my son!"

³ So Micah gave the 1,100 pieces of silver back to his mother. Then his mother said, "I dedicate this silver to the LORD for my son's benefit. I want to make a carved idol and a metal idol. So now I'm giving the silver back to you."

⁴ When Micah returned the silver to his mother, she took 200 pieces of the silver and gave it to a silversmith. He made a carved idol and a metal idol. Both were placed in Micah's home. ⁵ Micah owned a shrine. He also made an ephod*ᵃ* and household idols. He ordained one of his

---

ᵃ 17:5 *Ephod* is a technical term for a part of the priest's clothes. Its exact usage and shape are unknown.

sons to be his priest. [6] In those days Israel didn't have a king. Everyone did whatever he considered right.

[7] There was a young man from Bethlehem in Judah. (Bethlehem belongs to the family of Judah.) He was a Levite but was living in Bethlehem. [8] This man left Bethlehem in Judah to live wherever he could find ˌa placeˌ. He came to Micah's house in the mountains of Ephraim to carry on his work.

[9] Micah asked him, "Where do you come from?"

The man told him, "I'm a Levite from Bethlehem in Judah. I'm going to live wherever I can find ˌa placeˌ."

[10] Micah told him, "Stay with me! Be a father and a priest to me. I'll give you ten pieces of silver a year, a set of clothes, and your room and board."

The Levite accepted the offer [11] and agreed to live with Micah. The young man became like one of Micah's sons. [12] Micah ordained the Levite. So the young man became his priest and a part of his family.

[13] Then Micah said, "Now I know that the LORD will be good to me. I have a Levite for my priest."

Micah Brings Idolatry to the Tribe of Dan

18 [1] In those days Israel didn't have a king. And in those days the tribe of Dan was looking for a place to live. Up to that time they had not received land as an inheritance among the tribes of Israel as they should have. [2] So all the families of Dan sent out five qualified men from Zorah and Eshtaol. They were sent to spy throughout the land and explore it. They were told, "Go and explore the land!"

They came to Micah's house in the mountains of Ephraim. They spent the night there. [3] While they were at Micah's house, they recognized the young Levite's voice. So they stopped to ask him, "Who brought you here? What are you doing here? Why are you here?"

[4] The Levite told them what Micah had done for him and added, "Micah hired me, so I became his priest."

[5] They said to him, "Please find out from God if our journey will be successful."

[6] The priest told them, "Go in peace. The LORD approves of your journey."

[7] The five men left there and came to the city of Laish. They saw that the people there lived without a care. These people were like the people of Sidon. They were peaceful and secure. There was no one around who threatened to take away their property by force. They were far from the people of Sidon and totally independent.

[8] The men went back to their relatives in Zorah and Eshtaol. Their relatives asked them, "What did you find?"

[9] They replied, "Get up, let's attack Laish. We saw the land. It's very good!

"Don't just sit there! Go at once and take the land. [10] When you get there, you will come to a secure people. The land is wide open to you. God will hand it over to you. It's a place where you will have everything you could want."

[11] So 600 men from the tribe of Dan left Zorah and Eshtaol armed for war. [12] They camped at Kiriath Jearim in Judah. This is why the place just west of Kiriath Jearim is still called Mahaneh Dan [The Camp of Dan] today. [13] From there they marched to the mountains of Ephraim as far as Micah's house. [14] Then the five men who had gone to spy throughout the land around Laish spoke up. They said to the other men of Dan, "Do you know that there's an ephod, a carved idol, a metal idol, and household idols in these houses? What do you think we should do?"

[15] So they stopped and entered Micah's house and greeted the young Levite. [16] The 600 armed men from Dan stood at the entrance to the city. [17] The five men who had gone to spy throughout the land went inside. They took the carved idol, the ephod, the household idols, and the metal idol. The priest stood at the entrance to the city with the 600 armed men. [18] When these men entered Micah's house and took the carved idol, the ephod, the household idols, and the metal idol, the priest asked them, "What are you doing?"

[19] They told him, "Keep quiet! Don't say a word! Come with us and be our father and priest. Is it better for you to be a priest for one man's house or for a tribe in Israel and its families?"

[20] The priest was content. He took the ephod, the household idols, and the carved idol and went with the people. [21] When they left, they put their children, livestock, and property in front of them.

[22] When they had already gone some distance from Micah's house, Micah's neighbors were called together to help him catch up to the people of Dan. [23] They shouted at them. But the people of Dan turned around and said to Micah, "What's your problem? Why did you call your neighbors together to attack us?"

²⁴ Micah answered, "You've taken away the gods I made as well as my priest. What do I have left? How can you say to me, 'What's your problem?' "

²⁵ The people of Dan replied, "Don't make another sound, or some violent men will attack you. Then you and your family will lose your lives." ²⁶ The people of Dan went on their way. Micah saw they were stronger than he was, so he turned around and went home.

²⁷ The people of Dan took what Micah had made and the man who had become his priest and went to the city of Laish. They attacked a peaceful and secure people, killed them all with swords, and burned their city. ²⁸ There was no one to rescue them because their city was far from Sidon and totally independent. The city was in the valley that belonged to Beth Rehob. The people of Dan rebuilt the city and lived in it. ²⁹ They named the city Dan in honor of their ancestor Dan, Israel's son. Originally, the city was called Laish.

³⁰ The people of Dan set up the carved idol for themselves. Jonathan (son of Gershom and grandson of Moses) and his descendants were priests for Dan's tribe until the people living in that land were taken captive. ³¹ So they set up for themselves the carved idol Micah had made. It stayed there the whole time the house of God was at Shiloh.

Sexual Immorality

19 ¹ In those days when Israel didn't have a king, there was a Levite who lived in a remote area in the mountains of Ephraim. He took a woman from Bethlehem in Judah to be his concubine.ᵃ ² But she was unfaithful to him. She left him and went to her father's home, to Bethlehem in Judah. When she had been there four months, ³ her husband went to persuade her to come back home. He took along his servant and two donkeys.

She took her husband into her father's house. Her father was thrilled to see him. ⁴ He made the Levite stay there with him, celebrating for three days.

⁵ On the fourth day they got up early in the morning to leave, but the woman's father told his son-in-law, "Eat something to keep up your strength and then you can go." ⁶ So they both sat down and ate and drank together. The woman's father said to his son-in-law, "Why don't you spend the night and enjoy yourself?" ⁷ When the Levite started to leave, his father-in-law urged him to stay another night, so he did.

⁸ On the morning of the fifth day, the Levite got up early to leave. The woman's father said, "Eat something to keep up your strength!" So they spent the time eating until late afternoon. ⁹ The Levite started to leave with his concubine and his servant. But his father-in-law said to him, "It's already evening. Please stay another night. It's too late to leave now. Stay here, and enjoy yourself. Tomorrow you can start out early to go home." ¹⁰ But the Levite refused to spend another night.

He left and traveled as far as Jebus (now called Jerusalem). He had with him two saddled donkeys and his concubine. ¹¹ By the time they were near Jebus, it was very late in the day. The Levite's servant said to him, "Let's go spend the night in Jebus."

¹² The Levite told him, "We'll never go into a city of foreigners. They're not Israelites. We'll go on to Gibeah." ¹³ He told his servant, "Let's go someplace else. We'll spend the night either at Gibeah or Ramah."

¹⁴ So they went on. It was sunset by the time they arrived at Gibeah. (Gibeah belonged to the tribe of Benjamin.) ¹⁵ They went to spend the night there. The Levite entered Gibeah and sat down in the city square, because no one offered to take them home for the night.

¹⁶ That evening an old man came into the city from his work in the fields. He was from the mountain region of Ephraim but lived in Gibeah. The other people who lived there were from the tribe of Benjamin. ¹⁷ He saw the traveler in the city square. So the old man asked, "Where do you come from? And where are you going?"

¹⁸ The Levite replied, "We're on our way from Bethlehem in Judah to a remote area in the mountains of Ephraim. That's where I'm from. I had gone to Bethlehem in Judah. Now I'm going to the LORD's house, but no one has offered to take me into his home. ¹⁹ We have straw and fodder for our donkeys. I even have bread and wine for myself, the woman, and my servant. We have everything we need."

²⁰ Then the old man said, "Welcome! Let me take care of your needs. Just don't spend the night in the city square." ²¹ So he took the Levite to his house and fed the donkeys. After they washed, they ate and drank.

²² While they were enjoying themselves, some worthless men from the city surrounded the house and pounded on the door. They told the old man, the owner of the house, "Bring out the man who came to your house so that we can have sex with him."

²³ The owner went out to them. He told them, "No, my friends! Please don't do anything so evil! This man is a guest in my home. Don't do such a godless thing! ²⁴ Here, let me bring out

---

ᵃ 19:1 A concubine is considered a wife except she has fewer rights under the law.

my virgin daughter and this man's concubine. Rape them, and do with them whatever you want. Just don't do such a godless thing to this man."

²⁵ But the men refused to listen to him. So the Levite grabbed his concubine and forced her outside. They had sex with her and abused her all night until morning. They let her go when the sun was coming up. ²⁶ At daybreak, the woman came to the door of the house where her husband was and collapsed. She was still there when it became light.

²⁷ Her husband got up in the morning, opened the doors of the house, and was about to leave. His wife (that is, his concubine) was lying at the door of the house with her hands on the doorstep. ²⁸ The Levite said to her, "Get up! Let's go!" But she did not answer. So he put her on the donkey and left for home.

²⁹ When he arrived home, he got a knife. He took his concubine and cut her limb from limb into 12 pieces. Then he sent the pieces throughout the territories of Israel.

³⁰ Everyone who saw it said, "Never has such a thing happened or been seen from the time the people of Israel came out of Egypt until today. Think about it! Form a plan, and speak out!"

Israel Slaughters the Tribe of Benjamin

20 ¹ All the people of Israel from Dan to Beersheba and from Gilead came to Mizpah. The congregation stood united in the presence of the LORD. ² The leaders of all Israel's tribes took their places in the congregation of God's people. There were 400,000 foot soldiers with swords. ³ The people of Benjamin heard that Israel had come to Mizpah.

The people of Israel said, "Tell us how such an evil thing could happen."

⁴ The Levite, the husband of the murdered woman, answered, "My concubine*ᵃ* and I went to Gibeah in Benjamin to spend the night. ⁵ The citizens of Gibeah came to attack me. They surrounded the house where I was staying that night. They intended to kill me, but instead, they raped my concubine until she died. ⁶ So I took my concubine and cut her into pieces. Then I sent the pieces throughout the territory of Israel. I did this because the citizens of Gibeah did this perverted and godless thing in Israel. ⁷ All you people of Israel, tell me what you think. Give me your advice right now!"

⁸ All the people stood united, saying, "None of us will go to his tent or return to his house. ⁹ This is what we'll do to Gibeah. We'll decide by lot who should attack it.*ᵇ* ¹⁰ We'll take one-tenth*ᶜ* of all the men from the tribes of Israel to get supplies for the troops. When the troops go to Gibeah in the territory of Benjamin they can punish the citizens of Gibeah for the godless thing they did in Israel." ¹¹ So all the men of Israel assembled. They stood united against the city.

¹² The tribes of Israel sent men throughout the tribe of Benjamin. They asked, "How could such an evil thing happen among you? ¹³ Now hand over those worthless men in Gibeah. We must put them to death to rid ourselves of this kind of evil in Israel."

But the men of Benjamin refused to listen to the men of Israel. ¹⁴ So the men of Benjamin went from their towns and assembled at Gibeah to go to war with the men of Israel. ¹⁵ That day 26,000 men armed with swords came from Benjamin's cities and organized for battle along with 700 of Gibeah's best men. ¹⁶ Out of all these troops, the best 700 were left-handed. Each could sling a stone at a hair and not miss.

¹⁷ The men of Israel (Benjamin not included) totaled 400,000 soldiers armed with swords.

¹⁸ The men of Israel went to Bethel. They asked God, "Who will go first to fight Benjamin?"

The LORD answered, "Judah will go first."

¹⁹ The Israelites got up early in the morning and camped at Gibeah. ²⁰ So the men of Israel went to war with the men of Benjamin. The Israelites formed their battle line facing Gibeah. ²¹ That day the men of Benjamin came out from Gibeah. They slaughtered 22,000 of Israel's men.

²² But Israel's troops got reinforcements. They formed their battle line where they had formed it on the first day. ²³ The Israelites went and cried in the presence of the LORD until evening. They asked the LORD, "Should we continue to wage war against our close relatives, the men of Benjamin?"

The LORD answered, "Go fight them!"

²⁴ On the second day the Israelite troops advanced against Benjamin. ²⁵ Benjamin went out from Gibeah to meet them. This time they slaughtered 18,000 men from Israel who were armed with swords. ²⁶ Then all the men of Israel and all the troops went to Bethel. They sat there and cried in the presence of the LORD and fasted that day until evening. Then they sacrificed burnt offerings and fellowship offerings to the LORD.

²⁷ In those days the ark of God's promise was at Bethel. ²⁸ (Phinehas, son of Eleazar and grandson of Aaron, served in front of it.) So the people of Israel asked the LORD, "Should we continue to wage war against our close relatives, the men of Benjamin? Or should we stop?"

ᵃ 20:4 A concubine is considered a wife except she has fewer rights under the law.   *ᵇ* 20:9 Hebrew meaning uncertain.
ᶜ 20:10 Or "10 out of every battalion, 100 out of every regiment, and 1,000 out of every company."

The LORD answered, "Go! Tomorrow I will hand them over to you."

²⁹ Then Israel placed troops in ambush around Gibeah. ³⁰ On the third day the men of Israel went to fight the men of Benjamin. They formed their battle line facing Gibeah as they did before. ³¹ The men of Benjamin went out to attack Israel's troops and were led away from the city. They started to inflict casualties as before. They killed about 30 men from Israel in the open country and on the roads to Bethel and Gibeah. ³² The men of Benjamin shouted, "They're defeated as before!"

But the men of Israel had said, "Let's flee in order to lead them from the city to the roads." ³³ So the men of Israel left their positions. They formed their battle line at Baal Tamar. Meanwhile, those waiting in ambush rushed from their position to the west of Gibeah. ³⁴ Then 10,000 of Israel's best men attacked Gibeah. The battle was fierce. But Benjamin's men didn't realize their own evil was about to overtake them. ³⁵ So the LORD defeated them in front of Israel. On that day the Israelites slaughtered 25,100 men from Benjamin who were armed with swords. ³⁶ Then the men of Benjamin realized they were defeated.

The Israelites had allowed the men of Benjamin to take back some ground. The Israelites relied on those waiting in ambush near Gibeah. ³⁷ The men in ambush quickly charged toward Gibeah. They spread out in the city and killed everyone. ³⁸ The men of Israel had arranged with those waiting in ambush that they would make a big column of smoke rise from the city as a signal. ³⁹ Then the men of Israel would turn around in the battle.

The men of Benjamin had already killed about 30 men of Israel. They even said, "Israel is completely defeated, just like in the first battle."

⁴⁰ But when the column of smoke started to rise from the city, the men of Benjamin turned around and saw the whole city going up in smoke. ⁴¹ Then the men of Israel turned around, and the men of Benjamin panicked. They realized that their evil had overtaken them. ⁴² They turned in front of Israel toward the road to the desert. But the battle caught up with the men of Benjamin. Israel slaughtered whoever came out of the cities on the road to the desert. ⁴³ They closed in on the men of Benjamin and pursued them without stopping. They overtook them east of Gibeah. ⁴⁴ There were 18,000 experienced men from Benjamin who died in battle. ⁴⁵ The others turned and fled into the desert to Rimmon Rock. But the men of Israel killed 5,000 more on the roads. They caught up with another 2,000 and killed them near Gidom. ⁴⁶ In all, 25,000 men from Benjamin who were armed with swords were killed that day. They were all experienced men.

⁴⁷ But 600 men turned and fled into the desert to Rimmon Rock. They stayed at Rimmon Rock for four months.

⁴⁸ Then the men of Israel went back to attack the rest of the territory of Benjamin. They killed all the people and cattle they found in every city. They also burned down every city they came to.

Israel Provides Wives for the Surviving Men of Benjamin

21 ¹ The men of Israel had taken this oath in Mizpah: "None of us will ever let our daughters marry anyone from Benjamin."

² The people went to Bethel and sat there in the presence of God until evening. They cried very loudly, ³ "LORD God of Israel, why has this happened among us? Why should one tribe be missing today in Israel?"

⁴ The next day the people got up early. They built an altar there and sacrificed burnt offerings and fellowship offerings. ⁵ The people asked, "Is there any family from Israel that did not take part in the assembly in the presence of the LORD?" They had taken a solemn oath that whoever had not come into the presence of the LORD at Mizpah must be put to death.

⁶ The people of Israel felt sorry for their close relatives, the men of Benjamin. They said, "Today one tribe has been excluded from Israel. ⁷ What will we do to provide wives for the men who are left? We swore to the LORD that we would not let any of our daughters marry them." ⁸ Then they asked, "Is there any family from Israel that did not come into the presence of the LORD at Mizpah?" No one from Jabesh Gilead had come to the assembly in the camp. ⁹ So they questioned the people, and there was no one there from Jabesh Gilead.

¹⁰ The congregation sent 12,000 soldiers. They ordered them, "Go and kill the people of Jabesh Gilead, including the women and children. ¹¹ These are your directions: Claim every female who has gone to bed with a man, and claim every male. Claim them for the LORD by destroying them."

¹² Among the people of Jabesh Gilead they found 400 unmarried women who had never gone to bed with a man. They brought them to the camp at Shiloh in Canaan.

¹³ Then the whole congregation sent messengers to the men of Benjamin at Rimmon Rock and offered them peace. ¹⁴ So the men of Benjamin came back at that time. These men were

given the women from Jabesh Gilead who had been kept alive. However, the congregation had not found enough women for all of them.

¹⁵ The congregation felt sorry for the people of Benjamin because the LORD had broken the unity of the tribes of Israel. ¹⁶ The leaders of the congregation asked, "What should we do to provide wives for the men who are left, since the women in Benjamin have been killed?"

¹⁷ Some said, "Benjamin's men who survived must be allowed to have families. No tribe of Israel should be wiped out. ¹⁸ However, we can't give them any of our daughters as wives. The people of Israel have taken an oath that whoever gives wives to the men of Benjamin is under a curse."

¹⁹ Others said, "Every year the LORD's festival is held at Shiloh. Shiloh is north of Bethel, east of the highway going from Bethel to Shechem, and south of Lebonah." ²⁰ So they told the men of Benjamin, "Hide in the vineyards and ²¹ watch. When the young women of Shiloh come out to take part in the dances, come out of the vineyards. Each of you catch a woman from Shiloh to be your wife. Then go back to the territory of Benjamin. ²² When their fathers or brothers come to us to complain, we'll tell them, 'Have pity on them, since we didn't provide a wife for each man in the battle. You won't be guilty because you didn't give them the wives yourselves.' "

²³ The men of Benjamin did just that. They captured the number of wives they needed from the women who were dancing and went home. So they rebuilt their cities and lived in them.

²⁴ At that time the people of Israel left. Each man went to his tribe and family. They all went home.

²⁵ In those days Israel didn't have a king. Everyone did whatever he considered right.

RUTH

The Move to Moab and Tragedy

1 ¹ In the days when the judges were ruling, there was a famine in the land. A man from Bethlehem in Judah went with his wife and two sons to live for a while in the country of Moab. ² The man's name was Elimelech, his wife's name was Naomi, and the names of their two sons were Mahlon and Chilion. They were descendants of Ephrathah from Bethlehem in the territory of Judah. They went to the country of Moab and lived there.

³ Now, Naomi's husband Elimelech died, and she was left alone with her two sons. ⁴ Each son married a woman from Moab. One son married a woman named Orpah, and the other son married a woman named Ruth. They lived there for about ten years. ⁵ Then both Mahlon and Chilion died as well. So Naomi was left alone, without her two sons or her husband.

Departure From Moab

⁶ Naomi and her daughters-in-law started on the way back from the country of Moab. (While they were still in Moab she heard that the Lord had come to help his people and give them food. ⁷ So she left the place where she had been living, and her two daughters-in-law went with her.) They began to walk back along the road to the territory of Judah.

Naomi's Appeal to Her Daughters-in-law

⁸ Then Naomi said to her two daughters-in-law, "Go back! Each of you should go back to your mother's home. May the Lord be as kind to you as you were to me and to our loved ones who have died. ⁹ May the Lord repay each of you so that you may find security in a home with a husband."

When she kissed them goodbye, they began to cry loudly. ¹⁰ They said to her, "We are going back with you to your people."

¹¹ But Naomi said, "Go back, my daughters. Why should you go with me? Do I have any more sons in my womb who could be your husbands? ¹² Go back, my daughters. Go, because I am too old to get married again. If I said that I still have hope. . . . And if I had a husband tonight. . . . And even if I gave birth to sons, ¹³ would you wait until they grew up and stay single just for them? No, my daughters. My bitterness is much worse than yours because the Lord has sent me so much trouble."

¹⁴ They began to cry loudly again. Then Orpah kissed her mother-in-law goodbye, but Ruth held on to her tightly. ¹⁵ Naomi said, "Look, your sister-in-law has gone back to her people and to her gods. Go back with your sister-in-law."

¹⁶ But Ruth answered, "Don't force me to leave you. Don't make me turn back from following you. Wherever you go, I will go, and wherever you stay, I will stay. Your people will be my people, and your God will be my God. ¹⁷ Wherever you die, I will die, and I will be buried there with you. May the Lord strike me down if anything but death separates you and me!"

¹⁸ When Naomi saw that Ruth was determined to go with her, she ended the conversation.

Naomi Arrives in Bethlehem

¹⁹ So both of them went on until they came to Bethlehem. When they entered Bethlehem, the whole town was excited about them. "This can't be Naomi, can it?" the women asked.

²⁰ She answered them, "Don't call me Naomi [Sweet]. Call me Mara [Bitter] because the Almighty has made my life very bitter. ²¹ I went away full, but the Lord has brought me back empty. Why do you call me Naomi when the LORD has tormented me and the Almighty has done evil to me?"

²² When Naomi came back from the country of Moab, Ruth, her Moabite daughter-in-law, came along with her. They happened to enter Bethlehem just when the barley harvest began.

Ruth Gathers Grain in the Field of Boaz

2 ¹ Naomi had a relative. He was from Elimelech's side of the family. He was a man of outstanding character named Boaz.

² Ruth, who was from Moab, said to Naomi, "Please let me go to the field of anyone who will be kind to me. There I will gather the grain left behind by the reapers."

Naomi told her, "Go, my daughter."

³ So Ruth went. She entered a field and gathered the grain left behind by the reapers. Now it happened that she ended up in the part of the field that belonged to Boaz, who was from Elimelech's family.

⁴ Just then, Boaz was coming from Bethlehem, and he said to his reapers, "May the LORD be with all of you!"

They answered him, "May the LORD bless you!"

⁵ Boaz asked the young man in charge of his reapers, "Who is this young woman?"

⁶ The young man answered, "She's a young Moabite woman who came back with Naomi from the country of Moab. ⁷ She said, 'Please let me gather grain. I will only gather among the bundles behind the reapers.' So she came here and has been on her feet from daybreak until now. She just sat down this minute in the shelter."

Boaz Speaks With Ruth

⁸ Boaz said to Ruth, "Listen, my daughter. Don't go in any other field to gather grain, and don't even leave this one. Stay here with my young women. ⁹ Watch where my men are reaping, and follow the young women in that field. I have ordered my young men not to touch you. When you're thirsty, go to the jars and drink some of the water that the young men have drawn."

¹⁰ Ruth immediately bowed down to the ground and said to him, "Why are you so helpful? Why are you paying attention to me? I'm only a foreigner."

¹¹ Boaz answered her, "People have told me about everything you have done for your mother-in-law after your husband died. They told me how you left your father and mother and the country where you were born. They also told me how you came to people that you didn't know before. ¹² May the LORD reward you for what you have done! May you receive a rich reward from the LORD God of Israel, under whose protection you have come for shelter."

¹³ Ruth replied, "Sir, may your kindness to me continue. You have comforted me and reassured me, and I'm not even one of your own servants."

¹⁴ When it was time to eat, Boaz told her, "Come here. Have some bread, and dip it into the sour wine." So she sat beside the reapers, and he handed her some roasted grain. She ate all she wanted and had some left over.

¹⁵ When she got up to gather grain, Boaz ordered his servants, "Let her gather grain even among the bundles. Don't give her any problems. ¹⁶ Even pull some grain out of the bundles and leave it for her to gather. Don't give her a hard time about it."

Ruth and Naomi Talk About Boaz

¹⁷ So Ruth gathered grain in the field until evening. Then she separated the grain from its husks. She had about half a bushel of barley. ¹⁸ She picked it up and went into the town, and her mother-in-law saw what she had gathered. Ruth also took out what she had left over from lunch and gave it to Naomi.

¹⁹ Her mother-in-law asked her, "Where did you gather grain today? Just where did you work? May the man who paid attention to you be blessed."

So Ruth told her mother-in-law about the person with whom she worked. She said, "The man I worked with today is named Boaz."

²⁰ Naomi said to her daughter-in-law, "May the Lord bless him. The Lord hasn't stopped being kind to people—living or dead." Then Naomi told her, "That man is a relative of ours. He is a close relative, one of those responsible for taking care of us."

²¹ Ruth, who was from Moab, told her, "He also said to me, 'Stay with my younger workers until they have finished the harvest.'"

²² Naomi told her daughter-in-law Ruth, "It's a good idea, my daughter, that you go out to the fields with his young women. If you go to someone else's field, you may be molested."

²³ So Ruth stayed with the young women who were working for Boaz. She gathered grain until both the barley harvest and the wheat harvest ended. And she continued to live with her mother-in-law.

Naomi's Plan for Ruth's Marriage

3 ¹ Naomi, Ruth's mother-in-law, said to her, "My daughter, shouldn't I try to look for a home that would be good for you? ² Isn't Boaz, whose young women you've been working with, our relative? He will be separating the barley from its husks on the threshing floorᵃ tonight. ³ Freshen up, put on some perfume, dress up, and go down to the threshing floor. Don't let him know that you're there until he's finished eating and drinking. ⁴ When he lies down, notice the

---

ᵃ 3:2 A threshing floor is an outdoor area where grain is separated from its husks.

place where he is lying. Then uncover his feet, and lie down there. He will make it clear what you must do."

⁵ Ruth answered her, "I will do whatever you say."

Ruth at the Feet of Boaz

⁶ Ruth went to the threshing floor and did exactly as her mother-in-law had directed her. ⁷ Boaz had eaten and drunk to his heart's content, so he went and lay at the edge of a pile of grain. Then she went over to him secretly, uncovered his feet, and lay down.

⁸ At midnight the man was shivering. When he turned over, he was surprised to see a woman lying at his feet. ⁹ "Who are you?" he asked.

She answered, "I am Ruth. Spread the corner of your garment over me because you are a close relative who can take care of me."

¹⁰ Boaz replied, "May the Lord bless you, my daughter. This last kindness—that you didn't go after the younger men, whether rich or poor—is better than the first. ¹¹ Don't be afraid, my daughter. I will do whatever you say. The whole town knows that you are a woman who has strength of character. ¹² It is true that I am a close relative of yours, but there is a relative closer than I. ¹³ Stay here tonight. In the morning if he will agree to take care of you, that is good. He can take care of you. But if he does not wish to take care of you, then, I solemnly swear, as the Lord lives, I will take care of you myself. Lie down until morning."

Ruth Returns to Bethlehem

¹⁴ So Ruth lay at his feet until morning. Then she got up early before anyone could be recognized. At that moment Boaz thought to himself, "I hope that no one will ever know that this woman came to the threshing floor."

¹⁵ Then Boaz told Ruth, "Stretch out the cape you're wearing and hold it tight." So she held it tight while he measured out six measures of barley. Then he placed it on her ͵back͵ and went into the town.

¹⁶ When Ruth returned, her mother-in-law Naomi asked, "How did things go, my daughter?"

Ruth told Naomi everything the man had done for her. ¹⁷ She said, "He gave me these six measures of barley and told me not to come back to you empty-handed."

¹⁸ Naomi replied, "Stay here, my daughter, until you know how it turns out. The man won't rest unless he settles this matter today."

Boaz Assumes Responsibility for Ruth

4 ¹ Boaz went to the city gate and sat there. Just then, the relative about whom he had spoken was passing by. Boaz said, "Please come over here and sit, my friend." So the man came over and sat down.

² Then Boaz chose ten men who were leaders of that city and said, "Sit here." So they also sat down.

³ Boaz said to the man, "Naomi, who has come back from the country of Moab, is selling the field that belonged to our relative Elimelech. ⁴ So I said that I would inform you. Buy it in the presence of these men sitting here and in the presence of the leaders of our people. If you wish to buy back the property, you can buy back the property. But if you do not wish to buy back the property, tell me. Then I will know that I am next in line because there is no other relative except me."

The man said, "I'll buy back the property."

⁵ Boaz continued, "When you buy the field from Naomi, you will also assume responsibility for the Moabite Ruth, the dead man's widow. This keeps the inheritance in the dead man's name."

⁶ The man replied, "In that case I cannot assume responsibility for her. If I did, I would ruin my inheritance. Take all my rights to buy back the property for yourself, because I cannot assume that responsibility."

⁷ (This is the way it used to be in Israel concerning buying back property and exchanging goods: In order to make every matter legal, a man would take off his sandal and give it to the other man. This was the way a contract was publicly approved in Israel.) ⁸ So when the man said to Boaz, "Buy it for yourself," he took off his sandal.

⁹ Then Boaz said to the leaders and to all the people, "Today you are witnesses that I have bought from Naomi all that belonged to Elimelech and all that belonged to Chilion and Mahlon. ¹⁰ In addition, I have bought as my wife the Moabite Ruth, Mahlon's widow, to keep the inheritance in the dead man's name. In this way the dead man's name will not be cut off from his relatives or from the public records. Today you are witnesses."

¹¹ All the people who were at the gate, including the leaders, said, "We are witnesses. May the Lord make this wife, who is coming into your home, like Rachel and Leah, both of whom

built our family of Israel. So show your strength of character in Ephrathah and make a name for yourself in Bethlehem. ¹²Also, from the descendant whom the Lord will give you from this young woman, may your family become like the family of Perez, the son whom Tamar gave birth to for Judah."

Ruth Gives Birth to David's Ancestor

¹³Then Boaz took Ruth home, and she became his wife. He slept with her, and the Lord gave her the ability to become pregnant. So she gave birth to a son.

¹⁴The women said to Naomi, "Praise the Lord, who has remembered today to give you someone who will take care of you. The child's name will be famous in Israel. ¹⁵He will bring you a new life and support you in your old age. Your daughter-in-law who loves you is better to you than seven sons, because she has given birth."

¹⁶Naomi took the child, held him on her lap, and became his guardian.

¹⁷The women in the neighborhood said, "Naomi has a son." So they gave him the name Obed.

He became the father of Jesse, who was the father of David.

The Ancestry of David

¹⁸This is the account of Perez and his family.
   Perez was the father of Hezron.
¹⁹**Hezron** was the father of Ram.
   Ram was the father of Amminadab.
²⁰**Amminadab** was the father of Nahshon.
   Nahshon was the father of Salmon.
²¹**Salmon** was the father of Boaz.
   Boaz was the father of Obed.
²²**Obed** was the father of Jesse.
   Jesse was the father of **David**.

1 SAMUEL

Samuel's Birth

1 ¹ There was a man named Elkanah from Ramathaim Zophim in the mountains of Ephraim. He was the son of Jeroham, grandson of Elihu, great-grandson of Tohu, whose father was Zuph from the tribe of Ephraim. ² Elkanah had two wives, one named Hannah, the other Peninnah. Peninnah had children, but Hannah had none. ³ Every year this man would go from his own city to worship and sacrifice to the LORD of Armies at Shiloh. Eli's two sons, Hophni and Phinehas, served there as priests of the LORD.

⁴ Whenever Elkanah offered a sacrifice, he would give portions of it to his wife Peninnah and all her sons and daughters. ⁵ He would also give one portion to Hannah because he loved her, even though the LORD had kept her from having children. ⁶ Because the LORD had made her unable to have children, her rival ⌊Peninnah⌋ tormented her endlessly in order to make her miserable. ⁷ This happened year after year. Whenever Hannah went to the LORD's house, Peninnah would make her miserable, and Hannah would cry and not eat. ⁸ Her husband Elkanah would ask her, "Hannah, why are you crying? Why haven't you eaten? Why are you so downhearted? Don't I mean more to you than ten sons?"

⁹ One day, after Hannah had something to eat and drink in Shiloh, she got up. (The priest Eli was sitting on a chair by the door of the Lord's temple.) ¹⁰ Though she was resentful, she prayed to the LORD while she cried. ¹¹ She made this vow, "LORD of Armies, if you will look at my misery, remember me, and give me a boy, then I will give him to you for as long as he lives. A razor will never be used on his head." ¹² While Hannah was praying a long time in front of the LORD, Eli was watching her mouth. ¹³ She was praying silently. Her voice couldn't be heard; only her lips were moving. Eli thought she was drunk.

¹⁴ "How long are you going to stay drunk?" Eli asked her. "Get rid of your wine."

¹⁵ Hannah responded, "No, sir. I'm not drunk. I'm depressed. I'm pouring out my heart to the LORD. ¹⁶ Don't take me to be a good-for-nothing woman. I was praying like this because I've been troubled and tormented."

¹⁷ Eli replied, "Go in peace, and may the God of Israel grant your request."

¹⁸ "May you continue to be kind to me," she said. Then the woman went her way and ate. She was no longer sad.ᵃ

¹⁹ Early in the morning Elkanah and his family got up and worshiped in front of the LORD. Then they returned home to Ramah. Elkanah made love to his wife Hannah, and the LORD remembered her. ²⁰ Hannah became pregnant and gave birth to a son. She named him Samuel [God Hears], because she said, "I asked the LORD for him."

Samuel's Childhood

²¹ To keep his vow, Elkanah and his entire household again went to offer the annual sacrifice to the LORD. ²² But Hannah didn't go. She told her husband, "I'll wait until the boy is weaned. Then I'll bring him and present him to the LORD, and he'll stay there permanently."

²³ "Do what you think is best," her husband Elkanah told her. "Wait until you've weaned him. May the LORD keep his word." The woman stayed and nursed her son until she had weaned him.

²⁴ As soon as she had weaned Samuel, she took him with her. She also brought a three-year-old bull,ᵇ half a bushel of flour, and a full wineskin. She brought him to the LORD's house at Shiloh while the boy was ⌊still⌋ a child. ²⁵ Then the parents butchered the bull and brought the child to Eli. ²⁶ "Sir," Hannah said, "as sure as you live, I'm the woman who stood here next to you and prayed to the LORD. ²⁷ I prayed for this child, and the LORD granted my request. ²⁸ In return, I am giving him to the LORD. He will be dedicated to the LORD for his whole life."

And they worshiped the LORD there.

ᵃ 1:18 English equivalent difficult.   ᵇ 1:24 Dead Sea Scrolls, Greek, Latin, Syriac; Masoretic Text "three bulls." (See verse 25.)

Hannah's Prayer

2 [1] Hannah prayed out loud,

> "My heart finds joy in the LORD.
> My head is lifted to the LORD.
> My mouth mocks my enemies.
>   I rejoice because you saved ˌmeˌ.
> [2] There is no one holy like the LORD.
> There is no one but you, O LORD.
> There is no Rock like our God.

> [3] "Do not boast
>   ˌorˌ let arrogance come out of your mouth
>   because the LORD is a God of knowledge,
>   and he weighs ˌourˌ actions.

> [4] "The bows of the warriors are broken,
>   but those who stumble are armed with strength.
> [5] Those who were well-fed hire themselves out for a piece of bread,
>   but those who were hungry hunger no more.
> Even the woman who was childless gives birth to seven children,
>   but the mother of many children grieves all alone.

> [6] "The LORD kills, and he gives life.
> He makes ˌpeopleˌ go down to the grave, and he raises them up ˌagainˌ.
> [7]   The LORD causes poverty and grants wealth.
> He humbles ˌpeopleˌ; he also promotes them.
> [8]   He raises the poor from the dust.
> He lifts the needy from the trash heap
>   in order to make them sit with nobles
>   and even to make them inherit a glorious throne.

> "The pillars of the earth are the LORD's.
> He has set the world on them.
> [9]   He safeguards the steps of his faithful ones,
>   but wicked people are silenced in darkness
>   because humans cannot succeed by their own strength.

> [10] "Those who oppose the LORD are broken into pieces.
> He thunders at them from the heavens.
> The LORD judges the ends of the earth.
>   He gives strength to his King
>   and lifts the head of his Messiah."[a]

[11] Then Elkanah went home to Ramah. But the boy ˌSamuelˌ served the LORD under the priest Eli.

The Sins of Eli's Sons

[12] Eli's sons, ˌHophni and Phinehas,ˌ were good-for-nothing priests; they had no faith in the LORD. [13] Now, this was how the priests dealt with the people who were offering sacrifices: While the meat was boiling, the priest's servant would come with a three-pronged fork in his hand. [14] Then he would stick it into the pot, kettle, cauldron, or pan. Whatever the fork brought up ˌfrom the potˌ belonged to the priest. This is what the priests did in Shiloh to all the people of Israel who came there ˌto sacrificeˌ. [15] But ˌin the case of Eli's sons,ˌ even before the people burned the fat, their servants would come and say to the man who was sacrificing, "Give the meat to the priest to roast. He doesn't want boiled meat from you. He wants it raw."

[16] If the man said to the servant, "First let the fat be burned, then take as much as you want," the servant would say to him, "Give it to me now, or I'll take it by force." [17] The sin of Eli's sons was a serious matter to the LORD, because these men were treating the offerings made to the LORD with contempt.

---

[a] 2:10 Or "Anointed One."

The Faithfulness of Samuel's Family

¹⁸ Meanwhile, Samuel continued to serve in front of the LORD. As a boy he was ˻already˼ wearing a linen ephod.^b ¹⁹ His mother would make him a robe and bring it to him every year when she went with her husband to offer the annual sacrifice.

²⁰ Eli would bless Elkanah (and his wife) and say, "May the LORD give you children from this woman in place of the one which she has given to the LORD." Then they would go home.

²¹ The LORD came to Hannah. She became pregnant ˻five times˼ and had three sons and two daughters. Meanwhile, the boy Samuel grew up in front of the LORD.

Eli's Family Condemned

²² Now, Eli was very old, and he had heard everything that his sons were doing to all Israel and that they were sleeping with the women who served at the gate of the tent of meeting. ²³ So he asked them, "Why are you doing such things? I hear about your wicked ways from all these people. ²⁴ Sons, the report that I hear the people of the LORD spreading isn't good! ²⁵ If one person sins against another, God will take care of him. However, when a person sins against the LORD, who will pray for him?" But they wouldn't listen to their father's warning— the LORD wanted to kill them.

²⁶ The boy Samuel continued to grow and gained the favor of the LORD and the people.

²⁷ Then a man of God came to Eli and said to him, "This is what the LORD says: I revealed myself to your ancestors when they were under Pharaoh's control in Egypt. ²⁸ I chose ˻one of your ancestors˼ out of all the tribes of Israel to serve as my priest, to sacrifice burnt offerings on my altar, to burn incense, and to wear the ephod in my presence. And I gave your ancestors the right to keep portions of the sacrifices that the people of Israel burned on the altar. ²⁹ Why do you show no respect for my sacrifices and grain offerings that I have commanded people to make in my dwelling place? Why do you honor your sons more than me by making yourselves fat on the best of all the sacrifices offered by my people Israel?

³⁰ "Therefore, the LORD God of Israel declares: I certainly thought that your family and your father's family would always live in my presence.

"But now the LORD declares: I promise that I will honor those who honor me, and those who despise me will be considered insignificant. ³¹ The time is coming when I will break your strength and the strength of your father's house so that no one will grow old in your family. ³² You will see distress in my dwelling place. In spite of the good that I do for Israel, no one in your family will live to an old age. ³³ Any man in your family whom I do not remove from my altar will have his eyes fail, and he^c will be heartbroken. And all your descendants will die in the prime of life. ³⁴ What is going to happen to your two sons, Hophni and Phinehas, will be a sign to you: Both of them will die on the same day. ³⁵ Then I will appoint a faithful priest to serve me. He will do everything I want him to do. I will give him faithful descendants, and he will always live as my anointed one. ³⁶ Then anyone who is left from your household will bow down in front of him to get a coin or a loaf of bread and say, 'Please appoint me to one of the priestly classes so that I may eat a piece of bread.' "

The LORD Calls Samuel

3 ¹ The boy Samuel was serving the LORD under Eli. In those days a prophecy from the LORD was rare; visions were infrequent. ² One night Eli was lying down in his room. His eyesight had begun to fail so that he couldn't see well. ³ The lamp in God's temple^a hadn't gone out yet, and Samuel was asleep in the temple of the LORD where the ark of God was kept.

⁴ Then the LORD called Samuel. "Here I am," Samuel responded. ⁵ He ran to Eli and said, "Here I am. You called me."

"I didn't call ˻you˼," Eli replied. "Go back to bed." So Samuel went back and lay down.

⁶ The LORD called Samuel again. Samuel got up, went to Eli, and said, "Here I am. You called me."

"I didn't call ˻you˼, son," he responded. "Go back to bed." ⁷ Samuel had no experience with the LORD, because the word of the LORD had not yet been revealed to him.

⁸ The LORD called Samuel a third time. Samuel got up, went to Eli, and said, "Here I am. You called me."

Then Eli realized that the LORD was calling the boy. ⁹ "Go, lie down," Eli told Samuel. "When he calls you, say, 'Speak, LORD. I'm listening.' " So Samuel went and lay down in his room.

¹⁰ The LORD came and stood there. He called as he had called the other times: "Samuel! Samuel!" And Samuel replied, "Speak. I'm listening."

---

^b 2:18 *Ephod* is a technical term for a part of the priest's clothes. Its exact usage and shape are unknown.   ^c 2:33 Dead Sea Scrolls and Greek; Masoretic Text "you."   ^a 3:3 According to Exodus 27:21, each night the priests were to light a lamp in the tent of meeting which was to burn from dusk to dawn.

¹¹ Then the LORD said to Samuel, "I am going to do something in Israel that will make the ears of everyone who hears it ring. ¹² On that day I am going to do to Eli and his family everything I said from beginning to end. ¹³ I told him that I would hand down a permanent judgment against his household because he knew about his sons' sin—that they were cursing God*ᵇ—but he didn't try to stop them. ¹⁴ That is why I have taken an oath concerning Eli's family line: No offering or sacrifice will ever ˌbe able toˌ make peace for the sins that Eli's family committed."

¹⁵ Samuel remained in bed until morning. Then he opened the doors of the LORD's house. But Samuel was afraid to tell Eli about the vision.

¹⁶ Then Eli called Samuel. "Samuel, my son!" he said.

"Here I am," he responded.

¹⁷ "What did the LORD tell you?" he asked. "Please don't hide anything from me. May God strike you dead if you hide anything he told you from me."

¹⁸ So Samuel told Eli everything.

Eli replied, "He is the LORD. May he do what he thinks is right."

¹⁹ Samuel grew up. The LORD was with him and didn't let any of his words go unfulfilled. ²⁰ All Israel from Dan to Beersheba knew Samuel was the LORD's appointed prophet. ²¹ The LORD continued to appear in Shiloh, since the LORD revealed himself to Samuel in Shiloh through the word of the LORD. And Samuel spoke to all Israel.ᶜ

The Army Sends for the Ark

4 ¹ Israel went to fight against the Philistines and camped near Ebenezer while the Philistines camped at Aphek. ² The Philistines organized their troops to meet Israel in battle. As the battle spread,ᵃ the Philistines defeated Israel and killed about 4,000 soldiers in the field.

³ When the troops came back to the camp, the leaders of Israel asked, "Why has the LORD used the Philistines to defeat us today? Let's get the ark of the LORD's promise from Shiloh so that he may be with us and save us from our enemies." ⁴ The troops sent some men who brought back the ark of the promise of the LORD of Armies—who is enthroned over the angels.ᵇ Eli's two sons, Hophni and Phinehas, came along with God's ark. ⁵ When the LORD's ark came into the camp, all Israel shouted so loudly that the earth rang with echoes.

⁶ As the Philistines heard the noise, they asked, "What's ˌallˌ this shouting in the Hebrew camp?" The Philistines found out that the LORD's ark had come into the camp. ⁷ Then they were frightened and said, "A god has come into ˌtheirˌ camp." They also said, "Oh no! Nothing like this has ever happened before. ⁸ We're in trouble now! Who can save us from the power of these mighty gods? These are the gods who struck the Egyptians with every kind of plague in the desert. ⁹ Be strong, Philistines, and act like men, or else you will serve the Hebrews as they served you. Act like men and fight."

The Ark Captured

¹⁰ The Philistines fought and defeated Israel. Every ˌIsraeliteˌ soldier fled to his tent. It was a major defeat in which 30,000 Israelite foot soldiers died. ¹¹ The ark of God was captured. Both of Eli's sons, Hophni and Phinehas, died.

¹² A man from the tribe of Benjamin ran from the front line of the battle. He went to Shiloh that day with his clothes torn and dirt on his head.ᶜ ¹³ When he arrived, Eli was sitting on a chair beside the road, watching. He was worried about the ark of God. The man went into the city to tell the news. The whole city cried out. ¹⁴ Hearing the cry, Eli asked, "What is this commotion?" So the man went quickly to tell Eli the news. ¹⁵ (Eli was 98 years old, and his eyesight had failed so that he couldn't see.)

¹⁶ The man told Eli, "I'm the one who came from the battle. I fled from the front line today."

"What happened, son?" Eli asked.

¹⁷ "Israel fled from the Philistines," the messenger answered. "Our troops suffered heavy casualties. Your two sons, Hophni and Phinehas, also are dead, and the ark of God has been captured."

¹⁸ When the messenger mentioned the ark of God, Eli fell from his chair backwards toward the gate. He broke his neck, and he died. (The man was old and heavy.) He had judgedᵈ Israel for 40 years.

¹⁹ His daughter-in-law, Phinehas' wife, was pregnant. When she heard the news that the ark of God had been captured and her father-in-law and her husband were dead, she went into labor prematurely and gave birth to a son. ²⁰ As she was dying, the women helping her said, "Don't be afraid. You've given birth to a son." But she didn't answer or pay attention.

ᵇ 3:13 Ancient scribal tradition, Greek, and Latin; Masoretic Text "cursing themselves." At times some scribes would alter the text when they thought it was disrespectful to God.   ᶜ 3:21 This sentence is the first part of 1 Samuel 4:1 in the Hebrew Bible and most English Bibles.   ᵃ 4:2 Hebrew meaning uncertain.   ᵇ 4:4 Or "cherubim."   ᶜ 4:12 Tearing one's clothes and throwing dirt on one's head was a sign of mourning.   ᵈ 4:18 Eli served as a God-appointed political/religious leader of Israel like the judges in the book of Judges.

[21] She called the boy Ichabod [No Glory], saying, "Israel's glory is gone," because the ark of God had been captured and because her father-in-law and her husband ˌdiedˌ. [22] "Israel's glory is gone because the ark of God has been captured," she said.

The Ark in Philistia

5 [1] After the Philistines had captured the ark of God, they brought it from Ebenezer to Ashdod. [2] They brought it into the temple of Dagon and placed it beside Dagon. [3] Early the next day the people of Ashdod saw that Dagon had fallen forward on the ground in front of the LORD's ark. So they took Dagon and put him back in his place. [4] But the next morning they saw that Dagon had ˌagainˌ fallen forward on the ground in front of the LORD's ark. Dagon's head and his two hands were cut off ˌand were lyingˌ on the temple's threshold. The rest of Dagon's body was intact.[a] [5] This is why the priests of Dagon and everyone else who comes into Dagon's temple in Ashdod still don't step on the temple's threshold.

[6] The LORD dealt harshly with the people of Ashdod. He destroyed them by striking the people in the vicinity of Ashdod with tumors. [7] When the people of Ashdod realized what was happening, they said, "The ark of the God of Israel must not stay with us, because their God is dealing harshly with us and our god Dagon." [8] The people of Ashdod called together all the Philistine rulers. "What should we do with the ark of the God of Israel?" they asked.

"The ark of the God of Israel must be taken to Gath," the rulers said.[b] So the people took the ark of the God of Israel there.

[9] But after they had moved it,[c] the LORD threw the city into a great panic: He struck all the important and unimportant people in the city, and they were covered with tumors. [10] So the people of Gath sent the ark of God to Ekron. But when the ark of God came to Ekron, the people of Ekron cried out, "They brought the ark of the God of Israel here to kill us." [11] They called together all the Philistine rulers. "Send the ark of the God of Israel away," they said. "Let it go back to its own place so that it won't kill us or our people." There was a fear of death throughout the city, where God dealt ˌwith themˌ very harshly. [12] The people who didn't die were struck with tumors. So the cry of the city went up to heaven.

The Ark Is Returned to Israel

6 [1] The ark of the LORD had been in Philistine territory seven months [2] when the Philistines called for priests and people skilled in explaining omens. The Philistines asked, "What should we do with the ark of the LORD? Tell us how to return it to its ˌproperˌ place."

[3] The priests answered, "If you're returning the ark of the God of Israel, don't send it away empty, but by all means return it to its ˌproperˌ place with a guilt offering. Then you will be healed, and you will know why he would not turn his anger away from you."

[4] The Philistines asked, "What kind of guilt offering should we give him?"

The priests answered, "Five gold tumors and five gold mice for the ˌfiveˌ Philistine rulers because all of you and your rulers suffer from the same plague. [5] Make models of your tumors and your mice which are destroying the country, and give glory to the God of Israel. Maybe he will no longer be so hard on you, your gods, and your country. [6] Why should you be as stubborn as the Egyptians and their Pharaoh were? After he toyed with the Egyptians, didn't they send the Israelites on their way? [7] Now get a new cart ready for two dairy cows that have never been yoked. Hitch the cows to the cart. Take their calves away, and leave them in their stall. [8] Take the ark of the LORD, and put it on the cart. Put the gold objects which you're giving him as a guilt offering in a box beside the ark. Send the cart on its way, [9] but then watch where it goes. If it goes up the road to its own country toward Beth Shemesh, then this disaster is the LORD's doing. But if not, we'll know it wasn't his hand that struck us, but what happened to us was an accident."

[10] The people did this. They took two dairy cows, hitched them to a cart, and shut the calves in the stall. [11] They put the ark of the LORD and the box containing the gold mice and the models of their hemorrhoids on the cart. [12] The cows went straight up the road to Beth Shemesh. Continually mooing, they stayed on the road and didn't turn right or left. The rulers of the Philistines followed them to the border of Beth Shemesh.

[13] The people of Beth Shemesh were harvesting wheat in the valley. When they looked up and saw the ark, they were overjoyed. [14] The cart came into the field of Joshua of Beth Shemesh and stopped there by a large rock. The people chopped up the wood of the cart and sacrificed the cows as a burnt offering to the LORD. [15] (The Levites had already taken down ˌfrom the cartˌ the ark of the LORD and the box which contained the gold objects and put them on the large rock.) The people of Beth Shemesh presented burnt offerings and sacrifices to the LORD that day. [16] After the five rulers of the Philistines saw this, they went back to Ekron that same day.

---

[a] 5:4 Greek; Masoretic Text "Only Dagon was left."   [b] 5:8 Dead Sea Scrolls, Greek read "The citizens of Gath said, 'Let the ark of God be brought to us.'"   [c] 5:9 Dead Sea Scrolls add "to Gath."

¹⁷ The gold hemorrhoids which the Philistines sent as a guilt offering to the LORD were for the cities of Ashdod, Gaza, Ashkelon, Gath, and Ekron. ¹⁸ And the number of gold mice was the same as the number of Philistine cities belonging to the five rulers, including walled cities and farm villages. The large rock on which they put the ark of the LORD is a witness.ᵃ It is still there today in the field of Joshua of Beth Shemesh.

¹⁹ God struck down some of the people from Beth Shemesh because they looked inside the ark of the LORD. He struck down 70 people.ᵇ The people mourned because the LORD struck them with such a great blow. ²⁰ The people of Beth Shemesh asked, "Who can stand before the LORD, this holy God? And to which people will he go when he leaves us?" ²¹ They sent messengers to the people living at Kiriath Jearim to say, "The Philistines have brought back the ark of the LORD. Come and take it back with you."

7 ¹ The men of Kiriath Jearim came to take the LORD's ark and brought it into Abinadab's house on the hill. They gave Abinadab's son Eleazar the holy occupation of guarding the LORD's ark.

Israel Admits It Has Sinned

² A long time passed after the ark came to stay at Kiriath Jearim. For 20 years the entire nation of Israel mournfully sought the LORD.

³ Samuel told the entire nation of Israel, "If you are returning to the LORD wholeheartedly, get rid of the foreign gods you have, including the statues of the goddess Astarte. Make a commitment to the LORD, and serve only him. Then he will rescue you from the Philistines."

⁴ So the Israelites got rid of the statues of Baal and Astarte and served only the LORD. ⁵ Then Samuel said, "Gather all the Israelites together at Mizpah, and I will pray to the LORD for you." ⁶ So the Israelites gathered together at Mizpah. They drew some water, poured it out in front of the LORD, and fasted that day. They confessed, "We have sinned against the LORD." So Samuel judged Israel in Mizpah.

The Philistines Defeated

⁷ When the Philistines heard that the Israelites had gathered at Mizpah, the Philistine rulers came to attack Israel. The Israelites heard ⸤about the Philistine plan⸥ and were afraid of them. ⁸ The Israelites said to Samuel, "Don't turn a deaf ear to us! Don't stop crying to the LORD our God for us! Ask him to save us from the Philistines!"

⁹ Then Samuel took a lamb, one still feeding on milk, and sacrificed it as a burnt offering to the LORD. Samuel cried to the LORD on behalf of Israel, and the LORD answered him. ¹⁰ While Samuel was sacrificing the burnt offering, the Philistines came to fight against Israel. On that day the LORD thundered loudly at the Philistines and threw them into such confusion that they were defeated by Israel. ¹¹ Israel's soldiers left Mizpah, pursued the Philistines, and killed them as far as Beth Car.

¹² Then Samuel took a rock and set it up between Mizpah and Shen. He named it Ebenezer [Rock of Help] and said, "Until now the LORD has helped us."

¹³ The power of the Philistines was crushed, so they didn't come into Israel's territory again. The LORD restrained the Philistines as long as Samuel lived. ¹⁴ The cities between Ekron and Gath which the Philistines took from Israel were returned to Israel. And Israel recovered the territory controlled by these cities from the Philistines. There was also peace between Israel and the Amorites.

¹⁵ Samuel judged Israel as long as he lived. ¹⁶ Every year he went around to Bethel, Gilgal, and Mizpah in order to judge Israel in all those places. ¹⁷ Then he would return home to Ramah. There, too, he judged Israel. And in Ramah he built an altar to the LORD.

Israel Rejects the LORD as King

8 ¹ When Samuel was old, he made his sons judges over Israel. ² The name of his firstborn son was Joel; the name of his second son was Abijah. They were judges in Beersheba. ³ The sons didn't follow their father's example but turned to dishonest ways of making money. They took bribes and denied people justice.

⁴ Then all the leaders of Israel gathered together and came to Samuel at Ramah. ⁵ They told him, "You're old, and your sons aren't following your example. Now appoint a king to judge us so that we will be like all the other nations."

⁶ But Samuel considered it wrong for them to request a king to judge them. So Samuel prayed to the LORD. ⁷ The LORD told Samuel, "Listen to everything the people are saying to you. They haven't rejected you; they've rejected me. ⁸ They're doing just what they've done since I

ᵃ 6:18 Hebrew meaning uncertain.   ᵇ 6:19 "70 people" is found in a few Hebrew manuscripts and the writings of the ancient Jewish historian Josephus. Masoretic Text and Greek read "50,070 people."

took them out of Egypt—leaving me and serving other gods. [9] Listen to them now, but be sure to warn them and tell them about the rights of a king."

[10] Then Samuel told the people who had asked him for a king everything the LORD had said. [11] Samuel said, "These are the rights of a king:

He will draft your sons, make them serve on his chariots and horses, and make them run ahead of his chariots.

[12] He will appoint them to be his officers over 1,000 or over 50 soldiers, to plow his ground and harvest his crops, and to make weapons and equipment for his chariots.

[13] He will take your daughters and have them make perfumes, cook, and bake.

[14] He will take the best of your fields, vineyards, and olive orchards and give them to his officials.

[15] He will take a tenth of your grain and wine and give it to his aids and officials.

[16] He will take your male and female slaves, your best cattle,[a] and your donkeys for his own use.

[17] He will take a tenth of your flocks.

In addition, you will be his servants.

[18] "When that day comes, you will cry out because of the king whom you have chosen for yourselves. The LORD will not answer you when that day comes."

[19] But the people refused to listen to Samuel. They said, "No, we want a king! [20] Then we, too, will be like all the other nations. Our king will judge us, lead us out ˻to war˼, and fight our battles."

[21] When Samuel heard everything the people had to say, he reported it privately to the LORD. [22] The LORD told him, "Listen to them, and give them a king."

Then Samuel told the people of Israel, "Go ˻back˼ to your own cities."

Saul Searches for His Father's Donkeys

9 [1] There was a man from the tribe of Benjamin whose name was Kish. He was a son of Abiel, grandson of Zeror, and great-grandson of Becorath, whose father was Aphiah, a descendant of Benjamin. Kish was a powerful man. [2] He had a son named Saul, a handsome, young man. No man in Israel was more handsome than Saul. He stood a head taller than everyone else.

[3] When some donkeys belonging to Saul's father Kish were lost, Kish told Saul, "Take one of the servants with you, and go look for the donkeys."

[4] They went through the mountains of Ephraim and the region of Shalisha without finding the donkeys. Then Saul and his servant went through the region of Shaalim, but the donkeys weren't there. The men went through the territory of Benjamin but ˻still˼ didn't find them. [5] When they came to the territory of Zuph, Saul told his servant who was with him, "Let's go back, or my father will stop worrying about the donkeys and worry about us ˻instead˼."

Saul Seeks Samuel's Advice

[6] The servant responded, "There's a man of God in this city, a highly respected man. Everything he says is sure to happen. Let's go there. Maybe he'll tell us which way we should go."

[7] "If we go," Saul asked his servant, "what could we bring the man since the food in our sacks is gone? There's no present we can bring the man of God. What do we have?"

[8] The servant again answered Saul, "Look, here! I have one-tenth of an ounce of silver. I'll give it to the man of God. Then he'll tell us where to find the donkeys."

[9] (Formerly in Israel, when a person went to ask God ˻a question˼, he would say, "Come, let's go to the seer," because a person we now call a prophet used to be called a seer.)

[10] Saul told his servant, "That's a good idea! Come on, let's go." They went to the city where the man of God was.

[11] As they were going up the hill to the city, they met girls coming out to get water. They asked the girls, "Is the seer here?"

[12] The girls answered, "He's there ahead of you. Hurry! He ˻just˼ went into the city today since the people are offering a sacrifice on the worship site. [13] As you go into the city, you can find him before he goes to the worship site to eat. The people will not eat until he comes, since he blesses the sacrifice. Then those who are invited may eat. Go. You should be able to find him now."

[14] So Saul and his servant went to the city. As they entered it, Samuel was coming toward them on his way to the worship site. [15] Now, the LORD had revealed the following message to Samuel one day before Saul came: [16] "About this time tomorrow I will send you a man from the territory of Benjamin. Anoint him to be ruler of my people Israel. He will save my people from the Philistines because I've seen my people's ˻suffering˼ and their cry has come to me."

[17] When Samuel noticed Saul, the LORD told him, "There's the man I told you about. This man will govern my people."

---

[a] 8:16 Greek; Masoretic Text "best young men."

18 Saul approached Samuel inside the gateway and said, "Please tell me where the seer's house is."

19 Samuel replied, "I'm the seer. Go ahead of me to the worship site. You will eat with me today. In the morning I'll let you go after I tell you all that's on your mind. **20** Don't trouble yourself about the donkeys that were lost three days ago because they've been found. Who will have all that is desirable in Israel? Won't it be you and your father's family?"

21 Saul replied, "I am a man from the tribe of Benjamin, the smallest tribe of Israel. My family is the most insignificant of all the families of the tribe of Benjamin. So why are you saying such things to me?"

22 Samuel brought Saul and his servant to the banquet hall and had them sit at the head of the guests—about 30 people. **23** Samuel said to the cook, "Bring me the portion of the sacrificial meat that I gave you and told you to put aside." **24** So the cook picked up the leg and thigh[a] and laid it in front of Saul. Samuel said, "This was kept in order to be laid in front of you. Eat it. When I invited people to the feast, I set it aside for you."[b] Saul ate with Samuel that day.

25 Then they left the worship site for the city. They spread blankets on the roof for Saul, and he slept there.[c]

26 At dawn Samuel called to Saul on the roof, "Get up! ˌIt's time forˌ me to send you away." Saul got up, and both he and Samuel went outside. **27** As they were going toward the city limits, Samuel told Saul, "Have the servant go ahead of you." (He went ahead.) "But you stay here, and I will tell you God's word."

Saul Anointed by Samuel

10 **1** Samuel took a flask of olive oil, poured it on Saul's head, kissed him, and said, "The LORD has anointed you to be ruler of his people Israel. You will rule his people and save them from all their enemies. This will be the sign that the LORD has anointed you[a] to be ruler of his people. **2** When you leave me today, two men will be at Rachel's grave on the border of Benjamin at Zelzah. They'll tell you, 'We've found the donkeys you went looking for. Your father no longer cares about them. Instead, he's worried about you. He keeps asking, "What can I do ˌto findˌ my son?" ' **3** Keep going until you come to the oak tree at Tabor. There you will find three men on their way to worship God at Bethel: One will be carrying three young goats, one will be carrying three loaves of bread, and one will be carrying a ˌfullˌ wineskin. **4** They will greet you and give you two loaves of bread, which you should accept from them. **5** After that, you will come to the hill of God, where the Philistines have a military post. When you arrive at the city, you will meet a group of prophets prophesying as they come from the worship site. They will be led by men playing a harp, a tambourine, a flute, and a lyre. **6** Then the LORD's Spirit will come over you. You will be a different person while you prophesy with them. **7** When these signs happen to you, do what you must, because God is with you. **8** Go ahead of me to Gilgal. Then I will come to sacrifice burnt offerings and make fellowship offerings. Wait seven days until I come to tell you what to do."

Saul's Anointing Confirmed by Signs

9 When Saul turned around to leave Samuel, God changed Saul's attitude. That day all these signs happened. **10** When Saul came to the hill, a group of prophets came to meet him, and God's Spirit came over him. He prophesied with them. **11** When all who had known him before saw how he prophesied with the prophets, the people asked one another, "What has happened to the son of Kish? Is Saul one of the prophets?" **12** But a man from that place asked, "But who's the chief prophet?" So it became a proverb: "Is Saul one of the prophets?" **13** And when he had finished prophesying, he came to the worship site.

14 Saul's uncle asked him and his servant, "Where did you go?"

Saul answered, "To look for the donkeys, and when we couldn't find them, we went to Samuel."

15 Saul's uncle said, "Please tell me what Samuel said to you."

16 "He assured us the donkeys had been found," Saul answered his uncle. But Saul didn't tell him what Samuel said ˌabout his becoming kingˌ.

The LORD Chooses Saul

17 Samuel called the people to ˌcome into the presence ofˌ the LORD at Mizpah. **18** He said to the Israelites, "This is what the LORD God of Israel says: I brought Israel out of Egypt and rescued you from the power of the Egyptians and all the kings who were oppressing you. **19** But now you have rejected your God, who saves you from all your troubles and distresses. You said, 'No! Place a king over us.' Now then, stand in front of the LORD by your tribes and family groups."

---

a 9:24 Hebrew meaning uncertain.   *b* 9:24 Hebrew meaning of this sentence uncertain.   *c* 9:25 Greek; Masoretic Text reads ". . . for the city, and he spoke with Saul on the roof, and they got up early."   *a* 10:1 "to be ruler of his people. . . has anointed you" Greek; Masoretic Text omits these words.

[20] When Samuel had all the tribes of Israel come forward, the tribe of Benjamin was chosen. [21] When he had the tribe of Benjamin come forward by families, the family of Matri was chosen. Then Saul, the son of Kish, was chosen. They looked for him but couldn't find him. [22] They asked the LORD again, "Has he arrived here yet?"

The LORD answered, "He's hiding among the baggage."

[23] They ran and got him from there. As he stood among the people, he was a head taller than everyone else. [24] Samuel asked the people, "Do you see whom the LORD has chosen? There is no one like him among all the people."

Then all the people shouted, "Long live the king!"

[25] Samuel explained the laws concerning kingship to the people. He wrote the laws on a scroll, which he placed in front of the LORD. Then Samuel sent the people back to their homes. [26] Saul also went home to Gibeah. With him went some soldiers whose hearts God had touched. [27] However, some good-for-nothing people asked, "How can this man save us?" They despised him and wouldn't bring him presents, but he didn't respond.

Saul Defeats Ammon

11 [1] King Nahash of Ammon was severely oppressing the tribes of Gad and Reuben. He would poke out everyone's right eye and allow no one to rescue Israel. There was no one among the Israelites east of the Jordan River whose right eye King Nahash of Ammon had not poked out. However, seven thousand men had escaped from the Ammonites and gone to Jabesh Gilead. About a month later[a] Nahash the Ammonite blockaded Jabesh Gilead. All the men of Jabesh said to Nahash, "Make a treaty with us, and we'll serve you."

[2] Nahash the Ammonite responded, "I'll make a treaty with you on this one condition: I'll poke out everyone's right eye and bring disgrace on all Israel."

[3] The leaders of Jabesh told him, "Give us seven days so that we can send messengers throughout the territory of Israel. And if there's no one to save us, we'll surrender to you."

[4] The messengers came to Saul's town, Gibeah. When they told the people the news, the people cried loudly. [5] Just then Saul was coming from the field behind some oxen. "Why are these people crying?" Saul asked. So they told him the news about the men of Jabesh. [6] When he heard this news, God's Spirit came over him, and he became very angry. [7] Saul took a pair of oxen, cut them in pieces, and sent them by messengers throughout the territory of Israel with the following message: "This is what will be done to the oxen of anyone who doesn't follow Saul and Samuel ˌinto battleˌ." So the people became terrified by the LORD, and they came out united ˌbehind Saulˌ. [8] When Saul counted them at Bezek, there were 300,000 troops from Israel and 30,000 troops from Judah. [9] They told the messengers who had come, "This is what you are to say to the men of Jabesh Gilead: 'Tomorrow, by the time the sun gets hot, you will be rescued.' " When the men of Jabesh received the message, they were overjoyed.

[10] They said ˌto Nahashˌ, "Tomorrow we'll surrender to you, and you may do to us whatever you think is right."

[11] The next day Saul arranged the army in three divisions. They came into the ˌAmmoniteˌ camp during the morning hours and continued to defeat the Ammonites until it got hot that day. The survivors were so scattered that no two of them were left together.

[12] Then the people asked Samuel, "Who said that Saul shouldn't rule us? Let us have them, and we'll kill them."

[13] But Saul said, "No one will be killed today, because today the LORD saved Israel."

[14] Samuel told the troops, "Come, let's go to Gilgal and there acknowledge ˌSaul'sˌ kingship." [15] Then all the troops went to Gilgal, and there in the LORD's presence, they confirmed Saul as their king. There they sacrificed fellowship offerings to the LORD. Saul and all of Israel's soldiers celebrated.

Samuel's Spotless Leadership

12 [1] Then Samuel said to all Israel, "I have listened to everything you have said to me and appointed a king over you. [2] And now, here is the king who will lead you. I am old and gray, but my sons are with you. I have led you from my youth until this day. [3] Here I am. Testify against me in front of the LORD and in front of his anointed king. Did I take anyone's ox? Did I take anyone's donkey? Did I cheat or oppress anyone? Did I take a bribe from anyone to look the other way? ˌIf so,ˌ I will give it all back."

[4] They answered, "You didn't cheat us, oppress us, or take anything from anyone."

[5] Samuel told them, "The LORD is a witness to what you've said, and his anointed king is a witness today that you've found nothing in my hands."

"He is a witness," they answered.

---

[a] 11:1 Dead Sea Scrolls and the ancient Jewish historian Josephus add this first part of verse 1 between chapters 10 and 11 (usually denoted as verse 10:27b).

⁶ Samuel told the people, "The LORD appointed Moses and Aaron and brought your ancestors out of Egypt. ⁷ Now, stand up while I put you on trial in front of the LORD and cite all the righteous things the LORD did for you and your ancestors. ⁸ When your ancestors went with Jacob to Egypt ˌand were oppressed˷, they cried out to the LORD, who sent Moses and Aaron to bring them out of Egypt. The LORD settled them in this place. ⁹ But they forgot the LORD their God. So he handed them over to Sisera, who was the commander of the army of Hazor, to the Philistines, and to the king of Moab. All of them fought against your ancestors. ¹⁰ Then they cried out to the LORD and said, 'We have sinned. We have abandoned the LORD and served other gods and goddesses—the Baals and the Astartes. But rescue us from our enemies now, and we will serve you.'

¹¹ "Then the LORD sent Jerubbaal, Bedan, Jephthah, and Samuel and rescued you from your enemies on every side so that you could live securely. ¹² But when you saw King Nahash of Ammon coming to attack you, you told me, 'No, a king should rule over us,' though the LORD your God was your king.

The New Kingship

¹³ "Now, here is the king you have chosen, the one you asked for. See, the LORD has put a king over you. ¹⁴ If you fear the LORD, serve him, obey him, and don't rebel against what he says, then you and your king will follow the LORD your God. ¹⁵ But if you don't obey the LORD, if you rebel against what he says, then the LORD will be against you as he was against your ancestors. ¹⁶ Now then, stand still and watch this great thing the LORD is going to do right before your eyes. ¹⁷ Isn't the wheat being harvested today? I will call on the LORD, and he'll send thunder and rain. Then you will realize what a wicked thing you did in the LORD's presence when you asked for a king."

¹⁸ Then Samuel called on the LORD. That day the LORD sent thunder and rain so that all the people feared the LORD and Samuel very much.

¹⁹ All the people pleaded with Samuel, "Pray to the LORD your God for us so that we will not die. We have added ˌanother˷ evil thing to all our other sins by asking for a king."

²⁰ "Don't be afraid," Samuel told the people. "You did do all these evil things. But don't turn away from the LORD. Instead, serve the LORD wholeheartedly. ²¹ Don't turn away to follow other gods. They can't help or rescue you, because they don't exist. ²² For the sake of his great name, the LORD will not abandon his people, because the LORD wants to make you his people. ²³ It would be unthinkable for me to sin against the LORD by failing to pray for you. I will go on teaching you the way that is good and right. ²⁴ Fear the LORD, and serve him sincerely. Consider the great things he did for you. ²⁵ But if you go on doing what is evil, you and your king will be wiped out."

The LORD Rejects Saul as King

13 ¹ Saul was ˌthirty˷ years old when he became king, and he was king of Israel ˌforty-two˷ years.ᵃ

² Saul chose 3,000 men from Israel; 2,000 of them were stationed with Saul at Michmash and in the mountains of Bethel, and 1,000 were stationed with Jonathan at Gibeah in Benjamin. But the rest of the people he sent home.

³ Jonathan defeated the Philistine troops at Geba, and the Philistines heard about it. With the sounding of the ram's horn throughout the land, Saul announced, "Listen, Hebrews!" ⁴ (So all Israel listened.) "I, Saul, have defeated the Philistine troops, and now Israel has become offensive to the Philistines!" All the troops rallied behind Saul at Gilgal.

⁵ The Philistines assembled to fight against Israel. They had 30,000 chariots, 6,000 horsemen, and as many soldiers as the sand on the seashore. They camped at Michmash, east of Beth Aven. ⁶ When the Israelites saw they were in trouble because the army was hard-pressed, they hid in caves, in thorny thickets, among rocks, in pits, and in cisterns. ⁷ Some Hebrews crossed the Jordan River into the territory of Gad and Gilead. But Saul remained in Gilgal, and all the people who followed him trembled ˌin fear˷.

⁸ He waited seven days, the time set by Samuel. But Samuel had not come to Gilgal, and the troops began to scatter. ⁹ Then Saul said, "Bring me the animals for the burnt offering and the fellowship offerings." So he sacrificed the burnt offering. ¹⁰ As he finished sacrificing the burnt offering, Samuel came, and Saul went to greet him.

¹¹ Samuel asked, "What have you done?"

Saul replied, "I saw the troops were scattering. You didn't come when you said you would, and the Philistines were assembling at Michmash. ¹² So I thought, 'Now, the Philistines will come against me at Gilgal, but I haven't sought the LORD's favor.' I felt pressured into sacrificing the burnt offering."

ᵃ 13:1 The text of 1 Samuel 13:1 is problematic in all traditions. Some late Greek manuscripts state Saul was 30 years old when he became king. The ancient Jewish historian Josephus and Acts 13:21 state that Saul ruled for 40 years.

¹³ "You did a foolish thing," Samuel told Saul. "You didn't follow the command of the LORD your God. ⌐If you had,⌐ the LORD would have established your kingdom over Israel permanently. ¹⁴ But now your kingdom will not last. The LORD has searched for a man after his own heart. The LORD has appointed him as ruler of his people, because you didn't follow the command of the LORD."

¹⁵ Samuel left Gilgal. The rest of the people followed Saul to meet the soldiers. They went from Gilgal*ᵇ* to Gibeah in Benjamin, where Saul counted the troops who were still with him— about 600 men. ¹⁶ Saul, his son Jonathan, and the troops who were with them stayed at Geba in Benjamin while the Philistines camped at Michmash.

¹⁷ Raiding parties left the Philistine camp in three columns. One column turned onto the road to Ophrah to the region of Shual. ¹⁸ Another column turned onto the road to Beth Horon. And one turned onto the road toward the region that overlooks the valley of Zeboim and the desert.

¹⁹ No blacksmith could be found in the entire land of Israel. In this way the Philistines kept the Hebrews from making swords and spears. ²⁰ Everyone in Israel had to go to the Philistines to sharpen the blade of his plow, his mattock, ax, or sickle. ²¹ The price was a pim*ᶜ* for plow blades and mattocks, and one-tenth of an ounce of silver to sharpen a mattock*ᵈ* or set a metal point on a cattle-prod. ²² So on the day of battle, not one sword or spear could be found among all the troops who were with Saul and Jonathan. But Saul and his son Jonathan had them.

²³ Now, Philistine troops had gone out to the pass at Michmash.

Jonathan Defeats the Philistines

14 ¹ One day Saul's son Jonathan said to his armorbearer, "Let's go to the Philistine military post on the other side." But Jonathan didn't tell his father ⌐he was going⌐.

² Saul was staying on the outskirts of Gibeah under a pomegranate tree at Migron. He had with him about 600 men ³ in addition to Ahijah, the son of Ichabod's brother Ahitub, who was the son of Phinehas and the grandson of Eli, the LORD's priest at Shiloh. Ahijah was wearing the priestly ephod.*ᵃ*

The troops didn't know Jonathan had left. ⁴ There was a cliff on each side of the mountain pass where Jonathan searched for a way to cross over to attack the Philistine military post. The name of one ⌐cliff⌐ was Bozez, and the name of the other was Seneh. ⁵ One cliff stood like a pillar on the north facing Michmash, the other stood south facing Geba.

⁶ Jonathan said to his armorbearer, "Let's go to the military post of these uncircumcised people. Maybe the LORD will act on our behalf. The LORD can win a victory with a few men as well as with many."

⁷ His armorbearer answered him, "Do whatever you have in mind. Go ahead! I agree with you."

⁸ Jonathan continued, "Listen, we'll cross over to the Philistines and show ourselves to them. ⁹ If they say to us, 'Stay where you are until we come to you,' then we'll stay where we are and not go up to them. ¹⁰ But if they say to us, 'Come up here,' then we'll go up, because that will be our sign that the LORD has handed them over to us."

¹¹ So both of them showed themselves to the Philistine troops. The Philistines said, "Look, some Hebrews are coming out of the holes they were hiding in."

¹² "Come up here," the men of the military post said to Jonathan and his armorbearer. "We have something to show you."

Jonathan told his armorbearer, "Follow me up ⌐to the military post⌐ because the LORD has handed the troops over to Israel."

¹³ Jonathan climbed up ⌐the cliff⌐, and his armorbearer followed him. Jonathan struck down the Philistines. His armorbearer, who was behind him, finished killing them. ¹⁴ In their first slaughter Jonathan and his armorbearer killed about twenty men within about a hundred yards. ¹⁵ There was panic among the army in the field and all the troops in the military post. The raiding party also trembled ⌐in fear⌐. The earth shook, and there was a panic sent from God.

¹⁶ Saul's watchmen at Gibeah in Benjamin could see the crowd ⌐in the Philistine camp⌐ dispersing in all directions.

¹⁷ "Look around," Saul told the troops who were with him, "and see who has left ⌐our camp⌐." They looked and found that Jonathan and his armorbearer were not there.

¹⁸ Then Saul said to Ahijah, "Bring the priestly ephod," because Ahijah carried the ephod in front of Israel that day.*ᵇ* ¹⁹ While Saul was talking to the priest, the confusion in the Philistine camp grew worse and worse. Then Saul said to the priest, "Remove your hand ⌐from the ephod⌐."*ᶜ* ²⁰ Saul and all the troops with him assembled and went into battle. They found Philistine soldiers killing their fellow soldiers in wild confusion. ²¹ The Hebrews who had been

---

ᵇ 13:15 "Samuel . . . from Gilgal" Greek; Masoretic Text omits these words.   *ᶜ* 13:21 A pim was a measure of weight.
ᵈ 13:21 Hebrew meaning of "one-tenth . . . a mattock" uncertain.   *ᵃ* 14:3 *Ephod* is a technical term for a part of the priest's clothes. Its exact usage and shape are unknown.   *ᵇ* 14:18 Greek; Masoretic Text problematic: "Bring the ark of God because the ark of God that day and the sons of Israel."   *ᶜ* 14:19 Hebrew meaning uncertain.

with the Philistines before this and had been stationed in the camp now joined the Israelites who were with Saul and Jonathan. **²²** When all the men of Israel who had been hiding in the mountains of Ephraim heard that the Philistines were fleeing, they also pursued the Philistines in battle. **²³** So the LORD saved Israel that day.

Saul's Curse

Now, the battle moved beyond Beth Aven. **²⁴** Israel's soldiers were driven hard that day. Saul made the troops swear, "Cursed is anyone who eats food before the evening comes and before I've gotten revenge on my enemies." So none of his troops tasted any food. **²⁵** The entire land had honeycombs,*ᵈ* and there was honey on the ground. **²⁶** When the troops entered the woods, the honey was flowing. But no one put his hand to his mouth, because the troops were afraid of violating their oath.

²⁷ Jonathan hadn't heard that his father forced the troops to take an oath. So he stretched out the tip of the staff he had in his hand and dipped it in the honeycomb. When he put it to his mouth, his eyes lit up. **²⁸** Then one of the soldiers told him, "Your father forced the troops to take a solemn oath: 'Cursed is anyone who eats food today.' "

Now, the army was exhausted. **²⁹** Jonathan answered, "My father has brought trouble to the country. See how my eyes lit up when I tasted a little of this honey? **³⁰** If only the troops had eaten some of the enemies' food, which they found today. We would have killed more Philistines."

³¹ That day they struck down the Philistines from Michmash to Aijalon, but the troops were thoroughly exhausted. **³²** So the troops seized the Philistines' belongings. They took sheep, cows, and calves, and butchered them on the ground. The troops ate the meat with blood still in it. **³³** Some ˻soldiers˼ told Saul, "The troops are sinning against the LORD by eating meat with blood in it."

Saul replied, "You have been unfaithful. Roll a large rock over to me now." **³⁴** Then Saul said, "Spread out through the troops, and tell them, 'Each of you, bring me your ox or your sheep, and butcher it here, and eat. But don't sin against the LORD by eating meat with blood in it.' "

So each of the soldiers brought his ox with him that night and butchered it there.

³⁵ Then Saul built an altar to the LORD; it was the first time he had built an altar to the LORD.

³⁶ Saul said ˻to his men˼, "Let's attack the Philistines tonight and take their possessions until the light of dawn. And let's not leave any of them ˻alive˼."

"Do whatever you think is best," they responded.

But the priest said, "Let's consult God first."

³⁷ Then Saul asked God, "Should I attack the Philistines? Will you hand them over to Israel?" But he received no answer that day.

³⁸ So Saul ordered all the leaders of the troops, "Come here! Find out what sin was committed today. **³⁹** I solemnly swear, as the LORD and Savior of Israel lives, even if it is my son Jonathan ˻who did it˼, he must die." But not one of the soldiers replied.

⁴⁰ Saul told all Israel, "You stand on one side, and my son Jonathan and I will stand on the other side."

"Do whatever you think is best," the troops responded to Saul.

⁴¹ Then Saul said to the LORD, "O God of Israel, why didn't you answer me today? If this sin is mine or my son Jonathan's, LORD God of Israel, ˻let the priest˼ draw Urim. But if it is in your people Israel,*ᵉ* ˻let him˼ draw Thummim." Jonathan and Saul were chosen, and the people were freed ˻from guilt˼.

⁴² "Choose between me and my son Jonathan," Saul said. Then Jonathan was chosen.

⁴³ "Tell me," Saul asked Jonathan. "What did you do?"

So Jonathan told him, "I tasted a little honey on the tip of the staff I had in my hand. And for that I am to die?"

⁴⁴ Saul said, "May God do worse things to me than are in this curse if you do not die, Jonathan!"

⁴⁵ The troops asked Saul, "Should Jonathan die after he has won this great victory in Israel? That would be unthinkable! We solemnly swear, as the LORD lives, not a single hair of his head will fall to the ground, because he has done this with God's help today." So the troops rescued Jonathan from death. **⁴⁶** Then Saul stopped pursuing the Philistines. So the Philistines returned to their own land.

Summary of Saul's Reign

⁴⁷ When Saul had taken over the kingdom of Israel, he fought against his enemies on every side—against Moab, the Ammonites, Edom, the kings of Zobah, and the Philistines. Wherever

---

ᵈ 14:25 Or "The entire land came into the woods."   *ᵉ* 14:41 "Why didn't you . . . your people Israel" Greek, Latin; Masoretic Text omits these words.

he turned, he was victorious. [48] He acted forcefully and defeated Amalek. He rescued Israel from the enemies who looted their possessions.

[49] Saul's sons were Jonathan, Ishvi, and Malchishua. The names of his two daughters were Merab (the firstborn daughter) and Michal (the younger daughter). [50] The name of Saul's wife was Ahinoam, the daughter of Ahimaaz. The name of the commander of his army was Abner, the son of Saul's uncle Ner. [51] Kish (Saul's father) and Ner (Abner's father) were the sons of Abiel.

[52] There was intense warfare with the Philistines as long as Saul lived. Whenever any warrior or any skilled fighting man came to Saul's attention, Saul would enlist him in the army.

Saul Disobeys the Lord

15 [1] Samuel told Saul, "The LORD sent me to anoint you king of his people Israel. Now listen to the LORD's words. [2] This is what the LORD of Armies says: I will punish Amalek for what they did to Israel. They blocked Israel's way after the Israelites came from Egypt. [3] Now go and attack Amalek. Claim everything they have for God by destroying it. Don't spare them, but kill men and women, infants and children, cows and sheep, camels and donkeys."

[4] Saul organized the troops, and he counted them at Telaim: 200,000 foot soldiers and 10,000 men from Judah. [5] Saul went to the city of Amalek and set an ambush in the valley. [6] Then Saul said to the Kenites, "Get away from the Amalekites so that I won't destroy you with them. You were kind to all the Israelites when they came from Egypt." So the Kenites left the Amalekites.

[7] Saul attacked the Amalekites from Havilah to Shur, east of Egypt. [8] He captured King Agag of Amalek alive. But he claimed all the people for God by destroying them. [9] Saul and the army spared Agag and the best sheep and cows, the fattened animals, the lambs, and all the best ˌpropertyˏ. The army refused to claim them for God by destroying them. But everything that was worthless and weak the army did claim for God and destroy.

The Lord Rejects Saul

[10] Then the LORD spoke to Samuel: [11] "I regret that I made Saul king. He turned away from me and did not carry out my instructions." Samuel was angry, and he prayed to the LORD all night. [12] Early in the morning he got up to meet Saul. Samuel was told, "Saul went to Carmel to set up a monument in his honor. Then he left there and went to Gilgal."

[13] Samuel came to Saul, who said, "The LORD bless you. I carried out the LORD's instructions." [14] However, Samuel asked,

"But what is this sound of sheep in my ears
and this sound of cows that I hear?"

[15] Saul answered, "The army brought them from the Amalekites. They spared the best sheep and cows to sacrifice to the LORD your God. But the rest they claimed for God and destroyed."

[16] "Be quiet," Samuel told Saul, "and let me tell you what the LORD told me last night."

"Speak," Saul replied.

[17] Samuel said, "Even though you don't consider yourself great, you were the head of Israel's tribes. The LORD anointed you king of Israel. [18] And the LORD sent you on a mission. He said, 'Claim those sinners, the Amalekites, for me by destroying them. Wage war against them until they're wiped out.' [19] Why didn't you obey the LORD? Why have you taken their belongings and done what the LORD considers evil?"

[20] "But I did obey the LORD," Saul told Samuel. "I went where the LORD sent me, brought ˌbackˏ King Agag of Amalek, and claimed the Amalekites for God. [21] The army took some of their belongings—the best sheep and cows were claimed for God—in order to sacrifice to the LORD your God in Gilgal."

[22] Then Samuel said,

"Is the LORD as delighted with burnt offerings and sacrifices
    as he would be with your obedience?
To follow instructions is better than to sacrifice.
To obey is better than sacrificing the fat of rams.
[23]   The sin of black magic is rebellion.
    Wickedness and idolatry are arrogance.
Because you rejected the word of the LORD,
    he rejects you as king."

[24] Then Saul told Samuel, "I have sinned by not following the LORD's command or your instructions. I was afraid of the people and listened to them. [25] Now please forgive my sin and come back with me so that I may worship the LORD."

²⁶ Samuel told Saul, "I will not go back with you because you rejected what the LORD told you. So the LORD rejects you as king of Israel." ²⁷ When Samuel turned to leave, Saul grabbed the hem of his robe, and it tore. ²⁸ Samuel told him, "The LORD has torn the kingdom of Israel from you today. He has given it to your neighbor who is better than you. ²⁹ In addition, the Glory of Israel does not lie or change his mind, because he is not a mortal who changes his mind."

³⁰ Saul replied, "I have sinned! Now please honor me in front of the leaders of my people and in front of Israel. Come back with me, and let me worship the LORD your God." ³¹ Then Samuel turned and followed Saul, and Saul worshiped the LORD.

³² "Bring me King Agag of Amalek," Samuel said.

Agag came to him trembling.ᵃ "Surely, the bitterness of death is past,"ᵇ Agag said.

³³ But Samuel said, "As your sword made women childless, so your mother will be made childless among women." And Samuel cut Agag in pieces in the presence of the LORD at Gilgal.

³⁴ Then Samuel went to Ramah, and Saul went to his home at Gibeah. ³⁵ Samuel didn't see Saul again before he died, though Samuel mourned over Saul. And the LORD regretted that he had made Saul king of Israel.

David Chosen to Be King

16 ¹ The LORD asked Samuel, "How long are you going to mourn for Saul now that I have rejected him as king of Israel? Fill a flask with olive oil and go. I'm sending you to Jesse in Bethlehem because I've selected one of his sons to be king."

² "How can I go?" Samuel asked. "When Saul hears about it, he'll kill me."

The LORD said, "Take a heifer with you and say, 'I've come to sacrifice to the LORD.' ³ Invite Jesse to the sacrifice. I will reveal to you what you should do, and you will anoint for me the one I point out to you."

⁴ Samuel did what the LORD told him. When he came to Bethlehem, the leaders of the city, trembling with fear, greeted him and said, "May peace be with you."

⁵ "Greetings," he replied, "I have come to sacrifice to the LORD. Perform the ceremonies to make yourselves holy, and come with me to the sacrifice." He performed the ceremonies for Jesse and his sons and invited them to the sacrifice. ⁶ When they came, he saw Eliab and thought, "Certainly, here in the LORD's presence is his anointed king."

⁷ But the LORD told Samuel, "Don't look at his appearance or how tall he is, because I have rejected him. God does not see as humans see.ᵃ Humans look at outward appearances, but the LORD looks into the heart."

⁸ Then Jesse called Abinadab and brought him to Samuel. But Samuel said, "The LORD has not chosen this one either."

⁹ Then Jesse had Shammah come to Samuel. "The LORD has not chosen this one either," Samuel said. ¹⁰ So Jesse brought seven ˌmoreˌ of his sons to Samuel, but Samuel told Jesse, "The LORD has not chosen ˌany ofˌ these. ¹¹ Are these all the sons you have?"

"There's still the youngest one," Jesse answered. "He's tending the sheep."

Samuel told Jesse, "Send someone to get him. We won't continue until he gets here."

¹² So Jesse sent for him. He had a healthy complexion, attractive eyes, and a handsome appearance. The LORD said, "Go ahead, anoint him. He is the one." ¹³ Samuel took the flask of olive oil and anointed David in the presence of his brothers. The LORD's Spirit came over David and stayed with him from that day on. Then Samuel left for Ramah.

David Plays the Lyre for Saul

¹⁴ Now, the LORD's Spirit had left Saul, and an evil spirit from the LORD tormented him. ¹⁵ Saul's officials told him, "An evil spirit from God is tormenting you. ¹⁶ Your Majesty, why don't you command us to look for a man who can play the lyre well? When the evil spirit from God comes to you, he'll strum a tune, and you'll feel better."

¹⁷ Saul told his officials, "Please find me a man who can play well and bring him to me."

¹⁸ One of the officials said, "I know one of Jesse's sons from Bethlehem who can play well. He's a courageous man and a warrior. He has a way with words, he is handsome, and the LORD is with him."

¹⁹ Saul sent messengers to Jesse to say, "Send me your son David, who is with the sheep."

²⁰ Jesse took six bushels of bread, a full wineskin, and a young goat and sent them with his son David to Saul. ²¹ David came to Saul and served him. Saul loved him very much and made David his armorbearer. ²² Saul sent ˌthis messageˌ to Jesse, "Please let David stay with me because I have grown fond of him."

²³ Whenever God's spirit came to Saul, David took the lyre and strummed a tune. Saul got relief ˌfrom his terrorˌ and felt better, and the evil spirit left him.

ᵃ 15:32 Or "Agag came to him in shackles."   ᵇ 15:32 Hebrew meaning uncertain.   ᵃ 16:7 Greek; Masoretic Text "Not that which humans see."

David and Goliath

17 ¹ The Philistines assembled their armies for war. They assembled at Socoh, which is in Judah, and camped between Socoh and Azekah at Ephes Dammim. ² So Saul and the army of Israel assembled and camped in the Elah Valley. They formed a battle line to fight the Philistines. ³ The Philistines were stationed on a hill on one side, and the Israelites were stationed on a hill on the other side. There was a ravine between the two of them. ⁴ The Philistine army's champion came out of their camp. His name was Goliath from Gath. He was ten feet tall.ᵃ ⁵ He had a bronze helmet on his head, and he wore a bronze coat of armor scales weighing 125 pounds. ⁶ On his legs he had bronze shin guards and on his back a bronze javelin. ⁷ The shaft of his spear was like the beam used by weavers. The head of his spear was made of 15 pounds of iron. The man who carried his shield walked ahead of him.

⁸ Goliath stood and called to the Israelites, "Why do you form a battle line? Am I not a Philistine, and aren't you Saul's servants? Choose a man, and let him come down to ‚fight‚ me. ⁹ If he can fight me and kill me, then we will be your slaves. But if I overpower him and kill him, then you will be our slaves and serve us." ¹⁰ The Philistine added, "I challenge the Israelite battle line today. Send out a man so that we can fight each other." ¹¹ When Saul and all the Israelites heard what this Philistine said, they were gripped with fear.

¹² David was a son of a man named Jesse from the region of Ephrath and the city of Bethlehem in Judah. Jesse had eight sons, and in Saul's day he was an old man.ᵇ ¹³ Jesse's three oldest sons joined Saul's army for the battle. The firstborn was Eliab, the second was Abinadab, the third was Shammah, ¹⁴ and David was the youngest. The three oldest joined Saul's army. ¹⁵ David went back and forth from Saul's camp to Bethlehem, where he tended his father's flock. ¹⁶ Each morning and evening for 40 days, the Philistine came forward and made his challenge.

¹⁷ Jesse told his son David, "Take this half-bushel of roasted grain and these ten loaves of bread to your brothers. Take them to your brothers in the camp right away. ¹⁸ And take these ten cheeses to the captain of the regiment. See how your brothers are doing, and bring back some news about them. ¹⁹ They, along with Saul and all the soldiers of Israel, are in the Elah Valley fighting the Philistines."

²⁰ David got up early in the morning and had someone else watch ‚the sheep‚. He took ‚the food‚ and went, as Jesse ordered him. He went to the camp as the army was going out to the battle line shouting their war cry. ²¹ Israel and the Philistines formed their battle lines facing each other. ²² David left the supplies behind in the hands of the quartermaster, ran to the battle line, and greeted his brothers. ²³ While he was talking to them, the Philistine champion, Goliath from Gath, came from the battle lines of the Philistines. He repeated his words, and David heard them. ²⁴ When all the men of Israel saw Goliath, they fled from him because they were terrified. ²⁵ The men of Israel said, "Did you see that man coming ‚from the Philistine lines‚? He keeps coming to challenge Israel. The king will make the man who kills this Philistine very rich. He will give his daughter to that man to marry and elevate the social status of his family."ᶜ

²⁶ David asked the men who were standing near him, "What will be done for the man who kills this Philistine and gets rid of Israel's disgrace? Who is this uncircumcised Philistine that he should challenge the army of the living God?"

²⁷ The soldiers repeated ‚to David‚ how the man who kills Goliath would be treated.

²⁸ Eliab, David's oldest brother, heard David talking to the men. Then Eliab became angry with David. "Why did you come here," he asked him, "and with whom did you leave those few sheep in the wilderness? I know how overconfident and headstrong you are. You came here just to see the battle."

²⁹ "What have I done now?" David snapped at him. "Didn't I ‚merely‚ ask a question?" ³⁰ He turned to face another man and asked the same question, and the other soldiers gave him the same answer.

³¹ What David said was overheard and reported to Saul, who then sent for him. ³² David told Saul, "No one should be discouraged because of this. I will go and fight this Philistine."

³³ Saul responded to David, "You can't fight this Philistine. You're just a boy, but he's been a warrior since he was your age."

³⁴ David replied to Saul, "I am a shepherd for my father's sheep. Whenever a lion or a bear came and carried off a sheep from the flock, ³⁵ I went after it, struck it, and rescued the sheep from its mouth. If it attacked me, I took hold of its mane, struck it, and killed it. ³⁶ I have killed lions and bears, and this uncircumcised Philistine will be like one of them because he has challenged the army of the living God." ³⁷ David added, "The LORD, who saved me from the lion and the bear, will save me from this Philistine."

ᵃ 17:4 Masoretic Text; Dead Sea Scrolls and Greek "seven feet tall."   ᵇ 17:12 Greek; Masoretic Text "he came a leader among men."   ᶜ 17:25 Hebrew meaning of "elevate the social status of his family" uncertain.

"Go," Saul told David, "and may the LORD be with you."

38 Saul put his battle tunic on David; he put a bronze helmet on David's head and dressed him in armor. **39** David fastened Saul's sword over his clothes and tried to walk, but he had never practiced doing this. "I can't walk in these things," David told Saul. "I've never had any practice doing this." So David took all those things off.

40 He took his stick with him, picked out five smooth stones from the riverbed, and put them in his shepherd's bag. With a sling in his hand, he approached the Philistine. **41** The Philistine, preceded by the man carrying his shield, was coming closer and closer to David. **42** When the Philistine got a good look at David, he despised him. After all, David was a young man with a healthy complexion and good looks.

43 The Philistine asked David, "Am I a dog that you come to ˒attack˒ me with sticks?" So the Philistine called on his gods to curse David. **44** "Come on," the Philistine told David, "and I'll give your body to the birds."

45 David told the Philistine, "You come to me with sword and spear and javelin, but I come to you in the name of the LORD of Armies, the God of the army of Israel, whom you have insulted. **46** Today the LORD will hand you over to me. I will strike you down and cut off your head. And this day I will give the dead bodies of the Philistine army to the birds and the wild animals. The whole world will know that Israel has a God. **47** Then everyone gathered here will know that the LORD can save without sword or spear, because the LORD determines every battle's outcome. He will hand all of you over to us."

48 When the Philistine moved closer in order to attack, David quickly ran toward the opposing battle line to attack the Philistine. **49** Then David reached into his bag, took out a stone, hurled it from his sling, and struck the Philistine in the forehead. The stone sank into Goliath's forehead, and he fell to the ground on his face. **50** So using ˒only˒ a sling and a stone, David proved to be stronger than the Philistine. David struck down and killed the Philistine, even though David didn't have a sword in his hand. **51** David ran and stood over the Philistine. He took Goliath's sword, pulled it out of its sheath, and made certain the Philistine was dead by cutting off his head.

When the Philistines saw their hero had been killed, they fled. **52** Then the soldiers of Israel and Judah rose up, shouted a battle cry, and pursued the Philistines as far as Gath and to the gates of Ekron. Wounded Philistines lay on the road to Shaaraim and all the way to Gath and Ekron. **53** When the Israelites came back from their pursuit of the Philistines, they looted all the goods in the Philistine camp. **54** David took the Philistine's head and brought it to Jerusalem, but he kept Goliath's armor in his tent.

55 As Saul watched David going out against the Philistine, he asked Abner, the commander of the army, "Abner, whose son is this young man?"

Abner answered, "I solemnly swear, as you live, Your Majesty, I don't know."

56 The king said, "Find out whose son this young man is."

57 When David returned from killing the Philistine, Abner brought him to Saul. David had the Philistine's head in his hand.

58 Saul asked him, "Whose son are you, young man?"

"The son of your servant Jesse of Bethlehem," David answered.

David's Love for Jonathan

18 **1** David finished talking to Saul. After that, Jonathan became David's closest friend. He loved David as much as ˒he loved˒ himself. **2** (From that day on Saul kept David ˒as his servant˒ and didn't let him go back to his family.) **3** So Jonathan made a pledge of mutual loyalty with David because he loved him as much as ˒he loved˒ himself. **4** Jonathan took off the coat he had on and gave it to David along with his battle tunic, his sword, his bow, and his belt.

5 David was successful wherever Saul sent him. Saul put him in charge of the fighting men. This pleased all the people, including Saul's officials.

David's Success Makes Saul Jealous

6 As they arrived, David was returning from a campaign against the Philistines. Women from all of Israel's cities came to meet King Saul. They sang and danced, accompanied by tambourines, joyful music, and triangles.ᵃ **7** The women who were celebrating sang,

> "Saul has defeated thousands
>   but David tens of thousands!"

ᵃ 18:6 Hebrew meaning uncertain.

[8] Saul became very angry because he considered this saying to be insulting. "To David they credit tens of thousands," he said, "but to me they credit ˌonlyˌ a few thousand. The only thing left for David is my kingdom." [9] From that day on Saul kept an eye on David.

[10] The next day an evil spirit from God seized Saul. He began to prophesy in his house while David strummed a tune on the lyre as he did every day. Now, Saul had a spear in his hand. [11] He raised the spear and thought, "I'll nail David to the wall." But David got away from him twice.

[12] Saul was afraid of David, because the LORD was with David but had left Saul. [13] So he kept David away. He made David captain of a regiment. David led the troops out ˌto battleˌ and back again. [14] He was successful in everything he undertook because the LORD was with him. [15] Saul noticed how very successful he was and became ˌeven moreˌ afraid of him. [16] Everyone in Israel and Judah loved David, because he led them in and out ˌof battleˌ.

[17] Finally, Saul said to David, "Here is my oldest daughter Merab. I will give her to you as your wife if you prove yourself to be a warrior for me and fight the LORD's battles." (Saul thought, "I must not lay a hand on him. Let the Philistines do that.")

[18] "Who am I?" David asked Saul. "And how important are my relatives or my father's family in Israel that I should be the king's son-in-law?"

[19] But when the time came to give Saul's daughter Merab to David, she was married to Adriel from Meholah. [20] However, Saul's daughter Michal fell in love with David. When Saul was told about it, the news pleased him. [21] Saul thought, "I'll give her to David. She will trap him, and the Philistines will get him." So he said to David a second time, "You will now be my son-in-law."

[22] Saul ordered his officers, "Talk to David in private. Tell him, 'The king likes you, and all his officers are fond of you. Become the king's son-in-law.' "

[23] When Saul's officers made it a point to say this, David asked, "Do you think it's easy to become the king's son-in-law? I am a poor and unimportant person."

[24] When the officers told Saul what David had said, [25] Saul replied, "Tell David, 'The king doesn't want any payment for the bride except 100 Philistine foreskins so that he can get revenge on his enemies.' " In this way Saul planned to have David fall into the hands of the Philistines. [26] When his officers told David this, David concluded that it was acceptable to become the king's son-in-law. Before the time was up, [27] David and his men went out and struck down 200 Philistines. David brought the foreskins, and they counted them out for the king so that David could become the king's son-in-law. Then Saul gave him his daughter Michal as his wife. [28] Saul realized that the LORD was with David and that his daughter Michal loved David. [29] Then Saul was even more afraid of David, and so Saul became David's constant enemy.

[30] The Philistine generals still went out ˌto fight Israelˌ. But whenever they went out ˌto fightˌ, David was more successful than the rest of Saul's officers. So David gained a good reputation.

Saul's Plan to Kill David

19 [1] Saul told his son Jonathan and all his officers to kill David. But Saul's son Jonathan was very fond of David, [2] so he reported to David, "My father Saul is trying to kill you. Please be careful tomorrow morning. Go into hiding, and stay out of sight. [3] I'll go out and stand beside my father in the field where you'll be. I'll speak with my father about you. If I find out anything, I'll tell you."

[4] So Jonathan spoke well of David to his father Saul. "You should not commit a sin against your servant David," he said. "He hasn't sinned against you. Instead, he has done some very fine things for you: [5] He risked his life and killed the Philistine Goliath, and the LORD gave all Israel a great victory. When you saw it, you rejoiced. Why then should you sin by shedding David's innocent blood for no reason?"

[6] Saul listened to Jonathan, and he promised, "I solemnly swear, as the LORD lives, he will not be killed." [7] Jonathan told David all of this. Then Jonathan took David to Saul. So David was returned to his former status in Saul's court.

Saul Tries to Kill David

[8] When war broke out again, David went to fight the Philistines. He defeated them so decisively that they fled from him. [9] Then an evil spirit from the LORD came over Saul while he was sitting in his house with his spear in his hand. David was strumming a tune. [10] Saul tried to nail David to the wall with his spear. But David dodged it, and Saul's spear struck the wall. David fled, escaping ˌfrom Saulˌ that night.

[11] Saul sent messengers to watch David's house and kill him in the morning. But Michal, David's wife, advised him, "If you don't save yourself tonight, you'll be dead tomorrow!" [12] So Michal lowered David through a window, and he ran away to escape. [13] Then Michal took some idols, laid them in the bed, put a goat-hair blanket at its head, and covered the idols with a garment.

¹⁴ When Saul sent messengers to get David, Michal said, "He's sick." ¹⁵ Then Saul sent the messengers back to see David themselves. Saul told them, "Bring him here to me in his bed so that I can kill him." ¹⁶ The messengers came, and there in the bed were the idols with the goat-hair blanket at its head.

¹⁷ Saul asked Michal, "Why did you betray me by sending my enemy away so that he could escape?"

Michal answered, "He told me, 'Let me go! Why should I kill you?' "

¹⁸ David escaped and went to Samuel at Ramah. He told Samuel everything Saul had done to him. Then he and Samuel went to the pastures and lived there.

¹⁹ When it was reported to Saul that David was in the pastures at Ramah, ²⁰ Saul sent messengers to get David. But when they saw a group of prophets prophesying with Samuel serving as their leader, God's Spirit came over Saul's messengers so that they also prophesied. ²¹ When they told Saul ˌabout thisˌ, he sent other messengers, but they also prophesied. Saul even sent a third group of messengers, but they also prophesied. ²² Then he went to Ramah himself. He went as far as the big cistern in Secu and asked ˌthe peopleˌ, "Where are Samuel and David?"

He was told, "Over there in the pastures at Ramah." ²³ As he went toward the pastures at Ramah, God's Spirit came over him too. He continued his journey, prophesying until he came to the pastures at Ramah. ²⁴ He even took off his clothes as he prophesied in front of Samuel and lay there naked all day and all night. This is where the saying, "Is Saul one of the prophets?" came from.

David Makes a Promise to Jonathan

20 ¹ David fled from the pastures at Ramah, came to Jonathan, and asked, "What have I done? What crime am I guilty of? What sin have I committed against your father that he's trying to kill me?"

² Jonathan answered, "That's unthinkable! You're not going to die! My father does nothing without telling me, whether it's important or not. Why should my father hide this from me? It's just not that way."

³ But David took an oath, saying, "Your father certainly knows that you support me, so he said ˌto himselfˌ, 'Jonathan must not know about this. It will bring him distress.' But I solemnly swear, as the Lord and you live, I'm only one step away from death."

⁴ Jonathan said to David, "I'll do whatever you say."

⁵ David replied, "Tomorrow is the New Moon Festival, when I should sit and eat at the king's ˌtableˌ. But let me go and hide in the countryside for two more nights. ⁶ If your father really misses me, tell him, 'David repeatedly begged me to let him run to Bethlehem, his hometown, because his relatives are offering the annual sacrifice there.' ⁷ If he says, 'Good!' then I will be safe. But if he gets really angry, then you'll know for sure that he has decided to harm me. ⁸ Now, be kind to me. After all, you forced me into an agreement with the Lord. If I have committed any crime, kill me yourself. Why bother taking me to your father?"

⁹ Jonathan answered, "That's unthinkable! If I knew for sure that my father had decided to harm you, I would have told you about it."

¹⁰ Then David asked, "Who will tell me whether or not your father gives you a harsh answer?"

¹¹ Jonathan said, "Let's go out into the country." So they went out into the country.

¹² "As the Lord God of Israel ˌis my witnessˌ," Jonathan continued, "I'll find out in the next two or three days how my father feels about you. If he does feel kindly toward you, then I will send someone to tell you. ¹³ If my father plans to harm you and I fail to tell you and send you away safely, may the Lord harm me even more. May the Lord be with you as he used to be with my father. ¹⁴ But as long as I live, ˌpromise me that you willˌ show me kindness because of the Lord. And even when I die, ¹⁵ never stop being kind to my family. The Lord will wipe each of David's enemies off the face of the earth. ¹⁶ At that time, if Jonathan's nameᵃ is cut off from David's family, then may the Lord punish David's house."ᵇ

¹⁷ Once again Jonathan swore an oath to David because of his love for David. He loved David as much as ˌhe lovedˌ himself. ¹⁸ "Tomorrow is the New Moon Festival," Jonathan told him, "and you will be missed when your seat is empty. ¹⁹ The day after tomorrow you will be missed even more.ᶜ So go to the place where you hid on that other occasion, and stay by the rock. ²⁰ I will shoot three arrows from beside it toward a target. ²¹ Then I will send out a boy and say, 'Go, find the arrows.' Now, if I tell the boy, 'Look, the arrows are next to you; get them,' then come ˌback with meˌ. You will be safe, and there will be no trouble. I swear it, as the Lord lives. ²² But if I tell the boy, 'The arrows are next to you,' then go, because the Lord

---

ᵃ 20:16 Greek; Masoretic Text omits "name."   ᵇ 20:16 Ancient scribal tradition; Masoretic Text "punish David's enemies." At times some scribes would alter the text when they thought it was disrespectful.   ᶜ 20:19 Hebrew meaning uncertain.

has sent you away. ²³ We have made a promise to each other, and the LORD is ˌa witnessˌ between you and me forever."

²⁴ So David hid in the countryside. When the New Moon Festival came, King Saul sat down to eat the festival meal. ²⁵ He sat in his usual seat by the wall, while Jonathan stood. Abner sat beside Saul, but David's place was empty. ²⁶ Saul didn't say anything that day, thinking, "Something has happened to him so that he's unclean.ᵈ He must be unclean." ²⁷ But on the second day of the month, David's place was still empty.

Saul asked his son Jonathan, "Why hasn't Jesse's son come to the meal either yesterday or today?"

²⁸ Jonathan answered Saul, "David repeatedly begged me ˌto let him goˌ to Bethlehem. ²⁹ David said to me 'Please let me go. Our relatives will offerˌa sacrifice in the city, and my brother ordered me to be there. If you will permit it, please let me go to see my brothers.' This is why he hasn't come to your banquet."

³⁰ Then Saul got angry with Jonathan. "Son of a crooked and rebellious woman!" he called Jonathan. "I know you've sided with Jesse's son. You have no shame. ˌYou actˌ as if you are your mother's son but not mine.ᵉ ³¹ As long as Jesse's son lives on earth, neither you nor your right to be king is secure. Now, send some men to bring him to me. He's a dead man!"

³² Jonathan asked his father, "Why should he be killed? What has he done?"

³³ Saul raised his spear to strike him. Then Jonathan knew his father was determined to kill David. ³⁴ Jonathan got up from the table very angry and ate nothing that second day of the month. He was worried sick about David because Jonathan had been humiliated by his own father.

³⁵ In the morning Jonathan went out to the country to the place he and David had agreed on. Jonathan had a young boy with him. ³⁶ "Run," he told the boy, "please find the arrows I shoot."

The boy ran, and Jonathan shot the arrow over him. ³⁷ When the boy reached the place where Jonathan's arrow ˌhad landedˌ, Jonathan called after him, "The arrows are next to you!" ³⁸ Jonathan added, "Quick! Hurry up! Don't stand there!" Jonathan's young servant gathered the arrows and came to his master. ³⁹ The boy had no idea what was going on, but Jonathan and David understood. ⁴⁰ Then Jonathan gave his weapons to the boy. He told the boy, "Take them back into town."

⁴¹ When the boy had left, David came out from the south side ˌof the rockˌ and quickly bowed down three times with his face touching the ground. Then they kissed each other and cried together, but David cried the loudest.ᶠ

⁴² "Go in peace!" Jonathan told David. "We have both taken an oath in the LORD's name, saying, 'The LORD will be ˌa witnessˌ between me and you and between my descendants and your descendants forever.' "ᵍ

So David left, and Jonathan went into the city.

David at Nob

21 ¹ David went to the priest Ahimelech at Nob. Ahimelech was trembling as he went toᵃ meet David. "Why are you alone?" he asked David. "Why is no one with you?"

² "The king ordered me to do something," David answered the priest Ahimelech, "and he told me, 'No one must know anything about this mission I'm sending you on and about the orders I've given you. I've stationedᵇ my young men at a certain place.' " ³ ˌDavid added,ˌ "Now, what do you have ˌto eatˌ? Give me five loaves of bread or whatever you can find."

⁴ "I don't have any ordinary bread," the chief priest answered David. "But there is holy bread for the young men if they haven't had sexual intercourse ˌtodayˌ."

⁵ David answered the priest, "Of course women have been kept away from us as usual when we go ˌon a missionˌ. The young men's bodies are kept holy even on ordinary campaigns. How much more then will their bodies be holy today?"

⁶ So the priest gave him holy ˌbreadˌ because he only had the bread of the presence which had been taken from the LORD's presence and replaced with warm bread that day.

⁷ That same day one of Saul's servants who was obligated to stay in the LORD's presence was there. His name was Doeg. A foreman for Saul's shepherds, he was from Edom.

⁸ David asked Ahimelech, "Don't you have a spear or a sword here? I didn't take either my spear or any other weapon because the king's business was urgent."

⁹ The chief priest answered, "The sword of Goliath the Philistine, whom you killed in the Elah Valley, is here. It is wrapped in a cloth behind the priestly ephod.ᶜ If you want to take it, take it. There's no other weapon here."

David said, "There's none like it. Let me have the sword."

ᵈ 20:26 "Unclean" refers to anything that Moses' Teachings say is not presentable to God.   ᵉ 20:30 English equivalent difficult.
ᶠ 20:41 Hebrew meaning uncertain.   ᵍ 20:42 1 Samuel 20:42b in English Bibles is 1 Samuel 21:1 in the Hebrew Bible.
ᵃ 21:1 1 Samuel 21:1–15 in English Bibles is 1 Samuel 21:2–16 in the Hebrew Bible.   ᵇ 21:2 Dead Sea Scrolls, Greek; Masoretic
Text "I've informed."   ᶜ 21:9 Ephod is a technical term for a part of the priest's clothes. Its exact usage and shape are unknown.

David at Gath

¹⁰That day David left. He was ⸢still⸣ fleeing from Saul when he came to King Achish of Gath. ¹¹Achish's officers asked, "Isn't this David, the king of ⸢his⸣ country? He's the one they used to sing about in the dances:

> 'Saul has defeated thousands
>   but David tens of thousands.' "

¹²When David realized what they had said, he was terrified of King Achish of Gath. ¹³So he changed his behavior ⸢when he was⸣ in their presence and acted insane ⸢as long as he was⸣ under their authority. He scribbled on the doors of the city gate and let his spit run down his beard. ¹⁴Achish said to his officers, "Look at him! Don't you see ⸢that he's⸣ insane? Why bring him to me? ¹⁵Do I have such a shortage of lunatics that you bring this man so that he can show me he is insane? Does this man have to come into my house?"

David in Judah and Moab

22 ¹So David escaped from that place and fled to the cave at Adullam. When his brothers and all ⸢the rest⸣ of his family heard about it, they went to him. ²Then everyone who was in trouble, in debt, or bitter about life joined him, and he became their commander. There were about four hundred men with him.
³From there David went to Mizpah in Moab. He asked the king of Moab, "Please let my father and mother stay with you until I know what God is going to do for me." ⁴He brought them to the king of Moab, and they stayed with him as long as David was living in his fortified camp.
⁵"Don't live in your fortified camp," the prophet Gad told David. "Go to the land of Judah." So David went to the forest of Hereth.

Saul Massacres the Priests at Nob

⁶Saul heard that David and his men had been found. Saul was staying in Gibeah under the tamarisk tree at the worship site[a] with his spear in his hand and all his officials standing around him. ⁷He said to his officials, "Listen here, men of Benjamin! Will Jesse's son give every one of you fields and vineyards? Will he make you all officers over a regiment or a battalion of soldiers? ⁸All of you are plotting against me, and no one informed me when my son entered into a loyalty pledge with Jesse's son. No one felt sorry for me and informed me that my son has encouraged my servant David to ambush me, as he's doing now."
⁹Then Doeg from Edom, standing with Saul's officials, answered him, "I saw Jesse's son when he came to Ahimelech, Ahitub's son, in Nob. ¹⁰Ahimelech prayed to the LORD for David and gave him food and the sword of Goliath the Philistine."
¹¹Then the king sent for the priest Ahimelech, who was Ahitub's son, and his entire family who were the priests in Nob. All of them came to the king. ¹²Saul said, "Listen here, son of Ahitub!"
"Yes, sir?" he responded.
¹³Saul asked him, "Why did you and Jesse's son plot against me? You gave him bread and a sword and prayed to God for him so that he can rise up against me and ambush me, as he's doing now."
¹⁴Ahimelech asked the king, "But whom among all your officials can you trust like David? Your Majesty, he's your son-in-law, the commander of your bodyguard. He's honored in your own household. ¹⁵Is this the first time I have prayed to God for him? Not at all! You shouldn't blame me or anyone in my family for this. I knew nothing at all about this."
¹⁶Saul said, "Ahimelech, you and your entire family are going to die."
¹⁷"Turn and kill the LORD's priests because they support David," the king said to the runners standing around him. "When they knew David was fleeing, they didn't inform me." But the king's men refused to attack the LORD's priests.
¹⁸So the king said to Doeg, "You turn and attack the priests." Doeg from Edom turned and attacked the priests, and that day he killed 85 men wearing the linen priestly ephod.[b] ¹⁹He also killed the people of Nob, the city of the priests. Using ⸢his⸣ sword, he killed men and women, children and infants, cows, donkeys, and sheep.
²⁰But Ahimelech, Ahitub's son, had one son who escaped. His name was Abiathar. He fled to David. ²¹Abiathar told David that Saul had killed the LORD's priests.
²²David told Abiathar, "I knew that day when Doeg from Edom was there that he would be certain to tell Saul. I am the one responsible[c] for all the lives of your family. ²³Stay with me. Don't be afraid. The one who is seeking my life is ⸢also⸣ seeking your life. However, you will be under my protection."

---

[a] 22:6 Greek; Masoretic Text "at Ramah."   [b] 22:18 *Ephod* is a technical term for a part of the priest's clothes. Its exact usage and shape are unknown.   [c] 22:22 Greek; Masoretic Text "I turned."

David Saves the City of Keilah

23 [1] David was asked, "Did you know that the Philistines are fighting against Keilah? They are robbing the threshing floors."[a]

[2] David asked the LORD, "Should I go and attack these Philistines?"

"Go," the LORD told David, "attack the Philistines, and save Keilah."

[3] David's men told him, "We're afraid of staying here in Judah. How much more ˌafraid do you think we'll beˌ if we go to Keilah against the Philistine army?"

[4] David asked the LORD again, and the LORD answered him. He said, "Go to Keilah. I'm giving you the power to defeat the Philistines."

[5] David and his men went to Keilah, fought the Philistines, drove off their livestock, and decisively defeated them. So David rescued the people who lived in Keilah.

[6] When Ahimelech's son Abiathar fled to David at Keilah, Abiathar brought a priestly ephod[b] with him.

[7] When Saul was told that David went to Keilah, Saul said, "God has delivered him into my hands. He has trapped himself by going into a city which has ˌa gate withˌ a double door ˌheld shut byˌ a bar." [8] So Saul called together all the troops to go to war and blockade Keilah, where David and his men were.

[9] When David learned that Saul was planning to harm him, he told the priest Abiathar, "Bring the ephod." [10] Then David said, "LORD God of Israel, I have actually heard that Saul is going to come to Keilah and destroy the city on account of me. [11] Will the citizens of Keilah hand me over to him? Will Saul come here as I have heard? LORD God of Israel, please tell me."

"He will come," the LORD answered.

[12] "Will the citizens of Keilah hand me and my men over to Saul?" David asked.

"They will hand you over," the LORD answered.

[13] So David and his men, about six hundred[c] in all, left Keilah. They went wherever they could go. Then Saul was told, "David has escaped from Keilah!" So he gave up the campaign. [14] David lived in fortified camps in the desert, and he lived in fortified camps in the mountains of the desert of Ziph. Saul was always searching for him, but God didn't let him capture David.

David in the Desert of Ziph

[15] David was afraid because[d] Saul had come to kill him at Horesh in the desert of Ziph. [16] Saul's son Jonathan came to David at Horesh. He strengthened David's ˌfaithˌ in the LORD.[e] [17] "Don't be afraid," he told David, "my father Saul won't find you. You will rule Israel, and I will be your second-in-command. Even my father Saul knows this." [18] Both of them made a pledge in the LORD's presence. David stayed in Horesh, and Jonathan went home.

[19] Then the men of Ziph went to Saul in Gibeah. They said, "David is hiding with us in fortified camps at Horesh on the hills of Hachilah, south of Jeshimon. [20] Come, Your Majesty, whenever you want. We will hand him over to you."

[21] Saul responded, "The LORD bless you for feeling sorry for me! [22] Please make more plans, and watch where he goes. Who has seen him there? I'm told he's very clever. [23] Watch and learn about all the hiding places where he may be hiding, and come back to me with the facts. Then I'll go with you, and if he's in the country, I'll search for him among all the families of Judah." [24] They left for Ziph ahead of Saul.

David in the Desert of Maon

David and his men were in the desert of Maon, in the plains south of Jeshimon. [25] When Saul and his men came to look for him, David was told the news. So he went to his mountain stronghold in the desert of Maon. Saul heard about it and pursued David into the desert of Maon. [26] Saul went on one side of the mountain, and David and his men went on the other side of the mountain. David was hurrying to get away from Saul, and Saul and his men were going around ˌthe mountainˌ toward David and his men, trying to capture them. [27] Then a messenger came to Saul and said, "Come quickly! The Philistines are raiding the country."

[28] Saul gave up pursuing David and went to fight the Philistines. So that place was called Slippery Rock.[f] [29] From there David went to stay in the fortified camps of En Gedi.

David Spares Saul's Life

24[a] [1] When Saul came back from ˌfightingˌ the Philistines, he was told "Now David is in the desert near En Gedi." [2] Then Saul took 3,000 of the best-trained men from all Israel and went to search for David and his men on the Rocks of the Wild Goats. [3] He came to some sheep

---

[a] 23:1 A threshing floor is an outdoor area where grain is separated from its husks.   [b] 23:6 *Ephod* is a technical term for a part of the priest's clothes. Its exact usage and shape are unknown.   [c] 23:13 Masoretic Text; Greek "four hundred."   [d] 23:15 Or "David saw that."   [e] 23:16 Dead Sea Scrolls, Greek; Masoretic Text "in God."   [f] 23:28 1 Samuel 23:29 in English Bibles is 1 Samuel 24:1 in the Hebrew Bible.   [a] 24:1 1 Samuel 24:1–22 in English Bibles is 1 Samuel 24:2–23 in the Hebrew Bible.

pens along the road where there was a cave. Saul went into ˌitˌ to relieve himself while David and his men were sitting further back in the cave.

⁴ David's men told him, "Today is the day the LORD referred to when he said, 'I'm going to hand your enemy over to you. You will do to him whatever you think is right.' "

David quietly got up and cut off the border of Saul's robe. **⁵** But afterward, David's conscience bothered him because he had cut off the border of Saul's robe. **⁶** He said to his men, "It would be unthinkable for me to raise my hand against His Majesty, the LORD's anointed king, since he is the LORD's anointed." **⁷** So David stopped*ᵇ* his men by saying this to them and didn't let them attack Saul.

Saul left the cave and went out onto the road. **⁸** Later, David got up, left the cave, and called to Saul, "Your Majesty!" When Saul looked back, David knelt down with his face touching the ground. **⁹** David asked Saul, "Why do you listen to rumors that I am trying to harm you? **¹⁰** Today you saw how the LORD handed you over to me in the cave. Although I was told to kill you, I spared you, saying, 'I will not raise my hand against Your Majesty because you are the LORD's anointed.' **¹¹** My master, look at this! The border of your robe is in my hand! Since I cut off the border of your robe and didn't kill you, you should know and be able to see I mean no harm or rebellion. I haven't sinned against you, but you are trying to ambush me in order to take my life. **¹²** May the LORD decide between you and me. May the LORD take revenge on you for what you did to me. However, I will not lay a hand on you. **¹³** It's like people used to say long ago, 'Wickedness comes from wicked people.' But I will not lay a hand on you. **¹⁴** Against whom has the king of Israel come out? Whom are you pursuing? A dead dog? One flea? **¹⁵** So the LORD must be the judge. He will decide between you and me. He will watch and take my side in ˌthisˌ matter and set me free from you."

¹⁶ When David finished saying this, Saul asked, "Is that you speaking, my servant David?" and Saul cried loudly. **¹⁷** He told David, "You are more righteous than I. You treated me well while I treated you badly. **¹⁸** Today you have proved how good you've been to me. When the LORD handed me over to you, you didn't kill me. **¹⁹** When a person finds an enemy, does he send him away unharmed? The LORD will repay you completely for what you did for me today. **²⁰** Now I know that you certainly will rule as king, and under your guidance the kingdom of Israel will prosper. **²¹** Swear an oath to the LORD for me that you will not wipe out my descendants or destroy my name in my father's family."

²² So David swore to Saul. Then Saul went home, and David and his men went to their fortified camp.

Samuel Dies

25 **¹** Samuel died, and all Israel gathered to mourn for him. They buried him at his home in Ramah. Then David went to the desert of Paran.

David, Nabal, and Abigail

² Now, there was a man in Maon whose business was in Carmel. He was a very rich man. He had 3,000 sheep and 1,000 goats. And he was shearing his sheep in Carmel. **³** This man's name was Nabal, and his wife's name was Abigail. She was sensible and beautiful, but he was harsh and mean. He was a descendant of Caleb.

⁴ While David was in the desert, he heard that Nabal was shearing his sheep. **⁵** So David sent ten young men and told them, "Go to Carmel, visit Nabal, and greet him for me. **⁶** Say to him, 'May you live ˌlongˌ! May you, your home, and all you have prosper! **⁷** I hear that your sheepshearers are with you. Your shepherds have been with us, ˌandˌ we have not mistreated them. Nothing of theirs has been missing as long as they've been in Carmel. **⁸** Ask your young men, and let them tell you. Be kind to my young men, since we have come on a special occasion. Please give us and your son David anything you can ˌspareˌ.' "

⁹ When David's young men came to Nabal, they repeated all of this to him for David, and then they waited.

¹⁰ "Who is David?" Nabal answered David's servants. "Who is Jesse's son? So many servants nowadays are leaving their masters. **¹¹** Should I take my bread, my water, and my meat that I butchered for my shearers and give them to men coming from who knows where?"

¹² David's young men returned and told him all this.

¹³ "Each of you put on your swords!" David told his men. And everyone, including David, put on his sword. About four hundred men went with David, while two hundred men stayed with the supplies.

¹⁴ One of the young men told Abigail, Nabal's wife, "David sent messengers from the desert to greet our master, who yelled at them. **¹⁵** Those men were very good to us. They didn't mis-

---

ᵇ 24:7 Hebrew meaning uncertain.

treat us, and we found that nothing was missing wherever we went with them when we were in the fields. ¹⁶ They were a wall protecting us day and night as long as we were watching the sheep near them. ¹⁷ Now, consider what you should do because our master and his whole household are doomed. And he's such a worthless man that it's useless to talk to him."

¹⁸ So Abigail quickly took 200 loaves of bread, 2 full wineskins, 5 butchered sheep, a bushel of roasted grain, 100 bunches of raisins, and 200 fig cakes and loaded them on donkeys. ¹⁹ "Go on ahead," she told her young men, "and I'll follow you." But she didn't tell her husband Nabal about it.

²⁰ She was riding on her donkey down a hidden mountain path when she met David and his men coming toward her. ²¹ David had thought, "I guarded this man's stuff in the desert for nothing! Not one of his possessions was missing. Yet, he has paid me back with evil when I was good to him. ²² May God punish me*ᵃ* if I leave even one of his men*ᵇ* alive in the morning."

²³ When Abigail saw David, she quickly got down from her donkey. She immediately bowed down in front of David with her face touching the ground. ²⁴ After she bowed at his feet, she said, "Sir, let me be held responsible for this wrong. Please let me speak with you. Please listen to my words. ²⁵ You shouldn't take this worthless person Nabal seriously. He is like his name. His name is Nabal [Godless Fool], and he's foolish. But I didn't see the young men you sent.

²⁶ "The LORD has kept you from spilling innocent blood and from getting a victory by your own efforts. Now, sir, I solemnly swear, as the LORD and you live, may your enemies and those who are trying to harm you end up like Nabal. ²⁷ Here is a gift I am bringing to you. May it be given to the young men who are in your service. ²⁸ Please forgive my offense. The LORD will certainly give you, sir, a lasting dynasty, because you are fighting the LORD's battles. May evil never be found in you as long as you live. ²⁹ Even though someone pursued you and sought your life, your life is wrapped in the bundle of life which comes from the LORD your God. But he will dispose of the lives of your enemies like stones thrown from a sling. ³⁰ When the LORD does all the good he promised and makes you ruler of Israel, ³¹ you shouldn't have a troubled conscience because you spilled blood for no good reason and claimed your own victory. When the LORD has given you success, remember me."

³² David said to Abigail, "Blessed be the LORD God of Israel, who sent you today to meet me. ³³ May your good judgment be blessed. Also, may you be blessed for keeping me from slaughtering people today and from getting a victory by my own efforts. ³⁴ But I solemnly swear—as the LORD God of Israel, who has kept me from harming you, lives—if you hadn't come to meet me quickly, Nabal certainly wouldn't have had one of his men left at dawn."

³⁵ Then David accepted what she brought him and told her, "Go home in peace. I've listened to what you've said and granted your request."

³⁶ When Abigail came to Nabal, he was holding a banquet in his home. It was like a king's banquet. He was in a good mood and very drunk, so she didn't tell him anything until dawn. ³⁷ But in the morning, when the effects of the wine had worn off, his wife told him what had happened. Nabal's heart failed, and he could not move.*ᶜ* ³⁸ About ten days later the LORD made him even more sick, and Nabal died.

³⁹ When David heard Nabal was dead, he said, "Blessed be the LORD, who defended me against the insults of Nabal and kept me from doing wrong. The LORD has turned Nabal's own wickedness back on him."

Then David sent men ˻on his behalf˼ to propose marriage to Abigail. ⁴⁰ When David's servants came to Abigail at Carmel, they told her, "David has sent us to you so that we can take you to him to be his wife."

⁴¹ She bowed down with her face touching the ground. "I am ready to serve," she said. "I am ready to wash the feet of my master's servants." ⁴² Then Abigail quickly got up and rode on a donkey with five of her female servants following her. So she went with David's messengers and became his wife.

⁴³ David also married Ahinoam of Jezreel. Both she and Abigail were his wives. ⁴⁴ Saul had given his daughter Michal, David's wife, to Palti, Laish's son, who was from Gallim.

Saul's Final Pursuit of David

26 ¹ The people of Ziph came to Saul at Gibeah. "David is hiding at the hill of Hachilah near Jeshimon," they said.

² Saul went to the desert of Ziph, taking with him 3,000 of Israel's best-trained men to search for David. ³ Saul camped by the road at the hill of Hachilah near Jeshimon, but David stayed in the desert. When he realized Saul had come to the desert for him, ⁴ David sent spies to confirm that Saul had arrived.

ᵃ 25:22 Greek; Masoretic Text "To David's enemies."   *ᵇ* 25:22 Hebrew uses a coarse term for "men" here and at verse 34.
ᶜ 25:37 English equivalent difficult.

⁵ Then David went to the place where Saul had camped. David saw the place where Saul and Ner's son Abner, the commander of the army, were lying. Saul was lying in the camp, and the troops were camped around him.

⁶ David asked Ahimelech the Hittite and Abishai, who was Zeruiah's son and Joab's brother, "Who will go with me to Saul in the camp?"

Abishai answered, "I'll go with you."

⁷ So David and Abishai went among ˌSaul'sˌ troops that night. Saul was lying asleep inside the camp with his spear stuck in the ground near his head. Abner and the soldiers were lying around him. ⁸ Abishai said to David, "Today God has turned your enemy over to you. Please let me nail him to the ground with one stab of the spear. I won't have to do it twice!"

⁹ "Don't kill him!" David told Abishai. "No one has ever attacked the LORD's anointed king and remained free of guilt. ¹⁰ I solemnly swear, as the LORD lives," David added, "the LORD will strike him. Either his time will come when he'll die ˌnaturallyˌ, or he'll go into battle and be swept away. ¹¹ It would be unthinkable for me to attack the LORD's anointed king. But please take that spear near his head and that jar of water, and let's go."

¹² David took the spear and the jar of water near Saul's head, and they left. All of them were asleep. No one saw them, knew about it, or woke up. The LORD had made them fall into a deep sleep.

¹³ David went over to the other side and stood on top of the hill some distance away. (There was a wide space between them.) ¹⁴ Then David called to the troops and to Ner's son Abner. "Won't you answer, Abner?" he asked.

"Who is calling the king?" Abner asked.

¹⁵ David asked Abner, "Aren't you a man? Is there anyone like you in Israel? Then why didn't you guard your master, the king? Someone came to kill His Royal Majesty. ¹⁶ What you've done isn't good. I solemnly swear, as the LORD lives, you are dead men. You didn't guard your master, the LORD's anointed king. Look at the king's spear and the jar of water that were near his head."

¹⁷ Saul recognized David's voice. "Is that your voice, my servant David?" he asked.

"It is my voice, Your Royal Majesty," David answered. ¹⁸ "Why are you pursuing me?" he added. "What have I done? What crime have I committed? ¹⁹ Your Majesty, please listen to my words. If the LORD has turned you against me, let him be satisfied with an offering. But if mere mortals ˌhave turned you against meˌ, let them be cursed by the LORD. They have prevented me from having a share of the LORD's inheritance. 'Go and serve other gods,' they tell me. ²⁰ Don't let my blood fall to the ground, away from the LORD's presence. The king of Israel has come to search for one flea like someone hunting a partridge in the hills."

²¹ "My servant David," Saul said, "I have sinned. Come back. I will not harm you again, because you valued my life today. I've acted like a fool and made a terrible mistake."

²² David responded, "Here's the king's spear. One of the young men should come over and get it. ²³ The LORD will reward any person who is righteous and faithful. The LORD handed you over to me today, but I refused to attack the LORD's anointed king. ²⁴ As I placed great value on your life today, may the LORD place great value on my life and rescue me from all trouble."

²⁵ Then Saul said, "Blessed are you, my servant David. You will accomplish many things and certainly will succeed."

So David went his way, while Saul returned home.

David at Ziklag

27 ¹ David said to himself, "One of these days Saul will sweep me away. The best thing for me to do is to make sure that I escape to Philistine territory. Then Saul will give up looking all over Israel for me, and I'll escape from him." ² So David went with his 600 men to King Achish of Gath, Moach's son. ³ David and his men stayed with Achish in Gath. Each one had his family, and David had his two wives, Ahinoam from Jezreel and Abigail (who had been Nabal's wife) from Carmel. ⁴ When Saul was told that David had fled to Gath, he didn't search for him anymore.

⁵ David said to Achish, "If you will permit me, let me have a place in one of the outlying towns so that I can live there. Why should I live in the royal city with you?" ⁶ So Achish immediately gave him Ziklag. (This is why Ziklag still belongs to the kings of Judah today.)

⁷ David stayed in Philistine territory for one year and four months. ⁸ Then David and his men went to raid the Geshurites, the Girzites, and the Amalekites. (They lived in the territory which extends from Telaimᵃ to Shur and Egypt.) ⁹ Whenever David attacked the territory, he left no man or woman alive. He also took sheep, cattle, donkeys, camels, and clothing and returned to Achish.

ᵃ 27:8 Greek; Masoretic Text "lived in the country for a long time."

[10] Achish would ask, "Whom did you raid today?"[b]

And David would answer, "the Negev in Judah," or "the portion of the Negev where the descendants of Jerahmeel live," or "the portion of the Negev where the Kenites live." [11] He did not bring a single man or woman back to Gath alive. He thought, "They could tell Achish what I ˌreallyˌ did." This was his practice as long as he lived in Philistine territory. [12] And Achish believed David. Achish thought, "He has definitely made his own people in Israel despise him. He'll be my servant from now on."

28 [1] At that time the Philistines had gathered their army to fight against Israel. Then Achish said to David, "You need to know that you and your men will be going with me into battle."

[2] "Very well," David responded to Achish, "you will then know what I can do."

"Very well," Achish told David, "I will make you my bodyguard for life."

Saul's Sin—The Occult

[3] Meanwhile, Samuel had died, and all Israel had mourned for him and buried him in his hometown Ramah. (Saul had rid the land of mediums and psychics.)

[4] The Philistines assembled and camped in Shunem. Saul also assembled the whole Israelite army, and they camped at Gilboa. [5] When Saul looked at the Philistine army, he was very afraid—terrified. [6] He prayed to the LORD, but the LORD didn't answer him through dreams, the Urim,[a] or prophets. [7] Saul told his officers, "Find me a woman who conjures up the dead. Then I'll go to her and ask for her services."

His officers told him, "There is a woman at Endor who conjures up the dead."

[8] After disguising himself by putting on other clothes, Saul left with two men and came to the woman that night. He said to her, "Please consult with a dead person for me. Conjure up the person I request."

[9] The woman told him, "You know that Saul rid the land of mediums and psychics. Why are you trying to trap me and have me killed?"

[10] But Saul took an oath in the LORD's name, "I solemnly swear, as the LORD lives, you will not be harmed if you do this."

[11] "Whom should I conjure up for you?" the woman asked.

"Conjure up Samuel for me," he answered.

[12] When the woman saw Samuel, she cried out loudly and asked, "Why did you deceive me? You're Saul!"

[13] "Don't be afraid," the king said to her. "What do you see?"

"I see a god rising from the ground," the woman answered.

[14] "In what form?" he asked her.

She answered, "An old man is coming up, and he's wearing a robe." Then Saul knew it was Samuel. Saul knelt down with his face touching the ground.

[15] Samuel asked Saul, "Why did you disturb me by conjuring me up?"

Saul answered, "I'm in serious trouble. The Philistines are at war with me, and God has turned against me and doesn't answer me anymore—either by the prophets or in dreams. So I've called on you to tell me what to do."

[16] Samuel said, "Why are you asking me when the LORD has turned against you and become your enemy? [17] The LORD has done to you ˌexactlyˌ what he spoke through me: The LORD has torn the kingship out of your hands and given it to your fellow Israelite David. [18] The LORD is doing this to you today because you didn't listen to him or unleash his burning anger on Amalek. [19] For the same reasons the LORD will hand you and Israel over to the Philistines. Tomorrow you and your sons will be with me. And then the LORD will hand Israel's army over to the Philistines."

[20] Immediately, Saul fell flat on the ground. He was frightened by Samuel's words. He also had no strength left, because he hadn't eaten anything all day or all night. [21] The woman came over to Saul and saw that he was terrified. "I listened to you," she told him, "and I took my life in my hands when I did what you told me to do. [22] Now please listen to me. I will serve you something to eat. Eat it so that you will have strength when you leave."

[23] But he refused. "I don't want to eat," he said. Nevertheless, his officers and the woman kept urging[b] him until he listened to them. So he got up from the ground and sat on the bed.

[24] The woman immediately butchered a fattened calf that she owned. She took flour, kneaded it, and baked some unleavened bread. [25] Then she served it to Saul and his officers. They ate and left that ˌsameˌ night.

---

[b] 27:10 Dead Sea Scrolls, Greek; Masoretic Text "Did you raid today?"   [a] 28:6 The Urim and Thummim were used by the chief priest to determine God's answer to questions.   [b] 28:23 Greek; Masoretic Text "the woman broke through."

The Philistines Reject David

29 [1] The Philistines assembled their whole army at Aphek, and Israel camped at the spring in Jezreel. [2] The Philistine leaders were marching by with their companies and regiments. David and his men were marching in the rear with Achish.

[3] The Philistine officers asked, "What are these Hebrews doing here?"

Achish asked the Philistine officers, "Isn't this David, the servant of King Saul of Israel, who has been with me now for a year or two? I've found nothing wrong with him from the day he defected until now."

[4] But the Philistine officers were angry with Achish. "Send the man back," the Philistine officers told him. "Return him to the place you assigned him. He shouldn't go with us into battle. He shouldn't ˌbe allowed toˌ become our enemy during the battle. Is this man going to try to regain his master's favor? He'll do it with the lives of our men! [5] Isn't this David of whom people sing in dances:

'Saul has defeated thousands
   but David tens of thousands'?"

[6] Then Achish called David and told him, "I solemnly swear, as the LORD lives, you are a dependable man. I consider your campaigning with me a good thing, because I've never found anything wrong with you from the day you came to me until now. But the rulers don't approve of you. [7] So leave peacefully without doing anything to displease the Philistine rulers."

[8] "What have I done?" David asked Achish. "What have you learned about me from the time I came to you until now? Why shouldn't I fight your enemies, Your Majesty?"

[9] Achish answered David, "I admit that in my judgment you're as good as God's Messenger. However, the Philistine officers said, 'He shouldn't go into battle with us.' [10] Get up early in the morning with Saul's servants who came with you, and go to the place I have assigned to you. Don't worry about the unkind words, because I still approve of you.[a] Get up in the morning, and leave when it's light."

[11] Early the next morning David and his men returned to Philistine territory, while the Philistines went to Jezreel.

David Defeats the Amalekites

30 [1] Two days later, when David and his men came to Ziklag, the Amalekites had raided the Negev, including Ziklag. They had attacked Ziklag and burned it. [2] Although they captured the young and old women who were there, they killed no one. Instead, they had taken ˌthe women and other prisonersˌ and gone away. [3] By the time David and his men came to the town, it had been burned down, and their wives, sons, and daughters had been taken captive. [4] Then David and his men cried loudly until they didn't have the strength to cry anymore. [5] The Amalekites also captured David's two wives, Ahinoam from Jezreel and Abigail (who had been Nabal's wife) from Carmel. [6] David was in great distress because the people in their bitterness said he should be stoned. (They were thinking of their sons and daughters. But David found strength in the LORD his God.)

[7] David told the priest Abiathar, Ahimelech's son, "Please bring me the priestly ephod."[a] So Abiathar brought David the ephod.

[8] Then David asked the LORD, "Should I pursue these troops? Will I catch up with them?"

"Pursue them," the LORD told him. "You will certainly catch up with them and rescue the captives."

[9] So David and his 600 men went to the Besor Valley, where some were left behind. [10] David and 400 men went in pursuit, while 200 men who were too exhausted to cross the Besor Valley stayed behind.

[11] David's men found an Egyptian in the open country and took him to David. They gave him food to eat and water to drink. [12] They gave him a slice of fig cake and two bunches of raisins. After he had eaten, he revived. (He hadn't eaten any food or drunk any water for three whole days.) [13] David asked him, "To whom do you belong? Where do you come from?"

"I'm an Egyptian, the slave of an Amalekite," the young man answered. "My master left me behind because I got sick three days ago. [14] We raided the portion of the Negev where the Cherethites live, the territory of Judah, the portion of the Negev where Caleb settled, and we burned down Ziklag."

[15] "Will you lead me to these troops?" David asked him.

He answered, "Take an oath in front of God that you won't kill me or hand me over to my master, and I'll lead you to these troops."

---

¹⁶ The Egyptian led him ⌊to them⌋. They were spread out all over the land, eating, and drinking. They were celebrating because they had taken so much loot from Philistine territory and from the land of Judah. ¹⁷ From dawn until evening the next day, David attacked them. No one escaped except 400 young men who rode away on camels. ¹⁸ David rescued everything the Amalekites had taken, including his two wives. ¹⁹ Nothing was missing—young or old, sons or daughters, the loot or anything else they had taken with them. David brought back everything. ²⁰ He took all the sheep and the cattle. His men drove the animals ahead of him and said, "This is David's loot."

²¹ David came to the 200 men who had been too exhausted to go with him and had stayed in the Besor Valley. They came to meet David and the people with him. As David approached the men, he greeted them. ²² Then every wicked and worthless man who had gone with David said, "Since they didn't go with us, they shouldn't be given any of the loot we recovered. Each of them should take only his wife and children and leave."

²³ But David said, "My brothers, don't do that with the things which the LORD has given us. He has protected us and handed the troops that attacked us over to us. ²⁴ Besides, who is going to pay attention to what you have to say in this matter? Certainly, the share of those who go into battle must be like the share of those who stay with the supplies. They will all share alike." ²⁵ From that time on he made this a rule and a custom in Israel as it is to this day.

²⁶ When David came to Ziklag, he sent part of the loot to his friends, the leaders of Judah. He said, "Here is a gift for you from the loot ⌊taken from⌋ the LORD's enemies." ²⁷ There were shares for those in Bethel, Ramoth in the Negev, Jattir, ²⁸ Aroer, Siphmoth, Eshtemoa, ²⁹ Racal, the cities belonging to the Jerahmeelites, the cities belonging to the Kenites, ³⁰ Hormah, Borashan, Athach, ³¹ Hebron, and to all the places David and his men visited from time to time.

The Death of Saul—1 Chronicles 10:1–14

31 ¹ When the Philistines were fighting against Israel, the men of Israel fled from the Philistines and were killed in battle on Mount Gilboa. ² The Philistines caught up to Saul and his sons. They killed Jonathan, Abinadab, and Malchishua, Saul's sons. ³ The heaviest fighting was against Saul. When the archers got him in their range, he was badly wounded by them.

⁴ Saul told his armorbearer, "Draw your sword! Stab me, or these godless men will come, stab me, and make fun of me." But his armorbearer refused because he was terrified. So Saul took the sword and fell on it. ⁵ When the armorbearer saw that Saul was dead, he also fell on his sword and died with him. ⁶ So Saul, his three sons, his armorbearer, and all his men died together that day.

⁷ When the people of Israel on the other side of the valley and across the Jordan River saw that the men of Israel had fled and that Saul and his sons were dead, they abandoned their cities. So the Philistines came to live in these cities.

⁸ The next day, when the Philistines came to strip the dead, they found Saul and his three sons lying on Mount Gilboa. ⁹ They cut off his head and stripped off his armor. Then they sent men throughout Philistine territory to tell the people this good news in their idols' temples. ¹⁰ They put his armor in the temple of their goddesses—the Asherahs—and fastened his corpse to the wall of Beth Shan.

¹¹ When the people living in Jabesh Gilead heard what the Philistines had done to Saul, ¹² all the fighting men marched all night and took the dead bodies of Saul and his sons from the wall of Beth Shan. They came back to Jabesh and burned the bodies there. ¹³ They took the bones and buried them under the tamarisk tree in Jabesh. Then they fasted seven days.

2 SAMUEL

The Report of Saul's Death

1 ¹ After Saul died and David returned from defeating the Amalekites,ᵃ David stayed in Ziklag two days. ² On the third day a man came from Saul's camp. His clothes were torn, and he had dirt on his head. When he came to David, he immediately bowed down with his face touching the ground.

³ "Where did you come from?" David asked him.

"I escaped from the camp of Israel," he answered.

⁴ "What happened?" David asked him. "Please tell me."

The man answered, "The army fled from the battle, and many of the soldiers died. Saul and his son Jonathan are dead too."

⁵ "How do you know Saul and his son Jonathan are dead?" David asked the young man who had brought him the news.

⁶ The young man answered, "I happened to be on Mount Gilboa. Saul was there leaning on his spear, and the chariots and horsemen were catching up with him. ⁷ When he looked back and saw me, he called to me, and I said, 'Yes?' "

⁸ "He asked me, 'Who are you?'

"I said to him, 'I'm an Amalekite.'

⁹ "He said to me, 'Please stand over me and kill me. I'm alive, but I'm suffering.'ᵇ

¹⁰ "So I stood over him and killed him, since I knew he couldn't survive after he had been wounded. And I took the crown that was on his head and the band that was on his arm and brought them here to you, sir."

¹¹ Then David grabbed his own clothes and tore them in grief. All the men with him did the same. ¹² They mourned, cried, and fasted until evening because Saul, his son Jonathan, the LORD's army, and the nation of Israel had been defeated in battle.

¹³ David asked the young man who had brought him the news, "Where are you from?"

And the young man answered, "I'm an Amalekite, the son of a foreign resident."

¹⁴ David asked, "Why weren't you afraid to take it upon yourself to destroy the LORD's anointed king?" ¹⁵ Then David called one of ₍his₎ young men and told him, "Come here and attack him." David's young man executed him ¹⁶ while David said, "You are responsible for spilling your own blood. You testified against yourself when you said, 'I killed the LORD's anointed king.' "

David's Lament

¹⁷ David wrote this song of mourning for Saul and his son Jonathan. ¹⁸ He said,

"Teach this *kesheth*ᶜ to the people of Judah."
(It is recorded in the Book of Jashar.)

¹⁹ "Your glory, Israel, lies dead on your hills.
See how the mighty have fallen!
²⁰ Don't tell the news in Gath.
Don't announce the victory in the streets of Ashkelon,
or the daughters of the Philistines will be glad,
and the daughters of godless men will celebrate.
²¹ You mountains in Gilboa,
may there be no dew or rain on you
or on your slopes,ᵇ
because warriors' shields were tarnished there.
Saul's shield was never rubbed with olive oil.
²² From the blood of those killed and the fat of the warriors,
Jonathan's bow did not turn away,
nor did Saul's sword return unused.
²³ Saul and Jonathan were loved and well-liked while they were living.

ᵃ 1:1 Some Hebrew manuscripts, Syriac; other Hebrew manuscripts, Greek "Amalek."   ᵇ 1:9, 21 Hebrew meaning uncertain.
ᶜ 1:18 Unknown musical term.

They were not separated even when they died.
They were swifter than eagles and stronger than lions.

24 Daughters of Israel, cry over Saul,
who dressed you in decorated, red clothes,
who put gold jewelry on your clothes.

25 See how the mighty have fallen in battle!
On your hills Jonathan was killed!

26 I am heartbroken over you, my brother Jonathan.
You were my great delight.
Your love was more wonderful to me than the love of women.

27 See how the mighty have fallen!
See how the weapons of war have been destroyed!"

David Becomes King of Judah

2 ¹ After this, David asked the LORD, "Should I go to one of the cities of Judah?"
"Go," the LORD answered him.
"Where should I go?" David asked.
"To Hebron," the LORD replied.

² David went there with his two wives, Ahinoam from Jezreel and Abigail (who had been Nabal's wife) from Carmel. ³ David took his men and their families with him, and they settled in the towns around Hebron. ⁴ Then the people of Judah came to Hebron and anointed David to be king over the tribe of Judah.

They told David, "The people of Jabesh Gilead were the ones who buried Saul." ⁵ So David sent messengers to the people of Jabesh Gilead. He said to them, "May the LORD bless you because you showed kindness to your master Saul by burying him. ⁶ May the LORD always show you kindness. I, too, will be good to you because you did this. ⁷ Now, be strong and courageous. Because your master Saul is dead, the tribe of Judah has anointed me to be their king."

Abner Makes Ishbosheth King of Israel

⁸ Ner's son Abner, commander of Saul's army, took Saul's son Ishbosheth[a] and brought him to Mahanaim. ⁹ Abner made him king of Gilead, Asher,[b] Jezreel, Ephraim, and Benjamin, that is, all Israel. ¹⁰ Saul's son Ishbosheth was 40 years old when he became king of Israel. He ruled for two years, but the tribe of Judah followed David. ¹¹ In Hebron David was king over the tribe of Judah for seven years and six months.

Conflicts Between Abner and Joab

¹² Ner's son Abner and the officers of Saul's son Ishbosheth went from Mahanaim to Gibeon. ¹³ Zeruiah's son Joab and David's officers also left ˏHebronˌ. Both groups met at the pool of Gibeon. They sat down there, one group on one side of the pool and the other group on the other side of the pool.

¹⁴ Abner said to Joab, "Let's have the young men hold a contest." Joab agreed. ¹⁵ The men got up and were counted as they passed by. Twelve were from the tribe of Benjamin (representing Saul's son Ishbosheth), and twelve were from David's officers. ¹⁶ Each one grabbed his opponent by the head, stuck his sword into his opponent's side, and they fell down together. Therefore, that place in Gibeon is called the Field of Enemies. ¹⁷ Fierce fighting broke out that day, and David's men defeated Abner and the men of Israel.

¹⁸ Zeruiah's three sons were there: Joab, Abishai, and Asahel. Asahel was as fast on his feet as a wild gazelle. ¹⁹ He chased Abner and refused to leave him alone. ²⁰ When Abner looked back, he asked, "Are you Asahel?"

"Yes," Asahel answered.

²¹ Abner told him, "Leave me alone! Catch one of the young men, and take his weapon."[c]

But Asahel refused to turn away from him. ²² So Abner spoke again to Asahel. "Stop following me," he said. "Why should I kill you? How could I look your brother Joab in the face again?"

²³ But Asahel refused to turn away. So Abner struck him with the butt of the spear. The spear went into his belly and came out his back. He fell down there and died on the spot. And everyone who came to the place where Asahel fell and died stopped there.

²⁴ But Joab and Abishai chased Abner. When the sun went down, they came to the hill of Ammah, opposite Giah on the road from Gibeon to the desert. ²⁵ The men of Benjamin rallied behind Abner, banding together and taking their position on top of a hill.

²⁶ Then Abner called to Joab, "Should this slaughter go on forever? Don't you know this will end in bitterness? How long will it be before you will call off your troops from chasing their relatives?"

---

[a] 2:8 Masoretic Text; 1 Chronicles 8:33, 9:39; Greek "Ishbaal."   [b] 2:9 Or "the Ashurites."   [c] 2:21 Hebrew meaning uncertain.

²⁷ Joab answered, "I solemnly swear, as God lives, if you had not spoken, the men would not have stopped chasing their relatives until morning." ²⁸ So Joab blew a ram's horn, and all the troops stopped. They didn't chase or fight Israel anymore.

²⁹ Abner and his men marched through the plains all that night. They crossed the Jordan River and passed through the entire Bithron until they came to Mahanaim.

³⁰ Joab returned from chasing Abner. When he had gathered all the troops, ˌonlyˌ 19 of David's officers and Asahel were missing. ³¹ However, David's officers had killed 360 of the men of Benjamin under Abner's command. ³² They took Asahel and buried him in his father's tomb in Bethlehem. Then Joab and his men marched all night and arrived at Hebron by daybreak.

3 ¹ As the war between the royal families of Saul and David dragged on, David's family became stronger and stronger, and Saul's family became weaker and weaker.

David's Sons—1 Chronicles 3:1–4

² Sons were born to David while he was in Hebron. His first son was Amnon, ˌbornˌ to Ahinoam from Jezreel. ³ The second was Chileab, ˌbornˌ to Abigail (who had been Nabal's wife) from Carmel. The third was Absalom, whose mother was Maacah (the daughter of King Talmai) from Geshur. ⁴ The fourth was Adonijah, whose mother was Haggith. The fifth was Shephatiah, whose mother was Abital. ⁵ The sixth was Ithream, ˌbornˌ to David's wife Eglah. These sons were born to David while he was in Hebron.

Abner's Death

⁶ During the war between the families of Saul and David, Abner strengthened his position in Saul's royal family. ⁷ Saul had a concubineᵃ named Rizpah (Aiah's daughter). Ishbosheth asked Abner, "Why did you have sex with my father's concubine?"

⁸ Ishbosheth's question made Abner very angry. "Have I been behaving like some Judean dog?"ᵇ he asked. "Until now I've been faithful to your father Saul's family, to his relatives and friends, and I haven't handed you over to David. But now you charge me with a crime because of this woman. ⁹ May God strike me dead unless I do for David what the LORD had promised him with an oath: ¹⁰ 'I, the LORD, will transfer the kingship from Saul's family and establish David's throne over Israel and Judah from Dan to Beersheba.'" ¹¹ Ishbosheth couldn't respond to a single word, because he was afraid of Abner.

¹² Then Abner sent messengers to David to speak on his behalf. "Who owns this country?" he asked. "Make an agreement with me," he said. "I'll support you and bring all Israel to you."

¹³ "Good!" David answered. "I'll make an agreement with you. But there's one condition: You can't come to see me unless you bring Michal, Saul's daughter, when you come."

¹⁴ Then David sent messengers to Saul's son Ishbosheth to say, "Give me my wife Michal. I made a payment of 100 Philistine foreskins for her."

¹⁵ So Ishbosheth sent men to take her from her husband Paltiel, son of Laish. ¹⁶ Her husband went with her and cried over her all the way to Bahurim. "Go home," Abner told him. So he went home.

¹⁷ Meanwhile, Abner sent the following message to the leaders of Israel: "For some time now you've wanted to make David your king. ¹⁸ Do it now, because the LORD said about David: 'I will save my people Israel from the Philistines and all their other enemies through my servant David.'" ¹⁹ Abner also spoke specifically to the people of Benjamin.

Then Abner went directly to David in Hebron to tell him everything Israel and the entire tribe of Benjamin had approved. ²⁰ So Abner came with 20 men to David in Hebron, and David had a feast for Abner and his men.

²¹ Abner told David, "I must go now so that I can gather all Israel for you, Your Majesty. They will make a treaty with you, and you will rule everything your heart desires." Then David dismissed Abner, who left peacefully.

²² Just then David's men and Joab were coming home from a raid with a lot of goods. Abner had been dismissed, so he was no longer with David in Hebron. ²³ When Joab came back with the whole army, he was told, "Ner's son Abner came to the king, but David dismissed him, and Abner left peacefully."

²⁴ Then Joab went to the king and asked, "What have you done? Abner came to see you. Why did you dismiss him and let him get away? ²⁵ Certainly you must know that Ner's son Abner came to deceive you, to find out about your movements and learn everything you're doing!"

²⁶ After leaving David, Joab sent messengers after Abner. They brought him back from the cistern of Sirah without David knowing about it. ²⁷ When Abner returned to Hebron, Joab took him aside in the gateway as if to talk to him privately. There he stabbed Abner in the belly. Abner died because he spilled the blood of Joab's brother Asahel.

ᵃ 3:7 A concubine is considered a wife except she has fewer rights under the law.   ᵇ 3:8 English equivalent difficult.

[28] Later when David heard about it, he said, "As far as the LORD is concerned, my kingdom and I are forever innocent of spilling the blood of Ner's son Abner. [29] May the blame fall on the head of Joab and all of his family. May there always be members of Joab's family who have oozing sores and skin diseases, who can only work a spindle,[c] who die in battle, and who never have any food." [30] (Joab and his brother Abishai killed Abner because he had killed their brother Asahel in the battle at Gibeon.)

[31] David told Joab and all the people with him, "Tear your clothes, put on sackcloth, and mourn for Abner." King David followed the open casket. [32] They buried Abner in Hebron. The king cried loudly at Abner's grave, and all the people cried. [33] The king sang a funeral song for Abner:

> Should Abner die like a godless fool?
> [34]   Your hands were not tied.
>   Your feet were not chained.
> You fell as one falls in front of wicked men.

And all the people continued to cry for him. [35] That entire day all the people tried to get David to eat some food. But David had taken an oath: "May God strike me dead if I taste any food or anything else before the sun goes down." [36] Then all the people understood and approved of this, as all the people approved of everything the king did. [37] That day all the people of Israel knew the king wasn't responsible for killing Ner's son Abner. [38] The king said to his officers, "Don't you know that today a leader, a great man, has fallen in Israel? [39] Today I'm weak, though I'm the anointed king. These men, Zeruiah's sons, are too cruel for me. May the LORD repay this evildoer as his evil deeds deserve."

Ishbosheth Is Murdered

4 [1] When Saul's son Ishbosheth heard that Abner had died in Hebron, he lost his courage, and all Israel was alarmed. [2] Saul's son had two men who were captains of raiding parties. One was named Baanah, and the other was named Rechab. They were the sons of Rimmon from Beeroth from the tribe of Benjamin.

(Beeroth was considered a part of Benjamin, [3] even though the people of Beeroth had fled to Gittaim. They still live there today. [4] In addition, Saul's son Jonathan had a son who was crippled. When the boy was five years old, the news about ˌthe death ofˌ Saul and Jonathan came from Jezreel. His nurse picked him up and fled ˌto Gittaimˌ. She was in a hurry when she left, and he fell ˌfrom her armsˌ and became disabled. His name was Mephibosheth.)

[5] Rechab and Baanah, the sons of Rimmon from Beeroth, came to Ishbosheth's home at the hottest time of the day. Ishbosheth was taking his midday nap [6] when they came into the house as though they were going to get some flour. Instead, they stabbed him in the belly. Then Rechab and his brother Baanah escaped. [7] (They had come into the house while Ishbosheth was sleeping on his bed in his bedroom. They stabbed him, killed him, and cut off his head.) They took his head and traveled all night along the road to the plains.

[8] They brought Ishbosheth's head to David at Hebron. "Here is the head of Ishbosheth, the son of your enemy Saul who tried to kill you," they told the king. "Today the LORD has given Your Royal Majesty revenge on Saul and his descendants."

[9] David responded to Rechab and his brother Baanah, the sons of Rimmon from Beeroth, [10] "I once seized a man who told me that Saul had died. He thought he was bringing good news. I killed him in Ziklag to reward him for his news. [11] How much more ˌshould I rewardˌ wicked men who kill an innocent man on his own bed in his home? The LORD has rescued me from every trouble. I solemnly swear, as the LORD lives,[a] I'll now seek revenge for his murder and rid the land of you." [12] So David gave an order to his young men, who executed Rechab and Baanah, cut off their hands and feet, and hung their dead bodies by the pond in Hebron. Then they took Ishbosheth's head and buried it in Abner's tomb in Hebron.

David Anointed King of Israel—*1 Chronicles 11:1–3; 3:4*

5 [1] All the tribes of Israel came to David at Hebron. "We are your own flesh and blood," they said. [2] "Even in the past when Saul ruled us, you were the one who led Israel in battle. The LORD has said to you, 'You will be shepherd of my people Israel, the leader of Israel.' "

[3] All the leaders of Israel had come to Hebron. King David made an agreement with them at Hebron in front of the LORD. So they anointed David king of Israel. [4] David was 30 years old when he became king, and he ruled for 40 years. [5] In Hebron he ruled Judah for seven years and six months. In Jerusalem he ruled for 33 years over all Israel and Judah.

---

[c] 3:29 Spinning yarn and thread was normally done only by women and therefore was something only the weakest of men would do.   [a] 4:11 The last part of verse 9 (in Hebrew) has been placed in verse 11 to express the complex Hebrew paragraph structure more clearly in English.

David Captures Jerusalem—1 Chronicles 11:4–9

⁶ The king and his men went to Jerusalem to attack the Jebusites, who lived in that region. The Jebusites told David, "You will never get in here. Even the blind and the lame could turn you away" (meaning that David could never get in there). ⁷ But David captured the fortress Zion (that is, the City of David). ⁸ That day David said, "Whoever wants to defeat the Jebusites must reach the lame and the blind who hate me by using the water shaft." So there is a saying, "The blind and the lame will not get into the palace."ᵃ ⁹ David lived in the fortress and called it the City of David. He built the city ˎof Jerusalemˎ around it from the Milloᵇ to the palace. ¹⁰ David continued to grow more powerful because the LORD Godᶜ of Armies was with him.

David's Palace, Wives, and Children in Jerusalem—1 Chronicles 14:1–7; 3:5–9

¹¹ Then King Hiram of Tyre sent messengers to David, along with cedarwood, carpenters, and stonemasons. They built a palace for David. ¹² So David realized that the LORD had established him as king of Israel and made his kingship famous for the sake of Israel, the LORD's people.

¹³ David married more concubinesᵈ and wives from Jerusalem after he had come there from Hebron, and he fathered more sons and daughters. ¹⁴ These are the names of the children born to him in Jerusalem: Shammua, Shobab, Nathan, Solomon, ¹⁵ Ibhar, Elishua, Nepheg, Japhia, ¹⁶ Elishama, Eliada, and Eliphelet.

David Defeats the Philistines—1 Chronicles 14:8–17

¹⁷ When the Philistines heard that David had been anointed king of Israel, all of them came to attack David. But David heard about it and went to the fortress. ¹⁸ The Philistines had come and overrun the valley of Rephaim.

¹⁹ David asked the LORD, "Should I attack the Philistines? Will you hand them over to me?"

The LORD answered David, "Attack! I will certainly hand the Philistines over to you."

²⁰ So David went to Baal Perazim and defeated the Philistines there. He said, "The LORD has overwhelmed my enemies in front of me like an overwhelming flood." That is why that place is called Baal Perazim [The LORD Overwhelms]. ²¹ The Philistines left their idols there, so David and his men carried the idols away.

²² The Philistines again attacked and overran the valley of Rephaim. ²³ David asked the LORD, and he answered, "Don't attack now, but circle around behind them, and come at them in front of the balsam trees. ²⁴ When you hear the sound of marching in the tops of the balsam trees, act immediately because the LORD has gone ahead of you to defeat the Philistine army." ²⁵ David did as the LORD ordered him and defeated the Philistines from Geba to Gezer.

David Brings the Ark to Jerusalem—1 Chronicles 13:5–14; 15:25–16:3, 43

6 ¹ David again assembled all the best soldiers in Israel, 30,000 men. ² He and all the people with him left Baalah in Judahᵃ to bring God's ark ˎto Jerusalemˎ. (The ark is called by the name of the LORD of Armies, who is enthroned over the angels.ᵇ) ³ David and his men put God's ark on a new cart and brought it from Abinadab's home on the hill. Uzzah and Ahio, Abinadab's sons, were guiding the new cart. ⁴ They brought it from Abinadab's home, with Ahio walking ahead of the ark. ⁵ David and the entire nation of Israel were celebrating in the LORD's presence with all kinds of instruments made from cypress woodᶜ and with lyres, harps, tambourines, sistrums,ᵈ and cymbals.

⁶ But when they came to Nacon's threshing floor,ᵉ the oxen stumbled. So Uzzah reached out for the ark of God and grabbed it. ⁷ The LORD became angry with Uzzah, so God killed him there for his lack of respect. He died beside the ark of God.

⁸ David was angry because the LORD had struck Uzzah so violently. (That place is still called Perez Uzzah [The Striking of Uzzah] today.) ⁹ David was afraid of the LORD that day. "How can the ark of the LORD come to my ˎcityˎ?" he asked. ¹⁰ So David wouldn't bring the ark of the LORD with him to the City of David. Instead, he rerouted it to the home of Obed Edom, who was from Gath. ¹¹ The ark of the LORD stayed at the home of Obed Edom from Gath for three months, and the LORD blessed Obed Edom and his whole family.

¹² King David was told, "The LORD has blessed Obed Edom's home and everything he owns because of the ark of God." Then David joyfully went to get the ark of God from Obed Edom's house and bring it to the City of David. ¹³ When those who carried the ark of the LORD had gone six steps, David sacrificed a bull and a fattened calf.

ᵃ 5:8 Or "temple."   ᵇ 5:9 The exact place referred to as "the Millo" is unknown.   ᶜ 5:10 Masoretic Text; Dead Sea Scrolls, Greek, 1 Chronicles 11:9 omit "God."   ᵈ 5:13 A concubine is considered a wife except she has fewer rights under the law.
ᵃ 6:2 Or "Baal in Judah" or "the citizens of Judah"; Dead Sea Scrolls and 1 Chronicles 13:6 "Baalah in Kiriath Jearim."
ᵇ 6:2 Or "cherubim."   ᶜ 6:5 Or "with all their might." See 1 Chronicles 13:8.   ᵈ 6:5 A type of rattle used as a musical instrument.
ᵉ 6:6 A threshing floor is an outdoor area where grain is separated from its husks.

¹⁴ Wearing a linen ephod,ᶠ David danced in the LORD's presence with all his might. ¹⁵ He and the entire nation of Israel brought the ark of the LORD with shouts of joy and the sounding of rams' horns. ¹⁶ When the ark of the LORD came to the City of David, Saul's daughter Michal looked out of a window and saw King David leaping and dancing in the LORD's presence, so she despised him.

¹⁷ The men carrying the ark set it in its place inside the tent David had put up for it. David sacrificed burnt offerings and fellowship offerings in the LORD's presence. ¹⁸ When David had finished sacrificing the burnt offerings and the fellowship offerings, he blessed the people in the name of the LORD of Armies. ¹⁹ He also distributed to all the people—to the whole crowd of Israelites, both men and women—one loaf of bread, one date cake, and one raisin cake. Then all the people went home.

²⁰ When David returned to bless his family, Saul's daughter Michal came out to meet him. "How dignified Israel's king was today! He was exposing himself before the eyes of the slave girls of his palace staff—like a mindless fool might expose himself!"

²¹ David answered Michal, "˖I didn't dance in front of the slave girls but˖ in front of the LORD. He chose me rather than your father or anyone in your father's house, and he appointed me leader of Israel, the LORD's people. I will celebrate in the LORD's presence, ²² and I will degrade myself even more than this. Even if I am humiliated in your eyes, I will be honored by these slave girls you speak about."

²³ So Saul's daughter Michal was childless her entire life.

David's Wish to Build a House for God—1 Chronicles 17:1–27

7 ¹ While King David was living in his house, the LORD gave him peace with all his enemies around him. ² So the king said to the prophet Nathan, "Look, I'm living in a house made of cedar, while the ark of God remains in the tent."

³ Nathan told the king, "Do everything you have in mind, because the LORD is with you."

⁴ But that same night the LORD spoke his word to Nathan: ⁵ "Say to my servant David, 'This is what the LORD says: Are you the one who will build me a house to live in? ⁶ I haven't lived in a house from the day I took Israel out of Egypt to this day. Instead, I moved around in a tent, the tent ˖of meeting˖. ⁷ In all the places I've moved with all the Israelites, did I ever ask any of the judgesᵃ of Israel whom I ordered to be shepherds of my people Israel why they didn't build me a house of cedar?'

⁸ "Now this is what you will say to my servant David: 'This is what the LORD of Armies says: I took you from the pasture where you followed sheep so that you could be the leader of my people Israel. ⁹ I was with you wherever you went, and I destroyed all your enemies in front of you. I will make your name famous like the names of the greatest people on earth. ¹⁰ I will make a place for my people Israel and plant them there. They will live in their own place and not be troubled anymore. The wicked will no longer oppress them as they used to do ¹¹ ever since I appointed judges to rule my people Israel. So I will give you peace with all your enemies. I, the LORD, tell you that I will make a house for you.

¹² " 'When the time comes for you to lie down in death with your ancestors, I will send one of your descendants, ˖one˖ who will come from you. I will establish his kingdom. ¹³ He will build a house for my name, and I will establish the throne of his kingdom forever. ¹⁴ I will be his Father, and he will be my Son. If he sins, I will punish him with a rod and with blows inflicted by people. ¹⁵ But I will never stop showing him my love as I did to Saul, whom I took out of your way. ¹⁶ Your royal house will remain in my presenceᵇ forever. Your throne will be established forever.' "

¹⁷ Nathan told David all these words and everything he had seen.

¹⁸ King David went into the tent and sat in front of the LORD. "Who am I, Almighty LORD," he asked, "and why is my house so important that you have brought me this far? ¹⁹ And even this you consider to be a small act, Almighty LORD. You've also spoken about the distant future of my house. Almighty LORD, this is the teaching about the man.

²⁰ "What more can I, David, say to you, Almighty LORD, since you know me so well! ²¹ You've done this great thing because of your promise and your own desire. You made it known to me.

²² "That is why you are great, LORD God. There is no one like you, and there is no other god except you, as we have heard with our own ears. ²³ Who is like your people Israel? It is the one nation on earth that God came to free in order to make its people his own, to make his nameᶜ known, and to do great and wonderful things for them. You forcedᵈ nations and their gods out of the way of your people, whom you freed from Egypt to be your own. ²⁴ You created the people of Israel to be your people forever. And you, LORD, became their God.

ᶠ6:14 *Ephod* is a technical term for a part of the priest's clothes. Its exact usage and shape are unknown.
ᵃ 7:7 1 Chronicles 17:6; Masoretic Text "tribes." ᵇ 7:16 Some Hebrew manuscripts, Greek, Latin, Syriac; other Hebrew manuscripts "in your presence." ᶜ 7:23 Or "its name." ᵈ 7:23 Greek and 1 Chronicles 17:21; Masoretic Text "Your land."

²⁵ "Now, LORD God, keep the promise you made to me and my house forever. Do as you promised. ²⁶ Your name will be respected forever when ‿people‿ say, 'The LORD of Armies is God over Israel.' And the house of your servant David will be established in your presence. ²⁷ You, LORD of Armies, God of Israel, have revealed it especially to me, saying, 'I will build a house for you.' That is why I have found the courage to offer this prayer to you. ·

²⁸ "Almighty LORD, you are God, and your words are trustworthy. You promised me this good thing. ²⁹ Now, please bless my house so that it may continue in your presence forever. Indeed, you, Almighty LORD, have promised it. With your blessing my house will be blessed forever."

David's Successes—1 Chronicles 18:1–17

8 ¹ After this, David defeated and crushed the Philistines. He took control of the main Philistine city from them.ᵃ

² He also defeated Moab, made the Moabites lie down on the ground, and measured them with a rope. He measured two lengths which were to be killed, and one length which was to be spared. So the Moabites became David's subjects and paid taxes ‿to him‿.

³ When David went to restore his control ‿over the territory‿ along the Euphrates River, he defeated Zobah's King Hadadezer, son of Rehob. ⁴ David took 1,700 horsemen and 20,000 foot soldiers from him. David also disabled all but 100 of their horses so that they couldn't pull chariots.

⁵ When the Arameans from Damascus came to help King Hadadezer of Zobah, David killed 22,000 of them. ⁶ David put troops in the Aramean kingdom of Damascus, and the Arameans became his subjects and paid taxes ‿to him‿. Everywhere David went, the LORD gave him victories.

⁷ David took the gold shields that belonged to Hadadezer'sᵇ servants, and he brought them to Jerusalem. ⁸ King David also took a large quantity of bronze from Betah and Berothai, Hadadezer's cities.

⁹ When King Toi of Hamath heard that David had defeated Hadadezer's whole army, ¹⁰ he sent his son Joram to greet King David and congratulate him for fighting and defeating Hadadezer. (There had often been war between Hadadezer and Toi.) Joram brought articles of gold, silver, and bronze with him. ¹¹ King David dedicated these articles to the LORD, along with the silver and gold he had dedicated from all the nations he conquered— ¹² from Edom, Moab, Ammon, the Philistines, Amalek, and from the goods taken from Zobah's King Hadadezer, son of Rehob.

¹³ David made a name for himself by killing 18,000 Edomitesᶜ in the Dead Sea region as he returned ‿to Jerusalem‿. ¹⁴ He put troops everywhere in Edom, and all the Edomites were David's subjects. Everywhere David went, the LORD gave him victories.

¹⁵ So David ruled all Israel. He did what was fair and right for all his people. ¹⁶ Zeruiah's son Joab was in charge of the army. Ahilud's son Jehoshaphat was the royal historian. ¹⁷ Ahitub's son Zadok and Abiathar's son Ahimelech were priests. Seraiah was the royal scribe. ¹⁸ Jehoiada's son Benaiah was commander of the Cherethites and the Pelethites. And David's sons were priests.ᵈ

David Keeps His Promise to Jonathan

9 ¹ David asked, "Is there anyone left in Saul's family to whom I can show kindness for Jonathan's sake?"

² Now, Saul's family had a servant whose name was Ziba. He was summoned to ‿come to‿ David. "Are you Ziba?" the king asked him.

"‿Yes,‿ I am," he answered.

³ David asked, "Is there someone left in Saul's family to whom I can show God's kindness?"

"Jonathan has a son who is disabled," Ziba answered.

⁴ "Where is he?" the king asked.

Ziba replied, "He is at the home of Machir, Ammiel's son, in Lo Debar."

⁵ So King David sent men to get him from the home of Ammiel's son Machir in Lo Debar. ⁶ When Mephibosheth (son of Jonathan and grandson of Saul) came to David, he quickly bowed down with his face touching the ground.

"Mephibosheth!" David said to him.

"Yes, sir," he answered.

⁷ "Don't be afraid," David told him, "I will certainly show you kindness for your father Jonathan's sake. I will give back to you all the land of your grandfather Saul, and you will always eat at my table."

ᵃ 8:1 Or "of Metheg Ammah."   ᵇ 8:7 Most Hebrew manuscripts; some Hebrew manuscripts, 1 Chronicles 18:7, Syriac, Targum "Hadadezer's servants carried."   ᶜ 8:13 A few Hebrew manuscripts, 1 Chronicles 18:12, Greek, Syriac; other Hebrew manuscripts "Arameans."   ᵈ 8:18 One Hebrew manuscript, Syriac, Targum, Latin; all other Hebrew manuscripts "Jehoiada's son Benaiah, the Cherethites, the Pelethites, and David's sons were priests."

⁸ Mephibosheth bowed down ⌊again⌋ and answered, "Who am I that you would look at a dead dog like me?"

⁹ Then the king called for Ziba, Saul's servant, and said to him, "I have given your master's grandson everything that belonged to Saul and his family. ¹⁰ You, your sons, and your servants should farm the land for him and harvest ⌊the crops⌋ so that your master's family will have food to eat. However, your master's grandson Mephibosheth will always eat at my table." (Ziba had 15 sons and 20 servants.)

¹¹ Ziba responded, "I will do everything you've commanded, Your Majesty." From then on, Mephibosheth ate at David's table as one of the king's sons.

¹² Mephibosheth had a young son whose name was Mica. Everyone who lived at Ziba's home became Mephibosheth's servant. ¹³ However, Mephibosheth, who was disabled, lived in Jerusalem. He always ate at the king's table.

David Defeats Ammon and Aram—1 Chronicles 19:1–19

10 ¹ Later the king of Ammon died, and his son Hanun became king in his place. ² David thought, "I will show kindness to Hanun as his father Nahash showed me kindness." So David sent his servants to comfort Hanun after his father's ⌊death⌋. But when David's servants entered Ammonite territory, ³ the Ammonite princes asked their master Hanun, "Do you think David is honoring your father because he sent men to comfort you? Hasn't David sent his men to explore the city, spy on it, and destroy it?" ⁴ So Hanun took David's men, shaved off half of each man's beard, cut off their clothes from the waist down, and sent them away.

⁵ After David was told ⌊what had happened⌋, he sent ⌊someone⌋ to meet them because they were deeply humiliated. The king said to them, "Stay in Jericho until your beards have grown back, and then return ⌊to Jerusalem⌋."

⁶ The Ammonites realized that they had made themselves offensive to David. So they hired the Arameans from Beth Rehob and Zobah (20,000 foot soldiers), ⌊the army of⌋ the king of Maacah (1,000 men), and the men of Tob (12,000 men).

⁷ After David heard about this, he sent Joab and all the elite troops. ⁸ The Ammonites formed a battle line at the entrance of the ⌊city⌋ gate, while the Arameans from Zobah and Rehob and the men from Tob and Maacah remained by themselves in the open country.

⁹ When Joab saw he was under attack in front and behind, he took the select troops of Israel and organized them for combat against the Arameans. ¹⁰ He put his brother Abishai in charge of the rest of the troops. Abishai organized them for combat against the Ammonites.

¹¹ Joab said, "If the Arameans are too strong for my ⌊troops⌋, be ready to help me. And if the Ammonites are too strong for your ⌊troops⌋, I'll come to help you. ¹² Be strong! Let's prove ourselves strong for our people and for the cities of our God, and the LORD will do what he considers right."

¹³ Then Joab and his troops advanced to fight the Arameans, and the Arameans fled. ¹⁴ When the Ammonites saw that the Arameans had fled, the Ammonites fled from Abishai and went into the city. So Joab stopped his campaign against the Ammonites and returned to Jerusalem.

¹⁵ Realizing that Israel had defeated them, the Arameans reassembled ⌊their troops⌋. ¹⁶ Hadadezer sent ⌊messengers⌋ to get Arameans from beyond the Euphrates River. The Arameans came to Helam with Shobach, the commander of Hadadezer's army, leading them.

¹⁷ When David was told ⌊about this⌋, he assembled Israel's army, crossed the Jordan River, and came to Helam. The Arameans formed a battle line against David's ⌊troops⌋ and fought him. ¹⁸ The Arameans fled from Israel, and David killed 700 chariot drivers and 40,000 horsemen. David struck Shobach dead.

¹⁹ When all the kings who were subject to Hadadezer saw that Israel had defeated them, they made peace with Israel and became their subjects. And the Arameans were afraid to help the Ammonites anymore.

David Takes Bathsheba—1 Chronicles 20:1

11 ¹ In the spring, the time when kings go out to battle, David sent Joab, his mercenaries, and Israel's army ⌊to war⌋. They destroyed the Ammonites and attacked Rabbah, while David stayed in Jerusalem.

² Now, when evening came, David got up from his bed and walked around on the roof of the royal palace. From the roof he saw a woman bathing, and she was very pretty. ³ David sent someone to ask about the woman. The man said, "She's Bathsheba, daughter of Eliam and wife of Uriah the Hittite." ⁴ So David sent messengers and took her. She came to him, and he went to bed with her. (She had just cleansed herself after her monthly period.) Then she went home. ⁵ The woman had become pregnant. So she sent someone to tell David that she was pregnant.

⁶ Then David sent a messenger to Joab, saying, "Send me Uriah the Hittite." So Joab sent Uriah to David. ⁷ When Uriah arrived, David asked him how Joab and the troops were and how the war was going.

⁸ "Go home," David said to Uriah, "and wash your feet." Uriah left the royal palace, and the king sent a present to him. ⁹ But Uriah slept at the entrance of the royal palace among his superior's mercenaries. He didn't go home.

¹⁰ When they told David, "Uriah didn't go home," David asked Uriah, "Didn't you just come from a journey? Why didn't you go home?"

¹¹ Uriah answered David, "The ark and ˌthe army ofˌ Israel and Judah are in temporary shelters, and my commander Joab and Your Majesty's mercenaries are living in the field. Should I then go to my house to eat and drink and go to bed with my wife? I solemnly swear, as sure as you're living, I won't do this!"

¹² David said to Uriah, "Then stay here today, and tomorrow I'll send you back." So Uriah stayed in Jerusalem that day and the next. ¹³ David summoned him, ate and drank with him, and got him drunk. But that evening Uriah went to lie down on his bed among his superior's mercenaries. He didn't go home.

¹⁴ In the morning David wrote a letter to Joab and sent it with Uriah. ¹⁵ In the letter he wrote, "Put Uriah on the front line where the fighting is heaviest. Then abandon him so that he'll be struck down and die."

¹⁶ Since Joab had kept the city under observation, he put Uriah at the place where he knew the experienced warriors were. ¹⁷ The men of the city came out and fought Joab. Some of the people, namely, some of David's mercenaries, fell and died—including Uriah the Hittite.

¹⁸ Then Joab sent ˌa messengerˌ to report to David all the details of the battle. ¹⁹ And he commanded the messenger, "When you finish telling the king about the battle, ²⁰ the king may become angry. He might ask you, 'Why did you go so close to the city to fight? Didn't you know they would shoot from the wall? ²¹ Who killed Jerubbesheth'sᵃ son Abimelech? Didn't a woman on the wall of Thebez throw a small millstone at him and kill him? Why did you go so close to the wall?' If the king asks this, then say, 'Your man Uriah the Hittite is also dead.' "

²² The messenger left, and when he arrived, he reported to David everything Joab told him to say.ᵇ ²³ The messenger said, "Their men overpowered us and came to attack us in the field. Then we forced them back to the entrance of the city gate. ²⁴ The archers on the wall shot down at your mercenaries, and some of Your Majesty's mercenaries died. Your man Uriah the Hittite is also dead."

²⁵ David said to the messenger, "This is what you are to say to Joab, 'Don't let this thing trouble you, because a sword can kill one person as easily as another. Strengthen your attack against the city, and destroy it.' Say this to encourage him."

²⁶ When Uriah's wife heard that her husband Uriah was dead, she mourned for him. ²⁷ When her mourning was over, David sent for her, brought her to his home, and she became his wife. Then she gave birth to a son. But the Lord considered David's actions evil.

Nathan Confronts David

12 ¹ So the Lord sent Nathan to David. Nathan came to him and said, "There were two men in a certain city. One was rich, and the other was poor. ² The rich man had a very large number of sheep and cows, ³ but the poor man had only one little female lamb that he had bought. He raised her, and she grew up in his home with his children. She would eat his food and drink from his cup. She rested in his arms and was like a daughter.

⁴ "Now, a visitor came to the rich man. The rich man thought it would be a pity to take one of his own sheep or cattle to prepare a meal for the traveler. So he took the poor man's lamb and prepared her for the traveler."

⁵ David burned with anger against the man. "I solemnly swear, as the Lord lives," he said to Nathan, "the man who did this certainly deserves to die! ⁶ And he must pay back four times the price of the lamb because he did this and had no pity."

⁷ "You are the man!" Nathan told David. "This is what the Lord God of Israel says: I anointed you king over Israel and rescued you from Saul. ⁸ I gave you your master Saul's house and his wives. I gave you the house of Israel and Judah. And if this weren't enough, I would have given you even more. ⁹ Why did you despise my word by doing what I considered evil? You had Uriah the Hittite killed in battle. You took his wife as your wife. You used the Ammonites to kill him. ¹⁰ So warfare will never leave your house because you despised me and took the wife of Uriah the Hittite to be your wife.

¹¹ "This is what the Lord says: I will stir up trouble against you within your own household, and before your own eyes I will take your wives and give them to someone close to you. He will go to bed with your wives in broad daylight. ¹² You did this secretly, but I will make this happen in broad daylight in front of all Israel."

ᵃ 11:21 Or "Jerubbaal's"; see Judges 9:1.   ᵇ 11:22 Greek adds, "And David was angry with Joab. 'Why did you go so close to the city to fight? Didn't you know you would be shot at from the wall? Who killed Abimelech, Jerubbaal's son? Didn't a woman throw a millstone on him from the wall? Why did you go so close to the wall?' "

¹³ Then David said to Nathan, "I have sinned against the LORD."

Nathan replied, "The LORD has taken away your sin; you will not die. ¹⁴ But since you have shown total contempt for the LORD by this affair, the son that is born to you must die." ¹⁵ Then Nathan went home.

The LORD struck the child that Uriah's wife had given birth to for David so that the child became sick. ¹⁶ David pleaded with God for the child; he fasted and lay on the ground all night. ¹⁷ The older leaders in his palace stood beside him to raise him up from the ground, but he was unwilling. And he wouldn't eat with them.

¹⁸ On the seventh day the child died. But David's officials were afraid to tell him that the child was dead. They thought, "While the child was alive, we talked to him, and he wouldn't listen to us. How can we tell him the child is dead? He may harm ˌhimselfˌ."

¹⁹ But when David saw that his officials were whispering to one another, he realized that the child was dead. "Is the child dead?" David asked them.

"ˌYes,ˌ he is dead," they answered.

²⁰ So David got up from the ground, bathed, anointed himself, and changed his clothes. He went into the LORD's house and worshiped. Then he went home and asked for food. They placed food in front of him, and he ate.

²¹ His officials asked him, "Why are you acting this way? You fasted and cried over the child when he was alive. But as soon as the child died, you got up and ate."

²² David answered, "As long as the child was alive, I fasted and cried. I thought, 'Who knows? The LORD may be gracious to me and let the child live.' ²³ But why should I fast now that he's dead? Can I bring him back? ˌSomedayˌ I'll go to him, but he won't come back to me."

²⁴ Then David comforted his wife Bathsheba. He went to bed with her, and she later gave birth to a son. David named him Solomon. The LORD loved the child ²⁵ and sent a message through the prophet Nathan to name the baby Jedidiah [The LORD's Beloved].

David Defeats the Ammonites—1 Chronicles 20:1–3

²⁶ Meanwhile, Joab fought against the Ammonite city of Rabbah and captured its royal fortress. ²⁷ So he sent messengers to tell David, "I fought against Rabbah and captured the fortress guarding its water supply. ²⁸ Gather the rest of the troops, surround the city, and capture it. Otherwise, I will capture the city, and it will be named after me."

²⁹ So David gathered all the troops and went to Rabbah. He fought against the city and captured it. ³⁰ He took the gold crown from the head of Rabbah's king and put it on his own head. (The crown weighed 75 pounds and contained a precious stone.) David also took a lot of goods from the city. ³¹ He brought out the troops who were there and put them to work with saws, hoes, and axes. He did the same to all the Ammonite cities. Then David and all the troops returned to Jerusalem.

The Rape of Tamar

13 ¹ After this, David's son Amnon fell in love with Tamar, the beautiful sister of David's son Absalom. ² Amnon was so obsessed with his half sister Tamar that he made himself sick. It seemed impossible for him to be alone with her because she was a virgin.

³ Amnon had a friend by the name of Jonadab, a son of David's brother Shimea. Jonadab was a very clever man. ⁴ He asked Amnon, "Why are you, the king's son, so worn out morning after morning? Won't you tell me?"

"I'm in love with Absalom's sister Tamar," he answered.

⁵ Then Jonadab told him, "Lie down on your bed. Act sick, and when your father comes to see you, say to him, 'Please let my sister Tamar come to feed me. She can prepare a meal in front of me as I watch her, and she can feed me.' "

⁶ So Amnon lay down and acted sick, and the king came to see him. Amnon asked the king, "Please let my sister Tamar come and make some bread in front of me, and she can feed me."

⁷ David sent for Tamar at the palace. "Please go to your brother Amnon's home," he said, "and prepare some food for him."

⁸ So Tamar went to her brother Amnon's home. He was lying down. She took dough, kneaded it, made flat bread in front of him, and cooked it. ⁹ Then she took the pan and served him ˌthe breadˌ. But he refused to eat.

"Have everyone leave me," he said. So everyone left him.

¹⁰ Amnon told Tamar, "Bring the food into the bedroom so that you can feed me."

Tamar took the bread she had prepared and brought it to her brother Amnon in the bedroom. ¹¹ When she handed it to him to eat, he grabbed her and said, "Come to bed with me, Tamar!"

¹² "No," she told him, "don't rape me! That shouldn't be done in Israel. Don't do this godless act! ¹³ Where could I go in my disgrace? And you will be considered one of the godless fools in Israel! Speak to the king. He won't refuse your request to marry me."

14 But Amnon wouldn't listen to her. He grabbed his sister and raped her.

15 Now, Amnon developed an intense hatred for her. His hatred for her was greater than the lust he had felt for her. "Get out of here," he told her.

16 She said to him, "No, sending me away is a greater wrong than the other thing you did to me!" But he wouldn't listen to her.

17 Then he called his personal servant and said, "Get rid of her. Put her out, and bolt the door behind her." **18** (She was wearing a long-sleeved gown. The king's virgin daughters wore this kind of robe.) So his servant took her out and bolted the door behind her. **19** Tamar put ashes on her head, tore the long-sleeved gown she had on, put her hands on her head, and went away crying.

20 Her brother Absalom asked her, "Has your brother Amnon been with you? Sister, be quiet for now. He's your brother. Don't dwell on this matter." So Tamar stayed there at the home of her brother Absalom and was depressed.

21 When King David heard about this, he became very angry. But David didn't punish his son Amnon. He favored Amnon because he was his firstborn son.ᵃ **22** Absalom wouldn't speak at all to Amnon. He hated Amnon for raping his sister Tamar.

The Murder of Amnon

23 Two years later Absalom had sheepshearers at Baal Hazor near Ephraim. He invited all the king's sons.ᵇ **24** Absalom went to the king and said, "Since I have sheepshearers, Your Majesty and your officials are invited ˎto feastˏ with me."

25 "No, Son," the king answered Absalom. "If we all go, we'll be a burden to you." Even when Absalom continued to urgeᶜ him, David did not want to go, though he did give Absalom his blessing.

26 So Absalom said, "If you won't go, then please let my brother Amnon go with us."

"Why should he go with you?" the king asked him. **27** But when Absalom urged him, he let Amnon and all ˎthe rest ofˏ the king's sons go with him.

28 Then Absalom gave an order to his servants. "Watch now," he said. "When Amnon begins to feel good from drinking ˎtoo muchˏ wine, I'll tell you, 'Attack Amnon.' Then kill him. Don't be afraid. I've given you the order, haven't I? Be strong and courageous."

29 Absalom's servants did to Amnon as Absalom had ordered. Then all the king's sons got up, mounted their mules, and fled. **30** While they were on their way, David heard this rumor: "Absalom has killed all the king's sons, and not a single one is left." **31** The king stood up, tore his clothes, and lay down on the ground. All his servants were standing beside him with their clothes torn ˎto show their griefˏ.

32 Then Jonadab, the son of David's brother Shimea, said, "Sir, don't think that all the young men, all the king's sons, have been killed. Only Amnon is dead. Absalom decided to do this the day his half brother raped his sister Tamar. **33** You shouldn't burden your heart with the idea that all the king's sons are dead, Your Majesty. Only Amnon is dead. **34** Absalom has fled."

When the servant who kept watch looked up, he saw many people coming down the road beside the mountain west of him. **35** Then Jonadab told the king, "The king's sons have come. It's just as I said." **36** When he finished speaking, the king's sons arrived and cried loudly. The king and all his men also cried very bitterly.

37 Absalom, however, fled to Geshur's King Talmai, Ammihud's son. But the king mourned for his son Amnon every day. **38** Absalom, having fled to Geshur, stayed there three years. **39** King David began to long for Absalom once people had consoled him over Amnon's death.

Absalom Returns to Jerusalem

14 **1** Joab, Zeruiah's son, knew the king was still thinking about Absalom. **2** So Joab sent ˎsomeoneˏ to Tekoa to get a clever woman from there. He told her, "Please act like a mourner, and dress in mourning clothes. Don't rub olive oil on yourself,ᵃ but act like a woman who has been mourning for the dead for a long time. **3** Go to the king, and tell him this. . . ." Then Joab told her exactly what to say.

4 The woman from Tekoa cameᵇ to the king and immediately bowed down with her face touching the ground. "Help ˎmeˏ, Your Majesty," she said.

5 The king asked her, "What can I do for you?"

She answered, "I'm a widow; my husband is dead. **6** I had two sons who quarreled in the field, and there was no one to separate them. One killed the other. **7** Then the entire family turned against me. They said, 'Give us the man who killed his brother so that we can kill him because he took his brother's life. We're going to destroy the one who ˎnowˏ would be the

---

ᵃ 13:21 Dead Sea Scrolls, Greek, Latin add this sentence.   ᵇ 13:23 The time when sheep were sheared was also a time of rejoicing and feasting.   ᶜ 13:25 Dead Sea Scrolls; Masoretic Text "press," also in verse 27.   ᵃ 14:2 A cosmetic treatment of the skin.   ᵇ 14:4 Many Hebrew manuscripts, Greek, Syriac, Targum, Latin; some Hebrew manuscripts "said."

heir.' In this way they wish to extinguish the ⸢one⸣ burning coal that is left for me. They will not let my husband's name or descendants remain on the face of the earth."

[8] "Go home," the king told the woman. "I will order someone to take care of this matter."

[9] The woman from Tekoa said to the king, "Let me be held responsible for the sin, Your Majesty. Let my father's family be held responsible. Your Majesty and your throne are innocent."

[10] The king said, "If anyone says anything against you, bring him to me. He'll never harm you again."

[11] She said, "Your Majesty, please pray to the LORD your God in order to keep an avenger from doing more harm by destroying my son."

"I solemnly swear, as the LORD lives," he said, "not a hair on your son's head will fall to the ground."

[12] The woman said, "Please let me say something else to you."

"Speak," he said.

[13] "Why have you devised something like this against God's people?" she said. "When you say this, you condemn yourself because you haven't brought back the one you banished! [14] We are all going to die; we are all like water that is poured on the ground and can't be gathered up. But doesn't God forgive a person? He never plans to keep a banished person in exile.

[15] "I've come to say this to you because the people have frightened me. So I thought, 'I will speak to the king about this. Maybe the king will do something for me, his subject. [16] Maybe the king will listen and rescue me, his subject, from the man who wants to cut off both me and my son from ⸢our⸣ God-given inheritance.' [17] I thought that you would reassure me. You are like God's Messenger, who is able to distinguish right from wrong. May the LORD your God be with you!"

[18] The king said to the woman, "Please don't refuse to answer the question I'm going to ask you."

The woman responded, "Please speak, Your Majesty."

[19] "Did Joab put you up to this?" the king asked.

The woman answered, "I solemnly swear on your life, Your Majesty, you are absolutely right. Yes, your servant Joab ordered me ⸢to do this⸣. He told me to say exactly what I said. [20] Your servant Joab has done this to portray the matter in a different light. You are as wise as God's Messenger, who knows everything on earth."

[21] Then the king told Joab, "This is what you'll do. Bring back the young man Absalom."

[22] Joab quickly bowed down with his face touching the ground, and he blessed the king. He said, "Today I know that you have been kind to me because you have done what I wanted."

[23] So Joab went to Geshur and brought Absalom back to Jerusalem. [24] But the king said, "Absalom should return to his own house. He will not see me." So Absalom returned to his house and didn't see the king.

[25] Now, no one in all Israel was praised for his good looks as much as Absalom was. He had no blemish from head to toe. [26] At the end of every year, he used to cut his hair because it became heavy for him. When he cut the hair on his head and weighed it, it weighed five pounds according to the royal standard. [27] Absalom had three sons and one daughter. His daughter Tamar was a beautiful woman.

[28] Absalom stayed in Jerusalem two full years without seeing the king. [29] So Absalom sent for Joab in order to send him to the king, but Joab refused to come. Absalom sent for him a second time, but he still refused to come. [30] So Absalom said to his servants, "Look, Joab's field is next to mine. He has barley in it. Go and set it on fire." So Absalom's servants set it on fire.

Joab's servants came to him ⸢in grief⸣ and said, "Absalom's servants have set ⸢your⸣ field on fire."[c]

[31] Then Joab immediately went to Absalom at his home. "Why did your servants set my field on fire?" he asked.

[32] Absalom answered Joab, "I sent someone to tell you to come here because I wanted to send you to the king to ask him why I had to come from Geshur. It would be better for me if I were still there. Let me see the king now! If I'm guilty of a sin, he should kill me."

[33] Joab went to the king and told him this. The king then called for Absalom, who came to the king and bowed down with his face touching the ground. And the king kissed Absalom.

David Overthrown

15 [1] Soon after this, Absalom acquired a chariot, horses, and 50 men to run ahead of him. [2] Absalom used to get up early and stand by the road leading to the city gate. When anyone had a case to be tried by King David, Absalom would ask, "Which city are you from?"

After the person had told him which tribe in Israel he was from, [3] Absalom would say, "Your case is good and proper, but the king hasn't appointed anyone to hear it." [4] He would add,

---

[c] 14:30 Dead Sea Scrolls, Greek, and Latin add this sentence.

"I wish someone would make me judge in the land. Then anyone who had a case to be tried could come to me, and I would make sure that he got justice." [5] When anyone approached him and bowed down, Absalom would reach out, take hold of him, and kiss him. [6] This is what he did for all Israelites who came to the king to have him try their case. So Absalom stole the hearts of the people of Israel.

[7] Four years later Absalom said to the king, "Let me go to Hebron and keep the vow I made to the LORD. [8] I made a vow while I was living at Geshur in Aram. I said, 'If the LORD will bring me back to Jerusalem, I will serve the LORD.' "

[9] "Go in peace," the king told him.

So he went to Hebron. [10] But Absalom sent his loyal supporters to all the tribes of Israel and said, "When you hear the sound of the ram's horn, say, 'Absalom has become king in Hebron.' "

[11] Two hundred men invited from Jerusalem went with Absalom. They went innocently, knowing nothing ˌabout Absalom's plansˌ. [12] While Absalom was offering sacrifices, he sent for Ahithophel, David's adviser, to come from his home in Giloh. Meanwhile, the conspiracy grew stronger, and the number of people siding with Absalom kept getting larger.

[13] Someone came to tell David, "The hearts of the people of Israel are with Absalom."

David Flees Jerusalem

[14] David told all his men who were with him in Jerusalem, "Let's flee immediately, or none of us will escape from Absalom. Let's leave right away, or he'll catch up to us and bring disaster on us when he massacres the city."

[15] The king's servants told him, "No matter what happens, we are Your Majesty's servants."

[16] The king left on foot, and his whole household followed him except ten concubines[a] whom the king left behind to take care of the palace. [17] As the king and his troops were leaving the city on foot, they stopped at the last house. [18] All his mercenaries passed by him; all the Cherethites, all the Pelethites, Ittai, and all 600 men who had followed him from Gath were marching past the king.

[19] The king asked Ittai from Gath, "Why should you go with us? Go back, and stay with King Absalom. You are a foreigner, an exile from your homeland. [20] You came to us just yesterday. Should I make you wander around with me when I don't even know where I'm going? Go back, and take your countrymen with you. ˌMay the LORDˌ always show you kindness."

[21] But Ittai answered the king, "I solemnly swear, as the LORD and the king live: Wherever you are, whether you're dead or alive, I'll be there."

[22] So David told Ittai, "Go ahead and keep marching." So Ittai from Gath marched on with all his men and all the families who were with him.

[23] The whole country was crying loudly as all the troops were passing by. The king was crossing the Kidron Valley, and all the people were moving down the road toward the desert. [24] Zadok and all the Levites with him were carrying the ark of God's promise. They set down the ark of God beside Abiathar until all the troops had withdrawn from the city.

[25] The king told Zadok, "Take God's ark back to the city. If the LORD looks favorably on me, he will allow me to come back and see both it and its[b] dwelling place again. [26] But if he says, 'I'm not pleased with you,' let him do to me what he considers right."

[27] "Aren't you a seer?"[c] the king asked Zadok the priest. "Go back to the city peacefully, and take your son Ahimaaz and Abiathar's son Jonathan with you. [28] I'll wait at the river crossings in the desert until I receive a message from you." [29] So Zadok and Abiathar took the ark of God back to Jerusalem and stayed there.

[30] David cried as he went up the Mount of Olives. He covered his head and walked barefoot. And all of the troops with him covered their heads and cried as they went.

[31] Then David was told, "Ahithophel is among those conspiring with Absalom." So David prayed, "LORD, make Ahithophel's advice foolish."

[32] When David came to the top ˌof the Mount of Olivesˌ where people worshiped God, Hushai from Archi's family was there to meet him. His clothes were torn, and he had dirt on his head. [33] David told him, "If you go with me, you will only be a burden to me. [34] But if you go back to the city and say to Absalom, 'Your Majesty, I'll be your servant. I was your father's servant in the past, but now I'll be your servant,' then you'll ˌhelp me byˌ undoing Ahithophel's advice. [35] The priests Zadok and Abiathar will be with you there. When you hear anything from the royal palace, tell it to the priests Zadok and Abiathar. [36] They have two sons with them: Zadok has Ahimaaz, and Abiathar has Jonathan. Send them to report to me anything you hear."

[37] So Hushai, David's friend, went to the city as Absalom was entering Jerusalem.

---

[a] 15:16 A concubine is considered a wife except she has fewer rights under the law.   [b] 15:25 Or "his."   [c] 15:27 A seer is a prophet.

16 ¹ When David had gone over the top ˌof the Mount of Olivesˌ, Ziba, Mephibosheth's servant, met him with a pair of saddled donkeys. They were loaded with 200 loaves of bread, 100 bunches of raisins, 100 pieces of ripened fruit, and a full wineskin.

² "Why did you bring these?" David asked Ziba.

"The donkeys are for the king's family to ride on," Ziba answered. "The bread and the ripe fruit are for ˌyourˌ servants to eat. The wine is for those who become tired and thirsty in the desert."

³ "Where is your master Saul's grandson?" the king asked.

"He's staying in Jerusalem," Ziba answered the king. "He said, 'Today the house of Israel will give me back my grandfather's kingdom.' "

⁴ The king told Ziba, "In that case everything that belonged to Mephibosheth now belongs to you."

"I sincerely thank you," said Ziba. "I hope to remain in your good graces, Your Majesty."

⁵ When King David came to Bahurim, a man who was a distant cousin of Saul came out cursing. His name was Shimei, son of Gera. ⁶ He threw stones at David and David's servants, although all the people and all the warriors were shielding David. ⁷ Shimei cursed and said, "Get out! Get out, you bloodthirsty man! You worthless person! ⁸ The LORD is paying you back for all the blood you spilled in the family of Saul, whom you succeeded as king. The LORD is giving the kingship to your son Absalom. Now you're in trouble because you're a bloodthirsty man."

⁹ Abishai, Zeruiah's son, asked the king, "Why should this dead dog curse you, Your Majesty? Let me go over there and tear off his head."

¹⁰ But the king said, "You don't think like me at all, sons of Zeruiah. Let him curse. If the LORD has told him, 'Curse David,' should anyone ask, 'Why do you do that?' " ¹¹ David told Abishai and all his servants, "My own son, my own flesh and blood, is trying to kill me. Why, then, shouldn't this Benjaminite do this? Leave him alone. Let him curse, since the LORD has told him to do it. ¹² Maybe the LORD will see my misery and turn his curse into a blessing for me today."

¹³ As David and his men went along the road, Shimei was walking along the hillside parallel to him. Shimei cursed, hurled stones, and threw dirt at David. ¹⁴ The king and all the people with him finally arrived ˌat their destinationˌ and rested there.

Absalom Enters Jerusalem

¹⁵ Meanwhile, Absalom and all Israel's troops came to Jerusalem, and Ahithophel was with him. ¹⁶ When David's friend Hushai from Archi's family came to Absalom, he said, "Long live the king! Long live the king!"

¹⁷ "Is that how loyal you are to your friend?" Absalom asked Hushai. "Why didn't you go with him?"

¹⁸ Hushai answered Absalom, "No, I want to be with the one whom the LORD, these people, and all Israel have chosen. I will be his ˌfriendˌ and stay with him. ¹⁹ And besides, whom should I serve? Shouldn't it be his son? As I served your father, so I'll serve you."

²⁰ Then Absalom asked Ahithophel, "What's your advice? What should we do?"

²¹ Ahithophel told Absalom, "Sleep with your father's concubinesᵃ whom he left to take care of the palace. Then all Israel will hear about how you have made your father despise you. Everyone who is with you will support you even more."

²² So a tent was put up on the roof for Absalom, and he slept with his father's concubines in plain sight of Israel.

²³ In those days both David and Absalom thought that Ahithophel's advice was like getting an answer from God.

Absalom Pursues David

17 ¹ Ahithophel said to Absalom, "Let me choose 12,000 men and leave tonight to go after David. ² I'll attack him while he's tired and weak, and I'll cause him to panic. All the people with him will flee, but I'll kill only him. ³ I'll return all the people to you as a bride is returned to her husband. Since you will be seeking the life of only one man,ᵃ all the people will have peace." ⁴ Absalom and all the leaders of Israel approved this plan.

⁵ Absalom said, "Please call Hushai, who is descended from Archi's family, and let us hear what he, too, has to say."

⁶ When Hushai arrived, Absalom said to him, "Ahithophel has told us his plan. Should we do what he says? If not, tell us."

⁷ "This time Ahithophel's advice is no good," Hushai said to Absalom. ⁸ "You know your father and his men. They are warriors as fierce as a wild bear whose cubs have been stolen.

ᵃ 16:21 A concubine is considered a wife except she has fewer rights under the law.   ᵃ 17:3 "as a bride . . . only one man" Greek; Hebrew meaning uncertain.

Your father is an experienced soldier. He will not camp with the troops tonight. [9] He has already hidden in one of the ravines or some other place. If some of our soldiers are killed in the initial attack, others will definitely hear about it and say, 'The troops that support Absalom have been defeated.' [10] Even the bravest man with a heart like a lion would lose his courage, because all Israel knows that your father is a warrior and the men with him are brave. [11] So my advice is to gather all Israel's troops from Dan to Beersheba, since they are as numerous as the sand on the seashore. Lead them into battle yourself. [12] Then we'll attack him wherever we find him. We'll fall on him as dew falls on the ground. Neither he nor any of his men will be left ˻alive˼. [13] If he retreats into a city, all Israel will bring ropes to that city and drag it into a valley so that not even a pebble will be found there."

[14] Absalom and all the people of Israel said, "The advice of Hushai from Archi's family is better than Ahithophel's advice." (The Lord had commanded Ahithophel's good advice to be defeated in order to ruin Absalom.)

[15] Then Hushai told the priests Zadok and Abiathar, "Ahithophel advised Absalom and the leaders of Israel to do one thing, but I advised them to do something else. [16] Now send messengers quickly to tell David, 'Don't rest tonight in the river crossings in the desert, but make sure you cross ˻the river˼, or Your Majesty and all the troops with him will be wiped out.' "

[17] Jonathan and Ahimaaz were waiting at En Rogel. They could not risk being seen coming into the city, so a servant girl was to go and tell them, and they were to go and tell King David. [18] But a young man saw Jonathan and Ahimaaz and told Absalom. So both of them left quickly and came to the home of a man in Bahurim who had a cistern in his courtyard, and they went down into it. [19] The man's wife took a cover, spread it over the top of the cistern, and scattered some grain[b] over it so that no one could tell it was there.

[20] Absalom's servants came to the woman at her home. "Where are Ahimaaz and Jonathan?" they asked.

The woman said, "They've crossed the stream."

The servants looked for them but did not find them. So Absalom's servants returned to Jerusalem.

[21] After Absalom's servants left, both men came out of the cistern and went and told King David. "Leave right away," they told David. "Cross the river quickly because this is what Ahithophel has advised against you. . . ."

[22] David and all the troops with him left to cross the Jordan River. When the dawn came, everyone had crossed the Jordan River.

[23] When Ahithophel saw that his advice hadn't been followed, he saddled his donkey, left, and went home to his own city. He gave instructions to his family. Then he hanged himself, died, and was buried in his father's tomb.

[24] David had ˻already˼ come to Mahanaim by the time Absalom and all the men of Israel with him crossed the Jordan River. [25] Absalom appointed Amasa to take Joab's place as commander of the army. (Amasa was the son of a man named Ithra, a descendant of Ishmael.[c] His mother was Abigail,[d] the daughter of Nahash and sister of Joab's mother Zeruiah.) [26] The Israelites and Absalom camped in the region of Gilead.

[27] When David came to Mahanaim, Shobi, son of Nahash from Rabbah in Ammon, and Machir, son of Ammiel from Lo Debar, and Barzillai from Rogelim in Gilead [28] brought ˻supplies˼ and food for David and his troops: bedding, bowls, pots, wheat, barley, flour, roasted grain, beans, lentils,[e] [29] honey, buttermilk, sheep, and calves. They brought these things because they thought, "The troops in the desert are hungry, exhausted, and thirsty."

David Defeats Absalom

18   [1] David called together the troops that were with him. He appointed commanders in charge of regiments and battalions. [2] David put a third of the troops under Joab's command, another third under Joab's brother Abishai (Zeruiah's son), and the last third under Ittai from Gath.

"I am going ˻into battle˼ with you," the king said to the troops.

[3] "You're not going ˻with us˼," the troops said. "If we flee, they won't care about us, and if half of us die, they won't care either. But you're worth 10,000 of us. It's better for you to be ready to send us help from the city."

[4] "I'll do what you think best," the king responded. So the king stood by the gate while all the troops marched out by battalions and regiments.

[5] The king ordered Joab, Abishai, and Ittai, "Treat the young man Absalom gently for my sake." All the troops heard him give all the commanders this order regarding Absalom.

---

[b] 17:19 Hebrew meaning uncertain.   [c] 17:25 Greek, 1 Chronicles 2:17; Masoretic Text "the Israelite."   [d] 17:25 Or "Ishmael's descendant Ithra, who slept with Abigail."   [e] 17:28 Greek, Latin, Syriac; Masoretic Text adds "and roasted grain."

⁶ So the troops went out to the country to fight Israel in the forest of Ephraim. ⁷ There David's men defeated Israel's army, and the massacre was sizable that day—20,000 men. ⁸ The fighting spread over the whole country. That day the woods devoured more people than the battle.

⁹ Absalom happened to come face to face with some of David's men. He was riding on a mule, and the mule went under the tangled branches of a large tree. Absalom's head became caught in the tree. So he was left hanging* in midair when the mule that was under him ran away. ¹⁰ A man who saw this told Joab, "I saw Absalom hanging in a tree."

¹¹ "What! You saw that!" Joab said to the man who told him. "Why didn't you strike him to the ground? Then I would have felt obligated to give you four ounces of silver and a belt."

¹² But the man told Joab, "Even if I felt the weight of 25 pounds of silver in my hand, I wouldn't raise my hand against the king's son. We heard the order the king gave you, Abishai, and Ittai: 'Protect the young man Absalom for my sake.'ᵇ ¹³ If I had done something treacherous to him, would you have stood by me? Like everything else, it wouldn't stay hidden from the king."

¹⁴ Then Joab said, "I shouldn't waste time with you like this." He took three sharp sticks and plunged them into Absalom's heart while he was still alive in the tree. ¹⁵ Then ten of Joab's armorbearers surrounded Absalom, attacked him, and killed him.

¹⁶ Joab blew the ram's horn to stop their ˏfightingˌ, and the troops returned from pursuing Israel. ¹⁷ They took Absalom, threw him into a huge pit in the forest, and piled a large heap of stones over him. Meanwhile, all Israel fled and went back to their homes.

¹⁸ (ˏWhile he was still living,ˌ Absalom had taken a rock and set it up for himself in the king's valley. He said, "I have no son to keep the memory of my name alive." He called the rock by his name, and it is still called Absalom's Monument today.)

¹⁹ Then Ahimaaz, Zadok's son, said, "Let me run and bring the king the good news that the Lᴏʀᴅ has freed him from his enemies."

²⁰ But Joab told him, "You won't be the man carrying good news today. You can carry the news some other day. You must not deliver the news today because the king's son is dead." ²¹ Then Joab said to a man from Sudan, "Go, tell the king what you saw." The messenger bowed down with his face touching the ground in front of Joab and then ran off.

²² Ahimaaz, Zadok's son, spoke to Joab again, "Whatever may happen, I also want to run after the Sudanese messenger."

"Now, son, why should you deliver the message?" Joab asked. "You won't be rewarded for this news."

²³ "Whatever happens, I'd like to run," ˏreplied Ahimaaz.ˌ

"Run," Joab told him. So Ahimaaz ran along the valley road and got ahead of the Sudanese messenger.

²⁴ David was sitting between the two gates while the watchman walked along the roof of the gate by the wall. As he looked, he saw a man running alone. ²⁵ The watchman called and alerted the king.

"If he's alone," the king said, "he has good news to tell." The runner continued to come closer. ²⁶ When the watchman saw another man running, the watchman called, "There's ˏanotherˌ man running alone."

The king said, "This one is also bringing good news."

²⁷ The watchman said, "It seems to me that the first one runs like Ahimaaz, Zadok's son."

"He's a good man," the king said. "He must be coming with good news."

²⁸ Then Ahimaaz came up to the king, greeted him, and bowed down in front of him. Ahimaaz said, "May the Lᴏʀᴅ your God be praised. He has handed over the men who rebelled against Your Majesty."

²⁹ "Is the young man Absalom alright?" the king asked.

Ahimaaz answered, "I saw a lot of confusion when Joab sent me away, but I didn't know what it meant."

³⁰ "Step aside, and stand here," the king said. He stepped aside and stood there.

³¹ Then the Sudanese messenger came. "Good news for Your Majesty!" he said. "Today the Lᴏʀᴅ has freed you from all who turned against you."

³² "Is the young man Absalom alright?" the king asked.

The Sudanese messenger answered, "May your enemies and all who turned against you be like that young man!"ᶜ

³³ The king was shaken ˏby the news.ˌ He went to the room above the gate and cried. "My son Absalom!" he said as he went. "My son, my son Absalom! I wish I had died in your place! Absalom, my son, my son!"

ª 18:9 Dead Sea Scrolls, Greek, Latin, Syriac; Masoretic Text "he was put."   ᵇ 18:12 Two Hebrew manuscripts, Greek, Syriac, Targum, Latin; meaning of other Hebrew manuscripts uncertain.   ᶜ 18:32 2 Samuel 18:33 in English Bibles is 2 Samuel 19:1 in the Hebrew Bible.

David Restored to the Throne

19^a ¹ Joab was told, "The king is crying and mourning for Absalom." ² The victory of that day was turned into mourning because all the troops heard that the king was grieving for his son. ³ That day the troops sneaked into the city as if they had fled from battle and were ashamed of it. ⁴ The king covered his face and cried loudly, "My son Absalom! Absalom, my son, my son!"

⁵ Then Joab came into the house. "Today you have made all your men feel ashamed," he said. "They saved your life and the lives of your sons, daughters, wives, and concubines^b today. ⁶ You love those who hate you and hate those who love you. Today, you have made it clear that your commanders and servants mean nothing to you. I think you would be pleased if Absalom were alive and all of us were dead. ⁷ Now, get up, go out, and encourage your men. I swear to you by the LORD that if you don't go out, no one will stay with you tonight, and that will be worse than all the trouble you've had in your entire life."

⁸ The king sat in the gateway. When all the troops were told, "The king is sitting in the gateway," they came to the king.

Meanwhile, Israel had fled and went back to their own homes. ⁹ All the people in all the tribes of Israel were arguing with one another, saying, "The king rescued us from our enemies and saved us from the Philistines, but now he has fled from Absalom and left the country. ¹⁰ However, Absalom, whom we anointed to rule us, has died in battle. Why is no one talking about bringing back the king?"

¹¹ What all Israel was saying reached the king at his house. So King David sent ˌthis messageˌ to the priests Zadok and Abiathar: "Ask the leaders of Judah, 'Why should you be the last ˌtribeˌ to bring the king back to his palace? ¹² You are my relatives, my own flesh and blood. Why should you be the last to bring back the king?' ¹³ And tell Amasa, 'Aren't you my flesh and blood? May God strike me dead unless you are given Joab's place to serve me always as the commander of the army.' "

¹⁴ All the people of Judah were in total agreement. So they sent the king this message: "Come back with all your servants."

¹⁵ The king came back to the Jordan River, and the people of Judah came to Gilgal to meet the king and bring him across the Jordan River. ¹⁶ Shimei, Gera's son from the tribe of Benjamin and the town of Bahurim, hurried down with the people of Judah to meet King David. ¹⁷ One thousand people from Benjamin were with him. And Ziba, the servant of Saul's family, rushed to the Jordan River across from the king. Ziba brought his 15 sons and 20 servants. ¹⁸ They crossed the river to bring over the king's family and to do anything else the king wanted.

Shimei, Gera's son, bowed down in front of the king as he was going to cross the Jordan River. ¹⁹ He pleaded with the king, "Don't remember the crime I committed the day you left Jerusalem. Don't hold it against me or even think about it, Your Majesty. ²⁰ I know I've sinned. Today I've come as the first of all the house of Joseph to meet you."

²¹ But Abishai, Zeruiah's son, replied, "Shouldn't Shimei be put to death for cursing the LORD's anointed king?"

²² David responded, "Are you sure we're from the same family, sons of Zeruiah? You are my enemies today. Should anyone in Israel be killed today? Don't I know that I'm king of Israel again?"

²³ The king promised Shimei, "You won't die," and the king swore to it.

²⁴ Mephibosheth, Saul's grandson, went to meet the king. He had not tended to his feet, trimmed his mustache, or washed his clothes from the day the king left until he came home safely. ²⁵ When he came from Jerusalem to meet the king, the king asked him, "Why didn't you go with me, Mephibosheth?"

²⁶ He answered, "My servant deceived me, Your Majesty. Since I am disabled, I said, 'Saddle the donkey for me, and I'll ride on it and go with the king.' ²⁷ He told you lies about me, Your Majesty. However, you are like God's Messenger. Do what you think is right. ²⁸ You could have killed anyone in my entire family, Your Majesty. Instead, you've seated me with those who eat at your table. So I no longer have the right to complain to the king."

²⁹ The king asked him, "Why do you keep talking about it? I've said that you and Ziba should divide the land."

³⁰ "Let him take it all," Mephibosheth told the king. "It's enough for me that you've come home safely."

³¹ Barzillai, the man from Gilead, came from Rogelim with the king to the Jordan River to send him on his way. ³² Barzillai was an elderly man, 80 years old. Because he was a very rich man, he had provided the king with food while he was staying at Mahanaim.

³³ The king told Barzillai, "Cross the river with me. I'll provide for you in Jerusalem."

---

^a 19:1 2 Samuel 19:1–43 in English Bibles is 2 Samuel 19:2–44 in the Hebrew Bible.   ^b 19:5 A concubine is considered a wife except she has fewer rights under the law.

³⁴ Barzillai replied, "I don't have much longer to live. I shouldn't go with Your Majesty to Jerusalem. **³⁵** I'm 80 years old now. How can I tell what is pleasant and what is not? Can I taste what I eat or drink? Can I still hear the singing of men and women? Why should I now become a burden to you, Your Majesty? **³⁶** I'll just cross the Jordan River with you. Why should you give me such a reward? **³⁷** Please let me go back so that I can die in my city near the grave of my father and mother. But here is Chimham. Let him go across with you. And do for him what you think is right."

³⁸ "Chimham will go across with me," the king said. "I will do for him whatever you want. Anything you wish I'll do for you."

³⁹ All the troops crossed the Jordan River, and then the king crossed. The king kissed Barzillai and blessed him. Then Barzillai went back home.

⁴⁰ The king crossed the river to Gilgal, and Chimham went with him. All the troops from Judah and half of the troops from Israel brought the king across.

⁴¹ Then all the people of Israel kept coming to the king. They asked, "Why did our cousins, the people of Judah, kidnap you and bring Your Majesty and your family and men across the Jordan River?"

⁴² All the people of Judah answered the people of Israel, "Because the king is our relative. Why are you angry about this? Did we eat the king's food, or did he give us any gifts?"*ᶜ*

⁴³ The people of Israel answered the people of Judah, "We have ten times your interest in the king and a greater claim on David than you have. Why, then, do you despise us? Weren't we the first to suggest bringing back our king?"

But the people of Judah spoke ˌevenˌ more harshly than the people of Israel.

Sheba's Rebellion

20 **¹** A good-for-nothing man by the name of Sheba, Bichri's son, from the tribe of Benjamin happened to be at Gilgal. He blew a ram's horn ˌto announceˌ,

"We have no share in David's kingdom.
We won't receive an inheritance from Jesse's son.
  Everyone to his own tent, Israel!"

² So all the people of Israel left David to follow Sheba, Bichri's son. But the people of Judah remained loyal to their king ˌon his wayˌ from the Jordan River to Jerusalem.

³ When David came to his palace in Jerusalem, he took the ten concubines*ᵃ* he had left to look after the palace and put them in a house under guard. He provided for them but no longer slept with them. So they lived like widows in confinement until they died.

⁴ The king told Amasa, "Call the people of Judah together for me, and in three days be here yourself." **⁵** Amasa went to call Judah together, but he took longer to do it than David had given him.

⁶ David then told Abishai, "Sheba, son of Bichri, will do us more harm than Absalom. Take my men and go after him, or he will find some fortified cities and take the best ones for himself."*ᵇ*

⁷ So Joab's men, the Cherethites, Pelethites, and all the soldiers went with Abishai. They left Jerusalem to pursue Sheba, Bichri's son. **⁸** When they were at the large rock in Gibeon, Amasa met them there. Joab wore a military uniform, and strapped over it at his hip was a sword in a scabbard. As he stepped forward, the sword dropped ˌinto his handˌ. **⁹** "How are you, my brother?" Joab asked Amasa. He took hold of Amasa's beard with his right hand to kiss him. **¹⁰** Amasa wasn't on his guard against the sword in Joab's ˌleftˌ hand. Joab stabbed him in the stomach, and his intestines poured out on the ground. (He died without being stabbed again.) Then Joab and his brother Abishai pursued Sheba, son of Bichri. **¹¹** One of Joab's young men stood beside Amasa*ᶜ* and said, "Anyone who favors Joab and is on David's side should follow Joab." **¹²** Amasa was wallowing in his blood in the middle of the road. When the man saw that all the troops stopped as they came to the body, he carried Amasa from the road to the field and threw a sheet over him. **¹³** As soon as he was moved from the road, everyone followed Joab and pursued Sheba, Bichri's son.

¹⁴ Sheba passed through all the tribes of Israel to Abel (Beth Maacah). All the Berites were gathered together and followed him to the city. **¹⁵** Joab's army came and attacked him in Abel (Beth Maacah). They put up a dirt ramp against the city, and it stood level with the outer wall. All the troops with Joab were trying to destroy the wall and tear it down.

¹⁶ Then a clever woman called from the city, "Listen, listen! Tell Joab to come here so that I can talk to him."

¹⁷ He came near, and she asked, "Are you Joab?"

ᶜ 19:42 Greek; Hebrew meaning uncertain.   *ᵃ* 20:3 Hebrew "concubines/wives"; a concubine is considered a wife except she has fewer rights under the law.   *ᵇ* 20:6 Hebrew meaning of this phrase uncertain.   *ᶜ* 20:11 Greek, Latin; Masoretic Text "him."

"I am," he answered.

"Listen to what I have to say," she told him.

"I'm listening," he answered.

[18] So she said, "There's an old saying: 'Be sure to ask at Abel ˌbefore doing anythingˌ. That's the way they settle matters.' [19] We are peaceful and faithful Israelites. Are you trying to destroy a mother city in Israel? Why should you swallow up what belongs to the LORD?"

[20] Joab answered, "That's unthinkable! I don't wish to swallow ˌitˌ up or destroy ˌitˌ. [21] That isn't the case. A man from the mountains of Ephraim by the name of Sheba, son of Bichri, has rebelled against King David. Give him to me, and I'll withdraw from the city."

"That's fine," the woman told Joab. "His head will be thrown to you from the wall." [22] Then the woman went to all the people with her clever plan. They cut off Sheba's head and threw it to Joab. He blew the ram's horn, and everyone scattered and withdrew from the city and went home. Joab went back to the king in Jerusalem.

David's Officials

[23] Now, Joab was put in charge of Israel's whole army. Benaiah, son of Jehoiada, was in charge of the Cherethites and Pelethites. [24] Adoram was in charge of forced labor. Jehoshaphat, son of Ahilud, was the royal historian. [25] Sheva was the royal scribe. Zadok and Abiathar were priests. [26] And Ira, a descendant of Jair, was a priest to David.

David and the People of Gibeon

21 [1] In the time of David, there was a famine for three successive years, and David asked the LORD's advice about it. The LORD answered, "It's because of Saul and his family. They are guilty of murder because they killed the people of Gibeon."

[2] (The Gibeonites were not a part of Israel but were left over from the Amorites. Although the Israelites had sworn ˌto spare themˌ, Saul, in his eagerness, tried to destroy them for Israel and Judah.)

The king called the Gibeonites [3] and asked them, "What can I do for you? What should I ˌgive youˌ to make peace with you so that you will bless what belongs to the LORD?"

[4] "We do not want silver or gold from Saul's family," the Gibeonites answered him. "And none of us wants to kill ˌanyoneˌ in Israel."

The king asked, "What are you saying that I should do for you?"

[5] They answered the king, "Give us seven of the male descendants of the man who wanted to finish us off. He planned to wipe us out to keep us from staying anywhere in Israel's territory. [6] We will execute them in the LORD's presence at Saul's town Gibeah." (It was Saul whom the LORD had chosen.)

"I will give them ˌto youˌ," the king said.

[7] But the king spared Mephibosheth, Jonathan's son and Saul's grandson, because of the oath in the LORD's name between David and Jonathan, son of Saul. [8] The king took Armoni and Mephibosheth, the two sons whom Rizpah (Aiah's daughter) gave birth to for Saul, and five sons whom Merab[a] (Saul's daughter) gave birth to for Adriel, son of Barzillai from Meholah. [9] The king handed them over to the Gibeonites, who executed them on the mountain in the LORD's presence. All seven died together. They were killed at the beginning of the harvest, when people started harvesting barley.

[10] Rizpah (Aiah's daughter) took sackcloth and stretched it out on the rock for herself from the beginning of the harvest until the sky rained on the dead bodies. She wouldn't let any birds land on them during the day or any wild animals come near them during the night.

[11] When David was told what Saul's concubine[b] Rizpah (Aiah's daughter) had done, [12] David went and took the bones of Saul and of his son Jonathan from the citizens of Jabesh Gilead. They had stolen them from the public square of Beth Shean, where the Philistines had hung them the day they killed Saul at Gilboa. [13] When David brought up the bones of Saul and Jonathan, his men gathered the bones of those who had been executed. [14] Then they buried the bones of Saul and his son Jonathan in the land of Benjamin, in Zela, in the tomb of Saul's father Kish. They did everything the king ordered. After that, God answered the prayers for the land.

The Giants of the Philistines Defeated—1 Chronicles 20:4–8

[15] Once again there was a battle between the Philistines and Israel. So David and his men went to fight the Philistines, but David became exhausted. [16] A descendant of Haraphah named Benob, who had a bronze spear weighing 7½ pounds which he wore on a new belt, captured David and intended to kill him. [17] But Abishai, son of Zeruiah, came to help David. He attacked

---

[a] 21:8 1 Samuel 18:19, two Hebrew manuscripts, some Greek manuscripts, Syriac, Targum; other Hebrew and Greek manuscripts "Mical."   [b] 21:11 A concubine is considered a wife except she has fewer rights under the law.

the Philistine and killed him. Then David's men swore an oath, saying, "You'll never go into battle with us again. The lamp of Israel must never be extinguished." [18] After this, there was another battle with the Philistines at Gob. Then Sibbecai from Hushah killed Saph, another descendant of Haraphah. [19] When more fighting broke out with the Philistines at Gob, Elhanan, son of Jaare Oregim from Bethlehem, killed Goliath of Gath. (The shaft of Goliath's spear was like a beam used by weavers.) [20] In another battle at Gath, there was a tall man who had a total of 24 fingers and toes: six fingers on each hand and six toes on each foot. He also was a descendant of Haraphah. [21] When he challenged Israel, Jonathan, son of David's brother Shimei, killed him. [22] These four were descendants of Haraphah from Gath, and David and his men killed them.

David's Song of Deliverance—*Psalm 18:1–50*

22 [1] David sang this song to the LORD when the LORD rescued him from all his enemies, especially from Saul. [2] He said,

> The LORD is my rock and my fortress and my Savior,
> [3]   my God, my rock in whom I take refuge, my shield,
>   the strength of my salvation, my stronghold,
>   my refuge, and my Savior who saved me from violence.
> [4] The LORD should be praised.
>   I called on him, and I was saved from my enemies.
>
> [5] The waves of death had surrounded me.
>   The torrents of destruction had overwhelmed me.
> [6]   The ropes of the grave had surrounded me.
>   The clutches of death had confronted me.
>
> [7] I called on the LORD in my distress.
>   I called to my God for help.
>   He heard my voice from his temple,
>   and my cry for help reached his ears.
>
> [8] Then the earth shook and quaked.
>   Even the foundations of the heavens trembled.
>   They shook violently because he was angry.
> [9] Smoke went up from his nostrils,
>   and a raging fire came out of his mouth.
>   Glowing coals flared up from it.
> [10] He spread apart the heavens
>   and came down with a dark cloud under his feet.
> [11] He rode on one of the angels[a] as he flew,
>   and he soared on the wings of the wind.
> [12] He surrounded himself with darkness.
>   He made the dark rain clouds his covering.
> [13] Out of the brightness in front of him, he made lightning.
> [14] The LORD thundered from heaven.
>   The Most High made his voice heard.
> [15] He shot arrows and scattered them.
>   He flashed streaks of lightning and threw them into confusion.
> [16]   Then the ocean floor could be seen.
>   The foundations of the earth were laid bare
>   at the LORD's stern warning,
>   at the blast of the breath from his nostrils.
>
> [17] He reached down from high above and took hold of me.
>   He pulled me out of the raging water.
> [18] He rescued me from my strong enemy
>   and from those who hated me,
>   because they were too strong for me.
> [19] On the day when I faced disaster, they confronted me,
>   but the LORD became my defense.
> [20]   He brought me out to a wide-open place.
>   He rescued me because he was pleased with me.

---

[a] 22:11 Or "cherubim."

²¹ The LORD rewarded me
    because of my righteousness,
    because my hands are clean.
He paid me back
²²   because I have kept the ways of the LORD
      and I have not wickedly turned away from my God,
²³   because all his judgments are in front of me
      and I have not turned away from his laws.
²⁴   I was innocent as far as he was concerned.
      I have kept myself from guilt.
²⁵ The LORD paid me back
    because of my righteousness,
    because he can see that I am clean.

²⁶ ⌊In dealing⌋ with faithful people you are faithful,
    with innocent warriors you are innocent,
²⁷   with pure people you are pure.
    ⌊In dealing⌋ with devious people you are clever.

²⁸ You save humble people,
    but your eyes bring down arrogant people.
²⁹ O LORD, you are my lamp.
    The LORD turns my darkness into light.
³⁰   With you I can attack a line of soldiers.
    With my God I can break through barricades.

³¹ God's way is perfect!
    The promise of the LORD has proven to be true.
      He is a shield to all those who take refuge in him.
³²   Who is God but the LORD?
        Who is a rock other than our God?
³³ God arms me with strength.^b
His perfect way sets me free.
³⁴   He makes my feet like those of a deer
      and gives me sure footing on high places.
³⁵   He trains my hands for battle
      so that my arms can bend an ⌊archer's⌋ bow of bronze.
³⁶ You have given me the shield of your salvation.
Your help makes me great.
³⁷ You make a wide path for me to walk on
    so that my feet do not slip.
³⁸ I chased my enemies and destroyed them.
I did not return until I had ended their lives.
³⁹ I ended their lives by shattering them.
    They were unable to get up.
    They fell under my feet.
⁴⁰ You armed me with strength for battle.
You made my opponents bow at my feet.
⁴¹ You made my enemies turn their backs to me,
    and I destroyed those who hated me.
⁴² They looked, but there was no one to save them.
They looked to the LORD, but he did not answer them.
⁴³   I beat them into a powder as fine as the dust on the ground.
    I crushed them and stomped on them like the dirt on the streets.
⁴⁴ You rescued me from my conflicts with my people.
You kept me as the leader of nations.
    A people I did not know will serve me.
⁴⁵   Foreigners will cringe in front of me.
      As soon as they hear of me, they will obey me.
⁴⁶   Foreigners will lose heart,
      although they are armed^c in their fortifications.

---

^b 22:33 Dead Sea Scrolls, Psalm 18:33, Greek, Syriac, Latin; Masoretic Text "my refuge is strength."   ^c 22:46 Hebrew
meaning uncertain.

⁴⁷ The LORD lives!
  Thanks be to my rock!
    May God, the rock of my salvation, be glorified.
⁴⁸ God gives me vengeance!
  He brings people under my authority.
⁴⁹ He frees me from my enemies.
    You lift me up above my opponents.
    You rescue me from violent people.
⁵⁰ That is why I will give thanks to you, O LORD, among the nations
    and make music to praise your name.
⁵¹ He gives great victories to his king.
  He shows mercy to his anointed,
    to David, and to his descendant[d] forever.

David's Last Words

23 ¹ These are the last words of David:

"Here is the declaration by David, son of Jesse—
the declaration by the man whom God raised up,[a]
  whom the God of Jacob anointed,
    the singer of Israel's psalms:

² "The Spirit of the LORD spoke through me.
His words were on my tongue.
³ The God of Israel spoke to them.
The rock of Israel told me,
  'The one who rules humans with justice rules with the fear of God.
⁴   He is like the morning light as the sun rises,
      like a morning without clouds,
      like the brightness after a rainstorm.
        The rain makes the grass grow from the earth.'

⁵ "Truly, God considers my house to be that way,
  because he has made a lasting promise[b] to me,
    with every detail arranged and assured.
  ‚He promised‚ everything that helps me,
    everything that pleases me.
  Truly, he makes these things happen.

⁶ "Worthless people are like thorns.
  All of them are thrown away, because they cannot be picked by hand.
⁷   A person who touches them uses iron ‚tools‚
      or the shaft of a spear.
  Fire[c] will burn them up completely wherever they are."

David's Three Fighting Men—*1 Chronicles 11:10–19*

⁸ These are the names of David's fighting men: Josheb Basshebeth from Tahkemon's family was leader of the three. He used a spear[d] to kill 800 men on one occasion.

⁹ Next in rank to him was Eleazar, another one of the three fighting men. He was the son of Dodo and grandson of Aho. Eleazar was with David at Pas Dammim[e] when the Philistines gathered there for battle. When the soldiers from Israel retreated, ¹⁰ he attacked and killed Philistines until his hand got tired and stuck to his sword. So the LORD won an impressive victory that day. The army returned to Eleazar, but they only returned to strip the dead.

¹¹ Next in rank to him was Shammah, the son of Agee from Harar. The Philistines had gathered at Lehi, where there was a field of ripe lentils. When the troops fled from the Philistines, ¹² he stood in the middle of the field and defended it by killing Philistines. So the LORD won an impressive victory.

¹³ At harvest time three of the thirty leading men came to David at the cave of Adullam when a troop from the Philistine army was camping in the valley of Rephaim. ¹⁴ While David was in the fortified camp, Philistine troops were at Bethlehem. ¹⁵ When David became thirsty, he said, "I wish I could have a drink of water from the well at the city gate of Bethlehem." ¹⁶ So the three

---

[d] 22:51 Or "to his descendants."   [a] 23:1 Dead Sea Scrolls, Greek; Masoretic Text "who was raised up high."
[b] 23:5 Or "covenant."   [c] 23:7 Or "The fire."   [d] 23:8 1 Chronicles 11:11; Greek "drew his sword"; Hebrew meaning of Masoretic Text uncertain.   [e] 23:9 1 Chronicles 11:13; Masoretic Text "when [the Philistines] challenged."

fighting men burst into the Philistine camp and drew water from the well. They brought it to David, but he refused to drink it. He poured it out ˎas an offeringˌ to the LORD and said, [17] "It's unthinkable that I would do this, LORD. This is the blood of men who risked their lives!" So he refused to drink it.

These are the things which the three fighting men did.

David's Thirty Fighting Men—*1 Chronicles 11:20–47*

[18] Joab's brother Abishai, Zeruiah's son, was the leader of the thirty. He used his spear to kill 300 men. He was as famous as the three [19] and was honored more than they were. So he became their captain, but he didn't become a member of the three.

[20] Benaiah, son of Jehoiada, was from Kabzeel and was a brave man who did many things. He killed two distinguished soldiers from Moab. He also went into a pit and killed a lion on the day it snowed. [21] And he killed a handsome Egyptian. The Egyptian had a spear in his hand. Benaiah went to him with a club, grabbed the spear from him, and killed him with it. [22] These are the things that Benaiah, son of Jehoiada, did. He was as famous as the three fighting men. [23] He was honored more than the thirty, but he was not a member of the three. David put him in charge of his bodyguards.

[24] One of the thirty was Joab's brother Asahel. ˎThe thirty leading men wereˌ

    Elhanan (son of Dodo) from Bethlehem,
[25] Shammah from Harod,
    Elika from Harod,
[26] Helez the Paltite,
    Ira (son of Ikkesh) from Tekoa,
[27] Abiezer from Anathoth,
    Mebunnai (son of Hushai),
[28] Zalmon (descendant of Ahohi),
    Maharai from Netophah,
[29] Heleb (son of Baanah) from Netophah,
    Ittai (son of Ribai) from Gibeah in Benjamin,
[30] Benaiah from Pirathon,
    Hiddai from the Gaash ravines,
[31] Abi Albon from Beth Arabah,
    Azmaveth from Bahurim,
[32] Elihba from Shaalbon,
    Bene Jashen,
[33] Jonathan (ˎson ofˌ Shammah the Hararite),
    Ahiam (son of Sharar the Hararite),
[34] Eliphelet (son of Ahasbai and grandson of a man from Maacah),
    Eliam (son of Ahithophel) from Gilo,
[35] Hezrai from Carmel,
    Paarai from Arabah,
[36] Igal (son of Nathan) from Zobah,
    Bani from the tribe of Gad,
[37] Zelek from Ammon,
    Naharai from Beeroth, armorbearer for Zeruiah's son Joab,
[38] Ira (descendant of Ithra),
    Gareb (descendant of Ithra),
[39] Uriah the Hittite—
    37 in all.

David's Sin—He Takes a Census—*1 Chronicles 21:1–30*

24 [1] The LORD became angry with Israel again, so he provoked David to turn against Israel. He said, "Go, count Israel and Judah."

[2] King David said to Joab, the commander of the army who was with him, "Go throughout the tribes of Israel from Dan to Beersheba and count the people. That way I will know how many there are."

[3] Joab responded to the king, "May the LORD your God multiply the people a hundred times over, and may Your Majesty ˎliveˌ to see it. But why does Your Majesty wish to do this?"

[4] However, the king overruled Joab and the commanders of the army. So they left the king ˎin orderˌ to count the people of Israel. [5] They crossed the Jordan River and camped at Aroer, south of the city in the middle of the valley. Then they went to Gad and to Jazer. [6] They went to Gilead and to Tahtim Hodshi and then to Dan Jaan and around toward Sidon. [7] They went to the fortified city of Tyre and all the cities of the Hivites and the Canaanites.

Then they went to Beersheba in the Negev of Judah. ⁸ When they had covered the whole country, they came to Jerusalem after 9 months and 20 days. ⁹ Joab reported the census figures to the king: In Israel there were 800,000 able-bodied men who could serve in the army, and in Judah there were 500,000.

¹⁰ After David counted the people, his conscience troubled him. David said to the LORD, "I have committed a terrible sin by what I have done. LORD, please forgive me because I have acted very foolishly."

¹¹ When David got up in the morning, the LORD spoke his word to the prophet Gad, David's seer.ᵃ ¹² "Go and tell David, 'This is what the LORD says: I'm offering you three choices. Choose the one you want me to do to you.' "

¹³ When Gad came to David, he told David this and asked, "Should seven years of famine come to you and your land, or three months during which you flee from your enemies as they pursue you, or should there be a three-day plague in your land? Think it over, and decide what answer I should give the one who sent me."

¹⁴ "I'm in a desperate situation," David told Gad. "Please let us fall into the LORD's hands because he is very merciful. But don't let me fall into human hands."

¹⁵ So the LORD sent a plague among the Israelites from that morning until the time he had chosen. Of the people from Dan to Beersheba, 70,000 died. ¹⁶ But when the Messenger stretched out his arm to destroy Jerusalem, the LORD changed his mind about the disaster. "Enough!" he said to the Messenger who was destroying the people. "Put down your weapon." The Messenger of the LORD was at the threshing floorᵇ of Araunah the Jebusite.

¹⁷ When David saw the Messenger who had been killing the people, he said to the LORD, "I've sinned. I've done wrong. What have these sheep done? Please let your punishment be against me and against my father's family."

¹⁸ That day Gad came to David and said to him, "Go, set up an altar for the LORD at Araunah the Jebusite's threshing floor."

¹⁹ David went as Gad had told him and as the LORD had commanded him. ²⁰ When Araunah looked down and saw the king and his men coming toward him, he went out and bowed down with his face touching the ground in front of the king. ²¹ "Why has Your Majesty come to me?" Araunah asked.

David answered, "To buy the threshing floor from you and to build an altar for the LORD. Then the plague on the people will stop."

²² Araunah said to David, "Take it, Your Majesty, and offer whatever you think is right. There are oxen for the burnt offering, and there are threshers and oxen yokesᶜ for firewood." ²³ All this Araunah gave to the king and said, "May the LORD your God accept you."

²⁴ "No!" the king said to Araunah. "I must buy it from you at a ₍fair₎ price. I won't offer the LORD my God burnt sacrifices that cost me nothing."

So David bought the threshing floor and the oxen for 1¼ pounds of silver. ²⁵ David built an altar for the LORD there and sacrificed burnt offerings and fellowship offerings. So the LORD heard the prayers for the country, and the plague on Israel stopped.

ᵃ 24:11 A seer is a prophet.   ᵇ 24:16 A threshing floor is an outdoor area where grain is separated from its husks.
ᶜ 24:22 A thresher is a device used to separate grain from its husks. A yoke is a wooden bar placed over the necks of
work animals so that they can pull plows or carts.

1 KINGS

David's Old Age

1 ¹ King David had grown old, and although he was covered with blankets, he couldn't get warm. ² His officials told him, "Your Majesty, let us search for a young woman who has never been married. She can stay with you and be your servant. She can lie in your arms and keep you warm."

³ So they searched throughout Israel for a beautiful, young woman. They found Abishag from Shunem and brought her to the king. ⁴ The woman was very beautiful. She became the king's servant and took care of him, but the king did not make love to her.

Adonijah Plots to Become King

⁵ Adonijah, son of Haggith,^a was very handsome. His mother gave birth to him after Maacah had Absalom.^b Adonijah was boasting that he was king. So he got a chariot and horses and 50 men to run ahead of him. ⁶ His father had never confronted him by asking why he was doing this. ⁷ But Adonijah had discussed his actions with Joab (son of Zeruiah) and with the priest Abiathar, so they supported him. ⁸ But the priest Zadok, Benaiah (son of Jehoiada), the prophet Nathan, Shimei, Rei, and David's ˌthirtyˌ fighting men did not join Adonijah.

⁹ Adonijah sacrificed sheep, cattle, and fattened calves at Zoheleth Rock near En Rogel. He had invited all his brothers, the king's ˌotherˌ sons, all the men of Judah, and the king's officials. ¹⁰ But he didn't invite the prophet Nathan, Benaiah, the fighting men, or his brother Solomon.

The Prophet Nathan Helps Solomon Become King

¹¹ Then Nathan asked Solomon's mother Bathsheba, "Haven't you heard that Adonijah, Haggith's son, has become king, and our master David doesn't ˌevenˌ know about it? ¹² Bathsheba, let me give you some advice about how to save your life and your son's life. ¹³ Go to King David and ask him, 'Your Majesty, didn't you swear to me that my son Solomon will be king after you, and that he will sit on your throne? Why is Adonijah acting as king?' ¹⁴ And while you're still there talking to the king, I'll come in and confirm what you have said."

¹⁵ Bathsheba went to the king in his private room. The king was very old, and Abishag from Shunem was taking care of him. ¹⁶ Bathsheba knelt and bowed down in front of the king. "What do you want?" the king asked.

¹⁷ "Sir," she answered, "you took an oath to the Lord your God. You said that my son Solomon will be king after you, and that he will sit on your throne. ¹⁸ But now, you see, Adonijah has become king, and you don't ˌevenˌ know anything about it, Your Majesty. ¹⁹ He has sacrificed many fattened calves, bulls, and sheep. He has invited all the king's sons, Abiathar the priest, and Joab the commander of the army ˌto his feastˌ. But he hasn't invited your servant Solomon. ²⁰ All Israel is looking to you, Your Majesty, to tell them who should succeed you on your throne. ²¹ Otherwise, my son Solomon and I will be treated like criminals when you lie down in death with your ancestors."

²² While she was still talking to the king, the prophet Nathan arrived. ²³ The servants told the king, "The prophet Nathan is here." When he came to the king, he bowed down in front of him. ²⁴ Nathan said, "Your Majesty, you must have said that Adonijah will be king after you and that he will sit on your throne, ²⁵ because today he went and sacrificed many bulls, fattened calves, and sheep. He invited all the king's sons, the army's commanders, and the priest Abiathar ˌto his feastˌ. They are eating and drinking with him and saying, 'Long live King Adonijah!' ²⁶ But he didn't invite me or the priest Zadok or Benaiah, who is Jehoiada's son, or your servant Solomon. ²⁷ Did you allow this to happen without telling me who would sit on your throne next?"

²⁸ Then King David answered, "Call Bathsheba in here." So she stood in front of him, ²⁹ and he swore an oath. He said, "I solemnly swear, as the Lord who has saved my life from all trouble lives, ³⁰ I will do today exactly what I swore to you by the Lord God of Israel. Your son Solomon will be king after me. He will sit on my throne."

---

^a 1:5 Adonijah's mother was Haggith; his father was David. He was David's oldest living son.   ^b 1:5 "very handsome. . . Absalom." These words are the last part of verse 6 (in Hebrew). They have been placed at the beginning of verse 5 to express the complex Hebrew sentence structure more clearly in English.

³¹ Then Bathsheba bowed down with her face touching the ground in front of the king. "May Your Majesty, King David, live forever!" she said.

³² King David said, "Summon the priest Zadok, the prophet Nathan, and Benaiah, son of Jehoiada." So they came to the king, ³³ and he said, "Take my officials with you. Put my son Solomon on my mule, and take him to Gihon. ³⁴ Have the priest Zadok and the prophet Nathan anoint him king of Israel there. Then blow the ram's horn and say, 'Long live King Solomon!' ³⁵ Follow him ₎back₎ here when he comes to sit on my throne. He will be king in place of me. I have appointed him to be the leader of Israel and Judah."

³⁶ "So be it!" Benaiah, son of Jehoiada, answered the king. "The LORD your God says so too. ³⁷ As the LORD has been with you, so may he be with Solomon. May Solomon be an even greater king than you, King David."

³⁸ Then the priest Zadok, the prophet Nathan, Benaiah (son of Jehoiada), the Cherethites, and the Pelethites put Solomon on King David's mule and brought him to Gihon. ³⁹ The priest Zadok took the container of olive oil from the tent and anointed Solomon. They blew the ram's horn, and all the people said, "Long live King Solomon!" ⁴⁰ All the people followed him, blew flutes, and celebrated so loudly that their voices shook the ground.

Adonijah's Plot Fails

⁴¹ Adonijah and all his guests heard this as they finished eating. When Joab heard the sound of the horn, he asked, "What's the reason for the noise in the city?" ⁴² He was still speaking when Jonathan, son of the priest Abiathar, arrived. "Come in," Adonijah said. "You're an honorable man, so you must be bringing good news."

⁴³ "Not at all," Jonathan answered Adonijah. "His Majesty King David has made Solomon king. ⁴⁴ The king has sent the priest Zadok, the prophet Nathan, Benaiah (son of Jehoiada), the Cherethites, and the Pelethites with him. They have put him on the king's mule. ⁴⁵ The priest Zadok and the prophet Nathan have anointed him king at Gihon. They have come from there celebrating, so the city is excited. That is the sound you heard. ⁴⁶ Solomon is now seated on the royal throne. ⁴⁷ Furthermore, the royal officials have come ₎to congratulate₎ His Majesty King David, saying, 'May your God make Solomon's name more famous than yours and his reign greater than your reign.' The king himself bowed down on his bed ⁴⁸ and said, 'Praise the LORD God of Israel who has let me see the heir to my throne.' "

⁴⁹ Adonijah's guests were frightened, so they got up and scattered in all directions. ⁵⁰ Adonijah was afraid of Solomon. He got up, went ₎to the tent of meeting,₎ and took hold of the horns of the altar.ᶜ ⁵¹ Someone told Solomon, "Adonijah is afraid of you, King Solomon. He is holding on to the horns of the altar and saying, 'Make King Solomon swear to me today that he will not have me killed.' "

⁵² Solomon said, "If he will behave like an honorable man, not one hair on his head will fall to the ground. But if he does ₎anything₎ wrong, he will die." ⁵³ King Solomon sent men to take him from the altar. Adonijah bowed down in front of King Solomon. "Go home," Solomon told him.

David's Advice to Solomon—1 Chronicles 29:26–30

2 ¹ When David was about to die, he instructed his son Solomon, ² "I'm about to leave this world. Be strong and mature. ³ Fulfill your duty to the LORD your God. Obey his directions, laws, commands, rules, and written instructions as they are recorded in Moses' Teachings. Then you'll succeed in everything you do wherever you may go. ⁴ ₎You'll succeed₎ because the LORD will keep the promise he made to me: 'If your descendants are faithful to me with all their hearts and lives, you will never fail to have an heir on the throne of Israel.'

⁵ "You know what Joab (Zeruiah's son) did to me and to the two commanders of Israel's army—Abner, son of Ner, and Amasa, son of Jether. Joab killed them. When there was peace, he shed blood as if it were wartime. With their blood he stained the belt around his waist and the shoes on his feet. ⁶ Use your wisdom. Don't let that gray-haired, old man go to his grave peacefully.

⁷ "Be kind to the sons of Barzillai from Gilead. Let them eat at your table. They helped me when I was fleeing from your brother Absalom.

⁸ "Shimei, son of Gera from Bahurim in Benjamin, is still with you. He cursed me repeatedly when I went to Mahanaim. But when he came to meet me at the Jordan River, I took an oath by the LORD and said, 'As long as I'm king, I won't have you killed.' ⁹ Now, don't let him go unpunished. You are wise and know what to do to him: Put that gray-haired, old man into his grave by slaughtering him."

¹⁰ David lay down in death with his ancestors and was buried in the City of David. ¹¹ He ruled as king of Israel for 40 years. He ruled for 7 years in Hebron and for 33 years in Jerusalem.

ᶜ 1:50 Holding on to the horns of the altar was an appeal for mercy.

Solomon Establishes His Authority

¹² Solomon sat on his father David's throne, and his power was firmly established. ¹³ Then Adonijah, son of Haggith, went to Bathsheba, Solomon's mother. "Is this a friendly visit?" she asked.

"Yes," he answered. ¹⁴ Then he added, "I have a matter ˌto discussˌ with you."

"What is it?" she asked.

¹⁵ He said, "You know the kingship was mine. All Israel expected me to be their king. But the kingship has been turned over to my brother because the LORD gave it to him. ¹⁶ Now I want to ask you for one thing. Don't refuse me."

"What is it?" she asked.

¹⁷ He said, "Please ask King Solomon to give me Abishag from Shunem as my wife. He will not refuse you."

¹⁸ "Very well," Bathsheba answered. "I will talk to the king for you."

¹⁹ Bathsheba went to King Solomon to talk to him on Adonijah's behalf. The king got up to meet her and bowed down in front of her. Then he sat on his throne. He had a throne brought for his mother, and she sat at his right side.

²⁰ "I'm asking you for one little thing," she said. "Don't refuse me."

"Ask, Mother," the king told her. "I won't refuse you."

²¹ She replied, "Let Abishag from Shunem be given to your brother Adonijah as his wife."

²² King Solomon then said, "Why do you ask that Abishag from Shunem be given to Adonijah? That would be the same as giving him the kingship. After all, he is my older brother. The priest Abiathar and Joab (Zeruiah's son) are supporting him."

²³ King Solomon took an oath by the LORD and said, "May God strike me dead if Adonijah doesn't pay with his life for this request! ²⁴ The LORD set me on my father David's throne and gave me a dynasty as he promised. So I solemnly swear, as the LORD who has established me lives, that Adonijah will be put to death today." ²⁵ King Solomon gave this task to Benaiah, son of Jehoiada. Benaiah attacked and killed Adonijah.

²⁶ The king told the priest Abiathar, "Go to your land in Anathoth. You deserve to die, but I won't kill you at this time because you carried the ark of the Almighty LORD ahead of my father David and because you shared all my father's sufferings." ²⁷ So Solomon removed Abiathar as the LORD's priest and fulfilled the LORD's word spoken at Shiloh about Eli's family.

²⁸ The news reached Joab. (He had supported Adonijah, although he hadn't supported Absalom.) So Joab fled to the LORD's tent and clung to the horns of the altar. ²⁹ After King Solomon heard that Joab had fled to the altar in the tent of the LORD, Solomon sent Benaiah, son of Jehoiada, to kill Joab.

³⁰ When Benaiah came to the tent of the LORD, he told Joab, "The king says, 'Come out.' "

"No," Joab answered, "I'll die here."

So Benaiah reported to the king what Joab had said and how he had answered.

³¹ The king answered, "Do as he said. Kill him, and bury him. You can remove the innocent blood—the blood which Joab shed—from me and my father's family. ³² The LORD will repay him for the slaughter he caused. Joab killed two honorable men who were better than he was. He used his sword to kill Abner (who was the son of Ner and the commander of Israel's army) and Amasa (who was the son of Jether and the commander of Judah's army). Joab did this without my father's knowledge. ³³ The responsibility for their blood will fall on Joab and his descendants forever. But may David, his descendants, family, and throne always receive peace from the LORD."

³⁴ Then Benaiah, son of Jehoiada, went and attacked Joab, killed him, and buried him at his home in the desert. ³⁵ The king then appointed Benaiah, son of Jehoiada, to replace Joab as commander of the army. King Solomon also replaced Abiathar with the priest Zadok.

³⁶ The king summoned Shimei and said to him, "Build a house for yourself in Jerusalem, and stay there. Don't leave ˌthe cityˌ to go anywhere else. ³⁷ But the day you leave and cross the brook in the Kidron Valley, you can be certain that you will die. You will be responsible for your own death."

³⁸ "Very well," Shimei answered. "I'll do just what Your Majesty said."

So Shimei stayed in Jerusalem for a long time. ³⁹ But after three years, two of Shimei's slaves fled to Gath's King Achish, son of Maacah. Shimei was told that his slaves were in Gath, ⁴⁰ so he saddled his donkey and went to Achish in Gath to search for his slaves. Shimei went to Gath and got his slaves.

⁴¹ After Solomon heard that Shimei had gone from Jerusalem to Gath and back, ⁴² he summoned Shimei. Solomon asked him, "Didn't I make you take an oath by the LORD? Didn't I warn you that if you left ˌthe cityˌ to go anywhere, you could be certain that you would die? Didn't you say to me, 'Very well. I'll do just what you said'? ⁴³ Why didn't you keep your oath to the LORD and obey the command I gave you? ⁴⁴ Shimei, you know in your heart all the evil that you

did to my father David. The LORD is going to pay you back for the evil you have done. [45] But King Solomon is blessed, and David's dynasty will always be firmly established by the LORD." [46] Then the king gave orders to Benaiah, son of Jehoiada. He went to attack and kill Shimei. Solomon's power as king was now firmly established.

Solomon's Marriage—*2 Chronicles 1:1*

3 [1] Solomon became the son-in-law of Pharaoh (the king of Egypt). After marrying Pharaoh's daughter, Solomon brought her to the City of David until he finished building his own house, the LORD's house, and the wall around Jerusalem.

[2] The people were still sacrificing at other worship sites because a temple for the name of the LORD had not yet been built. [3] Solomon loved the LORD and lived by his father David's rules. However, he still sacrificed and burned incense at these other worship sites.

Solomon Requests Wisdom From God—*2 Chronicles 1:2–13*

[4] King Solomon went to Gibeon to sacrifice because it was the most important place of worship. Solomon sacrificed 1,000 burnt offerings on that altar.

[5] In Gibeon the LORD appeared to Solomon in a dream at night. He said, "What can I give you?" [6] Solomon responded, "You've shown great love to my father David, who was your servant. He lived in your presence with truth, righteousness, and commitment. And you continued to show him your great love by giving him a son to sit on his throne today.

[7] "LORD my God, although I'm young and inexperienced, you've made me king in place of my father David. [8] I'm among your people whom you have chosen. They are too numerous to count or record. [9] Give me a heart that listens so that I can judge your people and tell the difference between good and evil. After all, who can judge this great people of yours?"

[10] The LORD[a] was pleased that Solomon asked for this. [11] God replied, "You've asked for this and not for a long life, or riches for yourself, or the death of your enemies. Instead, you've asked for understanding so that you can do what is right. [12] So I'm going to do what you've asked. I'm giving you a wise and understanding heart so that there will never be anyone like you. [13] I'm also giving you what you haven't asked for—riches and honor—so that no other king will be like you as long as you live. [14] And if you follow me and obey my laws and commands as your father David did, then I will also give you a long life."

[15] Solomon woke up and realized it had been a dream. He went to Jerusalem and stood in front of the ark of the LORD's promise. He sacrificed burnt offerings and fellowship offerings and held a banquet for all his officials.

Solomon's Wisdom in Action

[16] A short time later two prostitutes came to the king and stood in front of him. [17] One woman said to him, "Sir, this woman and I live in the same house. I gave birth ͵to a son͵ while she was with me in the house. [18] Two days later this woman also gave birth ͵to a son͵. We were alone. No one else was with us. Just the two of us were in the house. [19] That night this woman's son died because she rolled over on top of him. [20] So she got up during the night and took my son, who was beside me, while I was asleep. She held him in her arms. Then she laid her dead son in my arms. [21] When I got up in the morning to nurse my son, he was dead! I took a good look at him and realized that he wasn't my son at all!"

[22] The other woman said, "No! My son is alive—your son is dead."

The first woman kept on saying, "No! Your son is dead—my son is alive." So they argued in front of the king.

[23] The king said, "This one keeps saying, 'My son is alive—your son is dead,' and that one keeps saying, 'No! Your son is dead—my son is alive.' "

[24] So the king told his servants to bring him a sword. When they brought it, [25] he said, "Cut the living child in two. Give half to the one and half to the other."

[26] Then the woman whose son was still alive was deeply moved by her love for the child. She said to the king, "Please, sir, give her the living child. Please don't kill him!"

But the other woman said, "He won't be mine or yours. Cut him ͵in two͵."

[27] The king replied, "Give the living child to the first woman. Don't kill him. She is his mother."

[28] All Israel heard about the decision the king made. They respected the king very highly, because they saw he possessed wisdom from God to do what was right.

Solomon's Administration—*2 Chronicles 9:26*

4 [1] When King Solomon was the king of all Israel, [2] these were his officials:

Azariah, son of Zadok, was the ͵chief͵ priest.

[3] **Elihoreph** and **Ahijah,** the sons of Shisha, were scribes.

---

[a] 3:10 Many Hebrew manuscripts, Greek; other Hebrew manuscripts "Lord."

Jehoshaphat, son of Ahilud, was the royal historian.
⁴**Benaiah**, son of Jehoiada, was commander of the army.
Zadok and **Abiathar** were priests.
⁵**Azariah**, son of Nathan, was in charge of the district governors.
Zabud, son of Nathan, was the king's adviser.
⁶**Ahishar** was in charge of the palace.
Adoniram, son of Abda, was in charge of forced labor.

⁷Solomon appointed 12 district governors in Israel. They were to provide food for the king and his palace. Each one had to supply food for one month every year. ⁸Their names were

Benhur, who was in charge of the hills of Ephraim,
⁹**Bendeker**, who was in charge of Makaz, Shaalbim, Beth Shemesh, and Elon Beth Hanan, and
¹⁰**Benhesed**, who was in charge of Arubboth, Socoh, and the entire region of Hepher.
¹¹**Benabinadab** had the entire region of Dor.
(Solomon's daughter Taphath was his wife.)
¹²**Baana**, son of Ahilud, had Taanach, Megiddo, and all of Beth Shean.
(This was near Zarethan, below Jezreel, from Beth Shean to Abel Meholah and over to Jokmeam.)
¹³**Bengeber** was in charge of Ramoth Gilead; he had the settlements of Jair, a descendant of Manasseh, in Gilead.
He ˌalsoˌ had the territory of Argob in Bashan, 60 large cities with walls and bronze bars across their gates.
¹⁴**Ahinadab**, son of Iddo, was in charge of Mahanaim.
¹⁵**Ahimaaz** was in charge of Naphtali.
(He also married Solomon's daughter Basemath.)
¹⁶**Baana**, son of Hushai, was in charge of Asher and Aloth.
¹⁷**Jehoshaphat**, son of Paruah, was in charge of Issachar.
¹⁸**Shimei**, son of Ela, was in charge of Benjamin.
¹⁹**Geber**, son of Uri, was in charge of Gilead, the territory of King Sihon the Amorite and King Og of Bashan. (There was only one governor in that territory.)ᵃ

²⁰The people of Judah and Israel were as numerous as the sand on the seashore. They ate and drank and lived happily.ᵇ
²¹Solomon ruled all the kingdoms from the Euphrates River to the country of the Philistines and as far as the Egyptian border. These kingdoms paid taxes and were subject to Solomon as long as he lived.
²²Solomon's food supply for one day was 180 bushels of flour, 360 bushels of coarse flour, ²³10 fattened cows, 20 cows from the pasture, and 100 sheep in addition to deer, gazelles, fallow deer, and fattened birds. ²⁴He controlled all the territory west of the Euphrates River from Tiphsah to Gaza and all of its kings. So he lived in peace with all the neighboring countries. ²⁵As long as Solomon lived, Judah and Israel (from Dan to Beersheba) lived securely, everyone under his own vine and fig tree.
²⁶Solomon had stalls for 40,000 chariot horses. He also had 12,000 chariot soldiers.ᶜ ²⁷Each of the governors provided food for one month every year for King Solomon and all who ate at his table. The governors saw to it that nothing was in short supply. ²⁸They brought their quota of barley and straw for the chariot horses to the proper places.

Solomon's Wisdom

²⁹God gave Solomon wisdom—keen insight and a mind as limitless as the sand on the seashore. ³⁰Solomon's wisdom was greater than that of all the eastern people and all the wisdom of the Egyptians. ³¹He was wiser than anyone, than Ethan the Ezrahite, or Heman, Calcol, or Darda, Mahol's sons. His fame spread to all the nations around him.
³²Solomon spoke 3,000 proverbs and wrote 1,005 songs. ³³He described and classified trees—from the cedar in Lebanon to the hyssop growing out of the wall. He described and classified animals, birds, reptiles, and fish. ³⁴People came from every nation to hear his wisdom; they came from all the kings of the earth who had heard about his wisdom.

Preparations for Building the Temple—2 Chronicles 2:1–13, 15–18

5 ᵃ ¹King Hiram of Tyre sent his officials to Solomon when he heard that Solomon had been anointed king to succeed his father. Hiram had always been David's friend.

ᵃ 4:19 "There was . . . territory" Masoretic Text; Greek "There was also one governor in the territory of Judah."
ᵇ 4:20 1 Kings 4:21–34 in English Bibles is 1 Kings 5:1–14 in the Hebrew Bible.   ᶜ 4:26 Or "12,000 cavalry horses."
ᵃ 5:1 1 Kings 5:1–18 in English Bibles is 1 Kings 5:15–32 in the Hebrew Bible.

[2] Solomon sent word to Hiram, by saying, [3] "You know that my father David was surrounded by war. He couldn't build a temple for the name of the LORD our God until the LORD let him defeat his enemies. [4] But the LORD my God has surrounded me with peace. I have no rival and no trouble. [5] Now I'm thinking of building a temple for the name of the LORD my God as the LORD spoke to my father David: 'Your son, whom I will put on your throne to succeed you, will build a temple for my name.' [6] So order men to cut down cedars from Lebanon for me. My workers will work with your workers. I will pay you whatever wages you ask for your workers. You know we don't have any skilled lumberjacks like those from Sidon."

[7] Hiram was very glad to hear what Solomon had said. Hiram responded, "May the LORD be praised today. He has given David a wise son to rule this great nation."

[8] Hiram sent men to Solomon to say, "I've received the message you sent me. I will do everything you want in regard to the cedar and cypress logs. [9] My workers will bring logs from Lebanon to the sea, and I will have them make them into rafts to go by sea to any place you specify. There I will have them taken apart, and you can use them. You can pay me by providing food for my palace." [10] So Hiram gave Solomon all the cedar and cypress wood he wanted. [11] Solomon gave Hiram 120,000 bushels of wheat and 120,000 gallons of pure olive oil. Solomon paid Hiram this much every year.

[12] The LORD gave Solomon wisdom as he had promised. There was peace between Hiram and Solomon, and they made a treaty with one another.

[13] King Solomon forced 30,000 men from all over Israel to work for him. [14] He sent a shift of 10,000 men to Lebanon for a month. They would spend one month in Lebanon and two months at home. Adoniram was in charge of forced labor.

[15] Solomon had 70,000 men who carried heavy loads, 70,000 who quarried stone in the mountains, [16] and 3,300 foremen who were in charge of the workers. [17] The king commanded them to quarry large, expensive blocks of stone in order to provide a foundation of cut stone for the temple. [18] Solomon's workmen, Hiram's workmen, and men from Gebal quarried the stone and prepared the logs and stone to build the temple.

The Temple Built in Seven Years—*2 Chronicles 3:1–14*

6 [1] Solomon began to build the LORD's temple 480 years after Israel left Egypt. He began building in the month of Ziv (the second month) of the fourth year of his reign over Israel. [2] The temple that King Solomon built for the LORD was 90 feet long, 30 feet wide, and 45 feet high. [3] The entrance hall in front of the main room of the temple was the same length as the shorter side of the temple. It extended 15 feet in front of the temple. [4] He also made latticed windows for the temple.

[5] He built an annex containing side rooms all around the temple. This annex was next to the walls of the main building and the inner sanctuary. [6] The ˾interior of˽ the lowest story of the annex was 7½ feet wide, the second story was 9 feet wide, and the third story was 10½ feet wide. Solomon made ledges all around the temple so that this annex would not be fastened to the walls of the temple.

[7] The temple was built with stone blocks that were finished at the quarry. No hammer, chisel, or any other iron tool made a sound at the temple construction site.

[8] The entrance to the first story[a] was on the south side of the temple. A staircase went up to the middle story and then to the third story.

[9] When he had finished building the walls, he roofed the temple with rows of cedar beams and planks.[b] [10] He built ˾each story of the˽ annex 7½ feet high alongside the entire temple. Its cedar beams were attached to the temple.

[11] The LORD spoke to Solomon, saying, [12] "This concerns the temple you are building: If you live by my laws, follow my rules, and keep my commands, I will fulfill the promise I made about you to your father David. [13] I will live among the Israelites and never abandon my people."

[14] When Solomon had finished building the temple's ˾frame˽, [15] he began to line the inside walls of the temple with cedar boards. He paneled the inside of the temple with wood from floor to ceiling. He covered the floor of the temple with cypress planks.

[16] He sectioned off a 30-foot-long room at the rear of the temple with cedar boards from the floor to the rafters. He built it to serve as an inner room, the most holy place. [17] The 60-foot-long room at the front of the temple served as the main hall. [18] Gourds and flowers were carved into the cedar paneling inside the temple. Everything was ˾covered with˽ cedar. No stone could be seen.

[19] He prepared the inner room of the temple in order to put the ark of the LORD's promise there. [20] The inner room was 30 feet long, 30 feet wide, and 30 feet high. Solomon covered it and the cedar altar with pure gold. [21] He covered the inside of the temple with pure gold. He

---

[a] 6:8 Greek, Targum; Masoretic Text "second story."   [b] 6:9 Hebrew meaning uncertain.

put golden chains across the front of the inner room which was covered with gold. ²² He covered the entire inside of the temple with gold. He also covered the entire altar in the inner room with gold.

²³ In the inner room he made two 15-foot-tall angelsᶜ out of olive wood. ²⁴ Each wing of the angels was 7½ feet long. The distance from the tip of one wing to the tip of the other was 15 feet. ²⁵ Both angels had a 15-foot ˌwingspanˌ. Both had the same measurements and the same shape. ²⁶ Each was 15 feet high. ²⁷ Solomon put the angels in the inner room of the temple. The wings of the angels extended so that the wing of one of the angels touched the one wall, and the wing of the other touched the other wall. Their remaining wings touched each other in the center of the room. ²⁸ He covered the angels with gold.

²⁹ He carved angels, palm trees, and flowers into the walls all around the inner and outer rooms of the temple. ³⁰ He covered the floor of the inner and outer rooms of the temple with gold.

³¹ He made doors for the entrance to the inner room out of olive wood. The doorposts had five sides. ³² The two doors were ˌmade out ofˌ olive wood. He carved angels, palm trees, and flowers into them and covered them with gold. The gold was hammered onto the angels and the palm trees.

³³ In the same way he made square doorposts out of olive wood for the temple's entrance. ³⁴ He made two doors from cypress. Each of the doors had two folding panels. ³⁵ On them he carved angels, palm trees, and flowers. He evenly covered them with gold.

³⁶ He built the inner courtyard with three courses of finished stones and a course of finished cedar beams.

³⁷ In the month of Ziv of the fourth year of Solomon's reign, the foundation of the LORD's temple was laid. ³⁸ In the month of Bul (the eighth month) of the eleventh year ˌof his reignˌ, the temple was finished according to all its plans and specifications. He spent seven years building it.

The Palace Built in 13 Years

7 ¹ Solomon took 13 years to finish building his palace. ² He built a hall ˌnamedˌ the Forest of Lebanon. It was 150 feet long, 75 feet wide, and 45 feet high. It had four rows of cedar pillars supporting cedar beams. ³ The hall was covered with cedar above the side rooms, which were supported by 45 pillars (15 per row).ᵃ ⁴ The windows were in three rows facing each other on opposite sides ˌof the palaceˌ. ⁵ All the doors and doorframes were square. There were three doors facing each other on opposite sides ˌof the palaceˌ.

⁶ Solomon made the Hall of Pillars 75 feet long and 45 feet wide. In front of the hall was an entrance hall with pillars.

⁷ He made the Hall of Justice, where he sat on his throne and served as judge. The hall was covered with cedar from floor to ceiling.ᵇ

⁸ His own private quarters were in a different location than the Hall of Justice, but they were similar in design. Solomon also built private quarters like this for his wife, Pharaoh's daughter.

⁹ From the foundation to the roof, all these buildings, including the large courtyard, were built with high-grade stone blocks. The stone blocks were cut to size and trimmed with saws on their inner and outer faces. ¹⁰ The foundation was made with large, high-grade stones (some 12 feet long, others 15 feet long). ¹¹ Above ˌthe foundationˌ were cedar beams and high-grade stone blocks, which had been cut to size. ¹² The large courtyard had three layers of cut stone blocks and a layer of cedar beams, like the inner courtyard of the LORD's temple and the entrance hall.

The Temple Furnishings—2 Chronicles 2:13–14; 3:15–5:1

¹³ King Solomon had Hiram brought from Tyre. ¹⁴ Hiram was the son of a widow from the tribe of Naphtali. His father, a native of Tyre, was a skilled bronze craftsman. Hiram was highly skilled, resourceful, and knowledgeable about all kinds of bronze craftsmanship. He came to King Solomon and did all his ˌbronzeˌ work.

¹⁵ He made two bronze pillars. Each was 27 feet high and 18 feet in circumference. ¹⁶ He made two capitals of cast bronze to put on top of the pillars. Each capital was 7½ feet high. ¹⁷ He also made seven rows of filigree and chains for each capital. ¹⁸ After he made the pillars, he made two rows ˌof decorationsˌ around the filigree to cover the capitals which were above the pillars.ᶜ He made the capitals identical to each other. ¹⁹ The capitals on top of the pillars in the entrance hall were lily-shaped. ˌEachˌ was six feet high. ²⁰ Two hundred pomegranates in rows were directly above the bowl-shaped parts around the filigree on the capitals on both pillars.

²¹ Hiram set up the pillars in the temple's entrance hall. He set up the pillar on the right and named it Jachin [He Establishes]. Then he set up the pillar on the left and named it Boaz [In Him Is Strength]. ²² There were lily-shaped capitals at the top of the pillars. He finished the work on the pillars.

²³ Hiram made a pool from cast metal. It was 15 feet in diameter. It was round, 7½ feet high, and had a circumference of 45 feet. ²⁴ Under the rim were two rows of gourds all around the 45-foot circumference of the pool. They were cast in metal when the pool was cast. ²⁵ The pool was set on 12 metal bulls. Three bulls faced north, three faced west, three faced south, and three faced east. The pool was set on them, and their hindquarters were toward the center ˻of the pool˼. ²⁶ The pool was three inches thick. Its rim was like the rim of a cup, shaped like a lily's bud. It held 12,000 gallons.

²⁷ He made ten bronze stands. Each stand was 6 feet square and 4½ feet high. ²⁸ The stands were made this way: They had side panels set in frames. ²⁹ On the panels set in frames were lions, oxen, and angels.ᵈ These were also on the frames. Above and below the lions and the cattle were engraved designs. ³⁰ Each stand had four bronze wheels on bronze axles and four supports beneath the basin. The supports were made of cast metal with designs on the sides. ³¹ Each had a 1½-foot-deep opening in the center to the circular frame on top. The opening was round, formed like a pedestal, and was two feet ˻wide˼. Around the opening there were engravings. But the panels were square, not round. ³² The four wheels were under the panels, and the axles were attached to the stand. Each wheel was two feet high. ³³ The wheels were made like chariot wheels. The axles, rims, spokes, and hubs were all cast metal. ³⁴ The four supports at the four corners of each stand were part of the stand. ³⁵ The top of each stand had a round, nine-inch-high band. Above the stand were supports which were part of the panels. ³⁶ Hiram engraved angels, lions, palm trees, and designs in every available space on the supports and panels. ³⁷ This is the way he made the ten stands. All of them were cast in the same mold, identical in size and shape.

³⁸ Hiram also made ten bronze basins. Each basin held 240 gallons. Every basin was six feet ˻wide˼. There was one basin on each of the ten stands. ³⁹ He put five stands on the south side of the temple and five on the north side of the temple. He set the pool on the south side of the temple in the southeast ˻corner˼. ⁴⁰ Hiram also made pots, shovels, and bowls.

So Hiram finished all the work for King Solomon on the LORD's temple: ⁴¹ 2 pillars, the bowl-shaped capitals on top of the 2 pillars, and 2 sets of filigree to cover the 2 bowl-shaped capitals on top of the pillars, ⁴² 400 pomegranates for the 2 sets of filigree (2 rows of pomegranates for each filigree to cover the 2 bowl-shaped capitals on the pillars), ⁴³ 10 stands and 10 basins on the stands, ⁴⁴ 1 pool, 12 bulls under the pool, ⁴⁵ pots, shovels, and bowls. Hiram made all these utensils out of polished bronze for the LORD's temple at King Solomon's request. ⁴⁶ The king cast them in foundries in the Jordan Valley between Succoth and Zarethan. ⁴⁷ Solomon left all the products unweighed because so much bronze was used. No one tried to determine how much the bronze weighed.

⁴⁸ Solomon made all the furnishings for the LORD's temple: the gold altar, the gold table on which the bread of the presence was placed, ⁴⁹ lamp stands of pure gold (five on the south side and five on the north in front of the inner room), flowers, lamps, gold tongs, ⁵⁰ dishes, snuffers, bowls, saucers, incense burners of pure gold, the gold sockets for the doors of the inner ˻room˼ (the most holy place), and the doors of the temple.

⁵¹ All the work King Solomon did on the LORD's temple was finished. He brought the holy things that had belonged to his father David—the silver, gold, and utensils—and put them in the storerooms of the LORD's temple.

The LORD Comes to His Temple—2 Chronicles 5:2–14

8 ¹ Then Solomon assembled the respected leaders of Israel, all the heads of the tribes, and the leaders of the Israelite families. They came to King Solomon in Jerusalem to take the ark of the LORD's promise from the City of David (that is, Zion). ² All the people of Israel gathered around King Solomon at the Festival ˻of Booths˼ in the month of Ethanim, the seventh month.

³ When all the leaders of Israel had arrived, the priests picked up the LORD's ark. ⁴ They brought the ark, the tent of meeting, and all the holy utensils in it ˻to the temple˼. The priests and the Levites carried them ⁵ while King Solomon with the whole assembly from Israel were offering countless sheep and cattle sacrifices in front of the ark. ⁶ The priests brought the ark of the LORD's promise to its place in the inner room of the temple (the most holy place) under the wings of the angels.ᵃ

⁷ When the angels' outstretched wings were over the place where the ark ˻rested˼, the angels became a covering above the ark and its poles. ⁸ The poles were so long that their ends could be seen in the holy place by anyone standing in front of the inner room, but they couldn't be seen

---

ᵈ 7:29 Or "cherubim."   ᵃ 8:6 Or "cherubim."

outside. (They are still there today.) [9] There was nothing in the ark except the two stone tablets Moses put there at Horeb, where the LORD made a promise to the Israelites after they left Egypt.

[10] When the priests left the holy place, a cloud filled the LORD's temple. [11] The priests couldn't serve because of the cloud. The LORD's glory filled his temple.

Solomon Addresses the People—2 Chronicles 6:1–11

[12] Then Solomon said, "The LORD said he would live in a dark cloud. [13] I certainly have built you a high temple, a home for you to live in permanently."

[14] Then the king turned around and blessed the whole assembly of Israel while they were standing. [15] "Thanks be to the LORD God of Israel. With his mouth he made a promise to my father David; with his hand he carried it out. He said, [16] 'Ever since I brought my people Israel out of Egypt, I didn't choose any city in any of the tribes of Israel as a place to build a temple for my name. But now I've chosen David to rule my people Israel.'

[17] "My father David had his heart set on building a temple for the name of the LORD God of Israel. [18] However, the LORD said to my father David, 'Since you had your heart set on building a temple for my name, your intentions were good. [19] But you must not build the temple. Instead, your own son will build the temple for my name.' [20] The LORD has kept the promise he made. I have taken my father David's place, and I sit on the throne of Israel as the LORD promised. I've built the temple for the name of the LORD God of Israel. [21] I've made a place there for the ark which contains the LORD's promise that he made to our ancestors when he brought them out of Egypt."

Solomon's Prayer—2 Chronicles 6:12–42

[22] In the presence of the entire assembly of Israel, Solomon stood in front of the LORD's altar. He stretched out his hands toward heaven [23] and said,

> "LORD God of Israel,
>> there is no god like you in heaven above or on earth below.
>> You keep your promise[b] of mercy to your servants,
>>> who obey you wholeheartedly.

[24]   You have kept your promise to my father David, your servant.
>> With your mouth you promised it.
>> With your hand you carried it out as it is today.

[25]   "Now, LORD God of Israel,
>> keep your promise to my father David, your servant.
>> You said, 'You will never fail to have an heir
>>> sitting in front of me on the throne of Israel
>>>> if your descendants are faithful to me
>>>> as you have been faithful to me.'

[26]   "So now, God of Israel,
>> may the promise you made to my father David,
>> your servant, come true.

[27]   "Does God really live on earth?
>> If heaven itself, the highest heaven, cannot hold you,
>> then how can this temple that I have built?

[28]   Nevertheless, my LORD God, please pay attention to my prayer for mercy.
> Listen to my cry for help as I pray to you today.

[29]   Night and day may your eyes be on this temple,
>> the place about which you said, 'My name will be there.'
> Listen to me as I pray toward this place.

[30]   Hear the plea for mercy
>> that your people Israel and I pray toward this place.
> Hear us ˻when we pray˼ to heaven, the place where you live.
> Hear and forgive.

[31]   "If anyone sins against another person
>> and is required to take an oath
>>> and comes to take the oath in front of your altar in this temple,

[32]   then hear ˻that person˼ in heaven, take action, and make a decision.
>> Condemn the guilty person with the proper punishment,
>>> but declare the innocent person innocent.

---

[b] 8:23 Or "covenant."

33 "An enemy may defeat your people Israel
because they have sinned against you.
But when your people turn to you, praise your name, pray,
and plead with you in this temple,
34 then hear ‚them‚ in heaven, forgive the sins of your people Israel,
and bring them back to the land that you gave to their ancestors.

35 "When the sky is shut and there's no rain
because they are sinning against you,
and they pray toward this place, praise your name,
and turn away from their sin because you made them suffer,
36 then hear ‚them‚ in heaven.
Forgive the sins of your servants, your people Israel.
Teach them the proper way to live.
Then send rain on the land,
which you gave to your people as an inheritance.

37 "There may be famine in the land.
Plant diseases, heat waves, funguses, locusts,
or grasshoppers may destroy crops.
Enemies may blockade Israel's city gates.
During every plague or sickness
38 ‚hear‚ every prayer for mercy,
made by one person or by all the people in Israel,
whose consciences bother them,
who stretch out their hands toward this temple.
39 Hear ‚them‚ in heaven, where you live.
Forgive ‚them‚, and take action.
Give each person the proper reply.
(You know what is in their hearts,
because you alone know what is in the hearts of all people.)
40 Then, as long as they live in the land that you gave to our ancestors,
they will fear you.

41 "People will hear about your great name,
mighty hand, and powerful arm.ᶜ
So when people who are not Israelites
come from distant countries because of your name
42 to pray facing this temple,
43 hear ‚them‚ in heaven, the place where you live.
Do everything they ask you
so that all the people of the world may know your name
and fear you like your people Israel
and learn also that this temple which I built bears your name.

44 "When your people go to war against their enemies
(wherever you may send them)
and they pray to you, O LORD, toward the city you have chosen
and the temple I built for your name,
45 then hear their prayer for mercy in heaven,
and do what is right ‚for them‚.

46 "They may sin against you.
(No one is sinless.)
You may become angry with them and hand them over to an enemy
who takes them to ‚another‚ country as captives,
‚whether it is‚ far or near.
47 If they come to their senses,
are sorry for what they've done,
and plead with you in the land where they are captives,
saying, 'We have sinned. We have done wrong.
We have been wicked,'

ᶜ 8:41 The first sentence of verse 42 (in Hebrew) has been placed in verse 41 to express the complex Hebrew paragraph structure more clearly in English.

48 if they change their attitude toward you
        in the land of their enemies where they are captives,
    if they pray to you
        toward the land that you gave their ancestors,
            and the city you have chosen,
            and the temple I have built for your name,
49 then in heaven, the place where you live, hear their prayer for mercy.
    Do what is right for them.
50   Forgive your people, who have sinned against you.
        ˌForgiveˌ all their wrongs when they rebelled against you,
            and cause those who captured them to have mercy on them
51   because they are your own people
            whom you brought out of Egypt
                from the middle of an iron smelter.

52 "May your eyes always see my plea and your people Israel's plea
        so that you will listen to them whenever they call on you.
53 After all, you, LORD God, set them apart from all the people of the world
        to be your own as you promised through your servant Moses
            when you brought our ancestors out of Egypt."

Solomon Blesses the People

54 When Solomon finished praying this prayer for mercy to the LORD, he stood in front of the LORD's altar, where he had been kneeling with his hands stretched out toward heaven. 55 Then he stood and in a loud voice blessed the entire assembly of Israel, 56 "Thanks be to the LORD! He has given his people Israel rest, as he had promised. None of the good promises he made through his servant Moses has failed to come true. 57 May the LORD our God be with us as he was with our ancestors. May he never leave us or abandon us. 58 May he bend our hearts toward him. Then we will follow him and keep his commands, laws, and rules, which he commanded our ancestors ˌto keepˌ. 59 May these words which I have prayed to the LORD be near the LORD our God day and night. Then he will give me and his people Israel justice every day as it is needed. 60 In this way all the people of the world will know that the LORD is God and there is no other ˌgodˌ. 61 May your hearts be committed to the LORD our God. Then you will live by his laws and keep his commands as you have today."

Solomon Offers Sacrifices—*2 Chronicles 7:4–10*

62 Then the king and all Israel offered sacrifices to the LORD. 63 Solomon sacrificed 22,000 cattle and 120,000 sheep as fellowship offerings to the LORD. So the king and all the people of Israel dedicated the LORD's temple.
64 On that day the king designated the courtyard in front of the LORD's temple as a holy place. He sacrificed the burnt offerings, grain offerings, and the fat from the fellowship offerings because the bronze altar in front of the LORD was too small to hold all of them.
65 At that time Solomon and all Israel celebrated the Festival ˌof Boothsˌ. A large crowd had come from ˌthe territory betweenˌ the border of Hamath and the River of Egypt to be near the LORD our God for seven days.*d* 66 On the eighth day he dismissed the people. They blessed the king and went to their tents. They rejoiced with cheerful hearts for all the blessings the LORD had given his servant David and his people Israel.

The Lord Answers Solomon's Prayer—*2 Chronicles 7:11–22*

9 1 Solomon finished building the LORD's temple, the royal palace, and everything ˌelseˌ he wanted to build. 2 Then the LORD appeared to him a second time, as he had appeared to him in Gibeon. 3 The LORD said to him,

    "I have heard your prayer for mercy that you made to me.
    I have declared that this temple which you have built is holy
        so that my name may be placed there forever.
        My eyes and my heart will always be there.

4   "If you will be faithful to me as your father David was
        (with a sincere and upright heart),
            do everything I command,
                and keep my laws and rules,
5   then I will establish your royal dynasty over Israel forever

---

d 8:65 Greek; Masoretic Text adds ". . . and seven [more] days, fourteen days [total] ."

as I promised your father David when I said,
'You will never fail to have an heir on the throne of Israel.'
⁶ But if you and your descendants dare to turn away from me
and do not keep my commands and laws that I gave to you,
and follow and serve other gods and worship them,
⁷ then I will cut Israel out of the land I gave them.
I will reject this temple that I declared holy for my name.
Israel will be an example
and an object of ridicule for all the people of the world.
⁸ Everyone passing by this temple, as impressive as it is, will be appalled.
They will gasp and ask,
'Why did the LORD do these things to this land and this temple?'
⁹ They will answer ˌthemselvesˌ,
'They abandoned the LORD their God,
who brought their ancestors out of Egypt.
They adopted other gods, worshiped, and served them.
That is why the LORD brought this disaster on them.' "

Solomon Completes His Construction—2 Chronicles 8:1–18

¹⁰ It took Solomon 20 years to build the two houses (the LORD's house and the royal palace). ¹¹ ˌWhen King Solomon had finished,ˌ he gave King Hiram of Tyre 20 cities in Galilee. (Hiram had supplied Solomon with as much cedar and cypress lumber and gold as he wanted.) ¹² Hiram left Tyre to see the cities Solomon gave him. However, they didn't please him. ¹³ "What kind of cities have you given me, brother?" he asked. So he named it the region of Cabul [Good for Nothing]. (ˌThey'reˌ still ˌcalledˌ that today.) ¹⁴ Hiram had sent the king 9,000 pounds of gold.

¹⁵ This is the record of the forced laborers whom King Solomon drafted to build the LORD's house, his own house, the Millo,ᵃ the walls of Jerusalem, and ˌthe cities ofˌ Hazor, Megiddo, and Gezer. ¹⁶ (The king of Egypt captured Gezer, burned it down, and killed the Canaanites living there. Then he gave it to his daughter, Solomon's wife, as a wedding present.) ¹⁷ So Solomon rebuilt Gezer, Lower Beth Horon, ¹⁸ Baalath, Tadmor in the desert (inside the country), and ¹⁹ all the storage cities that he owned. He also built cities for his chariots, cities for his war horses, and whatever ˌelseˌ he wanted to build in Jerusalem, Lebanon, or the entire territory that he governed.

²⁰ The Amorites, Hittites, Perizzites, Hivites, and Jebusites had been left ˌin the landˌbecause the Israelites had not been able to claim them for God by destroying them.ᵇ They were not Israelites, ²¹ but they had descendants who were still in the land. Solomon drafted them for slave labor. (They are still ˌslavesˌ today.) ²² But Solomon didn't make any of the Israelites slaves. Instead, they were soldiers, officials, officers, generals, and commanders of his chariot and cavalry units.

²³ These were the officers in charge of Solomon's projects: 550 foremen for the people who did the work.

²⁴ Pharaoh's daughter moved from the City of David to the palace that Solomon had built for her. Then he built the Millo.

²⁵ Three times a year Solomon sacrificed burnt offerings and fellowship offerings on the altar he built for the LORD. He burnt them on the altar that was in the LORD's presence. And he finished the temple.

²⁶ King Solomon also built a fleet near the Red Sea coast at Ezion Geber by Elath in Edom. ²⁷ Hiram sent his own servants ˌwho wereˌ experienced seamen with the fleet. Along with Solomon's servants ²⁸ they went to Ophir, got 31,500 pounds of gold, and brought it to King Solomon.

The Queen of Sheba Visits Solomon—2 Chronicles 9:1–12

10 ¹ The queen of Sheba heard about Solomon's reputation. (He owed his reputation to the name of the LORD.) So she came to test him with riddles. ² She arrived in Jerusalem with a large group of servants, with camels carrying spices, a very large quantity of gold, and precious stones. When she came to Solomon, she talked to him about everything she had on her mind. ³ Solomon answered all her questions. No question was too difficult for the king to answer.

⁴ When the queen of Sheba saw all of Solomon's wisdom, the palace he built, ⁵ the food on his table, his officers' seating arrangement, the organization of his officials and the uniforms they wore, his cupbearers,ᵃ and the burnt offerings that he sacrificed at the LORD's temple, she was breathless. ⁶ She told the king, "What I heard in my country about your words and your

---

ᵃ 9:15 The exact place referred to as "the Millo" is unknown.   ᵇ 9:20 "because the Israelites. . . ." This clause from verse 21 (in Hebrew) has been placed in verse 20 to express the complex Hebrew paragraph structure more clearly in English.
ᵃ 10:5 A cupbearer was a trusted royal official who ensured that the king's drink was not poisoned.

wisdom is true! [7] But I didn't believe the reports until I came and saw it with my own eyes. I wasn't even told half of it. Your wisdom and wealth surpass the stories I've heard. [8] How blessed your men must be! How blessed these servants of yours must be because they are always stationed in front of you, listening to your wisdom! [9] Thank the LORD your God, who is pleased with you. He has put you on the throne of Israel. Because of your God's eternal love for the people of Israel, he has made you king so that you would maintain justice and righteousness."

[10] She gave the king 9,000 pounds of gold, a very large quantity of spices, and precious stones. Never again was such a large quantity of spices brought ˻into Israel˼ as those that the queen of Sheba gave King Solomon.

[11] Hiram's fleet that brought gold from Ophir also brought a large quantity of sandalwood and precious stones from Ophir. [12] With the sandalwood the king made supports for the LORD's temple and the royal palace, and lyres and harps for the singers. Never again was sandalwood like this imported ˻into Israel˼, nor has any been seen ˻there˼ to this day.

[13] King Solomon gave the queen of Sheba anything she wanted, whatever she asked for, besides what he had given her out of his royal generosity. Then she and her servants went back to her country.

Solomon's Wealth—2 Chronicles 9:13–25, 27–28; 1:14–17

[14] The gold that came to Solomon in one year weighed 49,950 pounds, [15] not counting ˻the gold˼ which came from the merchants, the traders' profits, all the Arab kings, and the governors of the country.

[16] King Solomon made 200 large shields of hammered gold, using 15 pounds of gold on each shield. [17] He also made 300 small shields of hammered gold, using four pounds of gold on each shield. The king put them in the hall ˻which he called˼ the Forest of Lebanon.

[18] The king also made a large ivory throne and covered it with fine gold. [19] Six steps led to the throne. Carved into the back of the throne was a calf's head. There were armrests on both sides of the seat. Two lions stood beside the armrests. [20] Twelve lions stood on six steps, one on each side. Nothing like this had been made for any other kingdom.

[21] All King Solomon's cups were gold, and all the utensils for the hall ˻which he called˼ the Forest of Lebanon were fine gold. (Nothing was silver, because it wasn't considered valuable in Solomon's time.) [22] The king had a fleet headed for Tarshish with Hiram's fleet. Once every three years the Tarshish fleet would bring gold, silver, ivory, apes, and monkeys.

[23] In wealth and wisdom King Solomon was greater than all the ˻other˼ kings of the world. [24] The whole world wanted to listen to the wisdom that God gave Solomon. [25] So everyone who came brought him gifts: articles of silver and gold, clothing, weapons, spices, horses, and mules. This happened year after year.

[26] Solomon built up ˻his army˼ with chariots and war horses. He had 1,400 chariots and 12,000 war horses. He stationed ˻some˼ in chariot cities and ˻others˼ with himself in Jerusalem. [27] The king made silver as common in Jerusalem as stones, and he made cedars as plentiful as fig trees in the foothills.

[28] Solomon's horses were imported from Egypt and Kue. The king's traders bought them from Kue for a fixed price. [29] Each chariot was imported from Egypt for 15 pounds of silver and each horse for 6 ounces of silver. For the same price they obtained horses to export to all the Hittite and Aramean kings.

Solomon's Idolatry

11 [1] King Solomon loved many foreign women in addition to Pharaoh's daughter. He loved Hittite women and women from Moab, Ammon, Edom, and Sidon. [2] They came from the nations about which the LORD had said to the people of Israel, "Never intermarry with them. They will surely tempt you to follow their gods." But Solomon was obsessed with their love. [3] He had 700 wives who were princesses and 300 wives who were concubines.[a] [4] In his old age, his wives tempted him to follow other gods. He was no longer committed to the LORD his God as his father David had been. [5] Solomon followed Astarte (the goddess of the Sidonians) and Milcom (the disgusting idol of the Ammonites). [6] So Solomon did what the LORD considered evil. He did not wholeheartedly follow the LORD as his father David had done. [7] Then Solomon built an illegal worship site on the hill east of Jerusalem for Chemosh (the disgusting idol of Moab) and for Molech (the disgusting idol of the Ammonites). [8] He did these things for each of his foreign wives who burned incense and sacrificed to their gods.

God Pronounces Judgment on Solomon

[9] So the LORD became angry with Solomon because his heart had turned from the LORD God of Israel, who had appeared to him twice. [10] God had given him commands about this. ˻He

---

[a] 11:3 A concubine is considered a wife except she has fewer rights under the law.

told him, not to follow other gods. But Solomon did not obey God's command. [11] The LORD told Solomon, "Because this is your attitude and you have no respect for my promises[b] or my laws that I commanded you to keep, I will certainly tear the kingdom away from you. I will give it to one of your servants. [12] But I will not do it in your lifetime because of your father David. I will tear it away from the hands of your son. [13] However, I will not tear the whole kingdom away from you. I will give your son one tribe for my servant David's sake and for the sake of Jerusalem, the city, that I chose."

Rebellions Against Solomon

[14] The LORD raised up Hadad the Edomite as a rival to Solomon. Hadad was from the Edomite royal family. [15] When David had conquered Edom, Joab, the commander of the army, went to bury those killed in battle and killed every male in Edom. [16] (Joab and all Israel stayed there six months until they had destroyed every male in Edom.) [17] Hadad was a young boy at the time. He and some of his father's Edomite servants fled to Egypt. [18] They left Midian and went to Paran. Taking some men from Paran with them, they went to Pharaoh (the king of Egypt). Pharaoh gave Hadad a home, a food allowance, and land.

[19] Pharaoh approved of Hadad. So he gave Hadad his sister-in-law, the sister of Queen Tahpenes, to be Hadad's wife. [20] Tahpenes' sister had a son named Genubath. Tahpenes presented the boy to Pharaoh in the palace, and Genubath lived in the palace among Pharaoh's children.

[21] When Hadad heard in Egypt that David had lain down in death with his ancestors and that Joab, the commander of the army, had died, he said to Pharaoh, "Let me go to my own country." [22] Pharaoh asked him, "What don't you have here that makes you eager to go home?"

"Nothing," he said. "But let me leave anyway."

[23] God also raised up Rezon, son of Eliada, as a rival to Solomon. Rezon fled from his master, King Hadadezer of Zobah, [24] after David killed the men of Zobah. Rezon gathered men and became the leader of a troop of warriors. They went to Damascus, settled there, and ruled a kingdom in Damascus. [25] In addition to the trouble that Hadad caused, Rezon was Israel's rival as long as Solomon lived. He ruled Aram and despised Israel.

[26] There was also Jeroboam, who was the son of Nebat and an Ephrathite from Zeredah. His mother Zeruah was a widow. He was one of Solomon's officers, but he rebelled against the king. [27] This was the situation when he rebelled against the king: Solomon was building the Millo[c] and repairing a break in the wall of, the City of David. [28] Solomon saw that Jeroboam was a very able and hard-working man. So he put Jeroboam in charge of all forced labor from the tribes of Joseph.

[29] At that time Jeroboam left Jerusalem. The prophet Ahijah from Shiloh met him on the road. The two of them were alone in the open country, and Ahijah had on new clothes. [30] Ahijah took his new garment and tore it into 12 pieces. [31] He told Jeroboam, "Take 10 pieces because this is what the LORD God of Israel says: I am going to tear the kingdom out of Solomon's hands and give ten tribes to you. [32] He will have one tribe left, because of my servant David and Jerusalem, the city I have chosen from all the tribes of Israel. [33] I will do this because he has abandoned me and worshiped Astarte (the goddess of the Sidonians), Chemosh (the god of Moab), and Milcom (the god of Ammon). He has not followed my ways. He did not do what I consider right or keep my laws and decrees as his father David did. [34] "I will not take the whole kingdom from him. Instead, I will allow him to be ruler as long as he lives because of my servant David whom I chose, who obeyed my commands and laws. [35] But I will take the kingdom away from his son and give you ten tribes. [36] I will give his son one tribe so that my servant David will always have a lamp in my presence in Jerusalem, the city where I chose to place my name.

[37] "I will choose you so that you can rule everything you desire. You will be king of Israel. [38] If you will do all I command you, follow my ways, and do what I consider right by obeying my laws and commands as my servant David did, then I will be with you. I will build a permanent dynasty for you as I did for David. And I will give you Israel. [39] I will make David's descendants suffer for this, but not always."

[40] Then Solomon tried to kill Jeroboam, but Jeroboam fled to King Shishak of Egypt. He stayed in Egypt until Solomon died.

Solomon's Death—2 Chronicles 9:29–31

[41] Aren't the rest of Solomon's acts—everything he did—and his wisdom written in the records of Solomon? [42] The length of Solomon's reign in Jerusalem over all Israel was 40 years. [43] Solomon lay down in death with his ancestors and was buried in the City of David. His son Rehoboam succeeded him as king.

---

[b] 11:11 Or "covenant."   [c] 11:27 The exact place referred to as "the Millo" is unknown.

King Rehoboam Foolishly Rejects Israel's Request—*2 Chronicles 10:1-19*

12 ¹ Rehoboam went to Shechem because all Israel had gone to Shechem to make him king. ² Jeroboam (Nebat's son) was still in Egypt, where he had fled from King Solomon. When he heard ⸤about Rehoboam⸥, he returned from Egypt.ᵃ ³ ⸤Israel⸥ sent for Jeroboam and invited him back. Jeroboam and the entire assembly of Israel went to speak to Rehoboam. They said, ⁴ "Your father made us carry a heavy burden. Reduce the hard work and lighten the heavy burden he put on us, and we will serve you."

⁵ He said to them, "Leave and come back the day after tomorrow." So the people left.

⁶ King Rehoboam sought advice from the older leaders who had served his father Solomon while he was still alive. He asked, "What do you advise? How should I respond to these people?"

⁷ They told him, "If you will serve these people today, humble yourself, and speak gently, then they will always be your servants."

⁸ But he ignored the advice the older leaders gave him. He sought advice from the young men who had grown up with him and were serving him. ⁹ He asked them, "What is your advice? How should we respond to these people who are asking me to lighten the burden my father put on them?"

¹⁰ The young men who had grown up with him answered, "This is what you should tell them: 'My little finger is heavier than my father's whole body.ᵇ ¹¹ If my father put a heavy burden on you, I will add to it. If my father punished you with whips, I will punish you with scorpions.' "

¹² So Jeroboam and all the people came back to Rehoboam two days later, as the king had instructed them. ¹³ The king answered the people harshly. He ignored the advice the older leaders gave him. ¹⁴ He spoke to them as the young men advised. He said, "If my father made your burden heavy, I will add to it. If my father punished you with whips, I will punish you with scorpions." ¹⁵ The king refused to listen to the people because the LORD was directing these events to carry out the promise he had made to Jeroboam (Nebat's son) through Ahijah from Shiloh.

¹⁶ When all Israel saw that the king refused to listen to them, the people answered the king,

> "What share do we have in David's kingdom?
> We won't receive an inheritance from Jesse's son.
>   To your own tents, Israel!
>   Now look after your own house, David!"

So Israel went home to their own tents. ¹⁷ But Rehoboam ruled the Israelites who lived in the cities of Judah.

¹⁸ Then King Rehoboam sent Adoram to Israel. He was in charge of forced labor, but they stoned him to death. So King Rehoboam got on his chariot as fast as he could and fled to Jerusalem. ¹⁹ Israel has rebelled against David's dynasty to this day.

King Jeroboam Establishes Idolatry in Israel—*2 Chronicles 11:1-17*

²⁰ When all Israel heard that Jeroboam had returned, they sent men to invite him to the assembly. They made him king of all Israel. Only the tribe of Judah remained loyal to David's dynasty.

²¹ When Rehoboam came to Jerusalem, he gathered all the people of Judah and the tribe of Benjamin, 180,000 of the best soldiers, to fight against the people of Israel and return the kingdom to Rehoboam, son of Solomon.

²² But God spoke his word to Shemaiah, the man of God. He said, ²³ "Speak to Judah's King Rehoboam, son of Solomon, and all the people of Judah and Benjamin, and the rest of the people. ²⁴ This is what the LORD says: Don't wage war against your relatives from Israel. Everyone, go home. What has happened is my doing." So they obeyed the word of the LORD. They returned ⸤home⸥, as the LORD told them.

²⁵ Jeroboam rebuilt Shechem in the hills of Ephraim and lived there. Then he left that place and built Penuel. ²⁶ He said to himself, "The kingdom will probably return to David's dynasty now. ²⁷ King Rehoboam of Judah, the former master of these people, will regain popularity if they go to sacrifice in the LORD's temple in Jerusalem. Then they will kill me and return to King Rehoboam of Judah."

²⁸ After seeking advice, the king made two golden calves. He said, "You've been worshiping in Jerusalem long enough. Israel, here are your gods who brought you out of Egypt." ²⁹ He put one in Bethel and the other in Dan. ³⁰ Worshiping them became ⸤Israel's⸥ sin. The people went as far as Dan to worship the one calf. ³¹ Jeroboam built worship sites on hilltops. He appointed men who were not descended from Levi to be priests.

³² Jeroboam appointed a festival on the fifteenth day of the eighth month, just like the festival in Judah. He went to the altar in Bethel to sacrifice to the calves he had made. He appointed priests from the illegal worship sites ⸤to serve⸥ in Bethel. ³³ He went to his altar in Bethel to

---

ᵃ 12:2 2 Chronicles 10:2, Greek, Latin; Masoretic Text "remained in Egypt."   ᵇ 12:10 Hebrew meaning uncertain.

burn an offering on the fifteenth day of the eighth month, ˌthe festivalˌ he had invented for the Israelites.

A Prophet Announces God's Judgment

13 ¹ A man of God from Judah had come to Bethel. When he arrived, Jeroboam was standing at the altar to offer a sacrifice. ² By a command of the LORD, this man condemned the altar. "Altar, altar! This is what the LORD says: There will be a son born in David's family line. His name will be Josiah. Here on you Josiah will sacrifice the priests from the illegal worship sites who offer sacrifices on you. Human bones will be burned on you."

³ That day the man of God ˌalsoˌ gave ˌthemˌ a miraculous sign, saying, "This is the sign that the LORD will give you: You will see the altar torn apart. The ashes on it will be poured ˌon the groundˌ."

⁴ When King Jeroboam heard the man of God condemning the altar in Bethel, he pointed to the man across the altar. "Arrest him," he said. But the arm that he used to point to the man of God was paralyzed so that he couldn't pull it back. ⁵ The altar was torn apart, and the ashes from the altar were poured ˌon the groundˌ. This was the miraculous sign the man of God performed at the LORD's command.

⁶ Then the king asked the man of God, "Please make an appeal to the LORD your God, and pray for me so that I can use my arm again." So the man of God made an appeal to the LORD, and the king was able to use his arm again, as he had earlier.

⁷ The king told the man of God, "Come home with me; have something to eat and drink, and I will give you a gift."

⁸ The man of God told the king, "Even if you gave me half of your palace, I would never go with you to eat or drink there. ⁹ When the LORD spoke to me, he commanded me not to eat or drink or go back on the same road I took." ¹⁰ So the man of God left on another road and didn't go back on the road he had taken to Bethel.

A Prophet Disobeys God

¹¹ An old prophet was living in Bethel. His sons told him everything the man of God did in Bethel that day and the exact words he had spoken to the king. When they told their father, ¹² he said to them, "Which road did he take?" (His sons had seen which road the man of God from Judah had taken.) ¹³ The old prophet told his sons, "Saddle the donkey for me." After they had saddled the donkey for him, he got on it.

¹⁴ He went after the man of God and found him sitting under an oak tree. The old prophet asked him, "Are you the man of God who came from Judah?"

"Yes," he answered.

¹⁵ "Come home with me, and eat a meal," the old prophet replied.

¹⁶ The man of God said, "I'm not allowed to go back with you. I'm not allowed to eat or drink with you. ¹⁷ When the LORD spoke to me, he told me not to eat or drink there or go back on the road I took to get there."

¹⁸ The old prophet said, "I'm also a prophet, like you. An angel spoke the word of the LORD to me. He said, 'Bring him home with you so that he may have something to eat and drink.' " (But the old prophet was lying.)

¹⁹ The man of God went back with him and ate and drank in his home. ²⁰ When they were sitting at the table, the LORD spoke his word to the old prophet who had brought back the man of God. ²¹ The LORD also called to the man of God. He said, "This is what the LORD says: You rebelled against the words from the LORD's mouth and didn't obey the command that the LORD your God gave you. ²² You came back, ate, and drank at this place about which he told you, 'Don't eat or drink there.' That is why your dead body will not be allowed to be placed in the tomb of your ancestors."

²³ After the old prophet had something to eat and drink, he saddled the donkey for the prophet whom he had brought back. ²⁴ The man of God left. A lion found him ˌas he traveledˌ on the road and killed him. His dead body was thrown on the road. The donkey and the lion were standing by the body. ²⁵ People who passed by saw the body lying on the road and the lion standing by the body. They talked about it in the city where the old prophet was living.

²⁶ When the old prophet who had brought the man of God back from the road heard about it, he said, "It's the man of God who rebelled against the words from the LORD's mouth! The LORD gave him to the lion. It tore him to pieces and killed him as the word of the LORD had told him."

²⁷ Then the old prophet told his sons to saddle his donkey for him. So they did. ²⁸ He found the body of the man thrown on the road. He also found the donkey and the lion standing beside it. The lion had not eaten the body, nor had it torn the donkey to pieces. ²⁹ The old prophet picked up the body of the man of God, laid it on the donkey, and brought it back. He came to his own city to mourn for him and to bury him. ³⁰ He laid the body of the man of

God in his own tomb and mourned over the man, saying, "Oh no, my brother, my brother!" [31] After he had buried the man of God, he said to his sons, "When I die, bury me in the tomb where the man of God was buried. Lay my bones beside his bones. [32] The things that he announced by a command of the LORD against the altar in Bethel and all the illegal worship sites in the cities of Samaria will happen."

[33] Even after this, Jeroboam didn't change his evil ways, but he once again made some men priests for the illegal worship sites. He took all who were willing and appointed them to be priests at the worship sites. [34] Appointing illegal priests became the sin of Jeroboam's family so that it had to be destroyed and wiped off the face of the earth.

Jeroboam's Son Dies

14 [1] At that time Abijah, son of Jeroboam, got sick. [2] Jeroboam told his wife, "Go to Shiloh, but disguise yourself so that people will not recognize you as my wife. The prophet Ahijah, who told me I would be king of these people, is there. [3] Take ten loaves of bread, some raisins,[a] and a jar of honey with you, and go to him. He will tell you what will happen to the boy." [4] Jeroboam's wife did this. She left, went to Shiloh, and came to the home of Ahijah.

Ahijah couldn't see. His eyesight had failed because he was old. [5] However, the LORD had told Ahijah, "Jeroboam's wife is coming to ask you about her son who is sick. When she comes, she will pretend to be someone else." He also told Ahijah what to say to her.

[6] Ahijah heard her footsteps when she came into the room. He said, "Come in. You're Jeroboam's wife. Why are you pretending to be someone else? I've been told to give you some terrible news. [7] Tell Jeroboam, 'This is what the LORD God of Israel says: I picked you out of the people and made you a leader over my people Israel. [8] I tore the kingdom away from David's heirs and gave it to you. But you have not been like my servant David. He obeyed my commands and faithfully followed me by doing only what I considered right. [9] You have done more evil things than everyone before you. You made other gods, metal idols, for yourself. You made me furious and turned your back to me.

[10] " 'That is why I will bring disaster on Jeroboam's house. I will destroy every male[b] in his house, whether slave or freeman in Israel. I will burn down Jeroboam's house. It will burn like manure until it is gone. [11] If anyone from Jeroboam's house dies in the city, dogs will eat him. If anyone dies in the country, birds will eat him.' The LORD has said this!

[12] "Get up, and go home. The moment you set foot in the city the child will die. [13] All Israel will mourn for him and bury him. He is the only one of Jeroboam's family who will be properly buried. He was the only one in Jeroboam's house in whom the LORD God of Israel found anything good. [14] The LORD will appoint a king over Israel. That king will destroy Jeroboam's house. This will happen today. It will happen right now.[c]

[15] "The LORD will strike Israel like cattails which shake in the water. He will uproot Israel from this good land which he gave their ancestors. He will scatter them beyond the Euphrates River because they dedicated poles to the goddess Asherah and made the LORD furious. [16] So the LORD will desert Israel because of Jeroboam's sins, the sins which he led Israel to commit."

[17] Jeroboam's wife got up, left, and went to Tirzah. When she walked across the threshold of her home, the boy died. [18] All Israel buried him and mourned for him as the LORD had said through his servant, the prophet Ahijah.

[19] Everything else concerning Jeroboam, his wars, and his reign is written in the official records of the kings of Israel. [20] Jeroboam ruled for 22 years. Then he lay down in death with his ancestors. His son Nadab succeeded him as king.

King Rehoboam of Judah—2 Chronicles 12:13–14

[21] Rehoboam, son of Solomon, ruled Judah. He was 41 years old when he began to rule. He ruled for 17 years in Jerusalem, the city that the LORD chose from all the tribes of Israel, the city where the LORD put his name. Rehoboam's mother was an Ammonite woman named Naamah.

[22] The people of Judah did what the LORD considered evil. Their sins made him more angry than anything their ancestors had done. [23] They built worship sites for themselves and put up large stones and Asherah poles to worship on every high hill and under every large tree. [24] There were even male prostitutes in the temples of idols throughout the land. The people of Judah did all the disgusting practices done by the nations that the LORD had forced out of the Israelites' way.

King Shishak Takes the Temple Treasures—2 Chronicles 12:2, 9–11, 15–16

[25] In the fifth year of Rehoboam's reign, King Shishak of Egypt attacked Jerusalem. [26] He took the treasures from the LORD's temple and the royal palace. He took them all. He took all the gold shields Solomon had made. [27] So King Rehoboam made bronze shields to replace

---

[a] 14:3 Or "cakes."   [b] 14:10 Hebrew uses a coarse term for "male" here.   [c] 14:14 Hebrew meaning of these two sentences uncertain.

them and put them by the entrance to the royal palace, where the captains of the guards were stationed. [28] Whenever the king went into the LORD's temple, guards carried the shields and then returned them to the guardroom. [29] Isn't everything else concerning Rehoboam—everything he did—written in the official records of the kings of Judah? [30] There was war between Rehoboam and Jeroboam as long as they lived. [31] Rehoboam lay down in death with his ancestors and was buried with them in the City of David. (His mother was an Ammonite woman named Naamah.) His son Abijam succeeded him as king.

King Abijam of Judah—2 Chronicles 13:1, 2, 22; 14:1

15 [1] In the eighteenth year of the reign of Jeroboam (Nebat's son), Abijam began to rule Judah. [2] He ruled for three years in Jerusalem. His mother was named Maacah, daughter of Abishalom. [3] He followed the sinful example his father had set and wasn't committed to the LORD his God as his ancestor David had been. [4] But for David's sake the LORD his God made Abijam a lamp in Jerusalem. He appointed David's descendant to rule after him and protected Jerusalem. [5] The LORD did this because David did what the LORD considered right: David never failed to do anything the LORD commanded him to do his entire life (except in the matter concerning Uriah the Hittite).

[6] There was war between Abijam[a] and Rehoboam throughout their lives.

[7] Isn't everything else about Abijam—everything he did—written in the official records of the kings of Judah? There was war between Abijam and Jeroboam. [8] Abijam lay down in death with his ancestors and was buried in the City of David. His son Asa succeeded him as king.

King Asa of Judah—2 Chronicles 14:2, 3; 15:16–18

[9] In Jeroboam's twentieth year as king of Israel, Asa began to rule as king of Judah. [10] He ruled 41 years in Jerusalem. His grandmother was named Maacah, daughter of Abishalom.

[11] Asa did what the LORD considered right, as his ancestor David had done. [12] He forced the male temple prostitutes out of the land and got rid of the idols his father had made. [13] He also removed his grandmother Maacah from the position of queen mother because she made a statue of the repulsive goddess Asherah. Asa cut the statue down and burned it in the Kidron Valley. [14] Although the illegal worship sites were not torn down, Asa remained committed to the LORD his entire life. [15] He brought into the LORD's temple the silver, the gold, and the utensils he and his father had set apart as holy.

King Asa's War With King Baasha—2 Chronicles 15:19; 16:1–6, 11–14; 17:1

[16] There was war between Asa and King Baasha of Israel as long as they lived. [17] King Baasha of Israel invaded Judah and fortified Ramah to keep anyone from going to or coming from King Asa of Judah.

[18] Then Asa took all the silver and gold that was left in the treasuries of the LORD's temple and the royal palace and turned them over to his officials. King Asa sent them to Damascus to Aram's King Benhadad, son of Tabrimmon and grandson of Hezion. [19] He said, "There's a treaty between you and me ͺasͺ there was between your father and my father. I'm sending you a present of silver and gold. Now break your treaty with King Baasha of Israel so that he will leave me alone."

[20] Benhadad did what King Asa requested. He sent his generals and their armies to attack the cities of Israel. He conquered Ijon, Dan, Abel Beth Maacah, and the entire area around Chinneroth with the entire territory of Naphtali. [21] When Baasha heard the news, he stopped fortifying Ramah and lived in Tirzah. [22] Then King Asa drafted everyone in Judah and excused no one. He made them carry the stones and lumber from Ramah. Baasha had been using those to fortify the city. King Asa used the materials to fortify Geba in Benjamin and Mizpah.

[23] Isn't everything else about Asa—all his heroic acts, everything he did, and the cities he fortified—written in the official records of the kings of Judah? But when he was old, he had a foot disease. [24] Asa lay down in death with his ancestors. He was buried with his ancestors in the city of his ancestor, David. His son Jehoshaphat succeeded him as king.

King Baasha Overthrows Nadab, Son of Jeroboam

[25] Nadab, son of Jeroboam, began to rule Israel in Asa's second year as king of Judah. He ruled for two years. [26] He did what the LORD considered evil, living as his father did, leading Israel into the same sins.

[27] Then Baasha, son of Ahijah from the tribe of Issachar, plotted against Nadab. Baasha assassinated him in the Philistine city of Gibbethon while Nadab and the Israelite forces were attacking it. [28] The assassination happened in Asa's third year as king of Judah. Baasha suc-

---

[a] 15:6 Some Hebrew manuscripts; other Hebrew manuscripts "Jeroboam."

ceeded Nadab as king of Israel. ²⁹ As soon as he was king, he killed everyone else in Jeroboam's family. He did not spare a soul, as the LORD had spoken through his servant Ahijah from Shiloh. ³⁰ This was because of Jeroboam's sins and the sins which he led Israel to commit. Those sins made the LORD God of Israel furious.

³¹ Isn't everything else about Nadab—everything he did—written in the official records of the kings of Israel? ³² There was war between Asa and Baasha as long as they lived.

³³ In Asa's third year as king of Judah, Baasha, son of Ahijah, began to rule Israel in Tirzah. He ruled for 24 years. ³⁴ He did what the LORD considered evil. He lived like Jeroboam and led Israel into committing the ˌsameˌ sins.

The LORD Condemns King Baasha

16 ¹ The LORD spoke his word to Jehu, Hanani's son, against Baasha. ² He said, "I raised you from the dust and made you leader of my people Israel. But you have lived like Jeroboam. You have led my people to sin, and their sins make me furious. ³ So I will destroy Baasha and his family. I will make his family like the family of Jeroboam (Nebat's son). ⁴ Dogs will eat anyone from Baasha's ˌfamilyˌ who dies in the city. Birds will eat anyone from his ˌfamilyˌ who dies in the country."

⁵ Isn't everything else about Baasha—what he did and his heroic acts—written in the official records of the kings of Israel? ⁶ Baasha lay down in death with his ancestors and was buried in Tirzah. His son Elah succeeded him as king. ⁷ In addition, the LORD spoke his word to the prophet Jehu, Hanani's son, against Baasha and his family because of all the things Baasha did which the LORD considered evil. Baasha's actions, which made the LORD furious, were like ˌthe sin ofˌ Jeroboam's family. The LORD was also furious because Baasha destroyed Jeroboam's family.

Zimri Overthrows King Elah, Son of Baasha

⁸ Elah, son of Baasha, began to rule Israel in Asa's twenty-sixth year as Judah's king. He ruled in Tirzah for two years. ⁹ But Zimri, the general who commanded half of Elah's chariots, plotted against him. Elah was getting drunk in Tirzah at Arza's house. (Arza was in charge of the palace in Tirzah.) ¹⁰ Zimri entered Arza's house, attacked Elah, and killed him in Asa's twenty-seventh year as king of Judah. Zimri succeeded Elah as king ˌof Israelˌ. ¹¹ At the beginning of Zimri's reign, as soon as he was on his throne, he killed Baasha's entire family. He didn't spare any of Baasha's maleᵃ relatives or friends. ¹² So Zimri destroyed Baasha's entire family, as the LORD had spoken through the prophet Jehu. ¹³ This was for all the sins committed by Baasha and his son Elah. They sinned, led Israel to sin, and made the LORD God of Israel furious because of their worthless idols. ¹⁴ Isn't everything else about Elah—everything he did—written in the official records of the kings of Israel?

King Zimri Rules for Seven Days

¹⁵ In Asa's twenty-seventh year as Judah's king, Zimri ruled for seven days in Tirzah while the army was camped near the Philistine city of Gibbethon. ¹⁶ When the army heard that Zimri had plotted ˌagainst the kingˌ and killed him, the Israelite troops in the camp made Omri, the commander of the army, king of Israel.

¹⁷ Omri and the Israelite troops with him left Gibbethon and attacked Tirzah. ¹⁸ When Zimri saw that the city had been captured, he went into the stronghold in the royal palace and burned down the palace over his own head. He died ¹⁹ because of the sins he had committed—the things the LORD considered evil. Zimri lived like Jeroboam and led Israel to sin. ²⁰ Isn't everything else about Zimri and his plot written in the official records of the kings of Israel?

Omri Defeats Tibni

²¹ Then the army of Israel was divided into two factions. Half of the army followed Tibni, son of Ginath, and wanted to make him king. The ˌotherˌ half followed Omri. ²² But the half which followed Omri was stronger than the half which followed Tibni, Ginath's son. Tibni died, and Omri became king. ²³ Omri began to rule Israel in Asa's thirty-first year as king of Judah. He ruled for 12 years, 6 of them in Tirzah.

²⁴ Omri bought a hill from Shemer for 150 pounds of silver. He fortified the hill and built the city of Samaria on it. He named the city after its former owner, Shemer.

King Omri of Israel

²⁵ Omri did what the LORD considered evil. He did more evil things than all ˌthe kingsˌ before him. ²⁶ He lived exactly like Jeroboam (Nebat's son). He sinned and led Israel to sin with worthless idols, and the Israelites made the LORD God of Israel furious.

ᵃ 16:11 Hebrew uses a coarse term for "male" here.

²⁷ Isn't everything else about Omri—what he did and his heroic acts—written in the official records of the kings of Israel? ²⁸ Omri lay down in death with his ancestors and was buried in Samaria. His son Ahab succeeded him as king.

King Ahab Introduces Worship of Baal Into Israel

²⁹ Ahab, son of Omri, began to rule Israel in Asa's thirty-eighth year as king of Judah. He ruled for 22 years in Samaria. ³⁰ Ahab, son of Omri, did what the LORD considered evil. He was worse than all ˬthe kingsˬ who were before him. ³¹ It wasn't enough that he committed the same sins as Jeroboam (Nebat's son). He also married Jezebel, daughter of King Ethbaal of Sidon. Ahab then served and worshiped Baal. ³² He built the temple of Baal in Samaria and set up an altar there. ³³ Ahab made poles dedicated to the goddess Asherah. He did more to make the LORD God of Israel furious than all the kings of Israel who came before him.

³⁴ In Ahab's time Hiel from Bethel rebuilt Jericho.

> Laying the foundation
>   cost him his firstborn son, Abiram.
> Setting up the city doors
>   cost him his youngest son, Segub.

The LORD had spoken this through Joshua, son of Nun.

Elijah Prophesies a Drought

17 ¹ Elijah, who was from Tishbe but had settled in Gilead, said to Ahab, "I solemnly swear, as the LORD God of Israel whom I serve lives, there will be no dew or rain during the next few years unless I say so."

² Then the LORD spoke his word to Elijah: ³ "Leave here, turn east, and hide beside the Cherith River, which is east of the Jordan River. ⁴ You can drink from the stream, and I've commanded ravens to feed you there."

⁵ Elijah left and did what the word of the LORD ˬhad told himˬ. He went to live by the Cherith River, which is east of the Jordan River. ⁶ Ravens brought him bread and meat in the morning and in the evening. And he drank from the stream.

⁷ But after some time the stream dried up because no rain had fallen in the land.

Elijah and the Widow at Zarephath

⁸ Then the LORD spoke his word to Elijah: ⁹ "Get up, go to Zarephath (which belongs to Sidon), and stay there. I've commanded a widow there to feed you."

¹⁰ He got up and went to Zarephath. As he came to the town's entrance, a widow was gathering wood. He called to her, "Please bring me a drink of water." ¹¹ As she was going to get it, he called to her again, "Please bring me a piece of bread too."

¹² She said, "I solemnly swear, as the LORD your God lives, I didn't bake any bread. I have one handful of flour in a jar and a little oil in a jug. I'm gathering wood. I'm going to prepare something for myself and my son so that we can eat it and then die."

¹³ Then Elijah told her, "Don't be afraid. Go home, and do as you've said. But first make a small loaf and bring it to me. Then prepare something for yourself and your son. ¹⁴ This is what the LORD God of Israel says: Until the LORD sends rain on the land, the jar of flour will never be empty and the jug will always contain oil."

¹⁵ She did what Elijah had told her. So she, Elijah, and her family had food for a long time. ¹⁶ The jar of flour never became empty, and the jug always contained olive oil, as the LORD had promised through Elijah.

¹⁷ Afterwards, the son of the woman who owned the house got sick. He got so sick that finally no life was left in him. ¹⁸ The woman asked Elijah, "What do you and I have in common, man of God?ᵃ Did you come here to remind me of my sin and kill my son?"

¹⁹ He said to her, "Give me your son." Elijah took him from her arms, carried him to the upstairs room where he was staying, and laid him on his own bed. ²⁰ Then he called to the LORD, "LORD my God, have you brought misery on the widow I'm staying with by killing her son?" ²¹ Then Elijah stretched himself over the boy three times and called to the LORD, "LORD my God, please make this child's life return to him." ²² The LORD heard Elijah's request, and the child's life returned to him. He was alive again.

²³ Elijah took the child, brought him down from the upstairs room of the house, and gave him to his mother. He said, "Look! Your son is alive."

²⁴ The woman said to Elijah, "Now I'm convinced that you are a man of God and that the word of the LORD from your mouth is true."

ᵃ 17:18 Hebrew meaning of this sentence uncertain.

Elijah Comes to King Ahab

18 ¹A while later in the third year of the drought, the LORD spoke his word to Elijah: "Present yourself to Ahab. I will allow rain to fall on the ground." ²So Elijah went to present himself to Ahab.

The famine was particularly severe in Samaria. ³Ahab sent for Obadiah, who was in charge of the palace. Obadiah was a devout worshiper of the LORD. ⁴(When Jezebel was killing the LORD's prophets, Obadiah had hidden 100 prophets in caves. He put 50 prophets in each cave and kept them alive by providing bread and water for them.) ⁵Ahab told Obadiah, "Let's go throughout the countryside to every spring and stream. If we can find grass, then we can keep the horses and mules alive and not lose any animals." ⁶So they split up in order to cover the entire countryside. Ahab went one way by himself, and Obadiah went the other way by himself.

⁷Obadiah was on the road when he met Elijah. Obadiah recognized him and immediately bowed down to the ground. "Is it you, my master Elijah?" he asked.

⁸"Yes," Elijah answered him. "Tell your master that Elijah is here."

⁹Obadiah asked, "What have I done wrong to make you hand me over to Ahab to be killed? ¹⁰I solemnly swear, as the LORD your God lives, my master has searched for you in every region and kingdom. When people would say, 'He isn't here,' my master made that kingdom or region take an oath that they hadn't found you.

¹¹"Now you say, 'Tell your master that Elijah is here.' ¹²This is what will happen: When I leave you, the LORD's Spirit will take you away to some unknown place. I'll tell Ahab, but he won't be able to find you. Then he will kill me.

"I have been faithful to the LORD since I was a child. ¹³Haven't you heard what I did when Jezebel killed the LORD's prophets? Haven't you heard how I hid 100 of the LORD's prophets in caves? I hid 50 prophets in each cave and provided bread and water for them. ¹⁴Now you say that I should tell my master that Elijah is here. He will kill me."

¹⁵Elijah said, "I solemnly swear, as the LORD of Armies whom I serve lives, I will present myself to Ahab."

¹⁶So Obadiah went to tell Ahab.

Elijah and the Prophets of Baal on Mount Carmel

Ahab went to meet Elijah. ¹⁷When he saw Elijah, Ahab said, "Is that you, you troublemaker of Israel?"

¹⁸Elijah answered, "I haven't troubled Israel. You and your father's family have done it by disobeying the LORD's commands and following the various Baal gods. ¹⁹Order all Israel to gather around me on Mount Carmel. And bring the 450 prophets of Baal and 400 prophets of Asherah who eat at Jezebel's table."

²⁰Ahab sent word to all the Israelites and brought the prophets together on Mount Carmel. ²¹Elijah stood up in front of all the people and asked them, "How long will you try to have it both ways? If the LORD is God, follow him; if Baal is God, follow him." The people didn't say a word.

²²So Elijah told the people, "I'm the only surviving prophet of the LORD, but there are 450 prophets of Baal. ²³Give us two bulls. Let the prophets of Baal choose one for themselves, cut it into pieces, lay it on the wood, but not set it on fire. I'll do the same with the other bull.

²⁴"You call on the name of your gods, but I will call on the name of the LORD. The god who answers by fire is the real God."

All the people answered, "That's fine."

²⁵Elijah told the prophets of Baal, "Choose one bull for yourselves. Prepare yours first, because there are more of you. Call on the name of your god, but don't set the wood on fire."

²⁶They took the bull he gave them, prepared it, and called on the name of Baal from morning until noon. They said, "Baal, answer us!" But there wasn't a sound or an answer. So they danced around the altar they had made. ²⁷At noon Elijah started to make fun of them. "Shout louder, since he is a god. Maybe he's thinking, relieving himself, or traveling! Maybe he's sleeping, and you have to wake him!"

²⁸So they shouted louder. They also cut themselves with swords and spears until their blood flowed. (This is what their ritual called for.) ²⁹In the afternoon they continued to rant and rave until the time for the evening sacrifice. But there was no sound, no answer, no attention given to them.

³⁰Then Elijah said to all the people, "Come over here." So all the people came to him. He rebuilt the LORD's altar that had been torn down. ³¹Elijah took 12 stones, one for each of the tribes named after Jacob's sons. (The LORD had spoken his word to Jacob: "Your name will be Israel.") ³²Elijah built an altar in the LORD's name with those stones. He also made a trench that could hold 12 quarts of grain around the altar. ³³He arranged the wood, cut up the bull, and put it on the wood.

³⁴ He said, "Fill four jars with water. Pour the water on the offering and on the wood." Then he said, "Do it again," and they did it again. Then he said, "Do it a third time," and they did it a third time. ³⁵ The water flowed around the altar, and even the trench was filled with water.

³⁶ When it was time to offer the sacrifice, the prophet Elijah stepped forward. He said, "LORD God of Abraham, Isaac, and Israel, make known today that you are God in Israel and that I'm your servant and have done all these things by your instructions. ³⁷ Answer me, LORD! Answer me! Then these people will know that you, LORD, are God and that you are winning back their hearts."

³⁸ So a fire from the LORD fell down and consumed the burnt offering, wood, stones, and dirt. The fire even dried up the water that was in the trench. ³⁹ All the people saw it and immediately bowed down to the ground. "The LORD is God!" they said. "The LORD is God!"

⁴⁰ Elijah told them, "Seize the prophets of Baal. Don't let any of them escape." The people seized them, and Elijah took them to the Kishon River and slaughtered them there.

The Drought Ends

⁴¹ Then Elijah told Ahab, "Get up, eat, and drink. It sounds like a heavy rain ⌊is coming⌋." ⁴² Ahab got up to eat and drink.

Elijah went to the top of Carmel and bowed down on the ground to pray. ⁴³ He said to his servant, "Please go back to ⌊Mount Carmel⌋, and look toward the sea."

He went up, looked, ⌊came back,⌋ and said, "There's nothing."

Seven times Elijah told him, "Go back."

⁴⁴ After the seventh time the servant said, "A little cloud like a man's hand is coming from the sea."

Elijah said, "Go and tell Ahab, 'Prepare ⌊your chariot⌋, and leave before the rain delays you.'"

⁴⁵ Gradually, the sky grew darker with clouds and wind, and there was a heavy rain. Ahab got into his chariot to go back to Jezreel. ⁴⁶ The LORD's power was on Elijah. He hiked up his robe and ran ahead of Ahab until they came to Jezreel.

Elijah Flees From Jezebel

19 ¹ Ahab told Jezebel everything Elijah had done, including how he had executed all the prophets. ² Then Jezebel sent a messenger to Elijah. She said, "May the gods strike me dead if by this time tomorrow I don't take your life the way you took the lives of Baal's prophets."

³ Frightened, Elijah fled to save his life. He came to Beersheba in Judah and left his servant there. ⁴ Then he traveled through the wilderness for a day. He sat down under a broom plant and wanted to die. "I've had enough now, LORD," he said. "Take my life! I'm no better than my ancestors." ⁵ Then he lay down and slept under the broom plant.

An angel touched him and said, "Get up and eat." ⁶ When he looked, he saw near his head some bread baked on hot stones and a jar of water. So he ate, drank, and went to sleep again. ⁷ The angel of the LORD came back and woke him up again. The angel said, "Get up and eat, or your journey will be too much for you."

⁸ He got up, ate, and drank. Strengthened by that food, he traveled for 40 days and nights until he came to Horeb, the mountain of God. ⁹ There he went into a cave and spent the night.

Then the LORD spoke his word to Elijah. He asked, "What are you doing here, Elijah?"

¹⁰ He answered, "LORD God of Armies, I have eagerly served you. The Israelites have abandoned your promises,ᵃ torn down your altars, and executed your prophets. I'm the only one left, and they're trying to take my life."

¹¹ God said, "Go out and stand in front of the LORD on the mountain."

As the LORD was passing by, a fierce wind tore mountains and shattered rocks ahead of the LORD. But the LORD was not in the wind. After the wind came an earthquake. But the LORD wasn't in the earthquake. ¹² After the earthquake there was a fire. But the LORD wasn't in the fire. And after the fire there was a quiet, whispering voice. ¹³ When Elijah heard it, he wrapped his face in his coat, went out, and stood at the entrance of the cave.

Then the voice said to him, "What are you doing here, Elijah?"

¹⁴ He answered, "LORD God of Armies, I have eagerly served you. The Israelites have abandoned your promises, torn down your altars, and executed your prophets. I'm the only one left, and they're trying to take my life."

¹⁵ The LORD told him, "Go back to the wilderness near Damascus, the same way you came. When you get there, anoint Hazael as king of Aram. ¹⁶ Anoint Jehu, son of Nimshi, as king of Israel. And anoint Elisha, son of Shaphat, from Abel Meholah as prophet to take your place. ¹⁷ If anyone escapes from Hazael's sword, Jehu will kill him. And if anyone escapes from Jehu's sword, Elisha will kill him. ¹⁸ But I still have 7,000 people in Israel whose knees have not knelt to worship Baal and whose mouths have not kissed him."

ᵃ 19:10 Or "covenant."

The Call of Elisha

19 Elijah found Elisha, son of Shaphat. Elisha was plowing behind 12 pairs of oxen. He was using the twelfth pair. Elijah took off his coat and put it on Elisha. **20** So Elisha left the oxen, ran after Elijah, and said, "Please let me kiss my father and mother goodbye. Then I will follow you."

"Go back," Elijah answered him. "I'm not stopping you."

21 Elisha left him, took two oxen, and butchered them. He boiled the meat, using the oxen's yoke*ᵇ* ˎfor firewoodˎ. He gave the meat to the people to eat. Then he left to follow and assist Elijah.

King Ahab Defeats King Benhadad

20 **1** King Benhadad of Aram gathered together his whole army. With him were 32 kings along with their horses and chariots. He went to blockade Samaria and fight against it. **2** He sent messengers into the city to King Ahab of Israel. They told Ahab, "This is what Benhadad says: **3** Your silver and gold are mine. Your beloved wives and children are mine."

4 The king of Israel answered, "As you say, Your Majesty. I and everything I have are yours."

5 But Benhadad sent messengers back ˎto Ahabˎ. They said, "Benhadad has sent this message to you: 'Your silver, gold, wives, and children are mine. Give ˎthem to meˎ. **6** At this time tomorrow I'm going to send my servants to search your palace and your servants' houses. They will take anything that you consider valuable.' "

7 Then the king of Israel called for all the leaders of the country. He said, "You can see how this man is looking for trouble. When he sent for my wives, children, silver, and gold, I didn't refuse him."

8 All the leaders and all the people told him, "Don't listen to him. Don't agree ˎto his demandsˎ."

9 Ahab told Benhadad's messengers, "Tell His Majesty, 'I did everything your messengers told me the first time, but I can't do this.' " The messengers left to take back his answer.

10 Then Benhadad sent Ahab the following message: "May the gods strike me dead if there will be enough dust left from Samaria to give a handful to each soldier who follows me."

11 The king of Israel answered, "The saying goes, 'Don't brag about a victory before you have even dressed for battle.' "

12 Benhadad heard this as he and his allies were drinking in their tents. He told his officers to get ready. So they got ready ˎto attackˎ the city.

13 Then a prophet came to King Ahab of Israel and said, "This is what the LORD says: Have you seen this large army? I will hand it over to you today. Then you will know that I am the LORD."

14 Ahab asked, "How ˎwill this be doneˎ?"

The prophet answered, "This is what the LORD says: by using the young officers of the district governors."

"Who will start the battle?" Ahab asked.

"You will," the prophet answered.

15 Ahab counted the young officers of the district governors. There were 232. After counting them, he counted all the Israelite soldiers. There were 7,000. **16** They attacked at noon, when Benhadad was in his tent getting drunk with the 32 kings who were his allies. **17** The young officers of the district governors went out first.

Benhadad had sent men ˎto watch the cityˎ. They informed him that some men had come out of Samaria.

18 He said, "Take them alive, whether they have come out to make peace or to fight."

19 The young officers of the district governors led an attack, and the troops followed them. **20** Each officer killed his opponent. The Arameans fled, and Israel pursued them. King Benhadad of Aram escaped on a horse with the cavalry. **21** The king of Israel went out and destroyed the horses and chariots and decisively defeated the Arameans.

Ahab Spares Benhadad

22 Then the prophet came to the king of Israel and said, "Reinforce your army. Consider what you have to do. When spring comes, the king of Aram will attack ˎagainˎ."

23 Meanwhile, the officers of King Benhadad of Aram told him, "Their god is a god of the hills. That is why they were stronger than we were. However, if we fight them on the plain, we will be stronger than they are. **24** This is what we must do: Remove all of the kings from their positions, and substitute governors for them. **25** Recruit an army with as many horses and chariots as the one which was defeated. Then, if we fight them on the plain, we will be stronger than they are." He took their advice and followed it.

26 Spring came, and Benhadad organized the Aramean army and went to Aphek to fight Israel. **27** When the Israelite ˎtroopsˎ had been organized and given provisions, they went to

---

ᵇ 19:21 A yoke is a wooden bar placed over the necks of work animals so that they can pull plows or carts.

meet the enemy. The Israelites, while camped opposite the Arameans who filled the country, seemed like two newborn goats.[a]

²⁸ The man of God came again. He said to the king of Israel, "This is what the LORD says: Because the Arameans said that the LORD is a god of the hills but not a god of the valleys, I will hand over their entire army to you. Then you will know that I am the LORD."

²⁹ They camped facing one another for seven days, and on the seventh day the battle started. The Israelites killed 100,000 Aramean foot soldiers in one day. ³⁰ The survivors fled to Aphek, the city where the wall fell on 27,000 of them. Benhadad had also fled. He came to the city and hid in an inner room.

³¹ His officers told him, "We have heard that the kings of Israel are merciful. Allow us to dress in sackcloth, put ropes around our necks, and go to the king of Israel. Maybe he'll let you live." ³² So they dressed in sackcloth and put ropes around their necks. They went to the king of Israel and said, "Your servant Benhadad says, 'Please let me live.'"

Ahab asked, "He's still alive? He's my brother."

³³ The men, watching for a good sign, were quick to take him at his word. "Benhadad is your brother," they said.

Ahab said, "Bring him here." When Benhadad arrived, Ahab had him come up on the chariot with him.

³⁴ Benhadad told him, "I will give back the towns my father took from your father. You may set up trading centers in Damascus as my father did in Samaria."

Ahab said, "If you will put this into a treaty, I will let you go." So Ahab made a treaty with Benhadad and let him go.

³⁵ A disciple of the prophets spoke to a friend as the word of the LORD had told him. ˎThe disciple said,ˌ "Punch me," but the man refused to punch him. ³⁶ The disciple said, "Since you didn't obey the LORD, a lion will kill you when you leave me." When the friend left, a lion found him and killed him.

³⁷ Then the disciple found another man. He said, "Punch me." The man punched him hard and wounded him.

³⁸ Then the prophet, disguised with a bandage over his eyes, waited for the king by the road. ³⁹ When the king passed by, the disciple called to him. "I went to fight in the battle. A man turned around and brought a prisoner to me. He said, 'Guard this prisoner. If he gets away, you will pay for his life with your own life or be fined 75 pounds of silver.' ⁴⁰ But while I was busy doing other things, he got away."

The king of Israel told him, "That's your own penalty. You have determined it yourself."

⁴¹ Then he quickly took the bandage off his eyes. The king of Israel recognized him as one of the prophets.

⁴² The prophet told him, "This is what the LORD says: You let the man go. He was claimed by God and should have been killed. For that reason your life will be taken in place of his life and your people in place of his people."

⁴³ Resentful and upset, the king of Israel went home to Samaria.

Ahab Takes Naboth's Vineyard

21 ¹ This is what happened next. Naboth from Jezreel had a vineyard in Jezreel next to the palace of King Ahab of Samaria.

² Ahab told Naboth, "Give me your vineyard. It will become my vegetable garden because it is near my house. I will give you a better vineyard for it. Or if you prefer, I will pay you a fair price for it."

³ Naboth told Ahab, "The LORD has forbidden me to give you what I inherited from my ancestors."

⁴ Resentful and upset, Ahab went home because of what Naboth from Jezreel had told him. (ˎNaboth had said,ˌ "I will not give you what I inherited from my ancestors.") So Ahab lay on the couch, turned his face ˎfrom everyoneˌ, and refused to eat.

⁵ His wife Jezebel came to him and asked, "Why are you so resentful of everything? Why don't you eat?"

⁶ He told her, "I talked to Naboth from Jezreel. I said to him, 'Sell me your vineyard. Or, if you like, I'll give you another vineyard for it.' But he said, 'I won't give you my vineyard.'"

⁷ His wife Jezebel said to him, "Aren't you king of Israel? Get up, eat, and cheer up. I'll give you the vineyard belonging to Naboth from Jezreel."

⁸ So Jezebel wrote letters, signed them with Ahab's name, and sealed them with his seal. She sent them to the respected leaders and nobles living in Naboth's city. ⁹ In these letters she wrote: "Announce a fast. Seat Naboth as leader of the people. ¹⁰ Have two good-for-nothing men

---

[a] 20:27 Hebrew meaning of this sentence uncertain.

sit opposite him and accuse him of cursing God and the king. Then stone him to death outside the city."

[11] The men in Naboth's city—the respected leaders and nobles who lived there—did what Jezebel asked them to do. They did just as she had written in the letters she sent. [12] They announced a fast and had Naboth seated as the leader of the people. [13] The two good-for-nothing men came in and sat opposite him. In front of the people, these men accused Naboth of cursing God and the king. So the people stoned him to death outside the city. [14] Then the leaders sent ˌthis messageˌ to Jezebel: "Naboth has been stoned to death."

[15] Jezebel received the message and said to Ahab, "Get up! Confiscate the vineyard which Naboth from Jezreel refused to sell you. He's dead now."

[16] When he heard about Naboth's death, Ahab went to confiscate the vineyard.

[17] Then the LORD spoke his word to Elijah from Tishbe: [18] "Go, meet King Ahab of Israel, who lives in Samaria. He went to confiscate Naboth's vineyard. [19] Tell him, 'This is what the LORD asks: Have you murdered someone just to confiscate ˌa vineyardˌ?' Then tell him, 'This is what the LORD says: At the place where the dogs licked up Naboth's blood, the dogs will lick up your blood.' "

[20] Ahab asked Elijah, "So you've found me, my enemy?"

Elijah answered, "I found you. Because you sold yourself to do what the LORD considers evil. [21] So I am going to bring evil on you. I will destroy your descendants. I will destroy every male[a] in Ahab's ˌhouseˌ, whether slave or freeman in Israel. [22] I will make your family like the family of Jeroboam (Nebat's son) and like the house of Baasha, son of Ahijah, because you made me furious. You led Israel to sin."

[23] Then the LORD also spoke ˌthrough Elijahˌ about Jezebel: "The dogs will eat Jezebel inside the walls of Jezreel. [24] If anyone from Ahab's ˌhouseˌ dies in the city, dogs will eat him. If anyone dies in the country, birds will eat him."

[25] There was no one else like Ahab. At the urging of his wife, he sold himself to do what the LORD considered evil. [26] He did many disgusting things as a result of worshiping idols as the Amorites had done. (The LORD confiscated their land for Israel.)

[27] When Ahab heard these things, he tore his clothes ˌin distressˌ, and dressed in sackcloth. He fasted, lay in sackcloth, and walked around depressed.

[28] Then the LORD spoke his word to Elijah from Tishbe: [29] "Do you see how Ahab is humbling himself in my presence? Because he's humbling himself in my presence, I will not let any evil happen to his family while he is alive. I will bring evil on it during his son's lifetime."

Micaiah Prophesies Against King Ahab—2 Chronicles 18:1–34

22 [1] For three years there was no war between Aram and Israel. [2] In the third year King Jehoshaphat of Judah went to visit the king of Israel.

[3] The king of Israel asked his staff, "Do you know that Ramoth in Gilead belongs to us, and we are doing nothing to take it back from the king of Aram?" [4] Then he asked Jehoshaphat, "Will you go with me to fight at Ramoth in Gilead?"

Jehoshaphat told the king of Israel, "I will do what you do. My troops will do what your troops do. My horses will do what your horses do." [5] Then Jehoshaphat said to the king of Israel, "But first, find out what the word of the LORD is ˌin this matterˌ."

[6] So the king of Israel called 400 prophets together. He asked them, "Should I go to war against Ramoth in Gilead or not?"

"Go," they said. "The Lord[a] will hand over Ramoth to you."

[7] But Jehoshaphat asked, "Isn't there a prophet of the LORD whom we could ask?"

[8] The king of Israel told Jehoshaphat, "We can ask the LORD through Micaiah, son of Imlah, but I hate him. He doesn't prophesy anything good about me, only evil."

Jehoshaphat answered, "The king must not say that."

[9] The king of Israel called for an officer and said, "Quick! ˌGetˌ Micaiah, son of Imlah!"

[10] The king of Israel and King Jehoshaphat of Judah were dressed in royal robes and seated on thrones. They were on the threshing floor[b] at the entrance to the gate of Samaria. All the prophets were prophesying in front of them. [11] Zedekiah, son of Chenaanah, made iron horns and said, "This is what the LORD says: With these horns you will push the Arameans to their destruction." [12] All the other prophets made the same prophecy. They said, "Attack Ramoth in Gilead, and you will win. The LORD will hand it over to you."

[13] The messenger who went to call Micaiah told him, "The prophets have all told the king the same good message. Make your message agree with their message. Say something good."

[14] Micaiah answered, "I solemnly swear, as the LORD lives, I will tell him whatever the LORD tells me."

---

[a] 21:21 Hebrew uses a coarse term for "male" here.   [a] 22:6 Some Hebrew manuscripts; many Hebrew manuscripts, Targum "The LORD."   [b] 22:10 A threshing floor is an outdoor area where grain is separated from its husks.

¹⁵ When he came to the king, the king asked him, "Micaiah, should we go to war against Ramoth in Gilead or not?"

Micaiah said to him, "Attack and you will win. The LORD will hand it over to you."

¹⁶ The king asked him, "How many times must I make you take an oath in the LORD's name to tell me nothing but the truth?"

¹⁷ So Micaiah said, "I saw Israel's troops scattered in the hills like sheep without a shepherd. The LORD said, 'These ˌsheepˌ have no master. Let each one go home in peace.' "

¹⁸ The king of Israel said to Jehoshaphat, "Didn't I tell you he wouldn't prophesy anything good about me, only evil?"

¹⁹ Micaiah added, "Then hear the word of the LORD. I saw the LORD sitting on his throne, and the entire army of heaven was standing near him on his right and his left. ²⁰ The LORD asked, 'Who will deceive Ahab so that he will attack and be killed at Ramoth in Gilead?' Some answered one way, while others said something else.

²¹ "Then the Spirit stepped forward, stood in front of the LORD, and said, 'I will deceive him.'

" 'How?' the LORD asked.

²² "The Spirit answered, 'I will go out and be a spirit that tells lies through the mouths of all of Ahab's prophets.'

"The LORD said, 'You will succeed in deceiving him. Go and do it.'

²³ "So, the LORD has put into the mouths of all these prophets of yours a spirit that makes them tell lies. The LORD has spoken evil about you."

²⁴ Then Zedekiah, son of Chenaanah, went to Micaiah and struck him on the cheek. "How did the LORD's Spirit leave me to talk to you?" he asked.

²⁵ Micaiah answered, "You will find out on the day you go into an inner room to hide."

²⁶ The king of Israel then said, "Send Micaiah back to Amon, the governor of the city, and to Joash, the prince. ²⁷ Say, 'This is what the king says: Put this man in prison, and feed him nothing but bread and water until I come home safely.' "

²⁸ Micaiah said, "If you really do come back safely, then the LORD wasn't speaking through me. Pay attention to this, everyone!"

²⁹ So the king of Israel and King Jehoshaphat of Judah went to Ramoth in Gilead. ³⁰ The king of Israel told Jehoshaphat, "I will disguise myself and go into battle, but you should wear your royal robes." So the king of Israel disguised himself and went into battle.

³¹ The king of Aram had given orders to the 32 chariot commanders. He said, "Don't fight anyone except the king of Israel."

³² When the chariot commanders saw Jehoshaphat, they said, "He must be the king of Israel." So they turned to fight him. But when Jehoshaphat cried out, ³³ the chariot commanders realized that he wasn't the king of Israel. They turned away from him.

³⁴ One man aimed his bow at random and hit the king of Israel between his scale armor and his breastplate. Ahab told his chariot driver, "Turn around, and get me away from these troops. I'm badly wounded." ³⁵ But the battle got worse that day, and the king was kept propped up in his chariot facing the Arameans. He died that evening. The blood from the wound had flowed into the chariot. ³⁶ At sundown a cry went through the army, "Every man to his own city! Every man to his own property!"

³⁷ When the king was dead, he was brought to Samaria to be buried. ³⁸ His chariot was washed at the pool of Samaria, where the prostitutes bathed. The dogs licked up his blood, as the LORD had predicted.

³⁹ Isn't everything else about Ahab—everything he did, the ivory palace he built, and all the cities he fortified—written in the official records of the kings of Israel? ⁴⁰ Ahab lay down in death with his ancestors. His son Ahaziah succeeded him as king.

King Jehoshaphat of Judah—*2 Chronicles 20:31–21:1*

⁴¹ Jehoshaphat, son of Asa, became king of Judah in Ahab's fourth year as king of Israel. ⁴² Jehoshaphat was 35 years old when he began to rule, and he ruled for 25 years in Jerusalem. His mother's name was Azubah, daughter of Shilhi. ⁴³ Jehoshaphat carefully followed the example his father Asa had set and did what the LORD considered right. ⁴⁴ But the illegal worship sites were not torn down. The people continued to sacrifice and burn incense at these worship sites.ᶜ Jehoshaphat made peace with the king of Israel.

⁴⁵ Isn't everything else about Jehoshaphat—the heroic acts he did and ˌthe warsˌ he fought—written in the official records of the kings of Judah? ⁴⁶ He rid the land of the male temple prostitutes who were left there from the time of his father Asa. ⁴⁷ There was no king in Edom; instead, a deputy ruled.

ᶜ 22:44 1 Kings 22:44b–53 in English Bibles is 1 Kings 22:45–54 in the Hebrew Bible.

⁴⁸ Jehoshaphat made Tarshish-style ships to go to Ophir for gold. But they didn't go because the ships were wrecked at Ezion Geber. ⁴⁹ Then Ahaziah, son of Ahab, said to Jehoshaphat, "Let my servants go with your servants in the ships." But Jehoshaphat refused.

⁵⁰ Jehoshaphat lay down in death with his ancestors and was buried with them in the city of his ancestor David. His son Jehoram succeeded him as king.

King Ahaziah of Israel

⁵¹ Ahaziah, son of Ahab, became king of Israel in Samaria during Jehoshaphat's seventeenth year as king of Judah. Ahaziah ruled Israel for two years. ⁵² He did what the LORD considered evil. He followed the example of his father and mother and of Jeroboam (Nebat's son) who led Israel to sin. ⁵³ Ahaziah served Baal, worshiped him, and made the LORD God of Israel furious, as his father had done.

2 KINGS

Elijah and King Ahaziah of Israel

1 ¹ After Ahab died, Moab rebelled against Israel. ² During the rebellion King Ahaziah fell through a window lattice in his upstairs room in Samaria and injured himself. So he sent messengers ⸂to Ekron⸃. He had told them, "Go ask Baalzebub, the god of Ekron, if I will recover from this injury."

³ Then the angel of the LORD said to Elijah from Tishbe, "Meet the messengers of the king of Samaria, and ask them, 'Do you seek advice from Baalzebub, the god of Ekron, because ⸂you think⸃ there is no God in Israel? ⁴ This is what the LORD says: You will not get up from the bed you are lying on. Instead, you will die there.' " Then Elijah left.

⁵ When the messengers returned, the king asked them, "Why have you come back so soon?"

⁶ They told him that a man came to meet them and said to them, "Go back to the king who sent you. Tell him, 'This is what the LORD says: Do you send messengers to seek advice from Baalzebub, the god of Ekron, because ⸂you think⸃ there is no God in Israel? You will not get up from the bed you are lying on. Instead, you will die there.' "

⁷ The king asked them, "What was the man like who told you this?"

⁸ They replied, "He was hairy and had a leather belt around his waist."

"That's Elijah from Tishbe," the king answered.

⁹ The king sent an army officer with 50 men to Elijah. When the officer found Elijah sitting on top of a hill, he told Elijah, "Man of God, the king says, 'Come down.' "

¹⁰ Elijah answered the officer, "If I'm a man of God, fire will come from heaven and burn up you and your 50 men." Then fire came from heaven and burned up the officer and his 50 men.

¹¹ The king sent another officer with 50 men to Elijah. The officer said, "Man of God, this is what the king says: Come here right away!"

¹² Elijah answered the officer, "If I'm a man of God, fire will come from heaven and burn up you and your 50 men." Then God's fire came from heaven and burned up the officer and his 50 men.

¹³ The king sent a third officer with 50 men. The officer of the third group went up the hill and knelt in front of Elijah. The officer begged him, "Man of God, please treat my life and the lives of these 50 servants of yours as something precious. ¹⁴ Fire has come from heaven and burned up the first two officers and their 100 men. But treat my life as something precious."

¹⁵ The angel of the LORD told Elijah, "Go with him. Don't be afraid of him." So Elijah got up and went with him to the king. ¹⁶ Elijah told the king, "This is what the LORD says: You sent messengers to seek advice from Baalzebub, the god of Ekron. Is this because ⸂you think⸃ there is no God in Israel whose word you can seek? You will not get up from the bed you are lying on. Instead, you will die there."

¹⁷ So Ahaziah died as the LORD had predicted through Elijah. Joram succeeded him as king because Ahaziah had no son.ᵃ ¹⁸ Isn't everything else about Ahaziah—the things he did—written in the official records of the kings of Israel?

Elijah Taken to Heaven

2 ¹ When the LORD was going to take Elijah to heaven in a windstorm, Elijah and Elisha left Gilgal. ² Elijah said to Elisha, "Please stay here because the LORD is sending me to Bethel."

Elisha answered, "I solemnly swear, as the LORD lives and as you live, I will not abandon you." So they went to Bethel.

³ Some of the disciples of the prophets at Bethel came to Elisha. They asked him, "Do you know that the LORD is going to take your master from you today?"

He answered, "Yes, I know. Be quiet."

⁴ Elijah said, "Elisha, please stay here because the LORD is sending me to Jericho."

Elisha answered, "I solemnly swear, as the LORD lives and as you live, I will not abandon you." So they went to Jericho.

⁵ Then some of the disciples of the prophets who were in Jericho approached Elisha. They asked, "Do you know that the LORD is going to take your master from you today?"

ᵃ 1:17 Greek; Masoretic Text ". . . succeeded him in Jehoshaphat's son Jehoram's second year as king of Judah, because Ahaziah had no son."

He answered, "Yes, I know. Be quiet."

[6] Elijah said to Elisha, "Please stay here because the LORD is sending me to the Jordan River."

Elisha answered, "I solemnly swear, as the LORD lives and as you live, I will not abandon you." [7] Fifty disciples of the prophets stood at a distance as Elijah and Elisha stood by the Jordan River. [8] Elijah took his coat, rolled it up, and struck the water with it. The water divided to their left and their right, and the two men crossed ˻the river˼ on dry ground.

[9] While they were crossing, Elijah asked Elisha, "What should I do for you before I'm taken from you?"

Elisha answered, "Let me inherit a double share of your spirit."

[10] Elijah said, "You have asked for something difficult. If you see me taken from you, it will be yours. Otherwise, it will not."

[11] As they continued walking and talking, a fiery chariot with fiery horses separated the two of them, and Elijah went to heaven in a windstorm.

[12] When Elisha saw this, he cried out, "Master! Master! Israel's chariot and horses!" When he couldn't see Elijah anymore, he grabbed his own garment and tore it in two ˻to show his grief˼. [13] Then he picked up Elijah's coat (which had fallen off Elijah), went back, and stood on the bank of the Jordan River. [14] He took the coat and struck the water with it. He asked, "Where is the LORD God of Elijah?" As he struck the water, it divided to his left and his right, and Elisha crossed ˻the river˼.

[15] The disciples of the prophets who were at Jericho saw him from a distance. They said, "Elijah's spirit rests on Elisha!" Then they went to meet him and bowed in front of him with their faces touching the ground. [16] They said to him, "There are 50 strong men here with us. Please let them go and search for your master. Maybe the LORD's Spirit lifted him up and dropped him on one of the hills or in one of the valleys."

Elisha answered, "Don't send them ˻to look˼." [17] But the disciples kept urging him ˻to send the men˼ until he was embarrassed. So he said, "Send them." They sent 50 men who searched for three days without finding him. [18] They returned to Elisha in Jericho, where he was waiting. He said, "Didn't I tell you not to go?"

Elisha Purifies Jericho's Water

[19] The people of the city ˻of Jericho˼ told Elisha, "This city's location is as good as you will ever find. But the water is bad, and the land cannot grow crops."

[20] Elisha said, "Bring me a new jar, and put salt in it." They brought it to him. [21] He went to the spring and threw the salt into it. Then he said, "This is what the LORD says: I have purified this water. No more deaths or crop failures will come from this water." [22] To this day the water is still pure, as Elisha had said.

[23] From there he went to Bethel. As he walked along the road, some boys came out of the city and mocked him. They said, "Go away, baldy! Go away!"

[24] Looking back, he saw them and cursed them in the LORD's name. Two bears came out of the woods and tore 42 of these youths apart. [25] He left that place, went to Mount Carmel, and returned to Samaria.

King Joram of Israel

3 [1] Joram,[a] son of Ahab, became king of Israel in Samaria during Jehoshaphat's eighteenth year as king of Judah. He ruled for 12 years. [2] He did what the LORD considered evil, but he didn't do what his father or mother had done. He put away the sacred stone that his father had set up and dedicated to Baal. [3] But he would not give up the sins that Jeroboam (Nebat's son) led Israel to commit. Joram would not turn away from those sins.

King Mesha of Moab Defeated

[4] King Mesha of Moab raised sheep. ˻Each year˼ he had to pay the king of Israel 100,000 male lambs and the wool from 100,000 rams. [5] But when Ahab died, the king of Moab rebelled against the ˻new˼ king of Israel. [6] King Joram immediately left Samaria to prepare Israel's army for war. [7] He sent this message to King Jehoshaphat of Judah: "The king of Moab has rebelled against me. Will you fight Moab with me?"

Jehoshaphat answered, "I'll go. I will do what you do. My troops will do what your troops do. My horses will do what your horses do."

[8] Joram asked, "Which road should we take?"

Jehoshaphat answered, "The road through the desert of Edom."

[9] So the king of Israel, the king of Judah, and the king of Edom took an indirect route ˻to Moab˼. After seven days they ran out of water for the army and the animals. [10] The king of Israel said, "Oh no! The LORD has put the three of us at the mercy of ˻the people of˼ Moab."

---

[a] 3:1 In the Masoretic Text this king of Israel is also called Jehoram, a longer form of Joram.

[11] But Jehoshaphat asked, "Isn't there a prophet of the LORD whom we could ask?"

One of the officials of the king of Israel answered, "Elisha, the son of Shaphat, is here. He used to be Elijah's assistant."[b]

[12] Jehoshaphat said, "The LORD's word is with him." So King Jehoshaphat of Judah, the king of Israel, and the king of Edom went to Elisha.

[13] Elisha asked the king of Israel, "Why did you come to me? Go to your father's prophets or your mother's prophets."

The king of Israel answered him, "No. The LORD has called the three of us in order to put us at Moab's mercy."

[14] Elisha answered, "I solemnly swear, as the LORD of Armies whom I serve lives, I wouldn't even bother to look at you or notice you if it weren't for my respect for King Jehoshaphat of Judah. [15] But get me someone to play some music."

While the musician was playing, the LORD's power came over Elisha. [16] He said, "This is what the LORD says: Make this valley full of ditches. [17] You will not see wind or rain, but this valley will be filled with water. You, your cattle, and your other animals will drink. [18] The LORD considers that an easy thing to do. In addition, he will put Moab at your mercy. [19] You will defeat every walled city and every important city. You will cut down every good tree, seal all the wells, and use rocks to ruin every good piece of land."

[20] That is what happened in the morning. At the time of the grain offering, water flowed from Edom and filled the countryside.

[21] All the people of Moab heard that the kings had come to fight them. So all men old enough to bear arms were called to fight. They stood at the border. [22] When the Moabites got up early in the morning as the sun was rising over the water, they saw the water from a distance. It was as red as blood. [23] They said, "It's blood! The kings have been fighting one another and have killed each other. Now, Moabites, let's take their goods!"

[24] So when the Moabites came to Israel's camp, the Israelites attacked them, and they fled from the Israelites. Israel went after the Moabites and defeated them. [25] Then Israel tore down the cities, each man throwing rocks on every good field until it was covered. They sealed every well and cut down every good tree. Only the stones ˌin the wallsˌ of Kir Hareseth were left. Soldiers surrounded Kir Hareseth and attacked it with slings and stones. [26] When the king of Moab saw he was losing the battle, he took 700 swordsmen to try to break through to the king of Edom. But they couldn't do it. [27] Then he took his firstborn son, who would have succeeded him as king, and sacrificed him on the wall as a burnt offering. There was bitter anger against the Israelites. So they went home to their own country.

Elisha and the Widow's Olive Oil

4 [1] One of the wives of a disciple of the prophets called to Elisha, "Sir, my husband is dead! You know how he feared the LORD. Now a creditor has come to take my two children as slaves."

[2] Elisha asked her, "What should I do for you? Tell me, what do you have in your house?"

She answered, "I have nothing in the house except a jar of olive oil."

[3] Elisha said, "Borrow many empty containers from all your neighbors. [4] Then close the door behind you and your children, and pour oil into all those containers. When one is full, set it aside."

[5] So she left him and closed the door behind her and her children. The children kept bringing containers to her, and she kept pouring. [6] When the containers were full, she told her son, "Bring me another container."

He told her, "There are no more containers." So the olive oil stopped flowing. [7] She went and told the man of God.

He said, "Sell the oil, and pay your debt. The rest is for you and your children."

Elisha Brings a Shunem Woman's Son Back to Life

[8] One day Elisha was traveling through Shunem, where a rich woman lived. She had invited him to eat ˌwith herˌ. So whenever he was in the area, he stopped in to eat.

[9] She told her husband, "I know he's a holy man of God. And he regularly travels past our house. [10] Let's make a small room on the roof and put a bed, table, chair, and lamp stand there for him. He can stay there whenever he comes to visit us."

[11] One day he came ˌto their houseˌ, went into the upstairs room, and rested there. [12] He told his servant Gehazi, "Call this Shunem woman."

Gehazi called her, and she stood in front of him. [13] Elisha said to Gehazi, "Ask her what we can do for her, since she has gone to a lot of trouble for us. Maybe she would like us to speak to the king or the commander of the army for her."

---

[b] 3:11 Or "He used to pour water on Elijah's hands."

She answered, "I'm already living among my own people."

¹⁴ "What should we do for her?" Elisha asked.

Gehazi answered, "Well, she has no son, and her husband is old."

¹⁵ Elisha said, "Call her." So Gehazi called her, and she stood in the doorway. ¹⁶ Elisha said, "At this time next spring, you will hold a baby boy in your arms."

She answered, "Don't say that, sir. Don't lie to me. You're a man of God."

¹⁷ But the woman became pregnant and had a son at that time next year, as Elisha had told her. ¹⁸ Several years later the boy went to his father, who was with the harvest workers. ¹⁹ ˌSuddenly,ˌ he said to his father, "My head! My head!"

The father told his servant, "Carry him to his mother."

²⁰ The servant picked him up and brought him to his mother. The boy sat on her lap until noon, when he died. ²¹ She took him upstairs and laid him on the bed of the man of God, left ˌthe roomˌ, and shut the door behind her. ²² She called her husband and said, "Please send me one of the servants and one of the donkeys. I will go quickly to the man of God and come back again."

²³ Her husband asked, "Why are you going to him today? It isn't a New Moon Festival or a day of worship."

But she said goodbye to him.

²⁴ She saddled the donkey. Then she told her servant, "Lead on. Don't slow down unless I tell you." ²⁵ So she came to the man of God at Mount Carmel.

When he saw her coming at a distance, he told his servant Gehazi, "There is the woman from Shunem. ²⁶ Run to meet her and ask her how she, her husband, and the boy are doing."

"Everyone's fine," she answered.

²⁷ When she came to the man of God at the mountain, she took hold of his feet. Gehazi went to push her away. But the man of God said, "Leave her alone. She is bitter. The LORD has hidden the reason from me. He hasn't told me."

²⁸ The woman said, "I didn't ask you for a son. I said, 'Don't raise my hopes.' "

²⁹ The man of God told Gehazi, "Put on a belt, take my shepherd's staff in your hand, and go. Whenever you meet anyone, don't stop to greet him. If he greets you, don't stop to answer him. Lay my staff on the boy's face."

³⁰ The boy's mother said, "I solemnly swear, as the LORD and you live, I will not leave without you." So Elisha got up and followed her.

³¹ Gehazi went ahead of them and put the staff on the boy's face, but there was no sound or sign of life. So Gehazi came back to meet the man of God. Gehazi told him, "The boy didn't wake up."

³² When Elisha came to the house, the dead boy was lying on Elisha's bed. ³³ He went into the room, closed the door, and prayed to the LORD. ³⁴ Then he lay on the boy, putting his mouth on the boy's mouth, his eyes on the boy's eyes, his hands on the boy's hands. He crouched over the boy's body, and it became warm. ³⁵ Elisha got up, walked across the room and came back, and then got back on the bed and crouched over him. The boy sneezed seven times and opened his eyes. ³⁶ Elisha called Gehazi and said, "Call the Shunem woman." Gehazi called her. When she came to him, he said, "Take your son."

³⁷ Then she immediately bowed at his feet. She took her son and left.

Elisha and the Poisoned Food

³⁸ When Elisha went back to Gilgal, there was a famine in the country. ˌOne day,ˌ while the disciples of the prophets were meeting with him, he told his servant, "Put a large pot on the fire, and cook some stew for the disciples of the prophets."

³⁹ One of them went into the field to gather vegetables and found a wild vine. He filled his clothes with wild gourds. Then he cut them into the pot of stew without knowing what they were. ⁴⁰ They dished out the food for the men to eat. As they were eating the stew, they cried out, "There's death in the pot, man of God!" So they couldn't eat it.

⁴¹ Elisha said, "Bring some flour." He threw it into the pot and said, "Dish it out for the people to eat." Then there was nothing harmful in the pot.

Elisha Feeds a Hundred People

⁴² A man from Baal Shalisha brought bread made from the first harvested grain, 20 barley loaves, and fresh grain to the man of God. The man of God said, "Give it to the people to eat."

⁴³ But his servant asked, "How can I set this in front of a hundred people?"

"Give it to the people to eat," the man of God said. "This is what the LORD says: They will eat and even have some left over."

⁴⁴ The servant set it in front of them. They ate and had some left over, as the LORD had predicted.

Elisha Heals Naaman

5 ¹ Naaman, the commander of the Aramean king's army, was respected and highly honored by his master. The LORD had given Aram a victory through Naaman. This man was a good soldier, but he had a skin disease. ² Once, when the Arameans went on raids, they had brought back a little girl from Israel. She became the servant of Naaman's wife. ³ The girl told her mistress, "If only my master were with the prophet in Samaria. Then the prophet could cure him of his skin disease."

⁴ Naaman went to his master and told him what the girl from Israel had said. ⁵ The king of Aram said, "You may go. I will also send a letter to the king of Israel." When Naaman left, he took 750 pounds of silver, 150 pounds of gold, and 10 sets of clothing with him. ⁶ He brought the letter to the king of Israel. It read, "I'm sending my officer Naaman with this letter. Cure him of his skin disease."

⁷ When the king of Israel read the letter, he tore his clothes ˻in distress˼. He asked, "Am I God? Can I kill someone and then bring him back to life? This man sends someone to me so that I can cure his skin disease! All of you should realize and understand that he's trying to pick a fight with me."

⁸ But when Elisha, the man of God, heard that the king of Israel had torn his clothes, he sent a messenger to the king. He asked, "Why did you tear your clothes? Please let Naaman come to me and find out that there is a prophet in Israel."

⁹ Naaman came with his horses and chariot and stopped at the entrance to Elisha's home. ¹⁰ Elisha sent a messenger to him. He said, "Wash yourself seven times in the Jordan River, and your skin will be healthy and clean."ᵃ

¹¹ But Naaman became angry and left. He said, "I thought he would at least come out ˻of his house˼, stand somewhere, call on the name of the LORD his God, wave his hand over the ˻infected˼ place, and heal the skin disease. ¹² The Abana and Pharpar Rivers in Damascus have better water than any of the rivers in Israel. Couldn't I wash in them and˙be clean?" So he turned around and left in anger.

¹³ But Naaman's servants went to him and said, "Master, if the prophet had asked you to do some extraordinary act, wouldn't you have done it? Why shouldn't you do as he said: 'Wash and be clean'?"

¹⁴ So he went to dip himself in the Jordan River seven times, as the man of God had instructed him. His skin became healthy again like a little child's skin. ¹⁵ Then he and all his men returned to the man of God. Naaman stood in front of Elisha and said, "Now I know that there's no god in the whole world, except the God of Israel. So please accept a present from me."

¹⁶ Elisha said, "I solemnly swear, as the LORD whom I serve lives, I will not accept it." Naaman urged him to take it, but he refused.

¹⁷ So Naaman said, "If you won't take it, please have someone give me as much dirt as a pair of mules can carry. From now on I will sacrifice to the LORD alone. I will not offer any burnt offering or sacrifice to any other gods. ¹⁸ May the LORD forgive me when my master goes to the temple of Rimmon to worship, leans on my arm, and I have to bow down in the temple of Rimmon. When I do this, may the LORD forgive me for this one thing."

¹⁹ Elisha told Naaman, "Go in peace."

After Elisha had left him and gone some distance, ²⁰ Gehazi, the servant of Elisha (the man of God), thought, "My master let this Aramean Naaman go without accepting what he had brought. As sure as the LORD lives, I'll run after Naaman and get something from him." ²¹ So Gehazi went after Naaman. When Naaman saw Gehazi running after him, he got down from his chariot to speak to him. "Is something wrong?" he asked.

²² Gehazi answered, "No. My master has sent me. He says, 'Just now two young men from the disciples of the prophets in the hills of Ephraim have arrived. Please give them 75 pounds of silver and two sets of clothing.' "

²³ Naaman replied, "Please let me give you 150 pounds of silver." Naaman urged him ˻to take the silver˼. Naaman tied up 150 pounds of silver in two bags with two sets of clothing. He gave them to a couple of his own servants to carry in front of Gehazi.

²⁴ When Gehazi came to the Ophel in Samaria, he took these things and put them away in the house. Then he dismissed the men, and they left. ²⁵ He went and stood in front of his master.

Elisha asked him, "Where were you, Gehazi?"

"I didn't go anywhere," he answered.

²⁶ Then Elisha said to him, "I went with you in spirit when the man turned around in his chariot to speak to you. How could you accept silver, clothes, olive orchards, vineyards, sheep, cattle, or slaves? ²⁷ Naaman's skin disease will cling to you and your descendants permanently!"

When he left Elisha, Gehazi had a disease that made his skin as flaky as snow.

ᵃ 5:10 "Clean" refers to anything that Moses' Teachings say is presentable to God.

Elisha and the Floating Ax Head

6 [1] The disciples of the prophets said to Elisha, "The place where we're staying is too small for us. [2] Let's go to the Jordan River. Each of us can get some logs and make a place for us to live there."

Elisha said, "Go ahead."

[3] Then one of the disciples asked, "Won't you please come with us?"

Elisha answered, "I'll go."

[4] So he went with them. They came to the Jordan River and began to cut down trees. [5] As one of them was cutting down a tree, the ax head fell into the water. He cried out, "Oh no, master! It was borrowed!"

[6] The man of God asked, "Where did it fall?" When he showed Elisha the place, Elisha cut off a piece of wood. He threw it into the water at that place and made the ax head float. [7] Elisha said, "Pick it up." The disciple reached for it and picked it up.

The Aramean Army Is Struck With Blindness

[8] Whenever the king of Aram was fighting against Israel, he asked for advice from his officers about where they were to camp.

[9] So the man of God would send a message to the king of Israel, "Be careful not to go by that place. The Arameans are hiding there." [10] Then the king of Israel would send someone to the place that the man of God told him about. Elisha warned them so that they would be on their guard. He did this repeatedly.

[11] The king of Aram was very angry about this. He called his officers and asked them, "Won't you tell me who among us is ˌa spyˌ for the king of Israel?"

[12] One of his officers answered, "No one, Your Majesty. Elisha, the prophet in Israel, tells the king of Israel everything you say—even what you say in your bedroom."

[13] The king said, "Find out where he is. Then I will send men to capture him."

The king was told, "He is in Dothan." [14] So the king sent horses and chariots and a large fighting unit there. They came at night and surrounded the city.

[15] When the servant of the man of God got up in the morning and went outside, he saw troops, horses, and chariots surrounding the city. Elisha's servant asked, "Master, what should we do?"

[16] Elisha answered, "Don't be afraid. We have more forces on our side than they have on theirs." [17] Then Elisha prayed, "LORD, please open his eyes so that he may see." The LORD opened the servant's eyes and let him see. The mountain around Elisha was full of fiery horses and chariots.

[18] As the Arameans came down to get him, Elisha prayed to the LORD, "Please strike these people with blindness." The LORD struck them with blindness, as Elisha had asked. [19] Elisha told them, "This isn't the way! This isn't the city. Follow me, and I will lead you to the man you're looking for." So he led them into Samaria. [20] When they came into Samaria, Elisha said, "LORD, open the eyes of these men, and let them see." The LORD opened their eyes and let them see that they were in the middle of Samaria.

[21] When the king of Israel saw them, he asked Elisha, "Master, should I kill them? Should I kill them?"

[22] Elisha answered, "Don't kill them. Do you kill everyone you take captive in combat? Give them food and water. Let them eat and drink. Then let them go back to their master."

[23] So the king prepared a great feast for them. They ate and drank, and then he sent them back to their master. After this, Aramean troops didn't raid Israel's territory anymore.

The Aramean Army Blockades Samaria

[24] Later King Benhadad of Aram assembled his whole army. They went to Samaria and blockaded it. [25] The shortages caused by the blockade of Samaria became so severe that a donkey's head sold for two pounds of silver and a half-pint of dove[a] manure for two ounces of silver.

[26] As the king of Israel was walking on the city wall, a woman cried to him, "Help me, Your Majesty!"

[27] He answered, "If the LORD doesn't help you, how can I help you? I can't give you something from the threshing floor[b] or the winepress." [28] Then the king asked her, "What's the matter?"

She answered, "This woman told me, 'Give up your son. Let's eat him today. We'll eat my son tomorrow.' [29] So we boiled my son and ate him. The next day I told her, 'Give up your son. We'll eat him,' but she hid her son."

[30] When the king heard the woman say this, he tore his clothes ˌin distressˌ. As he was walking on the city wall, the people saw that he was wearing sackcloth under his clothes.

---

[a] 6:25 Or "pigeon."   [b] 6:27 A threshing floor is an outdoor area where grain is separated from its husks.

³¹ He said, "May God strike me dead if the head of Elisha, son of Shaphat, stays on his ˻body˼ today."

³² Elisha was sitting in his home with the ˻city's˼ leaders. The king had sent one of his men ahead of him ˻to Elisha's house˼. But before the messenger arrived, Elisha asked the leaders, "Do you see how this murderer has sent someone to tear off my head? When the messenger comes, close the door. Hold it shut because the king will be following him."

³³ While he was still talking to them, the messenger arrived. He said to Elisha, "This severe famine is from the LORD. Why should I wait any longer for the LORD ˻to help us˼?"

7 ¹ Elisha answered, "Listen to the word of the LORD! This is what the LORD says: About this time tomorrow 24 cups of the best flour will sell for half an ounce of silver in the gateway to Samaria. And 48 cups of barley will sell for half an ounce of silver."

² The servant on whose arm the king was leaning answered the man of God, "Could this happen even if the LORD poured rain through windows in the sky?"

Elisha replied, "You will see it with your own eyes, but you won't eat any of it."

The Aramean Army Flees

³ Four men with skin diseases were at the entrance of the city gate. One of them asked, "Why are we sitting here waiting to die? ⁴ If we go into the city, the famine is also there, and we'll still die. But if we stay here, we'll die. So let's go to the Aramean camp. If they give us something to keep us alive, we'll live. But if they kill us, we'll die anyway." ⁵ So they started out at dusk to go into the Aramean camp. When they came to the edge of the camp, no one was there.

⁶ (The LORD had made the Aramean army hear what sounded like chariots, horses, and a large army. The Aramean soldiers said to one another, "The king of Israel has hired the Hittite and Egyptian kings to attack us!" ⁷ So at dusk they fled. They abandoned the camp as it was with its tents, horses, and donkeys and ran for their lives.)

⁸ When the men with skin diseases came to the edge of the camp, they went into a tent, ate and drank, and carried off the silver, gold, and clothes they found in that tent. They went away and hid them. Then they came back, went into another tent, carried off its contents, went away, and hid them.

⁹ Then they said to one another, "What we're doing is not right. This is a day of good news, and we're not telling anyone about it. If we wait until morning when it's light out, we'll be punished. Let's bring the news to the royal palace." ¹⁰ So they called the city gatekeepers and told them, "We went into the Aramean camp, and we didn't see or hear anyone. The horses and donkeys were still tied up. Even the tents were left exactly as they were."

¹¹ The gatekeepers announced the news to the royal palace. ¹² So the king got up at night and told his officers what the Arameans had planned for them. He said, "They know we're starving, so they've left the camp to hide in the countryside. They're thinking, 'When they've left the city, we'll capture them alive and get into the city.' "

¹³ One of his officers replied, "Please let some men take five of the horses that are left here. Those men will be no worse off than the rest of the Israelites who are dying. Let's send them to take a look." ¹⁴ So they took two chariots with horses, and the king sent them to follow the Aramean army and told them to find out what happened. ¹⁵ They followed them as far as the Jordan River and saw how the whole road was littered with clothes and equipment that the Arameans had thrown away in their hurry. The messengers returned and told the king about it.

¹⁶ So the people went out and looted the Aramean camp. Then 24 cups of the best flour sold for half an ounce of silver, and 48 cups of barley sold for half an ounce of silver, as the LORD had predicted.

¹⁷ The king appointed the servant on whose arm he used to lean to be in charge of the gate. But the people trampled him to death in the gateway, as the man of God had predicted when the king came to him. ¹⁸ (It happened exactly as the man of God told the king, "48 cups of barley will sell for half an ounce of silver. And 24 cups of the best flour will sell for half an ounce of silver. This will happen about this time tomorrow in the gateway to Samaria." ¹⁹ Then the servant answered the man of God, "Could this happen even if the LORD poured rain through windows in the sky?" Elisha answered, "You will see it with your own eyes, but you won't eat any of it.") ²⁰ So this is what happened to the king's servant: The people trampled him to death in the gateway.

Elisha Helps a Shunem Woman Get Her Land Back

8 ¹ Elisha had told the woman whose son he had brought back to life, "Go away with your family. Stay wherever you can. The LORD has decided to send a famine on this country, and it will last seven years."

²The woman did what the man of God told her. She and her family went to live in Philistine territory for seven years. ³At the end of seven years, the woman came home from Philistine territory but left again to make an appeal to the king about her house and land.

⁴The king was talking to Gehazi, the servant of the man of God. He said, "Please tell me about all the great things Elisha has done." ⁵While Gehazi was telling the king how Elisha brought a dead child back to life, the mother ˎcame toˌ make an appeal to the king about her house and land.

Gehazi said, "Your Majesty, this is the woman, and this is her son whom Elisha brought back to life."

⁶ When the king asked the woman ˎabout this,ˌ she told him the story. So the king assigned to her an attendant to whom he said, "Restore all that is hers, including whatever her property produced from the day she left the country until now."

Elisha Prophesies to Hazael

⁷Elisha went to Damascus. King Benhadad of Aram, who was sick, was told, "The man of God has come here."

⁸The king told Hazael, "Take a present, and meet the man of God. Ask the LORD through him, 'Will I recover from this illness?'"

⁹Hazael went to meet Elisha. He took with him a present and all kinds of goods from Damascus. He had loaded the goods on 40 camels. He stood in front of Elisha and said, "Your humble servant King Benhadad of Aram has sent me to you. He asks whether he will recover from this illness."

¹⁰Elisha replied, "Tell him that he will get better, although the LORD has shown me that he is actually going to die." ¹¹He stared at him until he became embarrassed. Then the man of God began to cry.

¹²"Sir, why are you crying?" Hazael asked.

Elisha answered, "I know the evil you will do to the Israelites: You will set their fortresses on fire, kill their best young men, smash their little children, and rip open their pregnant women."

¹³But Hazael asked, "How can a dog like me do such a significant thing?"

Elisha answered, "The LORD has shown me that you will become king of Aram." ¹⁴Hazael left Elisha and went to his master Benhadad, who asked him what Elisha had said.

Hazael answered, "He told me that you will get better."

¹⁵But the next day Hazael took a blanket, soaked it in water, and smothered the king with it. Hazael ruled as king in his place.

King Jehoram of Judah—2 Chronicles 21:2–11; 21:16–22:1

¹⁶Joram (Ahab's son) was in his fifth year as king of Israel when Jehoram,ᵃ son of King Jehoshaphat of Judah, began to rule. Jehoram ruled while Jehoshaphat was still king of Judah. ¹⁷He was 32 years old when he began to rule, and he ruled for 8 years in Jerusalem. ¹⁸He followed the ways of the kings of Israel, as Ahab's family had done, because his wife was Ahab's daughter. So he did what the LORD considered evil. ¹⁹But for David's sake the LORD didn't want to destroy Judah. The LORD had told David that he would always give him and his descendants a ˎshiningˌ lamp.

²⁰During Jehoram's time Edom rebelled against Judah and chose its own king. ²¹Jehoram took all his chariots to attack Zair. The Edomites and their chariot commanders surrounded him, but he got up at night, broke through their lines, and his troops fled home. ²²So Edom rebelled against Judah's rule and is still independent today. At that time Libnah also rebelled. ²³Isn't everything else about Jehoram—everything he did—written in the official records of the kings of Judah? ²⁴Jehoram lay down in death with his ancestors and was buried with them in the City of David. His son Ahaziah succeeded him as king.

King Ahaziah of Judah—2 Chronicles 22:2–6

²⁵Joram (Ahab's son) was in his twelfth year as king of Israel when Jehoram's son Ahaziah became king of Judah. ²⁶Ahaziah was 22 years old when he began to rule, and he ruled for one year in Jerusalem. His mother was Athaliah, the granddaughter of King Omri of Israel. ²⁷Ahaziah followed the ways of Ahab's family. He did what the LORD considered evil, as Ahab's family had done, because he was related to Ahab's family by marriage.

²⁸Ahaziah went with Ahab's son Joram to fight against King Hazael of Aram at Ramoth Gilead. There the Arameans wounded Joram. ²⁹King Joram returned to Jezreel to let his wounds heal. (He had been wounded by the Arameans at Ramah when he fought against King Hazael of Aram.) Then Jehoram's son Ahaziah went to Jezreel to see Ahab's son Joram, who was sick.

ᵃ 8:16 In the Masoretic Text this king of Judah is also called Joram, a shorter form of Jehoram.

Jehu Is Anointed King of Israel

9 ¹ The prophet Elisha called one of the disciples of the prophets. He said, "Put on your belt. Take this flask of olive oil, and go to Ramoth Gilead. ² When you arrive there, look for Jehu, son of Jehoshaphat and grandson of Nimshi. Go inside, and have him get up and leave his companions. Take him into an inner room. ³ Take the flask of oil, pour it on his head, and say, 'This is what the LORD says: I have anointed you king of Israel.' Then open the door and leave immediately."

⁴ The young man, the servant of the prophet, went to Ramoth Gilead. ⁵ When he arrived there, the army's generals were sitting together. He said, "I have something to tell you, General."

Jehu asked, "Which one of us?"

He answered, "You, General!"

⁶ Jehu got up and went into the house. The prophet poured olive oil on his head and told him, "This is what the LORD God of Israel says: I have anointed you king of the LORD's people, ⸢king⸣ of Israel. ⁷ You will destroy the family of your master Ahab. I will get revenge on Jezebel for shedding the blood of my servants the prophets and all the LORD's ⸢other⸣ servants. ⁸ Ahab's entire family will die. I will destroy every male*a* from Ahab's family, whether slave or freeman in Israel. ⁹ I will make Ahab's family like the family of Jeroboam (Nebat's son) and like the family of Baasha, son of Ahijah. ¹⁰ Dogs will eat Jezebel inside the walls of Jezreel, and no one will bury her." Then he opened the door and left.

¹¹ Jehu came out to his master's officials. One of them asked him, "Is everything alright? Why did this lunatic come to you?"

He answered, "You know the man and the kind of things he says."

¹² They said, "That's not an answer. Please tell us."

Jehu replied, "We talked for a while, and he said to me, 'This is what the LORD says: I have anointed you king of Israel.' "

¹³ Then each one of them immediately took off his coat and laid it on the stairs below him. They blew a ram's horn and said, "Jehu is king!"

Jehu Kills King Joram, King Ahaziah, and Queen Jezebel—2 Chronicles 22:7–9

¹⁴ So Jehu, son of Jehoshaphat and grandson of Nimshi, plotted against Joram. (Joram and all Israel were guarding Ramoth Gilead against King Hazael of Aram. ¹⁵ But King Joram had returned to Jezreel to recover from the wounds he received while fighting King Hazael of Aram.)

Then Jehu said, "If you want me to be king, don't let anyone escape from the city to take the news to Jezreel." ¹⁶ So Jehu got on his chariot and drove to Jezreel because Joram was lying in bed there. (King Ahaziah of Judah had come to see Joram.)

¹⁷ The watchman standing on the tower in Jezreel saw Jehu's troops coming. He said, "I see some troops."

So Joram said, "Take a chariot driver, send him to meet them, and ask, 'Is everything alright?' "

¹⁸ So a chariot driver rode off, met Jehu, and said, "The king asks, 'Is everything alright?' "

Jehu replied, "Why should that matter to you? Follow me."

So the watchman announced, "The messenger you sent has reached them, but he isn't coming back."

¹⁹ Then Joram sent out a second driver. When he came to them, he said, "The king asks, 'Is everything alright?' "

Jehu replied, "Why should that matter to you? Follow me."

²⁰ So the watchman announced, "He has reached them, but he isn't coming back. The troop's leader is driving like a lunatic, like Jehu, grandson of Nimshi."

²¹ "Hitch the horses to the chariot," Joram ordered. When that was done, King Joram of Israel and King Ahaziah of Judah went to meet Jehu, each in his own chariot. They found him in the field that belonged to Naboth from Jezreel.

²² When Joram saw Jehu, he asked, "Is everything alright, Jehu?"

Jehu answered, "How can everything be alright as long as your mother continues her idolatry and witchcraft?"

²³ As Joram turned his chariot around and tried to flee, he said to Ahaziah, "It's a trap, Ahaziah!" ²⁴ But Jehu took his bow and shot Joram between the shoulders. The arrow came out of his chest, and he slumped over in his chariot.

²⁵ Then Jehu said to his attendant Bidkar, "Take him away, and throw him into the field that belonged to Naboth from Jezreel. Remember when you and I were driving our chariots behind his father Ahab? The LORD revealed this prophecy about him: ²⁶ 'Just as I saw the blood of

---

a 9:8 Hebrew uses a coarse term for "male" here.

Naboth and his sons yesterday, I will pay you back in this field,' declares the LORD. Now take him and throw him into the field as the LORD predicted."

²⁷ When King Ahaziah of Judah saw this, he fled on the road leading to Beth Haggan. Jehu pursued him and ordered, "Shoot him down in his chariot." They shot him at Gur Pass, which is near Ibleam. Ahaziah continued to flee until he got to Megiddo, where he died. ²⁸ His servants brought him in a chariot to Jerusalem. They buried him in a tomb with his ancestors in the City of David. ²⁹ (Ahaziah had become king of Judah in the eleventh year that Joram, Ahab's son, was king of Israel.)

³⁰ When Jehu arrived in Jezreel, Jezebel heard about it. She put on eye shadow, fixed her hair, and looked out of a second-story window. ³¹ When Jehu entered the gateway, she asked, "Is everything alright, Zimri, murderer of your master?"

³² Looking up at the window, he asked, "Is anyone on my side? Anyone?" Then two or three eunuchs looked out at him.

³³ He said, "Throw her down." They threw her down, and some of her blood splattered on the wall and the horses. The horses trampled her.

³⁴ He went inside, ate, and drank. Then he said, "Take care of this woman who had a curse on her. After all, she was a king's daughter." ³⁵ But when they went out to bury her, they couldn't find any of her body except her skull, feet, and hands. ³⁶ They came back and told him.

Jehu said, "The LORD spoke through his servant Elijah from Tishbe. He said, 'Dogs will eat Jezebel's body inside the walls of Jezreel. ³⁷ Jezebel's corpse will be like manure on the ground in the fields surrounding Jezreel so that no one will be able to say that this is Jezebel.' "

Jehu Kills King Ahab's and King Ahaziah's Heirs

10 ¹ Ahab had 70 male heirs in Samaria. So Jehu wrote letters to the officials of Jezreel, the respected leaders, and the guardians of Ahab's descendants in Samaria. The letters read, ² "Your master's heirs are with you, and you have chariots, horses, fortified cities, and weapons. As soon as this letter reaches you, ³ choose the best and most honest of your master's heirs, and put him on Ahab's throne. Fight for your master's family."

⁴ But they panicked. They said, "If two kings couldn't stand up to him, how can we stand up to him?" ⁵ So the official in charge of the palace, the mayor of the city, the respected leaders, and the guardians sent this message to Jehu: "We are your servants. We'll do everything you tell us. We won't make anyone king. Do what you think is best."

⁶ So he wrote them a second letter. It read, "If you are on my side and ready to listen to me, bring the heads of your master's heirs to me in Jezreel about this time tomorrow."

The 70 male heirs were staying with the city's most powerful men. These men had raised them. ⁷ When the letter came to the men, they slaughtered all 70 heirs. They put the heads in baskets and sent them to Jehu in Jezreel. ⁸ A messenger told him, "They've brought the heads of the king's heirs."

Jehu said, "Put them in two piles at the entrance to the gateway until morning." ⁹ In the morning he stood there. He told the people, "You are innocent. I plotted against my master and killed him. But who killed all these men? ¹⁰ You can be sure that the word of the LORD spoken about Ahab's family will be fulfilled. The LORD will do what he said through his servant Elijah."

¹¹ Jehu also killed every member of Ahab's household who was left in Jezreel: all the most powerful men, friends, and priests. Not one of them was left.

¹² Then Jehu left for Samaria. When he came to Beth Eked of the Shepherds, ¹³ he found some relatives of King Ahaziah of Judah. "Who are you?" he asked.

They answered, "We're Ahaziah's relatives. We've come to greet the families of the king and the queen mother."

¹⁴ Jehu ordered, "Capture them!"

Jehu's men captured and slaughtered 42 of them at a cistern near Beth Eked. They didn't leave any survivors.

¹⁵ When he left that place, he met Jehonadab, son of Rechab, who was coming to meet him. Jehu greeted him and asked, "Are you as loyal to me as I am to you?"

"I am," Jehonadab answered.

So Jehu said, "If you are, give me your hand."

When he gave Jehu his hand, Jehu helped him up into the chariot. ¹⁶ Jehu said, "Come with me. See how devoted I am to the LORD." So he had Jehonadab ride on his chariot. ¹⁷ When they arrived in Samaria, Jehu killed the rest of Ahab's family, every member who was left in Samaria. He wiped them out, as the LORD had told Elijah.

Jehu Kills Baal's Prophets

¹⁸ Then Jehu brought all the people together. He said, "Ahab served Baal a little, but Jehu will serve him a lot. ¹⁹ Summon all the prophets, servants, and priests of Baal. Make sure no

one is missing because I have a great sacrifice to offer Baal. Whoever is missing will not live." (Jehu was deceiving ˌthemˌ. He actually wanted to destroy those who worshiped Baal.) ²⁰ Jehu said, "Call a holy assembly to honor Baal." So they did. ²¹ Jehu sent messengers to all the Israelites. All the worshipers of Baal came, and there wasn't one who didn't come. They went into the temple of Baal and filled it from one end to the other.

²² Then Jehu told the man in charge of the priests' robes, "Bring out the robes for all the worshipers of Baal." So he brought out robes for them. ²³ Jehu and Jehonadab, son of Rechab, went into the temple of Baal and said to the worshipers of Baal, "Make sure that there are no worshipers of the LORD here with you. Only the worshipers of Baal should be here." ²⁴ So they went in to offer sacrifices and burnt offerings. But Jehu had stationed 80 of his men outside. He said ˌto themˌ, "If any of the people I'm putting in your hands escape, you will pay for their lives with yours."

²⁵ When the burnt offerings had been made, Jehu said to the guards and attendants, "Kill them. Don't let anyone get away." So they used swords to kill the Baal worshipers and threw out the bodies until the guards and attendants came to the stronghold in the temple of Baal. ²⁶ Then they brought out the large sacred stone of the temple of Baal and burned it. ²⁷ They destroyed the sacred stone of Baal and the temple of Baal and made it into a latrine. It is still a latrine today.

²⁸ So Jehu got rid of Baal worship throughout Israel. ²⁹ But Jehu did not turn away from the sins that Jeroboam (Nebat's son) led Israel to commit—ˌthe worship ofˌ the golden calves that were at Bethel and Dan.

³⁰ The LORD said to Jehu, "You did what I consider right, and you did it well. You did everything I wanted done to Ahab's family. That is why four generations of your descendants will sit on the throne of Israel."

³¹ But Jehu didn't wholeheartedly obey the teachings of the LORD God of Israel. He didn't turn away from the sins that Jeroboam led Israel to commit. ³² So in those days the LORD began to take away some of Israel's territory. Hazael defeated Jehu's army throughout Israel's territory ³³ east of the Jordan River: the entire region of Gilead (the territory belonging to Gad, Reuben, and Manasseh) from Aroer, which is near the Arnon River, to Gilead and Bashan.

³⁴ Isn't everything else about Jehu—everything he did, all his heroic acts—written in the official records of the kings of Israel? ³⁵ Jehu lay down in death with his ancestors and was buried in Samaria. His son Jehoahaz succeeded him as king. ³⁶ Jehu ruled as king of Israel in Samaria for 28 years.

The Priest Jehoiada Opposes Queen Athaliah—2 Chronicles 22:10–23:21

11 ¹ When Ahaziah's mother, Athaliah, saw that her son was dead, she began to destroy the entire royal family. ² But Jehosheba, daughter of King Jehoram and sister of Ahaziah, took Ahaziah's son Joash. She saved him from being killed with the king's other sons, and in a bedroom she hid him and his nurse from Athaliah. So Joash wasn't killed ³ but was hidden with her in the LORD's temple for six years while Athaliah ruled the country.

⁴ In the seventh year of Athaliah's reign, Jehoiada sent for the company commanders of the Carites and the guards and had them come to him in the LORD's temple. He made an agreement with them, put them under oath in the LORD's temple, and showed them the king's son. ⁵ He ordered them, "This is what you must do: One third of you, those who are on duty on the day of worship, must guard the royal palace. ⁶ Another third must be at Sur Gate. And another third must be at the gate behind the guards. You will guard the king's residence.ᵃ ⁷ Then your two groups who ˌnormallyˌ go off duty on the day of worship must guard the king at the LORD's temple. ⁸ Surround the king. Each man should have his weapons in his hand. Kill anyone who tries to break through your ranks. Stay with the king wherever he goes."

⁹ The company commanders did as the priest Jehoiada had ordered them. Each commander took his men who were coming on duty on the day of worship as well as those who were about to go off duty and came to the priest Jehoiada. ¹⁰ He gave the commanders the spears and the shields that had belonged to King David but were now in the LORD's temple. ¹¹ The guards stood with their weapons in their hands. They were stationed around the king and around the altar and the temple (from the south side to the north side of the temple). ¹² Then Jehoiada brought out the king's son, gave him the crown and the religious instructions, and made him king by anointing him. As the guards clapped their hands, they said, "Long live the king!"

¹³ When Athaliah heard the noise made by the guards and the other people, she went into the LORD's temple, where the people were. ¹⁴ She looked, and the king was standing by the pillar according to custom. The commanders and the trumpeters were by his side. All the peo-

---

ᵃ 11:6 Hebrew meaning uncertain.

ple of the land were rejoicing and blowing trumpets. As Athaliah tore her clothes ⌞in distress⌟, she cried, "Treason, treason!"

[15] Then the priest Jehoiada ordered the company commanders who were in charge of the army, "Take her out of the temple. Use your sword to kill anyone who follows her." (The priest had said, "She must not be killed in the LORD's temple.") [16] So they arrested her as she came to the street where the horses enter the royal palace, and there she was killed.

[17] Jehoiada made a promise to the LORD on behalf of the king and his people that they would be the LORD's people. He made other promises between the king and the people. [18] Then all the people of the land went to the temple of Baal and tore it down. They smashed Baal's altars and his statues and killed Mattan, the priest of Baal, in front of the altars.

Next, the priest appointed officials to be in charge of the LORD's temple. [19] He took the company commanders of the Carites and the guards and all the people of the land, and they brought the king from the LORD's temple. They went down the street that goes through Guards' Gate to the royal palace. Then Joash sat on the royal throne. [20] All the people of the land were celebrating. But the city was quiet because they had killed Athaliah with a sword at the royal palace.[b]

King Joash of Judah—2 Chronicles 24:1–23

[21] Joash[c] was seven years old when he began to rule.

12[a] [1] Joash began to rule in Jehu's seventh year as king of Israel, and he ruled for 40 years in Jerusalem. His mother was Zibiah from Beersheba. [2] Joash did what the LORD considered right, as long as the priest Jehoiada instructed him. [3] But the illegal places of worship weren't torn down. The people continued to offer sacrifices and burn incense at these worship sites.

[4] Joash told the priests, "⌞Collect⌟ all the holy contributions that are brought into the LORD's temple—the money each person is currently required to bring and all the money brought voluntarily to the LORD's temple. [5] Each of the priests should receive it from the donors and use it to make repairs on the temple where they are needed."

[6] But by Joash's twenty-third year as king, the priests still had not repaired the temple. [7] So King Joash called for Jehoiada and the other priests and asked them, "Why aren't you repairing the damage in the temple? Don't take any more money from the donors ⌞for your own use⌟. Instead, use it to make repairs on the temple." [8] The priests agreed neither to receive money from the people ⌞for personal use⌟ nor to be responsible for repairing the temple.

[9] Then the priest Jehoiada took a box, drilled a hole in its lid, and put it at the right side of the altar as one comes into the LORD's temple. The priests who guarded the entrance put the money that was brought to the LORD's temple in the box. [10] Whenever they saw a lot of money in the box, the king's scribe and the chief priest would collect and count the money that was donated in the LORD's temple. [11] Then they would give the money that had been weighed to the men who had been appointed to work on the LORD's temple. They used it to pay the carpenters, builders, [12] masons, and stonecutters. They also used it to buy wood and cut stones to make repairs on the LORD's temple and to buy anything else that they needed for the temple repairs. [13] But no silver bowls, snuffers, dishes, trumpets, or any other gold and silver utensils were made for the LORD's temple with the money that was brought. [14] Instead, the money was given to the workmen, and they used it to repair the temple. [15] They didn't require the men who were entrusted with the money for the workers to give an account, because they were honest people. [16] The money from the guilt offerings and the offerings for sin was not brought into the LORD's temple. It belonged to the priests.

[17] At this time King Hazael of Aram fought against Gath and conquered it. He was also determined to attack Jerusalem. [18] So King Joash of Judah took all the gifts his ancestors Kings Jehoshaphat, Jehoram, and Ahaziah of Judah, had dedicated to the LORD, the things he had dedicated to the LORD, and all the gold that could be found in the storerooms of the LORD's temple and the royal palace. He sent these things to King Hazael of Aram, who called off the attack on Jerusalem.

King Joash Is Assassinated—2 Chronicles 24:24–27

[19] Isn't everything else about Joash—everything he did—written in the official records of the kings of Judah? [20] His own officials plotted against him and killed him at Beth Millo on the road that goes down to Silla. [21] Joash's officials Jozacar, son of Shimeath, and Jehozabad, son of Shomer, executed him. They buried him with his ancestors in the City of David. His son Amaziah succeeded him as king.

---

[b] 11:20 2 Kings 11:21 in English Bibles is 2 Kings 12:1 in the Hebrew Bible.   [c] 11:21 In the Masoretic Text this king of Judah is also called Jehoash, a longer form of Joash.   [a] 12:1 2 Kings 12:1–21 in English Bibles is 2 Kings 12:2–22 in the Hebrew Bible.

King Jehoahaz of Israel

13 [1] Ahaziah's son King Joash of Judah was in his twenty-third year as king of Judah when Jehoahaz,[a] son of Jehu, began to rule in Samaria as king of Israel. He ruled for 17 years. [2] He did what the LORD considered evil. He continued to commit the sins that Jeroboam (Nebat's son) led Israel to commit. He never gave up committing those sins. [3] So the LORD became angry with Israel and put it at the mercy of King Hazael of Aram and Hazael's son Benhadad as long as they lived.

[4] Then Jehoahaz pleaded with the LORD, and the LORD heard him because he saw how the Aramean king was oppressing Israel. [5] So the LORD gave the Israelites someone to save them, and they were freed from Aram's power. They were able to live in their homes again as they had done before. [6] But they didn't turn away from the sins that Jeroboam and his dynasty led Israel to commit. They continued to commit those sins. In addition, the pole dedicated to the goddess Asherah remained standing in Samaria.

[7] Jehoahaz had no army left except for 50 horses, 10 chariots, and 10,000 foot soldiers because the king of Aram had destroyed the rest. He had made them like dust that people trample. [8] Isn't everything else about Jehoahaz—everything he did, his heroic acts—written in the official records of the kings of Israel? [9] Jehoahaz lay down in death with his ancestors and was buried in Samaria. His son Jehoash[b] ruled as king in his place.

King Jehoash of Israel

[10] In Joash's thirty-seventh year as king of Judah, Jehoahaz's son Jehoash began to rule Israel in Samaria. He ruled for 16 years. [11] He did what the LORD considered evil and never gave up committing the sins that Jeroboam led Israel to commit. He continued to commit them. [12] Isn't everything else about Jehoash—everything he did, his heroic acts when he fought against King Amaziah of Judah—written in the official records of the kings of Israel? [13] Jehoash lay down in death with his ancestors and was buried with the kings of Israel in Samaria. Then Jeroboam claimed the throne.

The Death of Elisha

[14] Elisha became fatally ill. King Jehoash of Israel visited him, cried over him, and said, "Master! Master! Israel's chariot and horses!"

[15] Elisha told him, "Get a bow and some arrows." So he got a bow and some arrows. [16] Then Elisha told the king of Israel, "Take the bow in your hand." So the king picked up the bow. Elisha laid his hands on the king's hands. [17] Elisha said, "Open the window that faces east." So the king opened it. "Shoot," Elisha said, and the king shot. Then Elisha said, "That is the arrow of the LORD's victory, the arrow of victory against Aram. You will completely defeat the Arameans at Aphek." [18] Then Elisha said, "Take the arrows." So the king took them. "Stomp on them," he told the king of Israel. The king stomped three times and stopped.

[19] Then the man of God became angry with him. "You should have stomped five or six times!" he said. "Then you would have completely defeated the Arameans. But now you will only defeat the Arameans three times."

[20] Elisha died and was buried. Moabite raiding parties used to invade the country in the spring. [21] One day some people who were burying a man saw one of these raiding parties. So they quickly put the man into Elisha's tomb. But when the body touched Elisha's bones, the man came back to life and stood up.

[22] King Hazael of Aram oppressed Israel as long as Jehoahaz ruled. [23] But the LORD was kind and merciful to the Israelites because of his promise[c] to Abraham, Isaac, and Jacob. He didn't want to destroy the Israelites, and even now he hasn't turned away from them.

[24] King Hazael of Aram died, and his son Benhadad succeeded him as king. [25] Then Jehoash, son of Jehoahaz, reconquered the cities that Benhadad had taken from his father Jehoahaz. Jehoash defeated Benhadad three times and recovered those cities of Israel.

King Amaziah of Judah—2 Chronicles 25:1–13

14 [1] Jehoahaz's son King Jehoash was in his second year as king of Israel when King Amaziah, son of Joash of Judah, began to rule. [2] Amaziah was 25 years old when he began to rule, and he ruled for 29 years in Jerusalem. His mother was Jehoaddin from Jerusalem. [3] He did what the LORD considered right, but not exactly what his ancestor David had done. He did everything his father Joash had done. [4] But the illegal places of worship were still not torn down. The people continued to offer sacrifices and burn incense at these worship sites.

---

[a] 13:1 In the Masoretic Text this king of Israel is also called Joahaz, a shorter form of Jehoahaz.   [b] 13:9 In the Masoretic Text this king of Israel is also called Joash, a shorter form of Jehoash.   [c] 13:23 Or "covenant."

⁵ As soon as he had a firm control over the kingdom, he executed the officials who had killed his father, the former king. ⁶ But he didn't execute their children. He obeyed the LORD's command written in the Book of Moses' Teachings: "Parents must never be put to death for the crimes of their children, and children must never be put to death for the crimes of their parents. Each person must be put to death for his own crime."

⁷ Amaziah killed 10,000 Edomites in the Dead Sea region and took the city of Sela in battle. He gave it the name Joktheel, which is still its name today.

King Amaziah's Defeat and Death—*2 Chronicles 25:14–26:2*

⁸ Then Amaziah sent messengers to King Jehoash, son of Jehoahaz and grandson of Jehu of Israel, to declare war on Israel.

⁹ King Jehoash of Israel sent this message to King Amaziah of Judah: "A thistle in Lebanon sent a message to a cedar in Lebanon. It said, 'Let your daughter marry my son,' but a wild animal from Lebanon came along and trampled the thistle. ¹⁰ You certainly defeated Edom, and now you have become arrogant. Enjoy your fame, but stay home. Why must you invite disaster and your own defeat and take Judah with you?"

¹¹ But Amaziah wouldn't listen. So King Jehoash of Israel attacked, and King Amaziah of Judah met him in battle at Beth Shemesh in Judah. ¹² Israel defeated the army of Judah, and the Judeans fled to their homes. ¹³ King Jehoash of Israel captured King Amaziah, son of Joash and grandson of Ahaziah of Judah, at Beth Shemesh and went to Jerusalem. He tore down a 600-foot section of the wall around Jerusalem from Ephraim Gate to Corner Gate. ¹⁴ He took all the gold, silver, and all the utensils he found in the LORD's temple and in the royal palace treasury. He also took hostages. Then he returned to Samaria.

¹⁵ Isn't everything else about Jehoash—what he did, his heroic acts when he fought against King Amaziah of Judah—written in the official records of the kings of Israel? ¹⁶ Jehoash lay down in death with his ancestors and was buried with the kings of Israel in Samaria. His son Jeroboam succeeded him as king.

¹⁷ Joash's son King Amaziah of Judah lived 15 years after the death of Jehoahaz's son King Jehoash of Israel. ¹⁸ Isn't everything else about Amaziah written in the official records of the kings of Judah? ¹⁹ Conspirators in Jerusalem plotted against him, so he fled to Lachish. But they sent men to Lachish after him and killed him there. ²⁰ They brought him back by horse, and he was buried in Jerusalem, in the City of David, with his ancestors.

²¹ All the people of Judah took Azariah, who was 16 years old, and made him king in place of his father Amaziah. ²² Azariah rebuilt Elath and returned it to Judah after King Amaziah lay down in death with his ancestors.

King Jeroboam II of Israel

²³ Joash's son Amaziah was in his fifteenth year as king of Judah when Jehoash's son King Jeroboam of Israel began to rule in Samaria. Jeroboam ruled for 41 years. ²⁴ He did what the LORD considered evil. He didn't turn away from any of the sins that Jeroboam (Nebat's son) led Israel to commit.

²⁵ He restored Israel's boundaries from the border of Hamath to the Dead Sea as the LORD God of Israel predicted through his servant Jonah, the prophet from Gath Hepher and the son of Amittai. ²⁶ The LORD did this because he saw how bitterly everyone in Israel was suffering. No slave or free person could help Israel. ²⁷ Since the LORD had said he was not going to wipe out Israel's name completely, he saved them through Jeroboam, son of Jehoash.

²⁸ Isn't everything else about Jeroboam—everything he did, his heroic acts when he fought, how he recovered Damascus and Hamath for Israel[a]—written in the official records of the kings of Israel? ²⁹ Jeroboam lay down in death with his ancestors, the kings of Israel. His son Zechariah succeeded him as king.

King Azariah of Judah—*2 Chronicles 26:3–5*

15 ¹ In Jeroboam's twenty-seventh year as king of Israel, Amaziah's son Azariah[a] began to rule as king of Judah. ² He was 16 years old when he began to rule, and he ruled for 52 years in Jerusalem. His mother was Jecoliah from Jerusalem.

³ He did what the LORD considered right, as his father Amaziah had done. ⁴ But the illegal places of worship were still not torn down. The people continued to offer sacrifices and burn incense at these worship sites.

ᵃ 14:28 Syriac; Masoretic Text "for Judah in Israel."   ᵃ 15:1 In the Masoretic Text this king of Judah is also called Uzziah.

Azariah's Skin Disease—2 Chronicles 26:21–23

⁵ The LORD inflicted the king with a skin disease that lasted until the day the king died. So the king lived in a separate house. The king's son Jotham was in charge of the palace and governed the country.

⁶ Isn't everything else about Azariah—everything he did—written in the official records of the kings of Judah? ⁷ Azariah lay down in death with his ancestors and was buried with them in the City of David. His son Jotham succeeded him as king.

King Zechariah of Israel Rules for Six Months

⁸ In Azariah's thirty-eighth year as king of Judah, Jeroboam's son Zechariah was king of Israel in Samaria for six months. ⁹ He did what the LORD considered evil, as his ancestors had done. He didn't turn away from the sins that Jeroboam (Nebat's son) led Israel to commit. ¹⁰ Shallum, son of Jabesh, plotted against Zechariah, attacked him at Kabal Am, killed him, and succeeded him as king. ¹¹ Everything else about Zechariah is written in the official records of the kings of Israel. ¹² It happened exactly as the LORD had told Jehu: "Four generations of your descendants will sit on the throne of Israel."

King Shallum of Israel Rules for One Month

¹³ Shallum, son of Jabesh, became king in Azariah's thirty-ninth year as king of Judah. Shallum ruled for an entire month in Samaria. ¹⁴ Then Menahem, son of Gadi, came from Tirzah to Samaria, attacked Shallum (son of Jabesh), killed him, and succeeded him as king. ¹⁵ Everything else about Shallum—all about his conspiracy—is written in the official records of the kings of Israel. ¹⁶ Then Menahem attacked Tiphsah, everyone there, and its territory. Because the city didn't open its gates for him, he attacked it and ripped open all its pregnant women.

King Menahem of Israel

¹⁷ In Azariah's thirty-ninth year as king of Judah, Menahem, son of Gadi, began to rule as king of Israel. He ruled for 10 years in Samaria. ¹⁸ He did what the LORD considered evil. During his entire life he never turned away from the sins that Jeroboam (Nebat's son) led Israel to commit.

¹⁹ King Pul of Assyria came to ˌattack, the country. So Menahem gave Pul 75,000 pounds of silver to gain his support and help strengthen his hold on the kingdom. ²⁰ Menahem raised the money from all the wealthy men in Israel. Each gave 20 ounces of silver for the king of Assyria. Then the king of Assyria left the country. ²¹ Isn't everything else about Menahem—everything he did—written in the official records of the kings of Israel? ²² Menahem lay down in death with his ancestors, and his son Pekahiah succeeded him as king.

King Pekahiah of Israel

²³ In Azariah's fiftieth year as king of Judah, Menahem's son Pekahiah began to rule. Pekahiah was king of Israel in Samaria for two years. ²⁴ He did what the LORD considered evil. He didn't turn away from the sins that Jeroboam (Nebat's son) led Israel to commit. ²⁵ His officer Pekah, son of Remaliah, plotted against him. With 50 men from Gilead, Pekah attacked Pekahiah, Argob, and Arieh in the fortress of the royal palace in Samaria. Pekah killed him and succeeded him as king. ²⁶ Everything else about Pekahiah—everything he did—is written in the official records of the kings of Israel.

King Pekah of Israel

²⁷ In Azariah's fifty-second year as king of Judah, Pekah, son of Remaliah, began to rule Israel in Samaria. He ruled for 20 years. ²⁸ He did what the LORD considered evil. He did not turn away from the sins that Jeroboam (Nebat's son) led Israel to commit. ²⁹ In the days of King Pekah of Israel, King Tiglath Pileser of Assyria took Ijon, Abel Beth Maacah, Janoah, Kedesh, Hazor, Gilead, Galilee, and the entire territory of Naphtali. He also took the people away to Assyria as captives. ³⁰ Hoshea, son of Elah, plotted against Pekah, son of Remaliah. Hoshea attacked him and killed him. Hoshea began to rule as king in his place in the twentieth year that Jotham, son of Azariah, was king of Judah. ³¹ Everything else about Pekah—everything he did—is written in the official records of the kings of Israel.

King Jotham of Judah—2 Chronicles 27:1–9

³² In the second year that King Pekah, son of Remaliah, ruled Israel, Jotham, son of Azariah, began to rule as king of Judah. ³³ He was 25 years old when he began to rule. He ruled for 16 years in Jerusalem. His mother was Jerusha, daughter of Zadok. ³⁴ He did what the LORD considered right, as his father Azariah had done. ³⁵ But the illegal places of worship were not torn

down. The people continued to offer sacrifices and burn incense at these worship sites. Jotham built the Upper Gate of the LORD's temple. [36] Isn't everything else about Jotham—everything he did—written in the official records of the kings of Judah?

[37] In those days the LORD began to use King Rezin of Aram and Pekah, son of Remaliah, to attack Judah. [38] Jotham lay down in death with his ancestors and was buried with them in the city of his ancestor David. His son Ahaz succeeded him as king.

King Ahaz of Judah—2 Chronicles 28:1–27

16 [1] Pekah, son of Remaliah, was in his seventeenth year as king of Israel when King Ahaz, son of Jotham, began to rule as king of Judah. [2] Ahaz was 20 years old when he began to rule. He ruled for 26 years in Jerusalem. He didn't do what the LORD his God considered right, as his ancestor David had done. [3] He followed the example of the kings of Israel and even sacrificed his son by burning him alive. Sacrificing ⸤children⸥ was one of the disgusting things done by the nations that the LORD had forced out of the Israelites' way. [4] He offered sacrifices and burned incense as an offering at the illegal worship sites, which were on hills and under every large tree.

[5] Then King Rezin of Aram and King Pekah, son of Remaliah of Israel, came to wage war against Jerusalem. They blockaded Ahaz but couldn't get him to fight. [6] At that time King Rezin of Aram drove the Judeans out of Elath and gave it back to Edom.[a] The Edomites came to Elath and still live there today.

[7] Ahaz sent messengers to King Tiglath Pileser of Assyria to say, "I'm your servant, your son. Come and save me from the kings of Aram and Israel who are attacking me." [8] Ahaz took the silver and gold he found in the LORD's temple and in the treasury in the royal palace and sent them to the king of Assyria as a present.

[9] The king of Assyria listened to him and attacked Damascus. He captured it, took the people to Kir as captives, and killed Rezin.

[10] Then King Ahaz went to Damascus to meet King Tiglath Pileser of Assyria. He saw an altar there in Damascus. So King Ahaz sent the priest Urijah a model of the altar and a set of detailed plans. [11] Urijah built an altar exactly like the model King Ahaz sent from Damascus. He finished it before Ahaz returned home from Damascus.

[12] When the king came from Damascus, he saw the altar. The king approached the altar and went up to it. [13] He sacrificed his burnt offering and grain offering, poured out his wine offering, and sprinkled the blood of his fellowship offering on the altar. [14] But he moved the bronze altar dedicated to the LORD. It had been in front of the temple between his altar and the LORD's temple. Ahaz put it on the north side of his altar. [15] King Ahaz gave this command to the priest Urijah: "On this great altar you must burn the morning burnt offerings and the evening grain offering, the king's burnt offerings and grain offerings, and the burnt offerings, grain offerings, and wine offerings of all the people of the land. Sprinkle all the blood of the burnt offerings and ⸤other⸥ sacrifices on it. I will use the bronze altar for prayer." [16] The priest Urijah did what King Ahaz had commanded.

[17] King Ahaz cut off the side panels of the ⸤bronze⸥ stands ⸤used in the temple⸥ and removed the basin from each of them. He took the bronze pool down from the bronze bulls that were under it and set it on a stone base. [18] Ahaz removed the covered walkway used on the day of worship. This walkway had been built in the temple. He also removed the outer entrance for the king from the LORD's temple. He did this to please the king of Assyria. [19] Isn't everything else about Ahaz—the things he did—written in the official records of the kings of Judah? [20] Ahaz lay down in death with his ancestors and was buried with them in the City of David. His son Hezekiah succeeded him as king.

King Hoshea of Israel

17 [1] In Ahaz's twelfth year as king of Judah, Hoshea, son of Elah, began to rule as king of Israel in Samaria. He ruled for nine years. [2] He did what the LORD considered evil, but he didn't do what the kings of Israel before him had done.

The Fall of Samaria

[3] King Shalmaneser of Assyria defeated Hoshea, who became his servant and was required to make annual payments to him. [4] The king of Assyria found Hoshea to be a traitor. (Hoshea had sent messengers to King Dais of Egypt and had stopped making annual payments to the king of Assyria.) So the king of Assyria arrested him and put him in prison. [5] Then the king of Assyria attacked the entire country. He attacked Samaria and blockaded it for three years. [6] In Hoshea's ninth year as king of Israel, the king of Assyria captured Samaria and took the Israelites to Assyria as captives. He settled them in Halah, along the Habor River in Gozan, and in the cities of the Medes.

---

[a] 16:6 Masoretic Text "Aram." (The Hebrew words for "Aram" and "Edom" are nearly identical.)

[7] The Israelites sinned against the LORD their God, who brought them out of Egypt and rescued them, from the power of Pharaoh (the king of Egypt). They worshiped other gods [8] and lived by the customs of the nations that the LORD had forced out of the Israelites' way. They also did what their kings wanted them to do. [9] The Israelites secretly did things against the LORD their God that weren't right:

They built for themselves illegal places of worship in all of their cities, from the smallest watchtower to the largest, fortified city.

[10] They set up sacred stones and poles dedicated to the goddess Asherah on every high hill and under every large tree.

[11] At all the illegal places of worship, they sacrificed in the same way as the nations that the LORD had removed from the land ahead of them.

They did evil things and made the LORD furious.

[12] They served idols, although the LORD had said, "Never do this."

[13] The LORD had warned Israel and Judah through every kind of prophet and seer,[a] "Turn from your evil ways, and obey my commands and decrees as I commanded your ancestors in all my teachings, the commands I sent to you through my servants the prophets." [14] But they refused to listen. They became as impossible to deal with as their ancestors who refused to trust the LORD their God. [15] They rejected his decrees, the promise[b] he made to their ancestors, and the warnings he had given them. They went after worthless idols and became as worthless as the idols. They behaved like the nations around them, although the LORD had commanded them not to do that. [16] They abandoned all the commands of the LORD their God:

They made two calves out of cast metal.

They made a pole dedicated to the goddess Asherah.

They prayed to the entire army of heaven.

They worshiped Baal.

[17] They sacrificed their sons and daughters by burning them alive.

They practiced black magic and cast evil spells.

They sold themselves by doing what the LORD considered evil, and they made him furious.

[18] The LORD became so angry with Israel that he removed them from his sight. Only the tribe of Judah was left. [19] Even Judah didn't obey the commands of the LORD their God but lived according to Israel's customs. [20] So the LORD rejected all of Israel's descendants, made them suffer, handed them over to those who looted their property, and finally turned away from Israel.

[21] When he tore Israel away from the family of David, the people of Israel made Jeroboam (Nebat's son) king. Jeroboam forced Israel away from the LORD and led them to commit a serious sin. [22] The Israelites followed all the sins Jeroboam committed and never turned away from them. [23] Finally, the LORD turned away from Israel as he had said he would through all his servants, the prophets. So the people of Israel were taken from their land to Assyria as captives, and they are still there today.

Assyria Brings Foreign People to Settle in Israel

[24] The king of Assyria brought people from Babylon, Cuthah, Avva, Hamath, and Sepharvaim and settled them in the cities of Samaria in place of the Israelites. They took over Samaria and lived in its cities.

[25] When they first came to live there, they didn't worship the LORD. So the LORD sent lions to kill some of them. [26] Then someone said to the king of Assyria, "The people you took as captives and settled in the cities of Samaria don't know the customs of the god of that country, so he sent lions. Now the lions are killing them because they don't know the customs of the god of this country."

[27] The king of Assyria gave this command: "Bring one of the priests you captured from there. Let him go back to teach them the customs of the god of that country." [28] So one of the priests who had been taken prisoner from Samaria went to live in Bethel. He taught them how to worship the LORD.

[29] But each group that settled in Samaria, continued to make its own gods. They put them at the illegal places of worship, which the people of Samaria had made. Each group did this in the cities where they lived:

[30] The people from Babylon made Succoth Benoth.

The people from Cuth made Nergal.

The people from Hamath made Ashima.

[31] The people from Avva made Nibhaz and Tartak.

The people from Sepharvaim burned their children for Adrammelech and Anammelech, the gods of Sepharvaim.

---

[a] 17:13 A seer is a prophet.   [b] 17:15 Or "covenant."

[32] So while these people were worshiping the LORD, they also appointed all kinds of people to serve as priests for the shrines at their illegal places of worship. [33] They worshiped the LORD but also served their own gods according to the customs of the nations from which they had come.

[34] Today they are still following their customs, as they've done from the beginning. They don't fear the LORD or live by the decrees, customs, teachings, or commands that the LORD gave to the descendants of Jacob (whom he named Israel). [35] When the LORD made a promise to Israel, he commanded, "Never worship other gods, bow down to them, serve them, or sacrifice to them. [36] Instead, worship the LORD, who used his great power and a mighty arm to bring you out of Egypt. Bow down to the LORD, and sacrifice to him. [37] Faithfully obey the laws, rules, teachings, and commands that he wrote for you: 'Never worship other gods. [38] Never forget the promise I made to you. Never worship other gods. [39] Instead, worship the LORD your God, and he will rescue you from your enemies.' "

[40] The people of Israel had refused to listen and made up their own rules, as they had done from the beginning. [41] These ˻other˼ nations worshiped the LORD but also served their own idols. So did their children and their grandchildren. They still do whatever their ancestors did.

King Hezekiah of Judah—2 Chronicles 29:1–2

18 [1] King Hoshea, son of Elah, had been king in Israel for three years when King Hezekiah, son of Ahaz of Judah, began to rule as king. [2] Hezekiah was 25 years old when he began to rule, and he ruled for 29 years in Jerusalem. His mother was Abi, daughter of Zechariah.

[3] He did what the LORD considered right, as his ancestor David had done. [4] He got rid of the illegal places of worship, crushed the sacred stones, and cut down the poles dedicated to the goddess Asherah. He even crushed the bronze snake that Moses had made because up to that time the Israelites had been burning incense to it. They called it Nehushtan. [5] Hezekiah trusted the LORD God of Israel. No king among all the kings of Judah was like Hezekiah. [6] He was loyal to the LORD and never turned away from him. He obeyed the commands that the LORD had given through Moses, [7] so the LORD was with him. He succeeded in everything he tried: He rebelled against the king of Assyria and wouldn't serve him anymore. [8] He conquered the Philistines from the ˻smallest˼ watchtower to the ˻largest˼ fortified city all the way to Gaza and its territory.

The Fall of Samaria

[9] In Hezekiah's fourth year as king (which was the seventh year in the reign of King Hoshea, son of Elah of Israel) King Shalmaneser of Assyria attacked Samaria, blockaded it, [10] and captured it at the end of three years. Samaria was taken in Hezekiah's sixth year as king (which was Hoshea's ninth year as king of Israel). [11] The king of Assyria took the Israelites to Assyria as captives. He put them in Halah, along the Habor River in Gozan, and in the cities of the Medes. [12] This happened because they refused to obey the LORD their God and disregarded the conditions of the promise[a] he made to them. They refused to obey everything that Moses, the LORD's servant, had commanded.

The LORD Rescues Judah From the Assyrians—2 Chronicles 32:1–23; Isaiah 36:1–37:20

[13] In Hezekiah's fourteenth year as king, King Sennacherib of Assyria attacked all the fortified cities of Judah and captured them. [14] Then King Hezekiah of Judah sent this message to the king of Assyria at Lachish: "I have done wrong. Go away, and leave me alone. I'll pay whatever penalty you give me."

So the king of Assyria demanded that King Hezekiah of Judah pay 22,500 pounds of silver and 2,250 pounds of gold. [15] Hezekiah gave him all the silver that could be found in the LORD's temple and in the royal palace treasury. [16] At that time Hezekiah stripped ˻the gold˼ off the doors and doorposts of the LORD's temple. (˻Earlier˼ Hezekiah had them covered ˻with gold˼) He gave the gold to the king of Assyria.

[17] Then the king of Assyria sent his commander-in-chief, his quartermaster, and his field commander with a large army from Lachish to King Hezekiah at Jerusalem. They came there and stood at the channel for the Upper Pool on the road to the Laundryman's Field. [18] When they called for King Hezekiah, Eliakim, who was in charge of the palace and was the son of Hilkiah, Shebnah the scribe, and Joah, who was the royal historian and the son of Asaph, went out to the field commander.

[19] He said to them, "Tell Hezekiah, 'This is what the great king, the king of Assyria, says: What makes you so confident? [20] You give useless advice about getting ready for war. Whom, then, do you trust for support in your rebellion against me? [21] Now, look! When you trust Egypt, you're trusting a broken stick for a staff. If you lean on it, it stabs your hand and goes through

---

[a] 18:12 Or "covenant."

it. This is what Pharaoh (the king of Egypt) is like for everyone who trusts him. ²²Suppose you tell me, "We're trusting the LORD our God." He's the god whose places of worship and altars Hezekiah got rid of. He told Judah and Jerusalem, "Worship at this altar in Jerusalem." '

²³"Now, make a deal with my master, the king of Assyria. I'll give you 2,000 horses if you can put riders on them. ²⁴How can you defeat my master's lowest-ranking officers when you trust Egypt for chariots and horses?

²⁵"Have I come to destroy this place without the LORD on my side? The LORD said to me, 'Attack this country, and destroy it.' "

²⁶Then Eliakim (son of Hilkiah), Shebnah, and Joah said to the field commander, "Speak to us in Aramaic, since we understand it. Don't speak to us in the Judean language as long as there are people on the wall listening."

²⁷But the field commander asked them, "Did my master send me to tell these things only to you and your master? Didn't he send me to the men sitting on the wall who will have to eat their own excrement and drink their own urine with you?"

²⁸Then the field commander stood and shouted loudly in the Judean language, "Listen to the great king, the king of Assyria. ²⁹This is what the king says: Don't let Hezekiah deceive you. He can't rescue you from me. ³⁰Don't let Hezekiah get you to trust the LORD by saying, 'The LORD will certainly rescue us, and this city will not be put under the control of the king of Assyria.' ³¹Don't listen to Hezekiah, because this is what the king of Assyria says: Make peace with me! Come out and give yourselves up to me! Everyone will eat from his own grapevine and fig tree and drink from his own cistern. ³²Then I will come and take you away to a country like your own. It's a country with grain and new wine, a country with bread and vineyards, a country with olive trees, olive oil, and honey. Live! Don't die! Don't listen to Hezekiah when he tries to mislead you by saying to you, 'The LORD will rescue us.' ³³Did any of the gods of the nations rescue their countries from the king of Assyria? ³⁴Where are the gods of Hamath and Arpad? Where are the gods of Sepharvaim, Hena, and Ivvah? Did they rescue Samaria from my control? ³⁵Did the gods of those countries rescue them from my control? Could the LORD then rescue Jerusalem from my control?"

³⁶But the people were silent and didn't say anything to him because the king commanded them not to answer him.

³⁷Then Eliakim, who was in charge of the palace and was the son of Hilkiah, Shebna the scribe, and Joah, who was the royal historian and the son of Asaph, went to Hezekiah with their clothes torn in grief. They told him the message from the field commander.

19 ¹When King Hezekiah heard the message, he tore his clothes in grief, covered himself with sackcloth, and went into the LORD's temple. ²Then he sent Eliakim, who was in charge of the palace, Shebna the scribe, and the leaders of the priests, clothed in sackcloth, to the prophet Isaiah, son of Amoz. ³They said to him, "This is what Hezekiah says: Today is a day filled with misery, punishment, and disgrace. We are like a woman who is about to give birth but doesn't have the strength to do it. ⁴The LORD your God may have heard all the words of the field commander. His master, the king of Assyria, sent him to defy the living God. The LORD your God may punish him because of the message that the LORD your God heard. Pray for the few people who are left."

⁵So King Hezekiah's men went to Isaiah. ⁶Isaiah answered them, "Say this to your master, 'This is what the LORD says: Don't be afraid of the message that you heard when the Assyrian king's assistants slandered me. ⁷I'm going to put a spirit in him so that he will hear a rumor and return to his own country. I'll have him assassinated in his own country.' "

⁸The field commander returned and found the king of Assyria fighting against Libnah. He had heard that the king left Lachish. ⁹Now, Sennacherib heard that King Tirhakah of Sudan was coming to fight him.

Sennacherib sent messengers to Hezekiah, saying, ¹⁰"Tell King Hezekiah of Judah, 'Don't let the god whom you trust deceive you by saying that Jerusalem will not be put under the control of the king of Assyria. ¹¹You heard what the kings of Assyria did to all countries, how they totally destroyed them. Will you be rescued? ¹²Did the gods of the nations which my ancestors destroyed rescue Gozan, Haran, Rezeph, and the people of Eden who were in Telassar? ¹³Where is the king of Hamath, the king of Arpad, and the king of the cities of Sepharvaim, Hena, and Ivvah?' "

¹⁴Hezekiah took the letters from the messengers, read them, and went to the LORD's temple. He spread them out in front of the LORD ¹⁵and prayed to the LORD, "LORD of Armies, God of Israel, you are enthroned over the angels.^a You alone are God of all the kingdoms of the world. You made heaven and earth. ¹⁶Turn your ear toward me, LORD, and listen. Open your

---

^a 19:15 Or "cherubim."

eyes, LORD, and see. Listen to the message that Sennacherib sent to defy the living God. [17] It is true, LORD, that the kings of Assyria have leveled nations.[b] [18] They have thrown the gods from these countries into fires because these gods aren't real gods. They're only wooden and stone statues made by human hands. So the Assyrians have destroyed them. [19] Now, LORD our God, rescue us from Assyria's control so that all the kingdoms on earth will know that you alone are the LORD God."

Isaiah's Prophecy Against King Sennacherib of Assyria—Isaiah 37:21-38

[20] Then Isaiah, son of Amoz, sent a message to Hezekiah, "This is what the LORD God of Israel says: You prayed to me about King Sennacherib of Assyria. I have heard you. [21] This is the message that the LORD speaks to him,

'My dear people in Zion despise you and laugh at you.
My people in Jerusalem shake their heads behind your back.
[22]   Whom are you defying and slandering?
          Against whom are you shouting?
              Who are you looking at so arrogantly?
              It is the Holy One of Israel!
[23]   Through your servants[c] you defy the Lord and say,
          "With my many chariots I'll ride up the high mountains,
              up the slopes of Lebanon.
                  I'll cut down its tallest cedars and its finest cypresses.
                  I'll come to its most distant borders
                      and its most fertile forests.
[24]   I'll dig wells and drink foreign water.
                  I'll dry up all the streams of Egypt
                      with the trampling of my feet."

[25]   " 'Haven't you heard? I did this long ago.
          I planned it in the distant past.
              Now I make it happen so that you will turn fortified cities
                  into piles of rubble.
[26]   Those who live in these cities are weak, discouraged, and ashamed.
          They will be like plants in the field,
              like fresh, green grass on the roofs,
                  scorched before it sprouted.
[27]   I know when you ˌget upˌ and sit down,
          when you go out and come in,
              and how you rage against me.
[28]   Since you rage against me and your boasting has reached my ears,
          I will put my hook in your nose
              and my bridle in your mouth.
          I will make you go back the way you came.

[29] " 'And this will be a sign for you, Hezekiah: You will eat what grows by itself this year and next year. But in the third year you will plant and harvest, plant vineyards, and eat what is produced. [30] Those few people from the nation of Judah who escape will again take root and produce crops. [31] Those few people will go out from Jerusalem, and those who escape will go out of Mount Zion. The LORD is determined to do this.'
[32] "This is what the LORD says about the king of Assyria:

He will never come into this city,
    shoot an arrow here,
    hold a shield in front of it,
        or put up dirt ramps to attack it.
[33]   He will go back the way he came,
          and he won't come into this city,"
              declares the LORD of Armies.
[34]   "I will shield this city to rescue it for my sake
          and for the sake of my servant David."

[35] It happened that night. The LORD's angel went out and killed 185,000 ˌsoldiersˌ in the Assyrian camp. When the Judeans got up early in the morning, they saw all the corpses.

---

[b] 19:17 Greek; Masoretic Text "nations and their country."   [c] 19:23 Isaiah 37:24; Masoretic Text "kings."

36 Then King Sennacherib of Assyria left. He went home to Nineveh and stayed there. 37 While he was worshiping in the temple of his god Nisroch, Adrammelech and Sharezer assassinated him and escaped to the land of Ararat. His son Esarhaddon succeeded him as king.

Hezekiah's Illness—*2 Chronicles 32:24; Isaiah 38:1–8, 21–22*

20 ¹ In those days Hezekiah became sick and was about to die. The prophet Isaiah, son of Amoz, came to him and said, "This is what the LORD says: Give final instructions to your household, because you're about to die. You won't get well."

² Hezekiah turned to the wall and prayed to the LORD, ³ "Please, LORD, remember how I've lived faithfully and sincerely in your presence. I've done what you consider right." And he cried bitterly.

⁴ Isaiah hadn't gone as far as the middle courtyard when the LORD spoke his word to him: ⁵ "Go back and say to Hezekiah, leader of my people, 'This is what the LORD God of your ancestor David says: I've heard your prayer. I've seen your tears. Now I'm going to heal you. The day after tomorrow you will go to the LORD's temple. ⁶ I'll give you 15 more years to live. I'll rescue you and defend this city from the control of the king of Assyria for my sake and for the sake of my servant David.' "

⁷ Then Isaiah said, "Get a fig cake, and put it on the boil so that the king will get well."

⁸ Hezekiah asked Isaiah, "What is the sign that the LORD will heal me and that I'll go to the LORD's temple the day after tomorrow?"

⁹ Isaiah said, "This is your sign from the LORD that he will do what he promises. Do you want the shadow to go forward ten steps or come back ten steps?"

¹⁰ Hezekiah replied, "It's easy for the shadow to extend ten ₍more₎ steps forward. No, let it come back ten steps."

¹¹ Then the prophet Isaiah called on the LORD, and the LORD made the shadow that had gone down on Ahaz's stairway go back up ten steps.

Hezekiah Shows the Babylonians His Treasures—*2 Chronicles 32:31–33; Isaiah 39:1–8*

¹² At that time Baladan's son, King Merodach Baladan of Babylon, sent letters and a present to Hezekiah because he heard that Hezekiah had been sick. ¹³ Hezekiah was so happy with them that he showed the messengers his warehouse: the silver, gold, balsam, fine olive oil, his entire armory, and everything in his treasury. Hezekiah showed them everything in his palace and every corner of his kingdom.

¹⁴ Then the prophet Isaiah came to King Hezekiah and asked, "What did these men say? And where did they come from?"

Hezekiah answered, "They came to me from the distant country of Babylon."

¹⁵ Isaiah asked, "What did they see in your palace?"

Hezekiah answered, "They saw everything in my palace, and I showed them everything in my treasury."

¹⁶ Isaiah said to Hezekiah, "Hear the word of the LORD! ¹⁷ The LORD says, 'The days are going to come when everything in your palace, everything your ancestors have stored up to this day, will be taken away to Babylon. Nothing will be left. ¹⁸ Some of your own descendants will be taken away. They will become officials in the palace of the king of Babylon.' "

¹⁹ Hezekiah said to Isaiah, "The LORD's word that you have spoken is good." He added, "Isn't it enough if there is peace and security as long as I live?"

²⁰ Isn't everything else about Hezekiah, all his heroic acts and how he made the pool and tunnel to bring water into the city, written in the official records of the kings of Judah? ²¹ Hezekiah lay down in death with his ancestors. His son Manasseh succeeded him as king.

King Manasseh of Judah—*2 Chronicles 33:1–20*

21 ¹ Manasseh was 12 years old when he began to rule, and he ruled for 55 years in Jerusalem. His mother's name was Hephzibah.

² He did what the LORD considered evil by copying the disgusting things done by the nations that the LORD had forced out of the Israelites' way. ³ He rebuilt the illegal places of worship that his father Hezekiah had destroyed. He set up altars dedicated to Baal and made a pole dedicated to the goddess Asherah as King Ahab of Israel had done. Manasseh, like Ahab, worshiped and served the entire army of heaven. ⁴ He built altars in the LORD's temple, where the LORD had said, "I will put my name in Jerusalem." ⁵ In the two courtyards of the LORD's temple, he built altars for the entire army of heaven. ⁶ He burned his son as a sacrifice, consulted fortunetellers, cast evil spells, and appointed ₍royal₎ mediums and psychics. He did many things that made the LORD furious. ⁷ Manasseh had an idol of Asherah made. Then he set it up in the temple, where the LORD had said to David and his son Solomon, "I have chosen this temple and Jerusalem from all the tribes of Israel. I will put my name here forever. ⁸ I will never

again make Israel's feet wander from the land that I gave to their ancestors if they will obey all the commands and all the Teachings that my servant Moses gave them." [9] (But they wouldn't obey.) Manasseh misled Israel so that they did more evil things than the nations that the LORD had destroyed when the Israelites arrived in the land.

[10] Then the LORD spoke through his servants the prophets: [11] "King Manasseh of Judah has done disgusting things, things more evil than what the Amorites who ˌwere hereˌ before him had done. Manasseh has also made Judah sin by ˌworshipingˌ his idols. [12] So this is what I, the LORD God of Israel, said: I'm going to bring such a disaster on Jerusalem and Judah that the ears of everyone who hears about it will ring. [13] I will measure Jerusalem with the measuring line used for Samaria and the plumb line used for Ahab's dynasty. I will wipe out Jerusalem in the same way that a dish is wiped out and turned upside down. [14] I will abandon the rest of my people. I will put them under the control of their enemies, and they will become property that their enemies capture. [15] I will do this because they have done what I consider evil and have been making me furious from the time their ancestors left Egypt until this day."

[16] In addition to his sin that he led Judah to commit in front of the LORD, Manasseh also killed a lot of innocent people from one end of Jerusalem to the other. [17] Isn't everything else about Manasseh—everything he did, the sins he committed—written in the official records of the kings of Judah? [18] Manasseh lay down in death with his ancestors. He was buried in the garden of his own palace, in the garden of Uzza. His son Amon succeeded him as king.

King Amon of Judah—*2 Chronicles 33:21–25*

[19] Amon was 22 years old when he began to rule, and he ruled for 2 years in Jerusalem. His mother was Meshullemeth, daughter of Haruz from Jotbah. [20] He did what the LORD considered evil, as his father Manasseh had done. [21] He lived like his father in every way and worshiped and prayed to the idols his father had worshiped. [22] He abandoned the LORD God of his ancestors and didn't live the LORD's way. [23] Amon's officials plotted against him and killed him in his palace. [24] Then the people of the land killed everyone who had plotted against King Amon. They made his son Josiah king in his place. [25] Isn't everything else about Amon—the things he did—written in the official record of the kings of Judah? [26] He was buried in his tomb in the garden of Uzza. His son Josiah succeeded him as king.

King Josiah of Judah—*2 Chronicles 34:1–2*

22 [1] Josiah was 8 years old when he began to rule, and he was king for 31 years in Jerusalem. His mother was Jedidah, daughter of Adaiah from Bozkath. [2] Josiah did what the LORD considered right. He lived in the ways of his ancestor David and never stopped.

The Book of the LORD's Teachings Found in the Temple—*2 Chronicles 34:8–28*

[3] In Josiah's eighteenth year as king of Judah, he sent the scribe Shaphan, son of Azaliah and grandson of Meshullam, to the LORD's temple with these instructions: [4] "Go to the chief priest Hilkiah. Have him count the money that has been brought into the LORD's temple, ˌthe moneyˌ that the doorkeepers have collected from the people. [5] Give ˌsome ofˌ it to the foremen who are in charge of the LORD's temple. They should give it to the workmen who are making repairs on the LORD's temple. [6] (These workers include the carpenters, builders, and masons.) Also, use ˌthe rest ofˌ the money to buy lumber and quarried stones to repair the temple. [7] Since the workmen are honest, don't require them to account for the money you give them."

[8] The chief priest Hilkiah told the scribe Shaphan, "I have found the Book of Moses' Teachings in the LORD's temple." Hilkiah gave the book to Shaphan, who then read it.

[9] The scribe Shaphan went to the king and reported, "We have taken the money donated in the temple and have given it to the workmen who are in charge of the LORD's temple." [10] Then the scribe Shaphan told the king, "The priest Hilkiah has given me a book." And Shaphan read it to the king.

[11] When the king heard what the book of the Teachings said, he tore his clothes ˌin distressˌ. [12] Then the king gave an order to the priest Hilkiah, to Ahikam (son of Shaphan), Achbor (son of Micaiah), the scribe Shaphan, and the royal official Asaiah. He said, [13] "On behalf of the people, all of Judah, and me, ask the LORD about the words in this book that has been found. The LORD's fierce anger is directed towards us because our ancestors did not obey the things in this book or do everything written ˌin itˌ."[a]

[14] So the priest Hilkiah, Ahikam, Achbor, Shaphan, and Asaiah went to talk to the prophet Huldah. She was the wife of Shallum, son of Tikvah and grandson of Harhas. Shallum was in charge of the ˌroyalˌ wardrobe. Huldah was living in the Second Part of Jerusalem. [15] She told them, "This is what the LORD God of Israel says: Tell the man who sent you to me, [16] 'This is what the LORD says: I'm going to bring disaster on this place and on the people

---

[a] 22:13 Masoretic Text adds "about us."

living here according to everything written in the book that the king of Judah has read. [17] I will do this because they have abandoned me and sacrificed to other gods in order to make me furious. Therefore, my burning anger directed at this place will never be extinguished.' "

[18] ˻Huldah added,˼ "But tell Judah's king who sent you to me to ask the LORD a question, 'This is what the LORD God of Israel says about the words you heard: [19] You had a change of heart and humbled yourself in front of the LORD when you heard my words against this place and those who live here. I had said that those who live here will be destroyed and cursed. You also tore your clothes ˻in distress˼ and cried in front of me. So I will listen ˻to you˼, declares the LORD. [20] That is why I'm going to bring you to your ancestors. I'm going to bring you to your grave in peace, and your eyes will not see any of the disaster I'm going to bring on this place.' "

So they reported this to the king.

King Josiah's Religious Reforms—2 Chronicles 34:29–33, 4–7; 35:1–27; 36:1

23 [1] Then the king sent for all the respected leaders of Judah and Jerusalem to join him. [2] The king, everyone in Judah, everyone living in Jerusalem, the priests, the prophets, and all the people (young and old) went to the LORD's temple. Josiah read everything written in the Book of the Promise[a] found in the LORD's temple so that they could hear it. [3] The king stood beside the pillar and made a promise to the LORD that he would follow the LORD and obey his commands, instructions, and laws with all his heart and soul. He confirmed the terms of the promise written in this book. And all the people joined in the promise.

[4] Then the king ordered the chief priest Hilkiah, the priests who served under Hilkiah, and the doorkeepers to take out of the LORD's temple all the utensils that had been made for Baal, Asherah, and the entire army of heaven. Josiah burned the utensils outside Jerusalem in an open field near the Kidron Brook. Then he carried their ashes to Bethel.

[5] He got rid of the pagan priests whom the kings of Judah had appointed to sacrifice at the illegal places of worship in the cities of Judah and all around Jerusalem. They had been sacrificing to Baal, the sun god, the moon god, the zodiac, and the entire army of heaven. [6] He took the pole dedicated to the goddess Asherah from the temple to the Kidron Valley outside Jerusalem. He burned it in the Kidron Valley, ground it to dust, and threw its ashes on the tombs of the common people. [7] He tore down the houses of the male temple prostitutes who were in the LORD's temple, where women did weaving for Asherah.

[8] He brought all the priests out of the cities of Judah from Geba to Beersheba and made the places where those priests sacrificed unclean.[b] He tore down the worship site at the entrance of the Gate of Joshua, the gate named after the mayor of the city. (The worship site was to the left of anyone going through the city gate.)

[9] The priests of the illegal worship sites had never gone to the LORD's altar in Jerusalem. Instead, they ate their unleavened bread among the other worshipers.

[10] Josiah also made Topheth in the valley of Ben Hinnom unclean so that people would never again sacrifice their sons or daughters by burning them to the god Molech.

[11] He removed the horses that Judah's kings had dedicated to the sun god at the entrance of the LORD's temple. They were in the temple courtyard near the room of the eunuch Nathan Melech. He also burned the chariots of the sun god, [12] the altars that Judah's kings had made and placed on the roof of Ahaz's upstairs room, and the altars Manasseh had made in the two courtyards of the LORD's temple. The king tore them down from there, crushed them, and dumped their rubble in the Kidron Valley.

[13] The king made the illegal places of worship east of Jerusalem unclean. They were on the southern part of the Hill of Destruction. King Solomon of Israel had built them for Astarte (the disgusting goddess of the Sidonians), Chemosh (the disgusting god of Moab), and Milcom (the disgusting god of the Ammonites). [14] Josiah crushed the sacred stones, cut down the poles dedicated to Asherah, and filled their places with human bones. [15] He also tore down the altar at Bethel—the place of worship made by Jeroboam (Nebat's son), who had made Israel sin. He tore down both the altar and the place of worship. They burned the worship site, crushing it to powder and burning the pole dedicated to Asherah.

[16] When Josiah turned and saw the tombs on the hill there, he sent men to take the bones out of the tombs and burn them on the altar to make it unclean. This fulfilled the word of the LORD announced by the man of God. [17] Then he asked, "What is this monument that I see?"

The people of the city answered him, "It's the tomb of the man of God who came from Judah to announce that you would do these things to the altar of Bethel."

[18] So Josiah said, "Let him rest. Don't disturb his bones." So they left his bones with the bones of the prophet who had come from Samaria.

---

[a] 23:2 Or "Covenant."　　[b] 23:8 "Unclean" refers to anything that Moses' Teachings say is not presentable to God.

[19] Josiah also got rid of all the temples at the illegal places of worship in the cities of Samaria. The kings of Israel had built these places to make the LORD furious. He did to them everything that he had done to the worship places at Bethel. [20] He slaughtered all the priests of the illegal worship sites on their altars and then burned human bones on them. He went back to Jerusalem.

[21] The king ordered all the people to celebrate the Passover for the LORD their God as it is written in this Book of the Promise. [22] The Passover had never been celebrated like this during the time of the judges who governed Israel or during the entire time of the kings of Israel and Judah. [23] But in the eighteenth year of King Josiah's reign, this Passover was celebrated in Jerusalem for the LORD.

[24] Josiah also got rid of the mediums, psychics, family idols, other idols, and disgusting gods that could be seen in the land of Judah and in Jerusalem. He did this to confirm the words of the Teachings written in the book that the priest Hilkiah found in the LORD's temple.

[25] No king before Josiah had turned to the LORD with all his heart, soul, and strength, as directed in Moses' Teachings. No other ˌkingˌ was like Josiah.

[26] But the LORD still didn't turn his hot, burning anger from Judah. After all, Manasseh had done all these things to make him furious. [27] The LORD had said, "I will put Judah out of my sight as I put Israel out of my sight. I will reject Jerusalem, the city that I chose, and I will reject the temple where I said my name would be."

[28] Isn't everything else about Josiah—everything he did—written in the official records of the kings of Judah?

[29] In Josiah's days Pharaoh Necoh (the king of Egypt) came to help the king of Assyria at the Euphrates River. King Josiah went to attack Necoh. When Pharaoh saw him at Megiddo, Pharaoh killed him. [30] His officers put his dead body in a chariot and brought it from Megiddo to Jerusalem. They buried Josiah in his tomb.

King Jehoahaz of Judah—2 Chronicles 36:1–4

Then the people of the land took Josiah's son Jehoahaz, anointed him, and made him king in place of his father. [31] Jehoahaz was 23 years old when he became king, and he was king for 3 months in Jerusalem. His mother was Hamutal, daughter of Jeremiah from Libnah. [32] He did what the LORD considered evil, as his ancestors had done. [33] Pharaoh Necoh made him a prisoner at Riblah in the territory of Hamath during his reign[c] in Jerusalem and fined the country 7,500 pounds of silver and 75 pounds of gold.

[34] Then Pharaoh Necoh made Josiah's son Eliakim king in place of his father Josiah and changed Eliakim's name to Jehoiakim. He took Jehoahaz away to Egypt, where he died. [35] Jehoiakim gave Pharaoh the silver and the gold. But he had to tax the country to pay the silver Pharaoh had demanded. He taxed each person according to his wealth so that he could get the silver and gold from the people of the land and give it to Pharaoh Necoh.

King Jehoiakim of Judah—2 Chronicles 36:5–8

[36] Jehoiakim was 25 years old when he began to rule, and he was king for 11 years in Jerusalem. His mother was Zebidah, daughter of Pedaiah from Rumah. [37] Jehoiakim did what the LORD considered evil, as his ancestors had done.

24 [1] During Jehoiakim's reign King Nebuchadnezzar of Babylon attacked ˌJudahˌ, and Jehoiakim became subject to him for three years. Then Jehoiakim turned against him and rebelled.

[2] The LORD sent raiding parties of Babylonians, Arameans, Moabites, and Ammonites against Jehoiakim to destroy Judah as the LORD had predicted through his servants the prophets. [3] Without a doubt, this happened to Judah because the LORD had commanded it to happen. He wanted to remove the people of Judah from his sight because of Manasseh's sins—everything he had done, [4] including the innocent blood he had shed. He had a lot of innocent people in Jerusalem killed, and the LORD refused to forgive him.

[5] Isn't everything else about Jehoiakim—everything he did—written in the official records of the kings of Judah? [6] Jehoiakim lay down in death with his ancestors, and his son Jehoiakin succeeded him as king.

[7] The king of Egypt didn't leave his own country again because the king of Babylon had taken all the territory from the River of Egypt to the Euphrates River. This territory had belonged to the king of Egypt.

---

[c] 23:33 Or "to keep him from ruling."

King Jehoiakin of Judah—*2 Chronicles 36:9–10*

[8] Jehoiakin was 18 years old when he began to rule as king. He was king for three months in Jerusalem. His mother was Nehushta, daughter of Elnathan from Jerusalem. [9] Jehoiakin did what the LORD considered evil, as his father had done.

[10] At that time the officers of King Nebuchadnezzar of Babylon attacked Jerusalem. (The city was blockaded.) [11] King Nebuchadnezzar of Babylon arrived while his officers were blockading the city. [12] King Jehoiakin of Judah, his mother, officials, generals, and eunuchs surrendered to the king of Babylon. In the eighth year of his reign, the king of Babylon captured Jehoiakin. [13] He also took away all the treasures in the LORD's temple and the royal palace. As the LORD had predicted, Nebuchadnezzar stripped the gold off all the furnishings that King Solomon of Israel had made for the LORD's temple. [14] He captured all Jerusalem, all the generals, all the soldiers (10,000 prisoners), and all the craftsmen and smiths. Only the poorest people of the land were left. [15] He took Jehoiakin to Babylon as a captive. He also took the king's mother, wives, eunuchs, and the leading citizens of the land from Jerusalem as captives to Babylon. [16] The king of Babylon brought all 7,000 of the prominent landowners, 1,000 craftsmen and smiths, and all the men who could fight in war as captives to Babylon.

King Zedekiah of Judah—*2 Chronicles 36:11–13; Jeremiah 52:1–3*

[17] The king of Babylon made King Jehoiakin's Uncle Mattaniah king in his place and changed Mattaniah's name to Zedekiah. [18] Zedekiah was 21 years old when he began to rule, and he ruled for 11 years in Jerusalem. His mother was Hamutal, daughter of Jeremiah from Libnah. [19] Zedekiah did what the LORD considered evil, as Jehoiakim had done.

[20] The LORD became angry with Jerusalem and Judah and threw the people out of his sight. Zedekiah rebelled against the king of Babylon.

The Fall of Jerusalem—*2 Chronicles 36:19–21; Jeremiah 39:1–10; 40:5–9; 41:1–3, 16–18; 52:4–30*

25 [1] On the tenth day of the tenth month of the ninth year of Zedekiah's reign, King Nebuchadnezzar of Babylon attacked Jerusalem with his entire army. They set up camp and built dirt ramps around the city walls. [2] The blockade of the city lasted until Zedekiah's eleventh year as king. [3] On the ninth day of the fourth[a] month, the famine in the city became so severe that the common people had no food.

[4] The enemy broke through the city walls that night. All Judah's soldiers left on the road of the gate between the two walls beside the king's garden. While the Babylonians were attacking the city from all sides, the king took the road to the plain ˏof Jerichoˏ. [5] The Babylonian army pursued King Zedekiah and caught up with him in the plain of Jericho. His entire army had deserted him. [6] The Babylonians captured the king, brought him to the king of Babylon at Riblah, and passed sentence on him. [7] They slaughtered Zedekiah's sons as he watched, and then they blinded Zedekiah. They put him in bronze shackles and took him to Babylon.

[8] On the seventh day of the fifth month of Nebuchadnezzar's nineteenth year as king of Babylon, Nebuzaradan, who was the captain of the guard and an officer of the king of Babylon, came to Jerusalem. [9] He burned down the LORD's temple, the royal palace, and all the houses in Jerusalem. Every important building was burned down. [10] The entire Babylonian army that was with the captain of the guard tore down the walls around Jerusalem.

[11] Nebuzaradan, the captain of the guard, captured the few people left in the city, those who surrendered to the king of Babylon, and the rest of the population. [12] The captain of the guard left some of the poorest people in the land to work in the vineyards and on the farms.

[13] The Babylonians broke apart the bronze pillars of the LORD's temple, the stands, and the bronze pool in the LORD's temple. They shipped the bronze to Babylon. [14] They took the pots, shovels, snuffers, dishes, and all the bronze utensils used in the temple service. [15] The captain of the guard took all of the incense burners and bowls that were made of gold or silver. [16] The bronze from the two pillars, the pool, and the stands that Solomon had made for the LORD's temple couldn't be weighed. [17] One pillar was 27 feet high and had a bronze capital on it that was 4½ feet high. The filigree and the pomegranates around the capital were all made of bronze. The second pillar and its filigree were the same.

[18] The captain of the guard took the chief priest Seraiah, the second priest Zephaniah, and the 3 doorkeepers. [19] From the city he also took an army commander, 5 men who had access to the king whom he found in the city, the scribe who was in charge of the militia, and 60 of the common people whom he found in the city. [20] Nebuzaradan, the captain of the guard, took them and brought them to the king of Babylon at Riblah. [21] The king of Babylon executed them at Riblah in the territory of Hamath. So the people of Judah were captives when they left their land.

---

[a] 25:3 Jeremiah 39:2; 52:6; Masoretic Text omits "fourth."

²² King Nebuchadnezzar of Babylon appointed Gedaliah, son of Ahikam and grandson of Shaphan, to govern the remaining people in the land of Judah. ²³ When all the army commanders and their men heard that the king of Babylon had appointed Gedaliah, they went to Gedaliah at Mizpah. They were Ishmael (son of Nethaniah), Johanan (son of Kareah), Seraiah (son of Tanhumeth from Netophah), and Jaazaniah from Beth Maacah and their men. ²⁴ Gedaliah swore an oath to them and their men. He said, "Don't be afraid of the Babylonian officers. Live in this country, serve the king of Babylon, and you will prosper."

²⁵ In the seventh month Ishmael (son of Nethaniah and grandson of Elishama, a descendant of the kings) went with ten men to kill Gedaliah and the Judeans and Babylonians who were with him at Mizpah. ²⁶ Then people of all classes and the army commanders left for Egypt because they were afraid of the Babylonians.

King Jehoiakin Released From Prison—*Jeremiah 52:31–34*

²⁷ On the twenty-seventh day of the twelfth month of the thirty-seventh year of the imprisonment of King Jehoiakin of Judah, King Evil Merodach of Babylon, in the first year of his reign, freed King Jehoiakin of Judah from prison. ²⁸ He treated him well and gave him a special position higher than the other kings who were with him in Babylon. ²⁹ Jehoiakin no longer wore prison clothes, and he ate his meals in the king's presence as long as he lived. ³⁰ The king of Babylon gave him a daily food allowance as long as he lived.

1 CHRONICLES

The Genealogy of Isaac's Descendants—*Genesis 5:1–32; 10:1–32; 11:10–26; 25:1–4, 12–16; 36:1–43*

1 ¹ Adam, Seth, Enosh, ² Kenan, Mahalalel, Jared, ³ Enoch, Methuselah, Lamech, ⁴ Noah: Shem, Ham, and Japheth.

⁵ Japheth's descendants were Gomer, Magog, Madai, Javan, Tubal, Meshech, and Tiras. ⁶ Gomer's descendants were Ashkenaz, Riphath, and Togarmah. ⁷ Javan's descendants were the people from Elishah, Tarshish, Cyprus, and Rhodes.

⁸ Ham's descendants were Cush, Egypt, Put, and Canaan. ⁹ Cush's descendants were Seba, Havilah, Sabta, Raama, and Sabteca. Raama's descendants were Sheba and Dedan. ¹⁰ Cush was the father of Nimrod, the first mighty warrior on the earth. ¹¹ Egypt was the ancestor of the Ludites, Anamites, Lehabites, Naphtuhites, ¹² Pathrusites, Casluhites (from whom the Philistines came), and the Caphtorites. ¹³ Canaan was the father of Sidon his firstborn, then Heth, ¹⁴ also the Jebusites, the Amorites, the Girgashites, ¹⁵ the Hivites, the Arkites, the Sinites, ¹⁶ the Arvadites, the Zemarites, and the Hamathites.

¹⁷ The descendants of Shem were Elam, Asshur, Arpachshad, Lud, Aram, Uz, Hul, Gether, and Meshech. ¹⁸ Arpachshad was the father of Shelah, and Shelah was the father of Eber. ¹⁹ Two sons were born to Eber. The name of the one was Peleg [Division], because in his day the earth was divided. His brother's name was Joktan. ²⁰ Joktan was the father of Almodad, Sheleph, Hazarmaveth, Jerah, ²¹ Hadoram, Uzal, Diklah, ²² Ebal, Abimael, Sheba, ²³ Ophir, Havilah, and Jobab. All these were sons of Joktan.

²⁴ Shem, Arpachshad, Shelah, ²⁵ Eber, Peleg, Reu, ²⁶ Serug, Nahor, Terah, ²⁷ Abram (that is, Abraham). ²⁸ Abraham's sons were Isaac and Ishmael.

²⁹ This is their list of descendants: Ishmael's firstborn was Nebaioth, then Kedar, Adbeel, Mibsam, ³⁰ Mishma, Dumah, Massa, Hadad, Tema, ³¹ Jetur, Naphish, and Kedemah. These were the sons of Ishmael.

³² Keturah, Abraham's concubine,ᵃ gave birth to the following sons: Zimran, Jokshan, Medan, Midian, Ishbak, and Shuah. Jokshan's sons were Sheba and Dedan. ³³ The sons of Midian were Ephah, Epher, Hanoch, Abida, and Eldaah. All these were descendants of Keturah.

³⁴ Abraham was the father of Isaac. Isaac's sons were Esau and Israel. ³⁵ Esau's sons were Eliphaz, Reuel, Jeush, Jalam, and Korah. ³⁶ Eliphaz's sons were Teman and Omar, Zephi and Gatam, Kenaz and Amalek, son of Timna.ᵇ ³⁷ Reuel's sons were Nahath, Zerah, Shammah, and Mizzah. ³⁸ Seir's sons were Lotan, Shobal, Zibeon, Anah, Dishon, Ezer, and Dishan. ³⁹ Lotan's sons were Hori and Homam. Timna was Lotan's sister. ⁴⁰ Shobal's sons were Alian, Manahath, Ebal, Shephi, and Onam. Zibeon's sons were Aiah and Anah. ⁴¹ Anah's son was Dishon. Dishon's sons were Hamran, Eshban, Ithran, and Cheran. ⁴² Ezer's sons were Bilhan, Zaavan, and Jaakan. Dishan's sons were Uz and Aran.

⁴³ These were the kings who ruled Edom before any king ruled the people of Israel: Bela, son of Beor, and the name of his ˌcapitalˌ city was Dinhabah. ⁴⁴ After Bela died, Jobab, son of Zerah from Bozrah, succeeded him as king. ⁴⁵ After Jobab died, Husham from the land of the Temanites succeeded him as king. ⁴⁶ After Husham died, Hadad, son of Bedad, who defeated the Midianites in the country of Moab, succeeded him as king, and the name of his ˌcapitalˌ city was Avith. ⁴⁷ After Hadad died, Samlah from Masrekah succeeded him as king. ⁴⁸ After Samlah died, Shaul from Rehoboth on the river succeeded him as king. ⁴⁹ After Shaul died, Baal Hanan, son of Achbor, succeeded him as king. ⁵⁰ After Baal Hanan died, Hadad succeeded him as king, and the name of his ˌcapitalˌ city was Pai. His wife's name was Mehetabel, daughter of Matred and granddaughter of Mezahab. ⁵¹ Then Hadad died.

The tribal leaders of Edom were Timna, Aliah, Jetheth, ⁵² Oholibamah, Elah, Pinon, ⁵³ Kenaz, Teman, Mibzar, ⁵⁴ Magdiel, and Iram. These were the tribal leaders of Edom.

Israel's Twelve Sons—*Genesis 35:16–26*

2 ¹ These were Israel's sons: Reuben, Simeon, Levi, Judah, Issachar, Zebulun, ² Dan, Joseph, Benjamin, Naphtali, Gad, and Asher.

ᵃ 1:32 A concubine is considered a wife except she has fewer rights under the law.   ᵇ 1:36 Genesis 36:12, Greek; Masoretic Text "Kenaz, and Timnath, and Amalek."

Judah's Descendants—*Genesis 46:12*

3 Judah's sons were Er, Onan, and Shelah. These three were born to him by Bathshua, a Canaanite woman. The LORD considered Er, Judah's firstborn, evil, so the LORD killed Er. **4** Tamar, Judah's daughter-in-law, gave birth to Judah's sons Perez and Zerah. Judah had five sons in all.

5 Perez's sons were Hezron and Hamul. **6** Zerah's sons were Zimri, Ethan, Heman, Calcol, and Dara[a]—five in all. **7** Carmi's son was Achar, who caused trouble for Israel by taking goods that were claimed by God. **8** Ethan's son was Azariah.

9 The sons born to Hezron were Jerahmeel, Ram, and Chelubai. **10** Ram was the father of Amminadab. Amminadab was the father of Nahshon, leader of Judah's people. **11** Nahshon was the father of Salma, and Salma was the father of Boaz. **12** Boaz was the father of Obed, and Obed was the father of Jesse. **13** Jesse was the father of Eliab (his firstborn), Abinadab (his second son), Shimea (his third son), **14** Nethanel (his fourth son), Raddai (his fifth son), **15** Ozem (his sixth son), and David (his seventh son). **16** Their sisters were Zeruiah and Abigail. Zeruiah's three sons were Abishai, Joab, and Asahel. **17** Abigail was the mother of Amasa, whose father was Jether, a descendant of Ishmael.

18 Hezron's son was Caleb. Caleb and his wife Azubah had a son named Jerioth. Her other sons were Jesher, Shobab, and Ardon. **19** After Azubah died, Caleb married Ephrath. She gave birth to Hur. **20** Hur was the father of Uri, and Uri was the father of Bezalel.

21 Afterwards, Hezron slept with the daughter of Machir, the man who first settled Gilead. Hezron had married her when he was 60 years old. She gave birth to Segub. **22** Segub was the father of Jair, who had 23 towns in Gilead. **23** Geshur and Aram captured Havvoth Jair with Kenath and its villages (60 cities in all). All of these people were descendants of Machir, the man who first settled Gilead. **24** After Hezron died in Caleb Ephrathah, Hezron's wife Abijah gave birth to Ashhur, who first settled Tekoa.

25 Jerahmeel (the firstborn son of Hezron) fathered Ram (his firstborn), then Bunah, Oren, Ozem, and Ahijah. **26** Jerahmeel had another wife. Her name was Atarah, and she was the mother of Onam.

27 The sons of Ram (the firstborn son of Jerahmeel) were Maaz, Jamin, and Eker. **28** Onam's sons were Shammai and Jada. Shammai's sons were Nadab and Abishur. **29** The name of Abishur's wife was Abihail. She gave birth to Ahban and Molid. **30** Nadab's sons were Seled and Appaim, but Seled died without children. **31** Appaim's son was Ishi, and Ishi's son was Sheshan, and Sheshan's son was Ahlai. **32** The sons of Jada (Shammai's brother) were Jether and Jonathan. Jether died without children. **33** Jonathan's sons were Peleth and Zaza. These were the descendants of Jerahmeel.

34 Sheshan had no sons, but he had daughters. He had an Egyptian slave named Jarha. **35** Sheshan let Jarha marry one of his daughters. She gave birth to Attai. **36** Attai was the father of Nathan. Nathan was the father of Zabad. **37** Zabad was the father of Ephlal. Ephlal was the father of Obed. **38** Obed was the father of Jehu. Jehu was the father of Azariah. **39** Azariah was the father of Helez. Helez was the father of Eleasah. **40** Eleasah was the father of Sismai. Sismai was the father of Shallum. **41** Shallum was the father of Jekamiah. Jekamiah was the father of Elishama.

42 The descendants of Caleb (Jerahmeel's brother) were his firstborn son Mesha, who first settled Ziph, and the sons of Mareshah, who first settled Hebron. **43** Hebron's sons were Korah, Tappuah, Rekem, and Shema. **44** Shema was the father of Raham, who first settled Jorkeam. Rekem was the father of Shammai. **45** Shammai's son was Maon, who first settled Beth Zur. **46** Ephah, Caleb's concubine,[b] was the mother of Haran, Moza, and Gazez. Haran was the father of Gazez. **47** Jahdai's sons were Regem, Jotham, Geshan, Pelet, Ephah, and Shaaph. **48** Maacah, Caleb's concubine, was the mother of Sheber and Tirhanah. **49** Also, she was the mother of Shaaph, who first settled Madmannah, and of Sheva, who first settled Machbenah and Gibea. Caleb's daughter was Achsah. **50** These people were the descendants of Caleb.

The sons of Hur, the firstborn son of Ephrath, were Shobal, who first settled Kiriath Jearim, **51** Salma, who first settled Bethlehem, and Hareph, who first settled Beth Gadar. **52** Shobal, who first settled Kiriath Jearim, had these descendants: Haroeh, half of the Manahathites, **53** the families of Kiriath Jearim, the Ithrites, the Puthites, the Shumathites, and the Mishraites. From these people came the Zorahites and Eshtaolites.

54 The descendants of Salma, who first settled Bethlehem, were the Netophathites, Atroth, who first settled Beth Joab, half of the Manahathites, the Zorites, **55** and the families of scribes who lived at Jabez. These families were the people of Tira, Shimea, and Sucah. These people are the Kenites who came from Hammath. They first settled Beth Rechab.

---

[a] 2:6 Some Hebrew manuscripts; other Hebrew manuscripts, 1 Kings 5:11, Greek, Syriac, Targum, Egyptian "Darda."
[b] 2:46 A concubine is considered a wife except she has fewer rights under the law.

Judah's Descendants: The Royal Family—2 Samuel 3:2–5; 5:5, 13–16

3 [1] These were David's sons who were born to him while he was in Hebron: His first son was Amnon, ⌐born⌐ to Ahinoam from Jezreel. The second was Daniel, ⌐born⌐ to Abigail from Carmel. [2] The third was Absalom, ⌐born⌐ to Maacah (the daughter of King Talmai) from Geshur. The fourth was Adonijah, whose mother was Haggith. [3] The fifth was Shephatiah, ⌐born⌐ to Abital. The sixth was Ithream, ⌐born⌐ to David's wife Eglah. [4] Six sons were born to him in Hebron, where he ruled for seven years and six months. He ruled for 33 years in Jerusalem. [5] These ⌐children⌐ were born to David in Jerusalem: Shimea, Shobab, Nathan, and Solomon (the mother of these four was Ammiel's daughter Bathshua) and [6] Ibhar, Elishama, Eliphelet, [7] Nogah, Nepheg, Japhia, [8] Elishama, Eliada, and Eliphelet (nine ⌐by other wives⌐). [9] All of these were David's sons. Besides these, there were the sons of the concubines.[a] Tamar was their sister.

[10] Solomon's son was Rehoboam. Rehoboam's son was Abijah. Abijah's son was Asa. Asa's son was Jehoshaphat. [11] Jehoshaphat's son was Joram. Joram's son was Ahaziah. Ahaziah's son was Joash. [12] Joash's son was Amaziah. Amaziah's son was Azariah. Azariah's son was Jotham. [13] Jotham's son was Ahaz. Ahaz's son was Hezekiah. Hezekiah's son was Manasseh. [14] Manasseh's son was Amon. Amon's son was Josiah. [15] Josiah's firstborn son was Johanan, the second was Jehoiakim, the third was Zedekiah, and the fourth was Shallum. [16] Jehoiakim's son was Jeconiah, whose son was Zedekiah.

[17] The descendants of the prisoner Jeconiah were his son Shealtiel, [18] then Malchiram, Pedaiah, Shenazzar, Jekamiah, Hoshama, and Nedabiah. [19] Pedaiah's sons were Zerubbabel and Shimei. Zerubbabel's sons were Meshullam and Hananiah, and Shelomith was their sister. [20] There were also five other sons: Hashubah, Ohel, Berechiah, Hasadiah, and Jushab Hesed. [21] Hananiah's sons were Pelatiah and Jeshaiah. Jeshaiah's son was Rephaiah.[b] Rephaiah's son was Arnan. Arnan's son was Obadiah. Obadiah's son was Shecaniah.[c] [22] Shecaniah's son was Shemaiah. Shemaiah's six sons were Hattush, Igal, Bariah, Neariah, and Shaphat. [23] Neariah's three sons were Elioenai, Hizkiah, and Azrikam. [24] Elioenai's seven sons were Hodaviah, Eliashib, Pelaiah, Akkub, Johanan, Delaiah, and Anani.

More of Judah's Descendants

4 [1] Judah's descendants were Perez, Hezron, Carmi, Hur, and Shobal. [2] Reaiah, son of Shobal, was the father of Jahath. Jahath was the father of Ahumai and Lahad. These were the families of the Zorathites.

[3] These were the first settlers in Etam: Jezreel, Ishma, and Idbash. Their sister's name was Hazelelponi. [4] Penuel was the father of Gedor, and Ezer was the father of Hushah. These were the sons of Hur, the firstborn of Ephrathah, who first settled Bethlehem.

[5] Ashhur, who first settled Tekoa, had two wives, Helah and Naarah. [6] Naarah gave birth to Ahuzzam, Hepher, Temeni, and Haahashtari. These were Naarah's sons. [7] Helah's sons were Zereth, Izohar, and Ethnan. [8] Koz was the father of Anub and Zobebah, and he was the ancestor of the families of Aharhel, son of Harum.

[9] Jabez was more honorable than his brothers. His mother had named him Jabez [Painful], because she said that his birth was painful. [10] Jabez prayed to the God of Israel, "Please bless me and give me more territory. May your power be with me and free me from evil so that I will not be in pain." God gave him what he prayed for.

[11] Chelub, Shuhah's brother, was the father of Mehir, who was the father of Eshton. [12] Eshton was the first to settle Beth Rapha. He was the father of Paseah and Tehinnah, who first settled the city of Nahash. These were the men from Recah.

[13] Kenaz's sons were Othniel and Seraiah. The sons of Othniel were Hathath and Meonothai.[a] [14] Meonothai was the father of Ophrah. Seraiah was the father of Joab, who first settled the valley of Craftsmen. (It was named this because they were craftsmen.) [15] The sons of Caleb, son of Jephunneh, were Iru, Elah, and Naam. Elah's son was Kenaz.

[16] Jehallelel's sons were Ziph, Ziphah, Tiria, and Asarel. [17] Ezrah's sons were Jether, Mered, Epher, and Jalon. His wife gave birth to Miriam, Shammai, and Ishbah, who first settled Eshtemoa. [18] His Judean wife was the mother of Jered, who first settled Gedor, Heber, who first settled Soco, and Jekuthiel, who first settled Zanoah.

[19] The sons of Hodiah's wife, the sister of Naham, first settled Keilah of the Garmites and Eshtemoa of the Maacathites. [20] Shimon's sons were Amnon, Rinnah, Ben Hanan, and Tilon. Ishi's sons were Zoheth and Ben Zoheth.

[21] The descendants of Shelah, son of Judah, were Er, who first settled Lecah, Laadah, who first settled Mareshah, families of the guild of linen workers at Beth Ashbea, [22] Jokim, Joash,

---

[a] 3:9 A concubine is considered a wife except she has fewer rights under the law.   [b] 3:21 Some Hebrew manuscripts, Greek, Latin; other Hebrew manuscripts "and Jeshiah, the sons of Rephaiah."   [c] 3:21 Greek, Latin; Masoretic Text "the sons of Arnan, the sons of Obadiah, the sons of Shecaniah."   [a] 4:13 Greek; Masoretic Text omits "and Meonothai."

Saraph, and the men of Cozeba. Saraph ruled Moab and Jashubi Lehem (according to ancient records). ²³ They were the potters who lived at Netaim and Gederah. They lived there with the king and did his work.

Simeon's Descendants

²⁴ Simeon's sons were Nemuel, Jamin, Jarib, Zerah, and Shaul. ²⁵ Shaul's son was Shallum. Shallum's son was Mibsam. Mibsam's son was Mishma. ²⁶ Mishma's son was Hammuel. Hammuel's son was Zaccur. Zaccur's son was Shimei. ²⁷ Shimei had 16 sons and 6 daughters. But his brothers didn't have many children, so their entire family didn't become as large as the people of Judah.

²⁸ Simeon's descendants lived in Beersheba, Moladah, Hazar Shual, ²⁹ Bilhah, Ezem, Tolad, ³⁰ Bethuel, Hormah, Ziklag, ³¹ Beth Marcaboth, Hazar Susim, Beth Biri, and Shaaraim. These were their cities until David became king. ³² Their five cities were Etam, Ain, Rimmon, Tochen, and Ashan. ³³ They also had all the villages around these cities as far as the city of Baal. These places were where they lived, and they had their own genealogical records:

³⁴ Meshobab, Jamlech, Joshah (son of Amaziah), ³⁵ Joel, Jehu (son of Joshibiah, grandson of Seraiah, and great-grandson of Asiel), ³⁶ Elioenai, Jaakobah, Jeshohaiah, Asaiah, Adiel, Jesimiel, Benaiah, and ³⁷ Ziza (son of Shiphi, grandson of Allon, great-grandson of Jedaiah, a descendant of Shimri and Shemaiah). ³⁸ These who are mentioned by name were leaders in their families, and the number of people in their households increased.

³⁹ They moved to the outskirts of Gedor, on the east side of the valley, to find pasture for their flocks. ⁴⁰ They found pasture that was rich and good. The land was vast, peaceful, and quiet because the Hamites used to live there. ⁴¹ In the days of King Hezekiah of Judah, the men listed here knocked down tents and killed the Meunites. They claimed the Meunites for God and destroyed them. (Even today no Meunites live there.) They lived in that land in place of the Meunites in order to have pasture for their flocks. ⁴² Ishi's sons Pelatiah, Neariah, Rephaiah, and Uzziel led 500 of Simeon's male descendants to Mount Seir. ⁴³ They killed the Amalekites who were left. Simeon's descendants still live there today.

Reuben's Descendants

5 ¹ These are the sons of Reuben, Israel's firstborn. (Although he was the firstborn, his rights as firstborn were given to his nephews, Joseph's sons, because he dishonored his father's bed. However, Joseph couldn't be listed in the genealogy as the firstborn son. ² Even though Judah was more prominent than his brothers and the prince was to come from him, Joseph received the rights as firstborn.)

³ The sons of Reuben, Israel's firstborn, were Hanoch, Pallu, Hezron, and Carmi. ⁴ Joel's son was Shemaiah. Shemaiah's son was Gog. Gog's son was Shimei. ⁵ Shimei's son was Micah. Micah's son was Reaiah. Reaiah's son was Baal. ⁶ Baal's son was Beerah. King Tiglath Pilneser of Assyria took him away as a captive. He was leader of the tribe of Reuben. ⁷ Beerah's brothers according to their families, when they were enrolled in the genealogical records according to their ancestry, were as follows: The first was Jeiel, then Zechariah ⁸ and Bela (son of Azaz, grandson of Shema, and great-grandson of Joel).

Reuben's descendants lived in Aroer as far as Nebo and Baal Meon. ⁹ Some of them lived eastward as far as the edge of the desert that extends to the Euphrates River, because they had so much livestock in Gilead. ¹⁰ In Saul's day they fought a war against the Hagrites, defeated them, and lived in their tents throughout the entire region east of Gilead.

Gad's Descendants

¹¹ Gad's descendants lived next to Reuben's descendants in Bashan as far ₍east₎ as Salcah. ¹² One family descended from Gad's first son Joel. Another family descended from Gad's second son Shapham. Other families descended from Gad's sons Janai and Shaphat in Bashan. ¹³ Their seven relatives by families were Michael, Meshullam, Sheba, Jorai, Jacan, Zia, and Eber. ¹⁴ These were the sons of Abihail, who was the son of Huri, grandson of Jaroah, and great-grandson of Gilead. Gilead was the son of Michael, grandson of Jeshishai, great-grandson of Jahdo, and great-great-grandson of Buz. ¹⁵ Ahi, son of Abdiel and grandson of Guni, was the head of their families. ¹⁶ They lived in Gilead, in Bashan and its villages, and in the entire pastureland of Sharon to its extreme edges. ¹⁷ All these people were recorded in genealogical records in the days of King Jotham of Judah and King Jeroboam of Israel.

Reuben, Gad, and Manasseh Fight Hagar's Descendants

¹⁸ The descendants of Reuben, Gad, and half of the tribe of Manasseh had 44,760 soldiers ready to go to war. They were skilled fighters who could carry shields and swords and shoot arrows. ¹⁹ They went to war against Hagar's descendants (including Jetur, Naphish, and Nodab) ²⁰ and received help while fighting them. Hagar's descendants and the nations with

them were handed over to Reuben's descendants. They had called out to God during the battle, and he answered their prayers because they trusted him. ²¹ They confiscated the Hagrites' livestock: 50,000 of their camels, 250,000 sheep and goats, and 2,000 donkeys. They captured 100,000 people. ²² Many were killed in battle because this was God's war. Reuben, Gad, and half of the tribe of Manasseh lived in the Hagrites' land until the Assyrians captured them.

The Leaders of the Tribe of Manasseh East of the Jordan River

²³ Half of the tribe of Manasseh lived in the land from Bashan to Baal Hermon, Senir, and Mount Hermon. The tribe members were numerous. ²⁴ These were the heads of Manasseh's families: Epher, Ishi, Eliel, Azriel, Jeremiah, Hodaviah, and Jahdiel. They were soldiers who were famous heads of their families.

The Assyrians Capture Gad, Reuben, and Half of the Tribe of Manasseh

²⁵ But Gad, Reuben, and half of the tribe of Manasseh were unfaithful to the God of their ancestors. They chased after the gods of the people of the land as if they were prostitutes. God had destroyed these people as the Israelites arrived. ²⁶ Then the God of Israel led King Pul of Assyria (King Tiglath Pilneser of Assyria) to take Reuben, Gad, and half of the tribe of Manasseh into captivity. He brought them to Halah, Habor, Hara, and the Gozan River. They are still there today.

Levi's Descendants

6ᵃ ¹ Levi's sons were Gershon, Kohath, and Merari. ² Kohath's sons were Amram, Izhar, Hebron, and Uzziel. ³ Amram's children were Aaron, Moses, and Miriam. Aaron's sons were Nadab, Abihu, Eleazar, and Ithamar.

⁴ Eleazar was the father of Phinehas. Phinehas was the father of Abishua. ⁵ Abishua was the father of Bukki. Bukki was the father of Uzzi. ⁶ Uzzi was the father of Zerahiah. Zerahiah was the father of Meraioth. ⁷ Meraioth was the father of Amariah. Amariah was the father of Ahitub. ⁸ Ahitub was the father of Zadok. Zadok was the father of Ahimaaz. ⁹ Ahimaaz was the father of Azariah. Azariah was the father of Johanan. ¹⁰ Johanan was the father of Azariah. (He was the one who served as priest in the temple Solomon built in Jerusalem.) ¹¹ Azariah was the father of Amariah. Amariah was the father of Ahitub. ¹² Ahitub was the father of Zadok. Zadok was the father of Shallum. ¹³ Shallum was the father of Hilkiah. Hilkiah was the father of Azariah. ¹⁴ Azariah was the father of Seraiah. Seraiah was the father of Jehozadak. ¹⁵ Jehozadak was taken captive when the LORD used Nebuchadnezzar to take Judah and Jerusalem away into captivity.

¹⁶ Levi's sons were Gershom, Kohath, and Merari. ¹⁷ These are the names of Gershom's sons: Libni and Shimei. ¹⁸ Kohath's sons were Amram, Izhar, Hebron, and Uzziel. ¹⁹ Merari's sons were Mahli and Mushi.

These are the descendants of Levi's sons. They are grouped by families:

²⁰ Gershom's son was Libni. Libni's son was Jahath. Jahath's son was Zimmah. ²¹ Zimmah's son was Joah. Joah's son was Iddo. Iddo's son was Zerah. Zerah's son was Jeatherai.

²² These were Kohath's descendants: Kohath's son was Amminadab. Amminadab's son was Korah. Korah's son was Assir. ²³ Assir's son was Elkanah. Elkanah's son was Ebiasaph. Ebiasaph's son was Assir. ²⁴ Assir's son was Tahath. Tahath's son was Uriel. Uriel's son was Uzziah. Uzziah's son was Shaul. ²⁵ Elkanah's sons were Amasai and Ahimoth. ²⁶ Ahimoth's son was Elkanah. Elkanah's son was Zophai. Zophai's son was Nahath. ²⁷ Nahath's son was Eliab. Eliab's son was Jeroham. Jeroham's son was Elkanah. ²⁸ Samuel's sons were Joel, who was his firstborn, and Abijah, who was his second son.

²⁹ These were Merari's descendants: Merari's son was Mahli. Mahli's son was Libni. Libni's son was Shimei. Shimei's son was Uzzah. ³⁰ Uzzah's son was Shimea. Shimea's son was Haggiah. Haggiah's son was Asaiah.

³¹ David put men in charge of the music in the LORD's temple after the ark was placed there permanently. ³² They served as musicians in the courtyard in front of the tent of meeting until Solomon built the LORD's temple in Jerusalem. They performed their duties according to the regulations set down for them.

³³ These are the men who served (their descendants also served):

The musician Heman was from Kohath's family line. Heman was the son of Joel, who was the son of Samuel, ³⁴ who was the son of Elkanah, who was the son of Jeroham, who was the son of Eliel, who was the son of Toah, ³⁵ who was the son of Zuph, who was the son of Elkanah, who was the son of Mahath, who was the son of Amasai, ³⁶ who was the son of Elkanah, who was the son of Joel, who was the son of Azariah, who was the son of Zephaniah, ³⁷ who was the son of Tahath, who was the son of Assir, who was the

ᵃ 6:1 1 Chronicles 6:1–81 in English Bibles is 1 Chronicles 5:27–6:66 in the Hebrew Bible.

son of Ebiasaph, who was the son of Korah, [38] who was the son of Izhar, who was the son of Kohath, who was the son of Levi, who was the son of Israel.

[39] Heman's relative Asaph stood on his right. He was the son of Berechiah, who was the son of Shimea, [40] who was the son of Michael, who was the son of Baaseiah, who was the son of Malchiah, [41] who was the son of Ethni, who was the son of Zerah, who was the son of Adaiah, [42] who was the son of Ethan, who was the son of Zimmah, who was the son of Shimei, [43] who was the son of Jahath, who was the son of Gershom, who was the son of Levi.

[44] On the left was Ethan, one of Heman's relatives descended from Merari. Ethan was the son of Kishi, who was the son of Abdi, who was the son of Malluch, [45] who was the son of Hashabiah, who was the son of Amaziah, who was the son of Hilkiah, [46] who was the son of Amzi, who was the son of Bani, who was the son of Shemer, [47] who was the son of Mahli, who was the son of Mushi, who was the son of Merari, who was the son of Levi.

[48] Their relatives, the Levites, were assigned all the other duties in the tent, the house of God.

[49] Aaron and his descendants offered sacrifices on the altar for burnt offerings and on the altar for incense. They did all the work in the most holy place and removed Israel's sins to make Israel acceptable to God. They did exactly what God's servant Moses had commanded.

[50] These were Aaron's descendants: His son was Eleazar. Eleazar's son was Phinehas. Phinehas' son was Abishua. [51] Abishua's son was Bukki. Bukki's son was Uzzi. Uzzi's son was Zerahiah. [52] Zerahiah's son was Meraioth. Meraioth's son was Amariah. Amariah's son was Ahitub. [53] Ahitub's son was Zadok. Zadok's son was Ahimaaz.

The Cities Belonging to Levi's Descendants

[54] These are the places where Levi's descendants lived, the places where they settled in the territory chosen for them when lots were drawn:

The ˌfirstˌ lot was drawn for the descendants of Aaron from the family descended from Kohath. [55] They were given Hebron in the territory of Judah as well as the pastureland around it, [56] but the fields belonging to the city and its villages were given to Caleb, son of Jephunneh. [57] Aaron's descendants were given Hebron as a city of refuge, Libnah with its pastureland, Jattir, Eshtemoa with its pastureland, [58] Hilen with its pastureland, Debir with its pastureland, [59] Ashan with its pastureland, and Beth Shemesh with its pastureland. [60] From the tribe of Benjamin, Aaron's descendants received Geba with its pastureland, Alemeth with its pastureland, and Anathoth with its pastureland. There was a total of 13 cities for their families.

[61] The rest of Kohath's descendants received 10 cities chosen by lot from the families of half of the tribe of Manasseh. [62] The families of Gershom's descendants were given 13 cities chosen by lot from the tribes of Issachar, Asher, Naphtali, and ˌthe part ofˌ the tribe of Manasseh that lived in Bashan. [63] The families of Merari's descendants were given 12 cities chosen by lot from the tribes of Reuben, Gad, and Zebulun.

[64] So the Israelites gave the Levites the cities with their pasturelands. [65] They gave ˌthemˌ the cities chosen by lot and mentioned here by name from the tribes of Judah, Simeon, and Benjamin.

[66] Some of the families of Kohath's descendants had cities chosen by lot from the tribe of Ephraim. [67] They were given these cities of refuge: Shechem with its pastureland in the hills of Ephraim, Gezer with its pastureland, [68] Jokmeam with its pastureland, Beth Horon with its pastureland, [69] Aijalon with its pastureland, and Gath Rimmon with its pastureland. [70] From half of the tribe of Manasseh, they were given Aner with its pastureland and Bileam with its pastureland for the families of the rest of Kohath's descendants.

[71] Gershom's descendants received Golan in Bashan with its pastureland and Ashtaroth with its pastureland from the families of half of the tribe of Manasseh. [72] From the tribe of Issachar, they received Kedesh with its pastureland, Daberath with its pastureland, [73] Ramoth with its pastureland, and Anem with its pastureland. [74] From the tribe of Asher, they received Mashal with its pastureland, Abdon with its pastureland, [75] Hukok with its pastureland, and Rehob with its pastureland. [76] From the tribe of Naphtali, they received Kedesh in Galilee with its pastureland, Hammon with its pastureland, and Kiriathaim with its pastureland.

[77] The rest of Merari's descendants received Rimmono with its pastureland and Tabor with its pastureland from the tribe of Zebulun. [78] From the tribe of Reuben,[b]

---

[b] 6:78 The last part of verse 79 has been moved to verse 78 to express the complex Hebrew sentence structure more clearly in English.

Merari's descendants received land east of the Jordan River and across from Jericho: Bezer in the wilderness with its pastureland, Jahzah with its pastureland, [79] Kedemoth with its pastureland and Mephaath with its pastureland. [80] From the tribe of Gad, they received Ramoth in Gilead with its pastureland, Mahanaim with its pastureland, [81] Heshbon with its pastureland, and Jazer with its pastureland.

Issachar's Descendants

7 [1] Issachar's four sons were Tola, Puah, Jashub, and Shimron. [2] Tola's sons were Uzzi, Rephaiah, Jeriel, Jahmai, Ibsam, and Shemuel. These men were heads of the families of Tola. They were soldiers grouped according to their ancestry. In David's day there were 22,600 of them. [3] The five descendants of Uzzi were Izrahiah and Izrahiah's sons Michael, Obadiah, Joel, and Isshiah. All of them were heads ˌof familiesˌ. [4] They had many wives and children. So in addition to these men grouped according to their ancestry and families, there were 36,000 soldiers. [5] Their relatives (that is, all of Issachar's families) were fighting men. A total of 87,000 of them was recorded in the genealogy.

Benjamin's Descendants

[6] Benjamin had three sons: Bela, Becher, and Jediael. [7] Bela's five sons were Ezbon, Uzzi, Uzziel, Jerimoth, and Iri. They were heads of families and fighting men. In the genealogy 22,034 of them were recorded. [8] Becher's sons were Zemirah, Joash, Eliezer, Elioenai, Omri, Jeremoth, Abijah, Anathoth, and Alemeth. These were all of Becher's sons. [9] In the genealogy 22,200 of them were recorded according to their ancestry (the heads of their families and fighting men). [10] Jediael's son was Bilhan. Bilhan's sons were Jeush, Benjamin, Ehud, Chenaanah, Zethan, Tarshish, and Ahishahar. [11] All of these men were Jediael's descendants. They headed families that produced 17,200 fighting men who could go to war. [12] The Shuppites and Huppites were Ir's descendants. The Hushites were descendants of someone else.

Naphtali's Descendants

[13] Naphtali's sons were Jahziel, Guni, Jezer, and Shallum. They were Bilhah's grandsons.

Manasseh's Descendants Who Lived West of the Jordan River

[14] Manasseh's sons were Asriel and Machir. Their mother was Manasseh's Aramean concubine.[a] Machir was the first to settle Gilead. [15] He married a wife from the Huppites and Shuppites. His wife's[b] name was Maacah. The name of his second son was Zelophehad. Zelophehad had only daughters. [16] Maacah, Machir's wife, had a son, and she named him Peresh. His brother's name was Sheresh, whose sons were Ulam and Rakem. [17] Ulam's son was Bedan. These were the people of Gilead, descendants of Machir (son of Manasseh). [18] Bedan's sister Hammolecheth gave birth to Ishhod, Abiezer, and Mahlah. [19] Shemida's sons were Ahian, Shechem, Likhi, and Aniam.

Ephraim's Descendants

[20] Ephraim's son was Shuthelah. Shuthelah's son was Bered. Bered's son was Tahath. Tahath's son was Eleadah. Eleadah's son was Tahath. [21] Tahath's son was Zabad. Zabad's son was Shuthelah.

Ephraim's sons Ezer and Elead were killed by the men of Gath when they came to take their livestock. [22] Their father Ephraim mourned a long time, even though his brothers tried to comfort him. [23] Then he slept with his wife, and she became pregnant. She gave birth to a son, and Ephraim named him Beriah [Tragedy], because tragedy had come to his home. [24] Beriah's daughter was Sheerah, who built Upper and Lower Beth Horon and Uzzen Sheerah. [25] Beriah's son was Rephah. Rephah's son was Resheph. Resheph's son was Telah. Telah's son was Tahan. [26] Tahan's son was Ladan. Ladan's son was Ammihud. Ammihud's son was Elishama. [27] Elishama's son was Nun. Nun's son was Joshua.

[28] The land and homes of Ephraim's descendants were in Bethel and its villages, Naaran to the east, Gezer with its villages to the west, Shechem and its villages, and as far as Gaza and its villages. [29] Next to Manasseh were Beth Shean and its villages, Taanach and its villages, Megiddo and its villages, and Dor and its villages. The descendants of Joseph, son of Israel, live in these cities.

Asher's Descendants

[30] Asher's sons were Imnah, Ishvah, Ishvi, and Beriah. Their sister was Serah. [31] Beriah's sons were Heber and Malchiel, who first settled Birzaith. [32] Heber was the father of Japhlet, Shomer, Hotham, and their sister Shua. [33] Japhlet's sons were Pasach, Bimhal, and Ashvath.

---

[a] 7:14 A concubine is considered a wife except she has fewer rights under the law.   [b] 7:15 Or "sister's."

These were Japhlet's sons. ³⁴ The sons of his brother Shomer were Rohgah, Jehubbah, and Aram. ³⁵ His brother Helem's sons were Zophah, Imna, Shelesh, and Amal. ³⁶ Zophah's sons were Suah, Harnepher, Shual, Beri, Imrah, ³⁷ Bezer, Hod, Shamma, Shilsha, Ithran, and Beera. ³⁸ Jether's sons were Jephunneh, Pispa, and Ara. ³⁹ Ulla's sons were Arah, Hanniel, and Rizia. ⁴⁰ All of these men were Asher's descendants—heads of their families, outstanding men, soldiers, and distinguished leaders. Their military roster had 26,000 recorded in it.

Benjamin's Descendants

8 ¹ Benjamin was the father of Bela (his firstborn), Ashbel (his second son), Aharah (his third son), ² Nohah (his fourth son), and Rapha (his fifth son). ³ Bela's sons were Addar, Gera, Abihud, ⁴ Abishua, Naaman, Ahoah, ⁵ Gera, Shephuphan, and Huram.

⁶ These were Ehud's sons, who were heads of the families living in Geba and who were taken away as captives to Manahath: ⁷ Naaman, Ahijah, and Gera. Gera led the rest of them away as captives. He was the father of Uzza and Ahihud.

⁸ Shaharaim divorced his wives Hushim and Baara. But later in Moab, ⁹ he and his wife Hodesh had the following sons: Jobab, Zibia, Mesha, Malcam, ¹⁰ Jeuz, Sachia, and Mirmah. All of Shaharaim's sons became heads of families. ¹¹ He and Hushim were the parents of Abitub and Elpaal. ¹² Elpaal's sons were Eber, Misham, and Shemed (who built Ono, Lod, and Lod's villages).

¹³ Beriah and Shema were the heads of the families who lived in Aijalon. They forced out the people living in Gath. ¹⁴ Their brothers*ᵃ* were Shashak and Jeremoth. ¹⁵ Beriah's sons were Zebadiah, Arad, Eder, ¹⁶ Michael, Ishpah, and Joha. ¹⁷ Elpaal's sons were Zebadiah, Meshullam, Hizki, Heber, ¹⁸ Ishmerai, Izliah, and Jobab. ¹⁹ Shimei's sons were Jakim, Zichri, Zabdi, ²⁰ Elienai, Zillethai, Eliel, ²¹ Adaiah, Beraiah, and Shimrath. ²² Shashak's sons were Ishpan, Eber, Eliel, ²³ Abdon, Zichri, Hanan, ²⁴ Hananiah, Elam, Anthothijah, ²⁵ Iphdeiah, and Penuel. ²⁶ Jeroham's sons were Shamsherai, Shehariah, Athaliah, ²⁷ Jaareshiah, Elijah, and Zichri. ²⁸ These were the heads of families listed by their ancestry. They were the heads of families. They lived in Jerusalem.

²⁹ Jeiel,ᵇ who first settled Gibeon, lived in Gibeon, and his wife's name was Maacah. ³⁰ His firstborn son was Abdon, then Zur, Kish, Baal, Nadab, ³¹ Gedor, Ahio, Zecher, ³² and Mikloth, who was the father of Shimeah. They lived next to their relatives in Jerusalem. ³³ Ner was the father of Kish. Kish was the father of Saul. Saul was the father of Jonathan, Malchishua, Abinadab, and Eshbaal. ³⁴ Jonathan's son was Meribbaal, and Meribbaal was the father of Micah. ³⁵ Micah's sons were Pithon, Melech, Tarea, and Ahaz. ³⁶ Ahaz was the father of Jehoaddah. Jehoaddah was the father of Alemeth, Azmaveth, and Zimri. Zimri was the father of Moza. ³⁷ Moza was the father of Binea. Binea's son was Raphah. Raphah's son was Eleasah. Eleasah's son was Azel. ³⁸ Azel had six sons. Their names were Azrikam, Bocheru, Ishmael, Sheariah, Obadiah, and Hanan. All of these men were Azel's sons. ³⁹ His brother Eshek's sons were Ulam (the firstborn), Jeush (the second son), and Eliphelet (the third son). ⁴⁰ Ulam's sons were soldiers, skilled archers. They had many sons and grandsons, 150 in all. All of these men were Benjamin's descendants.

The People Who Lived in Jerusalem

9 ¹ All Israel was recorded in the genealogies in the Book of the Kings of Israel and Judah. The Israelites were taken away to Babylon as captives because they had sinned. ² The first to settle again on their property in their own cities were ˌsomeˌ Israelites, the priests, the Levites, and the temple servants.

³ Jerusalem was settled by descendants of Judah, Benjamin, Ephraim, and Manasseh:

⁴ From the descendants of Perez, son of Judah, was Uthai, who was the son of Ammihud, grandson of Omri, and great-grandson of Imri. (Imri's father was Bani.) ⁵ From the descendants of Shilah were Asaiah (the firstborn) and his sons. ⁶ And from the descendants of Zerah were Jeuel and their relatives, 690 in all.

⁷ From the descendants of Benjamin were Sallu (son of Meshullam, grandson of Hodaviah, and great-grandson of Hassenuah), ⁸ Ibneiah (son of Jeroham), Elah (son of Uzzi and grandson of Michri), and Meshullam (son of Shephatiah, grandson of Reuel, and great-grandson of Ibniah), ⁹ and their relatives according to their ancestry. All of these men were heads of their families. A total of 956 of them lived in Jerusalem.

¹⁰ From the priests were Jedaiah, Jehoiarib, Jachin, ¹¹ and Azariah. Azariah was the son of Hilkiah, grandson of Meshullam, and great-grandson of Zadok. Zadok's father was Meraioth, the son of Ahitub (the official in charge of God's temple). ¹² Also from the priests were Adaiah (son of Jeroham, grandson of Pashhur, and great-grandson of Malchiah) and Maasai (son of Adiel,

---

ᵃ 8:14 Greek; Masoretic Text "Ahio."   ᵇ 8:29 Dead Sea Scrolls, Greek, Targum, Latin, 1 Chronicles 9:35; Masoretic Text omits "Jeiel."

grandson of Jahzerah, and great-grandson of Meshullam, whose father was Meshillemith, son of Immer). [13] Their relatives who were heads of their families totaled 1,760 soldiers. They served in God's temple and settled in Jerusalem.

[14] From the Levites descended from Merari were Shemaiah (son of Hasshub, grandson of Azrikam, and great-grandson of Hashabiah), [15] Bakbakkar, Heresh, Galal, Mattaniah (son of Mica, grandson of Zichri, and great-grandson of Asaph), [16] Obadiah (son of Shemaiah, grandson of Galal, and great-grandson of Jeduthun), and Berechiah (son of Asa and grandson of Elkanah, who lived in the villages belonging to the Netophathites).

[17] The gatekeepers were Shallum, Akkub, Talmon, Ahiman, and their relatives. (Shallum was in charge.) [18] Formerly, they were stationed at the king's gate on the east side. They were the gatekeepers for the Levite quarters.

[19] Shallum (son of Kore, grandson of Ebiasaph, great-grandson of Korah) and the members of his family (Korah's descendants) were responsible for serving as watchmen at the entrances to the tent, as their ancestors had been in charge of guarding the entrances to the LORD's camp. [20] (Phinehas, Eleazar's son, had been the official in charge of the gatekeepers, and the LORD was with him.) [21] Zechariah, son of Meshelemiah, was the keeper at the entrance to the tent of meeting. [22] The men chosen to be gatekeepers at the entrances totaled 212. Their genealogies were recorded in their villages. David and the seer[a] Samuel appointed them to these positions because they were trustworthy. [23] So they and their descendants were assigned to be gatekeepers for the LORD's house, that is, the tent.

[24] The gatekeepers were on the four sides (east, west, north, and south). [25] Their relatives had to come from their villages from time to time. They would come to serve under the gatekeepers' supervision for a period of seven days. [26] The four chief Levite gatekeepers were in charge of the rooms and treasures in God's temple because of their faithfulness. [27] They would spend the night stationed around God's temple because they had to guard it and open it every morning.

[28] Some of them were in charge of the utensils for worship. They would count them when they brought them in and when they took them out. [29] Other descendants of Korah were placed in charge of the utensils, the holy utensils, the flour, wine, olive oil, incense, and spices. [30] Some of the priests' sons prepared the mixture of spices. [31] Mattithiah, a Levite, the firstborn son of Shallum, Korah's descendant, was entrusted with preparing the flat bread. [32] Some of their Kohathite relatives were responsible for setting the bread out in rows every day of worship.

[33] These were the musicians who were the heads of the Levite families. They lived in rooms in the temple and were free from other duties because they were on duty day and night. [34] They were the heads of the Levite families according to their ancestry. These head Levites lived in Jerusalem.

Saul's Descendants

[35] Jeiel, who first settled Gibeon, lived in Gibeon, and his wife's name was Maacah. [36] His firstborn son was Abdon, then Zur, Kish, Baal, Nadab, [37] Gedor, Ahio, Zechariah, and Mikloth. [38] Mikloth was the father of Shimeam. They lived next to their relatives in Jerusalem. [39] Ner was the father of Kish. Kish was the father of Saul. Saul was the father of Jonathan, Malchishua, Abinadab, and Eshbaal. [40] Jonathan's son was Meribbaal, and Meribbaal was the father of Micah. [41] Micah's sons were Pithon, Melech, and Tarea. [42] Ahaz was the father of Jarah. Jarah was the father of Alemeth, Azmaveth, and Zimri. Zimri was the father of Moza. [43] Moza was the father of Binea. Binea's son was Rephaiah. Rephaiah's son was Eleasah. Eleasah's son was Azel. [44] Azel had six sons. Their names were Azrikam, Bocheru, Ishmael, Sheariah, Obadiah, and Hanan. All of these men were Azel's sons.

The Death of Saul—1 Samuel 31:1–13

10 [1] When the Philistines fought against Israel, the men of Israel fled from the Philistines and were killed in battle on Mount Gilboa. [2] The Philistines caught up to Saul and his sons. They killed Jonathan, Abinadab, and Malchishua, Saul's sons. [3] The heaviest fighting was against Saul. When the archers got him in their range, he was wounded by them.

[4] Saul told his armorbearer, "Draw your sword! Stab me, or these godless men will come and make fun of me." But his armorbearer refused because he was terrified. So Saul took the sword and fell on it. [5] When the armorbearer saw that Saul was dead, he also fell on the sword and died. [6] So Saul, his three sons, and his dynasty died together.

[7] When all the people of Israel in the valley saw that ˌtheir army ̖ had fled and that Saul and his sons were dead, they abandoned their cities. So the Philistines came to live in these cities.

[8] The next day, when the Philistines came to strip the dead, they found Saul and his sons lying on Mount Gilboa. [9] They stripped him and took his head and his armor. Then they sent

---

[a] 9:22 A seer is a prophet.

men throughout Philistine territory to tell their idols and the people this good news. [10] They put his armor in the temple of their gods and fastened his head to the temple of Dagon.

[11] When all the people of Jabesh Gilead heard about everything the Philistines had done to Saul, [12] all the fighting men came and took away the dead bodies of Saul and his sons and brought them to Jabesh. They buried the bones under the oak tree in Jabesh. Then they fasted seven days.

[13] So Saul died because of his unfaithfulness to the LORD: He did not obey the word of the LORD. He asked a medium to request information ˏfrom a dead personˎ. [14] He didn't request information from the LORD. So the LORD killed him and turned the kingship over to David, Jesse's son.

David Anointed King of Israel—2 Samuel 5:1–3

11 [1] All Israel gathered around David at Hebron. "We are your own flesh and blood," they said. [2] "Even in the past when Saul ruled, you were theˊone who led Israel on its campaigns to war. The LORD your God has said to you, 'You will be shepherd of my people Israel, the leader of my people Israel.' "

[3] All the leaders of Israel had come to Hebron. David made an agreement with them at Hebron in front of the LORD. So they anointed David king of Israel, as the LORD had spoken through Samuel.

David Captures Jerusalem—2 Samuel 5:6–10

[4] David and all Israel went to Jerusalem (that is, Jebus). The Jebusites were living in that region. [5] They told David, "You will never get in here." But David captured the fortress Zion (that is, the City of David).

[6] Now, David said, "Whoever is the first to kill a Jebusite will be made a general and a prince." Zeruiah's son Joab was the first to go ˏinto Jerusalemˎ, so he became the general. [7] David lived in the fortress, so it was called the City of David. [8] He built the city ˏof Jerusalemˎ around it, starting from the Millo[a] and making a complete circuit. Joab rebuilt the rest of the city. [9] David continued to grow more powerful because the LORD of Armies was with him.

David's Three Fighting Men—2 Samuel 23:8–17

[10] Now, these were the commanders of David's fighting men, who exercised power with him in his kingdom, and with all Israel they made him king according to the LORD's word to Israel. [11] The first of David's fighting men was Jashobeam, son of Hachmon, the leader of the three.[b] He used his spear to kill 300 men on one occasion. [12] Next in rank to him was Eleazar, another one of the three fighting men. He was the son of Dodo and grandson of Aho. [13] Eleazar was with David at Pas Dammim when the Philistines gathered there for battle. There was a field of ripe barley. When the troops fled from the Philistines, [14] they stood in the middle of the field and defended it by killing Philistines. So the LORD saved ˏthemˎ with an impressive victory. [15] Once three of the thirty leading men went down to David's rock at the cave of Adullam when the army of the Philistines was camping in the valley of Rephaim. [16] While David was in the fortified camp, Philistine troops were in Bethlehem.

[17] David was thirsty and said, "I wish I could have a drink of water from the cistern at the city gate of Bethlehem." [18] So the three burst into the Philistine camp and drew water from the cistern. They brought it to David, but he refused to drink it. He poured it out ˏas an offeringˎ to the LORD [19] and said, "It's unthinkable that I would do this, God. Should I drink the blood of these men who risked their lives? They had to risk their lives to get this water." So he refused to drink it.

These are the things which the three fighting men did.

David's Thirty Fighting Men—2 Samuel 23:18–39

[20] Joab's brother Abishai was the leader of the thirty. He used his spear to kill 300 men, but he was not one of the three, [21] although he was honored more than they were. So he became their captain but didn't become a member of the three.

[22] Benaiah, son of Jehoiada, was from Kabzeel and was a brave man who did many things. He killed two distinguished soldiers from Moab. He also went into a cistern and killed a lion on the day it snowed. [23] He killed an eight-foot-tall Egyptian. The Egyptian had a spear like a weaver's beam in his hand. But Benaiah went to him with a club, grabbed the spear away from him, and killed him with it. [24] These are the things that Benaiah, son of Jehoiada, did. He was as famous as the three fighting men. [25] He was honored more than the thirty, but he was not a member of the three. David put him in charge of his bodyguards.

---

[a] 11:8 The exact place referred to as "the Millo" is unknown.   [b] 11:11 2 Samuel 23:8, Greek; Masoretic Text "thirty."

26 The distinguished fighting men were
  Joab's brother Asahel,
  Elhanan (son of Dodo) from Bethlehem,
27 Shammoth from Harod,
  Helez the Pelonite,
28 Ira (son of Ikkesh) from Tekoa,
  Abiezer from Anathoth,
29 Sibbecai (son of Hushai),
  Ilai (descendant of Ahohi),
30 Maharai from Netophah,
  Heled (son of Baanah) from Netophah,
31 Ithai (son of Ribai) from Gibeah in Benjamin,
  Benaiah from Pirathon,
32 Hurai from the Gaash ravines,
  Abiel from Beth Arabah,
33 Azmaveth from Bahurim,
  Eliahba from Shaalbon,
34 Bene Hashem from Gizon,
  Jonathan (son of Shage the Hararite),
35 Ahiam (son of Sachar the Hararite),
  Eliphal (son of Ur),
36 Hepher the Mecherathite,
  Ahijah the Pelonite,
37 Hezro from Carmel,
  Naari (son of Ezbai),
38 Joel (son of Nathan),
  Mibhar (son of Hagri),
39 Zelek from Ammon,
  Naharai from Beroth, armorbearer for Zeruiah's son Joab,
40 Ira (descendant of Ithra),
  Gareb (descendant of Ithra),
41 Uriah the Hittite,
  Zabad (son of Ahlai),
42 Adina (son of Shiza) from the tribe of Reuben (who was leader of the
  tribe of Reuben and had his own group of thirty soldiers),
43 Hanan (son of Maacah),
  and Joshaphat the Mithnite,
44 Uzzia from Ashteroth,
  Shama and Jeiel (sons of Hotham from Aroer),
45 Jediael (son of Shimri) and
  his brother Joha the Tizite,
46 Eliel the Mahavite,
  Jeribai and Joshaviah (sons of Elnaam),
  Ithmah from Moab,
47 Eliel,
  Obed, and
  Jaasiel the Mezobaite.

The Men Who Helped David Become King

12 ¹These are the men who came to David at Ziklag when he was banished by Saul, son of Kish. They were among the soldiers who went into battle with David. ²They were armed with bows and could sling stones or shoot arrows with either their right or their left hands. They were Saul's relatives, from the tribe of Benjamin. ³Ahiezer was the leader, then Joash (they were the sons of Shemaah from Gibeah), Azmaveth's sons Jeziel and Pelet, Beracah and Jehu from Anathoth, ⁴Ishmaiah from Gibeon (one of the thirty fighting men and one of their leaders),ᵃ Jeremiah, Jahaziel, Johanan, and Jozabad from Gederah, ⁵Eluzai, Jerimoth, Bealiah, Shemariah, and Shephatiah from Haruph, ⁶Elkanah, Isshiah, Azarel, Joezer, and Jashobeam (Korah's descendants), ⁷and Joelah and Zebadiah, Jeroham's sons from Gedor.

⁸Some men left Gad to join David at the fortified camp in the desert. They were warriors, trained soldiers, able to fight with shields and spears. They looked like lions and were as fast as gazelles on the hills. ⁹Ezer was the first of these soldiers. The second was Obadiah. The

ᵃ 12:4 1 Chronicles 12:4b–40 in English Bibles is 1 Chronicles 12:5–41 in the Hebrew Bible.

third was Eliab. [10] The fourth was Mishmannah. The fifth was Jeremiah. [11] The sixth was Attai. The seventh was Eliel. [12] The eighth was Johanan. The ninth was Elzabad. [13] The tenth was Jeremiah. The eleventh was Machbannai. [14] These descendants of Gad were army officers. The least able one was in command of 100 men, and the best one was in command of 1,000. [15] In the first month of the year, these men crossed the Jordan River when it was flooding its banks. They chased away all the people in the valleys to the east and west.

[16] Some of the men of Benjamin and Judah came to David at the fortified camp. [17] David went to meet them. He told them, "If you've come to help me as friends would, then you may join me. But if you've come to betray me to my enemies, even though I haven't committed a crime, may the God of our ancestors see this and judge you."

[18] Then the Spirit gave Amasai, the leader of the thirty, the strength ˌto sayˌ,

"We are yours, David.
We are with you, son of Jesse.
  Success, success to you!
  Success to those who help you,
    because your God is helping you."

So David welcomed them and made them officers over his troops.

[19] Some men from Manasseh had deserted ˌSaul's armyˌ to join David when he went with the Philistines to attack Saul. (However, David didn't help the Philistines because their rulers sent him away after considering the matter. They said, "It will cost us our heads when he deserts and joins his master Saul.") [20] When David went to Ziklag, these men from Manasseh deserted to join him: Adnah, Jozabad, Jediael, Michael, Jozabad, Elihu, and Zillethai. Each one was an officer over 1,000 men in Manasseh. [21] They helped David fight raiding parties because they were all warriors, commanders in the army. [22] From day to day, men came to help David until he had an army as large as God's army.

[23] These are the numbers of the men equipped for war. The men joined David at Hebron to turn Saul's kingship over to David, as the LORD had said.

[24] From Judah's descendants there were 6,800 men equipped for war. They carried shields and spears.
[25] From Simeon's descendants there were 7,100 warriors.
[26] From Levi's descendants there were 4,600 [27] as well as Jehoiada (leader of Aaron's families). With him there were 3,700 men, [28] and Zadok, a young warrior from whose family came 22 officers.
[29] From Benjamin's descendants, Saul's relatives, there were 3,000 men, though most of them remained loyal to Saul's family. [30] From Ephraim's descendants there were 20,800 warriors who were famous among their families.
[31] From half of the tribe of Manasseh there were 18,000 who had been designated by name to make David king.
[32] From Issachar's descendants there were 200 leaders who understood the times and knew what Israel should do. Their relatives were under their command.
[33] From Zebulun there were 50,000 experienced soldiers. They were equipped for battle with every kind of weapon. Their loyalty was unquestioned.[b]
[34] From Naphtali there were 1,000 commanders. With them were 37,000 who fought with shields and spears.
[35] From Dan there were 28,600 ready for battle.
[36] From Asher there were 40,000 experienced soldiers ready for battle.
[37] From the east side of the Jordan River, from Reuben, Gad, and half the tribe of Manasseh, there were 120,000 soldiers ready to fight with all kinds of weapons.
[38] All of these soldiers, who were prepared for battle, came with a single purpose to Hebron—to make David king of all Israel. The rest of Israel also had agreed to make David king. [39] They ate and drank with David for three days because their relatives ˌin Judahˌ had provided enough for them. [40] Also, their neighbors as far as the territories of Issachar, Zebulun, and Naphtali brought food on donkeys, camels, mules, and oxen. There was plenty of flour, fig cakes, raisins, wine, olive oil, cattle, and sheep, because Israel was celebrating.

David Has the Ark Brought to Obed Edom's House—2 Samuel 6:1–11

13 [1] David consulted with every officer who commanded a regiment or battalion. [2] Then he told the whole assembly of Israel, "If you approve and if the LORD our God has con-

---

[b] 12:33 Hebrew meaning of this sentence uncertain.

sented,[a] we will send ˌan invitationˌ to the rest of our relatives in every region of Israel and to the priests and Levites in their cities and pasturelands so that they may join us. [3] Then we'll bring back our God's ark, which we ignored while Saul was king."

[4] The whole assembly agreed to this because the people considered it the right thing to do. [5] So David gathered all Israel from the Shihor River near Egypt to the border of Hamath in order to bring God's ark from Kiriath Jearim.

[6] David and all Israel went to Baalah in Kiriath Jearim, which is in Judah, to bring God's ark ˌto Jerusalemˌ. (The LORD is enthroned over the angels[b] ˌon the arkˌ where his name is used.) [7] David and his men put God's ark on a new cart from Abinadab's home. Uzzah and Ahio guided the cart. [8] David and all Israel were celebrating in God's presence with all their might, with songs, with lyres, harps, tambourines, cymbals, and trumpets.

[9] But when they came to Chidon's threshing floor,[c] the oxen stumbled. So Uzzah reached out to grab the ark. [10] The LORD became angry with Uzzah and killed him for reaching for the ark. He died in God's presence.

[11] David was angry because the LORD had struck Uzzah so violently. (That place is still called Perez Uzzah [The Striking of Uzzah] today.) [12] David was afraid of God that day. "How can I bring God's ark to my ˌcityˌ?" he asked. [13] So he didn't bring God's ark to his ˌhomeˌ, the City of David. Instead, he rerouted it to the home of Obed Edom, who was from Gath. [14] God's ark stayed at the home of Obed Edom with his family for three months, and the LORD blessed Obed Edom's family and everything he owned.

David's Palace, Wives, and Children in Jerusalem—2 Samuel 5:11–16

14 [1] King Hiram of Tyre sent messengers to David, along with cedarwood, masons, and carpenters to build a palace for David. [2] So David realized that the LORD had established him as king of Israel and that his kingdom was made famous for the sake of Israel, the LORD's people.

[3] David married more wives in Jerusalem and fathered more sons and daughters. [4] These are the names of the children who were born to him in Jerusalem: Shammua, Shobab, Nathan, Solomon, [5] Ibhar, Elishua, Elpelet, [6] Nogah, Nepheg, Japhia, [7] Elishama, Beeliada, and Eliphelet.

David Defeats the Philistines—2 Samuel 5:17–25

[8] When the Philistines heard that David had been anointed king of Israel, all of them came to attack David. But David heard about it and went out to meet them. [9] The Philistines had come and raided the valley of Rephaim.

[10] David asked God, "Should I attack the Philistines? Will you hand them over to me?"

The LORD answered him, "Attack! I will hand them over to you."

[11] So David ˌand his menˌ attacked and defeated the Philistines at Baal Perazim. David said, "Using my power like an overwhelming flood, God has overwhelmed my enemies." That is why they call that place Baal Perazim [The Lord Overwhelms]. [12] The Philistines left their gods there, so David ordered that the gods be burned.

[13] The Philistines again raided the valley. [14] Once more David asked God.

God answered him, "Don't go after them. Circle around, and come at them in front of the balsam trees. [15] As you hear the sound of marching in the tops of the balsam trees, then go out and fight because God has gone ahead of you to defeat the Philistine army."

[16] David did as God ordered him, and his men defeated the Philistine army from Gibeon to Gezer. [17] David's fame spread through all lands, and the LORD made all the nations fear him.

David Brings the Ark to Jerusalem—2 Samuel 6:12–19a

15 [1] After David constructed buildings for himself in the City of David, he prepared a place for God's ark and set up a tent for it. [2] Then David insisted that only the Levites carry God's ark because the LORD had chosen them to carry his ark and to serve him forever.

[3] David called together all Israel at Jerusalem to bring the LORD's ark to the place he had prepared for it. [4] David also called together Aaron's descendants and the Levites. [5] Leading Kohath's descendants was Uriel, who came with 120 of his relatives. [6] Leading Merari's descendants was Asaiah, who came with 220 of his relatives. [7] Leading Gershom's descendants was Joel, who came with 130 of his relatives. [8] Leading Elizaphan's descendants was Shemaiah, who came with 200 of his relatives. [9] Leading Hebron's descendants was Eliel, who came with 80 of his relatives. [10] Leading Uzziel's descendants was Amminadab, who came with 112 of his relatives.

[11] David called for the priests Zadok and Abiathar and for the Levites Uriel, Asaiah, Joel, Shemaiah, Eliel, and Amminadab. [12] He said to them, "You are the heads of the Levite families. You and your relatives must perform the ceremonies to make yourselves holy. Then bring the

---

[a] 13:2 Hebrew meaning uncertain.   [b] 13:6 Or "cherubim."   [c] 13:9 A threshing floor is an outdoor area where grain is separated from its husks.

ark of the LORD God of Israel to the place I prepared for it. ¹³ Because you weren't there the first time, the LORD our God struck us. We hadn't dedicated our lives to serving him in the way ͺhe ͺdesignated."

¹⁴ So the priests and the Levites made themselves holy in order to move the ark of the LORD God of Israel. ¹⁵ The Levites carried God's ark on their shoulders. They used poles as Moses had commanded according to the LORD's instructions.

¹⁶ David told the Levite leaders to appoint some of their relatives to serve as musicians. They were expected to play music on harps, lyres, and cymbals to produce joyful music for singing. ¹⁷ So the Levites appointed Heman, son of Joel, and from his relatives they appointed Asaph, Berechiah's son. From their own relatives, Merari's descendants, they appointed Ethan, son of Kushaiah. ¹⁸ In addition, they appointed their relatives from the second division: Zechariah,ᵃ Jaaziel, Shemiramoth, Jehiel, Unni, Eliab, Benaiah, Maaseiah, Mattithiah, Eliphelehu, and Mikneiah. Obed Edom and Jeiel were appointed gatekeepers. ¹⁹ The musicians Heman, Asaph, and Ethan were appointed to play bronze cymbals. ²⁰ Zechariah, Jaziel, Shemiramoth, Jehiel, Unni, Eliab, Maaseiah, and Benaiah were appointed to play harps according to *alamoth.*ᵇ ²¹ Mattithiah, Eliphelehu, Mikneiah, Obed Edom, Jeiel, and Azaziah were appointed to play lyres and to conduct the *sheminith.*ᵇ ²² Chenaniah, a Levite leader, instructed others how to sing prophetic songs because he was skilled at it. ²³ Berechiah and Elkanah were gatekeepers for the ark. ²⁴ The priests Shebaniah, Joshaphat, Nethanel, Amasai, Zechariah, Benaiah, and Eliezer blew trumpets in front of God's ark. Obed Edom and Jehiah were doorkeepers for the ark.

²⁵ So David, the leaders of Israel, and the army's commanders joyfully went to get the ark of the LORD's promise from Obed Edom's house. ²⁶ Because God helped the Levites who carried the ark of the LORD's promise, they sacrificed seven bulls and seven rams. ²⁷ David was dressed in a fine linen robe, as were all the Levites who carried the ark, the ͺLevites who were ͺsingers, and Chenaniah, the leader of the musicians' prophetic songs. David also wore a linen ephod.ᶜ

²⁸ All Israel brought the ark of the LORD's promise with shouts of joy and the sounding of rams' horns, trumpets, cymbals, harps, and lyres. ²⁹ When the ark of the LORD's promise came to the City of David, Saul's daughter Michal looked out of a window and saw King David dancing and celebrating, so she despised him.

16 ¹ The men carrying the ark set it inside the tent David had put up for it. They presented burnt offerings and fellowship offerings in God's presence. ² When David had finished sacrificing burnt offerings and fellowship offerings, he blessed the people in the name of the LORD. ³ He also distributed to every person in Israel—both men and women—a loaf of bread, a date cake, and a raisin cake.

The Levites Lead the Worship in Jerusalem—2 Samuel 6:19b–20a; Psalms 96:1–13; 105:1–15; 106:1, 47–48

⁴ David appointed some Levites to serve in front of the LORD's ark by offering prayers, thanks, and praise to the LORD God of Israel. ⁵ Asaph was the head; Zechariah was second, then Jeiel, Shemiramoth, Jehiel, Mattithiah, Eliab, Benaiah, Obed Edom, and Jeiel with harps and lyres. Asaph played the cymbals. ⁶ The priests Benaiah and Jahaziel played trumpets all the time in front of the ark of God's promise. ⁷ For the first time David entrusted Asaph and his relatives with the task of singing songs of thanks to the LORD:

⁸   "Give thanks to the LORD.
     Call on his name.
     Make known among the nations what he has done.
⁹   Sing to him.
     Make music to praise him.
     Meditate on all the miracles he has done.
¹⁰   Brag about his holy name.
     Let the hearts of those who seek the LORD rejoice.
¹¹   Search for the LORD and his strength.
     Always seek his presence.
¹²   Remember the miracles he performed,
         the amazing things he did and the judgments he pronounced,
¹³   you descendants of Israel, his servant,
         you descendants of Jacob, his chosen ones.

ᵃ 15:18 Greek; Masoretic Text adds "Ben," or "son."   ᵇ 15:20, 21 Unknown musical term.   ᶜ 15:27 *Ephod* is a technical term for a part of the priest's clothing. Its exact usage and shape are unknown.

14 "He is the LORD our God.
    His judgments are pronounced throughout the earth.
15 Remember his promise[a] forever,
    the word that he commanded for a thousand generations,
16   the promise that he made to Abraham,
      and his sworn promise to Isaac.
17 He confirmed it as a law for Jacob,
    as an everlasting promise to Israel,
18   by saying, 'I will give you Canaan.
      It is your share of the inheritance.'

19 "While they were few in number,
    a small group of foreigners living in that land,
20   they wandered from nation to nation
      and from one kingdom to another.
21 He didn't permit anyone to oppress them.
    He warned kings about them:
22   'Do not touch my anointed ones
      or harm my prophets.'

23 "Sing to the LORD, all the earth!
    Day after day announce that the LORD saves his people.
24   Tell people about his glory.
    Tell all the nations about his miracles.

25 "The LORD is great!
    He should be highly praised.
    He should be feared more than all ˌotherˌ gods
26   because all the gods of the nations are idols.
    The LORD made the heavens.
27 Splendor and majesty are in his presence.
    Strength and joy are where he is.

28 "Give to the LORD, you families of the nations.
    Give to the LORD glory and power.
29 Give to the LORD the glory his name deserves.
    Bring an offering, and come to him.
    Worship the LORD in ˌhisˌ holy splendor.
30   Tremble in his presence, all the earth!

"The earth stands firm; it cannot be moved.
31 Let the heavens rejoice and the earth be glad.
    Say to the nations, 'The LORD rules as king!'
32 Let the sea and everything in it roar like thunder.
    Let the fields and everything in them rejoice.
33   Then the trees in the forest will sing with joy
      in the presence of the LORD when he comes to judge the earth.

34 "Give thanks to the LORD because he is good,
    because his mercy endures forever.
35 Say, 'Rescue us, O God our Savior.
    Gather us and save us from the nations
      so that we may give thanks to your holy name
      and make your praise our glory.'
36 Thanks be to the LORD God of Israel
    from everlasting to everlasting."

Then all the people said amen and praised the LORD.
37 David left Asaph and his relatives to serve continually in front of the ark of the LORD's promise, as the daily work required. 38 David also left Obed Edom and 68 of his relatives ˌto serve thereˌ. Obed Edom (Jeduthun's son) and Hosah were to be gatekeepers. 39 David left Zadok and his priestly relatives to serve in the LORD's tent at the place of worship in Gibeon. 40 They were ordered to sacrifice burnt offerings to the LORD. This happened on the altar of burnt offerings continually, morning and evening, as written in the LORD's Teachings that he

---

a 16:15 Or "covenant."

gave Israel. **⁴¹** With Zadok and his relatives were Heman, Jeduthun, and the rest of the Levites who had been selected, chosen by name, to give thanks to the LORD ͺby singing,͵ "His mercy endures forever." **⁴²** Also, Heman and Jeduthun played trumpets, cymbals, and the ͺotherͺ musical instruments that accompany sacred songs. Jeduthun's sons were stationed at the gate. **⁴³** Then all the people went home. David went back to bless his family.

David's Wish to Build a House for God—2 Samuel 7:1–29

17 **¹** When David was living in his house, he said to the prophet Nathan, "I'm living in a house made of cedar, while the ark of the LORD's promise is inside a tent."
² Nathan told David, "Do everything you have in mind, because God is with you."
³ But that same night God spoke his word to Nathan: **⁴** "Say to David, my servant, 'This is what the LORD says: You must not build this house for me to live in. **⁵** I haven't lived in a house from the day I brought Israel out ͺof Egyptͺ to this day, but I've gone from tent site to tent site, moving the tent ͺof meetingͺ from one location ͺto anotherͺ. **⁶** In all the places I've moved with all Israel, did I ever ask any of the judges of Israel whom I ordered to be shepherds of my people why they didn't build me a house of cedar?'

⁷ "Now this is what you will say to my servant David: 'This is what the LORD of Armies says: I took you from the pasture where you followed sheep so that you could be the leader of my people Israel. **⁸** I was with you wherever you went, and I destroyed all your enemies in front of you. I will make your name like the names of the greatest people on earth. **⁹** I will make a place for my people Israel and plant them there. They will live in their own place and not be troubled anymore. The wicked will no longer frighten them as they used to do **¹⁰** ever since I appointed judges to rule my people Israel. I will crush all your enemies. I even tell you that I, the LORD, will build a house for you.

¹¹ " 'When the time comes for you to go and be with your ancestors, I will send one of your descendants. He will be one of your sons. I will establish his kingdom. **¹²** He will build a house for me, and I will establish his throne forever. **¹³** I will be his Father, and he will be my Son. And I will never stop showing him my love as I did to your predecessor. **¹⁴** I will place him in my royal house forever, and his throne will be established forever.' "

¹⁵ Nathan told David all these words and everything he had seen.
¹⁶ Then King David went into the tent and sat in front of the LORD. "Who am I, LORD God," he asked, "and why is my house so important that you have brought me this far? **¹⁷** And this you consider to be a small act, God. You've spoken about the distant future of my house. LORD God, you've shown me the generation of the great man.ᵃ
¹⁸ "What more can I do for you in light of the honor ͺyou have given͵ to me and since you know me so well! **¹⁹** LORD, you've done this great thing for my sake and your own desire. You made this great thing known to me.
²⁰ "LORD, there is no one like you, and there is no other god except you, as we have heard with our own ears. **²¹** Who is like your people Israel? It is the one nation on earth that God came to free in order to make its people his own, to make your name known, and to do great and wonderful things for them. You forced the nations and their gods out of the way of your people, whom you freed from Egypt. **²²** You made the people of Israel to be your people forever. And you, LORD, became their God.
²³ "Now, LORD, faithfully keep the promise you made to me and my house forever. Do as you promised. **²⁴** Your name will endure and be respected forever when ͺpeople͵ say, 'The LORD of Armies, the God of Israel, is Israel's God.' And the house of David, your servant, will be established in your presence. **²⁵** You, my God, have revealed especially to me that you will build me a house. That is why I have found ͺthe courage͵ to pray to you.
²⁶ "Almighty LORD, you are God. You promised me this good thing. **²⁷** Now, you were pleased to bless my house so that it may continue in your presence forever. Indeed, you, LORD, have blessed it. It will be blessed forever."

David's Successes—2 Samuel 8:1–18

18 **¹** After this, David defeated and crushed the Philistines. He took Gath and its surrounding villages from them.
² He also defeated Moab, and the Moabites became David's subjects and paid taxes ͺto him͵.
³ When David went to establish his control ͺover the territory͵ along the Euphrates River, he defeated King Hadadezer at Hamath. **⁴** David took 1,000 chariots, 7,000 horsemen, and 20,000 foot soldiers from him. David also disabled all but 100 of their horses so that they couldn't pull chariots.

ᵃ 17:17 Hebrew meaning of this sentence uncertain.

⁵ When the Arameans from Damascus came to help King Hadadezer of Zobah, David killed 22,000 of them. ⁶ David put troops in the Aramean kingdom of Damascus, and the Arameans became his subjects and paid taxes ˎto himˎ. Everywhere David went, the Lᴏʀᴅ gave him victories.
⁷ David took the gold shields that Hadadezer's servants carried, and he brought them to Jerusalem. ⁸ David also took a large quantity of bronze from Tibhath and Cun, Hadadezer's cities. (ˎLaterˎ Solomon used it to make the pool, pillars, and utensils ˎfor the templeˎ.)
⁹ When King Tou of Hamath heard that David had defeated the whole army of Zobah's King Hadadezer, ¹⁰ he sent his son Hadoram to greet King David and congratulate him for fighting and defeating Hadadezer. (There had often been war between Hadadezer and Tou.) ¹¹ King David dedicated all the articles of gold, silver, and bronze to the Lᴏʀᴅ, along with the silver and gold he had taken from other nations—from Edom, Moab, Ammon, the Philistines, and Amalek.
¹² Zeruiah's son Abishai killed 18,000 Edomites in the Dead Sea region. ¹³ He put troops in Edom, and all its people became David's subjects. Everywhere David went, the Lᴏʀᴅ gave him victories.
¹⁴ So David ruled all Israel. He did what was fair and right for all his people. ¹⁵ Zeruiah's son Joab was in charge of the army. Ahilud's son Jehoshaphat was the royal historian. ¹⁶ Ahitub's son Zadok and Abiathar's son Abimelech*ᵃ were priests. Shavsha was the royal scribe. ¹⁷ Jehoiada's son Benaiah was commander of the Cherethites and the Pelethites. And David's sons were his main officials.

David Defeats Ammon and Aram—2 Samuel 10:1–19

19 ¹ Later King Nahash of Ammon died, and his son became king in his place. ² David thought, "I will show kindness to Hanun because his father Nahash showed me kindness." So David sent messengers to comfort Hanun after his father's ˎdeathˎ. But when David's servants entered Ammonite territory to comfort Hanun, ³ the Ammonite princes asked Hanun, "Do you think David is honoring your father because he sent men to comfort you? Haven't his servants come to explore, destroy, and spy on the country?" ⁴ So Hanun took David's men, shaved them, cut off their clothes from the waist down, and sent them away.
⁵ After people told David ˎwhat had happenedˎ to the men, he sent ˎsomeoneˎ to meet them because they were deeply humiliated. The king said to them, "Stay in Jericho until your beards have grown back, and then return ˎto Jerusalemˎ."
⁶ The Ammonites realized that they had made themselves offensive to David. So Hanun and the Ammonites sent 75,000 pounds of silver to hire chariots and horses from the Arameans in Upper Mesopotamia, Maacah, and Zobah. ⁷ They hired 32,000 chariots and the king of Maacah with his army. They camped near Medeba. The Ammonites gathered for the battle from their cities.
⁸ After David heard about this, he sent Joab and all the elite troops. ⁹ The Ammonites formed a battle line at the entrance of the city, while the Arameans from Zobah and Rehob and the kings who had come remained by themselves in the open country.
¹⁰ When Joab saw he was under attack in front and behind, he took the select troops of Israel and organized them for combat against the Arameans. ¹¹ He put his brother Abishai in charge of the rest of the troops. They organized for combat against the Ammonites.
¹² Joab said, "If the Arameans are too strong for my ˎtroopsˎ, be ready to help me. And if the Ammonites are too strong for your ˎtroopsˎ, I'll help you. ¹³ Be strong! Let's prove ourselves strong for our people and for the cities of our God, and the Lᴏʀᴅ will do what he considers right."
¹⁴ Then Joab and his troops advanced to fight the Arameans, and the Arameans fled. ¹⁵ When the Ammonites saw that the Arameans had fled, they, too, fled from Joab's brother Abishai and went into the city. So Joab returned to Jerusalem.
¹⁶ Realizing that Israel had defeated them, the kings sent ˎmessengersˎ to get ˎotherˎ Arameans from beyond the Euphrates River. Shophach, the commander of Hadadezer's army, led them.
¹⁷ When David was told ˎabout thisˎ, he assembled Israel's army, crossed the Jordan, and confronted them. David formed a battle line against the Arameans, and they fought him. ¹⁸ The Arameans fled from Israel, and David killed 7,000 chariot drivers and 40,000 foot soldiers. David also killed Shophach. ¹⁹ When all the kings who were subject to Hadadezer saw that Israel had defeated them, they made peace with David and became his subjects. And the Arameans were no longer willing to help the Ammonites.

David Defeats the Philistines—2 Samuel 11:1; 12:26–31; 21:15–22

20 ¹ In the spring, the time when kings go out to battle, Joab led the army ˎto warˎ. They destroyed the Ammonites and came to Rabbah to attack it, while David stayed in

---

ᵃ 18:16 Most Hebrew manuscripts; some Hebrew manuscripts, 2 Samuel 8:17, Greek, Syriac, Latin, Arabic "Ahimelech."

Jerusalem. Joab defeated Rabbah and tore it down. ² He took the gold crown from the head of Rabbah's king and put it on David's head. (The crown was found to weigh 75 pounds, and in it was a precious stone.) David also took a lot of goods from the city. ³ He brought out the troops who were there and put them to work with saws, hoes, and axes.ᵃ He did the same to all the Ammonite cities. Then David and all the troops returned to Jerusalem.

⁴ After this, war broke out with the Philistines at Gezer. Then Sibbecai from Hushahᵇ killed Sippai, a descendant of Haraphah, and the Philistines were defeated. ⁵ When more fighting broke out with the Philistines, Elhanan, son of Jair, killed Lahmi, the brother of Goliath from Gath. (The shaft of Lahmi's spear was like a beam used by weavers.) ⁶ In another battle at Gath, there was a tall man who had 24 fingers and toes: six fingers on each hand and six toes on each foot. He also was a descendant of Haraphah. ⁷ When he challenged Israel, Jonathan, son of David's brother Shimea, killed him. ⁸ These ˌmenˌ were the descendants of Haraphah from Gath, and David and his men killed them.

David Counts the People—*2 Samuel 24:1–25*

21 ¹ Satan attempted to attack Israel by provoking David to count the Israelites. ² David said to Joab and the leaders of the people, "Go, count Israel from Beersheba to Dan. Bring me ˌthe results, so that I may know how many ˌpeopleˌ there are."

³ Joab responded, "May the LORD multiply his people a hundred times over. But, Your Majesty, aren't they all your servants? Why are you trying to do this? Why do you wish to make Israel guilty of ˌthisˌ sin?"

⁴ However, the king overruled Joab. So Joab left, went throughout Israel, and returned to Jerusalem. ⁵ Joab reported the census figures to David: In Israel there were 1,100,000 men who could serve in the army, and in Judah there were 470,000 who could serve in the army. ⁶ Joab didn't include Levi and Benjamin in the number because he was disgusted with the king's order.

⁷ God considered the census to be sinful, so he struck Israel ˌwith a plagueˌ.

⁸ David said to God, "I have committed a terrible sin by doing this thing. Forgive me because I have acted very foolishly."

⁹ The LORD spoke to Gad, David's seer.ᵃ ¹⁰ "Go and tell David, 'This is what the LORD says: I'm offering you three choices. Choose the one you want me to do to you.' "

¹¹ When Gad came to David, he said, "This is what the LORD says: 'Take your pick: ¹² either three years of famine, or three months during which your enemies will chase you away when their swords catch up to you, or three days of the LORD's sword—a plague in the land with the Messenger of the LORD destroying the whole country of Israel.' Decide what answer I should give the one who sent me."

¹³ "I'm in a desperate situation," David told Gad. "Please let me fall into the LORD's hands because he is extremely merciful. But don't let me fall into human hands."

¹⁴ So the LORD sent a plague on Israel, and 70,000 Israelites died. ¹⁵ God also sent a Messenger to Jerusalem to destroy it, but as he was destroying it, the LORD reconsidered and changed his mind about the disaster. "Enough!" he said to the destroying Messenger. "Put down your weapon." The Messenger of the LORD was standing by the threshing floorᵇ of Ornan the Jebusite.

¹⁶ When David looked up, he saw the Messenger of the LORD standing between heaven and earth. The Messenger had a sword in his hand and stretched it over Jerusalem. David and the leaders were dressed in sackcloth. They bowed down with their faces touching the ground. ¹⁷ David said to God, "I'm the one who ordered the people to be counted. I am the one who sinned and did wrong. What have these sheep done? LORD my God, let your punishment be against me and my father's family, but don't punish your people with a plague."

¹⁸ The LORD's Messenger told Gad to tell David to go and set up an altar for the LORD at Ornan the Jebusite's threshing floor. ¹⁹ David went as Gad had told him in the LORD's name.

²⁰ Now, Ornan had turned around and seen the Messenger. Ornan's four sons who were with him hid, but Ornan kept on threshing the wheat. ²¹ When David arrived, Ornan looked up and saw him. So he left the threshing floor and bowed down with his face touching the ground in front of David. ²² David said to Ornan, "Let me have the land this threshing floor is on. I'll build an altar for the LORD on it. Sell it to me for the full price. Then the plague on the people will stop."

²³ Ornan said to David, "Take it, Your Majesty, and do whatever you think is right. I'll give you oxen for the burnt offering, threshersᶜ for firewood, and wheat for the grain offering. I'll give you everything."

ᵃ 20:3 One Hebrew manuscript, 2 Samuel 12:31; other Hebrew manuscripts "saws."   ᵇ 20:4 Or "a descendant of Hushah."
ᵃ 21:9 A seer is a prophet.   ᵇ 21:15 A threshing floor is an outdoor area where grain is separated from its husks.
ᶜ 21:23 Threshers are devices used to separate grain from its husks.

²⁴ "No," King David told Ornan, "I insist on buying it for the full price. I won't take what is yours for the LORD and offer burnt sacrifices that cost me nothing." ²⁵ So David gave Ornan 15 pounds of gold for that place.

²⁶ David built an altar for the LORD there and sacrificed burnt offerings and fellowship offerings. He called on the LORD, and the LORD answered him by ˏsendingˌ fire from heaven on the altar for burnt offerings. ²⁷ So the LORD spoke to the Messenger, and he put his sword back in its scabbard.

²⁸ At that time, when David saw the LORD had answered him at the threshing floor of Ornan the Jebusite, he offered sacrifices there. ²⁹ The LORD's tent that Moses made in the desert and the altar for burnt offerings were at the worship site at Gibeon. ³⁰ However, David couldn't go there to consult God because he was frightened by the sword of the LORD's Messenger.

22 ¹ Then David said, "This is where the LORD God's temple will be. Israel's altar for burnt offerings will also be here."

David Helps Solomon Prepare to Build the Temple

² David ordered the foreigners living in Israel to gather. He appointed some of them to cut stones to build God's temple. ³ David prepared a large quantity of iron for nails and fittings on the doors of the gates. He also prepared so much bronze that it couldn't be weighed. ⁴ The men of Sidon and Tyre brought David so many cedar logs that the logs couldn't be counted.

⁵ David thought, "My son Solomon is young and inexperienced, and the temple that will be built for the LORD must be magnificent, large, famous, praised, and honored in all other countries. I'll prepare ˏthe building materialsˌ for him." So David prepared many materials ˏfor Solomonˌ before he died.

⁶ He summoned his son Solomon and commanded him to build a temple for the LORD God of Israel. ⁷ David told his son Solomon, "I had my heart set on building a temple for the name of the LORD, my God. ⁸ But the LORD spoke his word to me by saying, 'You have caused a lot of bloodshed and fought in a lot of wars. You must not build a temple for my name because you have caused so much bloodshed in my presence. ⁹ You will have a son who will be a peaceful man. I will give him peace from all the enemies around him. His name will be Solomon [Peace], and in his time I will give Israel peace and quiet. ¹⁰ He will build a temple for my name. He will be my son, and I will be his father. I will establish the throne of his kingdom permanently over Israel.' "

¹¹ ˏDavid continued,ˌ "Now, son, the LORD will be with you. You will be successful, and you will build the temple of the LORD your God as he predicted you would. ¹² The LORD will give you insight and understanding as he commands you to take charge of Israel and to follow the Teachings of the LORD your God. ¹³ Then you will succeed if you will carefully obey the laws and decrees the LORD commanded Moses to give to Israel. Be strong and courageous. Don't be afraid or terrified.

¹⁴ "Despite my troubles I've made preparations for the LORD's temple. There are 7,500,000 pounds of gold, 75,000,000 pounds of silver, and so much bronze and iron that it can't be weighed. I've also prepared wood and stones, and you may add to them. ¹⁵ You have many kinds of workers: stonecutters, masons, carpenters, and men skilled in every kind of work. ¹⁶ The gold, silver, bronze, and iron are more than can be counted. So get to work! May the LORD be with you."

¹⁷ David ordered all the leaders of Israel to help his son Solomon. ¹⁸ ˏDavid said,ˌ "Isn't the LORD your God with you? Hasn't he given you peace with all your neighbors? He put the people who live in this country under my power, and the country has been conquered by the LORD and his people. ¹⁹ So dedicate your hearts and lives to serving the LORD your God. Start building the holy place of the LORD God so that you can bring the ark of the LORD's promise and God's holy utensils into the temple that will be built for the LORD's name."

The Levites Are Organized to Serve in the Temple

23 ¹ When David had grown old and had lived out his years, he made his son Solomon king of Israel. ² He gathered all the officials of Israel and the priests and Levites. ³ Every male Levite who was at least 30 years old was counted. There were 38,000. ⁴ Of these, 24,000 were appointed to supervise the work on the LORD's temple, 6,000 were appointed to be officers and judges, ⁵ 4,000 were appointed to be gatekeepers, and 4,000 were appointed to praise the LORD with the instruments David had made for praising God. ⁶ David organized the Levites into divisions based on which of Levi's sons (Gershon, Kohath, or Merari) they were descended from.

⁷ Ladan and Shimei were Gershon's descendants. ⁸ Ladan had three sons: Jehiel was the first, then Zetham, and Joel. ⁹ Shimei had three sons: Shelomith, Haziel, and Haran. They were the heads of Ladan's families. ¹⁰ Shimei's sons were Jahath, Zina,ᵃ Jeush, and Beriah. They

---

ᵃ 23:10 Most Hebrew manuscripts; one Hebrew manuscript, Greek, Latin "Ziza" (see verse 11).

were Shimei's four sons. [11] Jahath was the first, and Ziza was the second. Jeush and Beriah didn't have many sons, so they were given an assignment as one family. [12] Kohath had four sons: Amram, Izhar, Hebron, and Uzziel. [13] Amram's sons were Aaron and Moses. Aaron and his sons were forever designated to dedicate the most holy things ˏto Godˏ, to offer sacrifices to the LORD, to serve him, and always give the blessing in his name. [14] The sons of Moses, the man of God, were counted with the tribe of Levi. [15] Moses' sons were Gershom and Eliezer. [16] Gershom's only son was Shebuel. [17] Eliezer's only son was Rehabiah. Eliezer had no other sons, but Rehabiah had many sons. [18] Izhar's only son was Shelomith. [19] Hebron's first son was Jeriah; his second was Amariah; his third was Jahaziel; his fourth was Jekameam. [20] Uzziel's first son was Micah; his second was Isshiah.

[21] Merari's sons were Mahli and Mushi. Mahli's sons were Eleazar and Kish. [22] Eleazar died without having any sons. He only had daughters. Their cousins, the sons of Kish, married them. [23] Mushi had three sons: Mahli, Eder, and Jeremoth.

[24] These were Levi's descendants, who were grouped according to their families. The heads of their families were registered by name as they were counted. Everyone who served in the LORD's temple was at least 20 years old. [25] David had said, "The LORD God of Israel has given his people rest. He will now live in Jerusalem forever. [26] The Levites will no longer have to carry the tent and all the utensils used in worship."

[27] David's last instructions were to count the Levites who were at least 20 years old. [28] They were appointed to stand beside Aaron's descendants to serve in the LORD's temple. They were appointed to be in charge of the courtyards and the temple rooms, to ensure that all the holy things were clean,[b] and to serve in God's temple. [29] They were also responsible for the rows of bread, the flour for the grain offerings, the unleavened bread wafers, and the bread made in frying pans. In addition, they were responsible for mixing the ingredients and keeping track of all weights and measures. [30] They were appointed to stand to give thanks and praise to the LORD every morning. They were appointed to do the same thing in the evening. [31] They were appointed to stand in front of the LORD in the required numbers whenever burnt offerings were made—on weekly worship days, at New Moon Festivals, and on appointed annual festivals. [32] They were appointed to follow the regulations for the tent of meeting and the holy place and to help their relatives, Aaron's descendants, as they served in the LORD's temple.

The Organization of the Priests

24 [1] The divisions of Aaron's descendants were as follows: Aaron's sons were Nadab and Abihu, Eleazar and Ithamar. [2] Nadab and Abihu died before their father died, and neither had any children. So Eleazar and Ithamar served as priests.

[3] David, Eleazar's descendant Zadok, and Ithamar's descendant Ahimelech divided Aaron's descendants into groups for service. [4] Since Eleazar's descendants had more men who were family heads than Ithamar's descendants, they were divided so that Eleazar's descendants had 16 family leaders and Ithamar's descendants had 8 family leaders. [5] Both groups were divided impartially by drawing lots so that there were officers for the holy place and officers for God among both Eleazar's and Ithamar's descendants. [6] The scribe Shemaiah was a son of Nethanel and a descendant of Levi. Shemaiah recorded their names in the presence of the king, the princes, the priest Zadok, Ahimelech (son of Abiathar), and the family leaders of the priests and Levites. One family was chosen for Eleazar, another for Ithamar.

[7] The first lot drawn was for Jehoiarib, the second for Jedaiah, [8] the third for Harim, the fourth for Seorim, [9] the fifth for Malchiah, the sixth for Mijamin, [10] the seventh for Hakkoz, the eighth for Abijah, [11] the ninth for Jeshua, the tenth for Shecaniah, [12] the eleventh for Eliashib, the twelfth for Jakim, [13] the thirteenth for Huppah, the fourteenth for Jeshebeab, [14] the fifteenth for Bilgah, the sixteenth for Immer, [15] the seventeenth for Hezir, the eighteenth for Happizzez, [16] the nineteenth for Pethahiah, the twentieth for Jehezkel, [17] the twenty-first for Jachin, the twenty-second for Gamul, [18] the twenty-third for Delaiah, the twenty-fourth for Maaziah. [19] These were their priestly groups when they went to serve at the LORD's temple. Their ancestor Aaron made these rules for them, as the LORD God of Israel had commanded him.

The Organization of the Levites

[20] ˏThe following men were leadersˏ for Levi's descendants ˏfrom Kohathˏ:
  Jehdeiah (for Amram's descendants through Shubael),
[21]   Isshiah (ˏfor Amram's descendantsˏ through Rehabiah),
[22]   Jahath (for Izhar's descendants through Shelomoth),
[23]   Jeriah (for Hebron's descendants[a]),
  Amariah (the second ˏof Hebron's descendantsˏ),

---

[b] 23:28 "Clean" refers to anything that Moses' Teachings say is presentable to God.   [a] 24:23 Greek, 1 Chronicles 23:19; Masoretic Text lacks "for Hebron's descendants."

Jahaziel (the third ˌof Hebron's descendantsˌ),
Jekameam (the fourth ˌof Hebron's descendantsˌ),
24 Shamir (for Uzziel's descendants through Micah),
25   and Zechariah (for ˌUzziel'sˌ descendants through Micah's brother Isshiah).

26 The following men were leaders from Levi's descendants from Merari:
Mahli, Mushi, and Merari's son Jaaziah,
27 Shoham, Zaccur, and Ibri (for Merari's descendants through his son Jaaziah),
28 Eleazar (who had no sons, for Mahli's descendants),
29 Jerahmeel (for ˌMahli'sˌ descendants through Kish),
30 Mahli, Eder, and Jerimoth (for Mushi's descendants).

These were Levi's descendants according to their families. 31 They drew lots as their relatives, Aaron's descendants, had done. They drew them in front of King David, Zadok, Ahimelech, and the leaders of the families of the priests and Levites. The families of the oldest brother were treated the same way as those of the youngest.

David Appoints Musicians for the Temple

25 1 David and the army commanders appointed the sons of Asaph, Heman, and Jeduthun to serve as prophets with lyres, harps, and cymbals. This is the list of the men who performed this service:

2 From the sons of Asaph were Zaccur, Joseph, Nethaniah, and Asharelah. (They were directed by Asaph, who served as a prophet under the king's direction.)

3 From the sons of Jeduthun were Gedaliah, Zeri, Jeshaiah, Shimei, Hashabiah, Mattithiah. (The six brothers were directed by their father, the prophet Jeduthun. They thanked and praised the LORD as they played lyres.)

4 From the sons of Heman were Bukkiah, Mattaniah, Uzziel, Shebuel, Jerimoth, Hananiah, Hanani, Eliathah, Giddalti, Romamti Ezer, Joshbekashah, Mallothi, Hothir, and Mahazioth.
5 (All of them were the sons of the king's seer[a] Heman. They were given to him to make him prominent, as God had promised. So God gave Heman 14 sons and 3 daughters.)

6 All these ˌLevitesˌ sang at the LORD's temple under the direction of their fathers Asaph, Jeduthun, and Heman. They played cymbals, lyres, and harps for worship in God's temple under the direction of the king. 7 They, along with their relatives, were trained, skilled musicians for the LORD. There were 288 of them.

8 They drew lots for their assignment of duties, the youngest as well as the oldest, the skilled ˌmusiciansˌ along with the students.

9 The first lot drawn chose Joseph, the son of Asaph.
The second chose Gedaliah, his sons, and his relatives—12 men.
10 The third chose Zaccur, his sons, and his relatives—12 men.
11 The fourth chose Izri, his sons, and his relatives—12 men.
12 The fifth chose Nethaniah, his sons, and his relatives—12 men.
13 The sixth chose Bukkiah, his sons, and his relatives—12 men.
14 The seventh chose Jesarelah, his sons, and his relatives—12 men.
15 The eighth chose Jeshaiah, his sons, and his relatives—12 men.
16 The ninth chose Mattaniah, his sons, and his relatives—12 men.
17 The tenth chose Shimei, his sons, and his relatives—12 men.
18 The eleventh chose Azarel, his sons, and his relatives—12 men.
19 The twelfth chose Hashabiah, his sons, and his relatives—12 men.
20 The thirteenth chose Shubael, his sons, and his relatives—12 men.
21 The fourteenth chose Mattithiah, his sons, and his relatives—12 men.
22 The fifteenth chose Jeremoth, his sons, and his relatives—12 men.
23 The sixteenth chose Hananiah, his sons, and his relatives—12 men.
24 The seventeenth chose Joshbekashah, his sons, and his relatives—12 men.
25 The eighteenth chose Hanani, his sons, and his relatives—12 men.
26 The nineteenth chose Mallothi, his sons, and his relatives—12 men.
27 The twentieth chose Eliathah, his sons, and his relatives—12 men.
28 The twenty-first chose Hothir, his sons, and his relatives—12 men.
29 The twenty-second chose Giddalti, his sons, and his relatives—12 men.
30 The twenty-third chose Mahazioth, his sons, and his relatives—12 men.
31 The twenty-fourth chose Romamti Ezer, his sons, and his relatives—12 men.

---

a 25:5 A seer is a prophet.

David Appoints Gatekeepers for the Temple

26 [1] The following were the divisions of the gatekeepers: For Korah's descendants there was Meshelemiah, the son of Kore, from the descendants of Asaph. [2] Meshelemiah's sons were Zechariah (the firstborn), Jediael (the second), Zebadiah (the third), Jathniel (the fourth), [3] Elam (the fifth), Jehohanan (the sixth), and Eliehoenai (the seventh).

[4] ꞈAlso for Korah's descendants꞉ there were Obed Edom's sons Shemaiah (the firstborn), Jehozabad (the second), Joah (the third), Sachar (the fourth), Nethanel (the fifth), [5] Ammiel (the sixth), Issachar (the seventh), and Peullethai (the eighth). God had blessed Obed Edom. [6] His son Shemaiah had sons who ruled their families because they were soldiers. [7] Shemaiah's sons were Othni, and Othni's skilled brothers Rephael, Obed, Elzabad, as well as Elihu and Semachiah. [8] All of these people were Obed Edom's descendants. They, their sons, and their relatives were skilled and had the ability to perform the service. Obed Edom's family included 62 men.

[9] Meshelemiah's sons and relatives were 18 skilled men.

[10] From the descendants of Merari there were Hosah's sons. Shimri was the head, although he was not the firstborn. His father appointed him head. [11] Hosah's other sons were Hilkiah (the second), Tebaliah (the third), and Zechariah (the fourth). There were 13 sons and relatives of Hosah.

[12] These divisions of gatekeepers through their head men were assigned duties with their relatives to serve in the Lord's temple. [13] They drew lots by families, youngest and oldest alike, for every gate. [14] Shelemiah was chosen for the east side. His son Zechariah, a counselor who displayed insight, was chosen for the north side. [15] Obed Edom was chosen for the south side, and his sons were chosen for the storerooms. [16] Shuppim and Hosah were chosen for the west side with Shallecheth Gate at the gateway that goes to the palace.

One squad of guards served its watch after another. [17] On the east side there were six Levites. On the north there were four every day. On the south there were four every day. At the storerooms there were four, two at each entrance. [18] At the courtyard[a] on the west there were four Levites at the gateway to the palace and two at the courtyard itself. [19] These were the divisions of the gatekeepers among Korah's and Merari's descendants.

David Appoints Treasurers for the Temple

[20] Ahijah, a Levite, was in charge of the treasuries in God's temple and the treasuries of the gifts dedicated to God. [21] ꞈThere were also꞉ the descendants of Ladan, who was descended from Gershon. ꞈThose who served꞉ for Ladan, the descendant of Gershon, were the heads of Ladan's families: Jehiel [22] ꞈand꞉ Jehiel's sons Zetham and Joel. They were in charge of the treasuries in the Lord's temple. [23] For the descendants of Amram, Izhar, Hebron, and Uzziel, [24] there was Shebuel, a descendant of Moses' son Gershom. He was the highest-ranking official in charge of the treasuries. [25] From his relatives on Eliezer's side of the family was Shelomith. (Eliezer's son was Rehabiah; his grandson was Jeshaiah; his great-grandson was Joram. Joram's son was Zichri; his grandson was Shelomith.) [26] He and his relatives were in charge of all the treasuries of the gifts dedicated to God that King David, the heads of families, the commanders of regiments and battalions, and the commanders of the army had donated. [27] (They had donated some of the loot taken in battle to support the Lord's temple.) [28] Everything that Samuel the seer,[b] Saul (son of Kish), Abner (son of Ner), and Joab (son of Zeruiah) had donated—everything that had been donated—was under the supervision of Shelomith and his relatives.

David Appoints Levites to Oversee Israel's Worship

[29] From Izhar's descendants Chenaniah and his sons were assigned duties. They served as officials and judges outside ꞈthe temple꞉ in Israel. [30] From Hebron's descendants Hashabiah and his 1,700 skilled, male relatives were appointed to serve Israel west of the Jordan River. They did everything the Lord wanted them to do, and they served the king. [31] Jeriah was the head of Hebron's descendants. In the fortieth year of David's reign, the ancestry of Hebron's descendants was researched family by family. Warriors from these families were found at Jazer in Gilead. [32] Jeriah's relatives were 2,700 skilled men, who were heads of families. King David appointed them to be overseers in every matter involving God or the king for the tribes of Reuben, Gad, and half of the tribe of Manasseh.

David's Government Officials

27 [1] This is a list of Israelite family heads, regiment and battalion commanders, and officers who were serving the king in all the army's units. Throughout each year they came for a month at a time and then left. Each unit consisted of 24,000 men.

---

[a] 26:18 Hebrew meaning uncertain.   [b] 26:28 A seer is a prophet.

[2] Jashobeam, son of Zabdiel, was in charge of the first unit, the one during the first month. In his unit there were 24,000. [3] He was a descendant of Perez, and he was head of all of the army's officers for the first month.

[4] Dodai, Ahoh's descendant, was in charge of the unit during the second month. It was his unit. (Mikloth was one of its leaders.) In Dodai's unit there were 24,000.

[5] The third commander of the army during the third month was Benaiah, son of the priest Jehoiada. He was the head, and in his unit there were 24,000. [6] This Benaiah was one of the thirty fighting men and commander of the thirty as well as his own unit. His son was Ammizabad.

[7] Asahel, Joab's brother, was in charge of the fourth unit during the fourth month, and after him was his son Zebadiah. In his unit there were 24,000.

[8] Shamhuth, Izrah's descendant, was commander of the fifth unit during the fifth month. In his unit there were 24,000.

[9] Ira, the son of Ikkesh from Tekoa, was in charge of the sixth unit during the sixth month. In his unit there were 24,000.

[10] Helez, a Pelonite from the descendants of Ephraim, was in charge of the seventh unit during the seventh month. In his unit there were 24,000.

[11] Sibbecai, a descendant of Zerah from Hushah, was in charge of the eighth unit during the eighth month. In his unit there were 24,000.

[12] Abiezer, a member of the tribe of Benjamin from Anathoth, was in charge of the ninth unit during the ninth month. In his unit there were 24,000.

[13] Mahrai, a descendant of Zerah from Netophah, was in charge of the tenth unit during the tenth month. In his unit there were 24,000.

[14] Benaiah, a member of the tribe of Ephraim from Pirathon, was in charge of the eleventh unit during the eleventh month. In his unit there were 24,000.

[15] During the twelfth month, the twelfth unit was commanded by Heldai from Netophah. He was Othniel's descendant. In his unit there were 24,000.

[16] The following officers were in charge of the tribes of Israel:

for the tribe of Reuben	Eliezer, son of Zichri
for the tribe of Simeon	Shephatiah, son of Maacah
[17] for the tribe of Levi	Hashabiah, son of Kemuel
for the family of Aaron	Zadok
[18] for the tribe of Judah	Elihu, one of David's brothers
for the tribe of Issachar	Omri, son of Michael
[19] for the tribe of Zebulun	Ishmaiah, son of Obadiah
for the tribe of Naphtali	Jerimoth, son of Azriel
[20] for the tribe of Ephraim	Hoshea, son of Azaziah
for half of the tribe of Manasseh	Joel, son of Pedaiah
[21] for the half of Manasseh in Gilead	Iddo, son of Zechariah
for the tribe of Benjamin	Jaasiel, son of Abner
[22] for the tribe of Dan	Azarel, son of Jeroham

These were the commanders of Israel's tribes.

[23] David didn't count those under 20 years old, because the LORD had promised that the people of Israel would be as numerous as the stars in the sky. [24] Joab, son of Zeruiah, started to count them but didn't finish. God was angry with Israel because of this, and the report from it was never included in the official records of King David.

[25] These were all the commanders in charge of King David's property:[a]

for the royal treasuries	Azmaveth, son of Adiel
for the goods in the fields, cities, villages, and watchtowers	Jonathan, son of Uzziah
[26] for the farm workers in the fields	Ezri, son of Chelub
[27] for the vineyards	Shimei from Ramah
for storing wine that came from the vineyards	Zabdi from Shepham
[28] for the olive and fig trees in the foothills	Baal Hanan from Gedor
for storing olive oil	Joash
[29] for the herds grazing in Sharon	Shitrai from Sharon
for the herds in the valleys	Shaphat, son of Adlai
[30] for the camels	Obil, a descendant of Ishmael

---

[a] 27:25 The last part of verse 32 has been moved to the beginning of verse 25 to express the complex Hebrew paragraph structure more clearly in English.

| for the donkeys | Jehdeiah from Meronoth |
| ³¹ for the flocks | Jaziz from Hagar |

³² David's uncle Jonathan, an educated man who possessed insight, was David's adviser. Jonathan and Jehiel, son of Hachmoni, were in charge of the king's sons. ³³ Ahithophel was the king's adviser. Hushai, a descendant of Archi, was the king's friend. ³⁴ Jehoiada (son of Benaiah) and Abiathar succeeded Ahithophel. Joab was the commander of the royal army.

David's Public Assembly at Jerusalem

28 ¹ David held a meeting in Jerusalem for all the leaders of Israel—the leaders of the tribes, the leaders of the army units that served the king, the commanders of regiments and battalions, the officials in charge of all the property and livestock belonging to the king and his sons, the palace officials, the soldiers, and the fighting men.

² David stood in front of them and said, "Listen to me, my relatives and subjects. I had my heart set on building the temple where the ark of the LORD's promise could be placed. This temple would be a stool for our God's feet, and I have made preparations to build it. ³ But God told me, 'You must not build the temple for my name. You have fought wars and caused bloodshed.' ⁴ Yet, from my entire family the LORD God of Israel chose me to be king of Israel permanently. He had chosen the tribe of Judah to lead ˌIsraelˌ. From the families of Judah he chose my father's family. From among my father's sons he was pleased to make me king of all Israel. ⁵ And of all my sons (the LORD has given me many sons) he chose my son Solomon to sit on the throne of the LORD's kingdom to rule Israel.

⁶ "He told me, 'Your son Solomon will build my temple and my courtyards because I have chosen him to be my son. I will be his father. ⁷ I will establish his kingdom forever if he will remain determined to obey my commands and laws, as he is doing today.' ⁸ Now, ˌleaders, I order youˌ in the sight of Israel (the LORD's congregation) and as our God listens to dedicate your lives to doing everything the LORD your God has commanded. Then you will be able to possess this good land and leave it as an inheritance to your descendants.

⁹ "And you, my son Solomon, learn to know your father's God. Serve the LORD wholeheartedly and willingly because he searches every heart and understands every thought ˌwe haveˌ. If you dedicate your life to serving him, he will accept you. But if you abandon him, he will reject you from then on. ¹⁰ So be careful, because the LORD has chosen you to build the temple as his holy place. Be strong, and do it."

¹¹ Then David gave his son Solomon the plans for the entrance hall and the temple, its storerooms, upper rooms, inner rooms, and the room for the throne of mercy. ¹² He gave him plans for the courtyards of the LORD's temple and for all the rooms around it. (These rooms served as treasuries for God's temple and the gifts dedicated to God.) ¹³ He determined the divisions of priests and Levites. He planned all the work done for worship in the LORD's temple. He designed all the utensils for worship in the LORD's temple. ¹⁴ ˌDavid specifiedˌ the weight of gold to be used for each of the utensils for worship, ¹⁵ the weight of the gold lamp stands and their gold lamps (ˌthat is,ˌ the weight of gold for each lamp stand and its lamps), the weight of silver for each silver lamp stand and its lamps (according to the use of each lamp stand for worship), ¹⁶ the weight of gold for each table with the rows of bread, and the silver for the silver tables, ¹⁷ the pure gold for the forks, bowls, and pitchers, the weight of each gold bowl, the weight of each silver bowl, ¹⁸ and the refined gold for the altar of incense. He also gave Solomon the plans for the chariot, that is, the gold angelsᵃ with their wings spread to cover the ark of the LORD's promise. ¹⁹ ˌDavid said,ˌ "All this was written for me by the LORD's hand. He made all the details of the plan clear to me."

²⁰ David also told his son Solomon, "Be strong and courageous, and do the work. Don't be afraid or terrified. The LORD God, my God, will be with you. He will not abandon you before all the work on the LORD's temple is finished. ²¹ Here are also the divisions of the priests and Levites for every type of worship in God's temple. You have with you every skilled worker to do all the work. In addition, all the leaders and people are at your command."

29 ¹ Then King David said to the whole assembly, "My son Solomon, the one whom God has chosen, is young and inexperienced. Yet, the work is important because this palace is not for a person but for the LORD God. ² With all my might I gathered ˌthe materials,ˌ for the temple of my God: gold for gold objects, silver for silver objects, bronze for bronze objects, iron for iron objects, wood for wooden objects, onyx stones and settings, black stones, stones of different colors, gems, and marble. ³ Moreover, I delight in the temple of my God. I have a personal treasury of gold and silver that I'm giving to my God's temple in addition to everything else I gathered for the holy temple. ⁴ There are 225,000 pounds of gold from Ophir and 525,000 pounds of refined silver. They are to be used to cover the walls of the buildings, ⁵ to

---

ᵃ 28:18 Or "cherubim."

make gold objects, silver objects, and everything else the craftsmen will make. Who else is willing to make an offering and dedicate himself to the LORD today?"

⁶ Then the leaders of the families, the leaders of the tribes of Israel, the commanders of regiments and battalions, and the officials in charge of the king's work gave generously. ⁷ They gave 375,186 pounds of gold, 750,000 pounds of silver, 135,000 pounds of bronze, and 7,500,000 pounds of iron for the work on God's temple. ⁸ Whoever happened to have precious stones gave them to Jehiel, Gershon's descendant, for the treasury of the LORD's temple. ⁹ The people were overjoyed that the leaders gave so generously and wholeheartedly to the LORD.

King David was also overjoyed, and ¹⁰ he praised the LORD while the whole assembly watched. David said,

> "May you be praised, LORD God of Israel,
>> our father forever and ever.ᵃ
> ¹¹ Greatness, power, splendor, glory, and majesty are yours, LORD,
>> because everything in heaven and on earth is yours.
>>> The kingdom is yours, LORD,
>>>> and you are honored as head of all things.
> ¹² Riches and honor are in front of you.
>> You rule everything.
>>> You hold power and strength in your hands,
>>>> and you can make anyone great and strong.
> ¹³ "Our God, we thank you
>> and praise your wonderful name.
> ¹⁴ But who am I and who are my people
>> that you enable us to give so generously?
>> Everything comes from you.
>>> We give you only what has come from your hands.
> ¹⁵ To you we are all like our ancestors—
>> foreigners without permanent homes.
>>> Our days are as fleeting as shadows on the ground.
>>>> There's no hope ˻for them˼.

¹⁶ "LORD, our God, all this wealth that we gathered to build a temple for your holy name is from you. All of it is yours. ¹⁷ I know, my God, that you examine hearts and delight in honesty. With an honest heart I have willingly offered all these things. I've been overjoyed to see your people here offering so willingly to you. ¹⁸ LORD God of our ancestors Abraham, Isaac, and Israel, always watch over your people's deepest thoughts. Keep their hearts directed toward you. ¹⁹ Make my son Solomon completely committed ˻to you˼ so that he will obey your commands, requests, and laws and do everything to build the palace I have planned."

Solomon Is Made King

²⁰ Then David said to the whole assembly, "Praise the LORD your God!" So the whole assembly praised the LORD God of their ancestors and knelt in front of the LORD and the king.

²¹ The next day they sacrificed to the LORD. They sacrificed burnt offerings to the LORD: 1,000 bulls, 1,000 rams, 1,000 lambs, wine offerings, and many sacrifices for all Israel. ²² That day they ate and drank as they joyfully celebrated in front of the LORD. For the second time they made David's son Solomon king. On the LORD's behalf they anointed Solomon to be leader and Zadok to be the priest.

²³ Then Solomon sat on the LORD's throne as king in place of his father David. Solomon was successful and all Israel obeyed him. ²⁴ All the leaders and soldiers and all of King David's sons pledged their loyalty to King Solomon. ²⁵ The LORD made Solomon extremely powerful, as all Israel could see. The people of Israel gave him royal honor like no king of Israel before him ever had.

David's Reign—1 Kings 2:10–12

²⁶ David, son of Jesse, had ruled all Israel. ²⁷ He ruled as king of Israel for 40 years. He ruled for 7 years in Hebron and for 33 in Jerusalem. ²⁸ He died at a very old age. His long life was full of wealth and honor. Then his son Solomon succeeded him as king.

²⁹ Everything about King David from first to last is written in the records of the seerᵇ Samuel, the prophet Nathan, and the seer Gad. ³⁰ It includes everything about his reign, his power, and the things that happened to him, Israel, and all the other kingdoms.

ᵃ 29:10 Or "May you be praised forever and ever, LORD God of our ancestor Israel."   ᵇ 29:29 A seer is a prophet.

2 CHRONICLES

God Appears to Solomon—1 Kings 3:1–15; 10:26–29

1 ¹ Solomon, son of David, strengthened his position over the kingdom. The LORD his God was with him and made him very powerful.

² Solomon spoke to all Israel—to the commanders of regiments and battalions, judges, every prince, and the heads of Israel's families. ³ Then Solomon and the entire assembly went to the place of worship in Gibeon because God's tent of meeting was there. Moses, the LORD's servant, had made the tent in the desert. ⁴ (However, David had ⌐already⌐ brought God's ark from Kiriath Jearim to a place he had prepared for it. He had put up a tent for it in Jerusalem.) ⁵ The bronze altar that Bezalel, son of Uri and grandson of Hur, had made was in front of the LORD's tent. There Solomon and the assembly worshiped the LORD. ⁶ In the LORD's presence Solomon went to the bronze altar in front of the tent of meeting and sacrificed 1,000 burnt offerings on it.

⁷ That night God appeared to Solomon. He said, "What can I give you?"

⁸ Solomon responded to God, "You've shown great love to my father David, and you've made me king in his place. ⁹ Now, LORD God, you've kept the promise you made to my father David. You've made me king of people who are as numerous as specks of dust on the ground. ¹⁰ Give me wisdom and knowledge so that I may lead these people. After all, who can judge this great people of yours?"

¹¹ God replied to Solomon, "I know this request is from your heart. You didn't ask for riches, fortunes, honor, or the death of those who hate you. You didn't even ask for a long life. Instead, you've asked for wisdom and knowledge to judge my people, over whom I made you king. ¹² So wisdom and knowledge will be given to you. I will also give you riches, fortunes, and honor like no other king before or after you."

¹³ Solomon went from the tent of meeting at the place of worship in Gibeon to Jerusalem. And he ruled Israel.

¹⁴ Solomon built up ⌐his army⌐ with chariots and war horses. He had 1,400 chariots and 12,000 war horses. He stationed ⌐some⌐ in chariot cities and ⌐others⌐ with himself in Jerusalem.

¹⁵ The king made silver and gold as common in Jerusalem as stones, and he made cedars as plentiful as fig trees in the foothills.

¹⁶ Solomon's horses were imported from Egypt and Kue. The king's traders bought them from Kue for a fixed price. ¹⁷ They imported each chariot from Egypt for 15 pounds of silver and each horse for 6 ounces of silver. For the same price they obtained horses to export to all the Hittite and Aramean kings.

Solomon Assembles the Labor and Materials for the Temple—1 Kings 5:1–18; 7:13–14

2ᵃ ¹ Solomon gave orders to begin building the temple for the LORD's name and a royal palace for himself.

² Solomon drafted 70,000 men to carry heavy loads, 80,000 to quarry stones in the mountains, and 3,600 foremen. ³ Solomon sent word to King Huram of Tyre by saying, "Do what you did for my father David. You sent him cedar so that he could build a palace to live in. ⁴ I want to build the temple for the name of the LORD my God. I want to dedicate it to him, burn sweet-smelling incense in his presence, and have rows of bread there continually. I want to ⌐sacrifice⌐ burnt offerings every morning and evening, on weekly worship days, New Moon Festivals, and during the annual festivals appointed by the LORD our God. (⌐These festivals⌐ are always to be celebrated by Israel.) ⁵ The temple I am building will be great because our God is greater than all other gods. ⁶ But who is able to build him a temple when heaven itself, the highest heaven, cannot hold him? Who am I to build him a temple except as a place to sacrifice in his presence?

⁷ "Send me a man who has the skill to work with gold, silver, bronze, and iron as well as purple, dark red, and violet cloth. He should know how to make engravings with the skilled men whom my father David provided for me in Judah and Jerusalem. ⁸ Send me cedar, cypress, and sandalwood from Lebanon. I know that your servants are skilled Lebanese lumberjacks. My workers will work with your workers. ⁹ They'll prepare plenty of lumber for me, because the tem-

---

ᵃ 2:1 2 Chronicles 2:1–18 in English Bibles is 2 Chronicles 1:18–2:17 in the Hebrew Bible.

ple I want to build will be large and astonishing. ¹⁰ I will give your lumberjacks 120,000 bushels of ground wheat, 120,000 bushels of barley, 200,000 gallons of wine, and 200,000 gallons of olive oil."

¹¹ Then King Huram of Tyre responded to Solomon by sending a letter that said, "Because the LORD loves his people, he made you their king." ¹² Huram added, "May the LORD God of Israel be praised. He made the heavens and the earth and has given King David a wise son who has insight and intelligence and can build the LORD's temple and a royal palace. ¹³ And now, I'm sending a man with skill and intelligence—Huram Abi. ¹⁴ He was the son of a woman from the tribe of Dan, and his father is a native of Tyre. Huram knows how to work with gold, silver, bronze, iron, stone, wood, purple, violet, and dark red cloth, and linen. He also knows how to make all kinds of engravings and follow any set of plans that will be given to him. ⸤He can work⸥ with your skilled workmen and the skilled workmen of His Majesty David, your father. ¹⁵ Your Majesty may now send the wheat, barley, olive oil, and wine he promised the workers. ¹⁶ We will cut all the lumber you need in Lebanon. Then we will make rafts out of it and send them to you in Joppa by sea. You can take it ⸤from there⸥ to Jerusalem."

¹⁷ Solomon counted all the men who were foreigners in the land of Israel, as his father David had counted them. Solomon counted 153,600 foreigners. ¹⁸ He made 70,000 of them carry heavy loads, 80,000 of them quarry stone in the mountains, and 3,600 of them supervise the work as foremen.

The Temple Built and Furnished—*1 Kings 6:1–38; 7:13–51*

3 ¹ Solomon began to build the LORD's temple in Jerusalem on Mount Moriah, where the LORD appeared to his father David. There David had prepared the site on the threshing floor[a] of Ornan the Jebusite. ² He began to build on the second day in the second month of the fourth year of his reign.

³ This is how Solomon laid the foundation to build God's temple. It was 90 feet long and 30 feet wide. (They used the old standard measurement.) ⁴ The entrance hall in front of ⸤the main room⸥ was 30 feet wide (the same as the width of the temple) and 30 feet high. He covered its inside walls with pure gold. ⁵ He paneled the larger building with cypress, overlaid it with fine gold, and decorated it with ⸤designs in the form of⸥ palm trees and chains. ⁶ He covered the building with gems to beautify it and used gold from Parvaim. ⁷ He also overlaid the building, the rafters, the threshold, the walls, and the doors with gold, and he carved angels[b] into the walls.

⁸ He made the most holy place. It was as long as the temple was wide, 30 feet long. It was also 30 feet wide. He overlaid it with 45,000 pounds of fine gold. ⁹ The gold nails weighed 20 ounces. He also overlaid the upper rooms with gold.

¹⁰ In the most holy place he made two sculptured angels and covered them with gold. ¹¹ The combined length of the angels' wings was 30 feet. A wing of one of the angels was 7½ feet long and touched the wall of the building. Its other wing was 7½ feet long and touched one wing of the other. ¹² The wing of the other one of the angels was 7½ feet long and touched the other wall of the building. Its other wing was 7½ feet long and touched the wing of the first. So the angels' combined wingspan was 30 feet. ¹³ They stood on their feet and faced the main hall. ¹⁴ Solomon made the canopy of violet, purple, and dark red cloth and of linen and decorated it with angels.

¹⁵ He made two pillars for the front of the temple. They were 53 feet long, and the capital on each pillar was 7½ feet ⸤high⸥. ¹⁶ He made chains for the inner room and ⸤also⸥ put them on the capitals. He made 100 pomegranates and put them on the chains. ¹⁷ He set up the pillars in front of the temple, one on the right and the other on the left. He named the one on the right Jachin [He Establishes] and the one on the left Boaz [In Him Is Strength].

4 ¹ He made a bronze altar 30 feet long, 30 feet wide, and 15 feet high. ² Huram made a pool from cast metal. It was 15 feet in diameter. It was round, 7½ feet high, and had a circumference of 45 feet. ³ Under the rim were two rows of figurines shaped like bulls all around the 45-foot circumference of the pool. They were cast in metal when the pool was cast. ⁴ The pool was set on 12 metal bulls. Three bulls faced north, three faced west, three faced south, and three faced east. The pool was set on them, and their hindquarters were toward the center ⸤of the pool⸥. ⁵ The pool was three inches thick. Its rim was like the rim of a cup, shaped like a lily's bud. It held 18,000 gallons.

⁶ Huram also made ten basins for washing and put five on the south side and five on the north side. The priests rinsed the meat prepared for the burnt offerings in them. They used the pool to wash themselves.

⁷ Huram made ten gold lamp stands according to their specifications and put them in the temple, five on the south side and five on the north side. ⁸ He made ten tables and put them in the temple, five on the south side and five on the north side. And he made 100 gold bowls.

---

[a] 3:1 A threshing floor is an outdoor area where grain is separated from its husks.   [b] 3:7 Or "cherubim."

⁹ He also made the priests' courtyard and the large courtyard and its doors. He covered the doors with bronze. ¹⁰ He set the pool on the south side in the southeast ‸corner‸. ¹¹ Huram also made the pots, shovels, and bowls.

So Huram finished the work for King Solomon in God's temple: ¹² 2 pillars, bowl-shaped capitals on top of the 2 pillars, and 2 sets of filigree to cover the 2 bowl-shaped capitals on top of the pillars, ¹³ 400 pomegranates for the 2 sets of filigree (2 rows of pomegranates for each filigree to cover the 2 bowl-shaped capitals on the pillars), ¹⁴ 10 stands and 10ᵃ basins on the stands, ¹⁵ 1 pool and the 12 bulls under it, ¹⁶ pots, shovels, and three-pronged forks. Huram made all of them out of polished bronze for the LORD's temple at King Solomon's request. ¹⁷ The king cast them in foundries in the Jordan Valley between Succoth and Zeredah. ¹⁸ Solomon made so many of these products that no one tried to determine how much the bronze weighed.

¹⁹ Solomon made all the furnishings for God's temple: the gold altar, the gold tables on which the bread of the presence was placed, ²⁰ lamp stands and lamps of pure gold (to burn as directed in front of the inner room), ²¹ flowers, lamps, pure gold tongs, ²² snuffers, basins, dishes, incense burners of pure gold, the gold entrance to the temple, the gold doors of the inner ‸room‸ (the most holy place), and the gold doors of the temple.

5 ¹ All the work Solomon did on the LORD's temple was finished. He brought the holy things that had belonged to his father David—the silver, gold, and all the utensils—and put them in the storerooms of God's temple.

The LORD Comes to His Temple—1 Kings 8:1–11

² Then Solomon assembled the respected leaders of Israel, all the heads of the tribes, and the leaders of the Israelite families. They came to Jerusalem to take the ark of the LORD's promise from the City of David (that is, Zion). ³ All the men of Israel gathered around the king at the Festival ‸of Booths‸ in the seventh month.

⁴ When all the leaders of Israel had arrived, the Levites picked up the ark. ⁵ They brought the ark, the tent of meeting, and all the holy utensils in it ‸to the temple‸. The priests and the Levites carried them ⁶ while King Solomon and the whole assembly from Israel were offering countless sheep and cattle sacrifices in front of the ark. ⁷ The priests brought the ark of the LORD's promise to its place in the inner room of the temple (the most holy place) under the wings of the angels.ᵃ

⁸ The angels' outstretched wings were over the place where the ark ‸rested‸ so that the angels became a covering above the ark and its poles. ⁹ The poles were so long that their ends could be seen in the holy place by anyone standing in front of the inner room,ᵇ but they couldn't be seen outside. (They are still there today.) ¹⁰ There was nothing in the ark except the two tablets Moses placed there at Horeb, where the LORD made a promise to the Israelites after they left Egypt.

¹¹ All the priests who were present had performed the ceremonies to make themselves holy to God without regard to staying in their divisions. ¹² All the Levites who were musicians—Asaph, Heman, Jeduthun, their sons, and their relatives—were dressed in fine linen and stood east of the altar with cymbals, harps, and lyres. With the musicians were 120 priests blowing trumpets. When the priests left the holy place,ᶜ ¹³ the trumpeters and singers praised and thanked the LORD in unison. Accompanied by trumpets, cymbals, and other musical instruments, they sang in praise to the LORD: "He is good; his mercy endures forever." Then the LORD's temple was filled with a cloud. ¹⁴ The priests couldn't serve because of the cloud. The LORD's glory filled God's temple.

Solomon Addresses the People—1 Kings 8:12–21

6 ¹ Then Solomon said, "The LORD said he would live in a dark cloud. ² But I have built you a high temple, a home for you to live in permanently."

³ Then the king turned around and blessed the whole assembly from Israel while they were standing. ⁴ "Thanks be to the LORD God of Israel. With his mouth he made a promise to my father David; with his hand he carried it out. He said, ⁵ 'Ever since I brought my people Israel out of Egypt, I didn't choose any city from the tribes of Israel as a place to build a temple for my name. And I didn't choose any man to be prince over my people Israel. ⁶ But now I've chosen Jerusalem to be a place for my name; I've chosen David to rule my people Israel.'

⁷ "My father David had his heart set on building a temple for the name of the LORD God of Israel. ⁸ However, the LORD said to my father David, 'Since you had your heart set on building a temple for my name, your intentions were good. ⁹ But you must not build the temple. Instead, your own son will build the temple for my name.' ¹⁰ The LORD has kept the promise he made. I've taken my father David's place, and I sit on the throne of Israel as the LORD promised. I've built the temple for the name of the LORD God of Israel. ¹¹ I've put the ark which contains the LORD's promise to Israel there."

ᵃ 4:14 1 Kings 7:43, Greek; Masoretic Text "he made stands, and he made basins. . . ."   ᵃ 5:7 Or "cherubim."
ᵇ 5:9 A few Hebrew manuscripts, 1 Kings 8:8, Greek; other Hebrew manuscripts "The poles extended so long from the ark that their ends could be seen by anyone standing in front of the inner room."   ᶜ 5:12 The first part of verse 11 (in Hebrew) has been placed just before verse 13 to express the complex Hebrew sentence structure more clearly in English.

Solomon's Prayer—*1 Kings 8:22–53; Psalm 132:1, 8–10*

12 In the presence of the entire assembly of Israel, Solomon stood in front of the LORD's altar. He stretched out his hands ˌto prayˌ. **13** (Solomon had made a bronze platform 7½ feet long, 7½ feet wide, and 4½ feet high. He put it in the middle of the courtyard. He stood on the platform, knelt in front of the entire assembly, and stretched out his hands toward heaven.) **14** He said,

> "LORD God of Israel,
>> there is no god like you in heaven or on earth.
> You keep your promise[a] of mercy to your servants,
>> who obey you wholeheartedly.
> **15** You have kept your promise to my father David, your servant.
>> With your mouth you promised it.
>> With your hand you carried it out as it is today.
>
> **16** "Now, LORD God of Israel,
>> keep your promise to my father David, your servant.
>>> You said, 'You will never fail to have an heir
>>>> sitting in front of me on the throne of Israel
>>>> if your descendants are faithful to me
>>>>> as you have been faithful to me.'
>
> **17** "So now, LORD God of Israel,
>> may the promise you made to David, your servant, come true.
>
> **18** "Does God really live on earth with people?
>> If heaven itself, the highest heaven, cannot hold you,
>> then how can this temple that I have built?
> **19** Nevertheless, my LORD God, please pay attention to my prayer for mercy.
> Listen to my cry for help as I pray to you.
> **20** Day and night may your eyes be on this temple,
>> the place about which you said your name will be there.
> Listen to me as I pray toward this place.
> **21** Hear the plea for mercy
>> that your people Israel and I pray toward this place.
> Hear us in heaven, the place where you live.
> Hear and forgive.
>
> **22** "If anyone sins against another person
>> and is required to take an oath
>> and comes to take the oath in front of your altar in this temple,
> **23** then hear ˌthat personˌ in heaven, take action, and make a decision.
>> Repay the guilty person with the proper punishment,
>> but declare the innocent person innocent.
>
> **24** "An enemy may defeat your people Israel
>> because they have sinned against you.
>>> But when your people turn, praise your name, pray,
>>> and plead with you in this temple,
> **25** then hear ˌthemˌ in heaven, forgive the sins of your people Israel,
>> and bring them back to the land
>> that you gave to them and their ancestors.
>
> **26** "When the sky is shut and there's no rain
>> because they are sinning against you
>>> and they pray toward this place, praise your name,
>>> and turn away from their sin because you made them suffer,
> **27** then hear ˌthemˌ in heaven.
>> Forgive the sins of your servants, your people Israel.
>> Teach them the proper way to live.
>>> Then send rain on the land,
>>> which you gave to your people as an inheritance.
>
> **28** "There may be famine in the land.
>> Plant diseases, heat waves, funguses, locusts,

---

a 6:14 Or "covenant."

or grasshoppers may destroy crops.
Enemies may blockade Israel's city gates.
During every plague or sickness
29 ⌞hear⌟ every prayer for mercy
made by one person or by all the people in Israel,
all who know suffering or pain,
who stretch out their hands toward this temple.
30 Hear ⌞them⌟ in heaven, where you live.
Forgive ⌞them⌟, and give each person the proper reply.
(You know what is in their hearts,
because you alone know what is in people's hearts.)
31 Then, as long as they live in the land that you gave to our ancestors,
they will fear you and follow you.

32 "People who are not Israelites
will come from distant countries because of your great name,
mighty hand, and powerful arm.
When they come to pray facing this temple,
33 then hear ⌞them⌟ in heaven, the place where you live.
Do everything they ask you
so that all the people of the world may know your name
and fear you like your people Israel
and learn that this temple which I built bears your name.

34 "When your people go to war against their enemies
(wherever you may send them)
and they pray to you toward this city you have chosen
and the temple I built for your name,
35 then hear their prayer for mercy in heaven,
and do what is right ⌞for them⌟.

36 "They may sin against you.
(No one is sinless.)
You may become angry with them and hand them over to an enemy
who takes them to ⌞another⌟ country as captives,
⌞whether it is⌟ far or near.
37 If they come to their senses,
are sorry for what they've done,
and plead with you in the land where they are captives,
saying, 'We have sinned. We have done wrong.
We have been wicked,'
38 if they change their attitude toward you
in the land where they are captives,
if they pray to you
toward the land that you gave their ancestors,
and the city you have chosen,
and the temple I have built for your name,
39 then in heaven, the place where you live, hear their prayer for mercy.
Do what is right for them.
Forgive your people, who have sinned against you.

40 "Finally, my God, may your eyes be open and your ears attentive
to the prayers ⌞offered⌟ in this place.

41 "Now arise, and come to your resting place, LORD God—
you and the ark of your power.
Clothe your priests, LORD God, with salvation.
Let your godly ones rejoice in what is good.
42 LORD God, do not reject your anointed one.
Remember your mercy to your servant David!"

Solomon Offers Sacrifices—1 Kings 8:62–66

7 ¹ When Solomon finished praying, fire came down from heaven and consumed the burnt offerings and the other sacrifices, and the LORD's glory filled the temple. ² The priests couldn't go into the LORD's temple because the LORD's glory had filled the LORD's temple.

³ When all the Israelites saw the fire come down and the LORD's glory on the temple, they knelt down with their faces on the pavement. They worshiped and praised the LORD, ⌞by saying,⌟ "He is good; his mercy endures forever."

⁴ Then the king and all the people offered sacrifices to the LORD. ⁵ King Solomon offered 22,000 cattle and 120,000 sheep as sacrifices to the LORD. So the king and all the people dedicated God's temple.

⁶ The priests were standing at their posts. So were the Levites who had the LORD's musical instruments which King David made for praising the LORD with "his mercy endures forever" and which he used to offer praise. The priests were opposite the Levites blowing trumpets while all Israel was standing ⌞there⌟.

⁷ Solomon designated the courtyard in front of the LORD's temple as a holy place. He sacrificed the burnt offerings, grain offerings, and the fat because the bronze altar that he had made and that was in front of the LORD was not able to hold all of them.

⁸ At that time Solomon and all Israel celebrated the Festival ⌞of Booths⌟. A very large crowd had come from ⌞the territory between⌟ the border of Hamath and the River of Egypt. ⁹ On the eighth day there was an assembly. They had observed the dedication of the altar for seven days and celebrated the festival for ⌞another⌟ seven days. ¹⁰ On the twenty-third day of the seventh month, Solomon dismissed the people to their tents. They rejoiced with cheerful hearts for all the blessings the LORD had given David, Solomon, and his people Israel.

The LORD Answers Solomon's Prayer—1 Kings 9:1–9

¹¹ Solomon finished the LORD's temple and the royal palace and completed everything he had in mind for the LORD's temple and his own palace. ¹² Then the LORD appeared to him at night. He said to Solomon,

> "I have heard your prayer
> and have chosen this place for myself as a temple for sacrifices.
> ¹³ I may shut the sky so that there is no rain,
> or command grasshoppers to devour the countryside,
> or send an epidemic among my people.
> ¹⁴ However, if my people, who are called by my name,
> will humble themselves,
> pray, search for me, and turn from their evil ways,
> then I will hear ⌞their prayer⌟ from heaven, forgive their sins,
> and heal their country.
> ¹⁵ My eyes will be open,
> and my ears will pay attention to those prayers at this place.
> ¹⁶ I have chosen and declared this temple holy
> so that my name may be placed there forever.
> My eyes and my heart will always be there.
>
> ¹⁷ "If you will be faithful to me as your father David was,
> do everything I command,
> and obey my laws and rules,
> ¹⁸ then I will establish your royal dynasty
> as I said in a promise to your father David,
> 'You will never fail to have an heir ruling Israel.'
> ¹⁹ But if you and your descendants turn away from me
> and abandon my commands and laws that I gave you,
> and follow and serve other gods and worship them,
> ²⁰ then I will uproot Israel from the land I gave them.
> I will reject this temple that I declared holy for my name.
> I will make it an example
> and an object of ridicule for all the people of the world.
> ²¹ Everyone passing by this impressive temple will be appalled.
> They will ask,
> 'Why did the LORD do these things to this land and this temple?'
> ²² They will answer ⌞themselves⌟,
> 'They abandoned the LORD God of their ancestors,
> who brought them out of Egypt.
> They adopted other gods, worshiped, and served them.
> That is why he brought this disaster on them.' "

Solomon Completes His Construction—*1 Kings 9:10–28*

8 ¹ It took Solomon 20 years to build the LORD's house and his own house. ² He rebuilt the cities Huram gave him, and he had Israelites live in them.

³ Then Solomon went to Hamath Zobah and conquered it. ⁴ He rebuilt Tadmor in the desert and built all the storage cities in Hamath. ⁵ He rebuilt Upper Beth Horon and Lower Beth Horon into cities fortified with walls, double-door gates, and bars. ⁶ He also rebuilt, Baalath and all the storage cities that he owned. He built all the cities for his chariots, all the cities for his war horses, and whatever ˌelseˌ he wanted to build in Jerusalem, Lebanon, or the entire territory that he governed.

⁷ The Hittites, Perizzites, Hivites, and Jebusites had been left ˌin the landˌ because the Israelites had not been able to destroy them.ᵃ They were not Israelites, ⁸ but they had descendants who were still in the land. Solomon drafted them for slave labor. (They are still ˌslavesˌ today.) ⁹ But Solomon didn't make any of the Israelites slaves for his projects. Instead, they were the soldiers, officers, generals, and commanders of his chariot and cavalry units.

¹⁰ These were the officers in charge of King Solomon's projects: 250 foremen for the people who did the work.

¹¹ Solomon brought Pharaoh's daughter from the City of David to a palace he had built for her. He said, "My wife will not live in the palace of King David of Israel because these places where the LORD's ark has come are holy."

¹² Then Solomon sacrificed burnt offerings to the LORD on the LORD's altar that he built in front of the entrance hall. ¹³ He sacrificed every day, on weekly worship days, on the New Moon Festivals, and on the three annual festivals (the Festival of Unleavened Bread, the Festival of Weeks, and the Festival of Booths) as Moses had commanded. ¹⁴ As Solomon's father David had directed, he set up the divisions of priests for their service and the ˌdivisions ofˌ Levites for their appointed places. ˌThe Levitesˌ were to lead in praising ˌthe LORDˌ and to serve beside the priests by doing whatever needed to be done each day. Solomon also set up divisions of doorkeepers at every gate because this is what David, the man of God, had commanded. ¹⁵ No one neglected the king's orders to the priests or the Levites in any matter, including the ˌtemple'sˌ finances. ¹⁶ All of Solomon's work was carried out from the day the foundation of the LORD's temple was laid until it was completed. The LORD's temple was ˌnowˌ finished.

¹⁷ Then Solomon went to the coast near Ezion Geber and Elath in Edom. ¹⁸ Huram sent his own servants and his experienced sailors with ships to Solomon. They went with Solomon's servants to Ophir, got 33,750 pounds of gold, and brought it to King Solomon.

The Queen of Sheba Visits Solomon—*1 Kings 10:1–13*

9 ¹ The queen of Sheba heard about Solomon's reputation. So she came to Jerusalem to test him with riddles. She arrived with a large group of servants, with camels carrying spices, a large quantity of gold, and precious stones. When she came to Solomon, she talked to him about everything she had on her mind. ² Solomon answered all her questions. No question was too difficult for Solomon to answer.

³ When the queen of Sheba saw Solomon's wisdom, the palace he built, ⁴ the food on his table, his officers' seating arrangement, the organization of his officials and the uniforms they wore, his cupbearersᵃ and their uniforms, and the burnt offerings that he sacrificed at the LORD's temple, she was breathless. ⁵ She told the king, "What I heard in my country about your words and your wisdom is true! ⁶ But I didn't believe the reports until I came and saw it with my own eyes. I wasn't even told about half of the extent of your wisdom. You've surpassed the stories I've heard. ⁷ How blessed your men must be! How blessed these servants of yours must be because they are always stationed in front of you and listen to your wisdom! ⁸ Thank the LORD your God, who is pleased with you. He has put you on his throne to be king on behalf of the LORD your God. Because of your God's love for the people of Israel, he has established them permanently and made you king over them so that you would maintain justice and righteousness."

⁹ She gave the king 9,000 pounds of gold, a very large quantity of spices, and precious stones. Never was there such a large quantity of spices ˌin Israelˌ as those that the queen of Sheba gave King Solomon.

¹⁰ Huram's servants and Solomon's servants who brought gold from Ophir also brought sandalwood and precious stones. ¹¹ With the sandalwood the king made gateways to the LORD's temple and the royal palace, and lyres and harps for the singers. No one had ever seen anything like them in Judah.

ᵃ 8:7 "because the Israelites. . . ." This clause has been moved from verse 8 (in Hebrew) to express the complex Hebrew sentence structure more clearly in English.   ᵃ 9:4 A cupbearer was a trusted royal official who ensured that the king's drink was not poisoned.

¹² King Solomon gave the queen of Sheba anything she wanted, whatever she asked for, more than what she had brought him. Then she and her servants went back to her country.

Solomon's Wealth—1 Kings 5:1; 10:14–29

¹³ The gold that came to Solomon in one year weighed 49,950 pounds, ¹⁴ not counting ⌐the gold⌐ which the merchants and traders brought. All the Arab kings and governors of the land also brought gold and silver to Solomon.

¹⁵ King Solomon made 200 large shields of hammered gold, using 15 pounds of gold on each shield. ¹⁶ He also made 300 small shields of hammered gold, using 7½ pounds of gold on each shield. The king put them in the hall ⌐named⌐ the Forest of Lebanon.

¹⁷ The king also made a large ivory throne and covered it with pure gold. ¹⁸ Six steps led to the throne, which had a gold footstool attached to it. There were armrests on both sides of the seat. Two lions stood beside the armrests. ¹⁹ Twelve lions stood on six steps, one on each side. Nothing like this had been made for any other kingdom.

²⁰ All King Solomon's cups were gold, and all the utensils for the hall ⌐named⌐ the Forest of Lebanon were fine gold. (Silver wasn't considered valuable in Solomon's time.) ²¹ The king had ships going to Tarshish with Huram's sailors. Once every three years the Tarshish ships would bring gold, silver, ivory, apes, and monkeys.

²² In wealth and wisdom King Solomon was greater than all the ⌐other⌐ kings of the world. ²³ All the kings of the world wanted to listen to the wisdom that God gave Solomon. ²⁴ So everyone who came brought him gifts: articles of silver and gold, clothing, weapons, spices, horses, and mules. This happened year after year.

²⁵ Solomon had 4,000 stalls for horses and chariots, and 12,000 war horses. He stationed ⌐some⌐ in chariot cities and ⌐others⌐ with himself in Jerusalem. ²⁶ He ruled all the kings from the Euphrates River to the country of the Philistines and as far as the Egyptian border. ²⁷ The king made silver as common in Jerusalem as stones, and he made cedars as plentiful as fig trees in the foothills. ²⁸ Horses were imported for Solomon from Egypt and from all other countries.

Solomon's Death—1 Kings 11:41–43

²⁹ Aren't the rest of Solomon's acts from first to last written in the records of Nathan the prophet, in the prophecy of Ahijah from Shiloh, and in Iddo the seer's[b] visions about Jeroboam (son of Nebat)?

³⁰ Solomon ruled in Jerusalem over all Israel for 40 years. ³¹ Solomon lay down in death with his ancestors and was buried in the City of David. His son Rehoboam succeeded him as king.

King Rehoboam Foolishly Rejects Israel's Request—1 Kings 12:1–19

10 ¹ Rehoboam went to Shechem because all Israel had gone to Shechem to make him king. ² Jeroboam (Nebat's son) was still in Egypt, where he had fled from King Solomon. When he heard ⌐about Rehoboam⌐, he returned from Egypt. ³ ⌐Israel⌐ sent for Jeroboam and invited him back. Jeroboam and all Israel went to speak to Rehoboam. They said, ⁴ "Your father made us carry a heavy burden. Reduce the hard work and lighten the heavy burden he put on us, and we will serve you."

⁵ He said to them, "Come back the day after tomorrow." So the people left.

⁶ King Rehoboam sought advice from the older leaders who had served his father Solomon while he was still alive. He asked, "What do you advise? How should I respond to these people?"

⁷ They told him, "If you are good to these people and try to please them by speaking gently to them, then they will always be your servants."

⁸ But he ignored the advice the older leaders gave him. He sought advice from the young men who had grown up with him and were serving him. ⁹ He asked them, "What is your advice? How should we respond to these people who are asking me to lighten the burden my father put on them?"

¹⁰ The young men who had grown up with him answered, "This is what you should tell them: 'My little finger is heavier than my father's whole body.[a] ¹¹ If my father put a heavy burden on you, I will add to it. If my father punished you with whips, I will punish you with scorpions.' "

¹² So Jeroboam and all the people came back to Rehoboam two days later, as the king had instructed them. ¹³ The king answered them harshly. He ignored the older leaders' advice. ¹⁴ He spoke to them as the young men advised. He said, "If my father made your burden heavy, I will add to it. If my father punished you with whips, I will use scorpions." ¹⁵ The king refused to listen to the people because the LORD was directing these events to carry out the promise he had made to Jeroboam (Nebat's son) through Ahijah from Shiloh.

¹⁶ When all Israel saw that the king refused to listen to them, the people answered the king,

---

ᵇ 9:29 A seer is a prophet.   ᵃ 10:10 Hebrew meaning uncertain.

"What share do we have in David's kingdom?
We won't receive an inheritance from Jesse's son.
Everyone to his own tent, Israel!
Now look after your own house, David!"

So all Israel went home to their own tents. **¹⁷** But Rehoboam ruled the Israelites who lived in the cities of Judah.
¹⁸ Then King Rehoboam sent Hadoram to the Israelites. He was in charge of forced labor, but they stoned him to death. So King Rehoboam got on his chariot as fast as he could and fled to Jerusalem. **¹⁹** Israel has rebelled against David's dynasty to this day.

Israel's Priests Come to Judah—1 Kings 12:21–33

11 **¹** When Rehoboam came to Jerusalem, he gathered the people of Judah and Benjamin, 180,000 of the best soldiers, to fight against Israel and return the kingdom to Rehoboam. **²** But God spoke his word to Shemaiah, the man of God. He said, **³** "Speak to Judah's King Rehoboam, son of Solomon, and all Israel in Judah and Benjamin. **⁴** This is what the LORD says: Don't wage war against your relatives. Everyone, go home. What has happened is my doing." So they obeyed the word of the LORD. They turned back from their attack on Jeroboam.

⁵ Rehoboam lived in Jerusalem and built fortified cities in Judah. **⁶** He rebuilt Bethlehem, Etam, Tekoa, **⁷** Beth Zur, Soco, Adullam, **⁸** Gath, Mareshah, Ziph, **⁹** Adoraim, Lachish, Azekah, **¹⁰** Zorah, Aijalon, and Hebron. These were fortified cities in Judah and Benjamin. **¹¹** He strengthened them and put army officers with reserves of food, olive oil, and wine in them. **¹²** In each city he stored shields and spears. He made the cities very secure. So Rehoboam held on to Judah and Benjamin.

¹³ The priests and Levites in every region of Israel sided with Rehoboam. **¹⁴** The priests abandoned their land and property and went to Judah and Jerusalem because Jeroboam and his descendants rejected them as the LORD's priests. **¹⁵** Instead, Jeroboam appointed ⌊his own⌋ priests for the illegal worship sites and the goat and calf statues he had made as idols. **¹⁶** People from every tribe of Israel who were determined to seek the LORD God of Israel followed the Levitical priests to Jerusalem to sacrifice to the LORD God of their ancestors.

¹⁷ So they strengthened the kingdom of Judah by supporting Rehoboam, son of Solomon, for three years. During ⌊those⌋ three years they lived the way David and Solomon had lived.

Rehoboam's Family

¹⁸ Rehoboam married Mahalath, daughter of Jerimoth. (Jerimoth was the son of David and Abihail. Abihail was the daughter of Eliab, son of Jesse.) **¹⁹** Mahalath gave birth to the following sons: Jeush, Shemariah, and Zaham. **²⁰** After marrying Mahalath, he married Maacah, Absalom's granddaughter. She gave birth to Abijah, Attai, Ziza, and Shelomith. **²¹** Rehoboam loved Maacah, Absalom's granddaughter, more than all his other wives and concubines.[a] (He had 18 wives and 60 concubines. He fathered 28 sons and 60 daughters.)

²² Rehoboam appointed Abijah, son of Maacah, as family head and prince among his brothers. By doing this, Rehoboam could make him king. **²³** He wisely placed his sons in every region of Judah and Benjamin, in every fortified city. He gave them allowances and obtained many wives for them.

King Shishak Takes the Temple Treasures—1 Kings 14:21–31

12 **¹** When Rehoboam had established his kingdom and made himself strong, he and all Israel abandoned the LORD's teachings. **²** In the fifth year of Rehoboam's reign, King Shishak of Egypt attacked Jerusalem. This happened because all Israel was not loyal to the LORD. **³** Shishak had 1,200 chariots, 60,000 horses, and an army of countless Libyans, Sukkites, and Sudanese from Egypt.

⁴ He captured the fortified cities in Judah and then came to Jerusalem.

⁵ The prophet Shemaiah came to Rehoboam and the leaders of Judah who had gathered in Jerusalem because of Shishak. Shemaiah said to them, "This is what the LORD says: You have abandoned me, so I will abandon you. I will hand you over to Shishak." **⁶** Then the commanders of Israel and the king humbled themselves. "The LORD is right!" they said.

⁷ When the LORD saw that they had humbled themselves, he spoke his word to Shemaiah: "They have humbled themselves. I will not destroy them. In a little while I will give them an escape. I will not use Shishak to pour my anger on Jerusalem. **⁸** But they will become his servants so that they can learn the difference between serving me and serving foreign kings."

---

[a] 11:21 A concubine is considered a wife except she has fewer rights under the law.

[9] King Shishak of Egypt attacked Jerusalem and took the treasures from the LORD's temple and the royal palace. He took them all. He took the gold shields Solomon had made. [10] So King Rehoboam made bronze shields to replace them and put them by the entrance to the royal palace, where the captains of the guards were stationed. [11] Whenever the king went into the LORD's temple, guards carried the shields and then returned them to the guardroom.

[12] After Rehoboam humbled himself, the LORD was no longer angry with him and didn't completely destroy him. So things went well in Judah.

[13] King Rehoboam strengthened his position in Jerusalem and ruled. He was 41 years old when he began to rule. He ruled for 17 years in Jerusalem, the city that the LORD chose from all the tribes of Israel, the city where the LORD put his name. (Rehoboam's mother was an Ammonite woman named Naamah.) [14] He did evil things because he was not serious about dedicating himself to serving the LORD.

[15] Aren't the events concerning Rehoboam from first to last written in the records of the prophet Shemaiah and the records of the seer[a] Iddo in the genealogies? There was war between Rehoboam and Jeroboam as long as they lived. [16] Rehoboam lay down in death with his ancestors and was buried in the City of David. His son Abijah succeeded him as king.

King Abijah's War With King Jeroboam—1 Kings 15:1–8

13 [1] In the eighteenth year of the reign of Jeroboam, Abijah began to rule Judah. [2] He ruled for three years in Jerusalem. His mother was named Micaiah, daughter of Uriel from Gibeah.

There was war between Abijah and Jeroboam.

[3] Abijah prepared for battle with an army of 400,000 of the best soldiers, while Jeroboam arranged to oppose him with 800,000 of the best professional soldiers.

[4] Then Abijah stood on Mount Zemaraim in the mountains of Ephraim. He called out, "Jeroboam and all Israel, listen to me! [5] Don't you know that the LORD God of Israel gave the kingdom of Israel to David and his descendants forever in a permanent promise?[a] [6] But Jeroboam (Nebat's son) rebelled against his master. He had been the servant of David's son Solomon. [7] Worthless, good-for-nothing men gathered around him. They opposed Rehoboam, son of Solomon, when Rehoboam was too young and inexperienced to challenge them. [8] Do you now intend to challenge the LORD's kingdom, which has been placed in the hands of David's descendants? You are a large crowd, and you have the gold calves that Jeroboam made to be your gods. [9] You forced out the LORD's priests who were Aaron's descendants, and you forced out the Levites so that you could appoint your own priests, as the people in foreign countries do. Anyone who has a young bull and seven rams can be ordained as a priest of nonexistent gods.

[10] "However, the LORD is our God. We haven't abandoned him. The priests who serve the LORD are Aaron's descendants, and the Levites assist them. [11] They sacrifice burnt offerings to the LORD every morning and every evening. They offer sweet-smelling incense and rows of bread on the clean[b] table. The lamps on the gold lamp stand burn every evening. We're following the instructions the LORD our God gave us, but you have abandoned him. [12] God is with us as our leader. His priests will sound their trumpets to call ˌthe armyˌ to fight you. Men of Israel, don't wage war against the LORD God of your ancestors. You won't succeed."

[13] But Jeroboam had set an ambush to attack them from behind. So Jeroboam's army was in front of Judah, and the ambush was behind them. [14] When Judah's soldiers looked around, the battle was in front of them and behind them. They cried out to the LORD, the priests blew the trumpets, [15] and the men of Judah shouted. When they shouted, God attacked Jeroboam and all Israel in front of Abijah and Judah. [16] The Israelites fled from Judah's ˌarmyˌ, and God handed them over to Judah. [17] So Abijah and his men defeated them decisively, and 500,000 of the best men of Israel were killed. [18] So the Israelites were humbled at that time, and the men of Judah won because they trusted the LORD God of their ancestors. [19] Abijah pursued Jeroboam and captured some of his cities: Bethel and its villages, Jeshanah and its villages, and Ephron and its villages.

[20] Jeroboam never regained power during Abijah's time. The LORD caused Jeroboam to become sick, and Jeroboam died.

[21] But Abijah became strong. He married 14 wives and fathered 22 sons and 16 daughters. [22] Everything else about Abijah—how he lived and what he said—is written in the history by the prophet Iddo.

14[a] [1] Abijah lay down in death with his ancestors and was buried in the City of David. His son Asa succeeded him as king. In Asa's time the land had peace for ten years.

---

[a] 12:15 A seer is a prophet.   [a] 13:5 Or "covenant."   [b] 13:11 "Clean" refers to anything that Moses' Teachings say is presentable to God.   [a] 14:1 2 Chronicles 14:1–15 in English Bibles is 2 Chronicles 13:23–14:14 in the Hebrew Bible.

King Asa of Judah—1 Kings 15:9–15

[2] Asa did what the LORD his God considered good and right.

[3] He got rid of the altars of foreign gods, broke down the sacred stones, and cut down the poles dedicated to the goddess Asherah. [4] He told the people of Judah to dedicate their lives to serving the LORD God of their ancestors and follow his teachings and commands. [5] He got rid of the illegal places of worship and the altars for incense in all the cities of Judah. The kingdom was at peace during his reign.

[6] He built fortified cities in Judah because the land had peace. There was no war during those years because the LORD gave him a time of peace. [7] So Asa told Judah, "Let's build these cities and make walls around them with towers and doors that can be barred. The country is still ours because we have dedicated our lives to serving the LORD our God. We have dedicated our lives to him, and he has surrounded us with peace." So they built the cities, and everything went well.

[8] Asa had an army of 300,000 Judeans who were armed with large shields and spears and 280,000 Benjaminites who were armed with small shields and bows. All of these men were good fighting men.

[9] Then Zerah from Sudan came with 1,000,000 men and 300 chariots to attack Asa. Zerah got as far as Mareshah. [10] Asa went to confront him, and the two armies set up their battle lines in the Zephathah Valley at Mareshah.

[11] Asa called on the LORD his God. He said, "LORD, there is no one except you who can help those who are not strong so that they can fight against a large ‚army‚. Help us, LORD our God, because we are depending on you. In your name we go against this large crowd. You are the LORD our God. Don't let anyone successfully oppose you."

[12] The LORD attacked the Sudanese army in front of Asa and Judah. The Sudanese army fled. [13] Asa and his troops pursued them as far as Gerar. Many of the Sudanese died in battle. As a result, the Sudanese army couldn't fight again. It was crushed in front of the LORD and his army. The LORD's army captured a lot of goods. [14] It attacked all the cities around Gerar because the cities were afraid of the LORD. The army looted all the cities because there were many things to take. [15] It also attacked those who were letting their cattle graze and captured many sheep and camels. Then it returned to Jerusalem.

15 [1] God's Spirit came to Azariah, son of Oded. [2] Azariah went to Asa and said to him, "Listen to me, Asa and all ‚you men from Judah and Benjamin. The LORD is with you when you are with him. If you will dedicate your lives to serving him, he will accept you. But if you abandon him, he will abandon you. [3] For a long time Israel was without the true God, without a priest who taught ‚correctly‚, and without Moses' Teachings. [4] But when they were in trouble, they turned to the LORD God of Israel. When they searched for him, he let them find him. [5] At those times no one could come and go in peace, because everyone living in the land had a lot of turmoil. [6] One nation crushed another nation; one city crushed another. God had tormented them with every kind of trouble. [7] But you must remain strong and not become discouraged. Your actions will be rewarded."

[8] When Asa heard the prophet Oded's words of prophecy, he was encouraged and put away the detestable idols from all of Judah, Benjamin, and the cities he had captured in the mountains of Ephraim. He also repaired the LORD's altar in front of the LORD's entrance hall.

[9] Then Asa gathered all the people from Judah and Benjamin and the foreigners who had come from Ephraim, Manasseh, and Simeon. (Many of them had come to him from Israel when they saw that Asa's God, the LORD, was with him.) [10] In the third month of the fifteenth year of Asa's reign, they gathered in Jerusalem. [11] On that day they sacrificed to the LORD a part of the loot they had brought with them: 700 cattle and 7,000 sheep. [12] They made an agreement with one another to dedicate their lives to serving the LORD God of their ancestors with all their heart and soul. [13] All people (young or old, male or female) who refused to dedicate their lives to the LORD God of Israel were to be killed. [14] Asa and the people swore their oath to the LORD with shouts, singing, and the blowing of trumpets and rams' horns. [15] All the people of Judah were overjoyed because of the oath, since they took the oath wholeheartedly. They took great pleasure in looking for the LORD, and he let them find him. So the LORD surrounded them with peace.

[16] King Asa also removed his grandmother Maacah from the position of queen mother because she made a statue of the repulsive goddess Asherah. Asa cut the statue down, crushed it, and burned it in the Kidron Valley. [17] Although the illegal worship sites in Israel were not taken down, Asa remained committed ‚to the LORD‚ his entire life. [18] He brought into God's temple the silver, the gold, and the utensils he and his father had set apart as holy.

King Asa's War With King Baasha—1 Kings 15:16–24

[19] There was no war until the thirty-fifth year of Asa's reign.

16 ¹ In the thirty-sixth year of Asa's reign, King Baasha of Israel invaded Judah and fortified Ramah to keep anyone from going to or coming from King Asa of Judah. ² Then Asa brought out all the silver and gold that was left in the treasuries of the LORD's temple and the royal palace. He sent them to Damascus to Aram's King Benhadad. ³ He said, "There's a treaty between you and me ˎasˌ there was between your father and my father. I'm sending you silver and gold. Now break your treaty with King Baasha of Israel so that he will leave me alone."

⁴ Benhadad did what King Asa requested. He sent his generals and their armies to attack the cities of Israel. He conquered Ijon, Dan, Abel Maim, and all the storage cities in the territory of Naphtali. ⁵ When Baasha heard the news, he stopped fortifying Ramah and abandoned his work on it.

⁶ Then King Asa took everyone in Judah ˎto Ramahˌ. He made them carry the stones and lumber from Ramah. Baasha had been using those to fortify the city. Asa used the materials to fortify Geba in Benjamin and Mizpah.

⁷ At that time the seer[a] Hanani came to King Asa of Judah and said to him, "Because you depended on the king of Syria and did not depend on the LORD your God, the army of the king of Aram has escaped your grasp. ⁸ Weren't the Sudanese and Libyans a large army with many chariots and drivers? But when you depended on the LORD, he handed them over to you. ⁹ The LORD's eyes scan the whole world to find those whose hearts are committed to him and to strengthen them. You acted foolishly in this matter. So from now on, you will have to fight wars."

¹⁰ Asa was furious at the seer. He was so angry with Hanani that he put Hanani in prison. Asa also oppressed some of the people at that time in his reign.

¹¹ Everything about Asa from first to last is written in the Book of the Kings of Judah and Israel. ¹² In the thirty-ninth year of his reign, Asa got a foot disease that became progressively worse. Instead of asking the LORD for help, he went to doctors.

¹³ Asa lay down in death with his ancestors. He died in the forty-first year of his reign. ¹⁴ They buried him in the tomb that he had prepared for himself in the City of David. They laid him on a bed full of spices and blended perfumes. And they burned a bonfire in his honor.

King Jehoshaphat of Judah

17 ¹ Asa's son Jehoshaphat succeeded him as king. Jehoshaphat strengthened himself ˎto wage warˌ against Israel. ² He put troops in all the fortified cities of Judah and placed military posts in Judah and in the cities of Ephraim that his father Asa had captured.

³ The LORD was with Jehoshaphat, who lived in the old way like his ancestor David. Jehoshaphat didn't dedicate his life to serving other gods—the Baals. ⁴ Instead, he dedicated his life to his ancestor's God and lived by God's commands. Jehoshaphat did not do what Israel was doing. ⁵ So the LORD established Jehoshaphat's power over the kingdom. All the people of Judah gave gifts to Jehoshaphat, and he had a lot of riches and honor. ⁶ He had the confidence to live the way the LORD wanted him to live. He also got rid of the illegal places of worship and poles dedicated to the goddess Asherah in Judah.

⁷ In the third year of his reign, he sent his officers Ben Hail, Obadiah, Zechariah, Nethanel, and Micaiah to teach in the cities of Judah. ⁸ With them were the Levites Shemaiah, Nethaniah, Zebadiah, Asahel, Shemiramoth, Jehonathan, Adonijah, Tobijah, Tob Adonijah, and the priests Elishama and Jehoram. ⁹ They taught in Judah. They had the Book of the LORD's Teachings with them when they taught the people in all the cities of Judah.

¹⁰ Fear of the LORD came to all the kingdoms around Judah. As a result, they didn't wage war against Jehoshaphat. ¹¹ Some of the Philistines brought gifts and silver as taxes. The Arabs also brought him flocks: 7,700 rams and 7,700 male goats. ¹² So Jehoshaphat became more and more powerful. He built fortresses and cities where supplies were stored in Judah. ¹³ He had large supplies of food in the cities of Judah and an army of professional soldiers with him in Jerusalem. ¹⁴ The following is a breakdown of these soldiers. They are listed by families. Judah's regimental commanders were Commander Adnah (with 300,000 fighting men), ¹⁵ next to him Commander Jehohanan (with 280,000), ¹⁶ and next to him Amasiah, Zichri's son, who volunteered to serve the LORD (with 200,000 fighting men). ¹⁷ From Benjamin there was the fighting man Eliada (with 200,000 armed men with bows and shields), ¹⁸ and next to him was Jehozabad (with him was an army of 180,000 armed men). ¹⁹ These were the men who served the king in addition to those whom the king put in the fortified cities throughout Judah.

Micaiah Prophesies Against King Ahab—1 Kings 22:1–40

18 ¹ Jehoshaphat was wealthy and honorable and became Ahab's in-law. ² A few years later he went to visit Ahab in Samaria. Ahab slaughtered many sheep and cattle for a ban-

---

[a] 16:7 A seer is a prophet.

quet in honor of Jehoshaphat and the people who were with him. And Ahab persuaded Jehoshaphat to attack Ramoth in Gilead with him.

³ King Ahab of Israel asked King Jehoshaphat of Judah, "Will you go with me to Ramoth in Gilead?"

Jehoshaphat told the king of Israel, "I will do what you do. My troops will do what your troops do. We will join your troops in battle." ⁴ Then Jehoshaphat said to the king of Israel, "But first, find out what the word of the LORD is in this matter."

⁵ So the king of Israel called 400 prophets together. He asked them, "Should we go to war against Ramoth in Gilead or not?"

"Go," they said. "God will hand over Ramoth to you."

⁶ But Jehoshaphat asked, "Isn't there a prophet of the LORD whom we could ask?"

⁷ The king of Israel told Jehoshaphat, "We can ask the LORD through Micaiah, son of Imla, but I hate him. Nothing he prophesies about me is good; it's always evil."

Jehoshaphat answered, "The king must not say that."

⁸ The king of Israel called for an officer and said, "Quick! Get Micaiah, son of Imla!"

⁹ The king of Israel and King Jehoshaphat of Judah were dressed in royal robes and seated on thrones. They were sitting on the threshing floorᵃ at the entrance to the gate of Samaria. All the prophets were prophesying in front of them. ¹⁰ Zedekiah, son of Chenaanah, made iron horns and said, "This is what the LORD says: With these horns you will push the Arameans to their destruction." ¹¹ All the other prophets made the same prophecy. They said, "Attack Ramoth in Gilead, and you will win. The LORD will hand it over to you."

¹² The messenger who went to call Micaiah told him, "The prophets have all told the king the same good message. Make your message agree with their message. Say something good."

¹³ Micaiah answered, "I solemnly swear, as the LORD lives, I will tell him whatever my God says to me."

¹⁴ When he came to the king, the king asked him, "Micaiah,ᵇ should we go to war against Ramoth in Gilead or not?"

Micaiah said, "Attack and you will win. They will be handed over to you."

¹⁵ The king asked him, "How many times must I make you take an oath in the LORD's name to tell me nothing but the truth?"

¹⁶ So Micaiah said, "I saw Israel's troops scattered in the hills like sheep without a shepherd. The LORD said, 'These sheep have no master. Let each one go home in peace.' "

¹⁷ The king of Israel said to Jehoshaphat, "Didn't I tell you he wouldn't prophesy anything good about me?"

¹⁸ Micaiah added, "Then hear the word of the LORD. I saw the LORD sitting on his throne, and the entire army of heaven was standing on his right and his left. ¹⁹ The LORD asked, 'Who will deceive King Ahab of Israel so that he will attack and be killed at Ramoth in Gilead?' Some answered one way, while others were saying something else.

²⁰ "Then the Spirit stepped forward, stood in front of the LORD, and said, 'I will deceive him.'

" 'How?' the LORD asked.

²¹ "The Spirit answered, 'I will go out and be a spirit that tells lies through the mouths of all of Ahab's prophets.'

"The LORD said, 'You will succeed in deceiving him. Go and do it.'

²² "So the LORD has put into the mouths of these prophets of yours a spirit that makes them tell lies. The LORD has spoken evil about you."

²³ Zedekiah, son of Chenaanah, went to Micaiah and struck him on the cheek. "Which way did the Spirit go when he left me to talk to you?" he asked.

²⁴ Micaiah answered, "You will find out on the day you go into an inner room to hide."

²⁵ The king of Israel then said, "Send Micaiah back to Amon, the governor of the city, and to Joash, the prince. ²⁶ Say, 'This is what the king says: Put this man in prison, and feed him nothing but bread and water until I return home safely.' "

²⁷ Micaiah said, "If you really do come back safely, then the LORD wasn't speaking through me. Pay attention to this, everyone!"

²⁸ So the king of Israel and King Jehoshaphat of Judah went to Ramoth in Gilead. ²⁹ The king of Israel told Jehoshaphat, "I will disguise myself and go into battle, but you should wear your royal robes." So the king of Israel disguised himself and went into battle.

³⁰ The king of Aram had given orders to the chariot commanders. He said, "Don't fight anyone except the king of Israel."

³¹ When the chariot commanders saw Jehoshaphat, they said, "He must be the king of Israel." So they surrounded him in order to fight him. But when Jehoshaphat cried out, the

---

ᵃ 18:9 A threshing floor is an outdoor area where grain is separated from its husks.   ᵇ 18:14 1 Kings 22:15; Masoretic Text "Micah."

LORD helped him. God drew them away from him, ³² and the chariot commanders realized that Jehoshaphat wasn't the king of Israel. Then they turned away from him.

³³ One man aimed his bow at random and hit the king of Israel between his scale armor and his breastplate. Ahab told the chariot driver, "Turn around, and get me away from these troops. I'm badly wounded." ³⁴ But the battle got worse that day, and the king propped himself up in his chariot facing the Arameans until evening. At sundown he died.

King Jehoshaphat's Religious Reforms

19 ¹ King Jehoshaphat of Judah returned safely to his home in Jerusalem. ² Jehu, son of the seer^a Hanani, asked King Jehoshaphat, "Why do you help wicked people and love those who hate the LORD? The LORD's anger is directed toward you because you have done this. ³ However, you've done some good things: You've burned the Asherah poles in this country, and you've wholeheartedly dedicated your life to serving God."

⁴ While Jehoshaphat was living in Jerusalem, he regularly went to the people between Beersheba and the mountains of Ephraim. He brought the people back to the LORD God of their ancestors. ⁵ He appointed judges in the country, in each fortified city of Judah. ⁶ He told the judges, "Pay attention to what you're doing. When you judge, you aren't doing it for a human but for the LORD. He will be with you when you hear a case. ⁷ May you have the fear of the LORD in you. Be careful about what you do. The LORD our God is never unjust. He is impartial and never takes bribes."

⁸ In Jerusalem Jehoshaphat also appointed some Levites, priests, and family heads from Israel to administer the LORD's laws and decide cases. They lived in Jerusalem. ⁹ He ordered them, "Do this wholeheartedly—with the fear of the LORD and with faithfulness. ¹⁰ Warn your relatives living in other cities about every case they bring to you, even if the case involves bloodshed or commands, rules, or regulations derived from Moses' Teachings. Then your relatives will not become guilty in front of the LORD. Otherwise, he will become angry with you and your relatives. Do this, and you won't be guilty ˌof anythingˌ. ¹¹ Now, the chief priest Amariah will be in charge of you in every matter involving the LORD. Zebadiah, who is the son of Ishmael and the leader of the tribe of Judah, will be in charge of every matter involving the king. The Levites will serve as officers of the court. Be strong, and do your job. May the LORD be with those who do right."

King Jehoshaphat Defeats Judah's Enemies

20 ¹ Later the Moabites, Ammonites, and some of the Meunites^a came to wage war against Jehoshaphat. ² Some men reported to Jehoshaphat, "A large crowd is coming against you from the other side of the Dead Sea, from Edom.^b The crowd is already in Hazazon Tamar" (also called En Gedi).

³ Frightened, Jehoshaphat decided to ask for the LORD's help. He announced a fast throughout Judah. ⁴ The people of Judah gathered to seek the LORD's help. They came from every city in Judah.

⁵ In the new courtyard at the LORD's temple, Jehoshaphat stood in front of the people. ⁶ He said, "LORD God of our ancestors, aren't you the God in heaven? You rule all the kingdoms of the nations. You possess power and might, and no one can oppose you. ⁷ Didn't you, our God, force those who were living in this country out of Israel's way? Didn't you give this country to the descendants of your friend Abraham to have permanently? ⁸ His descendants have lived in it and built a holy temple for your name in it. They said, ⁹ 'If evil comes in the form of war, flood,^c plague, or famine, we will stand in front of this temple and in front of you because your name is in this temple. We will cry out to you in our troubles, and you will hear us and save us.'

¹⁰ "The Ammonites, Moabites, and the people of Mount Seir have come here. However, you didn't let Israel invade them when they came out of Egypt. The Israelites turned away from them and didn't destroy them. ¹¹ They are now paying us back by coming to force us out of your land that you gave to us. ¹² You're our God. Won't you judge them? We don't have the strength to face this large crowd that is attacking us. We don't know what to do, so we're looking to you."

¹³ All the people from Judah, their infants, wives, and children were standing in front of the LORD. ¹⁴ Then the LORD's Spirit came to Jahaziel. (He was the son of Zechariah, grandson of Benaiah, great-grandson of Jeiel, whose father was Mattaniah, a Levite descended from Asaph.) ¹⁵ Jahaziel said, "Pay attention to me, everyone from Judah, everyone living in Jerusalem, and King Jehoshaphat. This is what the LORD says to you: Don't be frightened or terrified by this large crowd. The battle isn't yours. It's God's. ¹⁶ Tomorrow go into battle against them. They will be coming up the Ziz Pass. You will find them at the end of the valley in front of the Jeruel Desert. ¹⁷ You won't fight this battle. ˌInstead,ˌ take your position, stand

---

^a 19:2 A seer is a prophet.   ^a 20:1 Greek; Masoretic Text "and some of the Ammonites."   ^b 20:2 One Hebrew manuscript, Latin; other Hebrew manuscripts "Aram."   ^c 20:9 Greek; Masoretic Text "judgment."

still, and see the victory of the LORD for you, Judah and Jerusalem. Don't be frightened or terrified. Tomorrow go out to face them. The LORD is with you."

¹⁸ Jehoshaphat bowed down with his face touching the ground. Everyone from Judah and the people who lived in Jerusalem immediately bowed down in front of the LORD. ¹⁹ The Levites, descendants of Kohath and Korah, stood up to praise the LORD God of Israel with very loud songs.

²⁰ They got up early in the morning and went to the desert of Tekoa. As they were leaving, Jehoshaphat stopped and said, "Listen to me, people of Judah and those living in Jerusalem. Trust the LORD your God, and believe. Believe his prophets, and you will succeed."

²¹ After he had advised the people, he appointed people to sing to the LORD and praise him for the beauty of his holiness. As they went in front of the troops, they sang, "Thank the LORD because his mercy endures forever!" ²² As they started to sing praises, the LORD set ambushes against the Ammonites, Moabites, and the people of Mount Seir who had come into Judah. They were defeated. ²³ Then the Ammonites and Moabites attacked the people from Mount Seir and annihilated them. After they had finished off the people of Seir, they helped destroy one another.

²⁴ The people of Judah went to the watchtower in the desert and looked for the crowd. Corpses were lying on the ground. No one had escaped. ²⁵ When Jehoshaphat and his troops came to take the loot, they found among them a lot of goods, clothes,^d and valuables. They found more than they could carry. They spent three days collecting the loot. ²⁶ On the fourth day they gathered in the valley of Beracah. Because they thanked the LORD there, that place is still called the valley of Beracah [Thanks] today.

²⁷ All the men of Judah and Jerusalem returned to Jerusalem. They rejoiced while Jehoshaphat led them. The LORD gave them a reason to rejoice about ˌwhat had happened toˌ their enemies. ²⁸ So they brought harps, lyres, and trumpets to the LORD's temple in Jerusalem. ²⁹ The fear of the LORD came over the kingdoms in that area when they heard how the LORD waged war against Israel's enemies. ³⁰ Jehoshaphat's kingdom was peaceful, since his God surrounded him with peace.

Summary of Jehoshaphat's Reign—1 Kings 22:41–50

³¹ Jehoshaphat ruled as king of Judah. He was 35 years old when he began to rule, and he ruled for 25 years in Jerusalem. His mother's name was Azubah, daughter of Shilhi. ³² Jehoshaphat carefully followed the example his father Asa had set and did what the LORD considered right. ³³ But the illegal worship sites on the hills were not torn down. The people still didn't have their hearts set on the God of their ancestors.

³⁴ Everything else about Jehoshaphat from first to last is written in the records of Jehu, son of Hanani, which is included in the Book of the Kings of Israel.

³⁵ After this, King Jehoshaphat of Judah allied himself with King Ahaziah of Israel, who led him to do evil. ³⁶ Jehoshaphat joined him in making ships to go to Tarshish. They made the ships in Ezion Geber. ³⁷ Then Eliezer, son of Dodavahu from Mareshah, prophesied against Jehoshaphat. He said, "The LORD will destroy your work because you have allied yourself with Ahaziah." So the ships were wrecked and couldn't go to Tarshish.

King Jehoram of Judah—1 Kings 22:51; 2 Kings 8:17–19

21 ¹ Jehoshaphat lay down in death with his ancestors and was buried with them in the City of David. His son Jehoram succeeded him as king. ² He had the following brothers, sons of Jehoshaphat: Azariah, Jehiel, Zechariah, Azariahu, Michael, and Shephatiah. All were the sons of King Jehoshaphat of Israel. ³ Their father gave them many gifts: silver, gold, and other expensive things, along with fortified cities in Judah. But Jehoshaphat gave the kingdom to Jehoram, who was the firstborn.

⁴ After Jehoram had taken over his father's kingdom, he strengthened his position and then executed all his brothers and some of the officials of Israel. ⁵ Jehoram was 32 years old when he became king, and he ruled for 8 years in Jerusalem. ⁶ He followed the ways of the kings of Israel, as Ahab's family had done, because his wife was Ahab's daughter. So he did what the LORD considered evil. ⁷ But the LORD, recalling the promise^a he had made to David, didn't want to destroy David's family. The LORD had told David that he would always give him and his descendants a ˌshiningˌ lamp.

Edom Wins Independence From Judah—2 Kings 8:20–24a

⁸ During Jehoram's time Edom rebelled against Judah and chose its own king. ⁹ Jehoram took all his chariot commanders to attack. The Edomites and their chariot commanders surrounded him, but he got up at night and broke through their lines. ¹⁰ So Edom rebelled against Judah's rule and is still independent today. At the same time Edom rebelled, Libnah rebelled

---

^d 20:25 Latin; Masoretic Text "corpses."   ^a 21:7 Or "covenant."

because Jehoram had abandoned the LORD God of his ancestors. ¹¹ Jehoram made illegal places of worship in the hills of Judah. This caused the inhabitants of Jerusalem to chase after foreign gods as if they were prostitutes. So he led Judah astray.

¹² Then a letter came to him from the prophet Elijah. It read, "This is what the LORD God of your ancestor David says: You haven't followed the ways of your father Jehoshaphat or the ways of King Asa of Judah. ¹³ Instead, you have followed the ways of the kings of Israel. You, like Ahab's family, have caused Judah and the inhabitants of Jerusalem to chase after foreign gods as if they were prostitutes. You have killed your brothers, your father's family. Your brothers were better than you. ¹⁴ The LORD will strike a great blow to your people, your sons, your wives, and all your property because you did this. ¹⁵ You will suffer from a chronic intestinal disease until your intestines come out."

¹⁶ The LORD prompted the Philistines and the Arabs who lived near the people of Sudan to attack Jehoram. ¹⁷ They fought against Judah, broke into the country, and took away everything that could be found in the royal palace. They even took Jehoram's sons and wives. The only son left was Ahaziah,ᵇ Jehoram's youngest son. ¹⁸ After this, the LORD struck Jehoram with an incurable intestinal disease. ¹⁹ Two years later, as his life was coming to an end, his intestines fell out because of his sickness. He died a painful death.

His people did not make a bonfire in his honor as they had done for his ancestors. ²⁰ He was 32 years old when he became king, and he ruled for 8 years in Jerusalem. No one was sorry to see him die. He was buried in the City of David but not in the tombs of the kings.

King Ahaziah of Judah—2 Kings 8:24b–29; 9:14–29

22 ¹ The people of Jerusalem made Jehoram's youngest son Ahaziah king in his place, because the raiders who came to the camp with the Arabs had killed all the older sons. So Jehoram's son Ahaziah became king of Judah. ² Ahaziahᵃ was 42 years old when he began to rule, and he ruled for one year in Jerusalem. His mother was Athaliah, the granddaughter of Omri. ³ Ahaziah also followed the ways of Ahab's family, because his mother gave him advice that led him to sin. ⁴ He did what the LORD considered evil, as Ahab's family had done. After his father died, they advised him to do what Ahab's family had done. They did this to destroy him.

⁵ Ahaziah followed their advice and went with Ahab's son King Joramᵇ of Israel to fight against King Hazael of Aram at Ramoth Gilead. There the Arameans wounded Joram. ⁶ Joram returned to Jezreel to let his wounds heal. (He had been wounded by the Arameans at Ramah when he fought against King Hazael of Aram.) Then Jehoram's son Ahaziahᶜ went to Jezreel to see Ahab's son Joram, who was sick.

⁷ God brought about Ahaziah's downfall when he went to Joram. He went with Joram to meet Jehu, grandson of Nimshi. (The LORD had anointed Jehu to destroy Ahab's family.) ⁸ When Jehu was executing judgment on Ahab's family, he found Judah's leaders (Ahaziah's nephews) who were serving Ahaziah, and he killed them. ⁹ He searched for Ahaziah, and Jehu's men captured him while he was hiding in Samaria. They brought him to Jehu and killed him. Then they buried him. They explained, "Ahaziah is Jehoshaphat's grandson. Jehoshaphat dedicated his life to serving the LORD with all his heart." But no one in Ahaziah's family was able to rule as king.

The Priest Jehoiada Opposes Queen Athaliah—2 Kings 11:1–20

¹⁰ When Ahaziah's mother, Athaliah, saw that her son was dead, she began to destroy the entire royal family of the house of Judah. ¹¹ But Jehoshebath, daughter of the king and sister of Ahaziah, took Ahaziah's son Joash. She saved him from being killed with the king's other sons, and she put him and his nurse in a bedroom. Jehoshebath was the daughter of King Jehoram and wife of Jehoiada the priest. Because she was also Ahaziah's sister, she hid Joash from Athaliah. So he wasn't killed. ¹² Joash was with the priests. He was hidden in God's temple for six years while Athaliah ruled the country.

23 ¹ In the seventh year of Athaliah's reign, Jehoiada strengthened his position by making an agreement with the company commanders: Azariah, son of Jeroham, Ishmael, son of Jehohanan, Azariah, son of Obed, Maaseiah, son of Adaiah, and Elishaphat, son of Zichri. ² They went around Judah, gathered the Levites from all the cities of Judah and the leaders of the families of Israel, and came to Jerusalem. ³ The whole assembly made an agreement with the king in God's temple.

Then Jehoiada said to them, "Here is the king's son. He should be king, as the LORD said about David's descendants. ⁴ This is what you must do: One third of you, the priests and

---

ᵇ 21:17 In the Masoretic Text this king of Judah is also called Jehoahaz, an alternate form of Ahaziah.   ᵃ 22:2 In the Masoretic Text this king of Judah is also called Jehoahaz, an alternate form of Ahaziah.   ᵇ 22:5 In the Masoretic Text this king of Israel is also called Jehoram, a longer form of Joram.   ᶜ 22:6 Some Hebrew manuscripts, 2 Kings 8:29, Greek, Syriac, Latin; other Hebrew manuscripts "Azariah."

Levites who are on duty on the day of worship, must guard the gates. ⁵ Another third must be at the royal palace. And another third must be at Foundation Gate. All the people must be in the courtyards of the LORD's temple. ⁶ No one should come into the LORD's temple except the priests and the Levites who are on duty with them. They may enter because they are holy, but all other people should follow the LORD's regulations. ⁷ The Levites should surround the king. Each man should have his weapon in his hand. Kill anyone who tries to come into the temple. Stay with the king wherever he goes."

⁸ So the Levites and all the Judeans did what the priest Jehoiada had ordered them. Each took his men who were coming on duty on the day of worship as well as those who were about to go off duty. Jehoiada had not dismissed the priestly divisions.

⁹ Jehoiada gave the commanders the spears and the small and large shields that had belonged to King David but were now in God's temple. ¹⁰ All the troops stood with their weapons drawn. They were stationed around the king and around the altar and the temple (from the south side to the north side of the temple). ¹¹ Then they brought out the king's son, gave him the crown and the religious instructions, and Jehoiada and his sons made him king by anointing him. They said, "Long live the king!"

¹² When Athaliah heard the people running and praising the king, she went into the LORD's temple, where the people were. ¹³ She looked, and the king was standing by the pillar at the entrance. The commanders and the trumpeters were by his side. All the people of the land were rejoicing and blowing trumpets. The singers were leading the celebration with songs accompanied by musical instruments. As Athaliah tore her clothes ⸢in distress⸣, she said, "Treason, treason!"

¹⁴ Then the priest Jehoiada brought the company commanders who were in charge of the army out ⸢of the temple⸣. He said to them, "Take her out of the temple. Use your sword to kill anyone who follows her." (The priest had said, "Don't kill her in the LORD's temple.") ¹⁵ So they arrested her as she entered Horse Gate of the royal palace, and they killed her there.

¹⁶ Jehoiada made a promise to the LORD on behalf of the king and his people that they would be the LORD's people. ¹⁷ Then all the people went to the temple of Baal and tore it down. They smashed Baal's altars and his statues and killed Mattan, the priest of Baal, in front of the altars.

¹⁸ Next, Jehoiada appointed officials to be in charge of the LORD's temple under the direction of the priests and Levites.ᵃ (David had arranged them in divisions for the LORD's temple. They were appointed to sacrifice burnt offerings to the LORD as it is written in Moses' Teachings. They made these offerings with joy and singing as David had directed.) ¹⁹ Jehoiada appointed gatekeepers for the gates of the LORD's temple so that no one who was uncleanᵇ for any reason could enter.

²⁰ He took the company commanders, the nobles, the people's governors, and all the people of the land, and they brought the king from the LORD's temple. They went through Upper Gate to the royal palace and seated the king on the royal throne. The nobles, the governors of the people, and ²¹ all the people of the land were celebrating. But the city was quiet because they had killed Athaliah with a sword.

King Joash of Judah—2 Kings 11:21–12:14

24 ¹ Joashᵃ was 7 years old when he began to rule, and he ruled for 40 years in Jerusalem. His mother was Zibiah from Beersheba. ² Joash did what the LORD considered right, as long as the priest Jehoiada lived.

³ Jehoiada got Joash two wives, and Joash had sons and daughters.

⁴ After this, Joash wanted to renovate the LORD's temple. ⁵ He gathered the priests and the Levites and said to them, "Go to the cities of Judah, and collect money throughout Israel to repair the temple of your God every year. Do it immediately!" But the Levites didn't do it immediately.

⁶ So the king called for the chief priest Jehoiada and asked him, "Why didn't you require the Levites to bring the contributions from Judah and Jerusalem? The LORD's servant Moses and the assembly had required Israel to give contributions for the use of the tent containing the words of God's promise." ⁷ (The sons of that wicked woman Athaliah had broken into God's temple and used all the holy things of the LORD's temple ⸢to worship⸣ other gods—the Baals.)

⁸ The king issued an order, and they made a box and placed it outside the gate of the LORD's temple. ⁹ Then they issued a proclamation in Judah and Jerusalem that the contributions should be brought to the LORD. (In the desert the LORD's servant Moses had required Israel to make contributions.) ¹⁰ All the officials and all the people were overjoyed. They brought the money and dropped it into the box until it was full. ¹¹ Whenever the Levites brought the box to

---

ᵃ 23:18 A few Hebrew manuscripts, Greek, Syriac, Latin; most Hebrew manuscripts "Levitical priests."   ᵇ 23:19 "Unclean" refers to anything that Moses' Teachings say is not presentable to God.   ᵃ 24:1 In the Masoretic text this king of Judah is also called Jehoash, a longer form of Joash.

the king's officers and they saw a lot of money, the king's scribe and the chief priest's officer would empty the box and put it back in its place. They would do this every day, so they collected a lot of money. [12] The king and Jehoiada would give the money to the foremen who were working on the LORD's temple, and they hired masons and carpenters to renovate the LORD's temple. They also hired men who worked with iron and bronze to repair the LORD's temple. [13] As the men worked, the project progressed under the foremen's guidance. They restored God's temple to its proper condition and reinforced it.

[14] When they finished, they brought the rest of the money to the king and Jehoiada, who used it to make utensils for the LORD's temple. They made dishes and gold and silver utensils for the service and for the offerings. As long as Jehoiada lived, they sacrificed burnt offerings in the LORD's temple.

Joash's Sin Leads to His Assassination—2 Kings 12:17–21

[15] When Jehoiada was old and had lived out his years, he died. He was 130 years old when he died. [16] He was buried in the City of David with the kings because of the good he had done in Israel for God and the temple.

[17] After he died, the officials of Judah bowed in front of the king with their faces touching the ground. Then the king listened to their advice. [18] They abandoned the temple of the LORD God of their ancestors and worshiped idols and the poles dedicated to the goddess Asherah. This offense of theirs brought God's anger upon Judah and Jerusalem.

[19] The LORD sent them prophets to bring them back to himself. The prophets warned them, but they wouldn't listen. [20] God's Spirit gave Zechariah, son of the priest Jehoiada, strength. Zechariah stood in front of the people and said to them, "This is what God says: Why are you breaking the LORD's commands? You won't prosper that way! The LORD has abandoned you because you have abandoned him." [21] But they plotted against Zechariah, and by the king's order they stoned him to death in the courtyard of the LORD's temple. [22] King Joash did not remember how kind Zechariah's father, Jehoiada, had been to him. Instead, he killed Jehoiada's son. As Zechariah died, he said, "May the LORD see ˌthisˌ and get revenge!"

[23] At the end of the year, the Aramean army attacked Joash. They came to Judah and Jerusalem and destroyed all the people's leaders. The Arameans sent all the loot they took from Judah and Jerusalem to the king of Damascus. [24] The Aramean army had come with a small number of men, but the LORD handed Joash's large army over to them because Joash's soldiers had abandoned the LORD God of their ancestors. So the Arameans carried out ˌthe LORD'sˌ judgment on Joash. [25] When the Arameans withdrew, they left him suffering from many wounds. His own officials plotted against him for murdering the son of the priest Jehoiada. They killed Joash in his bed. When he died, they buried him in the City of David, but they didn't bury him in the tombs of the kings. [26] These were the men who conspired against him: Zabad, son of an Ammonite woman named Shimeath, and Jehozabad, son of a Moabite woman named Shimrith. [27] The record about his sons, the many divine revelations against him, and the rebuilding of God's temple is in the notes made in the Book of the Kings. His son Amaziah succeeded him as king.

King Amaziah of Judah—2 Kings 14:1–7

25 [1] Amaziah was 25 years old when he began to rule, and he ruled for 29 years in Jerusalem. His mother was Jehoaddan from Jerusalem. [2] He did what the LORD considered right, but he did not do it wholeheartedly. [3] As soon as he had firm control over the kingdom, he executed the officials who killed his father, the former king. [4] But he didn't execute their children. He obeyed the LORD's command written in the Book of Moses' Teachings: "Parents must never be put to death for the crimes of their children, and children must never be put to death for the crimes of their parents. Each person must be put to death for his own crime."

[5] Amaziah called the people of Judah together and assigned them by families to regiment and battalion commanders for all of Judah and Benjamin. He organized those who were at least 20 years old and found that he had 300,000 of the best men for the army, those who could handle a spear and a shield. [6] He also hired 100,000 soldiers from Israel for 7,500 pounds of silver.

[7] But a man of God came to him and said, "Your Majesty, Israel's army must not go with you, because the LORD isn't with Israel. He's not with these men from Ephraim. [8] If you go into battle with them, no matter how courageous you are, God will use the enemy to defeat you, because God has the power to help you or to defeat you."

[9] Amaziah asked the man of God, "What should I do about the 7,500 pounds of silver I gave the troops from Israel?"

The man of God answered, "The LORD can give you much more than that."

[10] Then Amaziah dismissed the troops that had come to him from Ephraim. But they became furious with Judah and returned home.

¹¹ Amaziah courageously led his troops. When he came to the Dead Sea region, he killed 10,000 men from Seir.ᵃ ¹² The Judeans captured another 10,000 alive, took them to the top of a cliff, and threw them off the top of the cliff so that they were dismembered.

¹³ The troops that Amaziah sent back so that they couldn't go with him into battle raided the towns in Judah from Samaria to Beth Horon. They killed 3,000 people and took a lot of goods.

King Amaziah's Sin Leads to His Defeat—2 Kings 14:8–20

¹⁴ After Amaziah came back from defeating the Edomites, he brought the gods of the people of Seir, set them up as his gods, bowed down to them, and burned sacrifices to them. ¹⁵ The LORD became angry with Amaziah. He sent him a prophet who asked him, "Why do you dedicate your life to serving the gods of those people? Those gods couldn't save their own people from you."

¹⁶ As he was talking, the king asked him, "Did we make you an adviser to the king? Stop! Do you want me to have you killed?"

The prophet stopped. He said, "I know that God has decided to destroy you because you did this, but you refuse to listen to my advice."

¹⁷ After getting advice ˏfrom his advisersˌ, King Amaziah of Judah sent messengers to King Jehoash,ᵇ son of Jehoahaz and grandson of Jehu of Israel, to declare war on Israel.

¹⁸ King Jehoash of Israel sent this message to King Amaziah of Judah: "A thistle in Lebanon sent a message to a cedar in Lebanon. It said, 'Let your daughter marry my son,' but a wild animal from Lebanon came along and trampled the thistle. ¹⁹ You say you defeated Edom, and now you've become arrogant enough to look for more fame. Stay home! Why must you invite disaster and your own defeat and take Judah with you?"

²⁰ But Amaziah wouldn't listen. (God made this happen because he wanted to hand over the Judeans to Jehoash because they had sought help from Edom's gods.) ²¹ So King Jehoash of Israel attacked, and King Amaziah of Judah met him in battle at Beth Shemesh in Judah. ²² Israel defeated the army of Judah, and the Judeans fled to their homes. ²³ King Jehoash of Israel captured King Amaziah, son of Joash and grandson of Ahaziah of Judah, at Beth Shemesh and brought him to Jerusalem. He tore down a 600-foot section of the wall around Jerusalem from Ephraim Gate to Corner Gate. ²⁴ ˏHe tookˌ all the gold, silver, and all the utensils he found in God's temple with Obed Edom and in the royal palace treasury. He also took hostages. Then he returned to Samaria.

²⁵ Joash's son King Amaziah of Judah lived 15 years after the death of Jehoahaz's son King Jehoash of Israel. ²⁶ Isn't everything else about Amaziah, from beginning to end, written in the Book of the Kings of Judah and Israel? ²⁷ After Amaziah turned away from the LORD, conspirators in Jerusalem plotted against him. Amaziah fled to Lachish, but they sent men to Lachish after him and killed him there. ²⁸ They brought him back by horse and buried him in the city of Judah with his ancestors.

King Uzziah of Judah—2 Kings 14:21–15:3

26 ¹ All the people of Judah took Uzziah, who was 16 years old, and made him king in place of his father Amaziah. ² Uzziah rebuilt Elath and returned it to Judah after King Amaziah lay down in death with his ancestors. ³ Uzziah was 16 years old when he began to rule, and he ruled for 52 years in Jerusalem. His mother was Jecoliah from Jerusalem. ⁴ He did what the LORD considered right, as his father Amaziah had done. ⁵ He dedicated his life to serving God in the days of Zechariah, who taught him to fear God. As long as he dedicated his life to serving the LORD, the LORD gave him success.

⁶ Uzziah went to wage war against the Philistines. He tore down the walls of Gath, Jabneh, and Ashdod. He built cities near Ashdod and elsewhere among the Philistines. ⁷ God helped him when he attacked the Philistines, the Arabs who lived in Gur Baal, and the Meunites. ⁸ The Ammonites paid taxes to Uzziah, and his fame spread to the border of Egypt because he became very powerful. ⁹ Uzziah built towers in Jerusalem at Corner Wall, Valley Gate, and the Angle, and he reinforced them. ¹⁰ He built towers in the desert. He dug many cisterns because he had a lot of herds in the foothills and the plains. He had farmers and vineyard workers in the mountains and the fertile fields because he loved the soil.

¹¹ Uzziah had an army of professional soldiers. They were ready to go to war in their companies based on the number organized by the scribe Jeiel and the officer Maaseiah. They were commanded by Hananiah, one of the king's officials. ¹² The total number of family heads among these warriors was 2,600. ¹³ Under them was an army of 307,500 soldiers. They were a powerful force that could support the king against the enemy. ¹⁴ For the entire army Uzziah prepared shields, spears, helmets, armor, bows, and stones for slings. ¹⁵ In Jerusalem he made

---

ᵃ 25:11 Seir is another name for Edom.   ᵇ 25:17 In the Masoretic Text this king of Israel is also called Joash, a shorter form of Jehoash.

machines designed by inventive people. The machines were placed on the towers and corners to shoot arrows and hurl large stones.

King Uzziah Is Cursed With a Skin Disease—*2 Kings 15:5–7*

Uzziah's fame spread far and wide because he had strong support until he became powerful. [16] But when he became powerful, his pride destroyed him. He was unfaithful to the LORD his God. He went into the LORD's temple to burn incense on the incense altar. [17] The priest Azariah went in after him with 80 of the LORD's courageous priests. [18] They opposed King Uzziah. They said to him, "Uzziah, you have no right to burn incense as an offering to the LORD. That right belongs to the priests, Aaron's descendants, who have been given the holy task of burning incense. Get out of the holy place because you have been unfaithful. The LORD God will not honor you for this."

[19] Uzziah, who held an incense burner in his hand, became angry. While he was angry with the priests, a skin disease broke out on his forehead. This happened in front of the priests in the LORD's temple as Uzziah was at the incense altar. [20] When the chief priest Azariah and all the priests turned toward him, a skin disease was on his forehead. They rushed him away. Uzziah was in a hurry to get out because the LORD had inflicted him ˏwith the diseaseˏ.

[21] King Uzziah had a skin disease until the day he died. Since he had a skin disease, he lived in a separate house and was barred from the LORD's temple. His son Jotham was in charge of the royal palace and governed the country.

[22] Everything else about Uzziah, from beginning to end, is recorded by the prophet Isaiah, son of Amoz. [23] Uzziah lay down in death with his ancestors and was buried with them in a field containing tombs that belonged to the kings. People said, "He had a skin disease." His son Jotham succeeded him as king.

King Jotham of Judah—*2 Kings 15:32–38*

27 [1] Jotham was 25 years old when he began to rule. He ruled for 16 years in Jerusalem. His mother was Jerushah, daughter of Zadok. [2] He did what the LORD considered right, as his father Uzziah had done. But unlike his father, he didn't ˏillegallyˏ enter the LORD's temple. Nevertheless, the people continued their corrupt ways.

[3] Jotham built the Upper Gate of the LORD's temple and did extensive building of the wall at the Ophel. [4] He built cities in the hills of Judah, and he built forts and towers in the wooded areas. [5] He fought with the king of the Ammonites and conquered them. That year the Ammonites gave him 7,500 pounds of silver, 60,000 bushels of wheat, and 60,000 bushels of barley. The Ammonites gave him the same amount for two more years. [6] Jotham grew powerful because he was determined to live as the LORD his God wanted.

[7] Everything else about Jotham—all his wars and his life—is written in the Book of the Kings of Israel and Judah. [8] He was 25 years old when he began to rule as king. He ruled for 16 years in Jerusalem. [9] Jotham lay down in death with his ancestors, and they buried him in the City of David. His son Ahaz succeeded him as king.

King Ahaz of Judah—*2 Kings 16:1–20*

28 [1] Ahaz was 20 years old when he began to rule. He ruled for 26 years in Jerusalem. He didn't do what the LORD considered right, as his ancestor David had done. [2] He followed the example of the kings of Israel and even made metal idols for worshiping other gods—the Baals. [3] He burned sacrifices in the valley of Ben Hinnom and sacrificed his son by burning him alive, one of the disgusting things done by the nations that the LORD had forced out of the Israelites' way. [4] He offered sacrifices and burned incense as an offering at the illegal worship sites, which were on hills and under every large tree.

[5] So the LORD his God handed him over to the king of Aram, who defeated him, captured many prisoners, and brought them to Damascus. He also handed him over to the king of Israel, who decisively defeated him. [6] In one day Pekah, son of Remaliah, killed 120,000 soldiers in Judah because they had abandoned the LORD God of their ancestors. [7] Zichri, a fighting man from Ephraim, killed Maaseiah, who was the king's son, Azrikam, who was in charge of the palace, and Elkanah, who was the king's second-in-command. [8] The Israelites captured 200,000 women, boys, and girls from their relatives ˏthe Judeansˏ. They also took a lot of goods from Judah and brought them to Samaria.

[9] A prophet of the LORD named Oded was there. He went to meet the army coming home to Samaria. He said to them, "The LORD God of your ancestors handed Judah over to you in his anger. You killed them in a rage that reaches up to heaven. [10] Now you intend to enslave the men and women of Judah and Jerusalem. But aren't you also guilty of sinning against the LORD your God? [11] Listen to me. Return these prisoners you have captured from your relatives, because the LORD is very angry with you."

¹² Then Azariah, son of Jehohan, Berechiah, son of Meshillemoth, Jehizkiah, son of Shallum, and Amasa, son of Hadlai (some leaders of Ephraim) opposed those coming home from the army. ¹³ They said to the army, "Don't bring the prisoners here. You'll make us responsible for this sin against the LORD. Do you intend to add to all our sins? The LORD is very angry with Israel because we have already sinned."

¹⁴ So the army left the prisoners and the loot in front of the leaders and the whole assembly. ¹⁵ Then the men who were mentioned by name took charge of the prisoners and gave clothes from the loot to all the prisoners who were naked. They provided clothes for them, gave them sandals, gave them something to eat and drink, and let them bathe. They put everyone who was exhausted on donkeys and brought them to Jericho (the City of Palms) near their own people. Then they returned to Samaria.

¹⁶ At that time King Ahaz sent for help from the kings of Assyria. ¹⁷ The Edomites had again invaded and defeated Judah and captured prisoners. ¹⁸ The Philistines had raided the foothills and the Negev in Judah. They captured and began living in Beth Shemesh, Aijalon, Gederoth, Soco and its villages, Timnah and its villages, and Gimzo and its villages. ¹⁹ The LORD humbled Judah because of King Ahaz of Israel. Ahaz had spread sin throughout Judah and was unfaithful to the LORD.

²⁰ King Tillegath Pilneser of Assyria attacked Ahaz. Instead of strengthening Ahaz, Tillegath Pilneser made trouble for him. ²¹ Ahaz took some of the things from the LORD's temple, the royal palace, and the princes, and he gave them to the king of Assyria. But that didn't help him. ²² When he had this trouble, King Ahaz became more unfaithful to the LORD. ²³ He sacrificed to the gods of Damascus, the gods who had defeated him. He thought, "The gods of the kings of Aram are helping them. I'll sacrifice to them so that they will help me." But they ruined him and all Israel.

²⁴ Ahaz collected the utensils in God's temple, cut them up, and closed the doors to the LORD's temple. He made altars for himself on every corner in Jerusalem. ²⁵ And in each city of Judah, he made places of worship to sacrifice to other gods. So he made the LORD God of his ancestors angry.

²⁶ Everything else about him—everything from beginning to end—is written in the Book of the Kings of Judah and Israel. ²⁷ Ahaz lay down in death with his ancestors and was buried in the city of Jerusalem because they didn't put him into the tombs of the kings of Israel. His son Hezekiah succeeded him as king.

King Hezekiah Rededicates the Temple—2 Kings 18:1–3

29 ¹ Hezekiah began to rule as king when he was 25 years old. He ruled for 29 years in Jerusalem. His mother was Abijah, daughter of Zechariah. ² He did what the LORD considered right, as his ancestor David had done.

³ In the first month of his first year as king, he opened the doors of the LORD's temple and repaired them. ⁴ He brought the priests and Levites together in the square on the east side ˎof the templeˎ.

⁵ He said to them, "Listen to me, Levites. Perform the ceremonies to make the temple of the LORD God of your ancestors holy. Remove anything that has been corrupted from the holy place. ⁶ Our ancestors were unfaithful and did what the LORD our God considered evil. They deserted him. They turned away from the LORD's tentᵃ and turned their backs on him. ⁷ They also shut the doors of the ˎtemple'sˎ entrance hall, extinguished the lamps, and didn't burn incense or sacrifice burnt offerings in the holy place to the God of Israel. ⁸ So the LORD was angry with Judah and Jerusalem. He made them something that shocks and terrifies people and that people ridicule, as you can see with your own eyes. ⁹ Our fathers were killed in battle, and our sons, daughters, and wives are prisoners because of this. ¹⁰ Now I intend to make a pledge to the LORD God of Israel so that he may turn his burning anger away from us. ¹¹ Don't be negligent, my sons. The LORD has chosen you to stand in front of him, serve him, be his servants, and burn sacrifices."

¹² So the Levites started to work.
     From Kohath's descendants were Mahath, son of Amasai, and Joel, son of Azariah.
     From Merari's descendants were Kish, son of Abdi, and Azariah, son of Jehallelel.
     From Gershon's descendants were Joah, son of Zimmah, and Eden, son of Joah.
¹³ From Elizaphan's descendants were Shimri and Jeiel.
     From Asaph's descendants were Zechariah and Mattaniah.
¹⁴ From Heman's descendants were Jehiel and Shimei.
     From Jeduthun's descendants were Shemaiah and Uzziel.

ᵃ 29:6 Or "the place where the LORD lives."

¹⁵ These men gathered their relatives and performed the ceremonies to make themselves holy. Then they obeyed the king's order from the LORD's word and entered the temple to make it clean.ᵇ ¹⁶ The priests entered the LORD's temple to make it clean. They carried into the courtyard every unclean thing that they found in the LORD's temple. Then the Levites took the unclean items outside the city to the Kidron Brook. ¹⁷ They started on the first day of the first month. On the eighth day they went into the LORD's entrance hall, and for eight days they performed the ceremonies to make the LORD's temple holy. They finished on the sixteenth day of the first month.

¹⁸ Then they went to King Hezekiah. They said ˌto himˌ, "We have made all of the LORD's temple clean. This includes the altar for burnt offerings, all its utensils, the table for the rows of bread and all its utensils, ¹⁹ and all the utensils King Ahaz refused to use during his reign when he was unfaithful. We have restored them and made them holy. They are in front of the LORD's altar."

²⁰ Early in the morning Hezekiah gathered the leaders of the city and went to the LORD's temple. ²¹ They brought seven bulls, seven rams, seven lambs, and seven male goats as an offering for sin for the kingdom, the holy place, and Judah. Hezekiah told the priests, Aaron's descendants, to sacrifice the animals on the LORD's altar.

²² So they slaughtered the bulls, and the priests sprinkled the blood on the altar. Then they slaughtered the rams and sprinkled the blood on the altar. After that, they slaughtered the lambs and sprinkled the blood on the altar. ²³ Then they brought the male goats for the offering for sin in front of the king and the assembly, who laid their hands on them. ²⁴ The priests slaughtered the goats and made their blood an offering for sin at the altar to make peace with the LORD for Israel. The king had said that the burnt offerings and offerings for sin should be for all Israel.

²⁵ He had the Levites stand in the LORD's temple with cymbals, harps, and lyres as David, the king's seerᶜ Gad, and the prophet Nathan had ordered. This command came from the LORD through his prophets. ²⁶ The Levites stood with David's instruments, and the priests had the trumpets. ²⁷ Then Hezekiah ordered the sacrificing of burnt offerings on the altar. When the burnt offerings started, the songs to the LORD started. These songs were accompanied by trumpets and the instruments of King David of Israel. ²⁸ The whole assembly bowed down with their faces touching the ground, singers began to sing, and the trumpets blew until the burnt offering was finished. ²⁹ When the burnt offerings were finished, the king and everyone who was with him kneeled and bowed down. ³⁰ Then King Hezekiah and the leaders told the Levites to praise the LORD with the words of David and the seer Asaph. They joyfully sang praises, bowed down, and worshiped.

³¹ Hezekiah said, "You have dedicated your lives to the LORD. Come, bring sacrifices and thank offerings to the LORD's temple."

The assembly brought sacrifices and thank offerings, and everyone who was willing brought burnt offerings. ³² The burnt offerings brought by the assembly totaled 70 bulls, 100 rams, and 200 lambs. All of these were burnt offerings to the LORD. ³³ The animals dedicated as holy sacrifices were 600 bulls and 3,000 sheep. ³⁴ But the priests needed more help to skin all the burnt offerings. So their relatives, the Levites, helped them until the work was completed and the priests could make themselves holy. The Levites were more diligent in making themselves holy than the priests were. ³⁵ There were many burnt offerings in addition to the fat of the fellowship offerings and wine offerings that accompanied the burnt offerings. So the worship in the LORD's temple was reestablished. ³⁶ Hezekiah and all the people were overjoyed because of what God had done for the people. Everything had happened so quickly.

Hezekiah Celebrates the Passover

30 ¹ Hezekiah sent a message to all Israel and Judah and wrote letters to the tribes of Ephraim and Manasseh. He invited them to come to the LORD's temple in Jerusalem to celebrate the Passover of the LORD God of Israel.

² The king, his officials, and the whole assembly in Jerusalem decided to celebrate the Passover in the second month. ³ They couldn't celebrate it at the regular time because not enough priests had performed the ceremonies to make themselves holy and the people hadn't gathered in Jerusalem. ⁴ The king and the whole assembly considered their plan to be the right thing to do. ⁵ So they decided to send an announcement throughout Israel from Beersheba to Dan. They summoned everyone to come to Jerusalem to celebrate the Passover of the LORD God of Israel. These people had not celebrated it in large numbers as the written instructions said they should.

⁶ Messengers took letters from the king and his officials throughout Israel and Judah. The king's order said, "Israelites, return to the LORD God of Abraham, Isaac, and Israel. Then he will return to the few of you who escaped from the power of the kings of Assyria. ⁷ Don't be

---

ᵇ 29:15 "Clean" refers to anything that Moses' Teachings say is presentable to God.   ᶜ 29:25 A seer is a prophet.

like your ancestors and your relatives who were unfaithful to the LORD God of their ancestors. He made them something that shocks people, as you have seen. [8] Don't be impossible to deal with like your ancestors. Reach out for the LORD. Come to his holy place that he made holy forever. Serve the LORD your God, and he will turn his burning anger away from you. [9] When you return to the LORD, your relatives and children will find compassion from those who captured them. They will return to this land. The LORD your God is merciful and compassionate. He will not turn his face away from you if you return to him."

[10] So the messengers went from city to city in the territories of Ephraim and Manasseh, as far as Zebulun. But the people ridiculed them. [11] However, some people from Asher, Manasseh, and Zebulun humbled themselves and came to Jerusalem. [12] Also, God guided the people of Judah so that they united to carry out the command which the king and the leaders gave from the LORD's word.

[13] Many people gathered in Jerusalem to celebrate the Festival of Unleavened Bread in the second month. They formed a large assembly.

[14] Then the people got rid of the ˌidols'ˌ altars in Jerusalem. They got rid of all the altars for incense by dumping them in the Kidron Valley.

[15] They slaughtered the Passover lamb on the fourteenth day of the second month. The priests and Levites were ashamed, so they performed the ceremonies to make themselves holy. Then they brought burnt offerings to the LORD's temple. [16] They stood in their regular places as instructed by Moses' Teachings. (Moses was a man of God.) The priests sprinkled the blood they received from the Levites. [17] Many people in the assembly had not made themselves holy. So the Levites had to kill the Passover lambs for all who weren't clean[a] and couldn't make their lambs holy for the LORD.

[18] Many people from Ephraim, Manasseh, Issachar, and Zebulun had not made themselves clean. So they ate the Passover, but not in the way the written instructions said they should. Hezekiah prayed for them: "May the good LORD forgive [19] those who have their hearts set on dedicating their lives to serving God. May the LORD God of their ancestors do this for those who are not clean as required for the holy place." [20] The LORD listened to Hezekiah and healed the people.

[21] So the Israelites in Jerusalem celebrated the Festival of Unleavened Bread for seven days with great joy. Each day the Levites and priests praised the LORD in song. They played the LORD's instruments loudly. [22] Hezekiah spoke encouraging words to all the Levites who had the skills to serve the LORD. They ate the festival meals for seven days, sacrificed fellowship offerings, and confessed their sins to the LORD God of their ancestors.

[23] Then the whole assembly decided to celebrate the festival for seven more days. So they joyfully celebrated for seven more days. [24] King Hezekiah of Judah provided 1,000 bulls and 7,000 sheep as sacrifices for the assembly. The leaders provided 1,000 bulls and 10,000 sheep for the assembly. So a large number of priests were able to perform the ceremonies to make themselves holy.

[25] The whole assembly from Judah, the priests, the Levites, the whole assembly from Israel, the foreigners who came from Israel, and those who lived in Judah rejoiced. [26] The city of Jerusalem was filled with joy. Nothing like this had happened in Jerusalem since the days of King Solomon of Israel.

[27] Then the Levitical priests blessed the people. Their voices were heard, and their prayers went to God's holy place in heaven.

Hezekiah Reforms Judah's Worship

31 [1] When this was over, all the Israelites who were there went to the cities in Judah. They crushed the sacred stones, cut down the poles dedicated to the goddess Asherah, and tore down the illegal places of worship and the altars throughout Judah, Benjamin, Ephraim, and Manasseh. The Israelites destroyed all of these things. Then all the Israelites returned to their own cities. Each person went to his own property.

[2] Hezekiah assigned the priests and the Levites to divisions. Each priest or Levite was put in a division based on the service he performed: sacrificing burnt offerings, sacrificing fellowship offerings, serving, giving thanks, or praising within the gates of the LORD's camp.

[3] He set aside part of the king's property for burnt offerings, the morning and evening offerings, burnt offerings on the weekly worship days, the New Moon Festivals, and the annual festivals, as it is written in the LORD's Teachings. [4] He told the people living in Jerusalem to give the priests and Levites the portions they were due so that they could devote themselves to the LORD's Teachings. [5] As soon as the word spread, the Israelites brought plenty of offerings from the first of their produce: grain, new wine, fresh olive oil, honey, and every crop from the fields. They brought large quantities, a tenth of everything. [6] The people of Israel and Judah who were

---

[a] 30:17 "Clean" refers to anything that Moses' Teachings say is presentable to God.

living in the cities of Judah brought a tenth of their cattle and sheep and a tenth of the holy things they had dedicated to the LORD their God. They piled these holy things in heaps. [7] In the third month they started piling them up, and in the seventh month they finished. [8] When Hezekiah and the leaders saw the heaps, they praised the LORD and his people Israel.

[9] Hezekiah asked the priests and the Levites about the heaps. [10] The chief priest Azariah from Zadok's family said, "Since the people started to bring the offerings to the LORD's temple, we have had all we wanted to eat and plenty to spare. The LORD has blessed his people, and there's a lot left over."

[11] Then Hezekiah told them to prepare storerooms in the LORD's temple. After they had prepared them, [12] they faithfully brought in the contributions, the offerings of one-tenth of the crops, and the gifts dedicated to God. The Levite Conaniah was in charge of these things, and his brother Shimei was his assistant. [13] King Hezekiah and Azariah, who was in charge of God's temple, appointed Jehiel, Azaziah, Nahath, Asahel, Jerimoth, Jozabad, Eliel, Ismachiah, Mahath, and Benaiah to serve under Conaniah and his brother Shimei. [14] Kore, son of Imnah the Levite, was the gatekeeper at East Gate and had to take care of the freewill offerings made to God. His responsibility was to distribute the offerings made to the LORD and the holy gifts dedicated to God. [15] Eden, Miniamin, Jeshua, Shemaiah, Amariah, and Shecaniah served under him in the cities belonging to the priests. They were to distribute the offerings faithfully to all their relatives, young and old, by their divisions. [16] They were appointed to distribute them to males who were at least three years old. The way they were enrolled in the genealogical records did not matter. The six men who served under Kore were to distribute the offerings to everyone who went to the LORD's temple to perform the daily service that each division was responsible for. [17] They were to distribute offerings to the priests who were enrolled by families and to the Levites who were at least 20 years old. Distribution was based on the way they served in their divisions. [18] The priests and Levites were enrolled with their wives, sons, daughters, and other people who depended on them—the whole community. The priests and Levites had to be faithful in keeping themselves holy for the holy work. [19] Men were appointed to give a portion of the offerings to all the males in the priestly families and to everyone listed in the genealogies of the Levites. These men were Aaron's descendants, priests who lived in the pasturelands of every Levite city.

[20] This is what Hezekiah did throughout Judah. He did what was good and right and true to the LORD his God. [21] Hezekiah incorporated Moses' Teachings and commands into worship and dedicated his life to serving God. Whatever he did for the worship in God's temple, he did wholeheartedly, and he succeeded.

God Saves Judah From the Assyrians—2 Kings 18:13–19:37; Isaiah 36:1–37:38

32 [1] After everything Hezekiah had done so faithfully, King Sennacherib of Assyria came to invade Judah. He set up camp ⸤to attack⸥ the fortified cities. He intended to conquer them himself.

[2] When Hezekiah saw that Sennacherib had come to wage war against Jerusalem, [3] he, his officers, and his military staff made plans to stop the water from flowing out of the springs outside the city. They helped him do it. [4] A large crowd gathered as they stopped all the springs and the brook that flowed through the land. They said, "Why should the kings of Assyria find plenty of water?"

[5] Hezekiah worked hard. He rebuilt all the broken sections of the wall, made the towers taller, built another wall outside ⸤the city wall⸥, strengthened the Millo[a] in the City of David, and made plenty of weapons and shields. [6] He appointed military commanders over the troops and gathered the commanders in the square by the city gate. He spoke these words of encouragement: [7] "Be strong and courageous. Don't be frightened or terrified by the king of Assyria or the crowd with him. Someone greater is on our side. [8] The king of Assyria has human power on his side, but the LORD our God is on our side to help us and fight our battles." So the people were encouraged by what King Hezekiah of Judah said.

[9] After this, while King Sennacherib of Assyria and all his royal forces were attacking Lachish, he sent his officers to King Hezekiah of Judah and to all of the people in Judah who were in Jerusalem to say: [10] "This is what King Sennacherib of Assyria says: Why are you so confident as you live in Jerusalem while it is blockaded? [11] Isn't Hezekiah misleading you and abandoning you to die from hunger and thirst when he says, 'The LORD our God will rescue us from the king of Assyria?' [12] Isn't this the same Hezekiah who got rid of the LORD's places of worship and altars and told Judah and Jerusalem, 'Worship and sacrifice at one altar?' [13] Don't you know what I and my predecessors have done to the people of all other countries? Were any of the gods of these other nations ever able to rescue their countries from me? [14] Were the gods of these nations able to rescue their people from my control? My predecessors claimed and destroyed those nations. Is your God able to rescue you from my control? [15] Don't let Hezekiah deceive you

---

[a] 32:5 The exact place referred to as "the Millo" is unknown.

or persuade you like this. Don't believe him. No god of any nation or kingdom could save his people from me or my ancestors. Certainly, your God will not rescue you from me!" ¹⁶ Sennacherib's officers said more against the LORD God and his servant Hezekiah. ¹⁷ Sennacherib wrote letters cursing the LORD God of Israel. These letters said, "As the gods of the nations in other countries couldn't rescue their people from me, Hezekiah's God cannot rescue his people from me." ¹⁸ Sennacherib's officers shouted loudly in the Judean language to the troops who were on the wall of Jerusalem. They tried to frighten and terrify the troops so that they could capture the city. ¹⁹ They spoke about the God of Jerusalem as if he were one of the gods made by human hands and worshiped by the people in other countries.

²⁰ Then King Hezekiah and the prophet Isaiah, son of Amoz, prayed about this and called to heaven. ²¹ The LORD sent an angel who exterminated all the soldiers, officials, and commanders in the Assyrian king's camp. Humiliated, Sennacherib returned to his own country. When he went into the temple of his god, some of his own sons killed him with a sword. ²² So the LORD saved Hezekiah and the people living in Jerusalem from King Sennacherib of Assyria and from everyone else. The LORD gave them peace with all their neighbors.

²³ Many people still went to Jerusalem to bring gifts to the LORD and expensive presents to King Hezekiah of Judah. From then on, he was considered important by all the nations.

Other Events in Hezekiah's Life—2 Kings 20:1–21; Isaiah 38:1–8, 21–22; 39:1–8

²⁴ In those days Hezekiah became sick and was about to die. He prayed to the LORD, who answered him and gave him a miraculous sign. ²⁵ But Hezekiah was conceited, so he didn't repay the LORD for his kindness. The LORD became angry with him, with Judah, and with Jerusalem. ²⁶ Hezekiah and the people living in Jerusalem humbled themselves when they realized they had become conceited. So the LORD didn't vent his anger on them during Hezekiah's time.

²⁷ Hezekiah became richer and was highly honored. He prepared storerooms for himself to hold silver, gold, precious stones, spices, shields, and all kinds of valuables. ²⁸ He made sheds to store his harvests of grain, new wine, and fresh olive oil, and he made barns for all his cattle and stalls for his flocks. ²⁹ He made cities for himself because he had many sheep and cattle. God had given him a lot of property. ³⁰ Hezekiah was the one who stopped the water from flowing from the upper outlet of Gihon. He channeled the water directly underground to the west side of the City of David. Hezekiah succeeded in everything he did.

³¹ When the leaders of Babylon sent ambassadors to ask him about the miraculous sign that had happened in the land, God left him. God did this to test him, to find out everything that was in Hezekiah's heart.

³² Everything else about Hezekiah, including his devotion to God, is written in the vision of the prophet Isaiah, son of Amoz, and in the records of the kings of Judah and Israel. ³³ Hezekiah lay down in death with his ancestors. He was buried in the upper tombs of David's descendants. When Hezekiah died, all of Judah and the people in Jerusalem honored him. His son Manasseh succeeded him as king.

King Manasseh of Judah—2 Kings 21:1–20

33 ¹ Manasseh was 12 years old when he began to rule, and he ruled for 55 years in Jerusalem.

² He did what the LORD considered evil by copying the disgusting things done by the nations that the LORD had forced out of the Israelites' way. ³ He rebuilt the illegal places of worship that his father Hezekiah had torn down. He set up altars dedicated to other gods—the Baals—and made a pole dedicated to the goddess Asherah as King Ahab of Israel had done. Manasseh, like Ahab, worshiped and served the entire army of heaven. ⁴ He built altars in the LORD's temple, where the LORD had said, "My name will be in Jerusalem forever." ⁵ In the two courtyards of the LORD's temple, he built altars for the entire army of heaven. ⁶ He burned his son as a sacrifice in the valley of Ben Hinnom, consulted fortunetellers, cast evil spells, practiced witchcraft, and appointed royal mediums and psychics. He did many things that made the LORD furious. ⁷ Manasseh had a carved idol made. Then he set it up in God's temple, where God had said to David and his son Solomon, "I have chosen this temple and Jerusalem from all the tribes of Israel. I will put my name here forever. ⁸ I will never again remove Israel from the land that I set aside for their ancestors if they will obey all the commands, all the teachings, the ordinances, and the regulations I gave through Moses." ⁹ Manasseh misled Judah and the inhabitants of Jerusalem so that they did more evil things than the nations that the LORD had destroyed when the Israelites arrived in the land.

¹⁰ When the LORD spoke to Manasseh and his people, they wouldn't even pay attention. ¹¹ So the LORD made the army commanders of the king of Assyria invade Judah. They took Manasseh captive, put a hook in his nose, put him in bronze shackles, and brought him to Babylon.

[12] When he experienced this distress, he begged the LORD his God to be kind and humbled himself in front of the God of his ancestors. [13] He prayed to the LORD, and the LORD accepted his prayer and listened to his request. The LORD brought him back to his kingdom in Jerusalem. Then Manasseh knew that the LORD is God.

[14] After this, Manasseh rebuilt the outer wall of the City of David from west of Gihon Spring in the valley to the entrance of Fish Gate. He made the wall go around the Ophel, and he built it very high. He put army commanders in every fortified city in Judah.

[15] Manasseh got rid of the foreign gods and the idol in the LORD's temple. He got rid of the altars he had built in the temple on the LORD's mountain and in Jerusalem. [16] He built the LORD's altar and sacrificed fellowship offerings and thank offerings on it. And he told Judah to serve the LORD God of Israel. [17] The people continued to sacrifice at the illegal places of worship, but they sacrificed only to the LORD their God.

[18] Everything else about Manasseh—including his prayer to his God and the words that the seers[a] spoke to him in the name of the LORD God of Israel—are in the records of the kings of Israel. [19] His prayer and how God accepted it are written in the records of Hozai. The things he did before he humbled himself are also written there. This includes all his sins and unfaithfulness and the places where he built illegal worship sites and set up idols and poles dedicated to the goddess Asherah.

[20] Manasseh lay down in death with his ancestors. They buried him in his own palace. His son Amon succeeded him as king.

King Amon of Judah—2 Kings 21:19–26

[21] Amon was 22 years old when he began to rule, and he ruled for 2 years in Jerusalem. [22] He did what the LORD considered evil, as his father Manasseh had done. Amon sacrificed to all the idols his father Manasseh had made, and he worshiped them. [23] He didn't humble himself in front of the LORD as his father Manasseh had humbled himself. Instead, Amon continued to sin.

[24] His officials plotted against him and killed him in his palace. [25] Then the people of the land killed everyone who had plotted against King Amon. They made his son Josiah king in his place.

King Josiah Reforms Judah's Worship—2 Kings 22:1–2; 23:4–20

34 [1] Josiah was 8 years old when he began to rule, and he was king for 31 years in Jerusalem. [2] He did what the LORD considered right. He lived in the ways of his ancestor David and never stopped living this way.

[3] In the eighth year of his reign, while he was still a boy, he began to dedicate his life to serving the God of his ancestor David. In his twelfth year as king, he began to make Judah and Jerusalem clean[a] by destroying the illegal places of worship, poles dedicated to the goddess Asherah, carved idols, and metal idols. [4] He had the altars of the various Baal gods torn down. He cut down the incense altars that were above them. He destroyed the Asherah poles, carved idols, and metal idols. He ground them into powder and scattered the powder over the tombs of those who had sacrificed to them. [5] He burned the bones of the priests on their altars. So he made Judah and Jerusalem clean. [6] In the cities of Manasseh, Ephraim, Simeon, and as far as Naphtali, he removed all their temples,[b] [7] tore down the altars, beat the Asherah poles and idols into powder, and cut down all the incense altars everywhere in Israel. Then he went back to Jerusalem.

King Josiah Rededicates Judah to God's Promise—2 Kings 22:3–23:4

[8] In the eighteenth year of his reign as he was making the land and the temple clean, Josiah sent Shaphan, son of Azaliah, Maaseiah, the mayor of the city, and Joah, the royal historian and son of Joahaz, to repair the temple of the LORD his God. [9] They came to the chief priest Hilkiah and gave him the money that had been brought to God's temple, the money that the Levite doorkeepers had collected from the tribes of Manasseh and Ephraim, from all who were left in Israel, from everyone in the tribes of Judah and Benjamin, and from the inhabitants of Jerusalem. [10] They gave the money to the foremen who were in charge of the LORD's temple. These foremen gave it to the workmen who were restoring and repairing the temple. [11] (These workers included carpenters and builders.) They were to buy quarried stones and wood for the fittings and beams of the buildings that the kings of Judah had allowed to become run-down. [12] The men did their work faithfully under the supervision of Jahath and Obadiah (Levites descended from Merari), and Zechariah and Meshullam (descendants of Kohath). The Levites, who were skilled musicians, [13] also supervised the workers and directed all the workmen on the various jobs. Some of the Levites served as scribes, officials, or gatekeepers.

[14] When they brought out the money that had been deposited in the LORD's temple, the priest Hilkiah found the book of the LORD's Teachings written by Moses. [15] Hilkiah told the

---

[a] 33:18 Seers are prophets.   [a] 34:3 "Clean" refers to anything that Moses' Teachings say is presentable to God.
[b] 34:6 Hebrew meaning of "he removed all their temples" uncertain.

scribe Shaphan, "I have found the book of the Teachings in the LORD's temple." Hilkiah gave the book to Shaphan.

¹⁶ Shaphan took the book to the king and reported, "We are doing everything you told us to do. ¹⁷ We took the money that was donated in the LORD's temple and gave it to the supervisors and the workmen." ¹⁸ Then the scribe Shaphan told the king, "The priest Hilkiah has given me a book." And Shaphan read it to the king.

¹⁹ When the king heard what the Teachings said, he tore his clothes ˌin distressˌ. ²⁰ Then the king gave an order to Hilkiah, Ahikam (son of Shaphan), Abdon (son of Micah), the scribe Shaphan, and the royal official Asaiah. He said, ²¹ "On behalf of those who are left in Israel and Judah and me, ask the LORD about the words in this book that was found. The LORD's fierce anger has been poured on us because our ancestors did not obey the word of the LORD by doing everything written in this book."

²² So Hilkiah and the king's officials went to talk to the prophet Huldah about this matter. She was the wife of Shallum, son of Tokhath and grandson of Hasrah. Shallum was in charge of the ˌroyalˌ wardrobe. Huldah was living in the Second Part of Jerusalem.

²³ She told them, "This is what the LORD God of Israel says: Tell the man who sent you to me, ²⁴ 'This is what the LORD says: I'm going to bring disaster on this place and on the people living here according to the curses written in the book that was read to the king of Judah. ²⁵ I will do this because they have abandoned me and sacrificed to other gods in order to make me furious. Therefore, my anger will be poured on this place and will never come to an end.' "

²⁶ ˌHuldah added,ˌ "Tell Judah's king who sent you to me to ask the LORD a question, 'This is what the LORD God of Israel says about the words you heard: ²⁷ You had a change of heart and humbled yourself in front of God when you heard my words against this place and those who live here. You humbled yourself, tore your clothes ˌin distressˌ, and cried in front of me. So I will listen ˌto youˌ, declares the LORD. ²⁸ That is why I'm going to bring you to your ancestors. I'm going to bring you to your grave in peace, and your eyes will not see any of the disaster I'm going to bring on this place and those who live here.' "

So they reported this to the king.

²⁹ Then the king sent for all the respected leaders of Judah and Jerusalem to join him. ³⁰ The king, everyone in Judah, everyone living in Jerusalem, the priests, the Levites, and all the people (young and old) went up to the LORD's temple. He read everything written in the Book of the Promise[c] found in the LORD's temple so that they could hear it. ³¹ The king stood in his place and made a promise to the LORD that he would follow the LORD and obey his commands, instructions, and laws with all his heart and soul. He said he would live by the terms of the promise written in this book. ³² He also made all those found in Jerusalem and Benjamin join with him ˌin the promiseˌ. Then the people of Jerusalem lived according to the promise of God, the God of their ancestors.

³³ Josiah got rid of all the disgusting idols throughout Israelite territory. He made all people found in Israel serve the LORD their God. As long as he lived, they didn't stop following the LORD God of their ancestors.

King Josiah Celebrates the Passover—2 Kings 23:21–23

35 ¹ Josiah celebrated the Passover for the LORD in Jerusalem. The Passover lamb was slaughtered on the fourteenth day of the first month. ² Josiah appointed the priests to their duties and encouraged them to serve in the LORD's temple. ³ He told the Levites, who instructed all Israel and performed ceremonies to make themselves holy to the LORD, "Put the holy ark in the temple that Solomon, son of David and king of Israel, built. It shouldn't be carried on your shoulders any longer. Serve the LORD your God and his people Israel. ⁴ Get yourselves ready with the family groups of your divisions, which are listed in the records of King David of Israel and the records of his son Solomon. ⁵ Stand in the holy place representing the family divisions of your relatives, the people ˌof Israelˌ. Let the Levites be considered a part of each family.[a] ⁶ Slaughter the Passover lamb, perform the ceremonies to make yourselves holy, and prepare ˌthe lambsˌ for the other Israelites as the LORD instructed ˌusˌ through Moses."

⁷ Josiah provided the people with 33,000 sheep and goats to be sacrificed as Passover offerings for all who were present. In addition, he provided 3,000 bulls. (These animals were the king's property.) ⁸ His officials also voluntarily gave animals to the people, priests, and Levites. Hilkiah, Zechariah, and Jehiel, the men in charge of God's temple, gave the priests 2,600 sheep and goats and 300 bulls for Passover sacrifices. ⁹ Conaniah and his brothers Shemaiah and Nethanel, and Hashabiah, Jeiel, and Jozabad, the leaders of the Levites, gave the Levites 5,000 sheep and goats and 500 bulls as Passover sacrifices.

---

^c 34:30 Or "Covenant."   ^a 35:5 Hebrew meaning of this sentence uncertain.

[10] So the service was prepared. The priests took their positions with the Levites according to their divisions, as the king had ordered. [11] They slaughtered the Passover lambs. The priests sprinkled the blood with their hands while the Levites skinned the lambs. [12] They set aside the burnt offerings to give them to the laypeople according to their family divisions. The laypeople could then present them to the LORD as written in the Book of Moses. The Levites did the same with the bulls. [13] They roasted the Passover lambs according to the directions. They boiled the holy offerings in pots, kettles, and pans and immediately served them to all the people. [14] Later, they prepared ˎthe animalsˏ for themselves and for the priests because the priests (Aaron's descendants) were sacrificing the burnt offerings and the fat until that evening.

So the Levites prepared ˎthe animalsˏ for themselves and the priests. [15] The singers (Asaph's descendants) were in their places as David, Asaph, Heman, and the king's seer[b] Jeduthun had commanded. The gatekeepers were stationed at each gate. They didn't need to leave their work, because their relatives, the Levites, prepared ˎanimalsˏ for them.

[16] So everything was arranged that day for the worship of the LORD. The Passover was celebrated, and the burnt offerings were sacrificed on the LORD's altar as King Josiah had commanded. [17] The Israelites who were present celebrated the Passover at that time. They also celebrated the Festival of Unleavened Bread for seven days.

[18] Never had a Passover like this been celebrated in Israel during the time of the prophet Samuel or the kings of Israel. They did not celebrate the Passover as Josiah celebrated it with priests, Levites, all of Judah, the people of Israel who could be found, and the inhabitants of Jerusalem. [19] In the eighteenth year of Josiah's reign, this Passover was celebrated.

Josiah's Sin Leads to His Death—2 Kings 23:28–30a

[20] After all this, when Josiah had repaired the temple, King Neco of Egypt came to fight a battle at Carchemish at the Euphrates River. Josiah went to attack him. [21] But Neco sent messengers to Josiah to say, "What's your quarrel with me, king of Judah? I'm not attacking you. I've come to fight those who are at war with me. God told me to hurry. God is with me, so stop now or else he will destroy you."

[22] But Josiah would not stop his attack. He disguised himself as he went into battle. He refused to listen to Neco's words, which came from God, and he went to fight in the valley of Megiddo.

[23] Some archers shot King Josiah. The king told his officers, "Take me away because I'm badly wounded."

[24] His officers took him out of the chariot and brought him to Jerusalem in his other chariot. He died and was buried in the tombs of his ancestors. All Judah and Jerusalem mourned for Josiah. [25] Jeremiah sang a funeral song about Josiah. All the male and female singers still sing funeral songs about Josiah today. This became a tradition in Israel. They are written in ˎthe Book ofˏ the Funeral Songs.

[26] Everything else about Josiah—including his devotion to God by following what is written in the LORD's Teachings [27] and his acts from first to last—are written in the records of the kings of Israel and Judah.

King Jehoahaz of Judah—2 Kings 23:30b–35

36 [1] Then people of the land took Josiah's son Jehoahaz and made him king in Jerusalem in place of his father. [2] Jehoahaz was 23 years old when he became king, and he was king in Jerusalem for 3 months. [3] The king of Egypt removed him from office in Jerusalem and fined the country 7,500 pounds of silver and 75 pounds of gold. [4] The king of Egypt made Jehoahaz's brother Eliakim king of Judah and Jerusalem and changed Eliakim's name to Jehoiakim. Neco took Jehoahaz away to Egypt.

King Jehoiakim of Judah—2 Kings 23:36–24:7

[5] Jehoiakim was 25 years old when he began to rule, and he ruled for 11 years in Jerusalem. He did what the LORD his God considered evil. [6] King Nebuchadnezzar of Babylon attacked Jehoiakim and put him in bronze shackles to take him to Babylon. [7] Nebuchadnezzar also brought some of the utensils of the LORD's temple to Babylon. He put them in his palace in Babylon.

[8] Everything else about Jehoiakim—the disgusting things he did and all the charges against him—is written in the Book of the Kings of Israel and Judah. His son Jehoiakin succeeded him as king.

King Jehoiakin of Judah—2 Kings 24:8–17

[9] Jehoiakin was eight years old when he began to rule as king. He was king for three months and ten days in Jerusalem. He did what the LORD considered evil.

---

[b] 35:15 A seer is a prophet.

¹⁰ In the spring King Nebuchadnezzar sent for Jehoiakin and brought him to Babylon with the valuable utensils from the LORD's temple. Nebuchadnezzar made Jehoiakin's uncle Zedekiah king of Judah and Jerusalem.

King Zedekiah of Judah—*2 Kings 24:18–25:21; Jeremiah 39:1–10; 52:1–27*

¹¹ Zedekiah was 21 years old when he began to rule, and he ruled for 11 years in Jerusalem. ¹² He did what the LORD his God considered evil and didn't humble himself in front of the prophet Jeremiah, who spoke for the LORD. ¹³ Zedekiah also rebelled against King Nebuchadnezzar. Nebuchadnezzar had made Zedekiah swear an oath of allegiance to him in God's name. But Zedekiah became so stubborn and so impossible to deal with that he refused to turn back to the LORD God of Israel.

¹⁴ All the officials, the priests, and the people became increasingly unfaithful and followed all the disgusting practices of the nations. Although the LORD had made the temple in Jerusalem holy, they made the temple unclean.ᵃ ¹⁵ The LORD God of their ancestors repeatedly sent messages through his messengers because he wanted to spare his people and his dwelling place. ¹⁶ But they mocked God's messengers, despised his words, and made fun of his prophets until the LORD became angry with his people. He could no longer heal them.

¹⁷ So he had the Babylonian king attack them and execute their best young men in their holy temple. He didn't spare the best men or the unmarried women, the old people or the sick people. God handed all of them over to him. ¹⁸ He brought to Babylon each of the utensils from God's temple, the treasures from the LORD's temple, and the treasures of the king and his officials. ¹⁹ They burned God's temple, tore down Jerusalem's walls, burned down all its palaces, and destroyed everything of value. ²⁰ The king of Babylon took those who weren't executed to Babylon to be slaves for him and his sons. They remained captives until the Persian Empire began to rule. ²¹ This happened so that the LORD's words spoken through Jeremiah would be fulfilled. The land had its years of rest and was made acceptable ˍagainˌ. While it lay in ruins, ˍthe land had its, 70 years of rest.

King Cyrus Allows the Jews to Return From Babylon—*Ezra 1:1–3*

²² The promise the LORD had spoken through Jeremiah was about to come true in Cyrus' first year as king of Persia. The LORD inspired the king to make this announcement throughout his whole kingdom and then to put it in writing.

²³ This is what King Cyrus of Persia says: The LORD God of heaven has given me all the kingdoms of the world. And he has ordered me to build a temple for him in Jerusalem (which is in Judah). May the LORD God be with all of you who are his people. You may go.

ᵃ 36:14 "Unclean" refers to anything that Moses' Teachings say is not presentable to God.

EZRA

Cyrus Allows the Jews to Return From Babylon—2 Chronicles 36:22–23

1 ¹ The promise the LORD had spoken through Jeremiah was about to come true in Cyrus' first year as king of Persia. The LORD inspired the king to make this announcement throughout his whole kingdom and then to put it in writing.

² This is what King Cyrus of Persia says: The LORD God of heaven has given me all the kingdoms of the world. And he has ordered me to build a temple for him in Jerusalem (which is in Judah). ³ May God be with all of you who are his people. You may go to Jerusalem (which is in Judah) and build a temple for the LORD God of Israel. He is the God who is in Jerusalem. ⁴ All who ˎchoose toˎ remain behind, wherever they may be living, should provide the people who are leaving with silver, gold, supplies, livestock, and freewill offerings to be used in God's temple in Jerusalem.

Sheshbazzar Returns With the Temple Furnishings

⁵ Then the heads of the families of Judah and Benjamin, the priests, and the Levites— everyone God had inspired—came forward to rebuild the LORD's temple in Jerusalem. ⁶ All their neighbors ˎwho were remaining behindˎ provided them with articles made from silver and gold, supplies, livestock, and valuable gifts besides everything that was freely offered. ⁷ King Cyrus brought out the utensils belonging to the LORD's temple. Nebuchadnezzar had taken these utensils from Jerusalem and put them in the temple of his own god. ⁸ King Cyrus of Persia put the treasurer Mithredath in charge of bringing them out. So Mithredath made a list of them for Prince Sheshbazzar of Judah.ᵃ ⁹ This is the inventory:

gold dishesᵇ	30
silver dishes	1,000
knivesᵇ	29
¹⁰ gold bowls	30
other silver bowls	410
other utensils	1,000

¹¹ The gold and silver utensils totaled 5,400.

Sheshbazzar took all these utensils with him when the exiles left Babylon to go to Jerusalem.

Those Who Returned With Zerubbabel—Nehemiah 7:6–7

2 ¹ These were the people in the province. They were the ones who left the place where the exiles had been taken captive. (King Nebuchadnezzar of Babylon had taken them to Babylon.) These exiles returned to Jerusalem and Judah. All of them went to their own cities. ² They went with Zerubbabel, Jeshua, Nehemiah, Seraiah, Reelaiah, Mordecai, Bilshan, Mispar, Bigvai, Rehum, and Baanah.

Families Listed by Ancestor—Nehemiah 7:8–25

This is the number of Israelite men from the people in exile:

³	the descendants of Parosh	2,172
⁴	of Shephatiah	372
⁵	of Arah	775
⁶	of Pahath Moab, that is, of Jeshua and Joab	2,812
⁷	of Elam	1,254
⁸	of Zattu	945
⁹	of Zaccai	760
¹⁰	of Bani	642
¹¹	of Bebai	623
¹²	of Azgad	1,222
¹³	of Adonikam	666
¹⁴	of Bigvai	2,056

ᵃ 1:8 Or "for Sheshbazzar, the leader of Judah."   ᵇ 1:9 Hebrew meaning of this word uncertain.

15 of Adin	454
16 of Ater, that is, Hezekiah	98
17 of Bezai	323
18 of Jorah	112
19 of Hashum	223
20 of Gibbar	95

Families Listed by Cities—*Nehemiah 7:26–38*

21 The people of Bethlehem	123
22 of Netophah	56
23 of Anathoth	128
24 of Azmaveth	42
25 of Kiriath Jearim, Chephirah, and Beeroth	743
26 of Ramah and Geba	621
27 of Michmas	122
28 of Bethel and Ai	223
29 of Nebo	52
30 of Magbish	156
31 of the other Elam	1,254
32 of Harim	320
33 of Lod, Hadid, and Ono	725
34 of Jericho	345
35 of Senaah	3,630

Priests—*Nehemiah 7:39–42*

36 These priests returned from exile:

the descendants of Jedaiah (through the family of Jeshua)	973
37 of Immer	1,052
38 of Pashhur	1,247
39 of Harim	1,017

Levites—*Nehemiah 7:43–45*

40 These Levites returned from exile:

the descendants of Jeshua and Kadmiel, that is, of Hodaviah	74

41 These singers returned from exile:

the descendants of Asaph	128

42 These gatekeepers returned from exile:

the descendants of Shallum, Ater, Talmon, Akkub, Hatita, and Shobai	139

Temple Servants—*Nehemiah 7:46–56*

43 These temple servants returned from exile: the descendants of Ziha, Hasupha, Tabbaoth, **44** Keros, Siaha, Padon, **45** Lebanah, Hagabah, Akkub, **46** Hagab, Shalmai, Hanan, **47** Giddel, Gahar, Reaiah, **48** Rezin, Nekoda, Gazzam, **49** Uzza, Paseah, Besai, **50** Asnah, Meunim, Nephusim, **51** Bakbuk, Hakupha, Harhur, **52** Bazluth, Mehida, Harsha, **53** Barkos, Sisera, Temah, **54** Neziah, and Hatipha.

Descendants of Solomon's Servants—*Nehemiah 7:57–60*

55 These descendants of Solomon's servants returned from exile: the descendants of Sotai, Hassophereth, Peruda, **56** Jaalah, Darkon, Giddel, **57** Shephatiah, Hattil, Pochereth Hazzebaim, and Ami.

58 The temple servants and the descendants of Solomon's servants totaled 392.

Those of Unknown Origin—*Nehemiah 7:61–65*

59 The following people came from Tel Melah, Tel Harsha, Cherub, Addan, and Immer, but they couldn't prove they were Israelites on the basis of their father's family or their genealogy: **60** the descendants of Delaiah, Tobiah, and Nekoda. These people totaled 652.

61 These descendants of the priests ˌcouldn't prove their families were Israelitesˌ: the descendants of Hobaiah, Hakkoz, and Barzillai (who had married one of the daughters of Barzillai from Gilead and took that ˌfamilyˌ name). **62** These people searched for their ˌfamilyˌ names in the genealogical records, but their names couldn't be found there. For this reason they were considered contaminated and couldn't be priests. **63** The governor told them not to eat any of the most holy food until a priest could use the Urim and Thummim[a] ˌto settle the problemˌ.

---

[a] 2:63 The Urim and Thummim were used by the chief priest to determine God's answer to questions.

The Total of the People and Animals Returning From Exile—Nehemiah 7:66–69

⁶⁴ The whole assembly totaled 42,360. ⁶⁵ In addition to the male and female servants who numbered 7,337, they also had 200 male and female singers. ⁶⁶ They had 736 horses, 245 mules, ⁶⁷ 435 camels, and 6,720 donkeys.

Gifts Given for the Temple—Nehemiah 7:70–73

⁶⁸ When some of the heads of the families came to the LORD's temple in Jerusalem, they contributed freewill offerings to help rebuild God's temple on its ˍformerˍ site. ⁶⁹ They contributed as much as they could to the treasury for this work: 1,030 pounds of gold, 5,740 pounds of silver, and 100 robes for the priests.

⁷⁰ The priests, the Levites, some of the people, the singers, the gatekeepers, and the temple servants settled in their own cities. All the other Israelites settled in their own cities.

Worship at the Temple Site Begins Again

3 ¹ When the seventh month came, the people gathered together in Jerusalem. (The Israelites had already settled in their cities.) ² Then Jozadak's son Jeshua and his relatives ˍwho wereˍ priests and Shealtiel's son Zerubbabel and his relatives built an altar for the God of Israel. They built it in order to sacrifice burnt offerings. They ˍfollowed the directionsˍ written in Moses' Teachings. (Moses was a man of God.) ³ So they rebuilt the altar on its original site, though they were afraid of the people in the neighboring regions. They sacrificed burnt offerings on it to the LORD every morning and evening.

⁴ Following the written directions, they celebrated the Festival of Booths. Each day they sacrificed the required number of burnt offerings. ⁵ After that, they sacrificed the daily burnt offerings, the offerings for the New Moon Festival and all the other holy festivals of the LORD, and all the freewill offerings brought to the LORD. ⁶ They started to bring these burnt offerings to the LORD on the first day of the seventh month, even though the foundation of the LORD's temple had not yet been laid.

Work on the Temple Begins

⁷ So they gave money to the stonecutters and carpenters. Then they gave food, drink, and olive oil to the men from Sidon and Tyre in exchange for cedar, which the men would bring by sea from Lebanon to Joppa as King Cyrus of Persia had authorized them to do.

⁸ Zerubbabel (who was Shealtiel's son), Jeshua (who was Jozadak's son), and the rest of the Jews, (the priests, Levites, and all the others who had come back from exile to Jerusalem) began to rebuild the temple. This happened in the second month of the second year following their return to ˍthe siteˍ of God's house in Jerusalem. They began by appointing the Levites who were at least 20 years old to direct the work on the LORD's house. ⁹ Then Jeshua with his sons and relatives and Kadmiel with his sons who were Judah's descendants joined Henadad's family and their sons and relatives, the Levites, in directing those working on God's house.

A Celebration After the Laying of the Temple's Foundation

¹⁰ The builders laid the foundation of the LORD's temple. Then the priests who were dressed in their robes took their places with trumpets, and the Levites who were Asaph's descendants took their places with cymbals to praise the LORD according to the instructions of King David of Israel. ¹¹ As they praised and gave thanks to the LORD, they sang antiphonally:

"He is good; his mercy toward Israel endures forever."

Then all the people shouted, "Praise the LORD," because the foundation for the house of the LORD had been laid.

¹² But many of the priests, Levites, and the heads of the families who were old enough to have seen the first temple with their own eyes began to sob when they saw the foundation of this temple. Many others shouted for joy. ¹³ No one could distinguish between the joyful shouts and the loud sobbing because the people were shouting so loudly. The noise was heard from far away.

The Samaritans Stop the Work

4 ¹ When the enemies of Judah and Benjamin heard that the people who returned from exile were building a temple for the LORD God of Israel, ² they approached Zerubbabel and the heads of the families. They told them, "We want to help you build because we worship the same God you worship. We have been sacrificing to himᵃ since the time of King Esarhaddon of Assyria, who brought us here."

ᵃ 4:2 Dead Sea Scrolls, Greek, Syriac, Egyptian; Masoretic Text "We have not sacrificed."

³ But Zerubbabel, Jeshua, and the rest of the heads of Israel's families told them, "It isn't right for your people and our people to build a temple for our God together. We must build it alone for the LORD God of Israel, as King Cyrus of Persia ordered us to do."

⁴ Then the people of that region discouraged the people of Judah and made them afraid to continue building. ⁵ They bribed officials to keep the people of Judah from carrying out their plans throughout the reign of King Cyrus of Persia until the reign of King Darius of Persia.

⁶ When Xerxes began to rule, the enemies of Judah and Jerusalem wrote a letter in which they made an accusation against the inhabitants of Judah and Jerusalem.

⁷ Bishlam, Mithredath, Tabeel, and the rest of their group wrote to him when Artaxerxes was king of Persia. The letter was written with the Aramaic script and translated into the Aramaic language.

⁸ Rehum the commander and Shimshai the scribe wrote another letter against ‚the people of‚ Jerusalem to King Artaxerxes. ⁹ At that time, Rehum the commander and Shimshai the scribe were with the others of their group—the people from Denya, Partakka, Tarpel, Persia, Erech, Babylon, Susa, (that is, those of Elam), ¹⁰ and the rest of the people whom the great and noble Assurbanipal deported. (Assurbanipal settled them in the cities of Samaria and the rest of the lands west of the Euphrates River.) ¹¹ This is the copy of the letter they sent to him:

To King Artaxerxes,
From your servants, the people west of the Euphrates:

¹² Your Majesty, you should know that the Jews who came to us from you are now in Jerusalem. They are rebuilding that rebellious and wicked city. They are close to finishing the walls. The foundations are already in place. ¹³ You should also know that if this city is rebuilt and its walls are finished, the Jews will no longer pay taxes, fees, and tolls.

Ultimately, this will hurt the king's income. ¹⁴ Now, because we are paid by your palace, it isn't right for us to watch something happen that will dishonor the king. So we are sending this letter to inform you ¹⁵ that you should search the official records of your predecessors. You will find in those official records that this city has been rebellious and has been a threat to kings and provinces. This city has a history of rebelliousness. That's why this city was destroyed. ¹⁶ We want the king to know that if this city is rebuilt and its walls are finished, you will have nothing left ‚of your province‚ west of the Euphrates River.

¹⁷ Then the king sent this reply:

To Rehum the commander, Shimshai the scribe, and the rest of their group living in
    Samaria, and to others west of the Euphrates River:
I wish you peace and prosperity!

¹⁸ The letter you sent me has been read word for word in my presence. ¹⁹ I gave the order, and a search was made. I discovered that this city has a long history of uprisings against kings. Its inhabitants are guilty of treason and rebellion. ²⁰ Jerusalem has had powerful kings who have ruled the whole ‚province‚ west of the Euphrates. Taxes, fees, and tolls were paid to them. ²¹ So order these men to stop rebuilding. Keep this city from being rebuilt until I give the order. ²² Be careful not to neglect your duty in this matter. Why should I, the king, suffer any more harm?

²³ Rehum the commander, Shimshai the scribe, and their group hurried to Jerusalem after hearing a copy of King Artaxerxes' letter. They forced the Jews to stop rebuilding.

²⁴ Then the work on God's temple in Jerusalem was stopped. Nothing more was done until Darius' second year as king of Persia.

Work Resumed on the Temple

5 ¹ The prophet Haggai and Zechariah, grandson of Iddo, prophesied to the Jews in Judah and Jerusalem in the name of Israel's God, who was over them. ² Then Zerubbabel, who was Shealtiel's son, and Jeshua, who was Jozadak's son, began to rebuild God's temple in Jerusalem. God's prophets were with them and supported them.

³ At the same time, Governor Tattenai ‚from the province‚ west of the Euphrates River, Shethar Bozenai, and their group went to the Jews and asked them, "Who gave you permission to rebuild this temple and finish its walls?" ⁴ They also asked the Jews for the names of the men who were working on this building.

⁵ But the leaders of the Jews were under God's watchful eye. They couldn't be stopped until Darius received a report and sent a reply to it.

Permission Requested From Darius

⁶ Here is a copy of the letter Governor Tattenai ˎfrom the provinceˎ west of the Euphrates River, Shethar Bozenai and his group (the Persians west of that river) sent to King Darius. ⁷ They sent him the following report:

To King Darius,
We wish you peace and prosperity in everything you do.

⁸ Your Majesty should know that we went to the province of Judah, to the temple of the great God. The temple is being built with large stones and with wooden beams laid in its walls. The builders are doing an excellent job and making rapid progress. ⁹ We asked their leaders the following question: "Who gave you permission to rebuild this temple and finish its walls?" ¹⁰ For your information, we also asked them for their names so that we would have a record of the men who were their leaders. ¹¹ This was their reply to us:

"We areˎ the servants of the God of heaven and earth. We are rebuilding the temple that was originally built many years ago by a great king of Israel. ¹² But because our ancestors made the God of heaven angry, he handed them over to King Nebuchadnezzar of Babylon (a Chaldean). So Nebuchadnezzar destroyed this temple and deported its people to Babylon.

¹³ "However, in the first year of the reign of King Cyrus of Babylon, Cyrus gave permission for God's temple to be rebuilt. ¹⁴ In addition, Cyrus took out of a temple in Babylon the gold and silver utensils that belonged to God's temple. (Nebuchadnezzar had taken them out of God's temple in Jerusalem and brought them into a temple in Babylon.) Cyrus gave them to a man named Sheshbazzar, whom he had made governor. ¹⁵ Cyrus told him, 'Take these utensils. Place them in the temple in Jerusalem. Rebuild God's temple on its original site.' ¹⁶ Then Sheshbazzar laid the foundation of God's temple in Jerusalem. The temple has been under construction from that time until now, but it still isn't finished."

¹⁷ If it pleases Your Majesty, allow someone to search the king's archives in Babylon to determine whether King Cyrus gave permission for the temple of God to be rebuilt in Jerusalem. Then please send us Your Majesty's decision on this matter.

King Darius Finds King Cyrus' Memorandum

6 ¹ Then King Darius gave the order to search the library where the archives were stored in Babylon. ² A scroll was found in the palace of Ecbatana, which is in the province of Media. This was written on it:

MEMORANDUM

³ Date: Cyrus' first year as king
From: King Cyrus
Subject: God's temple in Jerusalem.

The temple should be rebuilt as a place to offer sacrifices. Its foundation should be laid. It should be 90 feet high and 90 feet wide ⁴ with three rows of large stones and a row of wood. The king's palace will pay for it. ⁵ In addition, Cyrus took out of a temple in Babylon the gold and silver utensils that belonged to God's temple. (Nebuchadnezzar had taken them out of God's temple in Jerusalem and brought them into a temple in Babylon.) They should be returned to their proper place in the temple in Jerusalem. You should put each one in God's temple.

⁶ Governor Tattenai ˎfrom the provinceˎ west of the Euphrates, Shethar Bozenai, and those of your group (the Persians west of the river):
You must stay away from there. ⁷ Don't interfere with the work on God's temple. Let the governor of the Jews and the leaders of Judah rebuild God's temple on its ˎoriginalˎ foundation. ⁸ I am issuing this decree about how you must help the Jewish leaders rebuild God's temple:

The cost ˎfor thisˎ should be paid out of the king's own money from the taxes ˎon the provinceˎ west of the Euphrates. Full payment should be made to these men so that the work is not interrupted. ⁹ Also, whatever the priests in Jerusalem need for burnt offerings to the God of heaven—young bulls, rams, lambs, wheat, salt, wine, and olive oil—should be provided for them each day. Make sure that

---

ᵃ 6:11 Hebrew meaning of this word uncertain.

nothing is omitted. [10] Then they can offer sacrifices that please the God of heaven and pray for the life of the king and his sons.

[11] I am also issuing a decree that if anyone tampers with my orders, that person should be impaled on a beam torn from his own house and his house should be turned into a pile of rubble.[a] [12] May the God whose name is worshiped there cause the downfall of each king and nation who tries to tamper with my orders or tries to destroy the temple of the God in Jerusalem.

I, Darius, have issued a decree. It's to be carried out exactly as ordered.

[13] Then Governor Tattenai ˌfrom the provinceˌ west of the Euphrates River, Shethar Bozenai, and their group did exactly what King Darius had ordered. [14] So the Jewish leaders continued to make progress because of the message from the prophet Haggai and Zechariah, the grandson of Iddo. They finished building as the God of Israel had ordered and as Cyrus, Darius, and Artaxerxes (the kings of Persia) had ordered. [15] This temple was finished on the third day of the month of Adar in the sixth year of King Darius' reign.

The Temple Is Completed and Dedicated

[16] Then the people of Israel, the priests, the Levites, and the others who had returned from exile celebrated at the dedication of God's temple. [17] At the dedication of God's temple, they sacrificed 100 bulls, 200 rams, and 400 lambs. They sacrificed 12 male goats as an offering for sin, one goat for each of the tribes of Israel.

[18] The priests were assigned to their divisions and the Levites to their groups ˌto leadˌ the worship of God in Jerusalem by following the directions written in the Book of Moses.

The Passover Is Celebrated

[19] On the fourteenth day of the first month, those who had returned from exile celebrated the Passover. [20] Since the priests and Levites had cleansed themselves, all of them were ˌnowˌ clean.[b] They killed the Passover lambs for all the people who had returned from exile, for the rest of the priests, and for themselves. [21] The lambs were eaten by the Israelites who had returned from exile and by all who had separated themselves from the unclean practices of the non-Jews in the land to worship the LORD God of Israel. [22] So for seven days they celebrated the Festival of Unleavened Bread because the LORD had made them joyful. The LORD had made the king of Assyria change his mind so that he supported the people in their work on the temple of God, the God of Israel.

Ezra's Family Background

7 [1] After these things, during the reign of King Artaxerxes of Persia, Ezra left Babylon. Ezra was the son of Seraiah, who was the son of Azariah, who was the son of Hilkiah, [2] who was the son of Shallum, who was the son of Zadok, who was the son of Ahitub, [3] who was the son of Amariah, who was the son of Azariah, who was the son of Meraioth, [4] who was the son of Zerahiah, who was the son of Uzzi, who was the son of Bukki, [5] who was the son of Abishua, who was the son of Phinehas, who was the son of Eleazer, who was the son of Aaron (the first priest).

[6] As a scribe, Ezra was an expert in Moses' Teachings, which the LORD God of Israel had given. The king gave Ezra everything he requested because the LORD his God was guiding him.

[7] Some Israelites (including priests, Levites, singers, gatekeepers, and temple servants) went to Jerusalem in Artaxerxes' seventh year as king. [8] In that same year in the fifth month, Ezra arrived in Jerusalem. [9] He had left Babylon on the first day of the first month, and on the first day of the fifth month, he arrived in Jerusalem, since his God was good to him. [10] Ezra was determined to study the LORD's Teachings, live by them, and teach their rules and regulations in Israel.

King Artaxerxes' Letter to Ezra

[11] This is a copy of the letter that King Artaxerxes gave Ezra the priest and scribe, a man with a thorough knowledge of the LORD's commands and laws for Israel:

[12] From: Artaxerxes, king of kings
To: Ezra the priest, a scribe for the Teachings of the God of Heaven:
           I wish you peace and prosperity!

[13] I have issued a decree that any Israelites who are in my kingdom and want to go with you to Jerusalem may go. This also includes the priests and Levites. [14] I, the king, and my seven advisers are sending you to evaluate the situation in Judah and Jerusalem on the

---

[b] 6:20 "Clean" refers to anything that Moses' Teachings say is presentable to God.

basis of your God's Teachings, which you hold in your hands. [15] Also, you must take the silver and gold that the king and his advisers willingly contributed to the God of Israel, the God whose temple is in Jerusalem. [16] Take any silver and gold that you find in the whole province of Babylon when you take the gifts contributed by the people and the priests. They willingly contributed these gifts for the temple of their God in Jerusalem. [17] You must use this money to buy bulls, rams, lambs, grain, and wine to offer on the altar of the temple of your God in Jerusalem. [18] You and your relatives may do whatever you think is right with the rest of the silver and gold. However, what you do must conform to the will of your God. [19] The utensils that have been given to you so that they can be used in your God's temple must all be presented to the God of Jerusalem. [20] You may use the king's treasury to pay for anything else that you must provide for your God's temple.

[21] I, King Artaxerxes, order all the treasurers ˌin the provinceˌ west of the Euphrates River to do exactly what Ezra the priest, a scribe for the Teachings of the God of Heaven, asks you to do. [22] ˌYou may give himˌ up to 7,500 pounds of silver, 100 measures of wheat, 600 gallons of wine, 600 gallons of olive oil, and as much salt as he needs. [23] Whatever the God of heaven has commanded must be carried out in detail for the temple of the God of heaven. Why should God become angry with the king's empire and his sons? [24] Furthermore, we are notifying you that you are forbidden to make any priest, Levite, singer, gatekeeper, servant, or worker in the temple of this God pay any taxes, fees, or tolls.

[25] You, Ezra, using your God's wisdom—the Teachings you hold in your hands—will appoint judges and administrators for all the people who know your God's Teachings and live ˌin the provinceˌ west of the Euphrates River. In addition, you will teach anyone who doesn't know the Teachings.

[26] Whoever will not strictly follow your God's Teachings and the king's orders should be promptly exiled, have his goods confiscated, be imprisoned or be sentenced to die.

[27] ˌI, Ezra, said:ˌ Thanks be to the LORD God of our ancestors. He put this into the king's mind to make the LORD's temple in Jerusalem beautiful. [28] He made the king, his advisers, and all the king's powerful officials treat me kindly.

I was encouraged because the LORD my God was guiding me. So I gathered leaders in Israel to go with me.

The List of Those Returning From Babylon

8 [1] These are the leaders of the families and the genealogy of those who left Babylon with me during the reign of King Artaxerxes:

[2]	from the family of Phinehas:	Gershom
	from the family of Ithamar:	Daniel
[3]	from the family of David:	Hattush, son of Shecaniah
	from the family of Parosh:	Zechariah, with 150 males whose genealogies were known
[4]	from the family of Pahath Moab:	Eliehoenai, son of Zerahiah, with 200 males
[5]	from the family of Zattu:[a]	Shecaniah, son of Jahaziel, with 300 males
[6]	from the family of Adin:	Ebed, son of Jonathan, with 50 males
[7]	from the family of Elam:	Jeshaiah, son of Athaliah, with 70 males
[8]	from the family of Shephatiah:	Zebadiah, son of Michael, with 80 males
[9]	from the family of Joab:	Obadiah, son of Jehiel, with 210 males
[10]	from the family of Bani:[b]	Shelomith, son of Josiphiah, with 160 males
[11]	from the family of Bebai:	Zechariah, son of Bebai, with 38 males
[12]	from the family of Azgad:	Johanan, son of Hakkatan, with 110 males
[13]	from the family of Adonikam:	Eliphelet, Jeuel, and Shemaiah, who arrived later with 60 males
[14]	from the family of Bigvai:	Uthai and Zabbud, with 70 males.

---

[a] 8:5 Greek; Masoretic Text omits "of Zattu."   [b] 8:10 Greek; Masoretic Text omits "of Bani."

The People Prepare for Their Journey

¹⁵ I had this group gather by the river that flows to Ahava, and we camped there for three days. I noticed laypeople and priests there, but I didn't find any Levites. ¹⁶ Then I sent for Eliezer, Ariel, Shemaiah, Elnathan, Jarib, Elnathan, Nathan, Zechariah, and Meshullam (who were leading men) and for Joiarib and Elnathan (who were wise). ¹⁷ I sent them to Iddo, the leader in Casiphia. I told them to tell Iddo and his relatives, the temple servants in Casiphia, that they should bring us men who can serve in our God's temple. ¹⁸ God was guiding us, so Iddo and his relatives brought us someone competent, Sherebiah, who was a descendant of Mahli, Levi, and Israel. They brought us 18 of Sherebiah's sons and relatives. ¹⁹ They also brought Hashabiah, Jeshaiah (who was a descendant of Merari), 20 of Jeshaiah's relatives and their sons, ²⁰ and 220 temple servants. They were descended from the temple servants whom David and his officials had appointed to work for the Levites. These were all listed by name.

²¹ Then I announced a fast there at the Ahava River so that we might humble ourselves in the presence of our God to ask him for a safe journey for ourselves, for our little ones, and for all our goods. ²² I was ashamed to ask the king for an armed escort with cavalry to help us against an enemy attack on the way. We had already told the king, "Our God works things out for the good of everyone who dedicates his life to serving him, but his power and his anger oppose everyone who abandons him." ²³ So we fasted and asked our God for a safe journey, and he answered our prayer.

²⁴ Then I selected 12 leaders from the priests—Sherebiah, Hashabiah, and 10 of their relatives. ²⁵ I weighed for them the silver, the gold, and the utensils. These were the contributions that the king, his advisers, his officials, and all the Israelites had contributed for our God's temple. ²⁶ I weighed the contributions for them to guard: about 24 tons of silver, 100 silver utensils weighing 150 pounds apiece, 7,500 pounds of gold, ²⁷ 20 gold bowls weighing 18 pounds apiece, and two utensils of fine polished bronze that were as precious as gold. ²⁸ I told them, "You and the utensils are holy to the LORD. The silver and gold are freewill offerings to the LORD God of your ancestors. ²⁹ Guard them carefully. In Jerusalem, inside the storerooms of the LORD's temple, weigh these items. Do this in front of the chief priests, Levites, and the leaders of Israel's families." ³⁰ So the priests and the Levites took charge of the silver, the gold, and the utensils. They were responsible for bringing these items to the temple of our God in Jerusalem.

The People Arrive in Jerusalem

³¹ Then we left the Ahava River on the twelfth day of the first month to go to Jerusalem. God was guiding us, and he rescued us from our enemies and from ambushes along the way. ³² When we reached Jerusalem, we rested for three days. ³³ On the fourth day we weighed the silver, the gold, and the utensils in our God's temple. We put them under the supervision of Meremoth, son of the priest Uriah, as well as Eleazar, the son of Phinehas. The Levites, Jeshua's son Jozabad, and Binnui's son Noadiah, assisted them. ³⁴ Everything was counted and weighed, and the entire weight was recorded at that time.

³⁵ The exiles who had come back from captivity sacrificed burnt offerings to the God of Israel: 12 bulls for all Israel, 96 rams, 77 lambs, and 12 male goats for an offering for sin. All of these animals were burnt offerings for the LORD.

³⁶ The exiles delivered the king's orders to the king's satraps and governors in the province, west of the Euphrates River. These officials then gave their support to the people and the temple of God.

Ezra Leads the People in Prayer

9 ¹ After these things had been done, the leaders came to me and said, "The people of Israel, including the priests and Levites, have failed to keep themselves separate from the neighboring groups of people and from the disgusting practices of the Canaanites, Hittites, Perizzites, Jebusites, Ammonites, Moabites, Egyptians, and Amorites. ² The Israelites and their sons have married some of these foreign women. They have mixed our holy race with the neighboring groups of people. Furthermore, the leaders and officials have led the way in being unfaithful."

³ When I heard this, I tore my clothes in distress, pulled hair from my scalp and my beard, and sat down in shock. ⁴ Since the former exiles had been unfaithful, everyone who gathered around me there trembled at the words of the God of Israel. I sat in shock until the evening sacrifice. ⁵ At the evening sacrifice I got up from my misery, and with my clothes torn, I knelt down, stretched out my hands to the LORD my God in prayer, ⁶ and said,

"I am ashamed, my God. I am embarrassed to look at you. Our sins have piled up over our heads, and our guilt is so overwhelming that it reaches heaven. ⁷ From our ancestors' days until now, we have been deep in guilt. Our kings and our priests have been handed over to foreign kings to be executed. We have been taken captive, robbed, and humiliated, as we still are today because of our sins. ⁸ And now, for a brief moment, the LORD our God has been kind enough to leave us a few survivors from Babylon and to give us a secure hold on his holy place. Our God has made our eyes light up and has given us new opportunities while we were slaves. ⁹ We are slaves, but our God hasn't abandoned us in our slavery. Instead, he has made the kings of Persia treat us kindly. He did this to give us an opportunity to rebuild our God's temple and restore its ruins and to give us a protective wall in Judah and Jerusalem.

¹⁰ "And now, our God, what can we say after all this? We have abandoned your commandments! ¹¹ The commandments you gave us through your servants the prophets, said, 'The land you are going to take possession of has been polluted by its perverted people and by their disgusting practices that have filled it with wickedness from one end to another. ¹² So never let your daughters marry their sons or your sons marry their daughters, and never seek peace or trade with them. Then you will be strong, be able to eat the good things the land produces, and be able to give this land as a long-lasting inheritance to your children.'

¹³ "After all that has happened to us because of the evil things we have done and because of our overwhelming guilt, you, our God, have punished us far less than we deserve and have permitted a few of us to survive. ¹⁴ If we break your commandments again and intermarry with people doing these disgusting things, you will become even more angry with us until you finally destroy us and no survivors are left. ¹⁵ LORD God of Israel, because you are fair, a few of us continue to remain as survivors. Look at us. All of us are guilty. None of us can stand in your presence because of this."

The People Take Action

10 ¹ While Ezra was praying, confessing ˌthese sinsˌ, crying, and throwing himself down in front of God's temple, a large crowd of Israelite men, women, and children gathered around him. They also began to cry bitterly. ² Then Shecaniah, son of Jehiel, one of the descendants of Elam, interrupted by saying to Ezra, "We have been unfaithful to our God by marrying foreign women who came from the people around us. However, there is still hope for Israel. ³ So we must now make a promise to our God to get rid of all foreign women and the children born from them, as my lord ˌEzraˌ and the others who tremble at the commandments of our God have advised us to do. We must do what Moses' Teachings tell us. ⁴ Get up! It's your duty to take action. We are with you, so be strong and take action."

⁵ Then Ezra got up and made the leaders, priests, Levites, and all the rest of Israel swear to do what they had said. So they took an oath. ⁶ Then Ezra left the front of God's temple and went to the room of Jehohanan, son of Eliashib. Ezra didn't eat any food or drink any water while he was there. He was mourning because these former exiles had been so unfaithful.

⁷ Then he sent a proclamation throughout Judah and Jerusalem that all the former exiles must gather in Jerusalem. ⁸ If any of them didn't come within three days as the leaders and the older men had advised, then they would lose all their property and be excluded from the community of former exiles. ⁹ Then all the men of Judah and Benjamin gathered within three days in Jerusalem. On the twentieth day of the ninth month, all the people sat in the courtyard of God's temple. They were trembling because of this matter and shivering because of the heavy rain.

¹⁰ Ezra the priest stood up and said to them, "You have been unfaithful by marrying foreign women, and now you have added to Israel's guilt. ¹¹ Confess to the LORD God of your ancestors what you have done, and do what he wants. Separate yourselves from the people of this land and from your foreign wives."

¹² Then the whole assembly shouted in reply, "Yes! We will do as you say. ¹³ But the crowd is too large, and it's the rainy season. We can't take care of this outside. Besides, there are so many of us who are involved in this sin that it can't be taken care of in a day or two. ¹⁴ Let our leaders represent the whole community. At a set time, everyone who has married a foreign woman must meet with the leaders and judges of each city until our God's burning anger has turned away from us in this matter."

¹⁵ (Only Jonathan, Asahel's son, and Jahzeiah, Tikvah's son, opposed this. Meshullam and Shabbethai, the Levite, supported Jonathan and Jahzeiah.)

¹⁶ The former exiles did this. Ezra the priest chose men who were heads of families. He chose one from each family division. (They were all ˌlistedˌ by name.) They sat down on the first day of the tenth month to investigate the matter. ¹⁷ By the first day of the first month, they had finished dealing with all the men who had married foreign women.

¹⁸ Among the descendants of the priests, the following were married to foreign women: Maaseiah, Eliezer, Jarib, and Gedaliah, a descendant of Jeshua (who was Jozadak's son) and

his brothers. [19] They shook hands as a pledge that they would get rid of their wives. They sacrificed a ram from their flock as an offering for guilt because they were guilty.

Those Who Were Guilty of Marrying Foreign Women

[20]	From the descendants of Immer:	Hanani and Zebadiah
[21]	From the descendants of Harim:	Maaseiah, Elijah, Shemaiah, Jehiel, and Uzziah
[22]	From the descendants of Pashhur:	Elioenai, Maaseiah, Ishmael, Nethanel, Jozabad, and Elasah
[23]	From the Levites:	Jozabad, Shimei, Kelaiah (that is, Kelita), Pethahiah, Judah, and Eliezer
[24]	From the singers:	Eliashib
	From the gatekeepers:	Shallum, Telem, and Uri
[25]	From the other Israelites:	
	From the descendants of Parosh:	Ramiah, Izziah, Malchiah, Mijamin, Eleazar, Malchiah, and Benaiah
[26]	From the descendants of Elam:	Mattaniah, Zechariah, Jehiel, Abdi, Jeremoth, and Elijah
[27]	From the descendants of Zattu:	Elioenai, Eliashib, Mattaniah, Jeremoth, Zabad, and Aziza
[28]	From the descendants of Bebai:	Jehohanan, Hananiah, Zabbai, and Athlai
[29]	From the descendants of Bani:	Meshullam, Malluch, Adaiah, Jashub, Sheal, and Jeremoth
[30]	From the descendants of Pahath Moab:	Adna, Chelal, Benaiah, Maaseiah, Mattaniah, Bezalel, Binnui, and Manasseh
[31]	From the descendants of Harim:	Eliezer, Isshiah, Malchiah, Shemaiah, Shimeon, [32] Benjamin, Malluch, and Shemariah
[33]	From the descendants of Hashum:	Mattenai, Mattattah, Zabad, Eliphelet, Jeremai, Manasseh, and Shimei
[34]	From the descendants of Bani:	Maadai, Amram, Uel, [35] Benaiah, Bedeiah, Cheluhi, [36] Vaniah, Meremoth, Eliashib, [37] Mattaniah, Mattenai, Jaasau
[38]	From the descendants of Binnui:	Shimei, [39] Shelemiah, Nathan, Adaiah, [40] Machnadebai, Shashai, Sharai, [41] Azarel, Shelemiah, Shemariah, [42] Shallum, Amariah, and Joseph
[43]	From the descendants of Nebo:	Jeiel, Mattithiah, Zabad, Zebina, Jaddai, Joel, and Benaiah

[44] All of these men had married foreign women. Some of these women had given birth to children.[a]

---

[a] 10:44 Hebrew meaning of this sentence uncertain.

NEHEMIAH

Distressing News

1 ¹ These are the words of Nehemiah, son of Hacaliah:
During the month of Chislev, in Artaxerxes' twentieth year as king, while I was in the fortress at Susa, ² one of my brothers, Hanani, arrived with some men from Judah. I asked them about the Jews who had survived captivity and about Jerusalem. ³ They told me, "Those who survived captivity are in the province. They are enduring serious troubles and being insulted. The wall of Jerusalem has been broken down, and its gates have been destroyed by fire."

Nehemiah's Prayer

⁴ When I heard this, I sat down and cried. I mourned for days. I continued to fast and pray to the God of heaven. ⁵ I said,

"Lᴏʀᴅ God of heaven, great and awe-inspiring God, you faithfully keep your promise*ᵃ* and show mercy to those who love you and obey your commandments. ⁶ Open your eyes, and pay close attention with your ears to what I, your servant, am praying. I am praying to you day and night about your servants the Israelites. I confess the sins that we Israelites have committed against you as well as the sins that my father's family and I have committed. ⁷ We have done you a great wrong. We haven't obeyed the commandments, laws, or regulations that you gave us through your servant Moses. ⁸ Please remember what you told us through your servant Moses: 'If you are unfaithful, I will scatter you among the nations. ⁹ But if you return to me and continue to obey my commandments, though your people may be driven to the most distant point on the horizon, I will come and get you from there and bring you to the place where I chose to put my name.' ¹⁰ These are your servants and your people whom you have saved by your great power and your strong hand. ¹¹ Lord, please pay attention to my prayer and to the prayers of all your other servants who want to worship your name. Please give me success today and make this man, King Artaxerxes, show me compassion."

I was cupbearer*ᵇ* to the king at this time.

The King Shows Compassion to Nehemiah

2 ¹ In the month of Nisan, in Artaxerxes' twentieth year as king, after some wine was brought for the king, I picked up the cup of wine and gave it to the king. I had never been sad in his presence before.
² The king asked me, "Why do you look so sad? You aren't sick, are you? You must be troubled about something." (I was really afraid.)
³ "May the king live forever!" I said to the king. "Why shouldn't I look sad when the city, the place where my ancestors are buried, is in ruins and its gates are burned down?"
⁴ "What do you want?" the king asked me.
So I prayed to the God of heaven, ⁵ and I asked the king, "If it pleases Your Majesty, and you are willing to grant my request, let me go to Judah, to the city where my ancestors are buried, so that I can rebuild it."
⁶ Then, while the queen was sitting beside him, the king asked me, "How long will you be gone, and when will you come back?" When I gave him a specific date, he was willing to let me go.
⁷ I also asked the king, "If it pleases Your Majesty, let me have letters addressed to the governors ͺof the provinceͺ west of the Euphrates River. In the letters tell them to grant me safe conduct until I arrive in Judah. ⁸ Also, let me have a letter addressed to Asaph, the supervisor of Your Majesty's forest. In the letter order him to give me wood for the gates of the fortress near the temple, for the city wall, and for the house I'll move into." (The king let me have the letters, because God was guiding me.)

ᵃ 1:5 Or "covenant." *ᵇ* 1:11 A cupbearer was a trusted official who ensured that the king's drink was not poisoned.

Nehemiah Goes to Jerusalem

[9] I went to the governors ˻of the province˼ west of the Euphrates River and gave them the king's letters. (The king had sent army officers and cavalry to be with me.) [10] But when Sanballat the Horonite and Tobiah the Ammonite servant heard this, they were very upset that someone had come to give the people of Israel so much assistance.

Nehemiah Surveys the Damage to Jerusalem's Walls

[11] I went to Jerusalem and was there for three days. [12] During the night I went out with a few men without telling anyone what my God had inspired me to do for Jerusalem. The only animal I had was the one I was riding. [13] I went through Valley Gate that night toward Snake Fountain and Dung Gate and examined the places where the walls of Jerusalem were broken down and where its gates had been burned. [14] Passing through Fountain Gate, I arrived at King's Pool, but the animal I was riding couldn't get through. [15] So I went through the valley that night and examined the wall. Then I turned back, entered Valley Gate, and returned.

[16] The officials didn't know where I had gone or what I had done. I hadn't yet told the Jews, the priests, the leaders, the other officials, or any of the rest who would be doing the work. [17] Then I told them, "You see the trouble we're in. Jerusalem is in ruins, and its gates are burned down. Let's rebuild the wall of Jerusalem, and we will no longer be insulted." [18] Then I told them that my God had been guiding me and what the king had told me.

They replied, "Let's begin to rebuild." So they encouraged one another to begin this God-pleasing work.

[19] When Sanballat the Horonite, Tobiah the Ammonite servant, and Geshem the Arab heard about this, they made fun of us and ridiculed us. They asked, "What are you doing? Are you going to rebel against the king?"

[20] "The God of heaven will give us success," I answered them. "We, his servants, are going to rebuild. You have no property or claim or historic right in Jerusalem."

A List of the People Rebuilding Jerusalem's Walls

3 [1] The chief priest Eliashib and his relatives, the priests, started by rebuilding Sheep Gate. They dedicated it and set its doors in place. They rebuilt as far as the Tower of the Hundred, which they dedicated, and then as far as the Tower of Hananel. [2] The men from Jericho were rebuilding next to Eliashib. Zaccur, son of Imri, was next to them. [3] The sons of Hassenaah rebuilt Fish Gate. They laid its beams and set its doors, locks, and bars in place. [4] Next to them Meremoth, son of Uriah and grandson of Hakkoz, made repairs. Next to them Meshullam, son of Berechiah and grandson of Meshezabel, made repairs. Next to them Zadok, son of Baana, made repairs. [5] Next to them the men from Tekoa made repairs. However, the nobles wouldn't lower themselves to work under supervisors.

[6] Joiada, Paseah's son, and Meshullam, Besodeiah's son, made repairs on Old Gate. They laid its beams and set its doors, locks, and bars in place. [7] Next to them Melatiah from Gibeon and Jadon from Meronoth, with men from Gibeon and Mizpah, made repairs on the wall. They did this under the authority of the governor ˻from the province˼ west of the Euphrates River. [8] Next to them Uzziel, Harhaiah's son, a goldsmith, made repairs. Next to him Hananiah, a perfume maker, made repairs. They left out part of Jerusalem as far as Broad Wall. [9] Next to them Rephaiah, Hur's son, an official in charge of half a district of Jerusalem, made repairs. [10] Next to them Jedaiah, Harumaph's son, made repairs across from his own home. Next to them Hattush, Hashabneiah's son, made repairs. [11] Malchiah, Harim's son, and Hasshub, Pahath Moab's son, made repairs on a section that included the Tower of the Ovens. [12] Next to them Shallum, Hallohesh's son, an official in charge of half a district of Jerusalem, made repairs with the help of his daughters.

[13] Hanun and the people of Zanoah repaired Valley Gate. They rebuilt it and set its doors, locks, and bars in place, and they repaired 1,500 feet of the wall, as far as Dung Gate. [14] Dung Gate itself was repaired by Malchiah, Rechab's son, the official in charge of the district of Beth Hakkerem. He rebuilt it and set its doors, locks, and bars in place.

[15] Shallun, Col Hozeh's son, the official in charge of the district of Mizpah, repaired Fountain Gate. He rebuilt it, put a roof over it, and set its doors, locks, and bars in place. He also made repairs on the wall of the Pool of Shelah by the King's Garden as far as the stairs going down from the City of David. [16] After him Nehemiah, Azbuk's son, the official in charge of half the district of Beth Zur, made repairs all the way to a point across from the tombs of David as far as the pool and the soldiers' barracks. [17] After him the Levites, including Rehum (Bani's son), made repairs. Next to him Hashabiah, the official in charge of half the district of Keilah, made repairs for his district. [18] After him their relatives made repairs. This included Binnui, Henadad's son, the official in charge of half the district of Keilah. [19] Next to him Ezer, Jeshua's son, the official in charge of Mizpah, repaired a section across from the ascent to the Armory at the Angle.

[20] After him Baruch, Zabbai's son,[a] made repairs on a section from the Angle to the door of the house of the chief priest Eliashib. [21] After him Meremoth, son of Uriah and grandson of Hakkoz, made repairs on a section from the door of Eliashib's house to the end of Eliashib's house. [22] After him the priests who lived in that area made repairs. [23] After them Benjamin and Hasshub made repairs across from their own homes. After them Azariah, son of Maaseiah and grandson of Ananiah, made repairs next to his home. [24] After him Binnui, Henadad's son, made repairs on a section from Azariah's home to the Angle and to the corner of the wall. [25] Palal, Uzai's son, made repairs across from the Angle and the upper tower that projects from the king's palace to the guards' courtyard. After him Pedaiah, Parosh's son, [26] and the temple servants who were living on the Ophel made repairs on the wall as far as a point across from Water Gate toward the east and the projecting tower. [27] After him the men from Tekoa repaired a section across from the large projecting tower as far as the Wall of the Ophel.

[28] Above Horse Gate the priests made repairs. Each priest made repairs across from his own home. [29] After them Zadok, Immer's son, made repairs across from his own home. After him Shemaiah, Shecaniah's son, the guard at East Gate, made repairs. [30] After him Hananiah, Shelemiah's son, and Hanun, Zalaph's sixth son, repaired another section. After him Meshullam, Berechiah's son, made repairs across from his living quarters. [31] After him Malchiah, one of the goldsmiths, made repairs as far as the building that housed the temple servants and merchants across from Inspection Gate and as far as the upper room at the corner. [32] The goldsmiths and merchants made repairs between the upper room at the corner and Sheep Gate.

Sanballat Ridicules the Jews

4[a] [1] When Sanballat heard we were rebuilding the wall, he became enraged and made fun of the Jews. [2] In front of his allies and the army from Samaria, he said, "What do these miserable Jews think they're doing? Can they rebuild it by themselves? Are they going to offer sacrifices? Can they finish it in a day? Will they get the stones out of the rubbish heaps, burned as these stones are, and give them new strength?"

[3] Tobiah the Ammonite, who was beside Sanballat, said, "Even a fox would make their stone wall collapse if it walked on top of what they're building!"

Nehemiah Overcomes Opposition From Sanballat

[4] ˻Nehemiah prayed,˼ "Our God, hear us. We are despised. Turn their insults back on them, and let them be robbed in the land where they are prisoners. [5] Don't ignore their guilt, and don't let their sins disappear from your records. They have insulted you in front of these builders."

[6] So we rebuilt the wall, which was rebuilt to about half its ˻original˼ height. The people worked with determination.

[7] When Sanballat, Tobiah, the Arabs, the Ammonites, and the people from Ashdod heard that the repair work on the walls of Jerusalem was making progress and that the gaps were being filled in, they became furious. [8] All of them plotted to attack Jerusalem to create confusion. [9] But we prayed to our God and set guards to protect us day and night.

[10] Then the people of Judah said, "The work crews are worn out, and there is too much rubble. We can't continue to rebuild the wall."

[11] Our enemies said, "Before they know what is happening or see a thing, we will be right in the middle of them. We'll kill them and bring the work to an end."

[12] Jews who were living near our enemies warned us ten times that our enemies would attack us from every direction.[b]

[13] That is why I positioned people by their families behind the wall where it was lowest and most exposed. The people were armed with swords, spears, and bows. [14] I looked them over and proceeded to tell the nobles, the leaders, and the rest of the people, "Don't be afraid of our enemies. Remember how great and awe-inspiring the LORD is. Fight for your brothers, your sons, your daughters, your wives, and your homes."

[15] When our enemies heard that we knew about their plots and that God had prevented their plans from being successful, we all went back to the work on the wall. Each person performed his own job. [16] From that day on, half of my men worked on the wall, and the other half were wearing body armor and holding spears, shields, and bows. The leaders stood behind all the Judeans [17] who were rebuilding the wall. The workers who were carrying loads did the work with one hand and held their weapons with the other, [18] and each builder had his sword fastened to his side. The man who was supposed to sound the trumpet alarm was with me. [19] I told the nobles, the leaders, and the rest of the people, "So much work has to be done in different places that we are widely separated from one another on the wall. [20] When you hear the trumpet, assemble around me. Our God will fight for us!"

---

[a] 3:20 Masoretic Text; Dead Sea Scrolls, Syriac, Latin, Egyptian "Zaccai's son." [a] 4:1 Nehemiah 4:1–23 in English Bibles is Nehemiah 3:33–4:17 in the Hebrew Bible. [b] 4:12 Hebrew meaning of this verse uncertain.

²¹ So we continued to work. Half of us held spears from early dawn until the stars came out. ²² At that time I told the people, "Every man and his servant should stay overnight in Jerusalem so that we can set a guard at night and work during the day." ²³ My brothers, my servants, and the guards assigned to me never changed their clothes. Neither did I. We each kept our weapons at hand.

The Poor Complain About Their Rich Relatives

5 ¹ Then some of the people, the men and their wives, complained publicly about their Jewish relatives. ² Some of them said, "We have large families! We need some grain ˌif we are goingˌ to eat and stay alive." ³ Others said, "We've had to mortgage our fields, our vineyards, and our homes in order to get some grain because of this famine." ⁴ Others said, "We've had to borrow money to pay the king's taxes on our fields and vineyards. ⁵ We have the same flesh and blood as our relatives. Our children are just like theirs. Yet, we have to force our sons and daughters to become slaves. Some of our daughters have already become slaves. But we can't do anything else when our fields and vineyards belong to others."

Nehemiah Stops the Rich From Taking Advantage of the Poor

⁶ I became furious when I heard their complaint and what they had to say. ⁷ After thinking it over, I confronted the nobles and the leaders. I told them, "You are charging interest on loans made to your own relatives." I arranged for a large meeting to deal with them. ⁸ Then I told them, "We have done our best to buy back our Jewish relatives who had been sold to other nations. Now you are selling your Jewish relatives so that we have to buy them back again!" They were unable to say anything. ⁹ I added, "What you're doing is wrong. Shouldn't you live in the fear of our God to keep our enemies from ridiculing us? ¹⁰ My brothers, my servants, and I are lending money and grain to the poor. But we must stop charging them interest. ¹¹ You must return their fields, their vineyards, their olive orchards, and their homes today. Also, you must return the interest on the money, grain, new wine, and olive oil you've been charging them."

¹² They responded, "We'll return it and not try to get it from them ˌagainˌ. We'll do what you say." Then I called the priests and made them swear to do what they promised. ¹³ I brushed off my clothes and said, "In the same way, may God brush off from home and work everyone who refuses to keep this promise. In the same way, may everyone be brushed off and left with nothing." Then the whole congregation said amen and praised the LORD. The people did what they had promised.

Nehemiah Never Takes What Is Rightfully His as Governor

¹⁴ During the 12 years that I was governor of Judah, from the twentieth year of King Artaxerxes' reign to the thirty-second year of his reign, my brothers and I never ate any food that was paid for by the governor's food allowance. ¹⁵ Those who were governors before me had made life difficult for the people by taking from them food and wine plus one pound of silver. Even the governors' servants took advantage of their power over the people. But I didn't do that, because I feared God. ¹⁶ Instead, I put my best effort into the work on this wall, and we bought no land. All my men gathered here for work. ¹⁷ I fed 150 Jewish leaders and their people who came to us from the surrounding nations. ¹⁸ Preparing one ox and six choice sheep was necessary every day. Poultry was prepared for me. Once every ten days a supply of wine was ordered. Yet, in spite of all this, I never demanded anything from the governor's food allowance, because these people were already carrying a heavy load.

Nehemiah's Prayer

¹⁹ Remember me, my God. Consider everything that I have done for these people.

Sanballat Tries to Harm Nehemiah

6 ¹ Sanballat, Tobiah, Geshem the Arab, and the rest of our enemies heard that I had rebuilt the wall and that no gaps had been left in it (although at that time I had not yet hung the doors in the city gates). ² Then Sanballat and Geshem sent this message to me: "Let's meet in Hakkephirim on the plain of Ono." They were planning to harm me.

³ I sent messengers to tell them, "I'm working on an important project and can't get away. Why should the work stop while I leave to meet with you?" ⁴ They sent the same message to me four times, and I answered them the same way. ⁵ When Sanballat sent me the same message a fifth time, his servant held in his hand an unsealed letter. ⁶ In it was written:

It has been reported throughout the nations, and Geshem has confirmed it, that you and the Jews are planning to rebel. That's why you're rebuilding the wall. According to this report, you want to become their king. ⁷ You've appointed prophets to announce about you in Jerusalem, 'There's a king in Judah!' This report will get back to the king. So let's talk about this.

⁸ Then I sent someone to tell him, "None of your accusations are true. You are making them up out of your own imagination."

⁹ They were all trying to intimidate us. They thought we would give up and not finish the work. But God made me strong.

¹⁰ ₎One day₎ I went to the home of Shemaiah, son of Delaiah and grandson of Mehetabel. Shemaiah who was confined to his house, said, "Let's meet in the house of God, inside the temple, and close the temple doors. Some men are coming at night to kill you."

¹¹ But I asked, "Should a man like me run away? Would a man like me go into the temple to save his life? I won't go."

¹² Then I realized that God hadn't sent him. Instead, Tobiah and Sanballat had hired him to prophesy against me. ¹³ He was hired to intimidate me into doing this so that I would sin. Then they could give me a bad reputation in order to discredit me.

¹⁴ ₎Nehemiah prayed,₎ "My God, remember what Tobiah and Sanballat have done. Also, remember the female prophet Noadiah and the rest of the prophets who have been trying to intimidate me."

The Wall Rebuilt in Spite of Opposition

¹⁵ The wall was finished on the twenty-fifth day of the month of Elul. The wall took 52 days to finish. ¹⁶ When all our enemies heard about this, all the surrounding nations were afraid and lost their self-confidence. They realized we had done this work with the help of our God.

Traitors on the Inside

¹⁷ In those days the nobles of Judah sent many letters to Tobiah, and Tobiah sent many letters back to them. ¹⁸ Many in Judah had promised to support Tobiah because he was the son-in-law of Shecaniah, Arah's son. In addition, Tobiah's son Jehohanan had married the daughter of Meshullam, Berechiah's son. ¹⁹ The nobles were singing Tobiah's praises to me and reporting to him what I said. Tobiah kept sending letters to intimidate me.

Nehemiah Places Hanani and Hananiah in Charge of Guarding the City Gates

7 ¹ The gatekeepers, the singers, and the Levites were assigned their duties after the wall had been rebuilt and I had hung the doors. ² I put my brother Hanani and Hananiah, the commander of the fortress, in charge of Jerusalem. Hananiah was a trustworthy man, and he feared God more than most people do. ³ I told them, "The gates of Jerusalem should not be opened at the hottest time of the day. While the ₎gatekeepers₎ are still standing there, they should shut the doors and bar them. Order some of the men in Jerusalem to stand guard, some at their posts and others in front of their homes." ⁴ The city was large and wide-open. Few people were in it, and no houses were being built.

The First Jewish Exiles Who Returned to Jerusalem

⁵ Then my God put the idea into my head that I should gather the nobles, leaders, and people so that they could check their genealogy. I found the book with the genealogy of those who came back the first time. I found the following written in it:

⁶ These were the people in the province. They were the ones who left the place where the exiles had been taken captive. King Nebuchadnezzar of Babylon had taken them captive. They returned to Jerusalem and Judah. All of them went to their own cities. ⁷ They went with Zerubbabel, Jeshua, Nehemiah, Azariah, Raamiah, Nahamani, Mordecai, Bilshan, Mispereth, Bigvai, Nehum, and Baanah.

Families Listed by Ancestor—Ezra 2:3–20

This is the number of Israelite men from the people in exile:

⁸	the descendants of Parosh	2,172
⁹	of Shephatiah	372
¹⁰	of Arah	652
¹¹	of Pahath Moab, that is, of Jeshua and Joab	2,818
¹²	of Elam	1,254
¹³	of Zattu	845
¹⁴	of Zaccai	760
¹⁵	of Binnui	648
¹⁶	of Bebai	628
¹⁷	of Azgad	2,322
¹⁸	of Adonikam	667
¹⁹	of Bigvai	2,067
²⁰	of Adin	655

21	of Ater, that is, Hezekiah	98
22	of Hashum	328
23	of Bezai	324
24	of Hariph	112
25	of Gibeon	95

Families Listed by Towns—Ezra 2:21–35

26	the people of Bethlehem and Netophah	188
27	of Anathoth	128
28	of Beth Azmaveth	42
29	of Kiriath Jearim, Chephirah, and Beeroth	743
30	of Ramah and Geba	621
31	of Michmas	122
32	of Bethel and Ai	123
33	of the other Nebo	52
34	of the other Elam	1,254
35	of Harim	320
36	of Jericho	345
37	of Lod, Hadid, and Ono	721
38	of Senaah	3,930

Priests—Ezra 2:36–39

39	These priests returned from exile: the descendants of Jedaiah (through the family of Jeshua)	973
40	of Immer	1,052
41	of Pashhur	1,247
42	of Harim	1,017

Levites—Ezra 2:40–42

43	These Levites returned from exile: the descendants of Jeshua, that is, of Kadmiel ⸤and⸥ of Hodeiah	74
44	These singers returned from exile: the descendants of Asaph	148
45	These gatekeepers returned from exile: the descendants of Shallum, Ater, Talmon, Akkub, Hatita, and Shobai	138

Temple Servants—Ezra 2:43–54

46 These temple servants returned from exile: the descendants of Ziha, Hasupha, Tabbaoth, **47** Keros, Sia, Padon, **48** Lebanah, Hagabah, Shalmai, **49** Hanan, Giddel, Gahar, **50** Reaiah, Rezin, Nekoda, **51** Gazzam, Uzza, Paseah, **52** Besai, Meunim, Nephusheshim, **53** Bakbuk, Hakupha, Harhur, **54** Bazlith, Mehida, Harsha, **55** Barkos, Sisera, Temah, **56** Neziah, and Hatipha.

Descendants of Solomon's Servants—Ezra 2:55–58

57 These descendants of Solomon's servants returned from exile: the descendants of Sotai, Sophereth, Perida, **58** Jaala, Darkon, Giddel, **59** Shephatiah, Hattil, Pochereth Hazzebaim, and Amon. **60** The temple servants and the descendants of Solomon's servants totaled 392.

Those of Unknown Origin—Ezra 2:59–63

61 The following people came from Tel Melah, Tel Harsha, Cherub, Addan, and Immer, but they couldn't prove they were Israelites on the basis of their father's family or their genealogy: **62** the descendants of Delaiah, Tobiah, and Nekoda. These people totaled 642. **63** These priests ⸤couldn't prove they were Israelites⸥: the descendants of Hobaiah, Hakkoz, and Barzillai (who had married one of the daughters of Barzillai from Gilead and took that ⸤family⸥ name). **64** These people searched for their ⸤family⸥ names in the genealogical records, but their names couldn't be found there. For this reason they were considered contaminated and couldn't be priests. **65** The governor told them not to eat any of the most holy food until a priest could use the Urim and Thummim[a] ⸤to settle the problem⸥.

The Total of the People and Animals Returning From Exile—Ezra 2:64–67

66 The whole assembly totaled 42,360. **67** In addition to the male and female servants who numbered 7,337, they also had 245 male and female singers. **68** They had 736 horses, 245 mules,[b] **69** 435 camels, and 6,720 donkeys.

---

[a] 7:65 The Urim and Thummim were used by the chief priest to determine God's answer to questions. [b] 7:68 Some Hebrew manuscripts omit "They had . . . mules." In those manuscripts verses 69–73 are numbered as 68–72.

Gifts Given for the Temple—Ezra 2:68–70

[70] Some of the heads of the families contributed to this work. The governor contributed the following to the treasury: nearly 18 pounds of gold, 50 bowls, and 530 robes for the priests. [71] Some of the heads of the families contributed to the treasury for this work: 337 pounds of gold and 3,215 pounds of silver. [72] The rest of the people contributed 337 pounds of gold, 2,923 pounds of silver, and 67 robes for the priests.

[73] The priests, Levites, the gatekeepers, the singers, some of the people, the temple servants, and the rest of Israel settled in their own cities. When the seventh month came, the people of Israel were in their own cities.

The Public Reading of Moses' Teachings

8 [1] ₊When the seventh month came,₊ all the people gathered together in the courtyard in front of Water Gate. They told Ezra the scribe to bring the Book of Moses' Teachings, which the Lord had commanded Israel ₊to follow₊. [2] Then Ezra the priest brought the Teachings in front of the assembly. This included men, women, and any ₊children₊ who could understand what they heard. This took place on the first day of the seventh month. [3] From daybreak until noon, he read from it in the courtyard in front of Water Gate to the men, women, and ₊children₊ who could understand it. All the people listened to the Book of Moses' Teachings.

[4] Ezra the scribe stood on a raised wooden platform made for this occasion. Mattithiah, Shema, Anaiah, Uriah, Hilkiah, and Maaseiah stood beside him on his right. Pedaiah, Mishael, Malchiah, Hashum, Hashbaddanah, Zechariah, and Meshullam stood beside him on his left. [5] Ezra, standing higher than all the other people, opened the book in front of all the people. As he opened it, all the people stood up. [6] Ezra thanked the LORD, the great God. All the people responded, "Amen! Amen!" as they raised their hands and then bowed with their faces to the ground and worshiped the LORD. [7] The Levites—Jeshua, Bani, Sherebiah, Jamin, Akkub, Shabbethai, Hodiah, Maaseiah, Kelita, Azariah, Jozabad, Hanan, and Pelaiah—explained the Teachings to the people while they were standing there. [8] They read the Book of God's Teachings clearly and explained the meaning so that the people could understand what was read.

[9] Then Nehemiah the governor, Ezra the priest and scribe, and the Levites who taught the people told them, "This is a holy day for the LORD your God. Don't mourn or cry." All the people were crying as they listened to the reading of God's Teachings. [10] Then he told them, "Go, eat rich foods, drink sweet drinks, and send portions to those who cannot provide for themselves. Today is a holy day for the Lord. Don't be sad because the joy you have in the LORD is your strength." [11] So the Levites calmed all the people by saying, "Listen. Today is a holy day. Don't be sad."

[12] Then all the people went to eat and drink and to send portions. They had a big, joyful celebration because they understood the words that had been explained to them.

The Festival of Booths Is Observed

[13] On the second day the leaders of the families of all the people, including the priests and the Levites, met with Ezra the scribe to study the words of God's Teachings. [14] They found written in the Teachings that the LORD had given an order through Moses that the people of Israel should live in booths during a festival in the seventh month. [15] They should announce this command and send this message throughout all their cities and Jerusalem: "Go to the mountains, and get branches—olive and wild olive, myrtle, palm, and other thick-leaved branches—to make booths as it is written."

[16] So the people went to get branches to make booths for themselves. Some made booths on their roofs, others in their courtyards, in the courtyards of God's temple, in the open area by Water Gate, or in the open area at Ephraim Gate.

[17] The whole assembly that had come back from exile made booths and lived in them. From the time of Jeshua (son of Nun) to that day, the people of Israel had not done this. There was a big, joyful celebration. [18] Day by day, from the first day of the festival to the last day, Ezra continued to read from the Book of God's Teachings. The people celebrated the festival for seven days, and on the eighth day, they had a closing festival assembly in accordance with the regulations.

A Day of Fasting and Confession

9 [1] When the Israelites assembled on the twenty-fourth day of this month, they fasted, wore sackcloth, and threw dirt on their heads. [2] Those who were descendants of Israel separated themselves from all foreigners. They stood and confessed their sins as well as the wicked things their ancestors had done. [3] They stood in their places, and for one-fourth of the day, ₊they listened as₊ the Book of the Teachings of the LORD their God was read, and for another fourth ₊of the day₊, they confessed their sins and worshiped the LORD their God.

A Day of Prayer

[4] Then Jeshua, Bani, Kadmiel, Shebaniah, Bunni, Sherebiah, Bani, and Chanani stood on the stairs built for the Levites and cried loudly to the LORD their God. [5] Then the Levites—Jeshua, Kadmiel, Bani, Hashabneiah, Sherebiah, Hodiah, Shebaniah, and Pethahiah—said, "Stand up, and thank the LORD your God:

Creation

From everlasting to everlasting your glorious name is praised
  and lifted high above all blessing and praise.
[6] You alone are the LORD.
You made heaven, the highest heaven, with all its armies.
You made the earth and everything on it,
  the seas and everything in them.
You give life to them all, and the armies of heaven worship you.

Abraham

[7] You are the LORD, the God who chose Abram
  and took him from Ur of the Chaldeans
    and gave him the name Abraham.
[8] You found that his heart was faithful to you.
You made a promise[a] to him to give the land of the Canaanites, Hittites,
  Amorites, Perizzites, Jebusites, and Girgashites to his descendants.
You kept your promise because you are fair.

The Exodus

[9] You saw how our ancestors suffered in Egypt,
  and you heard them crying at the Red Sea.
[10] You performed miraculous signs and did amazing things to Pharaoh
  and all his servants and all the people in his land
    because you knew how arrogantly
      they were treating our ancestors.
You made a name for yourself, a name which remains to this day.
[11] You divided the sea in front of them
  so that they could walk through the sea on dry ground.
You threw into deep water those who pursued your people
  as someone throws a stone into raging water.

Wandering in the Wilderness

[12] You led them during the day by a column of smoke
  and during the night by a column of fire to give them light
    to see the way they should go.
[13] You came from heaven to Mount Sinai
  and spoke with them from heaven.
You gave them fair rules, trustworthy teachings,
  and good laws and commandments.
[14] You taught them about your holy day of worship.
You gave them commandments, laws, and teachings
  through your servant Moses.
[15] You gave them bread from heaven to satisfy their hunger
  and made water flow from a rock to quench their thirst.
You told them to take possession of the land
  that you swore you would give them.
[16] But they—our own ancestors—acted arrogantly.
  They became stubborn and wouldn't obey your commands.
[17] They refused to listen.
  They forgot the miracles you performed for them.
  They became stubborn and appointed a leader
    to take them back to slavery ˌin Egyptˌ.
But you are a forgiving God,
  one who is compassionate, merciful, patient,
  and always ready to forgive.
You never abandoned them,

---

[a] 9:8 Or "covenant."

18   even when they made a metal statue of a calf for themselves
        and said, 'This is your god who took you out of Egypt.'
    They committed outrageous sins.

19   But because of your endless compassion,
      you didn't abandon them in the desert.
          The column of smoke didn't leave them during the day,
            but it led them on their way.
          The column of fire didn't leave them during the night,
            but it gave them light to see the way they should go.

20   You gave them your good Spirit to teach them.
    You didn't keep your manna to yourself.
    You gave them water to quench their thirst.

21   You provided for them in the desert for 40 years,
      and they had everything they needed.
    Their clothes didn't wear out, and their feet didn't swell.

Conquest of Canaan

22   You gave kingdoms and nations to the Israelites
      and assigned them their boundaries.
          So they took possession of the land of Sihon,
            the land of the king of Heshbon,
              and the land of King Og of Bashan.

23   You made their children as numerous as the stars in the sky.
    You brought them into the land you told their parents to enter and possess.

24   Their children took possession of the land.
    You defeated for them the Canaanites, who lived in the land.
    You handed the Canaanite kings and their people over to them
      to do whatever they wanted with the Canaanites.

25   The Israelites captured fortified cities and a rich land.
    They took possession of houses filled with all sorts of good things,
      cisterns, vineyards, olive trees,
        and plenty of fruit trees.
          So they ate and were satisfied and grew fat.
          They enjoyed the vast supply of good things you gave them.

Israel's Rebellion

26   But they were defiant and rebelled against you.
    They threw your teachings over their shoulders
      and killed your prophets who warned them to turn back to you.
          They committed outrageous sins.

27   You handed them over to their enemies, who made them suffer.
      When they began to suffer, they cried to you.
    You heard them from heaven.
    You gave them saviors to rescue them from their enemies
      because of your endless compassion.

28   As soon as they felt some relief,
      they were again doing what you considered evil.
    You abandoned them to their enemies, who conquered them.
    They cried to you again, and you heard them from heaven.
    You rescued them many times because of your compassion.

29   You warned them in order to bring them back to your teachings,
      but they became arrogant and would not obey your commandments.
    They sinned by not following your regulations.
      If anyone follows them, he will find life in them.
    But they gave you the cold shoulder,
      became impossible to deal with, and wouldn't listen.

30   You were patient with them for many years.
    You warned them by your Spirit through your prophets.
      However, they wouldn't listen.
          So you handed them over to the people in the surrounding nations.

31   But your compassion is endless.
      You didn't destroy them or abandon them.
        You are a merciful and compassionate God.

The Present

32 And now, our God, you are the great, mighty, and awe-inspiring God.
  You faithfully keep your promises.
 Do not consider all the hardships
    that we have been going through as unimportant.
      The hardships have come to our kings, leaders, priests, prophets,
        ancestors, and all your people
          from the time of the kings of Assyria until now.

33 But you were fair about everything that has happened to us.
  You have been faithful, but we have been wicked.

34 Our kings, leaders, priests, and ancestors didn't obey your teachings.
  They didn't pay attention to your commandments or the warnings
    that you gave them.

35 When they lived in their own kingdom and enjoyed the many good things
    that you gave them in a vast, fertile land
      which was set in front of them, they didn't serve you
        or turn away from their wicked lives.

36 Look ˛at us˺ now. We're slaves!
  In the land you gave our ancestors,
    they could eat its produce and ˛enjoy˺ its good things.
      But now we're slaves!

37 The many products ˛from our land˺ go to the kings you put over us.
  This is because of our sins.
    These kings have control over our bodies,
      and they do as they please with our livestock.
        We are in agony.[b]

An Agreement in Writing

38 "We are making a binding agreement ˛and putting it˺ in writing because of all this. Our leaders, Levites, and priests are putting their seals on the document."

10[a] **1** The following people sealed the agreement: Governor Nehemiah (son of Hacaliah), Zedekiah, **2** Seraiah, Azariah, Jeremiah, **3** Pashhur, Amariah, Malchiah, **4** Hattush, Shebaniah, Malluch, **5** Harim, Meremoth, Obadiah, **6** Daniel, Ginnethon, Baruch, **7** Meshullam, Abijah, Mijamin, **8** Maaziah, Bilgai, and Shemaiah. These were the priests.

9 These were the Levites: Jeshua (son of Azaniah), Binnui (of the sons of Henadad), Kadmiel, **10** and their relatives Shebaniah, Hodiah, Kelita, Pelaiah, Hanan, **11** Mica, Rehob, Hashabiah, **12** Zaccur, Sherebiah, Shebaniah, **13** Hodiah, Bani, and Beninu.

14 These were the leaders of the people: Parosh, Pahath Moab, Elam, Zattu, Bani, **15** Bunni, Azgad, Bebai, **16** Adonijah, Bigvai, Adin, **17** Ater, Hezekiah, Azzur, **18** Hodiah, Hashum, Bezai, **19** Hariph, Anathoth, Nebai, **20** Magpiash, Meshullam, Hezir, **21** Meshezabel, Zadok, Jaddua, **22** Pelatiah, Hanan, Anaiah, **23** Hoshea, Hananiah, Hasshub, **24** Hallohesh, Pilha, Shobek, **25** Rehum, Hashabnah, Maaseiah, **26** Ahiah, Hanan, Anan, **27** Malluch, Harim, and Baanah.

28 The rest of the people took an oath. These people included the priests, Levites, gate-keepers, singers, temple servants, and all who had separated themselves from the inhabitants of the land for the sake of God's Teachings. Their wives, sons, daughters, and everyone who is capable of understanding also took an oath. **29** They joined their relatives, the nobles, in binding themselves with a curse and an oath to follow God's teachings given by Moses, God's servant. They also bound themselves to follow all the commandments, rules, and regulations of the LORD our Lord.

30 We will not allow our daughters to marry the inhabitants of the land or allow their daughters to marry our sons. **31** If the inhabitants of the land bring merchandise or grain to sell on the day of worship, we won't buy anything from them on the day of worship or any other holy day. During the seventh year, we won't plant the fields or collect any debts.

32 Also, we take upon ourselves the obligation to give an eighth of an ounce of silver every year for worship in our God's temple: **33** for rows of the bread of the presence, and for the daily grain offerings and daily burnt offerings, on the weekly days of worship, and on the New Moon Festivals, and at the appointed annual festivals, for the holy gifts and offerings for sin that make peace with God for Israel, and for all the other work in the temple of our God.

---

[b] 9:37 Nehemiah 9:38 in English Bibles is Nehemiah 10:1 in the Hebrew Bible.   [a] 10:1 Nehemiah 10:1–39 in the English Bible is Nehemiah 10:2–40 in the Hebrew Bible.

³⁴ We priests, Levites, and laypeople have drawn lots to decide the order in which the heads of our families should bring wood to our God's temple to burn on the altar of the LORD our God at appointed times every year according to the directions in the Teachings. ³⁵ We have drawn lots to decide who should bring the first produce harvested and the first fruit from every tree each year to the LORD's temple. ³⁶ Following the directions in the Teachings, we have drawn lots to decide who should bring the firstborn of our sons, our cattle, and our flocks to the priests serving in our God's temple. ³⁷ Also, we have drawn lots to decide who should bring the best of our coarse flour, contributions, fruit from every tree, new wine, and olive oil to the priests, to the storerooms. We will bring for the Levites one-tenth of the produce from our fields, because the Levites are the ones who collect one-tenth of the produce from all our farm communities. ³⁸ A priest—one of Aaron's descendants—should be with the Levites when they collect the tenth. Then the Levites should bring one-tenth of these tenths to our God's temple, into the rooms of the storehouses there. ³⁹ The Israelites and the Levites should bring into the storerooms their contributions of grain, new wine, and olive oil. They should bring these products to the place where the utensils of the holy place are and where the priests who serve and the gatekeepers and the singers are. We won't neglect our God's temple.

New Residents for Jerusalem

11 ¹ The leaders of the people settled in Jerusalem. The rest of the people drew lots to bring one out of every ten to live in Jerusalem, the holy city. The remaining nine-tenths were supposed to live in the other cities. ² The people blessed everyone who willingly offered to live in Jerusalem.

³ These were the officials of the province who settled in Jerusalem. Some Israelites, priests, Levites, temple servants, and descendants of Solomon's servants settled in the cities of Judah. They lived on their own property in their own cities.

⁴ Some of the descendants of Judah and of Benjamin settled in Jerusalem. The descendants of Judah were Athaiah, who was the son of Uzziah, who was the son of Zechariah, who was the son of Amariah, who was the son of Shephatiah, who was the son of Mahalalel, who was the son of Perez; ⁵ Maaseiah was the son of Baruch, who was the son of Col Hozeh, who was the son of Hazaiah, who was the son of Adaiah, who was the son of Joiarib, who was the son of Zechariah, who was the son of Shiloni. ⁶ All the descendants of Perez who settled in Jerusalem were 468 outstanding men. ⁷ These are the descendants of Benjamin: Sallu, who was the son of Meshullam, who was the son of Joed, who was the son of Pedaiah, who was the son of Kolaiah, who was the son of Maaseiah, who was the son of Ithiel, who was the son of Jeshaiah, ⁸ and after him, Gabbai ˻and˼ Sallai. ˻The number of Benjamin's descendants˼ totaled 928. ⁹ Joel, son of Zichri, was in charge, and Judah, son of Senuah, was second-in-command over the city.

¹⁰ These were the priests: Jedaiah (son of Joiarib), Jachin, ¹¹ Seraiah, who was the son of Hilkiah, who was the son of Meshullam, who was the son of Zadok, who was the son of Meraioth, who was the son of Ahitub, who was the supervisor of God's temple. ¹² From Seraiah's relatives 822 did the work in the temple. Also, Adaiah worked in the temple. He was the son of Jeroham, who was the son of Pelaliah, who was the son of Amzi, who was the son of Zechariah, who was the son of Pashhur, who was the son of Malchiah. ¹³ Adaiah's relatives, the heads of the families, totaled 242. Amashsai was the son of Azarel, who was the son of Ahzai, who was the son of Meshillemoth, who was the son of Immer. ¹⁴ Their relatives, who were warriors, totaled 128. The man in charge of them was Zabdiel, son of Haggedolim.

¹⁵ These were the Levites: Shemaiah who was the son of Hasshub, who was the son of Azrikam, who was the son of Hashabiah, who was the son of Bunni. ¹⁶ Shabbethai and Jozabad, Levite leaders, who were in charge of the work outside God's temple. ¹⁷ Mattaniah was the son of Mica, who was the son of Zabdi, who was the son of Asaph, the leader who led the prayer of thanksgiving. The Levite leader Bakbukiah was the second-in-command among his relatives; and so was Abda who was the son of Shammua, who was the son of Galal, who was the son of Jeduthum. ¹⁸ All the Levites in the holy city totaled 284.

¹⁹ These were the gatekeepers: Akkub, Talmon, and their relatives who guarded the gates totaled 172.

²⁰ The rest of the Israelites, priests, and Levites lived in all the cities of Judah. Everyone lived on his own inherited property. ²¹ But the temple servants lived on Mount Ophel with Ziha and Gishpa in charge of them.

²² The man in charge of the Levites in Jerusalem was Uzzi, who was the son of Bani, who was the son of Hashabiah, who was the son of Mattaniah, who was the son of Mica from Asaph's descendants who were the singers in charge of worship in God's temple. ²³ They were under orders from the king, orders that determined which duties they should perform day by

day. **24** Pethahiah, son of Meshezabel, one of the descendants of Zerah, Judah's son, was the king's adviser on all matters concerning the people.

25 Many people lived in villages that had fields. Some people of Judah lived in Kiriath Arba and its villages, in Dibon and its villages, in Jekabzeel and its villages, **26** in Jeshua, Moladah, and Beth Pelet, **27** in Hazar Shual, in Beersheba and its villages, **28** in Ziklag, and in Meconah and its villages, **29** in En Rimmon, Zorah, Jarmuth, **30** Zanoah, and Adullam and their villages, in Lachish and its fields, and in Azekah and its villages. So they settled in the land from Beersheba to the Valley of Hinnom.

31 Benjamin's descendants live in the area of Geba, in Michmash, Aija, Bethel and its villages, **32** in Anathoth, Nob, Ananiah, **33** Hazor, Ramah, Gittaim, **34** Hadid, Zeboim, Neballat, **35** Lod, Ono, and in the valley of the Craftsmen. **36** Some divisions of Levites in Judah were assigned to Benjamin.

The Priest and Levites Who Returned to Jerusalem With Zerubbabel

12 **1** These are the priests and Levites who came back with Zerubbabel (Shealtiel's son) and Jeshua: Seraiah, Jeremiah, Ezra, **2** Amariah, Malluch, Hattush, **3** Shecaniah, Rehum, Meremoth, **4** Iddo, Ginnethoi, Abijah, **5** Mijamin, Maadiah, Bilgah, **6** Shemaiah, Joiarib, Jedaiah, **7** Sallu, Amok, Hilkiah, and Jedaiah. These were the leaders of the priests and of their relatives at the time of Jeshua.

8 The Levites were Jeshua, Binnui, Kadmiel, Sherebiah, Judah, and Mattaniah, who with his relatives was in charge of the thanksgiving hymns. **9** Their relatives Bakbukiah and Unno stood across from them in worship.

10 Jeshua was the father of Joiakim. Joiakim was the father of Eliashib. Eliashib was the father of Joiada. **11** Joiada was the father of Jonathan. Jonathan was the father of Jaddua.

12 At the time of Joiakim, these were the priests who were the leaders of their families: From Seraiah, Meraiah; from Jeremiah, Hananiah; **13** from Ezra, Meshullam; from Amariah, Jehohanan; **14** from Malluchi, Jonathan; from Shebaniah, Joseph; **15** from Harim, Adna; from Meraioth, Helkai; **16** from Iddo, Zechariah; from Ginnethon, Meshullam; **17** from Abijah, Zichri; from Miniamin, from Moadiah, Piltai; **18** from Bilgah, Shammua; from Shemaiah, Jehonathan; **19** from Joiarib, Mattenai; from Jedaiah, Uzzi; **20** from Sallai, Kallai; from Amok, Eber; **21** from Hilkiah, Hashabiah; from Jedaiah, Nethanel.

22 The names of the family heads of the Levites and the priests at the time of Eliashib, Joiada, Johanan, and Jaddua were recorded until the reign of Darius the Persian. **23** The names of the family heads of the Levites were recorded in the Book of Chronicles until the time of Johanan, grandson of Eliashib. **24** The heads of the Levites were Hashabiah, Sherebiah, and Jeshua (son of Kadmiel). They and their relatives stood in groups across from one another to sing hymns of praise and thanksgiving antiphonally as David, the man of God, had ordered. **25** Mattaniah, Bakbukiah, Obadiah, Meshullam, Talmon, and Akkub were gatekeepers standing guard at the storehouses by the gates. **26** They lived in the days of Joiakim, son of Jeshua, grandson of Jozadak, and in the days of Nehemiah the governor and of Ezra the priest and scribe.

Jerusalem's Walls Are Dedicated to God

27 When the wall of Jerusalem was going to be dedicated, they went to wherever the Levites lived and had them come to Jerusalem to celebrate the dedication joyfully with hymns of thanksgiving, with songs and cymbals, and with harps and lyres. **28** So the groups of singers came together from the countryside around Jerusalem, from the villages of Netophah, **29** from Beth Gilgal, and from the region of Geba and Azmaveth. The singers had built villages for themselves around Jerusalem. **30** The priests and the Levites cleansed themselves. Then they cleansed the people, the gates, and the wall.

31 Then I had the leaders of Judah come up on the wall, and I arranged two large choirs to give thanks and march in procession. One choir went to the right on the wall to Dung Gate. **32** Hoshaiah and half of the leaders of Judah followed them. **33** Azariah, Ezra, Meshullam, **34** Judah, Benjamin, Shemaiah, and Jeremiah also followed. **35** So did some priests with trumpets: Zechariah, who was the son of Jonathan, who was the son of Shemaiah, who was the son of Mattaniah, who was the son of Micaiah, who was the son of Zaccur, who was the son of Asaph. **36** Also, these relatives of Zechariah followed: Shemaiah, Azarel, Milalai, Gilalai, Maai, Nethanel, Judah, and Hanani with the musical instruments of David, the man of God. Ezra the scribe led them. **37** At Fountain Gate they went straight up the stairs of the City of David. There the wall rises past David's palace and reaches Water Gate on the east.

38 The other choir went to the left. I followed them with the other half of the people. We walked on the wall, past the Tower of the Ovens, as far as Broad Wall, **39** then past Ephraim Gate, over Old Gate and Fish Gate, and by the Tower of Hananel and the Tower of the Hundred, as far as Sheep Gate. The choir stopped at Guard's Gate. **40** So both choirs stood in

God's temple, as did I and the half of the leaders who were with me. [41] Likewise, these priests stood in God's temple: Eliakim, Maaseiah, Miniamin, Micaiah, Elioenai, Zechariah, and Hananiah with trumpets, [42] and Maaseiah, Shemaiah, Eleazar, Uzzi, Jehohanan, Malchiah, Elam, and Ezer. The singers sang under the direction of Jezrahiah.

[43] That day they offered many sacrifices and rejoiced because God had given them reason to rejoice. The women and children rejoiced as well. The sound of rejoicing in Jerusalem could be heard from far away.

[44] On that day men were put in charge of the storerooms for the contributions, the first produce harvested, and a tenth of the people's money. They stored in those rooms the gifts designated by Moses' Teachings for the priests and Levites from the fields around the cities. The people of Judah were pleased with the ministry of the priests and Levites. [45] They were doing what their God required, what needed to be done for cleansing. The singers and the gatekeepers did what David and his son Solomon had ordered them to do. [46] Long ago in the time of David and Asaph, there had been directors for the singers to lead ˴in singing˴ the songs of praise and hymns of thanksgiving to God. [47] At the time of Zerubbabel and Nehemiah, all the Israelites were giving gifts for the daily support of the singers and the gatekeepers. They set aside holy gifts for ˴the daily support of˴ the Levites, and the Levites set aside holy gifts for support of Aaron's descendants.

13 [1] On that day the Book of Moses was read while the people were listening. They heard the passage that no Ammonite or Moabite should ever be admitted into God's assembly. [2] (After all, they didn't welcome the Israelites with food and water. Instead, they hired Balaam to curse the Israelites. But our God turned the curse into a blessing.) [3] After the people heard this Teaching, they separated the non-Israelites from the Israelites.

[4] Even before this, the priest Eliashib, who was related to Tobiah and had been put in charge of the storerooms of our God's temple, [5] had provided a large room for Tobiah. Previously, this room had been used to store grain offerings, incense, utensils, a tenth of all the grain harvested, new wine, and olive oil. These things belonged by law to the Levites, singers, and gatekeepers. The contributions for the priests had also been stored there.

Nehemiah Evicts Tobiah From the Temple

[6] While all of this was taking place, I wasn't in Jerusalem. In the thirty-second year of King Artaxerxes' reign in Babylon, I returned to the king. Later, I asked the king for permission to return. [7] I went to Jerusalem and discovered the evil thing Eliashib had done by providing Tobiah with a room in God's temple. [8] I was furious. So I threw all of Tobiah's household goods out of the room. [9] Then I told them to cleanse the rooms, and I put back in there the utensils from God's temple, the offerings, and the incense.

Nehemiah Ensures That the Levites Receive Their Portion of the Offerings

[10] I learned that the Levites had not been given their portions. So each of the Levites and singers, who conducted the worship ˴in the temple˴, had left for their own fields. [11] I reprimanded the leaders. "Why is God's temple being neglected?" I asked. So I brought the Levites back together and put them back in their places of service. [12] Then all Judah brought a tenth of all the grain harvested, new wine, and olive oil to the storerooms. [13] I appointed the following men to be in charge of the storerooms: Shelemiah the priest, Zadok the scribe, and Pedaiah the Levite, and I appointed Hanan, son of Zaccur and grandson of Mattaniah to help them. Since they could be trusted, I made them responsible for distributing ˴the portions˴ to their relatives.

[14] ˴Nehemiah prayed,˴ "Remember me for what I have done, my God, and don't wipe out the good things that I have done for your temple and for the worship that is held there."

Nehemiah Ensures That No Work Is Done on the Day of Worship

[15] In those days I saw people in Judah stomping grapes in the winepresses on the day of worship. I saw them bringing in loads of wine, grapes, figs, and every other kind of load. They piled the loads on donkeys and brought them into Jerusalem on the day of worship. I warned them about selling food on that day. [16] People from Tyre who lived in Jerusalem were bringing in fish and all kinds of goods. They were selling them on the day of worship to the people of Judah, even in Jerusalem. [17] I reprimanded the nobles of Judah and asked them, "What is this evil thing you're doing? How dare you treat the day of worship as unholy! [18] Isn't this what your ancestors did, with the results that our God brought all these evils on us and on this city? Now you're making him even more angry with Israel by treating the day of worship as unholy."

[19] Before the day of worship, when the gates of Jerusalem were cleared of traffic, I ordered the doors to be shut and not to be reopened until after the day of worship. I stationed some of my men by the gates to make sure that no loads could be brought in on the day of worship.

²⁰ Once or twice merchants and those who sell all kinds of goods spent the night outside Jerusalem. ²¹ I warned them. "Why are you spending the night in front of the wall?" I asked them. "If you do it again, I'll arrest you." After that, they no longer came on the day of worship. ²² Then I told the Levites to cleanse themselves and guard the gates to keep the day of worship holy.

⌊Nehemiah prayed,⌋ "Remember me also for this, my God, and spare me, since you are very kind."

Nehemiah Dissolves Marriages to Foreigners

²³ In those days I saw some Jews who had married women from Ashdod, Ammon, and Moab. ²⁴ Half their children spoke the language of Ashdod or one of the other languages, but they couldn't understand the language of Judah well enough to speak it. ²⁵ So I reprimanded those Jews, cursed them, beat some of them, and pulled out their hair. I made them swear by God: "We won't allow our daughters to marry their sons, and we won't allow their daughters to marry us or our sons." ²⁶ I said, "Wasn't it because of marriages like these that King Solomon of Israel sinned? There wasn't a king like him among all nations. God loved him, and God made him king of all Israel. But his non-Israelite wives led him to sin. ²⁷ Should we follow your example, commit such a serious crime against our God, and be unfaithful to him by marrying non-Israelite women?"

²⁸ Even one of Joiada's sons was a son-in-law of Sanballat from Beth Horon. (Joiada was the son of the chief priest Eliashib.) I chased Joiada's son away from me.

²⁹ ⌊Nehemiah prayed,⌋ "Remember them, my God, because they have contaminated the priestly office and the promise[a] you made to the priests and Levites."

³⁰ So I cleansed them from everything that was foreign. I assigned duties to the priests and Levites. Each one had his own assignment. ³¹ I also arranged for delivering wood at regular times and for bringing the first produce to be harvested.

⌊Nehemiah prayed,⌋ "Remember me, my God, for my benefit."

ᵃ 13:29 Or "covenant."

ESTHER

Queen Vashti Disobeys King Xerxes

1 ¹ In the days of Xerxes the following events took place. This was the same Xerxes who ruled over 127 provinces from India to Sudan. ² At the time when King Xerxes sat on the royal throne in the fortress of Susa, ³ he held a banquet in the third year of his reign. The banquet was for all his officials and advisers, that is, the military officers of the Persians and Medes, the nobles and officials of the provinces who had access to him. ⁴ He showed them the enormous wealth of his kingdom and the costly splendor of his greatness for many days, 180 to be exact. ⁵ When those days were over, the king held a banquet lasting seven days. This banquet was held in the enclosed garden of the king's palace for all people in the fortress of Susa, whatever their rank.

⁶ The garden had white and violet linen curtains. These curtains were attached to silver rods and marble pillars by cords made of white and purple fine linen. Gold and silver couches were on a mosaic pavement of purple rock, white marble, pearl-like stone, and black marble. ⁷ People drank from golden cups. No two cups were alike. The king also provided plenty of royal wine out of his royal generosity. ⁸ The drinking followed this rule: Drink as you please. (The king had ordered all the waiters in his palace to let everyone do as he pleased.)

⁹ Queen Vashti also held a banquet for the women at the royal palace of King Xerxes.

¹⁰ On the seventh day when the king was drunk on wine, he ordered Mehuman, Biztha, Harbona, Bigtha, Abagtha, Zethar, and Carcas, the seven eunuchs who served under King Xerxes, ¹¹ to bring Queen Vashti in front of the king, wearing her royal crown. He wanted to show the people, especially the officials, her beauty, because she was very attractive. ¹² But Queen Vashti refused the king's command that the eunuchs delivered to her. As a result, the king became very angry, and his rage burned inside him.

¹³ Now, the king usually asked for advice from all the experts in royal decrees and decisions, ¹⁴ from those closest to him—Carshena, Shethar, Admatha, Tarshish, Meres, Marsena, and Memucan. These seven officials of the Persians and Medes had access to the king and held the highest rank in the kingdom. The king asked these wise men who knew the times,[a] ¹⁵ "According to the royal decrees, what must we do with Queen Vashti since she did not obey King Xerxes' command, which the eunuchs delivered?"

¹⁶ Then Memucan spoke up in the presence of the king and the officials, "Queen Vashti has done wrong, not only against the king but also against all the officials and all the people in every province of King Xerxes. ¹⁷ The news of what the queen has done will spread to all women, and they will despise their husbands. They will say, 'King Xerxes ordered Queen Vashti to be brought to him, but she would not come.' ¹⁸ Today the wives of the officials in Persia and Media who have heard what the queen did will talk back to all the king's officials. There will be contempt and short tempers. ¹⁹ If it pleases you, Your Majesty, issue a royal decree. It should be recorded in the decrees of the Persians and Medes, never to be repealed, that Vashti may never again appear in front of King Xerxes. Furthermore, Your Majesty, you should give her royal position to another woman who is more worthy than she. ²⁰ When you issue your decree, your whole kingdom, great as it is, will hear it. Then all the wives will honor their husbands, regardless of their status."

²¹ The king and his officials approved of this, and so the king did as Memucan suggested. ²² He sent official documents to all the king's provinces, to each province in its own script and to the people in each province in their own language: "Let every husband be the ruler in his own house and speak with authority."[b]

Esther Becomes Queen

2 ¹ Later, when King Xerxes got over his raging anger, he remembered Vashti, what she had done, and what had been decided against her.

² So the king's personal staff said to him, "Search for attractive young virgins for the king. ³ And appoint scouts in all the provinces of your kingdom to gather all the attractive young virgins and bring them to the fortress of Susa, to the women's quarters. There, in the care of the

---

[a] 1:14 The first part of verse 13 (in Hebrew) has been placed just before verse 15 to express the complex Hebrew sentence structure more clearly in English.   [b] 1:22 Hebrew meaning uncertain.

king's eunuch Hegai, the guardian of the women, they will have their beauty treatment. ⁴Then the young woman who pleases you, Your Majesty, will become queen instead of Vashti."

The king liked the suggestion, and so he did just that.

⁵In the fortress of Susa there was a Jew from the tribe of Benjamin named Mordecai. He was the son of Jair, the grandson of Shimei, and the great-grandson of Kish. ⁶ (Kish had been taken captive from Jerusalem together with the others who had gone into exile along with Judah's King Jehoiakin,ᵃ whom King Nebuchadnezzar of Babylon had carried away.) ⁷Mordecai had raised Hadassah, also known as Esther, his uncle's daughter, because she was an orphan. The young woman had a beautiful figure and was very attractive. When her father and mother died, Mordecai adopted her as his own daughter.

⁸When the king's announcement and decree were heard, many young women were gathered together and brought to the fortress of Susa. They were placed in the care of Hegai. Esther also was taken to the king's palace and placed in the care of Hegai, the guardian of the women. ⁹The young woman pleased him and won his affection. So he immediately provided her with the beauty treatment, a daily supply of food, and seven suitable female servants from the king's palace. Then he moved her and her servants to the best place in the women's quarters.

¹⁰Esther did not reveal her nationality or her family background, because Mordecai had ordered her not to. ¹¹Every day Mordecai would walk back and forth in front of the courtyard of the women's quarters to find out how Esther was and what was happening to her.

¹²Each young woman had her turn to go to King Xerxes after she had completed the required 12-month treatment for women. The time of beauty treatment was spent as follows: six months using oil of myrrh and six months using perfumes and other treatments for women.

¹³After that, the young woman would go to the king. Anything she wanted to take with her from the women's quarters to the king's palace was given to her. ¹⁴She would go in the evening and come back in the morning to the other quarters for women. There she would be in the care of the king's eunuch Shaashgaz, the guardian of the concubines.ᵇ She never went to the king again unless the king desired her and requested her by name.

¹⁵ (Esther was the daughter of Abihail, Mordecai's uncle. Mordecai had adopted her as his own daughter.)

When Esther's turn came to go to the king, she asked only for what the king's eunuch Hegai, the guardian of the women, advised. Everyone who saw Esther liked her. ¹⁶So Esther was taken to King Xerxes in his royal palace in the month of Tebeth, the tenth month, in the seventh year of his reign.

¹⁷Now, the king loved Esther more than all the other women and favored her over all the other virgins. So he put the royal crown on her head and made her queen instead of Vashti. ¹⁸Then the king held a great banquet for Esther. He invited all his officials and his advisers. He also declared that day a holiday in the provinces, and he handed out gifts from his royal generosity.

Mordecai Saves the King's Life

¹⁹When the virgins were gathered a second time, Mordecai was sitting at the king's gate. ²⁰Esther still had not revealed her family background or nationality, as Mordecai had ordered her. Esther always did whatever Mordecai told her, as she did when she was a child.

²¹In those days, while Mordecai was sitting at the king's gate, Bigthan and Teresh, two of the king's eunuchs who guarded the entrance, became angry and planned to kill King Xerxes. ²²But Mordecai found out about it and informed Queen Esther. Then Esther told the king, on behalf of Mordecai. ²³When the report was investigated and found to be true, the dead bodies of Bigthan and Teresh were hung on a pole. The matter was written up in the king's presence in his official record of daily events.

Haman's Plot

3 ¹Later, King Xerxes promoted Haman. (Haman was the son of Hammedatha and was from Agag.) He gave Haman a position higher in authority than all the other officials who were with him. ²All the king's advisers were at the king's gate, kneeling and bowing to Haman with their faces touching the ground, because the king had commanded it. But Mordecai would not kneel and bow to him.

³Then the king's advisers at the king's gate asked Mordecai, "Why do you ignore the king's command?" ⁴Although they asked him day after day, he paid no attention to them. So they informed Haman to see if Mordecai's actions would be tolerated, since Mordecai had told them that he was a Jew.

ᵃ 2:6 Masoretic Text "Jeconiah," an alternate form of Jehoiakin.   ᵇ 2:14 A concubine is considered a wife except she has fewer rights under the law.

[5] When Haman saw that Mordecai did not kneel and bow to him, Haman was infuriated. [6] Because the king's advisers had informed him about Mordecai's nationality, he thought it beneath himself to kill only Mordecai. So Haman planned to wipe out Mordecai's people—all the Jews in the entire kingdom of Xerxes.

[7] In Xerxes' twelfth year as king, *Pur* (which means *the lot*) was thrown in front of Haman for every day of every month, from Nisan, the first month, until Adar, the twelfth month.

[8] Now, Haman told King Xerxes, "Your Majesty, there is a certain nationality scattered among—but separate from—the nationalities in all the provinces of your kingdom. Their laws differ from those of all other nationalities. They do not obey your decrees. So it is not in your interest to tolerate them, Your Majesty. [9] If you approve, have the orders for their destruction be written. For this I will pay 750,000 pounds of silver to your treasurers to be put in your treasury."

[10] At that, the king removed his signet ring and gave it to Haman, the enemy of the Jews. (Haman was the son of Hammedatha and was from Agag.) [11] The king told Haman, "You can keep your silver and do with the people whatever you like."

Haman Prepares to Kill the Jews

[12] On the thirteenth day of the first month the king's scribes were summoned. All Haman's orders were written to the king's satraps, the governors of every province, and the officials of every people. They wrote to each province in its own script and to the people in each province in their own language. The orders were signed in the name of King Xerxes and sealed with the king's ring. [13] Messengers were sent with official documents to all the king's provinces. ˌThe people were orderedˌ to wipe out, kill, and destroy all the Jews—young and old, women and children—on a single day, the thirteenth day of the twelfth month, the month of Adar. Their possessions were also to be seized. [14] A copy of the document was made public in a decree to every province. All the people were to be ready for this day.

[15] The messengers hurried out as the king told them. The decree was also issued at the fortress of Susa. So the king and Haman sat down to drink a toast, but the city of Susa was in turmoil.

4 [1] When Mordecai found out about everything that had been done, he tore his clothes and put on sackcloth and ashes. He went into the middle of the city and cried loudly and bitterly. [2] He even went right up to the king's gate. (No one could enter it wearing sackcloth.)

[3] In every province touched by the king's command and decree, the Jews went into mourning, fasting, weeping, and wailing. Many put on sackcloth and ashes.

Esther's Problem

[4] Esther's servants and eunuchs came and informed her ˌabout Mordecaiˌ. The queen was stunned. She sent clothing for Mordecai to put on in place of his sackcloth, but he refused to accept it. [5] Then Esther called for Hathach, one of the king's eunuchs appointed to serve her. She commanded him to go to Mordecai and find out what was going on and why.

[6] So Hathach went out to Mordecai in the city square in front of the king's gate. [7] Mordecai informed him about everything that had happened to him. He told him the exact amount of silver that Haman had promised to pay into the king's treasury to destroy the Jews. [8] He also gave him a copy of the decree that was issued in Susa. The decree gave permission to exterminate the Jews. Hathach was supposed to show it to Esther to inform and command her to go to the king, beg him for mercy, and appeal to him for her people. [9] So Hathach returned and told Esther what Mordecai had said.

[10] Esther spoke to Hathach and commanded him to say to Mordecai, [11] "All the king's advisers and the people in the king's provinces know that no one approaches the king in the throne room without being summoned. By law that person must be put to death. Only if the king holds out the golden scepter to him will he live. I, myself, have not been summoned to enter the king's presence for 30 days now." [12] So Esther's servants told Mordecai what Esther said.

[13] Mordecai sent this answer back to Esther, "Do not imagine that just because you are in the king's palace you will be any safer than all the rest of the Jews. [14] The fact is, even if you remain silent now, someone else will help and rescue the Jews, but you and your relatives will die. And who knows, you may have gained your royal position for a time like this."

[15] Esther sent this reply back to Mordecai, [16] "Assemble all the Jews in Susa. Fast for me: Do not eat or drink at all for three entire days. My servants and I will also fast. After that, I will go to the king, even if it is against a royal decree. If I die, I die."

[17] Mordecai did just as Esther had commanded him.

Esther Brings Her Request to the King

5 [1] On the third day Esther put on her royal robes. She stood in the courtyard of the king's palace, facing the king's throne room. The king was sitting on the royal throne inside the palace, facing the entrance.

² When the king saw Queen Esther standing in the entrance, she won his favor. So the king held out the golden scepter that was in his hand to Esther. Esther went up to him and touched the top of the scepter.

³ Then the king asked her, "What is troubling you, Queen Esther? What would you like? Even if it is up to half of the kingdom, it will be granted to you."

⁴ So Esther answered, "If it pleases you, Your Majesty, come today with Haman to a dinner I have prepared for you."

⁵ The king replied, "Bring Haman right away, and do whatever Esther asks." So the king and Haman came to the dinner that Esther had prepared.

⁶ While they were drinking wine, the king asked Esther, "What is your request? It will be granted to you. What would you like? Even if it is up to half of the kingdom, it will be granted."

⁷ Esther answered, "My request? What would I like? ⁸ Your Majesty, come with Haman to a dinner I will prepare for you. And tomorrow I will answer you, Your Majesty. If I have found favor with you, Your Majesty, and if it pleases you, Your Majesty, may you ˎthenˎ grant my request and do what I would like."

Meanwhile, Haman Is Disgraced Because of Mordecai

⁹ When Haman left that day, he was happy and feeling good. But when Haman saw Mordecai at the king's gate, neither getting up nor trembling in his presence, Haman was furious with Mordecai. ¹⁰ However, Haman controlled himself. He went home and sent for his friends and his wife Zeresh.

¹¹ Then Haman began to relate in detail to them how very rich he was, the many sons he had, and all about how the king promoted him to a position over the officials and the king's advisers. ¹² Haman went on to say, "What's more, Queen Esther allowed no one except me to come with the king to the dinner she had prepared. And again tomorrow I am her invited guest together with the king. ¹³ Yet, all this is worth nothing to me every time I see Mordecai the Jew sitting at the king's gate."

¹⁴ Then his wife Zeresh and all his friends said to him, "Have a pole set up, 75 feet high, and in the morning ask the king to have Mordecai's ˎdead bodyˎ hung on it. Then go with the king to the dinner in good spirits."

Haman liked the idea, so he had the pole set up.

6 ¹ That night the king could not sleep. So he told ˎa servantˎ to bring the official daily records, and they were read to the king. ² The records showed how Mordecai had informed him that Bigthan and Teresh, two of the king's eunuchs who guarded the entrance, had plotted a rebellion against King Xerxes.

³ The king asked, "How did I reward and promote Mordecai for this?"

The king's personal staff replied, "Nothing was done for him."

⁴ The king asked, "Who is in the courtyard?" At that moment, Haman came through the courtyard to the king's palace to ask the king about hanging Mordecai on the pole he had prepared for him.

⁵ The king's staff answered him, "Haman happens to be standing in the courtyard."

"Let him come in," the king said.

⁶ So Haman came in. The king then asked him, "What should be done for the man whom the king wishes to reward?"

Haman thought to himself, "Whom would the king wish to reward more than me?" ⁷ So Haman told the king, "This is what should be done: ⁸ ˎThe servantsˎ should bring a royal robe that the king has worn and a horse that the king has ridden, one that has a royal crest on its head. ⁹ Give the robe and the horse to one of the king's officials, who is a noble. Put the robe on the man whom the king wishes to reward and have him ride on the horse in the city square. The king's servants are also to shout ahead of him, 'This is what is done for the man whom the king wishes to reward.' "

¹⁰ The king told Haman, "Hurry, take the robe and the horse as you said. Do this for Mordecai the Jew who sits at the king's gate. Do not omit anything you have said."

¹¹ So Haman took the robe and the horse. He put the robe on Mordecai and had him ride in the city square, shouting ahead of him, "This is what is done for the man whom the king wishes to reward."

¹² After that, Mordecai returned to the king's gate, but Haman hurried home. He was in despair and covered his head. ¹³ There, Haman began to relate in detail to his wife Zeresh and to all his friends everything that had happened to him. Then his counselors and his wife Zeresh told him, "You are starting to lose power to Mordecai. If Mordecai is of Jewish descent, you will never win out over him. He will certainly lead to your downfall."

14 While they were still speaking with him, the king's eunuchs arrived and quickly took Haman to the dinner Esther had prepared.

Esther Brings About Haman's Downfall

7 **1** So the king and Haman came to have dinner with Queen Esther. **2** On the second day, while they were drinking wine, the king asked Esther, "What is your request, Queen Esther? It will be granted to you. And what would you like? Even if it is up to half of the kingdom, it will be granted."

3 Then Queen Esther answered, "If I have found favor with you, Your Majesty, and if it pleases you, Your Majesty, spare my life. That is my request. And spare the life of my people. That is what I ask for. **4** You see, we—my people and I—have been sold so that we can be wiped out, killed, and destroyed. If our men and women had only been sold as slaves, I would have kept silent because the enemy is not worth troubling you about, Your Majesty."

5 Then King Xerxes interrupted Queen Esther and said, "Who is this person? Where is the person who has dared to do this?"

6 Esther answered, "Our vicious enemy is this wicked man Haman!" Then Haman became panic-stricken in the presence of the king and queen.

7 The king was furious as he got up from dinner and went into the palace garden. But Haman stayed to beg Queen Esther for his life, because he saw that the king had a terrible end in mind for him. **8** When the king returned from the palace garden to the palace dining room, Haman was falling on the couch where Esther was lying. The king thought, "Is he even going to rape the queen while I'm in the palace?" Then the king passed sentence on him, and servants covered Haman's face.

9 Harbona, one of the eunuchs present with the king, said, "What a coincidence! The 75-foot pole Haman made for Mordecai, who spoke up for the well-being of the king, is still standing at Haman's house."

The king responded, "Hang him on it!" **10** So servants hung Haman's ˎdead bodyˎ on the very pole he had prepared for Mordecai. Then the king got over his raging anger.

8 **1** On that same day King Xerxes gave the property of Haman, the enemy of the Jews, to Queen Esther. Also, Mordecai came to the king because Esther had told him how Mordecai was related to her. **2** Then the king took off his signet ring, which he had taken from Haman, and gave it to Mordecai. And Esther put Mordecai in charge of Haman's property.

Esther Brings Her Request to the King

3 Esther spoke again to the king. She fell down at his feet crying and begged him to have mercy and to undo the evil plot of Haman, who was from Agag, and his conspiracy against the Jews. **4** The king held out his golden scepter to Esther, and Esther got up and stood in front of the king. **5** She said, "Your Majesty, if it pleases you, and if I have found favor with you, if you consider my cause to be reasonable and if I am pleasing to you, cancel the official orders ˎconcerningˎ the plot of Haman (who was the son of Hammedatha and was from Agag). He signed ˎthe orderˎ to destroy the Jews in all your provinces, Your Majesty. **6** I cannot bear to see my people suffer such evil. And I simply cannot bear to see the destruction of my relatives."

7 King Xerxes said to Queen Esther and Mordecai the Jew, "I have given Haman's property to Esther, and Haman's ˎdead bodyˎ was hung on the pole because he tried to kill the Jews. **8** You write what you think is best for the Jews in the king's name. Seal it also with the king's signet ring, because whatever is written in the king's name and sealed with the king's signet ring cannot be canceled."

Mordecai Uses His Position to Save the Jews

9 At that time on the twenty-third day of Sivan, the third month, the king's scribes were summoned. What Mordecai had ordered was written to the Jews and to the satraps, governors, and officers of the 127 provinces from India to Sudan. It was written to each province in its own script, to each people in their own language, and to the Jews in their own script and their own language. **10** Mordecai wrote in King Xerxes' name and sealed the official documents with the king's signet ring. Then he sent them by messengers who rode special horses bred for speed. ˎHe wroteˎ **11** that the king had given permission for the Jews in every city to assemble, to defend themselves, to wipe out, to kill, and to destroy every armed force of the people and province that is hostile to them, even women and children, and to seize their goods. **12** ˎThis was permittedˎ on one day in all the provinces of King Xerxes, on the thirteenth day of Adar, the twelfth month. **13** The copy of the document was made public in a decree to every province for all people. On that day the Jews were to be ready to take revenge on their enemies.

¹⁴ The messengers rode the king's fastest horses. They left quickly, in keeping with the king's command. The decree was issued also in the fortress of Susa.

¹⁵ Mordecai went out from the presence of the king wearing the royal violet and white robe, a large gold crown, and a purple outer robe of fine linen. And the city of Susa cheered and rejoiced.

¹⁶ So the Jews were cheerful, happy, joyful, and successful. ¹⁷ In every province and every city where the king's message and decree arrived, the Jews were happy and joyful, feasting and enjoying a holiday. Then many common people pretended to be Jews because they were terrified of the Jews.

The Jews Defend Themselves

9 ¹ On the thirteenth day of Adar, the twelfth month, the king's command and decree were to be carried out. On that very day, when the enemies of the Jews expected to overpower them, the exact opposite happened: The Jews overpowered those who hated them.

² The Jews assembled in their cities throughout all the provinces of King Xerxes to kill those who were planning to harm them. No one could stand up against them, because all the people were terrified of them. ³ All the officials of the provinces, the satraps, the governors, and the king's treasurers assisted the Jews because they were terrified of Mordecai. ⁴ Mordecai was an important man in the king's palace. Moreover, his reputation was spreading to all the provinces, since Mordecai was becoming more and more powerful.

⁵ Then with their swords, the Jews attacked all their enemies, killing them, destroying them, and doing whatever they pleased to those who hated them. ⁶ In the fortress of Susa the Jews killed and wiped out 500 men. ⁷ They also killed Parshandatha, Dalphon, Aspatha, ⁸ Poratha, Adalia, Aridatha, ⁹ Parmashta, Arisai, Aridai, and Vaizatha. ¹⁰ These were the ten sons of Haman, who was the son of Hammedatha and the enemy of the Jews. But the Jews did not seize any of their possessions.

¹¹ On that day the number of those killed in the fortress of Susa was reported to the king. ¹² So the king said to Queen Esther, "In the fortress of Susa the Jews have killed and wiped out 500 men and Haman's 10 sons. What must they have done in the rest of the king's provinces! Now, what is your request? It will be granted to you. And what else would you like? It, too, will be granted."

¹³ Esther said, "If it pleases you, Your Majesty, allow the Jews in Susa to do tomorrow what was decreed for today. Let them hang Haman's ten sons on poles."

¹⁴ The king commanded this, issuing a decree in Susa. And so they hung Haman's ten sons ˏon polesˌ.

¹⁵ The Jews in Susa also assembled on the fourteenth day of the month of Adar and killed 300 men in Susa, but they did not seize any of their possessions. ¹⁶ The other Jews who were in the king's provinces had also assembled to defend and free themselves from their enemies. They killed 75,000 of those who hated them, but they did not seize any of their possessions. ¹⁷ This was on the thirteenth day of the month of Adar. On the fourteenth they rested and made it a day of feasting and celebration. ¹⁸ But the Jews in Susa had assembled on the thirteenth and fourteenth. They rested on the fifteenth and made it a day of feasting and celebration. ¹⁹ That is why the Jews who live in the villages and in the unwalled towns make the fourteenth day of the month of Adar a holiday for feasting and celebration. They also send gifts of food to one another.

The Festival of Purim Instituted by Esther and Mordecai

²⁰ Now, Mordecai wrote these things down and sent official letters to all the Jews in all the provinces of King Xerxes, near and far. ²¹ He established the fourteenth and fifteenth days of the month of Adar as days they must observe every year. ²² They were to observe them just like the days when the Jews freed themselves from their enemies. In that month their grief turned to joy and their mourning into a holiday. He declared that these days are to be days for feasting and celebrating and for sending gifts of food to one another, especially gifts to the poor.

²³ So the Jews accepted as tradition what they had begun, as Mordecai had written to them. ²⁴ It was because Haman, the enemy of all the Jews, had plotted against the Jews to destroy them. (Haman was the son of Hammedatha and was from Agag.) Haman had the *Pur* (which means *the lot*) thrown ˏin order to determine whenˌ to crush and destroy them. ²⁵ But when this came to the king's attention, he ordered, in the well-known letter, that the evil plan Haman had plotted against the Jews should turn back on his own head. As a result, they hung Haman and his sons on poles.

²⁶ So the Jews called these days Purim, based on the word *Pur*. Therefore, because of everything that was said in this letter—both what they had seen and what had happened to them— ²⁷ the Jews established a tradition for themselves and their descendants and for anyone who would join them. The tradition was that a person should never fail to observe these two days

every year, as they were described and at their appointed time. [28] So these days must be remembered and observed in every age, family, province, and city. These days of Purim must not be ignored among the Jews, and the importance of these days must never be forgotten by the generations to come.

[29] Abihail's daughter Queen Esther and Mordecai the Jew wrote with full authority in order to establish with this second letter the well-known celebration of Purim. [30] Mordecai sent official documents granting peace and security to all the Jews in the 127 provinces of the kingdom of Xerxes. [31] He did this in order to establish these days of Purim at the appointed time. Mordecai the Jew and Queen Esther established them for themselves, as they had established for themselves and their descendants the practices of fasting with sadness. [32] Esther's command had established these practices of Purim, and they are written in a book.

Mordecai's Greatness

10 [1] King Xerxes levied a tax on the country and the islands of the sea. [2] All his acts of power and might along with the whole account of the greatness of Mordecai, whom the king had promoted, are recorded in the history of the kings of the Medes and Persians. [3] Mordecai the Jew was ranked second only to King Xerxes. He was greatly respected by, and popular with, all of the other Jews, since he provided for the good of his people and spoke for the welfare of his fellow Jews.

JOB

Job's Life

1 ¹A man named Job lived in Uz. He was a man of integrity: He was decent, he feared God, and he stayed away from evil. ²He had seven sons and three daughters. ³He owned 7,000 sheep and goats, 3,000 camels, 1,000 oxen, 500 donkeys, and a large number of servants. He was the most influential person in the Middle East.

⁴His sons used to go to each other's homes, where they would have parties. (Each brother took his turn having a party.) They would send someone to invite their three sisters to eat and drink with them.

⁵When they finished having their parties, Job would send for them in order to cleanse them from sin. He would get up early in the morning and sacrifice burnt offerings for each of them. Job thought, "My children may have sinned and cursed God in their hearts." Job offered sacrifices for them all the time.

Satan Challenges the Lord

⁶One day when the sons of God came to stand in front of the Lord, Satan the Accuser came along with them.

⁷The Lord asked Satan, "Where have you come from?"

Satan answered the Lord, "From wandering all over the earth."

⁸The Lord asked Satan, "Have you thought about my servant Job? No one in the world is like him! He is a man of integrity: He is decent, he fears God, and he stays away from evil."

⁹Satan answered the Lord, "Haven't you given Job a reason to fear God? ¹⁰Haven't you put a protective fence around him, his home, and everything he has? You have blessed everything he does. His cattle have spread out over the land. ¹¹But now stretch out your hand, and strike everything he has. I bet he'll curse you to your face."

¹²The Lord told Satan, "Everything he has is in your power, but you must not lay a hand on him!" Then Satan left the Lord's presence.

Job's First Crisis

¹³One day when Job's sons and daughters were eating and drinking wine in their oldest brother's home, ¹⁴a messenger came to Job. He said, "While the oxen were plowing and the donkeys were grazing nearby, ¹⁵men from Sheba attacked. They took the livestock and massacred the servants. I'm the only one who has escaped to tell you."

¹⁶While he was still speaking, another ⌊messenger⌋ came and said, "A fire from God fell from heaven and completely burned your flocks and servants. I'm the only one who has escaped to tell you."

¹⁷While he was still speaking, another ⌊messenger⌋ came and said, "The Chaldeans formed three companies and made a raid on the camels. They took the camels and massacred the servants. I'm the only one who has escaped to tell you."

¹⁸While he was still speaking, another ⌊messenger⌋ came and said, "Your sons and your daughters were eating and drinking wine at their oldest brother's home ¹⁹when suddenly a great storm swept across the desert and struck the four corners of the house. It fell on the young people, and they died. I'm the only one who has escaped to tell you."

²⁰Job stood up, tore his robe in grief, and shaved his head. Then he fell to the ground and worshiped. ²¹He said,

> "Naked I came from my mother,
>   and naked I will return.
> The Lord has given,
>   and the Lord has taken away!
> May the name of the Lord be praised."

²²Through all this Job did not sin or blame God for doing anything wrong.

Satan Challenges the Lord Again

2 ¹One day when the sons of God came to stand in front of the Lord, Satan the Accuser came along with them.

² The LORD asked Satan, "Where have you come from?"

Satan answered the LORD, "From wandering all over the earth."

³ The LORD asked Satan, "Have you thought about my servant Job? No one in the world is like him! He is a man of integrity: He is decent, he fears God, and he stays away from evil. And he still holds on to his principles. You're trying to provoke me into ruining him for no reason."

⁴ Satan answered the LORD, "Skin for skin! Certainly, a man will give everything he has for his life. ⁵ But stretch out your hand, and strike his flesh and bones. I bet he'll curse you to your face."

⁶ The LORD told Satan, "He is in your power, but you must spare his life!"

Job's Second Crisis

⁷ Satan left the LORD's presence and struck Job with painful boils from the soles of his feet to the top of his head. ⁸ Job took a piece of broken pottery to scratch himself as he sat in the ashes.

⁹ His wife asked him, "Are you still holding on to your principles? Curse God and die!"

¹⁰ He said to her, "You're talking like a godless fool. We accept the good that God gives us. Shouldn't we also accept the bad?"

Through all this Job's lips did not utter one sinful word.

¹¹ When Job's three friends heard about all the terrible things that had happened to him, each of them came from his home—Eliphaz of Teman, Bildad of Shuah, Zophar of Naama. They had agreed they would go together to sympathize with Job and comfort him.

¹² When they saw him from a distance, they didn't even recognize him. They cried out loud and wept, and each of them tore his own clothes in grief. They threw dust on their heads. ¹³ Then they sat down on the ground with him for seven days and seven nights. No one said a word to him because they saw that he was in such great pain.

Job Speaks
Job Curses the Day He Was Born

3 ¹ After all this, Job ˻finally˼ opened his mouth and cursed the day he was born. ² Job said,

³　"Scratch out the day I was born
　　and the night that said, 'A boy has been conceived!'

⁴　"That day—
　　let it be pitch-black.
　　Let God above not ˻even˼ care about it.
　　Let no light shine on it.
⁵　　Let the darkness and long shadows claim it as their own.
　　Let a dark cloud hang over it.
　　Let the gloom terrify it.

⁶　"That night—
　　let the blackness take it away.
　　Let it not be included in the days of the year
　　　or be numbered among the months.
⁷　　Let that night be empty.
　　Let no joyful singing be heard in it.
⁸　　Let those who curse the day*ᵃ*
　　　(those who know how to wake up Leviathan*ᵇ*)
　　　　curse that night.
⁹　　Let its stars turn dark before dawn.
　　Let it hope for light and receive none.
　　Let it not see the first light of dawn
¹⁰　　　because it did not shut the doors of the womb ˻from which I came˼
　　　or hide my eyes from trouble.

Why Did I Survive at Birth?

¹¹　"Why didn't I die as soon as I was born
　　and breathe my last breath when I came out of the womb?
¹²　Why did knees welcome me?
　　Why did breasts let me nurse?
¹³　Instead of being alive,
　　I would now be quietly lying down.
　　I would now be sleeping peacefully.
¹⁴　I would be with the kings and the counselors of the world

ᵃ 3:8 Or "those who curse the sea."　　*ᵇ* 3:8 Hebrew meaning uncertain.

who built for themselves ˌwhat are nowˌ ruins.
15 I would be with princes
who had gold,
who filled their homes with silver.
16 I would be buried like a stillborn baby.
I would not exist.
I would be like infants who never saw the light.
17 There the wicked stop their raging.
There the weary are able to rest.
18 There the captives have no troubles at all.
There they do not hear the shouting of the slave driver.
19 There ˌyou findˌ both the unimportant and important people.
There the slave is free from his master.

Why Do I Go on Living?

20 "Why give light to one in misery
and life to those who find it so bitter,
21 to those who long for death but it never comes—
though they dig for it more than for buried treasure?
22 They are ecstatic,
delighted to find the grave.
23 Why give light to those whose paths have been hidden,
to those whom God has fenced in?

24 "When my food is in front of me, I sigh.
I pour out my groaning like water.
25 What I fear most overtakes me.
What I dread happens to me.
26 I have no peace!
I have no quiet!
I have no rest!
And trouble keeps coming!"

Eliphaz Speaks
Be Patient and Listen, Job

4 1 Then Eliphaz from Teman replied ˌto Jobˌ,

2 "If someone tries to talk to you, will you become impatient?
But who can keep from talking?
3 Certainly, you have instructed many people:
When hands were weak, you made them strong.
4 When someone stumbled, you lifted him up with your words.
When knees were weak, you gave them strength.
5 But trouble comes to you, and you're impatient.
It touches you, and you panic.
6 Doesn't your fear of God give you confidence
and your lifetime of integrity give you hope?

Only Evil People Suffer

7 "Now think about this:
Which innocent person ˌeverˌ died ˌan untimely deathˌ?
Find me a decent person who has been destroyed.
8 Whenever I saw those who plowed wickedness and planted misery,
they gathered its harvest.
9 God destroys them with his breath
and kills them with a blast of his anger.
10 Though the roar of the lion
and the growl of the ferocious lion ˌis loudˌ,
the young lions have had their teeth knocked out.
11 The old lions die without any prey ˌto eatˌ,
and the cubs of the lioness are scattered.

12 "I was told something secretly
and heard something whispered in my ear.
13 With disturbing thoughts from visions in the night,
when deep sleep falls on people,
14 fear and trembling came over me,
and all my bones shook.

15 A spirit passed in front of me.
   It made my hair stand on end.
16 Something stood there.
      I couldn't tell what it was.
   A vague image was in front of my eyes.
   I heard a soft voice:
17   'Can ˌanyˌ mortal be righteous to God?
      Can ˌanyˌ human being be pure to his maker?'

18 "You see, God doesn't trust his own servants,
   and he accuses his angels of making mistakes.
19   How much more will he accuse those who live in clay houses
         that have their foundation in the dust.
            Those houses can be crushed quicker than a moth!
20   From morning to evening, they are shattered.
         They will disappear forever without anyone paying attention.
21   Haven't the ropes of their tent been loosened?
            Won't they die without wisdom?

Eliphaz Continues: Seek God's Help, Job

5 1 "Cry out!
      Is there anyone to answer you?
      To which of the holy ones will you turn?
2 Certainly, anger kills a stubborn fool,
   and jealousy murders a gullible person.
3 I have seen a stubborn fool take root,
   but I quickly cursed his house.
4 His children are far from help.
   They are crushed at the city gate,
      and no one is there to rescue them.
5 What a stubborn fool gathers, hungry people eat.
   They take it even from among the thorns,
      and thirsty people pant after his wealth.ᵃ
6 Certainly, sorrow doesn't come from the soil,
   and trouble doesn't sprout from the ground.
7   But a person is born for trouble as surely as sparks fly up ˌfrom a fireˌ.

8 "But I would seek God's help
   and present my case to him.
9 He does great things that ˌweˌ cannot understand
   and miracles that ˌweˌ cannot count.
10 He gives rain to the earth
   and sends water to the fields.
11 He places lowly people up high.
   He lifts those who mourn to safety.
12 He keeps shrewd people from carrying out their plans
   so that they cannot do anything successfully.
13 He catches the wise with their own tricks.
   The plans of schemers prove to be hasty.
14   In the daytime they meet darkness
      and grope in the sunlight as if it were night.

15 "But he saves ˌother peopleˌ from their slander
   and the needy from the power of the mighty.
16   Then the poor have hope
      while wrongdoing shuts its mouth.

Blessing Comes When God Corrects You

17 "Blessed is the person whom God corrects.
   That person should not despise discipline from the Almighty.
18   God injures, but he bandages.
      He beats you up, but his hands make you well.
19 He will keep you safe from six troubles,
      and when the seventh one comes, no harm will touch you:

ᵃ 5:5 Hebrew meaning of the last two lines uncertain.

20 "In famine he will save you from death,
       and in war he will save you from the sword.

21 "When the tongue lashes out, you will be safe,
       and you will not be afraid of destruction when it comes.

22 "You will be able to laugh at destruction and starvation,
       so do not be afraid of wild animals on the earth.

23 "You will have a binding agreement with the stones in the field,
       and wild animals will be at peace with you.

24 "You will know peace in your tent.
     You will inspect your house and find nothing missing.

25 "You will find that your children are many
       and your descendants are like the grass of the earth.

26 "You will come to your grave at a ripe old age
       like a stack of hay in the right season.

27 "We have studied all of this thoroughly! This is the way it is.
     Listen to it, and learn it for yourself."

Job Speaks
God Has Attacked Me Without Cause

6 ¹ Then Job replied ˌto his friendsˌ,

2 "If only my grief could be weighed,
     if only my misery could be laid on the scales with it,
3   then they would be heavier than the sand of the seas.
         I spoke carelessly
4   because the arrows of the Almighty ˌhave found their targetˌ in me,
             and my spirit is drinking their poison.
           God's terrors line up in battle against me.

5 "Does a wild donkey bray when it's ˌeatingˌ grass,
       or does an ox make a sound over its hay?
6   Is tasteless food eaten without salt,
       or is there any flavor in the white of an egg?ᵃ
7   I refuse to touch such things.
           They are disgusting to me.ᵇ

8 "How I wish that my prayer would be answered—
       that God would give me what I'm hoping for,
9   that God would ˌfinallyˌ be willing to crush me,
       that he would reach out to cut me off.
10   Then I would still have comfort.
           I would be happy despite my endless pain,
             because I have not rejected the words of the Holy One.
11   What strength do I have ˌleftˌ that I can go on hoping?
     What goal do I have that I would want to prolong my life?
12   Do I have the strength of rocks?
       Does my body have the strength of bronze?
13   Am I not completely helpless?
         Haven't my skills been taken away from me?

You Have Not Treated Me Like True Friends
14 "A friend should treat a troubled person kindly,
       even if he abandons the fear of the Almighty.
15   My brothers have been as deceptive as seasonal rivers,
       like the seasonal riverbeds that flood.
16   They are dark with ice.
         They are hidden by snow.ᶜ
17   They vanish during a scorching summer.
           In the heat their riverbeds dry up.
18   They change their course.
         They go into a wasteland and disappear.

ᵃ 6:6 Hebrew meaning of "white of an egg" uncertain.   ᵇ 6:7 Hebrew meaning of this line uncertain.   ᶜ 6:16 Hebrew meaning of this verse uncertain.

19   Caravans from Tema look for them.
      Travelers from Sheba search for them.
20   They are ashamed because they relied on the streams.
          Arriving there, they are disappointed.

21   "So you are as unreliable to me ⸢as they are⸥.ᵈ
      You see something terrifying, and you are afraid.
22·   Did I ever say, 'Give me a gift,'
          or 'Offer me a bribe from your wealth,'
23   or 'Rescue me from an enemy,'
          or 'Ransom me from a tyrant'?
24   Teach me, and I'll be silent.
      Show me where I've been wrong.
25   How painful an honest discussion can be!
      In correcting me, you correct yourselves!
26   Do you think my words need correction?
          Do you think they're what a desperate person says to the wind?
27   Would you also throw dice for an orphan?
          Would you buy and sell your friend?

28   "But now, if you're willing, look at me.
      I won't lie to your face.
29   Please change your mind.
      Don't permit any injustice.
      Change your mind because I am still right about this!
30   Is there injustice on my tongue,
      or is my mouth unable to tell the difference between right and wrong?

Job Speaks About the Futility of Human Existence

7 ¹   "Isn't a mortal's stay on earth difficult
          like a hired hand's daily ⸢work⸥?
2   Like a slave, he longs for shade.
     Like a hired hand, he eagerly looks for his pay.
3   Likewise, I have been given months that are of no use,
             and I have inherited nights filled with misery.
4   When I lie down, I ask,
             'When will I get up?'
                 But the evening is long,
                 and I'm exhausted from tossing about until dawn.
5   My body is covered with maggots and scabs.
     My skin is crusted over with sores; then they ooze.
6   My days go swifter than a weaver's shuttle.
     They are spent without hope.
7   Remember, my life is only a breath,
         and never again will my eyes see anything good.
8   The eye that watches over me will no longer see me.
     Your eye will look for me, but I'll be gone.
9   As a cloud fades away and disappears,
         so a person goes into the grave and doesn't come back again.
10   He doesn't come back home again,
              and his household doesn't recognize him anymore.
11   So I won't keep my mouth shut,
         but I will speak from the distress that is in my spirit
         and complain about the bitterness in my soul.

Job Says to God: Leave Me Alone

12   "Am I the sea or a sea monster
         that you have set a guard over me?
13   When I say,
         'My couch may give me comfort.
     My bed may help me bear my pain,'
14   then you frighten me with dreams
             and terrify me with visions.
15   My throat would rather be choked.
             My bodyᵃ would prefer death ⸢to these dreams⸥.

ᵈ 6:21 Hebrew meaning of this line uncertain.   ᵃ 7:15 Or "bones."

16 I hate my life; I do not want to live forever.
　　Leave me alone because my days are so brief.

17 "What is a mortal that you should make so much of him,
　　that you should be concerned about him?

18 ⌊What is he⌋ that you should inspect him every morning
　　and examine him every moment?

19 Why don't you stop looking at me
　　long enough to let me swallow my spit?[b]

20 If I sin, what can I ⌊possibly⌋ do to you
　　since you insist on spying on people?
　　Why do you make me your target?
　　I've become a burden even to myself.

21 Why don't you forgive my disobedience
　　and take away my sin?
　　Soon I'll lie down in the dust.
　　Then you will search for me, but I'll be gone!"

Bildad Speaks
You Are Unjustly Accusing God of Doing Evil, Job

8 ¹Then Bildad from Shuah replied ⌊to Job⌋,

2 "How long will you say these things?
　　How long will your words be so windy?

3 Does God distort justice,
　　or does the Almighty distort righteousness?

4 If your children sinned against him,
　　he allowed them to suffer the consequences of their sinfulness.

5 If you search for God
　　and plead for mercy from the Almighty,

6 if you are moral and ethical,
　　then he will rise up on your behalf
　　and prove your righteousness by rebuilding your home.[a]

7 Then what you had in the past will seem small
　　compared with the great prosperity you'll have in the future.

Learn From Past Generations

8 "Ask the people of past generations.
　　Find out what their ancestors had learned.

9 We have only been around since yesterday, and we know nothing.
　　Our days on earth are only a fleeting shadow.

10 Won't their words teach you?
　　Won't they share their thoughts with you?

God Does Not Punish the Innocent Person

11 "Can papyrus grow up where there is no swamp?
　　Can rushes grow tall without water?

12 Even if they were fresh and not cut,
　　they would wither quicker than grass.

13 The same thing happens to all who forget God.
　　The hope of the godless dies.

14 His confidence is easily shattered.
　　His trust is a spider's web.

15 If one leans on his house, it collapses.
　　If one holds on to it, it will not support his weight.

16 He is like a well-watered plant in the sunshine.
　　The shoots spread over his garden.

17 Its roots weave through a pile of stones.
　　They cling to a stone house.

18 But when it is uprooted from its place,
　　⌊the ground⌋ denies it ⌊and says⌋, 'I never saw you!'

19 That is its joy in this life,
　　and others sprout from the same ground to ⌊take its place⌋.

---

[b] 7:19 English equivalent of this verse difficult.　　[a] 8:6 English equivalent of this line difficult.

20 "Certainly, God does not reject a person of integrity
    or give a helping hand to wicked people.
21 He will fill your mouth with laughter
    and your lips with happy shouting.
22 Those who hate you will be clothed with shame,
    and the tent of the wicked will cease to exist."

Job Speaks
The Futility of Arguing With God

9 ¹ Then Job replied ˏto his friendsˌ,

2 "Yes, I know that this is true.
    But how can a mortal be declared righteous to God?
3 If he wished to debate with God,
    he wouldn't be able to answer one question in a thousand.

4 "God is wise in heart and mighty in power.
    Who could oppose him and win?
5 He moves mountains without their knowing it,
    and he topples them in his anger.
6 He shakes the earth from its place,
    and its pillars tremble.
7 He commands the sun not to rise.
    He doesn't let the stars come out.
8 He stretches out the heavens by himself
    and walks on the waves of the sea.
9 He made ˏthe constellationsˌ Ursa Major, Orion, and the Pleiades,
    and the clusters of stars in the south.
10 He does great things that are unsearchable
    and miracles that cannot be numbered.
11 He passes alongside of me, and I don't even see him.
    He goes past me, and I don't even notice him.
12 He takes something away, ˏbutˌ who can stop him?
    Who is going to ask him, 'What are you doing?'
13 God does not hold back his anger.
    Even Rahab's[a] helpers bow humbly in front of him.

14 "How can I possibly answer God?
    How can I find the right words ˏto speakˌ with him?
15 Even if I were right, I could not answer ˏhimˌ.
    I would have to plead for mercy from my judge.
16 If I cried out and he answered me,
    I do not believe that he would listen to me.
17 He would knock me down with a storm
    and bruise me without a reason.
18 He would not let me catch my breath.
    He fills me with bitterness.
19 If it is a matter of strength,
    then he is the mighty one.
    If it is about justice,
    who will charge me with a crime?
20 If I am righteous, my own mouth would condemn me.
    It would declare that I am corrupt even if I am a man of integrity.
21 If I am a man of integrity, I have no way of knowing it.
    I hate my life!
22 It is all the same.
    That is why I say,
      'He destroys ˏbothˌ the man of integrity and the wicked.'
23 When a sudden disaster brings death,
    he makes fun of the despair of innocent people.
24 The earth is handed over to the wicked.
    He covers the faces of its judges.
      If he isn't the one ˏdoing thisˌ, who is?

---

[a] 9:13 Rahab is the name of a demonic creature who opposes God.

25 "My days go by more quickly than a runner.
   They sprint away.
   They don't see anything good.
26 They pass by quickly like boats made from reeds,
   like an eagle swooping down on its prey.
27 ˌEvenˌ if I say, 'I will forget my complaining;
   I will change my expression and smile,'
28 I ˌstillˌ dread everything I must suffer.
   I know that you won't declare me innocent.
29 I've already been found guilty.
   Why should I work so hard for nothing?
30 If I wash myself with lye soap*b*
   and cleanse my hands with bleach,
31 then you would plunge me into a muddy pit,
   and my own clothes would find me disgusting.
32 A human like me cannot answer God,
   'Let's take our case to court.'
33 There is no mediator between us
   to put his hand on both of us.
34 God should take his rod away from me,
   and he should not terrify me.*c*
35 Then I would speak and not be afraid of him.
   But I know that I am not like that.*d*

Job Says to God: I Hate My Life

10 1 "I hate my life.
        I will freely express my complaint.
   I will speak as bitterly as I feel.
2 I will say to God,
     'Don't condemn me.
       Let me know why you are quarreling with me.
3   What do you gain by mistreating me,
            by rejecting the work of your hands
               while you favor the plans of the wicked?
4 Do you actually have human eyes?
   Do you see as a mortal sees?
5   Are your days like a mortal's days?
     Are your years like a human's years?
6   Is that why you look for guilt in me
          and search for sin in me?
7 You know I'm not guilty,
     but there is no one to rescue me from your hands.

8 " 'Your hands formed me and made every part of me,
     then you turned to destroy me.*a*
9 Please remember that you made me out of clay
     and that you will return me to the dust again.
10 Didn't you pour me out like milk
     and curdle me like cheese?
11 Didn't you dress me in skin and flesh
     and weave me together with bones and tendons?
12 You gave me life and mercy.
   Your watchfulness has preserved my spirit.
13 But in your heart you hid these things.
   I know this is what you did.

14 " 'If I sin, you watch me
     and will not free me from my guilt.
15 How terrible it will be for me if I'm guilty!
     Even if I'm righteous, I dare not lift up my head.
   I am filled with disgrace
     while I look on my misery.
16 Like a proud, ferocious lion you hunt me down.

---

b 9:30 Or "with water made from snow."   *c* 9:33–34 Or "If there were a mediator between us to put his hand on both of us, he would remove his rod from me, and no longer terrify me."   *d* 9:35 Hebrew meaning of this line uncertain.
a 10:8 Hebrew meaning of this line uncertain.

17 You keep working your miracles against me.[b]
You keep finding new witnesses against me.
You keep increasing your anger toward me.
You keep bringing new armies against me.

18 " 'Why did you take me out of the womb?
I wish I had breathed my last breath
before anyone had laid eyes on me.
19 Then it would be as if I had never existed,
as if I had been carried from the womb to the tomb.

20 " 'Isn't my life short enough?
So stop ˻this˼, and leave me alone.
Let me smile a little
21 before I go away
to a land of darkness and gloom,
22 to a dismal land of long shadows and confusion
where light is as bright as darkness.
I'll never return.' "

Zophar Speaks
Your Words Call for an Answer, Job

11 ¹Then Zophar from Naama replied ˻to Job˼,

2 "Shouldn't someone answer this flood of words?
Should a good public speaker be acquitted?
3 Should your empty talk silence others
so that you can make fun of us without any shame?
4 You say, 'My teaching is morally correct,'
and, 'As you can see, I'm innocent.'
5 I only wish God would speak
and open his mouth ˻to talk˼ to you.
6 He would tell you the secrets of wisdom,
because ˻true˼ wisdom is twice ˻as great as your wisdom˼,[a]
and you would know that God forgets your sin.

God Can Do as He Pleases
7 "Can you discover God's hidden secrets,
or are you able to find the Almighty's limits?
8 ˻God's wisdom is˼ higher than heaven.
What can you do?
It is deeper than ˻the depths˼ of hell.
What can you know?
9 It is longer than the earth
and wider than the sea.
10 If God comes along and imprisons ˻someone˼
and then calls a court into session, who can stop him?
11 He knows who the scoundrels are.
And when he sees sin, doesn't he pay attention to it?
12 But an empty-headed person will gain understanding
when a wild donkey is born tame.

Confess Your Sin and Be Forgiven
13 "If you want to set your heart right,
then pray to him.
14 If you're holding on to sin, put it far away,
and don't let injustice live in your tent.
15 Then you will be able to show your face without being ashamed,
and you will be secure and unafraid.
16 ˻Then˼ you will forget your misery
and remember it like water that has flowed downstream.
17 Then your life will be brighter than the noonday sun.
The darkness in your life will become like morning.
18 You will feel confident because there's hope,
and you will look around and rest in safety.

---

[b] 10:16 Hebrew meaning of this verse uncertain.   [a] 11:6 Hebrew meaning of this line uncertain.

¹⁹ You will lie down with no one to frighten you,
      and many people will try to gain your favor.
²⁰ But the wicked will lose their eyesight.
      Their escape route will be closed.
        Their only hope is to take their last breath."[b]

Job Speaks
My Friends Have No Wisdom

12 ¹ Then Job replied ⸤to his friends⸥,

² "You certainly are ⸤wise⸥ people,
      and when you die, wisdom will die.
³ Like you, I have a mind.
      I am not inferior to you.
        But who doesn't know these things?
⁴ I am a laughingstock to my neighbors.
      I am one who calls on God and expects an answer.
   A man of integrity, a man who is righteous, has become a laughingstock.

⁵ "A person who has an easy life has no appreciation for misfortune.
      He thinks it is the fate of those who slip up.
⁶ ⸤But⸥ robbers' tents are prosperous,
      and there is security for those who provoke God,
        for those whose god is their power.[a]

⁷ "Instead, ask the animals, and they will teach you.
      Ask the birds, and they will tell you.
⁸ Or speak with the earth, and it will teach you.
      Even the fish will relate ⸤the story⸥ to you.
⁹ What creature doesn't know that the LORD's hands made it?
¹⁰   The life of every living creature
        and the spirit in every human body are in his hands.
¹¹ Doesn't the ear distinguish sounds
      and the tongue taste food?

Wisdom Comes From God
¹² "Wisdom is with the ancient one.
      The one who has had many days has insight.[b]
¹³ God has wisdom and strength.
      Advice and insight are his.
¹⁴   When he tears ⸤something⸥ down, it cannot be rebuilt.
        When he puts someone in prison, that person cannot be freed.
¹⁵   When he holds back the waters, there is a drought.
        When he releases them, they flood the earth.

¹⁶ "God has power and priceless wisdom.
   He owns ⸤both⸥ the deceiver and the person who is deceived.
¹⁷ He leads counselors away barefoot
      and makes fools out of judges.
¹⁸ He loosens kings' belts
      and strips them of their pants.
¹⁹ He leads priests away barefoot
      and misleads those who serve in a temple.
²⁰ He makes trusted advisers unable to speak
      and takes away the good judgment of respected leaders.
²¹ He pours contempt on influential people
      and unbuckles the belt of the mighty.
²² He uncovers mysteries ⸤hidden⸥ in the darkness
      and brings gloom into the light.
²³ He makes nations important and then destroys them.
   He makes nations large and leads them away.
²⁴ He takes away the common sense of a country's leaders
      and makes them stumble about in a pathless wilderness.
²⁵   They grope in the dark with no light,
        and he makes them stumble like drunks.

---

[b] 11:20 Hebrew meaning of this verse uncertain.   [a] 12:6 Hebrew meaning of this line uncertain.   [b] 12:12 Or "Wisdom is with the elderly, and understanding with those who have lived a long time."

Job Continues: You Are Not Listening to Me

13 ¹ "My eye has certainly seen all of this!
My ear has heard and understood it.
² After all, I know it as well as you do.
I am not inferior to you.
³ However, I want to speak to the Almighty,
and I wish to argue my case in front of God.
⁴ But you are smearing me with lies.
All of you are worthless physicians.
⁵ I wish you would keep silent.
For you, that would be wisdom.
⁶ Please listen to my argument,
and pay attention to my plea.

Your Wisdom Misrepresents God

⁷ "Will you talk wickedly for God
and talk deceitfully on his behalf?
⁸ Will you favor him
⌊as⌋ if you were arguing in court on God's behalf?
⁹ Will it go well when he cross-examines you?
Will you try to trick him as one mortal tricks another?
¹⁰ Will he really defend you
if you secretly favor ⌊him⌋?
¹¹ Doesn't his majesty terrify you?
Doesn't the fear of him fall upon you?
¹² "Your recollections are worthless proverbs.ᵃ
Your answers are absolutely useless.ᵇ
¹³ Be quiet, because I want to speak.
Let whatever may happen to me ⌊happen⌋!
¹⁴ I am biting off more than I can chew
and taking my life in my own hands.
¹⁵ If God would kill me, I would have no hope ⌊left⌋.ᶜ
Nevertheless, I will defend my behavior to his face.
¹⁶ This also will be my salvation
because no godless person could face him.

Job Speaks to God

¹⁷ "Listen carefully to my words.
Hear my declaration.
¹⁸ I have prepared my case.
I know that I will be declared righteous.
¹⁹ Who can make a case against me?
If someone could, I'd be silent and die.

²⁰ "Please don't do two things to me
so that I won't have to hide from you:
²¹ Stop oppressing me.
Don't let your terror frighten me.
²² Then call, and I'll answer.
Otherwise, I'll speak, and you'll answer me.
²³ How many crimes and sins have I committed?
Make me aware of my disobedience and my sin.
²⁴ Why do you hide your face ⌊from me⌋ and consider me your enemy?
²⁵ Are you trying to make a fluttering leaf tremble
or trying to chase dry husks?
²⁶ You write down bitter accusations against me.
You make me suffer for the sins of my youth.
²⁷ You put my feet in shackles.
You follow my trail by engraving marks on the soles of my feet.
²⁸ I am like worn-out wineskins,
like moth-eaten clothes.

ᵃ 13:12 Or "proverbs of ashes."   ᵇ 13:12 Or "are just answers of clay."   ᶜ 13:15 Or "If God would kill me, I would still have hope."

Job Continues: Consider My Frail Human Nature, God

14 ¹ "A person who is born of a woman is short-lived
and is full of trouble.
²   He comes up like a flower; then he withers.
He is like a fleeting shadow; he doesn't stay long.
³ You observe this
and call me to account to you.

⁴ "If only an unclean person could become clean![a]
It's not possible.
⁵ If the number of his days
and the number of his months are determined by you,
and you set his limit,
then he cannot go past it.
⁶ Look away from him, and he will cease to be.[b]
Meanwhile, he loves life as a laborer loves work.
⁷ There is hope for a tree when it is cut down.
It will sprout again.
Its shoots will not stop sprouting.
⁸ If its roots grow old in the ground
and its stump dies in the soil,
⁹   merely a scent of water will make it sprout
and grow branches like a plant.
¹⁰ But a human dies and is powerless.
A person breathes his last breath, and where is he?
¹¹ ˌAsˌ water drains out of a lake,
or ˌasˌ a river dries up completely,
¹²   so each person lies down
and does not rise until the heavens cease to exist.
He does not wake up.
He is not awakened from his sleep.
¹³ I wish you would hide me in Sheol
and keep me hidden there until your anger cools.
Set a specific time for me when you will remember me.

¹⁴ "If a person dies, will he go on living?
I will wait for my relief to come
as long as my hard labor continues.
¹⁵ You will call, and I will answer you.
You will long for the person your hands have made.
¹⁶ Though now you count my steps,
you will not keep ˌa record ofˌ my sins.
¹⁷ My disobedience will be closed up in a bag,
and you will cover over my sins.
¹⁸ As surely as a mountain falls
and rocks are dislodged,
¹⁹   ˌsoˌ water wears away stone,
floods wash away soil from the land,
and you destroy a mortal's hope.
²⁰ You overpower him forever, and he passes away.
You change his appearance and send him away.
²¹   His sons are honored, and he doesn't know it.
Or they become unimportant, and he doesn't realize it.
²²   He feels only his body's pain.
He is only worried about himself."

Eliphaz Speaks
You Are Speaking Sinfully, Job

15 ¹ Then Eliphaz from Teman replied ˌto Jobˌ,

² "Should a wise person answer with endless details
and fill his stomach with the east wind?
³ Should he argue with words that don't help,
with speeches that don't help ˌanyoneˌ?

---

[a] 14:4 "Unclean" refers to anything that Moses' Teachings say is not presentable to God. "Clean" refers to anything that
Moses' Teachings say is presentable to God.   [b] 14:6 Hebrew meaning uncertain.

⁴ Yes, you destroy the fear ⌊of God⌋
    and diminish devotion to God.
⁵ Your sin teaches you what to say.
    You choose ⌊to talk with⌋ a sly tongue.
⁶ Your ⌊own⌋ mouth condemns you, not I.
    Your lips testify against you.

You Are Not the Only Wise Person, Job

⁷ "Were you the first human to be born?
    Were you delivered before the hills ⌊existed⌋?
⁸ Did you listen in on God's council meeting
    and receive a monopoly on wisdom?
⁹ What do you know that we don't know?
    What do you understand that we don't?
¹⁰ Both the old and the gray-haired are among us.
    They are older than your father.
¹¹ Isn't God's comfort enough for you,
    even when gently spoken to you?
¹² Why have your emotions carried you away?
    Why do your eyes flash
¹³   when you turn against God
    and spit these words out of your mouth?
¹⁴ Why should a mortal be considered faultless
    or someone born of a woman be considered righteous?
¹⁵ If God doesn't trust his holy ones,
    and the heavens are not pure in his sight,
¹⁶ how much less will he trust the one who is disgusting and corrupt,
    the one who drinks wickedness like water.

I Want to Tell You What I Know

¹⁷ "I'll tell you; listen to me!
    I'll relate what I have seen.
¹⁸ I'll tell you what wise people have declared
    and what was not kept secret from their ancestors.
¹⁹   (The land was given to them alone,
      and no stranger passed through their land.)

The Tortured Life of the Wicked Person

²⁰ "The wicked person is tortured ⌊all his days⌋.
    Only a few years are reserved for the ruthless person.
²¹   Terrifying sounds are in his ears.
    While he enjoys peace, the destroyer comes to him.
²²   He doesn't believe he'll return from the dark.
    He is destined ⌊to be killed⌋ with a sword.
²³   He wanders around for food and asks, 'Where is it?'^a
    He knows that his ruin is close at hand.

²⁴ "The day of darkness^b troubles him.
    Distress and anguish terrify him
      like a king ready for battle.
²⁵ He stretches out his hand against God
    and attacks the Almighty like a warrior.
²⁶ He stubbornly charges at him with a thick shield.

²⁷ "His face is bloated with fat,
    and he is fat around the waist.
²⁸ He lives in ruined cities
    where no one dwells,
    in houses that are doomed to be piles of rubble.
²⁹ He won't get rich,
    and his wealth won't last.
      His possessions won't spread out over the land.

³⁰ "He won't escape the darkness.
    A flame will shrivel his branches.

---

^a 15:23 Or "He wanders around as if he were food for vultures."   ^b 15:24 The Hebrew text divides verses 23 and 24 at this point.

He will be blown away by his own breath.
31 He shouldn't trust in worthless things and deceive himself
because he will get worthless things in return.
32 It will happen before his time has come,
and his branch will not become green.
33 He will drop his unripened grapes like a vine
and throw off his blossoms like an olive tree
34   because a mob of godless people produces nothing,
and fire burns up the tents of those who offer bribes.[c]
35   They conceive trouble and give birth to evil.
Their wombs produce deception."

Job Speaks
My Friends Do Not Help Ease My Pain

16 ¹ Then Job replied ⸤to his friends⸥,

2 "I have heard many things like this before.
You are all pathetic at comforting me.
3 Will ⸤your⸥ long-winded speeches never end?
What disturbs you that you keep on answering ⸤me⸥?
4 I, too, could speak like you
if we could trade places.
I could string words together against you
and shake my head at you.
5 I could encourage you with my mouth,
and my quivering lips could ease ⸤your pain⸥.
6 If I speak, my pain is not eased.
If I stop talking, how much of it will go away?

7   "But now, God has worn me out.
You, ⸤God,⸥ have destroyed everyone who supports me.
8   You have shriveled me up, which itself is a witness ⸤against me⸥.
My frail body rises up and testifies against me.

Job Describes What God Has Done to Him
9 "God's anger tore me ⸤apart⸥ and attacked me.
He gritted his teeth at me.
My opponent looked sharply at me.
10   People gaped at me with wide-open mouths.
In scorn they slapped my cheeks.
They united against me.
11 God handed me over to unjust people
and threw me into the hands of wicked people.
12 I was at ease, and he shattered me.
He grabbed me by the back of the neck and smashed ⸤my skull⸥.
He set me up as his target,
13   and his archers surrounded me.
He slashes open my kidneys without mercy
and spills my blood[a] on the ground.
14 He inflicts wound after wound on me.
He lunges at me like a warrior.

15 "I have sewn sackcloth over my skin,
and I have thrown my strength in the dust.
16 My face is red from crying,
and dark shadows encircle my eyes,
17   although my hands have done nothing violent,
and my prayer is sincere.

Job Appeals His Case to Heaven
18 "Earth, don't cover my blood.
Don't ever let my cry ⸤for justice⸥ be stopped.
19 Even now, look! My witness is in heaven,
and the one who testifies for me is above,
20   the spokesman for my thoughts.[b]

---

[c] 15:34 Or "those who take bribes."   [a] 16:13 Or "bile."   [b] 16:20 Or "my friends mock me."

My eyes drip ˌwith tearsˌ to God
²² because in a few short years I will take the path of no return.ᶜ
²¹ But my witness will plead for a human in front of God.
The Son of Man will plead for his friend!

Job Pleads With God to Declare Him Honest

17 ¹ "My spirit is broken.
My days have been snuffed out.
The cemetery ˌis waitingˌ for me.
² Certainly, mockers are around me.
My eyes are focused on their opposition.
³ Please guarantee my bail yourself.
Who else will guarantee it with a handshake?
⁴ You have closed their minds so that they cannot understand.ᵃ
That is why you will not honor them.
⁵ (Whoever turns in friends to get their property
should have his children's eyesight fail.)

Job Says to His Friends: I'm Still Wiser Than You

⁶ "Now he has made me a laughingstock for many people.
Now they spit in my face.
⁷ Now my eyes are blurred from grief.
Now all my limbs are like a shadow.
⁸ Decent people are shocked by this,
and it stirs up the innocent against godless people.
⁹ Yet, the righteous person clings to his way,
and the one with clean hands grows stronger.

¹⁰ "But now, all of you, come and try again!
I won't find one wise man among you.
¹¹ My days are passing by.
My plans are broken.
My dreams ˌare shatteredˌ.
¹² You say that night is day.
Light has nearly become darkness.
¹³ If I look for the grave as my home
and make my bed in the darkness,
¹⁴ if I say to the pit, 'You are my father,'
and to the worm, 'You are my mother and sister,'
¹⁵ then where is my hope?
Can you see any hope left in me?
¹⁶ Will hope go down with me to the gates of the grave?
Will my hope rest with me in the dust?"

Bildad Speaks
Why Do You Think You Are So Great, Job?

18 ¹ Then Bildad from Shuah replied ˌto Jobˌ,

² "How long before your words will end?
Think it through, and then we'll talk.
³ Why do you think of us as cattle?
Why are we considered stupid in your eyes?
⁴ Why do you rip yourself apart in anger?
Should the earth be abandoned for your sake
or a boulder be dislodged?

What a Wicked Person Can Expect From Life

⁵ "Indeed, the light of the wicked is snuffed out.
The flame of his fire stops glowing.
⁶ The light in his tent becomes dark,
and the lamp above him is snuffed out.

⁷ "His healthy stride is shortened,
and his own planning trips him up.

ᶜ 16:22 Verse 22 has been placed before verse 21 to express the complex Hebrew sentence structure more clearly in English.
ᵃ 17:4 English equivalent difficult.

8 His own feet get him tangled in a net
     as he walks around on its webbing.
9   A trap catches his heel.
       A snare holds him.
10   A rope is hidden on the ground for him.
       A trap is on his path ˎto catchˏ him.

11 "Terrors suddenly pounce on him from every side
     and chase him every step he takes.
12 Hunger undermines his strength.
     Disaster is waiting beside him.
13 His skin is eaten away by disease.
     Death's firstborn son eats away at the limbs of his body.
14   He is dragged from the safety of his tent
       and marched off to the king of terrors.
15 Fire lives in his tent.
     Sulfur is scattered over his home.
16   His roots dry up under him.
       His branches wither over him.
17   All memory about him will vanish from the earth,
       and his reputation will not be known on the street corner.
18   He will be driven from the light into the dark
       and chased out of the world.
19   He will not have any children or descendants among his people
       or any survivor where he used to live.
20 People in the west are shocked by what happens to him.
     People in the east are seized with horror.
21 This is what happens to the homes of wicked people
     and to those who do not know God."

Job Speaks
Admit That God Is Mistreating Me

19 ¹ Then Job replied ˎto his friendsˏ,

2 "How long will you torment me
     and depress me with words?
3 You have insulted me ten times now.
     You're not even ashamed of mistreating me.
4 Even if it were true that I've made a mistake without realizing it,
     my mistake would affect only me.
5 If you are trying to make yourselves look better than me
     by using my disgrace as an argument against me,
6 then I want you to know that God has wronged me
     and surrounded me with his net.
7 Indeed, I cry, 'Help! I'm being attacked!' but I get no response.
     I call for help, but there is no justice.

What God Has Done to Me

8 "God has blocked my path so that I can't go on.
     He has made my paths dark.
9 He has stripped me of my honor.
     He has taken the crown off my head.
10 He beats me down on every side until I'm gone.
     He uproots my hope like a tree.
11 He is very angry at me.
     He considers me to be his enemy.
12 His troops assemble against me.
     They build a ramp to attack me
       and camp around my tent.

13 "My brothers stay far away from me.
     My friends are complete strangers to me.
14 My relatives and my closest friends have stopped coming.
     My house guests have forgotten me.
15 My female slaves consider me to be a stranger.
     I am like a foreigner to them.
16 I call my slave, but he doesn't answer, though I beg him.
17 My breath offends my wife.

I stink to my own children.
18   Even young children despise me.
          If I stand up, they make fun of me.
19   All my closest friends are disgusted with me.
          Those I love have turned against me.
20   I am skin and bones,
          and I have escaped only by the skin of my teeth.

21   "Have pity on me, my friends!
      Have pity on me because God's hand has struck me down.
22   Why do you pursue me as God does?
          Why are you never satisfied with my flesh?

Job's Confidence in His Defender
23   "I wish now my words were written.
      I wish they were inscribed on a scroll.
24   I wish they were forever engraved on a rock
          with an iron stylus and lead.ª
25   But I know that my defender lives,
          and afterwards, he will rise on the earth.
26   Even after my skin has been stripped off my body,
          I will see God in my own flesh.
27   I will see him with my own eyes,
          not with someone else's.
      My heart fails inside me!

Job Warns His Friends
28   "You say,
          'We will persecute him!
          The root of the problem is found in him.'
29   Fear death,
          because ˏyour angerˏ is punishable by death.
              Then you will know there is a judge."

Zophar Speaks
Here Is My Answer
20   ¹ Then Zophar from Naama replied ˏto Jobˏ.

2   "My disturbing thoughts make me answer,
          and because of them I am upset.
3   I have heard criticism that makes me ashamed,
              but a spirit beyond my understanding gives me answers.

A Wicked Person's Joy Is Short, His Pain Long
4   "Don't you know
          that from ancient times,
              from the time humans were placed on earth,
5   the triumph of the wicked is short-lived,
                  and the joy of the godless person lasts only a moment?
6   If his height reaches to the sky
          and his head touches the clouds,
7   he will certainly rotª like his own feces.
      Those who have seen him will say, 'Where is he?'
8   He will fly away like a dream and not be found.
          He will be chased away like a vision in the night.
9   Eyes that saw him will see him no more.
          His home will not look at him again.
10   His children will have to ask the poor for help.
          His own hands will have to give back his wealth.
11   His bones, once full of youthful vigor,
              will lie down with him in the dust.

12   "Though evil is sweet in his mouth
          and he hides it under his tongue. . . .

ª 19:24 The order of the lines has been reversed because the English equivalent is difficult.   ª 20:7 Or "he will be dead forever."

13 Though he savors it and won't let go of it
   and he holds it on the roof of his mouth,
14   the food in his belly turns sour.
     It becomes snake venom in his stomach.
15   He vomits up the riches that he swallowed.
       God forces them out of his stomach.
16 The godless person sucks the poison of snakes.
   A viper's fang kills him.
17 He won't be able to drink from the streams
   or from the rivers of honey and buttermilk.
18 He will give back what he earned without enjoying it.
   He will get no joy from the profits of his business
19   because he crushed and abandoned the poor.
   He has taken by force a house that he didn't build.
20 He will never know peace in his heart.
   He will never allow anything he desires to escape ˌhis graspˌ.
21   "Nothing is left for him to eat.
     His prosperity won't last.
22   ˌEvenˌ with all his wealth
     the full force of misery comes down on him.
23   Let that misery fill his belly.
       ˌGodˌ throws his burning anger at the godless person
         and makes his wrath come down on him like rain.
24   If that person flees from an iron weapon,
       a bronze bow will pierce him.
25   He pulls it out, and it comes out of his back.
       The glittering point comes out of his gallbladder.

   "Terrors come quickly to the godless person:
26   Total darkness waits in hiding for his treasure.
     A fire that no one fans will burn him.
       Whatever is left in his tent will be devoured.
27   Heaven exposes his sin.
     Earth rises up against him.
28   A flood will sweep away his house,
     a flash flood on the day of his anger.
29 This is the reward God gives to the wicked person,
   the inheritance God has appointed for him."

Job Speaks
Comfort Me by Listening to Me
21 ¹Then Job replied ˌto his friendsˌ,

2   "Listen carefully to my words,
     and let that be the comfort you offer me.
3   Bear with me while I speak.
     Then after I've spoken, you may go on mocking.
4   Am I complaining about a person?
     Why shouldn't I be impatient?
5   Look at me, and be shocked,
     and put ˌyourˌ hand over ˌyourˌ mouth.
6   When I remember it, I'm terrified,
     ˌandˌ shuddering seizes my body.

Wicked People Do Not Suffer for Their Sins
7   "Why do the wicked go on living, grow old,
     and even become more powerful?
8   They see their children firmly established with them,
       and they get to see their descendants.
9   Their homes are free from fear,
       and God doesn't use his rod on them.
10   Their bulls are fertile when they breed.
      Their cows give birth to calves and never miscarry.
11   They send their little children out ˌto playˌ
        like a flock of lambs,
          and their children dance around.
12   They sing with the tambourine and lyre,

and they are happy with the music of the flute.
13   They spend their days in happiness,
    and they go peacefully to the grave.
14 But they say to God,
  'Leave us alone.
  We don't want to know your ways.
15   Who is the Almighty that we should serve him?
    What do we gain if we pray to him?'
16 Anyhow, isn't their happiness in their own power?
  (The plan of the wicked is foreign to my way of thinking.)

17 "How often is the lamp of the wicked snuffed out?
  How often does disaster happen to them?
  How often does an angry God give them pain?
18 How often are they like straw in the wind
  or like husks that the storm sweeps away?

19 " ⌞You say,⌟ 'God saves a person's punishment for his children.'
    God should pay back that person
      so that he would know that it is a punishment.
20   His eyes should see his own ruin.
      He should drink from the wrath of the Almighty.
21   How can he be interested in his family after he's gone,
        when the number of his months is cut short?

No One Understands How God Deals With Humans

22 "Can anyone teach God knowledge?
  Can anyone judge the Most High?
23   One person dies in his prime
      and feels altogether happy and contented.
24   His stomach is full of milk,
        and his bones are strong and healthy.
25   Another person, never having tasted happiness,
      dies with a bitter soul.
26   Together they lie down in the dust,
      and worms cover them.

My Friends Have Betrayed Me

27 "You see, I know your thoughts
    and the schemes you plot against me
28   because you ask,
        'Where is the house of the influential person?
        Where is the tent where wicked people live?'
29   Haven't you asked travelers?
        But you didn't pay attention to their directions.
30 On the day of disaster the wicked person is spared.
  On the day of ⌞God's⌟ anger he is rescued.
31   Who will tell him to his face how he lived?
    Who will pay him back for what he did?
32   He is carried to the cemetery,
      and his grave is guarded.
33   The soil in the creekbed is sweet to him.
      Everyone follows him.
      Countless others went before him.
34 How can you comfort me with this nonsense
    when your answers continue to betray me?"

Eliphaz Speaks
Admit You Are Wicked, Job

22 ¹Then Eliphaz from Teman replied ⌞to Job⌟,

2 "Can a human be of any use to God
    when even a wise person is only useful to himself?
3 Is the Almighty pleased when you are righteous?
  Does he gain anything when you follow the path of integrity?
4 Does God correct you
    and bring you into a court of law because you fear him?

5 "Aren't you really very wicked?
Is there no end to your wrongdoing?
6 For no reason you take your brothers' goods as security for a loan
and strip them of their clothes.ᵃ
7 You don't even give a tired person a drink of water,
and you take food away from hungry people.
8 A strong person owns the land.
A privileged person lives in it.
9 You send widows away empty-handed,
and the arms of orphans are broken.
10 That is why traps are all around you
and great fear suddenly grips you.
11 ˻That is why˼ darkness surrounds you and you cannot see
and a flood of water covers you.

12 "Isn't God high above in the heavens?
Look how high the highest stars are!
13 You ask, 'What does God know?
Can he judge ˻anything˼ from behind a dark cloud?
14 Thick clouds surround him so that he cannot see.
He walks above the clouds.'ᵇ

15 "Are you following the old path that wicked people have taken?
16 They are snatched up before their time.
A river washes their foundation away.
17 They told God, 'Leave us alone!
What can the Almighty do for us?'
18 Yet, he filled their homes with good things.
(The plan of the wicked is foreign to my way of thinking.)
19 The righteous saw it and were glad,
and the innocent made fun of them by saying,
20 'Indeed, their wealth has been wiped out,
and a fire has burned up what ˻little˼ they had left.'

Make Peace With God

21 "Be in harmony and at peace with God.
In this way you will have prosperity.
22 Accept instruction from his mouth,
and keep his words in your heart.
23 If you return to the Almighty, you will prosper.
If you put wrongdoing out of your tent,
24 and lay your gold down in the dust,
and put your gold from Ophir among the pebbles in the rivers,
25 then the Almighty will become your gold
and your large supply of silver.
26 Then you will be happy with the Almighty
and look up toward God.
27 You will pray to him, and he will listen to you,
and you will keep your vow to him.
28 When you promise to do something, you will succeed,
and light will shine on your path.
29 When others are discouraged, you will say, 'Cheer up!'
Then he will save the humble person.ᶜ
30 He will rescue one who is not innocent.
That person will be rescued by your purity."

Job Speaks
Where Can I Find God?

23 ¹ Then Job replied ˻to his friends˼,

2 "My complaint is bitter again today.
I try hard to control my sighing.

3 "If only I knew where I could find God!
I would go where he lives.

ᵃ 22:6 Clothes were often used as security deposits for loans in biblical times.   ᵇ 22:14 English equivalent difficult.
ᶜ 22:29 Or "you will say, 'It's conceit.' But he will save the humble person."

⁴ I would present ˻my˼ case to him.
I would have a mouthful of arguments.
⁵ I want to know the words he would use to answer me.
I want to understand the things he would say to me.
⁶ Would he sue me and hide behind great legal maneuvers?
No, he certainly would press charges against me.
⁷ Then decent people could argue with him,
and I would escape my judgment forever.
⁸ However, if I go east, he isn't there.
If I go west, I can't find him.
⁹ If I go northward, where he is at work, I can't observe him.
If I turn southward, I can't see him.
¹⁰ ˻I can't find him˼ because he knows the road I take.
When he tests me,
˻I'll come out as pure as gold.
¹¹ I have followed his footsteps closely.
I have stayed on his path and did not turn from it.
¹² I have not left his commands behind.
I have treasured his words in my heart.

God Is Against Me

¹³ "But God is one of a kind.
Who can make him change his mind?
He does whatever he wants!
¹⁴ He will carry out ˻his˼ orders concerning me
as he does with so many other things.[a]
¹⁵ That is why I'm terrified of him.
When I think of it, I'm afraid of him.
¹⁶ God has discouraged me.
The Almighty has filled me with terror.
¹⁷ But I am not silenced by the dark
or by the thick darkness that covers my face.

Job Continues: Why Doesn't God Punish Those Who Do Evil?

24 ¹ "Why doesn't the Almighty set aside times ˻for punishment˼?
Why don't those who are close to him see his days ˻of judgment˼?

² "˻People˼ move boundary markers.
They steal flocks and tend them as shepherds.
³ They drive away the orphan's donkey.
They take the widow's ox as security for a loan.
⁴ They force needy people off the road.
All the poor people of the country go into hiding.
⁵ Like wild donkeys in the desert,
poor people go out to do their work, looking for food.
The plains provide food for their children.
⁶ They harvest animal food in the field ˻to feed themselves˼.
They pick the leftover grapes in the wicked person's vineyard.
⁷ All night they lie naked
without a covering from the cold.
⁸ They are drenched by the rainstorms in the mountains.
They hug the rocks because they can't find shelter.

⁹ "˻People˼ snatch the ˻nursing˼ orphan from a breast
and take a poor woman's baby as security for a loan.
¹⁰ ˻That is why˼ the poor go around naked.
They are hungry, yet they carry bundles of grain.
¹¹ They press out olive oil between rows ˻of olive trees˼.
They stomp on grapes in wine vats, yet they are thirsty.
¹² Those dying in the city groan.
Wounded people cry for help,
but God pays no attention to their prayers.

¹³ "Such people are among those who rebel against the light.
They are not acquainted with its ways.
They do not stay on its paths.

---

[a] 23:14 Hebrew meaning uncertain.

¹⁴ At dawn murderers rise; they kill the poor and needy.
        At night they become thieves.
¹⁵ Adulterers watch for twilight.
        They say, 'No one is watching us,' as they cover their faces.
¹⁶ In the dark, they break into houses,
        ˌbutˌ by day they lock themselves in.
        They do not ˌevenˌ know the light,
¹⁷   because morning and deep darkness are the same to them,
            because they are familiar with the terrors of deep darkness.
¹⁸ Such people are like scum on the surface of the water.
        Their property is cursed in the land.
        People do not travel the road that goes to their vineyards.
¹⁹ ˌJust asˌ drought and heat steal water from snow,
        so the grave steals people who sin.
²⁰   The womb forgets them.
            Worms feast on them.
                No one remembers them anymore,
                    and wickedness is snapped like a twig.
²¹ These men take advantage of childless women.
        These men show no kindness to widows.
²²   ˌGodˌ will drag away ˌtheseˌ mighty men by his power.
            These people may prosper,
                but they will never feel secure about life.
²³   ˌGodˌ may let them feel confident and self-reliant,
            but his eyes are on their ways.
²⁴   ˌSuch peopleˌ may be prosperous for a little while,
            but then they're gone.
        They are brought down low and disappear like everything else.^a
        They wither like heads of grain.

²⁵ "If it isn't so, who can prove I'm a liar
        and show that my words are worthless?"

Bildad Speaks
No One Is Righteous to God

25 ¹ Then Bildad from Shuah replied ˌto Jobˌ,

² "Authority and terror belong to God.
        He establishes peace in his high places.
³ Is there any ˌlimit to theˌ number of his troops?
        Is there anyone on whom his light does not rise?
⁴   How can a person be righteous to God?
        How can anyone born of a woman be pure?
⁵   Even the moon isn't bright,
            and the stars aren't pure in his sight.
⁶   How much less pure is a mortal—who is only a maggot—
                a descendant of Adam—who is only a worm!"

Job Speaks
My Friends Have Offered Useless Advice

26 ¹ Then Job replied ˌto his friendsˌ,

² "You have helped the person who has no power
        and saved the arm that isn't strong.
³ You have advised the person who has no wisdom
        and offered so much assistance.
⁴ To whom have you spoken ˌtheseˌ words,
        and whose spirit has spoken through you?

God's Power Over Creation

⁵ "The souls of the dead tremble beneath the water,
        and so do the creatures living there.
⁶ Sheol is naked in God's presence,
        and Abaddon has no clothing.

---

^a 24:24 Hebrew meaning of this line uncertain.

7   "He stretches out his heavens[a] over empty space.
     He hangs the earth on nothing whatsoever.
8   He holds the water in his thick clouds,
         and the clouds don't ˻even˼ split under its ˻weight˼.
9   He covers his throne[b]
         by spreading his cloud over it.
10   He marks the horizon on the surface of the water
         at the boundary where light meets dark.
11   The pillars of heaven tremble
         and are astonished when he yells at them.
12   With his power he calmed the sea.
         With his insight he killed Rahab ˻the sea monster˼.
13   With his wind the sky was cleared.
         With his hand he stabbed the fleeing snake.

14   "These are only glimpses of what he does.
         We ˻only˼ hear a whisper of him!
         Who can understand the thunder of his power?"

Job Continues: I Insist I Am Innocent

27   ¹ Job continued his poems and said,

2   "I swear an oath
         by God, the one who has taken away my rights,
         by the Almighty, who has made my life bitter:
3   'As long as there is one breath ˻left˼ in me
             and God's breath fills my nostrils,
4   my lips will not say anything wrong,
                 and my tongue will not mumble anything deceitful.'
5   It's unthinkable for me to admit that you are right.
         Until I breathe my last breath, I will never give up my claim of integrity.
6   I cling to my righteousness and won't let go.
     My conscience won't accuse me as long as I live.

7   "Let my enemy be ˻treated˼ like wicked people.
     Let anyone who attacks me be ˻treated˼ like unrighteous people.
8   After all, what hope does the godless person have when he is cut off,
         when God takes away his life?
9   Will God hear his cry when trouble comes upon him?
10   Can he be happy with the Almighty?
         Can he call on God at all times?

What God Has in Store for Wicked People

11   "I will teach you about God's power.
     I will not hide what the Almighty has done.
12   Certainly, you have all seen it.
         Why then do you chatter on about such nonsense?
13   This is what God has waiting for the wicked person,
         the inheritance that tyrants receive from the Almighty:
14   If he has many children, swords will kill them,
             and his descendants won't have enough food.
15   Those who survive him will be buried by a plague,
             and their widows won't cry ˻for them˼.
16   Though he collects silver like dust
             and piles up clothing like dirt,
17   righteous people will wear what he piles up,
                 and the innocent will divide the silver
                     ˻among themselves˼.
18   He builds his house like a moth,
         like a shack that a watchman makes.
19   He may go to bed rich, but he'll never be rich again.
         When he opens his eyes, nothing will be left.
20   Terrors overtake him like a flood.
         A windstorm snatches him away at night.
21   The east wind carries him away, and he's gone.

---

[a] 26:7 Or "the north."   [b] 26:9 Or "the face of the moon."

22   It sweeps him from his place.
           It hurls itself at him without mercy.
               He flees from its power.
23   It claps its hands over him.
           It whistles at him from his own place.

Job Continues: Wisdom Is Inaccessible to Humans

28   ¹ "There is a place where silver is mined
        and a place where gold is refined.
2   Iron is taken from the ground,
        and rocks are melted for ⌊their⌋ copper.
3   ⌊Humans⌋ bring an end to darkness ⌊there⌋,
        and search to the limit of the gloomy, pitch-black rock.
4   They open up a mineshaft far from civilization,
        where no one has set foot.
    ⌊In this shaft⌋ men dangle and swing back and forth.

5   "Above the ground food grows,
        but beneath it the food decays as if ⌊it were burned⌋ by fire.
6   That place's stones are sapphire.ᵃ
        Its dust contains gold.
7   No bird of prey knows the way to it.
        No hawk's eye has ever seen it.
8   No proud beast has ever walked on it.
        No ferocious lion has ever passed over it.
9   "Humans exert their power on the flinty rocks
        and overturn mountains at their base.
10   They cut out mineshafts in the rocks.
        Their eyes see every precious thing.
11   They exploreᵇ the sources of rivers
        so that they bring hidden treasures to light.

Wisdom Is Inaccessible to Decay and Death

12   "Where can wisdom be found?
        Where does understanding live?
13   No mortal knows where it is.ᶜ
        It cannot be found in this world of the living.
14   The deep ocean says, 'It isn't in me.'
        The sea says, 'It isn't with me.'
15   You cannot obtain it with solid gold
        or buy it for any amount of silver.
16   It can't be bought with the gold from Ophir
        or with precious onyx or sapphire.
17   Neither gold nor glass can equal its value.
        Nor can gold ornaments, jewels, or crystalᵃ
18   be exchanged for it.
        Wisdom is more valuable than gems.
19   Topaz from Ethiopia cannot equal its value.
        It cannot be bought for ⌊any amount of⌋ pure gold.

20   "Where does wisdom come from?
        Where does understanding live?
21   It is hidden from the eyes of every living being,
        hidden even from the birds in the air.
22   Decay and Death say,
        'We've heard a rumor about it.'

Wisdom Is Accessible Only to the Creator

23   "God understands the way to it.
        He knows where it lives
24   because he can see to the ends of the earth
        and observe everything under heaven.
25   When he gave the wind its force
          and measured the water ⌊in the sea⌋,

ᵃ 28:6, 17 Hebrew meaning uncertain.   ᵇ 28:11 Or "dam up."   ᶜ 28:13 Or "how valuable it is."

26   when he made rules for the rain
            and set paths for the thunderstorms,
27   then he saw it and announced it.
            He confirmed it and examined it.
28   So he told humans,
            'The fear of the Lord is wisdom!
            To stay away from evil is understanding.' "

Job Continues: My Glorious Past

29

1 Job continued his poems and said,

2   "If only my life could be like it used to be,
        in the days when God watched over me,
3   when he made his lamp shine on my head,
        when I walked through the dark in his light.
4   If only I were in the prime of my life ⌞again⌟,
        when God was an adviser in my tent.
5   When the Almighty was still with me
        and my children were around me,
6   my steps were bathed in buttermilk,
            and the rocks poured streams of olive oil on me.
7   When I went through the city gate
        and took my seat in the town square,
8   young men saw me and kept out of sight.
            Old men stood up straight out of respect ⌞for me⌟.
9   Princes held back ⌞their⌟ words
                and put their hands over their mouths.
10   The voices of nobles were hushed,
                and their tongues stuck to the roofs of their mouths.

11 "⌞Any⌟ ears that heard me blessed me.
        ⌞Any⌟ eyes that saw me spoke well of me,
12   because I rescued the poor who called ⌞for help⌟
            and the orphans who had no one to help them.
13 I received a blessing from the dying.
        I made the widow's heart sing for joy.
14 I put on righteousness, and it was my clothing.
        I practiced justice, and it was my robe and my turban.
15 I was eyes for the blind person.
        I was feet for the lame person.
16 I was father to the needy.
        I carefully investigated cases brought by strangers.
17 I broke the teeth of the wicked person
        and made him drop the prey out of his mouth.

18 "I thought, 'I may die in my own house,
        but I will make my days as numerous as the sand.
19 My roots will grow toward the water,
        and dew will lie on my branches all night.
20 My power will be fresh ⌞every day⌟,
        and the bow in my hand will remain new.'

21 "People listened to me eagerly,
        quietly waiting for my advice.
22 After I had spoken, they wouldn't speak again.
        After all, my words fell gently on them.
23 They were as eager to hear me as they were for rain.
        They opened their mouths wide as if waiting for a spring shower.
24 When I smiled at them, they could hardly believe it,
        but the expression on my face did not change.ᵃ
25 I decided how they should live.
    I sat as their leader.
    I lived like a king among his troops,
        like one who comforts mourners.

ᵃ 29:24 Hebrew meaning uncertain.

Job Talks About His Present Misery

30 ¹ "But now those who are younger than I am laugh at me.
I didn't think their fathers were fit to sit with the dogs of my flock.
² Of what use to me was the strength of their hands?
Their strength is gone.
³ Shriveled up from need and hunger,
they gnaw at the dry and barren ground during the night.ᵃ
⁴ They pick saltwort from the underbrush,
and the roots of the broom plant are their food.ᵇ
⁵ They are driven from the community.
People shout at them in the same way they shout at thieves.
⁶ They have to live in dry riverbeds,
in holes in the ground, and among rocks.
⁷ They howl in bushes
and huddle together under thornbushes.
⁸ Godless fools and worthless people
are forced out of the land with whips.

⁹ "And now they make fun of me with songs.
I have become a joke to them.
¹⁰ Since they consider me disgusting, they keep their distance from me
and don't hesitate to spit in my face.
¹¹ Because God has untied my cord and has made me suffer,
they are no longer restrained in my presence.
¹² They have attacked me on my right side like a mob.
They trip my feet
and then prepare ways to destroy me.ᶜ
¹³ Yes, they remove all traces of my path in order to destroy me.
No one is there to help me against them.
¹⁴ They come through a wide hole ͺin the wallͺ.
They crawl through the ruins.
¹⁵ Terrors are directed toward me.
They blow away my dignity like the wind.
My prosperity vanishes like a cloud.

¹⁶ "Now my life is pouring out of me.
Days of suffering seize me.
¹⁷ At night God pierces my bones.
My bodyᵈ doesn't rest.
¹⁸ With great strength he grabs my clothes.
He seizes me by the collar of my robe.
¹⁹ He throws me into the dirt
so that I become like dust and ashes.

Job Calls on God for Help

²⁰ "I call to you for help,
but you don't answer me.
I stand up, but you just look at me.
²¹ You have begun to treat me cruelly.
With your mighty hand you assault me.
²² You pick me up and let the wind carry me away.
You toss me around with a storm.
²³ I know you will lead me to death,
to the dwelling place appointed for all living beings.

Job Says: I Am Being Punished by God

²⁴ "But God doesn't stretch out his hand against one who is ruined
when that person calls for help in his disaster.
²⁵ Didn't I cry for the person whose days were difficult?
Didn't my soul grieve for the poor?
²⁶ When I waited for good, evil came.
When I looked for light, darkness came.
²⁷ My insides are churning and won't calm down.
Days of misery are ahead of me.

ᵃ 30:3 Hebrew meaning of this line uncertain.   ᵇ 30:4 Or "they use the roots of the broom plant for warmth."
ᶜ 30:12 Hebrew meaning of this verse uncertain.   ᵈ 30:17 Hebrew meaning uncertain.

28 I walk in the dark without the sun.
   I stand up in public and call for help.
29 I'm a brother to jackals
   and a companion of ostriches.
30 My skin turns dark and peels.
   My body burns with fever.
31 So my lyre is used for mourning
   and my flute for loud weeping.

Job Wonders What Sin He May Have Committed

31 1 "I have made an agreement with my eyes.
         Then how can I look with lust at a virgin?
2 What would God above do ˌto meˌ?
   What would be my inheritance from the Almighty on high?
3 Aren't there catastrophes for wicked people
   and disasters for those who do wrong?
4 Doesn't he see my ways
   and count all my steps?

5 "If I have walked with lies
   or my feet have run after deception,
6 ˌthenˌ let God weigh me on honest scales,
   and he will know I have integrity.

7 "If my steps have left the ˌproperˌ path,
   or my heart has followed ˌthe desire ofˌ my eyes,
   or my hands are stained ˌwith sinˌ,
8 ˌthenˌ let someone else eat what I have planted,
   and let my crops be uprooted.

9 "If I have been seduced by a woman
   or I have secretly waited near my neighbor's door,
10 ˌthenˌ let my wife grind for another ˌmanˌ,
   and let other ˌmenˌ kneel over her.
11 That would be a scandal,
   and that would be a criminal offense.
12 It would be a fire that burns even in Abaddon.
   It would uproot my entire harvest.

13 "If I have abused the rights of my servants, male or female,
   when they have disagreed with me,
14 then what could I do if God rises up?
   If he examines me, how could I answer him?
15 Didn't he who made me in my mother's belly make them?
   Didn't the same God form us in the womb?
16 "If I have refused the requests of the poor
   or made a widow's eyes stop ˌlooking for helpˌ,
17 or have eaten my food alone
   without letting the orphan eat any of it. . . .
18 (From my youth the orphan grew up with me
   as though I were his father,
   and from my birth I treated the widow kindly.)
19 If I have seen anyone die because he had no clothes
   or a poor person going naked. . . .
20 (If his body didn't bless me,
   or the wool from my sheep didn't keep him warm. . . .)
21 If I have shaken my fist at an orphan
   because I knew that others would back me up in court,
22 ˌthenˌ let my shoulder fall out of its socket,
   and let my arm be broken at the elbow.

23 "A disaster from God terrifies me.
   In the presence of his majesty I can do nothing.

24 "If I put my confidence in gold
   or said to fine gold, 'I trust you'. . . .
25 If I enjoyed being very rich
   because my hand had found great ˌwealthˌ. . . .
26 If I saw the light shine

⁰ or the moon move along in its splendor

27 so that my heart was secretly tempted,
and I threw them a kiss with my hand,

28 then that, too, would be a criminal offense,
and I would have denied God above.

29 "If I enjoyed the ruin of my enemy
or celebrated when harm came to him

30 (even though I didn't speak sinfully
by calling down a curse on his life). . . .

31 "If the people who were in my tent had said,
'We wish we had never filled ˌour stomachsˌ with his food'.·. . .

32 (The visitor never spent the night outside,
because I opened my door to the traveler.)

33 "If I have covered my disobedience like Adam
and kept my sin to myself,

34 because I dreaded the large, noisy crowd
and because the contempt of the ˌlocalˌ mobs terrified me
so that I kept quiet and didn't go outside. . . .

35 "If only I had someone who would listen to me!
Look, here is my signature!
Let the Almighty answer me.
Let the prosecutor write ˌhis complaintˌ on a scroll.

36 I would certainly carry it on my shoulder
and place it on my head like a crown.

37 I would tell him the number of my steps
and approach him like a prince.

38 "If my land has cried out against me,
and its furrows have wept. . . .

39 If I have eaten its produce without paying for it
and made its owners breathe their last,

40 ˌthenˌ let it grow thistles instead of wheat,
and foul-smelling weeds instead of barley."

This is the end of Job's words.

Elihu Decides to Speak to Job

32 ¹ These three men stopped answering Job because Job thought he was righteous. ² Then Elihu, son of Barachel, a descendant of Buz from the family of Ram, became very angry with Job because Job thought he was more righteous than God. ³ Elihu was also very angry with Job's three friends because they had found no answer. They made it look as if Godᵃ were wrong. ⁴ Elihu waited as they spoke to Job because they were older than he was. ⁵ When Elihu saw that the three men had no further responses, he became very angry.

Elihu Speaks
The Reason for Elihu's Discourse

⁶ So Elihu, son of Barachel, the descendant of Buz, replied ˌto Jobˌ,

"I am young, and you are old.
That's why I refrained from speaking
and was afraid to tell you what I know.

7 I thought, 'Age should speak,
and experience should teach wisdom.'

8 However, there is in humans a Spirit,
the breath of the Almighty, that gives them understanding.

9 People do not become wise merely because they live long.
They don't understand what justice is merely because they're old.

10 "That is why I say, 'Listen to me!
Let me tell you what I know.'

11 I waited for you to speak.
I listened for you to share your understanding
until you could find the right words.

ᵃ 32:3 Masoretic Text "Job." At times some scribes would alter the text when they thought it was disrespectful to God.

12 I've paid close attention to you,
     but none of you refuted Job.
          None of you has an answer to what he says.
13 So don't say, 'We've found wisdom.
     Let God, not humans, defeat him.'
14 Job did not choose his words to refute me,
     so I won't answer him with your speeches.

15 "Job's friends have been overwhelmed and don't have any more answers.
     They don't have another word to say.
16 Should I wait because they don't speak,
     because they stand there and don't have any more answers?

17 "I'll give my answer.
     I'll tell you what I know.
18 I'm full of words.
     The Spirit within me forces me ˻to speak˼.
19   My belly is like ˻a bottle of˼ wine that has not been opened,
          like new wineskins that are ready to burst.
20 I must speak to get relief.
     I must open my mouth and answer.
21 I won't be partial toward anyone
     or flatter anyone.
22 I don't know how to flatter.
     If I did, my maker would soon carry me away.

Elihu Continues: Listen, Job

33 ¹ "Please, Job, listen to my words
     and consider everything I say.
2 I've opened my mouth.
     The words are on the tip of my tongue.
3 My words are straight from the heart,
     and I sincerely speak the knowledge that is on my lips.

4 "God's Spirit has made me.
     The breath of the Almighty gives me life.
5   Answer me if you can.
     Present your case to me, and take your stand.
6   Indeed, I stand in front of God as you do.
          I, too, was formed from a piece of clay.
7   You certainly don't need to be terrified of me.
          I won't put too much pressure on you.

God Doesn't Have to Answer You, Job

8 "But you spoke directly to me,
     and I listened to your words.
9 ˻You said,˼ 'I'm pure—without any rebellious acts ˻against God˼.
     I'm clean; I have no sin.
10   God is only looking for an excuse to attack me.
     He considers me his enemy.
11   He puts my feet in the stocks and watches all my paths.'
12 You aren't right about this!
     I've got an answer for you:
          God is greater than any mortal.
13 Why do you quarrel with him
     since he doesn't answer any questions?

Two Ways God Warns People

14 "God speaks in one way,
     even in two ways without people noticing it:
15   In a dream, a prophetic vision at night,
          when people fall into a deep sleep,
          when they sleep on their beds,
16   he opens people's ears
               and terrifies them with warnings.
17   ˻He warns them˼ to turn away from doing ˻wrong˼

and to stop being arrogant.^a

18 He keeps their souls from the pit
   and their lives from crossing the River ˻of Death˼.

19 In pain on their sickbeds, they are disciplined
   with endless aching in their bones

20 so that their whole being hates food
   and they lose their appetite for a delicious meal.

21 Their flesh becomes so thin that it can't be seen.
   Their bones, not seen before, will be exposed.

22 Their souls approach the pit.
   Their lives come close to those already dead.

A Third Way God Warns People

23 "If they have a messenger for them,
   a spokesman, one in a thousand,
   to tell people what is right for them,

24 then he will have pity on them and say,
   'Free them from going into the pit.
   I have found a ransom.'

25 Then their flesh will become softer than a child's.
   They will go back to the days of their youth.

26 They will pray to God, who will be pleased with them.
   They will see God's face and shout for joy
   as he restores their righteousness.^b

27 Each one sings in front of other people and says,
   'I sinned and did wrong instead of what was right,
   and it did me no good.

28 The messenger has freed my soul from going into the pit,
   and my life will see the light.'

29 Truly, God does all this two or three times with people
30 to turn their souls away from the pit
   and to enlighten them with the light of life.

Pay Attention, Job

31 "Pay attention, Job! Listen to me!
   Keep quiet, and let me speak.

32 If you have a response, answer me.
   Speak, because I'd be happy if you were right.

33 If not, you listen to me.
   Keep quiet, and I'll teach you wisdom."

Elihu Continues: Listen, Everyone

34 ¹ Elihu continued to speak ˻to Job and his friends˼,

2 "Listen to my words, you wise men.
   Open your ears to me, you intelligent men.

3 The ear tests words
   like the tongue tastes food.

4 Let's decide for ourselves what is right
   and agree among ourselves as to what is good,

5 because Job has said,
   'I'm righteous, but God has taken away my rights.

6 I'm considered a liar in spite of my rights.
   I've been wounded by a deadly arrow,
   though I haven't been disobedient.'

7 What person is like Job,
   who drinks scorn like water,

8 who travels with troublemakers
   and associates with evil people?

9 He says, 'It doesn't do any good to try to please God.'

10 "You people who have understanding, listen to me.
   It is unthinkable that God would ever do evil
   or that the Almighty would ever do wicked things.

11 God will repay humanity for what it has done

---

^a 33:17 Or "and cover a person's pride."   ^b 33:26 Or "restores them to his righteousness."

and will give each person what he deserves.
¹² Certainly, God will never do anything evil,
and the Almighty will never pervert justice.
¹³ Who put him in charge of the earth?
Who appointed him to be over the whole world?
¹⁴ If he thought only of himself
and withdrew his Spirit and his breath,
¹⁵   all living beings would die together,
and humanity would return to dust.

God Is Fair

¹⁶ "If you understand, listen to this.
Open your ears to my words!
¹⁷   Should anyone who hates justice be allowed to govern?
Will you condemn the one who is righteous and mighty?
¹⁸   Should anyone ˌevenˌ say to a king,
'You good-for-nothing scoundrel!'
or to nobles, 'You wicked people!'
¹⁹   The one who is righteous and mighty
does not grant special favors to princes
or prefer important people over poor people
because his hands made them all.
²⁰ They die suddenly in the middle of the night.
People have seizures and pass away.
Mighty people are taken away but not by human hands.
²¹ God's eyes are on a person's ways.
He sees all his steps.
²²   There's no darkness or deep shadow
where troublemakers can hide.
²³ He doesn't have to set a time for a person
in order to bring him to divine judgment.
²⁴ He breaks mighty people into pieces without examining them
and puts others in their places.
²⁵ He knows what they do,
so he overthrows them at night, and they're crushed.
²⁶ In return for their evil, he strikes them in public,
²⁷   because they turned away from following him
and didn't consider any of his ways.
²⁸   They forced the poor to cry out to him,
and he hears the cry of those who suffer.
²⁹ If he keeps quiet, who can condemn him?
If he hides his face, who can see him
whether it is a nation or a single person?
³⁰ ˌHe does thisˌ so that godless people cannot rule
and so that they cannot trap people.

³¹ "But suppose such a person says to God, 'I am guilty,
I will stop my immoral behavior.
³²   Teach me what I cannot see.
If I've done wrong, I won't do it again.'
³³ Should God reward you on your own terms since you have rejected his?
You must choose, not I.
Tell me what you know. Speak!

Elihu Makes an Appeal to God

³⁴ "People of understanding, the wise people
who listen to me, will say,
³⁵   'Job speaks without knowledge.
His words show no insight.'

³⁶ "My Father, let Job be thoroughly tested
for giving answers like wicked people do.
³⁷   He adds disobedience to his sin.
He claps his hands to insult us.
He multiplies his words against God."

Elihu Continues: I Will Answer You and Your Friends, Job

35 ¹ Elihu continued to speak ˌto Job and his friendsˌ,

² "Do you think this is right
    when you say, 'My case is more just than God's,'
³   when you ask, 'What benefit is it to you?'
        and, 'What would I gain by sinning?'
⁴ I will answer you and your friends.

Human Behavior Cannot Change God

⁵ "Look at the heavens and see.
    Observe the clouds high above you.
⁶   If you've sinned, what effect can you have on God?
        If you've done many wrongs, what can you do to him?
⁷   If you're righteous, what can you give him,
        or what can he get from you?
⁸ Your wickedness affects only someone like yourself.
    Your righteousness affects only the descendants of Adam.
⁹   The weight of oppression makes them cry out.
        The power of mighty people makes them call for help.
¹⁰   But no one asks,
            'Where is God, my Creator,
                who inspires songs in the night,
¹¹   who teaches us more than he teaches the animals of the earth,
                who makes us wiser than the birds in the sky?'
¹²   Then they cry out, but he doesn't answer them
        because of the arrogance of ˌthoseˌ evil people.

¹³ "Surely, God doesn't listen to idle complaints.
    The Almighty doesn't even pay attention to them.
¹⁴   Although you say that you pay attention to him,
        your case is in front of him, but you'll have to wait for him.
¹⁵   And now ˌyou sayˌ that his anger doesn't punish ˌanyoneˌ
        and he isn't too concerned about evil.ᵃ
¹⁶ Job opens his mouth for no good reason
    and talks a lot without having any knowledge."

Elihu Continues: Hear Me Out

36 ¹ Elihu continued to speak ˌto Jobˌ,

² "Be patient with me a little longer, and I will show you
    that there is more to be said in God's defense.
³ I will get my knowledge from far away
    and prove that my Creator is fair.
⁴ Certainly, my words are not lies.
    The one who knows everything is ˌspeakingˌ with you.

God's Justice Is Beyond Human Understanding

⁵ "Certainly, God is mighty.
    He doesn't despise anyone.
    He is mighty and brave.
⁶   He doesn't allow the wicked person to live.
        He grants justice to those who are oppressed.
⁷   He doesn't take his eyes off righteous people.
        He seats them on thrones with kings to honor them forever.
⁸ However, if righteous people are bound in chains
        and tangled in ropes of misery,
⁹   he tells them what they've done wrong
            and that they've behaved arrogantly.
¹⁰   He makes them listen to his warning
            and orders them to turn away from wrong.

¹¹ "If righteous people listen and serve ˌhimˌ,
        they will live out their days in prosperity
            and their years in comfort.

ᵃ 35:15 Hebrew meaning of this verse uncertain.

12 But if they don't listen,
    they will cross the River ˌof Deathˌ
      and die like those who have no knowledge.
13 But those who have godless hearts remain angry.
    They don't even call for help when he chains them up.
14 They die while they're young,
    or they live on as male prostitutes in the temples of idols.
15 He rescues suffering people through their suffering,
    and he opens their ears through distress.

16 "Yes, he lured you away from the jaws of trouble
    into an open area where you were not restrained,
      and your table was covered with rich foods.
17 But you are given the judgment evil people deserve.
    A fair judgment will be upheld.
18 Be careful that you are not led astray with riches.
    Don't let a large bribe turn you ˌto evil waysˌ.
19 Will your riches save you from having to suffer?
    Will all your mighty strength help you?
20 Don't look forward to the night,
    when people disappear from their places.
21 Be careful! Don't turn to evil,
    because you have chosen evil instead of suffering.[a]

22 "God does great things by his power.
    Is there any teacher like him?
23 Who can tell him which way he should go?
    Who can say to him, 'You did wrong'?
24 Remember that you should praise his work.
    People have sung about it.
25 Every person has seen it.
    Mortals have looked at it from a distance.

26 "Certainly, God is so great
    that he is beyond our understanding.
      The number of his years cannot be counted.
27 He collects drops of water.
    He distills rain from his mist,
28   which then drips from the clouds.
    It pours down on many people.
29   Can anyone really understand how clouds spread out
      or how he thunders from his dwelling place?
30   Look, he scatters his flashes of lightning around him
      and covers the depths of the sea.
31 This is how he uses the rains to provide for people
    and to give them more than enough food.
32 He fills his hands with lightning
    and orders it to hit the target.
33 The thunder announces his coming.
    The storm announces his angry wrath.

Elihu Continues: God's Ways Are Beyond Human Understanding

37 1 "My heart pounds because of this
    and jumps out of its place.
2 Listen! Listen to the roar of God's voice,
    to the rumbling that comes from his mouth.
3   He flashes his lightning everywhere under heaven.
    His light flashes to the ends of the earth.
4   It is followed by the roar of his voice.
    He thunders with his majestic voice.
    He doesn't hold the lightning back when his thunder is heard.
5   God's voice thunders in miraculous ways.
    It does great things that we cannot understand.

---

[a] 36:21 Hebrew meaning of verses 17–21 uncertain. The first two words of verse 18 (in Hebrew) were added to the end of verse 17 to express the complex Hebrew sentence structure more clearly in English.

6 "He says to the snow, 'Fall to the ground,'
　　and to the pouring rain, 'Rain harder!'
7 He makes it impossible to do anything[a]
　　so that people will recognize his work.
8 　Animals go into their dens
　　　and stay in their lairs.
9 　A storm comes out of its chamber.
　　　It is cold because of the strong winds.[b]
10 　God's breath produces ice,
　　　and the seas freeze over.
11 　Yes, he loads the thick clouds with moisture
　　　and scatters his lightning from the clouds.
12 　He guides the clouds as they churn round and round
　　　　over the face of the inhabited earth
　　　　　to do everything he orders them.
13 Whether for discipline,
　　or for the good of his earth,
　　　or out of mercy,
　　　　he makes the storm appear.

14 "Open your ears to this, Job.
　Stop and consider God's miracles.
15 Do you know how God controls them
　　and makes the lightning flash from his clouds?
16 Do you know how the clouds drift
　　(these are the miracles of the one who knows everything),
17 you whose clothes are hot and sweaty,
　　when the earth is calm under a south wind?
18 Can you stretch out the skies with him
　　and make them as firm as a mirror made of metal?
19 Teach us what we should say to him.
　　We are unable to prepare a case because of darkness.
20 Should he be told that I want to speak?
　　Can a person speak when he is confused?
21 People can't look at the sun
　　when it's bright among the clouds
　　　or after the wind has blown and cleared those clouds away.
22 A golden light comes from the north.
　　A terrifying majesty is around God.
23 The Almighty, whom we can't reach,
　　is great in power and judgment,
　　　has more than enough righteousness,
　　　　and does not oppress.
24 That is why people should fear him.
　　He does not respect those who think they're wise."

The LORD Speaks
Who Is Able to Challenge Me?

38 1 Then the LORD answered Job out of the storm.

2 "Who is this that belittles my advice
　　with words that do not show any knowledge about it?
3 Brace yourself like a man!
　　I will ask you, and you will teach me.

The LORD Speaks About Creation
4 "Where were you when I laid the foundation of the earth?
　　Tell me if you have such insight.
5 Who determined its dimensions?
　　Certainly, you know!
　Who stretched a measuring line over it?
6 On what were its footings sunk?
　Who laid its cornerstone
7 　when the morning stars sang together
　　　and all the sons of God shouted for joy?

---

[a] 37:7 Or "He seals up every person's hand."　　[b] 37:9 Hebrew meaning uncertain.

8 "Who shut the sea behind gates
  when it burst through and came out of the womb,
9   when I clothed it with clouds
    and wrapped it up in dark clouds,
10   when I set a limit for it
    and put up bars and gates,
11   when I said, 'You may come this far but no farther.
    Here your proud waves will stop'?

12 "Have you ever given orders to the morning
  or assigned a place for the dawn
13   so that it could grab the earth by its edges
    and shake wicked people out of it?
14 The earth changes like clay stamped by a seal,
  and ˌparts of itˌ stand out like ˌfolds inˌ clothing.
15 Wicked people are deprived of their light,
  and an arm raised ˌin victoryˌ is broken.
16 Have you gone to the springs in the sea
  or walked through the valleys of the ocean depths?
17 Have the gateways to death been revealed to you,
  or have you seen the gateways to total darkness?
18 Have you ˌevenˌ considered how wide the earth is?
  Tell me, if you know all of this!

19 "What is the way to the place where light lives?
  Where is the home of darkness
20   so that you may lead it to its territory,
    so that you may know the path to its home?
21 You must know because you were born then
  and have lived such a long time!
22 Have you been to the warehouses where snow is stored
  or seen the warehouses for hail
23   that I have stored up for the time of trouble,
    for the day of battle and war?
24 Which is the way to the place where light is scattered
  and the east wind is spread across the earth?

25 "Who made a channel for the flooding rains
  and a path for the thunderstorms
26   to bring rain on a land where no one lives,
    on a desert where there are no humans,
27   to saturate the desolate wasteland
    in order to make it sprout with grass?
28 Does the rain have a father?
  Who gave birth to the dewdrops?
29 From whose womb came the ice,
  and who has given birth to the frost in the air?
30   The water hardens like a stone,
    and the surface of the ocean freezes over.

31 "Can you connect the chains of the ˌconstellationˌ Pleiades
  or untie the ropes of Orion?
32 Can you bring out the constellations at the right time
  or guide Ursa Major with its cubs?
33 Do you know the laws of the sky
  or make them rule the earth?
34 Can you call to the clouds
  and have a flood of water cover you?
35 Can you send lightning flashes so that they may go and say to you,
  'Here we are'?
36 Who put wisdom in the heart
  or gave understanding to the mind?[a]
37 Who is wise enough to count the clouds
  or pour out the water jars of heaven
38   when the dirt hardens into clumps
    and the soil clings together?

---

[a] 38:36 Hebrew meaning uncertain.

The Lioness

39 "Can you hunt prey for the lioness
and satisfy the hunger of her cubs
40   as they crouch in their dens
and lie ready to ambush from their lairs?

The Crow

41 "Who provides food for the crow
when its young ones cry to God
and wander around in need of food?

The Lord Continues: The Mountain Goats

39 1 "Do you know the time when the mountain goats give birth?
Do you watch the does when they are in labor?
2   Can you count the months they are pregnant
or know the time when they'll give birth?
3   They kneel down to give birth and deliver their young.
Then the pain of giving birth is over.
4   Their young are healthy and grow up in the wild.
They leave and don't come back.

The Wild Donkey

5 "Who lets the wild donkey go free?
Who unties the ropes of the wild donkey?
6   I gave it the desert to live in
and the salt flats as its dwelling place.
7   It laughs at the noise of the city
and doesn't ˌevenˌ listen to the shouting of its master.
8   It explores the mountains for its pasture
and looks for anything green.

The Wild Ox

9 "Will the wild ox agree to serve you,
or will it stay at night beside your feeding trough?
10   Can you guide a wild ox in a furrow,
or will it plow the valleys behind you?
11   Can you trust it just because it's so strong
or leave your labor to it?
12   Can you rely on it to bring your grain back
and take it to your threshing floor?ᵃ

The Ostrich

13 "Does the ostrich flap its wings in joy,
or do its wings lack feathers?ᵇ
14   It lays its eggs on the ground
and warms them in the dust.
15   It forgets that a foot may crush them
or a wild animal may trample them.
16   It acts harshly toward its young as if they weren't its own.
It is not afraid that its work is for nothing
17   because God has deprived it of wisdom
and did not give it any understanding.
18   It laughs at the horse and its rider when it gets up to flee.

The Horse

19 "Can you give strength to a horse
or dress its neck with a flowing mane?
20   Can you make it leap like a locust,
when its snorting causes terror?
21   It paws in strength and finds joy in its power.
It charges into battle.
22   It laughs at fear,
is afraid of nothing,

ᵃ 39:12 A threshing floor is an outdoor area where grain is separated from its husks.   ᵇ 39:13 Or "Do its wings compare well with the wings and feathers of the stork?"

and doesn't back away from swords.
23 A quiver of arrows rattles on it
along with the flashing spear and javelin.
24 Anxious and excited, the horse eats up the ground
and doesn't trust the sound of the ram's horn.
25 As often as the horn sounds, the horse says, 'Aha!'
and it smells the battle far away—
the thundering ‸orders‸ of the captains and the battle cries.

The Birds of Prey
26 "Does your understanding make a bird of prey fly
and spread its wings toward the south?
27 Is it by your order that the eagle flies high
and makes its nest on the heights?
28 It perches for the night on a cliff.
Its fortress is on a jagged peak.
29 From there it seeks food,
and its eyes see it from far away.
30 Its young ones feed on blood.
It is found wherever there are dead bodies."

The LORD Speaks

40

1 The LORD responded to Job,

2 "Will the person who finds fault with the Almighty correct him?
Will the person who argues with God answer him?"

Job Speaks
3 Job answered the LORD,

4 "I'm so insignificant. How can I answer you?
I will put my hand over my mouth.
5 I spoke once, but I can't answer—
twice, but not again."

The LORD Speaks
Can You Be Like Me, Job?
6 Then the LORD responded to Job out of a storm,

7 "Brace yourself like a man!
I will ask you, and you will teach me.

8 "Would you undo my justice?
Would you condemn me so that you can be righteous?
9 Do you have power like God's?
Can you thunder with a voice like his?
10 Then dress yourself in majesty and dignity.
Clothe yourself in splendor and glory.
11 Unleash your outbursts of anger.
Look at all who are arrogant, and put them down.
12 Look at all who are arrogant, and humble them.
Crush wicked people wherever they are.
13 Hide them completely in the dust,
and cover their faces in the hidden place.
14 Then even I will praise you
because your right hand can save you.

Can You Conquer Behemoth, Job?
15 "Look at Behemoth,[a] which I made along with you.
It eats grass as cattle do.
16 Look at the strength in its back muscles,
the power in its stomach muscles.
17 It makes its tail stiff like a cedar.
The ligaments of its thighs are intertwined.
18 Its bones are bronze tubes.
They are like iron bars.

---

[a] 40:15 The Hebrew word *Behemoth* means "beast, animal."

19 Behemoth is the first of God's conquests.
    Its maker approaches it with his sword.
20   The hills bring it food,
            and all the wild animals play there.
21 It lies down under the lotus plants
        in a hiding place among reeds and swamps.
22   Lotus plants provide it with cover.
                Poplars by the stream surround it.
23 Though the river flows powerfully against it, it's not alarmed.
        It's confident ˌeven˩ when the Jordan rushes against its mouth.
24   Can anyone blind its eyes[b]
                or pierce its nose with snares?

The Lord Continues: Can You Conquer Leviathan, Job?

41[a] ¹ "Can you pull Leviathan[b] out ˌof the water˩ with a fishhook
        or tie its tongue down with a rope?
2   Can you put a ring through its nose
        or pierce its jaw with a hook?
3   Will it plead with you for mercy
        or speak tenderly to you?
4   Will it make an agreement with you
        so that you can take it as your permanent slave?
5   Can you play with it like a bird
        or keep it on a leash for your girls?
6   Will traders bargain over it
        and divide it among the merchants?
7   Can you fill its hide with harpoons
        or its head with fishing spears?
8   Lay your hand on it.
        Think of the struggle!
            Don't do it again!
9   Certainly, any hope ˌof defeating it˩ is a false hope.
                Doesn't the sight of it overwhelm you?
10 No one is brave enough to provoke Leviathan.
        Then who can stand in front of me?[c]
11 Who can confront me that I should repay him?
        Everything under heaven belongs to me!

12 "I will not be silent about Leviathan's limbs,
        its strength, or its graceful form.
13 Who can skin its hide?
        Who can approach it with a harness?
14 Who can open its closed mouth?
        Its teeth are surrounded by terror.
15 Its back has rows of scales that are tightly sealed.
16   One is so close to the other
            that there is no space between them.
17   Each is joined to the other.
            They are locked together and inseparable.
18 When Leviathan sneezes, it gives out a flash of light.
        Its eyes are like the first rays of the dawn.
19   Flames shoot from its mouth.
            Sparks of fire fly from it.
20   Smoke comes from its nostrils
            like a boiling pot heated over brushwood.
21 Its breath sets coals on fire,
        and a flame pours from its mouth.
22 Strength resides in its neck,
        and power dances in front of it.
23 The folds of its flesh stick to each other.
        They are solid and cannot be moved.
24 Its chest is solid like a rock,
        solid like a millstone.

---

[b] 40:24 Or "catch it with a trap."   [a] 41:1 Job 41:1–34 in English Bibles is Job 40:25–41:26 in the Hebrew Bible.
[b] 41:1 Hebrew meaning uncertain.   [c] 41:10 Some Hebrew manuscripts; many Hebrew manuscripts "it."

²⁵ "The mighty are afraid when Leviathan rises.
    Broken down, they draw back.
²⁶ A sword may strike it but not pierce it.
    Neither will a spear, lance, or dart.
²⁷   It considers iron to be like straw
     and bronze to be like rotten wood.
²⁸ An arrow won't make it run away.
    Stones from a sling turn to dust against it.
²⁹   It considers clubs to be like stubble,
     and it laughs at a rattling javelin.
³⁰ Its underside is like sharp pieces of broken pottery.
    It stretches out like a threshing*^d* sledge on the mud.
³¹   It makes the deep sea boil like a pot.
     It stirs up the ocean like a boiling kettle.
³²   It leaves a shining path behind it
     so that the sea appears to have silvery hair.
³³ Nothing on land can compare to it.
    It was made fearless.
³⁴ It looks down on all high things.
    It is king of everyone who is arrogant."

Job Speaks
I Admit That I Was Wrong

42 ¹ Then Job answered the LORD,

² "I know that you can do everything
    and that your plans are unstoppable.

³ " You said, 'Who is this that belittles my advice
    without having any knowledge about it ?'
     Yes, I have stated things I didn't understand,
      things too mysterious for me to know.

⁴ " You said, 'Listen now, and I will speak.
    I will ask you, and you will teach me.'
⁵   I had heard about you with my own ears,
     but now I have seen you with my own eyes.
⁶   That is why I take back what I said,
    and I sit in dust and ashes to show that I am sorry."

Job's Life Is Restored

⁷ After the LORD had said those things to Job, the LORD said to Eliphaz from Teman, "I'm very angry with you and your two friends because you didn't speak what is right about me as my servant Job has done. ⁸ So take seven young bulls and seven rams. Go to my servant Job, and make a burnt offering for yourselves. My servant Job will pray for you. Then I will accept his prayer not to treat you as godless fools. After all, you didn't speak what is right about me as my servant Job has done."

⁹ Then Eliphaz of Teman, Bildad of Shuah, and Zophar of Naama went and did what the LORD had told them to do. And the LORD accepted Job's prayer.

¹⁰ After Job prayed for his friends, the LORD restored Job's prosperity and gave him twice as much as he had before . ¹¹ Then all his brothers and sisters and everyone who had previously known him came to him. They ate with him at his house, sympathized with him, and comforted him for all the evil the LORD had brought to him. Each one gave him some money*^a* and a gold ring.

¹² The LORD blessed the latter years of Job's life more than the earlier years. He had 14,000 sheep and goats, 6,000 camels, 2,000 oxen, and 1,000 donkeys. ¹³ He also had seven sons and three daughters. ¹⁴ He named the first daughter Jemimah, the second Cassia, and the third Keren Happuch. ¹⁵ Nowhere in the whole country could be found women who were as beautiful as Job's daughters. Their father gave them and their brothers an inheritance.

¹⁶ Job lived 140 years after this. He saw his children, grandchildren, and great-grandchildren.*^b* ¹⁷ Then at a very old age, Job died.

---

^d 41:30 Threshing is the process of beating stalks to separate them from the grain.   *^a* 42:11 Hebrew meaning uncertain.
^b 42:16 Or "grandchildren, four generations."

PSALMS

BOOK ONE
Psalms 1–41

PSALM 1

1 Blessed is the person who does not
　　follow the advice of wicked people,
　　　　take the path of sinners,
　　　　　　or join the company of mockers.
2 Rather, he delights in the teachings of the LORD
　　and reflects on his teachings day and night.
3 He is like a tree planted beside streams—
　　a tree that produces fruit in season
　　　　and whose leaves do not wither.
He succeeds in everything he does.[a]

4 Wicked people are not like that.
Instead, they are like husks that the wind blows away.
5 　　That is why wicked people will not be able to stand in the judgment
　　　　and sinners will not be able to stand where righteous people gather.

6 The LORD knows the way of righteous people,
　　but the way of wicked people will end.

PSALM 2

1 Why do the nations gather together?
Why do their people devise useless plots?
2 　　Kings take their stands.
　　Rulers make plans together
　　　　against the LORD and against his Messiah[a] by saying,
3 　　　　"Let's break apart their chains
　　　　　　and shake off their ropes."

4 The one enthroned in heaven laughs.
The LORD makes fun of them.
5 　　Then he speaks to them in his anger.
　　In his burning anger he terrifies them by saying,
6 　　　　"I have installed my own king on Zion, my holy mountain."

7 I will announce the LORD's decree.
He said to me:
　　"You are my Son.
　　　　Today I have become your Father.
8 　　　　Ask me, and I will give you the nations as your inheritance
　　　　　　and the ends of the earth as your own possession.
9 　　　　　　You will break them with an iron scepter.
　　　　　　You will smash them to pieces like pottery."

10 Now, you kings, act wisely.
Be warned, you rulers of the earth!
11 　　Serve the LORD with fear, and rejoice with trembling.
12 　　Kiss the Son, or he will become angry
　　　　and you will die on your way
　　　　　　because his anger will burst into flames.
Blessed is everyone who takes refuge in him.

---

[a] 1:3 Or "and its leaves do not wither, and whatever it produces thrives."　　[a] 2:2 Or "anointed one."

PSALM 3

A psalm by David when he fled from his son Absalom.

1 O Lord, look how my enemies have increased!
   Many are attacking me.
2 Many are saying about me,
   "Even with God ˏon his sideˏ,
      he won't be victorious." *Selah*

3 But you, O Lord, are a shield that surrounds me.
   You are my glory.
   You hold my head high.

4 I call aloud to the Lord,
   and he answers me from his holy mountain. *Selah*
5 I lie down and sleep.
   I wake up again because the Lord continues to support me.
6 I am not afraid of the tens of thousands
   who have taken positions against me on all sides.

7 Arise, O Lord!
Save me, O my God!
   You have slapped all my enemies in the face.
   You have smashed the teeth of wicked people.
8   Victory belongs to the Lord!
   May your blessing rest on your people. *Selah*

PSALM 4

For the choir director; with stringed instruments; a psalm by David.

1 Answer me when I call, O God of my righteousness.
   You have freed me from my troubles.
Have pity on me, and hear my prayer!

2 You important people,
   how long are you going to insult my honor?
   How long are you going to love what is empty
      and seek what is a lie? *Selah*
3 Know that the Lord singles out godly people for himself.
   The Lord hears me when I call to him.
4 Tremble and do not sin.
   Think about this on your bed and remain quiet. *Selah*
5 Offer the sacrifices of righteousness
   by trusting the Lord.

6 Many are saying, "Who can show us anything good?"
   Let the light of your presence shine on us, O Lord.
7   You put more joy in my heart
   than when their grain and new wine increase.
8 I fall asleep in peace the moment I lie down
   because you alone, O Lord, enable me to live securely.

PSALM 5

For the choir director; for flutes; a psalm by David.

1 Open your ears to my words, O Lord.
   Consider my innermost thoughts.
2 Pay attention to my cry for help, my king and my God,
   because I pray only to you.
3   In the morning, O Lord, hear my voice.
   In the morning I lay my needs in front of you,
      and I wait.

4 You are not a God who takes pleasure in wickedness.
   Evil will never be your guest.
5   Those who brag cannot stand in your sight.
You hate all troublemakers.

6 You destroy those who tell lies.
   The LORD is disgusted with bloodthirsty and deceitful people.

7 But I will enter your house because of your great mercy.
   Out of reverence for you, I will bow toward your holy temple.
8 O LORD, lead me in your righteousness because of those who spy on me.
   Make your way in front of me smooth.

9 Nothing in their mouths is truthful.
   Destruction comes from their hearts.
      Their throats are open graves.
         They flatter with their tongues.

10 Condemn them, O God.
   Let their own schemes be their downfall.
   Throw them out for their many crimes
      because they have rebelled against you.
11 But let all who take refuge in you rejoice.
   Let them sing with joy forever.
   Protect them, and let those who love your name triumph in you.
12 You bless righteous people, O LORD.
      Like a large shield, you surround them with your favor.

PSALM 6

For the choir director; with stringed instruments, on the *sheminith;*[a] a psalm by David.

1 O LORD, do not punish me in your anger
   or discipline me in your rage.
2 Have pity on me, O LORD, because I am weak.
   Heal me, O LORD, because my bones shake with terror.
3 My soul has been deeply shaken with terror.
   But you, O LORD, how long. . . ?

4 Come back, O LORD.
   Rescue me.
   Save me because of your mercy!
5 In death, no one remembers you.
   In the grave, who praises you?

6 I am worn out from my groaning.
   My eyes flood my bed every night.
   I soak my couch with tears.
7 My eyes blur from grief.
   They fail because of my enemies.

8 Get away from me, all you troublemakers,
   because the LORD has heard the sound of my crying.
9 The LORD has heard my plea for mercy.
   The LORD accepts my prayer.
10 All my enemies will be put to shame and deeply shaken with terror.
   In a moment they will retreat and be put to shame.

PSALM 7

A *shiggaion*[a] by David; he sang it to the LORD about the ˛slanderous˛ words of Cush, a descendant of Benjamin.

1 O LORD my God, I have taken refuge in you.
   Save me, and rescue me from all who are pursuing me.
2 Like a lion they will tear me to pieces
      and drag me off with no one to rescue me.

3 O LORD my God,
   if I have done this—
      if my hands are stained with injustice,

---

a 6:1, 7:1 Unknown musical term.

4   if I have paid back my friend with evil
         or rescued someone who has no reason to attack me—[b]

5   then let the enemy chase me and catch me.
         Let him trample my life into the ground.
         Let him lay my honor in the dust.   *Selah*

6   Arise in anger, O LORD.
     Stand up against the fury of my attackers.
     Wake up, my God.[c]
         You have already pronounced judgment.
7   Let an assembly of people gather around you.
             Take your seat high above them.
8   The LORD judges the people of the world.
     Judge me, O LORD,
         according to my righteousness,
         according to my integrity.

9   Let the evil within wicked people come to an end,
         but make the righteous person secure,
             O righteous God who examines thoughts and emotions.
10   My shield is God above,
         who saves those whose motives are decent.

11   God is a fair judge,
         a God who is angered by injustice every day.
12   If a person does not change, God sharpens his sword.
             By bending his bow, he makes it ready ₎to shoot₎.
13   He prepares his deadly weapons
                 and turns them into flaming arrows.
14   See how that person conceives evil,
         is pregnant with harm,
             and gives birth to lies.
15   He digs a pit and shovels it out.
     Then he falls into the hole that he made ₎for others₎.
16   His mischief lands back on his own head.
     His violence comes down on top of him.

17   I will give thanks to the LORD for his righteousness.
     I will make music to praise the name of the LORD Most High.

PSALM 8

For the choir director; on the *gittith;*[a] a psalm by David.

1   O LORD, our Lord, how majestic is your name throughout the earth!

     Your glory is sung above the heavens.[b]
2   From the mouths of little children and infants,
         you have built a fortress against your opponents
             to silence the enemy and the avenger.

3   When I look at your heavens,
         the creation of your fingers,
             the moon and the stars that you have set in place—
4   what is a mortal that you remember him
                 or the Son of Man that you take care of him?
5   You have made him a little lower than yourself.
         You have crowned him with glory and honor.
6   You have made him rule what your hands created.
         You have put everything under his control:
7   all the sheep and cattle, the wild animals,
8   the birds, the fish,
                 whatever swims in the currents of the seas.

9   O LORD, our Lord, how majestic is your name throughout the earth!

---

[b] 7:4; 8:1 Hebrew meaning of this line uncertain.   [c] 7:6 Greek; Masoretic Text "Wake up to me."
[a] 8:1 Unknown musical term.

PSALM 9

For the choir director; according to *muth labben;*[a] a psalm by David.[b]

1 I will give ˎyouˎ thanks, O LORD, with all my heart.
  I will tell about all the miracles you have done.
2 I will find joy and be glad about you.
  I will make music to praise your name, O Most High.

3 When my enemies retreat, they will stumble and die in your presence.
4   You have defended my just cause:
          You sat down on your throne as a fair judge.
5   You condemned nations.
          You destroyed wicked people.
          You wiped out their names forever and ever.
6 The enemy is finished—in ruins forever.
      You have uprooted their cities.
          Even the memory of them has faded.

7 Yet, the LORD is enthroned forever.
      He has set up his throne for judgment.
8   He alone judges the world with righteousness.
      He judges ˎitsˎ people fairly.
9 The LORD is a stronghold for the oppressed,
      a stronghold in times of trouble.
10 Those who know your name trust you, O LORD,
      because you have never deserted those who seek your help.

11 Make music to praise the LORD, who is enthroned in Zion.
   Announce to the nations what he has done.
12   The one who avenges murder has remembered oppressed people.
      He has never forgotten their cries.
13 Have pity on me, O LORD.
   Look at what I suffer because of those who hate me.
   You take me away from the gates of death
14   so that I may recite your praises one by one
          in the gates of Zion
              and find joy in your salvation.

15 The nations have sunk into the pit they have made.
      Their feet are caught in the net they have hidden ˎto trap othersˎ.
16 The LORD is known by the judgment he has carried out.
      The wicked person is trapped
          by the work of his own hands.   *Higgaion Selah*
17 Wicked people, all the nations who forget God,
      will return to the grave.
18 Needy people will not always be forgotten.
      Nor will the hope of oppressed people be lost forever.
19 Arise, O LORD.
      Do not let mortals gain any power.
      Let the nations be judged in your presence.
20   Strike them with terror, O LORD.
      Let the nations know that they are ˎonlyˎ mortal.   *Selah*

PSALM 10

1 Why are you so distant, LORD?
  Why do you hide yourself in times of trouble?

2 The wicked person arrogantly pursues oppressed people.
      He will be caught in the schemes that he planned.
3 The wicked person boasts about his selfish desires.
      He blesses robbers, but he curses the LORD.
4 He turns up his nose ˎand saysˎ, "God doesn't care."
      His every thought ˎconcludesˎ, "There is no God."
5   He always seems to succeed.

---

[a] 9:1 Or "*almuth labben*"; unknown musical term.   [b] 9:1 Some Hebrew manuscripts, Greek, and Latin treat Psalms 9 and 10 as one psalm.

Your judgments are beyond his understanding.
He spits at all his opponents.
6 He says to himself, "Nothing can shake me.
I'll never face any trouble."
7 His mouth is full of cursing, deception, and oppression.
Trouble and wrongdoing are on the tip of his tongue.
8 He waits in ambush in the villages.
From his hiding places he kills innocent people.
His eyes are on the lookout for victims.
9 He lies in his hiding place like a lion in his den.
He hides there to catch oppressed people.
He catches oppressed people when he draws them into his net.
10 ⌞His⌟ victims are crushed.
They collapse,
and they fall under ⌞the weight of⌟ his power.
11 He says to himself,
"God has forgotten.
He has hidden his face.
He will never see it!"

12 Arise, O Lord!
Lift your hand, O God.
Do not forget oppressed people!
13 Why does the wicked person despise God?
Why does he say to himself, "God doesn't care"?
14 You have seen ⌞it⌟; yes, you have taken note of trouble and grief
and placed them under your control.
The victim entrusts himself to you.
You alone have been the helper of orphans.
15 Break the arm of the wicked and evil person.
Punish his wickedness until you find no more.

16 The Lord is king forever and ever.
The nations have vanished from his land.
17 You have heard the desire of oppressed people, O Lord.
You encourage them.
You pay close attention to them
18 in order to provide justice for orphans and oppressed people
so that no mere mortal will terrify them again.

PSALM 11

For the choir director; by David.

1 I have taken refuge in the Lord.
How can you say to me:
"Flee to your mountain like a bird?
2 Wicked people bend their bows.
They set their arrows against the strings
to shoot in the dark at people whose motives are decent.
3 When the foundations ⌞of life⌟ are undermined,
what can a righteous person do?"

4 The Lord is in his holy temple.
The Lord's throne is in heaven.
His eyes see.
They examine Adam's descendants.
5 The Lord tests righteous people,
but he hates wicked people and the ones who love violence.
6 He rains down fire and burning sulfur upon wicked people.
He makes them drink from a cup filled with scorching wind.
7 The Lord is righteous.
He loves a righteous way of life.
Decent people will see his face.

PSALM 12

For the choir director; on the *sheminith;* a psalm by David.

1 Help, O Lord.
   No godly person is left.
   Faithful people have vanished from among Adam's descendants!
2 All people speak foolishly.
They speak with flattering lips. They say one thing but mean another.
3 May the Lord cut off every flattering lip
   and every bragging tongue
4   that has said,
      "We will overcome with our tongues.
      With lips such as ours, who can be our master?"

5 "Because oppressed people are robbed and needy people groan,
   I will now arise," says the Lord.
"I will provide safety for those who long for it."
6 The promises of the Lord are pure,
   like silver refined in a furnace[a] and purified seven times.
7 O Lord, you will protect them.
You will keep each one safe from those people forever.
8   Wicked people parade around
     when immorality increases among Adam's descendants.

PSALM 13

For the choir director; a psalm by David.

1 How long, O Lord? Will you forget me forever?
How long will you hide your face from me?
2 How long must I make decisions alone
   with sorrow in my heart day after day?
How long will my enemy triumph over me?

3 Look at me! Answer me, O Lord my God!
Light up my eyes,
   or else I will die
4   and my enemy will say, "I have overpowered him."
      My opponents will rejoice because I have been shaken.

5 But I trust your mercy.
My heart finds joy in your salvation.
6 I will sing to the Lord because he has been good to me.

PSALM 14[a]

For the choir director; by David.

1 Godless fools say in their hearts,
   "There is no God."
They are corrupt.
They do disgusting things.
   There is no one who does good things.
2 The Lord looks down from heaven on Adam's descendants
   to see if there is anyone who acts wisely,
     if there is anyone who seeks help from God.
3   Everyone has turned away.
     Together they have become rotten to the core.
      No one, not even one person, does good things.
4 Are all those troublemakers,
   those who devour my people as if they were devouring food,
     so ignorant that they do not call on the Lord?
5 There they are—panic-stricken
   because God is with the person who is righteous.
6 They put the advice of oppressed people to shame
   because the Lord is their refuge.

. [a] 12:6 Hebrew meaning uncertain.   [a] 14:1 Psalm 14 is virtually identical in wording to Psalm 53.

7 If only salvation for Israel would come from Zion!
   When the LORD restores the fortunes of his people,
      Jacob will rejoice.
      Israel will be glad.

PSALM 15

A psalm by David.

1 O LORD, who may stay in your tent?
   Who may live on your holy mountain?

2   The one who walks with integrity,
          does what is righteous,
          and speaks the truth within his heart.

3   The one who does not slander with his tongue,
          do evil to a friend,
          or bring disgrace on his neighbor.

4   The one who despises those rejected by God
          but honors those who fear the LORD.

       The one who makes a promise and does not break it,
          even though he is hurt by it.

5   The one who does not collect interest on a loan
          or take a bribe against an innocent person.

   Whoever does these things will never be shaken.

PSALM 16

A *miktam*[a] by David.

1 Protect me, O God, because I take refuge in you.
2 I said to the LORD,
      "You are my Lord. Without you, I have nothing good."
3 Those who lead holy lives on earth
      are the noble ones who fill me with joy.[b]
4 Those who quickly chase after other gods multiply their sorrows.
      I will not pour out their sacrificial offerings of blood
          or use my lips to speak their names.

5 The LORD is my inheritance and my cup.
      You are the one who determines my destiny.
6 Your boundary lines mark out pleasant places for me.
   Indeed, my inheritance is something beautiful.

7 I will praise the LORD, who advises me.
      My conscience warns me at night.
8 I always keep the LORD in front of me.
      When he is by my side, I cannot be moved.
9   That is why my heart is glad and my soul rejoices.
          My body rests securely
10   because you do not abandon my soul to the grave
              or allow your holy one to decay.
11 You make the path of life known to me.
      Complete joy is in your presence.
      Pleasures are by your side forever.

PSALM 17

A prayer by David.

1 Hear my plea for justice, O LORD.
   Pay attention to my cry.
   Open your ears to my prayer,
      ⸤which comes⸥ from lips free from deceit.

---

[a] 16:1 Unknown musical term.   [b] 16:3 English equivalent of this verse difficult.

² Let the verdict of my innocence come directly from you.
Let your eyes observe what is fair.

³ You have probed my heart.
You have confronted me at night.
You have tested me like silver,
     but you found nothing wrong.
I have determined that my mouth will not sin.
⁴ I have avoided cruelty because of your word.
     In spite of what others have done,
⁵   my steps have remained firmly in your paths.
          My feet have not slipped.
⁶ I have called on you because you answer me, O God.
     Turn your ear toward me.
     Hear what I have to say.
⁷ Reveal your miraculous deeds of mercy,
          O Savior of those who find refuge by your side
               from those who attack them.
⁸ Guard me as if I were the pupil in your eye.
     Hide me in the shadow of your wings.
⁹ Hide me from wicked people who violently attack me,
     from my deadly enemies who surround me.

¹⁰ They have shut out all feeling.^a
Their mouths have spoken arrogantly.
¹¹ They have tracked me down.
They have surrounded me.
They have focused their attention on throwing me to the ground.
¹²   Each one of them is like a lion eager to tear ⸤its prey⸥ apart
          and like a young lion crouching in hiding places.

¹³ Arise, O Lord; confront them!
Bring them to their knees!
     With your sword rescue my life from wicked people.
¹⁴ With your power rescue me from mortals, O Lord,
     from mortals who enjoy their inheritance only in this life.
          You fill their bellies with your treasure.
          Their children are satisfied ⸤with it⸥,
               and they leave what remains to their children.

¹⁵ I will see your face when I am declared innocent.
When I wake up, I will be satisfied ⸤with seeing⸥ you.

PSALM 18^a

For the choir director; by David, the servant of the Lord. He sang this song to the Lord
when the Lord rescued him from all his enemies, especially from Saul. He said,

¹ I love you, O Lord, my strength.
² The Lord is my rock and my fortress and my Savior,
     my God, my rock in whom I take refuge,
          my shield, and the strength of my salvation,
               my stronghold.
³ The Lord should be praised.
     I called on him, and I was saved from my enemies.

⁴ The ropes of death had become tangled around me.
     The torrents of destruction had overwhelmed me.
⁵   The ropes of the grave had surrounded me.
          The clutches of death had confronted me.

⁶ I called on the Lord in my distress.
     I cried to my God for help.
          He heard my voice from his temple,
               and my cry for help reached his ears.

---

^a 17:10 Hebrew meaning uncertain.   ^a 18:1 Psalm 18 is virtually identical in wording to 2 Samuel 22.

7 Then the earth shook and quaked.
   Even the foundations of the mountains trembled.
     They shook violently because he was angry.
8 Smoke went up from his nostrils,
   and a raging fire came out of his mouth.
     Glowing coals flared up from it.
9 He spread apart the heavens
   and came down with a dark cloud under his feet.
10 He rode on one of the angels[b] as he flew,
   and he soared on the wings of the wind.
11 He made the darkness his hiding place,
   the dark rain clouds his covering.
12 Out of the brightness in front of him,
   those rain clouds passed by with hailstones and lightning.
13 The LORD thundered in the heavens.
   The Most High made his voice heard with hailstones and lightning.
14 He shot his arrows and scattered them.
   He flashed streaks of lightning and threw them into confusion.
15   Then the ocean floor could be seen.
   The foundations of the earth were laid bare
     at your stern warning, O LORD,
      at the blast of the breath from your nostrils.

16 He reached down from high above and took hold of me.
   He pulled me out of the raging water.
17 He rescued me from my strong enemy
   and from those who hated me,
     because they were too strong for me.
18 On the day when I faced disaster, they confronted me,
   but the LORD came to my defense.
19   He brought me out to a wide-open place.
   He rescued me because he was pleased with me.

20 The LORD rewarded me
   because of my righteousness,
   because my hands are clean.
   He paid me back
21   because I have kept the ways of the LORD
   and I have not wickedly turned away from my God,
22   because all his judgments are in front of me
   and I have not turned away from his laws.
23   I was innocent as far as he was concerned.
     I have kept myself from guilt.
24 The LORD paid me back
   because of my righteousness,
   because he can see that my hands are clean.

25 ‚In dealing‚ with faithful people you are faithful,
   with innocent people you are innocent,
26   with pure people you are pure.
   ‚In dealing‚ with devious people you are clever.

27 You save humble people,
   but you bring down a conceited look.
28 O LORD, you light my lamp.
   My God turns my darkness into light.
29   With you I can attack a line of soldiers.
   With my God I can break through barricades.

30 God's way is perfect!
   The promise of the LORD has proven to be true.
   He is a shield to all those who take refuge in him.
31   Who is God but the LORD?
     Who is a rock except our God?
32 God arms me with strength
   and makes my way perfect.

---

[b] 18:10 Or "cherubim."

33 He makes my feet like those of a deer
    and gives me sure footing on high places.
34 He trains my hands for battle
    so that my arms can bend an ˌarcher'sˌ bow of bronze.
35 You have given me the shield of your salvation.
Your right hand supports me.
Your gentleness makes me great.
36 You make a wide path for me to walk on
    so that my feet do not slip.
37 I chased my enemies and caught up with them.
I did not return until I had ended their lives.
38 I wounded them so badly that they were unable to get up.
They fell under my feet.
39 You armed me with strength for battle.
You made my opponents bow at my feet.
40 You made my enemies turn their backs to me,
    and I destroyed those who hated me.
41 They cried out for help, but there was no one to save them.
They cried out to the Lord, but he did not answer them.
42 I beat them into a powder as fine as the dust blown by the wind.
I threw them out as though they were dirt on the streets.
43 You rescued me from my conflicts with the people.
You made me the leader of nations.
    A people I did not know will serve me:
44 As soon as they hear of me, they will obey me.
    Foreigners will cringe in front of me.
45 Foreigners will lose heart,
    and they will tremble when they come out of their fortifications.

46 The Lord lives!
    Thanks be to my rock!
    May God my Savior be honored.
47 God gives me vengeance!
He brings people under my authority.
48 He saves me from my enemies.
    You lift me up above my opponents.
    You rescue me from violent people.
49 That is why I will give thanks to you, O Lord, among the nations
    and make music to praise your name.
50 He gives great victories to his king.
He shows mercy to his anointed,
    to David, and to his descendant*c* forever.

PSALM 19

For the choir director; a psalm by David.

1 The heavens declare the glory of God,
    and the sky displays what his hands have made.
2 One day tells a story to the next.
One night shares knowledge with the next
3 without talking,
without words,
without their voices being heard.
4 ˌYet,ˌ their sound has gone out into the entire world,
    their message to the ends of the earth.
He has set up a tent in the heavens for the sun,
5 which comes out of its chamber like a bridegroom.
    Like a champion, it is eager to run its course.
6 It rises from one end of the heavens.
    It circles around to the other.
        Nothing is hidden from its heat.

7 The teachings of the Lord are perfect.
    They renew the soul.

---

c 18:50 Or "to his descendants."

The testimony of the LORD is dependable.
It makes gullible people wise.
8 The instructions of the LORD are correct.
They make the heart rejoice.
The command of the LORD is radiant.
It makes the eyes shine.
9 The fear of the LORD is pure.
It endures forever.
The decisions of the LORD are true.
They are completely fair.
10 They are more desirable than gold, even the finest gold.
They are sweeter than honey, even the drippings from a honeycomb.
11 As your servant I am warned by them.
There is a great reward in following them.

12 Who can notice every mistake?
Forgive my hidden faults.
13 Keep me from sinning.
Do not let anyone gain control over me.
Then I will be blameless,
and I will be free from any great offense.

14 May the words from my mouth and the thoughts from my heart
be acceptable to you, O LORD, my rock and my defender.

PSALM 20

For the choir director; a psalm by David.

1 The LORD will answer you in times of trouble.
The name of the God of Jacob will protect you.
2 He will send you help from his holy place
and support you from Zion.
3 He will remember all your grain offerings
and look with favor on your burnt offerings. *Selah*
4 He will give you your heart's desire
and carry out all your plans.

5 We will joyfully sing about your victory.
We will wave our flags in the name of our God.
The LORD will fulfill all your requests.

6 Now I know that the LORD will give victory to his anointed king.
He will answer him from his holy heaven
with mighty deeds of his powerful hand.
7 Some ⸢rely⸣ on chariots and others on horses,
but we will boast in the name of the LORD our God.
8 They will sink to their knees and fall,
but we will rise and stand firm.

9 Give victory to the king, O LORD.
Answer us when we call.

PSALM 21

For the choir director; a psalm by David.

1 The king finds joy in your strength, O LORD.
What great joy he has in your victory!
2 You gave him his heart's desire.
You did not refuse the prayer from his lips. *Selah*
3 You welcomed him with the blessings of good things
and set a crown of fine gold on his head.
4 He asked you for life.
You gave him a long life, forever and ever.
5 Because of your victory his glory is great.
You place splendor and majesty on him.
6 Yes, you made him a blessing forever.
You made him glad with the joy of your presence.

7   Indeed, the king trusts the LORD,
        and through the mercy of the Most High, he will not be moved.

8   Your hand will discover all your enemies.
     Your powerful hand will find all who hate you.
9   When you appear, you will make them ⸢burn⸣ like a blazing furnace.
        The LORD will swallow them up in his anger.
        Fire will devour them.
10   You will destroy their children from the earth
        and their offspring from among Adam's descendants.
11   Although they scheme and plan evil against you,
            they will not succeed.
12   They turn their backs ⸢and flee⸣
            because you aim your bow at their faces.[a]

13   Arise, O LORD, in your strength.
     We will sing and make music to praise your power.

PSALM 22

For the choir director; according to *ayyeleth hashachar;*[a] a psalm by David.

1   My God, my God,
        why have you abandoned me?
        Why are you so far away from helping me,
            so far away from the words of my groaning?
2   My God,
        I cry out by day, but you do not answer—
            also at night, but I find no rest.

3   Yet, you are holy, enthroned on the praises of Israel.
4   Our ancestors trusted you.
        They trusted, and you rescued them.
5   They cried to you and were saved.
        They trusted you and were never disappointed.

6   Yet, I am a worm and not a man.
     I am scorned by humanity and despised by people.
7   All who see me make fun of me.
        Insults pour from their mouths.
            They shake their heads and say,
8   "Put yourself in the LORD's hands.
                Let the LORD save him!
                Let God rescue him since he is pleased with him!"
9   Indeed, you are the one who brought me out of the womb,
        the one who made me feel safe at my mother's breasts.
10   I was placed in your care from birth.
        From my mother's womb you have been my God.

11   Do not be so far away from me.
        Trouble is near, and there is no one to help.
12   Many bulls have surrounded me.
            Strong bulls from Bashan have encircled me.
13   They have opened their mouths to attack me
            like ferocious, roaring lions.
14   I am poured out like water,
        and all my bones are out of joint.
            My heart is like wax.
                It has melted within me.
15   My strength is dried up like pieces of broken pottery.
     My tongue sticks to the roof of my mouth.
        You lay me down in the dust of death.
16   Dogs have surrounded me.
     A mob has encircled me.
        They have pierced my hands and feet.
17   I can count all my bones.
         People stare.

They gloat over me.
18 They divide my clothes among themselves.
They throw dice for my clothing.

19 Do not be so far away, O LORD.
Come quickly to help me, O my strength.
20 Rescue my soul from the sword,
my life from vicious dogs.
21 Save me from the mouth of the lion
and from the horns of wild oxen.

You have answered me.

22 I will tell my people about your name.
I will praise you within the congregation.
23 All who fear the LORD, praise him!
All you descendants of Jacob, glorify him!
Stand in awe of him, all you descendants of Israel.
24 The LORD has not despised or been disgusted
with the plight of the oppressed one.
He has not hidden his face from that person.
The LORD heard when that oppressed person
cried out to him for help.
25 My praise comes from you while I am among those assembled for worship.
I will fulfill my vows in the presence of those who fear the LORD.
26 Oppressed people will eat until they are full.
Those who look to the LORD will praise him.
May you live forever.
27 All the ends of the earth will remember and return to the LORD.
All the families from all the nations will worship you
28 because the kingdom belongs to the LORD
and he rules the nations.
29 All prosperous people on earth will eat and worship.
All those who go down to the dust will kneel in front of him,
even those who are barely alive.
30 There will be descendants who serve him,
a generation that will be told about the Lord.
31 They will tell people yet to be born about his righteousness—
that he has finished it.

PSALM 23

A psalm by David.

1 The LORD is my shepherd.
I am never in need.
2 He makes me lie down in green pastures.
He leads me beside peaceful waters.
3 He renews my soul.
He guides me along the paths of righteousness
for the sake of his name.
4 Even though I walk through the dark valley of death,
because you are with me, I fear no harm.
Your rod and your staff give me courage.

5 You prepare a banquet for me while my enemies watch.
You anoint my head with oil.
My cup overflows.

6 Certainly, goodness and mercy will stay close to me all the days of my life,
and I will remain in the LORD's house for days without end.

PSALM 24

A psalm by David.

1 The earth and everything it contains are the LORD's.
The world and all who live in it are his.
2 He laid its foundation on the seas
and set it firmly on the rivers.

3 Who may go up the LORD's mountain?
Who may stand in his holy place?
4 ⌞The one who⌟ has clean hands and a pure heart
   and does not long for what is false[a]
   or lie when he is under oath.
5 ⌞This person⌟ will receive a blessing from the LORD
   and righteousness from God, his savior.
6 This is the person who seeks him,
   who searches for the face of the God of Jacob.[b]   *Selah*

7 Lift your heads, you gates.
Be lifted, you ancient doors,
   so that the king of glory may come in.

8 Who is this king of glory?
   The LORD, strong and mighty!
   The LORD, heroic in battle!

9 Lift your heads, you gates.
Be lifted, you ancient doors,
   so that the king of glory may come in.

10 Who, then, is this king of glory?
   The LORD of Armies is the king of glory!   *Selah*

PSALM 25[a]

By David.

1 To you, O LORD, I lift my soul.
2 I trust you, O my God.
   Do not let me be put to shame.
   Do not let my enemies triumph over me.
3 No one who waits for you will ever be put to shame,
   but all who are unfaithful will be put to shame.
4 Make your ways known to me, O LORD,
   and teach me your paths.
5 Lead me in your truth and teach me
   because you are God, my savior.
     I wait all day long for you.
6 Remember, O LORD, your compassionate and merciful deeds.
   They have existed from eternity.
7 Do not remember the sins of my youth or my rebellious ways.
   Remember me, O LORD, in keeping with your mercy and your goodness.

8 The LORD is good and decent.
   That is why he teaches sinners the way they should live.
9 He leads humble people to do what is right,
   and he teaches them his way.
10 Every path of the LORD is ⌞one of⌟ mercy and truth
   for those who cling to his promise[b] and written instructions.

11 For the sake of your name, O LORD,
   remove my guilt, because it is great.
12 Who, then, is this person that fears the LORD?
   He is the one whom the LORD will teach which path to choose.
13 He will enjoy good things in life,
   and his descendants will inherit the land.
14 The LORD advises those who fear him.
   He reveals to them the intent of his promise.

15 My eyes are always on the LORD.
   He removes my feet from traps.
16 Turn to me, and have pity on me.
   I am lonely and oppressed.
17 Relieve my troubled heart,
   and bring me out of my distress.

---

[a] 24:4 Hebrew meaning uncertain.   [b] 24:6 A few Hebrew manuscripts, Greek, Syriac; Masoretic Text "your face, Jacob."
[a] 25:1 Psalm 25 is a poem in Hebrew alphabetical order.   [b] 25:10 Or "covenant."

¹⁸ Look at my misery and suffering,
 and forgive all my sins.
¹⁹ See how my enemies have increased in number,
 how they have hated me with vicious hatred!
²⁰ Protect my life, and rescue me!
Do not let me be put to shame.
 I have taken refuge in you.
²¹ Integrity and honesty will protect me because I wait for you.
²² Rescue Israel, O God, from all its troubles!

PSALM 26

By David.

¹ Judge me favorably, O LORD,
 because I have walked with integrity
 and I have trusted you without wavering.
² Examine me, O LORD, and test me.
Look closely into my heart and mind.
³ I see your mercy in front of me.
 I walk in the light of your truth.
⁴ I did not sit with liars,
 and I will not be found among hypocrites.
⁵ I have hated the mob of evildoers
 and will not sit with wicked people.
⁶ I will wash my hands in innocence.
 I will walk around your altar, O LORD,
⁷ so that I may loudly sing a hymn of thanksgiving
 and tell about all your miracles.

⁸ O LORD, I love the house where you live,
 the place where your glory dwells.

⁹ Do not sweep away my soul along with hardened sinners
 or my life along with bloodthirsty people.
¹⁰ Evil schemes are in their hands.
 Their right hands are full of bribes.
¹¹ But I walk with integrity.
 Rescue me, and have pity on me.
¹² My feet stand on level ground.
 I will praise the LORD with the choirs in worship.

PSALM 27

By David.

¹ The LORD is my light and my salvation.
 Who is there to fear?
The LORD is my life's fortress.
 Who is there to be afraid of?

² Evildoers closed in on me to tear me to pieces.
 My opponents and enemies stumbled and fell.
³ Even though an army sets up camp against me,
 my heart will not be afraid.
 Even though a war breaks out against me,
 I will still have confidence ˛in the LORD˳.

⁴ I have asked one thing from the LORD.
This I will seek:
 to remain in the LORD's house all the days of my life
 in order to gaze at the LORD's beauty
 and to search for an answer in his temple.
⁵ He hides me in his shelter when there is trouble.
He keeps me hidden in his tent.
He sets me high on a rock.
⁶ Now my head will be raised above my enemies who surround me.
I will offer sacrifices with shouts of joy in his tent.
I will sing and make music to praise the LORD.
⁷ Hear, O LORD, when I cry aloud.

Have pity on me, and answer me.
8 When you said,
"Seek my face,"
my heart said to you,
"O Lord, I will seek your face."[a]
9 Do not hide your face from me.
Do not angrily turn me away.
You have been my help.
Do not leave me!
Do not abandon me, O God, my savior!
10 Even if my father and mother abandon me,
the Lord will take care of me.
11 Teach me your way, O Lord.
Lead me on a level path
because I have enemies who spy on me.
12 Do not surrender me to the will of my opponents.
False witnesses have risen against me.
They breathe out violence.
13 I believe that I will see the goodness of the Lord
in this world of the living.

14 Wait with hope for the Lord.
Be strong, and let your heart be courageous.
Yes, wait with hope for the Lord.

PSALM 28

By David.

1 O Lord, I call to you.
O my rock, do not turn a deaf ear to me.
If you remain silent,
I will be like those who go into the pit.
2 Hear my prayer for mercy when I call to you for help,
when I lift my hands toward your most holy place.
3 Do not drag me away with wicked people,
with troublemakers who speak of peace with their neighbors
but have evil in their hearts.
4 Pay them back for what they have done,
for their evil deeds.
Pay them back for what their hands have done,
and give them what they deserve.
5 The Lord will tear them down and never build them up again,
because they never consider what he has done
or what his hands have made.

6 Thank the Lord!
He has heard my prayer for mercy!
7 The Lord is my strength and my shield.
My heart trusted him, so I received help.
My heart is triumphant; I give thanks to him with my song.
8 The Lord is the strength of his people
and a fortress for the victory of his Messiah.[a]
9 Save your people, and bless those who belong to you.
Be their shepherd, and carry them forever.

PSALM 29

A psalm by David.

1 Give to the Lord, you heavenly beings.
Give to the Lord glory and power.
2 Give to the Lord the glory his name deserves.
Worship the Lord in his holy splendor.

---

[a] 27:8 Hebrew meaning uncertain; Greek "My heart said to you, 'I have sought your face. O Lord, I will seek your face.' "
[a] 28:8 Or "anointed one."

³ The voice of the LORD rolls over the water.
  The God of glory thunders.
  The LORD shouts over raging water.
⁴ The voice of the LORD is powerful.
  The voice of the LORD is majestic.
⁵ The voice of the LORD breaks the cedars.
  The LORD splinters the cedars of Lebanon.
⁶ He makes Lebanon skip along like a calf
  and Mount Sirion like a wild ox.
⁷ The voice of the LORD strikes with flashes of lightning.
⁸ The voice of the LORD makes the wilderness tremble.
  The LORD makes the wilderness of Kadesh tremble.
⁹ The voice of the LORD splits the oaksᵃ
  and strips ⸤the trees of⸥ the forests bare.
  Everyone in his temple is saying, "Glory!"

¹⁰ The LORD sat enthroned over the flood.
   The LORD sits enthroned as king forever.
¹¹ The LORD will give power to his people.
   The LORD will bless his people with peace.

PSALM 30

A psalm by David sung at the dedication of the temple.

¹ I will honor you highly, O LORD,
  because you have pulled me out ⸤of the pit⸥
  and have not let my enemies rejoice over me.
² O LORD my God,
  I cried out to you for help,
  and you healed me.
³ O LORD, you brought me up from the grave.
  You called me back to life
  from among those who had gone into the pit.
⁴ Make music to praise the LORD, you faithful people who belong to him.
  Remember his holiness by giving thanks.
⁵ His anger lasts only a moment.
  His favor lasts a lifetime.
  Weeping may last for the night,
  but there is a song of joy in the morning.

⁶ When all was well with me, I said,
  "I will never be shaken."
⁷ O LORD, by your favor you have made my mountain stand firm.
  When you hid your face, I was terrified.
⁸ I will cry out to you, O LORD.
  I will plead to the LORD for mercy:
⁹ "How will you profit if my blood is shed,
  if I go into the pit?
  Will the dust ⸤of my body⸥ give thanks to you?
  Will it tell about your truth?"
¹⁰ Hear, O LORD, and have pity on me!
   O LORD, be my helper!
¹¹ You have changed my sobbing into dancing.
   You have removed my sackcloth and clothed me with joy
¹²   so that my soulᵃ may praise you with music and not be silent.
   O LORD my God, I will give thanks to you forever.

PSALM 31

For the choir director; a psalm by David.

¹ I have taken refuge in you, O LORD.
  Never let me be put to shame.
  Save me because of your righteousness.
²   Turn your ear toward me.

ᵃ 29:9 Hebrew meaning of "splits the oaks" uncertain.   ᵃ 30:12 Or "glory."

    Rescue me quickly.
    Be a rock of refuge for me,
       a strong fortress to save me.
3 Indeed, you are my rock and my fortress.
    For the sake of your name, lead me and guide me.
4   You are my refuge,
       so pull me out of the net that they have secretly laid for me.
5   Into your hands I entrust my spirit.
         You have rescued me, O Lord, God of truth.

6 I hate those who cling to false gods, but I trust the Lord.
7 I will rejoice and be glad because of your mercy.
    You have seen my misery.
    You have known the troubles in my soul.
8   You have not handed me over to the enemy.
    You have set my feet in a place where I can move freely.

9 Have pity on me, O Lord, because I am in distress.
    My eyes, my soul, and my body waste away from grief.
10   My life is exhausted from sorrow,
       my years from groaning.
    My strength staggers under ⸤the weight of⸥ my guilt,
       and my bones waste away.
11   I have become a disgrace because of all my opponents.
    I have become someone dreaded by my friends,
       even by my neighbors.
       Those who see me on the street run away from me.
12   I have faded from memory as if I were dead
    and have become like a piece of broken pottery.
13   I have heard the whispering of many people—
       terror on every side—
         while they made plans together against me.
         They were plotting to take my life.

14 I trust you, O Lord.
    I said, "You are my God."

15 My future is in your hands.
    Rescue me from my enemies, from those who persecute me.
16   Smile on me.
    Save me with your mercy.
17 O Lord, I have called on you, so do not let me be put to shame.
    Let wicked people be put to shame.
    Let them be silent in the grave.
18   Let ⸤their⸥ lying lips be speechless,
       since they speak against righteous people with arrogance and contempt.

19   Your kindness is so great!
    You reserve it for those who fear you.
       Adam's descendants watch
         as you show it to those who take refuge in you.
20   You hide them in the secret place of your presence
       from those who scheme against them.
    You keep them in a shelter,
       safe from quarrelsome tongues.
21 Thank the Lord!
    He has shown me the miracle of his mercy
       in a city under attack.
22 When I was panic-stricken, I said,
    "I have been cut off from your sight."
    But you heard my pleas for mercy when I cried out to you for help.
23 Love the Lord, all you godly ones!
    The Lord protects faithful people,
       but he pays back in full those who act arrogantly.
24 Be strong, all who wait with hope for the Lord,
       and let your heart be courageous.

PSALM 32

A psalm by David; a *maskil.*[a]

1 Blessed is the person whose disobedience is forgiven
   and whose sin is pardoned.
2 Blessed is the person whom the LORD no longer accuses of sin
   and who has no deceitful thoughts.

3 When I kept silent ˌabout my sinsˌ,
   my bones began to weaken because of my groaning all day long.
4 Day and night your hand lay heavily on me.
   My strength shriveled in the summer heat.   Selah

5 I made my sins known to you, and I did not cover up my guilt.
   I decided to confess them to you, O LORD.
   Then you forgave all my sins.   Selah

6 For this reason let all godly people pray to you
      when you may be found.
      Then raging floodwater will not reach them.

7 You are my hiding place.
   You protect me from trouble.
   You surround me with joyous songs of salvation.   Selah

8 ˌThe LORD says,ˌ
   "I will instruct you.
   I will teach you the way that you should go.
   I will advise you as my eyes watch over you.
9 Don't be stubborn like a horse or mule.
      ˌThey needˌ a bit and bridle in their mouth to restrain them,
         or they will not come near you."

10 Many heartaches await wicked people,
      but mercy surrounds those who trust the LORD.

11 Be glad and find joy in the LORD, you righteous people.
   Sing with joy, all whose motives are decent.

PSALM 33

1 Joyfully sing to the LORD, you righteous people.
      Praising ˌthe LORDˌ is proper for decent people.
2 Give thanks with a lyre to the LORD.
   Make music for him on a ten-stringed harp.
3 Sing a new song to him.
   Play beautifully and joyfully on stringed instruments.

4 The word of the LORD is correct,
      and everything he does is trustworthy.
5 The LORD loves righteousness and justice.
      His mercy fills the earth.
6 The heavens were made by the word of the LORD
      and all the stars by the breath of his mouth.
7 He gathers the water in the sea like a dam
      and puts the oceans in his storehouses.
8 Let all the earth fear the LORD.
   Let all who live in the world stand in awe of him.
9 He spoke, and it came into being.
   He gave the order, and there it stood.

10 The LORD blocks the plans of the nations.
   He frustrates the schemes of the people of the world.
11   The LORD's plan stands firm forever.
      His thoughts stand firm in every generation.
12 Blessed is the nation whose God is the LORD.
   Blessed are the people he has chosen as his own.

---

[a] 32:1 Unknown musical term.

13 The LORD looks down from heaven.
   He sees all of Adam's descendants.
14 From the place where he sits enthroned,
   he looks down upon all who live on earth.
15 The one who formed their hearts
   understands everything they do.

16 No king achieves a victory with a large army.
   No warrior rescues himself by his own great strength.
17 Horses are not a guarantee for victory.
   Their great strength cannot help someone escape.
18 The LORD's eyes are on those who fear him,
   on those who wait with hope for his mercy
19   to rescue their souls from death
      and keep them alive during a famine.

20 We wait for the LORD.
   He is our help and our shield.
21 In him our hearts find joy.
   In his holy name we trust.
22 Let your mercy rest on us, O LORD,
   since we wait with hope for you.

PSALM 34 [a]

By David when he pretended to be insane in the presence of Abimelech; Abimelech
threw him out, so David left.

1 I will thank the LORD at all times.
   My mouth will always praise him.
2 My soul will boast about the LORD.
   Those who are oppressed will hear it and rejoice.
3 Praise the LORD's greatness with me.
   Let us highly honor his name together.
4 I went to the LORD for help.
   He answered me and rescued me from all my fears.
5 All who look to him will be radiant. [b]
   Their faces will never be covered with shame.
6 Here is a poor man who called out.
   The LORD heard him and saved him from all his troubles.
7 The Messenger of the LORD camps around those who fear him,
   and he rescues them.
8 Taste and see that the LORD is good.
   Blessed is the person who takes refuge in him.
9 Fear the LORD, you holy people who belong to him.
   Those who fear him are never in need.
10 Young lions go hungry and may starve,
   but those who seek the LORD's help have all the good things they need.
11 Come, children, listen to me.
   I will teach you the fear of the LORD.
12 Which of you wants a full life?
   Who would like to live long enough to enjoy good things?
13   Keep your tongue from saying evil things
      and your lips from speaking deceitful things.
14 Turn away from evil, and do good.
   Seek peace, and pursue it!
15 The LORD's eyes are on righteous people.
   His ears hear their cry for help.
16 The LORD confronts those who do evil
   in order to wipe out all memory of them from the earth.
17 ˌRighteous people˛ cry out.
   The LORD hears and rescues them from all their troubles.
18 The LORD is near to those whose hearts are humble.
   He saves those whose spirits are crushed.
19 The righteous person has many troubles,

but the LORD rescues him from all of them.
20   The LORD guards all of his bones.
    Not one of them is broken.
21 Evil will kill wicked people,
    and those who hate righteous people will be condemned.
22 The LORD protects the souls of his servants.
    All who take refuge in him will never be condemned.

PSALM 35

By David.

1 O LORD, attack those who attack me.
    Fight against those who fight against me.
2   Use your shields, ˻both˼ small and large.
    Arise to help me.
3   Hold your spear to block the way of those who pursue me.
    Say to my soul, "I am your savior."

4 Let those who seek my life be put to shame and disgraced.
    Let those who plan my downfall be turned back in confusion.
5 Let them be like husks blown by the wind
    as the Messenger of the LORD chases them.
6 Let their path be dark and slippery
    as the Messenger of the LORD pursues them.
7 For no reason they hid their net in a pit.
    For no reason they dug the pit ˻to trap me˼.
8 Let destruction surprise them.
    Let the net that they hid catch them.
    Let them fall into their own pit and be destroyed.
9 My soul will find joy in the LORD
    and be joyful about his salvation.
10 All my bones will say, "O LORD, who can compare with you?
    You rescue the weak person from the one who is too strong for him
    and weak and needy people from the one who robs them."

11 Malicious people bring charges against me.
    They ask me things I know nothing about.
12 I am devastated
    because they pay me back with evil instead of good.
13 But when they were sick, I wore sackcloth.
    I humbled myself with fasting.
    When my prayer returned unanswered,
14   I walked around as if I were mourning for my friend or my brother.
    I was bent over as if I were mourning for my mother.

15 Yet, when I stumbled,
    they rejoiced and gathered together.
    They gathered together against me.
    Unknown attackers tore me apart without stopping.
16   With crude and abusive mockers,
    they grit their teeth at me.
17 O Lord, how long will you look on?
    Rescue me from their attacks.
    Rescue my precious life from the lions.
18   I will give you thanks in a large gathering.
    I will praise you in a crowd ˻of worshipers˼.

19 Do not let my treacherous enemies gloat over me.
    Do not let those who hate me for no reason wink ˻at me˼.
20   They do not talk about peace.
    Instead, they scheme against the peaceful people in the land.
21   They open their big mouths and say about me,
    "Aha! Aha! Our own eyes have seen it."
22 You have seen it, O LORD.
    Do not remain silent.
    O Lord, do not be so far away from me.
23   Wake up, and rise to my defense.
    Plead my case, O my God and my Lord.

24 Judge me by your righteousness, O LORD my God.
Do not let them gloat over me
25 or think, "Aha, just what we wanted!"
Do not let them say, "We have swallowed him up."
26 Let those who gloat over my downfall
be thoroughly put to shame and confused.
Let those who promote themselves at my expense
be clothed with shame and disgrace.
27 Let those who are happy when I am declared innocent
joyfully sing and rejoice.
Let them continually say, "The LORD is great.
He is happy when his servant has peace."
28 Then my tongue will tell about your righteousness,
about your praise all day long.

PSALM 36

For the choir director; by David, the LORD's servant.

1 There is an inspired truth about the wicked person
who has rebellion in the depths of his heart:
He is not terrified of God.
2 He flatters himself and does not hate or ˌeven˒ recognize his guilt.
3 The words from his mouth are ˌnothing butˌ trouble and deception.
He has stopped doing what is wise and good.
4 He invents trouble while lying on his bed
and chooses to go the wrong direction.
He does not reject evil.

5 O LORD, your mercy reaches to the heavens,
your faithfulness to the skies.
6 Your righteousness is like the mountains of God,
your judgments like the deep ocean.
You save people and animals, O LORD.
7 Your mercy is so precious, O God,
that Adam's descendants take refuge
in the shadow of your wings.
8 They are refreshed with the rich foods in your house,
and you make them drink from the river of your pleasure.
9 Indeed, the fountain of life is with you.
In your light we see light.
10 Continue to show your mercy to those who know you
and your righteousness to those whose motives are decent.
11 Do not let the feet of arrogant people step on me
or the hands of wicked people push me away.
12 Look at the troublemakers who have fallen.
They have been pushed down and are unable to stand up again.

PSALM 37[a]

By David.

1 Do not be preoccupied with evildoers.
Do not envy those who do wicked things.
2 They will quickly dry up like grass
and wither away like green plants.
3 Trust the LORD, and do good things.
Live in the land, and practice being faithful.
4 Be happy with the LORD,
and he will give you the desires of your heart.
5 Entrust your ways to the LORD.
Trust him, and he will act ˌon your behalfˌ.
6 He will make your righteousness shine like a light,
your just cause like the noonday sun.
7 Surrender yourself to the LORD, and wait patiently for him.

---

[a] 37:1 Psalm 37 is a poem in Hebrew alphabetical order.

Do not be preoccupied with ˌan evildoerˌ who succeeds in his way
    when he carries out his schemes.
8 Let go of anger, and leave rage behind.
    Do not be preoccupied.
       It only leads to evil.
9 Evildoers will be cut off ˌfrom their inheritanceˌ,
    but those who wait with hope for the LORD will inherit the land.

10 In a little while a wicked person will vanish.
    Then you can carefully examine where he was,
       but there will be no trace of him.
11 Oppressed people will inherit the land
    and will enjoy unlimited peace.
12 The wicked person plots against a righteous one
    and grits his teeth at him.
13 The Lord laughs at him
    because he has seen that his time is coming.
14 Wicked people pull out their swords and bend their bows
    to kill oppressed and needy people,
    to slaughter those who are decent.
15 ˌButˌ their own swords will pierce their hearts,
    and their bows will be broken.
16 The little that the righteous person has is better
    than the wealth of many wicked people.
17 The arms of wicked people will be broken,
    but the LORD continues to support righteous people.
18 The LORD knows the daily ˌstrugglesˌ of innocent people.
    Their inheritance will last forever.
19 They will not be put to shame in trying times.
    Even in times of famine they will be satisfied.
20 But wicked people will disappear.
    The LORD's enemies will vanish like the best part of a meadow.
    They will vanish like smoke.
21 A wicked person borrows, but he does not repay.
    A righteous person is generous and giving.
22 Those who are blessed by him will inherit the land.
    Those who are cursed by him will be cut off.

23 A person's steps are directed by the LORD,
    and the LORD delights in his way.
24 When he falls, he will not be thrown down headfirst
    because the LORD holds on to his hand.
25 I have been young, and now I am old,
    but I have never seen a righteous person abandoned
       or his descendants begging for food.
26   He is always generous and lends freely.
       His descendants are a blessing.
27 Avoid evil, do good, and live forever.
28 The LORD loves justice,
    and he will not abandon his godly ones.
    They will be kept safe forever,
    but the descendants of wicked people will be cut off.
29 Righteous people will inherit the land
    and live there permanently.
30 The mouth of the righteous person reflects on wisdom.
    His tongue speaks what is fair.
31 The teachings of his God are in his heart.
    His feet do not slip.
32 The wicked person watches the righteous person
    and seeks to kill him.
33 But the LORD will not abandon him to the wicked person's power
    or condemn him when he is brought to trial.
34 Wait with hope for the LORD, and follow his path,
    and he will honor you by giving you the land.
       When wicked people are cut off, you will see it.

35 I have seen a wicked person ˌacting likeˌ a tyrant,
    spreading himself out like a large cedar tree.

36 But he moved on, and now there is no trace of him.
    I searched for him, but he could not be found.
37 Notice the innocent person,
    and look at the decent person,
        because the peacemaker has a future.
38   But rebels will be completely destroyed.
            The future of wicked people will be cut off.
39 The victory for righteous people comes from the LORD.
    He is their fortress in times of trouble.
40 The LORD helps them and rescues them.
    He rescues them from wicked people.
    He saves them because they have taken refuge in him.

PSALM 38

A psalm by David; to be kept in mind.[a]

1 O LORD, do not angrily punish me
    or discipline me in your wrath.
2   Your arrows have struck me.
      Your hand has struck me hard.
3 No healthy spot is left on my body
    because of your rage.
  There is no peace in my bones
    because of my sin.

4 My guilt has overwhelmed me.
    Like a heavy load, it is more than I can bear.
5 My wounds smell rotten.
    They fester because of my stupidity.
6 I am bent over and bowed down very low.
    All day I walk around in mourning.
7 My insides are filled with burning pain,
    and no healthy spot is left on my body.
8 I am numb and completely devastated.
  I roar because my heart's in turmoil.
9 You know all my desires, O Lord,
    and my groaning has not been hidden from you.
10 My heart is pounding.
    I have lost my strength.
        Even the light of my eyes has left me.

11 My loved ones and my friends keep their distance
    and my relatives stand far away because of my sickness.
12 Those who seek my life lay traps for me.
   Those who are out to harm me talk about ruining me.
    All day long they think of ways to deceive me.
13 But I am like a person who cannot hear
    and like a person who cannot speak.
14 I am like one who cannot hear
    and who can offer no arguments.

15 But I wait with hope for you, O LORD.
   You will answer, O Lord, my God.
16 I said, "Do not let them gloat over me.
    When my foot slips,
        do not let them promote themselves at my expense."
17 I am ready to fall.
   I am continually aware of my pain.
18 I confess my guilt.
   My sin troubles me.

19 My mortal enemies are growing stronger.
    Many hate me for no reason.
20 They pay me back with evil instead of good,
    and they accuse me because I try to do what is good.

---

[a] 38:1 Hebrew meaning of "to be kept in mind" uncertain.

21 Do not abandon me, O LORD.
O my God, do not be so distant from me.
22 Come quickly to help me, O Lord, my savior.

PSALM 39

For the choir director; for Jeduthun; a psalm by David.

1 I said,
"I will watch my ways so that I do not sin with my tongue.
I will bridle my mouth while wicked people are in my presence."
2 I remained totally speechless.
I kept silent, although it did me no good.
While I was deep in thought, my pain grew worse.
3 My heart burned like a fire flaring up within me.
Then I spoke with my tongue:
4 "Teach me, O LORD, about the end of my life.
Teach me about the number of days I have left
so that I may know how temporary my life is.
5 Indeed, you have made the length of my days ˎonlyˏ a few inches.
My life span is nothing compared to yours.
Certainly, everyone alive is like a whisper in the wind.   Selah
6 Each person who walks around is like a shadow.
They are busy for no reason.
They accumulate riches without knowing who will get them."

7 And now, Lord, what am I waiting for?
My hope is in you!
8 Rescue me from all my rebellious acts.
Do not disgrace me in front of godless fools.
9 I remained speechless.
I did not open my mouth
because you are the one who has done this.
10 Remove the sickness you laid upon me.
My life is over because you struck me with your hand.
11 With stern warnings you discipline people for their crimes.
Like a moth you eat away at what is dear to them.
Certainly, everyone is like a whisper in the wind.   Selah

12 Listen to my prayer, O LORD.
Open your ear to my cry for help.
Do not be deaf to my tears,
for I am a foreign resident with you,
a stranger like all my ancestors.
13 Look away from me so that I may smile again
before I go away and am no more.

PSALM 40

For the choir director; a psalm by David.

1 I waited patiently for the LORD.
He turned to me and heard my cry for help.
2 He pulled me out of a horrible pit,
out of the mud and clay.
He set my feet on a rock
and made my steps secure.
3 He placed a new song in my mouth,
a song of praise to our God.
Many will see this and worship.
They will trust the LORD.
4 Blessed is the person
who places his confidence in the LORD
and does not rely on arrogant people
or those who follow lies.
5 You have done many miraculous things, O LORD my God.
You have made many wonderful plans for us.
No one compares to you!

I will tell others about your miracles,
   which are more than I can count.

6 You were not pleased with sacrifices and offerings.
You have dug out two ears for me.[a]
You did not ask for burnt offerings or sacrifices for sin.
7   Then I said, "I have come!
      (It is written about me in the scroll of the book.)
8   I am happy to do your will, O my God."
Your teachings are deep within me.
9 I will announce the good news of righteousness
   among those assembled for worship.
      I will not close my lips.
         You know that, O LORD.
10 I have not buried your righteousness deep in my heart.
I have been outspoken about your faithfulness and your salvation.
I have not hidden your mercy and your truth
   from those assembled for worship.

11 Do not withhold your compassion from me, O LORD.
May your mercy and your truth always protect me.
12   Countless evils have surrounded me.
      My sins have caught up with me so that I can no longer see.
         They outnumber the hairs on my head.
            I have lost heart.

13 O LORD, please rescue me!
Come quickly to help me, O LORD![b]
14 Let all those who seek to end my life
   be confused and put to shame.
Let those who want my downfall
   be turned back and disgraced.
15 Let those who say to me, "Aha! Aha!"
   be stunned by their own shame.
16 Let all who seek you rejoice and be glad because of you.
Let those who love your salvation continually say,
   "The LORD is great!"

17 But I am oppressed and needy.
May the Lord think of me.
   You are my help and my savior.
      O my God, do not delay!

PSALM 41

For the choir director; a psalm by David.

1 Blessed is the one who has concern for helpless people.
   The LORD will rescue him in times of trouble.
2   The LORD will protect him and keep him alive.
      He will be blessed in the land.
         Do not place him at the mercy of his enemies.
3   The LORD will support him on his sickbed.
      You will restore this person to health when he is ill.

4 I said, "O LORD, have pity on me!
   Heal my soul because I have sinned against you."
5 My enemies say terrible things about me:
   "When will he die, and when will his family name disappear?"
6 When one of them comes to visit me, he speaks foolishly.
   His heart collects gossip.
      ⌊Then⌋ he leaves to tell others.
7 Everyone who hates me whispers about me.
They think evil things about me and say,
8   "A devilish disease has attached itself to him.
   He will never leave his sickbed."
9 Even my closest friend whom I trusted,

---

[a] 40:6 Hebrew meaning of this line uncertain.   [b] 40:13 Verses 13–17 are virtually identical in wording to Psalm 70.

the one who ate my bread,
    has lifted his heel against me.
10 Have pity on me, O LORD!
    Raise me up so that I can pay them back
11   and my enemy cannot shout in triumph over me.
        When you do this, I know that you are pleased with me.
12 You defend my integrity,
    and you set me in your presence forever.

13   Thank the LORD God of Israel through all eternity!
                 Amen and amen!

BOOK TWO
Psalms 42–72

PSALM 42

For the choir director; a *maskil*[a] by Korah's descendants.

1 As a deer longs for flowing streams,
    so my soul longs for you, O God.
2 My soul thirsts for God, for the living God.
    When may I come to see God's face?
3 My tears are my food day and night.
    People ask me all day long, "Where is your God?"
4 I will remember these things as I pour out my soul:
    how I used to walk with the crowd
        and lead it in a procession to God's house.
    ⌊I sang⌋ songs of joy and thanksgiving
        while crowds of people celebrated a festival.

5   Why are you discouraged, my soul?
       Why are you so restless?
           Put your hope in God,
               because I will still praise him.
                   He is my savior and my God.

6 My soul is discouraged.
    That is why I will remember you
        in the land of Jordan, on the peaks of Hermon, on Mount Mizar.
7 One deep sea calls to another at the roar of your waterspouts.
    All the whitecaps on your waves have swept over me.[b]
8 The LORD commands his mercy during the day,
    and at night his song is with me—
        a prayer to the God of my life.
9   I will ask God, my rock,
       "Why have you forgotten me?
       Why must I walk around in mourning
           while the enemy oppresses me?"
10   With a shattering blow to my bones,
           my enemies taunt me.
               They ask me all day long, "Where is your God?"

11   Why are you discouraged, my soul?
       Why are you so restless?
           Put your hope in God,
               because I will still praise him.
                   He is my savior and my God.

PSALM 43

1 Judge me, O God,
    and plead my case against an ungodly nation.
    Rescue me from deceitful and unjust people.
2   You are my fortress, O God!

---

a 42:1 Unknown musical term.   *b* 42:7 Hebrew meaning of this verse uncertain.

Why have you rejected me?
Why must I walk around in mourning
while the enemy oppresses me?
3 Send your light and your truth.
Let them guide me.
Let them bring me to your holy mountain
and to your dwelling place.
4 Then let me go to the altar of God, to God my ͵highest͵ joy,
and I will give thanks to you on the lyre, O God, my God.

5 Why are you discouraged, my soul?
Why are you so restless?
Put your hope in God,
because I will still praise him.
He is my savior and my God.

PSALM 44

For the choir director; a *maskil* by Korah's descendants.

1 O God,
we have heard it with our own ears.
Our ancestors have told us
about the miracle you performed in their day,
in days long ago.
2 By your power you forced nations ͵out of the land͵,
but you planted our ancestors ͵there͵.
You shattered many groups of people,
but you set our ancestors free.[a]
3 It was not with their swords that they took possession of the land.
They did not gain victory with their own strength.
It was your right hand, your arm,
and the light of your presence ͵that did it͵,
because you were pleased with them.

4 You alone are my king, O God.
You won those victories for Jacob.
5 With you we can walk over our enemies.
With your name we can trample those who attack us.
6 I do not rely on my bow,
and my sword will never save me.
7 But you saved us from our enemies.
You put to shame those who hate us.
8 All day long we praise our God.
We give thanks to you forever.   *Selah*

9 But now you have rejected and disgraced us.
You do not even go along with our armies.
10 You make us retreat from the enemy.
Those who hate us rob us at will.
11 You hand us over to be butchered like sheep
and scatter us among the nations.
12 You sell your people for almost nothing,
and at that price you have gained nothing.
13 You made us a disgrace to our neighbors
and an object of ridicule and contempt to those around us.
14 You made our ͵defeat͵ a proverb among the nations
so that people shake their heads at us.
15 All day long my disgrace is in front of me.
Shame covers my face
16 because of the words of those who insult and slander us,
because of the presence of the enemy and the avenger.

17 Although all of this happened to us,
we never forgot you.
We never ignored your promise.[b]

---

[a] 44:2 Or "and you sent them away."   [b] 44:17 Or "covenant."

18 Our hearts never turned away.
Our feet never left your path.
19 Yet, you crushed us in a place for jackals
and covered us with the shadow of death.

20 If we forgot the name of our God
or stretched out our hands to pray to another god,
21 wouldn't God find out,
since he knows the secrets in our hearts?
22 Indeed, we are being killed all day long because of you.
We are thought of as sheep to be slaughtered.

23 Wake up! Why are you sleeping, O Lord?
Awake! Do not reject us forever!
24 Why do you hide your face?
Why do you forget our suffering and misery?
25 Our souls are bowing in the dust.
Our bodies cling to the ground.
26 Arise! Help us!
Rescue us because of your mercy!

PSALM 45

For the choir director; according to *shoshannim;*[a] a *maskil* by Korah's descendants;
a love song.

1 My heart is overflowing with good news.
I will direct my song to the king.
My tongue is a pen for a skillful writer.

2 You are the most handsome of Adam's descendants.
Grace is poured on your lips.
That is why God has blessed you forever.
3 O warrior, strap your sword to your side
with your splendor and majesty.
4 Ride on victoriously in your majesty
for the cause of truth, humility, and righteousness.
Let your right hand teach you awe-inspiring things.
5 Your arrows are sharp in the heart of the king's enemies.
Nations fall beneath you.
6 Your throne, O God, is forever and ever.
The scepter in your kingdom is a scepter for justice.
7 You have loved what is right and hated what is wrong.
That is why God, your God, has anointed you,
rather than your companions, with the oil of joy.
8 All your robes are ˌfragrantˌ with myrrh, aloes, and cassia.
From ivory palaces the music of stringed instruments delights you.
9 The daughters of kings are among your noble ladies.
The queen takes her place at your right hand
and wears gold from Ophir.

10 Listen, daughter! Look closely!
Turn your ear ˌtoward meˌ.
Forget your people, and forget your father's house.
11 The king longs for your beauty.
He is your Lord.
Worship him.

12 The people of Tyre, the richest people,
want to win your favor with a gift.
13 The daughter of the king is glorious inside ˌthe palaceˌ.
Her dress is embroidered with gold.
14 Wearing a colorful gown, she is brought to the king.
Her bridesmaids follow her.
They will be brought to you.
15 With joy and delight they are brought in.
They enter the palace of the king.

---

a 45:1 Unknown musical term.

16   Your sons will take the place of your father.
    You will make them princes over the whole earth.

17   I will cause your name to be remembered throughout every generation.
    That is why the nations will give thanks to you forever and ever.

PSALM 46

For the choir director; a song by the descendants of Korah; according to *alamoth.*[a]

1   God is our refuge and strength,
    an ever-present help in times of trouble.
2   That is why we are not afraid
    even when the earth quakes
      or the mountains topple into the depths of the sea.
3   Water roars and foams,
        and mountains shake at the surging waves.   *Selah*

4   There is a river
    whose streams bring joy to the city of God,
      the holy place where the Most High lives.
5   God is in that city.
    It cannot fall.
      God will help it at the break of dawn.
6   Nations are in turmoil, and kingdoms topple.
    The earth melts at the sound of ˻God's˼ voice.

7   The Lord of Armies is with us.
    The God of Jacob is our stronghold.   *Selah*

8   Come, see the works of the Lord,
    the devastation he has brought to the earth.
9   He puts an end to wars all over the earth.
      He breaks an archer's bow.
      He cuts spears in two.
      He burns chariots.
10   Let go ˻of your concerns˼!
    Then you will know that I am God.
      I rule the nations.
      I rule the earth.

11   The Lord of Armies is with us.
    The God of Jacob is our stronghold.   *Selah*

PSALM 47

For the choir director; a psalm by Korah's descendants.

1   Clap your hands, all you people.
    Shout to God with a loud, joyful song.
2   We must fear the Lord, the Most High.
    He is the great king of the whole earth.
3   He brings people under our authority
      and ˻puts˼ nations under our feet.
4   He chooses our inheritance for us,
      the pride of Jacob, whom he loved.   *Selah*

5   God has gone up with a joyful shout.
    The Lord has gone up with the sound of a ram's horn.
6   Make music to praise God.
      Play music for him!
    Make music to praise our king.
      Play music for him!
7   God is the king of the whole earth.
    Make your best music for him!
8   God rules the nations.
    He sits upon his holy throne.

---

[a] 46:1 Unknown musical term.

9 The influential people from the nations gather together
> as the people of the God of Abraham.
The rulers of the earth belong to God.
> He rules everything.

PSALM 48

A song; a psalm by Korah's descendants.

1 The LORD is great.
He should be highly praised.
> His holy mountain is in the city of our God.
2 Its beautiful peak is the joy of the whole earth.
Mount Zion is on the northern ridge.
> It is the city of the great king.
3 God is in its palaces.
He has proved that he is a stronghold.

4 The kings have gathered.
> They marched together.
5 ⸢When⸣ they saw ⸢Mount Zion⸣,
> they were astonished.
> They were terrified and ran away in fear.
6 Trembling seized them
> like the trembling that a woman experiences during labor.
7 With the east wind you smash the ships of Tarshish.

8 The things we had only heard about, we have now seen
> in the city of the LORD of Armies,
> in the city of our God.
> God makes Zion stand firm forever.   *Selah*
9 Inside your temple we carefully reflect on your mercy, O God.
10 Like your name, O God,
> your praise ⸢reaches⸣ to the ends of the earth.
Your right hand is filled with righteousness.
11 Let Mount Zion be glad
> and the cities of Judah rejoice
> because of your judgments.

12 Walk around Zion.
> Go around it.
> Count its towers.
13 Examine its embankments.
> Walk through its palaces.
Then you can tell the next generation,
14 "This God is our God forever and ever.
> He will lead us beyond death."

PSALM 49

For the choir director; a psalm by Korah's descendants.

1 Listen to this, all you people.
Open your ears, all who live in the world—
2 common people and important ones,
> rich people and poor ones.
3 My mouth will speak wise sayings,
> the insights I have carefully considered.
4 I will turn my attention to a proverb.
I will explain my riddle with the ⸢music of⸣ a lyre.
5 Why should I be afraid in times of trouble,
> when slanderers surround me with evil?
6 They trust their riches
> and brag about their abundant wealth.

7 No one can ever buy back another person
> or pay God a ransom for his life.
8 The price to be paid for his soul is too costly.
> He must always give up
9 in order to live forever and never see the pit.

10 Indeed, one can see that wise people die,
     that foolish and stupid people meet the same end.
         They leave their riches to others.
11 Although they named their lands after themselves,
     their graves[a] have become their homes for ages to come,
         their dwelling places throughout every generation.

12 But mortals will not continue here with what they treasure.
     They are like animals that die.

13 This is the final outcome for fools and their followers
     who are delighted by what they say: Selah
14   Like sheep, they are driven to hell
             with death as their shepherd.
                 (Decent people will rule them in the morning.)
         Their forms will decay in the grave,
             far away from their comfortable homes.
15 But God will buy me back from the power of hell
     because he will take me.   Selah
16 Do not be afraid when someone becomes rich,
     when the greatness of his house increases.
17   He will not take anything with him when he dies.
             His greatness cannot follow him.
18 Even though he blesses himself while he is alive
     (and they praise you when you do well for yourself),
19   he must join the generation of his ancestors,
             who will never see light ˌagainˌ.

20 Mortals, with what they treasure, still don't have understanding.
     They are like animals that die.

PSALM 50

A psalm by Asaph.

1 The LORD, the only true God, has spoken.
     He has summoned the earth
         from where the sun rises to where it sets.
2 God shines from Zion,
     the perfection of beauty.
3 Our God will come and will not remain silent.
     A devouring fire is in front of him
         and a raging storm around him.
4 He summons heaven and earth to judge his people:
5   "Gather around me, my godly people
         who have made a pledge to me through sacrifices."

6 The heavens announce his righteousness
     because God is the judge.   Selah

7 "Listen, my people, and I will speak.
     Listen, Israel, and I will testify against you:
         I am God, your God!
8 I am not criticizing you for your sacrifices or burnt offerings,
     which are always in front of me.
9 ˌButˌ I will not accept ˌanotherˌ young bull from your household
     or a single male goat from your pens.
10 Every creature in the forest,
     ˌevenˌ the cattle on a thousand hills, is mine.
11 I know every bird in the mountains.
     Everything that moves in the fields is mine.
12 If I were hungry, I would not tell you,
     because the world and all that it contains are mine.
13 Do I eat the meat of bulls or drink the blood of goats?
14 Bring ˌyourˌ thanks to God as a sacrifice,
     and keep your vows to the Most High.

---

a 49:11 Greek, Syriac, Targum; Masoretic Text "their insides."

15   Call on me in times of trouble.
         I will rescue you, and you will honor me."

16 But God says to wicked people,
      "How dare you quote my decrees
        and mouth my promises!ᵃ
17   You hate discipline.
      You toss my words behind you.
18   When you see a thief, you want to make friends with him.
        You keep company with people who commit adultery.
19   You let your mouth say anything evil.
        Your tongue plans deceit.
20   You sit and talk against your own brother.
        You slander your own mother's son.
21   When you did these things, I remained silent.
     ⌊That⌋ made you think I was like you.
       I will argue my point with you
         and lay it all out for you to see.
22 Consider this, you people who forget God.
      Otherwise, I will tear you to pieces,
        and there will be no one left to rescue you.
23 Whoever offers thanks as a sacrifice honors me.
    I will let everyone who continues in my way
      see the salvation that comes from God."

PSALM 51

For the choir director; a psalm by David when the prophet Nathan came to him after David's adultery with Bathsheba.

1 Have pity on me, O God, in keeping with your mercy.
    In keeping with your unlimited compassion, wipe out my rebellious acts.
2 Wash me thoroughly from my guilt,
    and cleanse me from my sin.
3   I admit that I am rebellious.
      My sin is always in front of me.
4 I have sinned against you, especially you.
    I have done what you consider evil.
      So you hand down justice when you speak,
        and you are blameless when you judge.

5 Indeed, I was born guilty.
    I was a sinner when my mother conceived me.
6 Yet, you desire truth and sincerity.ᵃ
    Deep down inside me you teach me wisdom.
7 Purify me from sin with hyssop,ᵇ and I will be clean.ᶜ
    Wash me, and I will be whiter than snow.
8   Let me hear ⌊sounds of⌋ joy and gladness.
     Let the bones that you have broken dance.
9 Hide your face from my sins,
    and wipe out all that I have done wrong.

10 Create a clean heart in me, O God,
     and renew a faithful spirit within me.
11 Do not force me away from your presence,
     and do not take your Holy Spirit from me.
12 Restore the joy of your salvation to me,
     and provide me with a spirit of willing obedience.

13 ⌊Then⌋ I will teach your ways to those who are rebellious,
     and sinners will return to you.
14 Rescue me from the guilt of murder,
     O God, my savior.
    Let my tongue sing joyfully about your righteousness!
15 O Lord, open my lips,

ᵃ 50:16 Or "covenant."   ᵃ 51:6 Hebrew meaning uncertain.   ᵇ 51:7 Branches from the hyssop plant were used in purification rites.   ᶜ 51:7 "Clean" refers to anything that Moses' Teachings say is presentable to God.

and my mouth will tell about your praise.
16 You are not happy with any sacrifice.
    Otherwise, I would offer one ˌto youˌ.
You are not pleased with burnt offerings.
17   The sacrifice pleasing to God is a broken spirit.
    O God, you do not despise a broken and sorrowful heart.
18 Favor Zion with your goodness.
Rebuild the walls of Jerusalem.
19   Then you will be pleased with sacrifices offered in the right spirit—
        with burnt offerings and whole burnt offerings.
            Young bulls will be offered on your altar.

PSALM 52

For the choir director; a *maskil;* a psalm by David when Doeg (who was from Edom)
told Saul that David had come to Ahimelech's home.

1 Why do you brag about the evil you've done, you hero?
    The mercy of God lasts all day long!
2 Your tongue makes up threats.
    It's like a sharp razor, you master of deceit.
3 You prefer evil to good.
    You prefer lying to speaking the truth.   *Selah*
4 You love every destructive accusation, you deceitful tongue!

5 But God will ruin you forever.
    He will grab you and drag you out of your tent.
    He will pull your roots out of this world of the living.   *Selah*
6   Righteous people will see ˌthisˌ and be struck with fear.
    They will laugh at you and say,
7   "Look at this person who refused to make God his fortress!
            Instead, he trusted his great wealth
                and became strong through his greed."

8 But I am like a large olive tree in God's house.
    I trust the mercy of God forever and ever.
9 I will give thanks to you forever
        for what you have done.
    In the presence of your godly people,
        I will wait with hope in your good name.

PSALM 53[a]

For the choir director; according to *mahalath,*[b] a *maskil* by David.

1 Godless fools say in their hearts,
    "There is no God."
They are corrupt.
They do disgusting things.
    There is no one who does good things.
2 God looks down from heaven on Adam's descendants
        to see if there is anyone who acts wisely,
            if there is anyone who seeks help from God.
3   Everyone has fallen away.
        Together they have become rotten to the core.
            No one, not even one person, does good things.
4 Are all those troublemakers,
        those who devour my people as if they were devouring food,
            so ignorant that they do not call on God?
5 There they are—panic-stricken—
    ˌbutˌ there was no reason to panic,
        because God has scattered the bones
            of those who set up camp against you.[c]
    You put them to shame.
        After all, God has rejected them.

---

[a] 53:1 Psalm 53 is virtually identical in wording to Psalm 14.   [b] 53:1 Unknown musical term.   [c] 53:5 Hebrew meaning uncertain.

⁶ If only salvation for Israel would come from Zion!
When God restores the fortunes of his people,
   Jacob will rejoice.
   Israel will be glad.

PSALM 54

For the choir director; on stringed instruments; a *maskil* by David when people from
the city of Ziph told Saul that David was hiding among them.

¹ O God, save me by your name,
   and defend me with your might.
² O God, hear my prayer,
   and open your ears to the words from my mouth.

³ Strangers have attacked me.
Ruthless people seek my life.
   They do not think about God.[a]   *Selah*

⁴ God is my helper!
The Lord is the provider for my life.
⁵   My enemies spy on me.
   Pay them back with evil.
   Destroy them with your truth!

⁶ I will make a sacrifice to you along with a freewill offering.
I will give thanks to your good name, O LORD.
⁷   Your name rescues me from every trouble.
   My eyes will gloat over my enemies.

PSALM 55

For the choir director; on stringed instruments; a *maskil* by David.

¹ Open your ears to my prayer, O God.
Do not hide from my plea for mercy.
² Pay attention to me, and answer me.
   My thoughts are restless, and I am confused
³   because my enemy shouts at me
   and a wicked person persecutes me.
      They bring misery crashing down on me,
      and they attack me out of anger.
⁴ My heart is in turmoil.
   The terrors of death have seized me.
⁵ Fear and trembling have overcome me.
Horror has overwhelmed me.
⁶ I said, "If only I had wings like a dove—
   I would fly away and find rest.
⁷   Indeed, I would run far away.
   I would stay in the desert.
⁸   I would hurry to find shelter
      from the raging wind and storm."   *Selah*

⁹ Completely confuse their language, O Lord,
   because I see violence and conflict in the city.
¹⁰ Day and night they go around on ˌtop ofˌ the city walls.
   Trouble and misery are everywhere.
¹¹ Destruction is everywhere.
   Oppression and fraud never leave the streets.[a]

¹² If an enemy had insulted me,
   then I could bear it.
If someone who hated me had attacked me,
   then I could hide from him.
¹³ But it is you, my equal,
   my best friend,
      one I knew so well!

---

[a] 54:3 Hebrew meaning of this line uncertain.   [a] 55:11 Or "its marketplace."

14   We used to talk to each other in complete confidence
            and walk into God's house with the festival crowds.

15 Let death suddenly take ˌwicked peopleˌ!
    Let them go into the grave while they are still alive,
        because evil lives in their homes as well as in their hearts.
16 But I call on God,
        and the LORD saves me.
17 Morning, noon, and night I complain and groan,
        and he listens to my voice.
18 With ˌhisˌ peace, he will rescue my soul
        from the war waged against me,
            because there are many ˌsoldiers fightingˌ against me.
19 God will listen.
        The one who has sat enthroned from the beginning
            will deal with them.   *Selah*
                They neverˌchange. They never fear God.
20 ˌMy best friendˌ has betrayed his friends.
        He has broken his solemn promise.
21   His speech is smoother than butter,
            but there is war in his heart.
        His words are more soothing than oil,
            but they are like swords ready to attack.
22 Turn your burdens over to the LORD,
        and he will take care of you.
        He will never let the righteous person stumble.
23 But you, O God, will throw ˌwicked peopleˌ into the deepest pit.
        Bloodthirsty and deceitful people will not live out half their days.
        But I will trust you.

PSALM 56

For the choir director; according to *yonath elem rechokim;*[a] a *miktam* by David when
the Philistines captured him in Gath.

1   Have pity on me, O God, because people are harassing me.
        All day long warriors oppress me.
2   All day long my enemies spy on me.
            They harass me.
            There are so many fighting against me.
3   Even when I am afraid, I still trust you.

4   I praise the word of God.
        I trust God.
        I am not afraid.
            What can mere flesh ˌand bloodˌ do to me?

5   All day long my enemies twist my words.
    Their every thought is an evil plan against me.
6   They attack, and then they hide.
    They watch my every step as they wait to take my life.
7   With the wrong they do, can they escape?
    O God, angrily make the nations fall.
8   (You have kept a record of my wanderings.
            Put my tears in your bottle.
                They are already in your book.)
9   Then my enemies will retreat when I call ˌto youˌ.
    This I know: God is on my side.

10   I praise the word of God.
        I praise the word of the LORD.
11   I trust God.
        I am not afraid.
            What can mortals do to me?

12 I am bound by my vows to you, O God.
    I will keep my vows by offering songs of thanksgiving to you.

---
[a] 56:1 Unknown musical term.

13 You have rescued me from death.
    You have kept my feet from stumbling
        so that I could walk in your presence, in the light of life.

PSALM 57

For the choir director; *al tashcheth;*[a] a *miktam* by David when he fled from Saul into the cave.

1   Have pity on me, O God. Have pity on me,
        because my soul takes refuge in you.
            I will take refuge in the shadow of your wings
                until destructive storms pass by.
2   I call to God Most High,
        to the God who does everything for me.
3   He sends his help from heaven and saves me.
    He disgraces the one who is harassing me.   *Selah*
    God sends his mercy and his truth!
4   My soul is surrounded by lions.
    I must lie down with man-eating lions.
        Their teeth are spears and arrows.
        Their tongues are sharp swords.
5   May you be honored above the heavens, O God.
            Let your glory extend over the whole earth.

6   ⸢My enemies⸣ spread out a net to catch me.
        (My soul is bowed down.)[b]
    They dug a pit to trap me,
        but then they fell into it.   *Selah*
7   My heart is confident, O God.
    My heart is confident.
    I want to sing and make music.[c]
8   Wake up, my soul![d]
    Wake up, harp and lyre!
    I want to wake up at dawn.
9   I want to give thanks to you among the people, O Lord.
    I want to make music to praise you among the nations
10   because your mercy is as high as the heavens.
        Your truth reaches the skies.

11   May you be honored above the heavens, O God.
            Let your glory extend over the whole earth.

PSALM 58

For the choir director; *al tashcheth;* a *miktam* by David.

1   Do you rulers really give fair verdicts?
    Do you judge Adam's descendants fairly?
2   No, you invent new crimes on earth,
            and your hands spread violence.

3   ⸢Even⸣ inside the womb wicked people are strangers ⸢to God⸣.
    From their birth liars go astray.
4   They have poisonous venom like snakes.
        They are like a deaf cobra that shuts its ears
5   so that it cannot hear the voice of a snake charmer
                or of anyone trained to cast spells.

6   O God, knock the teeth out of their mouths.
        Break the young lions' teeth, O Lᴏʀᴅ.
7   Let them disappear like water that drains away.
        When they aim their bows, let their arrows miss the target.[a]
8   Let them become like a snail that leaves behind a slimy trail
            or like a stillborn child who never sees the sun.

---

[a] 57:1 Unknown musical term.   [b] 57:6 Hebrew meaning of this line uncertain.   [c] 57:7 Verses 7–11 are virtually identical in wording to Psalm 108:1–5.   [d] 57:8 Or "my glory."   [a] 58:7 Hebrew meaning of this sentence uncertain.

9 Let ⌐God¬ sweep them away
    faster than a cooking pot is heated by burning twigs.[b]

10 Righteous people will rejoice when they see ⌐God¬ take revenge.
    They will wash their feet in the blood of wicked people.
11 Then people will say,
    "Righteous people certainly have a reward.
    There is a God who judges on earth."

PSALM 59

For the choir director; *al tashcheth;* a *miktam* by David when Saul sent men to watch David's home and kill him.

1 Rescue me from my enemies, O my God.
    Protect me from those who attack me.
2 Rescue me from troublemakers.
    Save me from bloodthirsty people.
3   They lie in ambush for me right here!
    Fierce men attack me, O LORD,
        but not because of any disobedience,
4   or any sin, or any guilt on my part.
    They hurry to take positions against me.
Wake up, and help me; see ⌐for yourself¬.
5 O LORD God of Armies, God of Israel,
    arise to punish all the nations.
    Have no pity on any traitors.   *Selah*

6   They return in the evening.
    They howl like dogs.
    They prowl the city.

7 See what pours out of their mouths—
    swords from their lips!
    ⌐They think,¬ "Who will hear us?"
8 O LORD, you laugh at them.
    You make fun of all the nations.

9 O my strength, I watch for you!
    God is my stronghold, my merciful God!

10 God will come to meet me.
    He will let me gloat over those who spy on me.
11 Do not kill them.
    Otherwise, my people may forget.
Make them wander aimlessly by your power.
Bring them down, O Lord, our shield,
12   ⌐because of¬ the sins from their mouths
        and the words on their lips.
Let them be trapped by their own arrogance
    because they speak curses and lies.
13 Destroy them in your rage.
Destroy them until not one of them is left.
    Then they will know that God rules Jacob
    to the ends of the earth.   *Selah*

14   They return in the evening.
    They howl like dogs.
    They prowl the city.

15 They wander around to find something to eat.
    If they are not full enough,
        they will stay all night.
16 But I will sing about your strength.
    In the morning I will joyfully sing about your mercy.
        You have been my stronghold
        and a place of safety in times of trouble.

---

[b] 58:9 Hebrew meaning uncertain.

17 O my strength, I will make music to praise you!
    God is my stronghold, my merciful God!

PSALM 60

For the choir director; according to *shushan eduth;*[a] a *miktam* by David; for teaching.
When David fought Aram Naharaim and Aram Zobah, and ˻when˼ Joab came back and
killed 12,000 men from Edom in the Dead Sea region.

1 O God, you have rejected us.
   You have broken down our defenses.
   You have been angry.
   Restore us!
2 You made the land quake.
   You split it wide open.
      Heal the cracks in it
      because it is falling apart.
3 You have made your people experience hardships.
   You have given us wine that makes us stagger.
4 Yet, you have raised a flag for those who fear you
      so that they can rally to it
      when attacked by bows ˻and arrows˼.   *Selah*
5 Save ˻us˼ with your powerful hand, and answer us
      so that those who are dear to you may be rescued.[b]

6 God has promised the following through his holiness:
   "I will triumph!
   I will divide Shechem.
   I will measure the valley of Succoth.
7   Gilead is mine.
      Manasseh is mine.
      Ephraim is the helmet on my head.
      Judah is my scepter.
8   Moab is my washtub.
      I will throw my shoe over Edom.
      I will shout in triumph over Philistia."

9 Who will bring me into the fortified city?
   Who will lead me to Edom?
10   Isn't it you, O God, who rejected us?
      Isn't it you, O God, who refused to accompany our armies?

11 Give us help against the enemy
      because human assistance is worthless.
12   With God we will display great strength.
       He will trample our enemies.

PSALM 61

For the choir director; on a stringed instrument; by David.

1 Listen to my cry for help, O God.
   Pay attention to my prayer.
2   From the ends of the earth, I call to you
      when I begin to lose heart.
   Lead me to the rock that is high above me.
3   You have been my refuge,
      a tower of strength against the enemy.
4 I would like to be a guest in your tent forever
      and to take refuge under the protection of your wings.   *Selah*
5   O God, you have heard my vows.
         You have given me the inheritance
         that belongs to those who fear your name.
6 Add days upon days to the life of the king.
   May his years endure throughout every generation.
7 May he sit enthroned in the presence of God forever.

---

a 60:1 Unknown musical term.   *b* 60:5 Verses 5–12 are virtually identical in wording to Psalm 108:6–13.

May mercy and truth protect him.
8   Then I will make music to praise your name forever,
          as I keep my vows day after day.

PSALM 62

For the choir director; according to Jeduthun; a psalm by David.

1   My soul waits calmly for God alone.
        My salvation comes from him.
2   He alone is my rock and my savior—my stronghold.
        I cannot be severely shaken.

3   How long will all of you attack a person?
     How long will you try to murder him,
        as though he were a leaning wall or a sagging fence?
4   They plan to force him out of his high position.
           They are happy to lie.
           They bless with their mouths,
              but in their hearts they curse.   *Selah*

5   Wait calmly for God alone, my soul,
        because my hope comes from him.
6   He alone is my rock and my savior—my stronghold.
        I cannot be shaken.

7   My salvation and my glory depend on God.
        God is the rock of my strength, my refuge.
8   Trust him at all times, you people.
     Pour out your hearts in his presence.
        God is our refuge.   *Selah*

9   Common people are only a whisper in the wind.
     Important people are only a delusion.
        When all of them are weighed on a scale, they amount to nothing.
        They are less than a whisper in the wind.
10   Do not count on extortion ˻to make you rich˼.
     Do not hope to gain anything through robbery.
        When riches increase, do not depend on them.

11   God has spoken once.
        I have heard it ˻said˼ twice:
           "Power belongs to God.
12   Mercy belongs to you, O Lord.
              You reward a person based on what he has done."

PSALM 63

A psalm by David when he was in the wilderness of Judah.

1   O God, you are my God.
        At dawn I search for you.
           My soul thirsts for you.
           My body longs for you
              in a dry, parched land where there is no water.
2   So I look for you in the holy place
        to see your power and your glory.
3   My lips will praise you
        because your mercy is better than life ˻itself˼.
4   So I will thank you as long as I live.
        I will lift up my hands ˻to pray˼ in your name.
5   You satisfy my soul with the richest foods.
        My mouth will sing ˻your˼ praise with joyful lips.
6   As I lie on my bed, I remember you.
        Through the long hours of the night, I think about you.
7   You have been my help.
        In the shadow of your wings, I sing joyfully.
8   My soul clings to you.
        Your right hand supports me.

⁹ But those who try to destroy my life
   will go into the depths of the earth.
¹⁰   They will be cut down by swords.
         Their dead bodies will be left as food for jackals.
¹¹ But the king will find joy in God.
     Everyone who takes an oath by God will brag,
         but the mouths of liars will be shut.

PSALM 64

For the choir director; a psalm by David.

¹ Hear my voice, O God, when I complain.
   Protect my life from a terrifying enemy.
² Hide me from the secret plots of criminals,
     from the mob of troublemakers.
³   They sharpen their tongues like swords.
       They aim bitter words like arrows
⁴   to shoot at innocent people from their hiding places.
       They shoot at them suddenly, without any fear.
⁵   They encourage one another in their evil plans.
       They talk about setting traps and say,
         "Who can see them?"
⁶   They search for the perfect crime and say,
         "We have perfected a foolproof scheme!"
           Human nature and the human heart are a mystery!

⁷ But God will shoot them with an arrow.
     Suddenly, they will be struck dead.
⁸ They will trip over their own tongues.
     Everyone who sees them will shake his head.
⁹ Everyone will be afraid and conclude,
     "This is an act of God!"
       They will learn from what he has done.

¹⁰ Righteous people will find joy in the LORD and take refuge in him.
   Everyone whose motives are decent will be able to brag.

PSALM 65

For the choir director; a psalm by David; a song.

¹ You are praised with silence in Zion, O God,
     and vows ⌞made⌟ to you must be kept.
² You are the one who hears prayers.
     Everyone will come to you.
³ Various sins overwhelm me.
     You are the one who forgives our rebellious acts.
⁴ Blessed is the person you choose
     and invite to live with you in your courtyards.
       We will be filled with good food from your house,
         from your holy temple.

⁵ You answer us with awe-inspiring acts ⌞done⌟ in righteousness,
     O God, our savior,
       the hope of all the ends of the earth and of the most distant sea,
⁶   the one who set the mountains in place with his strength,
       the one who is clothed with power,
⁷   the one who calms the roar of the seas,
         their crashing waves,
           and the uproar of the nations.
⁸ Those who live at the ends of the earth are in awe of your miraculous signs.
   The lands of the morning sunrise and evening sunset sing joyfully.

⁹ You take care of the earth, and you water it.
   You make it much richer than it was.
     (The river of God is filled with water.)
   You provide grain for them.
     Indeed, you even prepare the ground.
¹⁰ You drench plowed fields ⌞with rain⌟

and level their clumps of soil.
You soften them with showers
and bless what grows in them.

11 You crown the year with your goodness,
and richness overflows wherever you are.

12   The pastures in the desert overflow ˌwith richnessˌ.
The hills are surrounded with joy.

13   The pastures are covered with flocks.
The valleys are carpeted with grain.
All of them shout triumphantly. Indeed, they sing.

PSALM 66

For the choir director; a song; a psalm.

1 Shout happily to God, all the earth!
2 Make music to praise the glory of his name.
Make his praise glorious.
3 Say to God,
"How awe-inspiring are your deeds!
Your power is so great that your enemies will cringe in front of you.
4 The whole earth will worship you.
It will make music to praise you.
It will make music to praise your name."   *Selah*
5 Come and see what God has done—
his awe-inspiring deeds for Adam's descendants.
6 He turned the sea into dry land.
They crossed the river on foot.
We rejoiced because of what he did there.
7 He rules forever with his might.
His eyes watch the nations.
Rebels will not be able to oppose him.   *Selah*

8 Thank our God, you nations.
Make the sound of his praise heard.
9 He has kept us alive
and has not allowed us to fall.
10 You have tested us, O God.
You have refined us in the same way silver is refined.
11 You have trapped us in a net.
You have laid burdens on our backs.
12 You let people ride over our heads.
We went through fire and water,
but then you brought us out and refreshed us.

13 I will come into your temple with burnt offerings.
I will keep my vows to you,
14   the vows made by my lips and spoken by my ˌownˌ mouth
when I was in trouble.
15 I will offer you a sacrifice of fattened livestock for burnt offerings
with the smoke from rams.
I will offer cattle and goats.   *Selah*

16 Come and listen, all who fear God,
and I will tell you what he has done for me.
17   With my mouth I cried out to him.
High praise was on my tongue.
18 If I had thought about doing anything sinful,
the Lord would not have listened ˌto meˌ.
19 But God has heard me.
He has paid attention to my prayer.

20 Thanks be to God,
who has not rejected my prayer
or taken away his mercy from me.

PSALM 67

For the choir director; on stringed instruments; a psalm; a song.

1 May God have pity on us and bless us!
  May he smile on us.   *Selah*
2   Then your ways will be known on earth,
      your salvation throughout all nations.

3 Let everyone give thanks to you, O God.
  Let everyone give thanks to you.
4 Let the nations be glad and sing joyfully
      because you judge everyone with justice
      and guide the nations on the earth.   *Selah*
5 Let the people give thanks to you, O God.
  Let all the people give thanks to you.
6   The earth has yielded its harvest.
  May God, our God, bless us.
7 May God bless us,
      and may all the ends of the earth worship him.

PSALM 68

For the choir director; a psalm by David; a song.

1 God will arise.
  His enemies will be scattered.
  Those who hate him will flee from him.
2   Blow them away like smoke.
      Let wicked people melt in God's presence like wax next to a fire.

3 But let righteous people rejoice.
      Let them celebrate in God's presence.
      Let them overflow with joy.
4 Sing to God; make music to praise his name.
  Make a highway for him to ride through the deserts.*
      The LORD is his name.
  Celebrate in his presence.

5 The God who is in his holy dwelling place
      is the father of the fatherless and the defender of widows.
6 God places lonely people in families.
      He leads prisoners out of prison into productive lives,
          but rebellious people must live in an unproductive land.

7 O God, when you went in front of your people,
      when you marched through the desert,   *Selah*
8   the earth quaked and the sky poured
          in the presence of the God of Sinai,
          in the presence of the God of Israel.

9 You watered the land with plenty of rain, O God.
      You refreshed it when your land was exhausted.
10   Your flock settled there.
          Out of your goodness, O God,
              you provided for oppressed people.

11 The Lord gives instructions.
   The women who announce the good news are a large army.
12   ˻They say,˼ "The kings of the armies flee; they run away.
          The women who remained at home will divide the goods.
13   Though you stayed among the sheep pens,
              ˻you will be like˼ the wings of a dove covered with silver,
                  its feathers with yellow gold.
14   Meanwhile, the Almighty was still scattering kings there
                  like snow falling on Mount Zalmon."

---

a 68:4 Or "Lift a song to him who rides upon the clouds."

15   The mountain of Bashan is the mountain of God.
       The mountain of Bashan is the mountain with many peaks.
16   Why do you look with envy, you mountains with many peaks,
             at the mountain where God has chosen to live?
                 Certainly, the LORD will live there forever.

17   The chariots of God are twenty thousand in number,
             thousands upon thousands.
                 The Lord is among them.
                     ⌊The God of⌋ Sinai is in his holy place.
18   You went to the highest place.
       You took prisoners captive.
       You received gifts from people,
             even from rebellious people, so that the LORD God may live there.

19   Thanks be to the Lord,
           who daily carries our burdens for us.
               God is our salvation.   *Selah*
20   Our God is the God of victories.
       The Almighty LORD is our escape from death.

21   Certainly, God will crush the heads of his enemies
           ⌊and destroy even⌋ the hair on the heads
           of those who continue to be guilty.
22   The Lord said, "I will bring them back from Bashan.
       I will bring them back from the depths of the sea
23   so that you, ⌊my people,⌋ may bathe[b] your feet in blood
                 and the tongues of your dogs
                     may lick the blood of your enemies."

24   Your festival processions, O God, can be seen by everyone.
       They are the processions for my God, my king, into the holy place.
25   The singers are in front.
               The musicians are behind them.
               The young women beating tambourines are between them.
26   Thank God, the Lord, the source of Israel, with the choirs.
27   Benjamin, the youngest, is leading them,
                 ⌊next,⌋ the leaders of Judah with their noisy crowds,
                     ⌊then,⌋ the leaders of Zebulun,
                     ⌊then,⌋ the leaders of Naphtali.

28   Your God has decided you will be strong.
           Display your strength, O God,
               as you have for us before.
29   Kings will bring you gifts
           because of your temple high above Jerusalem.
30   Threaten the beast who is among the cattails,
           the herd of bulls with the calves of the nations,
               until it humbles itself with pieces of silver.
       Scatter the people who find joy in war.[c]
31   ⌊Ambassadors will come from Egypt.
       Sudan will stretch out its hands to God ⌊in prayer⌋.

32   You kingdoms of the world, sing to God.
       Make music to praise the Lord.   *Selah*
33   God rides through the ancient heaven, the highest heaven.
           Listen! He makes his voice heard, his powerful voice.
34   Acknowledge the power of God.
               His majesty is over Israel, and his power is in the skies.

35   God, the God of Israel, is awe-inspiring in his holy place.
       He gives strength and power to his people.
           Thanks be to God!

---

[b] 68:23 Greek, Targum, Syriac; Masoretic Text "shatter."   [c] 68:30 Hebrew meaning of this verse uncertain.

PSALM 69

For the choir director; according to *shoshannim;* by David.

1 Save me, O God!
   The water is already up to my neck!
2 I am sinking in deep mud.
   There is nothing to stand on.
   I am in deep water.
   A flood is sweeping me away.
3 I am exhausted from crying for help.
   My throat is hoarse.
   My eyes are strained ˻from˼ looking for my God.
4   Those who hate me for no reason
          outnumber the hairs on my head.
      Those who want to destroy me are mighty.
          They have no reason to be my enemies.
   I am forced to pay back what I did not steal.

5 O God, you know my stupidity,
   and the things of which I am guilty are not hidden from you.
6 Do not let those who wait with hope for you
   be put to shame because of me, O Almighty LORD of Armies.
   Do not let those who come to you for help
   be humiliated because of me, O God of Israel.

7 Indeed, for your sake I have endured insults.
   Humiliation has covered my face.
8 I have become a stranger to my ˻own˼ brothers,
   a foreigner to my mother's sons.
9 Indeed, devotion for your house has consumed me,
   and the insults of those who insult you have fallen on me.
10 I cried and fasted, but I was insulted for it.
11 I dressed myself in sackcloth, but I became the object of ridicule.
12   Those who sit at the gate gossip about me,
          and drunkards make up songs about me.

13 May my prayer come to you at an acceptable time, O LORD.
    O God, out of the greatness of your mercy,
          answer me with the truth of your salvation.
14 Rescue me from the mud.
    Do not let me sink ˻into it˼.
    I want to be rescued from those who hate me
    and from the deep water.
15 Do not let floodwaters sweep me away.
    Do not let the ocean swallow me up,
          or the pit close its mouth over me.
16 Answer me, O LORD, because your mercy is good.
    Out of your unlimited compassion, turn to me.
17 I am in trouble, so do not hide your face from me.
    Answer me quickly!
18 Come close, and defend my soul.
    Set me free because of my enemies.

19 You know that I have been insulted, put to shame, and humiliated.
    All my opponents are in front of you.
20 Insults have broken my heart, and I am sick.
    I looked for sympathy, but there was none.
    I looked for people to comfort me, but I found no one.
21   They poisoned my food,
              and when I was thirsty, they gave me vinegar to drink.

22 Let the table set for them become a trap
    and a snare for their friends.
23 Let their vision become clouded so that they cannot see.
    Let their thighs continually shake.

24 Pour your rage on them.
    Let your burning anger catch up with them.

25 Let their camp be deserted
     and their tents empty.

26 They persecute the one you have struck,
     and they talk about the pain of those you have wounded.
27 Charge them with one crime after another.
     Do not let them be found innocent.
28 Let their ˌnamesˌ be erased from the Book of Life.
     Do not let them be listed with righteous people.

29 I am suffering and in pain.
     Let your saving power protect me, O God.
30 I want to praise the name of God with a song.
     I want to praise its greatness with a song of thanksgiving.
31   This will please the LORD more than ˌsacrificingˌ an ox
     or a bull with horns and hoofs.
32 Oppressed people will see ˌthisˌ and rejoice.
     May the hearts of those who look to God for help be refreshed.

33 The LORD listens to needy people.
     He does not despise his own who are in prison.
34 Let heaven and earth, the seas, and everything that moves in them, praise him.
35 When God saves Zion, he will rebuild the cities of Judah.
     His servants will live there and take possession of it.
36   The descendants of his servants will inherit it.
     Those who love him will live there.

PSALM 70[a]

For the choir director; by David; to be kept in mind.

1 Come quickly to rescue me, O God!
  Come quickly to help me, O LORD!
2 Let those who seek my life
     be confused and put to shame.
  Let those who want my downfall
     be turned back and disgraced.
3 Let those who say, "Aha! Aha!"
     be turned back because of their own shame.
4 Let all who seek you rejoice and be glad because of you.
  Let those who love your salvation continually say,
     "God is great!"

5 But I am oppressed and needy.
  O God, come to me quickly.
     You are my help and my savior.
       O LORD, do not delay!

PSALM 71

1 I have taken refuge in you, O LORD.
  Never let me be put to shame.
2 Rescue me and free me because of your righteousness.
  Turn your ear toward me, and save me.
3   Be a rock on which I may live,
     a place where I may always go.
       You gave the order to save me!
     Indeed, you are my rock and my fortress.
4 My God, free me from the hands of a wicked person,
     from the grasp of one who is cruel and unjust.
5 You are my hope, O Almighty LORD.
  You have been my confidence ever since I was young.
6 I depended on you before I was born.
     You took me from my mother's womb.
       My songs of praise constantly speak about you.
7 I have become an example to many people,

---

[a] 70:1 Psalm 70 is virtually identical in wording to Psalm 40:13–17.

but you are my strong refuge.
8 My mouth is filled with your praise,
with your glory all day long.

9 Do not reject me when I am old
or abandon me when I lose my strength.
10 My enemies talk about me.
They watch me as they plot to take my life.
11 They say, "God has abandoned him.
Pursue him and grab him because there is no one to rescue him."
12 O God, do not be so distant from me.
O my God, come quickly to help me.
13 Let those who accuse me come to a shameful end.
Let those who want my downfall be covered
with disgrace and humiliation.
14 But I will always have hope.
I will praise you more and more.
15 My mouth will tell about your righteousness,
about your salvation all day long.
Even then, it is more than I can understand.
16 I will come with the mighty deeds of the Almighty Lord.
I will praise your righteousness, yours alone.

17 O God, you have taught me ever since I was young,
and I still talk about the miracles you have done.
18 Even when I am old and gray, do not abandon me, O God.
Let me live to tell the people of this age
what your strength has accomplished,
to tell about your power to all who will come.

19 Your righteousness reaches to the heavens, O God.
You have done great things.
O God, who is like you?
20 You have made me endure many terrible troubles.
You restore me to life again.
You bring me back from the depths of the earth.
21 You comfort me and make me greater than ever.

22 Because of your faithfulness, O my God,
even I will give thanks to you as I play on a lyre.
I will make music with a harp to praise you, O Holy One of Israel.
23 My lips will sing with joy when I make music to praise you.
My soul, which you have rescued, also will sing joyfully.
24 My tongue will tell about your righteousness all day long,
because those who wanted my downfall
have been disgraced and put to shame.

PSALM 72

By Solomon.

1 O God, give the king your justice
and the king's son[a] your righteousness
2   so that he may judge your people with righteousness
and your oppressed ⌊people⌋ with justice.

3 May the mountains bring peace to the people
and the hills bring righteousness.
4 May he grant justice to the people who are oppressed.
May he save the children of needy people
and crush their oppressor.
5 May they fear you as long as the sun and moon ⌊shine⌋,—
throughout every generation.
6 May he be like rain that falls on ⌊freshly⌋ cut grass,
like showers that water the land.
7 May righteous people blossom in his day.
May there be unlimited peace until the moon no longer ⌊shines⌋.

---

a 72:1 According to ancient Jewish and Christian tradition, "king" and "king's son" refer to the Messiah.

8 May he rule from sea to sea,
    from the Euphrates River to the ends of the earth.
9 May the people of the desert kneel in front of him.
    May his enemies lick the dust.
10 May the kings from Tarshish and the islands bring presents.
    May the kings from Sheba and Seba bring gifts.
11 May all kings worship him.
    May all nations serve him.

12   He will rescue the needy person who cries for help
        and the oppressed person who has no one's help.
13   He will have pity on the poor and needy
        and will save the lives of the needy.
14   He will rescue them from oppression and violence.
        Their blood will be precious in his sight.

15 May he live long.
    May the gold from Sheba be given to him.
    May ˻the people˼ pray for him continually.
    May ˻they˼ praise him all day long.
16 May there be plenty of grain in the land.
    May it wave ˻in the breeze˼ on the mountaintops,
        its fruit like ˻the treetops of˼ Lebanon.
    May those from the city flourish like the grass on the ground.
17 May his name endure forever.
    May his name continue as long as the sun ˻shines˼.
    May all nations be blessed through him and call him blessed.

18 Thank the LORD God, the God of Israel,
    who alone does miracles.
19 Thanks be to his glorious name forever.
    May the whole earth be filled with his glory.

                                    Amen and amen!

20 The prayers by David, son of Jesse, end here.

BOOK THREE
Psalms 73–89

PSALM 73

A psalm by Asaph.

1   God is truly good to Israel,
        to those whose lives are pure.

2   But my feet had almost stumbled.
        They had almost slipped
3   because I was envious of arrogant people
                when I saw the prosperity that wicked people enjoy.

4   They suffer no pain.
    Their bodies are healthy.
5   They have no drudgery in their lives like ordinary people.
    They are not plagued ˻with problems˼ like others.
6   That is why they wear arrogance like a necklace
        and acts of violence like clothing.
7   Their eyes peer out from their fat faces,[a]
        and their imaginations run wild.
8   They ridicule.
    They speak maliciously.
    They speak arrogantly about oppression.
9   They verbally attack heaven,
        and they order people around on earth.
10   That is why God's people turn to wickedness[a]

---
[a] 73:7, 10 Hebrew meaning uncertain.

and swallow their words.
11 Then wicked people ask, "What does God know?"
   "Does the Most High know anything?"
12 Look how wicked they are!
   They never have a worry.
     They grow more and more wealthy.

13 I've received no reward for keeping my life pure
   and washing my hands of any blame.
14 I'm plagued ˻with problems˼ all day long,
   and every morning my punishment ˻begins again˼.
15 If I had said, "I will continue to talk like that,"
   I would have betrayed God's people.

16 But when I tried to understand this,
   it was too difficult for me.
17 Only when I came into God's holy place
   did I ˻finally˼ understand what would happen to them.

18 You put them in slippery places
   and make them fall into ruin.
19 They are suddenly destroyed.
   They are completely swept away by terror!
20 As ˻someone˼ gets rid of a dream when he wakes up,
   so you, O Lord, get rid of the thought of them
     when you wake up.

21 When my heart was filled with bitterness
   and my mind was seized ˻with envy˼,
22 I was stupid, and I did not understand.
   I was like a dumb animal in your presence.
23 Yet, I am always with you.
   You hold on to my right hand.
24   With your advice you guide me,
       and in the end you will take me to glory.
25 As long as I have you,
   I don't need anyone else in heaven or on earth.
26 My body and mind may waste away,
   but God remains the foundation of my life
     and my inheritance forever.
27 Without a doubt, those who are far from you will die.
   You destroy all who are unfaithful to you.

28 Being united with God is my highest good.
   I have made the Almighty LORD my refuge
     so that I may report everything that he has done.

PSALM 74

A *maskil*[a] by Asaph.

1 Why, O God, have you rejected us forever?
  Why does your anger
    smolder against the sheep in your care?

2 Remember your congregation.
    Long ago you made it your own.
    You bought this tribe to be your possession.
      This tribe is Mount Zion, where you have made your home.
3 Turn your steps toward[b] these pathetic ruins.
    The enemy has destroyed everything in the holy temple.

4 Your opponents have roared inside your meeting place.
    They have set up their own emblems as symbols.
5   Starting from its entrance, they hacked away
        like a woodcutter in a forest.[c]
6 They smashed all its carved paneling with axes and hatchets.

---

[a] 74:1 Unknown musical term.   [b] 74:3 Hebrew meaning uncertain.   [c] 74:5 Hebrew meaning of this verse uncertain.

7   They burned your holy place to the ground.
      They dishonored the place where you live among us.
8   They said to themselves, "We will crush them."
      They burned every meeting place of God in the land.

9   We no longer see miraculous signs.
      There are no prophets anymore.
        No one knows how long this will last.
10   How long, O God, will the enemy insult us?
      Will the enemy despise you forever?
11   Why do you hold back your hand, especially your right hand?
      Take your hands out of your pockets.
        Destroy your enemies!*d*

12   And yet, from long ago God has been my king,
      the one who has been victorious throughout the earth.
13   You stirred up the sea with your own strength.
      You smashed the heads of sea monsters in the water.
14   You crushed the heads of Leviathan*e*
      and gave them to the creatures of the desert for food.
15   You opened the springs and brooks.
      You dried up the ever-flowing rivers.
16   The day and the night are yours.
      You set the moon and the sun in their places.
17   You determined all the boundaries of the earth.
      You created summer and winter.

18   Remember how the enemy insulted you, O Lord.
      Remember how an entire nation of godless fools despised your name.
19   Do not hand over the soul of your dove to wild animals.
      Do not forget the life of your oppressed people forever.
20   Consider your promise*f*
      because every dark corner of the land is filled with violence.
21   Do not let oppressed people come back in disgrace.
      Let weak and needy people praise your name.
22   Arise, O God!
      Fight for your own cause!
      Remember how godless fools insult you all day long.
23   Do not forget the shouting of your opponents.
      Do not forget the uproar made by those who attack you.

PSALM 75

For the choir director; *al tashcheth;* a psalm by Asaph; a song.

1   We give thanks to you, O God; we give thanks.
      You are present, and your miracles confirm that.

2   When I choose the right time,
      I will judge fairly.
3   When the earth and everyone who lives on it begin to melt,
      I will make its foundations as solid as rock.   *Selah*
4   I said to those who brag, "Don't brag,"
      and to wicked people,
        "Don't raise your weapons.
5   Don't raise your weapons so proudly
        or speak so defiantly."

6   The ˌauthorityˌ to reward someone does not ˌcomeˌ
      from the east,
       from the west,
        or ˌevenˌ from the wilderness.
7   God alone is the judge.
      He punishes one person and rewards another.
8   A cup is in the Lord's hand.
      (Its foaming wine is thoroughly mixed with spices.)
      He will empty it,

---

d 74:11 Hebrew meaning of this verse uncertain.   *e* 74:14 Hebrew meaning uncertain.   *f* 74:20 Or "covenant."

⌊and⌋ all the wicked people on earth
will have to drink every last drop.

9 But I will speak ⌊about your miracles⌋ forever.
I will make music to praise the God of Jacob.
10 I will destroy all the weapons of wicked people,
but the weapons of righteous people will be raised proudly.

PSALM 76

For the choir director; on stringed instruments; a psalm by Asaph; a song.

1 God is known in Judah.
His name is great in Israel.
2 His tent is in Salem.
His home is in Zion.
3   There he destroyed flaming arrows,
shields, swords, and weapons of war.   *Selah*

4 You are the radiant one.
You are more majestic than the ancient mountains.[a]
5   Brave people were robbed.
They died.
None of the warriors were able to lift a hand.
6   At your stern warning, O God of Jacob,
chariot riders and horses were put to sleep.

7 You alone must be feared!
Who can stand in your presence when you become angry?
8   From heaven you announced a verdict.
The earth was fearful and silent
9   when you rose to judge, O God,
when you rose to save every oppressed person on earth.   *Selah*

10 Even angry mortals will praise you.
You will wear the remainder of ⌊their⌋ anger.[b]
11   Make vows to the Lord your God, and keep them.
Let everyone around him bring gifts to the one who must be feared.
12   He cuts short the lives of influential people.
He terrifies the kings of the earth.

PSALM 77

For the choir director; according to Jeduthun; a psalm by Asaph.

1 Loudly, I cried to God.
Loudly, I cried to God
so that he would open his ears to ⌊hear⌋ me.
2 On the day I was in trouble, I went to the Lord for help.
At night I stretched out my hands in prayer without growing tired.
Yet, my soul refused to be comforted.

3 I sigh as I remember God.
I begin to lose hope as I think about him.   *Selah*
4   (You keep my eyelids open.)
I am so upset that I cannot speak.
5 I have considered the days of old,
the years long ago.
6 I remember my song in the night
and reflect ⌊on it⌋.
My spirit searches ⌊for an answer⌋:
7   Will the Lord reject ⌊me⌋ for all time?
Will he ever accept me?
8   Has his mercy come to an end forever?
Has his promise been canceled throughout every generation?
9   Has God forgotten to be merciful?
Has he locked up his compassion because of his anger?   *Selah*

---

[a] 76:4 Greek, Syriac; Masoretic Text "mountains of prey."   [b] 76:10 Hebrew meaning of this line uncertain.

10　　　Then I said, "It makes me feel sick
　　　　　　that the power of the Most High is no longer the same."[a]

11　　I will remember the deeds of the LORD.
　　　I will remember your ancient miracles.
12　　I will reflect on all your actions
　　　　and think about what you have done.

13　　O God, your ways are holy!
　　　　What god is as great as our God?
14　　You are the God who performs miracles.
　　　You have made your strength known among the nations.
15　　With your might you have defended your people,
　　　　the descendants of Jacob and Joseph.　　　　　　　　　　*Selah*

16　　The water saw you, O God.
　　　The water saw you and shook.
　　　　Even the depths of the sea trembled.
17　　The clouds poured out water.
　　　The sky thundered.
　　　　Even your arrows flashed in every direction.
18　　The sound of your thunder rumbled in the sky.[a]
　　　　Streaks of lightning lit up the world.
　　　　　The earth trembled and shook.

19　　Your road went through the sea.
　　　　Your path went through raging water,
　　　　　but your footprints could not be seen.
20　　Like a shepherd, you led your people.
　　　You had Moses and Aaron take them by the hand.

PSALM 78

A *maskil* by Asaph.

1　　Open your ears to my teachings, my people.
　　　Turn your ears to the words from my mouth.
2　　　I will open my mouth to illustrate points.
　　　　I will explain what has been hidden long ago,
3　　　　　things that we have heard and known about,
　　　　　things that our parents have told us.
4　　　　　　We will not hide them from our children.
　　　　　　We will tell the next generation
　　　　　　　about the LORD's power and great deeds
　　　　　　　　and the miraculous things he has done.

5　　He established written instructions for Jacob's people.
　　　He gave his teachings to Israel.
　　　He commanded our ancestors to make them known to their children
6　　　　so that the next generation would know them.
　　　　　Children yet to be born ˌwould learn themˌ.
　　　　They will grow up and tell their children
7　　　　　to trust God, to remember what he has done,
　　　　　　and to obey his commands.
8　　　　Then they will not be like their ancestors,
　　　　　a stubborn and rebellious generation.
　　　　　　Their hearts were not loyal.
　　　　　　Their spirits were not faithful to God.

9　　The men of Ephraim, well-equipped with bows ˌand arrowsˌ,
　　　　turned ˌand ranˌ on the day of battle.
10　　　They had not been faithful to God's promise.[a]
　　　　They refused to follow his teachings.
11　　　They forgot what he had done—
　　　　　the miracles that he had shown them.

---

[a] 77:10, 18 Hebrew meaning of this line uncertain.　　[a] 78:10 Or "covenant."

¹² In front of their ancestors he performed miracles
  in the land of Egypt, in the fields of Zoan.
¹³ He divided the sea and led them through it.
  He made the waters stand up like a wall.
¹⁴ He guided them by a cloud during the day
  and by a fiery light throughout the night.
¹⁵ He split rocks in the desert.
  He gave them plenty to drink, an ocean of water.
¹⁶ He made streams come out of a rock.
  He made the water flow like rivers.

¹⁷ They continued to sin against him,
  to rebel in the desert against the Most High.
¹⁸ They deliberately tested God by demanding the food they craved.
¹⁹ They spoke against God by saying,
  "Can God prepare a banquet in the desert?
²⁰ True, he did strike a rock,
    and water did gush out,
    and the streams did overflow.
  But can he also give us bread or provide us, his people, with meat?"

²¹ When the LORD heard this, he became furious.
  His fire burned against Jacob
    and his anger flared up at Israel
²²   because they did not believe God
        or trust him to save them.

²³ In spite of that, he commanded the clouds above
  and opened the doors of heaven.
²⁴ He rained manna down on them to eat
    and gave them grain from heaven.
²⁵ Humans ate the bread of the mighty ones,
    and God sent them plenty of food.

²⁶ He made the east wind blow in the heavens
  and guided the south wind with his might.
²⁷ He rained meat down on them like dust,
    birds like the sand on the seashore.
²⁸   He made the birds fall in the middle of his camp,
        all around his dwelling place.

²⁹ They ate more than enough.
  He gave them what they wanted,
³⁰   but they still wanted more.
      While the food was still in their mouths,
³¹   the anger of God flared up against them.
          He killed their strongest men
            and slaughtered the best young men in Israel.

³² In spite of all this, they continued to sin,
  and they no longer believed in his miracles.
³³ He brought their days to an end like a whisper in the wind.
  He brought their years to an end in terror.
³⁴ When he killed ˻some of˼ them, ˻the rest˼ searched for him.
  They turned from their sins and eagerly looked for God.
³⁵ They remembered that God was their rock,
    that the Most High was their defender.
³⁶ They flattered him with their mouths
    and lied to him with their tongues.
³⁷ Their hearts were not loyal to him.
  They were not faithful to his promise.

³⁸ But he is compassionate.
  He forgave their sin.
    He did not destroy them.
  He restrained his anger many times.
    He did not display all of his fury.
³⁹ He remembered that they were only flesh and blood,
    a breeze that blows and does not return.

⁴⁰ How often they rebelled against him in the wilderness!
How often they caused him grief in the desert!
⁴¹ Again and again they tested God,
  and they pushed the Holy One of Israel to the limit.
⁴² They did not remember his power—
  the day he freed them from their oppressor,
⁴³   when he performed his miraculous signs in Egypt,
    his wonders in the fields of Zoan.

⁴⁴ He turned their rivers into blood
  so that they could not drink from their streams.
⁴⁵ He sent a swarm of flies that bit them
  and frogs that ruined them.
⁴⁶ He gave their crops to grasshoppers
  and their produce to locusts.
⁴⁷ He killed their vines with hail
  and their fig trees with frost.
⁴⁸ He let the hail strike their cattle
  and bolts of lightning strike their livestock.
⁴⁹ He sent his burning anger, rage, fury, and hostility against them.
He sent an army of destroying angels.
⁵⁰ He cleared a path for his anger.
He did not spare them.
He let the plague take their lives.
⁵¹ He slaughtered every firstborn in Egypt,
  the ones born in the tents of Ham when their fathers were young.

⁵² But he led his own people out like sheep
  and guided them like a flock through the wilderness.
⁵³   He led them safely.
    They had no fear while the sea covered their enemies.
⁵⁴ He brought them into his holy land,
  to this mountain that his power had won.
⁵⁵   He forced nations out of their way
    and gave them the land of the nations as their inheritance.
    He settled the tribes of Israel in their own tents.

⁵⁶ They tested God Most High and rebelled against him.
They did not obey his written instructions.
⁵⁷ They were disloyal and treacherous like their ancestors.
They were like arrows shot from a defective bow.
⁵⁸ They made him angry because of their illegal worship sites.
They made him furious because they worshiped idols.

⁵⁹ When God heard, he became furious.
  He completely rejected Israel.
⁶⁰   He abandoned his dwelling place in Shiloh,
    the tent where he had lived among humans.
⁶¹ He allowed his power to be taken captive
  and handed his glory over to an oppressor.
⁶² He let swords kill his people.
  He was furious with those who belonged to him.
⁶³   Fire consumed his best young men,
    so his virgins heard no wedding songs.
⁶⁴   His priests were cut down with swords.
    The widows ˻of his priests˼ could not even weep ˻for them˼.
⁶⁵ Then the Lord woke up like one who had been sleeping,
  like a warrior sobering up from ˻too much˼ wine.
⁶⁶ He struck his enemies from behind
  and disgraced them forever.

⁶⁷ He rejected the tent of Joseph.
He did not choose the tribe of Ephraim,
⁶⁸   but he chose the tribe of Judah,
    Mount Zion which he loved.
⁶⁹ He built his holy place to be like the high heavens,
  like the earth which he made to last for a long time.

⁷⁰ He chose his servant David.
He took him from the sheep pens.

71 He brought him from tending the ewes that had lambs
    so that David could be the shepherd of the people of Jacob,
        of Israel, the people who belonged to the LORD.
72 With unselfish devotion David became their shepherd.
    With skill he guided them.

PSALM 79

A psalm by Asaph.

1 O God, the nations have invaded the land that belongs to you.
    They have dishonored your holy temple.
    They have left Jerusalem in ruins.
2 They have given the dead bodies of your servants
        to the birds for food.
    They have given the flesh of your godly ones
        to the animals.
3 They have shed the blood of your people around Jerusalem
        as though it were water.
            There is no one to bury your people.

4 We have become a disgrace to our neighbors,
    an object of ridicule and contempt to those around us.
5 How long, O LORD?
    Will you remain angry forever?
    Will your fury continue to burn like fire?
6 Pour your fury on the nations that do not know you,
    on the kingdoms that have not called you.
7 They have devoured Jacob.
    They have destroyed his home.
8 Do not hold the crimes of our ancestors against us.
    Reach out to us soon with your compassion,
        because we are helpless.
9 Help us, O God, our savior, for the glory of your name.
    Rescue us, and forgive our sins for the honor of your name.

10 Why should the nations ˎbe allowed toˌ say,
    "Where is their God?"
    Let us watch as the nations learn
        that there is punishment for shedding the blood of your servants.
11 Let the groans of prisoners come into your presence.
    With your powerful arm rescue those who are condemned to death.
12 Pay each one of our neighbors back
    with seven times the number of insults they used to insult you, O Lord.
13 Then we, your people, the flock in your pasture,
    will give thanks to you forever.
        We will praise you throughout every generation.

PSALM 80

For the choir director; according to *shoshannim eduth;* by Asaph; a psalm.

1 Open your ears, O Shepherd of Israel,
    the one who leads ˎthe descendants ofˌ Joseph like sheep,
    the one who is enthroned over the angels.[a]
2 Appear in front of Ephraim, Benjamin, and Manasseh.
    Wake up your power, and come to save us.

3 O God, restore us and smile on us
    so that we may be saved.

4 O LORD God, commander of armies, how long will you smolder in anger
        against the prayer of your people?
5 You made them eat tears as food.
    You often made them drink ˎtheir ownˌ tears.
6 You made us a source of conflict to our neighbors,
    and our enemies made fun of us.

---

a 80:1 Or "cherubim."

⁷ O God, commander of armies, restore us and smile on us
      so that we may be saved.

⁸ You brought a vine from Egypt.
    You forced out the nations and planted it.
⁹ You cleared the ground for it
      so that it took root and filled the land.
¹⁰   Its shade covered the mountains.
      Its branches covered the mighty cedars.
¹¹   It reached out with its branches to the Mediterranean Sea.
      Its shoots reached the Euphrates River.

¹² Why did you break down the stone fences around this vine?
      All who pass by are picking its fruit.
¹³   Wild boars from the forest graze on it.
      Wild animals devour it.
¹⁴ O God, commander of armies, come back!
      Look from heaven and see!
    Come to help this vine.
¹⁵ Take care of what your right hand planted,
      the son you strengthened for yourself.
¹⁶   The vine has been cut down and burned.
      Let them be destroyed by the threatening look on your face.

¹⁷ Let your power rest on the man you have chosen,
      the son of man you strengthened for yourself.
¹⁸   Then we will never turn away from you.
      Give us life again, and we will call on you.

¹⁹ O Lord God, commander of armies, restore us, and smile on us
      so that we may be saved.

PSALM 81

For the choir director; on the *gittith;*[a] by Asaph.

¹ Sing joyfully to God, our strength.
    Shout happily to the God of Jacob.
² Begin a psalm, and strike a tambourine.
    Play lyres and harps with their pleasant music.
³ Blow the ram's horn on the day of the new moon,
      on the day of the full moon,
      on our festival days.
⁴ This is a law for Israel,
      a legal decision from the God of Jacob.
⁵   These are the instructions God set in place for Joseph
      when Joseph rose to power over Egypt.

I heard a message I did not understand:
⁶   "I removed the burden from his shoulder.
      His hands were freed from the basket.
⁷ When you were in trouble, you called out ˌto meˌ, and I rescued you.
    I was hidden in thunder, but I answered you.
    I tested your ˌloyaltyˌ at the oasis of Meribah.   *Selah*
⁸   Listen, my people, and I will warn you.
      Israel, if you would only listen to me!
⁹   Never keep any strange god among you.
      Never worship a foreign god.
¹⁰ I am the Lord your God, the one who brought you out of Egypt.
      Open your mouth wide, and I will fill it.

¹¹ "But my people did not listen to me.
      Israel wanted nothing to do with me.
¹²   So I let them go their own stubborn ways
      and follow their own advice.
¹³ If only my people would listen to me!
    If only Israel would follow me!

---

[a] 81:1 Unknown musical term.

14 I would quickly defeat their enemies.
I would turn my power against their foes.
15   Those who hate the LORD would cringe in front of him,
and their time ᵧfor punishment, would last forever.
16 But I would feed Israel with the finest wheat
and satisfy them with honey from a rock."

PSALM 82

A psalm by Asaph.

1 God takes his place in his own assembly.
He pronounces judgment among the gods:
2   "How long are you going to judge unfairly?
How long are you going to side with wicked people?"   *Selah*

3 Defend weak people and orphans.
Protect the rights of the oppressed and the poor.
4 Rescue weak and needy people.
Help them escape the power of wicked people.

5 Wicked people do not know or understand anything.
As they walk around in the dark,
all the foundations of the earth shake.
6 I said, "You are gods.
You are all sons of the Most High.
7   You will certainly die like humans
and fall like any prince."

8 Arise, O God!
Judge the earth, because all the nations belong to you.

PSALM 83

A song; a psalm by Asaph.

1 O God, do not remain silent.
Do not turn a deaf ear to me.
Do not keep quiet, O God.

2 Look, your enemies are in an uproar.
Those who hate you hold their heads high.
3   They make plans in secret against your people
and plot together against those you treasure.
4   They say, "Let's wipe out their nation
so that the name of Israel will no longer be remembered."
5 They agree completely on their plan.
They form an alliance against you:
6   the tents from Edom and Ishmael,
Moab and Hagar,
7   Gebal, Ammon, and Amalek,
Philistia, along with those who live in Tyre.
8   Even Assyria has joined them.
They helped the descendants of Lot.   *Selah*
9 Do to them what you did to Midian,
to Sisera and Jabin at the Kishon River.
10   They were destroyed at Endor.
They became manure to fertilize the ground.
11 Treat their influential people as you treated Oreb and Zeeb.
Treat all their leaders like Zebah and Zalmunna.
12   They said, "Let's take God's pasturelands for ourselves."
13 O my God, blow them away like tumbleweeds,ᵃ
like husks in the wind.
14 Pursue them with your storms,
and terrify them with your windstorms
15   the way fire burns a forest

ᵃ 83:13 Or "whirling dust."

and flames set mountains on fire.[b]

16 Let their faces blush with shame, O LORD,
     so that they must look to you for help.
17 Let them be put to shame and terrified forever.
     Let them die in disgrace
18   so that they must acknowledge you.
         Your name is the LORD.
         You alone are the Most High God of the whole earth.

PSALM 84

For the choir director; on the *gittith;* a psalm by Korah's descendants.

1 Your dwelling place is lovely, O LORD of Armies!
2   My soul longs and yearns
         for the LORD's courtyards.
     My whole body shouts for joy to the living God.
3   Even sparrows find a home,
             and swallows find a nest for themselves.
         There they hatch their young
             near your altars, O LORD of Armies,
                 my king and my God.
4 Blessed are those who live in your house.
     They are always praising you.   *Selah*

5 Blessed are those who find strength in you.
     Their hearts are on the road ˌthat leads to youˌ.[a]
6   As they pass through a valley where balsam trees grow,[b]
         they make it a place of springs.
         The early rains cover it with blessings.[c]
7   Their strength grows as they go along
             until each one of them appears
             in front of God in Zion.

8 O LORD God, commander of armies, hear my prayer.
     Open your ears, O God of Jacob.   *Selah*
9   Look at our shield, O God.
     Look with favor on the face of your anointed one.
10 One day in your courtyards is better than a thousand ˌanywhere elseˌ.
     I would rather stand in the entrance to my God's house
         than live inside wicked people's homes.
11 The LORD God is a sun and shield.
     The LORD grants favor and honor.
     He does not hold back any blessing
         from those who live innocently.

12 O LORD of Armies, blessed is the person who trusts you.

PSALM 85

For the choir director; a psalm by Korah's descendants.

1 You favored your land, O LORD.
     You restored the fortunes of Jacob.
2 You removed your people's guilt.
     You pardoned all their sins.   *Selah*
3 You laid aside all your fury.
     You turned away from your burning anger.

4 Restore us, O God, our savior.
     Put an end to your anger against us.
5   Will you be angry with us forever?
     Will you ever let go of your anger in the generations to come?
6   Won't you restore our lives again
         so that your people may find joy in you?

---

[b] 83:15 Verse 15 (in Hebrew) has been placed in front of verse 14 to express the complex Hebrew sentence structure more clearly in English.   [a] 84:5 Hebrew meaning of this line uncertain.   [b] 84:6 Or "As they pass through the valley of Weeping."   [c] 84:6 Or "pools."

7 Show us your mercy, O LORD,
  by giving us your salvation.

8 I want to hear what God the LORD says,
  because he promises peace to his people, to his godly ones.
  But they must not go back to their stupidity.
9 Indeed, his salvation is near those who fear him,
  and ⸤his⸥ glory will remain in our land.

10 Mercy and truth have met.
   Righteousness and peace have kissed.
11 Truth sprouts from the ground,
   and righteousness looks down from heaven.
12 The LORD will certainly give us what is good,
   and our land will produce crops.
13 Righteousness will go ahead of him
   and make a path for his steps.

PSALM 86

A prayer by David.

1 Turn your ear ⸤toward me⸥, O LORD.
  Answer me, because I am oppressed and needy.
2 Protect me, because I am faithful ⸤to you⸥.
  Save your servant who trusts you. You are my God.
3 Have pity on me, O Lord,
  because I call out to you all day long.
4 Give me joy, O Lord,
  because I lift my soul to you.
5 You, O Lord, are good and forgiving,
  full of mercy toward everyone who calls out to you.
6 Open your ears to my prayer, O LORD.
  Pay attention when I plead for mercy.
7 When I am in trouble, I call out to you
    because you answer me.

8 No god is like you, O Lord.
  No one can do what you do.
9 All the nations that you have made
    will bow in your presence, O Lord.
    They will honor you.
10 Indeed, you are great, a worker of miracles.
   You alone are God.
11 Teach me your way, O LORD,
   so that I may live in your truth.
   Focus my heart on fearing you.
12 I will give thanks to you with all my heart, O Lord my God.
   I will honor you forever
13 because your mercy toward me is great.
   You have rescued me from the depths of hell.

14 O God, arrogant people attack me,
   and a mob of ruthless people seeks my life.
   They think nothing of you.
15 But you, O Lord, are a compassionate and merciful God.
   You are patient, always faithful and ready to forgive.
16 Turn toward me, and have pity on me.
   Give me your strength because I am your servant.
   Save me because I am the son of your female servant.
17 Grant me some proof of your goodness
   so that those who hate me may see it and be put to shame.
   You, O LORD, have helped me and comforted me.

PSALM 87

By Korah's descendants; a psalm; a song.

1 ⸤The city⸥ the LORD has founded ⸤stands⸥ on holy mountains.
2 The LORD loves the city of Zion

more than any other place in Jacob.
3 Glorious things are said about you, O city of God!   *Selah*

4 ⌊The LORD says,⌋ "I will add Egypt and Babylon
    as well as Philistia, Tyre, and Sudan
        to the list of those who acknowledge me.
            Each nation ⌊will claim that it⌋ was born there."

5 But it will be said of Zion,
    "Every race is born in it.
    The Most High will make it secure."
6 The LORD will record this in the Book of Nations:
    "Every race ⌊claims that it⌋ was born there."   *Selah*
7 Singers and dancers will sing,
    "Zion is the source of all our blessings."

PSALM 88

A song; a psalm by Korah's descendants; for the choir director; according to *mahalath leannoth,*[a] a *maskil* by Heman the Ezrahite.

1 O LORD God, my savior,
    I cry out to you during the day and at night.
2 Let my prayer come into your presence.
    Turn your ear to hear my cries.
3 My soul is filled with troubles,
    and my life comes closer to the grave.
4 I am numbered with those who go into the pit.
    I am like a man without any strength—
5 abandoned with the dead,
        like those who have been killed and lie in graves,
        like those whom you no longer remember,
            who are cut off from your power.
6 You have put me in the bottom of the pit—in deep, dark places.
7 Your rage lies heavily on me.
    You make all your waves pound on me.   *Selah*
8 You have taken my friends far away from me.
    You made me disgusting to them.
        I'm shut in, and I can't get out.
9 My eyes grow weak because of my suffering.
        All day long I call out to you, O LORD.
            I stretch out my hands to you ⌊in prayer⌋.

10 Will you perform miracles for those who are dead?
    Will the spirits of the dead rise and give thanks to you?   *Selah*
11 Will anyone tell about your mercy in Sheol
    or about your faithfulness in Abaddon?
12 Will anyone know about your miracles in that dark place
    or about your righteousness in the place where forgotten people live?

13 I cry out to you for help, O LORD,
    and in the morning my prayer will come into your presence.

14 Why do you reject my soul, O LORD?
    Why do you hide your face from me?
15 Ever since I was young, I have been suffering and near death.
    I have endured your terrors, and now I am in despair.[b]
16 Your burning anger has swept over me.
    Your terrors have destroyed me.
17 They swirl around me all day long like water.
    They surround me on all sides.
18 You have taken my loved ones and friends far away from me.
    Darkness is my only friend![b]

---

[a] 88:1 Unknown musical term.   [b] 88:15, 18 Hebrew meaning uncertain.

PSALM 89

A *maskil* by Ethan the Ezrahite.

1 I will sing forever about the evidence of your mercy, O LORD.
I will tell about your faithfulness to every generation.
2 I said, "Your mercy will last forever.
Your faithfulness stands firm in the heavens."

3 ⸤You said,⸥ "I have made a promise*a* to my chosen one.
I swore this oath to my servant David:
4 'I will make your dynasty continue forever.
I built your throne to last throughout every generation.' "   *Selah*

5 O LORD, the heavens praise your miracles
and your faithfulness in the assembly of the holy ones.
6 Who in the skies can compare with the LORD?
Who among the heavenly beings is like the LORD?
7 God is terrifying in the council of the holy ones.
He is greater and more awe-inspiring than those who surround him.
8 O LORD God of Armies, who is like you?
Mighty LORD, even your faithfulness surrounds you.
9 You rule the raging sea.
When its waves rise, you quiet them.
10 You crushed Rahab;*b* it was like a corpse.
With your strong arm you scattered your enemies.
11 The heavens are yours.
The earth is also yours.
You made the world and everything in it.
12 You created north and south.
Mount Tabor and Mount Hermon sing your name joyfully.
13 Your arm is mighty.
Your hand is strong.
Your right hand is lifted high.
14 Righteousness and justice are the foundations of your throne.
Mercy and truth stand in front of you.
15 Blessed are the people who know how to praise you.
They walk in the light of your presence, O LORD.
16 They find joy in your name all day long.
They are joyful in your righteousness
17 because you are the glory of their strength.
By your favor you give us victory.*c*
18 Our shield belongs to the LORD.
Our king belongs to the Holy One of Israel.

19 Once in a vision you said to your faithful ones:
"I set a boy above warriors.*d*
I have raised up one chosen from the people.
20 I found my servant David.
I anointed him with my holy oil.
21 My hand is ready to help him.
My arm will also give him strength.
22 No enemy will take him by surprise.
No wicked person will mistreat him.
23 I will crush his enemies in front of him
and defeat those who hate him.
24 My faithfulness and mercy will be with him,
and in my name he will be victorious.*e*
25 I will put his ⸤left⸥ hand on the sea
and his right hand on the rivers.
26 He will call out to me,
'You are my Father, my God, and the rock of my salvation.'

---

a 89:3 Or "covenant."   *b* 89:10 Rahab is the name of a demonic creature who opposes God.   *c* 89:17 Hebrew meaning of "give us victory" uncertain.   *d* 89:19 Hebrew meaning of this line uncertain.   *e* 89:24 Hebrew meaning of "he will be victorious" uncertain.

27 Yes, I will make him the firstborn.
   He will be the Most High to the kings of the earth.
28 My mercy will stay with him forever.
   My promise to him is unbreakable.
29 I will make his dynasty endure forever
   and his throne like the days of heaven.

30 "If his descendants abandon my teachings
   and do not live by my rules,
31 if they violate my laws
   and do not obey my commandments,
32 then with a rod I will punish their rebellion
   and their crimes with beatings.
33 But I will not take my mercy away from him
   or allow my truth to become a lie.
34 I will not dishonor my promise
   or alter my own agreement.
35 On my holiness I have taken an oath once and for all:
   I will not lie to David.
36 His dynasty will last forever.
   His throne will be in my presence like the sun.
37 Like the moon his throne will stand firm forever.
   It will be like a faithful witness in heaven."

38 But you have despised, rejected,
   and become angry with your anointed one.
39 You have refused to recognize the promise to your servant
   and have thrown his crown into the dirt.
40 You have broken through all his walls
   and have laid his fortified cities in ruins.
41 (Everyone who passed by robbed him.
   He has become the object of his neighbors' scorn.)
42 You held the right hand of his enemies high
   and made all of his adversaries rejoice.
43 You even took his sword out of his hand
   and failed to support him in battle.
44 You put an end to his splendor
   and hurled his throne to the ground.
45 You cut short the days of his youth
   and covered him with shame.   *Selah*

46 How long, O Lord? Will you hide yourself forever?
   How long will your anger continue to burn like fire?
47 Remember how short my life is!
   Have you created Adam's descendants for no reason?
48 Can a mortal go on living and never see death?
   Who can set himself free from the power of the grave?   *Selah*
49 Where is the evidence of your mercy, Lord?
   You swore an oath to David
   on ˻the basis of˼ your faithfulness.

50 Remember, O Lord,ᶠ how your servantᵍ has been insulted.
   Remember how I have carried in my heart ˻the insults˼ from so many people.
51 Your enemies insulted ˻me˼.
   They insulted your Messiahʰ every step he took.

52 Thank the Lord forever.
   Amen and amen!

ᶠ 89:50 Many Hebrew manuscripts; other Hebrew manuscripts "Lord."   ᵍ 89:50 Many Hebrew manuscripts, Greek, Syriac;
other Hebrew manuscripts "your servants."   ʰ 89:51 Or "anointed one."

BOOK FOUR
Psalms 90–106

PSALM 90

A prayer by Moses, the man of God.

¹ O Lord, you have been our refuge throughout every generation.
² Before the mountains were born,
  before you gave birth to the earth and the world, you were God.
    You are God from everlasting to everlasting.

³ You turn mortals back into dust
  and say, "Return, descendants of Adam."
⁴ Indeed, in your sight a thousand years are like a single day,
  like yesterday—already past—
  like an hour in the night.
⁵ You sweep mortals away.
  They are a dream.
  They sprout again in the morning like cut grass.
⁶   In the morning they blossom and sprout.
    In the evening they wither and dry up.

⁷ Indeed, your anger consumes us.
  Your rage terrifies us.
⁸   You have set our sins in front of you.
    You have put our secret sins in the light of your presence.
⁹ Indeed, all our days slip away because of your fury.
  We live out our years like one ˌlongˌ sigh.
¹⁰ Each of us lives for 70 years—
  or even 80 if we are in good health.
    But the best of them*ˌbringˌ trouble and misery.
    Indeed, they are soon gone, and we fly away.
¹¹ Who fully understands the power of your anger?
  A person fears you more when he better understands your fury.*ᵇ
¹² Teach us to number each of our days
  so that we may grow in wisdom.

¹³ Return, LORD! How long. . . ?
  Change your plans about ˌus,ˌ your servants.
¹⁴ Satisfy us every morning with your mercy
  so that we may sing joyfully and rejoice all our days.
¹⁵ Make us rejoice for as many days as you have made us suffer,
  for as many years as we have experienced evil.
¹⁶ Let ˌus,ˌ your servants, see what you can do.
  Let our children see your glorious power.
¹⁷ Let the kindness of the Lord our God be with us.
  Make us successful in everything we do.
    Yes, make us successful in everything we do.

PSALM 91

¹ Whoever lives under the shelter of the Most High
  will remain in the shadow of the Almighty.
² I will say to the LORD,
  "ˌYou areˌ my refuge and my fortress, my God in whom I trust."

³ He is the one who will rescue you from hunters' traps
  and from deadly plagues.
⁴ He will cover you with his feathers,
  and under his wings you will find refuge.
    His truth is your shield and armor.

⁵ You do not need to fear
  terrors of the night,
  arrows that fly during the day,

ᵃ 90:10 Hebrew meaning of "the best of them" uncertain.   *ᵇ* 90:11 Hebrew meaning of this line uncertain.

6   plagues that roam the dark,
      epidemics that strike at noon.
7   They will not come near you,
              even though a thousand may fall dead beside you
                  or ten thousand at your right side.

8   You only have to look with your eyes
          to see the punishment of wicked people.

9   You, O LORD, are my refuge!

      You have made the Most High your home.
10   No harm will come to you.
          No sickness will come near your house.
11   He will put his angels in charge of you
          to protect you in all your ways.
12   They will carry you in their hands
              so that you never hit your foot against a rock.
13   You will step on lions and cobras.
          You will trample young lions and snakes.

14   Because you love me, I will rescue you.
          I will protect you because you know my name.
15   When you call to me, I will answer you.
          I will be with you when you are in trouble.
          I will save you and honor you.
16   I will satisfy you with a long life.
          I will show you how I will save you.

PSALM 92

A psalm; a song; for the day of worship.

1   It is good to give thanks to the LORD,
          to make music to praise your name, O Most High.
2   It is good to announce your mercy in the morning
          and your faithfulness in the evening
3   on a ten-stringed instrument and a harp
              and with a melody on a lyre.

4   You made me find joy in what you have done, O LORD.
      I will sing joyfully about the works of your hands.
5   How spectacular are your works, O LORD!
          How very deep are your thoughts!

6   A stupid person cannot know
          and a fool cannot understand
7   that wicked people sprout like grass
              and all troublemakers blossom ˌlike flowersˌ,
                  only to be destroyed forever.

8   But you, O LORD, are highly honored forever.
9   Now look at your enemies, O LORD.
          Now look at your enemies.
              They disappear, and all troublemakers are scattered.

10   But you make me as strong as a wild bull,
          and soothing lotion is poured on me.
11   My eyes gloat over those who spy on me.
      My ears hear ˌthe criesˌ of evildoers attacking me.

12   Righteous people flourish like palm trees
          and grow tall like the cedars in Lebanon.
13   They are planted in the LORD's house.
          They blossom in our God's courtyards.
14   Even when they are old, they still bear fruit.
              They are always healthy and fresh.
15   They make it known that the LORD is decent.
                      He is my rock.
                      He is never unfair.

PSALM 93

1 The LORD rules as king! He is clothed with majesty.
  The LORD has clothed himself; he has armed himself with power.
    The world was set in place; it cannot be moved.

2 Your throne was set in place a long time ago.
  You are eternal.

3 The ocean rises, O LORD.
  The ocean rises with a roar.
  The ocean rises with its pounding waves.
4   The LORD above is mighty—
      mightier than the sound of raging water,
      mightier than the foaming waves of the sea.

5 Your written testimonies are completely reliable.
  O LORD, holiness is what makes your house beautiful for days without end.

PSALM 94

1 O LORD, God of vengeance,
    O God of vengeance, appear!
2 Arise, O Judge of the earth.
  Give arrogant people what they deserve.
3 How long, O LORD, will wicked people triumph?
  How long?

4 They ramble.
    They speak arrogantly.
      All troublemakers brag about themselves.
5 They crush your people, O LORD.
    They make those who belong to you suffer.
6   They kill widows and foreigners, and they murder orphans.
7   They say, "The LORD doesn't see it.
          The God of Jacob doesn't even pay attention to it."

8 Pay attention, you stupid people!
  When will you become wise, you fools?
9   God created ears.
      Do you think he can't hear?
    He formed eyes.
      Do you think he can't see?
10 He disciplines nations.
      Do you think he can't punish?
    He teaches people.
      Do you think he doesn't know anything?
11   The LORD knows that people's thoughts are pointless.

12 O LORD, blessed is the person
    whom you discipline and instruct from your teachings.
13   You give him peace and quiet from times of trouble
        while a pit is dug to trap wicked people.

14 The LORD will never desert his people
    or abandon those who belong to him.
15   The decisions of judges will again become fair,
        and everyone whose motives are decent will pursue justice.[a]

16 Who will stand up for me against evildoers?
  Who will stand by my side against troublemakers?
17   If the LORD had not come to help me,
        my soul would have quickly fallen silent ˌin deathˌ.

18 When I said, "My feet are slipping,"
    your mercy, O LORD, continued to hold me up.
19 When I worried about many things,
    your assuring words soothed my soul.

---

[a] 94:15 English equivalent of this verse difficult.

20   Are wicked rulers who use the law to do unlawful things
        able to be your partners?
21   They join forces to take the lives of righteous people.
        They condemn innocent people to death.
22   The LORD has become my stronghold.
  My God has become my rock of refuge.
23   He has turned their own wickedness against them.
        He will destroy them because of their sins.
        The LORD our God will destroy them.

PSALM 95

1   Come, let's sing joyfully to the LORD.
        Let's shout happily to the rock of our salvation.
2   Let's come into his presence with a song of thanksgiving.
        Let's shout happily to him with psalms.
3   The LORD is a great God and a great king above all gods.
4   In his hand are the deep places of the earth,
        and the mountain peaks are his.
5   The sea is his.
        He made it, and his hands formed the dry land.

6   Come, let's worship and bow down.
        Let's kneel in front of the LORD, our maker,
7   because he is our God
          and we are the people in his care,
            the flock that he leads.

If only you would listen to him today!
8   "Do not be stubborn like ˌmy people wereˌ at Meribah,
        like the time at Massah in the desert.
9   Your ancestors challenged me and tested me there,
        although they had seen what I had done.
10   For 40 years I was disgusted with those people.
  So I said, 'They are a people whose hearts continue to stray.
        They have not learned my ways.'
11   That is why I angrily took this solemn oath:
        'They will never enter my place of rest!' "

PSALM 96

1   Sing to the LORD a new song!
  Sing to the LORD, all the earth!
2   Sing to the LORD! Praise his name!
        Day after day announce that the LORD saves his people.
3   Tell people about his glory.
        Tell all the nations about his miracles.

4   The LORD is great!
        He should be highly praised.
        He should be feared more than all ˌotherˌ gods
5   because all the gods of the nations are idols.
  The LORD made the heavens.
6   Splendor and majesty are in his presence.
        Strength and beauty are in his holy place.

7   Give to the LORD, you families of the nations.
  Give to the LORD glory and power.
8   Give to the LORD the glory he deserves.
        Bring an offering, and come into his courtyards.
9   Worship the LORD ˌhisˌ holy splendor.
        Tremble in his presence, all the earth!

10   Say to the nations, "The LORD rules as king!"
  The earth stands firm; it cannot be moved.
  He will judge people fairly.
11   Let the heavens rejoice and the earth be glad.
        Let the sea and everything in it roar like thunder.
12   Let the fields and everything in them rejoice.

13 Then all the trees in the forest will sing joyfully
        in the LORD's presence because he is coming.
    He is coming to judge the earth.
        He will judge the world with righteousness
        and its people with his truth.

PSALM 97

1 The LORD rules as king.
        Let the earth rejoice.
        Let all the islands be joyful.
2 Clouds and darkness surround him.
    Righteousness and justice are the foundations of his throne.
3 Fire spreads ahead of him.
    It burns his enemies who surround him.
4 His flashes of lightning light up the world.
        The earth sees them and trembles.
5 The mountains melt like wax in the presence of the LORD,
        in the presence of the Lord of the whole earth.
6 The heavens tell about his righteousness,
        and all the people of the world see his glory.

7 Everyone who worships idols
        and brags about false gods will be put to shame.
    All the gods will bow to him.

8 Zion hears about this and rejoices.
    The people of Judah are delighted with your judgments, O LORD.
9 You, O LORD, the Most High, are above the whole earth.
    You are highest. You are above all the gods.
10 Let those who love the LORD hate evil.
    The one who guards the lives of his godly ones
        will rescue them from the power of wicked people.
11 Light dawns for righteous people*ᵃ*
        and joy for those whose motives are decent.
12 Find joy in the LORD, you righteous people.
    Give thanks to him as you remember how holy he is.

PSALM 98

A psalm.

1 Sing a new song to the LORD
        because he has done miraculous things.
            His right hand and his holy arm have gained victory for him.
2 The LORD has made his salvation known.
        He has uncovered his righteousness for the nations to see.
3 He has not forgotten to be merciful and faithful
        to Israel's descendants.
            All the ends of the earth have seen how our God saves ˎthemˏ.

4 Shout happily to the LORD, all the earth.
    Break out into joyful singing, and make music.
5 Make music to the LORD with a lyre,
        with a lyre and the melody of a psalm,
6   with trumpets and the playing of a ram's horn.
    Shout happily in the presence of the king, the LORD.

7 Let the sea, everything in it,
        the world, and those who live in it roar like thunder.
8 Let the rivers clap their hands
        and the mountains sing joyfully
9   in the LORD's presence
                because he is coming to judge the earth.

ᵃ 97:11 One Hebrew manuscript, Greek, Syriac, Latin; other Hebrew manuscripts "Light is planted for righteous people."

He will judge the world with justice
and its people with fairness.

PSALM 99

1 The LORD rules as king.
　Let the people tremble.
He is enthroned over the angels.[a]
　Let the earth quake.
2 The LORD is mighty in Zion.
He is high above all people.
3 　Let them give thanks to your great and fearful name.

　He is holy!

4 The king's strength is that he loves justice.
　You have established fairness.
　You have done what is fair and right for Jacob.

5 Highly honor the LORD our God.
Bow down at his footstool.

　He is holy!

6 Moses and Aaron were among his priests.
Samuel was among those who prayed to him.
　They called to the LORD, and he answered them.
7 　He spoke to them from a column of smoke.
They obeyed his written instructions and the laws that he gave them.
8 O LORD, our God, you answered them.
　You showed them that you are a forgiving God
　　and that you are a God who punishes their ˌsinfulˌ deeds.

9 Highly honor the LORD our God.
Bow at his holy mountain.

　The LORD our God is holy!

PSALM 100

A psalm of thanksgiving.

1 Shout happily to the LORD, all the earth.
2 Serve the LORD cheerfully.
Come into his presence with a joyful song.
3 Realize that the LORD alone is God.
　He made us, and we are his.[a]
　We are his people and the sheep in his care.
4 Enter his gates with a song of thanksgiving.
Come into his courtyards with a song of praise.
Give thanks to him; praise his name.

5 The LORD is good.
　His mercy endures forever.
　His faithfulness endures throughout every generation.

PSALM 101

A psalm by David.

1 I will sing about mercy and justice.
O LORD, I will make music to praise you.
2 I want to understand the path to integrity.
　When will you come to me?

　I will live in my own home with integrity.
3 　I will not put anything wicked in front of my eyes.
I hate what unfaithful people do.
　I want no part of it.

---

[a] 99:1 Or "cherubim."　　[a] 100:3 Many Hebrew manuscripts, Greek, Targum, Latin; other Hebrew manuscripts "and not we ourselves."

⁴ I will keep far away from devious minds.
  I will have nothing to do with evil.
⁵ I will destroy anyone who secretly slanders his neighbor.
  I will not tolerate anyone with a conceited look or arrogant heart.
⁶ My eyes will be watching the faithful people in the land
    so that they may live with me.
      The person who lives with integrity will serve me.

⁷ The one who does deceitful things will not stay in my home.
  The one who tells lies will not remain in my presence.

⁸ Every morning I will destroy all the wicked people in the land
    to rid the LORD's city of all troublemakers.

PSALM 102

A prayer by someone who is suffering, when he is weary and pours out his troubles in the LORD's presence.

¹ O LORD, hear my prayer,
    and let my cry for help come to you.
² Do not hide your face from me when I am in trouble.
  Turn your ear toward me.
  Answer me quickly when I call.
³ My days disappear like smoke.
  My bones burn like hot coals.
⁴ My heart is beaten down and withered like grass
    because I have forgotten about eating.
⁵ I am nothing but skin and bones
    because of my loud groans.
⁶ I am like a desert owl,
    like an owl living in the ruins.
⁷ I lie awake.
  I am like a lonely bird on a rooftop.
⁸ All day long my enemies insult me.
    Those who ridicule me use my name as a curse.
⁹ I eat ashes like bread
    and my tears are mixed with my drink
¹⁰   because of your hostility and anger,
      because you have picked me up and thrown me away.
¹¹ My days are like a shadow that is getting longer,
    and I wither away like grass.

¹² But you, O LORD, remain forever.
    You are remembered throughout every generation.
¹³   You will rise and have compassion on Zion,
      because it is time to grant a favor to it.
        Indeed, the appointed time has come.
¹⁴   Your servants value Zion's stones,
          and they pity its rubble.
¹⁵ The nations will fear the LORD's name.
  All the kings of the earth will fear your glory.
¹⁶ When the LORD builds Zion,
    he will appear in his glory.
¹⁷ He will turn his attention to the prayers
    of those who have been abandoned.
  He will not despise their prayers.
¹⁸ This will be written down for a future generation
    so that a people yet to be created may praise the LORD:
¹⁹   "The LORD looked down from his holy place high above.
      From heaven he looked at the earth.
²⁰   He heard the groans of the prisoners
          and set free those who were condemned to death.
²¹   The LORD's name is announced in Zion
            and his praise in Jerusalem
²²   when nations and kingdoms gather
                to worship the LORD."

23 He has weakened my strength along the way.
   He has reduced ˌthe number ofˌ my days.
24 I said, "My God, don't take me now in the middle of my life.
   Your years ˌcontinue onˌ throughout every generation.
25 Long ago you laid the foundation of the earth.
   Even the heavens are the works of your hands.
26 They will come to an end, but you will still go on.
      They will all wear out like clothing.
      You will change them like clothes,
         and they will be thrown away.
27   But you remain the same, and your life will never end.
28 The children of your servants will go on living ˌhereˌ.
   Their descendants will be secure in your presence."

PSALM 103

By David.

1 Praise the LORD, my soul!
  Praise his holy name, all that is within me.
2 Praise the LORD, my soul,
     and never forget all the good he has done:
3   He is the one who forgives all your sins,
        the one who heals all your diseases,
4   the one who rescues your life from the pit,
        the one who crowns you with mercy and compassion,
5   the one who fills your life with blessings
           so that you become young again like an eagle.

6 The LORD does what is right and fair
     for all who are oppressed.
7   He let Moses know his ways.
     He let the Israelites know the things he had done.
8 The LORD is compassionate, merciful, patient,
     and always ready to forgive.

9 He will not always accuse us of wrong
     or be angry ˌwith usˌ forever.
10 He has not treated us as we deserve for our sins
      or paid us back for our wrongs.

11 As high as the heavens are above the earth—
      that is how vast his mercy is toward those who fear him.
12 As far as the east is from the west—
      that is how far he has removed our rebellious acts from himself.
13 As a father has compassion for his children,
      so the LORD has compassion for those who fear him.

14 He certainly knows what we are made of.
      He bears in mind that we are dust.
15 Human life is as short-lived as grass.
      It blossoms like a flower in the field.
16   When the wind blows over the flower, it disappears,
         and there is no longer any sign of it.

17 But from everlasting to everlasting,
      the LORD's mercy is on those who fear him.
      His righteousness belongs
         to their children and grandchildren,
18   to those who are faithful to his promise,[a]
         to those who remember to follow his guiding principles.
19 The LORD has set his throne in heaven.
   His kingdom rules everything.

20 Praise the LORD, all his angels,
      you mighty beings who carry out his orders
      and are ready to obey his spoken orders.

---

[a] 103:18 Or "covenant."

21   Praise the LORD, all his armies,
      his servants who carry out his will.
22   Praise the LORD, all his creatures
      in all the places of his empire.
    Praise the LORD, my soul!

PSALM 104

1   Praise the LORD, my soul!
   O LORD my God, you are very great.
      You are clothed with splendor and majesty.
2   You cover yourself with light as though it were a robe.
      You stretch out the heavens as though they were curtains.
3   You lay the beams of your home in the water.
      You use the clouds for your chariot.
      You move on the wings of the wind.
4   You make your angels winds
        and your servants flames of fire.

5   You set the earth on its foundations
      so that it can never be shaken.
6   You covered the earth with an ocean as though it were a robe.
      Water stood above the mountains
7   and fled because of your threat.
   Water ran away at the sound of your thunder.
8   The mountains rose and the valleys sank
        to the place you appointed for them.
9   Water cannot cross the boundary you set
       and cannot come back to cover the earth.

10   You make water gush from springs into valleys.
      It flows between the mountains.
11   Every wild animal drinks ˌfrom themˌ.
      Wild donkeys quench their thirst.
12   The birds live by the streams.
       They sing among the branches.
13   You water the mountains from your home above.
   You fill the earth with the fruits of your labors.

14   You make grass grow for cattle
      and make vegetables for humans to use
        in order to get food from the ground.
15   You make wine to cheer human hearts,
      olive oil to make faces shine,
       and bread to strengthen human hearts.
16   The LORD's trees, the cedars in Lebanon which he planted,
      drink their fill.
17   Birds build their nests in them.
      Storks make their homes in fir trees.
18   The high mountains are for wild goats.
   The rocks are a refuge for badgers.

19   He created the moon, which marks the seasons,
      and the sun, which knows when to set.
20   He brings darkness, and it is nighttime,
      when all the wild animals in the forest come out.
21   The young lions roar for their prey
       and seek their food from God.
22   When the sun rises,
      they gather and lie down in their dens.
23   Then people go to do their work,
       to do their tasks until evening.

24   What a large number of things you have made, O LORD!
      You made them all by wisdom.
       The earth is filled with your creatures.
25   The sea is so big and wide with countless creatures,
        living things both large and small.
26   Ships sail on it,

and Leviathan,[a] which you made, plays in it.
27 All of them look to you to give them their food at the right time.
28   You give it to them, and they gather it up.
    You open your hand, and they are filled with blessings.
29   You hide your face, and they are terrified.
    You take away their breath, and they die and return to dust.
30   You send out your Spirit, and they are created.
    You renew the face of the earth.

31 May the glory of the LORD endure forever.
    May the LORD find joy in what he has made.
32   He looks at the earth, and it trembles.
    He touches the mountains, and they smoke.
33   I will sing to the LORD throughout my life.
        I will make music to praise my God as long as I live.
34 May my thoughts be pleasing to him.
    I will find joy in the LORD.
35 May sinners vanish from the world.
    May there no longer be any wicked people.
    Praise the LORD, my soul!

Hallelujah!

PSALM 105

1 Give thanks to the LORD.
    Call on him.
    Make known among the nations what he has done.
2 Sing to him.
    Make music to praise him.
    Meditate on all the miracles he has performed.
3 Brag about his holy name.
    Let the hearts of those who seek the LORD rejoice.
4 Search for the LORD and his strength.
    Always seek his presence.
5 Remember the miracles he performed,
        the amazing things he did, and the judgments he pronounced,
6   you descendants of his servant Abraham,
        you descendants of Jacob, his chosen ones.

7 He is the LORD our God.
    His judgments are pronounced throughout the earth.
8 He always remembers his promise,[a]
    the word that he commanded for a thousand generations,
9   the promise that he made to Abraham,
            and his sworn oath to Isaac.
10 He confirmed it as a law for Jacob,
    as an everlasting promise to Israel,
11   by saying, "I will give you the land of Canaan.
            It is your share of the inheritance."

12 While the people of Israel were few in number,
        a small group of foreigners living in that land,
13   they wandered from nation to nation,
            from one kingdom to another.
14 He didn't permit anyone to oppress them.
    He warned kings about them:
15   "Do not touch my anointed ones
        or harm my prophets."

16 He brought famine to the land.
    He took away their food supply.
17 He sent a man ahead of them.
    He sent Joseph, who was sold as a slave.
18   They hurt his feet with shackles,
        and cut into his neck with an iron collar.

---

[a] 104:26 Hebrew meaning uncertain.   [a] 105:8 Or "covenant."

19 The LORD's promise tested him through fiery trials
  until his prediction came true.
20 The king sent someone to release him.
  The ruler of nations set him free.
21 He made Joseph the master of his palace
  and the ruler of all his possessions.
22 Joseph trained the king's officers the way he wanted
  and taught his respected leaders wisdom.

23 Then Israel came to Egypt.
  Jacob lived as a foreigner in the land of Ham.
24 The LORD made his people grow rapidly in number
  and stronger than their enemies.
25 He changed their minds so that they hated his people,
  and they dealt treacherously with his servants.
26 He sent his servant Moses, and he sent Aaron, whom he had chosen.
27 They displayed his miraculous signs among them
  and did amazing things in the land of Ham.
28 He sent darkness and made ˌtheir landˌ dark.
  They did not rebel against his orders.
29 He turned their water into blood
  and caused their fish to die.
30 He made their land swarm with frogs,
  even in the kings' bedrooms.
31 He spoke, and swarms of flies and gnats
  infested their whole territory.
32 He gave them hail and lightning
  instead of rain throughout their land.
33 He struck their grapevines and fig trees
  and smashed the trees in their territory.
34 He spoke, and countless locusts and grasshoppers came.
35 They devoured all the plants in the land.
  They devoured the crops in the fields.
36 He killed all the firstborn sons,
  the first ones born in the land when their fathers were young.
37 He brought Israel out with silver and gold,
  and no one among his tribes stumbled.
38 The Egyptians were terrified of Israel,
  so they were glad when Israel left.
39 He spread out a cloud as a protective covering
  and a fire to light up the night.
40 The Israelites asked, and he brought them quail
  and filled them with bread from heaven.
41 He opened a rock, and water gushed
  and flowed like a river through the dry places.

42 He remembered his holy promise to his servant Abraham.
43 He brought his people out with joy,
  his chosen ones with a song of joy.
44 He gave them the lands of ˌotherˌ nations,
  and they inherited what others had worked for
45 so that they would obey his laws
  and follow his teachings.

Hallelujah!

PSALM 106

1 Hallelujah!

Give thanks to the LORD because he is good,
  because his mercy endures forever.
2 Who can speak about all the mighty things the LORD has done?
  Who can announce all the things for which he is worthy of praise?
3 Blessed are those who defend justice
  and do what is right at all times.

4 Remember me, O LORD, when you show favor to your people.
  Come to help me with your salvation

⁵   so that I may see the prosperity of your chosen ones,
          find joy in our people's happiness,
               and brag with the people who belong to you.

⁶   We have sinned, and so did our ancestors.
      We have done wrong.
      We are guilty.
⁷   When our ancestors were in Egypt,
             they gave no thought to your miracles.
                  They did not remember your numerous acts of mercy,
                       so they rebelled at the sea, the Red Sea.

⁸   He saved them because of his reputation
          so that he could make his mighty power known.
⁹   He angrily commanded the Red Sea, and it dried up.
      He led them through deep water as though it were a desert.
¹⁰   He rescued them from the power of the one who hated them.
      He rescued them from the enemy.
¹¹   Water covered their adversaries.
             Not one Egyptian survived.
¹²   Then our ancestors believed what he said.
                  They sang his praise.

¹³   They quickly forgot what he did.
      They did not wait for his advice.
¹⁴   They had an unreasonable desire ˌfor foodˌ in the wilderness.
          In the desert they tested God.
¹⁵   He gave them what they asked for.
          He ˌalsoˌ gave them a degenerative disease.

¹⁶   In the camp certain men became envious of Moses.
          They also became envious of Aaron, the LORD's holy one.
¹⁷   The ground split open and swallowed Dathan.
             It buried Abiram's followers.
¹⁸   A fire broke out among their followers.
                  Flames burned up wicked people.

¹⁹   At Mount Horeb they made ˌa statue ofˌ a calf.
      They worshiped an idol made of metal.
²⁰   They traded their glorious God*a*
             for the statue of a bull that eats grass.
²¹   They forgot God, their savior,
          the one who did spectacular things in Egypt,
²²   miracles in the land of Ham,
             and terrifying things at the Red Sea.
²³   God said he was going to destroy them,
          but Moses, his chosen one, stood in his way
             to prevent him from exterminating them.

²⁴   They refused ˌto enterˌ the pleasant land.
      They did not believe what he said.
²⁵   They complained in their tents.
      They did not obey the LORD.
²⁶   Raising his hand, he swore
             that he would kill them in the wilderness,
²⁷   kill their descendants among the nations,
                       and scatter them throughout various lands.

²⁸   They joined in worshiping the god Baal while they were at Peor,
          and they ate what was sacrificed to the dead.
²⁹   They infuriated God by what they did,
          and a plague broke out among them.
³⁰   Then Phinehas stood between God and the people,
          and the plague was stopped.
³¹   Because of this, Phinehas was considered righteous forever,
             throughout every generation.
³²   They made God angry by the water at Meribah.

---

a 106:20 Or "their glory."

33 Things turned out badly for Moses because of what they did,
       since they made him bitter so that he spoke recklessly.

34 They did not destroy the people as the LORD had told them.
35 Instead, they intermarried with other nations.
       They learned to do what other nations did,
36   and they worshiped their idols,
               which became a trap for them.
37 They sacrificed their sons and daughters to demons.
38 They shed innocent blood,
           the blood of their own sons and daughters
               whom they sacrificed to the idols of Canaan.
               The land became polluted with blood.
39 They became filthy because of what they did.
   They behaved like prostitutes.
40   The LORD burned with anger against his own people.
       He was disgusted with those who belonged to him.
41 He handed them over to other nations,
       and those who hated them ruled them.
42   Their enemies oppressed them
               and made them subject to their power.
43 He rescued them many times,
       but they continued to plot rebellion against him
       and to sink deeper because of their sin.
44 He saw that they were suffering
       when he heard their cry for help.
45 He remembered his promise*b* to them.
       In keeping with his rich mercy, he changed his plans.
46 He let them find compassion
       from all those who held them captive.

47 Rescue us, O LORD our God, and gather us from the nations
       so that we may give thanks to your holy name
       and make your praise our glory.

48   Thanks be to the LORD God of Israel
               from everlasting to everlasting.
               Let all the people say amen.

               Hallelujah!

BOOK FIVE
Psalms 107–150

PSALM 107

1 Give thanks to the LORD because he is good,
       because his mercy endures forever.

2 Let the people the LORD defended repeat these words.
       They are the people he defended from the power of their enemies
3   and gathered from other countries,
               from the east and from the west,
               from the north and from the south.
4 They wandered around the desert on a deserted road
       without finding an inhabited city.
5 They were hungry and thirsty.
   They began to lose hope.
6 In their distress they cried out to the LORD.
   He rescued them from their troubles.
7 He led them on a road that went straight to an inhabited city.

8 Let them give thanks to the LORD because of his mercy.
   He performed his miracles for Adam's descendants.
9 He gave plenty to drink to those who were thirsty.

---

b 106:45 Or "covenant."

He filled those who were hungry with good food.

10 Those who lived in the dark, in death's shadow
were prisoners in misery.
They were held in iron chains

11 because they had rebelled against God's words
and had despised the advice given by the Most High.

12 So he humbled them with hard work.
They fell down, but no one was there to help them.

13 In their distress they cried out to the LORD.
He saved them from their troubles.

14 He brought them out of the dark, out of death's shadow.
He broke apart their chains.

15 Let them give thanks to the LORD because of his mercy.
He performed his miracles for Adam's descendants.

16 He shattered bronze gates
and cut iron bars in two.

17 Fools suffered because of their disobedience
and because of their crimes.

18 All food was disgusting to them,
and they came near death's gates.

19 In their distress they cried out to the LORD.
He saved them from their troubles.

20 He sent his message and healed them.
He rescued them from the grave.

21 Let them give thanks to the LORD because of his mercy.
He performed his miracles for Adam's descendants.

22 Let them bring songs of thanksgiving as their sacrifice.
Let them tell in joyful songs what he has done.

23 Those who sail on the sea in ships,
who do business on the high seas,

24 have seen what the LORD can do,
the miracles he performed in the depths of the sea.

25 He spoke, and a storm began to blow,
and it made the waves rise high.

26 The sailors aboard ship rose toward the sky.
They plunged into the depths.
Their courage melted in the face of disaster.

27 They reeled and staggered like drunks,
and all their skills as sailors became useless.

28 In their distress they cried out to the LORD.
He led them from their troubles.

29 He made the storm calm down,
and the waves became still.

30 The sailors were glad that the storm was quiet.
He guided them to the harbor they had longed for.

31 Let them give thanks to the LORD because of his mercy.
He performed his miracles for Adam's descendants.

32 Let them glorify him when the people are gathered for worship.
Let them praise him in the company of respected leaders.

33 He changes rivers into a desert,
springs into thirsty ground,

34 and fertile ground into a layer of salt
because of the wickedness of the people living there.

35 He changes deserts into lakes
and dry ground into springs.

36 There he settles those who are hungry,
and they build cities to live in.

37 They plant in fields and vineyards
that produce crops.

38 He blesses them, and their numbers multiply,
and he does not allow a shortage of cattle.

39 They became few in number and were humiliated
because of oppression, disaster, and sorrow.

40 He poured contempt on their influential people
and made them stumble around in a pathless desert.
41 But now he lifts needy people high above suffering
and makes their families like flocks.
42 Decent people will see this and rejoice,
but all the wicked people will shut their mouths.

43 Let those who ˎthinkˏ they are wise
pay attention to these things
so that they may understand the LORD's blessings.

PSALM 108[a]

A song; a psalm by David.

1 My heart is confident, O God.
I want to sing and make music even with my soul.[b]
2 Wake up, harp and lyre!
I want to wake up at dawn.
3 I want to give thanks to you among the people, O LORD.
I want to make music to praise you among the nations
4 because your mercy is higher than the heavens.
Your truth reaches the skies.

5 May you be honored above the heavens, O God.
Let your glory extend over the whole earth.

6 Save ˎusˏ with your powerful hand, and answer us
so that those who are dear to you may be rescued.

7 God has promised the following through his holiness:
"I will triumph!
I will divide Shechem.
I will measure the valley of Succoth.
8 Gilead is mine.
Manasseh is mine.
Ephraim is the helmet on my head.
Judah is my scepter.
9 Moab is my washtub.
I will throw my shoe over Edom.
I will shout in triumph over Philistia."

10 Who will bring me into the fortified city?
Who will lead me to Edom?
11 Isn't it you, O God, who rejected us?
Isn't it you, O God, who refused to accompany our armies?

12 Give us help against the enemy
because human assistance is worthless.
13 With God we will display great strength.
He will trample our enemies.

PSALM 109

For the choir director; a psalm by David.

1 O God, whom I praise, do not turn a deaf ear to me.
2 Wicked and deceitful people have opened their mouths against me.
They speak against me with lying tongues.
3 They surround me with hateful words.
They fight against me for no reason.
4 In return for my love, they accuse me,
but I pray for them.[a]
5 They reward me with evil instead of good
and with hatred instead of love.

---

[a] 108:1 Verses 1–5 are virtually identical in wording to Psalm 57:7–11; verses 6–13 are virtually identical in wording to Psalm 60:5–12.   [b] 108:1 Or "my glory."   [a] 109:4 Or "but I am a man of prayer."

⁶ ⌊I said,⌋ "Appoint the evil one to oppose him.
Let Satan stand beside him.
⁷ When he stands trial,
let him be found guilty.
Let his prayer be considered sinful.
⁸ Let his days be few ⌊in number⌋.
Let someone else take his position.

⁹ "Let his children become fatherless and his wife a widow.
¹⁰ Let his children wander around and beg.
Let them seek help far from their ruined homes.
¹¹ Let a creditor take everything he owns.
Let strangers steal what he has worked for.
¹² Let no one be kind to him anymore.
Let no one show any pity to his fatherless children.
¹³ Let his descendants be cut off
and their family name be wiped out by the next generation.
¹⁴ Let the LORD remember the guilt of his ancestors
and not wipe out his mother's sin.
¹⁵ Let their guilt and sin always remain on record
in front of the LORD.
Let the LORD remove every memory of him*ᵇ* from the earth,
¹⁶ because he did not remember to be kind.

"He drove oppressed, needy,
and brokenhearted people to their graves.
¹⁷ He loved to put curses ⌊on others⌋,
so he, too, was cursed.
He did not like to bless ⌊others⌋,
so he never received a blessing.
¹⁸ He wore cursing as though it were clothing,
so cursing entered his body like water
and his bones like oil.
¹⁹ Let cursing be his clothing,
a belt he always wears."

²⁰ This is how the LORD rewards those who accuse me,
those who say evil things against me.

²¹ O LORD Almighty, deal with me out of the goodness of your name.
Rescue me because of your mercy.
²² I am oppressed and needy.
I can feel the pain in my heart.
²³ I fade away like a lengthening shadow.
I have been shaken off like a grasshopper.
²⁴ My knees give way because I have been fasting.
My body has become lean, without any fat.
²⁵ I have become the victim of my enemies' insults.
They look at me and shake their heads.
²⁶ Help me, O LORD my God.
Save me because of your mercy.
²⁷ Then they will know that this is your doing,
that you, O LORD, are the one who saved me.
²⁸ They may curse, but you will bless.
Let those who attack me be ashamed,
but let me rejoice.
²⁹ Let those who accuse me wear disgrace as though it were clothing.
Let them be wrapped in their shame as though it were a robe.

³⁰ With my mouth I will give many thanks to the LORD.
I will praise him among many people,
³¹ because he stands beside needy people
to save them from those who would condemn them to death.

ᵇ 109:15 Or "them."

PSALM 110

A psalm by David.

1   The Lord said to my Lord,
      "Sit in the highest position in heaven
         until I make your enemies your footstool."

2   The Lord will extend your powerful scepter from Zion.
      Rule your enemies who surround you.

3   Your people will volunteer when you call up your army.
         Your young people will come to you in holy splendor
            like dew in the early morning.*

4   The Lord has taken an oath and will not change his mind:
      "You are a priest forever, in the way Melchizedek was a priest."

5   The Lord is at your right side.
      He will crush kings on the day of his anger.
6   He will pass judgment on the nations
         and fill them with dead bodies.
            Throughout the earth he will crush ͺtheirͺ heads.
7   He will drink from the brook along the road.
      He will hold his head high.

PSALM 111*

1   Hallelujah!

    I will give thanks to the Lord with all my heart
       in the company of decent people and in the congregation.
2   The Lord's deeds are spectacular.
       They should be studied by all who enjoy them.
3   His work is glorious and majestic.
    His righteousness continues forever.
4   He has made his miracles unforgettable.
       The Lord is merciful and compassionate.
5   He provides food for those who fear him.
    He always remembers his promise.*
6   He has revealed the power of his works to his people
       by giving them the lands of other nations as an inheritance.
7   His works are done with truth and justice.
       ˙All his guiding principles are trustworthy.
8   They last forever and ever.
       They are carried out with truth and decency.
9   He has sent salvation to his people.
    He has ordered that his promise should continue forever.
       His name is holy and terrifying.
10 The fear of the Lord is the beginning of wisdom.
    Good sense is shown by everyone who follows ͺGod's guiding principlesͺ.
    His praise continues forever.

PSALM 112*

1   Hallelujah!

    Blessed is the person who fears the Lord
       and is happy to obey his commands.
2   His descendants will grow strong on the earth.
       The family of a decent person will be blessed.
3   Wealth and riches will be in his home.
       His righteousness continues forever.
4   Light will shine in the dark for a decent person.
             He is merciful, compassionate, and fair.

---

a 110:3 Or "You have the dew of your youth."   *a* 111:1 Psalm 111 is a poem in Hebrew alphabetical order.
b 111:5 Or "covenant."   *a* 112:1 Psalm 112 is a poem in Hebrew alphabetical order.

⁵ All goes well for the person who is generous and lends willingly.
　He earns an honest living.
⁶ 　He will never fail.
　A righteous person will always be remembered.
⁷ 　　He is not afraid of bad news.
　　His heart remains secure, full of confidence in the LORD.
⁸ 　　His heart is steady, and he is not afraid.
　　　In the end he will look triumphantly at his enemies.
⁹ 　　He gives freely to poor people.
　　His righteousness continues forever.
　　His head is raised in honor.
¹⁰ 　　　The wicked person sees this and becomes angry.
　　　He angrily grits his teeth and disappears.
　　　　The hope that wicked people have will vanish.

PSALM 113

¹ Hallelujah!

You servants of the LORD, praise him.
Praise the name of the LORD.
² Thank the name of the LORD now and forever.
³ From where the sun rises to where the sun sets,
　the name of the LORD should be praised.
⁴ The LORD is high above all the nations.
　His glory is above the heavens.
⁵ Who is like the LORD our God?
　He is seated on his high throne.
⁶ He bends down to look at heaven and earth.
⁷ He lifts the poor from the dust.
　He lifts the needy from a garbage heap.
⁸ He seats them with influential people,
　with the influential leaders of his people.
⁹ He makes a woman who is in a childless home
　a joyful mother.

Hallelujah!

PSALM 114

¹ When Israel left Egypt,
when Jacob's family left people who spoke a foreign language,
² 　Judah became his holy place and Israel became his kingdom.
³ 　　The Red Sea looked at this and ran away.
　　The Jordan River turned back.
⁴ 　　　The mountains jumped like rams.
　　　The hills jumped like lambs.
⁵ 　　Red Sea, why did you run away?
　　Jordan River, what made you turn back?
⁶ 　　　Mountains, what made you jump like rams?
　　　Hills, what made you jump like lambs?
⁷ Earth, tremble in the presence of the Lord,
　in the presence of the God of Jacob.
⁸ 　　He turns a rock into a pool filled with water
　　　and turns flint into a spring flowing with water.

PSALM 115

¹ Don't give glory to us, O LORD.
Don't give glory to us.
　Instead, give glory to your name
　　because of your mercy and faithfulness.
² Why should other nations say, "Where is their God?"
³ 　Our God is in heaven.
　　He does whatever he wants.
⁴ Their idols are made of silver and gold.

They were made by human hands.[a]

5 They have mouths, but they cannot speak.
They have eyes, but they cannot see.
6 They have ears, but they cannot hear.
They have noses, but they cannot smell.
7 They have hands, but they cannot feel.
They have feet, but they cannot walk.
They cannot ˎevenˎ make a sound with their throats.
8 Those who make idols end up like them.
So does everyone who trusts them.

9 Israel, trust the LORD.
He is your helper and your shield.
10 Descendants of Aaron, trust the LORD.
He is your helper and your shield.
11 If you fear the LORD, trust the LORD.
He is your helper and your shield.

12 The LORD, who is ˎalwaysˎ thinking about us, will bless us.
He will bless the descendants of Israel.
He will bless the descendants of Aaron.
13 He will bless those who fear the LORD,
from the least important to the most important.
14 May the LORD continue to bless you and your children.
15 You will be blessed by the LORD, the maker of heaven and earth.
16 The highest heaven belongs to the LORD,
but he has given the earth to the descendants of Adam.
17 Those who are dead do not praise the LORD,
nor do those who go into the silence ˎof the graveˎ.
18 But we will thank the LORD now and forever.

Hallelujah!

PSALM 116

1 I love the LORD because he hears my voice, my pleas for mercy.
2 I will call on him as long as I live
because he turns his ear toward me.
3 The ropes of death became tangled around me.
The horrors of the grave took hold of me.
I experienced pain and agony.
4 But I kept calling on the name of the LORD:
"Please, LORD, rescue me!"

5 The LORD is merciful and righteous.
Our God is compassionate.
6 The LORD protects defenseless people.
When I was weak, he saved me.
7 Be at peace again, my soul,
because the LORD has been good to you.

8 You saved me from death.
You saved my eyes from tears ˎandˎ my feet from stumbling.
9 I will walk in the LORD's presence in this world of the living.
10 I kept my faith even when I said,
"I am suffering terribly."
11 I also said when I was panic-stricken,
"Everyone is undependable."
12 How can I repay the LORD
for all the good that he has done for me?
13 I will take the cup of salvation
and call on the name of the LORD.
14 I will keep my vows to the LORD
in the presence of all his people.
15 Precious in the sight of the LORD
is the death of his faithful ones.

---

[a] 115:4 Verses 4–8 are virtually identical in wording to Psalm 135:15–18.

16 O Lord, I am indeed your servant.
  I am your servant,
    the son of your female servant.
  You have freed me from my chains.
17 I will bring a song of thanksgiving to you as a sacrifice.
  I will call on the name of the Lord.
18 I will keep my vows to the Lord
  in the presence of all his people,
19   in the courtyards of the Lord's house,
      in the middle of Jerusalem.

Hallelujah!

PSALM 117

1 Praise the Lord, all you nations!
  Praise him, all you people of the world!
2 His mercy toward us is powerful.
  The Lord's faithfulness endures forever.

Hallelujah!

PSALM 118

1 Give thanks to the Lord because he is good,
  because his mercy endures forever.
2 Israel should say,
    "His mercy endures forever."
3 The descendants of Aaron should say,
    "His mercy endures forever."
4 Those who fear the Lord should say,
    "His mercy endures forever."

5 During times of trouble I called on the Lord.
  The Lord answered me ⸢and⸣ set me free ⸢from all of them⸣.
6 The Lord is on my side.
  I am not afraid.
    What can mortals do to me?
7 The Lord is on my side as my helper.
  I will see ⸢the defeat of⸣ those who hate me.
8 It is better to depend on the Lord
  than to trust mortals.
9 It is better to depend on the Lord
  than to trust influential people.

10 All the nations surrounded me,
  ⸢but armed⸣ with the name of the Lord, I defeated them.
11 They surrounded me. Yes, they surrounded me,
  ⸢but armed⸣ with the name of the Lord, I defeated them.
12 They swarmed around me like bees,
  but they were extinguished like burning thornbushes.
  ⸢So armed⸣ with the name of the Lord, I defeated them.
13 They pushed hard to make me fall,
  but the Lord helped me.
14 The Lord is my strength and my song.
  He is my savior.

15 The sound of joyful singing and victory is heard
  in the tents of righteous people.
    The right hand of the Lord displays strength.
16   The right hand of the Lord is held high.
    The right hand of the Lord displays strength.
17 I will not die,
  but I will live and tell what the Lord has done.
18 The Lord disciplined me severely,
  but he did not allow me to be killed.

19 Open the gates of righteousness for me.
  I will go through them ⸢and⸣ give thanks to the Lord.

20 This is the gate of the LORD
    through which righteous people will enter.

21 I give thanks to you,
        because you have answered me.
            You are my savior.

22 The stone that the builders rejected
        has become the cornerstone.

23 The LORD is responsible for this,
        and it is amazing for us to see.

24 This is the day the LORD has made.
        Let's rejoice and be glad today!

25 We beg you, O LORD, save us!
    We beg you, O LORD, give us success!

26 Blessed is the one who comes in the name of the LORD.
        We bless you from the LORD's house.

27 The LORD is God, and he has given us light.
        March in a festival procession
            with branches to the horns of the altar.

28 You are my God, and I give thanks to you.
    My God, I honor you highly.

29 Give thanks to the LORD because he is good,
        because his mercy endures forever.

PSALM 119[a]

1 Blessed are those whose lives have integrity,
        those who follow the teachings of the LORD.

2 Blessed are those who obey his written instructions.
        They wholeheartedly search for him.

3 They do nothing wrong.
        They follow his directions.

4 You have commanded
        that your guiding principles be carefully followed.

5 I pray that my ways may become firmly established
        so that I can obey your laws.

6 Then I will never feel ashamed
            when I study all your commandments.

7 I will give thanks to you
        as I learn your regulations, which are based on your righteousness.

8 I will obey your laws.
        Never abandon me.

9 How can a young person keep his life pure?
        ⌊He can do it⌋ by holding on to your word.

10 I wholeheartedly searched for you.
        Do not let me wander away from your commandments.

11 I have treasured your promise in my heart
        so that I may not sin against you.

12 Thanks be to you, O LORD.
        Teach me your laws.

13 With my lips I have repeated
        every regulation that ⌊comes⌋ from your mouth.

14 I find joy in the way ⌊shown by⌋ your written instructions
        more than I find joy in all kinds of riches.

15 I want to reflect on your guiding principles
        and study your ways.

16 Your laws make me happy.
    I never forget your word.

17 Be kind to me so that I may live
        and hold on to your word.

18 Uncover my eyes
        so that I may see the miraculous things in your teachings.

19 I am a foreigner in this world.

---

[a] 119:1 Psalm 119 is a poem in Hebrew alphabetical order.

Do not hide your commandments from me.
20 My soul is overwhelmed with endless longing for your regulations.
21 You threaten arrogant people, who are condemned
   and wander away from your commandments.
22 Remove the insults and contempt that have fallen on me
   because I have obeyed your written instructions.
23 Even though influential people plot against me,
   I reflect on your laws.
24 Indeed, your written instructions make me happy.
   They are my best friends.

25 I am close to death.
   Give me a new life as you promised.
26 I told you what I have done, and you answered me.
   Teach me your laws.
27 Help me understand your guiding principles
   so that I may reflect on your miracles.
28 I am drowning in tears.
   Strengthen me as you promised.
29 Turn me away from a life of lies.
   Graciously provide me with your teachings.
30 I have chosen a life of faithfulness.
   I have set your regulations in front of me.
31 I have clung tightly to your written instructions.
   O Lord, do not let me be put to shame.
32 I will eagerly pursue your commandments
   because you continue to increase my understanding.

33 Teach me, O Lord, how to live by your laws,
   and I will obey them to the end.
34 Help me understand so that I can follow your teachings.
   I will guard them with all my heart.
35 Lead me on the path of your commandments,
   because I am happy with them.
36 Direct my heart toward your written instructions
   rather than getting rich in underhanded ways.
37 Turn my eyes away from worthless things.
   Give me a new life in your ways.
38 Keep your promise to me
   so that I can fear you.
39 Take away insults, which I dread,
   because your regulations are good.
40 I long for your guiding principles.
   Give me a new life in your righteousness.

41 Let your blessings reach me, O Lord.
   Save me as you promised.
42 Then I will have an answer for the one who insults me
   since I trust your word.
43 Do not take so much as a single word of truth from my mouth.
   My hope is based on your regulations.
44 I will follow your teachings forever and ever.
45 I will walk around freely
   because I sought out your guiding principles.
46 I will speak about your written instructions in the presence of kings
   and not feel ashamed.
47 Your commandments, which I love, make me happy.
48 I lift my hands ˌin prayerˌ because of your commandments,
   which I love.
   I will reflect on your laws.

49 Remember the word ˌyou gaveˌ me.
   Through it you gave me hope.
50 This is my comfort in my misery:
   Your promise gave me a new life.
51 Arrogant people have mocked me with cruelty,
   yet I have not turned away from your teachings.
52 I remembered your regulations from long ago, O Lord,
   and I found comfort ˌin themˌ.

⁵³ I am burning with anger because of wicked people,
   who abandon your teachings.
⁵⁴ Your laws have become like psalms to me
   in this place where I am only a foreigner.
⁵⁵ At night I remember your name, O LORD,
   and I follow your teachings.
⁵⁶ This has happened to me
   because I have obeyed your guiding principles.

⁵⁷ You are my inheritance, O LORD.
   I promised to hold on to your words.
⁵⁸ With all my heart I want to win your favor.
   Be kind to me as you promised.
⁵⁹ I have thought about my life,
   and I have directed my feet back to your written instructions.
⁶⁰ Without any hesitation I hurry to obey your commandments.
⁶¹ ⌊Though⌋ the ropes of wicked people are tied around me,
   I never forget your teachings.
⁶² At midnight I wake up to give thanks to you
   for the regulations, which are based on your righteousness.
⁶³ I am a friend to everyone who fears you
   and to everyone who follows your guiding principles.
⁶⁴ Your mercy, O LORD, fills the earth.
   Teach me your laws.

⁶⁵ You have treated me well, O LORD,
   as you promised.
⁶⁶ Teach me ⌊to use⌋ good judgment and knowledge,
   because I believe in your commandments.
⁶⁷ Before you made me suffer, I used to wander off,
   but now I hold on to your word.
⁶⁸ You are good, and you do good things.
   Teach me your laws.
⁶⁹ Arrogant people have smeared me with lies,
   ⌊yet⌋ I obey your guiding principles with all my heart.
⁷⁰ Their hearts are cold and insensitive,
   ⌊yet⌋ I am happy with your teachings.
⁷¹ It was good that I had to suffer
   in order to learn your laws.
⁷² The teachings ⌊that come⌋ from your mouth are worth more to me
   than thousands in gold or silver.

⁷³ Your hands created me and made me what I am.
   Help me understand so that I may learn your commandments.
⁷⁴ Those who fear you will see me and rejoice,
   because my hope is based on your word.
⁷⁵ I know that your regulations are fair, O LORD,
   and that you were right to make me suffer.
⁷⁶ Let your mercy comfort me
   as you promised.
⁷⁷ Let your compassion reach me so that I may live,
   because your teachings make me happy.
⁷⁸ Let arrogant people be put to shame
   because they lied about me,
      ⌊yet⌋ I reflect on your guiding principles.
⁷⁹ Let those who fear you turn to me
   so that they can come to know your written instructions.
⁸⁰ Let my heart be filled with integrity in regard to your laws
   so that I will not be put to shame.

⁸¹ My soul is weak from waiting for you to save me.
   My hope is based on your word.
⁸² My eyes have become strained from looking for your promise.
   I ask, "When will you comfort me?"
⁸³ Although I have become like a shriveled and dried out wineskin,
   I have not forgotten your laws.
⁸⁴ What is left of my life?

When will you bring those who persecute me to justice?
85   Arrogant people have dug pits to trap me
      in defiance of your teachings.
86   (All your commandments are reliable.)
   Those people persecute me with lies. Help me!
87   They almost wiped me off ˌthe face ofˌ the earth.
      But I did not abandon your guiding principles.
88   Give me a new life through your mercy
      so that I may obey the written instructions,
      ˌwhich cameˌ from your mouth.

89   O Lord, your word is established in heaven forever.
90   Your faithfulness endures throughout every generation.
         You set the earth in place, and it continues to stand.
91   All things continue to stand today because of your regulations,
            since they are all your servants.
92   If your teachings had not made me happy,
      then I would have died in my misery.
93   I will never forget your guiding principles,
      because you gave me a new life through them.
94   I am yours.
      Save me, because I have searched for your guiding principles.
95   The wicked people have waited for me in order to destroy me,
      ˌyetˌ I want to understand your written instructions.
96   I have seen a limit to everything else,
      ˌbutˌ your commandments have no limit.

97   Oh, how I love your teachings!
   They are in my thoughts all day long.
98   Your commandments make me wiser than my enemies,
      because your commandments are always with me.
99   I have more insight than all my teachers,
      because your written instructions are in my thoughts.
100   I have more wisdom than those with many years of experience,
      because I have obeyed your guiding principles.
101   I have kept my feet ˌfrom walkingˌ on any evil path
      in order to obey your word.
102   I have not neglected your regulations,
      because you have taught me.
103   How sweet the taste of your promise is!
   It tastes sweeter than honey.
104   From your guiding principles I gain understanding.
      That is why I hate every path that leads to lying.

105   Your word is a lamp for my feet
      and a light for my path.
106   I took an oath, and I will keep it.
      I took an oath to follow your regulations,
         which are based on your righteousness.
107   I have suffered so much.
      Give me a new life, O Lord, as you promised.
108   Please accept the praise I gladly give you, O Lord,
      and teach me your regulations.
109   I always take my life into my own hands,
      but I never forget your teachings.
110   Wicked people have set a trap for me,
      but I have never wandered away from your guiding principles.
111   Your written instructions are mine forever.
      They are the joy of my heart.
112   I have decided to obey your laws.
      They offer a reward that never ends.

113   I hate two-faced people,
      but I love your teachings.
114   You are my hiding place and my shield.
      My hope is based on your word.
115   Get away from me, you evildoers,
      so that I can obey the commandments of my God.

116 Help me God, as you promised, so that I may live.
      Do not turn my hope into disappointment.
117 Hold me, and I will be safe,
      and I will always respect your laws.
118 You reject all who wander away from your laws,
      because their lies mislead them.*b*
119 You get rid of all wicked people on earth as if they were rubbish.
      That is why I love your written instructions.
120 My body shudders in fear of you,
      and I am afraid of your regulations.

121 I have done what is fair and right.
      Do not leave me at the mercy of those who oppress me.
122 Guarantee my well-being.
      Do not let arrogant people oppress me.
123 My eyes are strained from looking for you to save me
      and from looking for the fulfillment of your righteous promise.
124 Treat me with kindness,
      and teach me your laws.
125 I am your servant.
      Help me understand
        so that I may come to know your written instructions.
126 It is time for you to act, O Lord.*c*
      Even though people have abolished your teachings,
127   I love your commandments more than gold, more than pure gold.
128   I follow the straight paths of your guiding principles.
      I hate every pathway that leads to lying.

129 Your written instructions are miraculous.
      That is why I obey them.
130 Your word is a doorway that lets in light,
      and it helps gullible people understand.
131 I open my mouth and pant
      because I long for your commandments.
132 Turn toward me, and have pity on me
      as you have pledged to do for those who love your name.
133 Make my steps secure through your promise,
      and do not let any sin control me.
134 Save me from human oppression
      so that I may obey your guiding principles.
135 Smile on me,
      and teach me your laws.
136 Streams of tears flow from my eyes
      because others do not follow your teachings.

137 You are righteous, O Lord,
      and your regulations are fair.
138 You have issued your written instructions.
      They are fair and completely dependable.
139 My devotion ˌfor your wordsˌ consumes me,
      because my enemies have forgotten your words.
140 Your promise has been thoroughly tested,
      and I love it.
141 I am unimportant and despised,
      ˌyetˌ I never forget your guiding principles.
142 Your righteousness is an everlasting righteousness,
      and your teachings are reliable.
143 Trouble and hardship have found me,
      but your commandments ˌstillˌ make me happy.
144 Your written instructions are always right.
      Help me understand ˌthemˌ so that I will live.

145 I have called out with all my heart. Answer me, O Lord.
      I want to obey your laws.

---

b 119:118 Hebrew meaning of this line uncertain.   *c* 119:126 One Hebrew manuscript, Latin; other Hebrew manuscripts "It is time to act for the Lord."

146 I have called out.
       Save me, so that I can obey your written instructions.
147 I got up before dawn, and I cried out for help.
       My hope is based on your word.
148 My eyes are wide-open throughout the nighttime hours
       to reflect on your word.
149 In keeping with your mercy, hear my voice.
       O LORD, give me a new life guided by your regulations.
150 Those who carry out plots against me are near,
         ⸢yet⸣ they are far away from your teachings.
151 You are near, O LORD,
         and all your commandments are reliable.
152 Long ago I learned from your written instructions
       that you made them to last forever.

153 Look at my misery, and rescue me,
       because I have never forgotten your teachings.
154 Plead my case ⸢for me⸣, and save me.
       Give me a new life as you promised.
155 Wicked people are far from being saved,
       because they have not searched for your laws.
156 Your acts of compassion are many in number, O LORD.
       Give me a new life guided by your regulations.
157 I have many persecutors and opponents,
         ⸢yet⸣ I have not turned away from your written instructions.
158 I have seen traitors,
       and I am filled with disgust.
         They have not accepted your promise.
159 See how I have loved your guiding principles!
       O LORD, in keeping with your mercy, give me a new life.
160 There is nothing but truth in your word,
       and all of your righteous regulations endure forever.

161 Influential people have persecuted me for no reason,
       but it is only your words that fill my heart with terror.
162 I find joy in your promise
       like someone who finds a priceless treasure.
163 I hate lying; I am disgusted with it.
       I love your teachings.
164 Seven times a day I praise you
       for your righteous regulations.
165 There is lasting peace for those who love your teachings.
       Nothing can make those people stumble.
166 I have waited with hope for you to save me, O LORD.
       I have carried out your commandments.
167 I have obeyed your written instructions.
       I have loved them very much.
168 I have followed your guiding principles and your written instructions,
       because my whole life is in front of you.

169 Let my cry for help come into your presence, O LORD.
       Help me understand as you promised.
170 Let my plea for mercy come into your presence.
       Rescue me as you promised.
171 Let my lips pour out praise
       because you teach me your laws.
172 Let my tongue sing about your promise
       because all your commandments are fair.
173 Let your hand help me
       because I have chosen ⸢to follow⸣ your guiding principles.
174 I have longed for you to save me, O LORD,
       and your teachings make me happy.
175 Let my soul have new life so that it can praise you.
       Let your regulations help me.

176 I have wandered away like a lost lamb.
         Search for me,
             because I have never forgotten your commandments.

PSALM 120

A song for going up to worship.

1 When I was in trouble, I cried out to the LORD,
         and he answered me.
2 O LORD, rescue me from lying lips
         and from a deceitful tongue.

3 You deceitful tongue, what can the LORD give you?
         What more can he do for you?
4   He will give you a warrior's sharpened arrows and red-hot coals.

5 How horrible it is to live as a foreigner in Meshech
         or to stay in the tents of Kedar.
6   I have lived too long with those who hate peace.
7   I am for peace, but when I talk about it,
             they only talk about war.

PSALM 121

A song for going up to worship.

1 I look up toward the mountains.
         Where can I find help?
2 My help comes from the LORD,
         the maker of heaven and earth.
3 He will not let you fall.
         Your guardian will not fall asleep.
4 Indeed, the Guardian of Israel never rests or sleeps.
5 The LORD is your guardian.
     The LORD is the shade over your right hand.
6   The sun will not beat down on you during the day,
             nor will the moon at night.
7 The LORD guards you from every evil.
         He guards your life.
8 The LORD guards you as you come and go,
         now and forever.

PSALM 122

A song by David for going up to worship.

1 I was glad when they said to me,
         "Let's go to the house of the LORD."
2 Our feet are standing inside your gates, Jerusalem.
3 Jerusalem is built to be a city
         where the people are united.[a]
4 All of the LORD's tribes go to that city
         because it is a law in Israel
             to give thanks to the name of the LORD.
5 The court of justice sits there.
         It consists of ˌprinces who areˌ David's descendants.

6 Pray for the peace of Jerusalem:
         "May those who love you prosper.
7   May there be peace inside your walls
             and prosperity in your palaces."
8 For the sake of my relatives and friends, let me say,
         "May it go well for you!"
9 For the sake of the house of the LORD our God,
         I will seek what is good for you.

---

[a] 122:3 Hebrew meaning of this verse uncertain.

PSALM 123

A song for going up to worship.

1 I look up to you,
   to the one who sits enthroned in heaven.
2 As servants depend on their masters,
   as a maid depends on her mistress,
      so we depend on the LORD our God
         until he has pity on us.
3 Have pity on us, O LORD.
   Have pity on us
      because we have suffered more than our share of contempt.
4 We have suffered more than our share of ridicule
      from those who are carefree.
   We have suffered more than our share of contempt
      from those who are arrogant.

PSALM 124

A song by David for going up to worship.

1 "If the LORD had not been on our side. . ."
   (Israel should repeat this.)
2 "If the LORD had not been on our side when people attacked us,
3   then they would have swallowed us alive
         when their anger exploded against us.
4 Then the floodwaters would have swept us away.
      An ˻overflowing˼ stream would have washed us away.
5   Then raging water would have washed us away."

6 Thank the LORD, who did not let them sink their teeth into us.
7 We escaped like a bird caught in a hunter's trap.
   The trap was broken, and we escaped.
8 Our help is in the name of the LORD, the maker of heaven and earth.

PSALM 125

A song for going up to worship.

1 Those who trust the LORD are like Mount Zion,
      which can never be shaken.
         It remains firm forever.
2 ˻As˼ the mountains surround Jerusalem,
      so the LORD surrounds his people now and forever.

3 A wicked ruler will not be allowed to govern
      the land set aside for righteous people.
         That is why righteous people do not use their power to do wrong.

4 Do good, O LORD, to those who are good,
      to those whose motives are decent.
5 But when people become crooked,
      the LORD will lead them away with troublemakers.

   Let there be peace in Israel!

PSALM 126

A song for going up to worship.

1 When the LORD restored the fortunes of Zion,
      it was as if we were dreaming.
2 Then our mouths were filled with laughter
      and our tongues with joyful songs.
   Then the nations said,
      "The LORD has done spectacular things for them."

3 The LORD has done spectacular things for us.
      We are overjoyed.
4 Restore our fortunes, O LORD,

as you restore streams ˎto dry riverbedsˎ in the Negev.
5 Those who cry while they plant
will joyfully sing while they harvest.
6 The person who goes out weeping, carrying his bag of seed,
will come home singing, carrying his bundles of grain.

PSALM 127

A song by Solomon for going up to worship.

1 If the LORD does not build the house,
it is useless for the builders to work on it.
If the LORD does not protect a city,
it is useless for the guard to stay alert.
2 It is useless to work hard for the food you eat
by getting up early and going to bed late.
The LORD gives ˎfoodˎ to those he loves while they sleep.

3 Children are an inheritance from the LORD.
They are a reward from him.
4 The children born to a man when he is young
are like arrows in the hand of a warrior.
5 Blessed is the man who has filled his quiver with them.
He will not be put to shame
when he speaks with his enemies in the city gate.

PSALM 128

A song for going up to worship.

1 Blessed are all who fear the LORD
and live his way.

2 You will certainly eat what your own hands have provided.
Blessings to you!
May things go well for you!
3 Your wife will be like a fruitful vine inside your home.
Your children will be like young olive trees around your table.
4 This is how the LORD will bless the person who fears him.
5 May the LORD bless you from Zion
so that you may see Jerusalem prospering
all the days of your life.
6 May you live to see your children's children.

Let there be peace in Israel!

PSALM 129

A song for going up to worship.

1 "From the time I was young, people have attacked me. . ."
(Israel should repeat this.)
2 "From the time I was young, people have attacked me,
but they have never overpowered me.
3 They have plowed my back ˎlike farmers plow fieldsˎ.
They made long slashes ˎlike furrowsˎ."
4 The LORD is righteous.
He has cut me loose
from the ropes that wicked people tied around me.
5 Put to shame all those who hate Zion.
Force them to retreat.
6 Make them be like grass on a roof,
like grass that dries up before it produces a stalk.
7 It will never fill the barns of those who harvest
or the arms of those who gather bundles.
8 Those who pass by will never say ˎto themˎ,
"May you be blessed by the LORD"
or "We bless you in the name of the LORD."

PSALM 130

A song for going up to worship.

1 O LORD, out of the depths I call to you.
2 O Lord, hear my voice.
   Let your ears be open to my pleas for mercy.
3 O LORD, who would be able to stand
      if you kept a record of sins?
4 But with you there is forgiveness
      so that you can be feared.
5 I wait for the LORD, my soul waits,
      and with hope I wait for his word.
6 My soul waits for the LORD
      more than those who watch for the morning,
      more than those who watch for the morning.
7 O Israel, put your hope in the LORD,
      because with the LORD there is mercy
         and with him there is unlimited forgiveness.
8   He will rescue Israel from all its sins.

PSALM 131

A song by David for going up to worship.

1 O LORD, my heart is not conceited.
   My eyes do not look down on others.
   I am not involved in things too big or too difficult for me.
2 Instead, I have kept my soul calm and quiet.
   My soul is content as a weaned child is content in its mother's arms.
3 Israel, put your hope in the LORD now and forever.

PSALM 132

A song for going up to worship.

1 O LORD, remember David and all the hardships he endured.
2   Remember how he swore an oath to the LORD
         and made this vow to the Mighty One of Jacob:
3   "I will not step inside my house,
4   get into my bed, shut my eyes, or close my eyelids
5   until I find a place for the LORD,
                a dwelling place for the Mighty One of Jacob."

6 Now, we have heard about the ark ⌞of the promise⌟ being in Ephrathah.
   We have found it in Jaar.
7 Let's go to his dwelling place.
   Let's worship at his footstool.
8 O LORD, arise, and come to your resting place
   with the ark of your power.
9 Clothe your priests with righteousness.
   Let your godly ones sing with joy.
10 For the sake of your servant David,
   do not reject your anointed one.
11 The LORD swore an oath to David.
   This is a truth he will not take back:
      "I will set one of your own descendants on your throne.
12   If your sons are faithful to my promise[a]
            and my written instructions that I will teach them,
            then their descendants will also sit on your throne forever."

13 The LORD has chosen Zion.
   He wants it for his home.
14   "This will be my resting place forever.
      Here I will sit enthroned because I want Zion.
15   I will certainly bless all that Zion needs.

---

[a] 132:12 Or "covenant."

16 I will satisfy its needy people with food.
I will clothe its priests with salvation.
Then its godly ones will sing joyfully.
17 There I will make a horn sprout up for David.
I will prepare a lamp for my anointed one.
18 I will clothe his enemies with shame,
but the crown on my anointed one will shine."

PSALM 133

A song by David for going up to worship.

1 See how good and pleasant it is
when brothers and sisters live together in harmony!
2 It is like fine, scented oil on the head,
running down the beard—down Aaron's beard—
running over the collar of his robes.
3 It is like dew on ˻Mount˼ Hermon,
dew which comes down on Zion's mountains.
That is where the LORD promised
the blessing of eternal life.

PSALM 134

A song for going up to worship.

1 Praise the LORD, all you servants of the LORD,
all who stand in the house of the LORD night after night.
2 Lift your hands toward the holy place, and praise the LORD.
3 May the LORD, the maker of heaven and earth, bless you from Zion.

PSALM 135

1 Hallelujah!

Praise the name of the LORD.
Praise him, you servants of the LORD
2 who are standing in the house of the LORD,
in the courtyards of the house of our God.
3 Praise the LORD because he is good.
Make music to praise his name because his name is beautiful.
4 The LORD chose Jacob to be his own
and chose Israel to be his own special treasure.

5 I know that the LORD is great,
that our Lord is greater than all the false gods.
6 The LORD does whatever he wants in heaven or on earth,
on the seas or in all the depths of the oceans.
7 He is the one who makes the clouds rise from the ends of the earth,
who makes lightning for the thunderstorms,
and who brings wind out of his storerooms.

8 He is the one who killed every firstborn male in Egypt.
He killed humans and animals alike.
9 He sent miraculous signs and amazing things into the heart of Egypt
against Pharaoh and all his officials.
10 He is the one who defeated many nations and killed mighty kings:
11 King Sihon of the Amorites,
King Og of Bashan,
and all the kingdoms in Canaan.
12 He gave their land as an inheritance,
an inheritance to his people Israel.
13 O LORD, your name endures forever.
O LORD, you will be remembered throughout every generation.
14 The LORD will provide justice for his people
and have compassion on his servants.

¹⁵ The idols of the nations are made of silver and gold.
    They were made by human hands.^a
¹⁶   They have mouths, but they cannot speak.
        They have eyes, but they cannot see.
¹⁷   They have ears, but they cannot hear.
        They cannot breathe.
¹⁸ Those who make idols end up like them.
    So does everyone who trusts them.

¹⁹ Descendants of Israel, praise the LORD.
    Descendants of Aaron, praise the LORD.
²⁰ Descendants of Levi, praise the LORD.
    You people who fear the LORD, praise the LORD.
²¹   Thank the LORD in Zion.
        Thank the one who lives in Jerusalem.

Hallelujah!

PSALM 136

¹ Give thanks to the LORD because he is good,

        because his mercy endures forever.

² Give thanks to the God of gods

        because his mercy endures forever.

³ Give thanks to the Lord of lords

        because his mercy endures forever.

⁴ Give thanks to the only one who does miraculous things—
        because his mercy endures forever.
⁵   to the one who made the heavens by his understanding—
        because his mercy endures forever.
⁶   to the one who spread out the earth on the water—
        because his mercy endures forever.
⁷   to the one who made the great lights—

        because his mercy endures forever.
⁸   the sun to rule the day—

        because his mercy endures forever.
⁹   the moon and stars to rule the night—

        because his mercy endures forever.

¹⁰ Give thanks to the one who killed the firstborn males in Egypt—
        because his mercy endures forever.
¹¹   He brought Israel out from among them—

        because his mercy endures forever.
¹²   with a mighty hand and a powerful arm—

        because his mercy endures forever.

¹³ Give thanks to the one who divided the Red Sea—
        because his mercy endures forever.
¹⁴   He led Israel through the middle of it—

        because his mercy endures forever.
¹⁵   He swept Pharaoh and his army into the Red Sea—
        because his mercy endures forever.

¹⁶ Give thanks to the one who led his people through the desert—
        because his mercy endures forever.

¹⁷ Give thanks to the one who defeated powerful kings—
        because his mercy endures forever.
¹⁸   He killed mighty kings—

        because his mercy endures forever.
¹⁹   King Sihon of the Amorites—

        because his mercy endures forever.
²⁰   and King Og of Bashan—

        because his mercy endures forever.
²¹   He gave their land as an inheritance—

        because his mercy endures forever.

---

^a 135:15 Verses 15–18 are virtually identical in wording to Psalm 115:4–8.

22   as an inheritance for his servant Israel—

           because his mercy endures forever.

23   He remembered us when we were humiliated—

           because his mercy endures forever.

24   He snatched us from the grasp of our enemies—

           because his mercy endures forever.

25   He gives food to every living creature—

           because his mercy endures forever.

26   Give thanks to the God of heaven

           because his mercy endures forever.

PSALM 137

1   By the rivers of Babylon, we sat down and cried
       as we remembered Zion.
2   We hung our lyres on willow trees.
3   It was there that those who had captured us demanded that we sing.
       Those who guarded us wanted us to entertain them.
       ⌊They said,⌋ "Sing a song from Zion for us!"

4   How could we sing the LORD's song in a foreign land?
5   If I forget you, Jerusalem,
       let my right hand forget ⌊how to play the lyre⌋.
6   Let my tongue stick to the roof of my mouth
       if I don't remember you,
       if I don't consider Jerusalem my highest joy.

7   O LORD, remember the people of Edom.
       Remember what they did the day Jerusalem ⌊was captured⌋.
       They said, "Tear it down! Tear it down to its foundation."
8   You destructive people of Babylon,
       blessed is the one who pays you back
           with the same treatment you gave us.
9   Blessed is the one who grabs your little children
       and smashes them against a rock.

PSALM 138

By David.

1   I will give thanks to you with all my heart.
    I will make music to praise you in front of the false gods.
2   I will bow toward your holy temple.
    I will give thanks to your name because of your mercy and truth.
       You have made your name and your promise greater than everything.

3   When I called, you answered me.
       You made me bold by strengthening my soul.[a]
4   All the kings of the earth will give thanks to you, O LORD,
       because they have heard the promises you spoke.
5   They will sing this about the ways of the LORD:
           "The LORD's honor is great!"
6   Even though the LORD is high above, he sees humble people ⌊close up⌋,
       and he recognizes arrogant people from a distance.

7   Even though I walk into the middle of trouble,
       you guard my life against the anger of my enemies.
       You stretch out your hand,
           and your right hand saves me.
8   The LORD will do everything for me.
    O LORD, your mercy endures forever.
    Do not let go of what your hands have made.

---

[a] 138:3 Hebrew meaning of this line uncertain.

PSALM 139

For the choir director; a psalm by David.

1 O LORD, you have examined me, and you know me.
2 You alone know when I sit down and when I get up.
   You read my thoughts from far away.
3 You watch me when I travel and when I rest.
   You are familiar with all my ways.
4   Even before there is a ˌsingleˌ word on my tongue,
        you know all about it, LORD.
5 You are all around me—in front of me and in back of me.
   You lay your hand on me.
6   Such knowledge is beyond my grasp.
      It is so high I cannot reach it.

7 Where can I go ˌto get awayˌ from your Spirit?
   Where can I run ˌto get awayˌ from you?
8   If I go up to heaven, you are there.
      If I make my bed in hell, you are there.
9   If I climb upward on the rays of the morning sun
         ˌorˌ land on the most distant shore of the sea where the sun sets,
10   even there your hand would guide me
            and your right hand would hold on to me.
11   If I say, "Let the darkness hide me
      and let the light around me turn into night,"
12   even the darkness is not too dark for you.
            Night is as bright as day.
            Darkness and light are the same ˌto youˌ.

13 You alone created my inner being.
   You knitted me together inside my mother.
14 I will give thanks to you
      because I have been so amazingly and miraculously made.
         Your works are miraculous, and my soul is fully aware of this.
15 My bones were not hidden from you
      when I was being made in secret,
         when I was being skillfully woven in an underground workshop.
16 Your eyes saw me when I was only a fetus.
      Every day ˌof my lifeˌ was recorded in your book
         before one of them had taken place.
17 How precious are your thoughts concerning me, O God!
   How vast in number they are!
18   If I try to count them,
         there would be more of them than there are grains of sand.
            When I wake up, I am still with you.

19 I wish that you would kill wicked people, O God,
      and that bloodthirsty people would leave me alone.
20   They say wicked things about you.
         Your enemies misuse your name.
21 Shouldn't I hate those who hate you, O LORD?
   Shouldn't I be disgusted with those who attack you?
22   I hate them with all my heart.
      They have become my enemies.

23 Examine me, O God, and know my mind.
   Test me, and know my thoughts.
24   See whether I am on an evil path.
      Then lead me on the everlasting path.

PSALM 140

For the choir leader; a psalm by David.

1 Rescue me from evil people, O LORD.
   Keep me safe from violent people.
2   They plan evil things in their hearts.
      They start fights every day.

3 They make their tongues as sharp as a snake's ˌfangˌ.
Their lips hide the venom of poisonous snakes. *Selah*

4 Protect me from the hands of wicked people, O LORD.
Keep me safe from violent people.
They try to trip me.
5 Arrogant people have laid a trap for me.
They have spread out a net with ropes.
They have set traps for me along the road. *Selah*

6 I said to the LORD, "You are my God."
O LORD, open your ears to hear my plea for pity.
7 O LORD Almighty, the strong one who saves me,
you have covered my head in the day of battle.
8 O LORD, do not give wicked people what they want.
Do not let their evil plans succeed,
ˌorˌ they will become arrogant. *Selah*

9 Let the heads of those who surround me
be covered with their own threats.
10 Let burning coals fall on them.
Let them be thrown into a pit, never to rise again.
11 Do not let slanderers prosper on earth.
Let evil hunt down violent people with one blow after another.

12 I know that the LORD will defend the rights of those who are oppressed
and the cause of those who are needy.
13 Indeed, righteous people will give thanks to your name.
Decent people will live in your presence.

PSALM 141

A psalm by David.

1 O LORD, I cry out to you, "Come quickly."
Open your ears to me when I cry out to you.
2 Let my prayer be accepted
as sweet-smelling incense in your presence.
Let the lifting up of my hands in prayer be accepted
as an evening sacrifice.

3 O LORD, set a guard at my mouth.
Keep watch over the door of my lips.
4 Do not let me be persuaded to do anything evil
or to become involved with wickedness,
with people who are troublemakers.
Do not let me taste their delicacies.

5 A righteous person may strike me or correct me out of kindness.
It is like lotion for my head.
My head will not refuse it,
because my prayer is directed against evil deeds.
6 When their judges are thrown off a cliff,
they will listen to what I have to say.
It will sound pleasant ˌto themˌ.
7 As someone plows and breaks up the ground,
so our bones will be planted at the mouth of the grave.[a]

8 My eyes look to you, LORD Almighty.
I have taken refuge in you.
Do not leave me defenseless.
9 Keep me away from the trap they set for me
and from the traps set by troublemakers.
10 Let wicked people fall into their own nets,
while I escape unharmed.

---

[a] 141:7 Hebrew meaning of verses 5–7 uncertain.

PSALM 142

A *maskil*[a] by David when he was in the cave; a prayer.

1 Loudly, I cry to the LORD.
  Loudly, I plead with the LORD for mercy.
2   I pour out my complaints in his presence
      and tell him my troubles.
3   When I begin to lose hope,
        you ˻already˼ know what I am experiencing.

  ˻My enemies˼ have hidden a trap for me on the path where I walk.
4 Look to my right and see that no one notices me.
    Escape is impossible for me.
      No one cares about me.

5 I call out to you, O LORD.
  I say, "You are my refuge,
    my own inheritance in this world of the living."
6 Pay attention to my cry for help
    because I am very weak.
  Rescue me from those who pursue me
    because they are too strong for me.
7 Release my soul from prison
    so that I may give thanks to your name.
      Righteous people will surround me
        because you are good to me.

PSALM 143

A psalm by David.

1 O LORD, listen to my prayer.
    Open your ears to hear my urgent requests.
    Answer me because you are faithful and righteous.
2 Do not take me to court for judgment,
    because there is no one alive
      who is righteous in your presence.

3 The enemy has pursued me.
    He has ground my life into the dirt.
    He has made me live in dark places
      like those who have died long ago.
4   That is why I begin to lose hope
      and my heart is in a state of shock.

5 I remember the days long ago.
  I reflect on all that you have done.
  I carefully consider what your hands have made.
6 I stretch out my hands to you in prayer.
    Like parched land, my soul thirsts for you.   *Selah*

7 Answer me quickly, O LORD.
    My spirit is worn out.
  Do not hide your face from me,
    or I will be like those who go into the pit.
8 Let me hear about your mercy in the morning,
    because I trust you.
  Let me know the way that I should go,
    because I long for you.
9 Rescue me from my enemies, O LORD.
    I come to you for protection.

10 Teach me to do your will, because you are my God.
   May your good Spirit lead me on level ground.
11 O LORD, keep me alive for the sake of your name.
   Because you are righteous, lead me out of trouble.
12 In keeping with your mercy, wipe out my enemies

---

[a] 142:1 Unknown musical term.

and destroy all who torment me,
because I am your servant.

PSALM 144

By David.

1 Thank the LORD, my rock,
who trained my hands to fight
and my fingers to do battle,
2 my merciful one, my fortress,
my stronghold, and my savior,
my shield, the one in whom I take refuge,
and the one who brings people under my authority.

3 O LORD, what are humans that you should care about them?
What are mere mortals that you should think about them?
4 Humans are like a breath of air.
Their life span is like a fleeting shadow.

5 O LORD, bend your heaven low, and come down.
Touch the mountains, and they will smoke.
6 Hurl bolts of lightning, and scatter them.
Shoot your arrows, and throw them into confusion.
7 Stretch out your hands from above.
Snatch me, and rescue me from raging waters
and from foreigners' hands.
8 Their mouths speak lies.
Their right hands take false pledges.

9 O God, I will sing a new song to you.
I will sing a psalm to you on a ten-stringed harp.
10 You are the one who gives victory to kings.
You are the one who snatches your servant David
away from a deadly sword.
11 Snatch me, and rescue me from foreigners' hands.
Their mouths speak lies.
Their right hands take false pledges.

12 May our sons be like full-grown, young plants.
May our daughters be like stately columns
that adorn the corners of a palace.
13 May our barns be filled with all kinds of crops.
May our sheep give birth to thousands of lambs,
tens of thousands in our fields.
14 May our cattle have many calves.[a]

May no one break in, and may no one be dragged out.
May there be no cries of distress in our streets.

15 Blessed are the people who have these blessings!
Blessed are the people whose God is the LORD!

PSALM 145[a]

A song of praise by David.

1 I will highly praise you, my God, the king.
I will bless your name forever and ever.
2 I will bless you every day.
I will praise your name forever and ever.

3 The LORD is great, and he should be highly praised.
His greatness is unsearchable.
4 One generation will praise your deeds to the next.
Each generation will talk about your mighty acts.
5 I will think about the glorious honor of your majesty
and the miraculous things you have done.

---

[a] 144:14 Hebrew meaning of this verse uncertain.   [a] 145:1 Psalm 145 is a poem in Hebrew alphabetical order.

6 People will talk about the power of your terrifying deeds,
   and I will tell about your greatness.
7 They will announce what they remember of your great goodness,
   and they will joyfully sing about your righteousness.
8 The LORD is merciful, compassionate, patient,
   and always ready to forgive.
9 The LORD is good to everyone
   and has compassion for everything that he has made.
10 Everything that you have made will give thanks to you, O LORD,
   and your faithful ones will praise you.
11 Everyone will talk about the glory of your kingdom
   and will tell the descendants of Adam about your might
12   in order to make known your mighty deeds
      and the glorious honor of your kingdom.
13 Your kingdom is an everlasting kingdom.
   Your empire endures throughout every generation.

14 The LORD supports everyone who falls.
   He straightens ˌthe backsˌ of those who are bent over.
15   The eyes of all creatures look to you,
      and you give them their food at the proper time.
16   You open your hand,
      and you satisfy the desire of every living thing.
17 The LORD is fair in all his ways
   and faithful in everything he does.
18 The LORD is near to everyone who prays to him,
   to every faithful person who prays to him.
19 He fills the needs of those who fear him.
   He hears their cries for help and saves them.
20 The LORD protects everyone who loves him,
   but he will destroy all wicked people.

21 My mouth will speak the praise of the LORD,
   and all living creatures will praise his holy name
      forever and ever.

PSALM 146

1 Hallelujah!

Praise the LORD, my soul!
2 I want to praise the LORD throughout my life.
I want to make music to praise my God as long as I live.

3 Do not trust influential people,
   mortals who cannot help you.
4   When they breathe their last breath, they return to the ground.
      On that day their plans come to an end.
5 Blessed are those who receive help from the God of Jacob.
   Their hope rests on the LORD their God,
6   who made heaven, earth,
      the sea, and everything in them.
   The LORD remains faithful forever.
7 He brings about justice for those who are oppressed.
   He gives food to those who are hungry.
   The LORD sets prisoners free.
8 The LORD gives sight to blind people.
The LORD straightens ˌthe backsˌ of those who are bent over.
The LORD loves righteous people.
9 The LORD protects foreigners.
The LORD gives relief to orphans and widows.
   But he keeps wicked people from reaching their goal.
10 The LORD rules as king forever.
Zion, your God rules throughout every generation.

Hallelujah!

PSALM 147

1 Hallelujah!

It is good to sing psalms to our God.
It is pleasant to sing ⌊his⌋ praise beautifully.

2 The LORD is the builder of Jerusalem.
   He is the one who gathers the outcasts of Israel together.
3 He is the healer of the brokenhearted.
   He is the one who bandages their wounds.
4 He determines the number of stars.
   He gives each one a name.
5 Our Lord is great, and his power is great.
   There is no limit to his understanding.
6 The LORD gives relief to those who are oppressed.
   He brings wicked people down to the ground.

7 Sing to the LORD a song of thanksgiving.
Make music to our God with a lyre.
8 He covers the sky with clouds.
   He provides rain for the ground.
   He makes grass grow on the mountains.
9 He is the one who gives food to animals
   and to young ravens when they call out.
10 He finds no joy in strong horses,
    nor is he pleased by brave soldiers.
11 The LORD is pleased with those who fear him,
    with those who wait with hope for his mercy.

12 Praise the LORD, Jerusalem!
Praise your God, Zion!
13 He makes the bars across your gates strong.
    He blesses the children within you.
14 He is the one who brings peace to your borders
    and satisfies your ⌊hunger⌋ with the finest wheat.
15 He is the one who sends his promise throughout the earth.
    His word travels with great speed.
16 He is the one who sends snow like wool
    and scatters frost like ashes.
17 He is the one who throws his hailstones like breadcrumbs.
    Who can withstand his chilling blast?
18 He sends out his word and melts his hailstones.
    He makes wind blow ⌊and⌋ water flow.
19 He speaks his word to Jacob,
    his laws and judicial decisions to Israel.
20 He has done nothing like this for any other nation.
    The other nations do not know the decisions he has handed down.

Hallelujah!

PSALM 148

1 Hallelujah!

Praise the LORD from the heavens.
Praise him in the heights above.
2 Praise him, all his angels.
Praise him, his entire heavenly army.
3 Praise him, sun and moon.
Praise him, all shining stars.
4 Praise him, you highest heaven
   and the water above the sky.
5 Let them praise the name of the LORD
   because they were created by his command.
6 He set them in their places forever and ever.
He made it a law that no one can break.

7 Praise the LORD from the earth.
Praise him, large sea creatures and all the ocean depths,

8   lightning and hail,
      snow and fog,
      strong winds that obey his commands,
9   mountains and all hills,
      fruit trees and all cedar trees,
10   wild animals and all domestic animals,
      crawling animals and birds,
11   kings of the earth and all its people,
      officials and all judges on the earth,
12   young men and women,
      old and young together.
13   Let them praise the name of the LORD
      because his name is high above all others.
        His glory is above heaven and earth.
14   He has given his people a strong leader,[a]
      someone praiseworthy for his faithful ones,
        for the people of Israel, the people who are close to him.

   Hallelujah!

PSALM 149

1   Hallelujah!

   Sing a new song to the LORD.
   Sing his praise in the assembly of godly people.
2   Let Israel find joy in their creator.
   Let the people of Zion rejoice over their king.
3   Let them praise his name with dancing.
   Let them make music to him with tambourines and lyres,
4   because the LORD takes pleasure in his people.
      He crowns those who are oppressed with victory.
5   Let godly people triumph in glory.
   Let them sing for joy on their beds.
6   Let the high praises of God be in their throats
      and two-edged swords in their hands
7   to take vengeance on the nations,
      to punish the people of the world,
8   to put their kings in chains
        and their leaders in iron shackles,
9   to carry out the judgment that is written against them.
        This is an honor that belongs to all his godly ones.

   Hallelujah!

PSALM 150

1   Hallelujah!

   Praise God in his holy place.
   Praise him in his mighty heavens.
2   Praise him for his mighty acts.
   Praise him for his immense greatness.
3   Praise him with sounds from horns.
   Praise him with harps and lyres.
4   Praise him with tambourines and dancing.
   Praise him with stringed instruments and flutes.
5   Praise him with loud cymbals.
   Praise him with crashing cymbals.

6   Let everything that breathes praise the LORD!

   Hallelujah!

---

[a] 148:14 Or "given his people strength."

PROVERBS

The Reasons for Proverbs

1 ¹ The proverbs of Solomon, David's son who was king of Israel, ⌐given⌐
² to grasp wisdom and discipline,
to understand deep thoughts,
³ to acquire the discipline of wise behavior—
righteousness and justice and fairness—
⁴ to give insight to gullible people,
to give knowledge and foresight to the young—
⁵ a wise person will listen and continue to learn,
and an understanding person will gain direction—
⁶ to understand a proverb and a clever saying,
the words of wise people and their riddles.

⁷ The fear of the LORD is the beginning of knowledge.
Stubborn fools despise wisdom and discipline.

Listen to Wisdom

⁸ My son,
listen to your father's discipline,
and do not neglect your mother's teachings,
⁹ because discipline and teachings
are a graceful garland on your head
and a ⌐golden⌐ chain around your neck.

¹⁰ My son,
if sinners lure you, do not go along.
¹¹ If they say,
"Come with us.
Let's set an ambush to kill someone.
Let's hide to ambush innocent people for fun.
¹² We'll swallow them alive like the grave,
like those in good health who go into the pit.
¹³ We'll find all kinds of valuable possessions.
We'll fill our homes with stolen goods.
¹⁴ Join us.
We'll split the loot equally."

¹⁵ My son,
do not follow them in their way.
Do not even set foot on their path,
¹⁶ because they rush to do evil
and hurry to shed blood.
¹⁷ It does no good to spread a net
within the sight of any bird.
¹⁸ But these people set an ambush for their own murder.
They go into hiding only to lose their lives.
¹⁹ This is what happens to everyone
who is greedy for unjust gain.
Greed takes away his life.

²⁰ Wisdom sings her song in the streets.
In the public squares she raises her voice.
²¹ At the corners of noisy streets she calls out.
At the entrances to the city she speaks her words,
²² "How long will you gullible people love being so gullible?
How long will you mockers find joy in your mocking?
How long will you fools hate knowledge?

23 "Turn to me when I warn you.
    I will generously pour out my spirit for you.
    I will make my words known to you.

24 "I called, and you refused to listen.
    I stretched out my hands to you, and no one paid attention.
25   You ignored all my advice.
        You did not want me to warn you.
26 I will laugh at your calamity.
    I will make fun of you
        when panic strikes you,
27   when panic strikes you like a violent storm,
        when calamity strikes you like a wind storm,
        when trouble and anguish come to you.

28 "They will call to me at that time, but I will not answer.
    They will look for me, but they will not find me,
29   because they hated knowledge
            and did not choose the fear of the LORD.
30 They refused my advice.
    They despised my every warning.
31   They will eat the fruit of their lifestyle.
        They will be stuffed with their own schemes.

32 "Gullible people kill themselves because of their turning away.
    Fools destroy themselves because of their indifference.
33   But whoever listens to me will live without worry
            and will be free from the dread of disaster."

The Benefit of Wisdom

2 1 My son,
        if you take my words ⸢to heart⸣
            and treasure my commands within you,
2   if you pay close attention to wisdom,
        and let your mind reach for understanding,
3   if indeed you call out for insight,
        if you ask aloud for understanding,
4   if you search for wisdom as if it were money
        and hunt for it as if it were hidden treasure,
5   then you will understand the fear of the LORD
        and you will find the knowledge of God.
6   The LORD gives wisdom.
        From his mouth come knowledge and understanding.
7   He has reserved priceless wisdom for decent people.
    He is a shield for those who walk in integrity
8   in order to guard those on paths of justice
            and to watch over the way of his godly ones.
9   Then you will understand what is right and just and fair—
            every good course ⸢in life⸣.

10 Wisdom will come into your heart.
    Knowledge will be pleasant to your soul.
11 Foresight will protect you.
    Understanding will guard you.

12 ⸢Wisdom will⸣ save you
        from the way of evil,
        from the person who speaks devious things,
13   from those who abandon the paths of righteousness
            to walk the ways of darkness,
14   from those who enjoy doing evil,
        from those who find joy in the deviousness of evil.
15   Their paths are crooked.
            Their ways are devious.

16 ⸢Wisdom will⸣ also save you
        from an adulterous woman,
        from a loose woman with her smooth talk,
17   who leaves ⸢her husband,⸣ the closest friend of her youth,
                and forgets her marriage vows to her God.

18   Her house sinks down to death.
      Her ways lead to the souls of the dead.
19   None who have sex with her come back.
        Nor do they ever reach the paths of life.

20   So walk in the way of good people
    and stay on the paths of righteous people.
21   Decent people will live in the land.
     People of integrity will remain in it.
22   But wicked people will be cut off from the land
       and treacherous people will be torn*a* from it.

Using Wisdom

3 1   My son,
    do not forget my teachings,
      and keep my commands in mind,
2   because they will bring you
        long life, good years, and peace.

3   Do not let mercy and truth leave you.
    Fasten them around your neck.
    Write them on the tablet of your heart.
4   Then you will find favor and much success
     in the sight of God and humanity.

5   Trust the LORD with all your heart,
    and do not rely on your own understanding.
6   In all your ways acknowledge him,
    and he will make your paths smooth.*a*
7   Do not consider yourself wise.
  Fear the LORD, and turn away from evil.
8   Then, your body will be healed,
     and your bones will have nourishment.

9   Honor the LORD with your wealth
    and with the first and best part of all your income.*b*
10   Then your barns will be full,
     and your vats will overflow with fresh wine.

11   Do not reject the discipline of the LORD, my son,
    and do not resent his warning,
12   because the LORD warns the one he loves,
     even as a father warns a son with whom he is pleased.

13   Blessed is the one who finds wisdom
    and the one who obtains understanding.
14   The profit ,gained, from ,wisdom, is greater than
      the profit ,gained, from silver.
        Its yield is better than fine gold.
15   ,Wisdom, is more precious than jewels,
    and all your desires cannot equal it.
16   Long life is in ,wisdom's, right hand.
     In ,wisdom's, left hand are riches and honor.
17   ,Wisdom's, ways are pleasant ways,
    and all its paths lead to peace.
18   ,Wisdom, is a tree of life
    for those who take firm hold of it.
    Those who cling to it are blessed.

19   By Wisdom the LORD laid the foundation of the earth.
    By understanding he established the heavens.
20   By his knowledge the deep waters were divided,
    and the skies dropped dew.

21   My son,
    do not lose sight of these things.
    Use priceless wisdom and foresight.
22   Then they will mean life for you,

---

a 2:22 Or "will be swept away."   *a* 3:6 Or "straight."   *b* 3:9 Or "harvest."

    and they will grace your neck.

23   Then you will go safely on your way,
    and you will not hurt your foot.

24   When you lie down, you will not be afraid.
    As you lie there, your sleep will be sweet.

25   Do not be afraid of sudden terror
    or of the destruction of wicked people when it comes.

26   The LORD will be your confidence.
    He will keep your foot from getting caught.

27   Do not hold back anything good
    from those who are entitled to it
      when you have the power to do so.

28   When you have the good thing with you, do not tell your neighbor,
    "Go away!
    Come back tomorrow.
    I'll give you something then."

29   Do not plan to do something wrong to your neighbor
    while he is sitting there with you and suspecting nothing.

30   Do not quarrel with a person for no reason
    if he has not harmed you.

31   Do not envy a violent person.
    Do not choose any of his ways.

32   The devious person is disgusting to the LORD.
    The LORD's intimate advice is with decent people.

33   The LORD curses the house of wicked people,
    but he blesses the home of righteous people.

34   When he mocks the mockers,
    he is gracious to humble people.

35   Wise people will inherit honor,
    but fools will bear disgrace.

Cherish Wisdom

4 1   Sons,
    listen to ˏyourˌ father's discipline,
      and pay attention in order to gain understanding.

2   After all, I have taught you well.
    Do not abandon my teachings.

3   When I was a boy ˏlearningˌ from my father,
    when I was a tender and only child of my mother,

4   they used to teach me and say to me,
    "Cling to my words wholeheartedly.
    Obey my commands so that you may live.

5   Acquire wisdom.
    Acquire understanding.
    Do not forget.
    Do not turn away from the words that I have spoken.

6   Do not abandon wisdom, and it will watch over you.
    Love wisdom, and it will protect you.

7   The beginning of wisdom is to acquire wisdom.
    Acquire understanding with all that you have.

8   Cherish wisdom.
      It will raise you up.
      It will bring you honor when you embrace it.

9   It will give you a graceful garland for your head.
    It will hand you a beautiful crown."

Stay on the Path of Wisdom

10   My son,
    listen and accept my words,
      and they will multiply the years of your life.

11   I have taught you the way of wisdom.
    I have guided you along decent paths.

12   When you walk, your stride will not be hampered.
    Even if you run, you will not stumble.

13   Cling to discipline.
          Do not relax your grip on it.
              Keep it because it is your life.
14   Do not stray onto the path of wicked people.
          Do not walk in the way of evil people.
15   Avoid it.
              Do not walk near it.
                  Turn away from it,
                      and keep on walking.
16   Wicked people cannot sleep
          unless they do wrong,
              and they are robbed of their sleep
                  unless they make someone stumble.
17   They eat food obtained through wrongdoing
                  and drink wine obtained through violence.

18   But the path of righteous people is like the light of dawn
          that becomes brighter and brighter until it reaches midday.
19   The way of wicked people is like deep darkness.
          They do not know what makes them stumble.

Stay Focused on Wisdom

20   My son,
          pay attention to my words.
          Open your ears to what I say.
21   Do not lose sight of these things.
          Keep them deep within your heart
22   because they are life to those who find them
              and they heal the whole body.
23   Guard your heart more than anything else,
          because the source of your life flows from it.
24   Remove dishonesty from your mouth.
          Put deceptive speech far away from your lips.
25   Let your eyes look straight ahead
          and your sight be focused in front of you.
26   Carefully walk a straight path,
          and all your ways will be secure.
27   Do not lean to the right or to the left.
          Walk away from evil.

Avoid Adultery

5 1   My son,
          pay attention to my wisdom.
          Open your ears to my understanding
2   so that you may act with foresight
                  and speak with insight.

3   The lips of an adulterous woman drip with honey.
          Her kiss is smoother than oil,
4   but in the end she is as bitter as wormwood,
                  as sharp as a two-edged sword.
5   Her feet descend to death.
          Her steps lead straight to hell.
6   She doesn't even think about the path of life.
              Her steps wander, and she doesn't realize it.

7   But now, sons,
          listen to me,
              and do not turn away from what I say to you.
8   Stay far away from her.
          Do not even go near her door.
9   Either you will surrender your reputation to others
              and the rest of your years to some cruel person,
10   or strangers will benefit from your strength
              and you will have to work hard in a pagan's house.
11   Then you will groan when your end comes,
          when your body and flesh are consumed.
              You will say,

12   "Oh, how I hated discipline!
        How my heart despised correction!
13   I didn't listen to what my teachers said to me,
            nor did I keep my ear open to my instructors.
14   I almost reached total ruin
            in the assembly and in the congregation."

15   Drink water out of your own cistern
        and running water from your own well.
16   Why should water flow out of your spring?
        Why should your streams flow into the streets?
17   They should be yours alone,
            so do not share them with strangers.
18   Let your own fountain be blessed,
        and enjoy the girl you married when you were young,
19   a loving doe and a graceful deer.[a]
        Always let her breasts satisfy you.
        Always be intoxicated with her love.
20   Why should you, my son,
            be intoxicated with an adulterous woman
            and fondle a loose woman's breast?

21   Each person's ways are clearly seen by the LORD,
        and he surveys all his actions.
22   A wicked person will be trapped by his own wrongs,
        and he will be caught in the ropes of his own sin.
23   He will die for his lack of discipline
        and stumble around because of his great stupidity.

Avoid Disaster

6 1   My son,
        if you guarantee a loan for your neighbor
            or pledge yourself for a stranger with a handshake,
2   you are trapped by the words of your own mouth,
                caught by your own promise.

3   Do the following things, my son, so that you may free yourself,
        because you have fallen into your neighbor's hands:
            Humble yourself,
                and pester your neighbor.
4   Don't let your eyes rest
                or your eyelids close.
5   Free yourself like a gazelle from the hand of a hunter
                and like a bird from the hand of a hunter.

6   Consider the ant, you lazy bum.
    Watch its ways, and become wise.
7   Although it has no overseer, officer, or ruler,
8   in summertime it stores its food supply.
            At harvest time it gathers its food.

9   How long will you lie there, you lazy bum?
    When will you get up from your sleep?
10   "Just a little sleep,
        just a little slumber,
        just a little nap."
11   Then your poverty will come ˌto youˌ like a drifter,
                and your need will come ˌto youˌ like a bandit.

12   A good-for-nothing scoundrel is a person who has a dishonest mouth.
13   He winks his eye,
            makes a signal with his foot,
                ˌandˌ points with his fingers.
14   He devises evil all the time with a twisted mind.
        He spreads conflict.
15   That is why disaster will come on him suddenly.
                In a moment he will be crushed beyond recovery.

---

[a] 5:19 Or "graceful goat."

16 There are six things that the LORD hates,
even seven that are disgusting to him:
17   arrogant eyes,
      a lying tongue,
      hands that kill innocent people,
18   a mind devising wicked plans,
      feet that are quick to do wrong,
19   a dishonest witness spitting out lies,
         and a person who spreads conflict among relatives.

More Advice About Avoiding Adultery

20 My son,
      obey the command of your father,
         and do not disregard the teachings of your mother.
21 Fasten them on your heart forever.
   Hang them around your neck.
22   When you walk around, they will lead you.
      When you lie down, they will watch over you.
      When you wake up, they will talk to you
23   because the command is a lamp,
            the teachings are a light,
               and the warnings from discipline are the path of life
24   to keep you from an evil woman
               and from the smooth talk of a loose woman.

25 Do not desire her beauty in your heart.
   Do not let her catch you with her eyes.
26   A prostitute's price is ˌonlyˌ a loaf of bread,
         but a married woman hunts for ˌyourˌ life itself.
27   Can a man carry fire in his lap
         without burning his clothes?
28   Can anyone walk on red-hot coals
         without burning his feet?
29 So it is with a man who has sex with his neighbor's wife.
      None who touch her will escape punishment.
30 People do not despise a thief who is hungry
      when he steals to satisfy his appetite,
31   but when he is caught,
         he has to repay it seven times.
            He must give up all the possessions in his house.

32 Whoever commits adultery with a woman has no sense.
   Whoever does this destroys himself.
33   An adulterous man will find disease*a* and dishonor,
         and his disgrace will not be blotted out,
34   because jealousy arouses a husband's fury.
            The husband will show no mercy when he takes revenge.
35   No amount of money will change his mind.
               The largest bribe will not satisfy him.

7 1 My son,
      pay attention to my words.
   Treasure my commands that are within you.
2 Obey my commands so that you may live.
   Follow my teachings just as you protect the pupil of your eye.
3 Tie them on your fingers.
   Write them on the tablet of your heart.
4 Say to wisdom, "You are my sister."
   Give the name "my relative" to understanding
5   in order to guard yourself from an adulterous woman,
         from a loose woman with her smooth talk.

6 From a window in my house I looked through my screen.
7 I was looking at gullible people
      when I saw a young man without much sense among youths.
8 He was crossing a street near her corner

---

a 6:33 Or "wounds."

and walking toward her house
9   in the twilight,
          in the evening,
          in the dark hours of the night.

10   A woman with an ulterior motive meets him.
          She is dressed as a prostitute.
11   She is loud and rebellious.
          Her feet will not stay at home.
12   One moment she is out on the street,
              the next she is at the curb,
                  on the prowl at every corner.
13   She grabs him and kisses him and brazenly says to him,
14   "I have some sacrificial meat.
              Today I kept my vows.
15   That's why I came to meet you.
              Eagerly, I looked for you,
                  and I've found you.
16   I've made my bed,
              with colored sheets of Egyptian linen.
17   I've sprinkled my bed with myrrh, aloes, and cinnamon.
18   Come, let's drink our fill of love until morning.
              Let's enjoy making love,
19   because my husband's not home.
              He has gone on a long trip.
20   He took lots of money with him.
              He won't be home for a couple of weeks."

21   With all her seductive charms, she persuades him.
      With her smooth lips, she makes him give in.
22   He immediately follows her
              like a steer on its way to be slaughtered,
              like a ram hobbling into captivity[a]
23   until an arrow pierces his heart,
              like a bird darting into a trap.
          He does not realize that it will cost him his life.

24   Now, sons,
          listen to me.
          Pay attention to the words from my mouth.
25   Do not let your heart be turned to her ways.
          Do not wander onto her paths,
26   because she has brought down many victims,
                  and she has killed all too many.
27   Her home is the way to hell
                  and leads to the darkest vaults of death.

Wisdom's Announcement

8 ¹   Does not wisdom call out?
      Does not understanding raise its voice?
2   ⌊Wisdom⌋ takes its stand on high ground,
              by the wayside where the roads meet,
3   near the gates to the city.
          At the entrance ⌊wisdom⌋ sings its song,
4   "I am calling to all of you,
              and my appeal is to all people.
5   You gullible people, learn how to be sensible.
              You fools, get a heart that has understanding.[a]
6   Listen! I am speaking about noble things,
              and my lips will say what is right.
7   My mouth expresses the truth,
              and wickedness is disgusting to my lips.
8   Everything I say is fair,
              and there is nothing twisted or crooked in it.
9   All of it is clear to a person who has understanding

---

[a] 7:22 Hebrew meaning of this line uncertain.   [a] 8:5 English equivalent difficult.

and right to those who have acquired knowledge.
10 Take my discipline, not silver,
and my knowledge rather than fine gold,
11 because wisdom is better than jewels.
Nothing you desire can equal it.

Wisdom's Authority

12 "I, Wisdom, live with insight,
and I acquire knowledge and foresight.
13 To fear the LORD is to hate evil.
I hate pride, arrogance, evil behavior, and twisted speech.
14 Advice and priceless wisdom are mine.
I, Understanding, have strength.
15 Through me kings reign,
and rulers decree fair laws.
16 Through me princes rule,
so do nobles and all fair judges.
17 I love those who love me.
Those eagerly looking for me will find me.
18 I have riches and honor,
lasting wealth and righteousness.
19 What I produce is better than gold, pure gold.
What I yield is better than fine silver.
20 I walk in the way of righteousness, on the paths of justice,
21 to give an inheritance to those who love me
and to fill their treasuries.

Wisdom as Creator

22 "The LORD already possessed me long ago,
when his way began,
before any of his works.
23 I was appointed from everlasting
from the first,
before the earth began.
24 I was born
before there were oceans,
before there were springs filled with water.
25 I was born
before the mountains were settled in their places
and before the hills,
26 when he had not yet made land or fields
or the first dust of the world.

27 "When he set up the heavens, I was there.
When he traced the horizon on the surface of the ocean,
28 when he established the skies above,
when he determined the currents in the ocean,
29 when he set a limit for the sea
so the waters would not overstep his command,
when he traced the foundations of the earth,
30 I was beside him as a master craftsman.[b]
I made him happy day after day,
I rejoiced in front of him all the time,
31 found joy in his inhabited world,
and delighted in the human race.

Wisdom as Lifegiver

32 "Now, sons, listen to me.
Blessed are those who follow my ways.
33 Listen to discipline, and become wise.
Do not leave my ways.
34 Blessed is the person who listens to me,
watches at my door day after day,
and waits by my doorposts.
35 Whoever finds me finds life

---

[b] 8:30 Hebrew meaning of "master craftsman" uncertain.

36   and obtains favor from the LORD.
          Whoever sins against me harms himself.
          All those who hate me love death."

Wisdom Hosts a Banquet

9 ¹ Wisdom has built her house.
          She has carved out her seven pillars.
²   She has prepared her meat.
          She has mixed her wine.
          She has set her table.
³   She has sent out her servant girls.
          She calls from the highest places in the city,
⁴   "Whoever is gullible turn in here!"

          She says to a person without sense,
⁵   "Come, eat my bread,
               and drink the wine I have mixed.
⁶   Stop being gullible and live.
          Start traveling the road to understanding."

Wisdom Prolongs Life

⁷   Whoever corrects a mocker receives abuse.
          Whoever warns a wicked person gets hurt.
⁸   Do not warn a mocker, or he will hate you.
          Warn a wise person, and he will love you.
⁹   Give advice to a wise person,
               and he will become even wiser.
               Teach a righteous person,
               and he will learn more.

¹⁰   The fear of the LORD is the beginning of wisdom.
          The knowledge of the Holy One is understanding.

¹¹   You will live longer because of me,
          and years will be added to your life.
¹²   If you are wise, your wisdom will help you.
          If you mock, you alone will be held responsible.

Stupidity Imitates Wisdom's Banquet

¹³   The woman Stupidity is loud, gullible, and ignorant.[a]
¹⁴   She sits at the doorway of her house.
          She is enthroned on the high ground of the city
¹⁵   and calls to those who pass by,
               those minding their own business,
¹⁶   "Whoever is gullible turn in here!"

          She says to a person without sense,
¹⁷   "Stolen waters are sweet,
               and food eaten in secret is tasty."
¹⁸   But he does not know
               that the souls of the dead are there,
               that her guests are in the depths of hell.

10 ¹ The proverbs of Solomon:

A Wise Son Is Righteous

          A wise son makes his father happy,
               but a foolish son brings grief to his mother.

²   Treasures gained dishonestly profit no one,
               but righteousness rescues from death.
³   The LORD will not allow a righteous person to starve,
               but he intentionally ignores the desires of a wicked person.

⁴   Lazy hands bring poverty,
               but hard-working hands bring riches.

---

[a] 9:13 Hebrew meaning of this verse uncertain.

⁵ Whoever gathers in the summer is a wise son.
Whoever sleeps at harvest time brings shame.

⁶ Blessings cover the head of a righteous person,
but violence covers the mouths of wicked people.

⁷ The name of a righteous person remains blessed,
but the names of wicked people will rot away.

Proverbs Concerning the Mouth

⁸ The one who is truly wise accepts commands,
but the one who talks foolishly will be thrown down headfirst.
⁹ Whoever lives honestly will live securely,
but whoever lives dishonestly will be found out.
¹⁰ Whoever winks with his eye causes heartache.
The one who talks foolishly will be thrown down headfirst.
¹¹ The mouth of a righteous person is a fountain of life,
but the mouths of wicked people conceal violence.
¹² Hate starts quarrels,
but love covers every wrong.

¹³ Wisdom is found on the lips of a person who has understanding,
but a rod is for the back of one without sense.
¹⁴ Those who are wise store up knowledge,
but the mouth of a stubborn fool invites ruin.
¹⁵ The rich person's wealth is ⸢his⸣ strong city.
Poverty ruins the poor.
¹⁶ A righteous person's reward is life.
A wicked person's harvest is sin.
¹⁷ Whoever practices discipline is on the way to life,
but whoever ignores a warning strays.

¹⁸ Whoever conceals hatred has lying lips.
Whoever spreads slander is a fool.
¹⁹ Sin is unavoidable when there is much talk,
but whoever seals his lips is wise.
²⁰ The tongue of a righteous person is pure silver.
The hearts of wicked people are worthless.
²¹ The lips of a righteous person feed many,
but stubborn fools die because they have no sense.

²² It is the LORD's blessing that makes a person rich,
and hard work adds nothing to it.
²³ Like the laughter of a fool when he carries out an evil plan,
so is wisdom to a person who has understanding.

Righteous People Contrasted to Wicked People

²⁴ That which wicked people dread happens to them,
but ⸢the LORD⸣ grants the desire of righteous people.
²⁵ When the storm has passed, the wicked person has vanished,
but the righteous person has an everlasting foundation.
²⁶ Like vinegar to the teeth,
like smoke to the eyes,
so is the lazy person to those who send him ⸢on a mission⸣.
²⁷ The fear of the LORD lengthens ⸢the number of⸣ days,
but the years of wicked people are shortened.
²⁸ The hope of righteous people ⸢leads to⸣ joy,
but the eager waiting of wicked people comes to nothing.
²⁹ The way of the LORD is a fortress for an innocent person
but a ruin to those who are troublemakers.
³⁰ A righteous person will never be moved,
but wicked people will not continue to live in the land.
³¹ The mouth of a righteous person increases wisdom,
but a devious tongue will be cut off.
³² The lips of a righteous person announce good will,
but the mouths of wicked people are devious.

The Value of Righteousness

11 ¹ Dishonest scales are disgusting to the LORD,
but accurate weights are pleasing to him.
² Arrogance comes,
then comes shame,
but wisdom remains with humble people.
³ Integrity guides decent people,
but hypocrisy leads treacherous people to ruin.

⁴ Riches are of no help on the day of fury,
but righteousness saves from death.
⁵ The righteousness of innocent people makes their road smooth,
but wicked people fall by their own wickedness.
⁶ Decent people are saved by their righteousness,
but treacherous people are trapped by their own greed.
⁷ At the death of a wicked person, hope vanishes.
Moreover, his confidence in strength vanishes.

⁸ A righteous person is rescued from trouble,
and a wicked person takes his place.
⁹ With his talk a godless person can ruin his neighbor,
but righteous people are rescued by knowledge.

¹⁰ When righteous people prosper, a city is glad.
When wicked people die, there are songs of joy.
¹¹ With the blessing of decent people a city is raised up,
but by the words of wicked people, it is torn down.

¹² A person who despises a neighbor has no sense,
but a person who has understanding keeps quiet.
¹³ Whoever gossips gives away secrets,
but whoever is trustworthy in spirit can keep a secret.
¹⁴ A nation will fall when there is no direction,
but with many advisers there is victory.
¹⁵ Whoever guarantees a stranger's loan will get into trouble,
but whoever hates the closing of a deal remains secure.
¹⁶ A gracious woman wins respect,
but ruthless men gain riches.
¹⁷ A merciful person helps himself,
but a cruel person hurts himself.
¹⁸ A wicked person earns dishonest wages,
but whoever spreads righteousness earns honest pay.
¹⁹ As righteousness leads to life,
so whoever pursues evil finds his own death.

²⁰ Devious people are disgusting to the LORD,
but he is delighted with those whose ways are innocent.
²¹ Certainly, an evil person will not go unpunished,
but the descendants of righteous people will escape.
²² ₎Like₎ a gold ring in a pig's snout,
₎so₎ is a beautiful woman who lacks good taste.
²³ The desire of righteous people ends only in good,
but the hope of wicked people ends only in fury.

²⁴ One person spends freely and yet grows richer,
while another holds back what he owes and yet grows poorer.
²⁵ A generous person will be made rich,
and whoever satisfies others will himself be satisfied.[a]
²⁶ People will curse the one who hoards grain,
but a blessing will be upon the head of the one who sells it.

²⁷ Whoever eagerly seeks good searches for good will,
but whoever looks for evil finds it.
²⁸ Whoever trusts his riches will fall,
but righteous people will flourish like a green leaf.
²⁹ Whoever brings trouble upon his family inherits ₎only₎ wind,
and that stubborn fool becomes a slave to the wise in heart.

---

^a 11:25 Or "and whoever gives someone a drink will also get a drink."

30   The fruit of a righteous person is a tree of life,
          and a winner of souls is wise.
31   If the righteous person is rewarded on earth,
          how much more the wicked person and the sinner!

12   ¹ Whoever loves discipline loves to learn,
              but whoever hates correction is a dumb animal.
2   A good person obtains favor from the LORD,
          but the LORD condemns everyone who schemes.
3   A person cannot stand firm on a foundation of wickedness,
          and the roots of righteous people cannot be moved.
4   A wife with strength of character is the crown of her husband,
          but the wife who disgraces him is like bone cancer.

5   The thoughts of righteous people are fair.
      The advice of wicked people is treacherous.
6   The words of wicked people are a deadly ambush,
              but the words*ᵃ* of decent people rescue.
7   Overthrow wicked people, and they are no more,
          but the families of righteous people continue to stand.

8   A person will be praised based on his insight,
          but whoever has a twisted mind will be despised.
9   Better to be unimportant and have a slave
          than to act important and have nothing to eat.
10   A righteous person cares ⌞even⌟ about the life of his animals,
          but the compassion of wicked people is ⌞nothing but⌟ cruelty.
11   Whoever works his land will have plenty to eat,
          but the one who chases unrealistic dreams has no sense.
12   A wicked person delights in setting a trap for ⌞other⌟ evil people,
          but the roots of righteous people produce ⌞fruit⌟.*ᵇ*
13   An evil person is trapped by his own sinful talk,
          but a righteous person escapes from trouble.
14   One person enjoys good things as a result of his speaking ability.
      Another is paid according to what his hands have accomplished.

15   A stubborn fool considers his own way the right one,
          but a person who listens to advice is wise.
16   When a stubborn fool is irritated, he shows it immediately,
          but a sensible person hides the insult.

17   A truthful witness speaks honestly,
          but a lying witness speaks deceitfully.
18   Careless words stab like a sword,
          but the words of wise people bring healing.
19   The word of truth lasts forever,
          but lies last only a moment.
20   Deceit is in the heart of those who plan evil,
          but joy belongs to those who advise peace.

21   No ⌞lasting⌟ harm comes to a righteous person,
          but wicked people have lots of trouble.
22   Lips that lie are disgusting to the LORD,
          but honest people are his delight.
23   A sensible person ⌞discreetly⌟ hides knowledge,
          but foolish minds preach stupidity.
24   Hard-working hands gain control,
          but lazy hands do slave labor.
25   A person's anxiety will weigh him down,
          but an encouraging word makes him joyful.
26   A righteous person looks out for his neighbor,
          but the path of wicked people leads others astray.
27   A lazy hunter does not catchᶜ his prey,
          but a hard-working person becomes wealthy.*ᵈ*
28   Everlasting life is on the way of righteousness.
      Eternal death is not along its path.

ᵃ 12:6 Or "mouths."   *ᵇ* 12:12 Hebrew meaning of this verse uncertain.   *ᶜ* 12:27 Hebrew meaning uncertain.
ᵈ 12:27 Hebrew meaning of this line uncertain.

A Wise Son Lives Righteously

13 ¹ A wise son listens to his father's discipline,
    but a mocker does not listen to reprimands.
² A person eats well as a result of his speaking ability,
    but the appetite of treacherous people ₎craves₎ violence.
³ Whoever controls his mouth protects his own life.
    Whoever has a big mouth comes to ruin.
⁴ A lazy person craves food and there is none,
    but the appetite of hard-working people is satisfied.
⁵ A righteous person hates lying,
    but a wicked person behaves with shame and disgrace.
⁶ Righteousness protects the honest way of life,
    but wickedness ruins a sacrifice for sin.

⁷ One person pretends to be rich but has nothing.
    Another pretends to be poor but has great wealth.
⁸ A person's riches are the ransom for his life,
    but the poor person does not pay attention to threats.
⁹ The light of righteous people beams brightly,
    but the lamp of wicked people will be snuffed out.
¹⁰ Arrogance produces only quarreling,
    but those who take advice gain wisdom.
¹¹ Wealth ₎gained₎ through injustice dwindles away,
    but whoever gathers little by little has plenty.
¹² Delayed hope makes one sick at heart,
    but a fulfilled longing is a tree of life.
¹³ Whoever despises ₎God's₎ words will pay the penalty,
    but the one who fears ₎God's₎ commands will be rewarded.

¹⁴ The teachings of a wise person are a fountain of life
    to turn ₎one₎ away from the grasp of death.
¹⁵ Good sense brings favor,
    but the way of treacherous people is always the same.^a
¹⁶ Any sensible person acts with knowledge,
    but a fool displays stupidity.
¹⁷ An undependable messenger gets into trouble,
    but a dependable envoy brings healing.
¹⁸ Poverty and shame come to a person who ignores discipline,
    but whoever pays attention to constructive criticism will be honored.

¹⁹ A fulfilled desire is sweet to the soul,
    but turning from evil is disgusting to fools.
²⁰ Whoever walks with wise people will be wise,
    but whoever associates with fools will suffer.
²¹ Disaster hunts down sinners,
    but righteous people are rewarded with good.
²² Good people leave an inheritance to their grandchildren,
    but the wealth of sinners is stored away for a righteous person.

²³ When poor people are able to plow, there is much food,
    but a person is swept away where there is no justice.
²⁴ Whoever refuses to spank his son hates him,
    but whoever loves his son disciplines him from early on.
²⁵ A righteous person eats to satisfy his appetite,
    but the bellies of wicked people are always empty.

Wise People Live Righteously

14 ¹ The wisest of women builds up her home,
    but a stupid one tears it down with her own hands.
² Whoever lives right fears the LORD,
    but a person who is devious in his ways despises him.
³ Because of a stubborn fool's words a whip is lifted against him,
    but wise people are protected by their speech.

⁴ Where there are no cattle, the feeding trough is empty,
    but the strength of an ox produces plentiful harvests.

---

^a 13:15 Masoretic Text; Greek "is their disaster."

5 A trustworthy witness does not lie,
　　but a dishonest witness breathes lies.
6 A mocker searches for wisdom without finding it,
　　but knowledge comes easily to a person who has understanding.

7 Stay away from a fool,
　　because you will not receive knowledge from his lips.
8 The wisdom of a sensible person guides his way of life,
　　but the stupidity of fools misleads them.
9 Stubborn fools make fun of guilt,
　　but there is forgiveness among decent people.

10 The heart knows its own bitterness,
　　and no stranger can share its joy.
11 The houses of wicked people will be destroyed,
　　but the tents of decent people will continue to expand.
12 There is a way that seems right to a person,
　　but eventually it ends in death.
13 Even while laughing a heart can ache,
　　and joy can end in grief.

14 A heart that turns ˎfrom Godˎ becomes bored with its own ways,
　　but a good person is satisfied with God's ways.
15 A gullible person believes anything,
　　but a sensible person watches his step.
16 A wise person is cautious and turns away from evil,
　　but a fool is careless[a] and overconfident.
17 A short-tempered person acts stupidly,
　　and a person who plots evil is hated.
18 Gullible people are gifted with stupidity,
　　but sensible people are crowned with knowledge.
19 Evil people will bow to good people.
Wicked people will bow at the gates of a righteous person.

20 A poor person is hated even by his neighbor,
　　but a rich person is loved by many.
21 Whoever despises his neighbor sins,
　　but blessed is the one who is kind to humble people.

22 Don't those who stray plan what is evil,
　　while those who are merciful and faithful plan what is good?
23 In hard work there is always something gained,
　　but idle talk leads only to poverty.
24 The crown of wise people is their wealth.
The stupidity of fools is just that—stupidity!
25 An honest witness saves lives,
　　but one who tells lies is dangerous.
26 In the fear of the LORD there is strong confidence,
　　and his children will have a place of refuge.
27 The fear of the LORD is a fountain of life
　　to turn ˎoneˎ away from the grasp of death.
28 A large population is an honor for a king,
　　but without people a ruler is ruined.

29 A person of great understanding is patient,
　　but a short temper is the height of stupidity.
30 A tranquil heart makes for a healthy body,
　　but jealousy is ˎlikeˎ bone cancer.
31 Whoever oppresses the poor insults his maker,
　　but whoever is kind to the needy honors him.
32 A wicked person is thrown down by his own wrongdoing,
　　but even in his death a righteous person has a refuge.
33 Wisdom finds rest in the heart of an understanding person.
Even fools recognize this.[b]

---

[a] 14:16 Hebrew meaning uncertain.　　[b] 14:33 Hebrew meaning of this line uncertain.

Wise Ways to Live

34 Righteousness lifts up a nation,
but sin is a disgrace in any society.
35 A king is delighted with a servant who acts wisely,
but he is furious with one who acts shamefully.

15 1 A gentle answer turns away rage,
but a harsh word stirs up anger.
2 The tongues of wise people give good expression to knowledge,
but the mouths of fools pour out a flood of stupidity.
3 The eyes of the LORD are everywhere.
They watch evil people and good people.
4 A soothing tongue is a tree of life,
but a deceitful tongue breaks the spirit.
5 A stubborn fool despises his father's discipline,
but whoever appreciates a warning shows good sense.
6 Great treasure is in the house of a righteous person,
but trouble comes along with the income of a wicked person.
7 The lips of wise people spread knowledge,
but a foolish attitude does not.

8 A sacrifice brought by wicked people is disgusting to the LORD,
but the prayers of decent people please him.
9 The way of wicked people is disgusting to the LORD,
but he loves those who pursue righteousness.
10 Discipline is a terrible ˌburdenˌ to anyone who leaves the ˌrightˌ path.
Anyone who hates a warning will die.
11 If Sheol and Abaddon lie open in front of the LORD
how much more the human heart!
12 A mocker does not appreciate a warning.
He will not go to wise people.

13 A joyful heart makes a cheerful face,
but with a heartache comes depression.
14 The mind of a person who has understanding searches for knowledge,
but the mouths of fools feed on stupidity.
15 Every day is a terrible day for a miserable person,
but a cheerful heart has a continual feast.

16 Better to have a little with the fear of the LORD
than great treasure and turmoil.
17 Better to have a dish of vegetables where there is love
than juicy steaks where there is hate.

18 A hothead stirs up a fight,
but one who holds his temper calms disputes.
19 The path of lazy people is like a thorny hedge,
but the road of decent people is an ˌopenˌ highway.

A Wise Son Brings Blessings to Others

20 A wise son makes his father happy,
but a foolish child despises its mother.

21 Stupidity is fun to the one without much sense,
but a person who has understanding forges straight ahead.
22 Without advice plans go wrong,
but with many advisers they succeed.
23 A person is delighted to hear an answer from his own mouth,
and a timely word—oh, how good!

24 The path of life for a wise person leads upward
in order to turn him away from hell below.
25 The LORD tears down the house of an arrogant person,
but he protects the property of widows.
26 The thoughts of evil people are disgusting to the LORD,
but pleasant words are pure to him.
27 Whoever is greedy for unjust gain brings trouble to his family,
but whoever hates bribes will live.

28 The heart of a righteous person carefully considers how to answer,
  but the mouths of wicked people pour out a flood of evil things.
29 The LORD is far from wicked people,
  but he hears the prayers of righteous people.

30 A twinkle in the eye delights the heart.
  Good news refreshes the body.
31 The ear that listens to a life-giving warning
  will be at home among wise people.

32 Whoever ignores discipline despises himself,
  but the person who listens to warning gains understanding.
33 The fear of the LORD is discipline ₍leading to₎ wisdom,
  and humility comes before honor.

Wisdom's Blessings Come From the LORD

16 1 The plans of the heart belong to humans,
  but an answer on the tongue comes from the LORD.
2 A person thinks all his ways are pure,
  but the LORD weighs motives.
3 Entrust your efforts to the LORD,
  and your plans will succeed.
4 The LORD has made everything for his own purpose,
  even wicked people for the day of trouble.
5 Everyone with a conceited heart is disgusting to the LORD.
  Certainly, ₍such a person₎ will not go unpunished.

6 By mercy and faithfulness, peace is made with the LORD.
  By the fear of the LORD, evil is avoided.
7 When a person's ways are pleasing to the LORD,
  he makes even his enemies to be at peace with him.
8 Better a few ₍possessions₎ gained honestly
  than many gained through injustice.
9 A person may plan his own journey,
  but the LORD directs his steps.

10 When a divine revelation is on a king's lips,
  he cannot voice a wrong judgment.
11 Honest balances and scales belong to the LORD.
  He made the entire set of weights.
12 Wrongdoing is disgusting to kings
  because a throne is established through righteousness.
13 Kings are happy with honest words,
  and whoever speaks what is right is loved.
14 A king's anger announces death,
  but a wise man makes peace with him.
15 When the king is cheerful, there is life,
  and his favor is like a cloud bringing spring rain.

16 How much better it is to gain wisdom than gold,
  and the gaining of understanding should be chosen over silver.
17 The highway of decent people turns away from evil.
  Whoever watches his way preserves his own life.

18 Pride precedes a disaster,
  and an arrogant attitude precedes a fall.
19 Better to be humble with lowly people
  than to share stolen goods with arrogant people.

20 Whoever gives attention to the LORD's word prospers,
  and blessed is the person who trusts the LORD.
21 The person who is truly wise is called understanding,
  and speaking sweetly helps others learn.
22 Understanding is a fountain of life to the one who has it,
  but stubborn fools punish themselves with their stupidity.
23 A wise person's heart controls his speech,
  and what he says helps others learn.
24 Pleasant words are ₍like₎ honey from a honeycomb—
  sweet to the spirit and healthy for the body.

Words of Advice to a Wise Son

25 There is a way that seems right to a person,
      but eventually it ends in death.
26 A laborer's appetite works to his advantage,
      because his hunger drives him on.
27 A worthless person plots trouble,
      and his speech is like a burning fire.
28 A devious person spreads quarrels.
      A gossip separates the closest of friends.
29 A violent person misleads his neighbor
      and leads him on a path that is not good.
30 Whoever winks his eye is plotting something devious.
      Whoever bites his lips has finished his evil work.

31 Silver hair is a beautiful crown found in a righteous life.
32 Better to get angry slowly than to be a hero.
      Better to be even-tempered than to capture a city.
33 The dice are thrown,
      but the LORD determines every outcome.

17 ¹ Better a bite of dry bread ˻eaten˼ in peace
      than a family feast filled with strife.
2 A wise slave will become master over a son who acts shamefully,
      and he will share the inheritance with the brothers.
3 The crucible is for refining silver and the smelter for gold,
      but the one who purifies hearts ˻by fire˼ is the LORD.
4 An evildoer pays attention to wicked lips.
      A liar opens his ears to a slanderous tongue.
5 Whoever makes fun of a poor person insults his maker.
      Whoever is happy ˻to see someone's˼ distress will not escape punishment.
6 Grandchildren are the crown of grandparents,
      and parents are the glory of their children.

The Consequences of Being a Fool

7 Refined speech is not fitting for a godless fool.
      How much less does lying fit a noble person!
8 A bribe seems ˻like˼ a jewel to the one who gives it.[a]
      Wherever he turns, he prospers.
9 Whoever forgives an offense seeks love,
      but whoever keeps bringing up the issue separates the closest of friends.

10 A reprimand impresses a person who has understanding
      more than a hundred lashes impress a fool.
11 A rebel looks for nothing but evil.
      Therefore, a cruel messenger will be sent ˻to punish˼ him.
12 Better to meet a bear robbed of its cubs
      than a fool ˻carried away˼ with his stupidity.
13 Whoever pays back evil for good—
      evil will never leave his home.
14 Starting a quarrel is ˻like˼ opening a floodgate,
      so stop before the argument gets out of control.
15 Whoever approves of wicked people
      and whoever condemns righteous people
        is disgusting to the LORD.

16 Why should a fool have money in his hand to buy wisdom
      when he doesn't have a mind to grasp anything?
17 A friend always loves,
      and a brother is born to share trouble.
18 A person without good sense closes a deal with a handshake.
      He guarantees a loan in the presence of his friend.
19 Whoever loves sin loves a quarrel.
      Whoever builds his city gate high invites destruction.
20 A twisted mind never finds happiness,
      and one with a devious tongue ˻repeatedly˼ gets into trouble.
21 The parent of a fool has grief,

ᵃ 17:8 Or "who receives it."

and the father of a godless fool has no joy.
22 A joyful heart is good medicine,
   but depression drains one's strength.
23 A wicked person secretly accepts a bribe to corrupt the ways of justice.
24 Wisdom is directly in front of an understanding person,
   but the eyes of a fool ˎare looking aroundˎ all over the world.

How Fools Live
25 A foolish son is a heartache to his father
   and bitter grief to his mother.

26 To punish an innocent person is not good.
   To strike down noble people is not right.
27 Whoever has knowledge controls his words,
   and a person who has understanding is even-tempered.

28 Even a stubborn fool is thought to be wise if he keeps silent.
   He is considered intelligent if he keeps his lips sealed.

18 1 A loner is out to get what he wants for himself.
   He opposes all sound reasoning.
2 A fool does not find joy in understanding
   but only in expressing his own opinion.

3 When wickedness comes, contempt also comes,
   and insult comes along with disgrace.
4 The words of a person's mouth are like deep waters.
   The fountain of wisdom is an overflowing stream.
5 It is not good to be partial toward a wicked person,
   thereby depriving an innocent person of justice.

6 By talking, a fool gets into an argument,
   and his mouth invites a beating.
7 A fool's mouth is his ruin.
   His lips are a trap to his soul.
8 The words of a gossip are swallowed greedily,
   and they go down into a person's innermost being.

How to Avoid Fools and Foolishness
9 Whoever is lazy in his work is related to a vandal.
10 The name of the LORD is a strong tower.
   A righteous person runs to it and is safe.
11 A rich person's wealth is his strong city
   and is like a high wall in his imagination.

12 Before destruction a person's heart is arrogant,
   but humility comes before honor.
13 Whoever gives an answer before he listens is stupid and shameful.
14 A person's spirit can endure sickness,
   but who can bear a broken spirit?
15 The mind of a person who has understanding acquires knowledge.
   The ears of wise people seek knowledge.
16 A gift opens doors for the one who gives it
   and brings him into the presence of great people.

17 The first to state his case seems right
   ˎuntilˎ his neighbor comes to cross-examine him.
18 Flipping a coin ends quarrels
   and settles ˎissuesˎ between powerful people.
19 An offended brother is more ˎresistantˎ than a strong city,
   and disputes are like the locked gate of a castle tower.

20 A person's speaking ability provides for his stomach.
   His talking provides him a living.
21 The tongue has the power of life and death,
   and those who love to talk will have to eat their own words.

22 Whoever finds a wife finds something good
   and has obtained favor from the LORD.
23 A poor person is timid when begging,
   but a rich person is blunt when replying.

24 Friends can destroy one another,[a]
    but a loving friend can stick closer than family.

19 ¹ Better to be a poor person who lives innocently
    than to be one who talks dishonestly and is a fool.
2 A person without knowledge is no good.
    A person in a hurry makes mistakes.
3 The stupidity of a person turns his life upside down,
    and his heart rages against the LORD.
4 Wealth adds many friends,
    but a poor person is separated from his friend.

5 A lying witness will not go unpunished.
    One who tells lies will not escape.
6 Many try to win the kindness of a generous person,
        and everyone is a friend to a person who gives gifts.
7 The entire family of a poor person hates him.
        How much more do his friends keep their distance from him!
            When he chases them with words, they are gone.
8 A person who gains sense loves himself.
    One who guards understanding finds something good.
9 A lying witness will not go unpunished.
    One who tells lies will die.

10 Luxury does not fit a fool,
        much less a slave ruling princes.
11 A person with good sense is patient,
        and it is to his credit that he overlooks an offense.
12 The rage of a king is like the roar of a lion,
        but his favor is like dew on the grass.

A Foolish Son Brings Ruin to Others
13 A foolish son ruins his father,
        and a quarreling woman is like constantly dripping water.
14 Home and wealth are inherited from fathers,
        but a sensible wife comes from the LORD.

15 Laziness throws one into a deep sleep,
        and an idle person will go hungry.
16 Whoever obeys the law preserves his life,
        ˎbutˎ whoever despises the LORD's ways will be put to death.

17 Whoever has pity on the poor lends to the LORD,
        and he will repay him for his good deed.
18 Discipline your son while there is still hope.
        Do not be the one responsible for his death.
19 A person who has a hot temper will pay for it.
        If you rescue him, you will have to do it over and over.
20 Listen to advice and accept discipline
        so that you may be wise the rest of your life.
21 Many plans are in the human heart,
        but the advice of the LORD will endure.
22 Loyalty is desirable in a person,
        and it is better to be poor than a liar.

23 The fear of the LORD leads to life,
        and such a person will rest easy without suffering harm.[a]
24 A lazy person puts his fork in his food.
        He doesn't even bring it back to his mouth.
25 Strike a mocker, and a gullible person may learn a lesson.
        Warn an understanding person, and he will gain more knowledge.

Foolproof Instructions
26 A son who assaults his father ˎandˎ who drives away his mother
        brings shame and disgrace.
27 If you stop listening to instruction, my son,
        you will stray from the words of knowledge.

---

[a] 18:24 Or "A person has friends as companions."   [a] 19:23 Hebrew meaning of this line uncertain.

28 A worthless witness mocks justice,
and the mouths of wicked people swallow up trouble.
29 Punishments are set for mockers
and beatings for the backs of fools.

20 1 Wine ˌmakes peopleˌ mock,
liquor ˌmakes themˌ noisy,
and everyone under their influence is unwise.
2 The rage of a king is like the roar of a lion.
Whoever makes him angry forfeits his life.
3 Avoiding a quarrel is honorable.
After all, any stubborn fool can start a fight.

4 A lazy person does not plow in the fall.ᵃ
He looks for something in the harvest but finds nothing.
5 A motive in the human heart is like deep water,
and a person who has understanding draws it out.
6 Many people declare themselves loyal,
but who can find someone who is ˌreallyˌ trustworthy?
7 A righteous person lives on the basis of his integrity.
Blessed are his children after he is gone.
8 A king who sits on his throne to judge sifts out every evil with his eyes.

9 Who can say,
"I've made my heart pure.
I'm cleansed from my sin"?
10 A double standard of weights and measures—
both are disgusting to the LORD.
11 Even a child makes himself known by his actions,
whether his deeds are pure or right.
12 The ear that hears,
the eye that sees—
the LORD made them both.
13 Do not love sleep or you will end up poor.
Keep your eyes open, and you will have plenty to eat.

14 "Bad! Bad!" says the buyer.
Then, as he goes away, he brags ˌabout his bargainˌ.
15 There are gold and plenty of jewels,
but the lips of knowledge are precious gems.
16 Hold on to the garment of one who guarantees a stranger's loan,
and hold responsible the person who makes a loan on behalf of a foreigner.
17 Food gained dishonestly tastes sweet to a person,
but afterwards his mouth will be filled with gravel.
18 Plans are confirmed by getting advice,
and with guidance one wages war.
19 Whoever goes around as a gossip tells secrets.
Do not associate with a person whose mouth is always open.

20 The lamp of the person who curses his father and mother
will be snuffed out in total darkness.ᵇ
21 An inheritance quickly obtained in the beginning
will never be blessed in the end.
22 Do not say, "I'll get even with you!"
Wait for the LORD, and he will save you.
23 A double standard of weights is disgusting to the LORD,
and dishonest scales are no good.
24 The LORD is the one who directs a person's steps.
How then can anyone understand his own way?
25 It is a trap for a person to say impulsively, "This is a holy offering!"
and later to have second thoughts about those vows.

26 A wise king scatters the wicked
and then runs them over.
27 A person's soul is the LORD's lamp.
It searches his entire innermost being.
28 Mercy and truth protect a king,

ᵃ 20:4 Fall was the start of the planting season in Palestine.   ᵇ 20:20 Or "snuffed out as darkness approaches."

and with mercy he maintains his throne.
29 While the glory of young men is their strength,
   the splendor of older people is their silver hair.
30 Brutal beatings cleanse away wickedness.
   Such beatings cleanse the innermost being.

The LORD Controls Wise and Foolish People

21 ¹The king's heart is like streams of water.
        Both are under the LORD's control.
           He turns them in any direction he chooses.
2 A person thinks everything he does is right,
     but the LORD weighs hearts.
3 Doing what is right and fair
     is more acceptable to the LORD than offering a sacrifice.
4 A conceited look and an arrogant attitude,
     which are the lamps of wicked people, are sins.

5 The plans of a hard-working person lead to prosperity,
     but everyone who is ˌalwaysˌ in a hurry ends up in poverty.
6 Those who gather wealth by lying are wasting time.
     They are looking for death.
7 The violence of wicked people will drag them away
     since they refuse to do what is just.
8 The way of a guilty person is crooked,
     but the behavior of those who are pure is moral.ª

9 Better to live on a corner of a roof
     than to share a home with a quarreling woman.
10 The mind of a wicked person desires evil
     and has no consideration for his neighbor.
11 When a mocker is punished, a gullible person becomes wise,
     and when a wise person is instructed, he gains knowledge.
12 A righteous person wisely considers the house of a wicked person.
     He throws wicked people into disasters.

13 Whoever shuts his ear to the cry of the poor will call and not be answered.
14 A gift ˌgivenˌ in secret calms anger,
     and a secret bribe calms great fury.
15 When justice is done, a righteous person is delighted,
     but troublemakers are terrified.
16 A person who wanders from the way of wise behavior
     will rest in the assembly of the dead.

17 Whoever loves pleasure will become poor.
   Whoever loves wine and expensive food will not become rich.
18 Wicked people become a ransom for righteous people,
     and treacherous people will take the place of decent people.
19 Better to live in a desert
     than with a quarreling and angry woman.
20 Costly treasure and wealth are in the home of a wise person,
     but a fool devours them.
21 Whoever pursues righteousness and mercy
     will find life, righteousness, and honor.

22 A wise man attacks a city of warriors
     and pulls down the strong defenses in which they trust.
23 Whoever guards his mouth and his tongue keeps himself out of trouble.
24 An arrogant, conceited person is called a mocker.
     His arrogance knows no limits.

25 The desire of a lazy person will kill him
     because his hands refuse to work.
26   All day long he feels greedy,
         but a righteous person gives and does not hold back.

27 The sacrifice of wicked people is disgusting,
     especially if they bring it with evil intent.

ª 21:8 Hebrew meaning of this verse uncertain.

28 A lying witness will die,
but a person who listens to advice will continue to speak.
29 A wicked person puts up a bold front,
but a decent person's way of life is his own security.

30 No wisdom, no understanding, and no advice
͵can stand up͵ against the LORD.
31 The horse is made ready for the day of battle,
but the victory belongs to the LORD.

22 1 A good name is more desirable than great wealth.
Respect is better than silver or gold.
2 The rich and the poor have this in common:
the LORD is the maker of them all.
3 Sensible people foresee trouble and hide ͵from it͵,
but gullible people go ahead and suffer ͵the consequence͵.
4 On the heels of humility (the fear of the LORD)
are riches and honor and life.

5 A devious person has thorns and traps ahead of him.
Whoever guards himself will stay far away from them.
6 Train a child in the way he should go,
and even when he is old he will not turn away from it.
7 A rich person rules poor people,
and a borrower is a slave to a lender.
8 Whoever plants injustice will harvest trouble,
and this weapon of his own fury will be destroyed.
9 Whoever is generous will be blessed
because he has shared his food with the poor.

10 Drive out a mocker, and conflict will leave.
Quarreling and abuse will stop.
11 Whoever loves a pure heart and whoever speaks graciously
has a king as his friend.
12 The LORD's eyes watch over knowledge,
but he overturns the words of a treacherous person.

13 A lazy person says,
"There's a lion outside!
I'll be murdered in the streets!"
14 The mouth of an adulterous woman is a deep pit.
The one who is cursed by the LORD will fall into it.
15 Foolishness is firmly attached to a child's heart.
Spanking will remove it far from him.
16 Oppressing the poor for profit
͵or͵ giving to the rich
certainly leads to poverty.

Listen to My Advice
17 Open your ears, and hear the words of wise people,
and set your mind on the knowledge I give you.
18 It is pleasant if you keep them in mind
͵so that͵ they will be on the tip of your tongue,
19 so that your trust may be in the LORD.
Today I have made them known to you, especially to you.
20 Didn't I write to you previously with advice and knowledge
21 in order to teach you the words of truth
so that you can give an accurate report to those who send you?

Living With Your Neighbor
22 Do not rob the poor because they are poor
or trample on the rights of an oppressed person at the city gate,
23 because the LORD will plead their case
and will take the lives of those who rob them.
24 Do not be a friend of one who has a bad temper,
and never keep company with a hothead,
25 or you will learn his ways
and set a trap for yourself.

26 Do not be ˌfoundˌ among those who make deals with a handshake,
   among those who guarantee other people's loans.
27 If you have no money to pay back a loan,
   why should your bed be repossessed?
28 Do not move an ancient boundary marker
   that your ancestors set in place.
29 Do you see a person who is efficient in his work?
   He will serve kings.
   He will not serve unknown people.

23 1 When you sit down to eat with a ruler,
   pay close attention to what is in front of you,
2   and put a knife to your throat if you have a big appetite.
3 Do not crave his delicacies,
   because this is food that deceives you.

4 Do not wear yourself out getting rich.
   Be smart enough to stop.
5 Will you catch only a fleeting glimpse of wealth before it is gone?
   It makes wings for itself like an eagle flying into the sky.

6 Do not eat the food of one who is stingy,
   and do not crave his delicacies.
7 As he calculates the cost to himself, this is what he does:
   He tells you, "Eat and drink,"
      but he doesn't really mean it.
8 You will vomit the little bit you have eaten
   and spoil your pleasant conversation.

9 Do not talk directly to a fool,
   because he will despise the wisdom of your words.
10 Do not move an ancient boundary marker
   or enter fields that belong to orphans,
11   because the one who is responsible for them is strong.
   He will plead their case against you.

Learning From Your Father
12 Live a more disciplined life,
   and listen carefully to words of knowledge.
13 Do not hesitate to discipline a child.
   If you spank him, he will not die.
14   Spank him yourself,
      and you will save his soul from hell.

15 My son,
   if you have a wise heart,
   my heart will rejoice as well.
16   My heart rejoices when you speak what is right.

17 Do not envy sinners in your heart.
   Instead, continue to fear the LORD.
18   There is indeed a future,
      and your hope will never be cut off.

19 My son,
   listen, be wise,
   and keep your mind going in the right direction.
20 Do not associate with those who drink too much wine,
   with those who eat too much meat,
21   because both a drunk and a glutton will become poor.
      Drowsiness will dress a person in rags.

22 Listen to your father since you are his son,
   and do not despise your mother because she is old.
23 Buy truth (and do not sell it),
   ˌthat is,ˌ buy wisdom, discipline, and understanding.
24 A righteous person's father will certainly rejoice.
   Someone who has a wise son will enjoy him.
25   May your father and your mother be glad.
      May she who gave birth to you rejoice.

26 My son,
    give me your heart.
    Let your eyes find happiness in my ways.
27   A prostitute is a deep pit.
    A loose woman is a narrow well.
28   She is like a robber, lying in ambush.
    She spreads unfaithfulness throughout society.

29 Who has trouble?
    Who has misery?
    Who has quarrels?
    Who has a complaint?
    Who has wounds for no reason?
    Who has bloodshot eyes?
30   Those who drink glass after glass of wine
    and mix it with everything.
31 Do not look at wine
    because it is red,
    because it sparkles in the cup,
    because it goes down smoothly.
32   Later it bites like a snake
    and strikes like a poisonous snake.
33   Your eyes will see strange sights,
    and your mouth will say embarrassing things.
34 You will be like someone lying down in the middle of the sea
    or like someone lying down on top of a ship's mast, saying,
35   "They strike me, but I feel no pain.
    They beat me, but I'm not aware of it.
    Whenever I wake up, I'm going to look for another drink."

24 1 Do not envy evil people
    or wish you were with them,
2   because their minds plot violence,
    and their lips talk trouble.

3 With wisdom a house is built.
    With understanding it is established.
4 With knowledge its rooms are filled
    with every kind of riches, both precious and pleasant.

5 A strong man knows how to use his strength,
    but a person with knowledge is even more powerful.
6   After all, with the right strategy you can wage war,
    and with many advisers there is victory.

7 Matters of wisdom are beyond the grasp of a stubborn fool.
    At the city gate he does not open his mouth.
8 Whoever plans to do evil will be known as a schemer.
9 Foolish scheming is sinful,
    and a mocker is disgusting to everyone.

10 If you faint in a crisis, you are weak.
11 Rescue captives condemned to death,
    and spare those staggering toward their slaughter.
12 When you say, "We didn't know this,"
    won't the one who weighs hearts take note of it?
    Won't the one who guards your soul know it?
    Won't he pay back people for what they do?

13 Eat honey, my son, because it is good.
    Honey that flows from the honeycomb tastes sweet.
14   The knowledge of wisdom is like that for your soul.
    If you find it, then there is a future,
    and your hope will never be cut off.

15 You wicked one,
    do not lie in ambush at the home of a righteous person.
    Do not rob his house.
16   A righteous person may fall seven times, but he gets up again.
    However, in a disaster wicked people fall.

17 Do not be happy when your enemy falls,
　　and do not feel glad when he stumbles.
18 　The LORD will see it, he won't like it,
　　　and he will turn his anger away from that person.

19 Do not get overly upset with evildoers.
Do not envy wicked people,
20 　because an evil person has no future,
　　and the lamps of wicked people will be snuffed out.

21 Fear the LORD, my son.
Fear the king as well.
　Do not associate with those who always insist upon change,
22 　because disaster will come to them suddenly.
　　Who knows what misery both may bring?

Learning From Wise People
23 These also are the sayings of wise people:

Showing partiality as a judge is not good.
24 　Whoever says to a guilty person, "You are innocent,"
　　will be cursed by people and condemned by nations.
25 　But people will be pleased with those who convict a guilty person,
　　and a great blessing will come to them.
26 Giving a straight answer is ˌlikeˌ a kiss on the lips.

27 Prepare your work outside,
　　and get things ready for yourself in the field.
　　　Afterwards, build your house.

28 Do not testify against your neighbor without a reason,
　　and do not deceive with your lips.
29 Do not say,
　　"I'll treat him as he treated me.
　　I'll pay him back for what he has done to me."

30 I passed by a lazy person's field,
　　the vineyard belonging to a person without sense.
31 I saw that it was all overgrown with thistles.
　　The ground was covered with weeds,
　　　and its stone fence was torn down.
32 When I observed ˌthisˌ, I took it to heart.
I saw it and learned my lesson.
33 　"Just a little sleep,
　　just a little slumber,
　　just a little nap."
34 　　Then your poverty will come like a drifter,
　　　and your need will come like a bandit.

25 ¹These also are Solomon's proverbs that were copied
　　by the men of King Hezekiah of Judah.

Advice for Kings
2 It is the glory of God to hide things
　　but the glory of kings to investigate them.
3 ˌLikeˌ the high heavens and the deep earth,
　　so the mind of kings is unsearchable.
4 Take the impurities out of silver,
　　and a vessel is ready for the silversmith to mold.
5 Take a wicked person away from the presence of a king,
　　and justice will make his throne secure.

6 Do not brag about yourself in front of a king
　　or stand in the spot that belongs to notable people,
7 　because it is better to be told, "Come up here,"
　　　than to be put down in front of a prince
　　　　whom your eyes have seen.

8 Do not be in a hurry to go to court.
　　What will you do in the end if your neighbor disgraces you?
9 　　Present your argument to your neighbor,

10 but do not reveal another person's secret.
Otherwise, when he hears about it, he will humiliate you,
and his evil report about you will never disappear.

11 ˌLikeˌ golden apples in silver settings,
ˌsoˌ is a word spoken at the right time.
12 ˌLikeˌ a gold ring and a fine gold ornament,
ˌsoˌ is constructive criticism to the ear of one who listens.
13 Like the coolness of snow on a harvest day,
ˌsoˌ is a trustworthy messenger to those who send him:
He refreshes his masters.
14 ˌLikeˌ a dense fog or a dust storm,
ˌsoˌ is a person who brags about a gift that he does not give.

15 With patience you can persuade a ruler,
and a soft tongue can break bones.
16 When you find honey, eat only as much as you need.
Otherwise, you will have too much and vomit.
17 Do not set foot in your neighbor's house too often.
Otherwise, he will see too much of you and hate you.

18 ˌLikeˌ a club and a sword and a sharp arrow,
ˌsoˌ is a person who gives false testimony against his neighbor.
19 ˌLikeˌ a broken tooth and a lame foot,
ˌsoˌ is confidence in an unfaithful person in a ˌtime ofˌ crisis.
20 ˌLikeˌ taking off a coat on a cold day
or pouring vinegar on baking soda,
so is singing songs to one who has an evil heart.

21 If your enemy is hungry, give him some food to eat,
and if he is thirsty, give him some water to drink.
22 ˌIn this wayˌ you will make him feel guilty and ashamed,
and the LORD will reward you.

23 ˌAsˌ the north wind brings rain,
so a whispering tongue brings angry looks.
24 Better to live on a corner of a roof
than to share a home with a quarreling woman.
25 ˌLikeˌ cold water to a thirsty soul,
so is good news from far away.
26 ˌLikeˌ a muddied spring and a polluted well,
ˌsoˌ is a righteous person who gives in to a wicked person.

27 Eating too much honey is not good,
and searching for honor is not honorable.[a]

28 ˌLikeˌ a city broken into ˌandˌ left without a wall,
ˌsoˌ is a person who lacks self-control.

All About Fools

26 1 Like snow in summertime and rain at harvest time,
so honor is not right for a fool.
2 Like a fluttering sparrow,
like a darting swallow,
so a hastily spoken curse does not come to rest.
3 A whip is for the horse,
a bridle is for the donkey,
and a rod is for the backs of fools.

4 Do not answer a fool with his own stupidity,
or you will be like him.
5 Answer a fool with his own stupidity,
or he will think he is wise.
6 Whoever uses a fool to send a message
cuts off his own feet and brings violence upon himself.

7 ˌLikeˌ a lame person's limp legs,
so is a proverb in the mouths of fools.

---

[a] 25:27 Hebrew meaning of this line uncertain.

8 Like tying a stone to a sling,
   so is giving honor to a fool.
9 ⌐Like⌐ a thorn stuck in a drunk's hand,
   so is a proverb in the mouths of fools.
10 ⌐Like⌐ many people who destroy everything,
   so is one who hires fools or drifters.
11 As a dog goes back to its vomit,
   ⌐so⌐ a fool repeats his stupidity.
12 Have you met a person who thinks he is wise?
   There is more hope for a fool than for him.

13 A lazy person says,
   "There's a ferocious lion out on the road!
   There's a lion loose in the streets!"
14 ⌐As⌐ a door turns on its hinges,
   so the lazy person turns on his bed.
15 A lazy person puts his fork in his food.
   He wears himself out as he brings it back to his mouth.
16 A lazy person thinks he is wiser than seven people who give a sensible answer.

17 ⌐Like⌐ grabbing a dog by the ears,
   ⌐so⌐ is a bystander who gets involved in someone else's quarrel.
18 Like a madman who shoots flaming arrows, arrows, and death,
19 so is the person who tricks his neighbor and says, "I was only joking!"

20 Without wood a fire goes out,
   and without gossip a quarrel dies down.
21 ⌐As⌐ charcoal fuels burning coals and wood fuels fire,
   so a quarrelsome person fuels a dispute.
22 The words of a gossip are swallowed greedily,
   and they go down into a person's innermost being.

23 ⌐Like⌐ a clay pot covered with cheap silver,
   ⌐so⌐ is smooth talk that covers up an evil heart.
24 Whoever is filled with hate disguises it with his speech,
   but inside he holds on to deceit.
25 When he talks charmingly, do not trust him
   because of the seven disgusting things in his heart.
26 His hatred is deceitfully hidden,
   but his wickedness will be revealed to the community.

27 Whoever digs a pit will fall into it.
   Whoever rolls a stone will have it roll back on him.
28 A lying tongue hates its victims,
   and a flattering mouth causes ruin.

All About Life

27 ¹ Do not brag about tomorrow,
   because you do not know what another day may bring.
2 Praise should come from another person and not from your own mouth,
   from a stranger and not from your own lips.
3 A stone is heavy, and sand weighs a lot,
   but annoyance caused by a stubborn fool is heavier than both.
4 Anger is cruel, and fury is overwhelming,
   but who can survive jealousy?

5 Open criticism is better than unexpressed love.
6 Wounds made by a friend are intended to help,
   but an enemy's kisses are too much to bear.[a]
7 One who is full despises honey,
   but to one who is hungry,
   even bitter food tastes sweet.
8 Like a bird wandering from its nest,
   so is a husband wandering from his home.

9 Perfume and incense make the heart glad,
   but the sweetness of a friend is a fragrant forest.[b]

---

[a] 27:6 Hebrew meaning of "are too much to bear" uncertain.   [b] 27:9 Or "is sincere advice."

¹⁰ Do not abandon your friend or your father's friend.
Do not go to a relative's home when you are in trouble.
   A neighbor living nearby is better than a relative far away.

¹¹ Be wise, my son, and make my heart glad
   so that I can answer anyone who criticizes me.
¹² Sensible people foresee trouble and hide.
Gullible people go ahead ˎandˎ suffer.
¹³ Hold on to the garment of one who guarantees a stranger's loan,
      and hold responsible the person
         who makes a loan in behalf of a foreigner.
¹⁴ Whoever blesses his friend early in the morning with a loud voice—
   his blessing is considered a curse.

¹⁵ Constantly dripping water on a rainy day is like a quarreling woman.
¹⁶ Whoever can control her can control the wind.
   He can even pick up olive oil with his right hand.ᶜ

¹⁷ ˎAsˎ iron sharpens iron,
   so one person sharpens the wits of another.
¹⁸ Whoever takes care of a fig tree can eat its fruit,
   and whoever protects his master is honored.
¹⁹ As a face is reflected in water,
   so a person is reflected by his heart.
²⁰ Hell and decay are never satisfied,
   and a person's eyes are never satisfied.

²¹ The crucible is for refining silver and the smelter for gold,
   but a person ˎis testedˎ by the praise given to him.
²² If you crush a stubborn fool in a mortar with a pestle along with grain,ᵈ
   ˎeven thenˎ his stupidity will not leave him.
²³ Be fully aware of the condition of your flock,
   and pay close attention to your herds.
²⁴ Wealth is not forever.
      Nor does a crown last from one generation to the next.

²⁵ ˎWhenˎ grass is cut short, the tender growth appears,
   and vegetables are gathered on the hills.
²⁶ Lambs ˎwill provideˎ you with clothing,
      and the money from the male goats will buy a field.
²⁷ There will be enough goat milk to feed you,
      to feed your family,
         and to keep your servant girls alive.

28

¹ A wicked person flees when no one is chasing him,
   but righteous people are as bold as lions.
² When a country is in revolt, it has many rulers,
      but only with a person who has understanding and knowledge
         will it last a long time.
³ A poor person who oppresses poorer people
   is like a driving rain that leaves no food.
⁴ Those who abandon ˎGod'sˎ teachings praise wicked people,
   but those who follow ˎGod'sˎ teachings oppose wicked people.
⁵ Evil people do not understand justice,
   but those who seek the LORD understand everything.
⁶ Better to be a poor person who has integrity
   than to be rich and double-dealing.

⁷ Whoever follows ˎGod'sˎ teachings is a wise son.
Whoever associates with gluttons disgraces his father.
⁸ Whoever becomes wealthy through ˎunfairˎ loans and interest
   collects them for the one who is kind to the poor.
⁹ Surely the prayer of someone who refuses
   to listen to ˎGod'sˎ teachings is disgusting.
¹⁰ Whoever leads decent people into evil will fall into his own pit,
   but innocent people will inherit good things.

ᶜ 27:16 Hebrew meaning of this line uncertain.   ᵈ 27:22 Hebrew meaning uncertain.

11 A rich person is wise in his own eyes,
    but a poor person with understanding sees right through him.
12 When righteous people triumph, there is great glory,
    but when wicked people rise, people hide themselves.
13 Whoever covers over his sins does not prosper.
    Whoever confesses and abandons them receives compassion.
14 Blessed is the one who is always fearful ⸤of sin⸥,
    but whoever is hard-hearted falls into disaster.

15 ⸤Like⸥ a roaring lion and a charging bear,
    ⸤so⸥ a wicked ruler is a threat to poor people.
16 A leader without understanding taxes ⸤his people⸥ heavily,
    but those who hate unjust gain will live longer.
17 A person burdened with the guilt of murder
    will be a fugitive down to his grave.
        No one will help him.

18 Whoever lives honestly will be safe.
    Whoever lives dishonestly will fall all at once.
19 Whoever works his land will have plenty to eat.
    Whoever chases unrealistic dreams will have plenty of nothing.

20 A trustworthy person has many blessings,
    but anyone in a hurry to get rich will not escape punishment.
21 Showing partiality is not good,
    because some people will turn on you even for a piece of bread.
22 A stingy person is in a hurry to get rich,
    not realizing that poverty is about to overtake him.

23 Whoever criticizes people will be more highly regarded in the future
    than the one who flatters with his tongue.
24 The one who robs his father or his mother
    and says, "It isn't wrong!" is a companion to a vandal.
25 A greedy person stirs up a fight,
    but whoever trusts the LORD prospers.

26 Whoever trusts his own heart is a fool.
    Whoever walks in wisdom will survive.
27 Whoever gives to the poor lacks nothing.
    Whoever ignores the poor receives many curses.

28 When wicked people rise, people hide.
    When they die, righteous people increase.

29 1 A person who will not bend after many warnings
    will suddenly be broken beyond repair.
2 When righteous people increase, the people ⸤of God⸥ rejoice,
    but when a wicked person rules, everybody groans.
3 A person who loves wisdom makes his father happy,
    but one who pays prostitutes wastes his wealth.
4 By means of justice, a king builds up a country,
    but a person who confiscates religious contributions tears it down.

5 A person who flatters his neighbor
    is spreading a net for him to step into.
6 To an evil person sin is bait in a trap,
    but a righteous person runs away from it[a] and is glad.
7 A righteous person knows the just cause of the poor.
    A wicked person does not understand this.
8 Mockers create an uproar in a city,
    but wise people turn away anger.

9 When a wise person goes to court with a stubborn fool,
    he may rant and rave,
        but there is no peace and quiet.
10 Bloodthirsty people hate an innocent person,
    but decent people seek ⸤to protect⸥ his life.
11 A fool expresses all his emotions,

---

[a] 29:6 Hebrew meaning of "runs away from it" uncertain.

but a wise person controls them.
12 If a ruler pays attention to lies,
   all his servants become wicked.

13 A poor person and an oppressor have this in common:
   The LORD gives both of them sight.
14 When a king judges the poor with honesty,
   his throne will always be secure.

15 A spanking and a warning produce wisdom,
   but an undisciplined child disgraces his mother.
16 When wicked people increase, crime increases,
   but righteous people will witness their downfall.
17 Correct your son, and he will give you peace of mind.
   He will bring delight to your soul.

18 Without prophetic vision people run wild,
   but blessed are those who follow ⌞God's⌟ teachings.
19 A slave cannot be disciplined with words.
   He will not respond, though he may understand.
20 Have you met a person who is quick to answer?
   There is more hope for a fool than for him.
21 Pamper a slave from childhood,
   and later he will be ungrateful.[b]

22 An angry person stirs up a fight,
   and a hothead does much wrong.
23 A person's pride will humiliate him,
   but a humble spirit gains honor.
24 Whoever is a thief's partner hates his own life.
   He will not testify under oath.
25 A person's fear sets a trap ⌞for him⌟,
   but one who trusts the LORD is safe.
26 Many seek an audience with a ruler,
   but justice for humanity comes from the LORD.
27 An unjust person is disgusting to righteous people.
   A decent person is disgusting to wicked people.

30

1 The words of Agur, son of Jakeh. Agur's prophetic revelation.

Agur Speaks About God

[To God]
   This man's declaration:
      "I'm weary, O God.
      I'm weary and worn out, O God.
2   I'm more ⌞like⌟ a dumb animal than a human being.
      I don't ⌞even⌟ have human understanding.
3   I haven't learned wisdom.
      I don't have knowledge of the Holy One.[a]

[To the audience]
4   "Who has gone up to heaven and come down?
      Who has gathered the wind in the palm of his hand?
      Who has wrapped water in a garment?
      Who has set up the earth from one end to the other?
      What is his name or the name of his son?
         Certainly, you must know!

5   "Every word of God has proven to be true.
      He is a shield to those who come to him for protection.
6   Do not add to his words,
      or he will reprimand you, and you will be found to be a liar.

---

^b 29:21 Hebrew meaning uncertain.   ^a 30:3 Or "holy ones."

A Prayer

[To God]
⁷   "I've asked you for two things.
      Don't keep them from me before I die:
⁸   Keep vanity and lies far away from me.
      Don't give me either poverty or riches.
          Feed me ˎonlyˏ the food I need,
⁹   or I may feel satisfied and deny you
                and say, 'Who is the LORD?'
             or I may become poor and steal
                and give the name of my God a bad reputation.

Against Slander

[To the audience]
¹⁰   "Do not slander a slave to his master.
          The slave will curse you,
              and you will be found guilty."

Four Kinds of People

¹¹   A certain kind of person curses his father
          and does not bless his mother.
¹²   A certain kind of person thinks he is pure
          but is not washed from his own feces.ᵇ
¹³   A certain kind of person looks around arrogantly
          and is conceited.
¹⁴   A certain kind of person,
          whose teeth are like swords
              and whose jaws are ˎlikeˏ knives,
                  devours oppressed people from the earth
                      and people from among humanity.

Human Bloodsuckers

¹⁵   The bloodsucking leech has two daughters—"Give!" and "Give!"

Four Things That Are Never Satisfied

      Three things are never satisfied.
      Four never say, "Enough!":
¹⁶   the grave,
          a barren womb,
          a land that never gets enough water,
          a fire that does not say, "Enough!"

Disrespectful Children—Their Punishment

¹⁷   The eye that makes fun of a father and hates to obey a mother
          will be plucked out by ravens in the valley and eaten by young vultures.

Four Things of Intrigue

¹⁸   Three things are too amazing to me,
          even four that I cannot understand:
¹⁹   an eagle making its way through the sky,
          a snake making its way over a rock,
          a ship making its way through high seas,
          a man making his way with a virgin.

About the Woman Who Commits Adultery

²⁰   This is the way of a woman who commits adultery:
          She eats, wipes her mouth,
              and says, "I haven't done anything wrong!"

Four Things That Are Intolerable

²¹   Three things cause the earth to tremble,
          even four it cannot bear up under:
²²   a slave when he becomes king,

ᵇ 30:12 Blunt Hebrew term but not considered vulgar.

23 a godless fool when he is filled with food,
a woman who is unloved when she gets married,
a maid when she replaces her mistress.

Four Things That Are Small—Yet Smart and Strong
24 Four things on earth are small,
yet they are very wise:
25 Ants are not a strong species,
yet they store their food in summer.
26 Rock badgers are not a mighty species,
yet they make their home in the rocks.
27 Locusts have no king,
yet all of them divide into swarms by instinct.
28 A lizard you can hold in your hands,
yet it can even be found in royal palaces.

Four Things That Move With Dignity
29 There are three things that walk with dignity,
even four that march with dignity:
30 a lion, mightiest among animals, which turns away from nothing,
31 a strutting rooster,*c*
a male goat,
a king at the head of his army.*d*

Keep Calm and Quiet
32 If you are such a godless fool as to honor yourself,
or if you scheme,
you had better put your hand over your mouth.
33   As churning milk produces butter
and punching a nose produces blood,
so stirring up anger*e* produces a fight.

31 ¹ The sayings of King Lemuel, a prophetic revelation, used by his mother to discipline him.

Advice to a Prince
2 "What, my son?
What, son to whom I gave birth?
What, son of my prayers?
3 Don't give your strength to women
or your power to those who ruin kings.

4 "It is not for kings, Lemuel.
It is not for kings to drink wine or for rulers to crave liquor.
5 Otherwise, they drink and forget what they have decreed
and change the standard of justice for all oppressed people.
6 Give liquor to a person who is dying
and wine to one who feels resentful.
7   Such a person drinks
and forgets his poverty
and does not remember his trouble anymore.

8 "Speak out for the one who cannot speak,
for the rights of those who are doomed.
9 Speak out,
judge fairly,
and defend the rights of oppressed and needy people."

A Poem in Hebrew Alphabetical Order
10 "Who can find a wife with a strong character?
She is worth far more than jewels.
11 Her husband trusts her with ˌallˌ his heart,
and he does not lack anything good.
12 She helps him and never harms him all the days of her life.

---

c 30:31 Hebrew meaning of this line uncertain.   *d* 30:31 Hebrew meaning of "at the head of his army" uncertain.
e 30:33 In Hebrew there is a play on words in verse 33 where the same verb is used to express all three actions.

13 "She seeks out wool and linen ⌞with care⌟
    and works with willing hands.
14 She is like merchant ships.
    She brings her food from far away.
15 She wakes up while it is still dark
    and gives food to her family
        and portions of food to her female slaves.

16 "She picks out a field and buys it.
    She plants a vineyard from the profits she has earned.
17 She puts on strength like a belt
    and goes to work with energy.
18 She sees that she is making a good profit.
    Her lamp burns late at night.

19 "She puts her hands on the distaff,
    and her fingers hold a spindle.
20 She opens her hands to oppressed people
    and stretches them out to needy people.
21 She does not fear for her family when it snows
    because her whole family
        has a double layer of clothing.
22 She makes quilts for herself.
    Her clothes are ⌞made of⌟ linen and purple cloth.

23 "Her husband is known at the city gates
    when he sits with the leaders of the land.

24 "She makes linen garments and sells them
    and delivers belts to the merchants.
25 She dresses with strength and nobility,
    and she smiles at the future.

26 "She speaks with wisdom,
    and on her tongue there is tender instruction.
27 She keeps a close eye on the conduct of her family,
    and she does not eat the bread of idleness.
28 Her children and her husband
    stand up and bless her.
In addition, he sings her praises, by saying,
29 'Many women have done noble work,
    but you have surpassed them all!'

30 "Charm is deceptive, and beauty evaporates,
    ⌞but⌟ a woman who has the fear of the LORD should be praised.
31 Reward her for what she has done,
    and let her achievements praise her at the city gates."

ECCLESIASTES

Introducing the Spokesman

1 [1] The words of the spokesman, the son of David and the king in Jerusalem.

The Theme

[2] "Absolutely pointless!" says the spokesman. "Absolutely pointless! Everything is pointless."

Life Is an Endless Circle

[3] What do people gain from all their hard work under the sun?

[4]   Generations come, and generations go,
     but the earth lasts forever.
[5]   The sun rises, and the sun sets,
     and then it rushes back to the place where it will rise ˻again˼.
[6]   The wind blows toward the south and shifts toward the north.
     Round and round it blows. It blows in a full circle.
[7]   All streams flow into the sea, but the sea is never full.
     The water goes back to the place where the streams began
       in order to ˻start˼ flowing again.

[8] All of these sayings are worn-out phrases. They are more than anyone can express, comprehend, or understand.
[9] Whatever has happened before will happen ˻again˼. Whatever has been done before will be done ˻again˼. There is nothing new under the sun. [10] Can you say that anything is new? It has already been here long before us. [11] Nothing from the past is remembered. Even in the future, nothing will be remembered by those who come after us.

The Spokesman Begins to Study Everything Under Heaven

[12] I, the spokesman, have been king of Israel in Jerusalem. [13] With all my heart I used wisdom to study and explore everything done under heaven.

The Spokesman's General Conclusion

Mortals are weighed down with a terrible burden that God has placed on them. [14] I have seen everything that is done under the sun. Look at it! It's all pointless. ˻It's like˼ trying to catch the wind.

[15]   No one can straighten what is bent.
     No one can count what is not there.

The Spokesman Begins to Study Life

[16] I thought to myself, "I have grown wiser than anyone who ˻has ruled˼ Jerusalem before me. I've had a lot of experience with wisdom and knowledge." [17] I've used my mind to understand wisdom and knowledge as well as madness and stupidity. ˻Now˼ I know that this is ˻like˼ trying to catch the wind.

[18]   With a lot of wisdom ˻comes˼ a lot of heartache.
     The greater ˻your˼ knowledge, the greater ˻your˼ pain.

The Spokesman Studies Laughter

2 [1] I thought to myself, "Now I want to experiment with pleasure and enjoy myself." But even this was pointless.
[2] I thought, "Laughter doesn't make any sense. What does pleasure accomplish?"

The Spokesman Studies Wine

[3] I explored ways to make myself feel better by drinking wine. I also explored ways to do ˻some˼ foolish things. During all that time, wisdom continued to control my mind. I was able to determine whether this was good for mortals to do during their brief lives under heaven.

The Spokesman Studies Personal Achievements

[4] I accomplished some great things:

> I built houses for myself.
> I planted vineyards for myself.
> [5] I made gardens and parks for myself.
> I planted every kind of fruit tree in them.
> [6] I made pools to water the forest of growing trees.
> [7] I bought male and female slaves.
>   In addition, slaves were born in my household.
> I owned more herds and flocks
>   than anyone in Jerusalem before me.
> [8] I also gathered silver and gold for myself.
> I gathered the treasures of kings and provinces.
> I provided myself with male and female singers
>   and the pleasures men have with one concubine[a] after another.

[9] So I grew richer than anyone in Jerusalem before me. Yet, my wisdom remained with me. [10] If something appealed to me, I did it. I allowed myself to have any pleasure I wanted, since I found pleasure in my work. This was my reward for all my hard work. [11] But when I turned to look at all that I had accomplished and all the hard work I had put into it, I saw that it was all pointless. ⸤It was like⸥ trying to catch the wind. I gained nothing ⸤from any of my accomplishments⸥ under the sun.

Death Is the Common Destiny of All Life

[12] Then I turned ⸤my attention⸥ to experience wisdom, madness, and foolishness. For instance, what can the man who replaces the king do? Only what has already been done. [13] But I saw that wisdom has an advantage over foolishness as light has an advantage over darkness. [14] A wise person uses the eyes in his head, but a fool walks in the dark. But I have also come to realize that the same destiny waits for both of them. [15] I thought to myself, "⸤If⸥ the destiny that waits for the fool waits for me as well, then what is the advantage in being wise?" So I thought that even this is pointless.

Without God Everything Is Pointless

[16] Neither the wise person nor the fool will be remembered for long, since both will be forgotten in the days to come. Both the wise person and the fool will die. [17] So I came to hate life because everything done under the sun seemed wrong to me. Everything was pointless. ⸤It was like⸥ trying to catch the wind. [18] I came to hate everything for which I had worked so hard under the sun, because I will have to leave it to the person who replaces me. [19] Who knows whether that person will be wise or foolish? He will still have control over everything under the sun for which I worked so hard and used my wisdom. Even this is pointless. [20] Then I fell into despair over everything for which I had worked so hard under the sun. [21] Here is someone who had worked hard with wisdom, knowledge, and skill. Yet, he must turn over his estate to someone else, who didn't work for it. Even this is pointless and a terrible tragedy. [22] What do people get from all of their hard work and struggles under the sun? [23] Their entire life is filled with pain, and their work is unbearable. Even at night their minds don't rest. Even this is pointless.

With God Even the Simplest Things Have a Point

[24] There is nothing better for people to do than to eat, drink, and find satisfaction in their work. I saw that even this comes from the hand of God. [25] Who can eat or enjoy themselves without God? [26] God gives wisdom, knowledge, and joy to anyone who pleases him. But to the person who continues to sin, he gives the job of gathering and collecting ⸤wealth⸥. The sinner must turn his wealth over to the person who pleases God. Even this is pointless. ⸤It's like⸥ trying to catch the wind.

Everything in God's Own Time

3 [1] Everything has its own time, and there is a specific time for every activity under heaven:

> [2] a time to be born and
> a time to die,
> a time to plant and

---

[a] 2:8 A concubine is considered a wife except she has fewer rights under the law.

a time to pull out what was planted,
3 a time to kill and
a time to heal,
a time to tear down and
a time to build up,
4 a time to cry and
a time to laugh,
a time to mourn and
a time to dance,
5 a time to scatter stones and
a time to gather them,[a]
a time to hug and
a time to stop hugging,
6 a time to start looking and
a time to stop looking,
a time to keep and
a time to throw away,
7 a time to tear apart and
a time to sew together,
a time to keep quiet and
a time to speak out,
8 a time to love and
a time to hate,
a time for war and
a time for peace.

God Gives Mortals a Sense of Eternity

9 What do working people gain from their hard labor? 10 I have seen mortals weighed down with a burden that God has placed on them. 11 It is beautiful how God has done everything at the right time. He has put a sense of eternity in people's minds. Yet, mortals still can't grasp what God is doing from the beginning to the end ˌof timeˌ.

12 I realize that there's nothing better for them to do than to be cheerful and enjoy what is good in their lives. 13 It is a gift from God to be able to eat and drink and experience the good that comes from every kind of hard work.

14 I realize that whatever God does will last forever. Nothing can be added to it, and nothing can be taken away from it. God does this so that people will fear him.

15 Whatever has happened ˌin the pastˌ is present now. Whatever is going to happen ˌin the futureˌ has already happened ˌin the pastˌ. God will call the past to account.[b]

Humans and Animals Meet the Same End

16 I saw something else under the sun:

There is wickedness where justice should be found.
There is wickedness where righteousness should be found.

17 I thought to myself, "God will judge righteous people as well as wicked people, because there is a specific time for every activity and every work that is done." 18 I thought to myself, "God is going to test humans in order to show them that they are ˌlikeˌ animals." 19 Humans and animals have the same destiny. One dies just like the other. All of them have the same breath ˌof lifeˌ. Humans have no advantage over animals. All ˌof lifeˌ is pointless. 20 All ˌlifeˌ goes to the same place. All ˌlifeˌ comes from the ground, and all of it goes back to the ground. 21 Who knows whether a human spirit goes upward or whether an animal spirit goes downward to the earth?

22 I saw that there's nothing better for people to do than to enjoy their work because that is their lot ˌin lifeˌ. Who will allow them to see what will happen after them?

Better Not to Have Been Born

4 1 Next, I turned to look at all the acts of oppression that make people suffer under the sun. Look at the tears of those who suffer! No one can comfort them. Their oppressors have ˌallˌ the power. No one can comfort those who suffer. 2 I congratulate the dead, who have already died, rather than the living, who still have to carry on. 3 But the person who hasn't been born yet is better off than both of them. He hasn't seen the evil that is done under the sun.

---

[a] 3:5 Hebrew meaning of these two lines uncertain.   [b] 3:15 Hebrew meaning of this sentence uncertain.

Hard Work Versus Laziness

⁴Then I saw that all hard work and skillful effort come from rivalry. Even this is pointless. ⸤It's like⸥ trying to catch the wind. ⁵A fool folds his hands and wastes away. ⁶One handful of peace and quiet is better than two handfuls of hard work and of trying to catch the wind.

Those Who Are All Alone

⁷Next, I turned to look at something pointless under the sun: ⁸There are people who are all alone. They have no children or other family members. So there is no end to all the hard work they have to do. Their eyes are never satisfied with riches. But ⸤they never ask themselves⸥ why they are working so hard and depriving themselves of good things. Even this is pointless and a terrible tragedy.

Two Are Better Than One

⁹Two people are better than one because ⸤together⸥ they have a good reward for their hard work. ¹⁰If one falls, the other can help his friend get up. But how tragic it is for the one who is ⸤all⸥ alone when he falls. There is no one to help him get up. ¹¹Again, if two people lie down together, they can keep warm, but how can one person keep warm? ¹²Though one person may be overpowered by another, two people can resist one opponent. A triple-braided rope is not easily broken.

Rulers and Fickle Citizens

¹³A young man who is poor and wise is better than an old, foolish king who won't take advice any longer.

¹⁴A young man came out of prison to rule as king, even though he had been born in poverty in that same kingdom. ¹⁵I saw all living people moving about under the sun. They sided with the second young man, the king's successor. ¹⁶There was no end to all those people, everyone whom he led.ᵃ But those who will come later will not be happy with the successor. Even this is pointless. ⸤It's like⸥ trying to catch the wind.

Don't Daydream or Speak Carelessly When You Worship

5ᵃ ¹Watch your step when you go to the house of God. It is better to go there and listen than to bring the sacrifices fools bring. Fools are unaware that they are doing ⸤something⸥ evil.

²Don't be in a hurry to talk. Don't be eager to speak in the presence of God. Since God is in heaven and you are on earth, limit the number of your words.

³Daydreaming comes when there are too many worries.
Careless speaking comes when there are too many words.

⁴When you make a promise to God, don't be slow to keep it because God doesn't like fools. Keep your promise. ⁵It is better not to make a promise than to make one and not keep it. ⁶Don't let your mouth talk you into committing a sin. Don't say in the presence of a ⸤temple⸥ messenger, "My promise was a mistake!" Why should God become angry at your excuse and destroy what you've accomplished?

⁷In spite of many daydreams, pointless actions, and empty words, you should still fear God.

Corrupt Officials Have Corrupt Officials Over Them

⁸Don't be surprised if you see poor people being oppressed, denied justice, or denied their rights in any district. One authority is watching over another, and they both have authorities watching over them. ⁹Yet, a king is an advantage for a country with cultivated fields.ᵇ

The Value of Money

¹⁰Whoever loves money will never be satisfied with money. Whoever loves wealth will never be satisfied with more income. Even this is pointless. ¹¹As the number of goods increase, so do the number of people who consume them. What do owners gain ⸤from all their goods⸥ except ⸤the opportunity⸥ to look at them?

¹²The sleep of working people is sweet, whether they eat a little or a lot. But the full stomachs that rich people have will not allow them to sleep.

Economic Ruin

¹³There is a painful tragedy that I have seen under the sun: Riches lead to the downfall of those who hoard them. ¹⁴These hoarded riches were then lost in bad business deals. The owners had children, but now they have nothing to give them. ¹⁵They came from their mother's

---

ᵃ 4:16 Or "everyone who lived before these [kings]."   ᵃ 5:1 Ecclesiastes 5:1–20 in English Bibles is Ecclesiastes 4:17–5:19 in the Hebrew Bible.   ᵇ 5:9 Hebrew meaning of this verse uncertain.

womb naked. They will leave as naked as they came. They won't even be able to take a handful of their earnings with them from all their hard work. [16] This also is a painful tragedy: They leave exactly as they came. What advantage do they gain from working so hard for the wind? [17] They spend their entire lives in darkness, in constant frustration, sickness, and resentment.

Conclusion: God Alone Gives Contentment

[18] At last I have seen what is good and beautiful: It is to eat and drink and to enjoy the good in all our hard work under the sun during the brief lives God gives us. That is our lot ˏin lifeˏ. [19] It is a gift from God when God gives some people wealth and possessions, the power to enjoy them, ˏthe abilityˏ to accept their lot in life, and ˏthe abilityˏ to rejoice in their own hard work. [20] These people won't give much thought to their brief lives because God keeps them occupied with the joy in their hearts.

The Rich Person and the Stillborn Baby

6 [1] There is a tragedy that I have seen under the sun. It is a terrible one for mortals. [2] God gives one person riches, wealth, and honor so that he doesn't lack anything he wants. Yet, God doesn't give him the power to enjoy any of them. Instead, a stranger enjoys them. This is pointless and is a painful tragedy.

[3] Suppose a rich person wasn't satisfied with good things ˏwhile he was aliveˏ and didn't even get an honorable burial ˏafter he diedˏ. Suppose he had a hundred children and lived for many years. No matter how long he would have lived, it ˏstillˏ would have been better for him to have been born dead. [4] A stillborn baby arrives in a pointless birth and goes out into the darkness. The darkness then hides its name. [5] Though it has never seen the sun or known anything, the baby finds more rest than the rich person. [6] Even if the rich person lives two thousand years without experiencing anything good—don't we all go to the same place?

More Pointless Challenges

[7] Everything that people work so hard for goes into their mouths, but their appetite is never satisfied.

[8] What advantage does a wise person have over a fool? What advantage does a poor person have in knowing how to face life?

[9] It is better to look at what is in front of you than to go looking for what you want. Even this is pointless. ˏIt's likeˏ trying to catch the wind.

[10] Whatever has happened ˏin the pastˏ already has a name. Mortals are already known for what they are. Mortals cannot argue with the one who is stronger than they.

[11] The more words there are, the more pointless they become. What advantage do mortals gain from this? [12] Who knows what may be good for mortals while they are alive, during the brief, pointless days they live? Mortals pass by like a shadow. Who will tell them about their future under the sun?

Proverbs About Life

7 [1] A good name is better than expensive perfume, and the day you die is better than the day you're born. [2] It is better to go to a funeral than to a banquet because that is where everyone will end up. Everyone who is alive should take this to heart! [3] Sorrow is better than laughter because, in spite of a sad face, the heart can be joyful. [4] The minds of wise people think about funerals, but the minds of fools think about banquets.

[5] It is better to listen to wise people who reprimand you than to fools who sing your praises. [6] The laughter of a fool is like the crackling of thorns burning under a pot. Even this is pointless.

[7] Oppression can turn a wise person into a fool, and a bribe can corrupt the mind.

[8] The end of something is better than its beginning. It is better to be patient than arrogant.

[9] Don't be quick to get angry, because anger is typical of fools. [10] Don't ask, "Why were things better in the old days than they are now?" It isn't wisdom that leads you to ask this!

Wisdom Gives Life

[11] Wisdom is as good as an inheritance. It is an advantage to everyone who sees the sun. [12] Wisdom protects us just as money protects us, but the advantage of wisdom is that it gives life to those who have it.

[13] Consider what God has done! Who can straighten what God has bent?

A Truth for Every Situation

[14] When times are good, be happy. But when times are bad, consider this: God has made the one time as well as the other so that mortals cannot predict their future.

Mortals Don't Get What They Deserve

¹⁵ I have seen it all in my pointless life:

Righteous people die in spite of being righteous.
Wicked people go on living in spite of being wicked.

¹⁶ Don't be too virtuous, and don't be too wise. Why make yourself miserable? ¹⁷ Don't be too wicked, and don't be a fool. Why should you die before your time is up? ¹⁸ It's good to hold on to the one and not let go of the other, because the one who fears God will be able to avoid both extremes.

The Advantages of Wisdom

¹⁹ Wisdom will help a wise person more than ten rulers can help a city. ²⁰ Certainly, there is no one so righteous on earth that he always does what is good and never sins.

²¹ Don't take everything that people say to heart, or you may hear your own servant cursing you. ²² Your conscience knows that you have cursed others many times.

²³ I used wisdom to test all of this. I said, "I want to be wise, but it is out of my reach." ²⁴ Whatever wisdom may be, it is out of reach. It is deep, very deep. Who can find out what it is? ²⁵ I turned my attention to study, to explore, and to seek out wisdom and the reason for things. I learned that wickedness is stupid and foolishness is madness.

²⁶ I find that a woman whose thoughts are ˻like˺ traps and snares is more bitter than death itself. Even her hands are ˻like˺ chains. Whoever pleases God will escape her, but she will catch whoever continues to sin.

²⁷ The spokesman said, "This is what I've found: I added one thing to another in order to find a reason for things. ²⁸ I am still seeking a reason for things, but have not found any. I found one man out of a thousand who had it, but out of all these I didn't find one woman. ²⁹ I have found only this: God made people decent, but they looked for many ways ˻to avoid being decent˺."^a

8 ¹ Who is really wise? Who knows how to explain things? Wisdom makes one's face shine, and it changes one's grim look.

The Power of Kings Versus the Power of Death

² I ˻advise˺ you to obey the king's commands because of the oath you took in God's presence. ³ Don't be in a hurry to leave the king's service. Don't take part in something evil, because he can do whatever he pleases. ⁴ Since a king's word has such power, no one can ask him what he is doing. ⁵ Whoever obeys his commands will avoid trouble. The mind of a wise person will know the right time and the right way ˻to act˺. ⁶ There is a right time and a right way ˻to act˺ in every situation. Yet, a terrible human tragedy hangs over people.

⁷ They don't know what the future will bring. So who can tell them how things will turn out? ⁸ No one has the power to prevent the spirit^a of life from leaving. No one has control over the day of his own death. There is no way to avoid the war ˻against death˺. Wickedness will not save wicked people ˻from dying˺.

Life Is Unfair

⁹ I have seen all of this, and I have carefully considered all that is done under the sun whenever one person has authority to hurt others. ¹⁰ Then I saw wicked people given an ˻honorable˺ burial. They used to go in and out of the holy place. They were praised in the city for doing such things. Even this is pointless.

The Need for Swift Justice

¹¹ When a sentence against a crime isn't carried out quickly, people are encouraged to commit crimes. ¹² A sinner may commit a hundred crimes and yet live a long life. Still, I know with certainty that it will go well for those who fear God, because they fear him. ¹³ But it will not go well for the wicked. They will not live any longer. Their lives are like shadows, because they don't fear God.

Enjoy Life

¹⁴ There is something being done on earth that is pointless. Righteous people suffer for what the wicked do, and wicked people get what the righteous deserve. I say that even this is pointless.

¹⁵ So I recommend the enjoyment ˻of life˺. People have nothing better to do under the sun than to eat, drink, and enjoy themselves. This joy will stay with them while they work hard during their brief lives which God has given them under the sun.

¹⁶ When I carefully considered how to study wisdom and how to look at the work that is done on earth (even going without sleep day and night), ¹⁷ then I saw everything that God has

---

^a 7:29 English equivalent difficult.   ^a 8:8 Or "breath."

done. No one is able to grasp the work that is done under the sun. However hard a person may search for it, he will not find ‚its meaning‚. Even though a wise person claims to know, he is not able to grasp it.

Everything Is in the Hands of God

9 ¹ Now, I have carefully thought about all this, and I explain it in this way: Righteous people and wise people, along with their accomplishments, are in God's hands. No one knows whether there will be love or hatred. ² Everything turns out the same way for everyone. All people will share the same destiny, whether they are righteous, wicked, or good, clean or unclean,ᵃ whether they offer sacrifices or don't offer sacrifices. Good people are treated like sinners. People who take oaths are treated like those who are afraid to take oaths.

Where There's Life, There's Hope

³ This is the tragedy of everything that happens under the sun: Everyone shares the same destiny. Moreover, the hearts of mortals are full of evil. Madness is in their hearts while they are still alive. After that, they join the dead. ⁴ But all who are among the living have hope, because a living dog is better than a dead lion. ⁵ The living know that they will die, but the dead don't know anything. There is no more reward for the dead when the memory of them has faded. ⁶ Their love, their hate, and their passions have already vanished. They will never again take part in anything that happens under the sun.

Enjoy Life With Your Wife

⁷ Go, enjoy eating your food, and drink your wine cheerfully, because God has already accepted what you've done. ⁸ Always wear clean clothes, and never go without lotion on your head. ⁹ Enjoy life with your wife, whom you love, during all your brief, pointless life. God has given you your pointless life under the sun. This is your lot ‚in life‚ and what you get for the hard work that you do under the sun.

Work With All Your Might

¹⁰ Whatever presents itself for you to do, do it with ‚all‚ your might, because there is no work, planning, knowledge, or skill in the grave where you're going.

Time and Unpredictable Events

¹¹ I saw something else under the sun. The race isn't ‚won‚ by fast runners, or the battle by heroes. Wise people don't necessarily have food. Intelligent people don't necessarily have riches, and skilled people don't necessarily receive special treatment. But time and unpredictable events overtake all of them. ¹² No one knows when his time will come. Like fish that are caught in a cruel net or birds caught in a snare, humans are trapped by a disaster when it suddenly strikes them.

Wisdom Is Despised

¹³ I also have seen this example of wisdom under the sun, and it made a deep impression on me. ¹⁴ There was a small town with a few soldiers in it, and a powerful king came to attack it. He surrounded it and blockaded it. ¹⁵ A poor, wise person was found in that town. He saved the town using his wisdom. But no one remembered that poor person. ¹⁶ So I said, "Wisdom is better than strength," even though that poor person's wisdom was despised, and no one listened to what he said.

¹⁷ One should pay more attention to calm words from wise people than shouting from a ruler of fools. ¹⁸ Wisdom is better than weapons of war, but one sinner can destroy much that is good.

10 ¹ Dead flies will make a bottle of perfume stink, and then it is spoiled. A little foolishness outweighs wisdom ‚and‚ honor.

Proverbs About Life in General

² A wise person's heart leads the right way. The heart of a fool leads the wrong way. ³ Even when a fool goes walking, he has no sense and shows everyone else that he's a fool.

⁴ If a ruler becomes angry with you, don't resign your position. If you remain calm, you can make up for serious offenses.

⁵ There is a tragedy that I've seen under the sun, an error often made by rulers. ⁶ Foolish people are often given high positions, and rich people are left to fill lower positions. ⁷ I have seen slaves sitting on horses and influential people going on foot like slaves.

ᵃ 9:2 "Clean" refers to anything that Moses' Teachings say is presentable to God. "Unclean" refers to anything that Moses' Teachings say is not presentable to God.

⁸Whoever digs a pit may fall into it. Whoever breaks through a stone wall may be bitten by a snake. ⁹Whoever works in a stone quarry may get hurt. Whoever splits wood may be injured.

¹⁰If an ax is blunt and the edge isn't sharpened, then one has to use more strength. But wisdom prepares the way for success. ¹¹If a snake bites before it has been charmed, then there is no advantage in being a snake charmer.

¹²A wise person's words win favors, but a fool's lips are self-destructive. ¹³A fool starts out by talking foolishness and ends up saying crazy things that are dangerous. ¹⁴He never stops talking. No one knows what the future will bring, or what will happen after ˌdeathˌ. Who can say! ¹⁵Fools wear themselves out with hard work, because they don't even know the way to town.

¹⁶How horrible it will be for any country where the king used to be a servant and where the high officials throw parties in the morning. ¹⁷A country is blessed when the king is from a noble family and when the high officials eat at the right time in order to get strength and not to get drunk.

¹⁸A roof sags because of laziness. A house leaks because of idle hands.

¹⁹A meal is made for laughter, and wine makes life pleasant, but money is the answer for everything.

²⁰Don't curse the king even in your thoughts, and don't curse rich people even in your bedroom. A bird may carry your words, or some winged creature may repeat what you say.

Live Boldly

11 ¹Throw your bread on the surface of the water, because you will find it again after many days.

²Divide what you have into seven parts, or even into eight, because you don't know what disaster may happen on earth.

³If the clouds are full of rain, they will let it pour down on the earth. If a tree falls north or south, the tree will remain where it fell.

⁴Whoever watches the wind will never plant. Whoever looks at the clouds will never harvest. ⁵Just as you don't know how the breath of life enters the limbs of a child within its mother's womb, you also don't understand how God, who made everything, works.

⁶Plant your seed in the morning, and don't let your hands rest until evening. You don't know whether this field or that field will be profitable or whether both of them will ˌturn outˌ equally well.

⁷Light is sweet, and it is good for one's eyes to see the sun. ⁸Even though people may live for many years, they should enjoy every one of them. But they should also remember there will be many dark days. Everything that is coming is pointless.

Remember Your Creator While You're Young

⁹You young people should enjoy yourselves while you're young. You should let your hearts make you happy when you're young. Follow wherever your heart leads you and whatever your eyes see. But realize that God will make you give an account for all these things when he judges everyone. ¹⁰Get rid of what troubles you or wears down your body, because childhood and youth are pointless.

12 ¹Remember your Creator when you are young,
   before the days of trouble come
      and the years catch up with you.
         They will make you say,
           "I have found no pleasure in them."

² Remember your Creator before the sun, the light, the moon,
    and the stars turn dark, ˌandˌ the clouds come back with rain.

³ Remember your Creator when those who guard the house tremble,
    strong men are stooped over,
      the women at the mill stop grinding
        because there are so few of them,
         ˌandˌ those who look out of the windows
           see a dim light.

⁴ Remember your Creator when the doors to the street are closed,
    the sound of the mill is muffled,
      you are startled at the sound of a bird,
        ˌandˌ those who sing songs become quiet.

⁵ Remember your Creator when someone is afraid of heights
    and of dangers along the road,
      the almond tree blossoms,

the grasshopper drags itself along,
‚and‚ the caper bush has ‚no‚ fruit.
Mortals go to their eternal rest, and mourners go out in the streets.

⁶ Remember your Creator before the silver cord is snapped,
the golden bowl is broken,
the pitcher is smashed near the spring,
and the water wheel is broken at the cistern.

⁷ Then the dust ‚of mortals‚ goes back to the ground as it was before,
and the breath of life goes back to God who gave it.

⁸ "Absolutely pointless!" says the spokesman. "Everything is pointless!"

Lifelong Duty—Fear God and Keep His Commands

⁹ Besides being wise, the spokesman also taught the people what he knew. He very carefully thought about it, studied it, and arranged it in many proverbs. ¹⁰ The spokesman tried to find just the right words. He wrote the words of truth very carefully.

¹¹ Words from wise people are like spurs. Their collected sayings are like nails that have been driven in firmly. They come from one shepherd. ¹² Be warned, my children, against anything more than these. People never stop writing books. Too much studying will wear out your body. ¹³ After having heard it all, this is the conclusion: Fear God, and keep his commands, because this applies to everyone. ¹⁴ God will certainly judge everything that is done. This includes every secret thing, whether it is good or bad.

SONG OF SONGS

1 [1] The most beautiful song of Solomon.

The Young Woman Arrives in Solomon's Palace

[Bride]
[2] Let him kiss me with the kisses of his mouth.
        Your expressions of love are better than wine,
[3]   better than the fragrance of cologne.
                (Cologne should be named after you.)
        No wonder the young women love you!
[4]   Take me with you. Let's run away.
        The king has brought me into his private rooms.

[The chorus of young women]
        We will celebrate and rejoice with you.
        We will praise your expressions of love more than wine.
        How right it is that the young women love you!

[Bride]
[5]   Young women of Jerusalem, I am dark and lovely
            like Kedar's tents,
            like Solomon's curtains.
[6]   Stop staring at me because I am so dark.
            The sun has tanned me.
        My brothers were angry with me.
        They made me the caretaker of the vineyards.
            I have not even taken care of my own vineyard.
[7]   Please tell me, you whom I love, where do you graze your flock?
        Where does your flock lie down at noon?
        ⌞Tell me,⌟ or I will be considered a prostitute
            ⌞wandering⌟ among the flocks of your companions.

[The chorus of young women]
[8]   If you do not know, most beautiful of women,
            follow the tracks of the flocks,
                and graze your young goats near the shepherds' tents.

Solomon Searches for the Young Woman's Love

[Groom]
[9]   My true love, I compare you to a mare among Pharaoh's stallions.
[10]   Your cheeks are lovely with ornaments,
            your neck with strings of pearls.

[The chorus of young women]
[11] We will make gold ornaments with silver beads for you.

[Bride]
[12]   While the king is at his table,
            my perfume fills the air with its fragrance.
[13] My beloved is a pouch of myrrh[a]
            that lies at night between my breasts.
[14] My beloved is a bouquet of henna flowers
            in the vineyards of En Gedi.

---

[a] 1:13 Myrrh is a fragrant resin used for perfumes, embalming, and deodorizers.

[Groom]
15   Look at you! You are beautiful, my true love!
      Look at you! You are so beautiful!
          Your eyes are like doves!

[Bride]
16   Look at you! You are handsome, my beloved, so pleasing to me!
          The leaf-scattered ground will be our couch.
17   The cedars will be the walls of our house.
          The cypress trees will be our rafters.

2 1   I am a rose of Sharon,
          a lily ˎgrowingˏ in the valleys.

[Groom]
2   Like a lily among thorns,
          so is my true love among the young women.

[Bride]
3   Like an apple tree among the trees in the forest,
          so is my beloved among the young men.
              I want to sit in his shadow.
                  His fruit tastes sweet to me.
4   He leads me into a banquet room
          and looks at me with love.
5   Strengthen me with raisins
                  and refresh me with apples
                      because I am weak from love.
6   His left hand is under my head.
      His right hand caresses me.

7   Young women of Jerusalem, swear to me
          by the gazelles
              or by the does in the field
                  that you will not awaken love
                      or arouse love before its proper time.

The Young Woman Remembers One Spring Day With Her Beloved

[Bride]
8   I hear my beloved's voice.
      Look! Here he comes,
          sprinting over the mountains,
          racing over the hills.
9   My beloved is like a gazelle or a young stag.
      Look! There he stands behind our wall,
          peeking through the window,
          looking through the lattice.
10   My beloved said to me,
      "Get up, my true love, my beautiful one, and come with me.
11   Look! The winter is past.
          The rain is over and gone.
12   Blossoms appear in the land.
          The time of the songbird has arrived.
          The cooing of the mourning dove is heard in our land.
13   The green figs ripen.
          The grapevines bloom and give off a fragrance.
      Get up, my true love, my beautiful one, and come with me.
14   My dove, in the hiding places of the rocky crevices,
              in the secret places of the cliffs,
          let me see your figure and hear your voice.
          Your voice is sweet, and your figure is lovely."

15   Catch the foxes for us,
          the little foxes that ruin vineyards.
              Our vineyards are blooming.

16 My beloved is mine, and I am his.
    He is the one who grazes his flock among the lilies.
17 When the day brings a cooling breeze and the shadows flee,
        turn around, my beloved.
            Run like a gazelle or a young stag
                on the mountains that separate us!

The Young Woman Dreams About Searching for Her Beloved

[Bride]

3 1 Night after night on my bed
          I looked for the one I love.
        I looked for him but did not find him.
     2   I will get up now and roam around the city,
                in the streets, and in the squares.
            I will look for the one I love.
            I looked for him but did not find him.
     3 The watchmen making their rounds in the city found me.
            ⌞I asked,⌟ "Have you seen the one I love?"
     4 I had just left them when I found the one I love.
        I held on to him and would not let him go
            until I had brought him into my mother's house,
                into the bedroom of the one who conceived me.

     5 Young women of Jerusalem, swear to me
            by the gazelles
                or by the does in the field,
                    that you will not awaken love
                        or arouse love before its proper time.

A Description of the Royal Procession

[The chorus of young women]
     6   Who is this young woman coming up from the wilderness
                like clouds of smoke?
                    She is perfumed with myrrh and incense
                        made from the merchants' scented powders.
     7 Look! Solomon's sedan chair!ᵃ
        Sixty soldiers from the army of Israel surround it.
     8   All of them are skilled in using swords,
                experienced in combat.
            Each one has his sword at his side
                and guards against the terrors of the night.
     9 King Solomon had a carriage made for himselfᵇ
            from the wood of Lebanon.
    10 He had its posts made out of silver,
            its top out of gold,
            its seat out of purple fabric.
        Its inside—with inlaid scenes of love—
            was made by the young women of Jerusalem.
    11 Young women of Zion, come out and look at King Solomon!
            Look at his crown,
                the crown his mother placed on him on his wedding day,
                    his day of joyful delight.

Solomon Is Charmed by the Young Woman

[Groom]

4 1 Look at you! You are beautiful, my true love.
        Look at you! You are so beautiful.
            Your eyes behind your veil are like doves.
            Your hair is like a flock of goats moving down Mount Gilead.

ᵃ 3:7 A sedan chair is a portable chair for carrying a person of high position.   ᵇ 3:9 English equivalent of this phrase difficult.

2   Your teeth are like a flock of sheep about to be sheared,
         sheep that come up from the washing.
            All of them bear twins, and not one has lost its young.

3   Your lips are like scarlet thread.
     Your mouth is lovely.
     Your temples behind your veil are like slices of pomegranate.

4   Your neck is like David's beautifully-designed[a] tower.
         A thousand round shields belonging to soldiers
            are hung on it.

5   Your breasts are like two fawns,
         like twin gazelles grazing among the lilies.

6   When the day brings a cool breeze and the shadows flee,
     I will go to the mountain of myrrh and the hill of incense.

7   You are beautiful in every way, my true love.
         There is no blemish on you.

8   You will come with me from Lebanon,
         from Lebanon as my bride.
     You will travel with me
         from the peak of Mount Amana,
         from the mountain peaks in Senir and Hermon,
         from the lairs of lions,
         from the mountains of leopards.

9   My bride, my sister, you have charmed me.[b]
     You have charmed me
         with a single glance from your eyes,
         with a single strand of your necklace.

10   How beautiful are your expressions of love, my bride, my sister!
     How much better are your expressions of love than wine
         and the fragrance of your perfume than any spice.

11   Your lips drip honey, my bride.
         Honey and milk are under your tongue.
            The fragrance of your clothing is like the fragrance of Lebanon.

12   My bride, my sister is a garden that is locked,
         a garden that is locked,
         a spring that is sealed.

13   You are paradise that produces
         pomegranates and the best fruits,
         henna flowers and nard,

14   nard and saffron,
         calamus,[c] cinnamon, and all kinds of incense,[d]
         myrrh, aloes, and all the best spices.

15   ˌYou areˌ a spring for gardens,
         a well of living water flowing from Lebanon.

[Bride]
16   Awake, north wind!
     Come, south wind!
     Blow on my garden!
         Let its spices flow from it.
            Let my beloved come to his garden,
               and let him eat his own precious fruit.

[Groom]
5 1 My bride, my sister, I will come to my garden.
      I will gather my myrrh with my spice.
      I will eat my honeycomb with my honey.
      I will drink my wine with my milk.
          Eat, my friends!
          Drink and become intoxicated with expressions of love!

---

[a] 4:4 Hebrew meaning of "beautifully-designed" uncertain.   [b] 4:9 "Brother" and "sister" are terms of endearment between lovers in ancient Near Eastern literature.   [c] 4:14 Calamus is a sweet-smelling spice.   [d] 4:14 Or "incense-producing trees."

The Young Woman Dreams of Marriage With Her Husband

[Bride]
² I sleep, but my mind is awake.
Listen! My beloved is knocking.

[Groom]
Open to me, my true love, my sister,
my dove, my perfect one.
My head is wet with dew,
my hair with the dewdrops of night.

[Bride]
³ I have taken off my clothes! Why should I put them on ˎagainˎ?
I have washed my feet! Why should I get them dirty ˎagainˎ?
⁴ My beloved put his hand through the keyhole.
My heart throbbed for him.
⁵ I got up to open for my beloved.
My hands dripped with myrrh,
and my fingers were drenched with liquid myrrh,
on the handles of the lock.
⁶ I opened for my beloved,
but my beloved had turned away. He was gone!
I almost died when he left.
I looked for him, but I did not find him.
I called for him, but he did not answer me.
⁷ The watchmen making their rounds in the city found me.
They struck me!
They wounded me!
Those watchmen on the walls took my robe from me!

⁸ Young women of Jerusalem, swear to me
that if you find my beloved
you will tell him I am hopelessly lovesick.

[The chorus of young women]
⁹ Most beautiful of women,
what makes your beloved better than any other beloved?
What makes your beloved better than any other beloved
that you make us swear this way?

[Bride]
¹⁰ My beloved is dazzling yet ruddy.
He stands out among 10,000 men.
¹¹ His head is the finest gold.
His hair is wavy, black as a raven.
¹² His eyes are set like doves bathing in milk.
¹³ His cheeks are like a garden of spices,
a garden that produces scented herbs.
His lips are lilies that drip with myrrh.
¹⁴ His hands are disks of gold set with emerald.
His chest is a block of ivory covered with sapphires.
¹⁵ His legs are columns of marble set on bases of pure gold.
His form is like Lebanon, choice as the cedars.
¹⁶ His mouth is sweet in every way.
Everything about him is desirable!
This is my beloved, and this is my friend, young women of Jerusalem.

[The chorus of young women]
6 ¹ Where did your beloved go, most beautiful of women?
Where did your beloved turn?
We will look for him with you.

[Bride]
² My beloved went to his garden,
to the beds of spices,
to graze his flock in the gardens and gather lilies.

3   I am my beloved's, and my beloved is mine.
      He is the one who grazes his flock among the lilies.

Solomon Desires the Young Woman More Than the Rest of His Wives

[Groom]
4   You are beautiful, my true love, like Tirzah,
          lovely like Jerusalem,
              awe-inspiring like those great cities.[a]
5   Turn your eyes away from me. They enchant me!

          Your hair is like a flock of goats moving down from Gilead.
6   Your teeth are like a flock of sheep,
              sheep that come up from the washing.
                  All of them bear twins, and not one has lost its young.
7   Your temples behind your veil are like slices of pomegranate.

8   There are 60 queens, 80 concubines,[b] and countless virgins,
9   but she is unique, my dove, my perfect one.
              Her mother thinks she is unique.
              She is pure to the one who gave birth to her.
      Her sisters saw her and blessed her.
      Queens and concubines saw her and praised her.

The Young Woman's Home in Shulam

[The chorus of young women]
10   Who is this young woman?
          She looks like the dawn.
          She is beautiful like the moon,
              pure like the sun,
                  awe-inspiring like those heavenly bodies.

[Bride]
11   I went to the walnut grove
          to look at the blossoms in the valley,
          to see if the grapevine had budded
              and if the pomegranates were in bloom.
12   I did not know that I had become
          like the chariots of my noble people.[c]

[The chorus of young women]
13   Come back! Come back, young woman from Shulam!
      Come back! Come back so that we may look at you!

[Bride]
      Why do you look at me, the young woman from Shulam,
          as you look at the dance of Mahanaim?

[The chorus of young women]
7[a] 1   How beautiful are your feet in their sandals, noble daughter!
      The curves of your thighs are like ornaments,
          like the work of an artist's hands.
2   Your navel is a round bowl.
          May it always be filled with spiced wine.
      Your waist is a bundle of wheat enclosed in lilies.
3   Your breasts are like two fawns,
          twins of a gazelle.
4   Your neck is like an ivory tower.
      Your eyes are like pools in Heshbon, pools by the gate of Bath Rabbim.
      Your nose is like a Lebanese tower facing Damascus.
5   You hold your head as high as Mount Carmel.
      Your dangling curls are royal beauty.
      Your flowing locks could hold a king captive.

---

[a] 6:4 Or "awe-inspiring as an army with flags."   [b] 6:8 A concubine is considered a wife except she has fewer rights under the law.   [c] 6:12 Song of Songs 6:13 in English Bibles is Song of Songs 7:1 in the Hebrew Bible.   [a] 7:1 Song of Songs 7:1–13 in English Bibles is Song of Songs 7:2–14 in the Hebrew Bible.

Solomon Longs for the Young Woman's Affection

[Groom]
6 How beautiful and charming you are, my love, with your elegance.
7 Young woman,
     your figure is like a palm tree,
       and your breasts are like its clusters.
8 I thought, "I will climb the palm tree
   and take hold of its fruit."
May your breasts be like clusters on the vine.
     May the fragrance of your breath be like apples.
9   May your mouth taste like the best wine . . .

[Bride]
     . . . that goes down smoothly to my beloved
       and glides over the lips of those about to sleep.*b*
10 I am my beloved's, and he longs for me.
11 Come, my beloved.
     Let's go into the field.
     Let's spend the night among the henna flowers.*c*
12   Let's go to the vineyards early.
     Let's see if the vines have budded,
       if the grape blossoms have opened,
       if the pomegranates are in bloom.
There I will give you my love.
13 The mandrakes*d* give off a fragrance,
     and at our door are all kinds of precious fruits.
I have saved new and old things
     for you alone, my beloved.

8 1 If only you were my brother,
     one who nursed at my mother's breasts.
If I saw you on the street,
     I would kiss you, and no one would look down on me.
2 I would lead you.
I would bring you into my mother's house.
     (She is the one who was my teacher.)
I would give you some spiced wine to drink,
     some juice squeezed from my pomegranates.
3 His left hand is under my head.
His right hand caresses me.

4 Young women of Jerusalem, swear to me
     that you will not awaken love
       or arouse love before its proper time!

The Young Woman's Love for Her Beloved

[The chorus of young women]
5 Who is this young woman coming from the wilderness
     with her arm around her beloved?

[Bride]
     Under the apple tree I woke you up.
     There your mother went into labor with you.
       There she went into labor
       and gave birth to you!
6 Wear me as a signet ring on your heart,
     as a ring on your hand.
Love is as overpowering as death.
Devotion is as unyielding as the grave.
     Love's flames are flames of fire,
       flames that come from the LORD.

---

b 7:9 Or "flowing gently over lips and teeth."   *c* 7:11 Or "in the villages."   *d* 7:13 Mandrakes were thought to stimulate sexual desire.

7 Raging water cannot extinguish love,
and rivers will never wash it away.
If a man exchanged all his family's wealth for love,
people would utterly despise him.

The Young Woman With Her Family and Her Beloved

[The brothers]
8 We have a little sister, and she has no breasts.
What will we do for our sister on the day she becomes engaged?
9 If she is a wall, we will build a silver barrier around her.
If she is a door, we will barricade her with cedar boards.

[Bride]
10 I am a wall, and my breasts are like towers.
So he considers me to be one who has found peace.[a]
11 Solomon had a vineyard at Baal Hamon.
He entrusted that vineyard to caretakers.
Each one was to bring 25 pounds of silver
in exchange for its fruit.
12 My own vineyard is in front of me.
That 25 pounds is yours, Solomon,
and 5 pounds go to those who take care of its fruit.

[Groom]
13 Young woman living in the gardens,
while your friends are listening to your voice,
let me hear. . . .

[Bride]
14 Come away quickly, my beloved.
Run like a gazelle or a young stag
on the mountains of spices.

---

[a] 8:10 In Hebrew there is a play on the words "peace" (*shalom*), "Solomon" (*Shlomo*), and "the young woman from Shulam" (*Shulamith*).

ISAIAH

1 ¹This is the vision which Isaiah, son of Amoz, saw about Judah and Jerusalem at the time of Kings Uzziah, Jotham, Ahaz, and Hezekiah.

The LORD Accuses Israel of Sin

² Listen, heaven, and pay attention, earth!
    The LORD has spoken,
       "I raised ˻my˼ children and helped them grow,
         but they have rebelled against me.
³ Oxen know their owners,
    and donkeys know where their masters feed them.
    But Israel doesn't know ˻its owner˼.
    My people don't understand ˻who feeds them˼.
⁴ "How horrible it will be for a nation that sins.
    ˻Its˼ people are loaded down with guilt.
      They are descendants of evildoers
        and destructive children.
    They have abandoned the LORD.
    They have despised the Holy One of Israel.
    They have turned their backs on him.
⁵ "Why do you still want to be beaten?
    Why do you continue to rebel?
      Your whole head is infected.
      Your whole heart is failing.
⁶ From the bottom of your feet to the top of your head
      there is no healthy spot left on your ˻body˼—
        only bruises, sores, and fresh wounds.
          They haven't been cleansed, bandaged,
           or soothed with oil.

⁷ "Your country is devastated.
    Your cities are burned down.
    Your fields are destroyed right before your eyes by foreigners.
      Your fields are devastated and taken over by foreigners.
⁸ My people Zion are left like a hut in a vineyard,
    like a shack in a cucumber field,
    like a city under attack."

⁹ If the LORD of Armies hadn't left us a few survivors,
    we would have been like Sodom and Gomorrah.

Israel's Corrupt Religion

¹⁰ Listen to the word of the LORD, you rulers of Sodom!
    Pay attention to the teachings from our God, you people of Gomorrah!
¹¹ The LORD asks, "What do your many animal sacrifices mean to me?
    I've had enough of your burnt offerings of rams
      and enough fat from your fattened calves.
    I'm not pleased with the blood of bulls, lambs, or male goats.
¹² When you appear in my presence,
    who asked you to trample on my courtyards?
¹³ Don't bring any more worthless grain offerings.
    Your incense is disgusting to me,
      so are your New Moon Festivals, your days of worship,
        and the assemblies you call.
    I can't stand your evil assemblies.
¹⁴ I hate your New Moon Festivals and your appointed festivals.
    They've become a burden to me,
      and I'm tired of putting up with them.
¹⁵ So when you stretch out your hands ˻in prayer˼,

I will turn my eyes away from you.
Even though you offer many prayers,
    I will not listen because your hands are covered with blood.

The LORD Invites Israel to Turn Away From Sin

16 "Wash yourselves! Become clean!
Get your evil deeds out of my sight.
Stop doing evil.
17 Learn to do good.
Seek justice.
Arrest oppressors.
Defend orphans.
Plead the case of widows."

18 "Come on now, let's discuss this!" says the LORD.
"Though your sins are bright red,
    they will become as white as snow.
Though they are dark red,
    they will become as white as wool.
19 If you are willing and obedient,
    you will eat the best from the land.
20 But if you refuse and rebel,
    you will be destroyed by swords."
The LORD has spoken.

Jerusalem's Future

21 How the faithful town has become a prostitute!
She was full of justice,
    and righteousness lived in her.
        But now murderers live there!
22 Your silver is not pure.
Your wine is watered down.
23 Your rulers are rebels, friends with thieves.
They all love bribes and run after gifts.
They never defend orphans.
They don't notice the widows' pleas.

24 That's why the Lord, the LORD of Armies, the Mighty One of Israel, says,

"How horrible it will be when I take revenge on my opponents!
I will avenge myself against my enemies.
25 I will turn my power against you.
I will remove your impurities with bleach.
I will get rid of all your impurities.
26 I will give you judges like you had long ago,
    advisers like you had in the beginning.
After that you will be called the Righteous City,
    the Faithful Town."

27 Zion will be pardoned by ˎthe LORD'sˏ justice,
    and those who return will be pardoned
        by ˎthe LORD'sˏ righteousness.
28 Rebels and sinners will be crushed at the same time,
    and those who abandon the LORD will come to an end.
29 You will be ashamed of the oaks that you wanted to worship
    and embarrassed by the garden that you have chosen for your gods.
30 You will be like an oak whose leaves wither
    and like a garden without water.
31 Strong people will become tinder for a fire,
    and their work will be the spark.
Both of them will burn together,
    and there will be no one to put out the fire.

The LORD Will Teach the Nations—Micah 4:1–3

2 ¹ This is the message which Isaiah, son of Amoz, saw about Judah and Jerusalem.

2 In the last days the mountain of the LORD's house
    will be established as the highest of the mountains
        and raised above the hills.

All the nations will stream to it.
3 Then many people will come and say,
  "Let's go to the mountain of the LORD,
    to the house of the God of Jacob.
      He will teach us his ways so that we may live by them."
  The teachings will go out from Zion.
  The word of the LORD will go out from Jerusalem.
4   Then he will judge disputes between nations
    and settle arguments between many people.
  They will hammer their swords into plowblades
    and their spears into pruning shears.
  Nations will never fight against each other,
    and they will never train for war again.
5 Come, descendants of Jacob,
  let's live in the light of the LORD.

Israel's Sins

6 LORD, you have abandoned your people, the descendants of Jacob,
  because they are filled with Eastern influences.
    They are fortunetellers like the Philistines,
      and they make deals with foreigners.
7   Their land is filled with silver and gold,
    and there is no end to their treasures.
  Their land is filled with horses,
    and there is no end to their chariots.
8   Their land is filled with idols,
    and they worship what their hands have shaped
      and what their fingers have molded.
9 People will be brought down. Everyone will be humbled.
  Do not forgive them.
10 Go in among the rocks and hide underground
  because of the LORD's terrifying presence
    and the honor of his majesty.
11 The eyes of arrogant people will be humbled.
  High and mighty people will be brought down.
    On that day the LORD alone will be honored.

The Day of the LORD's Judgment

12 The LORD of Armies will have his day
    against all who are arrogant and conceited
      and all who are proud of themselves (they will be humbled),
13   against all the towering and mighty cedars of Lebanon
    and all the oaks of Bashan,
14   against all the high mountains
    and all the lofty hills,
15   against every high tower
    and every fortified wall,
16   against all the large ships of Tarshish
    and all the beautiful boats.

17 Then arrogant people will be brought down,
  and high and mighty people will be humbled.
    On that day the LORD alone will be honored.
18   Then idols will disappear completely.
19 People will go into caves in the rocks
  and into holes in the ground
    because of the LORD's terrifying presence
      and the honor of his majesty
        when he rises to terrify the earth.
20 On that day people will throw to the moles and the bats
  the silver and gold idols that they made
    for themselves to worship.
21 They will go into caves in the rocks
  and into cracks in the cliffs
    because of the LORD's terrifying presence
      and the honor of his majesty
        when he rises to terrify the earth.

²² Stop trusting people.
Their life is in their nostrils.
How can they be worth anything?

The LORD's Judgment on Sinners in Zion

3 ¹ See now, the Lord, the LORD of Armies,
is going to take from Jerusalem and Judah
every kind of support
and their entire supply of food and water.
² ⸢He will take their⸣ heroes and soldiers,
judges and prophets,
fortunetellers and statesmen,
³ military leaders and civilian leaders,
counselors, skilled workers, and experts in magic.

⁴ "I will make boys their leaders.
Children will govern them."

⁵ People will oppress each other,
and everyone will oppress his neighbor.
The young will make fun of the old,
and common people will make fun of their superiors.
⁶ A person will grab one of his relatives
from his father's family and say,
"You have a coat.
You'll be our leader.
This pile of ruins will be under your control."
⁷ When that day comes the relative will cry out,
"I'm not a doctor!
I don't have any food or a coat in my home.
Don't make me a leader of our family."

⁸ Jerusalem has stumbled, and Judah has fallen,
because what they say and what they do is against the LORD.
They are defiant in his honored presence.
⁹ The look on their faces will be held against them.
They boast about their sins,
which are like ⸢those of the people of⸣ Sodom.
They don't even bother to hide them.
How horrible it will be for these people,
because they have brought disaster on themselves.

¹⁰ Tell the righteous that blessings will come to them.
They will taste the fruit of their labor.

¹¹ How horrible it will be for the wicked! Disaster will strike them.
What they have done will be done to them.
¹² "Children will oppress my people.
Women will rule them.
My people, your guides mislead you,
and you don't know which way to go."
¹³ The LORD takes his place in the courtroom.
He stands to judge his people.
¹⁴ The LORD presents his case to the respected leaders
and the officials of his people:
"You have burned down the vineyard!
Your houses are filled with goods stolen from the poor."
¹⁵ The Almighty LORD of Armies asks,
"How can you crush my people
and grind the faces of the poor ⸢into the ground⸣?"
¹⁶ The LORD adds,
"The women of Zion are arrogant.
They walk with their noses in the air,
making seductive glances,
taking short little steps,
jingling the ankle bracelets on their feet."
¹⁷ The Lord will cause sores ⸢to appear⸣
on the heads of the women of Zion,
and the LORD will make their foreheads bare.

[18] On that day the Lord will take away their fine things: jingling anklets, headbands, crescent-shaped necklaces, [19] pendants, bracelets, scarfs, [20] hats, ankle bracelets, blouses, perfume boxes, charms, [21] signet rings, nose rings, [22] fine robes, coats, shawls, purses, [23] mirrors, underwear, headdresses, and veils.

[24]   Instead of the smell of perfume, there will be the smell of decay.
        They will wear ropes instead of belts.
        They will have bald heads instead of beautiful hair.
        They will wear sackcloth instead of expensive clothes.
            Their beauty will be scarred.[a]
[25]   ˌWomen,ˌ your warriors will die in combat.
        Your mighty men will die in battle.
[26]   The gates of Zion will cry and grieve,
        and Zion will sit on the ground, exhausted.

4 [1]   When that day comes, seven women will grab one man and say,
        "We'll eat our own food and provide our own clothes.
            Just let us marry you for your name.
            Take away our disgrace."

The LORD's New Glory for Zion
[2]   When that day comes, the branch of the LORD
        will be beautiful and wonderful.
            The fruit of the land
            will be the pride and joy of Israel's survivors.

[3] Then whoever is left in Zion and whoever remains in Jerusalem will be called holy, everyone who is recorded among the living in Jerusalem. [4] The Lord will wash away the filth of Zion's people.[a] He will clean bloodstains from Jerusalem with a spirit of judgment and a spirit of burning. [5] The LORD will create a cloud of smoke during the day and a glowing flame of fire during the night over the whole area of Mount Zion and over the assembly. His glory will cover everything. [6] It will be a shelter from the heat during the day as well as a refuge and hiding place from storms and rain.

The Song About the Vineyard
5 [1] Let me sing a lovesong to my beloved about his vineyard:

        My beloved had a vineyard on a fertile hill.
[2]   He dug it up, removed its stones,
            planted it with the choicest vines,
                built a watchtower in it,
                and made a winepress in it.
            Then he waited for it to produce good grapes,
            but it produced only sour, wild grapes.

[3]   Now then, you inhabitants of Jerusalem and Judah,
        judge between me and my vineyard!
[4]   What more could have been done for my vineyard
        than what I have already done for it?
      When I waited for it to produce good grapes,
        why did it produce only sour, wild grapes?

[5]   Now then, let me tell you what I will do to my vineyard.
        I will tear away its hedge so that it can be devoured
        and tear down its wall so that it can be trampled.
[6]   I will make it a wasteland.
        It will never be pruned or hoed.
            Thorns and weeds will grow in it,
                and I will command the clouds not to rain on it.

[7]   The vineyard of the LORD of Armies is the nation of Israel,
        and the people of Judah are the garden of his delight.
      He hoped for justice but saw only slaughter,
        for righteousness but heard only cries of distress.

---

[a] 3:24 Dead Sea Scrolls; Masoretic Text "expensive clothes, instead of beauty."   [a] 4:4 Or "Zion's women."

Six Sins Condemned

⁸ How horrible it will be for you
who acquire house after house and buy field after field
until there's nothing left
and you have to live by yourself in the land.

⁹ With my own ears I heard the LORD of Armies say,
"Many houses will become empty.
Large, beautiful houses will be without people to live in them.
¹⁰ A ten-acre vineyard will produce only six gallons of wine,
and two quarts of seed will produce only four quarts of grain."

¹¹ How horrible it will be for those
who get up early to look for a drink,
who sit up late until they are drunk from wine.
¹² At their feasts there are lyres and harps,
tambourines and flutes, and wine.
Yet, they don't pay attention to what the LORD is doing
or see what his hands have done.

¹³ "My people will go into exile
because they don't understand what I'm doing.
Honored men will starve,
and common people will be parched with thirst."
¹⁴ That is why the grave's appetite increases.
It opens its mouth very wide
so that honored people and common people will go down into it.
Those who are noisy and joyous will go down into it.
¹⁵ People will be brought down. Everyone will be humbled.
And the eyes of arrogant people will be humbled.
¹⁶ The LORD of Armies will be honored when he judges.
The holy God will show himself to be holy when he does what is right.
¹⁷ Then lambs will graze as if they were in their own pasture,
and foreigners will eat among the ruins of the rich.

¹⁸ How horrible it will be for those
who string people along with lies and empty promises,
whose lives are sinful.
¹⁹ They say,
"Let God hurry and quickly do his work
so that we may see what he has in mind.
Let the plan of the Holy One of Israel happen quickly
so that we may understand what he is doing."

²⁰ How horrible it will be for those
who call evil good and good evil,
who turn darkness into light and light into darkness,
who turn what is bitter into something sweet
and what is sweet into something bitter.

²¹ How horrible it will be for those
who think they are wise
and consider themselves to be clever.

²² How horrible it will be for those
who are heroes at drinking wine,
who are champions at mixing drinks,
²³ who declare the guilty innocent for a bribe,
who take away the rights of righteous people.

The LORD Will Use Another Nation to Punish His People

²⁴ As flames burn up straw
and dry grass shrivels in flames,
so their roots will rot,
and their blossoms will blow away like dust.
They have rejected the teachings of the LORD of Armies
and have despised the word of the Holy One of Israel.

²⁵ That's why the anger of the LORD burns hot against his people,
and he is ready to use his power to strike them down.

The hills tremble,
and dead bodies lie like garbage in the streets.

Even after all this, his anger has not disappeared,
and he is still ready to use his power.

26 The LORD raises up a flag for the nations far away.
With a whistle he signals those at the ends of the earth.
Look, they are coming very quickly!
27 None of them grow tired or stumble.
None of them slumber or sleep.
The belts on their waists aren't loose
or their sandal straps broken.
28 Their arrows are sharpened; all their bows are ready to shoot.
Their horses' hoofs are as hard as flint.
Their chariot wheels are as quick as the wind.
29 They roar like a lioness.
They growl like a young lion.
They growl as they snatch their prey
and carry it off to where no one can rescue it.
30 On that day they will roar over their prey
as the sea roars.
If they look at the land,
they will see only darkness and distress.
Even the light will be darkened by thick clouds.

Isaiah Is Sent With a Message for the LORD's People

6 ¹ In the year King Uzziah died, I saw the Lord sitting on a high and lofty throne. The bottom of his robe filled the temple. ² Angels[a] were standing above him. Each had six wings: With two they covered their faces, with two they covered their feet, and with two they flew. ³ They called to each other and said,

"Holy, holy, holy is the LORD of Armies!
The whole earth is filled with his glory."

⁴ Their voices shook the foundations of the doorposts, and the temple filled with smoke. ⁵ So I said, "Oh, no!

I'm doomed.
Every word that passes through my lips is sinful.
I live among people with sinful lips.
I have seen the king, the LORD of Armies!"

⁶ Then one of the angels flew to me. In his hand was a burning coal that he had taken from the altar with tongs. ⁷ He touched my mouth with it and said, "This has touched your lips. Your guilt has been taken away, and your sin has been forgiven."
⁸ Then I heard the voice of the Lord, saying, "Whom will I send? Who will go for us?"
I said, "Here I am. Send me!"
⁹ And he said, "Go and tell these people,

'No matter how closely you listen, you'll never understand.
No matter how closely you look, you'll never see.'
10 Make these people close-minded.
Plug their ears.
Shut their eyes.
Otherwise, they may see with their eyes,
hear with their ears,
understand with their minds,
and return and be healed."

¹¹ I asked, "How long, O Lord?"
And he replied,

"Until the cities lie in ruins with no one living in them,
the houses have no people,
and the land is completely desolate.
12 The LORD will send his people far away,
and a large area in the middle of the land will be abandoned.

ᵃ 6:2 Or "Seraphim."

¹³ Even if one out of ten people is left in it,
    the land will be burned again.
      When a sacred oak or an oak is cut down, a stump is left.
      The holy seed will be the land's stump."

The Virgin Will Have a Child

7 ¹ When Ahaz, son of Jotham and grandson of Uzziah, was king of Judah, Aram's King Rezin and Israel's King Pekah, son of Remaliah, went to Jerusalem to attack it, but they couldn't defeat it. ² When word reached David's family that the Arameans had made an alliance with Ephraim, the hearts of the king and his people were shaken as the trees of the forest are shaken by the wind.

³ Then the LORD said to Isaiah, "Go out with your son Shear Jashub to meet Ahaz at the end of the ditch of the Upper Pool on the road to the Laundryman's Field. ⁴ Say to him, 'Be careful, stay calm, and don't be afraid. Don't lose heart because of the fierce anger of Rezin from Aram and Remaliah's son. These two are smoldering logs.' ⁵ Aram, Ephraim, and Remaliah's son have planned evil against you, saying, ⁶ 'Let's march against Judah, tear it apart, divide it among ourselves, and set up Tabeel's son as its king.' ⁷ This is what the Almighty LORD says:

    It won't take place; it won't happen.
⁸   The capital of Aram is Damascus,
    and the leader of Damascus is Rezin.
      Ephraim will be shattered within 65 years
      so that it will no longer be a nation.
⁹   The capital of Ephraim is Samaria,
    and the leader of Samaria is Remaliah's son.
      If you don't remain faithful,
      you won't remain standing.

¹⁰ Again the LORD spoke to Ahaz, ¹¹ "Ask the LORD your God for a sign. It can be anything you want."

¹² But Ahaz answered, "I won't ask; I wouldn't think of testing the LORD."

¹³ "Listen now, descendants of David," Isaiah said. "Isn't it enough that you try the patience of mortals? Must you also try the patience of my God? ¹⁴ So the Lord himself will give you this sign: A virgin will become pregnant and give birth to a son, and she will name him Immanuel [God Is With Us]. ¹⁵ He will eat cheese and honey until he knows how to reject evil and choose good. ¹⁶ Indeed, before the boy knows how to reject evil and choose good, the land of the two kings who terrify you will be deserted.

¹⁷ "The LORD will bring on you, your people, and your ancestor's family a time unlike any since Ephraim broke away from Judah. He will bring the king of Assyria. ¹⁸ On that day the LORD will whistle for the flies that are at the distant branches of the Nile River in Egypt and for the bees that are in Assyria. ¹⁹ All of them will come and settle in the deep valleys, in the cracks in the cliffs, on all the thornbushes, and at all the water holes.

²⁰ "On that day the Lord will hire the king of Assyria from beyond the Euphrates River to be a razor to shave the hair on your head, the hair on your legs, and even your beard. ²¹ On that day a person will keep alive a young cow and two sheep. ²² That person will eat cheese, because they will produce so much milk. Everyone who is left in the land will eat cheese and honey. ²³ On that day, in every place where there were 1,000 vines (worth 1,000 pieces of silver), there will be briars and thorns. ²⁴ People will come there with bows and arrows to hunt, because the whole land will be filled with briars and thorns. ²⁵ And you will no longer be able to go to all the hills which used to be cultivated because they will be filled with briars and thorns. It will be a place for turning oxen loose and letting sheep run."

Isaiah's Child Is a Sign of the LORD's Protection of Judah

8 ¹ The LORD said to me, "Take a large writing tablet, and write on it with a pen: 'Maher Shalal Hash Baz' [The Looting Will Come Quickly; the Prey Will Be Easy]. ² I will have these dependable witnesses testify: the priest Uriah and Zechariah (son of Jeberechiah)."

³ I slept with the prophet. She became pregnant and gave birth to a son. The LORD told me, "Name him Maher Shalal Hash Baz. ⁴ Before the boy knows how to say 'Daddy' or 'Mommy,' the wealth of Damascus and the loot from Samaria will be carried away to the king of Assyria."

Assyria Will Invade, But It Will Not Conquer Judah

⁵ The LORD spoke to me again. He said,

⁶   "These people have rejected the gently flowing water of Shiloah
    and find joy in Rezin and Remaliah's son."
⁷   That is why the Lord is going to bring against them

the raging and powerful floodwaters of the Euphrates River—
    the king of Assyria with all his power.
It will overflow all its channels and go over all its banks.
8 It will sweep through Judah.
It will overflow and pass through; it will be neck-high.
Its outspread wings will extend over your whole country, O Immanuel.

9 Be broken, you people. Be terrified.
Listen, all you distant parts of the earth.
    Prepare for battle, but be terrified.
    Prepare for battle, but be terrified.

10 Make plans for battle, but they will never succeed.
Give orders, but they won't be carried out,
    because God is with us!

Some in Jerusalem Will Stumble Because They Do Not Trust the Lord
11 This is what the Lord said with his powerful hand on me.

He warned me not to follow the ways of these people:
12 "Don't say that everything these people call a conspiracy
    is a conspiracy.
Don't fear what they fear.
Don't let it terrify you."
13 Remember that the Lord of Armies is holy.
    He is the one you should fear
        and the one you should be terrified of.
14 He will be a place of safety for you.
    But he will be a rock that makes people trip
        and a stumbling block for both kingdoms of Israel.
He will be a trap and a snare for those who live in Jerusalem.
15 Many will stumble.
    They will fall and be broken.
    They will be trapped and caught.

16 Tie up the written instructions.
Seal the teachings among my disciples.

17 I will wait for the Lord,
    who hides his face from the descendants of Jacob.
I will hope in him.
18 I am here with the children that the Lord has given me.
    We are signs and symbols in Israel
        from the Lord of Armies, who lives on Mount Zion.
19 People will say to you, "Ask for help from the mediums
    and the fortunetellers, who whisper and mutter."
Shouldn't people ask their God for help instead?
Why should they ask the dead to help the living?
20 They should go to the teachings and to the written instructions.
    If people don't speak these words,
        it is because it doesn't dawn on them.
21 They will pass through the land when they are hard-pressed and hungry.
    When they are hungry, they will be furious.
        —Then they will look up, cursing their king and God.
22 They will look at the earth and see only distress and gloom.
They will go in anguish and be forced into darkness.

9 ^a **1** But there will be no more gloom
    for the land that is in distress.
God humbled the lands of Zebulun and Naphtali in earlier times.
    But in the future he will bring glory to the road by the sea,
        to the land across the Jordan River,
        to Galilee, where foreigners live.

---

[a] 9:1 Isaiah 9:1–21 in English Bibles is Isaiah 8:23–9:20 in the Hebrew Bible.

A Child Will Be Born as the Prince of Peace

2 The people who walk in darkness will see a bright light.
The light will shine on those who live in the land of death's shadow.

3 You will expand the nation and increase its happiness.
It will be happy in your presence
like those who celebrate the harvest
or rejoice when dividing loot.
4 You will break the yoke*b* that burdens them,
the bar that is across their shoulders,
and the stick used by their oppressor,
as you did in the battle against Midian.
5 Every warrior's boot marching to the sound of battle
and every garment rolled in blood
will be burned as fuel in the fire.
6 A child will be born for us.
A son will be given to us.
The government will rest on his shoulders.
He will be named:
Wonderful Counselor,
Mighty God,
Everlasting Father,
Prince of Peace.
7 His government and peace will have unlimited growth.
He will establish David's throne and kingdom.
He will uphold it with justice and righteousness now and forever.
The Lord of Armies is determined to do this!

The Lord's Message Against His People

8 The Lord sent a message against Jacob.
The message is against Israel.
9 All the people of Ephraim
and the people who live in Samaria will know it.
With arrogant and conceited hearts they will say,
10 "Bricks have fallen,
but we will rebuild with hand-cut stones.
Fig trees have been cut down,
but we will replace them with cedars."
11 The Lord will set Rezin's oppressors against Israel
and will stir up its enemies—
12 the Arameans from the east and the Philistines from the west.
They will devour Israel with open mouths.

Even after all this, his anger will not disappear,
and he is still ready to use his power.

13 But the people have not returned to the one who struck them,
nor have they sought the Lord of Armies.
14 So in one day the Lord will cut off from Israel
both head and tail,
both palm branches and cattails.
15 Respected and honored leaders are the head.
Prophets who teach lies are the tail.
16 Those who guide these people lead them astray.
Those who are guided by them will be destroyed.
17 That is why the Lord isn't happy with their young men,
nor will he show compassion for their orphans and widows.
Every one of them is a godless evildoer,
and every mouth speaks foolishness.

Even after all this, his anger will not disappear,
and he is still ready to use his power.

18 Surely wickedness burns like fire.
It burns up briars and thorns.
It sets the underbrush in the forest on fire,

---

b 9:4 A yoke is a wooden bar placed over the necks of work animals so that they can pull plows or carts.

and it whirls upward in clouds of smoke.
¹⁹ The land is scorched by the fury of the LORD of Armies,
   and the people are like fuel for the fire.
No one shows concern for others:
²⁰   On the right, one gobbles up food and is still hungry.
   On the left, another eats and is never full.
   Each person eats the flesh from his own arm.
²¹ Manasseh is against Ephraim.
Ephraim is against Manasseh.
   Together they attack Judah.

Even after all this, his anger will not disappear,
   and he is still ready to use his power.

10

¹ How horrible it will be for those who make unjust laws
   and who make oppressive regulations.
²   They deprive the poor of justice.
   They take away the rights of the needy among my people.
   They prey on widows and rob orphans.
³ What will you do on the day
   you are called to account ˌfor these thingsˌ,
      when the disaster comes from far away?
Where will you run for help?
Where will you leave your wealth?
⁴   Nothing's left but to crouch among prisoners
      and to fall with those who are killed.

Even after all this, his anger will not disappear,
   and he is still ready to use his power.

The LORD's Message Against Assyria
⁵   "How horrible it will be for Assyria!
   It is the rod of my anger.
      My fury is the staff in the Assyrians' hands.
⁶ I send them against a godless nation.
In my fury I order them against the people
   to take their belongings, loot them,
      and trample on them like mud in the streets.
⁷ But that's not what they intend to do.
   Their minds don't work that way.
   Their purpose is to destroy and put an end to many nations.
⁸ They ask, 'Aren't all our commanders kings?
⁹   Isn't Calno like Carchemish?
   Isn't Hamath like Arpad?
   Isn't Samaria like Damascus?'
¹⁰ My power has reached kingdoms which have idols.
   They had more carved statues than Jerusalem or Samaria.
¹¹ I will do to Jerusalem and its idols
   what I've done to Samaria and its idols."

¹² When the Lord has finished all his work on Mount Zion and in Jerusalem, he will punish the king of Assyria for all his boasting and all his arrogance. ¹³ The king will say,

"I did this with my own two powerful hands.
I did this with my wisdom, because I am so clever.
I've eliminated the boundaries of nations.
I've looted treasuries.
I've brought down people like a mighty man.
¹⁴ I've found the riches of nations as one finds a nest.
I've gathered the whole world as one gathers abandoned eggs.
   Not one of them flapped a wing, opened its mouth, or peeped."

¹⁵   Can an ax attack the person who cuts with it?
Can a saw make itself greater than the person who saws with it?
   A rod cannot move the person who lifts it.
   A wooden stick cannot pick up a person.
¹⁶ That is why the Almighty LORD of Armies
   will send a degenerative disease against brave men.
      A flame will be turned into a raging fire under his power.
¹⁷ Israel's light will become a flame.

Its Holy One will become a fire.
He will burn up and devour the weeds and thornbushes in one day.

18 The majestic forest and the orchard
will destroy both body and soul.
They will be like a sick person wasting away.

19 The trees that remain in the forest will be so few that
a child could count them.

20 At that time the remaining few Israelites,
the survivors of Jacob's descendants
will no longer depend on the one who struck them.
They will only depend on the Lord, the Holy One of Israel.

21 A few, the remaining few of Jacob, will return to the mighty God.

22 Although your people Israel may be
as ˌnumerous asˌ the grains of sand on the seashore,
only a few will return.
Destruction will be complete and fair.

23 The Almighty Lord of Armies will carry out this destruction
throughout the world as he has determined.

24 The Almighty Lord of Armies says:
My people who live in Zion,
don't be afraid of the Assyrians when they strike with a rod
or when they raise their staff against you
as the Egyptians did.

25 Very soon I will unleash my fury,
and my anger will destroy them.

26 Then the Lord of Armies will raise his whip against them.
As he struck down Midian at the Rock of Oreb
and raised his staff over the water,
so he will lift it as he did in Egypt.

27 At that time their burden will be removed from your shoulders.
Their yoke* will be removed from your neck.
The yoke will be torn away because you have grown fat.

28 They come to Aiath.
They pass through Migron.
They store their equipment at Michmash.

29 They go through the mountain pass and lodge at Geba for the night.
The people in Ramah tremble; the people in Saul's Gibeah flee.

30 Cry aloud, you people in Gallim!
Pay attention, you people in Laishah and miserable Anathoth!

31 The people in Madmenah flee; those who live in Gebim take shelter.

32 This day they stopped at Nob.
They shake their fist at the mountain of my people Zion,
at the mountain of Jerusalem.

33 Now look! The Almighty Lord of Armies
will trim the branches with terrifying power.
The highest trees will be cut down.
The tallest ones will be brought down.

34 He will cut down the underbrush of the forest with an ax.
Lebanon will fall in front of the Mighty One.

The Lord's Kingdom Will Be Ruled by a Shoot From Jesse's Stump

11 ¹ Then a shoot will come out from the stump of Jesse,
and a branch from its roots will bear fruit.

2 The Spirit of the Lord will rest on him—
the Spirit of wisdom and understanding,
the Spirit of advice and power,
the Spirit of knowledge and fear of the Lord.

3 He will gladly bear the fear of the Lord.
He will not judge by what his eyes see
or decide by what his ears hear.

4 He will judge the poor justly.
He will make fair decisions for the humble people on earth.

ª 10:27 A yoke is a wooden bar placed over the necks of work animals so that they can pull plows or carts.

He will strike the earth with a rod from his mouth.
He will kill the wicked with the breath from his lips.
5   Justice will be the belt around his waist.
    Faithfulness will be the belt around his hips.

6 Wolves will live with lambs.
    Leopards will lie down with goats.
    Calves, young lions, and year-old lambs will be together,
        and little children will lead them.
7 Cows and bears will eat together.
    Their young will lie down together.
    Lions will eat straw like oxen.
8 Infants will play near cobras' holes.
    Toddlers will put their hands into vipers' nests.
9 They will not hurt or destroy anyone anywhere on my holy mountain.
    The world will be filled with the knowledge of the LORD
        like water covering the sea.
10 At that time the root of Jesse will stand as a banner
        for the people ˌto gather aroundˌ.
        The nations will come to him.
            His resting place will be glorious.

11 At that time the Lord will use his power again
        to recover what remains of his people
        in Assyria, Upper and Lower Egypt,
            Sudan, Elam, Babylonia, Hamath,
                and the islands of the sea.
12 He will raise a banner for the nations ˌto gather aroundˌ.
    He will gather the outcasts of Israel
        and bring together the scattered people of Judah
            from the four corners of the earth.
13 Ephraim's jealousy will vanish,
        and Judah's opponents will come to an end.
    Ephraim won't be jealous of Judah,
        and Judah won't oppose Ephraim.
14 They will swoop down on the slopes of Philistia in the west.
        Together they will loot the people of the east.
    They will conquer Edom and Moab.
        The people of Ammon will be subject to them.
15 The LORD will dry up the gulf of the Egyptian Sea.
    He will wave his hand over the Euphrates River with his scorching wind
        and divide it into seven streams
            so that people can walk over it in their sandals.
16 There will be a highway
        for the remaining few of his people left in Assyria
            like there was for Israel when it came out of Egypt.

A Hymn of Praise From the LORD's People in His Kingdom

12 ¹ At that time you will say,

"I will praise you, O LORD.
Although you had been angry with me,
    you turned your anger away from me, and you comforted me.
2 Look! God is my Savior.
    I am confident and unafraid,
        because the LORD is my strength and my song.
        He is my Savior."

³ With joy you will draw water from the springs of salvation.
⁴ At that time you will say,

"Praise the LORD.
Call on his name.
Make his deeds known among the nations.
Make them remember that his name is highly honored.
5 Make music to praise the LORD.
    He has done wonderful things.
        Let this be known throughout the earth.

⁶ Shout loudly, and sing with joy, people of Zion!
  The Holy One of Israel is great. He is among you."

Babylon Will Be Punished

13 ¹ This is the divine revelation which Isaiah, son of Amoz, saw about Babylon.

² Raise a banner on the bare mountaintop.
    Call loudly to them.
      Signal them with your hand to enter the nobles' gates.
³ I've commanded my holy ones.
  I've called my mighty men to carry out my anger.
    They find joy in my triumphs.
⁴ Listen to the noise on the mountains.
    It is like the sound of a large army.
    It is the sound of kingdoms and nations gathering together.
  The LORD of Armies is assembling his army for battle.
⁵ His army is coming from a distant land,
    from the ends of heaven.
  The LORD is coming with the weapons of his fury
    to destroy the whole world.

⁶ Cry loudly, for the day of the LORD is near.
    It will come like destruction from the Almighty.
⁷ That is why every hand will hang limp,
    and everyone's courage will fail.
⁸   They'll be terrified.
      Pain and anguish will seize them.
    They'll writhe like a woman giving birth to a child.
    They'll look at one another in astonishment.
      Their faces will be burning red.

⁹ The day of the LORD is going to come.
    It will be a cruel day with fury and fierce anger.
    He will make the earth desolate.
      He will destroy its sinners.
¹⁰ The stars in the sky and their constellations
    won't show their light anymore.
  The sun will be dark when it rises.
  The moon won't shine.

¹¹ I will punish the world for its evil
    and the wicked for their wrongdoing.
  I will put an end to arrogant people
    and humble the pride of tyrants.
¹² I will make people harder to find than pure gold
    and human beings more rare than gold from Ophir.
¹³ I will make heaven tremble,
    and the earth will be shaken from its place
      when the LORD of Armies is angry.
        At that time he will be very angry.

¹⁴ They'll be like hunted gazelle
    and like sheep with no one to gather them.
  Everyone will return to his own people
    and flee to his own land.
¹⁵ Whoever is found will be stabbed to death.
  Whoever is captured will be executed.
¹⁶   Their little children will be smashed to death right before their eyes.
    Their houses will be looted and their wives raped.

¹⁷ I'm going to stir up the Medes against them.
    They don't care for silver and aren't happy with gold.
¹⁸ But their bows will smash the youth.
    They'll have no compassion for babies,
      nor will they look with pity on children.

¹⁹ Babylon, the jewel of the kingdoms,
    the proud beauty of the Chaldeans,
      will be like Sodom and Gomorrah when God destroyed them.
²⁰ It will never be inhabited again,

and no one will live in it for generations.
Arabs won't pitch their tents there.
Shepherds won't let their flocks rest there.
21 Desert animals will lie down there.
Their homes will be full of owls.
Ostriches will live there,
and wild goats will skip about.
22 Hyenas will howl in Babylon's strongholds,
and jackals will howl in its luxurious palaces.

Its time has almost come.
Its days will not be extended.

Israel Will Be Rescued From Babylon

14 ¹ The LORD will have compassion for Jacob and again choose Israel.
He will resettle them in their own country.
Foreigners will join them
and unite with the descendants of Jacob.
2 People will take them
and bring them to their own place.
The nation of Israel will possess nations
as male and female slaves in the LORD's land.
They will take their captors captive
and rule their oppressors.

3 When that day comes, the LORD will give you relief
from your pain and suffering,
from the hard slavery you were forced to do.
4 Then you will mock the king of Babylon with this saying,
"How the tyrant has come to an end!
How his attacks have come to an end!"
5 The LORD has broken the staff of the wicked,
the scepter of rulers.
6 They struck the people with fury,
with blows that didn't stop.
They ruled nations in anger,
persecuting them without restraint.
7 The whole earth rests and is peaceful.
It breaks out into shouts of joy.
8 Even the cypresses rejoice over you.
The cedars of Lebanon say,
"Since you have fallen,
no lumberjack has come to attack us."

9 Sheol below wakes up to meet you when you come.
It wakes up the ghosts of the dead,
all who were leaders on earth.
It raises all who were kings of the nations from their thrones.
10 All of them will greet you,
"You also have become weak like us!
You have become like one of us!"
11 Your pride has been brought down to Sheol
along with the music of your harps.
Maggots are spread out ⌊like a bed⌋ under you,
and worms cover you.

12 How you have fallen from heaven, you morning star, son of the dawn!
How you have been cut down to the ground, you conqueror of nations!
13 You thought,
"I'll go up to heaven and set up my throne above God's stars.
I'll sit on the mountain far away in the north
where the gods assemble.
14 I'll go above the top of the clouds.
I'll be like the Most High."
15 But you've been brought down to Sheol,
to the deepest part of the pit.
16 Those who see you stare at you; they look at you closely and say,
"Is this the man who made the earth tremble,
who shook the kingdoms,

17   who made the world like a desert and tore down its cities,
            who didn't let his prisoners go home?"

18   All the kings of the nations, all of them,
            have been buried with honor, each in his own tomb.
19   But you are thrown out of your tomb like a rejected branch.
            You are covered with those who were killed in battle.
            You go down to the stones of the pit like a trampled corpse.
20   You won't be joined by the kings in the tomb,
            because you have destroyed your land and killed your people.

     The descendants of the wicked will never be mentioned again.
21   Prepare a place to slaughter their sons
            because of their ancestors' guilt.
                 They won't be able to rise, possess the earth,
                      and rebuild cities all over it.

22   "I'll rise up against them," declares the LORD of Armies.
     "I'll cut off the name of the survivors from Babylon,
            its offspring and descendants," declares the LORD.
23   "It will become the possession of herons.
            It will become pools of water.
     I'll sweep it with the broom of destruction," declares the LORD of Armies.

Assyria Will Be Punished
24   The LORD of Armies has taken an oath:
            "It will happen exactly as I've intended.
     It will turn out exactly as I've planned.
25   I'll crush Assyria on my land.
            I'll trample it underfoot on my mountains.
     Then its yoke[a] will be removed from my people,
            and its burden will be removed from their shoulders."

26   This is the plan determined for the whole earth.
     This is how he will use his power against all the nations.
27   The LORD of Armies has planned it. Who can stop it?
            He is ready to use his power. Who can turn it back?

The Philistines Will Be Punished
28 This was the divine revelation in the year King Ahaz died.

29   All you Philistines, don't rejoice
            that the rod of the one who struck you is broken,
                 because a viper will come from that snake's root,
                      and his descendant will be a flying, fiery serpent.
30   The poorest of the poor will eat,
            and the needy will lie down in safety.
                 But I will put your root to death with famine
                      and kill off your survivors.

31   Cry loudly in the gate!
            Cry out in the city!
                 Be frightened, all you Philistines!
     Smoke comes from the north,
            and there are no stragglers in its ranks.
32   How should we answer the messengers from the nations?
            Tell them that the LORD has laid Zion's foundation,
                 and his humble people will find refuge in it.

Moab Will Be Punished
15 ¹This is the divine revelation about Moab.

     In a single night Ar in Moab is laid waste and destroyed!
     In a single night Kir in Moab is laid waste and destroyed!
2   The people of Dibon go to the temple,
            to the worship sites, to cry.
     Moab wails over Nebo and Medeba.

---

a 14:25 A yoke is a wooden bar placed over the necks of work animals so that they can pull plows or carts.

Every head is shaved bald, and every beard is cut off.[a]
3 In their streets they wear sackcloth.
    On their roofs and in their city squares everyone wails and cries.
4 Heshbon and Elealeh also cry out.
    Their voices are heard as far away as Jahaz.
  Moab's armed men cry out.
    Their courage is gone.
5 My heart cries out for Moab.
    Its people flee as far as Zoar at Eglath Shelishiyah.
      They go up the mountain road to Luhith.
    They cry loudly over the destruction on the way to Horonaim.
6 The Nimrim Brook has run dry!
    The grass dries up,
      the vegetation withers,
        and nothing green is left.
7 That is why they carry the wealth that they have earned and stored up
    over Willow Ravine.
8 Cries for help echo throughout the land of Moab.
    Their wailing echoes as far as Eglaim.
    Their wailing echoes as far as Beer Elim.
9 The water in Dimon is red with blood,
    yet I will bring even more on Dimon.
      A lion will attack the fugitives from Moab
      and the survivors from Adamah.[b]

16 1 Send lambs to the ruler of the land.[a]
    Send lambs from Sela through the desert to my people at Mount Zion.
2 Moab's daughters are like fluttering birds,
    like scattered nestlings,
      at the shallow crossings of the Arnon River.

3 Give us advice.
    Make a decision.
      At high noon make your shadow as dark as night.
      Hide the fugitives.
        Don't betray the refugees.
4   Let the fugitives from Moab stay with you a while.
        Be their refuge from the destroyer.
  Ruthless people will come to an end.
    The destruction will end.
    The one who tramples others will be gone.
5 Then the LORD will set up a trusted king.
    He will rule faithfully.
    He is from the tent of David.
    He judges and searches for justice.
    He is quick to do what is right.

6 We've heard of the arrogance of Moab's people.
    They are very arrogant.
  We've heard of their boasting, arrogance, and conceit,
    but their boasts aren't true.
7 That is why Moab will wail.
    Everyone will wail for Moab.
  Mourn and grieve over the raisin cakes of Kir Hareseth.[b]
8 The fields of Heshbon and the vineyards of Sibmah wither.
  Rulers of the nations have cut off their grapes.
    The grapevines ˌonceˌ reached as far as Jazer
      and strayed out into the desert.
    Their shoots had spread out over the sea.
9 I will cry for the grapevines of Sibmah
    as Jazer cries for them.
      I will drench you with my tears, Heshbon and Elealeh.
  The shouts of joy for your ripened fruits
    and your harvest will be silenced.

---

[a] 15:2 The shaving of the head and the beard are signs of a people going into exile.   [b] 15:9 Or "the survivors in the countryside."
[a] 16:1 Masoretic Text; Targum "They have sent lambs to the ruler of the land."   [b] 16:7 Hebrew meaning of this line uncertain.

¹⁰ Joy and delight have vanished from the orchards.
     No songs are sung.
     No shouts are raised.
     No one stomps on grapes in the winepresses,
         because I have put an end to the shouts of joy.
¹¹ That is why my heart mourns for Moab like a harp.
     My soul mourns for Kir Hareseth.
¹² When the people of Moab appear at the worship site,
         they will only wear themselves out.
     They will come into the holy place to pray,
         but they won't be able to.

¹³ This is the message that the LORD spoke about Moab in the past. ¹⁴ But now the LORD says, "Moab's honor will be despised within three years. I will count them like workers count the years left of their contracts.ᶜ In spite of their great number, the survivors will be very few and powerless."

Damascus and Israel Will Be Punished

17

¹ This is the divine revelation about Damascus.

     "Damascus will no longer be a city.
         It will become a pile of rubble.
²   The cities of Aroer will be deserted.
         These cities will be used for sheep, which will lie down in them.
         There will be no one to disturb those sheep.
³   Fortified cities will disappear from Ephraim,
         and the kingdom will disappear from Damascus.
     The remaining few from Aram will share Israel's honor,"
         declares the LORD of Armies.

⁴   "When that day comes, the honor of Jacob's people will fade away,
         and they will become skin and bones.
⁵   That time will be like harvesting bundles of grain by the armful.
     It will be like gathering grain in the Rephaim Valley.
⁶   Only a few people will survive.
         They will be like an olive tree that has been beaten.
         Only two or three olives are left
             at the top of the highest branch,
                 four or five olives on the rest of the branches,"
                 declares the LORD God of Israel.

⁷   When that day comes, they will look to their maker,
         and their eyes will look to the Holy One of Israel.
⁸   They won't look to the altars made by their hands
         or to the Asherah poles or incense altars
             which their fingers molded.

⁹   When that day comes, the fortified cities
         which other people abandoned because of the Israelites
             will be like abandoned woods and undergrowth.
     So it will become a wasteland.

¹⁰   You have forgotten the God of your salvation.
     You haven't remembered the rock, your stronghold.
     Instead, you have planted the best plants
         and have set out the imported grapevines.
¹¹   On the day you plant, you will make it grow.ᵃ
     On the morning you set out the seedling, you will make it sprout.
         But the harvest will become a [rotting] pileᵇ
             on a day of grief and incurable pain.

¹²   How horrible it will be for many people!
         They will roar like the roaring sea.
     The noise that the people make
         will be like the noise from rushing water.
¹³   The people will make noise like raging water.

ᶜ 16:14 Hebrew meaning of this sentence uncertain.   ᵃ 17:11 Hebrew meaning of this line uncertain.   ᵇ 17:11 Or "But the harvest will flee."

But the Lord will yell at them, and they will run far away.
  They will be chased away
      like husks on the mountains being blown by the wind,
      like whirling dust being blown by a storm.
14 In the evening there will be sudden terror.
Before morning they will be gone.
This will be the fate of those who looted us,
  the destiny of those who robbed us.

Sudan Will Be Punished

18 ¹ How horrible it will be for the land of whirring wings
      which lies beyond the rivers of Sudan.
  ²   It sends messengers by sea
        in boats made of reeds
          ⌊skimming⌋ over the surface of the water.
      Go, swift messengers, to a tall and smooth-skinned people,
        a people ⌊who are⌋ feared far and near,
        a strong and aggressive nation,
          whose land is divided by rivers.
  ³ Look when someone raises a flag on the mountains.
Listen when someone blows a ram's horn,
  all you inhabitants of the world who live on the earth.

⁴ This is what the Lord says to me:

I will keep quiet and watch from my dwelling place.
  My presence will be like scorching heat in the sunshine,
      like heavy dew in the heat of the harvest.
  ⁵ Before the harvest, when blossoms are gone
and grapes are ripening from blossoms,
      he will cut off the shoots with pruning shears
        and chop off the spreading branches.
  ⁶ They will be left for the birds of prey on the mountains
and the wild animals.
      The birds of prey will feed on them in the summer,
        and all the wild animals on earth
          will feed on them in the winter.
  ⁷ At that time gifts will be brought to the Lord of Armies
from a tall and smooth-skinned people,
      a people ⌊who are⌋ feared far and near,
      a strong and aggressive nation,
        whose land is divided by rivers.
They will be brought to Mount Zion,
  the place where the name of the Lord of Armies is.

Egypt Will Be Punished

19 ¹ This is the divine revelation about Egypt.

The Lord is riding on a fast-moving cloud and is coming to Egypt.
  Egypt's idols will tremble in his presence.
  Egypt's courage will fail.

  ² "I will turn one Egyptian against another.
They will fight—
      brother against brother,
      neighbor against neighbor,
      city against city,
      kingdom against kingdom.
  ³ The Egyptians will lose courage.
  I will unravel their plans.
They will turn to idols, ghosts,
      mediums, and fortunetellers.
  ⁴ I will hand over the Egyptians to a harsh master.
  A strong king will rule them,"
      declares the Almighty Lord of Armies.

⁵   The water in the Nile River will be dried up,ᵃ
    and the river will be dry and empty.
⁶   The canals will stink.
        Egypt's streams will be emptied and dried up.
        The reeds and cattails will wither.
⁷   The rushes by the Nile, by the edge of the Nile,
            and all the fields planted beside the Nile
            will dry up, be blown away, and disappear.
⁸   Fishermen will cry.
        All who cast their lines into the Nile will mourn.
        Those who spread their nets on the water will sigh.
⁹   Linenworkers and weavers will be ashamed.
¹⁰ Egypt's weavers will be crushed.
        Those who work for money will be distressed.

¹¹ The leaders of Zoan are nothing but fools.
    The wisest of Pharaoh's counselors gives stupid advice.
        How can you tell Pharaoh,
        "I'm a descendant of wise men,
            a descendant of ancient kings"?
¹²   Where are your wise men now?
        Let them tell you.
            Let them explain what the LORD of Armies
                is planning against Egypt.
¹³ The leaders of Zoan are acting foolishly.
    The leaders of Memphis are led astray.
    The leaders who are the cornerstones of its tribes mislead the Egyptians.
¹⁴ The LORD mixes up their minds.
        So they lead the Egyptians astray
            like a drunk who staggers in his vomit.
¹⁵ No one—leaders or followers, important or unimportant—
        can do anything for Egypt.

¹⁶ At that time Egyptians will act like women. They will tremble and be terrified because the LORD of Armies will shake his fist at them. ¹⁷ The land of Judah will terrify the Egyptians. Whenever they are reminded of Judah, they will be terrified of it because of what the LORD of Armies is planning against it.

¹⁸ When that day comes, five cities in Egypt will have people that speak the language of Canaan and swear allegiance to the LORD of Armies. One of the cities will be called Heliopolis.ᵇ

¹⁹ When that day comes, an altar for the LORD will be in the middle of Egypt, and a stone marker for the LORD will be near its border. ²⁰ These objects will be a sign and a witness that the LORD of Armies is in Egypt. When the people cry to the LORD because of those who oppress them, he will send a savior and defender to rescue them. ²¹ So the LORD will make himself known to the Egyptians. The Egyptians will know the LORD when that day comes. They will worship with sacrifices and food offerings. They will make vows to the LORD and carry them out. ²² The LORD will strike Egypt with a plague. When he strikes them, he will also heal them. Then they will come back to the LORD. And he will respond to their prayers and heal them.

²³ When that day comes, a highway will run from Egypt to Assyria. The Assyrians will come to Egypt and the Egyptians to Assyria, and the Egyptians will worship with the Assyrians. ²⁴ When that day comes, Israel will be one-third ˌof God's peopleˌ, along with Egypt and Assyria. They will be a blessing on the earth. ²⁵ The LORD of Armies will bless them, saying, "My people Egypt, the work of my hands Assyria, and my possession Israel are blessed."

Those Who Were Allied With Egypt Will Be Ashamed

20 ¹ In the year when King Sargon of Assyria sent his commander-in-chief to fight against Ashdod, he captured it. ² At that time the LORD told Isaiah, son of Amoz, "Take off the sackcloth that you are wearing, and take off your sandals!" Isaiah did this and walked around barefoot and naked.

³ Then the LORD said, "My servant Isaiah has gone barefoot and naked for three years as a sign and as an omen to Egypt and Sudan. ⁴ The king of Assyria will lead away both the young and the old—captives from Egypt and exiles from Sudan. They will be barefoot and naked.

ᵃ 19:5 Or "Then the water of the sea will be dried up."   ᵇ 19:18 Dead Sea Scrolls, some Hebrew manuscripts, Greek, Targum, Latin; Egyptian; Masoretic Text "City of Destruction."

Their buttocks will be exposed in order to disgrace Egypt. ⁵ Then the people will be shattered and ashamed because Sudan was their hope and Egypt was their beauty. ⁶ When that day comes, those who live on this coastland will say, 'Look at what has happened to our hope. We ran ˻to Egypt˼ for help to be rescued from the king of Assyria. How can we escape?' "

Babylon Has Fallen

21 ¹ This is the divine revelation about the desert by the sea.

> Like a storm sweeping through the Negev,
>   an invader will come from the desert,
>   from a terrifying land.
> ² I was shown a harsh vision.
>   The traitor betrays.
>   The destroyer destroys.
>   Go to war, Elam!
>   Surround them, Media!
> I will put an end to all the groaning.
> ³ That is why my body is full of trembling.
> Pain grips me like the pain of childbirth.
>   I'm disturbed by what I hear.
>   I'm terrified by what I see.
> ⁴ I'm confused.
> I'm shaking with terror.
> The twilight hours I longed for make me tremble.
> ⁵ Set the table.
>   Spread the rugs ˻by the table˼.
>   Eat. Drink.
> Get up, you leaders!
> Prepare your shields for battle!

⁶ This is what the Lord says to me:

> Post a watchman.
>   Have him report whatever he sees.
> ⁷ He will see chariots, pairs of horsemen,
>   riders on donkeys, and riders on camels.
>   Let him watch carefully, very carefully.
> ⁸ The watchman*ᵃ* called,
>   "Sir, I stand on the watchtower every day.
>   Every night, I stand guard at my post.
> ⁹   Look! Here come chariots and horsemen in pairs."
> Then he said,
>   "Babylon has fallen! It has fallen!
>   All the idols they worship lie shattered on the ground."

> ¹⁰ You, my people, have been threshed and winnowed.*ᵇ*
>   I make known to you what I heard from the Lᴏʀᴅ of Armies,
>   the God of Israel.

Someone Calling From Seir

¹¹ This is the divine revelation about Dumah.*ᶜ*

> Someone is calling to me from Seir,
>   "Watchman, how much of the night is left?
>   Watchman, how much of the night is left?"
> ¹² The watchman answers,
>   "Morning is coming, and night will come again.
>   If you need to ask, come back and ask."

Arabia Will Be Punished

¹³ This is the divine revelation about Arabia.

> You caravan of travelers from the people of Dedan
>   will spend the night in the forest of Arabia.

ᵃ 21:8 Syriac, Dead Sea Scrolls; Masoretic Text, Targum "lion"; Greek "Uriah."　　*ᵇ* 21:10 Threshing is the process of beating stalks to separate them from the grain. Winnowing is the process of separating husks from grain.　　*ᶜ* 21:11 The exact location of Dumah is unknown.

¹⁴ Bring water for the thirsty,
    you inhabitants of the land of Tema.
Bring food to the fugitives.
¹⁵ They flee from swords,
    from swords ready to kill,
      from bows ready to shoot,
        and from the thick of battle.

¹⁶ This is what the Lord says to me: All of Kedar's honor will be gone in another year. I will count it like workers count the years left on their contracts.^d ¹⁷ The remaining number of archers, Kedar's mighty archers, will be few. The LORD God of Israel has spoken.

Judah Will Be Punished

22 ¹ This is the divine revelation about the valley of Vision.

    What's the matter with you?
    Why do all of you go up on the roofs?
²   You are a city filled with shouting,
      a town filled with noise and excitement.
    Your people weren't killed with swords.
    Your dead didn't die in battle.
³ All your leaders fled together
    and were captured without their bows and arrows.
All those who were found were taken prisoner
    before any of them could get far away.
⁴ That is why I say,
    "Turn away from me
      so that I can cry bitterly.
    Don't try to comfort me
      because of the destruction brought on my people."

⁵ The Almighty LORD of Armies has chosen a special day.
    It will be a day of confusion and trampling
      in the valley of Vision,
        ₐa day of, tearing down walls and crying for help
        in the mountains.
⁶ Elam takes its quiver of arrows,
    manned chariots, and horsemen.
Kir uncovers its shields.
⁷   Then your fertile valleys will be filled with chariots,
      and horsemen will stand ready in front of the gate.
⁸   On that day the LORD will remove the defenses of Judah.

    You will look for weapons in the House of the Forest.^a
⁹ You will see how many places in David's wall are broken.
    You will store water in the Lower Pool.
¹⁰ You will count the houses in Jerusalem.
    You will tear down those houses in order to fortify the walls.
¹¹ You will build a reservoir between the two walls
    to hold the water of the Old Pool.
      You didn't look to Jerusalem's maker.
      You didn't see the one who formed it long ago.
¹² On that day the Almighty LORD of Armies
    will call for crying and for mourning,
      for shaving your heads and for wearing sackcloth.
¹³ Instead, you will rejoice, celebrate,
    slaughter cattle, and butcher sheep.
You will eat meat, drink wine, and say,
    "Let's eat and drink because tomorrow we're going to die."

¹⁴ The LORD of Armies revealed this to me: "Certainly, this wrong will not be forgiven even when you die," says the Almighty LORD of Armies.

---

^d 21:16 Hebrew meaning of this sentence uncertain.   ^a 22:8 "The House of the Forest" is a storehouse for weapons and other items. It was built by Solomon as part of the temple complex.

Shebna's Position Will Be Given to Eliakim

¹⁵ This is what the Almighty LORD of Armies says:

Go to Shebna, the man in charge of the palace, and say ͺto himͺ,
¹⁶   "What are you doing here?
        What right do you have to dig a tomb for yourself?
        What right do you have to cut it out in a prominent place?
        What right do you have to carve out
            a resting place for yourself in the rock?
¹⁷ Look, mighty man!
        The LORD will throw you out.
        He will grab you.
¹⁸   He will wrap you up tightly like a turban.
        He will throw you far away into another land.
            There you will die.
            There your splendid chariots will remain.
            There you will become a disgrace to your master's household.

¹⁹   "I will remove you from your office
            and do away with your position.
²⁰ When that day comes, I will call my servant Eliakim, son of Hilkiah.
²¹ I will dress him in your linen robe
            and fasten it with your belt.
        I will give him your authority,
            and he will be like a father to those who live in Jerusalem
            and to the nation of Judah.
²²   I will place the key of the house of David around his neck.
        What he opens no one will shut.
        What he shuts no one will open.
²³   I will fasten him firmly in place like a peg,
            and he will be a source of honor for his father's household.
²⁴   They will hang on him the whole weight of his father's household,
            descendants and offspring and all the little utensils,
                from bowls to jars of every kind."

²⁵ The LORD of Armies declares,

    "On that day the peg which I firmly fastened in place will be removed.
        It will be cut off and will fall,
            and everything hanging on it will be destroyed."

The LORD has spoken.

Tyre Will Be Punished

23 ¹ This is the divine revelation about Tyre.

    Cry loudly, you ships of Tarshish!
        Your port at Tyre is destroyed.
        Word has come to the ships from Cyprus.
²   Be silent, you inhabitants of the coastland, you merchants from Sidon.
        Your messengers have crossed the sea.
³   The grain of Shihor is on the Mediterranean.
        The harvest of the Nile River is brought to Tyre.
        Tyre became the marketplace for the nations.

⁴   Be ashamed, Sidon, because the stronghold by the sea has spoken,
        "I've never been in labor or given birth.
        I've raised no sons.
        I've brought up no daughters."
⁵   When the news reaches Egypt,
        the Egyptians will shudder over the news about Tyre.

⁶   Travel to Tarshish!
        Cry loudly, you inhabitants of the seacoast!
⁷   Is this your bustling city founded in the distant past?
        Is this the city that sent its people to settle in distant lands?
⁸   Who planned such a thing against Tyre, the city that produced kings?
        Its merchants are princes.
        Its traders are among the honored people of the world.
⁹   The LORD of Armies planned this

in order to dishonor all arrogant people
  and to humiliate all the honored people of the world.
¹⁰ Travel through your country like the Nile, people of Tarshish.
  You no longer have a harbor.
¹¹ The L ORD has stretched his hand over the sea to shake kingdoms.
  He has commanded that Canaan's fortifications be destroyed.
¹² He says, "You will no longer be joyful,
  my dear abused people Sidon."
Get up, and travel to Cyprus.
  Even there you will find no rest.
¹³ Look at the land of the Babylonians.
  These people will be gone.
Assyria gave this land to the desert animals.
  Assyria set up battle towers,
    stripped palaces bare,
      and turned these places into ruins.

¹⁴ Cry loudly, you ships of Tarshish, because your fortress will be destroyed. ¹⁵ When that day comes, Tyre will be forgotten for 70 years, the lifetime of one king. At the end of the 70 years, Tyre will be like the prostitute in this song:

¹⁶ "Take your lyre.
  Go around in the city, you forgotten prostitute.
Make sweet music.
  Sing many songs so that you'll be remembered."

¹⁷ At the end of 70 years the L ORD will come to help Tyre. Then she will go back to earning money as a prostitute. She will become a prostitute for all the world's kingdoms. ¹⁸ Her profits and her earnings will be turned over to the L ORD for his holy purpose. It won't be stored or hoarded. Her merchandise will belong to those who live in the presence of the L ORD so that they will have plenty of food and expensive clothing.

The Lord's Great Triumph

24 ¹ The L ORD is going to turn the earth into a desolate wasteland.
  He will mar the face of the earth and scatter the people living on it.
² The same will happen to people and priests,
    male slaves and masters,
    female slaves and masters,
    buyers and sellers,
    lenders and borrowers,
    debtors and creditors.
³ The earth will be completely laid waste and stripped
    because the L ORD has spoken.

⁴ The earth dries up and withers.
  The world wastes away and withers.
  The great leaders of the earth waste away.
⁵ The earth is polluted by those who live on it
    because they've disobeyed the L ORD's teachings,
      violated his laws,
        and rejected the everlasting promise.^a
⁶ That is why a curse devours the earth,
    and its people are punished for their guilt.
  That is why those who live on the earth are burned up,
    and only a few people are left.
⁷ New wine dries up, and grapevines waste away.
  All happy people groan.
⁸ Joyful tambourine music stops.
    Noisy celebrations cease.
      Joyful harp music stops.
⁹ People no longer drink wine when they sing.
    Liquor tastes bad to its drinkers.
¹⁰ The ruined city lies desolate.
    The entrance to every house is barred shut.
¹¹ People in the streets call for wine.
  All joy passes away,

---

^a 24:5 Or "covenant."

and the earth's happiness is banished.
12 The city is left in ruins.
Its gate is battered to pieces.

13 That is the way it will be on earth among the nations.
They will be like an olive tree which has been shaken
or like what's left after the grape harvest.
14 They raise their voices.
They shout for joy.
From the sea they sing joyfully about the LORD's majesty.
15 Honor the LORD in the east.
Honor the name of the LORD God of Israel along the coastlands.
16 From the ends of the earth we hear songs of praise
that honor the Righteous One.

But I kept saying,
"I'm wasting away! I'm wasting away!
How horrible it is for me!
Traitors continue to betray,
and their treachery grows worse and worse."
17 Disasters, pits, and traps
are in store for those who live on earth.
18 Whoever flees from news of a disaster will fall into a pit.
Whoever climbs out of that pit will be caught in a trap.
The floodgates in the sky will be opened,
and the foundations of the earth will shake.
19 The earth will be completely broken.
The earth will shake back and forth violently.
The earth will stagger.
20 The earth will stumble like a drunk
and sway like a shack in the wind.
Its disobedience weighs heavy on it.
It will fall and not get up again.

21 On that day the LORD will punish heaven's armies in heaven
and earth's kings on earth.
22 They'll be gathered like prisoners in a jail
and locked in prison.
After a long time they'll be punished.
23 The moon will be embarrassed.
The sun will be ashamed,
because the LORD of Armies will rule
on Mount Zion and in Jerusalem.
He will be glorious
in the presence of his respected leaders.

The LORD Protects the Weak

25 ¹ O LORD, you are my God.
I will highly honor you; I will praise your name.
You have done miraculous things.
You have been completely reliable
in carrying out your plans from long ago.
2 You have turned cities into ruins,
fortified cities into piles of rubble,
and foreigners' palaces into cities that will never be rebuilt.
3 That is why strong people will honor you,
and cities ruled by the world's tyrants will fear you.
4 You have been a refuge for the poor,
a refuge for the needy in their distress,
a shelter from the rain, and shade from the heat.
(A tyrant's breath is like a rainstorm against a wall,
5 like heat in a dry land.)
You calm the uproar of foreigners.
The song of tyrants is silenced
like heat that is ˌreducedˌ by the shadow of a cloud.

Death Will Be Swallowed Up

6 On this mountain the LORD of Armies will prepare for all people
　a feast with the best foods,
　a banquet with aged wines,
　　with the best foods and the finest wines.
7 On this mountain he will remove
　the veil of grief covering all people
　and the mask covering all nations.
8 He will swallow up death forever.
　The Almighty LORD will wipe away tears from every face,
　　and he will remove the disgrace of his people from the whole earth.
　　The LORD has spoken.
9 On that day ˎhis peopleˌ will say,
　"This is our God; we have waited for him, and now he will save us.
　This is the LORD; we have waited for him.
　　Let us rejoice and be glad because he will save us."

10 The LORD's power will be on this mountain.
　　Moab will be trampled beneath him
　　　like straw that is trampled in a pile of manure.
11 The Moabites will stretch out their hands in the manure
　　like swimmers who stretch out their hands to swim.
　　ˎThe LORDˌ will humble those arrogant people
　　　despite the movements of their hands.ª
12 He will bring down Moab's high fortified walls,
　　level them, and throw them into the dust on the ground.

The LORD's People Praise Him for Salvation

26 ¹On that day this song will be sung in the land of Judah:

We have a strong city.
Its walls and fortifications provide safety.

2 Open the gates, and let the righteous nation come in,
　the nation that remains faithful.
3 With perfect peace you will protect those whose minds cannot be changed,
　because they trust you.
4 Trust the LORD always,
　because the LORD, the LORD alone, is an everlasting rock.
5 He has brought down those who live high in the towering city.
He levels it.
He levels it to the ground and throws it into the dust.
6 Feet trample it,
　　the feet of the oppressed,
　　the footsteps of the poor.

7 The path of the righteous is level.
　O Upright One, you make the road of the righteous smooth.
8 Certainly, we wait with hope for you, O LORD,
　ˎas we followˌ the path of your guiding principles.
　We want to remember you and your name.
9 With my soul I long for you at night.
　Yes, with my spirit I eagerly look for you.
When your guiding principles are on earth,
　those who live in the world learn to do what is right.
10 Although the wicked are shown pity,
　they do not learn to do what is right.
　They do what is wrong in the upright land
　　and do not see the majesty of the LORD.
11 O LORD, your power is visible, but they do not see it.
　They will see how devoted your people are,
　　and they will be put to shame.
Your burning anger will destroy your enemies.

12 O LORD, you will establish peace for us,
　since you have done everything for us.

ª 25:11 Hebrew meaning of "despite the movements of their hands" uncertain.

¹³ O LORD, our God, you are not the only master to rule us,
    but we acknowledge only you.
¹⁴ The wicked are dead.
    They are no longer alive.
        The spirits of the dead won't rise.
    You have punished them, destroyed them,
        and wiped out all memory of them.
¹⁵ You have expanded the nation, O LORD.
    You have expanded the nation.
    You are honored.
    You have extended all the land's boundaries.
¹⁶ O LORD, the people have come to you in trouble.
    They were humbled by oppression, by your discipline upon them.ᵃ
¹⁷ O LORD, when we are with you,
    we are like pregnant women ready to give birth.
        They writhe and cry out in their labor pains.
¹⁸ We were pregnant; we writhed with labor pains
        only to give birth to the wind.
    We weren't able to bring salvation to the land,
        and no new people were born on earth.
¹⁹ Your dead will live.
    Their corpses will rise.
    Those who lie dead in the dust will wake up and shout for joy,
        because your dew is a refreshing dew,
            and the earth will revive the spirits of the dead.

²⁰ My people, go to your rooms,
    and shut the doors behind you.
    Hide for a little while until his fury has ended.
²¹   The LORD is going to come out from his dwelling place
        to punish those who live on earth for their sins.
            The earth will uncover the blood shed on it
                and will no longer cover up its dead bodies.

The LORD's People Will Worship on His Holy Mountain

27 ¹ On that day the LORD will use his fierce and powerful sword
    to punish Leviathan,ᵃ that slippery snake,
        Leviathan, that twisting snake.
            He will kill that monster which lives in the sea.

² On that day sing about a delightful vineyard.
³   I, the LORD, watch over it.
    I water it continually.
    I watch over it day and night
        so that no one will harm it.
⁴   I am no longer angry.
        If only thorns and briars would confront me!
        I would fight them in battle and set all of them on fire.
⁵   Or else let them come to me for protection.
        Let them make peace with me.
            Yes, let them make peace with me.

⁶ In times to come Jacob will take root.
        Israel will blossom, bud,
            and fill the whole world with fruit.

⁷ Will the LORD hurt Israel as he hurt others who hurt them?
    Will he kill them as he killed others?
⁸ He punished Israel by sending it away.
    He removed it with a fierce blast from the east winds.ᵇ
⁹ In this way the wrongdoings of the descendants of Jacob are covered up.
    This is the way they will turn from their sins—
        when they turn all the altar stones into powdered chalk
        and no poles dedicated to the goddess Asherah
            or incense altars are left standing.

ᵃ 26:16 Hebrew meaning of this line uncertain.   ᵃ 27:1 Hebrew meaning uncertain.   ᵇ 27:8 Hebrew meaning of this verse uncertain.

¹⁰   The fortified city is isolated.
        The homestead is left deserted, abandoned like the desert.
        Calves will graze there.
                They will lie down.
                        They will feed on the branches.
¹¹   When the branches are dried up,
                they will be broken off.
        Women will come and build a fire with them.
                These people don't understand ⌊these things⌋.
                        That is why their maker won't have compassion on them,
                                and their Creator won't have pity on them.

¹²   On that day the LORD will begin his threshing*
                from the flowing stream of the Euphrates River
                        to the brook of Egypt.
        People of Israel, you will be gathered one by one.

¹³   On that day a ram's horn will be blown loudly.
                Those who are dying in Assyria
                        and those who are banished to Egypt
                                will come and worship the LORD
                                        on the holy mountain in Jerusalem.

Ephraim Will Fall

28 ¹ How horrible it will be for the arrogant drunks of Ephraim.
                Their glorious beauty is ⌊like⌋ a withered flower.
                        They are at the entrance to a fertile valley
                                where they lie drunk from wine.
²   The Lord has one who is strong and powerful.
                He is like a hailstorm, a destructive wind.
                He is like a thunderstorm, an overwhelming flood.
                He will throw them to the ground forcefully.
³   The arrogant drunks of Ephraim will be trampled underfoot.
⁴   Their glorious beauty is ⌊like⌋ a withered flower.
                They are at the entrance to a fertile valley.
                        They will be like figs that ripened early.
                                As soon as someone sees them,
                                        they will be taken and eaten.

⁵   When that day comes, the LORD of Armies will be
                like a glorious crown for his few remaining people.
⁶   He will give a spirit of justice to those who judge.
        He will give strength to those who defend the city gates in battle.

⁷   Priests and prophets stagger from wine and wobble from too much liquor.
                They stagger from too much liquor
                        and become confused from too much wine.
                They wobble because of their liquor.
                They stagger when they see visions.
                They swerve as they judge.
⁸   All the tables are covered with vomit and excrement.
                There isn't a clean place left.
⁹   To whom will they make the message understood?
        To whom will they explain this message?
                To children just weaned from milk?
                To those just taken from their ⌊mother's⌋ breasts?
¹⁰   They speak utter nonsense.*

¹¹   The LORD will speak to these people.
                He will mock them by speaking in a foreign language.
¹²   He will say to them,
                "This is a place for comfort.
                        This is a place of rest for those who are tired.
                                This is a place for them to rest."
        But they weren't willing to listen.
¹³   The LORD speaks utter nonsense to them.

ᶜ 27:12 Threshing is the process of beating stalks to separate them from the grain.   ᵃ 28:10 Or "Command for command, command for command, line for line, line for line, a little here, a little there." Also in verse 13.

That is why they will fall backwards.
That is why they will be hurt, trapped, and captured.

A Message to Jerusalem

14 So hear the word of the LORD, you foolish talkers
who rule the people in Jerusalem.
15 You say, "We made a treaty with death
and an agreement with the grave.
When the overwhelming disaster passes by,
it won't matter to us,
because we have taken refuge in our lies,
and falsehood is our hiding place."

16 This is what the Almighty LORD says:

I am going to lay a rock in Zion,
a rock that has been tested,
a precious cornerstone,
a solid foundation.
Whoever believes ˌin himˌ will not worry.
17 I will make justice a measuring line
and righteousness a plumb line.
Hail will sweep away your refuge of lies,
and floodwaters will wash away your hiding place.
18 Your treaty with death will be wiped away.
Your agreement with the grave will not stand.
When the overwhelming disaster passes by,
you will be trampled by it.
19   Each time it passes by it will take you.
It will pass by morning after morning,
during the day and during the night.
Understanding this message brings only terror.
20 The bed is too short to stretch out on.
The blanket is too narrow to serve as a cover.
21 The LORD will rise as he did on Mount Perazim.
He will wake up as he did in Gibeon Valley.
He will do his work, his unexpected work,
and perform his deeds, his mysterious deeds.
22 Now stop laughing, or your chains will be tightened,
because I have heard that the Almighty LORD of Armies
has finally determined to destroy the whole land.

23 Open your ears, and listen to me!
Pay attention, and hear me!
24 Does a farmer go on plowing every day so he can plant?
Does he continue to break up the soil and make furrows in the ground?
25   When he has smoothed its surface,
doesn't he scatter black cumin seed and plant cumin?
Doesn't he plant wild wheat in rows?
Doesn't he put barley in its own area
and winter wheat at its borders?
26 God will guide him in judgment,
and his God will teach him.

27 Black cumin isn't threshed[b] with a sledge,
and wagon wheels aren't rolled over cumin.
Black cumin is beaten with a rod
and cumin with a stick.
28 Grain is ground into flour, but the grinding eventually stops.
It will be threshed.
The wheels of his cart will roll over it,
but his horses won't crush it.
29 All of this has come from the LORD of Armies.
His counsel is wonderful, and his wisdom is great.

---

[b] 28:27 Threshing is the process of beating stalks to separate them from the grain.

The LORD's Word Will Be Hidden From Some but Revealed to Others

29 ¹ How horrible it will be for you Ariel, Ariel,[a]
the city where David camped.
Let year after year go by.
Let your annual festivals go on.

² I will torment Ariel,
and the city will be filled with people grieving and mourning.
The city will become like Ariel.

³ I will set up war camps all around you.
I will blockade you with towers.
I will put up mounds of dirt around you.

⁴ When you have fallen, you will speak as you lie on the ground.
Your words will be muffled by the dust.
Your voice will come out of the ground like that of a ghost.
Your words will be whispered from the dust.

⁵ Your many enemies will be like fine dust.
Your many foes will be like husks blown by the wind.
All of this will happen suddenly, unexpectedly.

⁶ The LORD of Armies will punish you
with thunder, earthquakes, and loud noises,
with windstorms, rainstorms, and fire storms.

⁷ The armies from all the nations will go to war against Ariel.
They will go to war against it, blockade it, and torment it.
All of this will be like a dream, like a vision in the night.

⁸ They will be like hungry people who dream that they're eating
and wake up to find they're hungry.
They will be like thirsty people who dream that they're drinking
and wake up to find they're lightheaded and parched with thirst.
This is what will happen to the armies from all the nations
that fight against Mount Zion.

⁹ If you confuse yourselves, you will be confused.
If you blind yourselves, you will be blinded.
You are drunk, but not from wine.
You stagger, but not from liquor.

¹⁰ The LORD has poured out on you a spirit of deep sleep.
He will shut your eyes. (Your eyes are the prophets.)
He will cover your heads. (Your heads are the seers.[b])

¹¹ To you all these visions will be like words in a book that is closed and sealed. You give this book to someone who can read, saying, "Please read this."
He answers, "I can't read it. It's sealed."
¹² Then you give the book to someone who can't read, saying, "Please read this."
He answers, "I can't read."
¹³ The Lord says,

"These people worship me with their mouths
and honor me with their lips.
But their hearts are far from me,
and their worship of me is ⌊based on⌋ rules made by humans.

¹⁴ That is why I am going to do something completely amazing
for these people once again.
The wisdom of their wise people will disappear.
The intelligence of their intelligent people will be hidden."

¹⁵ How horrible it will be for those
who try to hide their plans from the LORD.
Their deeds are done in the dark,
and they say, "No one can see us"
and "No one can recognize us."

¹⁶ You turn things upside down!
Is the potter no better than his clay?
Can something that has been made
say about its maker, "He didn't make me"?
Can a piece of pottery

---

[a] 29:1 *Ariel* is an unknown Hebrew word which may mean "lion of God," "mountain of God," or "fireplace."
[b] 29:10 A seer is a prophet.

say about the potter, "He doesn't understand"?

17 In a very short time Lebanon will be turned into a fertile field
and the fertile field will be considered a forest.

18 When that day comes, the deaf will hear the words written in the book.
The blind will see out of their gloom and darkness.

19 Humble people again will find joy in the LORD.
The poorest of people will find joy in the Holy One of Israel.

20 Tyrants will be gone.
Mockers will be finished.
All who look for ways to do wrong will come to an end:

21 those who make people sin with words,
those who lay traps for judges,
those who, without any reason, deny justice
to people who are in the right.

22 This is what the LORD, who saved Abraham, says about the descendants of Jacob:

Jacob will no longer be ashamed.
Jacob's face will no longer turn pale.

23 When they see all their children,
the children I made with my hands,
they will acknowledge my name as holy.
They will treat the Holy One of Jacob as holy.
They will stand in terror of the God of Israel.

24 Then those who are wayward in spirit will gain understanding,
and those who complain will accept instruction.

Judah Should Trust the LORD, Not Egypt

30 ¹ The LORD declares,

"How horrible it will be for those rebellious children.
They carry out plans, but not mine.
They make alliances against my will.
They pile sin on top of sin.

2 They go to Egypt without asking me.
They look for shelter under Pharaoh's protection
and look for refuge in Egypt's shadow.

3 But Pharaoh's protection will be their shame,
and the refuge in Egypt's shadow will be their disgrace.

4 Although Pharaoh's officials are in Zoan
and his messengers have reached Hanes,

5 the people of Judah will be put to shame
because that nation can't help them.
That nation can't give aid or help to them.
It can only offer shame and disgrace."

6 This is the divine revelation about the animals in the Negev.

"My people travel through lands
where they experience distress and hardship.
Lions and lionesses live there.
Vipers and poisonous snakes live there.
They carry their riches on the backs of young donkeys
and their treasures on the humps of camels
to a nation that can't help them.

7 Egypt's help is completely useless.
That is why I call it, 'Rahab[a] who sits still.'

8 Now, write this on a tablet for them, and inscribe it in a book
so that it will be there in the future as a permanent witness.

9 These people are rebellious and deceitful children,
children who refuse to listen to the LORD's teachings.

10 They say to the seers,[b] 'Don't see the future.'
They say to those who have visions,
'Don't have visions that tell us what is right.
Tell us what we want to hear. See illusions.

---

[a] 30:7 Rahab is the name of a demonic creature who opposes God.   [b] 30:10 A seer is a prophet.

11 Get out of our way! Stop blocking our path!
 Get the Holy One of Israel out of our sight.' "

¹² This is what the Holy One of Israel says:

 You have rejected this warning,
  trusted oppression and deceit,
  and leaned on them.
13 That is why your sin will be
  like a high wall with a bulging crack, ready to fall.
  All of a sudden it will fall.
14 It will break like pottery.
 It will be smashed, and nothing will be left of it.
  No piece will be big enough to carry live coals from a fireplace
   or to dip water from a reservoir.

¹⁵ This is what the Almighty LORD, the Holy One of Israel, says:

 You can be saved by returning to me.
 You can have rest.
 You can be strong by being quiet and by trusting me.
  But you don't want that.
16 You've said, "No, we'll flee on horses."
  So you flee.
 You've added, "We'll ride on fast horses."
  So those who chase you will also be fast.
17 One thousand people will flee when one person threatens them,
  and you will flee when five threaten you.
   Then you will be left alone
    like a flagpole on top of a mountain,
    like a signpost on a hill.
18 The LORD is waiting to be kind to you.
 He rises to have compassion on you.
  The LORD is a God of justice.
   Blessed are all those who wait for him.

The LORD Will Heal His People's Wounds

¹⁹ You will live in Zion, in Jerusalem. You won't cry anymore. The LORD will certainly have pity on you when you cry for help. As soon as he hears you, he will answer you. ²⁰ The Lord may give you troubles and hardships. But your teacher will no longer be hidden from you. You will see your teacher with your own eyes. ²¹ You will hear a voice behind you saying, "This is the way. Follow it, whether it turns to the right or to the left." ²² Then you will dishonor your silver-plated idols and your gold-covered statues. You will throw them away like clothing ruined by stains. You will say to them, "Get out!"

²³ The Lord will give you rain for the seed that you plant in the ground, and the food that the ground provides will be rich and nourishing. When that day comes, your cattle will graze in large pastures. ²⁴ The oxen and the donkeys which work the soil will eat a mixture of food that has been winnowed^c with forks and shovels. ²⁵ There will be brooks and streams on every lofty mountain and every high hill. When the day of the great slaughter comes, towers will fall. ²⁶ Then the light of the moon will be like the light of the sun. The light of the sun will be seven times as strong, like the light of seven days. When that day comes, the LORD will bandage his people's injuries and heal the wounds he inflicted.

27 The name of the LORD is going to come from far away.
  His anger is burning.
  His burden is heavy.
  His lips are filled with fury.
  His tongue is like a devouring flame.
28 His breath is like an overflowing stream.
  It rises neck high,
   sifting the nations with a sieve of destruction,
    placing a bit in the mouths of the people
     to lead them astray.
29 You will sing a song
  like the song you sing on a festival night.
 Your hearts will be happy like someone going out with a flute

---

^c 30:24 Winnowing is the process of separating husks from grain.

on the way to the LORD's mountain, to the rock of Israel.
³⁰ The LORD will make his majestic voice heard.
He will come down with all his might,
    with furious anger,
    with fire storms, windstorms, rainstorms, and hailstones.
³¹ At the sound of the LORD, the people of Assyria will be shattered.
He will strike them with his rod.
³² To the sound of tambourines and lyres, the LORD will pound on them.
He will fight them in battle, swinging his fists.
³³ Topheth was prepared long ago.
It was made ready for the king.
It was made deep and wide and piled high with plenty of burning logs.
The LORD's breath will be like a flood of burning sulfur,
    setting it on fire.

The LORD, Not the Egyptians, Will Protect His People From Assyria

31 ¹ How horrible it will be for those
    who go to Egypt for help,
    who rely on horses,
    who depend on many chariots,
    who depend on very strong war horses.
        They don't look to the Holy One of Israel.
        They don't seek the LORD.
²   He is wise and can bring about disaster.
        He doesn't take back his words.
        He rises against wicked people
            and against those who help troublemakers.
³ The Egyptians are humans, not gods.
    Their horses are flesh and blood, not spirit.
    When the LORD uses his powerful hand,
        the one who gives help will stumble,
        and the one who receives help will fall.
            Both will die together.

⁴ This is what the LORD said to me:

A lion, even a young lion, growls over its prey
    when a crowd of shepherds is called to fight it.
        It isn't frightened by their voices
        or disturbed by the noise they make.
So the LORD of Armies will come to fight for
    Mount Zion and its hill.
⁵ The LORD of Armies will defend Jerusalem like a hovering bird.
    He will defend it and rescue it.
    He will pass over it and protect it.
⁶ You people of Israel, return to the one
    whom you have so violently rebelled against.
⁷ When that day comes, all of you will reject
    the silver and gold idols
        that your sinful hands have made.
⁸ Then Assyrians will be killed with swords not made by human hands.
    Swords not made by human hands will destroy them.
    They will flee from battle,
        and their young men will be made to do forced labor.
⁹ In terror they will run to their stronghold,^a
    and their officers will be frightened at ⌞the sight of⌟ the battle flag.

The LORD declares this. His fire is in Zion and his furnace is in Jerusalem.

The LORD Will Pour Out His Spirit and Bring Peace

32 ¹ A king will rule with fairness,
        and officials will rule with justice.
² Then each ruler will be like a shelter from the wind
        and a hiding place from the rain.
    They will be like streams on parched ground
        and the shade of a large rock in a weary land.

^a 31:9 Hebrew meaning of this line uncertain.

3 Then the vision of those who can see won't be blurred,
   and the ears of those who can hear will pay attention.
4 Then those who are reckless will begin to understand,
   and those who stutter will speak quickly and clearly.
5 Godless fools will no longer be called nobles,
   nor will scoundrels be considered gentlemen.
6 Godless fools speak foolishness,
   and their minds plan evil
      in order to do ungodly things.
   They speak falsely about the LORD.
   They let people go hungry
   and withhold water from thirsty people.
7 The tricks of scoundrels are evil.
   They devise wicked plans in order to ruin poor people with lies,
      even when needy people plead for justice.
8 But honorable people act honorably
   and stand firm for what is honorable.

9 Get up, and listen to me, you pampered women.
   Hear what I say, you overconfident daughters.
10   In a little less than a year
         you overconfident women will tremble,
            because the grape harvest will fail
               and no fruit will be brought in ˎfrom the fieldsˎ.
11 Shudder, you pampered women.
   Tremble, you overconfident women.
   Take off your clothes, walk around naked,
      and wear sackcloth around your waists.
12 Beat your breasts as you mourn for the fields,
      for the vines bearing grapes.
13 Mourn for my people's land where thorns and briars will grow.
   Mourn for all the happy homes in a joyful city.
14 Palaces will be deserted.
   Noisy cities will be abandoned.
   Fortresses and watchtowers will become permanent caves.
      They will be a delight for wild donkeys and pastures for flocks
15   until the Spirit is poured on us from on high.
   Then the wilderness will be turned into a fertile field,
      and the fertile field will be considered a forest.
16 Then justice will live in the wilderness,
      and righteousness will be at home in the fertile field.
17 Then an act of righteousness will bring about peace,
      calm, and safety forever.
18 My people will live in a peaceful place,
      in safe homes and quiet places of rest.
19 The forest will be flattened because of hail,
      and the city will be completely leveled.
20 Blessed are those who plant beside every stream
      and those who let oxen and donkeys roam freely.

The LORD Will Rescue Jerusalem From Assyria

33 1 How horrible it will be for you, you destroyer,
      although you haven't been destroyed.
   How horrible it will be for you, you traitor,
      although you haven't been betrayed.
   When you've finished destroying, you will be destroyed.
   When you've finished being a traitor, you will be betrayed.

2 O LORD, have pity on us.
    We wait with hope for you.
   Be our strength in the morning.
      Yes, be our savior in times of trouble.
3 People flee from the noise of ˎyourˎ army.
   Nations scatter when you attack.
4 You nations, your loot is gathered as grasshoppers harvest a crop.
      Like swarming locusts, people rush for your loot.

5 The LORD is honored because he lives on high.
    He will fill Zion with justice and righteousness.
6   He will be the foundation of your future.
      The riches of salvation are wisdom and knowledge.
The fear of the LORD is ⌊your⌋ treasure.

7 Heroes cry in the streets.
    Messengers of peace cry bitterly.
8 Highways are deserted.
Travelers stop traveling.
Agreements are broken.
Witnesses[a] are rejected.
People are no longer respected.
9 The country grieves and wastes away.
Lebanon is ashamed and is decaying.
Sharon has become like a wilderness.
Bashan and Carmel are shaken.

10 The LORD says, "Now I will arise.
    Now I will get up.
    Now I will be lifted up."
11 You will be pregnant with hay.
You will give birth to straw.
Your breath will be a fire which will burn you up.
12 People will be cremated.
    They will be set on fire like dry thornbushes.

13 Hear what I have done, you people who are far away!
Acknowledge my might, you people who are near!
14 The sinners in Zion are terrified.
    Trembling seizes the ungodly.
Can any of us live through a fire that destroys?
Can any of us live through a fire that burns forever?
15   The person who does what is right and speaks the truth will live.
      He rejects getting rich by extortion and refuses to take bribes.
      He refuses to listen to those who are plotting murders.
      He doesn't look for evil things to do.
16   This person will live on high.
      His stronghold will be a fortress made of rock.
        He will have plenty of food
          and a dependable supply of water.

17 Your eyes will see how handsome the king is.
You will see a land that stretches into the distance.
18 Your mind will be thinking of the terrors ⌊in the past⌋.
    Where are the scribes?
    Where are the tax collectors?
    Where are those who counted the towers?
19 You will no longer see those savage people,
    those people with an unrecognizable language,
      with a foreign language that you can't understand.
20 Look at Zion, the city of our festivals.
Your eyes will see Jerusalem as a peaceful place.
    It is a tent that can't be moved.
      Its tent pegs will never be pulled out,
        and none of its ropes will be broken.
21 The LORD will be our mighty defender
    in a place surrounded by wide rivers and streams.
      Ships with oars won't travel on them.
      Stately ships won't sail on them.
22 The LORD is our judge.
The LORD is our lawgiver.
The LORD is our king.
The LORD is our savior.

---

[a] 33:8 Dead Sea Scrolls; Masoretic Text "Cities."

23   Your ropes hang loose,
         your mast isn't secure,
         and your sail isn't spread out.
     A large amount of loot will be distributed.
     Lame people will carry off your loot.
24   No one who lives ˌin Zion˒ will say, "I'm sick."
     The sins of its inhabitants will be forgiven.

The Fall of Edom Is a Glimpse of the Lᴏʀᴅ's Judgment

34 ¹ Come close, you nations, and listen.
         Pay attention, you people.
         The earth, everyone in it,
            the world, and everything on it will listen.
2   The Lᴏʀᴅ is angry with all the nations.
     He is furious with all their armies.
         He has claimed them for destruction.
         He has handed them over to be slaughtered.
3   Their dead bodies will be thrown out.
                A stench will rise from their corpses,
                   Mountains will be red with their blood.
4   All the stars in the sky will rot.
         The heavens will be rolled up like a scroll.
     The stars will fall
         like leaves from a grapevine,
         like green figs from a fig tree.
5   When my sword is covered ˌwith blood˒ in the heavens,
         it will fall on Edom
            and on the people I've claimed for destruction.
6   The Lᴏʀᴅ's sword is covered with blood.
         It is covered with fat,
            with the blood of lambs and goats,
            with the fat of rams' kidneys.
     The Lᴏʀᴅ will receive a sacrifice in Bozrah,
         a huge slaughter in the land of Edom.
7   Wild oxen will be killed with them,
         young bulls along with rams.
     Their land will be drenched with blood.
     Their dust will be covered with fat.

8   The Lᴏʀᴅ will have a day of vengeance,
         a year of revenge in defense of Zion.
9   Edom's streams will be turned to tar.
         Its soil will be turned to burning sulfur.
         Its land will become blazing tar.
10   They will not be extinguished day or night,
                and smoke will always go up from them.
     Edom will lie in ruins for generations.
         No one will ever travel through it.
11   Pelicans and herons will take possession of the land.
                Owls and crows will live there.
     He will stretch the measuring line of chaos
         and the plumb line of destruction over it.
12   There are no nobles to rule a kingdom.
         All of its princes have disappeared.
13   Its palaces are covered with thorns.
     Its fortresses have nettles and thistles.
         It will become a home for jackals
            and a place for ostriches.
14   Hyenas will meet with jackals.
            Male goats will call to their mates.
            Screech owls will rest there
                and find a resting place for themselves.
15   Owls will make their nests there, lay eggs, and hatch them.
            They will gather their young
                in the shadow of ˌtheir wings˒.
            Vultures also will gather there,
                each one with its mate.

¹⁶ Search the LORD's book, and read it.
    Not one of these animals will be missing.
    Not one will lack a mate,
       because the LORD has commanded it,
         and his Spirit will gather them together.
¹⁷ He is the one who throws dice for them,
    and his hand divides up ˌthe landˌ for them with a measuring line.
    They will possess it permanently
    and live there for generations.

The LORD's People Will Have Joy

35 ¹ The desert and the dry land will be glad,
    and the wilderness will rejoice and blossom.
² Like a lily the land will blossom.
    It will rejoice and sing with joy.
    It will have the glory of Lebanon, the majesty of Carmel and Sharon.
    Everyone will see the glory of the LORD, the majesty of our God.

³ Strengthen limp hands.
    Steady weak knees.
⁴ Tell those who are terrified,
    "Be brave; don't be afraid.
      Your God will come with vengeance, with divine revenge.
        He will come and rescue you."

⁵ Then the eyes of the blind will be opened,
    and the ears of the deaf will be unplugged.
⁶ Then those who are lame will leap like deer,
    and those who cannot speak will shout for joy.
    Water will gush out into the desert,
    and streams will gush out into the wilderness.
⁷ Then the hot sand will become a pool,
    and dry ground will have springs.
    Grass will become cattails and rushes
      in the home of jackals.
⁸ A highway will be there, a roadway.
    It will be called the Holy Road.
      Sinners won't travel on it.
    It will be for those who walk on it.
      Godless fools won't wander ˌonto itˌ.
⁹ Lions won't be there.
    Wild animals won't go on it.
      They won't be found there.
    But the people reclaimed ˌby the LORDˌ will walk ˌon itˌ.
¹⁰ The people ransomed by the LORD will return.
    They will come to Zion singing with joy.
      Everlasting happiness will be on their heads ˌas a crownˌ.
        They will be glad and joyful.
        They will have no sorrow or grief.

The LORD Rescues Judah From the Assyrians—2 Kings 18:13–19:19

36 ¹ In Hezekiah's fourteenth year as king, King Sennacherib of Assyria attacked all the fortified cities of Judah and captured them. ² Then the king of Assyria sent his field commander with a large army from Lachish to King Hezekiah at Jerusalem. He stood at the channel for the Upper Pool on the road to Laundryman's Field.

³ Eliakim, who was in charge of the palace and was the son of Hilkiah, Shebna the scribe, and Joah, who was the royal historian and the son of Asaph, went out to the field commander. ⁴ He said to them, "Tell Hezekiah, 'This is what the great king, the king of Assyria, says: What makes you so confident? ⁵ You give useless advice about getting ready for war. Whom, then, do you trust for support in your rebellion against me? ⁶ Look! When you trust Egypt, you're trusting a broken stick for a staff. If you lean on it, it stabs your hand and goes through it. This is what Pharaoh (the king of Egypt) is like for everyone who trusts him. ⁷ Suppose you tell me, "We're trusting the LORD our God." He's the god whose places of worship and altars Hezekiah got rid of. Hezekiah told Judah and Jerusalem, "Worship at this altar." '"

[8] "Now, make a deal with my master, the king of Assyria. I'll give you 2,000 horses if you can put riders on them. [9] How can you defeat my master's lowest-ranking officers when you trust Egypt for chariots and horses?

[10] "Have I come to destroy this country without the LORD on my side? The LORD said to me, 'Attack this country, and destroy it.' "

[11] Then Eliakim, Shebna, and Joah said to the field commander, "Speak to us in Aramaic, since we understand it. Don't speak to us in the Judean language as long as there are people on the wall listening."

[12] But the field commander asked, "Did my master send me to tell these things only to you and your master? Didn't he send me to the men sitting on the wall who will have to eat their own excrement and drink their own urine with you?"

[13] Then the field commander stood and shouted loudly in the Judean language, "Listen to the great king, the king of Assyria. [14] This is what the king says: Don't let Hezekiah deceive you. He can't rescue you. [15] Don't let Hezekiah get you to trust the LORD by saying, 'The LORD will certainly rescue us, and this city will not be put under the control of the king of Assyria.' [16] Don't listen to Hezekiah, because this is what the king of Assyria says: Make peace with me! Come out, and give yourselves up to me! Everyone will eat from his own grapevine and fig tree and drink from his own cistern. [17] Then I will come and take you away to a country like your own. It's a country with grain and new wine, a country with bread and vineyards. [18] Don't let Hezekiah mislead you by saying to you, 'The LORD will rescue us.' Did any of the gods of the nations rescue their countries from the king of Assyria? [19] Where are the gods of Hamath and Arpad? Where are the gods of Sepharvaim? Did they rescue Samaria from my control? [20] Did the gods of these countries rescue them from my control? Could the LORD then rescue Jerusalem from my control?"

[21] They were silent and didn't say anything to him because the king commanded them not to answer him.

[22] Then Eliakim, who was in charge of the palace and was son of Hilkiah, Shebna the scribe, and Joah, who was the royal historian and the son of Asaph, went to Hezekiah with their clothes torn in grief. They told him the message from the field commander.

37 [1] When King Hezekiah heard the message, he tore his clothes in grief, covered himself with sackcloth, and went into the LORD's temple. [2] Then he sent Eliakim, who was in charge of the palace, Shebna the scribe, and the leaders of the priests, clothed in sackcloth, to the prophet Isaiah, son of Amoz. [3] They said to him, "This is what Hezekiah says: Today is a day filled with misery, punishment, and disgrace. We are like a woman who is about to give birth but doesn't have the strength to do it. [4] The LORD your God may have heard the words of the field commander. His master, the king of Assyria, sent him to defy the living God. The LORD your God may punish him because of the message that the LORD your God heard. Pray for the few people who are left."

[5] So King Hezekiah's men went to Isaiah. [6] Isaiah answered them, "Say this to your master, 'This is what the LORD says: Don't be afraid of the message that you heard when the Assyrian king's assistants slandered me. [7] I'm going to put a spirit in him so that he will hear a rumor and return to his own country. I'll have him assassinated in his own country.' "

[8] The field commander returned and found the king of Assyria fighting against Libnah. He had heard that the king left Lachish. [9] Now, Sennacherib heard that King Tirhakah of Sudan was coming to fight him.

When he heard this, he again sent messengers to Hezekiah, saying, [10] "Tell King Hezekiah of Judah, 'Don't let the god whom you trust deceive you by saying that Jerusalem will not be put under the control of the king of Assyria. [11] You heard what the kings of Assyria did to all countries, how they totally destroyed them. Will you be rescued? [12] Did the gods of the nations which my ancestors destroyed rescue Gozan, Haran, Rezeph, and the people of Eden who were in Telassar? [13] Where is the king of Hamath, the king of Arpad, and the king of the cities of Sepharvaim, Hena, and Ivvah?' "

[14] Hezekiah took the letter from the messengers, read it, and went to the LORD's temple. He spread it out in front of the LORD [15] and prayed to the LORD, [16] "LORD of Armies, God of Israel, you are enthroned over the angels.[a] You alone are God of the kingdoms of the world. You made heaven and earth. [17] Turn your ear toward me, LORD, and listen. Open your eyes, LORD, and see. Listen to the entire message that Sennacherib sent to defy the living God. [18] It is true, LORD, that the kings of Assyria have leveled every country.[b] [19] They have thrown the gods from these countries into fires because these gods aren't real gods. They're only wooden and stone statues made by human hands. So the Assyrians have destroyed them. [20] Now, LORD our God, rescue us from Assyria's control so that all the kingdoms on earth will know that you alone are the LORD."

---

[a] 37:16 Or "cherubim."   [b] 37:18 Dead Sea Scrolls, Greek; Masoretic Text "every country and their country."

Isaiah's Prophecy Against King Sennacherib of Assyria—2 Kings 19:20–37

21 Then Isaiah, son of Amoz, sent a message to Hezekiah, "This is what the LORD God of Israel says: You prayed to me about King Sennacherib of Assyria. **22** This is the message that the LORD speaks to him,

> 'My dear people in Zion despise you and laugh at you.
> My people in Jerusalem shake their heads behind your back.
> **23**   Whom are you defying and slandering?
>   Against whom are you shouting?
>   Who are you looking at so arrogantly?
>   It is the Holy One of Israel!
> **24**   Through your servants you defy the Lord and say,
>   "With my many chariots I'll ride up the high mountains,
>   up the slopes of Lebanon.
>   I'll cut down its tallest cedars and its finest cypresses.
>   I'll come to its most distant heights
>   and its most fertile forests.
> **25**   I'll dig wells and drink water.
>   I'll dry up all the streams of Egypt
>   with the trampling of my feet."
>
> **26**   " 'Haven't you heard? I did this long ago.
>   I planned it in the distant past.
>   Now I make it happen so that you will turn fortified cities
>   into piles of rubble.
> **27**   Those who live in these cities are weak, discouraged, and ashamed.
>   They will be like plants in the field,
>   like fresh, green grass on the roofs,
>   dried up by the east wind.
> **28**   I know when you ˻get up˼ and sit down,
>   when you go out and come in,
>   and how you rage against me.
> **29**   Since you rage against me and your boasting has reached my ears,
>   I will put my hook in your nose
>   and my bridle in your mouth.
>   I will make you go back the way you came.

30 " 'And this will be a sign for you, Hezekiah: You will eat what grows by itself this year, and the next year you will eat what comes up by itself. But in the third year you will plant and harvest, plant vineyards, and eat what is produced. **31** Those few people from the nation of Judah who escape will again take root and produce crops. **32** Those few people will go out from Jerusalem, and those who escape will go out from Mount Zion. The LORD of Armies is determined to do this.'

33 "This is what the LORD says about the king of Assyria:

> He will never come into this city,
>   shoot an arrow here,
>   hold a shield in front of it,
>   or put up dirt ramps to attack it.
> **34**   He will go back the way he came,
>   and he won't come into this city,"
>   declares the LORD of Armies.
> **35**   "I will shield this city to rescue it for my sake
>   and for the sake of my servant David."

36 The LORD's angel went out and killed 185,000 ˻soldiers˼ in the Assyrian camp. When the Judeans got up early in the morning, they saw all the corpses. **37** Then King Sennacherib of Assyria left. He went home to Nineveh and stayed there. **38** While he was worshiping in the temple of his god Nisroch, Adrammelech and Sharezer, his sons, assassinated him and escaped to the land of Ararat. His son Esarhaddon succeeded him as king.

Hezekiah's Illness—2 Kings 20:1–11; 2 Chronicles 32:24

38 **1** In those days Hezekiah became sick and was about to die. The prophet Isaiah, son of Amoz, came to him and said, "This is what the LORD says: Give final instructions to your household, because you're about to die. You won't get well."

2 Hezekiah turned to the wall and prayed to the LORD. **3** "Please, LORD, remember how I've lived faithfully and sincerely in your presence. I've done what you consider right." And he cried bitterly.

[4] Then the LORD spoke his word to Isaiah, [5] "Go and say to Hezekiah, 'This is what the LORD God of your ancestor David says: I've heard your prayer. I've seen your tears. I'm going to give you 15 more years to live. [6] I'll rescue you and defend this city from the control of the king of Assyria.' "

[7] ⌞Isaiah said,⌟ "This is your sign from the LORD that he will do what he promises. [8] The sun made a shadow that went down the stairway of Ahaz's upper palace. I'm going to make the shadow go back ten steps." So the sun on the stairway went back up the ten steps it had gone down.

[9] King Hezekiah of Judah wrote this after he was sick and became well again:

[10]   I thought that in the prime of my life
          I would go down to the gates of Sheol
          and be robbed of the rest of my life.
[11]   I thought that I wouldn't see the LORD in this world.
       Even with all the people in the world,
          I thought I would never see another person.
[12]   My life was over.
          You rolled it up like a shepherd's tent.
          You rolled up my life like a weaver.
          You cut me off from the loom.
          You ended my life in one day.
[13]   I cried out until morning
          as if a lion had crushed all my bones.
          You ended my life in one day.
[14]   I chirped like swallows and cranes.
       I cooed like doves.
       My eyes were tired from looking up to heaven.
          I've suffered miserably, O Lord!
          Please help me!

[15]   What can I say now that he has spoken to me?
       He has done this.
       I will be careful the rest of my life because of my bitter experience.[a]
[16]   Lord, people live in spite of such things,
          and I have the will to live in spite of them.
          You give me health and keep me alive.
[17]   Now my bitter experience turns into peace.
          You have saved me and kept me from the rotting pit.
          You have thrown all my sins behind you.
[18]   Sheol doesn't thank you!
       Death doesn't praise you!
          Those who go down to the pit cannot expect you to be faithful.
[19]   Those who are living praise you as I do today.
          Fathers make your faithfulness known to their children.
[20]   The LORD is going to rescue me,
          so let us play stringed instruments.
          We live our lives in the LORD's temple.

[21] Then Isaiah said, "Take a fig cake, and place it over the boil so that the king will get well."
[22] Hezekiah asked, "What is the sign that I'll go to the LORD's temple?"[b]

Hezekiah Shows the Babylonians His Treasures—2 Kings 20:12–19; 2 Chronicles 32:31–33

39 [1] At that time Baladan's son, King Merodach Baladan of Babylon, sent letters and a present to Hezekiah. He had heard that Hezekiah had been sick and had recovered. [2] Hezekiah was so happy with them that he showed the messengers his warehouse: the silver, gold, balsam, fine olive oil, his entire armory, and everything in his treasury. Hezekiah showed them everything in his palace and every corner of his kingdom.

[3] Then the prophet Isaiah came to King Hezekiah and asked, "What did these men say? And where did they come from?"

Hezekiah answered, "They came to me from the distant country of Babylon."

[4] Isaiah asked, "What did they see in your palace?"

Hezekiah answered, "They saw everything in my palace, and I showed them everything in my treasury."

---

[a] 38:15 Hebrew meaning of this line uncertain.   [b] 38:22 Verses 21 and 22 have been placed after verse 6 to express the complex Hebrew paragraph structure more clearly in English. See 2 Kings 20:6–9.

⁵ Isaiah said to Hezekiah, "Hear the word of the LORD of Armies! ⁶ The LORD says, 'The days are going to come when everything in your palace, everything your ancestors have stored up to this day, will be taken away to Babylon. Nothing will be left. ⁷ Some of your own descendants will be taken away. They will become officials in the palace of the king of Babylon.'"

⁸ Hezekiah said to Isaiah, "The LORD's word that you have spoken is good." He added, "Just let there be peace and security as long as I live."

Comfort My People

40 ¹ "Comfort my people! Comfort them!" says your God.
   ² "Speak tenderly to Jerusalem and announce to it
         that its time of hard labor is over
            and its wrongs have been paid for.
               It has received from the LORD double for all its sins."

³ A voice cries out in the desert:

   "Clear a way for the LORD.
   Make a straight highway in the wilderness for our God.
⁴   Every valley will be raised.
         Every mountain and hill will be lowered.
         Steep places will be made level.
         Rough places will be made smooth.
⁵   Then the LORD's glory will be revealed
         and all people will see it together.
            The LORD has spoken."

⁶ A voice called, "Call out!"
   I asked, "What should I call out?"

   "Call out: All people are like grass,
      and all their beauty is like a flower in the field.
⁷   Grass dries up,
         and flowers wither when the LORD's breath blows on them.
            Yes, people are like grass.
⁸   Grass dries up,
         and flowers wither,
            but the word of our God will last forever."

⁹   Go up a high mountain, Zion.
         Tell the good news!
      Call out with a loud voice, Jerusalem.
         Tell the good news!
      Raise your voice without fear.
         Tell the cities of Judah:
            "Here is your God!"

¹⁰   The Almighty LORD is coming with power
         to rule with authority.
      His reward is with him,
         and the people he has won arrive ahead of him.
¹¹   Like a shepherd he takes care of his flock.
         He gathers the lambs in his arms.
         He carries them in his arms.
         He gently helps the sheep and their lambs.

God Gives Strength to Those Who Depend on Him

¹²   Who has measured the water of the sea[a] with the palm of his hand
         or measured the sky with the length of his hand?
      Who has held the dust of the earth in a bushel basket
         or weighed the mountains on a scale and the hills on a balance?
¹³   Who has directed the Spirit of the LORD
         or instructed him as his adviser?
¹⁴   Whom did he consult?
            Who gave him understanding?
            Who taught him the right way?

---

[a] 40:12 Dead Sea Scrolls; Masoretic Text "Who has measured the water."

Who taught him knowledge?
Who informed him about the way to understanding?

15 The nations are like a drop in a bucket
and are considered to be like dust on a scale.
The weight of the islands is like fine dust.
16 All the trees in Lebanon are not enough to burn an offering.
Its wild animals are not enough for a single burnt offering.
17 All the nations amount to nothing in his presence.
He considers them less than nothing and worthless.
18 To whom, then, can you compare God?
To what statue can you compare him?

19 Craftsmen make idols.
Goldsmiths cover them with gold.
Silversmiths make silver chains for them.
20 The poorest people choose wood that will not rot
and search out skillful craftsmen
to set up idols that will not fall over.
21 Don't you know?
Haven't you heard?
Haven't you been told from the beginning?
Don't you understand the foundations of the earth?
22 God is enthroned above the earth,
and those who live on it are like grasshoppers.
He stretches out the sky like a canopy
and spreads it out like a tent to live in.
23 He makes rulers unimportant
and makes earthly judges worth nothing.
24 They have hardly been planted.
They have hardly been sown.
They have hardly taken root in the ground.
Then he blows on them and they wither,
and a windstorm sweeps them away like straw.
25 "To whom, then, can you compare me?
Who is my equal?" asks the Holy One.

26 Look at the sky and see.
Who created these things?
Who brings out the stars one by one?
He calls them all by name.
Because of the greatness of his might and the strength of his power,
not one of them is missing.
27 Jacob, why do you complain?
Israel, why do you say,
"My way is hidden from the LORD,
and my rights are ignored by my God"?
28 Don't you know?
Haven't you heard?
The eternal God, the LORD, the Creator of the ends of the earth,
doesn't grow tired or become weary.
His understanding is beyond reach.
29 He gives strength to those who grow tired
and increases the strength of those who are weak.
30 Even young people grow tired and become weary,
and young men will stumble and fall.
31 Yet, the strength of those who wait with hope in the LORD
will be renewed.
They will soar on wings like eagles.
They will run and won't become weary.
They will walk and won't grow tired.

The Nations Chose Idols, but the LORD Chose Israel

41 ¹ "Be silent and listen to me, you coastlands.
Let the people gain new strength.
Let them come near and speak.
Let us come together for judgment.

2 "Who has raised up from the east
       someone to whom the LORD gives victory with every step he takes?
          Nations are handed over to him.
             He defeats kings.
             With his sword he turns them into dust.
             With his bow he turns them into straw blown by the wind.
3   He chases them, marching by safely
                on a path his feet have never traveled before.
4 Who has accomplished this?
   Who has determined the course of history from the beginning?
       I, the LORD, was there first, and I will be there to the end.
       I am the one!"

5 The coastlands have seen him and are afraid.
   The ends of the earth tremble.
       They have come near and gathered together.
6 People help their neighbors
       and say to their relatives, "Be brave!"
7 Craftsmen encourage goldsmiths.
   Metalsmiths encourage blacksmiths who work at their anvils.
       They say that their soldering is good.
          And they fasten things with nails so they won't move.

8 "But you are my servant Israel,
       Jacob, whom I have chosen,
          the descendant of Abraham, my dear friend.
9 I have taken you from the ends of the earth
       and called you from its most distant places.
   I said to you, 'You are my servant.
       I've chosen you; I haven't rejected you.'
10 Don't be afraid, because I am with you.
   Don't be intimidated; I am your God.
       I will strengthen you.
       I will help you.
       I will support you with my victorious right hand.

11 "Everyone who is angry with you
       will be ashamed and disgraced.
   Those who oppose you
       will be reduced to nothing and disappear.
12 You will search for your enemies,
       but you will not find them.
   Those who are at war with you
       will be reduced to nothing and no longer exist.
13 I, the LORD your God, hold your right hand
       and say to you, 'Don't be afraid; I will help you.'
14 Don't be afraid, Jacob, you worm.
   You people of Israel, I will help you,"
       declares the LORD, your Defender, the Holy One of Israel.
15 "I am going to make you into a new threshing[a] sledge
       with sharp, double-edged teeth.
   You will thresh the mountains and crush them to dust.
       You will turn the hills into straw.
16 You will winnow[b] them.
       The wind will carry them away.
       The windstorm will scatter them.
   But you will find joy in the LORD
       and praise the Holy One of Israel.

17 "The poor and needy are looking for water, but there is none.
       Their tongues are parched with thirst.
   I, the LORD, will answer them.
   I, the God of Israel, will not abandon them.
18   I will make rivers flow on bare hilltops.
       I will make springs flow through valleys.

---

[a] 41:15 Threshing is the process of beating stalks to separate them from the grain.   [b] 41:16 Winnowing is the process of separating husks from grain.

I will turn deserts into lakes.
I will turn dry land into springs.
19 I will plant cedar, acacia, myrtle, and wild olive trees in the desert.
I will place cedar, fir, and cypress trees together in the wilderness.
20 People will see and know.
Together they will consider and understand
   that the LORD's power has done this,
   that the Holy One of Israel has created it.

21 "Present your case," says the LORD.
"Bring forward your best arguments," says Jacob's king.
22 "Bring ˻your idols˼ so they can tell us what's going to happen.
   Explain past events that your idols told you about
      so that we may consider them
        and know what their outcome will be.
         Tell us about future events.
23 Tell us what's going to happen
   so that we may know that you are gods.
Yes, do something, good or evil,
   to intimidate us and make us afraid.
24 You are nothing!
You can't do anything!
   Whoever chooses you is disgusting.

25 "I have raised up someone from the north, and he has come.
He will call on my name from the east.
He will attack rulers as if they were mud,
   as if he were treading on clay like a potter.
26 Who revealed this from the beginning so that we could know it?
Who revealed this from the past so that we could say that he was right?
No one revealed it.
No one announced it.
No one heard your words.
27 I was the first to tell Zion, 'Look, here they are.'
I gave Jerusalem a messenger with the good news.
28 When I look, there is no one.
There is no one to advise them.
When I ask them a question,
   will they give an answer?
29 All of them are nothing.[c]
They can't do anything.
Their statues are nothing but air."

The LORD's Servant Will Bring Righteousness to the World

42 ¹ Here is my servant, whom I support.
Here is my chosen one, with whom I am pleased.
I have put my Spirit on him.
He will bring justice to the nations.
2 He will not cry out or raise ˻his voice˼.
He will not make his voice heard in the streets.
3 He will not break off a damaged cattail.
He will not even put out a smoking wick.
He will faithfully bring about justice.
4 He will not be discouraged or crushed
   until he has set up justice on the earth.
The coastlands will wait for his teachings.

5 The LORD God created the heavens and stretched them out.
He shaped the earth and all that comes from it.
He gave life to the people who are on it
   and breath to those who walk on it.

This is what the LORD God says:

6 I, the LORD, have called you to do what is right.
I will take hold of your hand.

---

c 41:29 Dead Sea Scrolls, Syriac, Targum; Masoretic Text "They are false."

I will protect you.
I will appoint you as my promise[a] to the people,
as my light to the nations.
7   You will give sight to the blind,
bring prisoners out of prisons,
and bring those who live in darkness
out of dungeons.
8   I am the LORD; that is my name.
I will not give my glory to anyone else
or the praise I deserve to idols.
9   What I said in the past has come true.
I will reveal new things before they happen.

A Song About the LORD, the Warrior

10   Sing a new song to the LORD.
Sing his praise from the ends of the earth,
you people who sail on the seas
and all the creatures that live in them,
you coastlands and all who live on them.
11   Let those who live in the desert and its cities raise their voices.
Let those who live in the settlements of Kedar praise him.
Let those who live in Sela sing for joy.
Let them shout from the tops of the mountains.
12   Let them give glory to the LORD
and announce his praise on the coastlands.
13   The LORD marches out like a warrior.
He prepares himself for battle like a soldier.
He shouts, gives the battle cry, and overpowers his enemies.

14   I have been silent for a long time.
I kept quiet and held myself back.
But like a woman in childbirth I will cry out.
I will gasp and pant.
15   I will lay waste to mountains and hills.
I will dry up all their vegetation.
I will turn rivers into islands.
I will dry up ponds.
16   I will lead the blind on unfamiliar roads.
I will lead them on unfamiliar paths.
I will turn darkness into light in front of them.
I will make rough places smooth.
These are the things I will do for them,
and I will never abandon them.
17   Then those who trust idols
and those who say to statues,
"You are our gods"
will be turned away and put to shame.

The LORD Will Bring Israel Home

18   Listen, you deaf people.
Look, you blind people, so that you can see.
19   Who is blind except my servant
or deaf like the messenger I send?
Who is blind like the one who has my trust
or blind like the servant of the LORD?
20   You have seen much, but you do not observe anything.
Your ears are open, but you hear nothing.
21   The LORD is pleased because he does what is right.
He praises the greatness of his teachings and makes them glorious.
22   But these people are robbed and looted.
They are all trapped in pits and hidden in prisons.
They have become prey with no one to rescue them.
They have become loot with no one to say, "Give it back."
23   Who among you will listen to this?
Is there anyone who will pay attention and listen in the future?

---

[a] 42:6 Or "covenant."

²⁴ Who gave Jacob away as loot
and handed Israel over to robbers?
Wasn't it the LORD, against whom we have sinned?
    They didn't want to live his way.
    They didn't obey his teachings.
²⁵ So he poured out his burning anger and the horrors of war on them.
    It engulfed them in flames, but they did not understand.
    It burned them, but they did not take it to heart.

43 ¹ The LORD created Jacob and formed Israel. Now, this is what the LORD says:

Do not be afraid, because I have reclaimed you.
    I have called you by name; you are mine.
² When you go through the sea, I am with you.
When you go through rivers, they will not sweep you away.
When you walk through fire, you will not be burned,
    and the flames will not harm you.
³ I am the LORD your God, the Holy One of Israel, your Savior.
    Egypt is the ransom I exchanged for you.
    Sudan and Seba are the price I paid for you.
⁴ Since you are precious to me, you are honored and I love you.
    I will exchange others for you.
        Nations will be the price I pay for your life.

⁵ Do not be afraid, because I am with you.
    I will bring your descendants from the east
        and gather you from the west.
⁶ I will say to the north, "Give them up,"
    and to the south, "Do not keep them."
Bring my sons from far away
    and my daughters from the ends of the earth.
⁷ Bring everyone who is called by my name,
    whom I created for my glory,
    whom I formed and made.
⁸ Bring the people who are blind but still have eyes,
    the people who are deaf but still have ears.
⁹ All nations have gathered together, and people have assembled.
    Who among them could have revealed this?
    Who among them could have foretold this to us?
        They should bring their witnesses to prove that they were right.
            Let the people hear them. Then they will say that it is true.

¹⁰ "You are my witnesses," declares the LORD.
"I have chosen you as my servant
    so that you can know and believe in me
        and understand that I am the one ˌwho did thisˌ.
No god was formed before me,
    and there will be none after me.
¹¹ I alone am the LORD,
    and there is no savior except me.
¹² I have revealed it to you, I have saved you,
    and I have announced it to you.
        There was no foreign ˌgodˌ among you.
You are my witnesses that I am God," declares the LORD.
¹³ "From the ˌfirstˌ day I was the one ˌwho did thisˌ.
    No one can rescue people from my power.
When I do something, who can undo it?"
¹⁴ This is what the LORD, your Defender, the Holy One of Israel, says:

For your sake I will send ˌan armyˌ to Babylon.
    I will bring back all the Babylonian refugees
        in the ships that they take pride in.
¹⁵ I am the LORD, your Holy One,
    the Creator of Israel, your King.

Despite the People of Israel's Past Sin, the LORD Will Forgive Them
¹⁶ The LORD makes a path through the sea
    and a road through the strong currents.

17 He leads chariots and horses, an army and reinforcements.
(They lie down together and do not get up ˌagainˌ.
They are extinguished and snuffed out like a wick.)

This is what the Lord says:

18 Forget what happened in the past,
and do not dwell on events from long ago.
19 I am going to do something new.
It is already happening. Don't you recognize it?
I will clear a way in the desert.
I will make rivers on dry land.
20 Wild animals, jackals, and ostriches will honor me.
I will provide water in the desert.
I will make rivers on the dry land for my chosen people to drink.
21 I have formed these people for myself.
They will praise me.

22 Jacob, you have not prayed to me.
Israel, you have grown tired of me.
23 You did not bring me sheep for your burnt offerings
or honor me with your sacrifices.
I did not burden you by requiring grain offerings
or trouble you by requiring incense offerings.
24 You did not buy me any sugar cane with ˌyourˌ money
or satisfy me with the best part of yourˌ sacrifices.
Rather, you burdened me with your sins
and troubled me with your wrongdoings.

25 I alone am the one who is going to wipe away your rebellious actions
for my own sake.
I will not remember your sins ˌanymoreˌ.
26 Remind me ˌof what happenedˌ.
Let us argue our case together.
State your case so that you can prove you are right.
27 Your first ancestor sinned,
and your priests rebelled against me.
28 That is why I will corrupt the leaders of the holy place.
I will claim Jacob for destruction.
I will set up Israel for ridicule.

44

1 But now listen, my servant Jacob,
Israel, whom I have chosen.
2 The Lord made you, formed you in the womb, and will help you.

This is what the Lord says:

Don't be afraid, my servant Jacob,
Jeshurun,*a* whom I have chosen.
3 I will pour water on thirsty ground and rain on dry land.
I will pour my Spirit on your offspring
and my blessing on your descendants.
4 They will spring up with the grass
as poplars spring up by streams.
5 One person will say, "I belong to the Lord."
Another will call on the name of Jacob.
Another will write on his hand, "The Lord's,"
and he will adopt the name of Israel.

The Nations Form Idols, But the Lord Formed Israel

6 The Lord is Israel's king and defender.
He is the Lord of Armies.

This is what the Lord says:

I am the first and the last,
and there is no God except me.
7 If there is anyone like me, let him say so.

---

a 44:2 "Jeshurun" is another name for Israel.

Let him tell me what happened
when I established my people long ago.
Then let him predict what will happen to them.
8 Don't be terrified or afraid.
Didn't I make this known to you long ago?
You are my witnesses.
Is there any God except me?
There is no ˌotherˌ rock; I know of none.

9 All who make idols are nothing. Their precious treasures are worthless. Their own witnesses do not see or know anything, so they will be put to shame. 10 Nothing comes from making gods or casting metal idols. 11 Everyone associated with the gods will be put to shame. The craftsmen themselves are only human. Let them all get together and take their stand. They will be frightened and ashamed together.
12 Blacksmiths shape iron into tools. They work them over the coals and shape them with hammers, working them with their strong arms. They get hungry, and their strength fails. If they don't drink water, they will faint.
13 Carpenters measure blocks of wood with ˌchalkˌ lines. They mark them with pens. They carve them with chisels and mark them with compasses. They carve them into forms of people, beautiful people, so the idols can live in shrines.
14 They cut down cedars for themselves. Then they choose fir trees or oaks. They let them grow strong among the trees in the forest. Then they plant cedars, and the rain makes them grow. 15 These trees become ˌfuelˌ for people to burn. So they take some of them and warm themselves with them. They start fires and bake bread. They also make gods from these trees and worship them. They make them into carved statues and bow in front of them. 16 Half of the wood they burn in the fire. Over this half they roast meat that they can eat until they are full. They also warm themselves and say, "Ah! We are warm. We can see the fire!" 17 But the rest of the wood they make into gods, carved statues. They bow to them and worship them. They pray to them, saying, "Rescue us, because you are our gods."
18 They don't know or understand anything. Their eyes are plastered shut, so they can't see. And their minds are closed, so they can't understand. 19 No one stops to think. No one has enough knowledge or understanding to say, "I burned half of the wood in the fire. I also baked bread over its coals. I roasted meat and ate it. Now I am making the rest of the wood into a disgusting thing and bowing to a block of wood." 20 They eat ashes because they are deceived. Their own misguided minds lead them astray. They can't rescue themselves or ask themselves, "Isn't what I hold in my right hand a false god?"

21 Remember these things, Jacob:
You are my servant, Israel.
I formed you; you are my servant.
Israel, I will not forget you.
22 I made your rebellious acts disappear like a thick cloud
and your sins like the morning mist.
Come back to me, because I have reclaimed you.

23 Sing with joy, you heavens, because the LORD has done this.
Rejoice, you deep places of the earth.
Break into shouts of joy, you mountains,
you forests and every tree in them.
The LORD has reclaimed Jacob.
He will display his glory in Israel.

Through Cyrus the LORD Will Set Israel Free
24 The LORD reclaimed you.
He formed you in the womb.

This is what the LORD says:

I, the LORD, made everything.
I stretched out the heavens by myself.
I spread out the earth all alone.
25 I cause the signs of false prophets to fail
and make fools of fortunetellers.
I make wise men retreat
and turn their knowledge into foolishness.

26 He confirms the word of his servant
and fulfills the plan of his messengers.
He says about Jerusalem, "It will be inhabited."
He says about the cities of Judah, "They will be rebuilt."

He says about their ruins, "I will restore them."
²⁷ He says to the deep water, "Dry up."
    So I will dry up your rivers.
²⁸ He says about Cyrus, "He is my shepherd.
    He will do everything I want him to do."
He says about Jerusalem, "It will be rebuilt."
He says about the temple, "Your foundation will be laid."

45 ¹ This is what the LORD says about Cyrus, his^a anointed one:

I have held him by his right hand
    so he could conquer the nations ahead of him,
        strip kings of their power,
           and open doors ahead of him
                so that the gates would not be shut.
² I will go ahead of you, Cyrus, and smooth out the rough places.
I will break down the bronze doors and cut through the iron bars.
³ I will give you treasures from dark places and hidden stockpiles.
    Then you will know that I, the LORD God of Israel,
        have called you by name.

⁴ For the sake of my servant Jacob,
    Israel, my chosen one,
        I have called you by name.
    I have given you a title of honor, although you don't know me.
⁵ I am the LORD, and there is no other.
    There is no other God besides me.
        I will strengthen you, although you don't know me,
⁶   so that from the east to the west people will know
           that there is no God except me.
I am the LORD, and there is no other.
⁷ I make light and create darkness.
I make blessings and create disasters.
I, the LORD, do all these things.

⁸ Rain down from above, you heavens,
    and pour down righteousness, you skies.
        Let the earth open.
           Let salvation and righteousness sprout.
                Let them spring up.
I, the LORD, have created them.

⁹ How horrible it will be for the one who quarrels with his maker.
    He is pottery among other earthenware pots.
        Does the clay ask the one who shapes it, "What are you making?"
        Does your work say to you, "There are no handles"?
¹⁰ How horrible it will be for the one
    who says to his father, "Why did you conceive me?"
        or to his mother, "Why did you go through labor pains for me?"

¹¹ The LORD is the Holy One and the maker of Israel.

This is what the LORD says:

Ask me about what is going to happen to my children!
Are you going to give me orders concerning my handiwork?
¹² I made the earth and created humans on it.
I stretched out the heavens with my own hands.
I commanded all the stars ˻to shine˼.
¹³ I prepared Cyrus for my righteous purpose.
I will make all his roads straight.
    He will build my city and let my exiles go free
        without any payment or any reward, says the LORD of Armies.

¹⁴ This is what the LORD says:

The products from Egypt, the merchandise from Sudan,
    and the important Sabaeans will come to you.

---

^a 45:1 Masoretic Text; Greek "my."

They will belong to you.
They will follow you.
They will come to you in chains.
They will bow to you and pray to you,
    "Certainly God is with you alone, and there is no other God."

15 Certainly, you are a God who has hidden himself.
    You are the God of Israel, the Savior!
16 Those who make idols will be ashamed and disgraced.
    They will go away completely disgraced.
17 Israel has been saved by the LORD forever.
    You will never again be ashamed or disgraced.

18 The LORD created the heavens.
    God formed the earth and made it.
    He set it up.
    He did not create it to be empty
        but formed it to be inhabited.

This is what the LORD says:

I am the LORD, and there is no other.
19 I haven't spoken privately or in some dark corner of the world.
I didn't say to Jacob's descendants,
    "Search for me in vain!"
I, the LORD, speak what is fair and say what is right.

20 Come here, you refugees from the nations.
    Ignorant people carry wooden idols
        and pray to gods that cannot save ˻anyone˼.
21 Speak and present your case. Yes, let them consult one another.
    Who revealed this in the distant past and predicted it long ago?
    Wasn't it I, the LORD?
        There is no other God except me.
        There is no other righteous God and Savior besides me.

22 Turn to me and be saved, all who live at the ends of the earth,
    because I am God, and there is no other.
23 I have bound myself with an oath.
A word has gone out from my righteous mouth
    that will not be recalled,
        "Every knee will bow to me
            and every tongue will swear ˻allegiance˼."
24 It will be said of me,
    "Certainly, righteousness and strength are found in the LORD alone."

All who are angry with him will come to him and be ashamed.
25 All the descendants of Israel will be declared righteous,
    and they will praise the LORD.

Babylon's Idols Will Go Into Captivity

46 1 The god Bel bows down; the god Nebo stoops low.
    Their statues are seated on animals and cattle.
        The gods that you carry are burdens, a load for weary people.
2 These gods stoop low and bow down together.
    They aren't able to escape with heavy loads.
    They go away into captivity.

3 Listen to me, descendants of Jacob,
    the few people left of the nation of Israel.
        I've carried you since your birth.
        I've taken care of you from the time you were born.
4   Even when you're old, I'll take care of you.
        Even when your hair turns gray, I'll support you.
    I made you and will continue to care for you.
    I'll support you and save you.

5 To whom will you compare me and make me equal?
To whom will you compare me so that we can be alike?

6 People pour gold out of their bags and weigh silver on scales.
    They hire a goldsmith. He makes it into a god.

They bow down and worship it.
7 They lift it on their shoulders and carry it.
They set the idol in its place, and it stands there.
It doesn't move from its place.
If they cry to it for help, it can't answer.
It can't rescue them from their distress.

8 Remember this, and take courage.
Recall your rebellious acts.
9 Remember the first events,
because I am God, and there is no other.
I am God, and there's no one like me.
10 From the beginning I revealed the end.
From long ago I told you things that had not yet happened, saying,
"My plan will stand, and I'll do everything I intended to do."
11 I will call a bird of prey from the east.
I will call someone for my plan from a faraway land.
I have spoken, and I will bring it about.
I have planned it, and I will do it.
12 Listen to me, you stubborn people who are far from being righteous.
13 I'll bring my righteousness near; it isn't far away.
My salvation will not be delayed.
I'll provide salvation for Zion
and bring my glory to Israel.

Babylon's Fall

47 ¹ Go, sit in the dirt,
virgin princess of Babylon!
Sit on the ground, not on a throne,
princess of the Babylonians!
You will no longer be called soft and delicate.
2 Take millstones and grind flour.
Remove your veil.
Take off your skirt.
Uncover your legs, and cross the river.
3 People will see you naked.
People will see your shame.
I will take revenge.
I won't spare anyone.

4 Our defender is the Holy One of Israel.
His name is the LORD of Armies.

5 Go into the dark, and sit in silence,
princess of the Babylonians!
You will no longer be called the queen of kingdoms.
6 I was angry with my people.
I dishonored those who belong to me.
I put them under your control.
You showed them no mercy.
You placed a heavy burden on old people.
7 You said, "I will always be a queen."
You didn't carefully consider these things
or keep in mind how they would end.

8 Now then, listen to this, you lover of pleasure.
You live securely and say to yourself,
"I'm the only one, and there's no one else.
I won't live as a widow.
I won't suffer the loss of children."
9 In one day both of these will happen to you instantly:
the loss of your children and your husband.
All this will happen to you in spite of
your evil magic and your many spells.
10 You feel safe in your wickedness
and say, "No one can see me."
Your wisdom and knowledge have led you astray,
so you say to yourself,
"I'm the only one, and there's no one else."

11 But evil will happen to you.
      You won't know how to keep it away.
    Disaster will strike you.
      You won't be able to stop it.
    Destruction will overtake you suddenly.
      You won't expect it.

12 Keep practicing your spells and your evil magic.
      You have practiced them ever since you were young.
        You may succeed.
        You may cause terror.
13 You are worn out by your many plans.
    Let your astrologers and your stargazers,
      who foretell the future month by month,
        come to you, rise up, and save you.
14 They are like straw.
      Fire burns them.
    They can't rescue themselves from the flames.
    There are no glowing coals to keep them warm
      and no fire for them to sit by.
15 This is how it will be for those who have worked with you,
      for those who have been with you ever since you were young.
        They will go their own ways,
          and there will be no one to save you.

The LORD Will Refine His People Before He Rescues Them From Babylon

48 ¹ Listen to this, descendants of Jacob!
      You are given the name of Israel.
      You are descended from Judah.*ᵃ*
      You take oaths by the name of the LORD.
      You acknowledge the God of Israel,
        but you are not honest or sincere.
2   You call yourselves ˏcitizensˏ of the holy city.
      You depend on the God of Israel.
        His name is the LORD of Armies.

3   From the beginning I revealed to you what would happen.
        These words came out of my mouth,
          and I made them known.
      Suddenly, I acted, and they happened.
4   I know that you are stubborn.
        Like iron, you are hardheaded.
        Like bronze, nothing gets through your thick skull.
5   That is why I revealed to you what would happen long ago.
        I told you about them before they happened.
      ˏI did thisˏ so you couldn't say,
        "My gods have done these things.
        My carved idols and my metal idols
          have commanded them to happen."
6   You've heard these words.
        Now look at all this.
        Won't you admit it?

    From now on I will reveal to you new things,
      hidden things that you do not know.
7   They are created now, not in the past.
      You haven't heard about them before today,
        so you can't say that you already knew about them.
8   You have never heard about them.
        You have never known about them.
          Your ears have never been open to hear them before.
      I know that you've acted very treacherously
        and that you have been called a rebel since you were born.
9   For my name's sake I'll be patient.
      For my glory's sake I'll hold my anger back from you,

ᵃ 48:1 Dead Sea Scrolls; Masoretic Text "the fountain of Judah."

      rather than destroy you.
10 I have refined you,
      but not like silver.
    I have tested you in the furnace of suffering.
11 I am doing this for myself, only for myself.
      Why should my name be dishonored?
    I will not give my glory to anyone else.

12 Listen to me, Jacob,
      Israel, whom I have called.
        I am the one.
          I am the first and the last.
13 My hand laid the foundation of the earth.
    My right hand stretched out the heavens.
      When I call for them, they both stand.
14 Gather together, all of you, and listen.
    What idol has revealed such things?
The LORD loves Cyrus.
    He will carry out the LORD's plan against Babylon.
    He will use his strength against the Babylonians.
15 I alone have spoken.
    I have called him.
      I will bring him here, and he will succeed.

16 Come here. Listen to this:
    From the beginning I have spoken nothing in private.
    From the time it took place, I was there.

Now the Almighty LORD has sent me and his Spirit.

17 This is what the LORD, your Defender, the Holy One of Israel, says:

I am the LORD your God.
    I teach you what is best for you.
    I lead you where you should go.
18 If only you had listened to my commands!
    Your peace would be like a river ˻that never runs dry˼.
    Your righteousness would be like waves on the sea.
19   Your descendants would be like sand.
    Your children would be like its grains.
      Their names would not be cut off or wiped out in my presence.
20 Leave Babylon; flee from the Babylonians!
    Shout for joy as you tell it and announce it.
      Shout it out to the ends of the earth.
        Say that the LORD has reclaimed his servant Jacob.
21 They weren't thirsty when he led them through the deserts.
    He made water flow from a rock for them.
    He split a rock, and water gushed out.

22 "There is no peace for the wicked," says the LORD.

The LORD's Servant Will Bring Salvation to the Nations

49 1 Listen to me, you islands.
    Pay attention, you people far away.
      Before I was born, the LORD chose me.
      While I was in my mother's womb, he recorded my name.
2 He made my tongue like a sharp sword
    and hid me in the palm of his hand.
He made me like a sharpened arrow
    and hid me in his quiver.

3 He said to me,
    "You are my servant Israel.
      I will display my glory through you."
4 But I said,
    "I have worked hard for nothing.
    I have used my strength, but I didn't accomplish anything.
      Yet, certainly my case is in the LORD's hands,
        and my reward is with my God."

⁵   The LORD formed me in the womb to be his servant
      in order to bring Jacob back to him
         and gather Israel to him.
            (The LORD honors me,
               and my God has become my strength.)

⁶ Now, the Lord says,

    "You are not just my servant
      who restores the tribes of Jacob
         and brings back those in Israel whom I have preserved.
    I have also made you a light for the nations
      so that you would save people all over the world."

⁷   The LORD is the defender of Israel, its Holy One.

   This is what the LORD says to the despised one, to the one scorned by the nation, to the slave of rulers:

    Kings will see ˏyouˏ and stand.
      Princes will see ˏyouˏ and bow.
         The LORD is faithful.
            The Holy One of Israel has chosen you.

⁸ This is what the LORD says:

    In the time of favor I will answer you.
    In the day of salvation I will help you.
    I will protect you.
    I will appoint you as my promise[a] to the people.
      You will restore the land.
      You will make them inherit the desolate inheritance.
⁹   You will say to the prisoners, "Come out,"
         and to those who are in darkness, "Show yourselves."

    They will graze along every path,
      and they will find pastures on every bare hill.
¹⁰   They will never be hungry or thirsty,
      nor will the sun or the burning, hot wind strike them.
         The one who has compassion on them will lead them
            and guide them to springs.
¹¹   I will turn all my mountains into roads,
      and my highways will be restored.
¹²   They will come from far away.
    They will come from the north and from the west,
      and they will come from the land of Sinim.

¹³   Sing with joy, you heavens!
    Rejoice, you earth!
    Break into shouts of joy, you mountains!
      The LORD has comforted his people
         and will have compassion on his humble people.

The LORD Has Not Forgotten Israel

¹⁴   But Zion said, "The LORD has abandoned me.
    My Lord has forgotten me."

¹⁵   Can a woman forget her nursing child?
    Will she have no compassion on the child from her womb?
    Although mothers may forget,
      I will not forget you.
¹⁶   I have engraved you on the palms of my hands.
    Your walls are always in my presence.
¹⁷   Your children will hurry back.
    Those who destroyed you and laid waste to you will leave you.
¹⁸   Look up, look around, and watch!
    All of your children are gathering together and returning to you.
      "I solemnly swear as I live," declares the LORD,

ᵃ 49:8 Or "covenant."

"you will wear all of them like jewels
and display them on yourself as a bride would."

19 Though you are destroyed and demolished and your land is in ruins,
you will be too crowded for ͺyourͺ people now.
Those who devoured you will be long gone.
20 The children taken from you will say to you,
"This place is too crowded for me.
Make room for me to live here."
21 Then you will ask yourself,
"Who has fathered these ͺchildrenͺ for me?
I was childless and unable to have children.
I was exiled and rejected.
Who raised these ͺchildren for meͺ?
I was left alone.
Where have they come from?"

22 This is what the Almighty LORD says:

I will lift my hand ͺto signalͺ the nations.
I will raise my flag for the people.
They will bring your sons in their arms
and carry your daughters on their shoulders.
23 Then kings will be your foster fathers,
and their queens will nurse you.
They will bow in front of you
with their faces touching the ground.
They will lick the dust at your feet.
Then you will know that I am the LORD.
Those who wait with hope for me will not be put to shame.

24 Can loot be taken away from mighty men
or prisoners be freed from conquerors?

25 This is what the LORD says:

Prisoners will be freed from mighty men.
Loot will be taken away from tyrants.
I will fight your enemies,
and I will save your children.
26 I will make your oppressors eat their own flesh,
and they will become drunk on their own blood
as though it were new wine.
Then all humanity will know that I am the LORD, who saves you,
the Mighty One of Jacob, who reclaims you.

The LORD's People Were Sold Because of Their Sin

50 ¹ This is what the LORD says:

Where are your mother's divorce papers?
Did I give her any to get rid of her?
To which of my creditors did I sell you?
You were sold because of your sins.
I got rid of your mother because of your rebellion.
2 Why was no one here when I came?
Why was no one here to answer when I called?
Am I too weak to reclaim you?
Don't I have the power to rescue you?
I dry up the sea with my command,
and I turn rivers into deserts.
Their fish stink because there is no water,
and people die of thirst.
3 I clothe the heavens in darkness
and cover them with sackcloth.

The LORD's Servant Trusts in the LORD's Help

4 The Almighty LORD will teach me what to say,
so I will know how to encourage weary people.
Morning after morning he will wake me
to listen like a student.

⁵ The Almighty Lᴏʀᴅ will open my ears.
   I will not rebel, nor will I turn away ˏfrom himˌ.
⁶ I will offer my back to those who whip me
   and my cheeks to those who pluck hairs out of my beard.
I will not turn my face away from those who humiliate me
   and spit on me.

⁷ The Almighty Lᴏʀᴅ helps me.
   That is why I will not be ashamed.
     I have set my face like a flint.
      I know that I will not be put to shame.
⁸ The one who pronounces me innocent is near.
   Who will bring a case against me?
     Let us confront each other!
   Who accuses me?
     Let him confront me!
⁹ The Almighty Lᴏʀᴅ helps me.
   Who will find me guilty?
     They will all wear out like a garment.
     Moths will eat them.

¹⁰ Who among you fears the Lᴏʀᴅ
   and obeys his servant?
Let those who walk in darkness and have no light
   trust the name of the Lᴏʀᴅ
     and depend upon their God.

¹¹ But all of you light fires
   and arm yourselves with flaming torches.
So walk in your own light
   and among the torches you have lit.

This is what you will receive from me:
   You will be tormented.

The Lᴏʀᴅ Will Save His People

51 ¹ Listen to me, you people who pursue what is right and seek the Lᴏʀᴅ.
   Look to the rock from which you were cut
     and to the quarry from which you were dug.
² Look to Abraham, your ancestor,
   and to Sarah, from whom you are descended.
When I called Abraham, he was childless.
   I blessed him and gave him many descendants.
³ So the Lᴏʀᴅ will comfort Zion.
   He will comfort all those who live among its ruins.
   He will make its desert like Eden.
   He will make its wilderness like the garden of the Lᴏʀᴅ.
     Joy and gladness will be found in it,
      thanksgiving and the sound of singing.

⁴ Pay attention to me, my people.
   Open your ears to hear me, my nation.
     My teachings will go out from me.
     My justice will become a light for the people.
⁵ My righteousness is near.
   My salvation is on the way.
I will bring justice to people.
     The coastlands put their hope in me,
      and they wait eagerly for me.
⁶ Look at the sky.
Look at the earth below.
   The sky will vanish like smoke.
   The earth will wear out like clothing,
     and those who live there will die like flies.
But my salvation will last forever,
   and my righteousness will never fail.

⁷ Listen to me, you people who know righteousness,
   you people who have my teachings in your hearts.
Don't be afraid of being insulted by people.

Don't be discouraged by their ridicule.
8   Moths will eat them like clothing.
      Worms will devour them like wool.
   But my righteousness will last forever,
      and my salvation will last throughout every generation.

9   Wake up! Wake up! Clothe yourself with strength, O Lord!
    Wake up as you did in days long past, as in generations long ago.
    Didn't you cut Rahab[a] into pieces and stab the serpent?
10   Didn't you dry up the sea, the water of the great ocean?
    You made a road in the depths of the sea
      so that the people reclaimed ˻by the Lord˼
      might pass through it.
11   The people ransomed by the Lord will return.
    They will come to Zion singing with joy.
      Everlasting happiness will be on their heads ˻as a crown˼.
        They will be glad and joyful.
        They will have no sorrow or grief.

12   I alone am the one who comforts you.
    Why, then, are you afraid of mortals, who must die,
      of humans, who are like grass?
13   Why have you forgotten the Lord, your Creator?
    He stretched out the heavens
      and laid the foundations of the earth.
    Why should you live in constant fear of the fury
      of those who oppress you,
      of those who are ready to destroy you?
    Where is the fury of those who oppress you?
14   Chained prisoners will be set free.
    They will not die in prison.
    They will not go without food.
15   I am the Lord your God who stirs up the sea
    and makes its waves roar.
      My name is the Lord of Armies.
16   I put my words in your mouth
    and sheltered you in the palm of my hand.
    I stretched out the heavens,
      laid the foundations of the earth,
        and said to Zion, "You are my people."

Wake Up, Jerusalem
17   Wake up! Wake up!
    Stand up, Jerusalem!
      You drank from the cup in the Lord's hand.
        That cup was filled with his anger.
      You drank from the bowl, the cup that makes people stagger,
        and you drained it!
18   From all the children she gave birth to,
    there was no one to guide her.
    From all the children she raised,
    there was no one to take her by the hand.
19   Twice as many disasters have happened to you.
    Who will feel sorry for you?
    Violence, destruction, famine, and war have happened to you.
    Who will comfort you?
20   Your children have fainted.
    They lie sleeping at every street corner.
    They are like an antelope caught in a net.
    They experience the anger of the Lord,
      the fury of your God.

21   Listen to this, you humble people
    who are drunk but not from wine.
22   The Lord your God defends his people.

---

[a] 51:9 Rahab is the name of a demonic creature who opposes God.

This is what your master says:

> I'm taking from your hand the cup that makes people stagger,
>> the bowl, the cup of my fury.
>>> You will never drink from it again.

23   I will put it in the hands of those who made you suffer.
>> They said to you, "Lie down so that we can walk over you."
>>> So you made your back like the ground
>>>> and like a street for them to cross.

Wake Up, Zion

52 ¹ Wake up! Wake up! Clothe yourself with strength, Zion!
>> Put on your beautiful clothes, holy city of Jerusalem.
>> Godless and evil people will no longer come to you.
²   Shake the dust from yourselves.
>> Get up, captive Jerusalem.
>> Free yourself from the chains around your neck, captive people of Zion.

³ This is what the LORD says: You were sold, but no price was paid. You will be bought back, but without money. ⁴ This is what the Almighty LORD says: In the beginning my people went to Egypt to live there as foreigners. Later the Assyrians oppressed them for no reason. ⁵ So what do I find here? asks the LORD. My people are taken away for no reason. Their rulers are screaming, declares the LORD. And my name is cursed all day long. ⁶ Now my people will know my name. When that day comes, ⌊they will know⌋ that I am the one who says, "Here I am!"

⁷   How beautiful on the mountains are the feet of the messenger
>> who announces the good news, "All is well."
>>> He brings the good news,
>>>> announces salvation,
>>>>> and tells Zion that its God rules as king.
⁸   Listen! Your watchmen raise their voices
>> and shout together joyfully.
>>> When the LORD brings Zion back,
>>>> they will see it with their own eyes.
⁹   Break out into shouts of joy, ruins of Jerusalem.
>> The LORD will comfort his people.
>> He will reclaim Jerusalem.
¹⁰   The LORD will show his holy power to all the nations.
>> All the ends of the earth will see the salvation of our God.

¹¹   Run away! Run away!
> Get away from there!
> Do not touch anything unclean.*
> Get away from it!
> Make yourselves pure,
>> you Levites who carry the utensils for the LORD's temple.

¹²   You will not go away in a hurry,
> nor will you go away quickly.
> The LORD will go ahead of you.
> The God of Israel will guard you from behind.

The Suffering Servant

¹³   My servant will be successful.
> He will be respected, praised, and highly honored.
¹⁴   Many will be shocked by him.ᵇ
>> His appearance will be so disfigured
>>> that he won't look like any other man.
>> His looks will be so disfigured
>>> that he will hardly look like a human.
¹⁵   He will cleanse many nations ⌊with his blood⌋.
> Kings will shut their mouths because of him.
>> They will see things that they had never been told.
>> They will understand things that they had never heard.

ᵃ 52:11 "Unclean" refers to anything that Moses' Teachings say is not presentable to God.   ᵇ 52:14 Two Hebrew manuscripts, Syriac, Targum; Masoretic Text "you."

53 ¹Who has believed our message?
To whom has the LORD's power been revealed?

²   He grew up in his presence like a young tree,
      like a root out of dry ground.
    He had no form or majesty that would make us look at him.
    He had nothing in his appearance that would make us desire him.

³   He was despised and rejected by people.
    He was a man of sorrows, familiar with suffering.
    He was despised like one from whom people turn their faces,
      and we didn't consider him to be worth anything.

⁴   He certainly has taken upon himself our suffering
      and carried our sorrows,
        but we thought that God had wounded him,
          beat him, and punished him.

⁵   He was wounded for our rebellious acts.
      He was crushed for our sins.
        He was punished so that we could have peace,
          and we received healing from his wounds.

⁶   We have all strayed like sheep.
      Each one of us has turned to go his own way,
        and the LORD has laid all our sins on him.

⁷   He was abused and punished,
      but he didn't open his mouth.
    He was led like a lamb to the slaughter.
    He was like a sheep that is silent
      when its wool is cut off.
        He didn't open his mouth.

⁸   He was arrested, taken away, and judged.
      Who would have thought that he would be removed
        from the world?
    He was killed because of my people's rebellion.

⁹   He was placed in a tomb with the wicked.
    He was put there with the rich when he died,
      although he had done nothing violent
        and had never spoken a lie.

¹⁰   Yet, it was the LORD's will to crush him with suffering.
    When the LORD has made his life a sacrifice for our wrongdoings,
      he will see his descendants for many days.
        The will of the LORD will succeed through him.

¹¹   He will see and be satisfied
      because of his suffering.
    My righteous servant will acquit many people
      because of what he has learned ˏthrough sufferingˏ.
    He will carry their sins as a burden.

¹²   So I will give him a share among the mighty,
      and he will divide the prize with the strong,
        because he poured out his life in death
          and he was counted with sinners.
          He carried the sins of many.
            He intercedes for those who are rebellious.

The LORD's Compassion for the Women Without Children

54 ¹Sing with joy, you childless women who never gave birth to children.
    Break into shouts of joy, you women who never had birth pains.
    "There will be more children of women who have been deserted
      than there are children of married women," says the LORD.

²   Expand the space of your tent.
    Stretch out the curtains of your tent, and don't hold back.
      Lengthen your tent ropes, and drive in the tent pegs.

³   You will spread out to the right and left.
    Your descendants will take over other nations,
      and they will resettle deserted cities.

⁴   Don't be afraid, because you won't be put to shame.
    Don't be discouraged, because you won't be disgraced.
    You'll forget the shame you've had since you were young.

5 You won't remember the disgrace of your husband's death anymore.
Your husband is your maker.
His name is the LORD of Armies.
Your defender is the Holy One of Israel.
He is called the God of the whole earth.

6 "The LORD has called you as if you were
a wife who was abandoned and in grief,
a wife who married young and was rejected," says your God.

7 "I abandoned you for one brief moment,
but I will bring you back with unlimited compassion.
8 I hid my face from you for a moment in a burst of anger,
but I will have compassion on you with everlasting kindness,"
says the LORD your defender.
9 "To me this is like Noah's floodwaters, when I swore an oath
that Noah's floodwaters would never cover the earth again.
So now I swear an oath not to be angry with you or punish you.
10 The mountains may move, and the hills may shake,
but my kindness will never depart from you.
My promise*a* of peace will never change,"
says the LORD, who has compassion on you.

11 "You suffering, comfortless, storm-ravaged city!
I will rebuild your city with precious stones.
I will reset your foundations with sapphires.
12 I will rebuild your towers with rubies,
your gates with sparkling stones,
and all your walls with precious stones."

13 All your children will be taught by the LORD,
and your children will have unlimited peace.
14 You will be established in righteousness.
You will be far from oppression,
so you will not be afraid.
You will be far from destruction,
so it won't come near you.

15 "If anyone attacks you, it will not be my doing.
Whoever attacks you will be defeated by you.
16 I've created blacksmiths to fan the coals into flames
and to produce useful weapons.
I've also created destroyers to bring destruction.
17 No weapon that has been made to be used against you will succeed.
You will have an answer for anyone who accuses you.
This is the inheritance of the LORD's servants.
Their victory comes from me," declares the LORD.

The LORD's Word Will Accomplish Its Task

55 1 "Listen! Whoever is thirsty, come to the water!
Whoever has no money can come, buy, and eat!
Come, buy wine and milk. You don't have to pay; it's free!
2 Why do you spend money on what cannot nourish you
and your wages on what does not satisfy you?
Listen carefully to me:
Eat what is good, and enjoy the best foods.
3 Open your ears, and come to me!
Listen so that you may live!
I will make an everlasting promise*a* to you—
the blessings I promised to David.
4 I made him a witness to people,
a leader and a commander for people.
5 You will summon a nation that you don't know,
and a nation that doesn't know you will run to you
because of the LORD your God,

---

a 54:10; 55:3 Or "covenant."

because of the Holy One of Israel.
    He has honored you."

6 Seek the LORD while he may be found.
    Call on him while he is near.
7 Let wicked people abandon their ways.
    Let evil people abandon their thoughts.
    Let them return to the LORD,
        and he will show compassion to them.
    Let them return to our God,
        because he will freely forgive them.

8 "My thoughts are not your thoughts,
    and my ways are not your ways," declares the LORD.
9 "Just as the heavens are higher than the earth,
    so my ways are higher than your ways,
        and my thoughts are higher than your thoughts."

10 "Rain and snow come down from the sky.
    They do not go back again until they water the earth.
        They make it sprout and grow
            so that it produces seed for farmers
                and food for people to eat.
11 My word, which comes from my mouth, is like the rain and snow.
    It will not come back to me without results.
    It will accomplish whatever I want
        and achieve whatever I send it to do."

12 You will go out with joy and be led out in peace.
    The mountains and the hills
        will break into songs of joy in your presence,
            and all the trees will clap their hands.
13 Cypress trees will grow where thornbushes grew.
    Myrtle trees will grow where briars grew.
        This will be a reminder of the LORD's name
            and an everlasting sign that will never be destroyed.

Salvation for All People

56 **1** This is what the LORD says:

Preserve justice, and do what is right.
    My salvation is about to come.
    My righteousness is about to be revealed.

2 Blessed is the one who does these things
    and the person who holds on to them.
Blessed is the one who keeps the day of worship from becoming unholy
    and his hands from doing anything wrong.

3 Foreigners who have joined the LORD should not say, "The LORD will separate us from his people." Castrated men should not say, "We're only dead trees!" **4** This is what the LORD says: ⌊I will remember⌋ the castrated men who keep my days of worship, choose what pleases me, and faithfully observe the conditions of my promise.*[a] **5** Inside my house and within my walls, I will give them something better than sons and daughters. I will give them a monument and a name. I will give them a permanent name that will not be forgotten. **6** And ⌊I will remember⌋ the foreigners who have joined the LORD to worship him, to love the LORD's name, and to be his servants. All of them will keep the day of worship from becoming unholy and will faithfully observe the conditions of my promise. **7** Then I will bring them to my holy mountain and make them happy in my house of prayer. Their burnt offerings and their sacrifices will be acceptable on my altar, because my house will be called a house of prayer for all nations.

8 The Almighty LORD, who gathers the scattered people of Israel, declares, "I will gather still others besides those I have already gathered."

The Sins of Israel Bring the Lord's Anger

9 All you animals in the field,
    all you animals in the forest,

---

a 56:4 Or "covenant."

       come and eat.
10 ⌐Israel's⌐ watchmen are blind.
       None of them know anything.
       All of them are like dogs that are unable to bark.
   They lie around dreaming; they love to sleep.
11 These dogs have huge appetites.
       They are never full.
   They are the shepherds,
       but they don't understand.
   All of them have turned to go their own ways.
       Each one seeks his own gain.
12 ⌐Each one cries,⌐
       "Let me get some wine,
          and we'll fill ourselves with liquor.
             And tomorrow will be like today, only better."

57
1 Righteous people die,
       and no one cares.
   Loyal people are taken away,
       and no one understands.
   Righteous people are spared when evil comes.
2 When peace comes,
       everyone who has lived honestly will rest on his own bed.

Israel's Idolatry
3 But you—come here,
       you children of witches,
          you descendants of adulterers and prostitutes!
4 Whom are you making fun of?
   Whom are you making a face at?
   Whom are you sticking out your tongue at?
       Aren't you rebellious children,
          descendants of liars?
5 You burn with lust under oak trees
       and under every large tree.
   You slaughter children in the valleys
       and under the cracks in the rocks.
6 Your idols are among the smooth stones in the ravine.
       They are your destiny.
   You have given them wine offerings
       and sacrificed grain offerings to them.
   Do you think I am pleased with all this?

7 You've made your bed on a high and lofty mountain.
   You've gone to offer sacrifices there.
8 You've set up your idols beside doors and doorposts.
   You've uncovered yourself to the idols.
       You've distanced yourself from me.
   You've made your bed with them.
   You've made a deal with those you have pleasure with in bed.
   You've seen them naked.
9 You've journeyed to the king with perfumed oils
       and put on plenty of perfume.
   You've sent your ambassadors far away
       and sent them down to Sheol.
10 You've tired yourself out with many journeys.
       You didn't think that it was hopeless.
   You've found renewed strength,
       so you didn't faint.

11 Whom did you dread and fear so much that you lied to me?
       You haven't remembered me or cared about me.
   I've been silent for a long time.
       Is that why you don't fear me?
12 I'll tell you about your righteous ways and what you have done,
       but they won't help you.
13 When you cry for help,
       let your collection of idols save you.

A wind will carry them all away.
A breath will take them away.
    But whoever trusts me will possess the land
        and inherit my holy mountain.

¹⁴ It will be said:
    "Build a road! Build a road!
    Prepare the way!
        Remove every obstacle in the way of my people!"

¹⁵ The High and Lofty One lives forever, and his name is holy.

This is what he says:

I live in a high and holy place.
    But I am with those who are crushed and humble.
        I will renew the spirit of those who are humble
        and the courage of those who are crushed.
¹⁶ I will not accuse you forever.
I will not be angry with you forever.
    Otherwise, the spirits, the lives of those I've made,
        would grow faint in my presence.
¹⁷ I was angry because of their sinful greed,
    so I punished them, hid ˎfrom themˏ, and remained angry.
        But they continued to be sinful.
¹⁸ I've seen their ˎsinfulˏ ways, but I'll heal them.
I'll guide them and give them rest.
I'll comfort them and their mourners.
¹⁹ I'll create praise on their lips:
    "Perfect peace to those both far and near."
"I'll heal them," says the LORD.
²⁰   But the wicked are like the churning sea.
        It isn't quiet,
        and its water throws up mud and slime.

²¹ "There is no peace for the wicked," says my God.

Worship the LORD as He Wants to Be Worshiped

58 ¹ Cry aloud! Don't hold back!
    Raise your voice like a ram's horn.
        Tell my people about their rebellion
        and the descendants of Jacob about their sins.
² They look for me every day and want to know my ways.
    They act as if they were a nation that has done what is right
        and as if they haven't disregarded God's judgment ˎon themˏ.
They ask me for just decrees.
They want God to be near them.

³ Why have we fasted if you are not aware of it?
Why have we inflicted pain on ourselves if you don't pay attention?

Don't you see that on the days you fast,
    you do what you want to do?
        You mistreat all your workers.
⁴ Don't you see that when you fast,
    you quarrel and fight and beat your workers?
        The way you fast today keeps you from being heard in heaven.
⁵ Is this the kind of fasting I have chosen?
    Should people humble themselves for ˎonlyˏ a day?
Is fasting just bowing your head like a cattail
    and making your bed from sackcloth and ashes?
Is this what you call fasting?
Is this an acceptable day to the LORD?

⁶ This is the kind of fasting I have chosen:
    Loosen the chains of wickedness,
        untie the straps of the yoke,ᵃ
        let the oppressed go free,

ᵃ 58:6 A yoke is a wooden bar placed over the necks of work animals so that they can pull plows or carts.

and break every yoke.
7   Share your food with the hungry,
      take the poor and homeless into your house,
        and cover them with clothes when you see ⸤them⸥ naked.
      Don't refuse to help your relatives.

8   Then your light will break through like the dawn,
      and you will heal quickly.
    Your righteousness will go ahead of you,
      and the glory of the LORD will guard you from behind.
9   Then you will call, and the LORD will answer.
    You will cry for help, and he will say, "Here I am!"

    Get rid of that yoke.
      Don't point your finger and say wicked things.

10 If you give some of your own food to ⸤feed⸥ those who are hungry
      and to satisfy ⸤the needs of⸥ those who are humble,
    then your light will rise in the dark,
      and your darkness will become as bright as the noonday sun.
11 The LORD will continually guide you
      and satisfy you even in sun-baked places.
    He will strengthen your bones.
      You will become like a watered garden
        and like a spring whose water does not stop flowing.
12 Your people will rebuild the ancient ruins
      and restore the foundations of past generations.
    You will be called the Rebuilder of Broken Walls
      and the Restorer of Streets Where People Live.

13 If you stop trampling on the day of worship
      and doing as you please on my holy day,
    if you call the day of worship a delight
      and the LORD's holy day honorable,
    if you honor it by not going your own way,
      by not going out when you want, and by not talking idly,
14 then you will find joy in the LORD.
      I will make you ride on the heights of the earth.
    I will feed you with the inheritance of your ancestor Jacob.
    The LORD has spoken.

The LORD Will Turn His People From Wrongdoing

59 ¹ The LORD is not too weak to save
      or his ear too deaf to hear.
2   But your wrongs have separated you from your God,
      and your sins have made him hide his face
        so that he doesn't hear you.
3   Your hands are stained with blood,
      and your fingers are stained with sin.
    You speak lies,
      and you mutter wicked things.
4   No one calls for justice,
      and no one pleads his case truthfully.
    People trust pointless arguments and speak lies.
    They conceive trouble and give birth to evil.
5   They hatch viper eggs
      and weave spiderwebs.
        Those who eat their eggs will die.
          When an egg is crushed, a poisonous snake is hatched.
6   Their webs can't be used for clothes,
      nor can they cover themselves with their works.
    Their works are evil.
    Their hands have committed acts of violence.
7   Their feet run to do evil.
      They hurry to shed innocent blood.
    Their plans are evil.
      Ruin and destruction are on their highways.
8   They don't know the way of peace.
      There's no justice on their highways.

They've made their paths crooked.
   Whoever walks on them will never know peace.

⁹ That is why justice is far from us,
   and righteousness doesn't reach us.
We hope for light, but we walk in darkness.
We hope for brightness, but we walk in gloom.
¹⁰ We grope like blind men along a wall.
We grope like people without eyes.
We stumble at noon as if it were twilight.
We are like dead people among healthy people.
¹¹ We all growl like bears.
We coo like doves.
We hope for justice, but there is none.
We hope for salvation, but it's far from us.

¹² You are aware of our many rebellious acts.
   Our sins testify against us.
   Our rebellious acts are with us.
We know our wrongdoings.
¹³ We have rebelled and denied the LORD.
We have turned away from our God.
We have spoken about oppression and revolt.
We have conceived and uttered lies in our hearts.
¹⁴ Justice is turned back,
   and righteousness stands far away.
Truth has fallen in the street,
   and honesty can't come in.
¹⁵ Truth is missing.
   Those who turn away from evil make themselves victims.

The LORD sees it, and he's angry
   because there's no justice.
¹⁶ He sees that there's no one to help.
He's astounded that there's no one to intercede.
   So with his own power he wins a victory.
   His righteousness supports him.
¹⁷ He puts on righteousness like a coat of armor
   and a helmet of salvation on his head.
He wears clothes of vengeance.
He wraps himself with fury as a coat.
¹⁸ He will pay them back according to their deeds.
He will pay back his opponents with wrath and punish his enemies.
He will pay back the people who live on the coastlands.
¹⁹ The people of the west will fear the name of the LORD.
   Those in the east will fear his glory.
He will come like a rushing stream.
   The wind of the LORD pushes him.

²⁰ "Then a Savior will come to Zion,
   to those in Jacob who turn from rebellion," declares the LORD.

²¹ "This is my promise[a] to them," says the LORD. "My Spirit, who is on you, and my words that I put in your mouth will not leave you. They will be with your children and your grandchildren permanently," says the LORD.

The LORD Will Be Jerusalem's Glory

60 ¹ Arise! Shine! Your light has come,
   and the glory of the LORD has dawned.
² Darkness now covers the earth,
   and thick darkness covers the nations.
But the LORD dawns,
   and his glory appears over you.
³ Nations will come to your light,
   and kings will come to the brightness of your dawn.

ᵃ 59:21 Or "covenant."

4 "Look up, look around, and watch.
      All of your people assemble and come to you.
         Your sons come from far away.
         Your daughters are carried in their arms.
5 Then you will see this and rejoice,
      and your heart will be thrilled with joy,
         because the riches of the sea will be brought to you.
            The wealth of the nations will come to you.

6 "Many camels will cover your ˎland˻,
      young camels from Midian and Ephah.
   Everyone from Sheba will come.
      They will bring gold and incense.
      They will sing the praises of the LORD.
7 All of the flocks from Kedar will gather and come to you.
   The rams of Nebaioth will serve you.
      They will be sacrificed as acceptable ˎofferings˻ on my altar.
      So I will honor my beautiful temple.

8 "Who are these people that fly by like clouds,
      like doves to their nests?
9 Certainly, the coastlands wait with hope for me.
      The ships from Tarshish are the first to bring your children
         from far away.
      Their silver and their gold comes with them
         to honor the name of the LORD your God, the Holy One of Israel,
            because he has honored you.

10 "Foreigners will rebuild your walls,
      and their kings will serve you.
         In my anger I struck you,
         but in my favor I have compassion on you.
11 Your gates will always be open.
      They will never be closed day or night
         so that people may bring you the wealth of nations,
            with their kings led as prisoners.
12 Nations and kingdoms that do not serve you will be destroyed.
   The nations will certainly be ruined.

13 "Lebanon's glory will come to you:
      Cedar, fir, and cypress trees will come to beautify my holy place,
      and I will honor the place where my feet rest.
14 The descendants of those who oppress you will bow in front of you.
   All who despise you will bow at your feet.
      They will call you the city of the LORD,
      Zion, the city of the Holy One of Israel.

15 "You have been abandoned and hated; no one has passed through you.
      But now I will make you a source of everlasting pride,
         a joy for all generations.
16 You will drink milk from other nations
      and nurse at royal breasts.
         Then you will know that I am the LORD, your Savior,
         the Mighty One of Jacob, your Defender.
17 I will bring gold instead of bronze.
   I will bring silver instead of iron,
      bronze instead of wood, and iron instead of stone.
   I will appoint peace as your governor and righteousness as your ruler.
18 No longer will you hear about violence in your land
      or desolation and destruction within your borders.
         You will call your walls Salvation and your gates Praise.
19 The sun will no longer be your light during the day,
      nor will the brightness of the moon give you light,
         But the LORD will be your everlasting light.
            Your God will be your glory.
20 Your sun will no longer go down,
      nor will your moon disappear.
         The LORD will be your everlasting light,
            and your days of sadness will be over.

21 Then all your people will be righteous,
    and they will possess the land permanently.
        They will be the seedling I have planted,
            the honored work of my hands.
22 The smallest of them will become a family.
    The weakest of them will become a mighty nation.
        At the right time I, the LORD, will make it happen quickly."

The LORD Will Anoint His Servant With His Spirit

61 ¹The Spirit of the Almighty LORD is with me
        because the LORD has anointed me
            to deliver good news to humble people.
    He has sent me
        to heal those who are brokenhearted,
        to announce that captives will be set free
            and prisoners will be released.
2 ⌊He has sent me⌋
        to announce the year of the LORD's good will
            and the day of our God's vengeance,
        to comfort all those who grieve.
3 ⌊He has sent me⌋
        to provide for all those who grieve in Zion,
        to give them crowns instead of ashes,
            the oil of joy instead of ⌊tears of⌋ grief,
                and clothes of praise instead of a spirit of weakness.

They will be called Oaks of Righteousness,
    the Plantings of the LORD,
        so that he might display his glory.

4 They will rebuild the ancient ruins.
    They will restore the places destroyed long ago.
    They will renew the ruined cities, the places destroyed generations ago.
5 Foreigners will come forward and become shepherds for your flocks,
    and children of foreigners will work your fields and vineyards.
6 You will be called the priests of the LORD.
    You will be called the servants of our God.
        You will consume the wealth of the nations.
        You will boast in their splendor.
7 You will receive a double measure of wealth instead of your shame.
    You will sing about your wealth instead of being disgraced.
        That is why you will have a double measure of wealth in your land.
            You will have everlasting joy.
8 I, the LORD, love justice.
    I hate robbery and wrongdoing.
    I will faithfully reward my people's work.
    I will make an everlasting promise[a] to them.
9 Then their offspring will be known among the nations
        and their descendants among the people.
            Everyone who sees them will recognize
                that they are the descendants whom the LORD has blessed.

10 I will find joy in the LORD.
    I will delight in my God.
        He has dressed me in the clothes of salvation.
        He has wrapped me in the robe of righteousness
            like a bridegroom with a priest's turban,
            like a bride with her jewels.
11 Like the ground that brings forth its crops
        and like a garden that makes the seed in it grow,
            so the Almighty LORD will make righteousness and praise
                spring up in front of all nations.

---

[a] 61:8 Or "covenant."

Jerusalem's Salvation Is Coming

62 ¹ For Zion's sake I will not remain silent.
For Jerusalem's sake I will not rest,
    until its righteousness shines like the dawn
      and its salvation burns brightly like a torch.
² The nations will see your righteousness.
All kings will see your glory.
You will be given a new name
    that the LORD will announce.
³ Then you will be a beautiful crown in the hand of the LORD,
    a royal crown in the hand of your God.
⁴ You will no longer be called Deserted,
    and your land will no longer be called Destroyed.
But you will be named My Delight,
    and your land will be named Married.
The LORD is delighted with you,
    and your land will be married.
⁵ As a young man marries a woman,
    so your sons will marry you.
As a bridegroom rejoices over his bride,
    so your God will rejoice over you.

⁶ I have posted watchmen on your walls, Jerusalem.
    They will never be silent day or night.
Whoever calls on the LORD, do not give yourselves any rest,
⁷   and do not give him any rest until he establishes Jerusalem
      and makes it an object of praise throughout the earth.
⁸ The LORD has sworn with his right hand and with his mighty arm,
    "I will never again let your enemies eat your grain,
      nor will foreigners drink the new wine which you made."
⁹   Those who harvest grain
      will eat it and praise the LORD.
    Those who gather grapes
      will drink wine in my holy courtyards.

¹⁰ Go through! Go through the gates!
Prepare a way for the people!
Build up! Build up the highway!
Clear away the stones!
Raise a flag for the people!

¹¹ The LORD has announced to the ends of the earth:
    "Tell my people Zion,
     'Your Savior is coming.
     His reward is with him,
       and the people he has won arrive ahead of him.' "

¹² They will be called Holy People, Those Reclaimed by the LORD,
    and you will be called Sought After, a City Not Deserted.

The LORD Alone Wins His Victory

63 ¹ Who is this coming from Bozrah in Edom
    with his clothes stained bright red?
Who is this dressed in splendor,
    going forward with great strength?

"It is I, the LORD. I am coming to announce my victory.
    I am powerful enough to save ˛you˛."

² Why are your clothes red
    and your garments like those who trample grapes in a winepress?

³ "I have trampled alone in the winepress.
    No one was with me.
In my anger I trampled on people.
In my wrath I stomped on them.
Their blood splattered my clothes
    so all my clothing has been stained.
⁴ I planned the day of vengeance.
The year for my reclaiming ˛you˛ has come.

⁵ I looked, but there was no help.
  I was astounded that there was no ⸢outside⸣ support.
      So with my own power I won a victory.
      My anger supported me.
⁶   In my anger I trampled on people.
      In my wrath I made them drunk
          and poured their blood on the ground."

The Lord's People Pray for His Help

⁷ I will acknowledge the Lord's acts of mercy,
      and ⸢sing⸣ the praises of the Lord,
          because of everything that the Lord has done for us.
              He has done many good things for the nation of Israel
                  because of his compassion and his unlimited mercy.
⁸ He said, "They are my people,
      children who will not lie to me."
          So he became their Savior.
⁹ In all their troubles he was troubled,
      and he was the Messenger who saved them.
  In his love and compassion he reclaimed them.
      He always held them and carried them in the past.
¹⁰ But they rebelled and offended his Holy Spirit.
      So he turned against them as their enemy; he fought against them.

¹¹ Then his people remembered Moses and the distant past.
      Where is the one who brought them out of the sea
          with the shepherds of his flock?
      Where is the one who put his Holy Spirit in them?
¹² Where is the one who sent his powerful arm
          to support the right hand of Moses?
      Where is the one who divided the water in front of them
          to make an everlasting name for himself?
¹³ Where is the one who led them through the deep water?
  Like horses in the wilderness,
      they didn't stumble.
¹⁴ Like animals going down into a valley,
      they were given rest by the Lord's Spirit.
          In this way you guided your people
              to make an honored name for yourself.

¹⁵ Look down and see from heaven, from your holy and beautiful dwelling.
      Where is your determination and might?
      Where is the longing of your heart and your compassion?
          Don't hold back.
¹⁶ You are our Father.
      Even though Abraham doesn't know us
          and Israel doesn't pay attention to us,
              O Lord, you are our Father.
                  Your name is our Defender From Everlasting.
¹⁷ O Lord, why do you let us wander from your ways
      and become so stubborn that we are unable to fear you?
          Return for the sake of your servants.
              They are the tribes that belong to you.

¹⁸ Your holy people possessed the land for a little while.
      Our enemies have trampled on your holy place.
¹⁹ We have become like those whom you never ruled,
      like those who are not called by your name.

64 ᵃ¹ If only you would split open the heavens and come down!
      The mountains would quake at your presence.
²   Be like the fire that kindles brushwood and makes water boil.
  Come down to make your name known to your enemies.
      ·The nations will tremble in your presence.
³ When you did awe-inspiring things that we didn't expect,
      you came down and the mountains quaked in your presence.

ᵃ 64:1 Isaiah 64:1–12 in English Bibles is Isaiah 63:19b–64:11 in the Hebrew Bible.

4 No one has ever heard,
    no one has paid attention,
        and no one has seen any god except you.
            You help those who wait for you.

5 You greeted the one who gladly does right and remembers your ways.
  You showed your anger, because we've sinned.
    We've continued to sin for a long time.
      Can we still be saved?
6 We've all become unclean,[b]
    and all our righteous acts are like permanently stained rags.
  All of us shrivel like leaves,
    and our sins carry us away like the wind.
7 No one calls on your name
  or tries to hold on to you.
    You have hidden your face from us.
    You have let us be ruined by our sins.

8 But now, LORD, you are our Father.
  We are the clay, and you are our potter.
  We are the work of your hands.
9 Don't be too angry, LORD.
  Don't remember our sin forever.
  Now look, we are all your people.
10 Your holy cities have become a desert.
  Zion has become a desert.
  Jerusalem is a wasteland.
11 Our holy and beautiful temple, where our ancestors praised you,
  has been burned to the ground.
    All that we valued has been ruined.
12 Despite these things, LORD, will you hold back?
  Will you be silent and make us suffer more than we can bear?

The LORD Answers His People's Prayer

65 **1** I was ready to answer those who didn't ask.
  I was found by those who weren't looking for me.
    I said, "Here I am! Here I am!"
    to a nation that didn't worship me.
2 I stretched out my hands all day long to stubborn people.
  They chose to go the wrong direction.
  They followed their own plans.
3 These people constantly and openly provoked me.
  They offered sacrifices in gardens
    and burnt incense on brick altars.
4 They sat among the graves and spent their nights in caves.
  They ate pork and in their pots made broth from unclean foods.
5 They said, "Stay away! Don't touch me!
  I'm holier than you are."
  They have become like smoke in my nose,
    like a smoldering fire all day long.

6 "Look! It is written in front of me.
  I will not be silent, but I will repay.
  I will repay you in full.
7 I will repay you for your sins
  and for the sins of your ancestors," says the LORD.
  They burnt incense on the mountains and slandered me on the hills,
  so I will be the first to pay them back in full.

8 This is what the LORD says:

When someone finds juice for new wine in a cluster of grapes,
  another person will say,
    "Don't destroy it, because there's a blessing in it."
In the same way, I will do this for my servants:
  I will not destroy everything.

---

[b] 64:6 "Unclean" refers to anything that Moses' Teachings say is not presentable to God.

⁹ I will bring ˌwith meˌ Jacob's descendant,
  one who will inherit my mountains from Judah.
    My chosen ones will inherit them.
    My servants will live there.
¹⁰ The Sharon Plain will be a pasture for flocks.
  The Achor Valley will be a resting place for cattle
    and for my people who search for me.
¹¹ You have abandoned the LORD
    and forgotten my holy mountain.
  You have prepared a table for the god of good fortune
    and offered cups full of spiced wine to the goddess of destiny.
¹² Now I will destine you for death.
  All of you will bow to be slaughtered.
    I called, but you didn't answer.
    I spoke, but you didn't listen.
      You did what I consider evil.
      You chose what I don't like.

¹³ This is what the LORD God says:

  My servants will eat, but you will be hungry.
  My servants will drink, but you will be thirsty.
  My servants will be glad, but you will be ashamed.
¹⁴ My servants will sing because of the gladness in their hearts.
    But you will cry because of your sadness
    and wail because of your depression.
¹⁵ Your name will be used as a curse by my chosen ones.
    The Almighty LORD will kill you
    and call his servants by another name.
¹⁶ Whoever asks for a blessing in the land
    will be blessed by the God of Truth.
  Whoever swears an oath in the land
    will swear by the God of Truth.
      Past troubles are forgotten.
      They are hidden from my eyes.

¹⁷ I will create a new heaven and a new earth.
    Past things will not be remembered.
    They will not come to mind.
¹⁸ Be glad, and rejoice forever in what I'm going to create,
    because I'm going to create Jerusalem to be a delight
    and its people to be a joy.
¹⁹ I will rejoice about Jerusalem and be glad about my people.
  Screaming and crying will no longer be heard in the city.
²⁰ There will no longer be an infant who lives for only a few days
    or an old man who doesn't live a long life.
  Whoever lives to be a hundred years old will be thought of as young.
  Whoever dies before he is a hundred years old will be cursed as a sinner.
²¹ They will build houses and live there.
    They will plant vineyards and eat fruit from them.
²² They will not build homes and have others live there.
    They will not plant and have others eat from it.
      My people will live as long as trees,
      and my chosen ones will enjoy what they've done.
²³ They will never again work for nothing.
  They will never again give birth to children who die young,
    because they will be offspring blessed by the LORD.
      The LORD will bless their descendants as well.
²⁴ Before they call, I will answer.
  While they're still speaking, I will hear.
²⁵ Wolves and lambs will feed together,
    lions will eat straw like oxen,
      and dust will be food for snakes.
  "They will not hurt or destroy anyone anywhere on my holy mountain,"
    says the LORD.

The People of the LORD's New Creation

66 ¹ This is what the LORD says:

Heaven is my throne.
The earth is my footstool.
Where can you build a house or resting place for me?
² I have made all these things.
"That is why all these things have come into being,"
declares the LORD.
I will pay attention to those
who are humble and sorry ⸢for their sins⸥
and who tremble at my word.

³ Whoever kills a bull is like someone who kills a person.
Whoever sacrifices a lamb is like someone who breaks a dog's neck.
Whoever offers a grain sacrifice
is like someone who ⸢offers⸥ pig's blood.
Whoever burns incense is like someone who worships an idol.
People have certainly chosen their own ways,
and their souls delight in detestable things.

⁴ So I will choose harsh treatment for them
and bring on them what they fear.
I called, but no one answered.
I spoke, but they didn't listen.
They did what I consider evil.
They chose what I don't like.

⁵ Listen to the word of the LORD, all who tremble at his word.

Your relatives, who hate you and exclude you for my name's sake, say,
"Let the LORD show his glory; then we will see your joy."
But they will be put to shame.
⁶ Listen to the uproar from the city.
Listen to the sound from the temple.
It is the sound of the LORD
paying back his enemies as they deserve.

⁷ Before a woman goes into labor, she gives birth.
Before she has labor pains, she delivers a child.
⁸ Who has heard of such a thing?
Who has seen such things?
Can a country be born in one day?
Can a nation be born in a moment?
When Zion went into labor,
she also gave birth to her children.
⁹ "Do I bring a mother to the moment of birth
and not let her deliver?" asks the LORD.
"Do I cause a mother to deliver
and then make her unable to have children?" asks your God.
¹⁰ All who love Jerusalem, be happy and rejoice with her.
All who mourn for her, be glad with her.
¹¹ You will nurse and be satisfied from her comforting breasts.
You will nurse to your heart's delight at her full breasts.

¹² This is what the LORD says:

I will offer you peace like a river
and the wealth of the nations like an overflowing stream.
You will nurse and be carried in Jerusalem's arms
and cuddled on her knees.
¹³ As a mother comforts her child,
so will I comfort you.
You will be comforted in Jerusalem.
¹⁴ When you see it, your heart will rejoice
and you will flourish like new grass.
The power of the LORD will be made known to his servants,
but he will condemn his enemies.
¹⁵ The LORD will come with fire
and with his chariots like a thunderstorm.

He will pay them back with his burning anger
and punish them with flames of fire.
¹⁶ The LORD will judge with fire,
and he will judge all people with his sword.
Many people will be struck dead by the LORD.

¹⁷ People make themselves holy
and prepare themselves for their garden rituals.
They go into the garden
and devour pork, disgusting things, and mice.
"They will come to an end at the same time,"
declares the LORD.
¹⁸ Because of their actions and their thoughts,^a
I am coming to gather the nations of every language.
They will come and see my glory.
¹⁹ I will set up a sign among them
and send some of their survivors to the nations:
to Tarshish, Put and Lud, Meshech, Rosh, Tubal, Javan,
and to the distant coastlands
who have not heard of my fame or seen my glory.
They will tell about my glory among the nations.
²⁰ They will bring all your relatives
from every nation like a grain offering to the LORD.
"They will come on horses, in chariots, in wagons,
on mules and camels to my holy mountain, Jerusalem,"
declares the LORD.
They will come like the people of Israel who bring
their grain offerings in clean dishes to the LORD's temple.
²¹ "I will make some of them priests and Levites," declares the LORD.
²² "The new heaven and earth that I am about to make
will continue in my presence," declares the LORD.
"So your descendants and your name
will also continue in my presence.
²³ From one month to the next and from one week to the next
all people will come to worship me," declares the LORD.
²⁴ Then they will go out
and look at the corpses of those who have rebelled against me.
The worms that eat them will not die.
The fire that burns them will not go out.
All humanity will be disgusted by them.

---

^a 66:18 Hebrew meaning of this line uncertain.

JEREMIAH

The Prophet Jeremiah

1 ¹ ⸢These are⸣ the words of Jeremiah, son of Hilkiah. He was one of the priests at Anathoth in the territory of Benjamin. ² The LORD spoke his word to Jeremiah when King Josiah, son of Amon, was in his thirteenth year as king of Judah. ³ The LORD also spoke when Jehoiakim, son of Josiah, was king of Judah and during the 11 years that Zedekiah, ⸢another⸣ son of Josiah, was king of Judah. The LORD continued to speak to Jeremiah until the people of Jerusalem were taken away into captivity in the fifth month of the year.

The LORD Gives Jeremiah a Message for His People

⁴ The LORD spoke his word to me,

⁵   "Before I formed you in the womb,
       I knew you.
   Before you were born,
       I set you apart for my holy purpose.
       I appointed you to be a prophet to the nations."

⁶ I, Jeremiah, said, "Almighty LORD, I do not know how to speak. I am only a boy!"
⁷ But the LORD said to me, "Don't say that you are only a boy. You will go wherever I send you. You will say whatever I command you to say. ⁸ Don't be afraid of people. I am with you, and I will rescue you," declares the LORD.
⁹ Then the LORD stretched out his hand and touched my mouth. The LORD said to me,

   "Now I have put my words in your mouth.
¹⁰   Today I have put you in charge of nations and kingdoms.
       You will uproot and tear down.
       You will destroy and overthrow.
       You will build and plant."

¹¹ Again the LORD spoke his word to me and asked, "Jeremiah, what do you see?"
   I answered, "I see a branch of an almond tree."
¹² Then the LORD said to me, "Right. I am watching to make sure that my words come true."ᵃ
¹³ Again the LORD spoke his word to me and asked, "What do you see?"
   I answered, "I see a boiling pot, and its top is tilted away from the north."
¹⁴ Then the LORD said to me,

   "Disaster will be poured out from the north
       on all those who live in the land.
¹⁵   I am going to call every family and kingdom from the north,"
       declares the LORD.
           "They will come, and they will set up their thrones
               at the entrance of Jerusalem's gates.
           They will attack all the walls around the city
               and all the cities of Judah.
¹⁶   I will pass sentence on my people because of all their wickedness.
       They abandoned me,
           burned incense to other gods,
               and worshiped what their hands have made.
¹⁷   Brace yourself, Jeremiah!
       Stand up, and say to them whatever I tell you to say.
       Don't be terrified in their presence,
           or I will make you ⸢even more⸣ terrified in their presence.
¹⁸   Today I have made you like a fortified city,
       an iron pillar, and a bronze wall.
           You will be able to stand up to the whole land.

ᵃ 1:11–12 There is a play on words here between Hebrew *shaked* (almond tree) and *shoked* (watching).

You will be able to stand up to Judah's kings,
    its officials, its priests, and ˌallˌ the common people.
¹⁹ They will fight you, but they will not defeat you.
    I am with you, and I will rescue you," declares the LORD.

The People Continue to Reject the LORD's Love for Them

2 ¹ The LORD spoke his word to me,

² "Go and announce to Jerusalem,
    'This is what the LORD says:
    I remember the unfailing loyalty of your youth,
        the love you had for me as a bride.
    I remember how you followed me into the desert,
        into a land that couldn't be farmed.
³ Israel was set apart for the LORD.
    It was the best part of the harvest.
    All who devoured it became guilty,
        and disaster struck them,' " declares the LORD.

⁴ Listen to the word of the LORD, descendants of Jacob,
    all the families in the nation of Israel.
⁵ This is what the LORD says:
What did your ancestors find wrong with me
    that they went so far away from me?
They followed worthless idols and became worthless themselves.
⁶ They didn't ask, "Where is the LORD,
    who brought us from Egypt?
    He led us through the desert,
        through a wasteland and its pits,
        a land of drought and the shadow of death.
        No one lives there or travels there."
⁷ I brought them into a fertile land
    to eat its fruit and its produce.
    They came and made my land unclean.^a
    They made my property disgusting.
⁸ The priests didn't ask, "Where is the LORD?"
    Those who deal with my teachings didn't know me.
    The rulers rebelled against me.
    The prophets prophesied in the name of Baal
        and followed statues that couldn't help them.

⁹ "That is why I am bringing charges against you," declares the LORD,
    "and I am bringing charges against your grandchildren.
¹⁰ Go over to the coasts of Cyprus, and see.
Send ˌsomeoneˌ to Kedar, and observe closely.
    See if there has ever been anything like this.
¹¹ Has any nation ever exchanged gods?
    (Their gods aren't really gods.)
Yet, my people have exchanged their Glory
    for something that doesn't help them.
¹² Be horrified over this, heaven.
Be terribly afraid," declares the LORD.
¹³ "My people have done two things wrong.
    They have abandoned me,
        the fountain of life-giving water.
    They have also dug their own cisterns,
        broken cisterns that can't hold water.

¹⁴ "Are the people of Israel slaves?
    Were they born into slavery?
        Why, then, have they become someone's property?
¹⁵ Young lions have roared very loudly at them.
    Young lions have turned the land into a wasteland.
    The cities have been burned down, and everyone has left.

---

^a 2:7 "Unclean" refers to anything that Moses' Teachings say is not presentable to God.

16 People from Noph and Tahpanhes have cracked your skulls, Israel.
17 You have brought this on yourself
    by abandoning the LORD your God
      when he led you on his way.
18 You won't gain anything by going to Egypt
    to drink water from the Nile River.
  You won't gain anything by going to Assyria
    to drink water from the Euphrates River.
19 Your own wickedness will correct you,
    and your unfaithful ways will punish you.
  You should know and see how evil and bitter it is for you
    if you abandon the LORD your God and do not fear me,"
      declares the Almighty LORD of Armies.

20 "Long ago you broke off your yoke,[b] tore off your chains,
    and said that you wouldn't be a slave.
  You lay down and acted like a prostitute
    on every high hill and under every large tree.
21 I planted you like a choice grapevine from the very best seed.
  Now you have turned against me and have become a wild vine.
22 Even if you wash with detergent and use a lot of soap,
    I would still see the stains from your wickedness,"
      declares the Almighty LORD.
23 "How can you say that you haven't dishonored yourselves
    and haven't followed other gods—the Baals?
      Look how you've behaved in the valley.
      Acknowledge what you've done.
  You are like a young camel that swiftly runs here and there.
24 You are like a wild donkey that is used to the desert,
    sniffing the wind while in heat.
  All who look for you won't get tired.
  They will find you during your monthly period.
25 Don't run until your feet are bare and your throats are dry.
  But you say that it's useless.
    You love foreign gods and follow them.

26 "As a thief feels ashamed when he's caught,
    so the nation of Israel will feel ashamed.
      Their kings, princes, priests,
        and prophets will also feel ashamed.
27 You call wood your father.
  You call stone your mother.
    You've turned your backs, not your faces, to me.
  But when you're in trouble, you ask me to come and rescue you.
28 Where are the gods that you made for yourselves?
    Let them come and rescue you when you're in trouble.
      You have as many gods as you have cities, Judah!

29 "Why do you complain about me?
    All of you have rebelled against me," declares the LORD.
30 "I have punished your children without results.
    They didn't respond to correction.
  You killed my prophets like a raging lion.

31 "Consider the word of the LORD, people of this generation.
    Haven't I been a desert, a land of thick darkness, for Israel?
      Why do my people say that they are free to wander around
        and no longer come to me?
32 A young woman can't forget her jewelry or a bride her veils.
    Yet, my people have forgotten me for countless days.
33   You carefully planned ways to look for love.
    You taught your ways to wicked women.
34   You have the blood from poor and innocent people
        on your clothes.

---

[b] 2:20 A yoke is a wooden bar placed over the necks of work animals so that they can pull plows or carts.

You didn't kill them for breaking in to your home.
³⁵ In spite of all this you say, 'I'm innocent.
God will turn his anger from me,
because I haven't sinned.'
³⁶ You change your mind so easily.
You will be put to shame by Egypt
as you were put to shame by Assyria.
³⁷ You will also leave this place with your hands over your head,
because the LORD has rejected those you trust.
You will not be helped by them."

3 ¹ A saying:

If a man divorces his wife
and she leaves him and marries another man,
her first husband shouldn't go back to her again.
The land would become thoroughly polluted.
"You have acted like a prostitute who has many lovers.
And now you want to come back to me!" declares the LORD.

² "Look at the bare hills, and see.
You have had sex with men in every place.
You sat by the roadside waiting for them like a nomad in the desert.
You have polluted the land with your prostitution and wickedness.
³ So the rain has been withheld, and there have been no spring showers.
Yet, you have the shameless look of a prostitute,
and you refuse to blush.
⁴ But now you are calling to me.
You say, 'Father! You have been my companion
ever since I was young.
⁵ He won't hold a grudge forever.
He won't always be angry.'
You have said and done all the evil things that you could."

The LORD Offers to Forgive the Ten Tribes of Israel Despite Their Idolatry

⁶ When Josiah was king, the LORD asked me, "Did you see what unfaithful Israel did? She went up every high mountain and under every large tree, and she acted like a prostitute there. ⁷ I thought that after she had done all this that she would come back to me. But she didn't come back, and her treacherous sister Judah saw her. ⁸ Judah saw that I sent unfaithful Israel away because of her adultery and that I gave Israel her divorce papers. But treacherous Judah, her sister, wasn't afraid. She also acted like a prostitute. ⁹ Because she wasn't concerned about acting like a prostitute, she polluted the land and committed adultery with standing stones and wood pillars. ¹⁰ Even after all this, Israel's treacherous sister Judah didn't wholeheartedly come back to me. She was deceitful," declares the LORD.

¹¹ Then the LORD said to me, "Unfaithful Israel was less guilty than treacherous Judah. ¹² Go and proclaim these things to the north:

" 'Come back, unfaithful Israel.
It is the LORD speaking.
I will no longer frown on you
because I'm merciful,' declares the LORD.
'I will no longer be angry with you.
¹³ Admit that you've done wrong!
You have rebelled against the LORD your God.
You have given yourself to strangers under every large tree.
You have not obeyed me,' declares the LORD.

¹⁴ "Come back, you rebellious people," declares the LORD. "I'm your husband. I will take you, one from every city and two from every family, and bring you to Zion. ¹⁵ I will give you shepherds after my own heart. They will be shepherds who feed you with knowledge and insight. ¹⁶ In those days you will be fertile, and your population will increase in the land," declares the LORD. "People will no longer talk about the ark of the LORD's promise. It will no longer come to mind. They won't remember it, miss it, or make another one. ¹⁷ At that time they will call Jerusalem the throne of the LORD. All nations will gather in Jerusalem because the name of the LORD will be found there. They will no longer follow their own stubborn, evil ways. ¹⁸ In those days the nation of Judah will live with the nation of Israel. They will come together from the land of the north to the land that I gave their ancestors as their own property.

19 "I wanted to treat you like children
   and give you a pleasant land,
      the most beautiful property among the nations.
   I thought that you would call me Father and wouldn't turn away from me.
20 But like a wife who betrays her husband,
      so you, nation of Israel, betrayed me," declares the LORD.

21 The sound of crying is heard on the hills.
   It is the crying and the pleading of the people of Israel.
      They have become crooked
         and have forgotten the LORD their God.
22 "Come back, you rebellious people,
      and I will forgive you for being unfaithful."

Here we are!
   We have come to you because you are the LORD our God.
23 Truly, the noise from the hills, from the mountains,
      is the noise of false worship.
   Truly, the LORD our God will rescue us.
24 Ever since we were young,
      the shameful worship ⌊of Baal⌋
         has taken everything our ancestors worked for,
            their flocks and herds, their sons and daughters.
25   We must lie down in our shame
            and be covered by our disgrace.
   Ever since we were young, we and our ancestors have sinned
      against the LORD our God.
   We haven't obeyed the LORD our God.

4 ¹ The LORD declares,

"If you come back, Israel,
if you come back to me,
if you take your disgusting idols out of my sight
   and you don't wander away from me,
² if you take the oath, "As the LORD lives . . ."
   in an honest, fair, and right way,
then the nations will be blessed,
   and they will be honored by me."

The LORD Will Bring Destruction on Judah From the North

³ This is what the LORD says to the people of Judah and to Jerusalem:

Plow your unplowed fields,
   and don't plant among thorns.
⁴ Be circumcised by the LORD,
   and get rid of the foreskins of your hearts,
      people of Judah and inhabitants of Jerusalem.
If you don't, my fury will flare up like a fire.
   It will burn, and no one will be able to put it out,
      because of the evil you do.

⁵ Report this message in Judah.
Make it heard in Jerusalem.
   Say, "Blow the ram's horn throughout the land."
      Shout loudly and say, "Gather together!
         Let's go into the fortified cities."
⁶ Raise the flag to signal people to go to Zion.
   Take cover!
      Don't just stand there!
I'm bringing disaster and widespread destruction from the north.
⁷ A lion has come out of its lair.
A destroyer of nations has set out.
   He has left his place to destroy your land.
      Your cities will be ruined, and no one will live in them.
⁸ So put on sackcloth, mourn, and cry
   because the LORD's burning anger hasn't turned away from us.

⁹ "When that day comes," declares the LORD,
   "the king and the leaders will lose their courage.
   The priests will be stunned.
   The prophets will be amazed and astonished."

¹⁰ I said, "Almighty LORD,
   you certainly have deceived these people and Jerusalem.
      You said that everything would go well for them,
         but a sword is held at their throats."

¹¹ At that time it will be said to these people and to Jerusalem:
   "A hot wind from the heights will blow in the desert
      on the tracks of my people.
      It will not be a wind that winnowsᵃ or cleanses.
¹²   It will be a stronger wind than that.
         It will come from me.
   Now, I will pass sentence on them."

¹³ The enemy comes up like clouds.
   His chariots are like a raging wind.
   His horses are faster than eagles.
How horrible it will be for us! We will be destroyed!
¹⁴ Jerusalem, wash the evil from your heart
   so that you may be rescued.
      Don't continue making evil plans.
¹⁵ A message is heard from Dan,
   and a report of disaster comes from the mountains of Ephraim.
¹⁶ Warn the nations about these things.
Bring them to the attention of Jerusalem.
   "Hostile troops are coming from a distant country.
      They are shouting battle cries against the cities of Judah.
¹⁷   They surround them like men guarding a field,
         because Judah has rebelled against me,"
            declares the LORD.
¹⁸   "You brought this on yourself.
         This is your punishment.
         It is bitter.
         It breaks your heart."

¹⁹ My anguish, my anguish!
   I writhe in pain.
      My heart is beating wildly!
      My heart is pounding!
   I can't keep quiet
      because I hear a ram's horn sounding the alarm for war.
²⁰ One disaster follows another.
   The whole land is ruined.
My tents are suddenly destroyed.
   Their curtains are torn in an instant.
²¹ How long must I see the battle flag and hear the sound of rams' horns?

²² "My people are fools. They don't know me.
   They are stupid people. They don't understand.
   They are experts in doing wrong,
      and they don't know how to do good."

²³ I see the earth. It's formless and empty.
   I see the sky. Its lights are gone.
²⁴ I see the mountains. They are shaking,
   and the hills are swaying.
²⁵ I see that there are no people,
   and every bird has flown away.
²⁶ I see that the fertile land has become a desert,
   and all its cities are torn down
      because of the LORD and his burning anger.

ᵃ 4:11 Winnowing is the process of separating husks from grain.

27 This is what the LORD says:

The whole earth will be ruined,
although I will not destroy it completely.
28 The earth will mourn, and the sky will grow black.
I have spoken, and I have planned it.
I won't change my plans, and I won't turn back.

29 All the people in the city will flee
at the sound of riders and archers.
They will go off into the thickets
and climb among the rocks.
The entire city will be abandoned, and no one will live in it.

30 You are going to be destroyed!
What are you going to do?
Why do you dress in red and put on gold jewelry?
Why do you wear eye shadow?
You are making yourself beautiful for nothing.
Your lovers reject you; they want to kill you.

31 I hear a woman in labor.
I hear the woman cry with anguish as she gives birth to her first child.
My people Zion are gasping for breath.
They are stretching out their hands, saying,
"How horrible it is for us!
We're defenseless in the presence of murderers!"

Judah's Complete Rejection of the LORD

5 **1** Walk around the streets of Jerusalem.
Look around, and think about these things.
Search the city squares.
See if you can find anyone
who does what is right and seeks the truth.
Then I will forgive Jerusalem.
2 People say, "As the LORD lives. . . ."
Yet, they lie when they take this oath.
3 LORD, your eyes look for the truth.
You strike these people, but they don't feel it.
You crush them, but they refuse to be corrected.
They are more stubborn than rocks.
They refuse to turn back.
4 I thought, "These are poor, foolish people.
They don't know the way of the LORD
and the justice that God demands.
5 Let me go to important people and speak to them.
They know the way of the LORD
and the justice that God demands."
But they, too, had broken off their yokes*
and torn off their chains.
6 That is why a lion from the forest will attack them.
A wolf from the wilderness will destroy them.
A leopard will lie in ambush outside their cities.
All who leave the cities will be torn to pieces,
because they rebel so often
and they become more and more unfaithful.

7 "Why should I forgive you?
Your children abandoned me.
They took godless oaths.
They committed adultery, even though I satisfied their needs.
They traveled in crowds to the houses of prostitutes.
8 They are like well-fed stallions that are wild with desire.
They neigh for their neighbors' wives.
9 I will punish them for these things," declares the LORD.

---

* 5:5 A yoke is a wooden bar placed over the necks of work animals so that they can pull plows or carts.

"I will punish this nation.

10 "Go among Jerusalem's rows of grapevines and destroy them,
    but don't destroy all of them.
Cut off the branches because they don't belong to the LORD.
11 The nations of Israel and Judah are unfaithful to me,"
    declares the LORD.
12 They lie about the LORD and say,
    "He doesn't exist!
      Nothing bad will happen to us.
      We won't experience war or famine.
13 The prophets are nothing but windbags.
The LORD hasn't spoken through them,
    so let what they say happen to them."

14 This is what the LORD God of Armies says:

Because you've talked like this,
    I'm going to put my words in your mouth like a fire.
      These people will be like wood.
      My words will burn them up.
15 Nation of Israel, I'm going to bring a nation from far away
    to attack you, declares the LORD.
      It is a nation that has lasted a long time.
      It is an ancient nation.
        You don't know the language of this nation.
        You can't understand what its people say.
16   Their arrow quivers are like open graves.
      They are all mighty warriors.
17   They will devour your harvest and your food.
      They will devour your sons and your daughters.
      They will devour your flocks and your cattle.
      They will devour your grapevines and your fig trees.
        With their swords they will destroy
        the fortified cities you trust.
18 Yet, even in those days, declares the LORD,
    I won't destroy all of you.

19 They will ask, "Why has the LORD our God done all this to us?" Answer them, "You have abandoned me and served foreign gods in your land. So you will serve foreigners in a land that isn't yours."

20 "Tell this to the descendants of Jacob, and make this heard in Judah:
21 Hear this, you stupid and senseless people!
    You have eyes, but you cannot see.
    You have ears, but you cannot hear.
22   Don't you fear me?" asks the LORD.
    "Don't you tremble in my presence?
      I made the sand a boundary for the sea,
        a permanent barrier that it cannot cross.
          Although the waves toss continuously,
          they can't break through.
          Although they roar, they can't cross it.
23 But these people are stubborn and rebellious.
    They have turned aside and wandered away from me.
24 They don't say to themselves,
    'We should fear the LORD our God.
      He sends rain at the right time,
        the autumn rain and the spring rain.
      He makes sure that we have harvest seasons.'
25 Your wickedness has turned these things away.
Your sins have kept good things away from you.

26 "Wicked people are found among my people.
    They lie in ambush like bird catchers.
    They set traps and catch people.
27 Like cages filled with birds, their houses are filled with deceit.

That is why they become powerful and rich.
²⁸   They grow big and fat.
Their evil deeds have no limits.
They have no respect for the rights of others.
They have no respect for the rights of orphans.
    But they still prosper.
They don't defend the rights of the poor.
²⁹ I will punish them for these things," declares the LORD.
"I will punish this nation.

³⁰ "Something horrible and disgusting is happening in the land:
³¹   Prophets prophesy lies.
Priests rule under the prophets' directions,
    and my people love this.
But what will you do in the end?"

The LORD's Rejection of Judah

6 ¹ "Take cover, people of Benjamin!
Run away from Jerusalem!
Blow the ram's horn in Tekoa.
Raise the flag over Beth Hakkerem,
    because disaster and widespread destruction
    are coming from the north.

² "My people Zion are like lovely pastures.
³ With their flocks, shepherds will come to them,
    pitch their tents all around them,
    and each of them will tend his own flock.
⁴ ⸤The shepherds say,⸥ 'Prepare yourselves for war against Zion.
    Let's attack at noon!
How horrible it will be for us. The day is passing,
    and the shadows of evening are growing longer.
⁵   Let's attack at night and destroy its palaces.' "

⁶This is what the LORD of Armies says:

Cut down its trees.
Build up dirt mounds to attack Jerusalem.
    This city must be punished.
    There is nothing but oppression in it.
⁷ As a well keeps its water fresh,
    so Jerusalem keeps its evil fresh.
        Violence and destruction can be heard in it.
        I see that it is sick and wounded.
⁸ Pay attention to my warning, Jerusalem,
    or I will turn away from you.
I will make your land desolate,
    a land where no one will live.

⁹This is what the LORD of Armies says:

Thoroughly pick through the faithful few of Israel
    like someone picks through a grapevine.
Like someone picking grapes, pass your hand over its branches again.

¹⁰ Whom can I speak to?
Whom can I give a warning to?
Who will listen?
    Their ears are plugged,
    and they aren't able to pay attention.
When the LORD speaks his word to them,
    they show contempt for it and object to it.
¹¹ I am filled with the anger of the LORD.
I am tired of holding it in.

"Pour it out on the children in the street
    and on the gangs of young men.
A man and his wife will be taken away

as well as very old people.
12 Their households, their fields, and their wives
        will be turned over to others.
    I will use my power against those who live in the land,"
        declares the LORD.
13 "All of them, from the least important to the most important,
        are eager to make money dishonestly.
    All of them, from prophets to priests, act deceitfully.
14 They treat my people's wounds as though they were not serious, saying,
        'Everything is all right! Everything is all right!'
            But it's not all right.
15 Are they ashamed when they do disgusting things?
        No, they're not ashamed.
            They don't even know how to blush.
    So they will die with those who die.
    They will be brought down when I punish them," says the LORD.

16 This is what the LORD says:

    Stand at the crossroads and look.
    Ask which paths are the old, reliable paths.
    Ask which way leads to blessings.
        Live that way, and find a resting place for yourselves.
            But you said that you wouldn't live that way.
17 I posted watchmen over you.
        Pay attention to the sound of the ram's horn.
            But you said that you wouldn't pay attention.
18 Listen, you nations,
        and learn, you witnesses, what will happen to them.
19 Listen, earth!
    I'm going to bring disaster on these people.
        It is the result of their own plots,
            because they won't pay attention to my words.
    They reject my teachings.
20 Incense that comes from Sheba is no good to me.
    Sugar cane that comes from a distant land is no good to me.
        I won't accept your burnt offerings.
        I'm not pleased with your sacrifices.

21 This is what the LORD says:

    I'm going to lay stumbling blocks in front of these people.
        Parents and children will stumble over them.
        Neighbors and their friends will die.

22 This is what the LORD says:

    An army is going to come from the north.
    A great nation is preparing itself in the distant parts of the earth.
23   Its people take hold of bows and spears.
        They are cruel and have no compassion.
        They sound like the roaring sea.
        They ride on horses.
        They march like soldiers ready for battle
            against my people Zion.

24 We have heard the news about them.
        Our hands hang limp.
    We are gripped by anguish and pain
        like a woman giving birth to a child.
25 Don't go into the field or walk on the road.
        The enemy has a sword.
            Terror is all around.
26 Wear sackcloth, and roll around in ashes, my people.
        Mourn as if you have lost your only child, and cry bitterly.
    The destroyer will suddenly attack us.

27 "Jeremiah, I have put you in charge of testing and refining my people.

You will know how to test their ways.
28   They are all vicious rebels.
     They go around slandering.
     They are all like bronze and iron.
     They corrupt themselves.
29 The bellows of the blast furnace blow fiercely
     to make the fire melt away the lead.
     It is useless to go on refining
          because the impurities can't be removed.
30 ⌊People⌋ will call them useless silver
     because the LORD has rejected them."

Judah Trusts the Wrong Things

7 ¹The LORD spoke his word to Jeremiah. He said, ² "Stand at the gate of the LORD's house, and announce from there this message: 'Listen to the word of the LORD, all you people of Judah who go through these gates to worship the LORD. ³ This is what the LORD of Armies, the God of Israel, says: Change the way you live and act, and I will let you live in this place. ⁴ Do not trust the words of this saying, "This is the LORD's temple, the LORD's temple, the LORD's temple!" It's a lie.

⁵ " 'Suppose you really change the way you live and act and you really treat each other fairly. ⁶ Suppose you do not oppress foreigners, orphans, and widows, or kill anyone in this place. And suppose you do not follow other gods that lead you to your own destruction. ⁷ Then I will let you live in this place, in the land that I gave permanently to your ancestors long ago.

⁸ " 'You are trusting the words of a saying. It's a lie that cannot help you. ⁹ You steal, murder, commit adultery, lie when you take oaths, burn incense as an offering to Baal, and run after other gods that you do not know. ¹⁰ Then you stand in my presence in the house that is called by my name. You think that you're safe to do all these disgusting things. ¹¹ The house that is called by my name has become a gathering place for thieves. I have seen what you are doing,' " declares the LORD.

¹² " 'But go to my place that was at Shiloh, where I first made a dwelling place for my name. See what I did to Shiloh because of the evil done by my people Israel. ¹³ You have done the same things the people did at Shiloh,' " declares the LORD. " 'Although I spoke to you again and again, you did not listen. When I called you, you did not answer. ¹⁴ So what I did to Shiloh I will now do to the house that is called by my name. This is the place I gave to you and to your ancestors, the place where you feel so safe. ¹⁵ I will force you out of my sight as I forced out all your relatives, all of Ephraim's descendants.'

¹⁶ "Jeremiah, don't pray for these people. Don't cry or pray for them. Don't plead with me, because I will not listen to you. ¹⁷ Don't you see what they are doing in the cities of Judah and in the streets of Jerusalem? ¹⁸ Children gather wood, fathers light fires, and women knead dough to make cakes for the queen of heaven. They pour out wine offerings to other gods in order to make me furious. ¹⁹ They aren't really provoking me," declares the LORD. "But they are ⌊harming⌋ themselves to their own shame.

²⁰ "This is what the Almighty LORD says: My anger and fury will be poured out on this place, on humans and animals, and on trees and crops. My anger and fury will burn and not be put out.

²¹ "This is what the LORD of Armies, the God of Israel, says: Add your burnt offerings to your sacrifices, and eat the meat. ²² When I brought your ancestors out of Egypt, I did not tell them anything about burnt offerings and sacrifices. ²³ But I did tell them this, 'Obey me, and I will be your God, and you will be my people. Live the way I told you to live so that things will go well for you.' ²⁴ But they didn't obey me or pay attention to me. They followed their own plans and their stubborn, evil ways. They went backward and not forward. ²⁵ From the time that your ancestors left Egypt until now, I have sent all my servants the prophets to you again and again. ²⁶ But you didn't obey me or pay attention to me. You became impossible to deal with, and you were worse than your ancestors.

²⁷ "Jeremiah, you will say all these things to them, but they will not obey you. You will call to them, but they will not respond to you. ²⁸ You will say to them, 'This is the nation that did not obey the LORD their God. They did not accept discipline. Truth has disappeared and vanished from their lips.'

²⁹ "Cut off your hair and throw it away. Sing a song of mourning on the bare hills, because in his anger the LORD has rejected and abandoned the people of this generation. ³⁰ The people of Judah have done what I consider evil," declares the LORD. "They set up their detestable idols in the house that is called by my name. They have made it unclean.ᵃ ³¹ They have built worship sites at Topheth in the valley of Ben Hinnom in order to burn their sons and daughters as sacrifices. I did not ask for this. It never entered my mind.

ᵃ 7:30 "Unclean" refers to anything that Moses' Teachings say is not presentable to God.

32 "That is why the days are coming," declares the LORD, "when that place will no longer be known as Topheth or the valley of Ben Hinnom. Instead, it will be known as Slaughter Valley. They will bury ˎpeopleˎ at Topheth because no other place will be left. **33** The dead bodies of these people will become food for birds and animals, and no one will be there to frighten them away. **34** In the cities of Judah and in the streets of Jerusalem, I will banish the sounds of joy and happiness and the sounds of brides and grooms, because the land will be a wasteland."

8 **1** The LORD declares, "At that time the bones of the kings and the leaders of Judah, the bones of the priests and the prophets, and the bones of the others who lived in Jerusalem will be taken out of their graves. **2** They will be spread out and exposed to the sun, the moon, and all the stars in the sky. These are the things that they had loved, served, gone after, sought, and worshiped. Their bones will not be gathered or buried, but they will become manure on the ground.

3 "Then the few who remain from these wicked people will want to die rather than live where I will scatter them," declares the LORD of Armies.

The LORD's Judgment on Judah's False Religion

4 "Say to them, 'This is what the LORD says:

When someone falls, he gets back up.
When someone turns away from me, he returns.
5   The people of Jerusalem turned away from me without ever returning.
They still cling to deceit.
They refuse to return.
6   I have paid attention and listened,
but they weren't honest.
They don't turn away from their wickedness and ask,
"What have we done?"
They go their own ways like horses charging into battle.
7   Even storks know when it's time to return.
Mourning doves, swallows, and cranes know
when it's time to migrate.
But my people don't know
that I, the LORD, am urging them to return.

8   " 'How can you say that you are wise
and that you have the LORD's teachings?
The scribes have used their pens to turn these teachings into lies.
9   Wise people are put to shame, confused, and trapped.
They have rejected the word of the LORD.
They don't really have any wisdom.
10   That is why I will give their wives to other men
and their fields to new owners.
All of them, from the least important to the most important,
are eager to make money dishonestly.
All of them, from prophets to priests, act deceitfully.
11   They treat my dear people's wounds
as though they were not serious, saying,
"Everything is all right! Everything is all right!"
But it's not all right.
12   Are they ashamed that they do disgusting things?
No, they're not ashamed.
They don't even know how to blush.
So they will die with those who die.
They will be brought down when I punish them,' " says the LORD.
13   " 'I would have gathered their harvest,' " declares the LORD,
" 'but there are no grapes on the vine.
There are no figs on the tree,
and the leaves have dried up.
What I have given them will be taken away.' "

14   Why are we just sitting here? Let's get up!
Let's go into the fortified cities and die there.
The LORD our God has condemned us to die.
He has given us poison to drink
because we have sinned against the LORD.
15   We hoped for peace, but nothing good has happened.

We hoped for a time of healing, but there's only terror.
16   The snorting of horses can be heard from Dan.
The neighing of stallions makes the whole land tremble.
They are coming to devour the land and everything in it,
the city and its people.

17   "I am going to send snakes among you,
vipers that can't be charmed.
They will bite you," declares the LORD.

Jeremiah's Grief Over His People's Punishment

18   Sorrow has overwhelmed me.
I am sick at heart!
19   The cry from my dear people comes from a distant land:
"Isn't the LORD in Zion?
Isn't Zion's king still there?"
They make me furious with their idols, with their foreign gods.

20   The harvest is past,
the summer has ended,
and we haven't been saved.

21   I am crushed because my dear people have been crushed.
I mourn; terror grips me.
22   Isn't there medicine in Gilead?
Aren't there doctors there?
Then why hasn't the health of my dear people been restored?

9 1   "I wish that my head were ˌfilledˌ with water
and my eyes were a fountain of tears
so that I could cry day and night
for my dear people who have been killed.
2   I wish I had a place to stay in the desert.
I would abandon my people and go away from them.
They are all adulterers,
a mob of traitors.
3   They use their tongues like bows that shoot arrows.
Lies and dishonesty rule the land.^b
They go from one evil thing to another,
and they don't know me," declares the LORD.
4   "Beware of your neighbors.
Don't trust your relatives.
Every relative cheats.
Every neighbor goes around slandering.
5   Everyone cheats his neighbor.
No one speaks the truth.
My people train their tongues to speak lies.
They wear themselves out doing wrong.
6   Oppression follows oppression.^c
Deceit follows deceit.
They refuse to acknowledge me," declares the LORD.

7 This is what the LORD of Armies says:

I will now refine them with fire and test them.
What else can I do for my dear people?
8   Their tongues are like deadly arrows.
They speak deceitfully.
People speak politely to their neighbors,
but they think of ways to set traps for them.
9   I will punish them for these things, declares the LORD.
I will punish this nation.
I still won't be satisfied.

---

^a 9:1 Jeremiah 9:1–26 in English Bibles is Jeremiah 8:23–9:25 in the Hebrew Bible.   ^b 9:3 Greek; Masoretic Text "They bend their tongue. Their bow is falsehood. And not for truth are they strong in the land."   ^c 9:6 Greek; Masoretic Text "Your sitting is in the midst of deceit."

10   I will cry and weep for the mountains.
      I will sing a funeral song for the pastures in the wilderness.
          They are destroyed so that no one can travel through them.
              No one can hear the sound of cattle.
                  Birds and cattle have fled.
                  They are gone.
11   I will turn Jerusalem into a pile of rubble, a home for jackals.
      I will destroy the cities of Judah so that no one can live there.
12   No one is wise enough to understand this.
      To whom has the LORD revealed this
          so that they can explain it?
      The land dies; it has been ruined like the desert
          so that no one can travel through it.

13 The LORD answered,

      "They've abandoned my teachings that I placed in front of them.
      They didn't obey me, and they didn't follow them.
14   They followed their own stubborn ways and other gods—the Baals,
          as their ancestors taught them."

15 This is what the LORD of Armies, the God of Israel, says:

      I am going to feed these people bitterness
          and give them poison to drink.
16   I will scatter them among nations
          that they and their ancestors haven't heard of.
      I will send armies after them until I've wiped them out.

17 This is what the LORD of Armies says:

      Consider this:
          Call for the women who cry at funerals.
          Send for those who are the most skilled.
18   They should come quickly and cry for us.
          Our eyes will run with tears.
          Our eyelids will flow with water.
19   The sound of crying is heard from Zion.
          "We're ruined! We're very ashamed.
              We must leave our land because our homes have been torn down."

20   Listen to the word of the LORD, you women,
          and open your ears to hear his words.
              Teach your daughters how to cry.
              Teach your neighbors funeral songs.
21   Death has come through our windows and entered our palaces.
      Death has cut down the children in the streets
          and the young men in the market places.

22 This is what the LORD says:

      Dead bodies will fall like manure on the field.
          They will be like grain that has been cut but not gathered.

The Lord Is the Only True God

23 This is what the LORD says:

      Don't let wise people brag about their wisdom.
      Don't let strong people brag about their strength.
      Don't let rich people brag about their riches.
24   If they want to brag, they should brag that they understand and know me.
          They should brag that I, the LORD, act out of love, righteousness,
              and justice on the earth.
                  This kind of bragging pleases me, declares the LORD.
25   "The days are coming," declares the LORD,
          "when I will punish all who are circumcised.
26   I will punish Egypt, Judah, Edom, Ammon, and Moab.
      I will punish all who shave the hair on their foreheads
          or live in the desert.
              Even though these nations are circumcised,
                  all Israel has uncircumcised hearts."

10 ¹ Listen to the message that the LORD has spoken to you, nation of Israel. ² This is what the LORD says:

Don't learn the practices of the nations.
Don't be frightened by the signs in the sky
  because the nations are frightened by them.
³ The religion of the people is worthless.
  Woodcutters cut down trees from the forest.
    The hands of craftsmen prepare them with axes.
⁴   Craftsmen decorate them with silver and gold
      and fasten them ˏtogetherˏ with hammers and nails
        so that they won't fall over.
⁵ These trees are like scarecrows in cucumber gardens.
  They aren't able to speak.
  They have to be carried, because they can't walk.
Don't be afraid of them.
  They can't harm you.
  They can't do you any good either.

⁶ No one is like you, O LORD.
  You are great.
  Your name is powerful.
⁷ Everyone fears you, O King of the Nations.
    This is what you deserve.
No one is like you among all the wise people in the nations
  or in all their kingdoms.
⁸ They are complete idiots.
  They learn nonsense from wooden idols.
⁹   Hammered silver is brought from Tarshish and gold from Uphaz.
      Craftsmen and goldsmiths shape these metals.
      The clothing for the idols is blue and purple,
        all made by skilled workers.
¹⁰ But the LORD is the only God.
  He is the living God and eternal king.
    The earth trembles when he is angry.
    The nations can't endure his fury.

¹¹ Tell them this: These gods will disappear from the earth
  and from under heaven because they didn't make heaven and earth.

¹² The LORD made the earth by his power.
  He set up the world by his skill.
  He stretched out the world by his understanding.
¹³ He speaks, and the water in the sky produces a storm.
  He makes clouds rise from the ends of the earth.
  He makes lightning flash with the rain.
  He brings wind out of his storehouses.

¹⁴ Everyone is stupid and ignorant.
  Metalsmiths are put to shame by their idols.
    Their statues are false ˏgodsˏ.
      They can't breathe.
¹⁵   They are worthless jokes.
        When they are punished, they disappear.
¹⁶ Jacob's God isn't like them.
  He made everything,
    and Israel is the tribe that belongs to him.
    His name is the LORD of Armies.

¹⁷ Pick up your bags. You are being blockaded.

¹⁸ This is what the LORD says:

I am going to throw out those who live in the land at this time
  and cause trouble for them so that they will feel it.

¹⁹ Oh, I'm wounded!
  My wound is serious.
  Then I thought that this is my punishment, and I will bear it.

20 My tent is destroyed, and all my ropes are broken.
    My children have left me and have disappeared.
      There's no one to set up my tent again
        or put up my tent curtains.
21 The shepherds are foolish.
    They don't look to the LORD for help.
  That is why they won't succeed,
    and all their flocks will be scattered.
22 The report has arrived.
  A tremendous uproar is coming from the land of the north.
  Its army will destroy Judah's cities
    and make them homes for jackals.
23 O LORD, I know that the way humans act is not under their control.
  Humans do not direct their steps as they walk.
24 Correct me, O LORD, but please be fair.
  Don't correct me when you're angry.
    Otherwise, you'll reduce me to nothing.
25 Pour out your fury on the nations who don't know you
  and on people who don't worship you.
    They have devoured the descendants of Jacob.
    They have devoured them completely.
    They have destroyed their homes.

Judah Has Disobeyed the Terms of the LORD's Promise

11 ¹ This is the message that the LORD spoke to Jeremiah. He said, ² "Listen to the terms of this promise,ᵃ and tell them to the people of Judah and to those who live in Jerusalem. ³ Say to them, 'This is what the LORD, the God of Israel, says: Cursed is anyone who doesn't listen to the terms of this promise. ⁴ I made this promise to your ancestors when I brought them out of Egypt, which was an iron smelter. I said, "Obey me, and do everything that I have told you to do. Then you will be my people, and I will be your God. ⁵ I will keep the oath I made to your ancestors and give them a land flowing with milk and honey, the land you still have today." ' "

I answered, "Yes, LORD."

⁶ The LORD said to me, "Announce all these things in the cities of Judah and in the streets of Jerusalem: Listen to the terms of this promise, and keep them. ⁷ I solemnly warned your ancestors when I brought them out of Egypt, and the warning still applies to you today. I solemnly warned them to obey me. ⁸ But they didn't obey me or pay attention to me. They followed their own stubborn, evil ways. So I punished them, because they did not keep all the terms of the promise, the terms that I commanded them to keep."

⁹ The LORD said to me, "Conspiracy exists among the people of Judah and among those who live in Jerusalem. ¹⁰ They've gone back to the evil ways of their ancestors and refused to obey my words. They are following other gods and worshiping them. The nations of Israel and Judah have rejected the promise that I made to their ancestors. ¹¹ This is what the LORD says: I'm going to bring a disaster on them that they can't escape. Although they will cry out to me, I won't listen to them. ¹² Then the cities of Judah and those who live in Jerusalem will cry to the gods to whom they've been sacrificing. But these gods will never rescue them when they're in trouble. ¹³ Judah, you have as many gods as you have cities. You have set up many altars ˌin Jerusalemˌ to sacrifice to Baal. You have as many altars as there are streets in Jerusalem. ¹⁴ Jeremiah, don't pray for these people. Don't cry or pray for them. I won't listen when they call to me for help in times of trouble.

15 "What right do these people I love have to be in my house
  when they do so many devious things?
  Can the meat from their sacrifices turn disaster away from them?
    They rejoice when they do evil."

16 The LORD called you a large olive tree
  that has beautiful fruit to look at.
  He will set fire to you with a mighty storm,
    and your branches will be broken.
17 The LORD of Armies planted you.
    He has pronounced disaster on you.
      This is because of the evil things

ᵃ 11:2 Or "covenant."

that Israel and Judah have done.
    They have made him furious by burning incense
      as an offering to Baal.

Jeremiah's Life Is Threatened

[18] The LORD revealed their plot to me so that I would understand. He showed me what they were doing. [19] I was like a trusting lamb brought to the slaughter. I didn't know that they were plotting against me. They were saying, "Let's destroy the tree with its fruit. Let's cut Jeremiah off from this world of the living so that we won't be reminded of him anymore."

[20]   O LORD of Armies, you judge fairly
     and test motives and thoughts.
  I want to see you take revenge on them,
    because I've brought my case to you.

[21] This is what the LORD says: The people of Anathoth want to kill you. They say, "Don't prophesy in the name of the LORD, or we'll kill you."
[22] This is what the LORD of Armies says: I'm going to punish them. The young men will die because of war. Their sons and daughters will die because of famine. [23] I will bring a disaster on the people of Anathoth. It will be a year of punishment. There will be no survivors.

Jeremiah's Question

12 [1]   O LORD, even if I would argue my case with you,
     you would always be right.
   Yet, I want to talk to you about your justice.
    Why do wicked people succeed?
    Why do treacherous people have peace and quiet?
[2]   You plant them, and they take root.
      They grow, and they produce fruit.
      They speak well of you with their lips,
        but their hearts are far from you.
[3] You know me, O LORD.
  You see me and test my devotion to you.
    Drag them away like sheep to be slaughtered.
    Prepare them for the day of slaughter.
[4] How long will the land mourn?
  How long will the plants in every field remain dried up?
    The animals and the birds are dying,
      because people are wicked.
    They think that God[a] doesn't know what they are doing.

The LORD's Reply

[5]   "If you have raced against others on foot, and they have tired you out,
    how can you compete with horses?
  If you stumble in open country,
    how can you live in the jungle along the Jordan River?
[6] Even your relatives and members of your father's household betray you.
    They have also formed a mob to find you.
      Don't trust them when they say good things about you.
[7] "I have abandoned my nation.
  I have left my own people.
  I have handed the people I love over to their enemies.
[8] My people have turned on me like a lion in the forest.
    They roar at me, so I hate them.
[9] My people are like a colorful bird of prey.
  Other birds of prey surround it.
    Go, gather all the animals in the field,
      and bring them to devour it.
[10] Many shepherds have destroyed my vineyard.
    They've trampled my property.
    They've turned my pleasant property into a wasteland.
[11] They've left it a wasteland.
      Devastated, it mourns in my presence.
      The whole land is destroyed,

---

[a] 12:4 Greek; Masoretic Text "he."

> but no one takes this to heart.
>
> 12 Looters swarm all over the bare hills in the desert.
>> The LORD's sword destroys them
>>> from one end of the land to the other.
>>>> No one will be safe.
>
> 13 My people planted wheat, but they harvested thorns.
>> They worked until they became sick, but they gained nothing by it.
>>> They were disappointed by their harvests
>>>> because of the burning anger of the LORD.

14 "This is what I, the LORD, say about all my evil neighbors who take the inheritance that I gave my people Israel: I am going to uproot those neighbors from their lands. I will also uproot the people of Judah from among them. 15 After I've uprooted them, I will have compassion on them again. I will return them to their inheritance and to their lands. 16 Suppose they learn carefully the ways of my people. Suppose they take an oath in my name, 'As the LORD lives . . .' as they taught my people to take an oath in ˌthe name ofˌ Baal. Then they will build homes among my people. 17 But suppose they don't listen. Then I will uproot that nation and destroy it," declares the LORD.

Jeremiah's Linen Belt

13 1 This is what the LORD said to me: "Buy a linen belt. Put it around your waist. Don't let it get wet." 2 So I bought the belt, as the LORD had told me, and put it around my waist. 3 The LORD spoke his word to me again. He said, 4 "Take the belt that you bought, the one you're wearing. Go to the Euphrates River, and bury it there in a crack in the rocks." 5 So I went and buried it by the Euphrates, as the LORD had told me.

6 After many days the LORD said to me, "Go to the Euphrates, and get the belt from where I told you to bury it." 7 So I went back to the Euphrates and dug it up. I got the belt from where I had buried it. Now the belt was ruined. It was good for nothing.

8 Then the LORD spoke his word to me. He said, 9 "This is what the LORD says: This is how I will destroy Judah's arrogance and Jerusalem's extreme arrogance. 10 These wicked people refuse to listen to me. They go their own stubborn ways and follow other gods in order to serve them and worship them. They are like this good-for-nothing belt. 11 As a belt clings to a person's waist, so I have made the entire nation of Israel and the entire nation of Judah cling to me," declares the LORD. "I did this so that they would be my people and bring fame, praise, and honor to me. However, they wouldn't listen.

12 "Give this message to them, 'This is what the LORD God of Israel says: Every bottle will be filled with wine.' Then they will say to you, 'We know that every bottle will be filled with wine.' 13 Say to them, 'This is what the LORD says: I'm going to make everyone who lives in this land drunk. The kings who sit on David's throne, the priests, the prophets, and all those who live in Jerusalem will become drunk. 14 Then I will smash them like bottles against each other. I will smash parents and children together, declares the LORD. I will have no pity, mercy, or compassion when I destroy them.' "

> 15 Listen, and pay attention!
>> Don't be arrogant. The LORD has spoken.
>
> 16 Honor the LORD your God before it gets dark,
>> before your feet stumble on the mountains in the twilight.
>> You will look for light,
>>> but the LORD will turn it into the shadow of death
>>>> and change it into deep darkness.
>
> 17 If you won't listen,
>> I will cry secretly over your arrogance.
>> I will cry bitterly, and my eyes will flow with tears
>>> because the LORD's flock will be taken captive.
>
> 18 Say to the king and his mother,
>> "Come down from your thrones,
>>> because your crowns have fallen off your heads."
>
> 19 The cities in the Negev will be locked up,
>> and there will be no one to reopen them.
>> All the people of Judah will be taken away into captivity.
>
> 20 Look up, and see those who are coming from the north.
>> Where is the flock that was given to you—your beautiful sheep?
>
> 21 What will you say
>> when God makes the people you thought were your friends
>>> your new masters?

Won't pain grip you like a woman in labor?
22 If you ask yourself,
"Why do these things happen to me?"
it's because you have so many sins.
Your clothes have been torn off
and your limbs are bare.
23 Can Ethiopians change the color of their skin
or leopards change their spots?
Can you do good
when you're taught to do wrong?
24 "I will scatter you like straw that is blown away by a desert wind.
25 This is your fate, the destiny I have planned for you,"
declares the LORD.
"You have forgotten me and trusted false gods.
26 I will also tear off your clothes,
and your shame will be seen.
27 I have seen you commit adultery and squeal with delight.
I have seen you act like a shameless prostitute
on the hills and in the fields.
How horrible it will be for you, Jerusalem!
Will you ever be clean?"[a]

The LORD Sends a Drought

14 1 The LORD spoke his word to Jeremiah about the drought.

2 Judah mourns; its gates fall apart.
The people of Judah sit in mourning on the ground.
Their cry goes up from Jerusalem.
3 Important people send their assistants out for water.
They go to the cisterns, but they don't find any water.
They come back with their containers empty.
They cover their heads, because they are ashamed and disgraced.
4 The ground is cracked because there has been no rain in the land.
The farmers are disappointed. They cover their heads.
5 Even deer in the fields give birth and abandon their young
because there's no grass.
6 Wild donkeys stand on the bare hills.
They sniff the air like jackals.
Their eyesight fails because they have no green plants.

7 Do something, LORD, for the sake of your name,
even though our sins testify against us.
We have been unfaithful and have sinned against you.
8 You are Israel's hope,
the one who saves it in times of trouble.
Why should you be like a stranger in the land,
like a traveler who stays only one night?
9 Why should you be like someone taken by surprise,
like a strong man who cannot help?
You, O LORD, are among us.
We are called by your name.
Don't leave us!

10 This is what the LORD says about these people: They love to wander. They don't keep their feet where they belong. So the LORD isn't happy with them. He will remember their crimes and punish their sins.

11 The LORD said to me, "Don't pray for the good of these people. 12 Even if they go without food, I won't listen to their cries for help. Even if they sacrifice burnt offerings and grain offerings, I won't be pleased with them. But I will destroy these people with wars, famines, and plagues."

13 Then I said, "Almighty LORD, prophets are saying to them, 'You won't see wars or famines, because I, the LORD, will give you lasting peace in this place.' "

14 Then the LORD told me, "These are the lies that the prophets are telling in my name: They claim that I sent them, commanded them, and spoke to them. They dreamed up the visions they tell you. Their predictions are worthless. They are the products of their own imagination.

---

[a] 13:27 "Clean" refers to anything that Moses' Teachings say is presentable to God.

¹⁵ "I didn't send these prophets. Yet, they prophesy in my name that there will be no wars or famines in this land. So this is what I, the LORD, say about them: Wars and famines will bring an end to these prophets. ¹⁶ The people they prophesy to will be thrown out into the streets of Jerusalem. They will be victims of famines and wars. No one will bury them, their wives, their sons, or their daughters. I will pour on them the destruction that they deserve.

¹⁷ "Say this to them:

'My eyes flow with tears day and night without stopping
    because my dear people will suffer massive destruction.
    It will be a very serious blow.' "
¹⁸   If I go to the field, I see those killed because of war.
    If I go to the city, I see those sick because of famine.
    Prophets and priests wander through a land they haven't heard of.
¹⁹   Have you completely rejected Judah?
    Do you despise Zion?
    Why have you struck us so hard that we cannot heal?
      We hope for peace, but no good comes from it.
      We hope for a time of healing, but there's only terror.
²⁰   O LORD, we realize our wickedness
        and the wrongs done by our ancestors.
      We have sinned against you.
²¹   For the sake of your name, don't despise us.
    Don't dishonor your glorious throne.
    Remember your promiseᵃ to us; don't break it.
²²   The worthless gods of the nations can't make it rain.
    By themselves, the skies can't give showers.
      But you can, O LORD our God.
      We have hope in you because you do all these things.

15 ¹ Then the LORD said to me, "Even if Moses and Samuel were standing in front of me, I would not feel sorry for these people. Send them away from me, and let them go. ² When they ask you where they should go, say to them, 'This is what the LORD says:

Those who are destined to die will die.
Those who are destined to die in wars will die in wars.
Those who are destined to die in famines will die in famines.
Those who are destined to die in captivity will die in captivity.'

³ "I will devise four ways to punish them," declares the LORD. "I will send swords to kill, dogs to drag away, and birds and animals to devour and destroy. ⁴ I will make these people a horrifying sight to all the kingdoms on the earth. This will happen because of what Judah's King Manasseh, son of Hezekiah, did in Jerusalem.

⁵   No one will take pity on you, Jerusalem.
    No one will mourn for you.
    No one will bother to ask how you are doing.
⁶   You have left me," declares the LORD.
      "You have turned your back on me.
      So I will use my power against you and destroy you.
    I'm tired of showing compassion to you.

⁷   "I will separate them with a winnowingᵃ shovel at the city gates.
    I will make them childless.
    I will destroy my people because they will not change their ways.
⁸   Their widows will be more numerous
      than the grains of sand on the seashore.
    At noontime I will send a destroyer against the mothers of young men.
    I will suddenly bring anguish and terror to them.
⁹   A mother who gives birth to seven sons will grow faint
      and breathe her last.
      She will die, ashamed and humiliated,
        while it is still daylight.
    I will put survivors from these people to death
      in the presence of their enemies," declares the LORD.

ᵃ 14:21 Or "covenant."   ᵃ 15:7 Winnowing is the process of separating husks from grain.

Jeremiah Complains Bitterly

¹⁰ I'm so miserable! Why did my mother give birth to me?
I am a man who argues and quarrels with the whole earth.
I have never lent or borrowed anything.
   Yet, everyone curses me.

¹¹ The LORD said,

"I will certainly rescue you for a good reason.
I will certainly make your enemies plead with you
   in times of disaster and in times of distress.
¹²   (No one can break iron, iron from the north, or bronze.)
¹³ I will give away your wealth and treasures as loot
   as the price for all the sins that you have committed
      throughout your territory.
¹⁴ I will make you serve your enemies in a land that you haven't heard of,
   because my anger has started a fire.
      It will burn you."

¹⁵ O LORD, you understand.
Remember me, take care of me,
   and take revenge on those who persecute me.
Be patient, and don't take me away.
You should know that I've been insulted because of you.

¹⁶ Your words were found, and I devoured them.
Your words are my joy and my heart's delight,
   because I am called by your name, O LORD God of Armies.
¹⁷ I didn't keep company with those who laugh and have fun.
I sat alone because your hand was on me.
   You filled me with outrage.
¹⁸ Why is my pain unending
   and my wound incurable, refusing to heal?
Will you disappoint me like a stream
   that dries up in summertime?

¹⁹ This is what the LORD says:

If you will return, I will take you back.
If you will speak what is worthwhile and not what is worthless,
   you will stand in my presence.
The people will return to you, but you will not return to them.
²⁰ I will make you like a solid bronze wall in front of these people.
They will fight you, but they will not defeat you.
   I am with you, and I will save you and rescue you,
      declares the LORD.
²¹ I will rescue you from the power of wicked people
   and free you from the power of tyrants.

The LORD Tells Jeremiah Not to Marry

16 ¹ The LORD spoke his word to me. He said, ² "Don't marry! Don't have any sons or daughters in this place! ³ This is what the LORD says about the sons and daughters born in this place and about the mothers and fathers who have children in this land: ⁴ They will die horrible deaths. No one will mourn for them or bury them. They will be like manure on the ground. Wars and famines will bring them to an end. Their bodies will be food for birds and animals.

⁵ "This is what the LORD says: Don't go into a house where people are grieving. Don't go to mourn or to grieve for them. I'm taking my peace, love, and compassion away from these people," declares the LORD. ⁶ "Old and young alike will die in this land. No one will mourn for them or bury them. No one will cut his own body or shave his own head for them. ⁷ No one will offer food to comfort those who mourn the dead. No one will give a consoling drink to those who have lost their fathers or mothers.

⁸ "Don't even go into a home where there is a banquet. Don't sit with them to eat and drink. ⁹ This is what the LORD of Armies, the God of Israel, says: I'm going to put a stop to the sounds of joy and happiness and the sounds of brides and grooms in this place. This will happen in your lifetime, while you watch.

¹⁰ "When you tell the people all these things, they will ask you, 'Why does the LORD threaten us with all these disasters? What have we done wrong? How have we sinned against the LORD

our God?' ¹¹ Then say to them, 'It's because your ancestors abandoned me, declares the LORD. They followed other gods, served them, worshiped them, and abandoned me. They didn't obey my teachings. ¹² You have done worse than your ancestors. All of you are following your own stubborn, evil ways that keep you from obeying me. ¹³ So I will throw you out of this land into a land that you and your ancestors haven't heard of. There you will serve other gods day and night because I will no longer have pity on you.'

¹⁴ "That is why the days are coming," declares the LORD, "when people will no longer begin an oath with, 'The LORD brought the people of Israel out of Egypt. As the LORD lives. . . .' ¹⁵ But they will say, 'The LORD brought the people of Israel out of the land of the north and all the lands where he had scattered them. As the LORD lives. . . .' They will say this because I will bring them back to the land that I gave their ancestors.

¹⁶ "I'm going to send for many fishermen," declares the LORD, "and they will catch the people of Israel. After that, I will send for many hunters, and they will hunt for them on every mountain and hill and even in the cracks in the rocks. ¹⁷ I see everything that they do. They can't hide anything from me. Their wickedness can't be hidden; I can see it. ¹⁸ First, I will have them pay twice as much for their wickedness and their sin, because they have polluted my land. They have filled my property with the lifeless statues of their detestable and disgusting idols."

¹⁹ The LORD is my strength and my fortress,
   my refuge in times of trouble.
Nations come to you from the most distant parts of the world
   and say, "Our ancestors have inherited lies,
      worthless and unprofitable gods."

²⁰ "People can't make gods for themselves.
   They aren't really gods.
²¹ That is what I will teach them.
   This time I will make my power and my strength known to them.
   Then they will know that my name is the LORD."

17 ¹ ˻The LORD says,˼ "Judah's sin is written with an iron pen.
   It is engraved with a diamond point
      on the tablet of their hearts and on the horns of their altars.
² Even their children remember their altars
   and their poles dedicated to the goddess Asherah
      beside large trees on high hills
³   and on mountains in the open country.^a
I will turn your wealth and all your treasures into loot.
I will do this because of your worship sites and your sin
   throughout all your territory.
⁴   You will lose the inheritance that I gave you.
I will make you serve your enemies in a land that you haven't heard of.
I will do this because you have stirred up the fire of my anger.
   It will burn forever.

⁵ "This is what the LORD says:

   Cursed is the person who trusts humans,
      who makes flesh and blood his strength
         and whose heart turns away from the LORD.
⁶ He will be like a bush in the wilderness.
He will not see when something good comes.
He will live in the dry places in the desert,
   in a salty land where no one can live.
⁷ Blessed is the person who trusts the LORD.
   The LORD will be his confidence.
⁸ He will be like a tree that is planted by water.
   It will send its roots down to a stream.
   It will not be afraid in the heat of summer.
      Its leaves will turn green.
   It will not be anxious during droughts.
   It will not stop producing fruit.

⁹ "The human mind is the most deceitful of all things. It is incurable.
   No one can understand how deceitful it is.

---

^a 17:3 Greek; Masoretic Text "on my mountain."

10 I, the LORD, search minds and test hearts.
    I will reward each person for what he has done.
    I will reward him for the results of his actions.
11 A person who gets rich dishonestly is like a partridge
    that hatches eggs it did not lay.
        During his lifetime, he will lose his wealth.
        In the end, he will be a godless fool."

12 Our holy place is a glorious throne,
    highly honored from the beginning.
13 O LORD, the Hope of Israel, all who abandon you will be put to shame.
    Those who turn away from you will be written in dust,
        because they abandon the LORD,
        the fountain of life-giving water.

14 Heal me, O LORD, and I will be healed.
    Rescue me, and I will be rescued.
    You are the one I praise.
15 People keep asking me,
    "Where is the word of the LORD?
    Let it come."
16 I have not run away from being your shepherd,
    and I have not longed for the day of destruction.
    You know what came out of my mouth.
17   Do not terrorize me.
        You are my refuge on the day of disaster.
18 Put my persecutors to shame,
    but do not let me be put to shame.
Terrify them,
    but do not let me be terrified.
Bring the day of disaster on them,
    and destroy them completely.

The Blessing That Comes From Observing the Day of Worship as a Holy Day

19 This is what the LORD said to me: Stand at People's Gate, where the kings of Judah go in and out. Then stand at every gate in Jerusalem. 20 Tell everyone: "Listen to the word of the LORD, you kings of Judah, all the people of Judah, and all those who live in Jerusalem, and go through these gates. 21 This is what the LORD says: Watch out! If you value your lives, do not carry anything on the day of worship or bring it through the gates of Jerusalem. 22 Do not bring anything out of your homes on the day of worship. Do not do any work, but observe the day of worship as a holy day, as I told your ancestors. 23 Your ancestors did not obey me or pay attention to me. They were impossible to deal with and would not listen or accept discipline.

24 "Now," declares the LORD, "you must listen to me and not bring anything through the gates of this city on the day of worship. You must observe the day of worship as a holy day by not doing any work on it. 25 If you do this, then the kings and princes who sit on David's throne will come through the gates of this city. They and their princes will ride in chariots and on horses along with the people of Judah and those who live in Jerusalem. This city will always have people living in it.

26 "People will come from the cities of Judah, from all around Jerusalem, from the territory of Benjamin, from the foothills, from the mountains, and from the Negev. They will bring burnt offerings, sacrifices, grain offerings, and incense. They will also bring thank offerings to the LORD's temple. 27 But you must listen to me and observe the day of worship as a holy day by not carrying anything through the gates of Jerusalem on the day of worship. If you don't do this, I will set its gates on fire. The fire will burn down the palaces in Jerusalem, and you won't be able to put it out."

The People of Israel Are Like Clay for a Potter

18 1 The LORD spoke his word to Jeremiah. He said, 2 "Go to the potter's house. There I will give you my message."

3 I went to the potter's house, and he was working there at his wheel. 4 Whenever a clay pot he was working on was ruined, he would rework it into a new clay pot the way he wanted to make it.

5 The LORD spoke his word to me. The LORD asked, 6 "Nation of Israel, can't I do with you as this potter does with clay? Nation of Israel, you are like the clay in the potter's hands.

⁷ "At one time I may threaten to tear up, break down, and destroy a nation or a kingdom. ⁸ But suppose the nation that I threatened turns away from doing wrong. Then I will change my plans about the disaster I planned to do to it.

⁹ "At another time I may promise to build and plant a nation or a kingdom. ¹⁰ But suppose that nation does what I consider evil and doesn't obey me. Then I will change my plans about the good that I promised to do to it.

¹¹ "Now say to the people of Judah and to those who live in Jerusalem, 'This is what the LORD says: I'm going to prepare a disaster and make plans against you. Turn from your evil ways, change your lives, and do good.'

¹² "But they will answer, 'It's useless! We'll live the way we want to. We'll go our own stubborn, evil ways.'

¹³ "This is what the LORD says:

Ask among the nations if anyone has ever heard anything like this.
  The people of Israel have done a very horrible thing.
¹⁴ The rocky slopes of Lebanon are never without snow.
  The cool mountain streams never dry up.
¹⁵   But my people have forgotten me.
    They burn incense as an offering to worthless idols,
      and they stumble along the way, on the ancient path.
    They go on side roads and not on major highways.
¹⁶ Their land will become desolate
  and something to be hissed at forever.
  Everyone who will pass by it will be stunned and shake his head.
¹⁷ Like the east wind I will scatter them in front of the enemy.
  On the day of their disaster,
    I will show them my back, not my face."

¹⁸ Then they said, "Let's plot against Jeremiah, because the teachings of the priests, the advice of wise people, and the word of the prophets won't disappear. Accuse him! Pay no attention to anything he says."

¹⁹ Pay attention to me, O LORD,
    and listen to what my accusers say.
²⁰ Good should not be paid back with evil.
    They dig a pit to take my life.
    Remember how I stood in your presence and pleaded for them
      in order to turn your anger away from them.
²¹ Now, hand their children over to famine.
    Pour out their ˎblood˒ by using your sword.
    Then their wives will become childless widows.
      Their husbands will be put to death.
      Their young men will be struck down in battle.
²² Make them cry out from their homes
    when you suddenly send troops against them,
      because they dug a pit to catch me and hid snares for my feet.
²³ But you, O LORD, know that they plan to kill me.
    Don't forgive their crimes.
    Don't wipe their sins out of your sight.
    Make them stumble in your presence.
    Deal with them when you get angry.

Israel Will Be Smashed Like a Clay Jar

19 ¹ This is what the LORD says: Go and buy a clay jar from a potter. Take along some of the leaders of the people and some of the leaders of the priests. ² Go to the valley of Ben Hinnom at the entrance to Potsherd Gate. Announce there the things I plan to do. ³ Say, "Listen to the word of the LORD, you kings of Judah and those who live in Jerusalem. This is what the LORD of Armies, the God of Israel, says: I'm going to bring such a disaster on this place that the ears of everyone who hears about it will ring.

⁴ "The people, their ancestors, and the kings of Judah have abandoned me. They have made this place unrecognizable by burning incense as an offering to other gods that they hadn't heard of. They have filled this place with the blood of innocent people. ⁵ They have built worship sites to burn their children as sacrifices to Baal. I didn't ask them or command them to do this. It never entered my mind.

⁶ "That is why the days are coming, declares the LORD, when this place will no longer be called Topheth or the valley of Ben Hinnom. Instead, it will be called Slaughter Valley. ⁷ I will smash the

plans of Judah and Jerusalem in this place. I will cut them down with swords in front of their enemies and with the hands of those who want to kill them. I will give their bodies as food to birds and to animals. ⁸ I will devastate this city. It will become something to hiss at. Everyone who goes by it will be stunned and hiss with contempt at all the disasters that happen to it. ⁹ I will make the people eat the flesh of their sons and daughters. They will eat each other's flesh during blockades and hardships that their enemies impose on them when they want to kill them."

¹⁰ ˻The LORD says,˼ "Then smash the jar in front of the men who went with you. ¹¹ Say to them, 'This is what the LORD of Armies says: I will smash these people and this city as this potter's jar was smashed beyond repair. They will bury ˻the dead˼ in Topheth until there's no other place to bury them. ¹² That's what I will do to this place and to those who live in it, declares the LORD. I will make this city like Topheth. ¹³ The houses in Jerusalem, the houses of the kings of Judah, and all the rooftops of the houses will be unclean*ᵃ* like this city Topheth. This is because people burned incense to the entire army of heaven and poured out wine offerings to other gods.' "

¹⁴ Then Jeremiah left Topheth, where the LORD had sent him to prophesy. He stood in the courtyard of the LORD's temple and said to all the people, ¹⁵ "This is what the LORD of Armies, the God of Israel, says: I'm going to bring on this city and on all its towns the disasters that I threatened. They've become impossible to deal with, and they refuse to obey me."

Pashhur Imprisons Jeremiah

20 ¹ Now the priest, Immer's son Pashhur, the chief officer of the LORD's temple, heard Jeremiah prophesying these things. ² Pashhur struck the prophet Jeremiah and put him in prison at Upper Benjamin Gate that was in the LORD's temple.

³ The next day when Pashhur took Jeremiah out of prison, Jeremiah said to him, "The LORD doesn't call you Pashhur, but he calls you Terror Everywhere. ⁴ This is what the LORD says: I'm going to make you terrify yourself and all your friends. Their enemies' swords will kill them, and you will see it with your own eyes. I will hand all of Judah over to the king of Babylon. He will take the people away as captives to Babylon or kill them with swords. ⁵ I will hand all the riches of this city over to their enemies. This will include all its produce, all its valuables, and all the treasures of the kings of Judah. Their enemies will loot them, take them away, and bring them to Babylon. ⁶ And you, Pashhur, and all those who live in your house will go into captivity. You will go to Babylon, and you will die there. You will be buried there together with all your friends to whom you prophesied these lies."

Jeremiah Prays to the LORD

⁷   O LORD, you have deceived me, and I was deceived.
           You overpowered me and won.
               I've been made fun of all day long.
                   Everyone mocks me.
⁸   Each time I speak, I have to cry out and shout,
           "Violence and destruction!"
       The word of the LORD has made me the object of insults
           and contempt all day long.
⁹   I think to myself, "I can forget the LORD
           and no longer speak his name."
       But ˻his word˼ is inside me like a burning fire shut up in my bones.
       I wear myself out holding it in, but I can't do it any longer.
¹⁰   I have heard many ˻people˼ whispering,
           "Terror is everywhere!
           Report him! Let's report him!"
       All my closest friends are waiting to see me stumble.
       They say, "Maybe he will be tricked.
           Then we can overpower him and take revenge on him."
¹¹   But the LORD is on my side like a terrifying warrior.
           That is why those who persecute me will stumble. They can't win.
               They will be very ashamed that they can't succeed.
                   Their eternal shame will not be forgotten.
¹²   But the LORD of Armies examines the righteous.
           He sees their motives and thoughts.
       I want to see you take revenge on them,
           because I've brought my case to you.
¹³   Sing to the LORD! Praise the LORD!

ᵃ 19:13 "Unclean" refers to anything that Moses' Teachings say is not presentable to God.

He has rescued the lives of needy people
from the power of wicked people.

¹⁴ Cursed is the day that I was born,
the day that my mother gave birth to me.
May it not be blessed.
¹⁵ Cursed is the man who made my father very happy with the news
that he had just become the father of a baby boy.
¹⁶ May that man be like the cities
that the LORD destroyed without pity.
May he hear a cry of alarm in the morning
and a battle cry at noon.
¹⁷ If only he had killed me while I was in the womb.
Then my mother would have been my grave,
and she would have always been pregnant.
¹⁸ Why did I come out of the womb?
All I've seen is trouble and grief.
I will finish my days in shame.

Jerusalem Will Be Captured by the Babylonians

21 ¹ The LORD spoke his word to Jeremiah when King Zedekiah sent Pashhur, son of Malchiah, and the priest Zephaniah, son of Maaseiah, to Jeremiah. They said, ² "Consult the LORD for us, because King Nebuchadnezzar of Babylon is attacking us. Maybe the LORD will perform miracles for us so that Nebuchadnezzar will retreat."

³ Jeremiah responded to them, "This is what you should say to Zedekiah, ⁴ This is what the LORD God of Israel says: I'm going to take your weapons away from you. You are using these weapons to fight the king of Babylon as well as the Babylonians who are now blockading you outside the wall. I will bring the Babylonians inside this city. ⁵ I will fight you in anger, fury, and rage with my powerful hand and my mighty arm. ⁶ I will defeat those who live in this city, both people and animals. They will die from a terrible plague. ⁷ Afterwards, declares the LORD, I will hand over Judah's King Zedekiah, his officials, the people, and everyone else in this city who survives the plague, war, and famine. They will be handed over to King Nebuchadnezzar of Babylon and to their enemies who want to kill them. Nebuchadnezzar will kill them with swords. He won't spare them, show them compassion, or care for them.'

⁸ "Say to these people, 'This is what the LORD says: I am going to give you the choice of life or death. ⁹ Those who live in this city will die in the war, famine, or plague. Those of you who go out and surrender to the Babylonians will live. You will escape with your lives. ¹⁰ I've decided to harm this city, not to do good to it, declares the LORD. It will be handed over to the king of Babylon, and he will burn it down.'

¹¹ "Say to the nation of the king of Judah, 'Listen to the word of the LORD, ¹² descendants of David. This is what the LORD says:

Judge fairly every morning.
Rescue those who have been robbed from those who oppress them.
Otherwise, my fury will break out and burn like fire.
No one will be able to put it out
because of the evil things you have done.

¹³ " 'I'm against you, Jerusalem.
You are the city that is in the valley
and on the rock in the plain,' "
declares the LORD.
" 'But you ask, "Who can attack us?
Who can enter our places of refuge?"

¹⁴ " 'I will punish you because of the evil things you have done,' "
declares the LORD.
" 'I will start a fire in your forests,
and it will burn up everything around you.' "

Warnings to the Wicked Kings

22 ¹ This is what the LORD says: Go to the palace of the king of Judah, and speak this message there: ² "Listen to the word of the LORD, you officials, you people who come into these gates, and you, king of Judah, the one sitting on David's throne. ³ "This is what the LORD says: Judge fairly, and do what is right. Rescue those who have been robbed from those who oppress them. Don't mistreat foreigners, orphans, or widows, and don't oppress them. Don't kill innocent people in this place. ⁴ If you do what I say, then the kings who sit on David's throne will ride through the gates of this palace in chariots and on horses along with their officials and their people. [5] But if you don't do what I say, I will take an oath on myself," declares the LORD, "that this palace will become a pile of rubble.

[6] "This is what the LORD says about the palace of the king of Judah:

> This palace is like Gilead to me,
>   like the top of Lebanon.
> I will certainly turn it into a desert,
>   into cities that no one lives in.
> [7] I will send people to destroy you.
>   They will have their own weapons.
>   They will cut down your finest cedar trees
>   and throw them on a fire.

[8] "People from many nations will pass by this city and ask each other, 'Why has the LORD done this to this important city?' [9] The answer will be: 'They rejected the promise[a] of the LORD their God. They worshiped other gods and served them.' "

> [10] Don't cry for the dead.
>   Don't shake your heads at them.
>   Cry bitterly for those who are taken away,
>   because they won't come back to see their homeland.

[11] This is what the LORD says about King Josiah's son Shallum, who succeeded his father as king of Judah and left this place: He will never come back here again. [12] He will die in the place where he was taken captive, and he will never see this land again.

> [13] "How horrible it will be for the person who builds his house dishonestly
>   and his upper rooms through injustice.
>   He makes his neighbors work for nothing
>   and doesn't pay them for their work.
> [14] He says, 'I will build a large house for myself with big upper rooms.'
>   He cuts out windows in it,
>   panels the rooms with cedar,
>   and paints them red.
> [15] Do you think you're a better king than others
>   because you use more cedar?
>   Your father ate and drank and did what is fair and right.
>   Everything went well for him.
> [16] He defended the cause of the poor and needy.
>   Everything went well for him.
>   Isn't this what it means to know me?" asks the LORD.
> [17] "But your eyes and your mind are set on nothing but dishonest profits.
>   You kill innocent people and violently oppress your people."

[18] This is what the LORD says about Jehoiakim, son of Judah's King Josiah:

> People won't mourn for him and say,
>   "How horrible it is for my brother and sister!"
> They won't mourn for him and say,
>   "How horrible it is for my master and his splendor!"
> [19] He will receive a donkey's burial.
>   He will be dragged off and thrown outside the gates of Jerusalem.

> [20] "Go to Lebanon and cry! Raise your voice in Bashan!
>   Cry out from Abarim, because all your lovers are defeated."

> [21] I spoke to you when you were prosperous,
>   but you said that you wouldn't listen.
>   This is how you've been ever since you were young.
>   You don't listen to me.
> [22] The wind will blow away all your shepherds,
>   and your lovers will go into captivity.
>   Then you will be ashamed and disgraced by all your wickedness.
> [23] You live in Lebanon and have your nest in the cedars.
>   But you will groan when pain strikes you,
>   pain like a woman giving birth to a child.

---

[a] 22:9 Or "covenant."

²⁴ "As I live," declares the LORD, "even though you, Jehoiakin,^b son of Judah's King Jehoiakim, are the signet ring on my right hand, I will pull you off my hand. ²⁵ I will hand you over to those who want to kill you, those you fear—King Nebuchadnezzar of Babylon and the Babylonians. ²⁶ I will throw you and your mother into another land. You weren't born there, but you will die there. ²⁷ You will want to return to this land, but you won't be allowed to come home."

²⁸   This Jehoiakin is like a rejected and broken pot that no one wants.
        Is that why he and his descendants will be thrown out
            and cast into another land they've never heard of?
²⁹   O land, land, land!
        Listen to the word of the LORD.

³⁰ This is what the LORD says:

        Write this about Jehoiakin: He will be childless.
        He won't prosper in his lifetime.
            None of his descendants will succeed him as king.
            They won't sit on David's throne and rule Judah again.

The Righteous Branch

23 ¹ "How horrible it will be for the shepherds who are destroying and scattering the sheep in my care," declares the LORD. ² "This is what I, the LORD God of Israel, said to the shepherds who take care of my people: You have scattered my sheep and chased them away. You have not taken care of them, so now I will take care of you by punishing you for the evil you have done," declares the LORD.
³ "Then I will gather the remaining part of my flock from all the countries where I chased them. I will bring them back to their pasture, and they will be fertile and increase in number. ⁴ I will put shepherds over them. Those shepherds will take care of them. My sheep will no longer be afraid or terrified, and not one of them will be missing," declares the LORD.

⁵   "The days are coming," declares the LORD,
        "when I will grow a righteous branch for David.
        He will be a king who will rule wisely.
        He will do what is fair and right in the land.
⁶   In his lifetime, Judah will be saved,
                and Israel will live in safety.
                    This is the name that he will be given:
                    The LORD Our Righteousness.

⁷ "That is why the days are coming," declares the LORD, "when people's oaths will no longer be, 'The LORD brought the people of Israel out of Egypt. As the LORD lives. . . .' ⁸ Instead, their oaths will be, 'The LORD brought the descendants of the nation of Israel out of the land of the north and all the lands where he^a had scattered them. As the LORD lives. . . .' At that time they will live in their own land.

Warnings to the False Prophets

⁹ " Say this about the prophets:

        I am deeply disturbed.
            All my bones tremble.
        I am like a drunk,
            like a person who has had too much wine,
                because of the LORD and his holy words.
¹⁰   The land is filled with adulterers.
        The land mourns because of the curse.
            Pastures in the wilderness have dried up.
                The people are evil,
                and they use their strength to do the wrong things.
¹¹   The prophets and priests are godless.
        Even in my temple I've found them doing evil," declares the LORD.
¹²   "That is why their own way will become
        like slippery paths in the dark.
        They will be chased away, and they will fall down in the dark.
            I will bring disaster on them.
                It is time for them to be punished," declares the LORD.

¹³ " ˌSay thisˌ about the prophets of Samaria:

I saw something disgusting.
The prophets of Samaria prophesied by Baal
and led my people Israel astray.

¹⁴ " ˌSay thisˌ about the prophets of Jerusalem:

I see something horrible.
The prophets of Jerusalem commit adultery and live a lie.
They support those who do evil
so that no one turns back from his wickedness.
They are all like Sodom to me,
and those who live in Jerusalem are like Gomorrah."

¹⁵ This is what the LORD of Armies says about the prophets:

I will give them wormwood to eat and poison to drink.
The prophets of Jerusalem have spread godlessness
throughout the land.

¹⁶ This is what the LORD of Armies says:

Don't listen to what the prophets are saying to you.
They fill you with false hope.
They speak about visions that they dreamed up.
These visions are not from the LORD.
¹⁷ They keep saying to those who despise me,
"The LORD says, 'Everything will go well for you.' "
They tell all who live by their own stubborn ways,
"Nothing bad will happen to you."
¹⁸ Who is in the LORD's inner circle
and sees and hears his word?
Who pays attention and listens to his word?
¹⁹ The storm of the LORD will come with his anger.
Like a windstorm, it will swirl down on the heads of the wicked.
²⁰ The anger of the LORD will not turn back
until he has done everything he intends to do.
In the last days you will understand this clearly.
²¹ I didn't send these prophets,
yet they ran ˌwith their messageˌ.
I didn't speak to them,
yet they prophesied.
²² If they had been in my inner circle,
they would have announced my words to my people.
They would have turned back from their evil ways
and the evil they have done.

²³ "I am a God who is near.
I am also a God who is far away," declares the LORD.
²⁴ "No one can hide so that I can't see him," declares the LORD.
"I fill heaven and earth!" declares the LORD.

²⁵ "I've heard the prophets who speak lies in my name. They say, 'I had a dream! I had a dream!' ²⁶ How long will these prophets continue to lie and deceive? ²⁷ They tell each other the dreams they had, because they want to make my people forget my name, as their ancestors forgot my name because of Baal. ²⁸ The prophet who has a dream should tell his dream. However, the person who has my word should honestly speak my word. What does grain have to do with straw?" asks the LORD. ²⁹ "Isn't my word like fire or like a hammer that shatters a rock?" asks the LORD. ³⁰ "I'm against the prophets who steal my words from each other," declares the LORD. ³¹ "I'm against the prophets who speak their own thoughts and say that they speak for me. ³² I'm against those who prophesy dreams they made up," declares the LORD. "They tell the dreams they made up and lead my people astray with their lies and their wild talk. I didn't send them or command them to go. They don't help these people at all," declares the LORD.

³³ "When these people, the prophets, or the priests ask you, 'What revelation has the LORD burdened you with now?' say to them, 'You are the burden! I will abandon you, declares the LORD.' ³⁴ Suppose the prophets, the priests, or these people say, 'This is the LORD's revelation!' I will punish them and their families. ³⁵ They should ask their neighbors and their relatives,

'What is the LORD's answer?' and 'What did the LORD say?' [36] They should never again say, 'This is the LORD's revelation,' because each person's word becomes the revelation. They will twist the words of the living God, the LORD of Armies, our God.

[37] "Jeremiah, say this to the prophets, 'What was the LORD's answer to you?' and 'What did the LORD say?' [38] Suppose they say, 'This is the LORD's revelation!' Then say, 'This is what the LORD says: Because you have said, "This is the LORD's revelation!" even though I commanded you not to repeat this saying, [39] I will certainly forget you. I will throw you out of my presence and out of the city that I gave you and your ancestors. [40] I will bring eternal disgrace and shame on you. It will never be forgotten.' "

The Two Fig Baskets

24 [1] King Nebuchadnezzar of Babylon took Jehoiakin[a] (son of King Jehoiakim of Judah), the princes of Judah, the skilled workers, and the builders from Jerusalem into captivity and brought them to Babylon. After this, the LORD showed me two baskets of figs set in front of the LORD's temple. [2] One basket had very good figs, like figs that ripen first. The other basket had very bad figs. These figs were so bad that they couldn't be eaten.

[3] Then the LORD asked me, "What do you see, Jeremiah?"

I answered, "Figs. Figs that are very good. I also see figs that are very bad, so bad that they can't be eaten."

[4] The LORD spoke his word to me, [5] "This is what the LORD God of Israel says: The captives of Judah, whom I sent away from here to Babylon, are like these good figs. I will look kindly on them. [6] I will watch over them for their own good, and I will bring them back to this land. I will build them up and not tear them down. I will plant them and not uproot them. [7] I will give them the desire to know that I am the LORD. They will be my people, and I will be their God, because they will wholeheartedly come back to me.

[8] "But this is what the LORD says about the bad figs that are so bad that they can't be eaten. The LORD says, 'Like these bad figs, I will abandon King Zedekiah of Judah, his princes, the remaining few in Jerusalem who stayed behind in this land, and those who are living in Egypt. [9] I will make them a horrifying sight to all the kingdoms of the earth. They will be a disgrace and an example. They will become something ridiculed and cursed wherever I scatter them. [10] I will send wars, famines, and plagues until they disappear from the land that I gave to them and their ancestors.' "

Judgment on Judah and the Nations

25 [1] The LORD spoke his word to Jeremiah about all the people of Judah when Jehoiakim, son of Josiah, was in his fourth year as king. (This was the first year that Nebuchadnezzar was king of Babylon.) [2] The prophet Jeremiah spoke to all the people of Judah and to everyone who lived in Jerusalem. He said, [3] "For 23 years, from the time that Josiah, son of Amon, was in his thirteenth year as king of Judah until today, the LORD continued to speak his word to me. So I have spoken to you again and again, but you have not listened.

[4] "Even though the LORD has sent all his servants the prophets to you, you haven't listened or paid attention to them. [5] The prophets said, 'Turn from your evil ways and the evil you have done, and live in the land that the LORD permanently gave to you and your ancestors. [6] Don't follow other gods to serve and worship them. Don't make me furious about the idols your hands have shaped. Then I won't harm you. [7] But you haven't listened to me, declares the LORD. You have made me furious about the idols your hands have shaped and ⌊have brought⌋ harm upon yourselves.'

[8] "This is what the LORD of Armies says: You did not listen to my words, [9] so I'm going to send for all the families from the north. I will also send for my servant King Nebuchadnezzar of Babylon, declares the LORD. I will bring the families from the north to attack this land, its people, and all these surrounding nations. I'm going to destroy them and turn them into something terrible, something ridiculed, and something permanently ruined. [10] I will take from them the sounds of joy and happiness, the sounds of brides and grooms, the sound of mills, and the light of lamps. [11] This whole land will be ruined and become a wasteland. These nations will serve the king of Babylon for 70 years.

[12] "When the 70 years are over, I will punish the king of Babylon and that nation for their crimes, declares the LORD. I will turn Babylon into a permanent wasteland. [13] I will bring on that land all the disasters I threatened to do to it, everything that Jeremiah prophesied against all the nations, everything written in this book. [14] Many nations and great kings will make slaves of the people of Babylon, and I will pay them back for what they have done."

[15] This is what the LORD God of Israel said to me: Take from my hand this cup filled with the wine of my fury, and make all the nations to whom I'm sending you drink from it. [16] When they drink from it, they will stagger and go insane because of the wars that I'm going to send them.

---

[a] 24:1 Masoretic Text "Jeconiah," an alternate form of Jehoiakin.

¹⁷ So I took the cup from the LORD's hand. I made all the nations to whom the LORD sent me drink from it: ¹⁸ Jerusalem and the cities of Judah as well as its kings and officials. When they drank from it, they became wastelands and ruins, something ridiculed and cursed, until today.

¹⁹ I also made these people drink from it: Pharaoh king of Egypt, his servants, officials, all his people, ²⁰ and all the foreign people living among them; all the kings of the land of Uz; all the kings of Philistia, those from the cities of Ashkelon, Gaza, and Ekron, and the people left in Ashdod; ²¹ Edom, Moab, and the people of Ammon; ²² all the kings of Tyre and Sidon, and the kings on the seacoast; ²³ Dedan, Tema, Buz, and all who shave the hair on their foreheads; ²⁴ all the kings of Arabia, and all the kings of the foreign people living in the desert; ²⁵ all the kings of Zimri, all the kings of Elam, and all the kings of Media; ²⁶ all the kings of the north, near and far, one after another—all the kingdoms of the earth. Last of all, the king of Sheshach will drink from the cup.

²⁷ The LORD said, "Say to them, 'This is what the LORD of Armies, the God of Israel, says: Drink, get drunk, vomit, fall down, and don't get up because of the wars that I'm going to send you.' ²⁸ But if they refuse to take the cup from your hand and drink from it, say to them, 'This is what the LORD of Armies says: You must drink from it! ²⁹ I am going to bring disaster on the city that is named after me. Do you think you'll go unpunished? You will not go unpunished! I'm declaring war on all those who live on earth, declares the LORD of Armies.'

³⁰ "That is why you will prophesy all these things to them and say,

> The LORD roars from above.
> He thunders from his holy dwelling place.
> He roars against his land.
> He shouts like those who stomp grapes.
> He shouts against all those who live on earth.
> ³¹ The sound is echoing to the ends of the earth
>   because the LORD has brought charges against the nations.
> He will judge all humans.
> He will kill the wicked, declares the LORD.'

³² "This is what the LORD of Armies says:

> Disaster is spreading from nation to nation.
> A great storm is brewing from the distant corners of the earth."

³³ On that day those killed by the LORD will stretch from one end of the earth to the other. They will not be mourned, taken away, or buried. They will become like manure on the ground.

> ³⁴ Mourn, you shepherds, and cry.
> Roll in the dust, you leaders of the flock.
> The time has come for you to be slaughtered.
> The time has come for you to be scattered,
>   and you will break like fine pottery.
> ³⁵ There will be no place for the shepherds to flee,
>   no escape for the leaders of the flock.
> ³⁶ The shepherds are crying
>   and the leaders of the flock are mourning
>   because the LORD is stripping their pasture.
> ³⁷ The peaceful pastures are destroyed by the LORD's burning anger.
> ³⁸ He has left his lair like a lion.
>   Their land has been ruined
>   because of the heat of the oppressor,
>   because of the fury of his anger.

Jeremiah Is Arrested

26 ¹ The LORD spoke his word when Judah's King Jehoiakim, son of Josiah, began to rule. He said, ² "This is what the LORD says: Stand in the courtyard of the LORD's temple, and speak to all the people who come from the cities of Judah to worship in the LORD's temple. Tell them everything that I command you to tell them. Don't leave out a single word. ³ Maybe they'll listen, and they'll turn from their evil ways. Then I'll change my plan about the disaster I intend to bring on them because of the evil they have done."

⁴ The LORD added, "Also say to them, 'This is what the LORD says: Suppose you don't listen to me and don't follow my teachings that I set in front of you. ⁵ Suppose you don't listen to the words of my servants the prophets, whom I sent to you again and again, even though you didn't listen. ⁶ Then I will do to this temple what I did to Shiloh. I will turn this city into something that will be cursed by all the nations on earth.' "

[7] The priests, the prophets, and all the people heard Jeremiah speaking these things in the LORD's temple. [8] But as soon as Jeremiah finished saying everything that the LORD had commanded him to say, the priests, the prophets, and all the people grabbed him and said, "You must die! [9] Why do you prophesy in the LORD's name that this temple will be like Shiloh and this city will become a pile of rubble with no one living here?" Then all the people crowded around Jeremiah in the LORD's temple.

[10] When the officials of Judah heard about these things, they went from the king's palace to the LORD's temple. They sat at the entrance of New Gate to the LORD's ˌtempleˌ. [11] Then the priests and the prophets said to the officials and all the people, "This man is condemned to die because he prophesied against this city as you yourselves have heard."

[12] Then Jeremiah said to all the officials and all the people, "The LORD sent me to prophesy everything that you have heard me say against this temple and against this city. [13] Now, change your ways and what you are doing, and listen to the LORD your God. Then the LORD will change his plan about the disaster that he intends to bring on you.

[14] "My life is in your hands. Do with me whatever you think is good and right. [15] But know for certain that if you put me to death, you, this city, and the people living in it will be guilty of killing an innocent person. The LORD has certainly sent me to speak all these things to you."

[16] Then the officials and all the people said to the priests and prophets, "This man should not be condemned to die. He has spoken to us in the name of the LORD our God."

[17] Then some of the leaders in the land got up and said to the entire crowd, [18] "Micah from Moresheth prophesied at the time of Judah's King Hezekiah and said to all the people of Judah, 'This is what the LORD of Armies says:

> Zion will be plowed like a field,
>> Jerusalem will become a pile of rubble,
>>> and the temple mountain will become a worship site
>>> covered with trees.'

[19] Did Judah's King Hezekiah and all the people of Judah put Micah to death? No! Hezekiah feared the LORD and sought the LORD's favor. So the LORD changed his plan about the disaster he intended to bring on them. But we are about to bring a bigger disaster on ourselves."

[20] There was another man prophesying in the name of the LORD. His name was Uriah, son of Shemaiah, from Kiriath Jearim. He prophesied against this city and this land as Jeremiah did. [21] When King Jehoiakim and all his personal troops and officials heard what Uriah said, the king wanted to put him to death. But Uriah heard about it and fled in fear to Egypt. [22] King Jehoiakim sent soldiers to Egypt: Elnathan (son of Achbor) and other soldiers along with him. [23] They brought Uriah from Egypt and took him to King Jehoiakim. The king executed Uriah and threw his body into the burial ground for the common people. [24] Ahikam, son of Shaphan, supported Jeremiah. So Jeremiah was not handed over to the people to be put to death.

The Yoke of Babylon Will Be on Judah

27 [1] When Zedekiah, son of King Josiah of Judah, began to rule, the LORD spoke his word to Jeremiah.

[2] This is what the LORD said to me: Make ˌleatherˌ straps and a wooden yoke,ᵃ and strap the yoke on your neck. [3] Then send messages to the kings of Edom, Moab, Ammon, Tyre, and Sidon, with messengers who have come to King Zedekiah of Judah in Jerusalem. [4] Give them an order for their masters: "This is what the LORD of Armies, the God of Israel, says: Say this to your masters, [5] 'I used my great strength and my powerful arm to make the earth along with the people and the animals on it. I give it to anyone I please. [6] Now I have handed all these countries over to my servant King Nebuchadnezzar of Babylon. I have even made wild animals serve him. [7] All nations will serve him, his son, and his grandson until Babylon is defeated. Then many nations and great kings will make him their slave.

[8] " 'Suppose nations or kingdoms won't serve or surrender to King Nebuchadnezzar of Babylon. I will punish those nations by wars, famines, and plagues, until I have put an end to them by Nebuchadnezzar's power, declares the LORD. [9] Don't listen to prophets, mediums, interpreters of dreams, fortunetellers, or sorcerers who tell you that you'll never serve the king of Babylon. [10] They are prophesying lies to you. They will cause you to be taken far from your lands. I'll scatter you, and you will die. [11] But suppose a nation surrenders to the king of Babylon and serves him. I will let it stay in its own land. People will farm the land and live on it,' " declares the LORD.

[12] I spoke the same message to King Zedekiah of Judah, "Surrender to the king of Babylon, serve him and his people, and you will stay alive. [13] Why should you and your people die in wars, famines, and plagues? The LORD has threatened the nations that don't serve the king of Babylon. [14] Don't listen to the prophets who tell you that you'll never serve the king of Babylon.

ᵃ 27:2 A yoke is a wooden bar placed over the necks of work animals so that they can pull plows or carts.

They are prophesying lies to you. [15] I didn't send them, declares the LORD. They prophesy lies in my name. So I will scatter you, and you and the prophets will die."

[16] I also spoke this message to the priests and all the people. "This is what the LORD said to me: Don't listen to the prophets who tell you that the utensils of the LORD's temple will be brought back from Babylon soon. They are prophesying lies to you. [17] Don't listen to them. Instead, serve the king of Babylon, and live. Why should this city be turned into rubble? [18] If they are prophets and the LORD is speaking to them, they should beg the LORD of Armies not to allow the utensils that are left in the LORD's temple, in the royal palace of Judah, and in Jerusalem to be taken away to Babylon.

[19-20] "Babylon's King Nebuchadnezzar took Jehoiakin,[b] son of King Jehoiakim of Judah, into captivity from Jerusalem to Babylon along with all the nobles of Judah and Jerusalem. But he didn't take the pillars, the bronze pool, the stands, and the rest of the utensils that are left in this city. [21] This is what the LORD of Armies, the God of Israel, says about the utensils that are left in the LORD's temple, in the royal palace of Judah, and in Jerusalem: [22] They will be taken to Babylon and stay there until I come for them, declares the LORD. I will take them from there and bring them back to this place."

Hananiah's False Prophecy

28 [1] In that same year, early in the rule of King Zedekiah of Judah, in the fifth month of his fourth year as king, the prophet Hananiah, son of Azzur, from Gibeon, spoke to me in the LORD's temple. He said to me in front of the priests and all the people, [2] "This is what the LORD of Armies, the God of Israel, says: I will break the yoke[a] of the king of Babylon. [3] Within two years I will bring back all the utensils of the LORD's temple that King Nebuchadnezzar of Babylon took from this place and carried off to Babylon. [4] I will also bring back to this place Jehoiakin, son of King Jehoiakim of Judah, and all the captives of Judah who went to Babylon, declares the LORD. So I will break the yoke of the king of Babylon."

[5] The prophet Jeremiah replied to the prophet Hananiah in front of the priests and all the people standing in the LORD's temple. [6] He said, "Amen! May the LORD do this! May the LORD make your prophecy come true and bring back the utensils of the LORD's temple and all the captives from Babylon to this place. [7] But now listen to this message that I am speaking to you and to all the people: [8] Long ago, the prophets who preceded you and me prophesied wars, disasters, and plagues against many countries and great kingdoms. [9] But the prophet who prophesied peace was recognized as a prophet that the LORD sent only if the message of the prophet came true."

[10] Then the prophet Hananiah took the yoke off the neck of the prophet Jeremiah and broke it. [11] Hananiah said in front of all the people, "This is what the LORD says: In the same way, I will break the yoke of King Nebuchadnezzar of Babylon off the neck of all the nations within two years." Then the prophet Jeremiah went on his way.

[12] After the prophet Hananiah broke the yoke off the neck of the prophet Jeremiah, the LORD spoke his word to Jeremiah. He said, [13] "Tell Hananiah, 'This is what the LORD says: You have broken the wooden yoke, but I[b] will replace it with an iron yoke. [14] This is what the LORD of Armies, the God of Israel, says: I will put an iron yoke on the necks of all these nations so that they will serve King Nebuchadnezzar of Babylon. They will serve him! I will even make wild animals serve him.' "

[15] Then Jeremiah told the prophet Hananiah, "Now listen, Hananiah, the LORD hasn't sent you. You have made these people believe a lie. [16] This is what the LORD says: I'm going to remove you from the face of the earth. You will die this year because you have encouraged rebellion against the LORD."

[17] So the prophet Hananiah died in the seventh month of that year.

Jeremiah Writes to the Captives in Babylon

29 [1] The prophet Jeremiah sent a letter from Jerusalem to the rest of the leaders among the captives. He also sent it to the priests, the prophets, and all the people that Nebuchadnezzar took away as captives from Jerusalem to Babylon. [2] (This was after King Jehoiakin[a] and his mother, the court officials, the leaders of Judah and Jerusalem, the craftsmen, and metal workers left Jerusalem.) [3] He sent the letter with Shaphan's son Elasah and Hilkiah's son Gemariah, whom King Zedekiah of Judah had sent to King Nebuchadnezzar in Babylon. The letter said:

[4] This is what the LORD of Armies, the God of Israel, says to all those who were taken captive from Jerusalem to Babylon: [5] Build houses, and live in them. Plant gardens, and eat what they produce. [6] Get married, and have sons and daughters. Find wives for your sons, and let your daughters get married so that they can have sons and daughters. Grow

---

[b] 27:19–20 Masoretic Text "Jeconiah," an alternate form of Jehoiakin.   [a] 28:2 A yoke is a wooden bar placed over the necks of work animals so that they can pull plows or carts.   [b] 28:13 Greek; Masoretic Text "you."   [a] 29:2 Masoretic Text "Jeconiah," an alternate form of Jehoiakin.

in number there; don't decrease. [7] Work for the good of the city where I've taken you as captives, and pray to the LORD for that city. When it prospers, you will also prosper.

[8] This is what the LORD of Armies, the God of Israel, says: Don't let the prophets or the mediums who are among you trick you. Don't even listen to your own dreams. [9] These people are prophesying lies to you in my name. I didn't send them, declares the LORD.

[10] This is what the LORD says: When Babylon's 70 years are over, I will come to you. I will keep my promise to you and bring you back to this place. [11] I know the plans that I have for you, declares the LORD. They are plans for peace and not disaster, plans to give you a future filled with hope. [12] Then you will call to me. You will come and pray to me, and I will hear you. [13] When you look for me, you will find me. When you wholeheartedly seek me, [14] I will let you find me, declares the LORD. I will bring you back from captivity. I will gather you from all the nations and places where I've scattered you, declares the LORD. I will bring you back from the place where you are being held captive.

[15] You've said that the LORD has given you prophets in Babylon. [16] But this is what the LORD says about the king who sits on David's throne and about all the people who live in this city, the people who are your relatives and who weren't taken away as captives: [17] The LORD of Armies says: I'm going to send them wars, famines, and plagues. These people are like rotten figs to me, figs that are so bad that they can't be eaten. [18] I will chase them with wars, famines, and plagues. I will make them a horrifying sight to all the kingdoms on the earth. They will become something cursed, ridiculed, and hissed at, and they will be a disgrace among all the nations where I scatter them. [19] They didn't listen to me, declares the LORD. I sent them my servants the prophets again and again, but they refused to listen, declares the LORD.

[20] So listen to the word of the LORD, all you captives who were sent away from Jerusalem to Babylon. [21] This is what the LORD of Armies, the God of Israel, says about Kolaiah's son Ahab and about Maaseiah's son Zedekiah, who prophesy lies to you in my name: I'm going to hand them over to King Nebuchadnezzar of Babylon. I will kill them as you watch. [22] Because of them, all the captives from Judah who are in Babylon will use this curse: May the LORD curse you as he cursed Zedekiah and Ahab, whom the king of Babylon burned to death. [23] They have done shameful things in Israel. They committed adultery with their neighbors' wives and spoke lies in my name. I didn't command them to do this. I know what they have done. I'm a witness, declares the LORD.

[24] The LORD says, "Say to Shemaiah from Nehelam, [25] 'This is what the LORD of Armies, the God of Israel, says: You sent letters in your own name to all the people who are in Jerusalem, to the priest Zephaniah, son of Maaseiah, and to all the priests. These letters said: [26] The LORD made you priest instead of Jehoiada so that there would be officials for the LORD's temple. You should put any lunatic who acts like a prophet in prison and in shackles. [27] Now, why haven't you arrested Jeremiah from Anathoth? After all, he acts like a prophet among you. [28] That's why Jeremiah sent this message to us in Babylon: You will be captives a long time. Build houses, and live in them. Plant gardens, and eat what they produce.' "

[29] The priest Zephaniah read this letter to the prophet Jeremiah.

[30] Then the LORD spoke his word to Jeremiah. He said, [31] "Send this message to all the captives: 'This is what the LORD says about Shemaiah from Nehelam: Shemaiah prophesied to you, but I didn't send him. He has made you believe a lie. [32] The LORD says: I will punish Shemaiah from Nehelam. I will also punish his descendants. No one from his family will be left alive. He will not see the blessings that I'm going to send my people, declares the LORD, because he has encouraged rebellion against the LORD.' "

Israel's Glorious Future

30 [1] The LORD spoke his word to Jeremiah. He said, [2] "This is what the LORD God of Israel says: Write in a book everything that I tell you. [3] The days are coming," declares the LORD, "when I will bring my people Israel and Judah back from captivity. I will bring them back to the land that I gave their ancestors, and they will take possession of it."

[4] This is the message that the LORD spoke about Israel and Judah: [5] "This is what the LORD says:

"We hear cries of fear, cries of panic, not cries of peace.
[6]　　Ask now, and see: Can a man give birth to a child?
　　　　Why, then, do I see every strong man holding his stomach in pain
　　　　　　like a woman giving birth to a child?
　　　　Why has every face turned pale?
[7]　　How terrible that day will be!
　　　　There will be no other day like it.

It will be a time of calamity for the descendants of Jacob,
but they will be rescued from it.

[8] "On that day," declares the LORD of Armies, "I will break the yokes[a] off your necks and tear off your ropes. Foreigners will no longer make you serve them. [9] You will serve the LORD your God and David your king. I will establish him for you.

[10] "Don't be afraid, my servant Jacob," declares the LORD.
Don't be terrified, Israel.
    I'm going to rescue you from a faraway place.
    I'm going to rescue your descendants from where they are captives.
        The descendants of Jacob will again have peace and security,
        and no one will frighten them.
[11] I am with you, and I will rescue you," declares the LORD.
    "I will completely destroy all the nations where I scattered you,
        but I will not completely destroy you.
        I will correct you with justice.
        I won't let you go entirely unpunished.

[12] "This is what the LORD says:

Your wound is incurable.
Your injury is beyond healing.
[13]   No one argues that you should be healed.
    No medicine will heal you.
[14]   All your lovers have forgotten you,
    and they don't want you anymore.
I've punished you as an enemy would.
I've corrected you as a cruel person would.
    You are very wicked, and you have many sins.
[15] Why do you cry about your wound, your injury that can't be cured?
I've done this to you.
    You are very wicked, and you have many sins.
[16] That is why everyone who devours you will be devoured,
    and all your enemies will be taken away as captives.
Those who looted you will be looted.
Those who stole from you in war will have things stolen from them.
[17] I'll restore your health and heal your wounds," declares the LORD.
    "People call you an outcast:
    Zion, no one cares for you.

[18] "This is what the LORD says:

I'm going to bring the captives back to Jacob's tents
    and show compassion on their homes.
Cities will be built on the ruins,
    and fortified palaces will be built in their rightful place.
[19] The people who live there will sing songs of praise,
    and the sound of laughter will be heard from there.
I'll make them numerous, and their number won't decrease.
I'll bring them honor, and they won't be considered unimportant.
[20] Their children will be like they were long ago.
Their community will be established in my presence,
    and I will punish everyone who oppresses them.
[21] Their leader will be someone from their own people.
Their ruler will come from among them.
    I'll bring him near, and he will come close to me.
    Who would dare to come near me?" asks the LORD.
[22] You will be my people, and I will be your God.
[23]   The storm of the LORD will come with his anger.
    Like a driving wind, it will swirl down on the heads of the wicked.
[24] The LORD's burning anger will not turn back
    until he has done everything he intends to do.
        In the last days you will understand this clearly.

---

[a] 30:8 A yoke is a wooden bar placed over the necks of work animals so that they can pull plows or carts.

Both Israel and Judah Will Be Rescued

31 ¹ "At that time," declares the LORD, "I will be the God of all the families of Israel, and they will be my people."

² This is what the LORD says:

The people who survived the wars have found favor in the desert.
> Israel went to find its rest.

³ The LORD appeared to me in a faraway place and said,

"I love you with an everlasting love.
> So I will continue to show you my kindness.
⁴   Once again I will build you up,
>> and you will be rebuilt, my dear people Israel.
> Once again you will take your tambourines,
>> and you will go dancing with happy people.
⁵   Once again you will plant vineyards on the mountains of Samaria.
>> Those who plant them will enjoy the fruit.
⁶ There will be a day when watchmen on the mountains of Ephraim
> will call out this message:
>> 'Arise! Let's go to Zion, to the LORD our God.' "

⁷ This is what the LORD says:

Sing a happy song about Jacob.
Sing joyfully for the leader of the nations.
Shout, sing praise, and say,
> "O LORD, rescue your people, the remaining few from Israel."

⁸ "I will bring them from the land of the north.
I will gather them from the farthest parts of the earth.
> Blind people and lame people will return
>> together with pregnant women and those in labor.
>>> A large crowd will return here.
⁹   They will cry as they return.
>>> They will pray as I bring them back.
I will lead them beside streams
> on a level path where they will not stumble.
>> I will be a Father to Israel,
>>> and Ephraim will be my firstborn.

¹⁰ "You nations, listen to the word of the LORD.
Tell it to the distant islands.
> Say, 'The one who scattered the people of Israel will gather them
>> and watch over them as a shepherd watches over his flock.'
¹¹   The LORD will free the descendants of Jacob
> and reclaim them from those who are stronger than they are.
¹² They will come and shout for joy on top of Mount Zion.
> They will stream to it to enjoy the LORD's blessings:
>> fresh grain, new wine, and olive oil, lambs and calves.
> Their lives will be like well-watered gardens,
>> and they will never suffer again.
¹³ Then young women will rejoice and dance
> along with young men and old men.
I will turn their mourning into joy.
I will comfort them.
I will give them joy in place of their sorrow.
¹⁴ I will satisfy the priests with rich food.
> My people will be filled with my blessings," declares the LORD.

¹⁵ This is what the LORD says:

A sound is heard in Ramah,
> the sound of crying in bitter grief.
>> Rachel is crying for her children.
>>> She refuses to be comforted,
>>>> because they are dead.

¹⁶ This is what the LORD says:

Stop your crying, and wipe away your tears.
You will be rewarded for your work, declares the LORD.
You will return from the land of the enemy.

[17] Your future is filled with hope, declares the LORD.
Your children will return to their own territory.

[18] "I have certainly heard Ephraim mourn and say,
'You disciplined me, and I was disciplined.
I was like a young, untrained calf.
Turn me, and I will be turned,
because you are the LORD my God.

[19] After I was turned around, I changed the way I thought and acted.
After I was taught a lesson, I hung my head in shame.
I was so ashamed and humiliated,
because of all the stupid things I have done
ever since I was young.'

[20] Is Ephraim my dear son? Is he a pleasant child?
Even though I have often spoken against him, I still think fondly of him.
That is why my heart longs for him,
and I will certainly have compassion on him," declares the LORD.

[21] Set up landmarks!
Put up road signs!
Remember the highway, the road on which you traveled.
Come back, my dear people Israel, come back to your cities.

[22] How long will you wander around, you unfaithful people?
The LORD will create something new on earth:
A woman will protect a man.

[23] This is what the LORD of Armies, the God of Israel, says: When I have brought them back from captivity, they will once again use this saying in Judah and in its cities:

"The LORD will bless you, home of righteousness, holy mountain.

[24] Judah and all its cities will live there together.
Farmers and shepherds will also live there.

[25] I will give those who are weary all they need.
I will refresh everyone who is filled with sorrow."

[26] At this, I woke up and looked around. My sleep had been pleasant.

[27] "The days are coming," declares the LORD, "when I will plant the nations of Israel and Judah with people and animals. [28] Once I watched over them to uproot them, to tear them down, and to wreck, ruin, and hurt them. Now I will watch over them to build them up and to plant them," declares the LORD. [29] "When those days come, people will no longer say, 'Fathers have eaten sour grapes, and their children's teeth are set on edge.' [30] But each person will die for his own sin. Whoever eats sour grapes will have his own teeth set on edge.

The New Promise

[31] "The days are coming," declares the LORD, "when I will make a new promise[a] to Israel and Judah. [32] It will not be like the promise that I made to their ancestors when I took them by the hand and brought them out of Egypt. They rejected that promise, although I was a husband to them," declares the LORD. [33] "But this is the promise that I will make to Israel after those days," declares the LORD: "I will put my teachings inside them, and I will write those teachings on their hearts. I will be their God, and they will be my people. [34] No longer will each person teach his neighbors or his relatives by saying, 'Know the LORD.' All of them, from the least important to the most important, will know me," declares the LORD, "because I will forgive their wickedness and I will no longer hold their sins against them."

[35] The LORD provides the sun to be a light during the day.
He orders the moon and stars to be lights during the night.
He stirs up the sea so that its waves roar.
His name is the LORD of Armies.

This is what the LORD says:

[36] Only if these laws stop working, declares the LORD,
will Israel's descendants stop being a nation in my presence.

---

[a] 31:31 Or "covenant."

³⁷ This is what the LORD says:

> Only if the heavens could be measured
>   or the foundations of the earth could be searched,
>   would I ever reject all of Israel's descendants
>   because of everything that they have done, declares the LORD.

³⁸ "The days are coming," declares the LORD, "when the city will be rebuilt for me from the Tower of Hananel to Corner Gate. ³⁹ A measuring line will stretch from there straight to the Hill of Gareb, and then it will turn to Goah. ⁴⁰ The whole valley, filled with its dead bodies and ashes, and the whole area to the Kidron Valley, as far as the corner of Horse Gate in the east, will be holy to the LORD. It will never be uprooted or torn down again."

Jeremiah Buys a Field

32 ¹ The LORD spoke his word to Jeremiah during Zedekiah's tenth year as king of Judah. (This was Nebuchadnezzar's eighteenth year as king.) ² At that time the army of the king of Babylon was blockading Jerusalem.

The prophet Jeremiah was locked up in the courtyard of the prison. This prison was in the palace of the king of Judah. ³ When King Zedekiah of Judah locked up Jeremiah, Zedekiah asked him, "Why are you prophesying? You are saying, 'This is what the LORD says: I'm going to hand this city over to the king of Babylon, and he will capture it. ⁴ King Zedekiah of Judah will not escape from the Babylonians. He will certainly be handed over to the king of Babylon. He will talk to Nebuchadnezzar in person and look him in the eye. ⁵ Nebuchadnezzar will take Zedekiah to Babylon, and Zedekiah will stay there until I deal with him, declares the LORD. When you fight the Babylonians, you won't win.' "

⁶ Jeremiah said, "The LORD spoke his word to me. He said, ⁷ 'Jeremiah, your cousin Hanamel, son of Shallum, is going to come to you and say, "Buy my field that is in Anathoth, because as the closest relative it is your responsibility to buy it.' "

⁸ "Then, as the LORD had said, my cousin Hanamel came to me in the courtyard of the prison. He said to me, 'Please buy my field that is in Anathoth in the territory of Benjamin. It is your responsibility to purchase it, because the rights of the closest relative belong to you. Buy it for yourself.' Then I knew that the LORD had spoken to me.

⁹ "So I bought the field in Anathoth from my cousin Hanamel and gave him the money. The field cost seven ounces of silver. ¹⁰ I signed the deed, sealed it, had people witness the signing of the deed, and paid out the silver. ¹¹ Then I took the sealed copy of the deed, containing the terms and conditions, as well as an unsealed copy. ¹² I gave the copies of the deeds to Baruch, son of Neriah and grandson of Mahseiah. I did this in the presence of my cousin Hanamel and the witnesses who had signed the deed and in the presence of all the Jews who were sitting in the courtyard of the prison. ¹³ Then I gave Baruch these orders: ¹⁴ 'This is what the LORD of Armies, the God of Israel, says: Take both of these documents, both the sealed and the unsealed copies of the deed. Put them in a clay jar so that they will last a long time. ¹⁵ This is what the LORD of Armies, the God of Israel, says: My people will again buy houses, fields, and vineyards in this land.'

¹⁶ "After I had given the copies to Baruch, son of Neriah, I prayed to the LORD. I prayed, ¹⁷ 'Almighty LORD, you made heaven and earth by your great strength and powerful arm. Nothing is too hard for you. ¹⁸ You show mercy to thousands of generations. However, you punish children for the wickedness of their parents. You, God, are great and mighty. Your name is the LORD of Armies. ¹⁹ You make wise plans and do mighty things. You see everything the descendants of Adam do. You reward them for the way they live and for what they do. ²⁰ You performed miraculous signs and amazing things in Egypt. To this day you are still doing them in Israel. You made a name for yourself that continues to this day. ²¹ You brought your people from Egypt with miraculous signs and amazing things, with a mighty hand and a powerful arm, and with great terror. ²² You gave them the land that you swore with an oath to give their ancestors, the land flowing with milk and honey. ²³ They entered and took possession of it. However, they refused to obey you or to follow your teachings. They didn't do anything you commanded them to do, so you brought all this disaster on them.

²⁴ " 'See how the dirt ramps have been built up around the city to capture it! Because of wars, famines, and plagues, the city will be handed over to the Babylonians who are attacking it. What you have threatened to do has happened, as you can see. ²⁵ Yet you, Almighty LORD, told me to buy a field with money and get witnesses to confirm it, although the city was handed over to the Babylonians.' "

²⁶ The LORD spoke his word to Jeremiah. He said, ²⁷ "I am the LORD God of all humanity. Nothing is too hard for me. ²⁸ This is what the LORD says: I'm going to hand this city over to the Babylonians and King Nebuchadnezzar of Babylon. They will capture it. ²⁹ "The Babylonians who are attacking this city will break in, set this city on fire, and burn it down. They will burn down the houses of people who made me furious by going up to the

roofs to burn incense to Baal and to pour out wine offerings to other gods. ³⁰ Ever since they
were young, the people of Israel and Judah have done what I consider evil. The people of Israel
have made me furious by what they've done," declares the LORD. ³¹ "The people in this city
have made me so angry and furious from the day they built it to this day. So now I must remove
this city from my presence.

³² "The people of Israel and Judah have made me furious because they are evil. The people,
their kings and officials, their priests and prophets, and the Judeans and those who live in
Jerusalem ³³ have turned their backs, not their faces to me. I taught them again and again, but
they refused to listen and learn. ³⁴ They set up their detestable idols in the temple that is called
by my name, and they dishonored it. ³⁵ In the valley of Ben Hinnom they built worship sites
for Baal to sacrifice their sons and daughters to Molech. I didn't ask them to do this. It never
entered my mind. I didn't make Judah sin.

³⁶ "You have said this about the city, 'Because of wars, famines, and plagues it will be handed
over to the king of Babylon.' Now this is what the LORD God of Israel says: ³⁷ I am going to
gather the people from all the lands where I scattered them in my anger, fury, and terrifying
wrath. I will bring them back to this place and make them live here securely. ³⁸ They will be
my people, and I will be their God. ³⁹ I will give them the same attitude and the same purpose
so that they will fear me as long as they live. This will be for their own good and for the good
of their children. ⁴⁰ I will make an eternal promise^a to them that I will never stop blessing them.
I will make them fear me so that they will never turn away from me. ⁴¹ I will enjoy blessing
them. With all my heart and soul I will faithfully plant them in this land.

⁴² "This is what the LORD says: As I brought all these disasters on these people, so I will
bring on them all these blessings that I have promised them. ⁴³ You have said that this land is
a wasteland, without people or animals living in it. You have also said that it has been handed
over to the Babylonians. But people will once again buy fields in this land. ⁴⁴ They will buy
fields for money, sign deeds, seal them, and have people witness the signing of the deeds. This
will happen in the territory of Benjamin, in the region of Jerusalem, in the cities of Judah, in
the cities on the mountains, in the hill country, and in the Negev because I will bring them
back from their captivity," declares the LORD.

The LORD Will Restore and Heal Judah

33 ¹ While Jeremiah was still being held in the courtyard of the prison, the LORD spoke his
word to him a second time. The LORD said, ² "I made ˌthe earthˌ, formed it, and set it in
place. My name is the LORD. This is what the LORD says: ³ Call to me, and I will answer you. I
will tell you great and mysterious things that you do not know. ⁴ The houses in this city and the
palaces of the kings of Judah have been torn down to be used against the dirt ramps and
weapons of the Babylonians. This is what the LORD God of Israel says about this: ⁵ The people
of Israel fought the Babylonians. Now their houses are filled with the bodies of their own people I killed in my anger and my fury. I will hide my face from this city because of its wickedness.

⁶ "But I will heal this city and restore it to health. I will heal its people, and I will give them peace
and security. ⁷ I will restore Judah and Israel and rebuild them as they were before. ⁸ I will cleanse
them from all the sins that they have committed against me. I will forgive them for all the sins that
they have committed against me and for rebelling against me. ⁹ Then Jerusalem will be my source
of joy, praise, and honor. All the nations on earth will hear about all the blessings that I will give to
Jerusalem. They will be afraid and tremble because of all the prosperity that I will provide for it.

¹⁰ "This is what the LORD says: You have said that this place is ruined and that no people or
animals live in it. It's true! The cities of Judah and the streets of Jerusalem are deserted. No
people or animals live there. But once again you will hear ¹¹ the sounds of joy and happiness
and the sounds of brides and grooms. You will hear those who bring thank offerings to the
LORD's temple say,

> 'Give thanks to the LORD of Armies because the LORD is good,
>   because his mercy endures forever.'

I will restore the fortunes of the land to what they were before," says the LORD.

¹² "This is what the LORD of Armies says: In this deserted place, where no people or animals
live, and in all its cities, there will once again be pastures where shepherds can rest their
flocks. ¹³ In the cities on the mountains, in the foothills, in the Negev, in the territory of
Benjamin, in the area around Jerusalem, and in the cities of Judah, shepherds will once again
count their sheep," says the LORD.

¹⁴ "The days are coming," declares the LORD, "when I will keep the promise that I made to
Israel and Judah. ¹⁵ In those days and at that time, I will cause a righteous branch to spring up
for David. He will do what is fair and right in the land. ¹⁶ In those days Judah will be saved and
Jerusalem will live securely. Jerusalem will be called The LORD Our Righteousness.

---

^a 32:40 Or "covenant."

¹⁷ "This is what the LORD says: David will never fail to have a descendant sitting on the throne of Israel. ¹⁸ The Levitical priests will never fail to have a descendant in my presence to sacrifice burnt offerings, to burn grain offerings, and to prepare daily sacrifices."

¹⁹ The LORD spoke his word to Jeremiah. He said, ²⁰ "This is what the LORD says: Suppose you could break my arrangement*ᵃ with day and night so that they wouldn't come at their proper time. ²¹ Then my arrangement with my servant David could be broken, and he would not have a descendant to rule on his throne. The arrangement with my servants the Levitical priests could also be broken. ²² I will multiply the descendants of my servant David and the Levites who serve me like the stars of heaven that cannot be counted and the sand on the seashore that cannot be measured."

²³ Then the LORD spoke his word to Jeremiah. He said, ²⁴ "Haven't you noticed what these people have said? They have said that the LORD has rejected the two families he has chosen. They despise my people, and they no longer consider them a nation.

²⁵ "This is what the LORD says: Suppose I hadn't made an arrangement with day and night or made laws for heaven and earth. ²⁶ Then I would reject the descendants of Jacob and of my servant David. I would not let any of David's descendants rule the descendants of Abraham, Isaac, and Jacob. However, I will restore their fortunes and love them."

King Zedekiah and the People Break Their Promise

34 ¹ The LORD spoke his word to Jeremiah when King Nebuchadnezzar of Babylon, his entire army, and all the kingdoms and people that he ruled were attacking Jerusalem and all its cities. He said, ² "This is what the LORD God of Israel says: Go to King Zedekiah of Judah, and tell him, 'The LORD says: I'm going to hand this city over to the king of Babylon, and he will burn it down. ³ You will not escape from him. You will certainly be captured and handed over to him. You will see the king of Babylon with your own eyes, and he will talk to you face to face. Then you will go to Babylon.

⁴ " 'Listen to the word of the LORD, King Zedekiah of Judah. This is what the LORD says about you: You will not die in war. ⁵ You will die peacefully. People will burn funeral fires for you as they did for your ancestors, the kings who lived before you. They will say, "Oh, master," as they mourn for you. I have spoken my word, declares the LORD.' "

⁶ The prophet Jeremiah told all these things to King Zedekiah of Judah in Jerusalem. ⁷ He did this when the army of the king of Babylon was attacking Jerusalem and the cities of Lachish and Azekah. These were the only fortified cities of Judah that were left.

⁸ The LORD spoke his word to Jeremiah after King Zedekiah and all the people in Jerusalem promised to free their slaves. ⁹ Everyone was supposed to free his Hebrew slaves, both male and female. No one was supposed to keep another Jew as a slave. ¹⁰ All the officials and all the people agreed and promised to free their male and female slaves and not to keep them as slaves anymore. So they set them free. ¹¹ But afterwards, they changed their minds and took back the men and women they had freed and made them their slaves again.

¹² The LORD spoke his word to Jeremiah. He said, ¹³ "This is what the LORD God of Israel says: I put a condition on the promiseᵃ I made to your ancestors when I brought them from Egypt, where they were slaves. I said, ¹⁴ 'Every seven years each of you must free any Hebrews who sold themselves to you. When they have served you for six years, you must set them free.' But your ancestors refused to obey me or listen to me. ¹⁵ Recently, you changed and did what I consider right. You agreed to free your neighbors, and you made a promise in my presence, in the temple that is called by my name. ¹⁶ Now you have changed again and dishonored me. You brought back the male and female slaves that you had set free to live their own lives. You have forced them to be your male and female slaves again.

¹⁷ "This is what the LORD says: You didn't obey me. You haven't freed your relatives and neighbors. Now I am going to free you," declares the LORD. "I will free you to die in wars, plagues, and famines. I will make all the kingdoms of the world horrified at the thought of you. ¹⁸ I will hand over the people who have rejected my promise. They have not kept the terms of the promise which they made in my presence when they cut a calf in two and passed between its pieces. ¹⁹ I will hand over the officials of Judah and Jerusalem, the palace officials, the priests, and all the common people who passed between the pieces of the calf. ²⁰ I will hand them over to their enemies who want to kill them, and their corpses will be food for birds and wild animals. ²¹ I will hand King Zedekiah of Judah and his officials over to their enemies who want to kill them and to the army of the king of Babylon, the army that has withdrawn from you. ²² I am going to give a command," declares the LORD. "I will bring that army back to this city to attack it, capture it, and burn it down. I will destroy the cities of Judah so that no one will live there."

ᵃ 33:20, 34:13 Or "covenant."

The Obedient Example of the Family of Rechab

35 [1] The Lord spoke his word to Jeremiah during the reign of Jehoiakim, son of King Josiah of Judah. He said, [2] "Go to the family of Rechab and talk to them. Take them into one of the side rooms in the Lord's temple, and offer them a drink of wine."

[3] I took Jaazaniah, who was the son of Jeremiah and the grandson of Habazziniah, and I took Jaazaniah's brothers and all his sons—the whole family of Rechab. [4] I brought them into the Lord's temple, into the side room of the sons of Hanan. (He was Igdaliah's son, the man of God.) It was next to the room of the officials and above the side room of Maaseiah, Shallum's son, the doorkeeper. [5] Then I set cups and pitchers filled with wine in front of the family of Rechab. I said to them, "Drink some wine."

[6] They answered, "We don't drink wine, because our ancestor Jonadab, Rechab's son, gave us this order: 'You and your descendants must never drink wine. [7] Never build any houses or plant any fields or vineyards. You must never have any of these things. You must always live in tents so that you may live for a long time in the land where you are staying.' [8] We, along with our wives, sons, and daughters, have obeyed our ancestor Jonadab, Rechab's son, in everything he ordered us to do. We have never drunk wine, [9] built houses to live in, or owned vineyards, pastures, or grain-fields. [10] We live in tents, and we have obeyed everything our ancestor Jonadab ordered us to do. [11] But when King Nebuchadnezzar of Babylon invaded this land, we said, 'Let's go to Jerusalem to escape the Babylonian and Aramean armies.' That's why we are living in Jerusalem."

[12] Then the Lord spoke his word to Jeremiah. He said, [13] "This is what the Lord of Armies, the God of Israel, says: Tell the people of Judah and those who live in Jerusalem, 'Won't you ever learn your lesson and obey my words? declares the Lord. [14] Jonadab, Rechab's son, ordered his descendants not to drink wine. This order has been carried out. His descendants have not drunk any wine to this day, because they have obeyed their ancestor's order. I have spoken to you again and again, but you have refused to listen to me. [15] I have sent all my servants the prophets to you again and again. They said, "Turn from your evil ways, do what is right, and don't follow other gods in order to serve them. Then you will live in the land that I gave you and your ancestors." However, you refused to listen to me or obey me. [16] The descendants of Jonadab, Rechab's son, have carried out the orders of their ancestor, but you refuse to listen to me.

[17] " 'This is what the Lord God of Armies, the God of Israel, says: I am going to bring on Judah and on all those who live in Jerusalem all the disasters that I threatened. I have spoken to them, but they didn't listen. I called to them, but they didn't answer.' "

[18] Then Jeremiah said to the family of Rechab, "This is what the Lord of Armies, the God of Israel, says: You obeyed the order of your ancestor Jonadab, followed all his instructions, and did exactly what he told you to do. [19] So this is what the Lord of Armies, the God of Israel, says: A descendant of Jonadab, Rechab's son, will always serve me."

Jeremiah's Prophecies Are Written, Read, and Burned

36 [1] In the fourth year of the reign of Jehoiakim, son of King Josiah of Judah, the Lord spoke his word to Jeremiah. He said, [2] "Take a scroll, and write on it everything that I have dictated to you about Israel, Judah, and all the other nations from the time I spoke to you during the reign of Josiah until today. [3] Maybe the nation of Judah will hear about all the disasters that I plan to bring on them, and they will turn from their wicked ways. Then I will forgive their wickedness and their sins."

[4] Then Jeremiah called Baruch, son of Neriah. Jeremiah dictated everything that the Lord had told him, and Baruch wrote it all down on a scroll. [5] Jeremiah told Baruch, "I'm no longer allowed to go to the Lord's temple. [6] On a day of fasting, you must read from the scroll the Lord's message that you wrote as I dictated. You must read it to the people in the Lord's temple. You must also read it to all the people of Judah when they come from their cities. [7] Maybe their prayers will come into the Lord's presence, and they will turn from their evil ways. The Lord has threatened these people with his terrifying anger and fury."

[8] Baruch, son of Neriah, did as the prophet Jeremiah commanded him. In the Lord's temple he read from the scroll everything that the Lord had said. [9] In the ninth month of the fifth year of the reign of Jehoiakim, son of King Josiah of Judah, a time for fasting was called. It was a time for all the people in Jerusalem and for everyone who was coming from any city in Judah to Jerusalem to fast in the Lord's presence. [10] Then Baruch read the scroll containing the words of Jeremiah. Baruch read it to all the people in the Lord's temple in the room of the scribe Gemariah, son of Shaphan, in the upper courtyard at the entrance of New Gate of the Lord's temple.

[11] Micaiah, who was the son of Gemariah and the grandson of Shaphan, heard Baruch read from the scroll everything the Lord had said. [12] Then he went down to the scribe's room in the king's palace where all the scribes were sitting. The scribe Elishama, Delaiah (son of Shemaiah), Elnathan (son of Achbor), Gemariah (son of Shaphan), Zedekiah (son of Hananiah), and all the other officials were there. [13] Micaiah told them everything he heard Baruch read from the scroll publicly. [14] Then all the officials sent Jehudi, who was the son of Nethaniah, the grandson of

Shelemiah, and the great-grandson of Cushi, to Baruch. Jehudi said to Baruch, "Bring the scroll that you read publicly, and come with me." Baruch, son of Neriah, took the scroll and went with him to see the officers. ¹⁵ They said to Baruch, "Please sit down, and read it to us."

So Baruch read it to them. ¹⁶ When they heard everything, they turned to each other in terror. They said to Baruch, "We must tell the king everything." ¹⁷ Then they asked Baruch, "Please tell us how you wrote all this. Did Jeremiah dictate it to you?"

¹⁸ Baruch answered, "He dictated everything to me, and I wrote it on the scroll in ink."

¹⁹ The officials said to Baruch, "You and Jeremiah must hide. Don't let anyone know where you are."

²⁰ After they put the scroll in the side room of the scribe Elishama, they went to the king in the courtyard and told him everything. ²¹ Then the king sent Jehudi to get the scroll. He took the scroll from the side room of the scribe Elishama. Jehudi read it to the king and all the officials standing by the king. ²² It was the ninth month, and the king was in his winter house sitting in front of the fire in the fireplace. ²³ As Jehudi read three or four columns, the king would cut them off with a scribe's knife and throw them into the fire in the fireplace. He did this until the whole scroll was burned up. ²⁴ The king and all his attendants didn't show any fear or tear their clothes in fear when they heard everything being read. ²⁵ Even when Elnathan, Delaiah, and Gemariah urged the king not to burn the scroll, he refused to listen to them. ²⁶ The king commanded Jerahmeel (the king's son), Seraiah (son of Azriel), and Shelemiah (son of Abdeel) to arrest the scribe Baruch and the prophet Jeremiah. But the LORD had hidden Baruch and Jeremiah.

²⁷ After the king burned up the scroll that Baruch had written and that Jeremiah had dictated, the LORD spoke his word to Jeremiah. He said, ²⁸ "Take another scroll, and write on it everything that was written on the scroll that King Jehoiakim of Judah burned. ²⁹ Say about King Jehoiakim of Judah, 'This is what the LORD says: You burned this scroll, and you asked Jeremiah, "Why did you write that the king of Babylon will certainly come to destroy this land and take away people and animals?" ³⁰ This is what the LORD says about King Jehoiakim of Judah: He will have no one to sit on David's throne, and his own corpse will be thrown out and exposed to the heat of day and the cold of night. ³¹ I will punish him, his descendants, and his attendants for their wickedness. They refused to listen. So I will bring on them, on those who live in Jerusalem, and on the people of Judah all the disasters that I have threatened.' "

³² Then Jeremiah took another scroll and gave it to the scribe Baruch, son of Neriah. As Jeremiah dictated, Baruch wrote on it everything that was on the scroll that King Jehoiakim of Judah had burned. They added many similar messages.

Jeremiah Advises Zedekiah

37 ¹ King Nebuchadnezzar of Babylon appointed Zedekiah, son of Josiah, to be king of Judah. Zedekiah succeeded Jehoiakin, son of Jehoiakim. ² But Zedekiah, his administrators, and the common people didn't listen to what the LORD had spoken through the prophet Jeremiah.

³ King Zedekiah sent Jehucal (son of Shelemiah) and the priest Zephaniah (son of Maaseiah) to the prophet Jeremiah. They asked him, "Please pray to the LORD our God for us."

⁴ Jeremiah was still free to come and go among the people. The people of Jerusalem hadn't put him in prison yet. ⁵ Pharaoh's army had come from Egypt, and when the Babylonians who were blockading Jerusalem heard this news, they retreated from Jerusalem.

⁶ The LORD spoke his word to the prophet Jeremiah. He said, ⁷ "This is what the LORD God of Israel says: Say this to the king of Judah, who sent you to get advice from me: 'Pharaoh's army has come out to help you. But it will go back to Egypt, its own land. ⁸ Then the Babylonians will return. They will attack the city, capture it, and burn it down.

⁹ " 'This is what the LORD says: Don't deceive yourselves by thinking that the Babylonians will leave you. They will not leave you. ¹⁰ Even if you would defeat the entire Babylonian army so that they had only a few badly wounded men left in their tents, they would get up and burn down this city.' "

¹¹ The Babylonian army had retreated from Jerusalem because Pharaoh's army was coming. ¹² So Jeremiah wanted to leave Jerusalem and go to the territory of Benjamin to take possession of his property there among the people. ¹³ But when he came to Benjamin Gate, the captain of the guard there, whose name was Irijah, son of Shelemiah and grandson of Hananiah, arrested the prophet Jeremiah. He said, "You're deserting to the Babylonians!"

¹⁴ Jeremiah answered, "That's a lie! I'm not deserting to the Babylonians." But Irijah wouldn't listen to him. Irijah arrested Jeremiah and took him to the officials. ¹⁵ The officials were so angry with Jeremiah that they beat him and put him in prison in the scribe Jonathan's house, which had been turned into a prison. ¹⁶ Jeremiah went into a prison cell, and he stayed there a long time.

¹⁷ Then King Zedekiah sent for Jeremiah, and the king asked him privately in the palace, "Is there any message from the LORD?"

Jeremiah answered, "Yes! There is a message from the LORD. You will be handed over to the king of Babylon." [18] Then Jeremiah asked King Zedekiah, "What crime have I committed against you, your administrators, or these people? Why have you put me in prison? [19] Where are the prophets who told you that the king of Babylon wouldn't attack you and this land? [20] But now, Your Majesty, please listen, and accept my plea for mercy. Don't return me to the scribe Jonathan's house, or I will die there."

[21] King Zedekiah gave the command to have Jeremiah put in the courtyard of the prison. He gave him a loaf of bread every day from the bakers' street until all the bread in the city was gone. So Jeremiah stayed in the courtyard of the prison.

Jeremiah Is Thrown Into a Muddy Cistern

38 [1] Shephatiah (son of Mattan), Gedaliah (son of Pashhur), Jucal (son of Shelemiah), and Pashhur (son of Malchiah) heard that Jeremiah was speaking to all the people. [2] They heard Jeremiah say, "This is what the LORD says: Those who stay in this city will die in wars, famines, or plagues. But those who surrender to the Babylonians will live. They will escape with their lives.

[3] "This is what the LORD says: This city will certainly be handed over to the army of the king of Babylon, and it will capture the city."

[4] Then the officials said to the king, "Have this man put to death. He discourages the soldiers who are left in this city and all the people by telling them such things. This man is not trying to help these people; he's trying to hurt them."

[5] King Zedekiah answered, "He's in your hands. I won't do anything to stop you."

[6] So they took Jeremiah and threw him into the cistern of Malchiah, the king's son. It was in the courtyard of the prison. They used ropes to lower Jeremiah into the cistern. There was no water in the cistern, only mud, and Jeremiah sank in the mud.

[7] But an official in the royal palace, Ebed Melech from Sudan, heard that they had put Jeremiah in the cistern. The king happened to be sitting at Benjamin Gate. [8] Ebed Melech left the royal palace and spoke to the king at Benjamin Gate. [9] "Your Majesty, everything that these men have done to the prophet Jeremiah is wrong. They have thrown him into the cistern, where he'll starve to death, because there's no more bread in the city."

[10] Then the king gave Ebed Melech from Sudan this command: "Take 30 men from here, and lift the prophet Jeremiah out of the cistern before he dies."

[11] So Ebed Melech took the men with him and went to the royal palace, to a room under the treasury. He took rags and torn clothes from there and lowered them with ropes to Jeremiah in the cistern. [12] Ebed Melech from Sudan said to Jeremiah, "Put these rags and torn clothes under your arms to protect you from the ropes." Jeremiah did. [13] They used the ropes to pull Jeremiah up and lift him out of the cistern. Then Jeremiah stayed in the courtyard of the prison.

[14] King Zedekiah sent for the prophet Jeremiah and brought him to the third entrance in the LORD's temple. "I'm going to ask you a question," the king said to Jeremiah. "Don't hide anything from me."

[15] Jeremiah answered Zedekiah, "If I answer you, you'll kill me. If I give you advice, you won't listen to me."

[16] So King Zedekiah secretly swore an oath to Jeremiah, "The LORD gave us life. As the LORD lives, I will not kill you or hand you over to these men who want to kill you."

[17] Jeremiah said to Zedekiah, "This is what the LORD God of Armies, the God of Israel, says: If you surrender to the officers of the king of Babylon, you will live, and this city will not be burned. You and your household will live. [18] But if you don't surrender to the officers of the king of Babylon, this city will be handed over to the Babylonians. They will burn it down, and you will not escape from them."

[19] King Zedekiah answered Jeremiah, "I'm afraid of the Jews who have deserted to the Babylonians. The Babylonians may hand me over to them, and they will torture me."

[20] Jeremiah said, "You will not be handed over to them. Obey the LORD by doing what I'm telling you. Then everything will go well for you, and you will live. [21] But if you refuse to surrender, this is what the LORD has shown me. [22] All the women who are left in the palace of Judah's king will be brought out to the officers of the king of Babylon. These women will say:

'Your trusted friends have misled you and used you.
Your feet are stuck in the mud, and your friends have deserted you.'

[23] "All your wives and children will be brought to the Babylonians. You will not escape from them. You will be captured by the king of Babylon, and this city will be burned down."   ·

Jeremiah and Zedekiah Make an Agreement

[24] Zedekiah said to Jeremiah, "Don't let anyone know about this conversation, or you will die. [25] The officials may find out that I've been talking with you. They may come to you and

say, 'Tell us what you said to the king and what the king said to you. Don't hide anything from us, or we'll kill you.' **26** If they come to you, say to them, 'I asked the king not to send me back to Jonathan's house to die there.' "

27 All the officials came to Jeremiah and questioned him. He told them exactly what the king had told him to say. So they stopped questioning him, because they hadn't heard his conversation with the king. **28** Jeremiah stayed in the courtyard of the prison until the day Jerusalem was captured.

Jerusalem Is Captured—*2 Kings 25:1–12; 2 Chronicles 36:19–21; Jeremiah 52:4–16*

39 **1** In the tenth month of Zedekiah's ninth year as king of Judah, King Nebuchadnezzar of Babylon attacked Jerusalem with his entire army and blockaded it. **2** On the ninth day of the fourth month of Zedekiah's eleventh year as king, they broke into the city.

3 Then all the officers of the king of Babylon came in and sat in Middle Gate: Nergal (the quartermaster), Samgar Nebo (the chief officer), Nergal (the quartermaster and the chief fortuneteller), and all the rest of the officers of the king of Babylon.

4 When King Zedekiah of Judah and all the soldiers saw them, they fled. They left the city at night by way of the king's garden through the gate between the two walls, and they took the road to the plain ˌof Jerichoˌ. **5** The Babylonian army pursued them and caught up with Zedekiah in the plain of Jericho. They arrested him and brought him to Babylon's King Nebuchadnezzar at Riblah in the territory of Hamath. The king of Babylon passed sentence on him. **6** The king of Babylon slaughtered Zedekiah's sons as Zedekiah watched at Riblah. He also slaughtered all the leaders of Judah. **7** Then he blinded Zedekiah, put him in bronze shackles, and took him to Babylon.

8 The Babylonians burned down the royal palace and the people's homes, and they tore down the walls of Jerusalem. **9** Nebuzaradan, Babylon's captain of the guard, captured the few people left in the city, those who surrendered to him, and the rest of the people. **10** But Nebuzaradan, the captain of the guard, left some poor people who had nothing in the land of Judah. At that time he gave them vineyards and farms.

11 King Nebuchadnezzar of Babylon gave Nebuzaradan an order concerning Jeremiah. He said, **12** "Take him, and look after him. Don't harm him in any way, but do for him whatever he asks." **13** Nebuzaradan (the captain of the guard), Nebushazban (the chief official), Nergal (the quartermaster and the chief fortuneteller), and all the other leaders of the king of Babylon sent for Jeremiah. **14** They took Jeremiah out of the courtyard of the prison and handed him over to Gedaliah, son of Ahikam and grandson of Shaphan, to take him home. So he lived among the people.

15 While Jeremiah was still confined in the courtyard of the prison, the LORD spoke his word to him. The LORD said, **16** "Say to Ebed Melech from Sudan, 'This is what the LORD of Armies, the God of Israel, says: I'm going to carry out my threat against this city by bringing disaster on it instead of prosperity. At that time these things will happen as you watch. **17** But at that time I will rescue you, declares the LORD. You will not be handed over to those you fear. **18** I will certainly rescue you. You will not die in war. You will escape with your life because you trusted me, declares the LORD.' "

Jeremiah Is Freed—*2 Kings 25:22–26*

40 **1** The LORD spoke his word to Jeremiah after Nebuzaradan, the captain of the guard, let him go at Ramah. Nebuzaradan found Jeremiah in chains along with the captives of Jerusalem and Judah who were being taken to Babylon. **2** The captain of the guard took Jeremiah aside and said to him, "The LORD your God threatened to bring this disaster on this place. **3** He has carried out his threat. The LORD did as he promised because you Israelites have sinned against him and refused to obey him. That is why this has happened to you. **4** Today I'm removing the chains from your hands. If you would like to come with me to Babylon, come, and I'll look after you. But if you don't want to come with me to Babylon, don't come. The whole land is yours. Go wherever you want.

5 "If you wish to remain,*ª* then go back to Gedaliah, son of Ahikam and grandson of Shaphan, whom the king of Babylon appointed to govern the cities of Judah. Live among the people with him, or go anywhere you want." The captain of the guard gave Jeremiah some food and a present and let him go. **6** Jeremiah went to Gedaliah, son of Ahikam, at Mizpah and lived with him among the people who were left in the land.

7 All the army commanders and their men who were in the field heard that the king of Babylon had appointed Gedaliah, son of Ahikam, to govern the country and some of the country's poorest men, women, and children who had not been taken away to Babylon. **8** These are the commanders who went with their men to Gedaliah at Mizpah: Ishmael (son of Nethaniah), Johanan and Jonathan (sons of Kareah), Seraiah (son of Tanhumeth), the sons of Ephai from

---

ª 40:5 Hebrew meaning of "If you wish to remain" uncertain.

Netophah, and Jezaniah, who was the son of a man from Maacah. [9] Gedaliah, son of Ahikam and grandson of Shaphan, swore an oath to them and their men. He said, "Don't be afraid to serve the Babylonians. Live in this country, serve the king of Babylon, and you will prosper. [10] I'm going to live in Mizpah and represent you when the Babylonians come to us. Gather grapes, summer fruit, and olive oil, and put them in storage jars. Live in the cities you have taken over."

[11] Now, all the Jews who were in Moab, Ammon, Edom, and in all the other countries heard that the king of Babylon had left a few survivors in Judah and had appointed Gedaliah, son of Ahikam and grandson of Shaphan, to govern them. [12] So all the Jews returned from all the places where they had been scattered. They came to Judah and to Gedaliah at Mizpah. They gathered a large harvest of grapes and summer fruit.

[13] Kareah's son Johanan and all the army commanders who were still in the country came to Gedaliah at Mizpah. [14] They asked him, "Do you know that King Baalis of the Ammonites has sent Ishmael, Nethaniah's son, to kill you?" However, Gedaliah, son of Ahikam, didn't believe them.

[15] Then Johanan, Kareah's son, secretly asked Gedaliah at Mizpah, "Let me kill Ishmael, Nethaniah's son. No one will know about it. Why should he kill you? All the Jews who have gathered around you would scatter. What is left of Judah would disappear."

[16] Gedaliah, son of Ahikam, told Johanan, Kareah's son, "Don't do that! What you are saying about Ishmael is a lie."

Gedaliah Is Assassinated by Ishmael—*2 Kings 25:25–26*

41 [1] In the seventh month Ishmael (son of Nethaniah and grandson of Elishama, a descendant of the royal family and of the king's officers) went with ten men to Gedaliah, son of Ahikam, at Mizpah. As they ate together at Mizpah, [2] Ishmael, son of Nethaniah, and the ten men who were with him got up, drew their swords, and killed Gedaliah, son of Ahikam and grandson of Shaphan. So they assassinated the man whom the king of Babylon had appointed to govern the land. [3] Ishmael also killed all the Jews who were with Gedaliah at Mizpah as well as the Babylonian soldiers that he found there.

[4] The day after the murder of Gedaliah, before anyone knew about it, [5] 80 men arrived from Shechem, Shiloh, and Samaria. Their beards were shaved off, their clothes were torn, and cuts were on their bodies. They brought grain offerings and incense to the LORD's temple. [6] Ishmael, son of Nethaniah, left Mizpah to meet them, crying as he went. When he met them, he said to them, "Come to Gedaliah, son of Ahikam." [7] When they came into the city, Ishmael, son of Nethaniah, and his men slaughtered them and threw them into a cistern. [8] However, ten men from the group had said to Ishmael, "Don't kill us! We have wheat, barley, olive oil, and honey hidden in the country." So he left them alone and didn't kill them along with the others.

[9] Now, the cistern where Ishmael threw all the bodies of the men he had killed was the same one that King Asa made as a part of his defense against King Baasha of Israel. Ishmael, son of Nethaniah, filled it with the bodies.

[10] Then Ishmael took captive the rest of the people who were at Mizpah. He captured the king's daughters and all the other people who had been left at Mizpah. They were the people whom Nebuzaradan, the captain of the guard, had put under the control of Gedaliah, son of Ahikam. Ishmael, son of Nethaniah, took them captive and left for Ammon.

[11] When Kareah's son Johanan and all the army commanders who were with him heard about all the crimes Ishmael, son of Nethaniah, had done, [12] they took all their men and went to fight Ishmael. They caught up with him at the large pool in Gibeon. [13] When all the people who were with Ishmael saw Kareah's son Johanan and all the army commanders who were with him, they were glad. [14] Then all the people Ishmael had taken captive at Mizpah turned and ran to Kareah's son Johanan. [15] Ishmael and eight of his men escaped from Johanan and fled to Ammon.

[16] Then Kareah's son Johanan and all the army commanders who were with him brought back the rest of the people of Mizpah whom he had rescued from Ishmael, son of Nethaniah, after Ishmael had killed Gedaliah, son of Ahikam. Johanan brought back men, women, children, soldiers, and commanders from Gibeon. [17] When they left Gibeon, they stayed near Bethlehem at Geruth Kimham on their way to Egypt. [18] They were afraid of the Babylonians because Ishmael had killed Gedaliah whom the king of Babylon had appointed to govern the land.

Jeremiah Warns the People of Judah Not to Go to Egypt

42 [1] Then all the army commanders along with Kareah's son Johanan and Hoshaiah's son Jezaniah and all the people, from the least important to the most important, came to the prophet Jeremiah. [2] They said to him, "Please listen to our request, and pray to the LORD your God for all of us who are left here. As you can see, there are only a few of us left. [3] Let the LORD your God tell us where we should go and what we should do."

[4] The prophet Jeremiah answered them, "I have listened to your request. I will pray to the LORD your God as you have requested, and I will tell you everything the LORD says. I won't keep anything from you."

[5] They said to Jeremiah, "May the LORD be a true and faithful witness against us if we don't do exactly what the LORD your God tells us to do. [6] We will obey the LORD our God to whom we are sending you, whether it's good or bad. Yes, we will obey the LORD our God so that everything will go well for us."

[7] After ten days the LORD spoke his word to Jeremiah. [8] So Jeremiah called Kareah's son Johanan, all the army commanders who were with him, and all the people from the least important to the most important. [9] Jeremiah said to them, "You sent me to plead your case humbly to the LORD. This is what the LORD God of Israel says: [10] Suppose you stay in this land. Then I will build you up and not tear you down. I will plant you and not uproot you. I will change my plans about the disaster I've brought on you. [11] Don't be afraid of the king of Babylon, whom you now fear. Don't be afraid of him, declares the LORD. I'm with you. I will save you and rescue you from his power. [12] I will have compassion on you. I will make him have compassion on you and return you to your land.

[13] "But suppose you say, 'We won't stay in this land,' and you disobey the LORD your God. [14] Then you say, 'We'll go to Egypt, where we won't have to see war, hear the sound of a ram's horn, or be hungry. We'll stay there.'

[15] "Now, listen to the word of the LORD, you people who are left in Judah. This is what the LORD of Armies, the God of Israel, says: Suppose you're determined to go to Egypt, and you go and live there. [16] Then the wars you fear will catch up with you in Egypt. The famines you dread will follow you to Egypt, and you will die there. [17] So all the people who decide to go and live in Egypt will die in wars, famines, and plagues. No one will survive or escape the disasters I will bring on them.

[18] "This is what the LORD of Armies, the God of Israel, says: As my anger and my fury were poured out on those who live in Jerusalem, so my fury will be poured out on you if you go to Egypt. You will become a curse word. You will become something ridiculed, cursed, and disgraced. You won't see this place again.

[19] "The LORD has told you people who are left in Judah not to go to Egypt. You need to know that I am warning you today. [20] You only deceived yourselves when you sent me to the LORD your God and said, 'Pray to the LORD our God for us, and tell us everything that the LORD our God says, and we'll do it.' [21] I have told you today, but you won't obey anything the LORD your God sent me to tell you. [22] But now, you need to know that you will die in wars, famines, or plagues in the place where you want to go and live."

Jeremiah Is Forced to Go to Egypt

43 [1] So Jeremiah finished telling all the people the message from the LORD their God. He told them everything the LORD their God sent him to tell them. [2] Azariah (son of Hoshaiah), Johanan (son of Kareah), and all the arrogant people said to Jeremiah, "You're lying! The LORD our God didn't send you to tell us that we must not go to live in Egypt. [3] But Baruch, son of Neriah, has turned you against us in order to hand us over to the Babylonians. Then they will kill us or take us as captives to Babylon."

[4] So Johanan (son of Kareah), all the army commanders, and all the people didn't obey the LORD. They didn't stay in Judah. [5] Johanan (son of Kareah) and all the army commanders took all the people who were left in Judah to Egypt. These were all the people who had come back to Judah from the places where they had been scattered. [6] They took men, women, children, and the king's daughters. They took every person whom Nebuzaradan, the captain of the guard, had left with Gedaliah, son of Ahikam and grandson of Shaphan, including the prophet Jeremiah and Baruch, son of Neriah. [7] They didn't listen to the LORD, so they went to Egypt. They went as far as Tahpanhes.

Jeremiah Prophesies That Egypt Will Be Invaded by Nebuchadnezzar

[8] Then the LORD spoke his word to Jeremiah in Tahpanhes. He said, [9] "Take some large stones, and bury them under the brick pavement at the entrance to the Pharaoh's palace in Tahpanhes. Do this while the people of Judah watch you. [10] Say to them, 'This is what the LORD of Armies, the God of Israel, says: I'm going to send for my servant King Nebuchadnezzar of Babylon. I will set his throne over these stones that I buried, and I will spread his royal canopy above them. [11] He will defeat Egypt. He will bring death to those who are supposed to die. He will capture those who are supposed to be captured. He will kill in battle those who are supposed to be killed in battle. [12] He[a] will set fire to the temples of Egypt's gods. He will burn down the temples and take their gods captive. Nebuchadnezzar will put on Egypt as his coat as a

---

[a] 43:12 Greek; Masoretic Text "I."

shepherd puts on his coat. He will leave Egypt peacefully. [13] At Beth Shemesh he will break the monuments in Egypt and burn down the temples of Egypt's gods.' "

The Jews in Egypt Will Be Punished for Their Idolatry

44 [1] The LORD spoke his word to Jeremiah about all the Jews living in Egypt at Migdol, Tahpanhes, Noph, and Pathros. [2] This is what the LORD of Armies, the God of Israel, says: You have seen all the disasters I brought on Jerusalem and on all the cities of Judah. Today they are deserted ruins. [3] It is because their people did evil, and they made me angry. They went to burn incense and serve other gods that neither you nor your ancestors heard of. [4] I have sent my servants the prophets to you again and again to tell you not to do these detestable things that I hate. [5] But you wouldn't listen or pay attention. You wouldn't turn from your wicked ways and wouldn't stop burning incense as an offering to other gods. [6] That is why my fury and anger were poured out and continued to burn in the cities of Judah and on the streets of Jerusalem. So they became the desolate ruin that they are today.

[7] Now, this is what the LORD God of Armies, the God of Israel, says: Why do you bring this terrible disaster on yourselves? Why do you keep destroying men, women, children, and babies from Judah until none are left? [8] Why do you make me angry by burning incense to other gods in Egypt, where you have come to live. You will destroy yourselves and be cursed and ridiculed by all the nations on earth. [9] Have you forgotten the wicked things done by your ancestors, by the kings of Judah and their wives, and by you and your wives in Judah and on the streets of Jerusalem? [10] You have not humbled yourselves even to this day. You haven't feared me or lived your lives by my teachings or by my decrees that I gave your ancestors.

[11] This is what the LORD of Armies, the God of Israel, says: I'm going to bring disaster on you and destroy all of Judah. [12] I will take away from Judah those who are left, those who were determined to go to live in Egypt. They will die in Egypt. All of them, from the least important to the most important, will die in wars and be brought to an end by famines. They will become something cursed, ridiculed, and disgraced. [13] I will punish those living in Egypt as I punished Jerusalem with wars, famines, and plagues. [14] None of the people of Judah who went to live in Egypt will survive or return to Judah, where they long to return and live. Only a few refugees will return there.

[15] Then all the men who knew that their wives were burning incense to other gods, all the women who were standing there, and all the people who lived at Pathros in Egypt answered Jeremiah. They said, [16] "We won't listen to the message that you have spoken to us in the LORD's name. [17] We will do everything we said we would do. We will burn incense to the queen of heaven and pour out wine offerings to her as our ancestors, our kings, and our officials did in the cities of Judah and on the streets of Jerusalem. We had plenty to eat then, and we lived comfortably and saw no disaster. [18] But since we stopped burning incense to the queen of heaven and pouring out wine offerings to her, we have had nothing but wars and famines."

[19] The women added, "When we burned incense to the queen of heaven, poured out wine offerings to her, and made cakes for her with her image on them, do you think our husbands didn't approve?"

[20] Then Jeremiah said to all the people, both men and women, to everyone who answered him, [21] "Doesn't the LORD remember that you burned incense in the cities of Judah and on the streets of Jerusalem along with your ancestors, your kings and your officials, and the people in the land? [22] The LORD could no longer bear the wicked and detestable things you did. That is why your land has become something ruined, destroyed, and cursed. No one lives in that land today. [23] You burned incense as offerings to other gods, sinned against the LORD, and wouldn't obey him. You didn't live by his teachings, decrees, or written instructions. That is why you have met with this disaster as it is today."

[24] Then Jeremiah said to all the people, including the women, "Listen to the word of the LORD, all you people of Judah who are in Egypt. [25] This is what the LORD of Armies, the God of Israel, says: You and your wives made promises, and you have kept them. You said, 'We will certainly do what we vow. We will burn incense to the queen of heaven and pour out wine offerings to her.'

"So go ahead. Keep your vows, and do what you vow. [26] But listen to the word of the LORD, all you people of Judah who live in Egypt. 'I swear by my great name,' says the LORD, 'that no one from Judah who lives anywhere in Egypt will ever again call on my name and take the oath, "As the Almighty LORD lives." [27] I am going to watch over them. I am going to watch over them to bring disasters, not blessings. In Egypt the people from Judah will die in wars and famines until everyone is gone. [28] Those who escape the wars will return to Judah from Egypt. Then all the people of Judah who went to live in Egypt will know whose words have come true, mine or theirs. [29] I will give you this sign,' declares the LORD. 'I will punish you in this place so that you will know that my threats of disaster will happen to you. [30] This is what the LORD says: I'm going to hand Pharaoh Hophra, king of Egypt, over to his enemies and to those who want to kill him, just as I handed over King Zedekiah of Judah to King Nebuchadnezzar of Babylon and to those who wanted to kill him.' "

The LORD's Promise to the Scribe Baruch

45 [1] This is the message that the prophet Jeremiah spoke to Baruch, son of Neriah. Baruch wrote these things on a scroll as Jeremiah dictated them during the fourth year that Jehoiakim, son of Josiah, was king of Judah. Jeremiah said, [2] "This is what the LORD God of Israel says to you, Baruch: [3] You said, 'I'm so miserable! The LORD has added grief to my pain. I'm worn out from groaning. I can't find any rest.'

[4] "Say this to Baruch, 'This is what the LORD says: I will tear down what I have built. I will uproot what I have planted throughout the earth. [5] Are you looking for great things for yourself? Don't look for them, because I'm going to bring disaster on all people, declares the LORD. But wherever you go I will let you escape with your life.' "

A Prophecy Against Egypt

46 [1] The LORD spoke this message to the prophet Jeremiah about the nations. [2] This is the message about Egypt, about the army of Pharaoh Neco, king of Egypt. King Nebuchadnezzar of Babylon defeated his army at Carchemish along the Euphrates River during the fourth year that Jehoiakim, son of Josiah, was king of Judah.

[3] "Get your large and small shields ready; advance into battle.
[4] Harness your horses. Mount up, you horsemen.
Take your positions, and put on your helmets.
Polish your spears.
Put on your armor.

[5] "What do I see in them?
They are terrified.
They are retreating.
Their warriors are defeated.
They flee without looking back.
Terror is all around them," declares the LORD.
[6] "The infantry can't flee.
The warriors can't escape.
They stumble and fall in the north by the Euphrates River.
[7] Who is this, rising like the Nile River,
like streams that flow swiftly?
[8] Egypt is like the rising Nile River,
like a river quickly overflowing its banks.
Egypt says, 'I will rise; I will cover the earth.
I will destroy cities and the people in them.'
[9] Go into battle, you horsemen.
Drive wildly, you chariot drivers.
March into battle, you warriors,
you warriors from Sudan and Put who carry shields,
you warriors from Lydia who use bows and arrows.
[10] That day belongs to the Almighty LORD of Armies.
It is a day of vengeance when he will take revenge on his enemies.
His sword will devour until it has had enough,
and it will drink their blood until it's full.
The Almighty LORD of Armies will offer them as sacrifices
in the north by the Euphrates River.
[11] Go to Gilead, and get medicine, dear people of Egypt.
You have used many medicines without results; you can't be cured.
[12] The nations have heard of your shame; your cry fills the earth.
One warrior will stumble over another,
and both will fall together."

[13] The LORD spoke this message to the prophet Jeremiah about the coming of King Nebuchadnezzar of Babylon, who will defeat Egypt.

[14] "Tell this in Egypt; announce this in Migdol.
Make it known in Memphis and in Tahpanhes.
Say, 'Take your positions, and get ready.
Swords will kill those around you.'
[15] Why should your soldiers be cut down?
They can't stand because the LORD will push them down.
[16] They have repeatedly stumbled, and now they have fallen.
They say to each other,

'Get up! Let's go back to our people,
   to the land where we were born,
      and escape our enemy's sword.'
17 There they will cry, 'Pharaoh, king of Egypt, is a big windbag.
   He has missed his chance.'

18 "As I live," declares the king, whose name is the LORD of Armies,
   "someone who is like Mount Tabor among the mountains will come.
   Someone who is like Mount Carmel by the sea will come.
19 Pack your bags, inhabitants of Egypt,
   because you will be taken away as captives.
      Memphis will become a dreary wasteland,
         a pile of rubble where no one lives.

20 "Egypt is like a beautiful cow,
   but a horsefly from the north will attack it.
21 Egypt's hired soldiers are like fattened calves.
   They will turn and run away together.
   They won't stand their ground.
      The day of destruction is coming.
         At that time they will be punished.
22 Egypt will hiss like a snake as it slithers away.
   Its enemies will come with full force.
   They will attack it with axes like those who chop wood.
23 They will cut down the forest," declares the LORD,
   "since Egypt can't be found.
They are more numerous than locusts; they can't be counted.
24 The people of Egypt will be put to shame.
They will be handed over to the people from the north."

25 The LORD of Armies, the God of Israel, says,

"I'm going to punish Amon, who is the god of Thebes.
I will also punish Pharaoh, Egypt, its gods, its kings,
   and whoever trusts Pharaoh.
26 I'll hand them over to those who want to kill them,
   to King Nebuchadnezzar of Babylon and his officers.
Afterward, they will live in peace as they did long ago,"
   declares the LORD.

27 "Don't be afraid, my servant Jacob.
Don't be terrified, Israel.
   I'm going to rescue you and your descendants from a faraway land,
      from the land where you are captives.
   Then Jacob's descendants will again have undisturbed peace,
      and no one will make them afraid.
28 Don't be afraid, my servant Jacob," declares the LORD.
   "I am with you.
   I will completely destroy all the nations where I scattered you,
      but I will not completely destroy you.
         I will correct you with justice.
            I won't let you go entirely unpunished."

A Prophecy Against Philistia

47 ¹ The LORD spoke this message to the prophet Jeremiah about the Philistines before
   Pharaoh defeated Gaza. ² This is what the LORD says:

Water is rising in the north.
   It will become an overflowing river.
      It will overflow the land and everything in it,
         the cities and those who live in them.
People will cry out and everyone who lives in the land will cry loudly.
3 They will hear the sound of galloping war horses,
   the rattling of enemy chariots,
      and the rumbling of their wheels.
Fathers who lack courage abandon their children.
4 The time has come to destroy all the Philistines,
   to cut off from Tyre and Sidon any Philistine

who might have escaped to get help.
The LORD will destroy the Philistines
    and anyone who is left from the island of Crete.
5 Gaza will shave its head in mourning.
Ashkelon will be destroyed.
How long will you cut yourselves, you people left on the plains?
6 You cry out, "Sword of the LORD,
    how long will you keep on fighting?
        Go back into your scabbard.
            Stay there and rest!"
7 How can the sword of the LORD rest?
    The LORD has ordered it to attack Ashkelon and the coast.
    He has put it there.

A Prophecy Against Moab

48 ¹ This is what the LORD of Armies, the God of Israel, says about Moab:

How horrible it will be for Nebo; it will be destroyed.
Kiriathaim will be put to shame; it will be captured.
    Its stronghold will be put to shame and torn down.
2 People will no longer praise Moab.
    The people in Heshbon will plan Moab's destruction.
    "Let's destroy that nation!"
You will be silenced, city of Madmen.
    Death will come after you.
3 People will cry out from Horonaim, "Looting and great destruction!"
4 Moab will be broken.
    Its little ones will cry out.
5 People go up the pass of Luhith, crying bitterly as they go.
    On the road down to Horonaim they have heard
        the distressful cry of destruction.
6   "Run away! Run for your lives!
                Run like a wild donkey in the desert."
7 Since you trust the things you do and your treasures,
    you will be captured.
Chemosh will go into captivity with all its priests and officials.
8 The destroyer will come to every city, and no city will escape.
The valley will be destroyed, and the plain will be laid waste
    as the LORD has threatened.
9 Put salt on Moab.
    It will be destroyed.
    Its cities will become deserted ruins.
10 Cursed are those who neglect doing the LORD's work.
Cursed are those who keep their swords from killing.
11 "Moab has lived securely ever since it was young.
    Its people are like wine left to settle in a jar.
        They aren't poured from one jar to another.
        They haven't gone into captivity.
            That is why its flavor has remained the same,
                and its aroma hasn't changed.
12 That is why the days are coming," declares the LORD,
    "when I will send people to pour Moab out of its jars
    and to smash its pitchers.
13 Then Moab will be ashamed of Chemosh
    as the nation of Israel was ashamed when it trusted Bethel.
14 "How can you say, 'We are soldiers and warriors'?
15   The enemy will attack Moab and destroy its cities.
        Its finest young men will be slaughtered,"
            declares the king, whose name is the LORD of Armies.
16 "Moab's destruction is coming near; disaster is coming quickly.
17 Mourn over it, all of its neighbors and everyone who knows its fame.
Say, 'Look at the strong staff, the beautiful rod, that is broken!'
18 "People of Dibon, come down from your place of honor

and sit on the dry ground.
The destroyers of Moab will attack you.
They will destroy your fortresses.
¹⁹ Stand by the road in Aroer, and watch.
Ask those who are fleeing
and those who are escaping what is happening.
²⁰ They will answer, 'Moab is disgraced; it is defeated.
Shout loudly, and cry.
Tell the news in Arnon that Moab is destroyed.'

²¹ "Judgment has come to all the cities on the plain: to Holon, Jahzah, Mephaath, ²² Dibon, Nebo, Beth Diblathaim, ²³ Kiriathaim, Beth Gamul, Beth Meon, ²⁴ Kerioth, Bozrah, and on all the cities of Moab, far and near.

²⁵ "Moab's horn is cut off, and its arm is broken,"
declares the LORD.
²⁶ "Get the people of Moab drunk; they have spoken against the LORD.
They will wallow in their own vomit, and people will laugh at them.
²⁷ People of Moab, didn't you laugh at the people of Israel?
Were they caught among thieves?
Whenever you talk about them you shake your heads in contempt.
²⁸ People of Moab, abandon your cities.
Live among the cliffs.
Be like doves that make their nests at the entrance of a cave.

²⁹ "We have heard about the arrogance of Moab's people.
They are very arrogant.
They are very arrogant, conceited, and boastful.
³⁰ I know how arrogant they are," declares the LORD,
"but it isn't right.
They brag and don't do what they say.
³¹ That is why I will weep for Moab and cry for all of Moab.
I will moan for the people of Kir Hareseth.
³² I will cry for you as Jazer cries.
I will cry for you, grapevines of Sibmah.
Your branches ⌊once⌋ spread as far as the sea,
and they reached as far as the sea of Jazer.
The destroyer will destroy your ripened fruits and your grapes.
³³ Joy and gladness have disappeared from the orchards and fields of Moab.
I will stop the wine flowing from the winepresses.
No one will stomp on grapes with shouts of joy.
There will be shouts, but not shouts of joy.

³⁴ "The cry will be heard from Heshbon to Elealeh and Jahaz. It will be heard from Zoar to Horonaim and Eglath Shelishiyah. Even the streams of Nimrim will dry up. ³⁵ I will stop those in Moab who come to worship sites, those who bring offerings to their gods," declares the LORD. ³⁶ "That is why I moan for Moab like a flute. I sound like a flute for the people of Kir Hareseth. The wealth they gained has disappeared.

³⁷ "Every head is shaved, and every beard is cut off. There are gashes on every hand and sackcloth on every waist. ³⁸ People in Moab will mourn on every rooftop and in every street. There will be mourning everywhere, because I will break Moab like a jar that no one wants," declares the LORD. ³⁹ "They will cry, 'Look how Moab is defeated! Moab turns away in shame!' Moab has become something ridiculed and something held in contempt by everyone around it.

⁴⁰ "This is what the LORD says:

The enemy will swoop down like eagles and spread their wings over Moab.
⁴¹ The cities will be taken, and the fortified places will be captured.
On that day Moab's soldiers will be like women in childbirth.
⁴² Moab will be destroyed as a nation,
because it spoke against the LORD.
⁴³ Disasters, pits, and traps are in store for those who live in Moab,"
declares the LORD.
⁴⁴ "Whoever flees from a disaster will fall into a pit.
Whoever climbs out of the pit will be caught in a trap.
I will bring a year of punishment to Moab," declares the LORD.
⁴⁵ "Those who flee will stand exhausted in the shadow of Heshbon.
A fire will come out of Heshbon and a flame from Sihon.

It will burn the foreheads of the people of Moab
and the skulls of those noisy people.
46 How horrible it will be for you, Moab.
You people of Chemosh will die.
Your sons will be taken away into exile,
and your daughters will be taken away into captivity.
47 But I will restore Moab in the last days," declares the Lord.

The judgment against Moab ends here.

A Prophecy Against Ammon

49 ¹ This is what the Lord says about the people of Ammon:

Doesn't Israel have any children? Doesn't it have any heirs?
Why, then, has the god Milcom[a] taken over the inheritance
of Gad's descendants?
Why do Milcom's people live in Gad's cities?
2 That is why the days are coming, declares the Lord,
when I will sound the battle cry against Rabbah,
where the people of Ammon live.
It will become a pile of rubble.
Its villages will be burned down.
Then Israel will take possession of its inheritance, says the Lord.
3 Cry loudly, Heshbon, because Ai is destroyed.
Cry, people of Rabbah, put on your sackcloth, and mourn.
Run back and forth between the walls.
Milcom will be taken away into captivity
with its priests and officials.
4 Why do you brag about your valleys,
your fertile valleys, you unfaithful people?
You trust your treasures.
You think, "Who would attack me?"
5 I am going to bring terror on you from all around,
declares the Almighty Lord of Armies.
Everyone will be scattered.
No one will gather the refugees.
6 But afterward, I will return the captives of Ammon, declares the Lord.

A Prophecy Against Edom—*Obadiah 1–5*

⁷ This is what the Lord of Armies says about Edom:

Is there no longer any wisdom in Teman?
Has wisdom disappeared from your people?
Has their wisdom vanished?
8 Turn and run.
Hide in deep caves, inhabitants of Dedan.
When I punish them,
I will bring disaster on the descendants of Esau.
9 If people come to pick your grapes,
won't they leave a few grapes behind?
If thieves come during the night,
won't they steal only until they've had enough?
10 Yet, I will strip the descendants of Esau.
I will find their hiding places.
They won't be able to hide.
Their children and relatives will be destroyed.
None of their neighbors will say,
11 "Abandon your orphans, and I will keep them alive.
Your widows can trust me."

¹² This is what the Lord says: If those who don't deserve to drink from the cup still drink from it, why should you go unpunished? You won't go unpunished. You must drink from it. ¹³ I take an oath on myself, declares the Lord, that Bozrah will become a pile of rubble. It will become something horrifying, ridiculed, ruined, and cursed. All its cities will lie in ruins permanently.

---

a 49:1 Or "Molech."

¹⁴ I heard a message from the LORD.
    A messenger was sent among the nations to say,
      "Assemble, and attack Edom.
        Get ready for battle."

¹⁵ "Edom, I will make you the smallest of nations
    and despised among humanity.
¹⁶   You have frightened other people.
    Your arrogance has deceived you.
      You live on rocky cliffs
        and occupy the highest places in the hills.
  Even though you build your nest as high as an eagle,
    I will bring you down from there," declares the LORD.
¹⁷ "Then Edom will become something horrible.
    Everyone who passes by it will be horrified
      and hiss at all its wounds.
¹⁸ Edom will be like Sodom, Gomorrah, and their neighboring cities
    when they were destroyed.
    No one will live there.
    No human will stay there," says the LORD.
¹⁹ "I will suddenly chase them from their places
  like a lion coming out of the jungle
    along the Jordan River into pastureland.
      I will appoint over Edom whomever I choose.
        Who is like me? Who can challenge me?
        Is there any leader who can stand up to me?"

²⁰ Listen to the plans that the LORD is making against Edom
  and the things he intends to do to those who live in Teman.
    He will surely drag away the little ones of the flock.
    He will surely destroy the pasture
      because of the people who live in Teman.
²¹ The earth will quake at the sound of their downfall.
  The sound of their crying will be heard at the Red Sea.
²² The enemy will swoop down like eagles
  and spread their wings over Bozrah.
    On that day Edom's soldiers will be like women in childbirth.

A Prophecy Against Damascus

²³ This is a message about Damascus.

"Hamath and Arpad are worried because they heard the bad news.
    They melt in fear.
    They are troubled like a sea that can't be calmed.
²⁴ The people of Damascus are weak.
    They turn to flee, but panic grips them.
    Anguish and pain grip them like a woman in labor.
²⁵ Why isn't that famous, happy city abandoned?
²⁶ That is why its young men will die in the streets,
    and its soldiers will be silenced that day,"
      declares the LORD of Armies.
²⁷ "I will set fire to the walls of Damascus
    and burn down Benhadad's palaces."

A Prophecy Against Kedar and Hazor

²⁸ This is about the tribe of Kedar and the kingdoms of Hazor that King Nebuchadnezzar of Babylon defeated. This is what the LORD says:

Get ready, attack Kedar,
    and loot the people from the east.
²⁹ Their tents and their flocks will be taken.
  Their tent curtains, utensils, and camels will be carried away.
    People will shout to them, "Terror is all around!"
³⁰ Run far away! Find a place to hide,
    inhabitants of Hazor, declares the LORD.
  King Nebuchadnezzar of Babylon has made plans against you

and intends to attack you.
³¹ Get ready! Attack the nation living peacefully and securely,
　　declares the LORD.
　　　　It is a nation with no gates or bars.
　　　　Its people live alone.
³² Their camels will be taken as prizes.
Their large herds will be taken as loot.
　　I will scatter to the winds
　　　　those who shave the hair on their foreheads.
　　I will bring disaster on them from every side,
　　　　declares the LORD.
³³ Hazor will be a place where only jackals live.
　　It will become a permanent wasteland.
　　　　No one will live there.
　　　　No human will stay there.

A Prophecy Against Elam

³⁴ Early in the rule of King Zedekiah of Judah, the LORD spoke his word to the prophet Jeremiah about Elam.
³⁵ This is what the LORD of Armies says:

I'm going to break the bows of Elam's archers,
　　the most important weapon of their strength.
³⁶ I'll bring the four winds
　　from the four corners of heaven against Elam
　　　　and scatter its people in every direction.
There won't be a nation
　　where Elam's refugees won't go.
³⁷ I'll defeat the people of Elam in the presence of their enemies,
　　in the presence of those who want to kill them.
I'll bring disaster with my burning anger, declares the LORD.
I'll send armies after them until I put an end to them.
³⁸ I'll set my throne in Elam and destroy its king and officials,
　　declares the LORD.
³⁹ But afterward, I'll return the captives of Elam, declares the LORD.

A Prophecy Against Babylon

50 ¹ This is the message that the LORD spoke about Babylon and the land of the Babylonians through the prophet Jeremiah.

² "Announce this among the nations, and spread the news.
Raise a flag, and announce it.
Don't hide anything.
　　Say, 'Babylon will be captured.
　　　　Bel will be put to shame.
　　　　Marduk will be filled with terror.
　　　　　　Babylon's statues will be put to shame.
　　　　　　Its idols will be filled with terror.'
³ A nation from the north will attack Babylon
　　and destroy its land so that no one will live in it.
　　　　People and animals will run away.

⁴ "In those days and at that time," declares the LORD,
　　"the people of Israel and Judah will cry as they go together
　　　　to seek the LORD their God.
⁵ They will ask which road goes to Zion and turn in that direction.
They will go there to make a permanent agreement with the LORD.
　　It will not be forgotten.
⁶ My people have been lost sheep.
　　Their shepherds have led them astray.
　　　　They wander around on the mountains.
　　　　They go from mountains to hills.
　　　　　　They have forgotten their resting place.
⁷ Everyone who finds them eats them.
　　Their enemies say, 'We're not guilty.

They have sinned against the LORD, their true pasture.
They have sinned against the LORD, the hope of their ancestors.'

8 "Run away from Babylon.
  Leave the land of the Babylonians.
  Be like the male goats that lead the flock.
9 I am going to stir up an alliance of strong nations from the north
  and bring it against Babylon.
    Those nations will take up positions against Babylon.
  Babylon will be captured from the north.
    Its enemy's arrows will be like skilled soldiers
    who don't come back empty-handed.
10 The Babylonians will become the prize.
  All who loot them will get everything they want,"
    declares the LORD.

11 "You are happy and excited.
  You have looted the people who belong to me.
  You dance around like calves on the grass
    and neigh like stallions.
12   But your mother will be greatly ashamed.
    The woman who gave birth to you will be disgraced.
  Babylon, you will be the least important nation.
  You will become a parched desert.
13 No one will live in Babylon because of the LORD's anger.
  It will be completely abandoned.
  Everyone who passes by Babylon will be horrified
    and hiss at all its wounds.

14 "Take up your positions around Babylon, all you archers with bows.
  Shoot at it; don't save any arrows,
    because the people of Babylon have sinned against the LORD.
15 Shout a war cry against them on every side.
    They'll surrender.
    Their towers will fall and their walls will be torn down.
  Since this is the LORD's vengeance, take revenge against them.
    Do to them what they did to others.
16 Don't allow anyone in Babylon to plant or harvest.
  Everyone will turn to his own people and flee to his own homeland
    because of the enemies' swords.

17 "The people of Israel are like scattered sheep that lions have chased.
    The first to devour them was the king of Assyria.
    The last to gnaw at their bones was King Nebuchadnezzar of Babylon.

18 "This is what the LORD of Armies, the God of Israel, says:

  I am going to punish the king of Babylon and his land
    as I punished the king of Assyria.
19 I will bring the people of Israel back to their pastures.
    They will eat on Mount Carmel and Mount Bashan.
    They will eat until they are full
    on the mountains of Ephraim and Gilead.
20 In those days and at that time," declares the LORD,
    "people will look for Israel's crimes, but they will find none.
    They will look for Judah's sins, but none will be found.
    I will forgive the faithful few whom I have spared.
21 "Attack the land of Merathaim
    and the people who live in Pekod.
  Claim them for me by killing them with a sword,"
    declares the LORD.
    "Do everything I commanded you.
22 The noise of battle and great destruction fills the land.
23 The hammer of the whole earth is broken and shattered.
  See how desolate Babylon is of all the nations!
24 I will set traps for you, Babylon.
    You will be caught, but you won't know it.

You will be found and captured
because you have opposed the LORD.

25 The LORD will open his armory
and bring out the weapons of his fury,
because the Almighty LORD of Armies
has a job to do in the land of the Babylonians.

26 Attack them from a distance,
open their storehouses,
pile up their corpses like piles of grain,
claim them for me by destroying them,
and don't leave anyone behind.

27 Kill all their young bulls.
Let them go to be slaughtered.
How horrible it will be for them when their time has come,
the time for them to be punished.

28 Listen! Fugitives and refugees from Babylon
are coming to Zion to tell about
the vengeance of the LORD our God, the vengeance for his temple.

29 "Call together the archers, the soldiers with bows, against Babylon.
Set up blockades around it. Don't let anyone escape.
Pay the people of Babylon back for what they have done.
Do to them what they did to others.
They have disobeyed the LORD, the Holy One of Israel.

30 That is why their young men will die in the streets,
and all their soldiers will be silenced that day,"
declares the LORD.

31 "I'm against you, you arrogant city,"
declares the Almighty LORD of Armies.
"Your day has come, the time when I will punish you.

32 Those arrogant people will stumble and fall,
and there will be no one to help them get up.
I will light a fire in their cities
that will burn up everything around them."

33 This is what the LORD of Armies says:

All the people of Israel and Judah are oppressed.
All their enemies have captured them.
They refuse to let them go.

34 Their defender is strong.
His name is the LORD of Armies.
He will certainly take up their cause
in order to bring rest to the land of Israel
and unrest to the people who live in Babylon.

35 "A sword will kill the Babylonians and everyone who lives in Babylon,"
declares the LORD.
"A sword will kill their officials and their wise men.

36 A sword will kill the false prophets.
They will become fools.
A sword will kill their soldiers and defeat them.

37 A sword will kill their horses, their chariots,
and all the foreigners within their ranks.
They will become women.
A sword will destroy their treasures, and they will be looted.

38 A drought will diminish their water supply, and it will dry up.
Babylon is a land of idols, statues that will go crazy with fear.

39 That is why desert animals will live with hyenas.
Desert owls will also live there.
It will no longer be inhabited or lived in for generations.

40 Babylon will be like Sodom, Gomorrah, and their neighboring cities
when I, God, destroyed them.
No one will live there.
No human will stay there," declares the LORD.

41 "People are going to come from the north.
A great nation and many kings will rise from the ends of the earth.
42 They will take hold of bows and spears.
They will be cruel and have no compassion.
They will sound like the sea when it roars.
They will ride horses.
They are ready for war, ready to attack you, people of Babylon.
43 The king of Babylon has heard reports about them, and he loses courage.
Anguish will grip him as pain grips a woman in labor.
44 I will suddenly chase them from their places
like a lion coming out of the jungle
along the Jordan River into pastureland.
I will appoint over Babylon whomever I choose.
Who is like me? Who can challenge me?
Is there any leader who can stand up to me?
45 Listen to the plans that the LORD is making against Babylon
and the things he intends to do to the land of the Babylonians.
He will surely drag away the little ones of the flock.
He will surely destroy the pasture because of the Babylonians.
46 The earth will quake at the news that Babylon has been captured.
Its cry will be heard among the nations."

51

1 This is what the LORD says:

I will stir up a destructive wind against Babylon
and against the people who live in Leb Kamai.
2 I will send people to winnow[a] Babylon,
to winnow it and strip its land bare.
They will attack it from every direction on the day of trouble.
3 Have the archers bend their bows.
Have them put on their armor.
Don't spare Babylon's young men.
Completely destroy its whole army.
4 Babylon's soldiers will fall down badly wounded in their streets.
They will lie dead in their own land.

5 Israel and Judah haven't been abandoned by their God, the LORD of Armies, although their land is guilty of abandoning the Holy One of Israel.

6 Run away from Babylon!
Run for your lives!
You shouldn't die because of Babylon's crimes.
This is the time for the vengeance of the LORD.
He will pay the people of Babylon back for what they have done.
7 Babylon was a golden cup in the LORD's hand.
It made the whole world drunk.
The nations drank its wine.
That is why the nations have gone insane.
8 Babylon will suddenly fall and be shattered.
Cry for it.
Bring medicine for its pain.
Maybe it can be healed.
9 We wanted to heal Babylon, but it couldn't be healed.
Let's abandon it and go to our own land.
God has judged Babylon.
Its judgment is complete.

10 The LORD has brought about our victory.
Let's announce in Zion what the LORD our God has done.

11 Sharpen the arrows; fill the quivers.
The LORD will stir up the spirit of the kings of the Medes
because his plan is to destroy Babylon.
The LORD will avenge his temple.

---

a 51:2 Winnowing is the process of separating husks from grain.

12   Raise your battle flag in front of the walls of Babylon.
         Strengthen the guards.
             Station watchmen.
                 Prepare ambushes.
      The LORD will carry out his plans
         against the people who live in Babylon.
13   Babylon, you live beside many rivers and are rich with treasures,
         but your end has come.
             The thread of your life has been cut off.
14   The LORD of Armies has taken an oath on himself:
         "I will certainly fill you with many enemy armies.
             They will swarm like locusts.
                 People will shout their victory over you."

15   The LORD made the earth by his power.
      He set up the world by his wisdom.
      He stretched out heaven by his understanding.
16   When he thunders, the water in the sky roars.
      He makes clouds rise from the ends of the earth.
      He sends lightning with the rain.
      He brings wind out of his storehouses.

17   Everyone is stupid and ignorant.
         Metalsmiths are put to shame by their idols.
             Their statues are false ˏgodsˎ.
18   They can't breathe.
                     They are worthless jokes.
                         When they are punished, they will disappear.
19   Jacob's God isn't like them.
         He made everything,
             and Israel is the tribe that belongs to him.
                 His name is the LORD of Armies.

20   "You are my war club and my weapon for battle.
      I will use you to crush nations.
      I will use you to destroy kingdoms.
21   I will use you to crush horses and their riders.
      I will use you to crush chariots and their drivers.
22   I will use you to crush men and women.
      I will use you to crush the old and the young.
      I will use you to crush young men and women.
23   I will use you to crush shepherds and their flocks.
      I will use you to crush farmers and their oxen.
      I will use you to crush governors and officials.

24   "In your presence I will pay back Babylon
         and all the people who live in Babylon
             for all the evil things that they did in Zion,"
                 declares the LORD.

25   "I am against you, Babylon, you destructive mountain.
         You have destroyed the whole earth," declares the LORD.
      "I will use my power against you,
         roll you off the cliffs,
             and make you a scorched mountain.
26   People won't find any stones in you to use as a cornerstone.
      They won't find any stones in you to use for a foundation.
         You will become permanent ruins," declares the LORD.

27   Raise your battle flag throughout the world.
      Blow the ram's horn among the nations.
         Prepare nations to attack Babylon.
             Tell the kingdoms of Ararat, Minni, and Ashkenaz to attack it.
                 Appoint a commander to lead the attack.
                     Bring up horses like a swarm of locusts.
28   Prepare nations to attack Babylon.
      Prepare the king of the Medes, their governors, all their deputies,

and all the countries that they rule.
29 The earth trembles and writhes in pain.
The LORD carries out his plans against Babylon
   to make Babylon a wasteland so that no one will live there.
30 The warriors of Babylon have stopped fighting.
   They stay in their fortified cities.
   Their strength has failed. They have become women.
   Their buildings are set on fire.
   The bars across their gates are broken.
31 Runners run to meet runners.
   Messengers follow messengers.
      They inform the king of Babylon that his entire city is captured.
32   The river crossings have been taken.
         The enemy has burned its marshes,
            and its soldiers are terrified.

33 This is what the LORD of Armies, the God of Israel, says:

   The people of Babylon are like a threshing floor*b*
      at the time it is trampled.
         Their harvest time will come soon.

34 King Nebuchadnezzar of Babylon has devoured us.
   He has thrown us into confusion.
   He has turned us into empty jars.
   He has swallowed us like a monster.
   He has filled his belly with our delicacies.
      Then he spit us out.
35 The people who live in Zion say,
   "May the violence done to us be done to Babylon."
   Jerusalem says,
   "May the people of Babylon be held responsible for our deaths."

36 This is what the LORD says:

   I am going to take up your cause and get revenge for you.
      I will dry up Babylon's sea and make its springs dry.
37 Babylon will become piles of rubble.
   It will become a dwelling place for jackals,
      something horrible, and an object of contempt,
         where no one lives.
38 Its people are like roaring lions and growling lion cubs.
39 When they are excited,
      I will prepare a feast for them
         and make them drunk so that they will shout and laugh.
            They will fall into a deep sleep and never wake up again,
               declares the LORD.
40 I will take them to be slaughtered like lambs, rams, and male goats.

41 "Sheshach has been captured.
   Babylon, the city that the whole world praised, has been taken captive.
42   What a horrifying sight Babylon will be to the nations!
         The sea will rise over Babylon,
            and its roaring waves will cover it.
43 Its cities will be ruined.
   It will become a desert, a land where no one lives
      and where no human travels.
44 I will punish Bel in Babylon.
   I will make Bel spit out everything that it has swallowed.
      Nations will no longer stream to Babylon,
         and its walls will fall.

45 "Leave it, my people!
      Run for your lives!
         Run from the burning anger of the LORD.
46 Don't lose courage or be afraid when rumors are heard in the land.

---

b 51:33 A threshing floor is an outdoor area where grain is separated from its husks.

One rumor comes one year; another rumor comes the next year.
    Rumors of violence are in the land.
    Rumors that one ruler will fight against another are in the land.
47 That is why the days are coming when I will punish Babylon's idols.
    The whole country will be put to shame,
        and all its soldiers will lie dead.
48 Then heaven and earth and everything in them will rejoice over Babylon,
    because destroyers from the north will attack it,"
    declares the LORD.

49 Because the people of Babylon have killed many Israelites
    and because they have killed many people throughout the earth,
        Babylon must fall.
50 You people who escaped from the sword, leave!
    Don't just stand there.
Remember the LORD in a distant land, and think about Jerusalem.
51 We have been put to shame, and we have been disgraced.
    Shame covers our faces, because foreigners have gone
        into the holy places of the LORD's temple.

52 "That is why the days are coming," declares the LORD,
    "when I will punish their idols,
        and those who are wounded will moan everywhere in the land.
53 The people of Babylon might go up to heaven.
They might fortify their strongholds.
    But destroyers will still come from me against them,"
    declares the LORD.

54 Cries of agony are heard from Babylon.
Sounds of terrible destruction are heard
    from the land of the Babylonians.
55 The LORD will destroy Babylon.
He will silence the loud noise coming from it.
    Waves of enemies will come roaring in like raging water.
    The noise will be heard everywhere.
56 A destroyer will attack Babylon,
    its soldiers will be captured,
        and their bows and arrows will be broken.

"I, the LORD, am a God who punishes evil.
I will certainly punish them.
57 I will make their officials and wise men drunk,
    along with their governors, officers, and soldiers.
        They will fall into a deep sleep and never wake up,"
        declares the king, whose name is the LORD of Armies.

58 This is what the LORD of Armies says:

The thick walls of Babylon will be leveled,
    and its high gates will be set on fire.
    People exhaust themselves for nothing.
    The nations wear themselves out only to have a fire.

59 This is the message that the prophet Jeremiah gave to Seraiah, son of Neriah and grandson of Mahseiah, when Seraiah went to Babylon with King Zedekiah of Judah in the fourth year of Zedekiah's rule. (Seraiah was the quartermaster.) 60 Jeremiah wrote on a scroll all the disasters that would happen to Babylon. He wrote all these things that have been written about Babylon. 61 Jeremiah said to Seraiah, "When you come to Babylon, see that you read all this. 62 Then say, 'LORD, you have threatened to destroy this place so that no person or animal will live here, and it will become a permanent ruin.' 63 When you finish reading this scroll, tie a stone to it and throw it into the middle of the Euphrates River. 64 Say, 'Babylon will sink like this scroll. It will never rise again because of the disasters that I will bring on it.' "
    The words of Jeremiah end here.

The Fall of Jerusalem—*2 Kings 24:18–25:26; 2 Chronicles 36:11–12; Jeremiah 39:1–10*

52 1 Zedekiah was 21 years old when he began to rule, and he ruled for 11 years in Jerusalem. His mother's name was Hamutal, daughter of Jeremiah from Libnah.

[2] Zedekiah did what the LORD considered evil, as Jehoiakim had done. [3] The LORD became angry with Jerusalem and Judah and threw the people out of his sight.

Zedekiah rebelled against the king of Babylon. [4] On the tenth day of the tenth month of the ninth year of Zedekiah's reign, King Nebuchadnezzar of Babylon attacked Jerusalem with his entire army. They set up camp and built dirt ramps around the city walls. [5] The blockade of the city lasted until Zedekiah's eleventh year as king. [6] On the ninth day of the fourth month, the famine in the city became so severe that the common people had no food.

[7] The enemy broke through the city walls, and all Judah's soldiers fled. They left the city at night through the gate between the two walls beside the king's garden. While the Babylonians were attacking the city from all sides, they took the road to the plain ₍of Jericho₎. [8] The Babylonian army pursued King Zedekiah and caught up with him in the plain of Jericho. His entire army had deserted him. [9] The Babylonians captured the king and brought him to the king of Babylon at Riblah in Hamath, where the king of Babylon passed sentence on him. [10] The king of Babylon slaughtered Zedekiah's sons as Zedekiah watched. He also slaughtered all the officials of Judah at Riblah. [11] Then he blinded Zedekiah and put him in bronze shackles. The king of Babylon took him to Babylon and put him in a prison, where he stayed until he died.

[12] On the tenth day of the fifth month of Nebuchadnezzar's nineteenth year as king of Babylon, Nebuzaradan, who was the captain of the guard and an officer of the king of Babylon, came to Jerusalem. [13] He burned down the LORD's temple, the royal palace, and all the houses in Jerusalem. Every important building was burned down. [14] The entire Babylonian army that was with the captain of the guard tore down the walls around Jerusalem.

[15] Nebuzaradan, the captain of the guard, captured the few people left in the city, those who surrendered to the king of Babylon, and the rest of the population. [16] But Nebuzaradan, the captain of the guard, left some of the poorest people in the land to work in the vineyards and on the farms.

[17] The Babylonians broke apart the bronze pillars of the LORD's temple, the stands, and the bronze pool in the LORD's temple. They shipped all the bronze to Babylon. [18] They took the pots, shovels, snuffers, bowls, dishes, and all the bronze utensils used in the temple service. [19] The captain of the guard also took pans, incense burners, bowls, pots, lamp stands, dishes, and the bowls used for wine offerings. The captain of the guard took all of the trays and bowls that were made of gold or silver. [20] The bronze from the 2 pillars, the pool, and the 12 bronze bulls under the stands that King Solomon had made for the LORD's temple couldn't be weighed. [21] One pillar was 27 feet high and 18 feet in circumference. It was three inches thick and hollow. [22] The capital that was on it was 7½ feet high with a filigree and pomegranates around it. They were all made of bronze. The second pillar was the same. It also had pomegranates. [23] There were 96 pomegranates on the sides. The total number of pomegranates on the surrounding filigree was 100.

[24] The captain of the guard took the chief priest Seraiah, the second priest Zephaniah, and the 3 doorkeepers. [25] From the city he also took an army commander, 7 men who had access to the king whom he found in the city, the scribe who was in charge of the militia, and 60 common people whom he found in the city. [26] Nebuzaradan, the captain of the guard, took them and brought them to the king of Babylon at Riblah. [27] The king of Babylon executed them at Riblah in the territory of Hamath. So the people of Judah were captives as they left their land.

[28] These are the people Nebuchadnezzar took captive: In his seventh year as king, he took 3,023 Jews. [29] In his eighteenth year, Nebuchadnezzar took 832 people from Jerusalem. [30] In Nebuchadnezzar's twenty-third year as king, Nebuzaradan, the captain of the guard, took away 745 Jews. In all, 4,600 people were taken away.

King Jehoiakin Released From Prison—2 Kings 25:27–30

[31] On the twenty-fifth day of the twelfth month of the thirty-seventh year of the imprisonment of King Jehoiakin of Judah, King Evil Merodach of Babylon, in the first year of his reign, freed King Jehoiakin of Judah and released him from prison. [32] He treated him well and gave him a special position higher than the other kings who were with him in Babylon. [33] Jehoiakin no longer wore prison clothes, and he ate his meals in the king's presence as long as he lived. [34] The king of Babylon gave him a daily food allowance as long as he lived.

LAMENTATIONS

The Prophet Speaks Out: No One Offers Comfort

1 [a] 1 "Look how deserted Jerusalem is!
  Once the city was crowded with people.
  Once it was important among the nations.
   Now it is a widow.
  Once it was a princess among the provinces.
   Now it does forced labor.
2 Jerusalem cries bitterly at night with tears running down its cheeks.
  Out of all those who love the city, no one offers it comfort.
  All of Jerusalem's friends have betrayed it and become its enemies.

3 "Judah has been exiled after ˌmuchˌ suffering and harsh treatment.
  Its ˌpeopleˌ live among the nations; they find no rest.
   Those who chased them caught up with them
    in places where there was no way out.

4 "The roads to Zion are deserted.[b]
  No one comes to the annual festivals.
  No one passes through any of its gates.[c]
   Its priests are groaning.
   Its young women are made to suffer.
   Zion is bitter.
5 Its opponents are now in control.
  Its enemies have no worries.
  The LORD made Zion suffer for its many rebellious acts.
  Its children go ahead of their opponents into captivity.
6 All splendor has abandoned the people of Zion.
  Its influential people were like deer that couldn't find any pasture.
  They ran without any strength ahead of the hunters.

7 "Now, during its suffering and oppression,
  Jerusalem remembers all the treasures it had from ancient times,
   when its people fell into the power of their enemies
    with no one to help them.
  Their opponents looked on, and they laughed at Jerusalem's downfall.
8 Jerusalem has sinned so much that it has become a filthy thing.
  Everyone who used to honor it now despises it.
   They've seen it naked.
   Jerusalem groans and turns away.
9 Jerusalem's own filth ˌcoversˌ its clothes.
  It gave no thought to its future.
  Its downfall was shocking.
   No one offers it comfort.
   'O LORD, look at my suffering,
    because my enemies have triumphed.'
10 The enemies laid their hands on all of the city's treasures.
  Jerusalem has seen the nations enter the holy place.
   'O Lord, they are the same people
    you have forbidden to enter your congregation.'
11 All the people are groaning as they beg for bread.
  They trade their treasures for food to keep themselves alive.
   'O LORD, look and see how despised I am!' "

---

[a] 1:1 Chapter 1 is a poem in Hebrew alphabetical order. [b] 1:4 Or "are in mourning." [c] 1:4 Or "All its gates are in despair."

Zion Speaks Out: No One Offers Comfort

12 "Doesn't this affect all of you who pass by?
    Look and see if there's any pain
        like the pain that the LORD has caused me,
        like the pain that he has made me suffer on the day of his fierce anger.
13   He sent fire from above.
        He made it go deep into my bones.
        He spread a net for my feet.
        He made me turn back.
        He has left me devastated.
        He has made me sick all day long.
14 My rebellious acts are a heavy burden for me.
        They were tied together by God's own hands.
        They were tied around my neck.
        He has weakened me ˌwith themˌ.
        The Lord has handed me over to people I cannot oppose.ᵈ
15 The Lord has treated all the warriors inside my ˌwallsˌ with contempt.
        He called an army to defeat my young men.
        The LORD trampled the people of Judah in a winepress.
16 I'm crying because of ˌallˌ these things.
        My eyes—my eyes flow with tears.
            No one can give me the comfort I need to keep me alive.
            Everyone is too far away from me.
                My children are devastated because my enemies have won."

17 Zion holds out its hands.
        No one offers it comfort.
    The LORD has given this order about Jacob:
        His own neighbors will become his opponents.
        Jerusalem has become a filthy thing among them.

18 "The LORD is right in what he did,
        because I rebelled against his word.
    Please listen, all you people, and look at my pain.
        My young women and young men have gone into captivity.
19 I called for those who love me, but they betrayed me.
        My priests and leaders breathed their last breath in the city,
            looking for food to keep themselves alive.

20 "O LORD, see the distress I'm in!
        My stomach is churning.
        My heart is pounding because I've been very bitter.
    In the streets swords kill my children.
    Inside the houses it's like death.

21 "All my enemies have heard that I am groaning.
        No one offers me comfort.
    All my enemies have heard about my disaster.
        They are happy that you did it.
            You have allowed the day to come, the one that you had announced.
            Let my enemies be like me now.ᵈ
22 Recall all of their wickedness.
        Then deal with them as you have dealt with me
            because of all my rebellious acts.
            I groan so much and feel so sick at heart."

The Prophet Speaks Out: The LORD Destroyed Zion

2ᵃ 1 "Look how the Lord has covered the people of Zion
        with the cloud of his anger!
        He has thrown down Israel's beauty from heaven to earth.
        He didn't ˌevenˌ remember his footstool on the day of his anger.
2   The Lord swallowed up all of Jacob's pastures without any pity.

ᵈ 1:14, 1:21 Hebrew meaning of this verse uncertain.   ᵃ 2:1 Chapter 2 is a poem in Hebrew alphabetical order.

He tore down the fortified cities of Judah in his fury.
He brought the kingdom ˌof Judahˌ and its leaders
    down to the ground in dishonor.
³ In his burning anger he cut off all of Israel's strength.
He withdrew his right hand when they faced their enemy.
He burned like a raging fire in ˌthe land ofˌ Jacob,
    destroying everything around him.
⁴ Like an enemy he bent his bow.
Like an opponent his right hand held the arrow steady.
He killed all the beautiful people.
He poured out his fury like fire on the tent of Zion's people.
⁵ The Lord became an enemy.
    He swallowed up Israel.
    He swallowed up all of its palaces.
    He destroyed its strongholds.
    He made the people of Judah mourn and moan.
⁶ He stripped his own booth as if it were a garden
    and destroyed his own festivals.
The LORD wiped out the memory of festivals and days of worship in Zion.
He expelled kings and priests because of his fierce anger.
⁷ The Lord rejected his altar and disowned his holy place.
    He handed the walls of Zion's palaces over to its enemies.
        The enemies made noise in the LORD's temple
        as though it were a festival day.
⁸ The LORD planned to destroy the wall of Zion's people.
    He marked it off with a line.
    He didn't take his hand away until he had swallowed it up.
    He made the towers and walls mourn.
        They are completely dejected.

The Prophet Describes Jerusalem's Destruction

⁹ "ˌZion'sˌ gates have sunk into the ground.
    ˌThe LORDˌ destroyed and shattered the bars across its ˌgatesˌ.
Its king and influential people are ˌscatteredˌ among the nations.
    There is no longer any instruction ˌfrom Moses' Teachingsˌ.
Its prophets can find no visions from the LORD.
¹⁰ The respected leaders of Zion's people sit silently on the ground.
    They throw dirt on their heads and put on sackcloth.
The young women of Jerusalem bow their heads to the ground.
¹¹ My eyes are worn out with tears.
My stomach is churning.
My heart is poured out on the ground
    because of the destruction of my people.
Little children and infants faint in the city streets.
¹² They're asking their mothers for some bread and wine
        as they faint like wounded people in the city streets.
        Their lives dwindle away in their mothers' arms.

The Prophet Speaks Out: The LORD Destroyed You

¹³ "What example can I give you?
What parallel can I show you, people of Jerusalem?
What comparison can I make that will comfort you, beloved people of Zion?
Your wounds are as deep as the sea.
Who can heal you?
¹⁴ Your prophets saw misleading visions about you.
    They painted a good picture of you.
    They didn't expose your guilt in order to make things better again.
    They gave you false prophecies that misled you.
¹⁵ Everyone who walks along the road shakes a fist at you.
    They hiss and shake their heads at Jerusalem's people:
        'Is this the city they used to call absolutely beautiful,
        the joy of the whole world?'
¹⁶ All your enemies gawk at you.

They hiss and grit their teeth.
They say, 'We've swallowed it up.
Yes, this is the day we've been waiting for.
At last we have seen it!'

17 The LORD has accomplished what he had planned to do.
He carried out the threat he announced long ago.
He tore you down without any pity, ⸢Jerusalem⸣.
He made your enemies gloat over you.
He raised the weapons of your opponents.

18 The hearts of Jerusalem's people
cried out to the LORD, the wall of Zion's people.
Let your tears run down like a river day and night.
Don't let them stop.
Don't let your eyes rest.

19 Get up! Cry out at night, every hour on the hour.
Pour your heart out like water in the presence of the LORD.
Lift up your hands to him ⸢in prayer⸣
for the life of your little children
who faint from hunger at every street corner."

Zion Speaks Out: The LORD Destroyed Me

20 "O LORD, look and consider:
Have you ever treated anyone like this?
Should women eat their own children,
the children they have nursed?
Should priests and prophets be killed in the Lord's holy place?

21 Young and old lie on the ground in the streets.
My young women and men are cut down by swords.
You killed them on the day of your anger.
You slaughtered them without any pity.

22 You have invited those who terrorize me on every side,
as though they were invited to a festival.
No one escaped or survived on the day of the LORD's anger.
My enemy has murdered the children I nursed and raised."

The Prophet—A Man of Despair

3[a] **1** "I am the man who has experienced suffering under the rod of God's fury.
2 God has driven me away
and made me walk in darkness instead of light.
3 He beat me again and again all day long.
4 He has made my flesh and my skin waste away.
He has broken my bones.
5 He has attacked me and surrounded me with bitterness and hardship.
6 He has made me live in darkness,
like those who died a long time ago.
7 He has blocked me so that I can't get out.
He has put heavy chains on me.
8 Even when I cry and call for help, he shuts out my prayer.
9 He has blocked my way with cut stones and made my paths crooked.
10 He is like a bear waiting to ambush me, like a lion in hiding.
11 He has forced me off the road I was taking, torn me to pieces,
and left me with nothing.
12 He has drawn his bow and made me the target for his arrows.
13 He has shot the arrows from his quiver into my heart.
14 I have become a laughingstock to all my people.
All day long ⸢they make fun of me⸣ with their songs.
15 He has filled me with bitterness.
He has made me drink wormwood.
16 He has ground my teeth with gravel.
He has trampled me into the dust.

---

[a] 3:1 Chapter 3 is a poem in Hebrew alphabetical order.

17 "My soul has been kept from enjoying peace.
   I have forgotten what happiness is.
18 I said, 'I've lost my strength ˌto liveˌ and my hope in the LORD.'
19 Remember my suffering and my ˌaimlessˌ wandering,
      the wormwood and poison.
20 My soul continues to remember ˌthese thingsˌ and is so discouraged.

The Prophet—A Man of Hope

21 "The reason I can ˌstillˌ find hope is that I keep this one thing in mind:
22   the LORD's mercy.
      We were not completely wiped out.
      His compassion is never limited.
23   It is new every morning.
         His faithfulness is great.
24   My soul can say, 'The LORD is my lot ˌin lifeˌ.
         That is why I find hope in him.'
25   The LORD is good to those who wait for him,
         to anyone who seeks help from him.

26   "It is good to continue to hope and wait silently
         for the LORD to save us.
27   It is good for people to endure burdens when they're young.
28   They should sit alone and remain silent
            because the LORD has laid these burdens on them.
29   They should put their mouths in the dust.
            Maybe a reason to hope exists.
30   They should turn their cheeks to the one who strikes them
            and take their fill of insults.

31   "The Lord will not reject ˌsuchˌ people forever.
32   Even if he makes us suffer,
         he will have compassion
            in keeping with the richness of his mercy.
33   He does not willingly bring suffering or grief to anyone,
34   crush any prisoner on earth underfoot,
35   deny people their rights in the presence of the Most High God,
36   or deprive people of justice in court.
            The Lord isn't happy to see ˌthese thingsˌ.
37   Who was it who spoke and it came into being?
         It was the Lord who gave the order.
38   Both good and bad come from the mouth of the Most High God.

39   "Why should any living mortal (any person)
         complain about being punished for sin?
40   Let us look closely at our ways and examine them
         and then return to the LORD.
41   Let us raise our hearts and hands to God in heaven.

42   "We have been disobedient and rebellious.
         You haven't forgiven us.
43   You covered yourself with anger and pursued us.
       · You killed without pity.
44   You covered yourself with a cloud
         so that no prayer could get through it.
45   You made us the scum and trash of the nations.
46   All our enemies gawk at us.
47   Panic and pitfalls have found us, so have devastation and destruction.

48   "Streams of tears run down from my eyes
         over the ruin of my dear people.
49   My eyes will keep flowing without stopping for a moment
50   until the LORD looks down from heaven and sees.
51   What I see with my eyes disturbs me deeply
         because of all the young women in my city.ᵇ

ᵇ 3:51 Hebrew meaning of this verse uncertain.

52 "Those who were my enemies for no reason hunted me like a bird.
53 They threw me alive into a pit and threw rocks at me.
54 　Water flowed over my head. I thought I was finished.

55 "I call your name from the deepest pit, O LORD.
56 Listen to my cry ⌊for help⌋.
Don't close your ears when I cry out for relief.
57 Be close at hand when I call to you. You told me not to be afraid.
58 Plead my case for me, O LORD. Reclaim my life.
59 Look at the wrong that has been done to me, O LORD.
Give me a fair verdict.
60 Look at all their malice, all their plots against me.
61 Listen to their insults, all their plots against me.
62 The words and thoughts of those who attack me
are directed against me all day long.
63 Look at them! Whether they are sitting or standing,
they make fun of me in their songs.
64 Pay them back, O LORD, for what they deserve,
for what their own hands have done.
65 Make them stubborn. Let your curse be on them.
66 Pursue them in anger, and wipe them out from under the LORD's heaven."

The Prophet Speaks Out: Zion's Suffering Was Worse Than Sodom's

4 [a] 1 "Look how the gold has become tarnished!
The fine gold has changed!
The sacred stones are scattered at every street corner.

2 "Zion's precious children, who are worth their weight in fine gold,
are now treated like clay pots,
like those made by a potter's hands.
3 Even jackals offer their breasts to nurse their young,
but the women of my people are as cruel as wild ostriches.
4 The tongues of nursing infants stick to the roofs of their mouths
because of their thirst.
Little children beg for bread,
but no one will break off a piece for them.
5 Those who used to eat delicacies are now destitute in the streets.
Those who used to wear expensive clothes now pick through piles of garbage.
6 The punishment for my people's wickedness has been more severe
than the punishment for the sins of Sodom.
Sodom was destroyed instantly, without one human hand touching it.
7 Zion's princes were purer than snow, whiter than milk.
Their bodies were more pink than coral.
Their hair was like sapphires.
8 Their faces are ⌊now⌋ blacker than soot.
No one recognizes them on the streets.
Their skin has shriveled on their bones.
It has become as dry as bark.
9 Those who were killed with swords are better off
than those who are dying from starvation.
Those who were stabbed bled to death.
The others are dying because there is nothing in the fields to eat.
10 The hands of loving mothers cooked their own children.
The children were used for food by my people
when they were being destroyed ⌊by a blockade⌋.
11 The LORD's fury has accomplished his purpose.
He unleashed his burning anger.
He started a fire in Zion that even burned its foundations.
12 Neither the kings of the earth nor anyone living on earth could believe
that enemies or invaders would ever get through the gates of Jerusalem.
13 ⌊They got through⌋ because of the sins of Jerusalem's prophets
and the crimes of its priests,
who spilled the blood of righteous people within it.

---

[a] 4:1 Chapter 4 is a poem in Hebrew alphabetical order.

14 My people staggered blindly through the streets.
    They were so contaminated with bloodstains
        that no one would touch their clothes.
15 'Get away! You're unclean,'ᵇ people yelled at them.
    'Get away! Get away! Don't touch anyone.'
        When they fled and wandered around,
            the people of the nations said, 'They can't stay here any longer.'
16 The LORD himself has scattered them.
    He will no longer look favorably on them.
        They no longer respected the priests,
            nor did they honor their older leaders."

The People of Zion Speak Out

17 "We are still straining our eyes, trying in vain to find help.
    We waited and waited for a nation that didn't save us.
18 ˌThe enemyˌ kept tracking us down,
        so we couldn't even go out into the streets.
            Our end was near.
            Our time was up.
            Our end had come.
19 Those who were hunting us were faster than eagles in the sky.
    They chased us in the mountains and ambushed us in the wilderness.
20 The person the LORD anointed ˌas kingˌ, who is the breath of our life,
        was caught in their pits.
            We had thought that we would live
                in our king's shadow among the nations."

The Prophet Speaks Out: Be Warned About Edom's Impending Doom

21 "Rejoice and be glad, people of Edom, inhabitants of the country of Uz.
    The cup ˌof the LORD's furyˌ will be passed to you next.
        You'll get drunk and take off all your clothes.
22 People of Zion, the punishment for your wickedness will end.
    The LORD will not let you remain in exile.
People of Edom, he will punish you for your wickedness.
    He will expose your sins."

A Prayer of the Prophet

5
1 "Remember, O LORD, what has happened to us.
    Take a look at our disgrace!

2 "The land we inherited has been turned over to strangers.
    Our homes have been turned over to foreigners.
3 We are orphans without a father.
    Our mothers are like widows.
4 We have to pay to drink our own water.
    We have to pay to chop our own wood.
5 ˌOur enemiesˌ are breathing down our necks.
    We are worn out ˌandˌ not permitted to rest.
6 We had to beg Egypt and Assyria for food.ᵃ
7 Our ancestors sinned.
        Now they are gone,
            ˌbutˌ we have to take the punishment for their wickedness.
8 Slaves rule us.
        There is no one to rescue us from them.
9 To get our food, we have to risk our lives
        in the heatᵇ of the desert.
10 Our skin is as hot as an oven from the burning heat of starvation.
11 Women in Zion are raped, so are the girls in the cities of Judah.
12 ˌOurˌ leaders are hung by their hands.
    ˌOurˌ older leaders are shown no respect.

ᵇ 4:15 "Unclean" refers to anything that Moses' Teachings say is not presentable to God.   ᵃ 5:6 Or "We made a pledge to Egypt and Assyria in order to get enough food."   ᵇ 5:9 Hebrew meaning of "in the heat" uncertain.

¹³ ⌊Our⌋ young men work at the mill,
     and ⌊our⌋ boys stagger under loads of wood.
¹⁴ ⌊Our⌋ older leaders have stopped meeting at the city gate,
     and ⌊our⌋ young men no longer play their music.
¹⁵ There is no joy left in our hearts.
     Our dancing has turned into mourning.
¹⁶ The crown has fallen from our head.
     Because we have sinned, it has been disastrous for us.
¹⁷   This is why we feel sick.
         This is why our eyes see less and less.
¹⁸   Foxes roam around on Mount Zion, which lies in ruins.

¹⁹ "But you, O LORD, sit enthroned forever,
     and your reign continues throughout every generation.
²⁰ Why have you completely forgotten us?
   Why have you abandoned us for such a long time?
²¹   O LORD, bring us back to you, and we'll come back.
       Give us back the life we had long ago,
²²   unless you have completely rejected us
             ⌊and⌋ are very angry with us."

EZEKIEL

Ezekiel Sees the LORD's Throne

1 ¹ On the fifth day of the fourth month in the thirtieth year, while I was living among the exiles by the Chebar River, the sky opened, and I saw visions from God. ² On the fifth day of the month, during the fifth year of the exile of King Jehoiakin, ³ the LORD spoke his word to the priest Ezekiel, son of Buzi, in Babylon by the Chebar River. The power of the LORD came over Ezekiel.

⁴ As I looked, I saw a storm coming from the north. There was an immense cloud with flashing lightning surrounded by a bright light. The middle of the lightning looked like glowing metal. ⁵ In the center of the cloud I saw what looked like four living creatures. They were shaped like humans, ⁶ but each of them had four faces and four wings. ⁷ Their legs were straight, their feet were like those of calves, and they glittered like polished bronze. ⁸ They had human hands under their wings on each of their four sides. All four of them had faces and wings. ⁹ Their wings touched each other. The creatures went straight ahead, and they did not turn as they moved.

¹⁰ Their faces looked like this: From the front, each creature had the face of a human. From the right, each one had the face of a lion. From the left, each one had the face of a bull. And from the back, each one had the face of an eagle. ¹¹ That is what their faces looked like. Their wings were spread out, pointing upward. Each creature had two wings with which they touched each other. The other two wings covered their bodies. ¹² Each of the creatures went straight ahead. They went wherever their spirit wanted to go, and they didn't turn as they moved. ¹³ The living creatures looked like burning coals and torches. Fire moved back and forth between the living creatures. The fire was bright, and lightning came out of the fire. ¹⁴ The living creatures ran back and forth like lightning.

¹⁵ As I looked at the living creatures, I saw a wheel on the ground beside each of them. ¹⁶ This is how the wheels looked and how they were made: They looked like beryl. All four wheels looked the same. They looked like a wheel within a wheel. ¹⁷ Whenever they moved, they moved in any of the four directions without turning as they moved. ¹⁸ The rims of the wheels were large and frightening. They were covered with eyes.

¹⁹ When the living creatures moved, the wheels moved with them. When the living creatures rose from the earth, the wheels rose. ²⁰ Wherever their spirit wanted to go, the creatures went. The wheels rose with them, because the spirit of the living creatures was in the wheels. ²¹ So whenever the creatures moved, the wheels moved. Whenever the creatures stood still, the wheels stood still. And whenever the creatures rose from the earth, the wheels rose with them, because the spirit of the living creatures was in the wheels.

²² Something like a dome was spread over the heads of the living creatures. It looked like dazzling crystal. ²³ Under the dome, each creature had two wings that were stretched out straight, touching one another. Each creature had two wings that covered its body. ²⁴ When the creatures moved, I heard the sound of their wings. The sound was like the noise of rushing water, like the thunder of the Almighty, like the commotion in an army camp. When the creatures stood still, they lowered their wings.

²⁵ A voice came from above the dome over their heads as they stood still with their wings lowered. ²⁶ Above the dome over their heads was something that looked like a throne made of sapphire. On the throne was a figure that looked like a human. ²⁷ Then I saw what he looked like from the waist up. He looked like glowing bronze with fire all around it. From the waist down, he looked like fire. A bright light surrounded him. ²⁸ The brightness all around him looked like a rainbow in the clouds. It was like the LORD's glory. When I saw it, I immediately bowed down, and I heard someone speaking.

Ezekiel's Vision of a Scroll

2 ¹ He said to me, "Son of man, stand up, and I will speak to you." ² As he spoke to me, the Spirit entered me, stood me on my feet, and I heard him speaking to me.

³ He said to me, "Son of man, I am sending you to the people of Israel. They are people from a nation that has rebelled against me. They and their ancestors have rebelled against me to this day. ⁴ I am sending you to these defiant and stubborn children. Tell them, 'This is what the Almighty LORD says.' ⁵ Whether these rebellious people listen or not, they will realize that a

prophet has been among them. ⁶ Son of man, don't be afraid of them or the things they say. Don't be afraid, even though thorns and thistles are around you and you live among scorpions. Don't let the things they say frighten you. Don't be terrified in their presence, even though they are rebellious people. ⁷ Speak my words to them whether they listen or not, because they are rebellious. ⁸ But you, son of man, listen to what I say. Don't be rebellious like those rebellious people. Open your mouth, and eat what I am giving to you."

⁹ As I looked, I saw a hand stretched out toward me. In it was a scroll. ¹⁰ He spread the scroll in front of me. There was writing on the front and back. There were funeral songs, songs of mourning, and horrible things written on it.

3 ¹ The LORD said to me, "Son of man, eat what you find. Eat this scroll. Then speak to the people of Israel." ² So I opened my mouth, and he gave me the scroll to eat.

³ He said to me, "Son of man, eat this scroll I'm giving you, and fill your stomach with it." So I ate it, and it tasted as sweet as honey in my mouth.

⁴ He said to me, "Son of man, go to the people of Israel, and speak my words to them. ⁵ I am not sending you to people whose language is hard to understand or difficult to speak. I am sending you to Israel. ⁶ I am not sending you to nations whose language is hard to understand, difficult to speak, or whose words you cannot understand. If I send you to those nations, they will certainly listen to you. ⁷ But the people of Israel will refuse to listen to you because they refuse to listen to me. All the people of Israel are very stubborn and hardheaded. ⁸ Yet, I will make you as stubborn and as hardheaded as they are. ⁹ I will make you as hard as a diamond, harder than stone. Don't be afraid of them. Don't be terrified in their presence, even though they are rebellious people."

¹⁰ He also said to me, "Son of man, take to heart everything I have spoken to you, and listen closely. ¹¹ Go to the exiles, to your people. Whether they listen or not, tell them, 'This is what the Almighty LORD says.'"

¹² Then the Spirit lifted me, and behind me I heard a loud thundering voice say, "Blessed is the LORD's glory, which left this place." ¹³ I also heard the noise of the wings of the living creatures touching one another and the noise of the wheels beside them as well as a loud rumbling. ¹⁴ Then the Spirit lifted me and took me away. I went away feeling bitter and angry. The strong power of the LORD came over me. ¹⁵ I went to Tel Abib, to the exiles who lived by the Chebar River. I sat there among them for seven days. I was stunned.

Ezekiel Is Appointed to Be a Watchman

¹⁶ After seven days the LORD spoke his word to me. He said, ¹⁷ "Son of man, I have made you a watchman over the people of Israel. Listen to what I say, and warn them for me. ¹⁸ Suppose I tell you that wicked people will surely die, but you don't warn them or speak out so that they can change their wicked ways in order to save their lives. Then these wicked people will die because of their sin, but I will hold you responsible for their deaths. ¹⁹ But suppose you warn the wicked people, and they don't turn from their wicked ways. Then they will die because of their sin, but you will save yourself. ²⁰ If righteous people turn from living the right way and do wrong, I will make them stumble, and they will die. If you don't warn them, they will die because of their sin, and the right things they did will not be remembered. I will hold you responsible for their deaths. ²¹ But if you warn righteous people not to sin, and they don't sin, they will certainly live because they listened to the warning. You will save yourself."

The LORD Gives Ezekiel Directions to Follow

²² The power of the LORD came over me. He said, "Get up, and go to the plain. I will speak to you there." ²³ I got up and went to the plain. The LORD's glory was standing there like the glory I saw by the Chebar River, and I immediately bowed down.

²⁴ Then the Spirit entered me and stood me on my feet. He talked to me. He said, "Go into your home, and shut yourself inside. ²⁵ People will tie you up with ropes, son of man, so that you can't go outside. ²⁶ I will make your tongue stick to the roof of your mouth so that you can't talk or criticize them, even though they are rebellious people. ²⁷ But when I speak to you, I will open your mouth. You will tell them, 'This is what the Almighty LORD says.' Some will listen, and some will refuse to listen. They are rebellious people."

Ezekiel Plays Out the Blockade of Jerusalem

4 ¹ The LORD said, "Son of man, take clay, put it in front of you, and draw a map of Jerusalem on it. ² Set up a blockade against it, build attack walls around it, put up dirt ramps around it, have troops ready to attack it, and place battering rams all around it. ³ Then take an iron pan, and set it up as a wall between you and the city. Turn your face toward the city as if you were going to attack it, and then attack it. This is a sign for the people of Israel.

⁴ "Then lie on your left side and take the punishment of the nation of Israel yourself. You will bear its punishment as many days as you lie on that side. ⁵ I have assigned to you one day

for each year its punishment will last. So for 390 days, you will bear the punishment for the sins of the nation of Israel. ⁶ When you finish this, you will lie down again, this time on your right side. You will bear the punishment for the sins of the nation of Judah for 40 days, one day for each year I have assigned to you. ⁷ Turn your face toward the blockaded Jerusalem. Shake your fist and prophesy against it. ⁸ I will tie you up with ropes so that you will not be able to turn from one side to the other until you have finished attacking ˌJerusalemˌ.

⁹ "Then take wheat, barley, beans, lentils, millet, and winter wheat. Put them in a container, and use them to make bread for yourself. Eat it during the 390 days that you are lying on your side. ¹⁰ The food that you eat should be weighed. Eat eight ounces of food every day at set times. ¹¹ Measure out two-thirds of a quart of water, and drink it at set times. ¹² Eat the bread as you would eat barley loaves. Bake the bread in front of people, using human excrement for fuel."

¹³ Then the LORD said, "In the same way, the people of Israel will eat unclean* bread among the nations where I scatter them."

¹⁴ I answered, "Almighty LORD, I have never dishonored myself. From the time I was young until now, I have never eaten an animal that died by itself or was killed by other wild animals. No unclean meat has ever entered my mouth."

¹⁵ He said to me, "I will let you use cow manure in place of human excrement. Bake your bread over it."

¹⁶ He also said to me, "Son of man, I am going to cut off the bread supply in Jerusalem. People will anxiously eat rationed bread and fearfully drink rationed water. ¹⁷ They will be shocked at the sight of each other because of the lack of food and water. They will waste away because of their sin."

The LORD Tells Ezekiel About the Fall of Jerusalem

5 ¹ ˌThe LORD said,ˌ "Son of man, take a sharp blade, and use it as a barber's razor to shave your head and beard. Take scales to weigh your hair and divide it ˌinto three even partsˌ. ² When the blockade is over, burn one-third of your hair in a fire in the middle of the city. Take another third, and cut it up with a blade around the city. Then scatter the remaining third to the wind, and I will draw a sword and go after it. ³ Take a few strands of hair, and wrap them in the hem of your clothes. ⁴ Later, take some of them, and throw them in a fire and burn them up. From there a fire will spread throughout the whole nation of Israel.

⁵ "This is what the Almighty LORD says: This is Jerusalem! I have placed it in the center of the nations with countries all around it. ⁶ The people of Jerusalem have rebelled against my rules and my laws more than the surrounding nations. They have rejected my rules, and they don't live by my laws.

⁷ "So this is what the Almighty LORD says: ˌPeople of Jerusalem,ˌ you have caused more trouble than the nations around you. You haven't lived by my laws or obeyed my rules. You haven't even lived up to the standards of the nations around you.

⁸ "So this is what the Almighty LORD says: I, too, am against you, and I will punish you in front of the nations. ⁹ Because of all the detestable things that you do, I will do things to you that I have never done before and will never do again. ¹⁰ That is why parents will eat their children, and children will eat their parents. I will punish you and scatter whoever is left to the wind.

¹¹ "As I live, declares the Almighty LORD, because you have dishonored my holy worship place with all your disgusting and detestable things, I will have you killed. I will not have compassion for you or feel sorry for you. ¹² One-third of you will die in plagues and be devoured in famines. Another third will die in battles against those around you. I will scatter the remaining third to the wind, and I will pursue them with a sword.

¹³ "I will unleash my anger. I will use my fury against you, and I will get revenge. When my fury is unleashed against you, you will know that I, the LORD, spoke to you while I was angry. ¹⁴ I will turn you into a wasteland and an object of ridicule among the nations around you and in the presence of everyone who passes by. ¹⁵ The nations that are around you will ridicule you and laugh at you. When I punish you because of my anger, fury, and fierce revenge, you will become something ridiculed and something horrible. I, the LORD, have spoken. ¹⁶ When I shoot my destructive arrows of famine at you, I will shoot to kill you. I will bring more and more famines into your land, and I will cut off your food supply. ¹⁷ I will send famines and wild animals against you, and they will rob you of your children. I will send plagues, violence, and wars to kill you. I, the LORD, have spoken."

A Prophecy Against the Mountains of Israel

6 ¹ The LORD spoke his word to me. He said, ² "Son of man, look toward the mountains of Israel, and prophesy against them. ³ Say this, 'You mountains of Israel, listen to the word

---

* 4:13 "Unclean" refers to anything that Moses' Teachings say is not presentable to God.

of the Almighty LORD! This is what the Almighty LORD says to the mountains and hills and to the ravines and valleys: I am going to attack you with a sword and destroy your worship sites. **4** Your altars will be destroyed, and your incense burners will be smashed. I will kill people in front of your idols. **5** I will lay the dead bodies of the people of Israel in front of your idols, and I will scatter their bones around your altars. **6** Wherever people live, the cities will be ruined, and the worship sites will be wrecked. Your altars will be ruined and demolished. Your idols will be smashed and completely destroyed. Your incense burners will be cut down, and everything you have done will be wiped out. **7** People will be killed, and they will fall among you. Then you will know that I am the LORD.

8 " 'But I will let some people live. Some people will escape the battle among the nations and be scattered throughout the countries. **9** Then those who escape will remember me among the nations where they are taken captive. I was hurt by their adulterous hearts, which turned away from me, and by their eyes, which lusted after idols. They will hate themselves for the evil and disgusting things that they have done. **10** Then you will know that I am the LORD and that the disaster I promised was not an empty threat.

11 " 'This is what the Almighty LORD says: Clap your hands, stomp your feet, and say, "Oh no!" because the people of Israel have done evil and disgusting things. So they will die in wars, famines, and plagues. **12** Plagues will kill those who are far away. Those who are near will die in wars, and anyone who is left and has escaped will die in famines. This is how I will unleash my anger. **13** Then you will know that I am the LORD.

" 'Those who are killed will lie beside the idols around their altars. They will lie on every high hill, on all the mountaintops, and under every large tree and every leafy oak. These are the places where they made offerings to their disgusting idols. **14** I will use my power against them and destroy the land, from the desert to Diblah. Then they will know that I am the LORD.' "

The LORD's Judgment on Israel

7 **1** The LORD spoke his word to me. He said, **2** "Son of man, this is what the Almighty LORD says to ˏthe people inˏ the land of Israel: The end is coming! The end is coming to the four corners of the earth. **3** Now the end is coming for you. I will send my anger against you. I will judge you for the way you have lived, and I will punish you for all the detestable things that you have done. **4** I will not have compassion for you or feel sorry for you. I will pay you back for the way you have lived and for the detestable things you have done. Then you will know that I am the LORD.

5 "This is what the Almighty LORD says: One disaster after another is coming. **6** The end is coming. The end ˈis coming. It is stirring itself up against you. It is coming! **7** Destruction is coming to you, inhabitants of the land. The time is coming. The day is near. There will be confusion. There will be no joy in the mountains. **8** Soon I will pour out my fury on you and unleash my anger on you. I will judge you for the way you have lived, and I will punish you for all the detestable things that you have done. **9** I will not have compassion or feel sorry. I will pay you back for the way you have lived and for the detestable things that you are still doing. Then you will know that I am the LORD and that I am the one attacking ˏyouˏ.

10 "The day is near! It is coming! Destruction is coming! Wrongdoing has blossomed. Arrogance has flourished. **11** Violence has grown into a weapon for punishing wickedness. None of the people will be left. None of that crowd, none of their wealth, and nothing of value will be left. **12** The time is coming. The day is near. Buyers will not rejoice, and sellers will not mourn, because ˏmyˏ fury will be against the whole crowd. **13** Sellers will not live long enough to buy back what they have sold. The visions against that crowd will not change. Because of their sins, none of the people will live. **14** They have blown a ram's horn, and everything is ready. But no one will go into battle, because my fury is against their whole crowd.

15 "Outside are swords, and inside are plagues and famines. Whoever is in a field will die in battle. Whoever is in the city will be devoured by famines and plagues. **16** Those who survive will escape to the mountains. They will moan like doves in the valleys. They will moan because of their sins. **17** Every hand will hang limp, and every knee will be as weak as water. **18** They will put on sackcloth, and horror will cover them. All their faces will be covered with shame, and every head will be shaved. **19** They will throw their silver and gold into the streets like garbage. Their silver and gold won't be able to rescue them on the day of the LORD's anger. It will no longer satisfy their hunger or fill their stomachs. Their silver and gold caused them to fall into sin. **20** They were proud of their beautiful jewels and used them to make disgusting and detestable statues ˏof false godsˏ. That is why I will make their jewels disgusting. **21** I will hand their jewels over to foreigners as loot and to the most evil people on earth as prizes. These foreigners will dishonor the people of Israel. **22** I will turn my face away from the people of Israel, and foreigners will dishonor my treasured place. Robbers will go in and dishonor it.

²³ "Get the chains ready! The land is filled with murder, and the city is filled with violence. ²⁴ So I will send the most evil nation, and it will take possession of people's houses. I will stop those who are strong from feeling proud, and their holy places will be dishonored. ²⁵ Anguish is coming. People will look for peace, but there will be none. ²⁶ One disaster will happen after another. One rumor will follow another. People will ask for a vision from a prophet. The teachings of priests and the advice of leaders will disappear. ²⁷ Kings will mourn, and princes will give up hope. The common people will lose their courage. I will give them what they deserve and judge them as they have judged others. Then they will know that I am the LORD."

Idolatry in Jerusalem

8 ¹ On the fifth day of the sixth month in the sixth year, I was sitting in my home. Judah's leaders were sitting in front of me. The power of the Almighty LORD came over me. ² As I looked, I saw something that looked like a human. From the waist down its body looked like fire, and from the waist up its body looked like glowing metal. ³ It stretched out what looked like a hand and grabbed me by the hair on my head. In these visions from God, the Spirit carried me between heaven and earth. He took me to Jerusalem, to the entrance to the north gate of the inner courtyard of the temple. That was where an idol that stirs up ˏGod'sˎ anger was located. ⁴ There I saw the glory of Israel's God as I did in the vision that I saw in the valley.

⁵ God said to me, "Son of man, look toward the north." So I looked toward the north, and there in the entrance to the north gate beside the altar, I saw the idol that stirs up ˏGod'sˎ anger.

⁶ He asked me, "Son of man, do you see what the people of Israel are doing? The people of Israel are doing very disgusting things here, things that will force me to go far away from my holy place. But you will see even more disgusting things."

⁷ Then he took me to the entrance of the courtyard. As I looked, I saw a hole in the wall. ⁸ He said to me, "Son of man, dig through the wall." So I dug through the wall, and I saw a door. ⁹ He said to me, "Go in, and see the wicked, disgusting things that the people of Israel are doing here." ¹⁰ So I went in and looked. I saw that the walls were covered with drawings of every kind of crawling creature, every kind of disgusting animal, and all the idols in the nation of Israel. ¹¹ In front of these drawings stood 70 of Israel's leaders. Jaazaniah, son of Shaphan, was standing with the leaders. Each of them was holding an incense burner in his hand, and a cloud of incense went up.

¹² God asked me, "Son of man, do you see what the leaders of the nation of Israel are doing in secret? Each of them is in the room where his god is, and each one of them is thinking, 'The LORD doesn't see me. The LORD has abandoned this land.' ".

¹³ Then he said to me, "You will see even more disgusting things that they are doing."

¹⁴ He brought me to the entrance of the north gate of the LORD's temple. Women were sitting there and crying for the god Tammuz. ¹⁵ He asked me, "Son of man, do you see this? You will see even more disgusting things than these."

¹⁶ Then he brought me into the inner courtyard of the LORD's temple. There at the entrance to the LORD's temple, between the entrance and the altar, were about 25 men who had their backs turned to the LORD's temple. They were facing east and worshiping the rising sun. ¹⁷ He asked me, "Son of man, do you see this? Isn't it bad enough that the people of Judah have done these disgusting things that you have seen here? Yet, they also fill the land with violence and continue to provoke me even more. Look how they insult me in the worst possible way.ᵃ ¹⁸ So I will take action because I'm angry, and I won't have compassion for them or feel sorry for them. Even if they shout in my ears, I won't listen to them."

The LORD Orders the Destruction of the Temple in Jerusalem

9 ¹ Then I heard the LORD call out with a loud voice. He said, "Come here, those who are going to punish this city. Each of you should bring your weapon with you." ² So six men came from the upper north gate. Each one brought a deadly weapon with him. Among them was a person dressed in linen who was carrying paper and pen. The men came in and stood by the bronze altar. ³ Then the glory of the God of Israel went up from the angels,ᵃ where it had been, to the temple's entrance. The LORD called to the person dressed in linen who was carrying paper and pen.

⁴ The LORD said to that person, "Go throughout the city of Jerusalem, and put a mark on the foreheads of those who sigh and groan about all the disgusting things that are being done in the city."

⁵ Then he said to the others as I was listening, "Follow him throughout the city and kill. Don't have any compassion, and don't feel sorry. ⁶ Kill old men, young men, old women, young

---

ᵃ 8:17 Hebrew meaning uncertain.　ᵃ 9:3 Or "cherubim."

women, and children. But don't come near anyone who has a mark on him. Start with my holy place." So they started with the old men in front of the temple.

[7] He said to them, "Dishonor the temple! Fill its courtyards with dead people, and then leave." So they went out and killed the people in the city.

[8] As they were killing people, I was left alone. So I immediately bowed down. I cried, "Almighty LORD, will you destroy everyone who is left in Israel while you pour out your anger on Jerusalem?"

[9] He answered me, "The wickedness of the nations of Israel and Judah is terrible. The land is filled with murder, and the city is filled with wrongdoing. They think that the LORD has abandoned the land and that he doesn't see. [10] But I will not have compassion or feel sorry. I will do to them what they have done to others."

[11] Then the person dressed in linen who was carrying paper and pen reported, "I did everything you commanded."

The Glory of the LORD Leaves His Temple

10 [1] As I looked at the dome over the heads of the angels,[a] I saw something that looked like a throne made of sapphire. [2] The LORD said to the person dressed in linen, "Go between the wheels under the angels, and fill your hands with burning coals. Then scatter them over the city." So he went between the wheels as I watched.

[3] The angels were standing on the south side of the temple as the person went. A cloud filled the inner courtyard. [4] The LORD's glory rose from the angels to the entrance of the temple, the cloud filled the temple, and the brightness of the LORD's glory filled the courtyard. [5] The sound of the angels' wings was heard as far as the outer courtyard. It was like the sound of the Almighty God when he speaks.

[6] After the LORD had commanded the person dressed in linen to take burning coals from between the wheels beside the angels, the person went in and stood beside one of the wheels. [7] One of the angels reached into the fire that was between the angels and took out some coals. This angel put them in the hands of the person dressed in linen. The person took them and left.

[8] The angels appeared to have what looked like human hands under their wings. [9] As I looked, I saw four wheels beside the angels, one wheel beside each of the angels. The wheels looked like beryl. [10] All four wheels looked the same. Each was like a wheel within a wheel. [11] Whenever the angels moved, they moved in any of the four directions without turning as they moved. They always moved in the direction they faced without turning as they moved. [12] Their entire bodies, their backs, hands, wings, and wheels were covered with eyes. Each of the angels had a wheel. [13] I heard that the wheels were called the whirling wheels. [14] Each of the angels had four faces. The first was the face of an angel, the second was the face of a human, the third was the face of a lion, and the fourth was the face of an eagle.

[15] The angels rose. These were the living creatures that I saw at the Chebar River. [16] When the angels moved, the wheels moved beside them. When the angels lifted their wings to rise from the ground, the wheels didn't leave their side. [17] When the angels stood still, the wheels stood still. When the angels rose, the wheels rose with them. The spirit of the living creatures was in the wheels. [18] Then the glory of the LORD left the temple's entrance and stood over the angels. [19] The angels lifted their wings and rose from the ground. I was watching them as they left with the wheels beside them. The angels stood at the door to the east gate of the LORD's temple, and the glory of the God of Israel was above them.

[20] These are the living creatures that I saw under the God of Israel at the Chebar River. I realized that they were angels. [21] Each had four faces and four wings, and under their wings were what looked like human hands. [22] Their faces looked exactly like the faces that I saw by the Chebar River. Each one went straight ahead.

Judgment on the Rulers of Israel

11 [1] Then the Spirit lifted me and took me to the east gate of the LORD's temple. (It's the gate that faces east.) Twenty-five men were at the entrance of the gate. I saw among them Azzur's son Jaazaniah and Benaiah's son Pelatiah. They were leaders of the people.

[2] Then the LORD said to me, "Son of man, these are the men who plan evil and give bad advice in this city. [3] They say, 'It's almost time to rebuild homes. This city is a cooking pot, and we're the meat.' [4] So prophesy against them. Prophesy, son of man."

[5] The LORD's Spirit came to me and told me to say, "This is what the LORD says: You are saying these things, nation of Israel. But I know what's going through your mind. [6] You have killed many people in this city and have filled its streets with corpses.

---

[a] 10:1 Or "cherubim."

[7] "So this is what the Almighty LORD says: The corpses that you put in the middle of the city are the meat, and the city is the cooking pot. I will force you out of the city. [8] You are afraid of swords, so I will bring swords to attack you, declares the Almighty LORD. [9] I will force you out of the city. I will hand you over to foreigners, and I will punish you. [10] You will die in battle. I will judge you at Israel's borders. Then you will know that I am the LORD. [11] The city will not be your cooking pot, and you will not be the meat in it. I will judge you at Israel's borders. [12] Then you will know that I am the LORD. You haven't lived by my laws, and you haven't obeyed my rules. You have followed the standards set by the nations around you."

[13] While I was prophesying, Benaiah's son Pelatiah died.

I immediately bowed down and cried out, "Almighty LORD, will you completely destroy all the remaining people in Israel?"

The Lord's Promise to Gather Israel From the Nations

[14] Then the LORD spoke his word to me. He said, [15] "Son of man, the people who live in Jerusalem are talking about your own relatives and about the entire nation of Israel. The people who live in Jerusalem say, 'They are far away from the LORD. This land has been given to us as our own property.'

[16] "So tell them, 'This is what the Almighty LORD says: Although I sent them far away among the nations and scattered them among the countries, I have been their sanctuary for a little while among the countries where they've gone.'

[17] "So tell them, 'This is what the Almighty LORD says: I will bring them together from the nations and gather them from the countries where I've scattered them. I will give them the land of Israel. [18] They will come and remove all the disgusting and detestable things that are there. [19] I will give them a single purpose and put a new spirit in them. I will remove their stubborn hearts and give them obedient hearts. [20] Then they will live by my laws and obey my rules. They will be my people, and I will be their God. [21] But as for those whose minds are set on following detestable and disgusting idols, I will pay them back for what they have done, declares the Almighty LORD.'"

The Glory of the Lord Leaves Jerusalem

[22] Then the angels[a] raised their wings, with the wheels beside them. The glory of the God of Israel was above them. [23] The LORD's glory left the middle of the city and stopped above the mountain east of the city.

[24] In this vision from God's Spirit, the Spirit lifted me and brought me to the exiles in Babylonia. Then the vision I saw left me.

[25] I told the exiles everything the LORD had shown me.

Ezekiel Plays Out Israel's Exile

12 [1] The LORD spoke his word to me. He said, [2] "Son of man, you are living among rebellious people. They have eyes, but they can't see. They have ears, but they can't hear because they are rebellious people.

[3] "Son of man, pack your bags as if you were going into exile. Let the people see you leave in the daylight. March like a captive from your place to another place as they watch. Maybe they will understand, even though they are rebellious people. [4] Let them see you in the daylight. Bring out your bags as if you were going into exile. In the evening let them see you leave like a captive going into exile. [5] Dig a hole through the wall of your house, and leave through it. [6] Let them see you put your bags on your shoulders and carry them out in the dark. Cover your face so that you won't see the land. I've made you a sign to warn the nation of Israel."

[7] I did what I was ordered to do. During the day I brought out bags as if I were going into exile. In the evening I dug a hole through the wall. I brought out my bags in the dark. I let the people see me as I carried my bags on my shoulders.

[8] The next morning the LORD spoke his word to me. He said, [9] "Son of man, didn't the rebellious nation of Israel ask you what you were doing?

[10] "Tell them, 'This is what the Almighty LORD says: This is the divine revelation about the prince from Jerusalem and about all the people of Israel who live there.'

[11] "Tell them, 'I am your warning sign. What I have done will happen to you. You will go into exile and into captivity. [12] The prince who is among you will put his bags on his shoulders in the dark and leave. People will dig holes in the wall to go through. The prince will cover his face so that he cannot see the land. [13] I will spread my net over him, and he will be caught in my net. I will bring him to Babylon, the land of the Babylonians, but he will not see it. And that's where he'll die. [14] I will scatter in every direction all those who are around him—his staff

---

[a] 11:22 Or "cherubim."

and all his troops. I will pursue them with my sword. [15] Then they will know that I am the LORD, because I will scatter them among the nations and force them into other countries. [16] However, I will spare a few of them from wars, famines, and plagues. Wherever they go among the nations, they will realize that everything they did was disgusting. Then they will know that I am the LORD.' "

[17] The LORD spoke his word to me. He said, [18] "Son of man, shake as you eat your food. Tremble and be worried as you drink your water.

[19] "Tell the people of this land, 'This is what the Almighty LORD says about the people who live in Jerusalem and in the land of Israel: They will be worried as they eat their food and terrified as they drink their water. Their country will be stripped of everything because everyone who lives there is violent. [20] The cities where people live will be destroyed, and the country will become a wasteland. Then they will know that I am the LORD.' "

[21] The LORD spoke his word to me. He said, [22] "Son of man, what is this proverb you have in Israel: 'Days go by, and every vision comes to nothing'?

[23] "Tell the people, 'This is what the Almighty LORD says: I will put a stop to the use of this proverb. You will no longer quote it in Israel.' Instead, tell them, 'The time is near when every vision will come true. [24] There will no longer be any false visions or flattering fortunetelling to the people. [25] I, the LORD, will speak. Everything that I say will happen without any more delay. I will say something, and it will happen during your lifetime, you rebellious people, declares the Almighty LORD.' "

[26] The LORD spoke his word to me. He said, [27] "Son of man, the people of Israel are saying, 'The vision that Ezekiel sees won't happen for a long time. What he prophecies will happen in the distant future.'

[28] "Tell them, 'This is what the Almighty LORD says: Everything that I say will no longer be delayed. Whatever I say will happen, declares the Almighty LORD.' "

False Prophets Condemned

13 [1] The LORD spoke his word to me. He said, [2] "Son of man, prophesy against the prophets of Israel. Tell those who make up their prophecies, 'Listen to the word of the LORD.

[3] " 'This is what the Almighty LORD says: How horrible it will be for the foolish prophets. They follow their own ideas, and they have seen nothing. [4] Israel, your prophets are like foxes among the ruins ˌof a cityˌ. [5] They haven't repaired the gaps in the wall or rebuilt the wall for the nation of Israel. So Israel will not be protected in battle on the day of the LORD. [6] These foolish prophets see false visions, and their predictions don't come true. They say, "The LORD said this." But the LORD hasn't sent them. Then they hope that their message will come true. [7] Prophets of Israel, haven't you seen false visions and predicted things that don't come true? Don't you say, "The LORD said this," even though I haven't said anything?

[8] " 'This is what the Almighty LORD says: Your predictions are false, and your visions are lies. That is why I'm against you, declares the Almighty LORD. [9] I will use my power against the prophets who see false visions and predict things that don't come true. They will not help my people make decisions or be recorded in the records of the nation of Israel. They won't even enter Israel. Then you will know that I am the LORD.

[10] " 'They have deceived my people by saying that everything is alright, but it's not alright. When someone builds a flimsy wall, the prophets cover it up with paint. [11] Tell those who cover up the wall with paint that their wall will fall down. Rain will pour down, hailstones will fall on it, and stormy winds will break it to pieces. [12] When the wall falls down, people will ask them, "Where's the paint that you used to cover the wall?"

[13] " 'This is what the Almighty LORD says: In my fury I'll cause a storm to break out. In my anger rain will pour down, and hailstones will destroy the wall. [14] I will tear down the wall that the prophets covered up with paint. I will level it and expose its foundation. When the wall falls, they will be destroyed by it. Then you will know that I am the LORD. [15] I will unleash my fury on the wall and on those who covered it up with paint.

" 'Then I will say to you, "The wall is gone, and so are those who painted it. [16] The prophets of Israel who prophesied to Jerusalem are gone. Those who said that everything was alright, when it wasn't alright, are gone, declares the Almighty LORD.' "

[17] "Son of man, look at the women among your people who make up prophecies, and prophesy against them.

[18] "Tell them, 'This is what the Almighty LORD says: How horrible it will be for women who sew magic charms for people's wrists and make magic veils of every size for people's heads. You want to trap people. You want to control the lives of my people for your own profit. [19] You dishonor me in front of my people for a few handfuls of barley and a few pieces of bread. You kill people who shouldn't die, and you spare the lives of people who shouldn't live. You lie to my people who are willing to listen.

²⁰ " 'This is what the Almighty LORD says: I'm against the magic charms that you use to trap people like birds. I will tear them from your arms and free the people that you have trapped. ²¹ I will tear off your magic veils and rescue my people from your power so that they will no longer be under your control. Then you will know that I am the LORD. ²² You have discouraged righteous people with your lies, even though I hadn't brought them any grief. You encouraged wicked people not to turn from their wicked ways to save their lives. ²³ That is why you will no longer see false visions or make predictions. I will rescue my people from your power. Then you will know that I am the LORD.' "

Idolaters Condemned

14 ¹ Some of Israel's leaders came to me and sat down in front of me. ² Then the LORD spoke his word to me. He said, ³ "Son of man, these people are devoted to their idols, and they are allowing themselves to fall into sin. Should they be allowed to ask me for help?

⁴ "So speak to them. Tell them, 'This is what the LORD says: Suppose an Israelite is devoted to idols and allows himself to fall into sin. Suppose he goes to a prophet ˛to ask for my help˛. I, the LORD, will give that Israelite an answer, the answer that his many idols deserve. ⁵ I will do this to recapture the hearts of the nation of Israel. They have deserted me because of their disgusting idols.'

⁶ "So tell the nation of Israel, 'This is what the Almighty LORD says: Change the way you think and act! Turn away from your idols, and don't return to any of your disgusting things. ⁷ Suppose an Israelite or a foreigner who lives in Israel deserts me by devoting himself to idols and by allowing himself to fall into sin. If he goes to a prophet to ask for my help, I, the LORD, will give him an answer. ⁸ I will reject him, and I will make an example of him. I will exclude him from my people. Then you will know that I am the LORD.

⁹ " 'If a prophet is tricked into giving a prophecy, it is I, the LORD, who tricked the prophet. I will use my power against you and destroy you from among my people Israel. ¹⁰ Both of you will suffer for your sins. The prophet will be as guilty as you are when you ask for his help. ¹¹ Then the people of Israel will no longer wander away from me. They will no longer dishonor me with all their sins. Then they will be my people, and I will be their God, declares the Almighty LORD.' "

¹² The LORD spoke his word to me. He said, ¹³ "Son of man, suppose a country sins against me by being unfaithful to me. I will use my power against it, cut off its food supply, send a famine to it, and destroy its people and animals. ¹⁴ Even if these three men—Noah, Daniel, and Job—were in that country, they would, by their righteousness, rescue only themselves," declares the Almighty LORD.

¹⁵ "Suppose I send wild animals through that country and they make it childless and turn it into such a wasteland that no one travels through it because of the animals. ¹⁶ As I live, declares the Almighty LORD, not even Noah, Daniel, and Job could rescue their own sons or daughters. They could rescue only themselves. And the country would become a wasteland.

¹⁷ "Suppose I bring a war against that country by saying, 'I will let a war go throughout this country.' Suppose I destroy the people and the animals in it. ¹⁸ As I live, declares the Almighty LORD, not even Noah, Daniel, and Job could rescue their sons or daughters. They could rescue only themselves.

¹⁹ "Suppose I send a plague into that country or pour out my fury on it by killing people and destroying animals. ²⁰ As I live, declares the Almighty LORD, not even Noah, Daniel, and Job could, by their righteousness, rescue their sons or daughters. They could rescue only themselves.

²¹ "This is what the Almighty LORD says: I will surely send four terrible punishments against Jerusalem. I will send wars, famines, wild animals, and plagues. They will destroy people and animals. ²² But some people will survive. Some of your sons and daughters will be brought out. When they come out to you, you will see how they live. Then you will be comforted after the disasters that I will bring on Jerusalem, after every disaster that I will bring against it. ²³ You will be comforted when you see how they live. Then you will know that everything I have done was done for a reason," declares the Almighty LORD.

Jerusalem Is Compared to Wood From a Wild Vine

15 ¹ The LORD spoke his word to me. He said, ² "Son of man, what good is the wood from a vine? Is it better than the wood from a tree in the forest? ³ Do people use it to make something? Do they make a peg from it to hang things on? ⁴ No! It is only thrown into the fire as fuel. The fire burns up both its ends and chars its middle. Then can it be used to make anything? ⁵ When the vine was in perfect condition, it couldn't be made into anything. How can it be used to make anything after the fire has burned and charred it?

⁶ "So this is what the Almighty LORD says: As a vine is taken from among the trees in the forest to be used to feed the fire, so I will take the people who live in Jerusalem to punish them.

⁷ I will turn against the people of Jerusalem. Even though they have escaped one fire, another fire will burn them. Then they will know that I am the LORD, because I will turn against them. ⁸ I will turn the country into a wasteland because they have been unfaithful," declares the Almighty LORD.

A Description of Jerusalem's Sins

16 ¹ The LORD spoke his word to me. He said, ² "Son of man, make known to the people of Jerusalem the disgusting things they have done. ³ Tell them, 'This is what the Almighty LORD says to the people of Jerusalem: Your birthplace and your ancestors were in the land of the Canaanites. Your father was an Amorite, and your mother was a Hittite. ⁴ When you were born, your umbilical cord wasn't cut. You weren't washed with water to make you clean. You weren't rubbed with salt or wrapped in cloth. ⁵ No one who saw you felt sorry enough for you to do any of these things. But you were thrown into an open field. You were rejected when you were born.

⁶ " 'Then I went by you and saw you kicking around in your own blood. I said to you, "Live." ⁷ I made you grow like a plant in the field. You grew up, matured, and became a young woman. Your breasts developed, and your hair grew. Yet, you were naked and bare.

⁸ " 'I went by you again and looked at you. You were old enough to make love to. So I spread my robe over you, and covered your naked body. I promised to love you, and I exchanged marriage vows with you. You became mine, declares the Almighty LORD.

⁹ " 'Then I bathed you with water, and I washed off your blood. I poured olive oil over you. ¹⁰ I put an embroidered dress on you and fine leather sandals on your feet. I dressed you in fine linen and covered you with silk. ¹¹ I gave you jewelry. I put bracelets on your wrists and a necklace around your neck. ¹² I put a ring in your nose, earrings on your ears, and a beautiful crown on your head. ¹³ So you wore gold and silver jewelry. You were dressed in fine linen, silk, and embroidered clothes. Your food was flour, honey, and olive oil. You were very beautiful, and eventually you became a queen. ¹⁴ You became famous in every nation because of your beauty. Your beauty was perfect because I gave you my glory, declares the Almighty LORD.

¹⁵ " 'But you trusted your beauty, and you used your fame to become a prostitute. You had sex with everyone who walked by. ¹⁶ You took some of your clothes and made your worship sites colorful. This is where you acted like a prostitute. Such things shouldn't happen. They shouldn't occur. ¹⁷ You took your beautiful gold and silver jewelry that I had given you and made male idols for yourself. Then you committed adultery with them. ¹⁸ You took off your embroidered clothes and covered the idols with them. You offered my olive oil and incense in their presence. ¹⁹ You also offered them sweet and fragrant sacrifices. You gave flour, olive oil, and honey—all the food that I gave you to eat. This is what happened, declares the Almighty LORD.

²⁰ " 'You took your sons and daughters, who belonged to me, and you sacrificed them as food to idols. Wasn't your prostitution enough? ²¹ You slaughtered my children and presented them as burnt offerings to idols. ²² With all the disgusting things that you did and all your acts of prostitution, you didn't remember the time when you were young. You didn't remember when you were naked and bare, kicking around in your own blood.

²³ " 'How horrible! How horrible it will be for you! declares the Almighty LORD. After all your wickedness, ²⁴ you built yourself platforms and illegal worship sites in every city square. ²⁵ You also built worship sites at the head of every street. You used your beauty to seduce people there. You offered your body to everyone who passed by. You increased your acts of prostitution. ²⁶ You had sex with your lustful neighbors, the Egyptians. You used your prostitution to make me angry.

²⁷ " 'So I used my power against you. I took away some of your land, and I handed you over to your greedy enemies, the Philistines, who were ashamed of what you had done.

²⁸ " 'You had sex with the Assyrians because you weren't satisfied. You still weren't satisfied. ²⁹ So you increased your acts of prostitution to include the land of the merchants, the Babylonians. Even after that, you weren't satisfied.

³⁰ " 'You have no will power! declares the Almighty LORD. You do everything a shameless prostitute does. ³¹ You build your platforms at the head of every street and place your illegal worship sites in every square. Yet, you aren't like other prostitutes, because you don't want to be paid. ³² You are an adulterous wife who prefers strangers to her husband. ³³ All prostitutes get paid. But you give gifts to all your lovers and bribe them to come to you from all directions to have sex with you. ³⁴ You are a different kind of prostitute. No one goes after you for favors. You are the opposite. You pay them, and you don't accept payment.

Jerusalem's Punishment

³⁵ " 'Listen to the word of the LORD, you prostitute. ³⁶ This is what the Almighty LORD says: You exposed yourself and uncovered your naked body when you gave yourself to your lovers

and to all your disgusting idols. You also killed your children and sacrificed their blood to these idols. [37] That is why I will gather all your lovers with whom you found pleasure. I will have all those who love you and hate you gather around. I will uncover your body for them, and they will see you naked. [38] I will punish you the same way that those who are guilty of prostitution and murder are punished. I will give you the death penalty in my fury and burning anger. [39] I will hand you over to your lovers. They will destroy your platforms and tear down your illegal worship sites. They will tear off your clothes, take away your beautiful jewelry, and leave you naked and bare. [40] They will also bring a mob against you. They will stone you and cut you into pieces with their swords. [41] They will burn your houses and punish you in the presence of many women. I will put an end to your prostitution, and you will no longer pay others. [42] Then I will rest from my fury against you, and I will stop being angry. I will be at peace. I will no longer be angry.

[43] " 'You didn't remember the time when you were young, and you made me very angry with all these things. So I will pay you back for what you have done, declares the Almighty LORD. Didn't you make wicked plans in addition to all your disgusting practices?

[44] " 'Everyone who uses proverbs will speak the following saying against you: Like mother, like daughter. [45] You are your mother's daughter. She rejected her husband and her children. You are exactly like your sisters. They rejected their husbands and their children. Your mother was a Hittite, and your father was an Amorite.

[46] " 'Your older sister was Samaria. She and her daughters lived north of you. Your younger sister is Sodom. She lives south of you with her daughters. [47] You didn't follow their ways. You didn't do the same disgusting things that they did. It only took you a little time to be more corrupt than they ever were. [48] As I live, declares the Almighty LORD, your sister Sodom and her daughters never did what you and your daughters have done. [49] This is what your sister Sodom has done wrong. She and her daughters were proud that they had plenty of food and had peace and security. They didn't help the poor and the needy. [50] They were arrogant and did disgusting things in front of me. So I did away with them when I saw this.

[51] " 'Samaria didn't commit half the sins you did. You have done many more disgusting things than they ever did. Because of all the disgusting things that you have done, you make your sisters look innocent. [52] You will have to suffer disgrace because you accused your sisters. Yet, your sins are more disgusting than theirs. They look like they are innocent compared to you. Be ashamed of yourself and suffer disgrace, because you have made your sisters look like they are innocent.

[53] " 'I will restore the fortunes of Sodom and her daughters, and Samaria and her daughters. I will also restore your fortune along with theirs. [54] You will have to suffer disgrace and be ashamed of everything you have done, including comforting them. [55] When Sodom and her daughters and Samaria and her daughters return to what they once were, you and your daughters will return to what you once were. [56] You didn't mention your sister Sodom when you were arrogant. [57] You didn't mention her before your wickedness was revealed. Now the daughters of Aram[a] and their neighbors despise you. The daughters of the Philistines also despise you. Those around you hate you. [58] You must suffer because of all the crude and disgusting things you have done, declares the LORD.

[59] " 'This is what the Almighty LORD says: I will give you what you deserve. You despised your marriage vows and rejected my promise.[b] [60] I will remember the promise that I made with you when you were young, and I will make it a promise that will last forever. [61] Then you will remember what you have done. You will be ashamed when I return your older and younger sisters to you. I will give them to you as daughters, but not because of my promise with you. [62] Then I will make my promise with you, and you will know that I am the LORD. [63] You will remember and be ashamed. You will never again open your mouth because of your disgrace when I forgive you for everything you did, declares the Almighty LORD.' "

Judah Is Compared to a Tree

17 [1] The LORD spoke his word to me. He said, [2] "Son of man, tell this riddle. Give this illustration to the nation of Israel. [3] Say, 'This is what the Almighty LORD says: A large eagle came to Lebanon. It had large wings with long, colorful feathers. It took hold of the top of a cedar tree. [4] It broke off the highest twig and carried it to a country of merchants. It planted the twig in a city of merchants.

[5] " 'Then it took a seedling from that country and planted the seedling in fertile soil. The eagle planted the seedling like a willow where there was plenty of water. [6] The plant sprouted and grew into a low vine that spread over the ground. Its branches turned upward toward the eagle, but its roots grew downward. So it became a vine, producing branches and growing shoots.

---

[a] 16:57 Some Hebrew manuscripts; other Hebrew manuscripts, Syriac "Edom."   [b] 16:59 Or "covenant."

⁷ " 'There was another large eagle with large wings and many feathers. Now, the vine stretched its roots toward this eagle and sent its branches toward the eagle so that the eagle could water it. The vine turned away from the garden where it was planted. ⁸ It was planted in good soil beside plenty of water so that it could grow branches, bear fruit, and become a wonderful vine.'

⁹ "Tell the nation of Israel, 'This is what the Almighty LORD says: Will this vine live and grow? Won't the first eagle uproot it and tear off its fruit? Then it will wither. All the leaves on its branches will wither. It won't take much strength or many people to pull the vine up by its roots. ¹⁰ It might be planted again, but will it live and grow? It will wither completely when the east wind blows on it. It will certainly wither in the garden where it is growing.' "

¹¹ The LORD spoke his word to me. He said, ¹² "Ask these rebellious people, 'Don't you know what this means?' Tell them, 'The king of Babylon came to Jerusalem and captured its king and its leaders. He brought them home with him to Babylon. ¹³ Then he took someone from the royal family, made a treaty with him, and made him promise to be loyal. He took away the leading citizens from Judah ¹⁴ so that it would remain a humiliated country and be unable to regain its power. The country could only survive by keeping the treaty. ¹⁵ But the king of Judah rebelled against the king of Babylon by sending his messengers to Egypt to get horses and many soldiers. Will the king of Judah succeed? Will anyone who does such things escape? He can't break a treaty and go unpunished.

¹⁶ " 'As I live, declares the Almighty LORD, the king of Judah will die in Babylonia. He will die in the country of the king who appointed him king of Judah. The king of Judah broke his promise and his treaty with the king of Babylon. ¹⁷ Even with a large army and many people, Pharaoh will not be able to help him in battle when the Babylonians put up dirt ramps and set up blockades to kill many people. ¹⁸ The king of Judah broke the promise and the treaty that he pledged to keep. He did all these things, and he can't go unpunished.

¹⁹ " 'So this is what the Almighty LORD says: As I live, I will certainly punish you for rejecting my promise and hating my treaty. ²⁰ I will spread my net over you to catch you in my trap. I will take you to Babylon and judge you there for rebelling against me. ²¹ The best of your troops will die in battle. Anyone who remains will be scattered in every direction that the wind blows. Then you will know that I, the LORD, have spoken.

²² " 'This is what the Almighty LORD says: I, too, will take hold of the top of a cedar tree. I will break off the highest twig and plant it on a high and lofty mountain. ²³ I will plant it on a high mountain in Israel. It will grow branches and produce fruit. It will become a magnificent cedar tree. Every kind of bird will nest in it and find a home in the shelter of its branches. ²⁴ Then all the trees in the field will know that I am the LORD. I cut down tall trees, and I make small trees grow tall. I dry up green trees, and I make dry trees grow. I, the LORD, have spoken, and I will do it.' "

Everyone Will Suffer for His Own Sins

18 ¹ The LORD spoke his word to me. He said, ² "What do you mean when you use this proverb about the land of Israel: 'Fathers have eaten sour grapes, and their children's teeth are set on edge'? ³ As I live, declares the Almighty LORD, you will no longer use this proverb in Israel. ⁴ The life of every person belongs to me. Fathers and their children belong to me. The person who sins will die.

⁵ "Suppose a righteous person does what is fair and right. ⁶ He doesn't eat at the illegal mountain worship sites or look for help from the idols of the nation of Israel. He doesn't dishonor his neighbor's wife or have sexual intercourse with a woman while she is having her period. ⁷ He doesn't oppress anyone. He returns what a borrower gives him as security for a loan. He doesn't rob anyone. He gives food to people who are hungry, and he gives clothes to those who are naked. ⁸ He doesn't lend money for interest or make an excessive profit. He refuses to do evil things, and he judges everyone fairly. ⁹ He lives by my rules and obeys my laws faithfully. This person is righteous. He will certainly live," declares the Almighty LORD.

¹⁰ "But suppose this person has a son who robs and murders. The son does all the things ¹¹ that his father never did. He eats at the illegal mountain worship sites. He dishonors his neighbor's wife. ¹² He oppresses the poor and needy. He robs. He doesn't return the security for a loan. He looks to idols for help. He does disgusting things. ¹³ He lends money for interest and makes excessive profits. Will this person live? He will not live. He has done all these disgusting things. So he must die, and he will be responsible for his own death.

¹⁴ "But suppose this person has a son. The son sees all the sins that his father does. He is afraid, so he doesn't do such things.ᵃ ¹⁵ He doesn't eat at the illegal mountain worship sites or

---

ᵃ 18:14 Many Hebrew manuscripts, Greek, Latin; other Hebrew manuscripts "Although he sees them, he doesn't do such things."

look for help from the idols of the nation of Israel. He doesn't dishonor his neighbor's wife. ¹⁶ He doesn't oppress anyone. He doesn't keep the security for a loan. He doesn't rob anyone. He gives food to people who are hungry, and he gives clothes to those who are naked. ¹⁷ He refuses to hurt the poor. He doesn't charge interest or make excessive profits. He obeys my rules and lives by my laws. He won't die for his father's sins. He will certainly live. ¹⁸ But his father has oppressed others, robbed his relative, and done what is wrong among his people. So the father will die because of his sin.

¹⁹ "But you ask, 'Why isn't the son punished for his father's sin?' It is because the son has done what is fair and right. He obeyed my rules and followed them. He will certainly live. ²⁰ The person who sins will die. A son will not be punished for his father's sins, and a father will not be punished for his son's sins. The righteousness of the righteous person will be his own, and the wickedness of the wicked person will be his own.

²¹ "But suppose a wicked person turns away from all the sins that he has done. He obeys all my laws and does what is fair and right. He will certainly live. He will not die. ²² All the rebellious things that he did will not be remembered. He will live because of the right things that he did. ²³ I don't want wicked people to die." declares the Almighty LORD. "I want them to turn from their evil ways and live.

²⁴ "But suppose a righteous person turns away from doing right and he does evil things. He does all the disgusting things that the wicked person did. Will he live? All the right things that he has done will not be remembered because of his unfaithfulness and because of his sin. He will die because of them.

²⁵ "But you say, 'The Lord's way is unfair.' Listen, nation of Israel, isn't my way fair? Isn't it your ways that are unfair? ²⁶ When a righteous person turns away from doing right and does evil things, he will die. He will die because of the evil things he has done. ²⁷ When a wicked person turns away from the wicked things that he has done and does what is fair and right, he will live. ²⁸ He realized what he was doing and turned away from all the rebellious things that he had done. He will certainly live. He will not die.

²⁹ "But the nation of Israel says, 'The Lord's way is unfair.' Isn't my way fair, nation of Israel? Isn't it your ways that are unfair?

³⁰ "That is why I will judge each of you by what you have done, people of Israel," declares the Almighty LORD. "Change the way you think and act. Turn away from all the rebellious things that you have done so that you will not fall into sin. ³¹ Stop all the rebellious things that you are doing. Get yourselves new hearts and new spirits. Why do you want to die, nation of Israel? ³² I don't want anyone to die," declares the Almighty LORD. "Change the way you think and act!"

Funeral Songs for Israel's Princes

19 ¹ Sing a funeral song for the princes of Israel. ² Say:

> Your mother was like a lioness.
> She lay down among the lions.
> She fed many cubs.
> ³ One of the cubs she raised became a young lion.
> He learned to tear apart the animals he hunted.
> He ate people.
> ⁴ The nations heard about him,
> caught him in their pit,
> and brought him with hooks to Egypt.
> ⁵ The lioness waited until she saw that there was no more hope.
> Then she took another one of her cubs
> and raised him into a young lion.
>
> ⁶ He became a young lion, and he prowled among the lions.
> He learned to tear apart the animals he hunted.
> He ate people.
> ⁷ He destroyed fortresses
> and turned cities into wastelands.
> The land and everyone living in it
> were terrified by the sound of his roar.
> ⁸ The nations from every region came together against him.
> They spread their net over him
> and caught him in their pit.

⁹   With hooks they put him in a cage
      and brought him to the king of Babylon.
    They put him in prison
      so that his roar wouldn't be heard anymore
        on the mountains of Israel.

¹⁰   Your mother was like a grapevine
      that was planted near water.
    It had a lot of fruit and many branches
      because there was plenty of water.
¹¹   Its branches were strong.
    They were used to make scepters for kings.
    It grew to be tall with many branches around it,
      and everyone saw it because of its many branches.
¹²   But in anger it was uprooted and thrown to the ground.
    The east wind dried up its fruit.
      Its strong branches broke off.
        They withered and were burned.
¹³   Now it is planted in the desert,
    in a dry and waterless land.
¹⁴   Fire has spread from the vine's main branch.
    Fire has destroyed its fruit.
    It no longer has any strong branches
      that could be used as a king's scepter.

This is a funeral song. It is to be used as a funeral song.

Israel's Past and Present Sins

20 ¹On the tenth day of the fifth month in the seventh year, some of the leaders of Israel came to ask for the LORD's help. They sat in front of me.

²Then the LORD spoke his word to me. He said, ³"Son of man, speak to the leaders of Israel. Tell them, 'This is what the Almighty LORD says: Are you coming to ask me for help? As I live, declares the Almighty LORD, you will not be allowed to ask me for help.'

⁴"Will you judge them? Will you judge them, son of man? Tell them about the disgusting things their ancestors did. ⁵Tell them, 'This is what the Almighty LORD says: When I chose Israel, I raised my hand and swore an oath to the descendants of Jacob's family. I made myself known to them in Egypt. I made a promise to them and said, "I am the LORD your God." ⁶At that time I promised to bring them out of Egypt to a land that I had chosen for them. This land is the most beautiful land, a land flowing with milk and honey. ⁷I said to them, "Get rid of the detestable idols that you look to for help. Don't dishonor yourselves with the disgusting idols of Egypt. I am the LORD your God."

⁸" 'But they rebelled against me and refused to listen to me. Not one of them got rid of the detestable idols that they looked to for help. They didn't abandon the disgusting idols of Egypt. So I was going to pour out my fury on them and unleash my anger on them in Egypt. ⁹But I acted so that my name would not be dishonored among the nations where they were living. While other nations were watching, I made myself known to them by bringing the Israelites out of Egypt.

¹⁰" 'So I brought the Israelites out of Egypt and led them into the desert. ¹¹I gave them my laws and made my rules known to them. If people obey them they will live. ¹²I also gave them certain days to worship me as a sign between us so that they would know that I, the LORD, made them holy.

¹³" 'But the people of Israel rebelled against me in the desert. They didn't live by my laws, and they rejected my rules. If people obey them, they will live. They dishonored the days to worship me. So I was going to pour out my fury on them in the desert and completely wipe them out. ¹⁴But I acted so that my name would not be dishonored among the nations who had watched me bring the Israelites out ˎof Egyptˏ. ¹⁵I also swore an oath to them in the desert. I swore that I would not bring them into the land that I had promised to give them. This land is the most beautiful land, a land flowing with milk and honey. ¹⁶They rejected my rules, and they didn't live by my laws. They dishonored the days to worship me, because their hearts chased disgusting idols. ¹⁷But I had compassion on them. I didn't destroy them or completely wipe them out in the desert. ¹⁸I said to their children in the desert, "Don't live by the laws of your ancestors. Don't obey their rules or dishonor yourselves with their disgusting idols. ¹⁹I am the LORD your God. Live by my laws. Obey my rules and follow them. ²⁰Set apart certain holy days to worship me. This will be a sign between me and you so that you will know that I am the LORD your God."

²¹ " 'But they rebelled against me. They didn't live by my laws, and they didn't obey my rules and follow them. If people obey them, they will live. They dishonored the days to worship me. So I was going to pour out my fury on them and unleash my anger on them in the desert. ²² But I didn't use my power so that my name would not be dishonored among the nations who had watched me bring the Israelites out ˌof Egypt˒. ²³ I raised my hand and swore an oath to them in the desert. I promised to scatter them among the nations and force them into other countries. ²⁴ They didn't follow my rules, and they rejected my laws. They dishonored the days to worship me, and they looked to their ancestors' disgusting idols for help. ²⁵ I also allowed them to follow laws that were no good and rules by which they could not live. ²⁶ I let them dishonor themselves when they sacrificed all their firstborn sons as gifts ˌto their false gods˒. I terrified them so that they would know that I am the LORD.'

²⁷ "Speak to the nation of Israel, son of man. Tell them, 'This is what the Almighty LORD says: Your ancestors insulted me again because they were unfaithful to me. ²⁸ I brought them to the land that I promised to give them. When they saw any high hill or any leafy tree, they made sacrifices and brought offerings there to make me angry. There they offered their sacrifices and poured out their wine offerings. ²⁹ Then I asked them, "What is this worship site you're going to?' " (So it is still called 'worship site' today.)

³⁰ "Tell the nation of Israel, 'This is what the Almighty LORD says: Will you dishonor yourselves the way your ancestors did? Will you chase their detestable idols like a prostitute? ³¹ You offer your children as sacrifices by burning them alive. You dishonor yourselves with all your disgusting idols to this day. Should you be allowed to ask me for help, nation of Israel?

" 'As I live, declares the Almighty LORD, you won't be allowed to ask me for help. ³² What you have in mind will never happen. You think that you want to be like other nations, like the different people in other countries. You want to serve wood and stone.

³³ " 'As I live, declares the Almighty LORD, I will rule you with a mighty hand and a powerful arm, and I will pour out my fury. ³⁴ I will bring you out from the nations and gather you from the countries where I have scattered you with my mighty hand and powerful arm. I will pour out my fury. ³⁵ I will bring you into the desert of the nations. There I will put you on trial face to face. ³⁶ I will put you on trial as I put your ancestors on trial in the desert of Egypt, declares the Almighty LORD. ³⁷ Then I will make you suffer punishment and make you keep the terms of the promise.ᵃ ³⁸ I will get rid of rebels and those who do wrong against me. I will bring you out of the land where you are living. You will never enter Israel. Then you will know that I am the LORD.

Israel's Future

³⁹ " 'Nation of Israel, this is what the Almighty LORD says: Serve your disgusting idols. But afterwards, you will listen to me. You will no longer dishonor my holy name with your gifts and your disgusting idols.

⁴⁰ " 'The entire nation of Israel, everyone in the land, will worship me on my holy mountain, the high mountain of Israel, declares the Almighty LORD. There I will accept you. There I will look for your offerings, your best gifts, and all your holy gifts. ⁴¹ When I bring you out from the nations and gather you from the countries where you have been scattered, I will accept you as if you were a pleasing sacrifice. Through you I will reveal myself as holy to the nations that are watching. ⁴² Then you will know that I am the LORD, because I will bring you to the land of Israel, the land that I promised to give your ancestors. ⁴³ There you will remember the way you lived and everything you did to dishonor yourselves. You will be disgusted by every wrong thing that you did. ⁴⁴ Then you will know that I am the LORD, because I will deal with you for the sake of my name. I will not deal with you based on the evil and corrupt things that you have done, nation of Israel, declares the Almighty LORD.' "ᵇ

The Burning Forest

⁴⁵ The LORD spoke his word to me. He said, ⁴⁶ "Son of man, turn to the south, preach against the south, and prophesy against the forest in the Negev. ⁴⁷ Tell the forest in the Negev, 'Listen to the word of the LORD. This is what the Almighty LORD says: I am about to set fire to you to destroy all your green trees and all your dry trees. The blazing fire will not be put out. It will burn the whole land from the south to the north. ⁴⁸ Then everyone will know that I, the LORD, started the fire. It will never be put out.' "

⁴⁹ Then I said, "Oh no! Almighty LORD, no! The people already say that I'm only telling stories."

The Sword of the LORD

21ᵃ ¹ The LORD spoke his word to me. He said, ² "Son of man, turn to Jerusalem, preach against the holy places. Prophesy against the land of Israel. ³ Tell the land of Israel,

---

ᵃ 20:37 Or "covenant."   ᵇ 20:44 Ezekiel 20:45–49 in English Bibles is Ezekiel 21:1–5 in the Hebrew Bible.   ᵃ 21:1 Ezekiel 21:1–32 in English Bibles is Ezekiel 21:6–37 in the Hebrew Bible.

'This is what the LORD says: I am against you. I will take my sword out of its scabbard and kill the righteous people and the wicked people among you. ⁴ I'm going to kill the righteous people and the wicked people among you. That is why my sword will come out of its scabbard to be used against everyone from the south to the north. ⁵ Then everyone will know that I, the LORD, have taken my sword from its scabbard, and I will not put it back again.'

⁶ "So, son of man, groan with a breaking heart and with bitter crying while the people watch you. ⁷ When they ask you why you are groaning, say, 'News has come that will discourage everyone. People's hands will hang limp, their hearts will lose courage, and their knees will become as weak as water. It's coming! It will surely take place!' declares the Almighty LORD."

⁸ The LORD spoke his word to me. He said, ⁹ "Son of man, prophesy. Tell them, 'This is what the Lord says:

> A sword, a sword is sharpened and polished,
> 10   It's sharpened to kill
>   and polished to flash like lightning.
>   How can we rejoice?
>   My son has refused to be disciplined or punished.ᵇ
> 11 The sword has been handed over to be polished,
>   to be placed in the hand.
> The sword is being sharpened and polished
>   to be placed in the hands of killers.
>
> 12 " 'Cry and mourn, son of man,
>   because the sword will be used against my people
>   and against all the princes of Israel.
>   I will throw the princes and my people on the sword.
>   So beat your breast, and grieve.
> 13 Testing will surely come.
>   What if you refuse to be disciplined again?
>   Won't you be tested? declares the Almighty LORD.
> 14 So prophesy, son of man.
>   Clap your hands!
>   Let the sword strike again and again.
>   It's the sword for killing.
>   It's the sword for killing many people.
>   It's the sword that surrounds them.
> 15 I have appointed my sword to slaughter people at all their gates
>   so that their hearts will sink and many will die.
>   Yes! It's ready to flash like lightning.
>   It's polished to kill.
> 16 Sword, cut to the right.
>   Cut to the left
>   or wherever your blade is turned.
> 17 I will also clap my hands and rest from my fury.
>   I, the LORD, have spoken.' "

The Sword of the King of Babylon

¹⁸ The LORD spoke his word to me. He said, ¹⁹ "Son of man, mark two roads that the king of Babylon and his sword can take. Both of these roads should start from the same country. Make a sign, and put it where the roads start to fork toward the cities. ²⁰ Mark the road that the king and his sword can take to the Ammonite city of Rabbah, and mark the road that leads to Judah and the fortified city of Jerusalem. ²¹ The king of Babylon will stop where the roads branch off, where there is a fork in the road. Then he will look for omens. He will shake some arrows, ask his household gods for help, and examine animal livers. ²² The omens will indicate that he should go to the right, to Jerusalem. So he will set up his battering rams there, give the order to kill, raise a battle cry, aim the battering rams against the city gates, put up ramps, and set up blockades. ²³ The people won't believe this because they have made treaties with other nations. But the king of Babylon will remind them of their sins, and they will be captured.

²⁴ "This is what the Almighty LORD says: You make people remember how sinful you are because you openly do wrong. You show your sins in everything you do. So you will be taken captive.

²⁵ "You dishonest and wicked prince of Israel, the time for your final punishment has come. ²⁶ This is what the Almighty LORD says: Take off your turban, and get rid of your crown. Things

---

ᵇ 21:10 Hebrew meaning of this sentence uncertain.

are going to change. Those who are unimportant will become important, and those who are important will become unimportant. ²⁷ Ruins! Ruins! I will turn this place into ruins! It will not be restored until its rightful owner comes. Then I will give it to him.

²⁸ "Son of man, prophesy. Tell them, 'This is what the Almighty LORD says about the Ammonites and their insults:

> A sword, a sword is drawn ready to kill.
>   It's polished to destroy and flash like lightning.
> ²⁹ People see false visions about you
>   and prophesy lies about you.
> The sword will be placed on the necks of dishonest, wicked people,
>   for whom the time of final punishment has come.
>
> ³⁰ " 'Return your sword to its scabbard.
>   In the place where you were created,
>   in the land where you were born,
>   there I will judge you.
> ³¹ I will pour out my fury on you
>   and breathe on you with my fiery anger.
> I will hand you over to cruel people who are skilled in destruction.
> ³² You will be fuel for the fire.
>   You will die in the land.
>   You will no longer be remembered.
>   I, the LORD, have spoken.' "

Jerusalem Is Judged Because of Its Murderous History

22 ¹ The LORD spoke his word to me. He said, ² "Will you judge, son of man? Will you judge the city of murderers? Then tell it about all the disgusting things that it has done. ³ Tell it, 'This is what the Almighty LORD says: Jerusalem, you are the city that murders people who live in you. Your time has come. You dishonor yourself with disgusting idols. ⁴ You are guilty because of the people you have killed. You are dishonored because of the disgusting idols you have made. You have brought an end to your days, and you have come to the end of your years. That is why I will make you a disgrace to the nations and a joke in every land. ⁵ Those near and those far away will mock you. Your name will be dishonored, and you will be filled with confusion.

⁶ " 'See how all the princes of Israel who live in you have used their power to murder people. ⁷ People in you hate their fathers and mothers. They oppress foreigners in you. They oppress orphans and widows in you. ⁸ You have despised my holy things and dishonored the day to worship me. ⁹ Some of your people slander. They want to kill people. People who live in you eat food sacrificed to idols at the worship sites on the hills, and they sin sexually. ¹⁰ Men have sex with their father's wives. They have sex with women when the women are having their periods and are unclean.ᵃ ¹¹ Men do disgusting things with their neighbors' wives. Some men sexually dishonor their daughters-in-law. Other men who live in you have sex with their sisters, their father's daughters. ¹² Other people take bribes to murder people. You collect interest and make excessive profits. You make profits by mistreating your neighbors. You have forgotten me, declares the Almighty LORD.

¹³ " 'I will use my power against you because of the excessive profits you have made and the murders you have committed. ¹⁴ Will you still be brave? Will you remain strong when I deal with you? I, the LORD, have spoken, and I will do it. ¹⁵ I will scatter you among the nations and force you into other countries. I will put an end to your uncleanness. ¹⁶ You will be dishonored in the sight of the nations. Then you will know that I am the LORD.' "

¹⁷ Then the LORD spoke his word to me. He said, ¹⁸ "Son of man, the people of Israel have become worthless to me. All of them are like copper, tin, iron, and lead in a smelting furnace. They are like the impurities left from silver. ¹⁹ This is what the Almighty LORD says: All of you have become worthless. That is why I'm going to gather you in Jerusalem. ²⁰ People gather silver, copper, iron, lead, and tin together in a smelting furnace to melt them with a fiery blast. In the same way, in my anger and fury I will gather you and put you in the city. I will melt you there. ²¹ Yes, I will gather you, breathe on you with my fiery anger, and melt you in the city. ²² You will be melted in the city like silver that is melted in a furnace. Then you will know that I, the LORD, have poured out my fury on you."

²³ The LORD spoke his word to me. He said, ²⁴ "Son of man, tell the city, 'You are an unclean land that has not had rain during the day of my anger. You have not been made clean.ᵇ ²⁵ Your

---

ᵃ 22:10 "Unclean" refers to anything that Moses' Teachings say is not presentable to God.   ᵇ 22:24 "Clean" refers to anything that Moses' Teachings say is presentable to God.

princes are like roaring lions who tear their prey into pieces. They eat people and take their treasures and precious belongings. They turn many women into widows. ²⁶ Your priests violate my teachings and dishonor my holy things. They don't distinguish between what is holy and what is unholy. They don't teach the difference between what is clean and what is unclean. They ignore the days to worship me. So I am dishonored among the people. ²⁷ Your leaders are like wolves that tear their prey into pieces. They murder and destroy people to make excessive profits. ²⁸ Your prophets cover up these things by seeing false visions and by prophesying lies. They say, "This is what the Almighty LORD says." Yet, the LORD hasn't spoken. ²⁹ The common people oppress and rob others. They do wrong to humble people and to poor people. They oppress foreigners for no reason.

³⁰ " 'I looked for someone among you who could build walls or stand in front of me by the gaps in the walls to defend the land and keep it from being destroyed. But I couldn't find anyone. ³¹ So I will pour out my anger on you, and with my fiery anger I will consume you. This is because of all the things you have done,' declares the Almighty LORD."

Samaria and Jerusalem Acted Like Prostitutes

23 ¹ The LORD spoke his word to me. He said, ² "Son of man, there were once two women, daughters of the same mother. ³ They became prostitutes in Egypt when they were young. There men fondled and caressed their breasts.

⁴ "The older girl was named Oholah, and the younger girl was named Oholibah. I married them, and they gave birth to sons and daughters. Oholah represents Samaria, and Oholibah represents Jerusalem. ⁵ Oholah acted like a prostitute, although she was my wife. She lusted after her Assyrian lovers who lived nearby. ⁶ They were governors and commanders clothed in purple. They were all handsome young men who rode on horses. ⁷ She became a prostitute for all the important men in Assyria. She dishonored herself with the idols of all those with whom she fell in love. ⁸ She continued the prostitution that she started in Egypt. When she was young, men went to bed with her, caressed her breasts, and treated her like a prostitute.

⁹ "That is why I handed her over to her lovers, to the Assyrians whom she lusted after. ¹⁰ They stripped her naked, took away her sons and daughters, and killed her with a sword. Women gossiped about how she was punished.

¹¹ "Even though her younger sister Oholibah saw this, Oholibah lusted after men more than her sister did. Oholibah's prostitution became worse than her sister's prostitution. ¹² She lusted after the Assyrians who were nearby. They were governors and commanders in full dress. They were mounted horsemen, all of them desirable young men. ¹³ I saw that she was dishonoring herself. Both sisters acted the same way. ¹⁴ Yet, she carried her prostitution even further. She saw pictures of men carved on walls. They were figures of Babylonian men, painted in bright red. ¹⁵ The men had belts around their waists and flowing turbans on their heads. All of them looked like Babylonian officers who were born in Babylon. ¹⁶ She fell in love with them at first sight and sent messengers to them in Babylonia. ¹⁷ So these men came from Babylon, went to bed with her, and dishonored her with their lust. After they had dishonored her, she turned away from them in disgust.

¹⁸ "She carried out her prostitution openly, and she lay around naked. I turned away from her in disgust as I had turned away from her sister. ¹⁹ She remembered how she had been a prostitute in Egypt when she was young. So she took part in even more prostitution. ²⁰ She lusted after her lovers, whose genitals were like those of donkeys and whose semen was like that of horses. ²¹ So she longed to do the sinful things she did when she was young in Egypt, when young men caressed and fondled her breasts.

²² "Oholibah, this is what the Almighty LORD says: I'm going to stir up your lovers against you. They are the lovers you turned away from in disgust. I will bring them against you from every side. ²³ I will bring men from Babylon and from all Babylonia, men from Pekod, Shoa, and Koa, as well as all the Assyrians. They are desirable young men, governors and commanders, military officers and important men. All of them ride on horses. ²⁴ They will attack you from the north,ᵃ with chariots and wagons and with a large number of troops. They will attack you from all around with small and large shields and with helmets. I have handed you over to them for punishment. They will punish you with their own kind of punishment. ²⁵ I will direct my burning anger against you so that they will deal with you in anger. They will cut off your nose and ears and kill everyone who remains. They will take your sons and your daughters and burn down whatever is left. ²⁶ They will rip off your clothes and take away your beautiful jewels. ²⁷ I will put a stop to your sinning and to your prostitution, which you began in Egypt. You won't desire these things anymore or remember Egypt anymore.

ᵃ 23:24 Hebrew meaning uncertain.

28 "This is what the Almighty LORD says: I'm going to hand you over to those you hate and to those you turned away from in disgust. 29 They will treat you hatefully and take away everything that you have worked for. They will leave you naked and bare. The shame of your prostitution will be revealed. 30 Your sinning and your prostitution have done this to you, because you lusted after the nations and dishonored yourself with their idols. 31 You've acted the same way as your sister. That is why I will put her cup in your hand. 32 This is what the Almighty LORD says:

> You will drink from your sister's cup,
>   a cup that is deep and wide.
> You will be scorned and mocked,
>   because this cup holds so much.
> 33   The cup of your sister Samaria will be filled
>   with drunkenness and sorrow.
> 34 You will drink from it and drain it.
> You will break it into pieces
>   and tear your breasts off your body.
> I have spoken, declares the Almighty LORD.

35 "This is what the Almighty LORD says: You have forgotten me and turned your back on me. So you will be punished for your sinning and prostitution."

36 The LORD said to me, "Son of man, will you judge Oholah and Oholibah and tell them about their disgusting practices? 37 They have committed adultery. Their hands are covered with blood. They commit adultery with their idols. They have sacrificed the children they gave birth to for me as burnt offerings to idols. 38 They have also done this to me: They have polluted my holy places when they do these things and dishonored the days to worship me. 39 When they sacrificed their children to their idols, they came into my holy place and dishonored it. That is what they've done in my temple.

40 "They even sent messengers to invite men to come from far away. When the men arrived, they washed themselves for the men, painted their eyes, and put on their jewels. 41 They sat on their fine couches with tables in front of them. They put my incense and my olive oil on their tables.

42 "I heard the noise from a carefree crowd. A large number of people came from the desert, and they put bracelets on the women's wrists and beautiful crowns on their heads. 43 Then I said, 'She is worn out from her acts of adultery.' Yet, men continued to have sex with her. 44 Men slept with her. They slept with those sinful women, Oholah and Oholibah just as they slept with a prostitute. 45 Righteous people will punish these women for adultery and for murder, because these women have committed adultery and their hands are covered with blood.

46 "This is what the Almighty LORD says: Bring together a mob against the people of Samaria and Jerusalem. Hand them over to terror and looting. 47 Then the mob will stone them and kill them with swords. The mob will kill their sons and daughters and burn their homes. 48 So I will put a stop to the sinning in the land, and all the women will be warned not to sin as they do. 49 They will be punished for their sins, and they will pay for their sin of idolatry. Then they will know that I am the Almighty LORD."

Judah Is Compared to a Boiling Pot

24 1 On the tenth day of the tenth month in the ninth year, the LORD spoke his word to me. He said, 2 "Son of man, write down today's date. The king of Babylon has surrounded Jerusalem this very day. 3 Tell these rebellious people a story. Tell them, 'This is what the Almighty LORD says:

> Put the pot on the fire; put it on.
> Pour water in it.
> 4   Cut the meat into pieces,
>   all the best pieces, the thigh and shoulder.
> Fill the pot with the meatiest bones
> 5   selected from the best sheep.
> Pile wood under the pot.
> Bring the mixture in the pot to a boil.
> Cook the bones that are in it well.

6 " 'This is what the Almighty LORD says:

> How horrible it will be for that city of murderers,
>   for that tarnished pot.
>   Its tarnish will not come off.

Empty the meat out of it piece by piece
   without choosing any particular piece.
⁷ Blood is still in that city.
   The blood was poured on a bare rock.
     It wasn't poured on the ground where dust would cover it.
⁸ In order to stir up my fury so that I would pay that city back,
   I put the blood of its victims on a bare rock.
     Now that blood can't be covered.

⁹ " 'This is what the Almighty LORD says:

How horrible it will be for that city of murderers.
   I, too, will pile the wood high.
¹⁰ Pile it high, and light the fire.
Cook the meat thoroughly, stir the mixture,
   and let the bones burn.
¹¹ Then set the empty pot on the coals
   so that it gets hot and its copper glows.
     Its impurities will melt away,
      and its tarnish will burn off.

¹² " 'I have worn myself out trying to clean this pot. Even the fire can't take away its thick tarnish. ¹³ I tried to clean you of your filthy lust, but you wouldn't clean yourself from your filth. You will never be clean until I unleash my fury on you. ¹⁴ I, the LORD, have spoken. It will happen, and I will do it. I will not ignore you, pity you, or change my plans. I will punish you because of the way you lived and because of everything you have done,' " declares the Almighty LORD.

Ezekiel's Silent Sorrow Over the Destruction of Jerusalem

¹⁵ Then the LORD spoke his word to me. He said, ¹⁶ "Son of man, with one blow I'm going to take away from you the person you love the most. But you must not mourn, cry, or let tears run down your face. ¹⁷ Groan silently. Don't grieve for the person who dies. Tie on your turban, and put on your sandals. Don't cover your face or eat the food that mourners eat."

¹⁸ So I spoke to the people in the morning, and in the evening my wife died. The next morning I did as I was ordered.

¹⁹ The people asked me, "Tell us, what do these things that you are doing mean to us?"

²⁰ I told them, "The LORD spoke his word to me. He said, ²¹ 'Tell the nation of Israel, "This is what the Almighty LORD says: I'm going to dishonor my holy place. You brag that my holy place gives you strength. It's the thing you love the most. It's your hearts' desire. So the sons and daughters that you left behind will die in battle. ²² Then you must do as I did. Don't cover your faces or eat the food that mourners eat. ²³ Leave your turbans on your heads and your sandals on your feet. Don't grieve or cry! You will waste away because of your guilt and groan to one another. ²⁴ Ezekiel is a sign to you. You will do everything he has done. Then you will know that I am the Almighty LORD." '

²⁵ "Son of man, on that day I will take their stronghold away from them. It makes them happy and proud. It is their hearts' desire and the thing they love the most. I will also take away their sons and daughters. ²⁶ On that day a refugee will come to you to tell you the news. ²⁷ On that very day your mouth will be opened, and you will talk to the refugee. You will speak and not be silent anymore. You will be a sign to them. Then they will know that I am the LORD."

Judgment on Ammon

25 ¹ The LORD spoke his word to me. He said, ² "Son of man, turn to the Ammonites and prophesy against them. ³ Tell the Ammonites, 'Listen to the word of the Almighty LORD. This is what the Almighty LORD says: You were glad when my holy place was dishonored, when the land of Israel was ruined, and when the nation of Judah went into exile. ⁴ That is why I'm going to hand you over to the people in the east. They will possess your land. They will set up their camps and pitch their tents among you. They will eat your crops and drink your milk. ⁵ I will turn Rabbah into a pasture for camels, and I will turn Ammon into a resting place for sheep. Then you will know that I am the LORD.

⁶ " 'This is what the Almighty LORD says: You clapped your hands and stomped your feet. You rejoiced and felt contempt for the land of Israel. ⁷ That is why I will use my power against you and hand you over to the nations as loot. I will wipe you out from among the nations, make you disappear, and destroy you. Then you will know that I am the LORD.

Judgment on Moab

8 " 'This is what the Almighty LORD says: Moab and Seir said, "The nation of Judah is like all the other nations." **9** That is why I'm going to open up the cities that protect Moab's borders. They are the beautiful cities of Beth Jeshimoth, Baal Meon, and Kiriathaim. **10** I will hand the Moabites and the Ammonites over to the people in the east. So the Ammonites will no longer be remembered among the nations. **11** I will punish Moab. Then they will know that I am the LORD.

Judgment on Edom

12 " 'This is what the Almighty LORD says: Edom took revenge on the nation of Judah and became guilty because of it. **13** So this is what the Almighty LORD says: I will use my power against Edom. I will wipe out people and animals. I will turn the land into ruins from Teman to Dedan. People will die in battle. **14** I will use my people Israel to take revenge on Edom. My people will deal with Edom based on my anger and my fury. Then the Edomites will know my revenge, declares the Almighty LORD.

Judgment on the Philistines

15 " 'This is what the Almighty LORD says: The Philistines have taken revenge with spiteful hearts. They have tried to destroy their long-time enemies. **16** So this is what the Almighty LORD says: I'm going to use my power against the Philistines, cut off the Cherethites, and destroy the people that are left on the coast. **17** I will take fierce revenge on them and punish them with fury. I will take revenge on them. Then they will know that I am the LORD.' "

Judgment on Tyre

26 **1** On the first day of the month in the eleventh year, the LORD spoke his word to me. He said, **2** "Son of man, Tyre said this about Jerusalem: 'The city that was the gateway for the nations is destroyed, and its doors are swung open to me. I'll get rich now that it's ruined.' **3** So this is what the Almighty LORD says: I am against you, Tyre. I will bring many nations against you as the waves on the sea rise. **4** They will destroy the walls of Tyre and tear down its towers. Then I will sweep up the dust and turn Tyre into a bare rock. **5** It will become a place by the sea where people spread their fishing nets. I have spoken, declares the Almighty LORD. It will become a prize for the nations. **6** The people in the villages and on the mainland will die in battle. Then they will know that I am the LORD.

7 "This is what the Almighty LORD says: From the north I'm going to bring King Nebuchadnezzar of Babylon against you, Tyre. He is the greatest king. He will bring horses, chariots, war horses, many people, and many troops. **8** He will destroy the villages on your mainland. He will set up blockades, put up dirt ramps, and raise his shields against you. **9** He will direct his battering rams against your walls, and he will cut down your towers with his axes. **10** He will have so many horses that their dust will cover you. The noise from the war horses, wagon wheels, and chariots will shake your walls when he enters your gates. He will enter as people enter a conquered city. **11** With his horses' hoofs he will trample all your streets. He will kill your people in battle, and your strong pillars will fall to the ground. **12** His troops will loot your riches and take your goods as prizes. They will destroy your walls and tear down your delightful homes. They will throw your stones, wood, and soil into the water.

13 "I will put a stop to your noisy songs, and the music from your harps will no longer be heard. **14** I will turn you into bare rock. You will become a place to spread fishing nets. You will never be rebuilt. I, the LORD, have spoken, declares the Almighty LORD.

15 "This is what the Almighty LORD says to Tyre: The people who live on the coast will shake with fear when they hear about your defeat. They will groan when your people are wounded and slaughtered. **16** Then the princes from the coast will come down from their thrones. They will remove their robes and take off their embroidered clothes. Dressed in terror, they will sit on the ground. They will tremble constantly and be shocked at you. **17** Then they will sing this funeral song for you:

> Tyre, you famous city, you have been destroyed.
> > You have been shattered by the sea.
> > > You and your people ruled the sea.
> > > > All your people terrified those who lived by the coast.
> **18** Your defeat will make the people who live by the coast tremble.
> > Your end will terrify the islands in the sea.

19 "This is what the Almighty LORD says: I will turn your city into ruins like cities that have no one living in them. I will bring the deep ocean over you, and the Mediterranean Sea will cover you. **20** I will bring you down with those who descend to the grave to join the people of long ago. I will make you live below the earth among the ancient ruins with those who go down to the grave. You will never return or take your place in the land of the living. ²¹ I will turn you into a terror, and you will no longer exist. People will look for you, but they will never see you again," declares the Almighty LORD.

A Funeral Song About Tyre

27 ¹ The LORD spoke his word to me. He said, ² "Son of man, sing a funeral song about Tyre. ³ Tyre is the city at the entrance to the sea. It is the merchant to the nations. Say to Tyre, 'This is what the Almighty LORD says:

Tyre, you used to brag about your perfect beauty.
⁴   Your home is the sea.

"'Your builders made your beauty perfect.
⁵   Your builders made all your boards from pine trees on Mount Hermon.
         They took cedar trees from Lebanon to make a mast for you.
⁶   They made your oars from oaks in Bashan.
         They made your deck from pine trees on the shores of Cyprus.
            It had ivory set in it.
⁷   Your sails were made out of fine embroidered linen from Egypt.
         They were like your flags.
         Your awnings were violet and purple.
            They came from the coasts of Elishah.
⁸   "'People from Sidon and Arvad used to row you.
         Your own skilled people were your sailors.
⁹   Master shipbuilders from Gebal went inside you to caulk your seams.
         All the ships on the sea and their sailors
            docked alongside you to trade with you.
¹⁰   People from Persia, Lud, and Put were soldiers in your army.
         They hung their shields and helmets inside you.
            Their victories made you look good.

¹¹ "'People from Arvad and Helech[a] were guards all around your walls. People from Gammad guarded your towers. They hung their shields all around your walls, making your beauty perfect.

¹² "'People from Tarshish traded with you because you were so very rich. They exchanged silver, iron, tin, and lead for your merchandise. ¹³ People from Greece, Tubal, and Meshech traded with you. They exchanged slaves and bronze items for your goods. ¹⁴ People from Beth Togarmah exchanged horses, war horses, and mules for your merchandise. ¹⁵ People from Dedan traded goods with you. You traded with many people on the coasts, and they brought you ivory and ebony as payment.

¹⁶ "'People from Syria traded with you because you had so many products. They exchanged emeralds, purple cloth, richly woven cloth, linen, coral, and rubies for your merchandise. ¹⁷ Judah and Israel traded with you. They exchanged wheat from Minnith, baked goods, honey, olive oil, and balsam for your goods. ¹⁸ People from Damascus traded with you because you had so many products. They exchanged wine from Helbon and wool from Sahar.

¹⁹ "'Danites and Greeks from Uzal traded for your merchandise. They exchanged wrought iron, cassia, and sugar cane for your goods. ²⁰ Dedan traded saddle blankets with you. ²¹ Arabia and all the officials of Kedar traded with you. They traded lambs, rams, and male goats. ²² The merchants from Sheba and Raamah traded with you. They traded the finest spices, precious stones, and gold for your merchandise. ²³ Haran, Canneh, Eden, the merchants from Sheba, Assyria, and Kilmad traded with you. ²⁴ In your marketplace they traded for beautiful clothes, purple robes, embroidered cloth, and many multicolored rugs with woven and twisted cords.

²⁵   "'Ships from Tarshish carried your goods.
         You were like a ship filled with heavy cargo in the sea.
²⁶   Your rowers took you out to the high seas,
         and an east wind wrecked you in the sea.
²⁷   Your wealth, your merchandise, and the goods you sell,
            your mariners and your sailors,
            your caulkers and your merchants,
            your soldiers and everyone else on board
               sank into the sea when your ship was wrecked.

ᵃ 27:11 Or "Celicia."

28   " 'When your sailors cried out, people on the shore trembled.
29   All the rowers, the sailors,
         and all the mariners came down from their ships
           and stood on the shore.
30   They cried loudly and bitterly over you.
     They put dust on their heads and covered themselves with ashes.
31   They shaved their heads because of you and put on sackcloth.
     They cried over you with bitterness and with bitter mourning.
32   They sang a funeral song for you with loud crying:
     "Who is like Tyre, the city destroyed in the sea?"
33   Your merchandise was sent overseas.
         You filled many people with your great wealth and your goods.
          You made the kings of the earth rich.
34   Now you are wrecked in the sea, at the bottom of the sea.
         Your goods and your whole crew sank with you.
35   All those who live on the coasts are horrified because of you.
         Their kings are terribly afraid.
         Their faces show their fear.
36   The merchants among the nations laugh at you.
           You have come to a terrible end,
             and you will never exist again.' "

Judgment on the King of Tyre

28   [1] The LORD spoke his word to me. He said, [2] "Son of man, tell the ruler of Tyre, 'This is what the Almighty LORD says:

In your arrogance you say,
     "I'm a god. I sit on God's throne in the sea."
         But you're only human and not a god,
          although you think you are a god.
3   You think that you are wiser than Daniel
         and that no secret can be hidden from you.
4   Because you are wise and understanding,
         you've made yourself rich.
          You saved gold and silver in your treasuries.
5   Because of your great skill in trading,
         you've made yourself very wealthy.
          You have become arrogant because of your wealth.

6 " 'This is what the Almighty LORD says:

You think you are wise like God.
7   That is why I am going to bring foreigners against you,
         the most ruthless foreigners among the nations.
     They will draw their swords against your fine wisdom
         and dishonor your greatness.
8   They will throw you into a pit,
         and you will die a violent death in the sea.
9   You will no longer say that you are a god
         when you face those who kill you.
     You will be a human, not a god, in the hands of those who kill you.
10   You will die at the hands of foreigners like a godless person.
     I have spoken,' " declares the LORD.

[11] The LORD spoke his word to me. He said, [12] "Son of man, sing a funeral song for the ruler of Tyre. Tell him, 'This is what the Almighty LORD says:

You were the perfect example,
     full of wisdom and perfect in beauty.
13   You were in Eden, God's garden.
     You were covered with every kind of precious stone:
         red quartz, topaz, crystal,
         beryl, onyx, gray quartz, sapphire,
         turquoise, and emerald.
     Your settings and your sockets

were made of gold when you were created.
14 I appointed an angel[a] to guard you:
  You were on God's holy mountain.
  You walked among fiery stones.
15 Your behavior was perfect from the time you were created,
  until evil was found in you.
16 You traded far and wide. You learned to be violent, and you sinned.
  So I threw you down from God's mountain in disgrace.
  The guardian angel forced you out from the fiery stones.
17 You became too proud because of your beauty.
  You wasted your wisdom because of your greatness.
    So I threw you to the ground
      and left you in front of the kings
        so that they could see you.
18 You dishonored your own holy places
  because of your many sins and dishonest trade.
    So I set fire to you to burn you up.
    I turned you into ashes on the ground
      in the presence of all who saw you.
19 All the nations who knew you are horrified because of you.
  You have come to a terrible end,
    and you will never exist again.' "

Judgment on Sidon Means Hope for Israel

20 The LORD spoke his word to me. He said, 21 "Son of man, turn to Sidon and prophesy against it. 22 Tell it, 'This is what the Almighty LORD says:

I'm against you, Sidon.
  I will show my greatness through you.
    Then people will know that I am the LORD,
      because I will punish you and show you how holy I am.
23 I will send a plague against you
  and make blood flow in your streets.
    Your people will fall dead.
      People with swords will attack you from every side.
    Then they will know that I am the LORD.
24 The nation of Israel will no longer be hurt
  by prickly thorns or sharp briars from everyone around them.
    Then they will know that I am the Almighty LORD.

25 " 'This is what the Almighty LORD says: When I gather the people of Israel from the nations where they were scattered, I will show that I am holy as the nations watch. The people of Israel will live in their own land, the land I gave to my servant Jacob. 26 They will live there in safety. They will build homes and plant vineyards. They will live in safety when I punish all the surrounding people who treat them with scorn. Then they will know that I am the LORD their God.' "

Judgment on Egypt

29 1 On the twelfth day of the tenth month in the tenth year, the LORD spoke his word to me. He said, 2 "Son of man, turn to Pharaoh, king of Egypt, and prophesy against him and against all Egypt. 3 Tell him, 'This is what the Almighty LORD says:

I'm against you, Pharaoh, king of Egypt.
  You are like a monster crocodile lying in the Nile River.
  You say, "The Nile River is mine. I made it for myself."

4 " 'I will put hooks in your jaws
  and make the fish in the Nile River stick to your scales.
  I will pull you out of your river
    with all the fish in the Nile sticking to your scales.
5 I will leave you in the desert, you and all the fish from the Nile.
  You will fall in an open field.
    No one will pick you up or bury you.
  I will feed you to wild animals and birds.

---

[a] 28:14 Or "one of the cherubim."

⁶   Then all those living in Egypt will know that I am the LORD.
      Egypt, you have become like a ˌbrokenˌ walking stick
         to the nation of Israel.
⁷   When Israel grabbed you, you splintered and tore up their shoulders.
      When they leaned on you, you broke, and they wrenched their backs.

⁸ " 'This is what the Almighty LORD says: I am going to attack you with a sword. I will kill people and animals. ⁹ Egypt will become a wasteland and a pile of rubble. Then you will know that I am the LORD. You said, "The Nile River is mine. I made it." ¹⁰ That is why I'm against you and the Nile River. I will turn Egypt into a pile of rubble. It will become a wasteland, from Migdol to Syene, all the way to the border of Sudan. ¹¹ No human or animal will walk through it, and no one will live there for 40 years. ¹² I will make Egypt the most desolate country in the world. For 40 years Egypt's cities will lie in ruins. They will be ruined more than any other city. I will scatter the Egyptians among the nations and force them into other countries.

¹³ " 'This is what the Almighty LORD says: After 40 years I will gather the Egyptians from the nations where they have been scattered. ¹⁴ I will bring back the Egyptian captives and return them to Pathros,ᵃ the land they came from. There they will be a weak kingdom. ¹⁵ They will be the weakest kingdom, and they will never rule the nations again. I will make them so weak that they will never rule the nations again. ¹⁶ The nation of Israel will never trust Egypt again. The people of Israel will remember how wrong they were whenever they turned to Egypt ˌfor helpˌ. Then they will know that I am the Almighty LORD.' "

¹⁷ On the first day of the first month in the twenty-seventh year, the LORD spoke his word to me. He said, ¹⁸ "Son of man, King Nebuchadnezzar of Babylon made his army fight hard against Tyre. Every soldier's head was worn bald, and every soldier's shoulder was rubbed raw. Yet, he and his army got no reward for their hard-fought battle against Tyre. ¹⁹ This is what the Almighty LORD says: I'm going to give Egypt to King Nebuchadnezzar of Babylon. He will carry off its wealth, take its prized possessions, and loot it. That will be the pay for his army. ²⁰ I have given him Egypt as pay for what he has done. Nebuchadnezzar and his army worked for me, declares the Almighty LORD.

²¹ "On that day I will make the people of Israel strong again, and I will give you, Ezekiel, something to say among them. Then they will know that I am the LORD."

Nebuchadnezzar Will Conquer Egypt

30 ¹ The LORD spoke his word to me. He said, ² "Son of man, prophesy. Say, 'This is what the Almighty LORD says:

      Cry for that day!
³   The day is near. The day of the LORD is near.
      It will be a gloomy day, a time of trouble for the nations.
⁴   There will be war in Egypt and anguish in Ethiopia.
      Many Egyptians will fall dead.
      People will take away Egypt's wealth,
         and its foundations will be torn down.
⁵   Sudan, Put, Lud, all the Arabs, the Libyans,
         and people from the promised land will die in battle.

⁶ " 'This is what the LORD says:

      All Egypt's allies will die.
      Egypt's strength will disappear.
         People will die in war from Migdol to Syene,
            declares the Almighty LORD.

⁷ " 'Egypt will become the most desolate country in the world, and Egypt's cities will lie in ruins. They will be ruined more than other cities. ⁸ Then they will know that I am the LORD, because I will set fire to Egypt and all her defenders will be killed. ⁹ On that day I will send messengers in ships to terrify those who live in safety in Sudan. The people of Sudan will be in anguish when Egypt is in trouble. That day is coming!

¹⁰ " 'This is what the Almighty LORD says: I will use King Nebuchadnezzar of Babylon to bring an end to Egypt. ¹¹ He and his troops, the most ruthless troops among the nations, will be brought to destroy the land. They will draw their swords to attack Egypt and fill the land with dead bodies. ¹² I will dry up the Nile River and sell the land to wicked people. I will have foreigners destroy the land and everything in it. I, the LORD, have spoken.

ᵃ 29:14 Or "southern Egypt."

¹³ " 'This is what the Almighty LORD says: I will destroy the statues and put an end to the idols in Memphis. A prince will never rise again in Egypt. I will spread fear throughout Egypt. ¹⁴ I will destroy Pathros, set fire to Zoan, and bring punishment on Thebes. ¹⁵ I will pour out my fury on Sin, Egypt's fortress, and I will kill many people in Thebes. ¹⁶ I will set fire to Egypt. Sin will be in much pain. Thebes will be broken into pieces, and Memphis will be in trouble every day. ¹⁷ The young men from Heliopolis and Bubastis will die in battle, and people from these cities will go into exile. ¹⁸ At Tahpanhes the day will turn dark when I break Egypt's power. Egypt's strong army will be defeated. Clouds will cover Egypt, and people from its villages will go into exile. ¹⁹ Then they will know that I am the LORD, because I will bring punishment on Egypt.' "

²⁰ On the seventh day of the first month in the eleventh year, the LORD spoke his word to me. He said, ²¹ "Son of man, I have broken the arm of Pharaoh, king of Egypt. His arm isn't bandaged, so it can't heal and be strong enough to hold a sword.

²² "This is what the Almighty LORD says: I'm against Pharaoh, king of Egypt. I will break both his arms, the healthy one and the broken one. I will make the sword fall from his hand. ²³ I will scatter the Egyptians among the nations and force them into other countries. ²⁴ I will make the arms of the king of Babylon strong. I will put my sword in his hand, but I will break Pharaoh's arms. Pharaoh will groan like a person who is dying. ²⁵ I will strengthen the arms of the king of Babylon, but Pharaoh's arms will fall. Then they will know that I am the LORD, because I will put my sword in the hand of the king of Babylon. He will strike Egypt with it. ²⁶ I will scatter the Egyptians among the nations and force them into other countries. Then they will know that I am the LORD."

Egypt Will Be Conquered as Assyria Was Conquered

31 ¹ On the first day of the third month in the eleventh year, the LORD spoke his word to me. He said, ² "Son of man, say to Pharaoh, king of Egypt, and his many people,

'Was there ever anyone as great as you?
³   What about Assyria?
        It was a cedar in Lebanon
            with fine branches that shaded the forest.
        It was very tall.
        Its top was among the clouds.
⁴   Water made the tree grow,
            and underground springs made it tall.
        Rivers flowed around the place where the tree was planted.
        Streams ran beside all the other trees around it.
⁵   That is why it grew taller than all the other trees in the field.
        Its branches became large and long because of so much water.
⁶   All the birds made their nests in its branches.
        All the wild animals gave birth to their young under it.
        All the powerful nations lived in its shade.
⁷   So the tree was big and beautiful with its long branches.
        Its roots reached down to many sources of water.
⁸   The cedar trees in God's garden couldn't compare to it.
        The pine trees couldn't equal its branches.
        The plane trees couldn't measure up to its branches.
            All the trees in God's garden couldn't match its beauty.
⁹   I was the one who made it beautiful with its many branches.
        This tree was the envy of all the trees in Eden, in God's garden.

¹⁰ " 'This is what the Almighty LORD says: The tree grew very tall, and its top reached the clouds. It became arrogant because it was so tall. ¹¹ So I handed it over to a mighty ruler among the nations, and he surely dealt with it. I forced it out because of its wickedness. ¹² Foreigners from the most ruthless nation cut it down and threw it away. Its branches fell on the mountains and in every valley. Its broken branches fell in every ravine in the land. All the nations in the world came out from under its shade and left. ¹³ All the birds perched on the fallen tree, and all the wild animals lived in its branches. ¹⁴ Then all the other trees growing by the water were kept from becoming arrogant because of their height, and their tops were no longer allowed to reach the clouds. So no tree, even if it is well-watered, will ever stand that tall. Every tree is going to die and go below the earth to join those who have died and gone down to the pit.

¹⁵ " 'This is what the Almighty LORD says: When the tree went down to the grave, I made people mourn. I covered the underground springs and held back the rivers. The many water sources stopped flowing. I made Lebanon mourn for the tree, and all the trees in the field

fainted as they grieved over it. [16] I made the nations tremble in fear at the sound of the tree's crash. I brought the tree down to the grave to join those who had gone down to the pit. Then all the trees in Eden, the choicest and best trees of Lebanon, and all the trees that were well-watered were comforted below the earth. [17] They had gone down with the tree in the grave to join others killed in battle. All who lived in its shadow were scattered among the nations.

[18] " 'This tree is you, Pharaoh, and all your many people. No tree in Eden has ever been as honorable and as great as you. But you will be brought down below the earth with the trees of Eden. You will lie among the godless people who were killed in battle, declares the Almighty LORD.' "

A Funeral Song About Pharaoh

32 [1] On the first day of the twelfth month in the twelfth year, the LORD spoke his word to me. He said, [2] "Son of man, sing a funeral song for Pharaoh, king of Egypt. Tell him,

> 'You think you are like a lion among the nations.
>> Instead, you are like a crocodile in the water.
>>> You splash around in the water.
>>> You stir up the water with your feet.
>>> You make the streams muddy.

[3] " 'This is what the Almighty LORD says: When many nations gather together, I will spread my net over you, and they will haul you up in a net. [4] I will throw you on the ground and toss you into an open field. I will make birds perch on you, and wild animals from all over the earth will feed on you. [5] I will scatter your flesh on the hills and fill the valleys with your rotting corpse. [6] I will drench the earth with your flowing blood all the way to the mountains. Ravines will be filled with your dead body.

[7] " 'When I put out your light, I will cover the sky and darken the stars. I will cover the sun with clouds, and the moon won't shine anymore. [8] I will darken all the lights shining in the sky above you. I will bring darkness over your land, declares the Almighty LORD.

[9] " 'I will make many people troubled when I spread the news of your destruction among the nations to countries that you haven't heard of. [10] Many people will be shocked by what I will do to you. Their kings will shudder when I swing my sword in their faces. When you die, all of them will tremble in fear for their own lives.

[11] " 'This is what the Almighty LORD says: The sword of the king of Babylon will attack you. [12] I will cut down your people with the swords of warriors. All of them will be the most ruthless warriors among the nations. They will shatter the pride of Egypt and destroy its many people. [13] I will also destroy all the animals beside its many water sources. The feet of humans and the hoofs of animals won't stir up the water anymore. [14] Then I will make its water clear and make its streams flow like oil, declares the Almighty LORD. [15] I will turn Egypt into a wasteland. I will take everything in the land, and I will kill all the people who live there. Then they will know that I am the LORD.'

[16] "This is a funeral song. The people from the nations will sing this song. They will sing it as they mourn for Egypt and its many people," declares the Almighty LORD.

The Egyptians Will Join the Other Nations in the Grave

[17] On the fifteenth day of the month in the twelfth year, the LORD spoke his word to me. He said, [18] "Son of man, cry for the many people of Egypt. Bring them down along with the other mighty nations. Send them down below the earth to be with those who have gone down to the pit.

[19] " Tell them, 'Are you more beautiful than anyone else? Go down and join the godless people.'

[20] "The Egyptians will lie among those who were killed in battle. A sword has been drawn. Drag Egypt and all its people away. [21] The mightiest warriors will say to Pharaoh from the grave, 'You and your defenders have come down, and you now lie with the godless people who were killed in battle.'

[22] "Assyria is there with its whole army, and the graves of its soldiers are all around it. All of its soldiers are dead. They have been killed in battle. [23] Their graves are in the deepest parts of the pit. Assyria's army lies around its grave. All of its soldiers are dead. They have been killed in battle. They once terrified people in the land of the living.

[24] "Elam is there with all its soldiers, and the graves of its soldiers are all around it. All of its soldiers are dead. They have been killed in battle. They went down below the earth as godless people. They once terrified people in the land of the living. Now they suffer disgrace with those who have gone down to the pit. [25] A bed has been made for Elam among the dead. The graves of its soldiers are all around it. The soldiers were godless people. They were killed in battle because they terrified others in the land of the living. Now they suffer disgrace with those who have gone down to the pit. They lie among the dead.

[26] "Meshech and Tubal are there with all their soldiers, and the graves of their soldiers are all around them. Their soldiers were all godless people. They were killed in battle because they terrified others in the land of the living. [27] They don't lie with the godless warriors who died and went down to the grave with their weapons of war. Their swords were placed under their heads. Their shields were placed on their bones because they terrified others in the land of the living.

[28] "You Egyptians will be crushed with the godless people, and you will lie with those who were killed in battle.

[29] "Edom is there with its kings and its princes. They used to be powerful, but now they lie with those who were killed in battle. They lie there with the godless people and with those who have gone down to the pit.

[30] "All the rulers from the north and all the people from Sidon are there. They, too, went down with the dead. They are disgraced because they terrified people with their power. They were godless people. Now they lie with those who were killed in battle. They suffer disgrace with those who went down to the pit.

[31] "Pharaoh and his army will see these things and be comforted over all the soldiers who have been killed in battle, declares the Almighty LORD. [32] I terrified people in the land of the living. Pharaoh and all his soldiers will be laid among the godless people who were killed in battle," declares the Almighty LORD.

Ezekiel Is Called to Be a Watchman

33 [1] The LORD spoke his word to me. He said, [2] "Son of man, speak to your people. Tell them, 'Suppose I bring war on this country, and the people of this country choose one of their men and make him their watchman. [3] If he sees the enemy coming to attack the country, he will blow his horn to warn the people. [4] If the people hear the horn and ignore the warning and the enemy comes and takes them, they will be responsible for their own deaths. [5] They heard the sound of the horn but ignored its warning. So they are responsible for their own deaths. If they had taken the warning, they would have saved themselves.

[6] " 'But if the watchman sees the enemy coming and doesn't blow his horn to warn the people and the enemy comes and kills someone, that watchman must die because of his sin. I will hold him responsible for their deaths.'

[7] "Son of man, I have appointed you as a watchman for the people of Israel. Listen to what I say, and warn them for me. [8] Suppose I say to a wicked person, 'You wicked person, you will certainly die,' and you say nothing to warn him to change his ways. That wicked person will die because of his sin, and I will hold you responsible for his death. [9] But if you warn a wicked person to turn from his ways and he doesn't turn from them, then he will die because of his sin. However, you will save yourself.

[10] "Son of man, say to the people of Israel, 'You have said this, "Our wickedness and our sins weigh us down, and we are rotting away because of them. How can we live?" '

[11] "Tell them, 'As I live, declares the Almighty LORD, I don't want wicked people to die. Rather, I want them to turn from their ways and live. Change the way you think and act! Turn from your wicked ways! Do you want to die, people of Israel?'

[12] "Son of man, say to your people, 'The right things that a righteous person has done will not save him when he rebels. The wicked things that a wicked person has done will not make him stumble when he turns from his wickedness. The righteous person will not live when he sins.' [13] I may promise the righteous person that he will certainly live. But if he trusts in the right things that he has done and he does evil, none of the right things that he has done will be remembered. He will die because of the evil things he has done. [14] I may warn the wicked person that he will certainly die. But suppose he turns from his sin and does what is fair and right. [15] He returns the security for a loan, pays back everything he stole, lives by the rules of life, and does nothing evil. Then he will certainly live. He will not die. [16] None of the sins that he has done will be remembered. He has done what is fair and right. He will certainly live.

[17] "But your people say, 'The Lord's way is unfair.' Yet, their ways are unfair. [18] If the righteous person turns from the right things that he has done and does evil, he will die because of it. [19] If the wicked person turns from his wickedness and does what is fair and right, he will live because of it. [20] Yet, the people of Israel say, 'The Lord's way is unfair.' I will judge each of you by your own ways, people of Israel."

[21] On the fifth day of the tenth month in the twelfth year of our captivity, a refugee from Jerusalem came to me. He said, "The city has been captured." [22] The evening before the refugee arrived, the power of the LORD came over me. On the morning the refugee arrived, the LORD made me speak. So I spoke, and I was no longer quiet.

[23] The LORD spoke his word to me. He said, [24] "Son of man, those who live in the ruined cities in Israel are saying, 'Abraham was only one person, and he was given the land. But we

are many. Certainly the land has been given to us.' ²⁵ So tell them, 'This is what the Almighty LORD says: You eat meat with blood in it. You look to your idols for help. You murder people. Should the land be given to you? ²⁶ You rely on your swords. You do disgusting things. You dishonor your neighbor's wife. Should the land be given to you?'

²⁷ "Tell them, 'This is what the Almighty LORD says: As I live, whoever is in the ruined cities will be killed in battle. Whoever is in the open field will become food for wild animals. Whoever is in fortified places and caves will die from plagues. ²⁸ I will turn the land into a barren wasteland. People will no longer brag about its power. The mountains of Israel will become so ruined that no one will travel through them. ²⁹ Then people will know that I am the LORD, when I make the land a barren wasteland because of all the disgusting things that they have done.'

³⁰ "Son of man, your people are talking about you by the walls and in the doorways of their homes. They are saying to each other, 'Let's go and hear the word that has come from the LORD.' ³¹ Then they come to you, as if they are still my people, and they sit down in front of you. They listen to what you say, but they don't do it. They say that they love me, but in their hearts they chase dishonest profits. ³² To them you are nothing more than a singer with a beautiful voice who sings love songs or a musician who plays an instrument. They listen to your words, but they don't do them. ³³ When all your words come true—and they certainly will come true—these people will know that a prophet has been among them."

The Promise of a New Shepherd for the LORD's Sheep

34 ¹ The LORD spoke his word to me. He said, ² "Son of man, prophesy against the shepherds of Israel. Prophesy to these shepherds. Tell them, 'This is what the Almighty LORD says: How horrible it will be for the shepherds of Israel who have been taking care of only themselves. Shouldn't shepherds take care of the sheep? ³ You eat the best parts of the sheep, dress in the wool, and butcher the finest sheep. Yet, you don't take care of the sheep. ⁴ You have not strengthened those that were weak, healed those that were sick, or bandaged those that were injured. You have not brought back those that strayed away or looked for those that were lost. You have ruled them harshly and violently. ⁵ So they were scattered because there was no shepherd. When they were scattered, they became food for every wild animal. ⁶ My sheep wandered over all the mountains and on every high hill. They were scattered throughout the whole earth. No one searched or looked for them.

⁷ " 'So, you shepherds, listen to the word of the LORD. ⁸ As I live, declares the Almighty LORD, because there is no shepherd, my sheep have become prey. My sheep have become food for every wild animal. My shepherds haven't searched for my sheep. They have taken care of only themselves, not my sheep. ⁹ So, you shepherds, listen to the word of the LORD. ¹⁰ This is what the Almighty LORD says: I am against the shepherds. I will demand that they hand over my sheep. I won't let them take care of my sheep anymore, and they will no longer take care of only themselves. I will rescue my sheep from their mouths, and my sheep will no longer be their food.

¹¹ " 'This is what the Almighty LORD says: I will search for my sheep myself, and I will look after them. ¹² As a shepherd looks after his flock when he is with his scattered sheep, so I will look after my sheep. I will rescue them on a cloudy and gloomy day from every place where they have been scattered. ¹³ I will bring them out from the nations, gather them from the countries, and bring them to their own land. I will take care of them on the mountains of Israel, by the streams, and in all the inhabited places of the land. ¹⁴ I will feed them in good pasture, and they will graze on the mountains of Israel. They will rest on the good land where they graze, and they will feed on the best pastures in the mountains of Israel. ¹⁵ I will take care of my sheep and lead them to rest, declares the Almighty LORD. ¹⁶ I will look for those that are lost, bring back those that have strayed away, bandage those that are injured, and strengthen those that are sick. I will destroy those that are fat and strong. I will take care of my sheep fairly.

¹⁷ " 'As for you, my sheep, this is what the Almighty LORD says: I will judge disputes between one sheep and another, between rams and male goats. ¹⁸ Isn't it enough for you to feed on the good pasture? Must you trample the rest of the pasture with your feet? You drink clean water. Must you muddy the rest of the water with your feet? ¹⁹ Must my sheep eat what your feet have trampled and drink what your feet have muddied?

²⁰ " 'So this is what the Almighty LORD says to them: I will judge disputes between the fat sheep and the skinny sheep. ²¹ You fat sheep push the skinny sheep with your sides and shoulders, and you knock down all the sick sheep with your horns. You have scattered them all over. ²² So I will rescue my sheep, and they will no longer be prey. I will judge between one sheep and another. ²³ Then I will place one shepherd over them, my servant David, and he will take care of them. He will take care of them and be their shepherd. ²⁴ I, the LORD, will be their God, and my servant David will be their prince. I, the LORD, have spoken.

²⁵ " 'I will promise them peace. I will remove the wild animals from the land so that my sheep can live safely in the wilderness and sleep in the woods. ²⁶ I will bless them and the

places around my hill. I will send rain at the right time. These showers will be a blessing to them. **27** Then the trees in the field will produce fruit, the land will yield crops, and my sheep will live safely in their land. Then they will know that I am the LORD, because I will break off the bars on their yokes[a] and rescue them from the people who made them slaves. **28** They will no longer be prey to the nations, and the wild animals will no longer eat them. They will live safely, and no one will frighten them. **29** I will give them a place that is known for its good crops. They will no longer experience hunger in the land, and they will no longer suffer the insults of other nations. **30** Then they will know that I, the LORD their God, am with them and that they, the people of Israel, are my people, declares the Almighty LORD. **31** You, my sheep, are the sheep in my pasture. You are mortal, and I am your God, declares the Almighty LORD.' "

Judgment on Edom

35 **1** The LORD spoke his word to me. He said, **2** "Son of man, turn to Mount Seir, and prophesy against it. **3** Tell it, 'This is what the Almighty LORD says:

I'm against you, Mount Seir.
> I will use my power against you,
>> and you will become a wasteland.
4 I will turn your cities into ruins,
>> and you will become a wasteland.
>>> Then you will know that I am the LORD.

5 " 'You have always been an enemy of Israel.
> You deserted the people of Israel in battle
>> when they were in trouble during their final punishment.
6 That is why, as I live, declares the Almighty LORD,
> I will let you be murdered.
> Murderers will pursue you.
Since you don't hate murdering people, murder will pursue you.
7 I will turn Mount Seir into a barren wasteland,
>> and I will destroy everyone who comes or goes from there.
8 I will fill your mountains with those who have been killed.
> Those killed in battle will fall on your hills
>> and in your valleys and ravines.
9 I will turn you into a permanent wasteland.
> Your cities will not be lived in.
>> Then you will know that I am the LORD.

10 " 'You said, "These two nations, Israel and Judah, along with their land, belong to us. We will take possession of them." But the LORD was there. **11** That is why, as I live, declares the Almighty LORD, I will do to you what you did to them. When you were angry and jealous, you acted hatefully toward them. **12** Then you will know that I, the LORD, heard all the insults that you spoke about the mountains of Israel. You said, "They have been deserted and handed over to us to use up." **13** You bragged and continually talked against me. I heard you.

14 " 'This is what the Almighty LORD says: The whole earth will be glad when I turn you into a wasteland. **15** You were happy when the land of Israel became a wasteland. I will do the same thing to you. You will become a wasteland, Mount Seir, and so will all of Edom. Then you will know that I am the LORD.' "

Blessings for the Mountains of Israel

36 **1** The LORD said, "Son of man, prophesy to the mountains of Israel. Tell them, 'Mountains of Israel, listen to the word of the LORD. **2** This is what the Almighty LORD says: Your enemies said this about you, "Aha! The ancient worship sites now belong to us." '

3 "So prophesy. Say, 'This is what the Almighty LORD says: Your enemies turned you into ruins and crushed you from every side. You became the possession of the rest of the nations, and people began to talk and gossip about you.

4 " 'Mountains of Israel, listen to the word of the Almighty LORD. This is what the Almighty LORD says to the mountains and hills, to the ravines and valleys, and to the empty ruins and abandoned cities that have become prey and are mocked by the rest of the surrounding nations: **5** In my fiery anger I have spoken against the rest of the nations and against all of Edom. The Edomites have taken possession of my land with wholehearted joy and with complete scorn. They forced out the people and took their land.'

---

[a] 34:27 A yoke is a wooden bar placed over the necks of work animals so that they can pull plows or carts.

⁶ "So prophesy about Israel. Tell the mountains and hills and the ravines and valleys, 'This is what the Almighty LORD says: I am speaking in my anger and fury because you have been insulted by the nations. ⁷ So this is what the Almighty LORD says: I raise my hand and swear that the nations which surround you will be insulted.

⁸ " 'But you, mountains of Israel, will grow branches and bear fruit for my people Israel. My people will come home soon. ⁹ I am for you. I will turn to you, and you will be plowed and planted. ¹⁰ I will increase the number of people who live on you. All the people of Israel, all of them, will live on you. The cities will be inhabited, and the ruins will be rebuilt. ¹¹ I will increase the number of people and animals that live on you. They will grow and become many. I will let people live on you as in the past, and I will make you better off than ever before. Then you will know that I am the LORD. ¹² I will bring people, my people Israel, to you. They will take possession of you, and you will be their inheritance. You will no longer take their children away from them.

¹³ " 'This is what the Almighty LORD says: People say that you devour your people and take the children away from your nation. ¹⁴ So you will no longer devour your people or take the children away from your nation, declares the Almighty LORD. ¹⁵ I will no longer let you hear the insults from the nations. You will no longer suffer the disgrace of the people. You will never again take the children away from your own nation, declares the Almighty LORD.' "

¹⁶ The LORD spoke his word to me. He said, ¹⁷ "Son of man, when the people of Israel lived in their land, they dishonored it by the way they lived and by everything they did. Their ways were as unclean*a* as a woman's menstrual period. ¹⁸ So I poured out my fury on them because they poured out blood on the land and they dishonored the land with their idols. ¹⁹ I forced them into other nations, and they became scattered among the nations. I judged them based on the way that they lived and based on everything that they had done. ²⁰ But wherever they went among the nations, they dishonored my holy name. People said about them, 'These are the LORD's people, yet they had to leave his land.' ²¹ I became concerned about my holy name because my people dishonored it among the nations wherever they went.

²² "So tell the people of Israel, 'This is what the Almighty LORD says: I am about to do something, people of Israel. I will not do this for your sake but for the sake of my holy name, which you have dishonored among the nations wherever you have gone. ²³ I will reveal the holiness of my great name, which has been dishonored by the nations, the name that you have dishonored among them. Then the nations will know that I am the LORD, because I will reveal my holiness among you as they watch, declares the Almighty LORD.

²⁴ " 'I will take you from the nations and gather you from every country. I will bring you back to your own land. ²⁵ I will sprinkle clean water on you and make you clean*b* instead of unclean. Then I will cleanse you from all your idols. ²⁶ I will give you a new heart and put a new spirit in you. I will remove your stubborn hearts and give you obedient hearts. ²⁷ I will put my Spirit in you. I will enable you to live by my laws, and you will obey my rules. ²⁸ Then you will live in the land that I gave your ancestors. You will be my people, and I will be your God. ²⁹ I will rescue you from all your uncleanness. I will make the grain grow so that you will never again have famines. ³⁰ I will make fruit grow on the trees and crops grow in the fields so that you will no longer suffer disgrace among the nations because of famines. ³¹ Then you will remember your evil ways and the bad things that you did, and you will hate yourselves for all these wicked and disgusting things. ³² I want you to know that I'm not doing this for your sake, declares the Almighty LORD. Be ashamed and disgraced because of your ways, people of Israel.

³³ " 'This is what the Almighty LORD says: On the day that I cleanse you from all your wickedness, I will cause your cities to be lived in again, and your ruins will be rebuilt. ³⁴ The wasteland will be plowed. It will no longer remain empty for everyone passing by to see. ³⁵ People will say, "This wasteland has become like the garden of Eden. The cities were destroyed. They were empty and ruined, but now they are fortified and have people living in them." ³⁶ The surrounding nations that are left will know that I, the LORD, have rebuilt the ruined places and planted crops in the land that was empty. I, the LORD, have spoken, and I will do it.'

³⁷ "This is what the Almighty LORD says: I will also let the people of Israel ask me to make them as numerous as sheep. ³⁸ They will be like the sheep for sacrifices, like the sheep in Jerusalem during the appointed festivals. Their ruined cities will be filled with flocks of people. Then they will know that I am the LORD."

The Valley of Dry Bones

37 ¹ The power of the LORD came over me. The LORD brought me out by his Spirit and put me down in the middle of a valley. The valley was filled with bones. ² He led me all around them. I saw that there were very many bones at the bottom of the valley, and they were very dry.

---

a 36:17 "Unclean" refers to anything that Moses' Teachings say is not presentable to God.   *b* 36:25 "Clean" refers to anything that Moses' Teachings say is presentable to God.

[3] Then he asked me, "Son of man, can these bones live?"

I answered, "Only you know, Almighty LORD."

[4] Then he said to me, "Prophesy to these bones. Tell them, 'Dry bones, listen to the word of the LORD. [5] This is what the Almighty LORD says to these bones: I will cause breath to enter you, and you will live. [6] I will put ligaments on you, place muscles on you, and cover you with skin. I will put breath in you, and you will live. Then you will know that I am the LORD.' "

[7] So I prophesied as I was commanded. While I was prophesying, suddenly there was a rattling noise, and the bones came together, one bone ˌattaching itselfˌ to another. [8] As I looked, I saw that ligaments were on them, muscles were on them, and skin covered them. Yet, there was no breath in them.

[9] Then the LORD said to me, "Prophesy to the breath!ᵃ Prophesy, son of man. Tell the breath, 'This is what the Almighty LORD says: Come from the four winds, Breath, and breathe on these people who were killed so that they will live.' "

[10] So I prophesied as he commanded me, and the breath entered them. Then they came to life and stood on their feet. There were enough of them to form a very large army.

[11] The LORD also said to me, "Son of man, all the people of Israel are like these bones. The people say, 'Our bones are dry, and our hope has vanished. We are completely destroyed.' [12] So prophesy. Tell them, 'This is what the Almighty LORD says: My people, I will open your graves and take you out of them. I will bring you to Israel. [13] Then, my people, you will know that I am the LORD, because I will open your graves and bring you out of your graves. [14] I will put my Spirit in you, and you will live. I will place you in your own land. Then you will know that I, the LORD, have spoken, and I have done it, declares the LORD.' "

[15] The LORD spoke his word to me again. He said, [16] "Son of man, take a stick and write on it: 'For Judah and for the Israelites who are associated with it.' Then take another stick and write on it, 'The stick of Ephraim, for Joseph and for all the people of Israel associated with it.' [17] Then join both sticks together so that they will be one in your hand. Your people will say to you, [18] 'Tell us what you mean by this.' [19] Then say to them, 'This is what the Almighty LORD says: I will take Joseph's stick, which is in Ephraim's hand, and the tribes of Israel associated with it, and I will put them with Judah's stick. I will make them into one stick. They will be one in my hand.' [20] When you hold the sticks in your hand, let the people see them.

[21] "Then tell them, 'This is what the Almighty LORD says: I will take the Israelites out of the nations where they've gone. I will gather them from everywhere and bring them to their own land. [22] I will form them into one nation in the land on the mountains of Israel. One king will rule all of them. They will no longer be two nations or be divided into two kingdoms. [23] They will no longer dishonor themselves with their idols, with their detestable things, or with their rebellious acts. I will forgive them for all the times they turned away from me and sinned. I will cleanse them so that they will be my people, and I will be their God.

[24] " 'My servant David will be their king, and all of them will have one shepherd. They will live by my rules, and they will obey my laws. [25] They will live in the land that I gave my servant Jacob, the land where their ancestors lived. They, their children, and their grandchildren will live in it permanently. My servant David will always be their prince. [26] I will promise them peace. This promiseᵇ will last forever. I will establish them, make them increase in number, and put my holy place among them permanently. [27] My dwelling place will be with them. I will be their God, and they will be my people. [28] Then the nations will know that I, the LORD, have set Israel apart as holy, because my holy place will be among them permanently.' "

The Destruction of Gog and Its Army

38 [1] The LORD spoke his word to me. He said, [2] "Son of man, turn to Gog from the land of Magog. He is the chief prince of ˌthe nations ofˌ Meshech and Tubal. Prophesy against him. [3] Tell him, 'This is what the Almighty LORD says: I am against you, Gog, chief prince of Meshech and Tubal. [4] I will turn you around and put hooks in your jaws. I will lead you out with all your military forces, with horses and riders. Your soldiers will be fully armed. They will carry large and small shields and be able to use swords. [5] Persia, Sudan, and Put will be with you. They, too, will have shields and helmets. [6] Gomer will come with all its troops and with the nation of Togarmah from the far north. There will be many armies with you.

[7] " 'Be prepared! Be prepared, you and all the soldiers assembled around you. You will be their leader. [8] After a long time you will be called to service. In the years to come, you will attack a land that has been rebuilt after a war. Its people have been gathered from many nations and brought to the mountains of Israel, mountains that have been ruined for a long time. These people were brought there from the nations, and all of them live there safely. [9] You will attack like a storm and cover the land like a cloud. Your troops and the many armies will be with you.

ᵃ 37:9 Or "Spirit."   ᵇ 37:26 Or "covenant."

¹⁰ " 'This is what the Almighty LORD says: At that time ideas will enter your head, and you will make wicked plans. ¹¹ You will say, "I'll attack a land with unwalled villages. I will attack peaceful people who live safely. All of them live without walls, locks, or gates. ¹² I will come to rob them and loot them. I will use my power against the ruins that people are living in again. I will use it against the people who were gathered from the nations. These people have cattle and property, and they live in the world."

¹³ " 'Sheba, Dedan, the merchants from Tarshish, and all their villages will ask you, "Did you come to rob these people of their possessions? Did you assemble all these soldiers to carry away large amounts of silver and gold and to take cattle and property?" '

¹⁴ "So prophesy, son of man. Tell Gog, 'This is what the Almighty LORD says: At that time my people Israel will live safely, and you will know it. ¹⁵ You will come from your place in the far north and many armies will be with you. All of you will ride on horses. You will be a large crowd and a mighty army. ¹⁶ You will attack my people Israel like a cloud that covers the land. In the days to come, I will let you attack my land so that nations will know me. I will use you for my holy purpose as they watch.

¹⁷ " 'This is what the Almighty LORD says: You are the one I spoke about long ago through my servants the prophets of Israel. They prophesied in those days that I would bring you to attack them. ¹⁸ On the day that Gog attacks the land of Israel, I will be filled with burning anger, declares the Almighty LORD. ¹⁹ In my fiery anger I tell you this. On that day there will be a large earthquake in the land of Israel. ²⁰ Fish, birds, wild animals, everything that crawls on the ground, and every person on earth will tremble in my presence. The mountains will be torn down, the cliffs will crumble, and every wall will fall to the ground. ²¹ I will declare war against Gog on all my mountains, declares the Almighty LORD. Each person will use his sword against his relative. ²² I will punish Gog with plagues and death. I will send rainstorms, large hailstones, fire, and burning sulfur on his troops and on the many armies with him. ²³ I will show my greatness and my holiness. I will reveal myself to many nations. Then they will know that I am the LORD.' "

39 ¹ The LORD said, "Son of man, prophesy against Gog. Tell it, 'This is what the Almighty LORD says: I am against you, Gog, the chief prince of Meshech and Tubal. ² I will turn you around and lead you. I will bring you from the far north and have you attack the mountains of Israel. ³ Then I will knock the bow out of your left hand and make you drop the arrows in your right hand. ⁴ You will die on the mountains of Israel with your troops and the armies that are with you. I will let you become food for every bird of prey and for every wild animal. ⁵ You will die in the open field because I said so, declares the Almighty LORD. ⁶ I will send fire on Magog and on those who live safely on the coasts. Then they will know that I am the LORD. ⁷ I will make my holy name known among my people Israel, and I will never let them dishonor my holy name again. Then the nations will know that I am the LORD, the Holy One in Israel.

⁸ " 'It's coming! It will happen! declares the Almighty LORD. This is the day I have spoken about. ⁹ Those living in the cities of Israel will go out. They will set fire to weapons and burn them. They will burn small and large shields, bows and arrows, and war clubs and spears. They will burn them for seven years. ¹⁰ They will not need to get wood from the field or cut down trees in the woods. They will make fires with the weapons. They will loot those who looted them, and they will grab things back from those who grabbed their things, declares the Almighty LORD.

¹¹ " 'When that day comes, I will give Gog a burial place in Israel. It will be in Travelers Valley, east of the Dead Sea. It will block those who travel through the valley. Gog and his whole army will be buried there. So it will be called the valley of Gog's troops. ¹² The people of Israel will be burying them there for seven months to make the land clean.ᵃ ¹³ All the common people will be burying them. The people of Israel will be honored on the day of my victory, declares the Almighty LORD.

¹⁴ " 'People will be chosen to go through the land and make it clean. With the help of others they will bury the dead soldiers that are still on the ground. At the end of seven months they will begin their search. ¹⁵ Whenever they go through the land and see a human bone, they will set up a marker beside it until the grave diggers have buried that bone in the valley of Gog's troops. ¹⁶ (A city named Hamonahᵇ will also be there.) In this way they will cleanse the land.'

¹⁷ "Son of man, this is what the Almighty LORD says: Tell every kind of bird and every wild animal, 'Assemble, and come together from all around for the sacrifice that I'm preparing for you. It will be a huge feast on the mountains of Israel. You can eat meat and drink blood there. ¹⁸ You can eat the meat of warriors and drink the blood of the princes of the earth. All of them will be killed like rams, lambs, goats, bulls and all the best animals of Bashan. ¹⁹ You can eat

---

ᵃ 39:12 "Clean" refers to anything that Moses' Teachings say is presentable to God.   ᵇ 39:16 There is a play on words here between Hebrew *hamon* (troops) and Hamonah.

the best meat until you are full and drink blood until you are drunk at the sacrifice that I am preparing for you. ²⁰ At my table you will be filled with horses and riders, warriors, and soldiers of every kind, declares the Almighty LORD.'

²¹ "I will show my greatness among the nations. All the nations will see how I will turn my power against them to punish them. ²² From that day on, the people of Israel will know that I am the LORD their God. ²³ Then the nations will know that the people of Israel went into captivity because they did wrong and rebelled against me. So I hid my face from them and handed them over to their enemies. They were killed in battle. ²⁴ I paid them back for their uncleanness and their sins, and I hid my face from them.

²⁵ "So this is what the Almighty LORD says: Now I will bring back Jacob's captives and have compassion for the whole nation of Israel. I will stand up for my holy name. ²⁶ When they live safely in a land where no one will frighten them, they will forget their shame and all the unfaithful things they have done against me. ²⁷ I will bring them back from the other nations and gather them from the countries of their enemies. Many nations will see that I am holy. ²⁸ Then my people will know that I am the LORD their God. I sent them into captivity among the nations, and I brought them back again to their land. I left none of them behind. ²⁹ I will no longer hide my face from them, because I will pour out my Spirit on the nation of Israel, declares the Almighty LORD."

The New Temple of God

40 ¹ It was the tenth day of the month in the beginning of the twenty-fifth year of our captivity and fourteen years after Jerusalem was captured. At that time the LORD's power came over me, and he brought me to Jerusalem. ² In visions, God brought me to Israel and set me down on a very high mountain. On the south side of the mountain were some buildings that looked like those in a city. ³ He brought me closer. I saw a man who looked like he was covered with bronze. The man was holding a linen tape measure and a measuring stick, and he stood in a gateway. ⁴ He said to me, "Son of man, look with your eyes, and listen with your ears. Pay close attention to everything I'm going to show you. You were brought here to be shown these things. Tell the nation of Israel everything that you see."

The East Gateway

⁵ I saw a wall that surrounded the temple. The man had a measuring stick that was 10½ feet long. He measured the wall. It was 10½ feet thick and 10½ feet high.

⁶ Then the man went to the gateway that faced east. He went up its steps and measured the entrance to the gateway. It was 10½ feet wide. ⁷ There were also guardrooms. Each guardroom was 10½ feet long and 10½ feet wide. The space between the guardrooms was 9 feet thick. And the entrance to the gateway by the entrance hall of the temple was 10½ feet wide. ⁸ He also measured the entrance hall of the gateway. ⁹ It extended 14 feet from the temple. Its recessed walls were 3½ feet thick. The gateway's entrance hall faced the temple.

¹⁰ Now, there were three guardrooms on each side of the eastern gateway. All three rooms on each side were the same size, and the recessed walls on each side were the same size. ¹¹ Then the man measured the width of the entrance to the gateway. It was 17½ feet wide, and the gateway was 23 feet long. ¹² There was a barrier about 21 inches in front of each guardroom. The guardrooms were 10½ feet square. ¹³ He measured the gateway from the top of one guardroom to the top of the opposite guardroom. It was 44 feet wide from one door to the opposite door. ¹⁴ He also measured the entrance hall. It was 35 feet wide. In front of the entrance hall to the gateway was a courtyard on all sides. ¹⁵ The total length of the gateway from the front of the outer part to the front of the inner part of the entrance hall was 87½ feet.

¹⁶ The guardrooms and recessed walls inside the gateway had small windows all around. The entrance hall also had windows all around on the inside. Pictures of palm trees were carved on the recessed walls.

The Outer Courtyard

¹⁷ Then the man brought me into the outer courtyard. I saw rooms there and pavement all around the courtyard. There were 30 rooms along the edge of the pavement. ¹⁸ The pavement in the lower courtyard ran alongside the gateways. It was as wide as it was long. ¹⁹ The man measured the distance from the inside of the lower gateway to the outside of the inner courtyard. It was 175 feet from east to north.

The North Gateway

²⁰ Then the man measured the length and width of the gateway, leading to the outer courtyard. This was the gateway that faced north. ²¹ Its three guardrooms, its recessed walls, and its entrance hall were the same size as those in the east gateway. The gateway was 87½ feet

long and 44 feet wide. ²² Its windows, recessed walls, and palm tree pictures were the same size as those in the east gateway. Seven steps went up to it and led to its entrance hall. ²³ The inner courtyard had a gateway opposite the north gate just like the east gateway. The man measured the distance from one gate to the other gate. It was 175 feet.

The South Gateway

²⁴ Then the man led me to the south side, and I saw a gateway that faced south. He measured its recessed walls and its entrance hall. They were the same size as those of the other gateways. ²⁵ The gateway and its entrance hall had windows on all sides like the windows in the other gateways. It was 87½ feet long and 44 feet wide. ²⁶ Seven steps went up to it and led to its entrance hall. Pictures of palm trees were carved on the recessed walls, one picture on each side. ²⁷ The inner courtyard had a gateway facing south. The man measured the distance from the gateway on the south side to its opposite gateway. It was 175 feet.

The Inner Courtyard

²⁸ Then the man brought me to the inner courtyard through the south gateway. He measured the south gateway. It was the same size as the others. ²⁹ Its guardrooms, recessed walls, and entrance hall were the same size as the other gateways. The guardrooms and the entrance hall had windows all around. The gateway was 87½ feet long and 44 feet wide. ³⁰ There were entrance halls all around the inner courtyard. They were all 44 feet long and 9 feet wide. ³¹ The entrance halls faced the outer courtyard. Pictures of palm trees were carved on the recessed walls, and eight steps led up to each gateway.

³² Then the man brought me to the east side of the inner courtyard. He measured the gateway. It was the same size as the others. ³³ Its guardrooms, recessed walls, and entrance halls were the same size as those of the other gateways. Its guardrooms and entrance hall had windows all around. The gateway was 87½ feet long and 44 feet wide. ³⁴ Its entrance hall faced the outer courtyard. Pictures of palm trees were carved on the recessed walls, and eight steps led up to the gateway.

³⁵ Then the man brought me to the north gateway. He measured it. It was the same size as the others. ³⁶ Its guardrooms, recessed walls, and entrance hall had windows all around. The gateway was 87½ feet long and 44 feet wide. ³⁷ Its recessed walls faced the outer courtyard. Pictures of palm trees were carved on the recessed walls, and eight steps led up to the gateway.

Special Rooms

³⁸ There was a room with a door that opened toward the entrance hall of the gateway. This is the room where the priests washed the animals for the burnt offerings. ³⁹ In the entrance hall of the gateway there were two tables on each side of the room. On these tables the animals were slaughtered for burnt offerings, offerings for sin, and guilt offerings. ⁴⁰ On each side of the entrance to the north gateway there were two tables, and on the other side of the entrance hall of the gateway there were two tables. ⁴¹ So there were four tables on each side of the gateway, eight tables in all, on which they slaughtered animals. ⁴² There were four tables made of cut stone for burnt offerings. They were 3 feet long, 3 feet wide, and 21 inches high. On these tables the priests laid the utensils that were used to slaughter animals for burnt offerings and sacrifices. ⁴³ Double-pronged hooks, three inches long, were attached to the wall all around the room, and the tables were for the meat of the animals. ⁴⁴ Outside the gateways to the inner courtyard were the rooms for the singers in the inner courtyards. One room was at the side of the north gateway. It faced south. The other room was at the side of the south gateway. It faced north. ⁴⁵ The man said to me, "This room that faces south is for the priests who serve in the temple. ⁴⁶ The room that faces north is for the priests who serve at the altar. These priests are Zadok's descendants. They are the only Levites who are able to come near the LORD and serve him." ⁴⁷ The man measured the courtyard. It was a perfect square—175 feet long and 175 feet wide. And the altar was in front of the temple.

⁴⁸ Then the man brought me to the entrance hall of the temple and measured its recessed walls. They were 9 feet on each side. The gateway was 24½ feet wide, and the walls on each side were 5 feet wide. ⁴⁹ The entrance hall was 35 feet long and 21 feet wide. Steps led up to it. Pillars stood by the recessed walls, one on each side of the entrance hall.

The Holy Place in the Temple

41 ¹ Then the man brought me into the holy place in the temple and measured the recessed walls. They were 10½ feet wide on each side. ² The entrance was 17½ feet wide, and on each side of the entrance the walls were 9 feet wide. Then he measured the length of the holy place. It was 70 feet long and 35 feet wide.

³ Then the man went inside and measured the passageway. It was 3½ feet thick. The entrance was 10½ feet high and 12 feet wide. ⁴ Then he measured the room at the end of the holy place. It was 35 feet long and 35 feet wide. The man said to me, "This is the most holy place."

⁵ Next, the man measured the temple wall. It was 10½ feet wide. The width of each side room around the temple was 7 feet. ⁶ The rooms were arranged on three different stories. There were 30 rooms on each story. These rooms had supports all the way around the temple wall, but these supports were not fastened to the temple wall. ⁷ The side rooms grew wider all the way around as they went up, story after story. The surrounding structure went from story to story all around the temple. The structure grew wider as it went higher. A stairway went from the first story through the second story to the third story.

⁸ I also saw a raised base all around the temple. This base was the foundation for the side rooms. It measured the full length of the measuring rod, 10½ feet. ⁹ The outer wall of the side rooms was 9 feet thick. There was an open area between the side rooms connected to the temple ¹⁰ and the priests' rooms. It was 35 feet wide and went all around the temple. ¹¹ The doors in the side rooms were entrances into the open area. There was one door to the north and another to the south. The base of the open area was 9 feet wide all the way around.

¹² At the far end of the open area, on the west side of the temple, was a building 122½ feet wide. The wall of the building was 9 feet thick all the way around, and it was 157½ feet long.

¹³ Then the man measured the temple. It was 175 feet long. This included the open area with the building and its walls. All together it was 175 feet long. ¹⁴ The eastern side of the temple, including the open area, was also 175 feet wide. ¹⁵ He also measured the length of the building facing the courtyard on the west side along with its corridors on both sides. It was 175 feet long.

The holy place and the most holy place were paneled. ¹⁶ The doorposts, the small windows, and the corridors of all three stories were paneled. The walls, from the floor up to the windows, were paneled. ¹⁷ In the space above the door to the most holy place and on the walls all around it, ¹⁸ there were pictures of angels*ᵃ* and palm trees. Palm trees were positioned between each of the angels, and each angel had two faces: ¹⁹ the face of a man, which was turned toward a palm tree on one side, and the face of a lion, which was turned toward a palm tree on the other side. These pictures were carved all around the temple. ²⁰ Pictures of angels and palm trees were carved on the walls from the floor to the space above the door.

²¹ The doorframes in the holy place were square. In front of the most holy place was something similar. ²² There was a wooden altar, 5 feet high and 3½ feet wide. Its corners, its base, and its sides were made of wood. Then the man told me, "This is the table that is in the presence of the LORD."

²³ The holy place and the most holy place had two doors. ²⁴ Each of the doors were double doors that swung open. ²⁵ Pictures of angels and palm trees were carved on the doors of the holy place as on the walls. There was a wooden roof hanging over the outer entrance hall. ²⁶ There were small windows and palm trees on both sides of the entrance hall, on the side rooms of the temple, and on the roofs.

The Courtyards of the LORD's New Temple

42 ¹ Then the man led me out toward the north to the outer courtyard. He brought me to the side rooms opposite both the open area and the northern building. ² The building that faced north was 175 feet long and 87½ feet wide. ³ Opposite the inner courtyard was an area that was 35 feet wide, and opposite the pavement of the outer courtyard were corridors facing corridors on all three stories. ⁴ In front of the side rooms was a walkway, 17½ feet wide and 175 feet long. The doors of these side rooms faced north.

⁵ The side rooms on the third story were narrower than those on the first or second stories of the building because the corridors took space away from them. ⁶ The rooms were in three stories. They didn't have pillars like the pillars in the courtyards. That is why the rooms on the third story were set farther back than those on the first and second stories. ⁷ There was a wall which ran parallel to the side rooms and the outer courtyard. It ran alongside the side rooms for 87½ feet. ⁸ The row of rooms in the outer courtyard was 87½ feet long. The rooms that faced the temple were 175 feet long. ⁹ These lower side rooms had an entrance on the east side. A person was able to enter the outer courtyard through them.

¹⁰ There were side rooms parallel to the wall of the courtyard on the south side.*ᵃ* They faced the open area and the building. ¹¹ There was a walkway in front of them like the one that was in front of the side rooms on the north side. These side rooms were as long and as wide as the northern rooms. They had the same exits, dimensions, and doors. ¹² The doors to the south

---

ᵃ 41:18 Or "cherubim."   *ᵃ* 42:10 Greek; Masoretic Text "east side."

rooms were the same as the doors to the north rooms. There was a doorway at the other end of the walkway that was parallel to the corresponding wall that ran eastward. People entered through that doorway.

¹³ Then the man said to me, "The northern and southern side rooms that face the open area are holy rooms. These rooms are where the priests who come near the LORD eat the holiest offerings. Because these rooms are holy, the priests keep the holiest offerings there: the grain offerings, the offerings for sin, and the guilt offerings. ¹⁴ Once the priests enter the holy place, they must not go out of the holy place into the outer courtyard until they leave behind the clothes that they wore as they served. These clothes are holy. The priests must put on other clothes. Then they can go into the area that is for the people."

¹⁵ When the man had finished measuring the inner part of the temple area, he led me out through the east gate. Then he measured all the way around the outer area. ¹⁶ He measured the east side with a measuring stick. It was 875 feet long according to the measuring stick. ¹⁷ He measured the north side. It was 875 feet long according to the measuring stick. ¹⁸ He measured the south side. It was 875 feet long according to the measuring stick. ¹⁹ He came around to the west side and measured it. It was 875 feet long according to the measuring stick. ²⁰ So he measured all four sides. There was a wall all around it. The wall was 875 feet long and 875 feet wide. It separated what was holy from what was unholy.

The Glory of the LORD Fills the New Temple

43 ¹ Then the man took me to the east gate. ² I saw the glory of the God of Israel coming from the east. His voice was like the sound of rushing water, and the earth was shining because of his glory. ³ This vision was like the one I saw when he came[a] to destroy Jerusalem and like the one I saw by the Chebar River. I immediately bowed down. ⁴ The LORD's glory came into the temple through the east gate.

⁵ The Spirit lifted me and brought me into the inner courtyard. I saw the LORD's glory fill the temple. ⁶ I heard someone speaking to me from inside the temple while the man was standing beside me. ⁷ The voice said to me, "Son of man, this is the place where my throne is and the place where my feet rest. This is where I will live among the Israelites forever. Then the people of Israel and their kings will no longer dishonor my holy name by acting like prostitutes, nor will they dishonor it with the dead bodies of their kings. ⁸ They put their doorway by my doorway and their doorposts by my doorposts. Only a wall separated me from them. They dishonored my holy name because of the disgusting things that they have done. So I destroyed them in my anger. ⁹ Now they must stop acting like prostitutes and take the dead bodies of their kings far away from me. Then I will live among them forever.

¹⁰ "Son of man, describe this temple to the people of Israel. Then they will be ashamed because of their sins. Let them study the plans. ¹¹ Suppose they are ashamed of everything that they have done. Then show them the design of the temple, its arrangements, its exits and entrances—its entire design. Tell them about all its rules and regulations. Then write these things down for them so that they can remember its design and follow all its rules.

¹² "This is a regulation of the temple: The whole area all the way around the top of the mountain is most holy. Yes, this is a regulation of the temple."

The Altar in the New Temple

¹³ These are the measurements of the altar, using royal measurements. (The royal measuring stick was 21 inches long.) The base of the altar was 21 inches high and 21 inches wide. All around the edge of the altar was a rim measuring 9 inches wide. This was the height of the altar: ¹⁴ From the base on the ground to the lower ledge it was 3½ feet high, and from the lower ledge to the upper ledge it was 7 feet high and 21 inches wide. ¹⁵ The place where the sacrifices were burned was 7 feet high. There were four horns above it. ¹⁶ It was square, 21 feet wide and 21 feet long. ¹⁷ The upper ledge was also square. It was 24½ feet long and 24½ feet wide. It had a rim all the way around that was 10½ inches wide. Its base was 21 inches. The steps to the altar faced east.

¹⁸ Then the man said to me, "Son of man, this is what the Almighty LORD says: These are the rules for sacrificing burnt offerings and for sprinkling blood on the altar after the altar is built. ¹⁹ Give a young bull to the priests as an offering for sin. These priests are Zadok's descendants, men from the tribe of Levi, who can come near me and serve me. ²⁰ Take some of the bull's blood, and put it on the altar's four horns, on the four corners of the ledge, and on the rim all the way around the altar. When you do this, you will remove sin from the altar and make peace with the LORD. ²¹ Then take a young bull as an offering for sin, and burn it in the place appointed near the temple, outside the holy place.

---

[a] 43:3 Some Hebrew manuscripts, Greek, Latin; other Hebrew manuscripts "When I came."

²² "On the second day bring a male goat that has no defects as an offering for sin. Remove sin from the altar as you did with the young bull. ²³ When you finish removing sin, offer a young bull and a ram that have no defects. ²⁴ Offer them to the LORD. The priests must throw salt on them and offer them as burnt offerings to the LORD. ²⁵ Every day for seven days you must sacrifice a goat, a young bull, and a ram from the flock as an offering for sin. They must be animals that have no defects. ²⁶ For seven days the priests should make peace with the LORD at the altar, purify it, and consecrate it. ²⁷ When those days are over, on the eighth day, the priests must sacrifice burnt offerings and fellowship offerings on the altar. Then I will accept them, declares the Almighty LORD."

The East Gate Is Sealed Shut

44 ¹ Then the man took me back to the outer east gate of the holy place, and the gate was shut. ² The LORD said to me, "This gate will stay shut and will not be opened. No one may enter through it because the LORD God of Israel entered through it. It must be kept shut. ³ Only the prince may sit there and eat food in the presence of the LORD. He will enter through the entrance hall of the gateway and leave the same way."

⁴ The man brought me through the north gate in front of the temple. When I looked, I saw the LORD's glory fill the LORD's temple. I immediately bowed down.

The People Serving in the New Temple

⁵ The LORD said to me, "Son of man, pay close attention. Look, and listen to everything I'm going to tell you. Listen to all the rules and regulations for the LORD's temple. Pay close attention to everyone who enters the temple and leaves from the holy place. ⁶ Tell the rebellious people of Israel, 'This is what the Almighty LORD says: I've had enough of all the disgusting things that you have done, people of Israel. ⁷ You brought godless foreigners*a* into my holy place. You dishonored my temple when you offered fat and blood to me. You rejected my promise so that you could do all your disgusting things. ⁸ You didn't take care of my holy things. You put foreigners in charge of my temple. ⁹ So this is what the Almighty LORD says: Any godless foreigner who lives among the Israelites may not enter my holy place.

¹⁰ " 'Some Levites went far away from me when Israel wandered off to follow their idols. They must be punished for their sins. ¹¹ They could have served in my holy place. They could have guarded the gates of the temple. They could have served in the temple by slaughtering the animals for the burnt offerings and the sacrifices for the people. They could have stood in front of the people and served them. ¹² But they served the people by standing in front of their idols and by making Israel fall into sin. So I raised my hand and swore that they would be punished for their sins, declares the LORD. ¹³ They must not come near me and serve me as priests. They must not come near any of my holy things or my most holy things. They must suffer disgrace because of the disgusting things that they have done. ¹⁴ I will assign them all of the less important work in the temple.

¹⁵ " 'But the priests who are Levites and descendants of Zadok took care of my holy place when the Israelites wandered away from me. They may come near me and serve me, and they may stand in my presence. They may bring fat and blood to me, declares the Almighty LORD. ¹⁶ They may enter my holy place, come near my table to serve me, and take care of everything I gave them. ¹⁷ When they enter the gateways to the inner courtyard, they must wear linen clothes. They must have no wool on them while they serve in the gateways to the inner courtyard and in the temple. ¹⁸ They must wear linen turbans on their heads and linen undergarments. They must not wear anything that makes them sweat. ¹⁹ When they go out among the people in the outer courtyard, they must take off the clothes that they wore as they served. They must leave their clothes in the side rooms of the holy place and put on other clothes so that they do not transfer the holiness from their clothes to the people.

²⁰ " 'They must not shave their heads or let their hair grow long. They must keep the hair on their heads trimmed. ²¹ None of the priests may drink wine when they enter the inner courtyard. ²² They must not marry widows or women who have been divorced. They may marry only virgins from the nation of Israel or widows of priests. ²³ They must teach my people the difference between what is holy and what is unholy. They must show the people how to tell the difference between what is clean and what is unclean.*b* ²⁴ In all disputes the priests must act as judges and make decisions based on my laws. They must obey my rules and my regulations at all my festivals. They must observe holy days to worship me.

²⁵ " 'A priest must not make himself unclean by going near a dead body. But a priest may become unclean if the dead person is his father, mother, son, daughter, brother, or unmarried

---

a 44:7 Or "foreigners whose hearts and bodies are uncircumcised."   *b* 44:23 "Clean" refers to anything that Moses' Teachings say is presentable to God. "Unclean" refers to anything that Moses' Teachings say is not presentable to God.

sister. ²⁶ After a priest is made clean, he must wait seven days. ²⁷ When he enters the inner courtyard of the holy place to serve in the holy place, he must bring his offering for sin, declares the Almighty LORD.

²⁸ " 'The priests will have no inheritance. I am their inheritance. Don't give them any possessions in Israel. The priests belong to me. ²⁹ They will eat grain offerings, offerings for sin, and guilt offerings. Everything in Israel that is devoted to the LORD will belong to them. ³⁰ The priests should have the best of all the first ripened fruits. The best of every gift from all your contributions must go to the priests. The best of your dough must go to the priests. This will cause a blessing to rest on your home. ³¹ The priests must never eat any bird or animal that has died naturally or was killed by other wild animals.

Land for the Priests, Levites, and the Prince

45 ¹ " 'Divide the land by drawing lots for the property you will inherit. Set aside an area 43,750 feet long and 35,000 feet wide for the LORD. The entire area will be holy. ² An area of 875 feet square will be for the holy place with an open area 87½ feet wide. ³ Measure off an area 43,750 feet long and 17,500 feet wide. The holy place, that is, the most holy place, will be in this area. ⁴ This holy part of the land will belong to the priests who serve in the holy place, the priests who come near to serve the LORD. They will use this place for their homes, and it will be the location for the holy place. ⁵ An area 43,750 feet long and 17,500 feet wide will belong to the Levites who serve in the temple. It will be given to them so that they have cities to live in.

⁶ " 'You must designate an area 8,750 feet wide and 43,750 feet long as the city's property. It will be located alongside the holy area. It will belong to all the people of Israel.

⁷ " 'The prince will have all the land on both sides of the holy area and on both sides of the property belonging to the city. From the western boundary of the holy area, his land will extend to the Mediterranean Sea. From the eastern boundary of the holy area, his land will extend to the eastern border ˌof the countryˌ. His territory will be as large as the territory of one of the tribes. ⁸ This land will belong to the prince in Israel. Then my princes will no longer oppress my people. They will give land to each tribe of the nation of Israel.

Honest Weights and Measures for the LORD's People

⁹ " 'This is what the Almighty LORD says: I've had enough of you, you princes of Israel. Stop your violence and looting, and do what is fair and right. Stop evicting my people, declares the Almighty LORD. ¹⁰ You must have honest scales and honest dry and liquid measures. ¹¹ The dry and liquid measures must always be the same: The ephah and the bath should hold the same as one-tenth of a homer. The homer must be the standard measure.^a ¹² One shekel must weigh 20 gerahs. One mina must weigh 60 shekels.^b

Rules for Worship

¹³ " 'This is the contribution you must give to the LORD: seventeen percent of your wheat and seventeen percent of your barley. ¹⁴ You must give one percent of your olive oil using the standard measure. ¹⁵ You must take one sheep out of every 200 from the well-watered pastures of Israel. You must sacrifice them with grain offerings, burnt offerings, and fellowship offerings to make peace with the LORD, declares the Almighty LORD. ¹⁶ All the common people must give this contribution to the prince in Israel. ¹⁷ Then the prince is responsible to provide burnt offerings, grain offerings, and wine offerings at the annual festivals, the New Moon Festivals, the weekly days of worship, and all the other appointed festivals of the nation of Israel. He must prepare offerings for sin, grain offerings, burnt offerings, and fellowship offerings to make peace with the LORD for the nation of Israel.

¹⁸ " 'This is what the Almighty LORD says: On the first day of the first month, take a young bull that has no defects and remove sin from the holy place. ¹⁹ The priest must take some blood from the offering for sin and put it on the doorposts of the temple, on the four corners of the ledge of the altar, and on the doorposts of the gateways of the inner courtyard. ²⁰ You must do the same on the seventh day of the month for everyone who unintentionally does something wrong and is unaware of it. So you must make peace with the LORD for the temple.

²¹ " 'On the fourteenth day of the first month, you will celebrate the Passover, a festival lasting seven days when unleavened bread is eaten. ²² At that time the prince must prepare for himself and for all the common people a young bull as an offering for sin. ²³ Every day during the seven days of the festival, he must prepare burnt offerings for the LORD: seven young bulls that have no defects, seven rams that have no defects, and one male goat as an offering for sin.

---

^a 45:11 A homer was about 60 gallons as a liquid measure or 6 bushels as a dry measure.   ^b 45:12 A shekel was about four-tenths of an ounce.

[24] He must also give as a grain offering a half-bushel for each young bull and a half-bushel for each ram. He must also give one gallon of olive oil for every half-bushel of grain. [25] On the fifteenth day of the seventh month, at the Festival of Booths, he must do the same as on those seven days. He must prepare the same offerings for sin, burnt offerings, grain offerings, and olive oil.

46 [1] " 'This is what the Almighty LORD says: The east gate of the inner courtyard must be closed during the six working days, but it must be opened on the weekly day of worship. It must also be opened on the New Moon Festival. [2] The prince must enter from the outside through the entrance hall of the gateway. He must stand by the doorposts of the gateway. Then the priests must prepare the prince's burnt offerings and fellowship offerings. He must worship at the entrance of the gateway and then leave. The gate must not be closed until evening. [3] The common people must worship at the door of the gateway in the presence of the LORD on the weekly days of worship and on New Moon Festivals. [4] The prince must offer to the LORD six lambs that have no defects and one ram that has no defects as a burnt offering on the day of worship. [5] The grain offering that is to be brought with the ram must be a half-bushel, and the grain offering that is to be brought with the lambs must be whatever the prince can bring. One gallon of olive oil must be brought with each half-bushel of grain. [6] On the first day of the month, the burnt offering must be one young bull, six lambs, and one ram—all animals that have no defects. [7] With each young bull and each ram the offering must include a half-bushel of grain, and with each lamb the offering must be whatever the prince wants to bring. One gallon of olive oil must be offered with each half-bushel of grain. [8] When the prince enters, he must enter through the entrance hall of the gateway. He must enter and leave the same way.

[9] " 'The people will enter the LORD's presence at the time of the appointed festivals. Those entering through the north gate to worship must leave through the south gate. Those entering through the south gate must leave through the north gate. They must not leave through the same gate they entered. They must leave through the opposite gate. [10] The prince must be among them. When they enter, he must enter. When they leave, he must leave.

[11] " 'On festival days and at appointed festivals, a grain offering of a half-bushel must be brought with each young bull, and a half-bushel must be brought with each ram. But with the lambs, the prince may bring whatever he wants to bring. One gallon of olive oil must be brought with each half-bushel of grain. [12] When the prince prepares a freewill burnt offering, either a burnt offering or a fellowship offering to the LORD, the east gate must be opened for him. He must sacrifice burnt offerings and fellowship offerings as he does on the day of worship. When he leaves, the gate must be shut after him.

[13] " 'Prepare a year-old lamb that has no defects every day as a burnt offering to the LORD. Do this every morning. [14] Also, prepare a grain offering with it every morning: three-and-a-third quarts of grain and one-and-a-third quarts of olive oil to moisten the flour. It will be a grain offering dedicated to the LORD. These rules are to be followed always. [15] Prepare the lamb, the grain offering, and the olive oil every morning as a daily burnt offering.

[16] " 'This is what the Almighty LORD says: Suppose the prince offers one of his sons a gift from his property. The gift will belong to his descendants because it is their inheritance. [17] But suppose the prince offers a gift from his property to one of his servants. The gift will belong to the servant only until the year of freedom. Then the gift will go back to the prince. Only his sons can inherit his property. [18] The prince must not take any of the people's property. He must not force them to give up their property. He must give his own property as an inheritance to his sons so that none of my people will be separated from their property.' "

[19] The man brought me through a passage beside the gateway to the side rooms that faced north. These rooms were reserved for the priests. He showed me a place on the west side of the rooms. [20] He said to me, "This is the place where the priests must boil the meat for the guilt offering and the offering for sin. This is the place where they must bake grain offerings so that they don't have to bring the offerings into the outer courtyard. This way they won't transfer holiness to the people."

[21] Then the man led me to the outer courtyard and took me past the four corners of the courtyard. I saw that in each corner of the courtyard there was a smaller courtyard. [22] The smaller courtyards that were in each of the four corners of the courtyard were 60 feet long and 45 feet wide. All four of the smaller courtyards in the corners of the courtyard were the same size. [23] Around each of the four courtyards were stone walls, and these walls were equipped with fireplaces.

[24] Then the man said to me, "These are the kitchens where the temple servants must boil the people's sacrifices."

Water Flowing From the Temple

47 ¹ Then the man took me back to the door of the temple. I saw water flowing from under the entrance of the temple toward the east. (The temple faced east.) The water was flowing under the south side of the temple, south of the altar. ² Then he led me through the north gate and around to the outer east gate. The water was flowing down the south side of the gate.

³ With a measuring line in his hand, the man went eastward. He measured off 1,500 feet and led me through the water. The water came up to my ankles. ⁴ Then he measured off another 1,500 feet and led me through the water. The water came up to my knees. He measured off another 1,500 feet and led me through the water. The water came up to my waist. ⁵ Then he measured another 1,500 feet. But the water had risen so much that it became a river which I couldn't cross. The river was too deep to cross except by swimming. ⁶ Then he asked me, "Son of man, do you see this?"

⁷ Then the man led me back along the bank of the river. As I went back, I saw many trees on both sides of the river. ⁸ Then the man said to me, "This water flows through the land to the east, down into the Jordan Valley, and into the Dead Sea. When the water flows into the Dead Sea, it will replace the salt water there with fresh water. ⁹ Wherever the river flows, there will be many fish and animals. The river will make the water in the Dead Sea fresh. Wherever the river flows, it will bring life. ¹⁰ From En Gedi to En Eglaim people will be standing on the shore of the sea with their fishing nets spread out. As many kinds of fish will be there as there are in the Mediterranean Sea. ¹¹ But the water in the swamps and marshes won't become fresh. It will remain salty. ¹² All kinds of fruit trees will grow on both sides of the river. Their leaves won't wither, and they won't fail to produce fruit. Each month they will produce fresh fruit because this water flows from the holy place. The fruit will be good food, and the leaves will be used for healing."

Dividing the Land for the Lord's People

¹³ This is what the Almighty LORD says: These are the borders of the land that is to be divided among the 12 tribes of Israel. Joseph gets two parts. ¹⁴ Divide the land equally. I raised my hand and swore that I would give the land to your ancestors. So this land will be your inheritance.

¹⁵ This is the northern border for the land: On the north side the border will run from the Mediterranean Sea all the way to Hethlon and Hamath Pass. It will run through the city of Zedad and through ¹⁶ Berothah and Sibraim, which are between the borders of Damascus and Hamath. It will run to Hazer Hatticon, which is on the border of Hauran. ¹⁷ So the border will run from the Mediterranean Sea to Hazar Enon on the border of Damascus. The border of Hamath will lie to the north. This is the north side.

¹⁸ On the east side the border will run between Hauran and Damascus. The Jordan River will serve as the border between Gilead and the land of Israel. The border will continue from the Dead Sea down to Tamar. This is the east side.

¹⁹ On the south side the border will run from Tamar to the oasis at Meribah in Kadesh along the ravine to the Mediterranean Sea. This is the southern border.

²⁰ On the west side the Mediterranean Sea is the border up to a point opposite Hamath Pass. This is the west side.

²¹ Divide this land among yourselves for each of the tribes of Israel. ²² Divide it by drawing lots. This land will be for you. It will also be for the foreign residents who live among you and have given birth to children while they lived with you. Think of them as Israelites. They will draw lots with you for their inheritance among the tribes of Israel. ²³ Foreign residents will receive their share of the inheritance with the people of the tribe among whom they are living, declares the Almighty LORD.

48 ¹ These are the names of the tribes. Beginning at the northern border, **Dan** will have one part of the land. It will extend from the road to Hethlon to Hamath Pass and Hazar Enon, on the northern border of Damascus near Hamath, from the eastern border to the western border.

² **Asher** will have one part of the land and border Dan on the south. It will extend from the eastern border to the western border.

³ **Naphtali** will have one part of the land and border Asher on the south. It will extend from the eastern border to the western border.

⁴ **Manasseh** will have one part of the land and border Naphtali on the south. It will extend from the eastern border to the western border.

⁵ **Ephraim** will have one part of the land and border Manasseh on the south. It will extend from the eastern border to the western border.

⁶ **Reuben** will have one part of the land and border Ephraim on the south. It will extend from the eastern border to the western border.

⁷ **Judah** will have one part of the land and border Reuben on the south. It will extend from the eastern border to the western border.

⁸ The land that you set aside as a special gift for the LORD will border Judah on the south. It will be 43,750 feet wide, and it will be as long as one of the sections of the tribes. It will extend from the eastern border to the western border, and the holy place will be in the middle of it.

⁹ This special land that you set aside for the LORD will be 43,750 feet long and 17,500 feet wide. ¹⁰ This holy area will belong to the priests. On the north side it will be 43,750 feet long. On the west side it will be 17,500 feet wide. On the east side it will be 17,500 feet wide. On the south side it will be 43,750 feet long. The LORD's holy place will be in the middle of it. ¹¹ This land that has been set apart will belong to the priests who are descendants of Zadok. They took care of my holy place. They didn't wander away with the Israelites as the Levites did. ¹² So they will have a special portion from the land. It will be the holiest part of land, next to the land belonging to the Levites.

¹³ Alongside the land belonging to the priests will be the land belonging to the Levites. It will be 43,750 feet long and 17,500 feet wide. ¹⁴ They must not sell any of it or trade any of it. They must not let others have the best part of the land, because the land is the LORD's and it is holy.

¹⁵ A strip of land, 8,750 feet wide by 43,750 feet long, will be left for cities, homes, and pastures. The city will be in the middle of it. ¹⁶ These will be the measurements for the city: On the north side it will be 7,875 feet long. On the south side it will be 7,875 feet long. On the east side it will be 7,875 feet wide. And on the west side it will be 7,875 feet wide. ¹⁷ The city's pastureland will be 4,375 feet on the north, 4,375 feet on the south, 4,375 feet on the east, and 4,375 feet on the west. ¹⁸ The rest of the land borders the holy area and runs lengthwise. This land will be 17,500 feet on its east side and 17,500 feet on its west side. It will be used to provide food for the city workers. ¹⁹ City workers from all the tribes in Israel will farm it. ²⁰ The whole area will be 43,750 feet square. You must give this land as a special gift to the LORD along with the city property.

²¹ Whatever is left on the east side and west side of the holy area and the city property will belong to the prince. This land will extend eastward from the holy area to the eastern border, and it will extend westward to the western border. Both of these areas are as long as one of the sections of the tribes. These areas belong to the prince, and the holy area with the holy place of the temple will be between them. ²² So the Levites' property and the city's property will be between the prince's part of the land. What is between Judah's and Benjamin's boundaries will belong to the prince.

²³ This is what the rest of the tribes will receive: **Benjamin** will have one part of the land. It will extend from the eastern border to the western border.

²⁴ **Simeon** will have one part of the land and border Benjamin on the south. It will extend from the eastern border to the western border.

²⁵ **Issachar** will have one part of the land and border Simeon on the south. It will extend from the eastern border to the western border.

²⁶ **Zebulun** will have one part of the land and border Issachar on the south. It will extend from the eastern border to the western border.

²⁷ **Gad** will have one part of the land and border Zebulun on the south. It will extend from the eastern border to the western border.

²⁸ The southern border of Gad will run south from Tamar to the oasis at Meribah in Kadesh, and it will run along the Brook of Egypt to the Mediterranean Sea. ²⁹ This is the land you will divide as your inheritance among the tribes of Israel, and these are their areas, declares the Almighty LORD.

The New City of God

³⁰ These will be the exits for the city: The north side will be 7,875 feet long. ³¹ The gates of the city will be named after the tribes of Israel. The three gates on the north side will be Reuben Gate, Judah Gate, and Levi Gate.

³² The east side will be 7,875 feet long. The three gates on the east side will be Joseph Gate, Benjamin Gate, and Dan Gate.

³³ The south side will be 7,875 feet long. The three gates on the south side will be Simeon Gate, Issachar Gate, and Zebulun Gate.

³⁴ The west side will be 7,875 feet long. The three gates on the west side will be Gad Gate, Asher Gate, and Naphtali Gate.

³⁵ The city will measure about 31,500 feet all the way around. From then on the city's name will be: The LORD Is There.

DANIEL

Daniel and His Friends Remain Faithful to God

1 ¹ In the third year of the reign of King Jehoiakim of Judah, King Nebuchadnezzar of Babylon came to Jerusalem and attacked it. ² The Lord handed King Jehoiakim of Judah and some utensils from God's temple over to Nebuchadnezzar. Nebuchadnezzar took the utensils to the temple of his god in Babylonia and put them in the temple treasury.

³ The king told Ashpenaz, the chief-of-staff, to bring some of the Israelites, the royal family, and the nobility. ⁴ They were to be young men who were healthy, good-looking, knowledgeable in all subjects, well-informed, intelligent, and able to serve in the king's palace. They were to be taught the language and literature of the Babylonians.

⁵ The king arranged for them to get a daily allowance of the king's rich food and wine. They were to be trained for three years. After that, they were to serve the king. ⁶ Among these young men were some Judeans: Daniel, Hananiah, Mishael, and Azariah. ⁷ The chief-of-staff gave them ₎Babylonian₎ names: To Daniel he gave the name Belteshazzar. To Hananiah he gave the name Shadrach. To Mishael he gave the name Meshach. And to Azariah he gave the name Abednego.

⁸ Daniel made up his mind not to harm himself by eating the king's rich food and drinking the king's wine. So he asked the chief-of-staff for permission not to harm himself in this way. ⁹ God made the chief-of-staff kind and compassionate toward Daniel. ¹⁰ The chief-of-staff told Daniel, "I'm afraid of my master, the king. The king determined what you should eat and drink. If he sees that you look worse than the other young men your age, he would have my head cut off."

¹¹ The chief-of-staff put a supervisor in charge of Daniel, Hananiah, Mishael, and Azariah. Daniel said to the supervisor, ¹² "Please test us for ten days. Give us only vegetables to eat and water to drink. ¹³ Then compare us to the young men who are eating the king's rich food. Decide how to treat us on the basis of how we look."

¹⁴ The supervisor listened to them about this matter and tested them for ten days. ¹⁵ After ten days they looked healthier and stronger than the young men who had been eating the king's rich food. ¹⁶ So the supervisor took away the king's rich food and wine and gave them vegetables.

¹⁷ God gave these four men knowledge, wisdom, and the ability to understand all kinds of literature. Daniel could also understand all kinds of visions and dreams.

¹⁸ At the end of the three-year training period, the chief-of-staff brought all the young men to Nebuchadnezzar. ¹⁹ The king talked to them and found no one like Daniel, Hananiah, Mishael, and Azariah among all of them. So these four men served the king. ²⁰ Whenever the king asked them about things that required wisdom and insight, he found that they knew ten times more than all the magicians and psychics in his whole kingdom.

²¹ Daniel served the royal palace until the first year of King Cyrus ₎of Persia₎.

Nebuchadnezzar's Dream About a Statue Made of Four Metals

2 ¹ During the second year of Nebuchadnezzar's reign, he had some dreams. He was troubled, but he stayed asleep. ² The king sent for the magicians, psychics, sorcerers, and astrologers so that they could tell him what he had dreamed. So they came to the king.

³ The king said to them, "I had a dream, and I'm troubled by it. I want to know what the dream was."

⁴ The astrologers spoke to the king in Aramaic, "Your Majesty, may you live forever! Tell us the dream, and we'll interpret it for you."

⁵ The king answered the astrologers, "I meant what I said! If you don't tell me the dream and its meaning, you will be torn limb from limb, and your houses will be turned into piles of rubble. ⁶ But if you tell me the dream and its meaning, I will give you gifts, awards, and high honors. Now tell me the dream and its meaning."

⁷ Once more they said, "Your Majesty, tell us the dream, and we'll tell you its meaning."

⁸ The king replied, "I'm sure you're trying to buy some time because you know that I meant what I said. ⁹ If you don't tell me the dream, you'll all receive the same punishment. You have agreed among yourselves to make up a phony explanation to give me, hoping that things will change. So tell me the dream. Then I'll know that you can explain its meaning to me."

¹⁰ The astrologers answered the king, "No one on earth can tell the king what he asks. No other king, no matter how great and powerful, has ever asked such a thing of any magician,

psychic, or astrologer. ¹¹ What you ask is difficult, Your Majesty. No one can tell what you dreamed except the gods, and they don't live with humans."

¹² This made the king so angry and furious that he gave an order to destroy all the wise advisers in Babylon. ¹³ So a decree was issued that the wise advisers were to be killed, and some men were sent to find Daniel and his friends and kill them.

¹⁴ While Arioch, the captain of the royal guard, was leaving to kill the wise advisers in Babylon, Daniel spoke to him using shrewd judgment. ¹⁵ He asked Arioch, the royal official, "Why is the king's decree so harsh?" So Arioch explained everything to Daniel.

¹⁶ Daniel went and asked the king to give him some time so that he could explain the dream's meaning. ¹⁷ Then Daniel went home and told his friends Hananiah, Mishael, and Azariah about this matter. ¹⁸ He told them to ask the God of heaven to be merciful and to explain this secret to them so that they would not be destroyed with the rest of the wise advisers in Babylon.

¹⁹ The secret was revealed to Daniel in a vision during the night. So Daniel praised the God of heaven. ²⁰ He said,

> "Praise God's name from everlasting to everlasting
>   because he is wise and powerful.
> ²¹ He changes times and periods of history.
> He removes kings and establishes them.
> He gives wisdom to those who are wise
>   and knowledge to those who have insight.
> ²² He reveals deeply hidden things.
> He knows what is in the dark,
>   and light lives with him.
> ²³ God of my ancestors, I thank and praise you.
> You gave me wisdom and power.
> You told me the answer to our question.
> You told us what the king wants to know."

²⁴ Then Daniel went to Arioch, whom the king had appointed to destroy Babylon's wise advisers. Daniel told him, "Don't destroy Babylon's wise advisers. Take me to the king, and I'll explain the dream's meaning to him."

²⁵ Arioch immediately took Daniel to the king. He told the king, "I've found one of the captives from Judah who can explain the dream's meaning to you, Your Majesty."

²⁶ The king asked Daniel (who had been renamed Belteshazzar), "Can you tell me the dream I had and its meaning?"

²⁷ Daniel answered the king, "No wise adviser, psychic, magician, or fortuneteller can tell the king this secret. ²⁸ But there is a God in heaven who reveals secrets. He will tell King Nebuchadnezzar what is going to happen in the days to come. This is your dream, the vision you had while you were asleep: ²⁹ Your Majesty, while you were lying in bed, thoughts about what would happen in the future came to you. The one who reveals secrets told you what is going to happen. ³⁰ This secret wasn't revealed to me because I'm wiser than anyone else. It was revealed so that you could be told the meaning and so that you would know your innermost thoughts.

³¹ "Your Majesty, you had a vision. You saw a large statue. This statue was very bright. It stood in front of you, and it looked terrifying. ³² The head of this statue was made of fine gold. Its chest and arms were made of silver. Its stomach and hips were made of bronze. ³³ Its legs were made of iron. Its feet were made partly of iron and partly of clay. ³⁴ While you were watching, a stone was cut out, but not by humans. It struck the statue's iron-and-clay feet and smashed them. ³⁵ Then all at once, the iron, clay, bronze, silver, and gold were smashed. They became like husks on a threshing floor^a in summer. The wind carried them away, and not a trace of them could be found. But the stone that struck the statue became a large mountain which filled the whole world. ³⁶ This is the dream. Now we'll tell you its meaning.

³⁷ "Your Majesty, you are the greatest king. The God of heaven has given you a kingdom. He has given you power, strength, and honor. ³⁸ He has given you control over people, wild animals, and birds, wherever they live. He has made you ruler of them all. You are the head of gold. ³⁹ Another kingdom, inferior to yours, will rise to power after you. Then there will be a third kingdom, a kingdom of bronze, that will rule the whole world. ⁴⁰ There will also be a fourth kingdom. It will be as strong as iron. (Iron smashes and shatters everything.) As iron crushes things, this fourth kingdom will smash and crush all the other kingdoms. ⁴¹ You also saw the feet and toes. They were partly potters' clay and partly iron. This means that there will be a divided kingdom which has some of the firmness of iron. As you saw, iron was mixed with

---

^a 2:35 A threshing floor is an outdoor area where grain is separated from its husks.

clay. **42** The toes were partly iron and partly clay. Part of the kingdom will be strong, and part will be brittle. **43** As you saw, iron was mixed with clay. So the two parts of the kingdom will mix by intermarrying, but they will not hold together any more than iron can mix with clay. **44** "At the time of those kings, the God of heaven will establish a kingdom that will never be destroyed. No other people will be permitted to rule it. It will smash all the other kingdoms and put an end to them. But it will be established forever. **45** This is the stone that you saw cut out from a mountain, but not by humans. It smashed the iron, bronze, clay, silver, and gold. The great God has told you what will happen in the future, Your Majesty. The dream is true, and you can trust that this is its meaning."

46 King Nebuchadnezzar immediately bowed down on the ground in front of Daniel. He ordered that gifts and offerings be given to Daniel. **47** The king said to Daniel, "Your God is truly the greatest of gods, the Lord over kings. He can reveal secrets because you were able to reveal this secret."

48 Then the king promoted Daniel and gave him many wonderful gifts. Nebuchadnezzar made Daniel governor of the whole province of Babylon and head of all Babylon's wise advisers. **49** With the king's permission, Daniel appointed Shadrach, Meshach, and Abednego to govern the province of Babylon. But Daniel stayed at the king's court.

Shadrach, Meshach, and Abednego Refuse to Worship an Idol

3 **1** King Nebuchadnezzar made a gold statue 90 feet high and 9 feet wide. He set it up in a recessed area in the wall*a* in the province of Babylon. **2** King Nebuchadnezzar sent messengers to assemble the satraps, governors, mayors, military advisers, treasurers, judges, officers, and all the other provincial officials to dedicate the statue he had set up. **3** Then the satraps, governors, mayors, military advisers, treasurers, judges, officers, and all the other provincial officials assembled to dedicate the statue King Nebuchadnezzar had set up. They stood in front of the statue.

4 The herald called out loudly, "People of every province, nation, and language! **5** When you hear the sound of rams' horns, flutes, lyres, harps, and three-stringed harps playing at the same time with all other kinds of instruments, bow down and worship the gold statue that King Nebuchadnezzar has set up. **6** Whoever doesn't bow down and worship will immediately be thrown into a blazing furnace." **7** As soon as they heard the sound of rams' horns, flutes, lyres, harps, and three-stringed harps with all other kinds of instruments, all the people from every province, nation, and language bowed down and worshiped the gold statue King Nebuchadnezzar had set up.

8 After that happened, some astrologers came forward and brought charges against the Jews. **9** They addressed King Nebuchadnezzar, "Your Majesty, may you live forever! **10** Your Majesty, you gave an order that everyone who hears the sound of rams' horns, flutes, lyres, harps, and three-stringed harps at the same time with all other kinds of instruments should bow down and worship the gold statue. **11** Your order said that whoever doesn't bow down and worship will be thrown into a blazing furnace. **12** There are certain Jews whom you appointed to govern the province of Babylon: Shadrach, Meshach, and Abednego. These men didn't obey your order, Your Majesty. They don't honor your gods or worship the statue that you set up."

13 Then, in a fit of rage and anger, Nebuchadnezzar summoned Shadrach, Meshach, and Abednego. Immediately, they were brought to the king. **14** Nebuchadnezzar asked them, "Shadrach, Meshach, and Abednego, is it true that you don't honor my gods or worship the gold statue that I set up? **15** When you hear the sound of the rams' horns, flutes, lyres, harps, and three-stringed harps playing at the same time with all other kinds of instruments, will you bow down and worship the gold statue I made? If you don't worship it, you will immediately be thrown into a blazing furnace. What god can save you from my power then?"

16 Shadrach, Meshach, and Abednego answered King Nebuchadnezzar, "We don't need to answer your last question. **17** If our God, whom we honor, can save us from a blazing furnace and from your power, he will, Your Majesty. **18** But if he doesn't, you should know, Your Majesty, we'll never honor your gods or worship the gold statue that you set up."

19 Nebuchadnezzar was so filled with anger toward Shadrach, Meshach, and Abednego that his face turned red. He ordered that the furnace should be heated seven times hotter than normal. **20** He told some soldiers from his army to tie up Shadrach, Meshach, and Abednego so that they could be thrown into the blazing furnace. **21** Then the three men were thrown into the blazing furnace. They were wearing their clothes, hats, and other clothing. **22** The king's order was so urgent and the furnace was so extremely hot that the men who carried Shadrach, Meshach, and Abednego were killed by the flames from the fire. **23** So these three men— Shadrach, Meshach, and Abednego—fell into the blazing furnace. They were still tied up.

---

a 3:1 Or "in the plain of Dura."

²⁴ Then Nebuchadnezzar was startled. He sprang to his feet. He asked his advisers, "Didn't we throw three men into the fire?"

"That's true, Your Majesty," they answered.

²⁵ The king replied, "But look, I see four men. They're untied, walking in the middle of the fire, and unharmed. The fourth one looks like a son of the gods."

²⁶ Then Nebuchadnezzar went to the door of the blazing furnace and said, "Shadrach, Meshach, and Abednego—servants of the Most High God—come out here."

Shadrach, Meshach, and Abednego came out of the fire. ²⁷ The king's satraps, governors, mayors, and advisers gathered around the three men. They saw that the fire had not harmed their bodies. The hair on their heads wasn't singed, their clothes weren't burned, and they didn't smell of smoke.

²⁸ Nebuchadnezzar said, "Praise the God of Shadrach, Meshach, and Abednego. He sent his angel and saved his servants, who trusted him. They disobeyed the king and risked their lives so that they would not have to honor or worship any god except their own God. ²⁹ So I order that people from every province, nation, or language who say anything slanderous about the God of Shadrach, Meshach, and Abednego will be torn limb from limb. Their houses will be turned into piles of rubble. No other god can rescue like this."

³⁰ Then the king promoted Shadrach, Meshach, and Abednego to higher positions in the province of Babylon.

A Letter From Nebuchadnezzar About His Insanity

4 ᵃ ¹ From King Nebuchadnezzar.
  To the people of every province, nation, and language in the world.

I wish you peace and prosperity. ² I am pleased to write to you about the miraculous signs and amazing things the Most High God did for me.

³   His miraculous signs are impressive.
      He uses his power to do amazing things.
      His kingdom is an eternal kingdom.
      His power lasts from one generation to the next.

⁴ I, Nebuchadnezzar, was living comfortably at home. I was prosperous while living in my palace. ⁵ I had a dream that terrified me. The visions I had while I was asleep frightened me. ⁶ So I ordered all the wise advisers in Babylon to be brought to me to tell me the dream's meaning. ⁷ The magicians, psychics, astrologers, and fortunetellers came to me. I told them the dream, but they couldn't tell me its meaning. ⁸ Finally, Daniel came to me. (He had been renamed Belteshazzar after my god ˎBelˌ.) The spirit of the holy gods is in him.

I told him the dream: ⁹ "Belteshazzar, head of the magicians, I know the spirit of the holy gods is in you. No secret is too hard for you ˎto uncoverˌ. Tell me the meaning of the visions I had in my dream. ¹⁰ These are the visions I had while I was asleep: I was looking, and I saw an oak tree in the middle of the earth. It was very tall. ¹¹ The tree grew, and it became strong enough and tall enough to reach the sky. It could be seen everywhere on earth. ¹² It had beautiful leaves and plenty of fruit, enough to feed everyone. Wild animals found shade under it. Birds came to live in its branches. It fed every living creature.

¹³ "I was seeing these visions as I was asleep. I saw a guardian, a holy being, come down from heaven. ¹⁴ He shouted loudly, 'Cut down the oak tree! Cut off its branches! Strip off its leaves! Scatter its fruit! Make the animals under it run away, and make the birds fly from its branches. ¹⁵ But leave the stump and its roots in the ground. Secure it with an iron and bronze chain in the grass in the field. Let it get wet with the dew from the sky. And let it get its share of the plants on the ground with the animals. ¹⁶ Let its human mind be changed, and give it the mind of an animal. Let it remain like this for seven time periods. ¹⁷ The guardians have announced this decision. The holy ones have announced this so that every living creature will know that the Most High has power over human kingdoms. He gives them to whomever he wishes. He can place the lowest of people in charge of them.' "

¹⁸ ˎI said,ˌ "This is the dream I, King Nebuchadnezzar, had. Now you, Belteshazzar, tell me its meaning because the wise advisers in my kingdom can't tell it to me. However, you can, because the spirit of the holy gods is in you."

¹⁹ Then Daniel (who had been renamed Belteshazzar) was momentarily stunned. What he was thinking frightened him. I told him, "Belteshazzar, don't let the dream and its meaning frighten you."

ᵃ 4:1 Daniel 4:1–37 in English Bibles is Daniel 3:31–4:34 in the Hebrew Bible.

Belteshazzar answered, "Sir, I wish that the dream were about those who hate you and its meaning were about your enemies. ²⁰ You saw an oak tree grow and become strong enough and tall enough to reach the sky. It could be seen everywhere on earth. ²¹ It had beautiful leaves and plenty of fruit, enough to feed everyone. Wild animals lived under it, and birds made their homes in its branches. ²² You are that tree, Your Majesty. You grew and became strong and mighty until you reached the sky. Your power reaches the most distant part of the world. ²³ You saw a guardian, a holy being, come down from heaven. He said, 'Cut down the oak tree! Destroy it! But leave the stump and its roots in the ground. Secure it with an iron and bronze chain in the field. Let it get wet with the dew from the sky. Let it get its share of the plants on the ground with the wild animals for seven time periods.'

²⁴ "This is the meaning, Your Majesty. The Most High has decided to apply it to you, Your Majesty. ²⁵ You will be forced away from people and live with the wild animals. You will eat grass like cattle. The dew from the sky will make you wet. And seven time periods will pass until you realize that the Most High has power over human kingdoms and that he gives them to whomever he wishes. ²⁶ Since I said that the stump and the tree's roots were to be left, your kingdom will be restored to you as soon as you realize that heaven rules.

²⁷ "That is why, Your Majesty, my best advice is that you stop sinning, and do what is right. Stop committing the same errors, and have pity on the poor. Maybe you can prolong your prosperity."

²⁸ All this happened to King Nebuchadnezzar. ²⁹ Twelve months later, he was walking around the royal palace in Babylon. ³⁰ The king thought, "Look how great Babylon is! I built the royal palace by my own impressive power and for my glorious honor." ³¹ Before the words came out of his mouth, a voice said from heaven, "King Nebuchadnezzar, listen to this: The kingdom has been taken from you. ³² You will be forced away from people and live with the wild animals. You will eat grass like cattle. And seven time periods will pass until you realize that the Most High has power over human kingdoms and that he gives them to whomever he wishes." ³³ Just then the prediction about Nebuchadnezzar came true. He was forced away from people and ate grass like cattle. Dew from the sky made his body wet until his hair grew as long as eagles' feathers and his nails grew as long as birds' claws.

³⁴ At the end of the seven time periods, I, Nebuchadnezzar, looked up to heaven, and my mind came back to me. I thanked the Most High, and I praised and honored the one who lives forever, because his power lasts forever and his kingdom lasts from one generation to the next. ³⁵ Everyone who lives on earth is nothing compared to him. He does whatever he wishes with the army of heaven and with those who live on earth. There is no one who can oppose him or ask him, "What are you doing?"

³⁶ Just then my mind came back to me. My royal honor and glory were also given back to me. My advisers and nobles wanted to meet with me ˌagainˌ. I was given back my kingdom and made extraordinarily great. ³⁷ Now I, Nebuchadnezzar, will praise, honor, and give glory to the King of Heaven. Everything he does is true, his ways are right, and he can humiliate those who act arrogantly.

The Handwriting on the Wall

5 ¹ King Belshazzar threw a large banquet for 1,000 nobles and drank wine with them. ² As they were tasting the wine, Belshazzar ordered that the gold and silver utensils which his grandfather Nebuchadnezzar had taken from the temple in Jerusalem be brought to him. He wanted to drink from them with his nobles, his wives, and his concubines.ᵃ

³ So the servants brought the gold utensils that had been taken from God's temple in Jerusalem. The king, his nobles, wives, and concubines drank from them. ⁴ They drank the wine and praised their gods made of gold, silver, bronze, iron, wood, or stone.

⁵ Suddenly, the fingers of a person's hand appeared and wrote on the plaster wall opposite the lamp stand of the royal palace. The king watched as the hand wrote. ⁶ Then the king turned pale, and his thoughts frightened him. His hip joints became loose, and his knees knocked against each other.

⁷ The king screamed for the psychics, astrologers, and fortunetellers to be brought to him. He told these wise advisers of Babylon, "Whoever reads this writing and tells me its meaning will be dressed in purple, wear a gold chain on his neck, and become the third-highest ruler in the kingdom." ⁸ All the king's wise advisers came, but they couldn't read the writing or tell the king its meaning. ⁹ King Belshazzar was terrified, and his face turned pale. His nobles didn't know what to do.

¹⁰ The discussion between the king and his nobles brought the queen herself into the banquet hall. The queen said, "Your Majesty, may you live forever! Don't let your thoughts

---

ᵃ 5:2 A concubine is considered a wife except she has fewer rights under the law.

frighten you, and don't turn pale. [11] There's a man in your kingdom who has the spirit of the holy gods. In the days of your grandfather, he was found to have insight, good judgment, and wisdom like the wisdom of the gods. Your grandfather, King Nebuchadnezzar, made him head of the magicians, psychics, astrologers, and fortunetellers. [12] This Daniel (who had been renamed Belteshazzar) was found to have knowledge, judgment, and an extraordinary spirit. He has the ability to interpret dreams, solve riddles, and untangle problems. Now, call Daniel, and he will tell ˻you˼ what it means."

[13] So Daniel was taken to the king. The king asked him, "Are you Daniel, one of the captives that my grandfather brought from Judah? [14] I've heard that you have the spirit of the gods and that you have insight, good judgment, and extraordinary wisdom. [15] The wise advisers and the psychics were brought to me to read this writing and tell me its meaning. But they couldn't tell me its meaning. [16] I have heard that you can interpret such things and untangle problems. If you can read the writing and tell ˻me˼ its meaning, you will be dressed in purple, wear a gold chain on your neck, and become the third-highest ruler in the kingdom."

[17] Daniel told the king, "Keep your gifts. Give your gifts and awards to someone else. I'll still read the writing for you and tell you its meaning.

[18] "Your Majesty, the Most High God gave your grandfather Nebuchadnezzar a kingdom, might, honor, and glory. [19] People from every province, nation, and language trembled and were terrified by him, because God gave him power. Nebuchadnezzar killed whomever he wanted to kill, and he kept alive whomever he wanted to keep alive. He promoted whomever he wanted to promote, and he demoted whomever he wanted to demote. [20] But when he became so arrogant and conceited that he became overconfident, he was removed from the royal throne. His honor was taken away from him. [21] He was chased away from people, and his mind was changed into an animal's mind. He lived with wild donkeys, ate grass like cattle, and his body became wet with dew from the sky. This happened until he realized that the Most High God has power over human kingdoms. God puts whomever he wishes in charge of them.

[22] "Belshazzar, you are one of Nebuchadnezzar's successors. You didn't remain humble, even though you knew all this. [23] But you made yourself greater than the Lord of heaven. You had the utensils from his temple brought to you. You, your nobles, wives, and concubines drank wine from them. You praised your gods made of silver, gold, bronze, iron, wood, or stone. These gods can't see, hear, or know anything. You didn't honor God, who has power over your life and everything you do. [24] So he sent the hand to write this inscription. [25] This is what has been written: Numbered, Numbered, Weighed, and Divided. [26] This is its meaning: Numbered—God has numbered the days of your kingdom and will bring it to an end. [27] Weighed—you have been weighed on a scale and found to be too light. [28] Divided—your kingdom will be divided and given to the Medes and Persians."[b]

[29] Then Belshazzar ordered that Daniel be dressed in purple and wear a gold chain on his neck. He made Daniel the third-highest ruler in the kingdom. [30] That night King Belshazzar of Babylon was killed.[c] [31] Darius the Mede took over the kingdom. He was 62 years old.

Daniel in the Lion's Den

6[a] [1] Darius decided it would be good to appoint 120 satraps to rule throughout the kingdom. [2] Over these satraps were three officials. Daniel was one of these officials. The satraps were to report to these three officials so that the king wouldn't be cheated.

[3] This man, Daniel, distinguished himself among the other officials and satraps because there was an extraordinary spirit in him. The king thought about putting him in charge of the whole kingdom. [4] So the other officials and satraps tried to find something to accuse Daniel of in his duties for the kingdom. But they couldn't find anything wrong because he was trustworthy. No error or fault could be found. [5] These men said, "We won't find anything to accuse this man, Daniel, unless we find it in his religious practices."

[6] So these officials and satraps went to the king as a group. They said to him, "May King Darius live forever! [7] All the officials, governors, satraps, advisers, and mayors agree that the king should make a statute and enforce a decree. The decree should state that for the next 30 days whoever asks for anything from any god or person except you, Your Majesty, will be thrown into a lions' den. [8] Your Majesty, issue this decree, and sign it. According to the law of the Medes and Persians no one could change it or repeal it." [9] So Darius signed the written decree.

[10] When Daniel learned that the document had been signed, he went to his house. An upper room in his house had windows that opened in the direction of Jerusalem. Three times each day he got down on his knees and prayed to his God. He had always praised God this way.

---

[b] 5:28 There is a play on words here between Aramaic *peres* (divided) and *paras* (Persians).   [c] 5:30 Daniel 5:31 in English Bibles is Daniel 6:1 in the Hebrew Bible.   [a] 6:1 Daniel 6:1–28 in English Bibles is Daniel 6:2–29 in the Hebrew Bible.

¹¹ One of those times the men came in as a group and found Daniel praying and pleading to his God. ¹² Then they went and spoke to the king about his decree. ˌThey asked,ˌ "Didn't you sign a decree which stated that for 30 days whoever asks for anything from any god or person except you, Your Majesty, will be thrown into a lions' den?"

The king answered, "That's true. According to the law of the Medes and Persians the decree can't be repealed."

¹³ They replied, "Your Majesty, Daniel, one of the captives from Judah, refuses to obey your order or the decree that you signed. He prays three times each day."

¹⁴ The king was very displeased when he heard this. He tried every way he could think of to save Daniel. Until sundown he did everything he could to rescue him.

¹⁵ Then Daniel's accusers gathered in front of the king. They said to him, "Remember, Your Majesty, the Medes and Persians have a law that no decree or statute the king makes can be changed."

¹⁶ So the king gave the order, and Daniel was brought to him and thrown into the lions' den. The king told Daniel, "May your God, whom you always worship, save you!"

¹⁷ A stone was brought and placed over the opening of the den. The king put his seal on the stone, using his ring and the rings of his nobles, so that Daniel's situation could not be changed.

¹⁸ Then the king went to his palace and spent the night without food or company. He couldn't get to sleep. ¹⁹ At dawn, as soon as it was light, the king got up and quickly went to the lions' den. ²⁰ As he came near the den where Daniel was, the king called to Daniel with anguish in his voice, "Daniel, servant of the living God! Was God, whom you always worship, able to save you from the lions?"

²¹ Daniel said to the king, "Your Majesty, may you live forever! ²² My God sent his angel and shut the lions' mouths so that they couldn't hurt me. He did this because he considered me innocent. Your Majesty, I haven't committed any crime."

²³ The king was overjoyed and had Daniel taken out of the den. When Daniel was taken out of the den, people saw that he was completely unharmed because he trusted his God.

²⁴ The king ordered those men who had brought charges against Daniel to be brought to him. They, their wives, and their children were thrown into the lions' den. Before they reached the bottom of the den, the lions attacked them and crushed all their bones.

²⁵ Then King Darius wrote to the people of every province, nation, and language all over the world:

I wish you peace and prosperity.

²⁶ I decree that in every part of my kingdom people should tremble with terror in front of Daniel's God, the living God who continues forever. His kingdom will never be destroyed. His power lasts to the end ˌof timeˌ. ²⁷ He saves, rescues, and does miraculous signs and amazing things in heaven and on earth. He saved Daniel from the lions.

²⁸ This man, Daniel, prospered during the reign of Darius and the reign of Cyrus the Persian.

Daniel's Vision About Four Animals

7 ¹ In Belshazzar's first year as king of Babylon, Daniel had a dream. He saw a vision while he was asleep. He wrote down the main parts of the dream.

² In my visions at night I, Daniel, saw the four winds of heaven stirring up the Mediterranean Sea. ³ Four large animals, each one different from the others, came out of the sea.

⁴ The first animal was like a lion, but it had wings like an eagle. I watched until its wings were plucked off and it was lifted off the ground. It was made to stand on two feet like a human and was given a human mind.

⁵ I saw a second animal. It looked like a bear. It was raised on one side and had three ribs in its mouth between its teeth. It was told, "Get up, and eat as much meat as you want."

⁶ After this, I saw another animal. It looked like a leopard. On its back it had four wings, like the wings of a bird. The animal also had four heads. It was given power to rule.

⁷ After this, I saw a fourth animal in my vision during the night. It was terrifying, dreadful, extraordinarily strong, and had large iron teeth. It devoured and crushed its victims and trampled whatever was left. It acted differently from all the other animals that I had seen before. It had ten horns. ⁸ While I was thinking about the horns, another horn, a little horn, came up among them. It uprooted three of the other horns. This horn had eyes like human eyes and a mouth that spoke impressive things.

⁹   I watched until thrones were set up
       and the Ancient One, who has lived for endless years, sat down.

His clothes were as white as snow
  and the hair on his head was like pure wool.
His throne was fiery flames,
  and its wheels were burning fire.
10   A river of fire flowed.
  It came from him.
Thousands and thousands served him.
Ten thousand times ten thousand were stationed in front of him.
The court convened,
  and the books were opened.

[11] I continued to watch because of the impressive words that the horn was speaking. I watched until the animal was killed. Its body was destroyed and put into a raging fire. [12] The power of the rest of the animals was taken away, but they were allowed to live for a period of time.

[13] In my visions during the night, I saw among the clouds in heaven someone like the Son of Man.[a] He came to the Ancient One, who has lived for endless years, and was presented to him. [14] He was given power, honor, and a kingdom. People from every province, nation, and language were to serve him. His power is an eternal power that will not be taken away. His kingdom will never be destroyed.

[15] I, Daniel, was deeply troubled, and my visions frightened me. [16] I went to someone who was standing there and asked him to tell me the truth about all this. So he told me what all this meant. He said, "These four large animals are four kingdoms that will rise to power on the earth. [18] But the holy people of the Most High will take possession of the kingdom and keep it forever and ever."

[19] Then I wanted to know the truth about the fourth animal, which was so different from all the others. It was very terrifying and had iron teeth and bronze claws. It devoured and crushed its victims, and trampled whatever was left. [20] I also wanted to know about the ten horns on its head and about the other horn that had come up and made three of the horns fall out. That horn had eyes and a mouth that spoke impressive things. It appeared to be bigger than the others. [21] I saw that horn making war against the holy people and defeating them. [22] It did this until the Ancient One, who has lived for endless years, came and judged in favor of the holy people of the Most High. The time came when the holy people took possession of the kingdom.

[23] He said, "The fourth animal will be the fourth of these kingdoms on earth. It will be different from all other kingdoms. It will devour, trample, and crush the whole world. [24] The ten horns are ten kings that will rise to power from that kingdom. Another king will rise to power after them. He will be different from the kings who came before him, and he will humble three kings. [25] He will speak against the Most High God, oppress the holy people of the Most High, and plan to change the appointed times and laws. The holy people will be handed over to him for a time, times, and half of a time. [26] But judgment will be handed down, his power will be taken away, and he will be completely and permanently destroyed. [27] The kingdom, along with the power and greatness of all the kingdoms under heaven, will be given to the holy people of the Most High. Their kingdom is eternal. All other powers will serve and obey them."

[28] Here is the end of the matter. I, Daniel, was terrified by my thoughts, and I turned pale. I kept this to myself.

Daniel's Vision About the Ram and the Goat

8 [1] In Belshazzar's third year as king, I, Daniel, saw a vision. This vision came after the one I saw earlier. [2] In my vision I saw myself in the fortress of Susa in the province of Elam. In my vision I saw myself at Ulai Gate. [3] I looked up and saw a single ram standing beside the gate. The ram had two long horns, one longer than the other, though the longer one had grown up later. [4] I saw the ram charging west, north, and south. No other animal could stand in front of it, and no one could escape from its power. It did anything it pleased and continued to grow.

[5] As I was watching closely, I saw a male goat coming from the west. It crossed the whole earth without touching it. This goat had a prominent horn between its eyes. [6] The goat was coming toward the two-horned ram that I had seen standing beside the gate. It furiously ran at the ram. [7] I saw it come closer to the ram. The goat was extremely angry with the ram, so it attacked the ram. It broke both of the ram's horns. The ram didn't have the strength to stand up against the goat. So the ram was thrown down on the ground and trampled. No one could rescue the ram from the goat's power.

[8] The male goat became very important. But when the goat became powerful, his large horn broke off. In its place grew four horns. They corresponded to the four winds of heaven.

---

[a] 7:13 Or "like a human."

⁹ Out of one of the horns came a small horn. It gained power over the south, the east, and the beautiful land. ¹⁰ It continued to gain power until it reached the army of heaven. It threw some of the army of heaven, the stars, down on the ground and trampled them. ¹¹ Then it attacked the commander of the army so that it took the daily burnt offering from him and wrecked his holy place. ¹² In its rebelliousness it was given an army to put a stop to the daily burnt offering. It threw truth on the ground. The horn was successful in everything it did.ᵃ

¹³ Then I heard a holy one speaking. Another holy one said to the one who was speaking, "How long will the things in this vision—the daily burnt offering, the destructive rebellion, the surrender of the holy place, and the trampling of the army—take place?"

¹⁴ He told me, "For 2,300 evenings and mornings. Then the holy place will be made acceptable to God."

· ¹⁵ Now as I, Daniel, watched the vision and tried to understand it, I saw someone who looked like a man standing in front of me. ¹⁶ I heard a man in Ulai ˻Gate˼ call loudly, "Gabriel, explain the vision to this man."

¹⁷ Gabriel came up beside me, and when he came, I was terrified and immediately knelt down.

He said to me, "Son of man, understand that the vision is about the end times." ¹⁸ As he spoke to me, I fainted facedown on the ground, but he touched me and made me stand up. ¹⁹ He said, "I will tell you what will happen in the last days, ˻the time of God's˼ anger, because the end time has been determined.

²⁰ "The two-horned ram that you saw represents the kingdoms of Media and Persia. ²¹ The hairy male goat is the kingdom of Greece, and the large horn between its eyes is its first king. ²² The horn broke off, and four horns replaced it. Four kingdoms will come out of that nation, but they won't be as strong as the first king was.

²³ "In the last days of those kingdoms, when rebellions are finished, a stern-looking king who understands mysterious things will rise to power. ²⁴ He will become very strong, but not by his own strength. He will cause astounding destruction and will be successful in everything he does. He will destroy those who are powerful along with some holy people. ²⁵ He will cleverly use his power to deceive others successfully. He will consider himself to be great and destroy many people when they don't expect it. He will oppose the Commander of Commanders, but he will be defeated, though not by any human power. ²⁶ The vision about the ˻2,300˼ evenings and mornings that was explained to you is true. Seal the vision, because it is about things that will happen in the distant future."

²⁷ I, Daniel, was exhausted and sick for days. Then I got up and worked for the king. The vision horrified me because I couldn't understand it.

Daniel's Prayer About Jerusalem Is Answered

9 ¹ Xerxes' son Darius, who was a Mede by birth, was made ruler of the kingdom of Babylon. ² In the first year of his reign, I, Daniel, learned from the Scriptures the number of years that Jerusalem would remain in ruins. The LORD had told the prophet Jeremiah that Jerusalem would remain in ruins for 70 years. ³ So I turned to the Lord God and looked to him for help. I prayed, pleaded, and fasted in sackcloth and ashes.

⁴ I prayed to the LORD my God. I confessed and said, "Lord, you are great and deserve respect as the only God. You keep your promiseᵃ and show mercy to those who love you and obey your commandments. ⁵ We have sinned, done wrong, acted wickedly, rebelled, and turned away from your commandments and laws. ⁶ We haven't listened to your servants the prophets, who spoke in your name to our kings, leaders, ancestors, and all the common people. ⁷ You, Lord, are righteous. But we—the men of Judah, the citizens of Jerusalem, and all the Israelites whom you scattered in countries near and far—are still ashamed because we have been unfaithful to you. ⁸ We, our kings, leaders, and ancestors are ashamed because we have sinned against you, LORD.

⁹ "But you, Lord our God, are compassionate and forgiving, although we have rebelled against you. ¹⁰ We never listened to you or lived by the teachings you gave us through your servants the prophets. ¹¹ All Israel has ignored your teachings and refused to listen to you. So you brought on us the curses you swore in an oath, the curses written in the Teachings of your servant Moses. We sinned against you. ¹² So you did what you said you would do to us and our rulers by bringing a great disaster on us. Nowhere in the world has anything ever happened like what has happened to Jerusalem. ¹³ This entire disaster happened to us, exactly as it was written in Moses' Teachings. LORD our God, we never tried to gain your favor by turning from our wrongs and dedicating ourselves to your truth. ¹⁴ So you were prepared to bring this disaster on us. LORD our God, you are righteous in everything you do. But we never listened to you.

ᵃ 8:12 Hebrew meaning of this verse uncertain.   ᵃ 9:4 Or "covenant."

[15] "Lord our God, you brought your people out of Egypt with your strong hand and made yourself famous even today. We have sinned and done evil things. [16] Lord, since you are very righteous, turn your anger and fury away from your city, Jerusalem, your holy mountain. Jerusalem and your people are insulted by everyone around us because of our sins and the wicked things our ancestors did.

[17] "Our God, listen to my prayer and request. For your own sake, Lord, look favorably on your holy place, which is lying in ruins. [18] Open your ears and listen, my God. Open your eyes and look at our ruins and at the city called by your name. We are not requesting this from you because we are righteous, but because you are very compassionate. [19] Listen to us, Lord. Forgive us, Lord. Pay attention, and act. Don't delay! Do this for your sake, my God, because your city and your people are called by your name."

[20] I continued to pray, confessing my sins and the sins of my people Israel. I humbly placed my request about my God's holy mountain in front of the LORD my God. [21] While I was praying, the man Gabriel, whom I had seen in the first vision, came to me about the time of the evening sacrifice. He was exhausted. [22] He informed me, "Daniel, this time I have come to give you insight. [23] As soon as you began to make your request, a reply was sent. I have come to give you the reply because you are highly respected. So study the message, and understand the vision.

[24] "Seventy sets of seven time periods have been assigned for your people and your holy city. These time periods will serve to bring an end to rebellion, to stop sin, to forgive wrongs, to usher in everlasting righteousness, to put a seal on a prophet's vision, and to anoint the Most Holy One. [25] Learn, then, and understand that from the time the command is given to restore and rebuild Jerusalem until the anointed prince comes, seven sets of seven time periods and sixty-two sets of seven time periods will pass. Jerusalem will be restored and rebuilt with a city square and a moat during the troubles of those times. [26] But after the sixty-two sets of seven time periods, the Anointed One[b] will be cut off and have nothing. The city and the holy place will be destroyed with the prince who is to come.[c] His end will come with a flood until the end of the destructive war that has been determined. [27] He will confirm his promise with many for one set of seven time periods. In the middle of the seven time periods, he will stop the sacrifices and food offerings. This will happen along with disgusting things that cause destruction until ˌthose time periodsˌ come to an end. It has been determined that this will happen to those who destroy ˌthe cityˌ."

An Angel Comes to Daniel With a Message

10 [1] In Cyrus' third year as king of Persia, a message was revealed to Daniel (who had been renamed Belteshazzar). The message was true. It was about a great war. Daniel understood the message because he was given insight during the vision.

[2] During those days I, Daniel, mourned for three whole weeks. [3] I didn't eat any good-tasting food. No meat or wine entered my mouth. I didn't wash myself until the entire three weeks were over.

[4] On the twenty-fourth day of the first month, I was by the great Tigris River. [5] When I looked up, I saw a man dressed in linen, and he had a belt made of gold from Uphaz around his waist. [6] His body was like beryl. His face looked like lightning. His eyes were like flaming torches. His arms and legs looked like polished bronze. When he spoke, his voice sounded like the roar of a crowd. [7] I, Daniel, was the only one who saw the vision. The men with me didn't see the vision. Yet, they started to tremble violently, and they quickly hid themselves. [8] So I was left alone to see this grand vision. I had no strength left in me. My face turned deathly pale, and I was helpless. [9] I heard the man speak, and as I listened to his words, I fainted facedown on the ground.

[10] Then a hand touched me and made my hands and knees shake. [11] The man said to me, "Daniel, you are highly respected. Pay attention to my words. Stand up, because I've been sent to you." When he said this to me, I stood up, trembling. [12] He told me, "Don't be afraid, Daniel. God has heard everything that you said ever since the first day you decided to humble yourself in front of your God so that you could learn to understand things. I have come in response to your prayer. [13] The commander of the Persian kingdom opposed me for 21 days. But then Michael, one of the chief commanders, came to help me because I was left alone with the kings of Persia. [14] I have come to explain to you what will happen to your people in the last days, because the vision is about times still to come."

[15] When he said this to me, I bowed down with my face touching the ground and was silent. [16] Then someone who looked like a human touched my lips. I opened my mouth and began to talk. I said to the person standing in front of me, "Sir, because of this vision, pain has overwhelmed me, and I'm helpless. [17] How can I talk to you, sir? I have no strength left, and the wind has been knocked out of me."

---

[b] 9:26 Or "Messiah."   [c] 9:26 Or "The people of the prince who is to come will destroy the city and the holy place."

¹⁸ Again, the person who looked like a human touched me, and I became stronger. ¹⁹ He said, "Don't be afraid. You are highly respected. Everything is alright! Be strong! Be strong!"

As he talked to me, I became stronger. I said, "Sir, tell me what you came to say. You have strengthened me."

²⁰ He asked, "Do you know why I have come to you? Now I will return to fight the commander of Persia. When I go, the commander of Greece will come. ²¹ However, I will tell you what is inscribed in the true writings. No one will support me when I fight these commanders **11** except your commander, Michael. ¹ During Darius the Mede's first year as king, I strengthened and defended Michael."

Greece Will Conquer Persia

² ˌThe person who looked like a human continued,ˌ "What I am about to tell you is the truth. Three more kings will rule Persia. Then there will be a fourth, who will become much richer than all the others. As he becomes strong through his wealth, he will turn everyone against the kingdom of Greece.

³ "Then a warrior-king will come. He will rule a vast empire and do as he pleases. ⁴ But as soon as he is established, his kingdom will be broken into pieces and divided in the directions of the four winds of heaven. The empire will not be given to his descendants. It will no longer be like his empire, since it will be uprooted and given to others.

The Northern and Southern Kings

⁵ "The southern king will be strong, but one of his officers will become stronger than he is and rule a vast empire. ⁶ After a few years the southern and northern kings will make an alliance. The southern king's daughter will go to the northern king to make peace. She won't hold on to her power, and the alliance won't last. She, those who came with her, and the one who fathered*ᵃ* and protected her will be given away.

⁷ "At that time a shoot will grow from her roots to replace her father. He will attack the northern army, enter the stronghold of the northern king, fight against them, and be victorious. ⁸ He will take the metal statues of their gods and their precious utensils of silver and gold back to Egypt. He will rule for more years than the northern king. ⁹ He will invade the southern kingdom and return to his own country.

¹⁰ "Then his sons will prepare for war. They will assemble a large number of forces so that they can overwhelm ˌthe enemyˌ and pass through its land. They will return and wage war all the way to the stronghold. ¹¹ The southern king will be outraged. He will go to fight the northern king, who will raise a large army that will fall into the southern king's hands. ¹² When that army is captured, the southern king will become conceited. Although he will dominate tens of thousands of people, he will not always be strong.

¹³ "The northern king will return and raise an army larger than the first one. After a few years he will invade with a large army and a lot of equipment. ¹⁴ In those times many people will rebel against the southern king, and violent men from your own people will rebel in keeping with this vision, but they will be defeated. ¹⁵ Then the northern king will come, build dirt attack ramps, and capture a fortified city. The southern forces will not be able to withstand him. Even their best troops will not be strong enough. ¹⁶ The invader will do as he pleases, and no one will be able to withstand his attack. He will rise to power in the beautiful land and it will be completely under his control.

¹⁷ "Then the northern king will decide to invade with the power of his entire kingdom, and some decent men will invade with him. He will give the southern king his daughter as a wife in order to destroy the southern kingdom. But this will not succeed or help him. ¹⁸ Then he will turn his attention to the coastlands and capture many of them. But a commander will silence the insults that the northern king makes and even insult him.*ᵇ* ¹⁹ He will turn back toward the fortresses in his own country, but he will stumble, fall, and disappear.

²⁰ "Another king will take his place. He will have a cruel official go out in royal splendor. But in a few days the king will be destroyed, although not in anger or war.

²¹ "A contemptible person will take his place. He will not be given royal splendor. He will invade when people are feeling secure, and he will seize the kingdom using false promises. ²² He will overwhelm large forces and defeat them, including the prince of the promise.*ᶜ* ²³ After an alliance has been made with him, he will act deceitfully and rise to power with only a few people. ²⁴ When people feel secure, he will invade the richest parts of the provinces and do something that none of his predecessors ever did. He will distribute loot and wealth to his followers. He will invent new ways of attacking fortifications. But this will last only for a little while.

ᵃ 11:6 Most Hebrew manuscripts; one Hebrew manuscript, some Greek manuscripts "her son."　ᵇ 11:18 Hebrew meaning of this sentence uncertain.　ᶜ 11:22 Or "covenant."

²⁵ "With a large army he will summon his power and courage against the southern king, who will prepare for war with a large, strong army. But the southern king won't be able to withstand him because of the schemes devised against him. ²⁶ People who eat the king's rich food will ruin him. His army will be overwhelmed, and many will die in battle. ²⁷ The two kings will both plan to do evil. They will sit at the same table and tell lies. But they will not succeed, because the end must wait until the appointed time. ²⁸ The northern king will return to his country with a lot of wealth. He will be determined to fight against the holy promise. He will take action and return to his own country.

²⁹ "At the appointed time he will again invade the south, but this time will be different from the first. ³⁰ Ships will come from the west to attack him, and he will be discouraged and turn back. Angry at the holy promise, he will return, take action, and favor those who abandon the holy promise. ³¹ His forces will dishonor the holy place (the fortress), take away the daily burnt offering, and set up the disgusting thing that causes destruction. ³² With flattery he will corrupt those who abandon the promise. But the people who know their God will be strong and take action.

³³ "People who are wise will help many to understand. But for some time they will be defeated by swords and flames. They will be captured and looted. ³⁴ As they are being defeated, they will get a little help, but many who are not sincere will join them. ³⁵ Some of the wise people will be defeated in order to refine, purify, and make them white until the end times. But the appointed time is still to come.

³⁶ "The king will do as he pleases. He will highly honor himself above every god. He will say amazing things against the God of gods. He will succeed until God's anger is over, because what has been decided must be done. ³⁷ He will have no interest in the gods of his ancestors or desire for women. He will have no interest in any god, because he will make himself greater than anyone else. ³⁸ Instead, he will honor the god of fortresses. With gold, silver, precious stones, and other expensive things he will honor a god his ancestors never heard of. ³⁹ With the help of a foreign god, he will deal with strong fortresses. He will give high honors to those who acknowledge him, make them rulers over many people, and distribute land for a price.

⁴⁰ "In the end times the southern king will attack him. The northern king will rush at him like a storm with chariots, horses, and many ships. He will invade countries, overwhelm them, and pass through their land. ⁴¹ He will invade the beautiful land, and tens of thousands will be defeated. But Edom, Moab, and the leaders of the Ammonites will escape from his power. ⁴² He will use his power against many countries. Even Egypt will not escape. ⁴³ He will control gold and silver treasures and all Egypt's treasuries. Libya and Sudan will surrender to him. ⁴⁴ But news from the east and the north will frighten him. He will leave very angry to destroy and exterminate many. ⁴⁵ He will pitch his royal tents between the seas at a beautiful holy mountain. When he comes to his end, there will be no one to help him."

12 ¹ ⌞The person who looked like a human continued,⌟ "At that time Michael, the great commander, will stand up on behalf of the descendants of your people. It will be a time of trouble unlike any that has existed from the time there have been nations until that time. But at that time your people, everyone written in the book, will be rescued. ² Many sleeping in the ground will wake up. Some will wake up to live forever, but others will wake up to be ashamed and disgraced forever. ³ Those who are wise will shine like the brightness on the horizon. Those who lead many people to righteousness will shine like the stars forever and ever.

⁴ "But you, Daniel, keep these words secret, and seal the book until the end times. Many will travel everywhere, and knowledge will grow."

The Words Are Sealed Up

⁵ When I, Daniel, looked up, I saw two men standing there. One man stood on one side of the river, and the other one stood on the other side. ⁶ One of them asked the man dressed in linen clothes who was above the river, "How long will it be until these miracles are over?" ⁷ I heard the man dressed in linen clothes who was above the river. He raised his right hand and left hand to heaven and swore an oath by the one who lives forever. He said, "It will be for a time, times, and half of a time. When the power of the holy people has been completely shattered, then all these things will be finished."

⁸ I heard him, but I did not understand. So I asked him, "Sir, how will these things end?"

⁹ He replied, "Go, Daniel. These words are to be kept secret and sealed until the end times. ¹⁰ Many will be purified, made white, and refined. But wicked people will do wicked things, and none of them will understand. Only wise people will understand. ¹¹ From the time the daily burnt offering is taken away and the disgusting thing that causes destruction is set up, there will be 1,290 days. ¹² Blessed are those who wait until they reach 1,335 days. ¹³ But go on until the end. You will rest, and you will rise for your inheritance at the end of time."

HOSEA

The Prophet Hosea

1 [1] The Lord spoke his word to Hosea, son of Beeri, when Uzziah, Jotham, Ahaz, and Hezekiah were kings of Judah and when Jeroboam, son of Joash, was king of Israel.

Hosea Marries a Prostitute

[2] When the Lord first spoke to Hosea, the Lord told him, "Marry a prostitute, and have children with that prostitute. The people in this land have acted like prostitutes and abandoned the Lord." [3] So Hosea married Gomer, daughter of Diblaim. She became pregnant and had a son.

[4] The Lord told Hosea, "Name him Jezreel. In a little while I will punish Jehu's family for the people they slaughtered at Jezreel. Then I will put an end to the kingdom of Israel. [5] On that day I will break Israel's bows and arrows in the valley of Jezreel."

[6] Gomer became pregnant again and had a daughter. The Lord told Hosea, "Name her Lo Ruhamah [Unloved]. I will no longer love the nation of Israel. I will no longer forgive them. [7] Yet, I will love the descendants of Judah. I will rescue them because I am the Lord their God. I won't use bows, swords, wars, horses, or horsemen to rescue them."

[8] After Gomer had weaned Lo Ruhamah, she became pregnant again and had a son. [9] The Lord said, "Name him Lo Ammi [Not My People]. You are no longer my people, and I am no longer your God.[a, b]

[10] "Yet, the Israelites will become as numerous as the grains of sand on the seashore. No one will be able to measure them or count them. Wherever they were told, 'You are not my people,' they will be told, 'You are the children of the living God.' [11] The people of Judah and Israel will be gathered together. They will appoint one leader for themselves, and they will grow in the land. The day of Jezreel will be a great day.

Israel Is the Lord's Unfaithful Wife

2 [a][1] "So call your brothers Ammi [My People],
and call your sisters Ruhamah [Loved].

[2] "Plead with your mother; plead with her.
 She no longer acts like my wife.
 She no longer treats me like her husband.
Tell her to stop acting like a prostitute.
Tell her to remove the lovers from between her breasts.
[3] If she refuses, I will strip her.
 I will leave her as naked as the day she was born.
 I will turn her into a dry and barren land,
  and she will die of thirst.
[4] I won't love her children,
  because they are children of a prostitute.
[5] Their mother acted like a prostitute.
The woman who became pregnant with them did shameful things.
 She said, 'I'll chase after my lovers.
 They will give me food and water,
  wool and linen, olive oil and wine.'

[6] "That is why I will block her way with thornbushes
  and build a wall so that she can't get through.
[7] She will run after her lovers, but she won't catch them.
She will search for them, but she won't find them.
 Then she will say, 'I'll go back to my first husband.
 Things were better for me than they are now.'

---

[a] 1:9 Or "I am no longer I Am to you." (See Exodus 3:14.)   [b] 1:9 Hosea 1:10–11 in English Bibles is Hosea 2:1–2 in the Hebrew Bible.   [a] 2:1 Hosea 2:1–23 in English Bibles is Hosea 2:3–25 in the Hebrew Bible.

⁸ "She doesn't believe that I gave her grain, new wine, and olive oil.
> I gave her plenty of silver and gold,
>> but she used it to make statues of Baal.

⁹ That is why I will take back my grain when it has ripened
> and my new wine when it's in season.
I will take away the wool and the linen
> that I gave her to cover her naked body.

¹⁰ I will show her naked body to her lovers,
> and no one will rescue her from my power.

¹¹ I will put an end to all her celebrations:
> her annual festivals, her New Moon Festivals,
> her weekly worship days—all her appointed festivals.

¹² I will destroy her grapevines and fig trees.
> She said that they were gifts from her lovers.
I will turn her vineyards into a forest, and wild animals will devour them.

¹³ I will punish her for all the times she burned incense
> as an offering to other gods—the Baals.
>> She put on her rings and jewelry,
>>> and she chased after her lovers.
>>>> She forgot me," declares the LORD.

The LORD Continues to Love Israel

¹⁴ "That is why I'm going to win her back.
> I will lead her into the desert.
> I will speak tenderly to her.

¹⁵ I will give her vineyards there.
> I will make the valley of Achor [Disaster] a door of hope.
>> Then she will respond as she did when she was young,
>>> as she did when she came out of Egypt.

¹⁶ "On that day she will call me her husband," declares the LORD.
> "She will no longer call me her master.^b

¹⁷ I won't allow her to say the names of other gods called Baal.
> She will never again call out their names.

¹⁸ "On that day I will make an arrangement with the wild animals,
> the birds, and the animals that crawl on the ground.
I will destroy all the bows, swords, and weapons of war,
> so people can live safely.

¹⁹ "Israel, I will make you my wife forever.
> I will be honest and faithful to you.
> I will show you my love and compassion.

²⁰ I will be true to you, my wife.
> Then you will know the LORD.

²¹ "On that day I will answer your ˌprayersˌ," declares the LORD.
> "I will speak to the sky,
> it will speak to the earth,

²² and the earth will produce grain, new wine, and olive oil.
>> You will produce many crops, Jezreel.

²³ I will plant my people in the land.
> Those who are not loved I will call my loved ones.
> Those who are not my people I will call my people.
Then they will say, 'You are our God!' "

Hosea's Adulterous Wife

3 ¹ Then the LORD told me, "Love your wife again, even though she is loved by others and has committed adultery. Love her as I, the LORD, love the Israelites, even though they have turned to other gods and love to eat raisin cakes."

² So I bought her for 23 ounces of silver and 10 bushels of barley. ³ Then I told her, "You must wait for me a long time. Don't be a prostitute or offer yourself to any man. I will wait for you."

---

^b 2:16 Or "her Baal."

[4] In the same way, the Israelites will wait a long time without kings or officials, without sacrifices or sacred stones, and without ephods[a] or family idols. [5] After that, the Israelites will turn and look to the LORD their God and David their king. They will come trembling to the LORD for his blessings in the last days.

The LORD's Legal Case Against Israel

4 [1] Listen to the word of the LORD, you Israelites. The LORD has brought these charges against those who live in the land:

"There is no faith, no love, and no knowledge of God in the land.
[2] There is cursing, lying, murdering, stealing, and adultery.
People break ˌmy lawsˌ, and there is one murder after another.
[3] That is why the land is drying up,
and everyone who lives in it is passing away.
Wild animals, birds, and fish are dying.

[4] "No one should accuse other people or bring charges against them.
My case is against you priests.
[5] During the day you stumble,
and during the night the prophets stumble with you.
So I will destroy your mother, ˌthe nation of Israelˌ.
[6] I will destroy my people because they are ignorant.
You have refused to learn,
so I will refuse to let you be my priests.
You have forgotten the teachings of your God,
so I will forget your children.
[7] The more priests there are,
the more they sin against me.
So I will turn their glory into shame.
[8] They feed on the sins of my people,
and they want them to do wicked things.
[9] So the priests will be punished like the people.
I will punish them for their wicked ways
and pay them back for what they have done.

[10] "They will eat, but they'll never be full.
They will have sex with prostitutes, but they'll never have children.
They have abandoned the LORD.
[11] Prostitutes, old wine, and new wine have robbed them of their senses.
[12] My people ask their wooden idols for help.
A piece of wood tells them what to do.
A spirit of prostitution leads them astray.
They commit adultery
by giving themselves to other gods.
[13] They offer sacrifices on mountaintops,
and they burn incense on the hills
under oaks, poplars, and other trees.
They think that these trees provide good shade.

"That is why your daughters become prostitutes,
and your daughters-in-law commit adultery.
[14] Yet, I will not punish your daughters when they become prostitutes
or your daughters-in-law when they commit adultery.
The men go to prostitutes
and offer sacrifices with temple prostitutes.
These foolish people will be trampled.

[15] "Israel, you act like a prostitute.
Don't let Judah become guilty too.
Don't go to Gilgal.
Don't go to Beth Aven.
Don't take the oath, 'As the LORD lives. . . .'

---

[b] 3:4 *Ephod* is a technical term for part of the priest's clothes. Its exact usage and shape are unknown.

16   "The people of Israel are as stubborn as a bull.
     How can the LORD feed them like lambs in an open pasture?
17   The people of Ephraim have chosen to worship idols. Leave them alone!
18   When they're done drinking their wine,
     they continue to have sex with the prostitutes.
       Their rulers dearly love to act shamefully.
19   The wind will carry them away in its wings,
         and their sacrifices will bring them shame.

The LORD Announces the Verdict Against Israel

5   1   "Listen to this, you priests!
    Pay attention, nation of Israel!
    Open your ears, royal family!
     This is my decision about you.
    You set traps at Mizpah
     and spread out nets on Mount Tabor.
2   You are deeply involved in sin.
    So I will punish all of you.[a]
3   I know Ephraim,
    and Israel isn't a stranger to me.
    Now, Ephraim, you are acting like a prostitute,
     and Israel is unclean.[b]

4   "The wicked things that the people have done
    keep them from returning to their God.
      They have a spirit of prostitution,
       and they don't know the LORD.
5   The people of Israel's arrogance testifies against them.
    Israel and Ephraim stumble because of their sins,
     and Judah stumbles with them.
6   They go with their sheep and their cattle to search for the LORD,
    but they can't find him.
     He has left them.
7   They have been unfaithful to the LORD,
    because their children do not belong to him.
    Now their New Moon ˎFestivalsˎ will devour them and their fields.

8   "Blow the ram's horn in Gibeah.
    Blow the trumpet in Ramah.
    Sound the alarm at Beth Aven, you descendants of Benjamin.
9   Ephraim will become a wasteland
     when the time for punishment comes.
      I will make the truth known among the tribes of Israel.
10   The leaders of Judah are like those who move boundary markers.
    I will pour my fury on them like water.
11   Ephraim is oppressed—crushed by punishment,
    because its people are determined to chase idols.[c]
12   I will destroy Ephraim as a moth destroys clothing.
    I will destroy the nation of Judah as rot destroys wood.

13   "When Ephraim saw that he was sick
    and when Judah saw his own wounds,
      Ephraim went to Assyria to ask the great king for help.[d]
       But the king couldn't cure them or heal their wounds.
14   I will be like a lion to Ephraim
    and like a young lion to the nation of Judah.
    I will carry ˎthemˎ off, and no one will rescue ˎthemˎ.
15   I will go back to my place until they admit that they are guilty.
    Then they will search for me.
     In their distress they will eagerly look for me."

---

[a] 5:2 Hebrew meaning of this verse uncertain. [b] 5:3 "Unclean" refers to anything that Moses' Teachings say is not presentable to God. [c] 5:11 Greek, Syriac, Targum; Masoretic Text "to chase commands." [d] 5:13 Or "to ask King Jareb for help."

Israel Rejected the LORD's Promise

6 ¹ Let's return to the LORD.
   Even though he has torn us to pieces,
      he will heal us.
   Even though he has wounded us,
      he will bandage our wounds.
² After two days he will revive us.
      On the third day he will raise us
         so that we may live in his presence.
³ Let's learn about the LORD.
   Let's get to know the LORD.
      He will come to us as sure as the morning comes.
      He will come to us like the autumn rains and the spring rains
         that water the ground.

⁴ "What should I do with you, Ephraim?
   What should I do with you, Judah?
      Your love is like fog in the morning.
         It disappears as quickly as the morning dew.
⁵ That is why I cut ˌyouˌ down by sending the prophets.
   I killed you with the words from my mouth.
      My judgments shined on you like light.
⁶ I want your loyalty, not your sacrifices.
   I want you to know me, not to give me burnt offerings.

⁷ "Like Adam, you rejected the promise.ᵃ
   You were unfaithful to me.
⁸ Gilead is a city filled with troublemakers.
   It is stained with bloody footprints.
⁹ The priests are like gangs of robbers who lie in ambush for a person.
   They murder on the road to Shechem.
      Certainly, they have committed a crime.

¹⁰ "I have seen horrible things in the nation of Israel.
   Ephraim is acting like a prostitute,
      and Israel is unclean.ᵇ

¹¹ "Yet, Judah, I have set a harvest time for you
      when I bring my people back from captivity.

7 ¹ "Whenever I want to heal Israel,
      all I can see is Ephraim's sin and Samaria's wickedness.
         People cheat each other.
         They break into houses and steal.
         They rob people in the streets.
² They don't realize that I remember
      all the evil things they've done.
         Now their sins surround them.
            Their sins are in my presence.

³ "They make kings happy with the wicked things they do.
   They make officials happy with the lies they tell.
⁴ They all commit adultery.
      They are like a heated oven,
         an oven so hot that a baker doesn't have to fan its flames
            when he makes bread.
⁵ On the day of the king's celebration,
      the officials become drunk from wine,
         and the king joins mockers.
⁶ They become hot like an oven while they lie in ambush.
   All night long their anger smolders,
      but in the morning it burns like a raging fire.

ᵃ 6:7 Or "You have walked all over my promise as if it were dirt."   ᵇ 6:10 "Unclean" refers to anything that Moses'
Teachings say is not presentable to God.

⁷ They are all as hot as an oven.
  They consume their judges ˌlike a fireˎ.
    All their kings die in battle, and none of them calls to me.

Israel Turns to Other Nations for Help

⁸ "Ephraim mixes with other nations.
  Ephraim, you are like a half-baked loaf of bread.
⁹   Foreigners are using up your strength, but you don't realize it.
    You have become a gray-haired, old man, but you don't realize it.
¹⁰ Israel, your arrogance testifies against you,
    but even after all this, you don't turn to the LORD your God
      or look to him for help.
¹¹ Ephraim, you are like a silly, senseless dove.
    You call for Egypt and run to Assyria for help.
¹²   When you go, I will spread my net over you.
      I will snatch you out of the air like a bird.
      I will punish you for all the evil things you have done.

¹³ "How horrible it will be for these people.
    They have run away from me.
    They must be destroyed because they've rebelled against me.
      I want to reclaim them, but they tell lies about me.
¹⁴   They don't pray to me sincerely,
      even though they cry in their beds
        and make cuts on their bodies
          while praying for grain and new wine.
    They have turned against me.
¹⁵   I trained them and made them strong.
      Yet, they plan evil against me.
¹⁶ They don't return to the Most High.
    They are like a defective bow.
      Their officials will die in battle
        because they curse.
        The people in Egypt will ridicule them for this.

The LORD Will Punish Israel for Its Rebellion

8 ¹ "Sound the alarm on the ram's horn.
    The enemy swoops down on the LORD's temple like an eagle.
      The people of Israel have rejected my promise
        and rebelled against my teachings.
²   They cry out to me, 'We acknowledge you as our God.'
³   However, they have rejected what is good.
      The enemy will persecute them.

⁴ "They chose their own kings, kings I didn't approve.
    They chose their own princes, princes I didn't know.
    They chose to make idols with their own silver and gold.
      Because of this, they will be destroyed.
⁵ Get rid of your calf-shaped idol, Samaria.
    My anger burns against these people.
      How long will they remain unclean?ᵃ
⁶ Samaria's calf-shaped idol was made in Israel.
    Skilled workers made it.
      It is not a god.
      It will be smashed to pieces.

⁷ "The people of Israel plant the wind, but they harvest a storm.
    A field of grain that doesn't ripen will never produce any grain.
    Even if it did produce grain, foreigners would eat it all.
⁸   Israel will be swallowed up.
      It has already mixed in with the other nations.
      It has become worthless.

ᵃ 8:5 "Unclean" refers to anything that Moses' Teachings say is not presentable to God.

⁹ . "The people of Israel went to Assyria.
   They were like wild donkeys wandering off alone.
   The people of Ephraim sold themselves to their lovers.
¹⁰ Even though they sold themselves among the nations,
   I will gather them now.
   They will suffer for a while under the burdens of kings and princes.

¹¹ "The more altars that the people of Ephraim build
   to make offerings to pay for their sins,
   the more places they have for sinning.
¹² I have written many things for them in my teachings,
   but they consider these things strange and foreign.
¹³ They offer sacrifices to me and eat the meat of sacrifices,
   but I, the LORD, do not accept these sacrifices.
   Now I will remember their wickedness
   and punish them because of their sins.
   They will go back to Egypt.
¹⁴ The people of Israel have built palaces,
   and they have forgotten their maker.
   The people of Judah have built many fortified cities.
   I will send a fire on their cities and burn down their palaces."

9 ¹ Israel, don't rejoice.
   Don't celebrate as other nations do.
   You have been unfaithful to your God.
   You have sold sex on every threshing floor.ᵃ
² There won't be enough grain to feed people.
   There won't be enough wine to go around.

³ The people of Ephraim won't stay in the LORD's land.
   They will return to Egypt,
   and they will eat uncleanᵇ food in Assyria.
⁴ They won't pour wine offerings to the LORD,
   and their sacrifices won't please him.
   Their sacrifices will be like the food that mourners eat.
   All who eat this food will be unclean.
   Their food will only satisfy their hunger.
   It will not be brought ˌas an offeringˌ to the LORD's temple.

⁵ What will they do on the day of an appointed festival
   or on the LORD's festival days?
⁶ Even if they escape without being destroyed,
   Egypt will capture them
   and Memphis will bury them.
   Weeds will grow over their silver treasures.
   Thorns will grow over their tents.
⁷ The time for them to be punished will come.
   The time for them to pay for their sins will come.
   ˌWhen this happens,ˌ Israel will know it.
   ˌThey think thatˌ prophets are fools
   and that spiritual people are crazy.
   They have sinned a lot, and they are very hostile.
⁸ . Prophets are God's watchmen over Ephraim.
   Yet, traps are set on every prophet's path,
   and people are hostile in the temple of their God.
⁹ People have deeply corrupted themselves as they once did at Gibeah.
   God will remember their wickedness
   and punish them because of their sins.

Israel Is Like Rotten Grapes or Rotten Figs
¹⁰ ˌThe LORD said,ˌ "When I found Israel,
   it was like finding grapes in the desert.

ᵃ 9:1 A threshing floor is an outdoor area where grain is separated from its husks.   ᵇ 9:3 "Unclean" refers to anything that Moses' Teachings say is not presentable to God.

When I saw your ancestors,
  it was like seeing the first figs of the harvest.
    But they went to Baal Peor and worshiped shameful idols.
      They became as disgusting as the things they worshiped.

11 "Ephraim's glory will fly away like a bird.
  There will be no more pregnancies, births, or babies.
12 Even if they bring up children,
  I will take those children away before they grow up.
  Yes, how horrible it will be for them when I leave them.
13 I have seen Ephraim, like Tyre, planted in a pleasant place.
  But the people of Ephraim will bring out their children
    to be killed."

14 Lord, give them what they deserve.
  Make the women miscarry,
    or else make them unable to nurse their babies.

15 "All Ephraim's wickedness began in Gilgal; I hated the people there.
  I will force them out of my temple because of their wickedness,
    and I won't love them anymore.
  All their officials are rebellious.

16 "The people of Ephraim are like sick plants.
  Their roots are dried up.
  They have no fruit.
    Even if they were to have children,
      I would kill their dear children."

17 My God will reject them
  because they refused to listen to him.
    They will wander among the nations.

Israel Is Like a Rotten Vine

10 ¹The people of Israel are like vines that used to produce fruit.
  The more fruit they produced,
    the more altars they built.
  The more their land produced,
    the more stone markers they set up ˪to honor other gods˪.
2 They are hypocrites. Now they must take their punishment.
  God will tear down their altars and destroy their stone markers.
3   So they'll say,
      "We have no king because we didn't fear the Lord.
      Even if we had a king, he couldn't do anything for us."
4 They say many things. They lie when they take oaths,
  and they make promises they don't intend to keep.
    That's why lawsuits spring up
      like poisonous weeds in the furrows of a field.

5 Those who live in Samaria fear the calf-shaped idol at Beth Aven.
  The people will mourn over it.
  The priests will cry loudly
    because its glory will be taken away into captivity.
6 The thing itself will be carried to Assyria
  as a present to the great king.ᵃ
    Ephraim will be disgraced.
    Israel will be ashamed because of its plans.
7 The king of Samaria will be carried away
  like a piece of wood on water.
8 The illegal worship sites of Aven will be destroyed.
  Israel sins there.
    Thorns and weeds will grow over those altars.
      People will say to the mountains, "Cover us!"
        and to the hills, "Fall on us!"

ᵃ 10:6 Or "to King Jareb."

9 Israel, you have sinned ever since the incident at Gibeah.
  You never change.
  War will overtake the wicked people in Gibeah.
10 "I will punish them when I'm ready.
  Armies will gather to attack them.
  They will be punished for their many sins.

Israel Is Like a Cow That Threshed Grain

11 "Ephraim is like a trained calf that loves to thresh[b] grain.
  I will put a yoke[c] on its beautiful neck.
  I will harness Ephraim.
   Judah must plow.
   Jacob must break up the ground.

12 "Break new ground.
  Plant righteousness,
    and harvest the fruit that your loyalty will produce for me."

  It's time to seek the LORD!
   When he comes, he will rain righteousness on you.
13 You have planted wickedness and harvested evil.
  You have eaten the fruit that your lies produced.
  You have trusted your own power and your many warriors.
14 So your army will hear the noise of battle.
  All your fortresses will be destroyed
    like the time Shalman destroyed Beth Arbel in battle.
     Mothers and their children were smashed to death.
15 This is what will happen to you, Bethel,
  because you have done many wicked things.
    At daybreak, the king of Israel will be completely destroyed.

Israel Is Like a Bad Son

11 **1** "When Israel was a child, I loved him,
    and I called my son out of Egypt.
2 The more I called them,[a] the farther they went away.
   They sacrificed to other gods—the Baals,
    and they burned incense to idols.
3 I was the one who taught the people of Ephraim to walk.[b]
  I took them by the hand.
    But they didn't realize that I had healed them.
4 I led them with cords of human kindness, with ropes of love.
  I removed the yokes[c] from their necks.
    I bent down and fed them.

5 "They will not return to Egypt.
  Instead, Assyria will rule them
    because they have refused to return to me.
6 War will sweep through their cities,
   demolish their city gates,
    and put an end to their plans.
7 My people are determined to turn away from me.
   Even if they call to the Most High,
    he will not pardon them.

8 "How can I give you up, Ephraim?
  How can I hand you over, Israel?
  How can I make you like Admah?
  How can I treat you like Zeboim?
   I have changed my mind.
    I am deeply moved.

---

[b] 10:11 Threshing is the process of beating stalks to separate them from the grain.   [c] 10:11 A yoke is a wooden bar placed over the necks of work animals so that they can pull plows or carts.   [a] 11:2 Greek; Masoretic Text "The more they called them."   [b] 11:3 Or "I was the one who guided Ephraim."   [c] 11:4 A yoke is a wooden bar placed over the necks of work animals so that they can pull plows or carts.

⁹ I will not act on my burning anger.
I will not destroy Ephraim again.
  I am God, not a human.
  I am the Holy One among you,
    and I will not come to you in anger.

¹⁰ "My people will follow me when I roar like a lion.
  When I roar, my children will come trembling from the west.
¹¹   They will come trembling like birds from Egypt
    and like doves from Assyria.
      I will settle them in their own homes,"
        declares the LORD.ᵈ

¹² "Ephraim surrounds me with lies.
The nation of Israel surrounds me with deceit."
  Judah rebels against God, against the Holy One who is faithful.

The People of Israel Ignored What the LORD Had Done for Them

12 ᵃ¹The people of Ephraim try to catch the wind
  and try to chase the east wind all day.
They are very violent and destructive.
They make treaties with Assyria and take olive oil to Egypt.

² The LORD brings charges against Judah and punishes Jacob
    because of the way their people act.
He will pay them back for what they have done.
³ Their ancestor Jacob held on to his brother's heel
    while the two of them were in their mother's womb.
When Jacob became a man, he struggled with God.
⁴   He struggled with the Messenger and won.
    Jacob cried and pleaded with him.
    Jacob found him at Bethel,
      and he talked with him there.
⁵ The LORD is the God of Armies.
The LORD is the name by which he is remembered.
⁶   Return to your God.
  Be loyal and fair, and always wait with hope for your God.

⁷ ˌThe LORD says,ˌ "The merchants use dishonest scales.
  They love to cheat people.
⁸ The people of Ephraim say, 'We're rich. We've made a fortune.
  With all this wealth, no one will find us guilty of any sin.'
⁹ I am the LORD your God.
I brought you out of Egypt.
I will make you live in tents again
  as you did during your appointed festivals.
¹⁰ I spoke to the prophets and gave them many visions.
I taught lessons through the prophets."ᵇ

¹¹ The people of Gilead are evil.
  They are worthless.
  They sacrifice bulls in Gilgal.
    But their altars will become like piles of rubble
      beside a plowed field.
¹² Jacob fled to the country of Syria.
  Israel worked to get a wife; he took care of sheep to pay for her.
¹³ The LORD used a prophet to bring the people of Israel out of Egypt.
  He used a prophet to take care of them.

¹⁴ The people of Ephraim made the LORD bitter.
  He will hold them guilty of murder.
    The Lord will pay them back for their insults.

ᵈ 11:11 Hosea 11:12 in English Bibles is Hosea 12:1 in the Hebrew Bible.   ᵃ 12:1 Hosea 12:1–14 in English Bibles is Hosea 12:2–15 in the Hebrew Bible.   ᵇ 12:10 Or "I brought destruction through the prophets."

The People of Israel Will Be Punished for Their Idolatry

13 [1] When the tribe of Ephraim spoke, people trembled.
The people of Ephraim were important in Israel.
Then they became guilty of worshiping Baal,
so they must die.

[2] They keep on sinning more and more.
They make idols from silver for themselves.
These idols are skillfully made.
All of them are the work of craftsmen.
People say this about the Israelites: "They offer human sacrifices
and kiss calf-shaped idols."

[3] That is why they will be like fog in the morning
and like morning dew that disappears quickly.
They will be like straw blown away from threshing floors.[a]
They will be like smoke rising from chimneys.

[4] "I am the LORD your God. I brought you out of Egypt.
You have known no god besides me.
There is no savior except me.

[5] I took care of you[b] in the desert, in a dry land.

[6] When I fed you, you were full.
When you were full, you became arrogant.
That is why you forgot me.

[7] So I will be like a lion.
Like a leopard I will wait by the road to ambush you.

[8] Like a bear that has lost her cubs, I will attack you.
I will rip you open.
Like a lion I will devour you.
Like a wild animal I will tear you apart.

[9] You are destroying yourself, Israel.
You are against me, your helper.

[10] "Where, now, is your king, the one who is supposed to save you?
Where in all your cities are your judges?
You said, 'Give us kings and officials!'

[11] I gave you a king when I was angry,
and I took him away when I was furious.

[12] "Ephraim's wickedness is on record.
The record of the people's sins is safely stored away.

[13] They have the opportunity to live again,
but they are not smart enough to take it.
They are like a baby who is about to be born
but won't come out of its mother's womb.

[14] "I want to free them from the power of the grave.
I want to reclaim them from death.
Death, I want to be a plague to you.
Grave, I want to destroy you.[c]
I won't even think of changing my plans."

[15] The people of Ephraim have become important among their relatives.
However, the LORD's scorching wind will come from the east.
It will blow out of the desert.
Then their springs will run dry,
and their wells will dry up.
The wind will destroy every precious thing in their storehouses.[d]

[16] The people of Samaria are guilty as charged
because they rebelled against their God.
They will be killed in war,

---

[a] 13:3 A threshing floor is an outdoor area where grain is separated from its husks.   [b] 13:5 Greek; Masoretic Text "I knew you."   [c] 13:14 Or "Death, where is your plague? Grave, where is your destruction?"   [d] 13:15 Hosea 13:16 in English Bibles is Hosea 14:1 in the Hebrew Bible.

their children will be smashed to death,
  and their pregnant women will be ripped open.

The Lord Offers to Forgive Israel

14 [a]**1** Israel, return to the LORD your God.
  You have stumbled because of your sins.
2 Return to the LORD, and say these things to him:
  "Forgive all our sins, and kindly receive us.
  Then we'll praise you with our lips.
3 Assyria cannot save us.
  We won't ride on horses anymore.
  We will never again say
    that the things our hands have made are our gods.
      You love orphans."

4 ˌThe LORD says,ˌ "I will cure them of their unfaithfulness.
I will love them freely.
I will no longer be angry with them.
5 I will be like dew to the people of Israel.
  They will blossom like flowers.
  They will be firmly rooted like cedars from Lebanon.
6 They will be like growing branches.
  They will be beautiful like olive trees.
  They will be fragrant like cedars from Lebanon.
7 They will live again in God's shadow.
  They will grow like grain.
  They will blossom like grapevines.
  They will be as famous as the wines from Lebanon.

8 "The people of Ephraim will have nothing more to do with idols.
  I will answer them and take care of them.
    I am like a growing pine tree.
      Their fruit comes from me."

9 Wise people will understand these things.
A person with insight will recognize them.
  The LORD's ways are right.
    Righteous people live by them.
    Rebellious people stumble over them.

---

[a] 14:1 Hosea 14:1–9 in English Bibles is Hosea 14:2–10 in the Hebrew Bible.

JOEL

The Prophet Joel

1 ¹ This is what the LORD said to Joel, son of Pethuel.

Judah Is Plagued With Locusts and Famine

² Listen to this, you leaders!
   Open your ears, all inhabitants of this land!
      Nothing like this has ever happened in your lifetime
      or in your ancestors' lifetime.
³ Tell your children about it.
   Have your children tell their children.
   Have your grandchildren tell their children.
⁴   What young locusts leave, mature locusts will eat.
    What mature locusts leave, adult locusts will eat.
    What adult locusts leave, grasshoppers will eat.

⁵ Wake up and cry, you drunks!
   Cry loudly, you wine drinkers!
     New wine has been taken away from you.
⁶ A strong nation attacked my land.
   It has too many soldiers to count.
     They have teeth like lions.
     They have fangs like grown lions.
⁷   They destroyed my grapevines.
     They ruined my fig trees.
       They stripped off what they could eat,
        threw the rest away,
          and left the branches bare.

⁸ Cry loudly like a young woman who is dressed in sackcloth,
   mourning for the man she was going to marry.
⁹ Grain offerings and wine offerings
   are no longer brought to the LORD's temple.
    The priests, the LORD's servants, mourn.
¹⁰ Israel's fields are ruined, and the ground is dried up.
   The grain has been destroyed.
   The new wine has dried up.
   The olive oil has run out.
¹¹   Be sad, you farmers!
    Cry loudly, you grape growers!
      Mourn for the wheat and the barley.
        The harvest is destroyed in the field.
¹² The grapevines are dried up.
   The fig trees are withered.
   The pomegranate, palm, and apricot trees,
     as well as all the trees in the orchards, have died.
       Yes, the joy of these people has died too.

¹³ Put on your sackcloth and mourn, you priests.
   Cry loudly, you servants of the altar.
   Spend the night in sackcloth, you servants of my God.
    Grain offerings and wine offerings
     are withheld from your God's temple.
¹⁴ Schedule a time to fast!
   Call for an assembly!

Gather the leaders and everyone who lives in the land.
Bring them to the temple of the LORD your God,
and cry to the LORD for help.

15 This will be a terrible day!
The day of the LORD is near,
and it will come like destruction from the Almighty.

16 Food disappears right before our eyes.
Happiness and rejoicing disappear from our God's temple.
17 Seeds shrivel up in their shells.ᵃ
Storehouses are destroyed.
Barns are ruined.
The grain has dried up.
18 The animals groan.
Herds of cattle wander around confused.
There's no pasture for them.
Even flocks of sheep are suffering.

19 O LORD, I cry to you for help!
Fire has burned up the open pastures.
Flames have burned up all the trees in the orchards.
20 Even wild animals long for you.
Streams run dry.
Fire has burned up the open pastures.

The Day of the LORD

2 ¹ Blow the ram's horn in Zion.
Sound the alarm on my holy mountain.
Everyone who lives in the land should tremble,
because the day of the LORD is coming.
Certainly, it is near.
2 It is a day of darkness and gloom,
a day of clouds and overcast skies.
A large and mighty army
will spread over the mountains like the dawn.ᵃ
Nothing like this has ever happened.
Nothing like this will ever happen again.

3 In front of this army a fire burns.
Behind it flames are blazing.
In front of it the land is like the garden of Eden.
Behind it the land is like a barren desert.
Nothing escapes it!

4 The soldiers look like horses.
They run like war horses.
5 As they leap on mountaintops,
they sound like rattling chariots,
like crackling fire burning up straw,
and like a mighty army prepared for battle.

6 People are terrified in their presence.
Every face turns pale.

7 They run like warriors.
They climb walls like soldiers.
They march straight ahead.
They do not leave their places.
8 They do not crowd one another.
They keep in their own lines.
Even when they break through the defenses,
they do not break their ranks.
9 They rush into the city.

ᵃ 1:17 Hebrew meaning of this line uncertain.   ᵃ 2:2 Or "like darkness."

They run along the wall.
They climb into houses.
They enter through windows like thieves.

10   The earth quakes in their presence,
and the sky shakes.
The sun and the moon turn dark,
and the stars no longer shine.
11   The LORD shouts out orders to his army.
His forces are very large.
The troops that carry out his commands are mighty.
The day of the LORD is extremely terrifying.
Who can endure it?

The LORD Invites the People to Return to Him
12   "But even now," declares the LORD,
"return to me with all your heart—
with fasting, crying, and mourning."

13   Tear your hearts, not your clothes.
Return to the LORD your God.
He is merciful and compassionate,
patient, and always ready to forgive
and to change his plans about disaster.
14   Who knows?
He may reconsider and change his plan
and leave a blessing for you.
Then you could give grain offerings and wine offerings
to the LORD your God.

15   Blow the ram's horn in Zion.
Schedule a time to fast.
Call for an assembly.
16   Gather the people.
Prepare them for a holy meeting.
Assemble the leaders.
Gather the children, even the nursing infants.

Grooms leave their rooms.
Brides leave their chambers.
17   The priests who serve the LORD cry
between the altar and the entrance to the temple.
They say,
"Spare your people, O LORD.
Don't let the people who belong to you become a disgrace.
Don't let the nations ridicule them.
Why should people ask, 'Where is their God?' "

The LORD Will Give Earthly Blessings to His People
18   Then the LORD became concerned about his land,
and he had pity on his people.
19   The LORD said to his people,
"I am going to send grain, new wine, and olive oil to you.
You will be satisfied with them.
I will no longer make you a disgrace among the nations.

20   "I will keep the northern ˻army˼ far from you,
and I will force it into a dry and barren land.
The soldiers in front will be forced into the eastern sea.
The soldiers in back will be forced into the western sea.
A foul odor will rise from the dead bodies.
They will stink."

He has done great things!
21   Land, do not be afraid.

Be glad and rejoice.
The LORD has done great things!
22   Wild animals, do not be afraid.
The pastures in the wilderness have turned green.
The trees have produced their fruit.
There are plenty of figs and grapes.
23   People of Zion, be glad and find joy in the LORD your God.
The LORD has given you the Teacher of Righteousness.[b]
He has sent the autumn rain and the spring rain as before.
24   The threshing floors[c] will be filled with grain.
The vats will overflow with new wine and olive oil.

25   "Then I will repay you for the years
that the mature locusts, the adult locusts,
the grasshoppers, and the young locusts ate your crops.
(They are the large army that I sent against you.)
26   You will have plenty to eat, and you will be full.
You will praise the name of the LORD your God,
who has performed miracles for you.
My people will never be ashamed again.
27   You will know that I am in Israel.
I am the LORD your God, and there is no other.
My people will never be ashamed again.[d]

The LORD Will Pour His Spirit on All People

28   "After this, I will pour my Spirit on everyone.
Your sons and daughters will prophesy.
Your old men will dream dreams.
Your young men will see visions.
29   In those days I will pour my Spirit on servants,
on both men and women.
30   I will work miracles in the sky and on the earth:
blood, fire, and clouds of smoke.
31   The sun will become dark,
and the moon will become as red as blood
before the terrifying day of the LORD comes."

32   Then whoever calls on the name of the LORD will be saved.
Those who escape will be on Mount Zion and in Jerusalem.
Among the survivors will be those whom the LORD calls,
as the LORD has promised.

The LORD Will Rescue His People

3[a] 1   "In those days and at that time,
I will bring back the captives of Judah and Jerusalem.
2   I will gather all the nations.
I will bring them down to the valley of Jehoshaphat.[b]
I will judge them there.
They scattered the Israelites, the people who belong to me,
among the nations.
They divided my land.
3   They threw dice for my people.
They traded boys for prostitutes.
They sold girls so that they could buy wine to drink.

4   "Now what do you have against me, Tyre and Sidon
and all the regions of Philistia?
Are you paying me back for something I have done?
If you are paying me back,
I will quickly pay you back for what you have done.

---

[b] 2:23 Or "The LORD has given you plenty of autumn rain."   [c] 2:24 A threshing floor is an outdoor area where grain is separated from its husks.   [d] 2:27 Joel 2:28–32 in English Bibles is Joel 3:1–5 in the Hebrew Bible.   [a] 3:1 Joel 3:1–21 in English Bibles is Joel 4:1–21 in the Hebrew Bible.   [b] 3:2 Or "the valley where the LORD judges."

⁵ You took my silver and my gold.
  You brought my finest treasures to your temples.
⁶ You sold the people of Judah and Jerusalem to the Greeks.
  That way you could send them far away from their land.
⁷ I am going to make them leave the place where you sold them.
  I will pay you back for what you have done.
⁸ I will sell your sons and daughters to the people of Judah.
  They will sell them to the people of Sheba,
    a nation that is far away."
    The LORD has spoken.

⁹ Announce this among the nations:
  Prepare yourselves for war.
    Wake up the warriors.
      Have all the warriors come near and attack.
¹⁰ Hammer your plowblades into swords
     and your pruning shears into spears.
       Weaklings should say that they are warriors.

¹¹ Hurry from every direction, and gather there, all you nations.
   O LORD, bring your soldiers.
¹² Wake up, you nations.
   Come to the valley of Jehoshaphat.
     There I will sit to judge all the surrounding nations.

¹³ Cut them down like grain.
   The harvest is ripe.
   Stomp on them as you would stomp on grapes.
     The winepress is full.
     The vats overflow.
       The nations are very wicked.
¹⁴ There are many, many people in the valley of decision.
   The day of the LORD is near in the valley of decision.
¹⁵ The sun and the moon will turn dark.
   The stars will no longer shine.
¹⁶ The LORD will roar from Zion,
     and his voice will thunder from Jerusalem.
       The sky and the earth will shake.
   The LORD will be a refuge for his people.
   He will be a stronghold for the people of Israel.

¹⁷ "You will know that I am the LORD your God.
   I live on my holy mountain, Zion.
     Jerusalem will be holy.
       Foreigners will never invade it again.
¹⁸ On that day new wine will cover the mountains.
   Milk will flow on the hills.
   Water will flow in all the brooks of Judah.
   A spring will flow from the LORD's temple.
     It will water the valley of Shittim.
¹⁹ Egypt will become a wasteland.
   Edom will become a barren desert.
     This is because the nations were cruel to Judah.
       They murdered innocent people in their land.
²⁰ People will always live in Judah.
   People will live in Jerusalem from now on.
²¹   I will punish those who murder."ᶜ
       The LORD lives in Zion!

ᶜ 3:21 Hebrew meaning of this line uncertain.

AMOS

1 ¹These are the words of Amos, one of the sheep farmers from Tekoa. He saw ˌa visionˌ about Israel during the reigns of Judah's King Uzziah and Israel's King Jeroboam, son of Joash. This happened two years before the earthquake.
² He said:

The LORD roars from Zion,
  and his voice thunders from Jerusalem.
The pastures of the shepherds are turning brown,
  and the top of ˌMountˌ Carmel is dried up.

Damascus Will Be Judged for Its Crimes

³ This is what the LORD says:

Because Damascus has committed three crimes, and now a fourth crime,
  I will not change my plans.
    The Arameans have crushed ˌthe people ofˌ Gilead
      with iron-spiked threshing*ᵃ* sledges.
⁴   I will send a fire on the house of Hazael
      and burn down the palaces of Ben Hadad.
⁵   I will break the bars ˌon the gatesˌ of Damascus.
    I will cut off those living in Aven Valley
      and the one who holds the scepter in Beth Eden.
The people of Aram will go into captivity at Kir.

The LORD has said this.

Gaza Will Be Judged for Its Crimes

⁶ This is what the LORD says:

Because Gaza has committed three crimes, and now a fourth crime,
  I will not change my plans.
    The Philistines have taken all the people captive
      in order to hand them over to the Edomites.
⁷   I will send a fire on the walls of Gaza
      and burn down its palaces.
⁸   I will cut off those living in Ashdod
      and the one who holds the scepter in Ashkelon.
    I will turn my power against Ekron.
The rest of the Philistines will die.

The Almighty LORD has said this.

Tyre Will Be Judged for Its Crimes

⁹ This is what the LORD says:

Because Tyre has committed three crimes, and now a fourth crime,
  I will not change my plans.
    The Tyrians have handed all the people over to the Edomites.
      The Tyrians didn't remember their treaty with their relatives.
¹⁰   I will send a fire on the walls of Tyre
      and burn down its palaces.

ᵃ 1:3 Threshing is the process of beating stalks to separate them from the grain.

Edom Will Be Judged for Its Crimes

11 This is what the LORD says:

> Because Edom has committed three crimes, and now a fourth crime,
>   I will not change my plans.
>   The Edomites pursued their relatives with swords.
>   They refused to show any compassion to them.
>   Their anger was unstoppable.
>   They refused to control their fury.
> **12**   I will send a fire on Teman
>   and burn down the palaces of Bozrah.

Ammon Will Be Judged for Its Crimes

13 This is what the LORD says:

> Because Ammon has committed three crimes, and now a fourth crime,
>   I will not change my plans.
>   The Ammonites enlarged their territory
>   by ripping open pregnant women in Gilead.
> **14**   I will set fire to the walls of Rabbah
>   and burn down its palaces
>   while troops are shouting on the day of battle
>   and winds are howling on the day of the storm.
> **15**   Their king will go into captivity along with his officials.

The LORD has said this.

Moab Will Be Judged for Its Crimes

2 **1** This is what the LORD says:

> Because Moab has committed three crimes, and now a fourth crime,
>   I will not change my plans.
>   The Moabites have cremated Edom's king.
> **2**   I will send a fire on Moab
>   and burn down the palaces of Kerioth.
>   Moab will die during the noise of battle
>   while troops are shouting and rams' horns are blowing.
> **3**   I will take their judges away from them.
>   I will kill all their officials at the same time.

The LORD has said this.

Judah Will Be Judged for Its Crimes

4 This is what the LORD says:

> Because Judah has committed three crimes, and now a fourth crime,
>   I will not change my plans.
>   The people of Judah have rejected the LORD's Teachings
>   and haven't kept his laws.
>   They have been led astray by false teachings,
>   the same ones their ancestors followed.
> **5**   I will send a fire on Judah
>   and burn down the palaces of Jerusalem.

Israel Will Be Judged for Its Crimes

6 This is what the LORD says:

> Because Israel has committed three crimes, and now a fourth crime,
>   I will not change my plans.
>   The people of Israel sell the righteous for money
>   and the needy for a pair of sandals.
> **7**   They stomp the heads of the poor into the dust.
>   They push the humble out of the way.
>   Father and son sleep with the same woman.
>   They dishonor my holy name.

8   Beside every altar, they spread themselves out on clothes
          taken as security.
      In the temples of their gods, they drink the wine
          that they bought with fines.

9   I destroyed the Amorites in front of them,
          although the Amorites were as tall as cedars and as strong as oaks.
      I destroyed their fruit above the ground and their roots below it.

10   I brought you out of Egypt.
      I led you through the desert for 40 years
          so that you could take possession of the land of the Amorites.
11   I also sent you prophets from among your children
          and Nazirites from among your youths.
      Isn't that so, people of Israel?

   The Lord has declared this.

12   You made the Nazirites drink wine.
      You commanded the prophets to stop prophesying.

13   I am going to crush you as an overloaded wagon crushes a person.
14   Runners will not be able to escape.
      Strong men will find that their strength is useless.
      Soldiers will not be able to save themselves.
15   Archers will not stand their ground.
      Fast runners will not be able to escape.
      Horsemen will not be able to save themselves.
16   Brave soldiers will run away naked that day.

   The Lord has declared this.

The Lord Will Punish Israel for Its Immoral Behavior

3 ¹ Listen to this message which I, the Lord, have spoken against you Israelites, against your whole family that I brought out of Egypt.

2   Out of all the families on earth, I have known no one else but you.
      That is why I am going to punish you for all your sins.

3   Do two people ever walk together without meeting first?
4   Does a lion roar in the forest if it has no prey?
      Does a young lion growl in its den unless it has caught something?
5   Does a bird land in a trap on the ground if there's no bait in it?
      Does a trap spring up from the ground unless it has caught something?
6   If a ram's horn sounds an alarm in a city, won't the people be alarmed?
      If there is a disaster in a city, hasn't the Lord done it?
7   Certainly, the Almighty Lord doesn't do anything
        unless he first, reveals his secret to his servants the prophets.
8   The lion has roared. Who isn't afraid?
      The Almighty Lord has spoken. Who can keep from prophesying?

9   Announce in the palaces of Ashdod and in the palaces of Egypt,
      "Gather together on the mountains of Samaria.
        See the widespread confusion and oppression in Samaria."
10   Those who collect profits in their palaces
      through violent and destructive acts
        don't know how to do what is right, declares the Lord.

11 This is what the Almighty Lord says:

    An enemy will surround your land,
      strip you of your defenses,
      and loot your palaces.

12 This is what the Lord says:

    As a shepherd rescues two legs or a piece of an ear out of a lion's mouth,
      so the Israelites living in Samaria will be rescued,

ˌhaving onlyˌ a corner of a bed or a piece of a couch.ᵃ

¹³ Listen, and testify against the descendants of Jacob,
   declares the Almighty LORD, the God of Armies.
¹⁴ On the day I punish Israel for its disobedience,
   I will also destroy the altars at Bethel.
      The horns of the altar will be cut off and will fall to the ground.
¹⁵ I will tear down winter houses as well as summer houses.
   Houses ˌdecoratedˌ with ivory will be destroyed.
   Mansions will be demolished, declares the LORD.

The LORD Will Punish the Women of Samaria

4 ¹ Listen to this message, you cows of Bashan who live on Mount Samaria.
   You women oppress the poor and abuse the needy.
   You say to your husbands, "Get some wine! Let's drink!"

² Almighty LORD has taken an oath on his holiness:
   Surely, the time is going to come
      when you will be taken away on hooks,
         and the rest of you on fishhooks.
³ Each of you will leave ˌthe cityˌ
      through breaks in the wall, one woman ahead of another.
         You will be thrown into a garbage dump.

   The LORD declares this.

⁴ Go to Bethel and sin.
   Go to Gilgal and sin even more.
   Bring your sacrifices every morning.
   Bring a tenth of your income every three days.
⁵ Burn bread as a thank offering.
   Brag and boast about your freewill offerings.
      This is what you people of Israel love to do.

   The Almighty LORD declares this.

⁶ I left you with nothing to eat in any of your cities.
   I left you with no food in your entire land.
   And you still didn't return to me, declares the LORD.

⁷ I stopped the rain from falling
      three months before the harvest.
   I sent rain on one city and not on another.
      One field had rain.
      Another field had none and dried up.
⁸ So people from two or three cities staggered
         as they walked to another city in order to get a drink of water.
            But they couldn't get enough.
   And you still didn't return to me, declares the LORD.

⁹ I struck your ˌcropsˌ with blight and mildew.
      Locusts repeatedly devoured your gardens, vineyards,
         fig trees, and olive trees.
   And you still didn't return to me, declares the LORD.

¹⁰ I sent plagues on you as I did to Egypt.
   With swords I killed your best young men along with your captured horses.
   I made the stench from your camps fill your noses.
   And you still didn't return to me, declares the LORD.

¹¹ I destroyed some of you as I destroyed Sodom and Gomorrah.
      You were like a burning log snatched from a fire.
   And you still didn't return to me, declares the LORD.

¹² This is what I will do to you, Israel.
      Prepare to meet your God.
         This is what I will do to you, Israel!

ᵃ 3:12 Or "a couch of Damascus."

13   God forms the mountains and creates the wind.
    He reveals his thoughts to humans.
    He makes dawn and dusk ˎappearˎ.
    He walks on the high places of the earth.
    His name is the LORD God of Armies.

A Funeral Song About Israel

5   ¹ Listen to this message, this funeral song that I sing about you, nation of Israel:

2   The people of Israel have fallen,
        never to rise again.
    They lie abandoned in their own land.
        There is no one to help them.

³ This is what the Almighty LORD says:

    The city that sends 1,000 troops off to war
        will have ˎonlyˎ 100 left.
    The one that sends 100 troops off to war
        will have ˎonlyˎ 10 left for the nation of Israel.

A Threefold Call to Turn Away From Sin

⁴ This is what the LORD says to the nation of Israel:

    Search for me and live!
5   But don't search ˎfor meˎ at Bethel.
        Don't go to Gilgal.
            Don't travel to Beersheba.
        Gilgal will certainly go into exile.
    Bethel will come to nothing.
6   Search for the LORD and live!
        If you don't, he will spread like a fire through the house of Joseph
            and burn it down.
            Bethel will have no one to put it out.

7   You, Israel, turn justice into poison
        and throw righteousness on the ground.

8   God made the ˎconstellationsˎ Pleiades and Orion.
    He turns deep darkness into dawn.
    He turns day into night.
    He calls for water from the sea
        to pour it over the face of the earth.
    His name is the LORD.
9   He destroys strongholds and ruins fortresses.

10   Israel, you hate anyone who speaks out against injustice.
    You are disgusted by anyone who speaks the truth.
11   You trample on the poor
        and take their wheat from them for taxes.
            That is why you build houses from hand-cut stones,
                but you will not live in them.
            You plant beautiful vineyards,
                but you will not drink their wine.
12   I know that your crimes are numerous and your sins are many.
        You oppress the righteous by taking bribes.
        You deny the needy access to the courts.
13   That is why a wise person remains silent at such times,
                because those times are so evil.

14   Search for good instead of evil so that you may live.
        Then the LORD God of Armies will be with you, as you have said.
15   Hate evil and love good.
        Then you will be able to have justice in your courts.
            Maybe the LORD God of Armies
                will have pity on the faithful few of Joseph.

16 This is what the LORD, the Almighty God of Armies, says:

> There will be loud crying in every city square,
>> and people will say in every street, "Oh, no!"
> They will call on farmers to mourn
>> and on professional mourners to cry loudly.

17 There will be loud crying in every vineyard,
>> because I will pass through your land ˎwith deathˎ.

The LORD has said this.

The Terrifying Day of the LORD

18 How horrible it will be for those who long for the day of the LORD!
>> Why do you long for that day?
> The day of the LORD is one of darkness and not light.

19 It is like a person who flees from a lion
>> only to be attacked by a bear.
> It is like a person who goes home and puts his hand on the wall
>> only to be bitten by a snake.

20 The day of the LORD brings darkness and not light.
> It is pitch black, with no light.

The LORD Rejects Israel's Worship

21 I hate your festivals; I despise them.
> I'm not pleased with your religious assemblies.

22 Even though you bring me burnt offerings and grain offerings,
> I won't accept them.
> I won't even look at the fellowship offerings of your choicest animals.

23 Spare me the sound of your songs.
> I won't listen to the music of your harps.

24 But let justice flow like a river
>> and righteousness like an ever-flowing stream.

25 Did you bring me sacrifices and grain offerings
> in the desert for 40 years, nation of Israel?

26 You carried along the statues of ˎthe godˎ Sikkuth as your king
> and the star Kiyyun,
>> the gods you made for yourselves.

27 I will send you into exile beyond Damascus,
> says the LORD, whose name is the God of Armies.

The Fall of Samaria

6 **1** How horrible it will be for those who are at ease in Zion,
> for those who feel secure on the mountain of Samaria,
>> and for the heads of the leading nations,
>>> to whom the nation of Israel comes.

2 Go to Calneh and look.
>> Go from there to the great city of Hamath.
>>> Then go to Gath, the city of the Philistines.
> Are you better than these kingdoms?
> Is their territory larger than yours?

3 How horrible it will be for those who think that a day of disaster is far away.
> They bring the reign of violence closer.

4 How horrible it will be for those who sleep on ivory beds.
> They sprawl out on their couches
>> and eat lambs from their flocks and calves from their stalls.

5 How horrible it will be for those who make up songs as they strum a harp.
> Like David, they write all kinds of songs for themselves.

6 How horrible it will be for those who drink wine by the jugful.
> They rub the finest oils all over themselves
>> and are not sorry for the ruin ˎof the descendantsˎ of Joseph.

7 That is why they will now be the first to go into exile.
> The celebrating of those sprawled around the banquet table will stop.

8 The Almighty LORD has sworn an oath on himself.
The LORD God of Armies declares:
   I am disgusted with Jacob's pride,
     and I hate his palaces.
       So I will hand over the city and everything in it.
9 If ten people are left in one house, they will die.
10 If a relative or a mortician
   comes to take the dead bodies out of the house
   and asks someone who is inside the house,
     "Is there anyone else with you?"
       that person will answer, "No."
         "Hush," he will add.
           "We shouldn't mention the name of the LORD!"
11 The LORD is going to give the command
   to level big houses and flatten little houses.

12 Do horses run on rocks?
Does a farmer plow the sea with oxen?
   Yet, you have turned justice into something deadly
     and what is righteous into poison.
13 How horrible it will be for those who rejoice over Lo Debar
   and who say, "We were strong enough to capture Karnaim by ourselves."

14 I am going to lead a nation to attack you, nation of Israel,
   declares the LORD God of the Armies of the Nations.
They will oppress you from the border of Hamath to the valley of Arabah.

The LORD Threatens to Bring a Famine by Locusts

7 ¹ This is what the Almighty LORD showed me: He was preparing swarms of locusts when the second crop was being harvested. It was the harvest that followed the harvest for the king. ² When the locusts had finished eating every plant in the land, I said, "Almighty LORD, please forgive us! How can ˎthe descendants ofˎ Jacob survive? There are so few of them."
³ The LORD changed his plans about this. "This won't happen," the LORD said.

The LORD Threatens to Bring a Drought by Fire

⁴ This is what the Almighty LORD showed me: The Almighty LORD was calling for judgment by fire. The fire dried up the ocean and burned up the land. ⁵ Then I said, "Almighty LORD, please stop! How can ˎthe descendants ofˎ Jacob survive? There are so few of them."
⁶ The LORD changed his plans about this. "This won't happen either," the Almighty LORD said.

The LORD Refuses to Overlook Israel's Sin

⁷ This is what he showed me: The Lord was standing by a wall built with the use of a plumb line, and he had a plumb line in his hand. ⁸ He asked me, "What do you see, Amos?"
I answered, "A plumb line."
Then the Lord said, "I'm going to hold a plumb line in the middle of my people Israel. I will no longer overlook what they have done. ⁹ The worship sites of Isaac will be destroyed, and the holy places of Israel will be in ruins. I will attack Jeroboam's heirs with my sword."

Amaziah Opposes Amos

¹⁰ Then Amaziah, the priest at Bethel, sent a message to King Jeroboam of Israel. It read, "Amos is plotting against you among the people of Israel. The country isn't able to endure everything he is saying. ¹¹ Amos says that Jeroboam will be killed with a sword and that Israel cannot avoid being taken from its land into exile."
¹² Then Amaziah said to Amos, "You seer,ᵃ run away to Judah! Eat there, and prophesy there! ¹³ But don't ˎeverˎ prophesy again in Bethel, because this is the king's holy place and the king's palace."
¹⁴ Amos responded, "I'm not a prophet, and I'm not a disciple of the prophets. I am a rancher and a grower of figs. ¹⁵ But the LORD took me away from herding the flock and said to me, 'Prophesy to my people Israel.'
¹⁶ "Now listen to the word of the LORD: You said, 'Stop prophesying against Israel, and stop preaching against the descendants of Isaac.'
¹⁷ "However, this is what the LORD says: Your wife will become a prostitute in the city, and your sons and daughters will be killed with swords. Your land will be surveyed and divided up, and you will die in an uncleanᵇ land. Israel cannot avoid being taken from its land into exile."

ᵃ 7:12 A seer is a prophet.   ᵇ 7:17 "Unclean" refers to anything that Moses' Teachings say is not presentable to God.

The End Has Come for Israel

8 ¹ This is what the Almighty LORD showed me: a basket of ripe summer fruit. ² He asked, "What do you see, Amos?"

"A basket of ripe summer fruit," I answered.

Then the LORD said to me, "My people Israel are now ripe. I will no longer overlook what they have done. ³ On that day the songs of the temple will become loud cries," declares the Almighty LORD. "There will be dead bodies scattered everywhere. Hush!"

⁴ Listen to this, those who trample on the needy
   and ruin those who are oppressed in the world.
⁵ You say to yourselves,
   "When will the New Moon Festival be over
      so that we can sell more grain?
When will the day of worship be over
      so that we can sell more wheat?
   We can shrink the size of the bushel baskets,
      increase the cost,
         and cheat with dishonest scales.
⁶   We can buy the poor with money
         and the needy for a pair of sandals.
   We can sell the husks mixed in with the wheat."

⁷ The LORD has sworn an oath by Jacob's pride:
   "I will never forget anything that they have done."

⁸ The land will tremble because of this.
Everyone who lives in it will mourn.
   The entire land will rise like the Nile,
      be tossed about, and then sink like Egypt's river.

⁹ On that day, declares the Almighty LORD,
   I will make the sun go down at noon
      and darken the earth in broad daylight.
¹⁰ I will turn your festivals into funerals
      and all your songs into funeral songs.
   I will put sackcloth around everyone's waist
      and shave everyone's head.
   I will make that day seem like a funeral for an only child,
      and its end will be bitter.

¹¹ The days are going to come, declares the Almighty LORD,
      when I will send a famine throughout the land.
   It won't be an ordinary famine or drought.
      Instead, there will be a famine of hearing the words of the LORD.
¹²   People will wander from sea to sea
         and roam from the north to the east,
            searching for the word of the LORD.
            But they won't find it.

¹³ On that day beautiful young women and strong young men
      will faint because of their thirst.
¹⁴ ⌞How horrible it will be for⌟ those who swear by Ashimah,ᵃ
      the idol of Samaria, and say,
         "I solemnly swear, Dan, as your god lives. . . ."
         "I solemnly swear as long as there is a road to Beersheba. . . ."
   Those who say this will fall and never get up again.

The LORD Will Sift Israel out of All the Nations

9 ¹ I saw the Lord standing by the altar, and he said:

   Strike the tops of the pillars so that the foundations shake.
      Cut off everyone's head.
         I will kill with a sword all who are left.

ᵃ 8:14 Hebrew meaning uncertain.

None of them will be able to get away.
None of them will be able to escape.

2 Even if they dig their way into Sheol,
   my hand will take them from there.
Even if they go up to heaven,
   I will bring them down from there.
3 Even if they hide on top of Mount Carmel,
   I will look for them and take them from there.
Even if they hide from me at the bottom of the sea,
   I will command a sea snake to bite them.
4 Even if they go into exile ahead of their enemies,
   I will command a sword to kill them.
I will keep my eyes on them
   so that I can bring disaster on them and not help them.

5 The Almighty LORD of Armies touches the earth.
   It quakes, and all who live on it mourn.
      All of it rises like the Nile
         and sinks like Egypt's river.
6 The one who builds stairs up to heaven
   and sets their foundation on the earth,
the one who calls for the water in the sea
   and pours it over the face of the earth—
His name is the LORD.

7 You people of Israel are like the people from Sudan, says the LORD.
Didn't I bring Israel from Egypt?
Didn't I bring the Philistines from Crete and the Arameans from Kir?

8 I, the Almighty LORD, have my eyes on this sinful kingdom.
   I will wipe it off the face of the earth.
But I won't totally destroy the descendants of Jacob, declares the LORD.
9 I'm going to give the order.
I will sift the nation of Israel out of all the nations
   as if I were using a sieve.
Not one pebble will fall to the ground.
10 All the sinners among my people are thinking,
   "Destruction will not catch up to us or run into us."
      In spite of this, they will be killed with swords.

The LORD Will Restore His People
11 On that day I will set up David's fallen tent.
   I will repair the holes in it.
   I will restore its ruined places.
   I will rebuild them as they were a long time ago.
12 They will capture the few survivors of Edom
   and all the other nations that were under my authority,
      declares the LORD, who will do these things.

13 The days are going to come, declares the LORD,
   when the one who plows will catch up to the one who harvests,
      and the one who stomps on grapes will catch up to the one who plants.
         New wine will drip from the mountains
            and flow from all the hills.
14 I will restore my people Israel.
   They will rebuild the ruined cities and live in them.
   They will plant vineyards and drink the wine from them.
   They will plant gardens and eat their fruit.
15 I will plant the people of Israel in their land,
   and they won't be uprooted again from the land that I gave them,
      says the LORD your God.

OBADIAH

Edom's Fall—*Jeremiah 49:14–16*

¹ This is the vision of Obadiah.

This is what the Almighty LORD says about Edom:

> We have heard a message from the LORD.
>> A messenger was sent among the nations to say,
>>> "Get ready! Let's go to war against Edom."

² "Edom, I will make you the smallest of nations.
>> Others will despise you.

³ Your arrogance has deceived you.
>>> You live on rocky cliffs.
>>> You make your home up high.
>>> You say to yourself,
>>>> 'No one can bring me down to earth.'

⁴ Even though you fly high like an eagle
>> and build your nest among the stars,
>>> I will bring you down from there," declares the LORD.

⁵ "If thieves or looters come to you during the night,
>> won't they steal only until they've had enough?
>>> You will be ruined!
> If people come to pick your grapes,
>> won't they leave a few grapes behind?

⁶ But you, Esau,ª will lose everything.
>> Even your hidden treasures will be looted.

⁷ All your allies will force you to leave your land.
> The people who are at peace with you will deceive you.
>> Those who eat food with you will set traps for you,
>>> and you won't even know about it.

⁸ "On that day I will destroy the wise people in Edom
>> and take wisdom away from Esau's mountain," declares the LORD.

⁹ "Teman, your warriors will be terrified.
> Everyone on Esau's mountain will be slaughtered.

Why Edom Will Be Destroyed

¹⁰ "Because of the violence you did to Jacob, your relative,
>> you will be covered with shame.
>> You will be destroyed forever.

¹¹ While you stood there doing nothing,
>> strangers carried off Jacob's wealth.
>>> Foreigners entered his gates and threw dice for Jerusalem.
>>> You acted like one of them.

¹² Don't gloat over your relative's misfortune
> or be happy when the people of Judah are destroyed.
> Don't brag so much when they're in distress.

¹³ Don't march through the gates of my people when disaster strikes
> or gloat over their misery when disaster strikes.
> Don't take their wealth when disaster strikes.

¹⁴ Don't stand at the crossroads to kill their refugees.
> Don't hand over their survivors when they're in distress.

ª 6 Esau was the son of Isaac and the ancestor of the people of Edom.

The Day of the LORD

¹⁵ "The day of the LORD is near for all nations.
>   Edom, you will be treated as you have treated others.
>   You will get back what you have given.
¹⁶ As you, Israel, drank on my holy mountain,
>   so all nations will drink in turn.
>   They will drink and guzzle down everything in it.
>   They will be like those who have never existed.

¹⁷ "But refugees will live on Mount Zion.
>   It will be holy.
> The descendants of Jacob will get back their possessions.
¹⁸ The descendants of Jacob will be like a fire.
> The descendants of Joseph will be like a flame.
>   But the descendants of Esau will be like straw.
>   They will be burned and destroyed.
>   There will be no one left among the descendants of Esau."
>   The LORD has spoken.

¹⁹ "People from the Negev will take possession of Esau's mountain.
> People from the foothills will take possession of Philistia.
>   They will take possession of the lands of Ephraim and Samaria,
>   and ˏthe descendants ofˏ Benjamin will take possession of Gilead.
²⁰ Exiles from Israel will take possession of Canaan.
>   They will possess land as far as Zarephath.
> Exiles from Jerusalem who are in Sepharad
>   will take possession of the cities in the Negev.
²¹ Those who are victorious will come from Mount Zion
>   to rule Esau's mountain.
>   The kingdom will belong to the LORD."

JONAH

Jonah Tries to Run Away From the LORD

1 ¹ The LORD spoke his word to Jonah, son of Amittai. He said, ² "Leave at once for the important city, Nineveh. Announce to the people that I can no longer overlook the wicked things they have done."

³ Jonah immediately tried to run away from the LORD by going to Tarshish. He went to Joppa and found a ship going to Tarshish. He paid for the trip and went on board. He wanted to go to Tarshish to get away from the LORD.

⁴ The LORD sent a violent wind over the sea. The storm was so powerful that the ship was in danger of breaking up. ⁵ The sailors were afraid, and they cried to their gods for help. They began to throw the cargo overboard to lighten the ship's load.

Now, Jonah had gone below deck and was lying there sound asleep. ⁶ The captain of the ship went to him and asked, "How can you sleep? Get up, and pray to your God. Maybe he will notice us, and we won't die."

⁷ Then the sailors said to each other, "Let's throw dice to find out who is responsible for bringing this disaster on us." So they threw dice, and the dice indicated that Jonah was responsible.

⁸ They asked him, "Tell us, why has this disaster happened to us? What do you do for a living? Where do you come from? What country are you from? What nationality are you?"

⁹ Jonah answered them, "I'm a Hebrew. I worship the LORD, the God of heaven. He is the God who made the sea and the land."

¹⁰ Then the men were terrified. They knew that he was running away from the LORD, because he had told them. They asked Jonah, "Why have you done this?"

¹¹ The storm was getting worse. So they asked Jonah, "What should we do with you to calm the sea?"

¹² He told them, "Throw me overboard. Then the sea will become calm. I know that I'm responsible for this violent storm."

¹³ Instead, the men tried to row harder to get the ship back to shore, but they couldn't do it. The storm was getting worse.

¹⁴ So they cried to the LORD for help: "Please, LORD, don't let us die for taking this man's life. Don't hold us responsible for the death of an innocent man, because you, LORD, do whatever you want." ¹⁵ Then they took Jonah and threw him overboard, and the sea became calm. ¹⁶ The men were terrified of the LORD. They offered sacrifices and made vows to the LORD.ᵃ

¹⁷ The LORD sent a big fish to swallow Jonah. Jonah was inside the fish for three days and three nights.

Jonah's Prayer Inside the Fish

2ᵃ ¹ From inside the fish Jonah prayed to the LORD his God. ² Jonah prayed:

> "I called to the LORD in my distress,
>   and he answered me.
> From the depths of my ˎwateryˏ grave I cried for help,
>   and you heard my cry.
³
>   You threw me into the deep, into the depths of the sea,
>   and water surrounded me.
>   All the whitecaps on your waves have swept over me.
⁴
>   "Then I thought,
>   'I have been banished from your sight.
>   Will I ever see your holy temple again?'

ᵃ 1:16 Jonah 1:17 in English Bibles is Jonah 2:1 in the Hebrew Bible.   ᵃ 2:1 Jonah 2:1–10 in English Bibles is Jonah 2:2–11 in the Hebrew Bible.

5   "Water surrounded me, threatening my life.
           The deep ˌseaˌ covered me completely.
               Seaweed was wrapped around my head.
6   I sank to the foot of the mountains.
       I sank to the bottom,
           where bars held me forever.
       But you brought me back from the pit, O Lᴏʀᴅ, my God.

7   "As my life was slipping away, I remembered the Lᴏʀᴅ.
           My prayer came to you in your holy temple.
8   Those who hold on to worthless idols abandon their loyalty ˌto youˌ.
9   But I will sacrifice to you with songs of thanksgiving.
       I will keep my vow.
           Victory belongs to the Lᴏʀᴅ!"

10 Then the Lᴏʀᴅ spoke to the fish, and it spit Jonah out onto the shore.

Nineveh Turns From Its Wicked Ways

3 ¹ Then the Lᴏʀᴅ spoke his word to Jonah a second time. He said, ² "Leave at once for the important city, Nineveh. Announce to the people the message I have given you."

³ Jonah immediately went to Nineveh as the Lᴏʀᴅ told him. Nineveh was a very large city. It took three days to walk through*ᵃ it. ⁴ Jonah entered the city and walked for about a day. Then he said, "In forty days Nineveh will be destroyed."

⁵ The people of Nineveh believed God. They decided to fast, and everyone, from the most important to the least important, dressed in sackcloth.

⁶ When the news reached the king of Nineveh, he got up from his throne, took off his robe, put on sackcloth, and sat in ashes. ⁷ Then he made this announcement and sent it throughout the city:

"This is an order from the king and his nobles: No one is to eat or drink anything. This includes all people, animals, cattle, and sheep. ⁸ Every person and animal must put on sackcloth. Cry loudly to God for help. Turn from your wicked ways and your acts of violence. ⁹ Who knows? God may reconsider his plans and turn from his burning anger so that we won't die."

10 God saw what they did. He saw that they turned from their wicked ways. So God reconsidered his threat to destroy them, and he didn't do it.

The Lᴏʀᴅ Has to Remind Jonah About His Mercy

4 ¹ Jonah was very upset about this, and he became angry. ² So he prayed to the Lᴏʀᴅ, "Lᴏʀᴅ, isn't this what I said would happen when I was still in my own country? That's why I tried to run to Tarshish in the first place. I knew that you are a merciful and compassionate God, patient, and always ready to forgive and to reconsider your threats of destruction. ³ So now, Lᴏʀᴅ, take my life. I'd rather be dead than alive."

⁴ The Lᴏʀᴅ asked, "What right do you have to be angry?"

⁵ Jonah left the city and sat down east of it. He made himself a shelter there. He sat in its shade and waited to see what would happen to the city. ⁶ The Lᴏʀᴅ God made a plant grow up beside Jonah to give him shade and make him more comfortable. Jonah was very happy with the plant.

⁷ At dawn the next day, God sent a worm to attack the plant so that it withered. ⁸ When the sun rose, God made a hot east wind blow. The sun beat down on Jonah's head so that he was about to faint. He wanted to die. So he said, "I'd rather be dead than alive."

⁹ Then God asked Jonah, "What right do you have to be angry over this plant?"

Jonah answered, "I have every right to be angry—so angry that I want to die."

10 The Lᴏʀᴅ replied, "This plant grew up overnight and died overnight. You didn't plant it or make it grow. Yet, you feel sorry for this plant. ¹¹ Shouldn't I feel sorry for this important city, Nineveh? It has more than 120,000 people in it as well as many animals. These people couldn't tell their right hand from their left."

ᵃ 3:3 Or "around."

MICAH

The Prophet Micah

1 ¹The LORD spoke his word to Micah, who was from Moresheth, when Jotham, Ahaz, and Hezekiah were kings of Judah. This is the vision that Micah saw about Samaria and Jerusalem.

The Capital Cities of Israel and Judah Destroyed

2 Listen, all you people!
Pay attention, earth and all who are on it.
   The Almighty LORD will be a witness against you.
   The Lord will be a witness from his holy temple.

3 The LORD is going to come from his place.
He is going to come down and step on the worship places of the earth.

4   Mountains will melt under him like wax near a fire.
   Valleys will split apart like water pouring down a steep hill.

5 All this is because of Jacob's crime and Israel's sin.
   What is Jacob's crime? Isn't it Samaria?
   What is Judah's worship place? Isn't it Jerusalem?

6 So I will turn Samaria into a pile of rubble,
   a place for planting vineyards.
I will roll its stones down into a valley and expose its foundations.

7   All its idols will be smashed to pieces.
   All its wages for being a prostitute will be burned.
   All its statues will be turned into a pile of rubble.
      Samaria collected its wages for being a prostitute.
      That money will again pay for prostitutes.

8 I will mourn and cry because of this.
I will walk around barefoot and naked.
I will cry like a jackal and mourn like an ostrich.

9   Samaria's wounds are incurable.
      The news about Samaria, will come to Judah.
      It will reach the gates of my people in Jerusalem.

10   Don't report it in Gath. Don't cry there.ª
   Roll in the dust of Beth Leaphrah.

11 Pass by, naked and ashamed, inhabitants of Shaphir.
Don't come out, inhabitants of Zaanan.
   Beth Ezel is in mourning.
      It will take its support away from you.

12 Wait anxiously for good, inhabitants of Maroth.
   From the LORD disaster will come on the gates of Jerusalem.

13 Harness the horses to the chariots, inhabitants of Lachish.
   You were the first to lead the people of Zion into sin.
      The rebellious acts of Israel are found in you.

14   That is why you will give farewell gifts to Moresheth Gath.
   The town of Achzib will betray the kings of Israel.

15 I will again bring a conqueror against the inhabitants of Mareshah.
   The glory of Israel will come to Adullam.

16 Shave your head in mourning for the children you love.
   Make yourselves as bald as vultures
      because your children will be taken from you into exile.

ª 1:10 Or "I rolled in the dust of Beth Leaphrah."

Israel's Sins Are Condemned

2 ¹ How horrible it will be for those who invent trouble
and work out plans for disaster while in bed.
When the morning dawns, they carry out their plans
because they are able to.
² They desire ⸤other people's⸥ fields, so they seize them.
They desire ⸤people's⸥ houses, so they take them.
They cheat a man and his family,
a man and his inheritance.

³ So this is what the LORD says:

I'm planning a disaster to punish your family.
You won't be able to rescue yourselves.
You will no longer be able to walk proudly.
This will be a time of disaster.
⁴ When that day comes, people will make fun of you.
They will sing this sad song about you:
"We are completely ruined.
The LORD gives our people's possessions ⸤to others⸥.
He takes them from us.
He divides our fields among our captors."
⁵ That is why none of you in the LORD's assembly will draw lots
to divide your property.

⁶ Your prophets say, "Don't prophesy!
Don't prophesy such things!
Disgrace will never overtake us."
⁷ Should the descendants of Jacob be asked:
Has the Spirit of the LORD become impatient with you?
Has he done these things?
Are his words good for those who live honestly?

⁸ Recently, my people have turned into enemies.
You take coats from those who pass by without a care
as they return from war.
⁹ You force the women among my people out of their pleasant homes
and take my glory away from their children forever.
¹⁰ Get up, and go away!
This is not a place to rest!
It will be destroyed, completely destroyed,
because it offends me.
¹¹ Liars and frauds may go around and say,
"We will preach to you about wine and liquor."
They would be just the type of preacher you want.

Israel Will Be Gathered Again by the LORD

¹² I will surely gather all of you, Jacob.
I will surely bring together the few people left in Israel.
I will gather them together like sheep in a pen,
like a flock in its pasture.
They will make a lot of noise
because there will be so many people.
¹³ ⸤The LORD⸥ will open the way and lead them.
They will break out, go through the gate, and leave.
Their king will travel in front of them.
The LORD will lead the people.

Israel's Sinful Leaders—Rulers, Prophets, and Priests

3 ¹ Then I said:

Listen, you leaders of Jacob, you rulers of the nation of Israel.
You should know justice.

² You hate good and love evil.

You strip the skin off my people and the flesh off their bones.
3 You eat my people's flesh.
You strip off their skin.
You break their bones to pieces.
You chop them up like meat for a pot, like stew meat for a kettle.
4   Then you will cry to the LORD,
but he will not answer you.
He will hide his face from you at that time
because you have done evil things.

5 This is what the LORD says about the prophets who mislead my people:

When they have something to eat, they say, "All is well!"
But they declare a holy war against those who don't feed them.
6 That is why you will have nights without visions.
You will have darkness without revelations.
The sun will set on the prophets,
and the day will turn dark for them.
7 Seers[a] will be put to shame.
Those who practice witchcraft will be disgraced.
All of them will cover their faces, because God won't answer them.

8 But I am filled with the power of the LORD's Spirit,
with justice, and with strength.
So I will tell ˌthe descendants ofˌ Jacob about their crimes
and ˌthe nation ofˌ Israel about its sins.

9 Listen to this, you leaders of the descendants of Jacob,
you rulers of the nation of Israel.
You despise justice and pervert everything that is right.
10   You build Zion on bloodshed and Jerusalem on wickedness.
11   Your leaders exchange justice for bribes.
Your priests teach for a price.
Your prophets tell the future for money.
But they rely on the LORD when they say,
"After all, the LORD is with us.
Nothing bad will happen to us."
12 Because of you,
Zion will be plowed like a field,
Jerusalem will become a pile of rubble,
and the temple mountain will become a worship site
covered with trees.

The LORD Will Teach the Nations—Isaiah 2:2–4

4 1 In the last days the mountain of the LORD's house
will be established as the highest of the mountains
and raised above the hills.
People will stream to it.
2 Then many nations will come and say,
"Let's go to the mountain of the LORD,
to the house of the God of Jacob.
He will teach us his ways so that we may live by them."
The teachings will go out from Zion.
The word of the LORD will go out from Jerusalem.
3   Then he will judge disputes between many people
and settle arguments between many nations far and wide.
They will hammer their swords into plowblades
and their spears into pruning shears.
Nations will never fight against each other,
and they will never train for war again.
4 They will sit under their grapevines and their fig trees,
and no one will make them afraid.
The LORD of Armies has spoken.

---

[a] 3:7 A seer is a prophet.

⁵ All the nations live by the names of their gods,
   but we will live by the name of the LORD our God forever.

⁶ "When that day comes," declares the LORD,
   "I will gather those who are lame.
   I will bring together those who are scattered
      and those whom I have injured.
⁷ I will change those who are lame into a faithful people.
   I will change those who are forced away into a strong nation."
The LORD will rule them on Mount Zion now and forever.
⁸ You, Jerusalem, watchtower of the flock,
   stronghold of the people of Zion,
      your former government will come back to you.
         The kingdom will return to the people of Jerusalem.

⁹ Now why are you crying so loudly?
   Don't you have a king?
   Has your counselor died?
   Pain grips you like a woman in labor.
¹⁰ Daughter of Zion, writhe in pain and groan like a woman in labor.
   Now you will leave the city,
      live in the open fields,
         and go to Babylon.
            There you will be rescued.
            There the LORD will reclaim you from your enemies.

¹¹ But now many nations gather against you.
   They say, "Let's dishonor Zion and gloat over it."
¹² They don't know the thoughts of the LORD or understand his plan.
   He will bring them together
      like cut grain on the threshing floor.ᵃ
¹³ Get up and thresh,ᵇ people of Zion.
   I will make your horns as hard as iron
      and your hoofs as hard as bronze.
         You will smash many nations into small pieces.
            You will claim their loot for the LORD,
               their wealth for the Lord of the whole earth.
5ᵃ ¹ Now, gather your troops, you city of troops.
      We are under attack.
   Enemies will strike the judge of Israel on the cheek with a stick.

The LORD's Leader for Israel

² You, Bethlehem Ephrathah,
   are too small to be included among Judah's cities.
      Yet, from you Israel's future ruler will come for me.
         His origins go back to the distant past, to days long ago.
³ That is why the LORD will abandon Israel
   until the time a mother has a child.
   Then the rest of the LORD's people will return to the people of Israel.
⁴ The child will become the shepherd of his flock.
   ˌHe will lead themˌ with the strength of the LORD,
      with the majestic name of the LORD his God.
   They will live in safety
      because his greatness will reach the ends of the earth.
⁵ This man will be their peace.

When the Assyrians invade our land and trample our palaces,
   we will attack them with seven shepherds and eight leaders.
⁶ They will rule Assyria with their swords
      and the country of Nimrod with drawn swords.
   They will rescue us from the Assyrians
      when they come into our land
         and walk within our territory.

ᵃ 4:12 A threshing floor is an outdoor area where grain is separated from its husks.   ᵇ 4:13 Threshing is the process of beating stalks to separate them from the grain.   ᵃ 5:1 Micah 5:1–15 in English Bibles is Micah 4:14–5:14 in the Hebrew Bible.

7   Then the few people left from Jacob will be among many people
        like dew from the LORD, like showers on the grass.
            They do not put their hope in humans or wait for mortals.
8   The few people left from Jacob will be among the nations,
        among many people.
            They will be like a lion among animals in the forest,
                like a young lion among flocks of sheep.
            When a lion hunts,
                it tramples ˌits victimsˌ and tears ˌthemˌ to pieces,
                    and there is no one to rescue them.
9   You will use your power against your opponents,
        and all your enemies will be destroyed.

10 "When that day comes," declares the LORD,
        "I will destroy your horses
            and demolish your chariots.
11 I will destroy the cities in your land
        and tear down all your fortresses.
12 I will destroy your sorcerers,
        and you will have no more fortunetellers.
13 I will destroy your idols and your sacred monuments.
        You will no longer worship what your hands have made.
14 I will pull out your poles dedicated to the goddess Asherah.
        I will wipe out your cities.
15 I will take revenge with great anger
        on the nations that do not obey me."

The LORD's Lawsuit Against His People

6 1   Now listen to what the LORD is saying,
        "Stand up! Plead your case in front of the mountains,
            and let the hills listen to your request.
2   Listen to the LORD's lawsuit, you mountains.
    Listen, you strong foundations of the earth.
    The LORD has filed a lawsuit against his people.
        He is arguing his case against Israel.

3   "My people, what have I done to you?
        How have I tried your patience? Answer me!
4   I brought you out of Egypt and freed you from slavery.
    I sent Moses, Aaron, and Miriam to lead you.
5   My people, remember what King Balak of Moab planned ˌto do to youˌ
        and how Balaam, son of Beor, responded to him.
    Remember ˌyour journeyˌ from Shittim to Gilgal[a]
        so that you may know the victories of the LORD."

6   What should I bring when I come into the LORD's presence,
        when I bow in front of the God of heaven?
    Should I bring him year-old calves as burnt offerings?
7   Will the LORD be pleased with thousands of rams
        or with endless streams of olive oil?
    Should I give him my firstborn child because of my rebellious acts?
    Should I give him my young child for my sin?
8   You mortals, the LORD has told you what is good.
        This is what the LORD requires from you:
            to do what is right,
                to love mercy,
                    and to live humbly with your God.

9   The voice of the LORD calls out to the city.
        (The fear of your name is wisdom.)
    "Listen, you tribe assembled in the city.[b]
10 I have cursed all the wicked people who use their money for evil
        and use inaccurate weights and measures.

---

[a] 6:5 Hebrew meaning of this line uncertain.   [b] 6:9 Greek; Masoretic Text "Listen to the stick and the one who appointed it."

¹¹ I cannot tolerate dishonest scales
 and bags filled with inaccurate weights.
¹² The rich people in the city are violent.
 Those who live in the city speak lies,
 and their tongues speak deceitfully.
¹³ I have begun to strike you with heavy blows
 and to ruin you because of your sins.
¹⁴ You will eat, but you won't be full.
 So you will always be hungry.
 You will put things away, but you won't save them.
 Anything you save I will destroy.
¹⁵ You will plant, but you won't harvest.
 You will crush olives, but you won't rub the oil on your skin.
 You will make new wine, but you won't drink it.
¹⁶ You have kept Omri's laws
 and all the practices of the descendants of Ahab,
 and you have followed their advice.
 That is why I will ruin you.
 Your people will be ridiculed.
 You will bear the disgrace of my people."

The Lord's People Confess Their Sin

7 ¹ Poor me!
 I am like those gathering summer fruit,
 like those picking grapes.
 But there aren't any grapes to eat
 or any ripened figs that I crave.
² Faithful people are gone from the earth,
 and no one is decent.
 All people lie in ambush to commit murder.
 They trap each other with nets.
³ Their hands are skilled in doing evil.
 Officials ask for gifts.
 Judges accept bribes.
 Powerful people dictate what they want.
 So they scheme together.^a
⁴ The best of them is like a briar.
 The most decent person is sharper than thornbushes.
 The day you thought you would be punished has come.
 Now is the time you will be confused.
⁵ Don't trust your neighbors.
 Don't have confidence in ˌyourˌ friends.
 Keep your mouth shut even when a woman is lying in your arms.
⁶ A son treats his father with contempt.
 A daughter rebels against her mother.
 A daughter-in-law rebels against her mother-in-law.
 People's enemies are the members of their own families.

⁷ I will look to the Lord.
 I will wait for God to save me.
 I will wait for my God to listen to me.

⁸ Don't laugh at me, my enemies.
 Although I've fallen, I will get up.
 Although I sit in the dark, the Lord is my light.
⁹ I have sinned against the Lord.
 So I will endure his fury
 until he takes up my cause and wins my case.
 He will bring me into the light,
 and I will see his victory.
¹⁰ Then my enemies will see this, and they will be covered with shame,
 because they asked me, "Where is the Lord your God?"

---

^a 7:3 Hebrew meaning of this line uncertain.

Now I look at them.
They are trampled like mud in the streets.

11 The day for rebuilding your walls
and extending your borders is coming.
12 When that day comes, your people will come to you
from Assyria and the cities of Egypt,
from Egypt to the Euphrates River,
from sea to sea, and from mountain to mountain.
13 The earth will become a wasteland for those who live on it
because of what the people living there have done.

14 With your shepherd's staff, take care of your people,
the sheep that belong to you.
They live alone in the woods, in fertile pastures.
Let them feed in Bashan and Gilead like before.
15 Let us see miracles
like the time you came out of Egypt.
16 Nations will see this and be ashamed in spite of all their strength.
They will put their hands over their mouths.
Their ears will become deaf.
17 They will lick dust like snakes,
like animals that crawl on the ground.
They will come out of their hiding places trembling.
They will turn away from your presence in fear, O LORD our God.
They will be afraid of you.
18 Who is a God like you?
You forgive sin
and overlook the rebellion of your faithful people.
You will not be angry forever,
because you would rather show mercy.
19 You will again have compassion on us.
You will overcome our wrongdoing.
You will throw all our sins into the deep sea.
20 You will be faithful to Jacob.
You will have mercy on Abraham
as you swore by an oath to our ancestors long ago.

NAHUM

Nahum's Vision

1 ¹ This is a revelation from the Lord about Nineveh. This book contains the vision of Nahum from Elkosh.

Who Can Withstand the Lord's Anger?

² God does not tolerate rivals. The Lord takes revenge.
The Lord takes revenge and is full of anger.
The Lord takes revenge against his enemies
and holds a grudge against his foes.
³ The Lord is patient and has great strength.
The Lord will never let the guilty go unpunished.
Raging winds and storms mark his path,
and clouds are the dust from his feet.
⁴ He yells at the sea and makes it dry.
He dries up all the rivers.
Bashan and Carmel wither.
The flowers of Lebanon wither.
⁵ The mountains quake because of him.
The hills melt.
The earth draws back in his presence.
The world and all who live in it draw back as well.
⁶ Who can stand in the presence of his rage?
Who can oppose his burning anger?
He pours out his rage like fire
and smashes the rocky cliffs.

Why Does Nineveh Oppose the Lord?

⁷ The Lord is good.
ˌHe is˴ a fortress in the day of trouble.
He knows those who seek shelter in him.
⁸ He will put an end to Nineveh
with a devastating flood.
He will pursue his enemies with darkness.
⁹ What do you think about the Lord?
He is the one who will bring Nineveh to an end.
This trouble will never happen again.
¹⁰ ˌThe people of Nineveh will be˴ like tangled thorns
and like people drunk on their own drink.
They will be completely burned up like very dry straw.
¹¹ From you, Nineveh, a person who plans evil against the Lord sets out.
His advice is wicked.

Nineveh Will Fall

¹² This is what the Lord says:
Though the people of Nineveh are physically fit and many in number,
they will be cut down and die.
Though I have humbled you, Judah,
I will not humble you again.
¹³ But now I will break Nineveh's yoke[a] off of you
and tear its chains from you.

¹⁴ The Lord has given this command about you, Nineveh:
You will no longer have descendants to carry on your name.

---

[a] 1:13 A yoke is a wooden bar placed over the necks of work animals so that they can pull plows or carts.

I will remove the wooden and metal idols from the temple of your gods.
I will prepare your grave because you are worthless.[b]

An Army Will Conquer Nineveh

¹⁵ There on the mountains are the feet of a messenger
who announces the good news: "All is well!"
Celebrate your festivals, Judah! Keep your vows!
This wickedness will never pass your way again.
It will be completely removed.

2[a] 1 The one who will scatter you is coming to attack you.
Guard your fortress!
Keep a lookout on the road!
Prepare for battle!
Be very courageous!

² The LORD will restore Jacob's glory like Israel's glory,
although enemies have looted it
and have destroyed its vines.

³ The shields of his warriors are painted red.
His soldiers have red uniforms.
The metal on his chariots flashes fiery red,
so do the spears when they are waved
on the day he prepares for battle.

⁴ Chariots are racing madly through the streets,
rushing this way and that in the city squares.
They look like torches, like lightning, as they dart about.

⁵ He remembers his best fighting men.
They stumble over themselves as they march.
They hurry to Nineveh's wall.
The shield has been set up for the battering ram.

⁶ The gates of the rivers are opened, and the palace melts away.

Nineveh's Treasures Will Be Taken

⁷ The LORD has determined:
"It will be stripped.
It will be carried away.
Its young women will be mourning like doves
as they beat their breasts."

⁸ Nineveh was like a pool of water from its first day on.
But now its people are fleeing.
"Stop! Stop!"
But no one turns around.

⁹ Steal the silver! Steal the gold!
There is no end to what is stored here—
everything a person could ever want.

¹⁰ Nineveh is destroyed, deserted, demolished.
Hearts are melting.
Knees are knocking.
Every stomach becomes upset.
Every face turns pale.

Nineveh Will Be Destroyed

¹¹ Where is the lions' den,
that feeding place for young lions?
Where are the lion, the lioness, and the lion cub who moved about
with no one to terrify them?

¹² The lion tore its prey to pieces to feed its cubs.
It strangled the prey for its mates.
It used to fill its caves with torn carcasses
and its dens with torn flesh.

---

[b] 1:14 Nahum 1:15 in English Bibles is Nahum 2:1 in the Hebrew Bible.   [a] 2:1 Nahum 2:1–13 in English Bibles is Nahum 2:2–14 in the Hebrew Bible.

13   "I am against you, Nineveh," declares the LORD of Armies.
        "I will send your chariots up in smoke,
            and a sword will kill your young lions.
      I will remove your prey from the earth,
            and no one will ever hear the voice of your messengers again."

Nineveh's Punishment for Sin

3 1   How horrible it will be for that city of bloody violence!
        It is completely full of lies and stolen goods—never without victims.
   2   The sound of the whip!
            The sound of rattling wheels!
        Horses gallop!
            Chariots bounce along!
   3   Horses charge!
            Swords flash!
                Spears glitter!
        Many are killed!
            Dead bodies pile up!
                There is no end to the corpses!
        People trip over corpses
   4   because of Nineveh's constant prostitution,
                this very charming mistress of evil magic.
        She used to sell
            nations her prostitution
                and people her evil magic."
   5   "I am against you, Nineveh," declares the LORD of Armies.
        "I will lift up your dress over your face.
        I will show nations your naked body and kingdoms your disgrace.
   6   I will throw filth on you.
        I will make you look like a fool.
        I will make you a sight to be seen.
   7   Everyone who sees you will run from you, saying,
            'Nineveh has been violently destroyed!
                Who will feel sorry for her?'
        Where can I find anyone to comfort you?"

Nineveh Will Not Escape Punishment

   8   Are you better than No-amon,[a] which sits by the streams of the Nile
            with water surrounding her?
                The sea was ˌherˌ defense.
                The water was her wall.
   9   Sudan and Egypt were her endless strength.
                Put and the Lybians were her help.
  10   Even she went into captivity and was exiled.
        Even her little children were smashed to death at every street corner.
            Soldiers tossed dice for her important men,
                and all her best men were bound in chains.
  11   Even you, Nineveh, will stagger like a drunk.
            You will disappear.
        Even you will look for a fortress ˌto escapeˌ from the enemy.
  12   All your defenses will be like fig trees with the earliest figs.
                When shaken, the figs fall into the mouth of the eater.
  13   Look at your soldiers; they're women!
        The gates of your country are wide open to your enemies.
            Fire has destroyed the bars of your gates.

Nineveh's Strength Will Not Save Her

  14   Store water for the siege!
            Strengthen your defenses!
                Step into the claypits and trample the clay!
                    Grab the brick mold!

---

[a] 3:8 The city No-amon, also called Thebes, was the capital of southern Egypt.

15 Fire will consume you there.
A sword will cut you down.
It will consume you like locusts.
    Multiply like locusts!
    Multiply like hungry locusts!
16 You have produced more businessmen than there are stars in the sky.
  ⌊They are⌋ like locusts that attack and then fly away.
17 Your officers are like locusts,
    and your scribes are like swarms of locusts
       that settle on the fences when it is cold.
          The sun rises, and they scatter in every direction.
             No one knows where they've gone.
18 Your shepherds, king of Assyria, have fallen into a deep sleep.
Your best fighting men are at rest.
Your people are scattered on the mountains,
    and there is no one to gather them.
19 There is no relief for your collapse.
Your wound is fatal.
    All who hear the news about you will clap their hands.
      Who hasn't suffered from your endless evil?

HABAKKUK

Habakkuk's Vision

1 ¹ The divine revelation that the prophet Habakkuk saw.

Habakkuk's Question

² How long, O LORD, am I to cry for help,
   but you will not listen?
I cry out to you, "There's violence!"
   yet you will not come to the rescue.
³ Why do you make me see wrongdoing?
   And why do you watch wickedness?
Destruction and violence are in front of me.
Quarrels and disputes arise.
⁴ That is why your teaching is numbed,
   and justice is never carried out.
      Wicked people surround righteous people
         so that when justice is carried out, it's perverted.

The LORD's Answer

⁵ Look among the nations and watch.
Be amazed and astonished.
I am going to do something in your days
   that you would not believe even if it were reported to you.
⁶ I am going to send the Babylonians,
   that fierce and reckless nation.
They will march throughout the earth
   to take possession of lands that don't belong to them.
⁷ They will be terrifying and fearsome.
They will carry out their own kind of justice and honor.
⁸ Their horses will be faster than leopards
      and quicker than wolves in the evening.
   Their riders will gallop along proudly.
   Their riders will come from far away.
They will fly like an eagle that swoops down for its prey.
⁹ They will all come for violence.
   Every face will be directed forward.
They will gather prisoners like sand.
¹⁰ They will make fun of kings and treat rulers as a joke.
They will laugh at every fortified city
   and build a dirt ramp to capture it.
¹¹ They will move quickly and pass through like the wind.
      So they will be guilty,
         because their own strength is their god.

Habakkuk's Question

¹² Didn't you exist before time began, O LORD, my God, my Holy One?
   We will not die!
O LORD, you have appointed the Babylonians to bring judgment.
O Rock, you have destined them to correct us.
¹³ Your eyes are too pure to look at evil.
You can't watch wickedness.
   Why do you keep watching treacherous people?
   Why are you silent when wicked people swallow those
      who are more righteous than they are?

¹⁴ You make all people like the fish in the sea,
      like schools of sea life that have no ruler.
¹⁵ The Babylonians pull them all up with fishhooks,
         drag them away in nets,
            and gather them in dragnets.
               So they rejoice and are happy.
¹⁶ That is why they sacrifice to their nets and burn incense to their dragnets.
      They are rich and well fed because of them.
¹⁷ Will they keep on emptying their nets
      and always kill nations without mercy?

Habakkuk Waits for the Lord's Answer

2 ¹ I will stand at my guard post.
      I will station myself on the wall.
      I will watch to see what he will say to me
         and what answer I will get to my complaint.

The Lord's Answer

² Then the Lord answered me,
      "Write the vision.
         Make it clear on tablets
            so that anyone can read it quickly.
³ The vision will still happen at the appointed time.
      It hurries toward its goal.
      It won't be a lie.
   If it's delayed, wait for it.
      It will certainly happen.
      It won't be late.

⁴ "Look at the proud person. He is not right in himself.
      But the righteous person will live because of his faithfulness.ᵃ
⁵ Also because wine is treacherous
      he is arrogant and never rests.
      He has a large appetite like the grave.
      He is like death—never satisfied.
      He gathers all the nations to himself.
      He collects all the people to himself.
⁶ Won't all of them ridicule him,
      directing clever sayings and riddles at him, like:

" 'How horrible it will be for the one who makes himself rich
      with what is not his own
         and makes himself wealthy on loans.
            How long will this go on?'
⁷ Won't your creditors suddenly rise up
      and those who are going to shake you wake up?
         Then you will become their prize.
⁸ You have looted many nations.
      All the rest of the people will loot you
         because of the slaughter and violence done
            to lands, cities, and all their inhabitants.

⁹ " 'How horrible it will be for the one who uses violence
      to get things for his own household
         in order to set his nest up high
            and save himself from disaster.'
¹⁰ You have planned disgrace for your household
      by cutting off many people and forfeiting your own life.
¹¹ A stone in the wall will cry out.
      A beam in the roof will answer it.

¹² " 'How horrible it will be for the one who builds a city by slaughter
      and founds a town by crime.'

ᵃ 2:4 Masoretic Text; Greek "live because of my faith."

¹³   Isn't it from the LORD of Armies
           that people grow tired only to feed the flames
               and nations exhaust themselves for nothing?
¹⁴   But the earth will be filled with the knowledge of the LORD's glory
           like the water covers the sea.

¹⁵   " 'How horrible it will be for the one who makes his neighbor drink
           from the bowl of God's rage,
               making him drunk in order to stare at his nakedness.'
¹⁶   You are filled with disgrace rather than glory.
           Drink! Yes you! And expose yourself as godless.
               The cup in the LORD's right hand will come around to you,
                   and disgrace will cover your glory.
¹⁷   The violence done to Lebanon will overwhelm you,
           and the destruction done to the animals will terrify you
               because of the slaughter and violence done
                   to lands, cities, and all their inhabitants.

¹⁸   "What benefit is there in a carved idol
           when its maker has carved it?
       What benefit is there in a molded statue, a teacher of lies,
           when its maker has molded it?
       The one who formed it trusts himself
           to make worthless idols that cannot speak.
¹⁹   'How horrible it will be for the one
           who says to a piece of wood, "Wake up!"
               and to a stone that cannot talk, "Get up!" '
       Can that thing teach ˌanyoneˌ?
           Just look at it!
               It's covered with gold and silver,
                   but there's absolutely no life in it."

²⁰   The LORD is in his holy temple.
           All the earth should be silent in his presence.

A Psalm

3 ¹ A prayer of the prophet Habakkuk; according to *shigionoth*.ᵃ

²   LORD, I have heard the report about you.
       LORD, I fear your work.
           In the course of the years, renew it.
           In the course of the years, reveal it.
           In all this chaos, remember to be merciful.

³   God comes from Teman.   *Selah*
       The Holy One comes from Mount Paran.
           His splendor covers the heavens.
           His praise fills the earth.
⁴   His brightness is like the sunlight.
               Rays of light ˌstreamˌ from his hand.
                   That is where his power is hidden.
⁵   Diseases go ahead of him.
           Plagues follow after him.
⁶   He stands and shakes the earth.
       He casts a glance and startles the nations.
           The oldest mountains break apart.
           The ancient hills sink.
           The ancient paths belong to him.
⁷   I see trouble in the tents of Cushan.
       I see trembling in the tents of Midian.

⁸   The LORD is not angry with the rivers, is he?
           If you are angry with the rivers,

ᵃ 3:1 Unknown musical term.

> if you are furious with the sea,
>   ⌐why⌐ do you ride your horses,
>   your chariots of salvation?

9 You get your bow ready for action,
>   for the arrows ⌐you⌐ promised.   *Selah*
> You split the land with rivers.

10 The mountains look at you. They writhe in pain.
> Floodwaters pass by.
> The deep ocean roars. Its waves rise up high.

11 The sun and the moon stand still.
>   They scatter at the light of your arrows,
>   at the bright lightning of your spear.

12 You march through the earth with fury.
> You trample the nations in anger.

13 You go out to save your people,
>   to save your anointed.*b*
> You crush the leader of the wicked household,
>   stripping him bare from head to toe.   *Selah*

14 You pierce the leader of his gang with his own arrows.
>   His soldiers come like a violent storm to scatter me.
>   They are arrogant like those who secretly eat up the poor.

15 You march with your horses into the sea,
>   into the mighty raging waters.

16 I have heard, so there's trembling within me.
> At the report my lips quivered.
> A rotten feeling has entered me.
>   I tremble where I stand.
>   I wait for the day of trouble
>   to come to the people who will attack us.

17 Even if the fig tree does not bloom
>   and the vines have no grapes,
> even if the olive tree fails to produce
>   and the fields yield no food,
> even if the sheep pen is empty
>   and the stalls have no cattle—

18 even then,
>   I will be happy with the LORD.
>   I will truly find joy in God, who saves me.

19 The LORD Almighty is my strength.
>   He makes my feet like those of a deer.
>   He makes me walk on the mountains.

For the choir director; on stringed instruments.

---

b 3:13 Or "to save with your anointed."

ZEPHANIAH

Zephaniah's Prophecy

1 ¹ This is the word that the LORD spoke to Zephaniah, who was the son of Cushi, the grandson of Gedaliah, and the great-grandson of Amariah, son of Hezekiah. The LORD spoke his word in the days of Judah's King Josiah, son of Amon.

The LORD Will Judge the Earth

² "I will gather everything on the face of the earth
   and put an end to it," declares the LORD.
³ "I will put an end to humans and animals.
I will put an end to
   the birds in the sky,
      the fish in the sea,
         and the sins that make people fall, together with the sinners.
I will remove all people from the face of the earth," declares the LORD.

The LORD Will Judge Judah

⁴ "I will use my power against Judah
   and against those who live in Jerusalem.
I will remove the faithful few of Baal from this place
   and the names of the pagan priests along with my priests.
⁵ I will remove those who worship all the stars in the sky on their rooftops
   and those who worship by swearing loyalty to the LORD
      while also swearing loyalty to the god Milcom.ᵃ
⁶ I will remove those who have turned away from following the LORD
   and those who no longer seek the LORD or ask him for help."

⁷ Be silent in the presence of the Almighty LORD,
   because the day of the LORD is near.
The LORD has prepared a sacrifice.
   He has invited his special guests.

⁸ "On the day of the LORD's sacrifice I will punish the officials,
   the king's sons, and all who dress in foreign clothing.ᵇ
⁹ On that day I will punish all who jump over the doorway
   and all who fill their master's house with violence and deception.
¹⁰ On that day a loud cry will come from Fish Gate,
   a howling from the Second Part of the city,
      and a loud crashing sound from the hills," declares the LORD.
¹¹   "Howl, inhabitants of the Mortar,ᶜ
            because all the merchants will be destroyed
               and all who handle money will be killed.

¹² "At that time I will search Jerusalem with lamps and punish those
   who are satisfied with their hardened lifestyle,
      who think that the LORD won't do anything—good or bad.
¹³   Their wealth will be looted.
            Their homes will be demolished.
            They will build houses, but they won't live in them.
            They will plant vineyards, but they won't drink their wine."

The Day of the LORD

¹⁴   The frightening day of the LORD is near.
      It is near and coming very quickly.

ᵃ 1:5 Or "to their king." ᵇ 1:8 Wearing foreign clothing was a sign of worshiping foreign gods. ᶜ 1:10–11 The Mortar was in the northern part of Jerusalem, the Second Part of the city, which could be entered through the Fish Gate.

Listen! Warriors will cry out bitterly on the day of the LORD.
¹⁵ That day will be a day of overflowing fury,
    a day of trouble and distress,
    a day of devastation and desolation,
    a day of darkness and gloom,
    a day of clouds and overcast skies,
¹⁶   a day of rams' horns and battle cries
      against the fortified cities
        and against the high corner towers.
¹⁷ "I will bring such distress on humans that they will walk like they are blind,
    because they have sinned against the LORD."
Their blood will be poured out like dust
    and their intestines like manure.
¹⁸ Their silver and their gold will not be able to rescue them
    on the day of the LORD's overflowing fury.
The whole earth will be consumed by his fiery anger,
    because he will put an end, a frightening end,
      to those who live on earth.

A Call for Judah to Turn Away From Sin

2 ¹ Gather yourselves together!
    Yes, gather together, you shameless nation,
²   before the decree is carried out
     ˌandˌ the day passes like windblown husks,
    before the LORD's burning anger comes to you,
    before the day of the LORD's anger comes to you.
³ Search for the LORD, all you humble people in the land
    who carry out his justice.
Search for what is right.
Search for humility.
    Maybe you will find shelter on the day of the LORD's anger.

The LORD Will Judge His People's Enemies

⁴ Gaza will be deserted,
    and Ashkelon will be destroyed.
Ashdod will be driven out at noon,
    and Ekron will be torn out by the roots.
⁵ How horrible it will be for those who live on the seacoast,
    for the nation from Crete.
The word of the LORD is against you, Canaan, the land of the Philistines:
    "I will destroy you so that no one will be living there."
⁶ The seacoast will become pastureland
    with meadows for shepherds
      and fenced-off places for sheep.
⁷ The coast will belong to the faithful few from the nation of Judah.
    There they will graze their sheep.
    In the evening they will lie down in the houses of Ashkelon.
The LORD their God will take care of them
    and will restore their fortunes.

⁸ "I have heard the insults from Moab and the mockery from Ammon.
    They insulted my people and bragged about their territory.
⁹ Therefore, I solemnly swear, as I live,"
    declares the LORD of Armies, the God of Israel,
"Moab will become like Sodom, and Ammon will become like Gomorrah:
    a place of weeds, salt pits, and ruins forever.
The faithful few of my people will loot them,
    and those who are left in my nation will take possession of them."

¹⁰ This is what they will get for their sinful pride,
    because they insulted the people who belong to the LORD of Armies
      and made themselves greater than them.

¹¹ The LORD will terrify them,
because he will make all the gods of the earth waste away.
So every person from every coast and nation will bow to him.

¹² "Even you, the people from Sudan,
you will also die by my sword."

¹³ The LORD will use his power against the north and destroy Assyria.
He will turn Nineveh into a deserted ruin,
a dried up wasteland like the desert.
¹⁴ Flocks will lie down in it along with animals of every kind.
Even pelicans and herons will nest on top of its columns.
Listen! A bird will sing in a window.
The doorway will be in ruins,
because the LORD will expose the cedar beams.
¹⁵ Is this the arrogant city?
Is this the city that used to live securely,
the city that used to think to itself,
"I'm the only one, and no one else exists but me"?
What a wasteland it is now, a resting place for wild animals!
All who pass by it will hiss and make an obscene gesture.

Jerusalem Will Be Destroyed

3 ¹ How horrible it will be for that rebellious
and corrupt place, the city of violence.
² It obeys no one.
It does not accept correction.
It does not trust the LORD.
It does not draw close to its God.
³ Its officials are ˌlikeˌ roaring lions.
Its judges are ˌlikeˌ wolves in the evening.
They leave nothing to gnaw on for the morning.
⁴ Its prophets are reckless and unfaithful.
Its priests contaminate what is holy.
They violate the teachings.
⁵ The righteous LORD is in that city.
He does no wrong.
He brings his judgment to light every morning.
He does not fail.
But those who are perverted are shameless.

⁶ "I will cut off the nations.
Their towers will be destroyed.
I will demolish their streets.
No one will walk through them.
Their cities will be completely destroyed.
Not a single person will be left.
No one will be living there.
⁷ I said ˌto my peopleˌ,
'You will fear me.
You will accept correction!'
Then their homeland would not be wiped out
even though I have punished them.
Still, they continued to be corrupt in everything they did."
⁸ The LORD declares, "Just wait!
One day I will stand up as a witness.
I have decided to gather nations,
to bring kingdoms together,
and to pour my rage, my burning anger, on them.
The whole land will be consumed by my fiery fury.

Israel Will Turn Away From Sin

⁹ "Then I will give all people pure lips
to worship the LORD
and to serve him with one purpose.

10   From beyond the rivers of Sudan
     my worshipers, my scattered people, will bring my offering.
11   On that day you will no longer be ashamed
     of all your rebellious acts against me.
  Then I will remove your arrogance
     and never again will you act proud on my holy mountain.
12   So with you I will leave a faithful few, a humble and poor people.
     They will seek refuge in the name of the LORD.
13   The faithful few in Israel will not do wrong, tell lies,
     or use their tongues to deceive others.
  They will graze their sheep and lie down,
     and there will be no one to terrify them."

Israel's Joyful Song

14   Sing happily, people of Zion!
     Shout loudly, Israel!
        Celebrate and rejoice with all your heart, people of Jerusalem.
15   The LORD has reversed the judgments against you.
     He has forced out your enemies.
  The king of Israel, the LORD, is with you.
     You will never fear disaster again.
16   On that day Jerusalem will be told,
     "Do not be afraid, Zion!
     Do not lose courage!"
17   The LORD your God is with you.
     He is a hero who saves you.
       He happily rejoices over you,
          renews you with his love,
            and celebrates over you with shouts of joy.

Israel Will Return Home

18   "I will gather those among you who are troubled because of the festivals.
     They bear a burden of disgrace.
19   At that time
     I will deal with all who have overpowered you.
     I will rescue those who are lame.
     I will gather those who have been scattered.
     I will make them praised and famous in all the world,
       though they had been ashamed.
20   At that time I will bring you ˌhomeˌ.
     Yes, at that time I will gather you together.
  I will make you famous and praised among all the people of the earth
     when I restore your fortunes right before your eyes," says the LORD.

HAGGAI

A Call to Rebuild the LORD's House

1 ¹ On the first day of the sixth month in Darius' second year as king, the LORD spoke his word through the prophet Haggai to Zerubbabel (who was the son of Shealtiel and was governor of Judah) and to the chief priest Joshua (who was the son of Jehozadak). He said, ² "This is what the LORD of Armies says: These people say it's not the right time to rebuild the house of the LORD."

³ Then the LORD spoke his word through the prophet Haggai. He said, ⁴ "Is it time for you to live in your paneled houses while this house lies in ruins? ⁵ Now, this is what the LORD of Armies says: Carefully consider your ways! ⁶ You planted a lot, but you harvested little. You eat, but you're never full. You drink, but you're still thirsty.ᵃ You wear clothing, but you never have enough to keep you warm. You spend money as fast as you earn it. ⁷ This is what the LORD of Armies says: Carefully consider your ways!

⁸ "Go to the mountains, get lumber, and build the house. I will be pleased with it, and I will be honored," declares the LORD.

⁹ "You expected a lot, but you received a little. When you bring something home, I blow it away. Why?" declares the LORD of Armies. "It's because my house lies in ruins while each of you is busy working on your own house. ¹⁰ It is because of you that the sky has withheld its dew and the earth has withheld its produce. ¹¹ I called for a drought on the land, the hills, and on the grain, the new wine, the olive oil, and whatever the ground produces, on humans and animals, and on all your hard work."

The Work on the House Resumes

¹² Then Zerubbabel (who was the son of Shealtiel), the chief priest Joshua (who was the son of Jehozadak), and the faithful few who returned from Babylon obeyed the LORD their God. They also obeyed the words of the prophet Haggai because the LORD their God had sent him and because the people feared the LORD.

¹³ Then Haggai, the messenger of the LORD who had received the LORD's message, said to the people, "I am with you, declares the LORD."

¹⁴ The LORD inspired them ˌto rebuild his houseˌ. So Zerubbabel (who was the son of Shealtiel and was governor of Judah), the chief priest Joshua (who was the son of Jehozadak), and the faithful few who returned from Babylon began working on the house of the LORD of Armies, their God. ¹⁵ They began on the twenty-fourth day of the sixth month in Darius' second year as king.

The New House Will Be Greater Than the Old One

2 ¹ On the twenty-first day of the seventh month, the LORD spoke his word through the prophet Haggai. He said, ² "Now, speak to Zerubbabel (who is the son of Shealtiel and is governor of Judah), the chief priest Joshua (who is the son of Jehozadak), and the faithful few who returned from Babylon. ³ Ask them, 'Is there anyone among the faithful few who saw this house in its former glory? How does it look to you now? Doesn't it seem like nothing to you?'

⁴ "But now, Zerubbabel, be strong," declares the LORD. "Chief Priest Joshua (son of Jehozadak), be strong. Everyone in the land, be strong," declares the LORD. "Work, because I am with you," declares the LORD of Armies. ⁵ "This is the promise I made to you when you came out of Egypt. My Spirit remains with you. Don't be afraid.

⁶ "This is what the LORD of Armies says: Once again, in a little while,ᵃ I am going to shake the sky and the earth, the sea and the dry land. ⁷ I will shake all the nations, and the one whom all the nations desire will come. Then I will fill this house with glory, says the LORD of Armies. ⁸ The silver is mine, and the gold is mine, declares the LORD of Armies. ⁹ This new house will be more glorious than the former, declares the LORD of Armies. And in this place I will give ˌthemˌ peace, declares the LORD of Armies."

ᵃ 1:6 Or "You have ˌwineˌ to drink but not enough to become drunk."   ᵃ 2:6 Hebrew meaning uncertain.

Though the People Are Sinful, the Lord Will Bless Them

¹⁰ On the twenty-fourth day of the ninth month in Darius' second year as king, the Lord spoke his word to the prophet Haggai. He said, ¹¹ "This is what the Lord of Armies says: Ask the priests for a decision. ¹² Suppose a person carries meat set aside for a holy purpose and he folds it up in his clothes. If his clothes touch bread, boiled food, wine, oil, or any kind of food, does that make the food holy?"

The priests answered, "No."

¹³ Haggai asked, "Suppose a person becomes unclean*b* by touching a corpse. If he touches any of these things, does that make them unclean?"

The priests answered, "That makes them unclean."

¹⁴ Then Haggai answered, "In the same way, I have decided that these people are unclean, and so is this nation, declares the Lord. So is everything they do. Whatever offering they bring is unclean.

¹⁵ "And from now on, carefully consider this. Consider how things were before one stone was laid on another in the temple of the Lord. ¹⁶ When anyone came to a pile of grain ˌto getˌ 20 measures, there would be only 10. And when anyone came to a wine vat to draw out 50 measures, there would be only 20 in it. ¹⁷ I infested all your work with blight and mildew and struck it with hail. But you didn't come back to me, declares the Lord. ¹⁸ Carefully consider from now on, from the twenty-fourth day of the ninth month, from the day when the foundation of the house of the Lord was laid. Carefully consider: ¹⁹ Is there any seed left in the barn? The vine, the fig tree, the pomegranate, and the olive tree still haven't produced. But from now on I will bless you."

A Promise to Zerubbabel

²⁰ The Lord spoke his word to Haggai a second time on the twenty-fourth day of the month. He said, ²¹ "Say to Zerubbabel (governor of Judah), 'I am going to shake the heavens and the earth. ²² I will overthrow the thrones of kingdoms and destroy the power of nations. I will overthrow chariots and their riders, and the horses will fall along with their riders. They will kill one another with swords. ²³ On that day, declares the Lord of Armies, I will take you, my servant Zerubbabel (son of Shealtiel), declares the Lord. I will make you like a signet ring, because I have chosen you, declares the Lord of Armies.' "

---

b 2:13 "Unclean" refers to anything that Moses' Teachings say is not presentable to God.

ZECHARIAH

Turn From Your Evil Ways

1 ¹ In the eighth month of Darius' second year as king, the LORD spoke his word to the prophet Zechariah, who was the son of Berechiah and the grandson of Iddo. He said, ² "The LORD was very angry with your ancestors. ³ Tell the people, 'This is what the LORD of Armies says: Return to me, declares the LORD of Armies, and I will return to you, says the LORD of Armies.' ⁴ Don't be like your ancestors, who heard the earlier prophets preach to them, 'This is what the LORD of Armies says: Turn from your evil ways and your evil deeds.' But they didn't listen or pay attention to me, declares the LORD. ⁵ Your ancestors—where are they now? And the prophets—are they still alive? ⁶ Didn't my warnings and my laws, which I've commanded my servants the prophets ₊to preach₊, finally catch up with your ancestors? Then your ancestors turned away from their sins and said, 'The LORD of Armies has done to us what he had planned to do. He has dealt with us as our ways and deeds deserve.' "

The LORD Will Comfort Zion

⁷ On the twenty-fourth day of the eleventh month (the month of Shebat) in Darius' second year as king, the LORD spoke his word to the prophet Zechariah, who was the son of Berechiah and the grandson of Iddo.

⁸ During that night I saw a man riding on a red horse. He was standing among the myrtle trees in a ravine. Behind him were red, chestnut, and white horses.

⁹ "What do these horses mean, sir?" I asked.

The angel who was speaking with me answered, "I will show you what they mean."

¹⁰ The man standing among the myrtle trees explained, "They're the horses the LORD has sent to patrol the earth." ¹¹ Then they reported to the Messenger of the LORD standing among the myrtle trees, "We have patrolled the earth. The whole world is at rest and in peace."

¹² Then the Messenger of the LORD said, "LORD of Armies, how much longer until you show compassion to Jerusalem and the cities of Judah? You've been angry with them for 70 years." ¹³ The LORD responded to the angel who was speaking with me, using kind and comforting words.

¹⁴ The angel who was speaking with me said, "Announce: This is what the LORD of Armies says: I'm very jealous about Jerusalem and Zion, ¹⁵ and I'm very angry with the nations who think they are at ease. I was only a little angry, but they made things worse. ¹⁶ This is what the LORD of Armies says: I have returned to Jerusalem with compassion. My house will be rebuilt in it, declares the LORD of Armies. A measuring line will be used to rebuild Jerusalem.

¹⁷ "Announce again: This is what the LORD of Armies says: My cities will overflow with prosperity once more. The LORD will again comfort Zion and will again choose Jerusalem."[a]

Punishment for the Nations That Scattered Judah

¹⁸ I looked up and saw four animal horns. ¹⁹ So I asked the angel who was speaking with me, "What do these horns mean?"

He said to me, "These are the horns ₊of the nations₊ that scattered Judah, Israel, and Jerusalem."

²⁰ Then the LORD showed me four craftsmen. ²¹ I asked, "What are they going to do?"

He answered, "Those horns scattered Judah so widely that no one could lift up his head. But the craftsmen have come to terrify them, to throw down the horns of the nations. The nations raised their horns to scatter the land of Judah."

The LORD Will Choose Jerusalem

2[a] ¹ I looked up and saw a man with a measuring line in his hand. ² I asked him, "Where are you going?"

He answered, "I am going to measure Jerusalem to see how wide and how long it is."

---

[a] 1:17 Zechariah 1:18–21 in English Bibles is Zechariah 2:1–4 in the Hebrew Bible.   [a] 2:1 Zechariah 2:1–13 in English Bibles is Zechariah 2:5–17 in the Hebrew Bible.

³ Then the angel who was speaking with me left. Another angel came out to meet him ⁴ and said to him, "Run, and say to that young man, 'Jerusalem will be inhabited like an unwalled village because it will have so many people and animals in it. ⁵ I will be a wall of fire around it, declares the LORD. I will be the glory within it.'

⁶ "Hurry, hurry! Flee from the land of the north, declares the LORD. I've scattered you to the four winds of heaven. ⁷ Hurry, Zion! Escape, you inhabitants of Babylon! ⁸ This is what the LORD of Armies says: Afterwards, the Glory sent me to the nations who looted you. Whoever touches you touches the apple of his eye. ⁹ I'm going to shake my fist at the nations, and their own slaves will loot them. Then you will know that the LORD of Armies has sent me. ¹⁰ Sing for joy and rejoice, people of Zion. I'm going to come and live among you, declares the LORD. ¹¹ On that day many nations will join the LORD and become my people. I will live among you. Then you will know that the LORD of Armies has sent me to you. ¹² The LORD will claim Judah as his own in the holy land and will again choose Jerusalem.

¹³ "Everyone be silent in the presence of the LORD. He is waking up and setting out from his holy dwelling place."

The LORD Will Send His Servant, the Branch

3 ¹ Then he showed me Joshua, the chief priest, standing in front of the Messenger of the LORD. Satan the Accuser was standing at Joshua's right side to accuse him. ² The LORD said to Satan, "I, the LORD, silence you, Satan! I, the LORD, who has chosen Jerusalem, silence you! Isn't this man like a burning log snatched from a fire?"

³ Joshua was wearing filthy clothes and was standing in front of the Messenger. ⁴ The Messenger said to those who were standing in front of him, "Remove Joshua's filthy clothes." Then he said to Joshua, "See, I have taken your sin away from you, and I will dress you in fine clothing."

⁵ So I said, "Put a clean turban on his head." They put a clean turban on his head and dressed him while the Messenger of the LORD was standing there.

⁶ The Messenger of the LORD advised Joshua, ⁷ "This is what the LORD of Armies says: If you live according to my ways and follow my requirements, you will govern my temple and watch over my courtyards. Then I will give you free access to walk among those standing here.

⁸ "Listen, Chief Priest Joshua and your friends sitting with you. These men are a sign of things to come: I'm going to bring my servant, the Branch.

⁹ "Look at the stone I have set in front of Joshua. That one stone has seven eyes.ᵃ I am engraving an inscription on it," declares the LORD of Armies. "I will remove this land's sin in a single day. ¹⁰ On that day," declares the LORD of Armies, "each of you will invite your neighbor to sit under your vine and fig tree."

The LORD's House Will Be Rebuilt

4 ¹ The angel who was speaking with me returned and woke me up as one might wake up someone who is sleeping. ² He asked me, "What do you see?"

I answered, "I see a solid gold lamp stand with a bowl on top and seven lamps on it. There are seven spouts for each lamp that is on top of it. ³ There are also two olive trees beside it, one on the right of the bowl and the other on its left."

⁴ I asked the angel who was speaking with me, "What do these things mean, sir?"

⁵ Then the angel asked me, "Don't you know what they mean?"

"No, sir," I answered.

⁶ Then he replied, "This is the word the LORD spoke to Zerubbabel: You won't ₍succeed₎ by might or by power, but by my Spirit, says the LORD of Armies. ⁷ What a high mountain you are! In front of Zerubbabel you will become a plain. He will bring out the topmost stone with shouts of 'Blessings, blessings on it!' "

⁸ Then the LORD spoke his word to me. He said, ⁹ "Zerubbabel's hands have laid the foundation of this house, and his hands will finish it. Then you will know that the LORD of Armies has sent me to you. ¹⁰ Who despised the day when little things began to happen? They will be delighted when they see the plumb line in Zerubbabel's hand. (These seven eyes of the LORD roam over all the earth.)"

¹¹ I asked the angel, "What do these two olive trees at the right and the left of the lamp stand mean?" ¹² Again I asked him, "What is the meaning of the two branches from the olive trees next to the two golden pipes that are pouring out gold?"

¹³ He asked me, "Don't you know what these things mean?"

"No, sir," I answered.

¹⁴ So he said, "These are the two anointed ones who are standing beside the Lord of the whole earth."

ᵃ 3:9 Or "facets."

Sinners Will Be Separated From the Lord's People

5 **1** I looked up again and saw a flying scroll. **2** The angel asked me, "What do you see?"

"I see a flying scroll," I answered. "It's 30 feet long and 15 feet wide."

3 Then he said to me, "This is a curse that will go out all over the earth. The one side of the scroll says that every thief will be forced away. The other side of the scroll says that everyone who takes an oath will be forced away. **4** I will send out a curse, declares the LORD of Armies, and it will enter the houses of thieves and the houses of those who take oaths in my name. It will stay in their houses and destroy the timber and stone."

Wickedness Will Be Removed From the Land

5 The angel who was speaking with me came forward. He said, "Look up, and see what's coming."

6 "What is it?" I asked.

"A basket is coming," he said. Then he added, "This is what the people's sins look like all over the earth."ᵃ **7** A lead cover ˌon the basketˌ was raised, and a woman was sitting in the basket. **8** The angel said, "This is wickedness," and he pushed her back into the basket and forced the lead cover down on top of it.

9 I looked up and saw two women coming forward with wind in their wings. They had wings like those of a stork. They carried the basket into the sky.

10 I asked the angel who was speaking with me, "Where are they taking the basket?"

11 He answered me, "They are going to build a house for it in Shinar [Babylonia]. When the house is ready, they will set the basket there on a stand."

The Lord's Victory Throughout the Earth

6 **1** I looked up again and saw four chariots going out from between the two mountains. They were mountains of bronze. **2** The first chariot had red horses. The second had black horses. **3** The third had white horses. And the fourth had strong, spotted horses. **4** I asked the angel who was speaking with me, "What do these horses mean, sir?"

5 The angel answered, "They are the four spirits of heaven. They are going out after standing in the presence of the Lord of the whole earth. **6** The chariot with the black horses is going toward the north, and the white horses are following them. The spotted ones are going toward the south."

7 When these strong horses went out, they were eager to patrol the earth.

He said, "Go, patrol the earth!" And they patrolled the earth.

8 Then he called out to me, "Look! Those who went to the north have made my Spirit rest in the north."

Priest and King

9 The LORD spoke his word to me. He said, **10** "Take an offering from the exiles Heldai, Tobijah, and Jedaiah, who have arrived from Babylon. This same day go to the house of Josiah, son of Zephaniah. **11** Take the silver and gold, make a crown, and put it on the head of Chief Priest Joshua, son of Jehozadak. **12** Then say to him, 'This is what the LORD of Armies says: Here is the man whose name is Branch. He will branch out from where he is, and he will rebuild the LORD's temple. **13** He will rebuild the LORD's temple and receive royal honor. He will sit and rule from his throne. He will be a priest on his throne. There will be a peaceful understanding between them. **14** The crown will be a reminder to Helem, Tobijah, Jedaiah, and Hen (son of Zephaniah) in the LORD's temple. **15** Those who are far away will come and rebuild the LORD's temple. Then you will know the LORD of Armies has sent me to you. This will happen if you obey the LORD your God completely.' "

You Should Have Obeyed the Lord's Prophets

7 **1** On the fourth day of the ninth month (the month of Chislev) in Darius' fourth year as king, the LORD spoke his word to Zechariah. **2** Now, ˌthe people fromˌ Bethel sent Sharezer and Regem Melech with their menᵃ to ask the LORD for a blessing. **3** They asked the priests from the house of the LORD of Armies as well as the prophets, "Should we mourn and fast in the fifth month as we have done for so many years?"

4 Then the LORD of Armies spoke his word to me. He said, **5** "Tell all the people of the land and the priests, 'When you fasted and mourned in the fifth and seventh months these past 70 years, did you really do it for me? **6** When you ate and drank, didn't you do it to benefit yourselves? **7** Aren't these the same words that the LORD announced through the earlier prophets,

---

ᵃ 5:6 One Hebrew manuscript, Greek, Syriac; other Hebrew manuscripts "This is their eye all over the earth."
ᵃ 7:2 Or "Bethel Sharezer sent Regem Melech with his men."

when Jerusalem and its surrounding cities were inhabited and undisturbed and the Negev and the foothills were still inhabited?' "

⁸ Then the LORD spoke his word to Zechariah. He said, ⁹ "This is what the LORD of Armies says: Administer real justice, and be compassionate and kind to each other. ¹⁰ Don't oppress widows, orphans, foreigners, and poor people. And don't even think of doing evil to each other.

¹¹ "But people refused to pay attention. They shrugged their shoulders at me and shut their ears so that they couldn't hear. ¹² They made their hearts as hard as flint so that they couldn't hear the LORD's teachings, the words that the LORD of Armies had sent by his Spirit through the earlier prophets. So the LORD of Armies became very angry.

¹³ "When I called, they wouldn't listen. So now when they call, I won't listen, says the LORD of Armies. ¹⁴ I used a windstorm to scatter them among all the nations, nations they hadn't even heard of. They left behind a land so ruined that no one is able to travel through it. They have turned a pleasant land into a wasteland."

What the LORD Will Do for Zion

8 ¹ The LORD of Armies spoke his word.

² This is what the LORD of Armies says:

> I am very jealous about Zion.
> I am fiercely possessive of it.

³ This is what the LORD says:

> I will return to Zion and live in Jerusalem.
> Jerusalem will be called the City of Truth.
> The mountain of the LORD of Armies will be called the holy mountain.

⁴ This is what the LORD of Armies says:

> Old men and old women will again sit in the streets of Jerusalem.
> Each will have a cane in hand because of old age.
⁵   The city will be filled with boys and girls playing in the streets.

⁶ This is what the LORD of Armies says:

> It may seem impossible to the few remaining people in those days,
> but will it seem impossible to me? declares the LORD of Armies.

⁷ This is what the LORD of Armies says:

> I am going to save my people
> from the land where the sun rises
> and from the land where the sun sets.
⁸   I will bring them back, and they will live in Jerusalem.
> They will be my people, and I will be their God, who is faithful and just.

⁹ This is what the LORD of Armies says:

> Be strong so that the temple might be rebuilt,
> you people who are presently listening
> to the words from the mouths of the prophets
> who spoke when the foundation
> for the house of the LORD of Armies was laid.
¹⁰   Before that time there was no money to hire any person or animal.
> No one who traveled was safe from the enemy.
> I turned every person against his neighbor.
¹¹   But now I won't deal with the few remaining people
> as I did in earlier times, declares the LORD of Armies.
¹²   Seeds will thrive in peacetime.
> Vines will produce their grapes.
> The land will yield its crops.
> The sky will produce its dew.
> I will give the few remaining people
> all these things as an inheritance.
¹³   Just as you, people of Judah and people of Israel,
> have been a curse among the nations,
> so I will now save you,
> and you will become a blessing.

Don't be afraid. Let your hands work hard.

14 This is what the LORD of Armies says:

When your ancestors made me angry,
   I made plans to destroy you, declares the LORD of Armies,
      and I didn't change my plans.
15 So now I have again made plans, but this time to do good
   to Jerusalem and the people of Judah.
Don't be afraid.
16 You must do these things:
   Speak the truth to each other.
   Give correct and fair verdicts for peace in your courts.
17   Don't even think of doing evil to each other.
   Don't enjoy false testimony.
      I hate all these things, declares the LORD.

Many Nations Will Come to the LORD's People

18 The LORD of Armies spoke his word to me again.

19 This is what the LORD of Armies says:

The fast in the fourth month, the fast in the fifth month,
the fast in the seventh month, and the fast in the tenth month
   will become joyful and glad occasions
      as well as happy festivals for the nation of Judah.
         So love truth and peace.

20 This is what the LORD of Armies says:

People and citizens from many cities are going to come.
21 The citizens of one city will come to another city, saying,
   "Let's make a habit of going to ask the LORD for a blessing
      and to seek the LORD of Armies.
         I'm also going."
22 Many people and powerful nations will come
   to seek the LORD of Armies in Jerusalem
      and to ask the LORD for a blessing.

23 This is what the LORD of Armies says:

In those days ten people from every language found among the nations
   will take hold of the clothes of a Jew. They will say,
      "Let us go with you
         because we have heard that God is with you."

The LORD Protects His House

9 **1** This is the divine revelation.

The word of the LORD is against the land of Hadrach
   and will rest on Damascus
2   and also Hamath, which borders on it,
   and Tyre and Sidon, though they are very wise.
      (The eyes of humanity and of all the tribes of Israel are on the LORD.)[a]

3 Tyre built itself a fortress.
   It piled up silver like dust
      and gold like mud in the streets.
4 The Lord will take away its possessions.
   He will throw its wealth into the sea
      and burn the city down.
5 Ashkelon will see ˏthisˏ and be afraid.
   Gaza will also be in great pain,
      also Ekron, because its hope will fade.
         Gaza will lose its king.

---

[a] 9:2 This sentence has been moved from verse 1 to express the complex Hebrew paragraph structure more clearly in English.

Ashkelon will no longer be lived in.
⁶ A mixed race will live in Ashdod,
  and I will cut off the Philistines' arrogance.
⁷ I will remove the blood from their mouths
  and the disgusting things from between their teeth.
    Then only a few of them will be left for our God
      like a tribe in Judah,
        and Ekron will be like a Jebusite.
⁸ I will camp in front of my house
  as a guard against those who come and go.
    No oppressors will pass through them,
      because I have seen it with my own eyes.ᵇ

The Lord Sends His King

⁹ Rejoice with all your heart, people of Zion!
  Shout in triumph, people of Jerusalem!
  Look! Your King is coming to you:
    He is righteous and victorious.
    He is humble and rides on a donkey,
      on a colt, a young pack animal.
¹⁰ Heᶜ will make sure there are no chariots in Ephraim
    or war horses in Jerusalem.
      There will be no battle bows.
    He will announce peace to the nations.
    He will rule from sea to sea
      and from the ˌEuphratesˌ River to the ends of the earth.

¹¹ I will set your captives free from the waterless pit
    because of the blood that sealed my promiseᵈ to you.
¹² Return to your fortress, you captives who have hope.
    Today I tell you that I will return to you double ˌblessingsˌ.
¹³ I will bend Judah as my bow
    and draw my bow with Ephraim ˌas its arrowˌ.
  I will stir up your people, Zion, against your people, Greece,
    and I will use you like a warrior's sword.

¹⁴ The Lord will appear over them,
    and his arrow will go out like lightning.
  The Almighty Lord will blow the ram's horn
    and will march in the storms from the south.
¹⁵ The Lord of Armies will defend them.
    They will destroy and trample the stones used in slings.
    They will drink and shout as if they were drunk.
    They will be filled like a sacrificial bowl
      ˌused for sprinklingˌ the corners of the altar.
¹⁶ On that day the Lord their God will rescue them
    as the flock of his people.
      They will certainly sparkle in his land like jewels in a crown.
¹⁷   They will be beautiful and lovely.ᵉ
          Young men will prosper on grain,
            and young women will prosper on new wine.

The Lord's People Will Be Victorious

10 ¹ Ask the Lord for rain in the springtime.
        The Lord makes thunderstorms.
      He gives everyone rain showers for the plants in the field.
² The idols speak lies.
    The fortunetellers see false visions.
      They speak about false dreams.
        They give useless comfort.
  That is why people wander around like sheep.
    . They are troubled because there is no shepherd.

ᵇ 9:8 Hebrew meaning of verses 7–8 uncertain.   ᶜ 9:10 Greek, Syriac; Masoretic Text "I."   ᵈ 9:11 Or "covenant."
ᵉ 9:17 Or "He will be beautiful and lovely."

3 "My burning anger is directed against the shepherds.
    I will punish the male goats.
        The LORD of Armies takes care of his flock, the people of Judah.
            He makes them like his splendid war horse."

4 From them will come a cornerstone,
    from them a tent peg,
        from them a battle bow,
            from them every leader.
5 Together they will be like warriors
    who trample the enemy in the mud on the streets.
They will fight because the LORD is with them.
They will put to shame those who ride on horses.

6 "I will strengthen the people of Judah.
    I will rescue Joseph's people.
    I will bring them back, because I have compassion for them.
        It will be as though I had never rejected them,
            because I am the LORD their God, and I will answer them.
7 The people of Ephraim will be like mighty warriors.
        Their hearts will be glad as if they had some wine ˻to drink˼.
        Their sons will see it and be glad.
        Their hearts will find joy in the LORD.
8 I will signal them with a whistle
        and gather them because I have reclaimed them.
        They will be as numerous as they have ever been.
9 Although I have scattered them among the nations,
    they will remember me even in faraway places.
        They will live with their children and then return.
10 I will bring them back from Egypt.
I will gather them from Assyria.
I will bring them to Gilead and to Lebanon,
    and there won't be enough room for them."

11 The LORD will pass through a sea of distress,
        strike the waves in the sea,
            and dry up all the deep places of the Nile River.
The pride of Assyria will be humiliated,
    and the scepter of Egypt will depart.

12 "I will strengthen them in the LORD.
    They will live in his name," declares the LORD.

Zechariah Is Told to Take Care of the Sheep

11 1 Open your doors, Lebanon,
        so that fire will be able to burn down your cedars.
2 Cry, cypress trees,
        because the cedars have fallen
            and the stately trees have been destroyed.
Cry, oak trees of Bashan,
        because your dense forest has fallen down.
3 Listen! The shepherds are crying,
        because their rich pastures are destroyed.
Listen! The young lions are roaring,
        because the lush banks of the Jordan are destroyed.

4 This is what the LORD my God says: Take care of the sheep that are about to be slaughtered. 5 Those who buy them will kill them and go unpunished. Those who sell them will say, "Praise the LORD! I've become rich!" Even their own shepherds will have no pity on them.

6 The LORD declares, "I will no longer have pity on those who live in the land. I am going to hand the people over to their neighbors and their king, who will crush the land. And I won't rescue any of them from their power."

7 So I became the shepherd of the sheep that were to be slaughtered and also of the oppressed sheep. I took two shepherd staffs and named one Favor and the other Unity. And I took care of the sheep. 8 I got rid of three shepherds in one month. I became impatient with the sheep, and they also became disgusted with me. 9 So I said, "I won't be your shepherd. Let those that are dying die. Let those that are missing stay missing. And let those that are left devour each other."

[10] Then I took my staff called Favor and broke it in pieces, to break the promise[a] that I had made to all the nations. [11] So it was broken on that day, and the oppressed among the sheep who were watching me realized that it was the word of the LORD.

[12] Then I said to them, "If it's alright with you, pay me my wages. But if it's not, don't." And they paid me my wages—30 pieces of silver.

[13] The LORD told me, "Give it to the potter." So I took the 30 pieces of silver. Such a magnificent price was set by them! I gave the pieces of silver to the potter at the house of the LORD.

[14] Then I broke my second staff, called Unity, in pieces, to break off the brotherhood between Judah and Israel.

[15] Then the LORD said to me, "Use the equipment of a foolish shepherd again. [16] I'm about to place a shepherd in the land. He will not take care of those that are dying. He will not search for the young. He will not heal those that have broken their legs or support those that can still stand. But he will eat the meat of the fat animals and tear off their hoofs.

[17]   "How horrible it will be for the foolish shepherd who abandoned the sheep.
        A sword will strike his arm and his right eye.
        His arm will be completely withered.
        His right eye will be completely blind."

The LORD Will Save Jerusalem

12 [1] This is the prophetic revelation, the word of the LORD about Israel. The LORD—who spread out the heavens, laid the foundation of the earth, and forms the spirit in a person—says, [2] "I'm going to make Jerusalem like a cup ˌof wineˌ that makes all the surrounding people stagger. They will attack Judah along with Jerusalem. [3] On that day I will make Jerusalem a stone too heavy for all the nations to lift. All who try to lift it will be severely injured. All the nations in the world will gather ˌto fightˌ against Jerusalem."

[4] The LORD declares, "On that day I will strike every horse with panic and every rider with madness. I will watch over the people of Judah, but I will strike all the horses of the nations blind. [5] Then the leaders of Judah will think to themselves, 'The people who live in Jerusalem are strong because of the LORD of Armies, their God.'

[6] "On that day I will make the leaders of Judah like a fire on a pile of wood and like a burning torch among freshly cut straw. They will burn up all the surrounding nations to the right and to the left. But the people of Jerusalem will remain safe in Jerusalem."

[7] "The LORD will save Judah's tents first so that the honor of David's family and the honor of those who live in Jerusalem will not be greater than the honor of Judah. [8] On that day the LORD will defend those who live in Jerusalem so that even those who stumble will be like David, and David's family will be like God, like the Messenger of the LORD ahead of them.

[9] "On that day I will seek to destroy all the nations who attack Jerusalem.

The People of Jerusalem Will Look at the One They Stabbed

[10] "I will pour out the Spirit of blessing and mercy on David's family and on those who live in Jerusalem. They will look at me, whom they have stabbed. Then they will mourn for him as one mourns for an only son, and they will cry bitterly for him as one cries for a firstborn son. [11] On that day the mourning in Jerusalem will be as intense as the mourning at Hadad Rimmon in the plain of Megiddo. [12] The land will mourn, each family by itself: the family of David by itself, and the wives by themselves; the family of Nathan by itself, and the wives by themselves; [13] the family of Levi by itself, and the wives by themselves; the family of Shimei by itself, and the wives by themselves. [14] All the families that are left ˌwill mournˌ, each by itself, and the wives by themselves."

13 [1] ˌThe LORD declares,ˌ "On that day a fountain will be opened for David's family and for those who live in Jerusalem to wash away ˌtheirˌ sin and stain.

False Prophets Will Be Judged

[2] "On that day," declares the LORD of Armies, "I will wipe away the names of the idols from the land. They will no longer be remembered. I will also remove the ˌfalseˌ prophets and the unclean[a] spirit from the land.

[3] "If a man still prophesies, his father and his mother, who gave birth to him, will say, 'You don't deserve to live because you speak lies in the name of the LORD.' Then his father and his mother, who gave birth to him, will stab him when he prophesies.

[4] "On that day every prophet will be ashamed of his vision when he prophesies. He won't deceive people by dressing ˌlike a prophetˌ in a coat made of hair. [5] He will say, 'I am not a prophet. I'm a farmer. I've owned this land since I was a child.'

[6] "When someone asks him, 'What are these scars on your chest?' he will answer, 'I was hurt at my friend's house.'

---

[a] 11:10 Or "covenant."   [a] 13:2 "Unclean" refers to anything that Moses' Teachings say is not presentable to God.

The Shepherd Struck, the Sheep Scattered

7 "Arise, sword, against my shepherd,
　　against the man who is my friend," declares the LORD of Armies.
"Strike the shepherd, and the sheep will be scattered.
　　Then I will turn my hand against the little ones."

8 The LORD declares,

"Throughout the land two-thirds will be cut off and die.
　　Yet, one-third will be left in it.
9 I will bring this third ‚of the people‚ through the fire.
I will refine them as silver is refined.
I will test them as gold is tested.
　　They will call on me, and I will answer them.
　　　　I will say, 'They are my people.'
　　　　They will reply, 'The LORD is our God.' "

The LORD Will Fight the Nations

14 1 A day is going to come for the LORD when the loot you have taken will be divided among you. 2 I will gather all the nations to Jerusalem for battle. The city will be captured, the houses looted, and the women raped. Half of the people in the city will go into exile, but the rest of the people won't be taken from the city.

3 Then the LORD will go out and fight against those nations as he does when he fights a battle. 4 On that day his feet will stand on the Mount of Olives, just east of Jerusalem. The Mount of Olives will be split in two, forming a very large valley from east to west. Half of the mountain will move toward the north, and the other half will move toward the south. 5 Then you will flee to the valley of my mountains, because this valley between the mountains will go as far as Azel.[a] You will flee as you did from the earthquake at the time of King Uzziah of Judah. The LORD my God will come, and all the holy ones will be with him.

6 On that day there will be neither heat nor freezing cold.[a] 7 There will be one day—a day known to the LORD—with no difference between day and night. It will be light even in the evening.

Living Water From Jerusalem

8 On that day living water will flow out from Jerusalem, half of it to the Dead Sea and the other half to the Mediterranean Sea. It will continue in summer and in winter.

9 The LORD will be king over all the earth. On that day the LORD will be the only Lord and his name the only name.

10 The whole earth will become like the plains from Geba to Rimmon, south of Jerusalem. Jerusalem will rise and remain on its site, from Benjamin Gate to the place of First Gate, Corner Gate, and from the Tower of Hananel to the king's winepresses. 11 People will live there, and it will never be threatened with destruction. Jerusalem will live securely.

12 This will be the plague the LORD will use to strike all the people from the nations that have gone to war against Jerusalem. Their flesh will rot while they are standing on their feet. Their eyes will rot in their sockets, and their tongues will rot in their mouths.

13 On that day a large-scale panic from the LORD will spread among them. One person will grab the hand of another, and one will attack the other. 14 Judah will also fight in Jerusalem. The wealth of all the surrounding nations will be collected, a very large amount of gold, silver, and clothes. 15 A similar plague will also affect horses, mules, camels, donkeys, and all other animals in those camps.

16 Everyone who is left from all the nations that attacked Jerusalem will come every year to worship the king, the LORD of Armies, and to celebrate the Festival of Booths. 17 If any of the families on the earth won't go to Jerusalem to worship the king, the LORD of Armies, then rain won't fall on them. 18 If the people of Egypt won't go or enter Jerusalem, then ‚rain won't fall‚ on them. The plague the LORD uses to strike the nations will affect those who won't come to celebrate the Festival of Booths. 19 This will be ‚the punishment‚ for Egypt's sin and for the sin of all the nations that won't go to celebrate the Festival of Booths.

20 On that day "Holy to the LORD" will be written on the bells of the horses. And the cooking pots in the house of the LORD will be like the bowls in front of the altar. 21 Yes, every pot in Jerusalem and in Judah will be holy to the LORD of Armies. All who come to sacrifice will take some of them and cook in them. On that day there will no longer be any Canaanite[b] in the house of the LORD of Armies.

---

[a] 14:5, 6 Hebrew meaning uncertain.　　[b] 14:21 Or "merchant."

MALACHI

"I Loved Jacob, but Esau I Hated"

1 ¹ This is a divine revelation. The LORD spoke his word to Israel through Malachi. ² "I loved you," says the LORD.

"But you ask, 'How did you love us?'

"Wasn't Esau Jacob's brother?" declares the LORD. "I loved Jacob, ³ but Esau I hated. I turned his mountains into a wasteland and left his inheritance to the jackals in the desert.

⁴ "The descendants of Esau may say, 'We have been beaten down, but we will rebuild the ruins.'

"Yet, this is what the LORD of Armies says: They may rebuild, but I will tear it down. They will be called 'the Wicked Land' and 'the people with whom the LORD is always angry.' ⁵ You will see these things with your own eyes and say, 'Even outside the borders of Israel the LORD is great.'

The Priests Offer Unacceptable Sacrifices to the LORD

⁶ "This is what the LORD of Armies says: A son honors his father, and a servant honors his master. So if I am a father, where is my honor? If I am a master, where is my respect? You priests despise my name.

"But you ask, 'How have we despised your name?'

⁷ "You offer contaminated food on my altar.

"But you ask, 'Then how have we contaminated you?'

"When you say that the LORD's table may be despised. ⁸ When you bring a blind animal to sacrifice, isn't that wrong? When you bring a lame or a sick animal, isn't that wrong? Try offering it to your governor. Would he accept it from you? Would he welcome you?" asks the LORD of Armies.

⁹ "Now try asking God to be kind to you. This is what you are doing! Will he welcome you?" asks the LORD of Armies.

¹⁰ "I wish one of you would shut the doors ⌊to my house⌋ so that you could not light fires on my altar for no reason. I'm not pleased with you," says the LORD of Armies, "and I won't accept your offerings.

¹¹ "From the nations where the sun rises to the nations where the sun sets, my name will be great. Incense and pure offerings will be offered everywhere in my name, because my name will be great among the nations," says the LORD of Armies. ¹² "But you dishonor it when you say that the Lord's table may be contaminated and that its food may be despised.

¹³ "You say, 'Oh what a nuisance it is,' and you sniff at it in disgust," says the LORD of Armies. "You bring stolen, lame, and sick animals. When you bring such offerings, should I accept them from you?" asks the LORD.

¹⁴ "Cheaters are under a curse. They have male animals in their flocks that they vow to give ⌊as a sacrifice⌋. But they sacrifice second-rate ones to the Lord instead. I am a great king," says the LORD of Armies. "Among the nations my name is respected.

The Priests Do Not Teach the LORD's Word Correctly

2 ¹ "And now, you priests, this warning is for you. ² If you won't listen and if you won't consider giving honor to my name," says the LORD of Armies, "then I'll send a curse on you, and I'll curse the blessings you give. Yes, I've already cursed them because you don't carefully consider this.

³ "I'm going to punish your descendants. I'm going to spread excrement on your faces, the excrement from your festival sacrifices. You will be discarded with it. ⁴ Then you will know that I sent you this warning so that my promise*a* to Levi will continue," says the LORD of Armies. ⁵ "I promised Levi life and peace. I gave them to him so that he would respect me. He respected me and stood in awe of my name. ⁶ The teaching that came from his mouth was true. Nothing unjust was found on his lips. He lived with me in peace and honesty and turned many people away from sin.

---

a 2:4 Or "covenant."

⁷ "A priest's lips should preserve knowledge. Then, because he is the messenger for the LORD of Armies, people will seek instruction from his mouth.
⁸ "But you have turned from the ˻correct˼ path and caused many to stumble over my teachings. You have corrupted the promise made to Levi," says the LORD of Armies. ⁹ "So I have made you disgusting, and I have humiliated you in front of all the people, because you have not followed my ways. You have been unfair when ˻applying˼ my teachings."

The People Break Their Marriage Vows

¹⁰ Don't all of us have the same father? Hasn't the same God created us? Why are we unfaithful to each other? And why do we dishonor the promise given to our ancestors? ¹¹ Judah has been unfaithful! A disgusting thing has been done in Israel and Jerusalem. Judah has dishonored the holy place that the LORD loves and has married a woman who worships a foreign god. ¹² May the LORD exclude anyone who does this, whoever he may be. May he exclude them from Jacob's tents and from bringing offerings to the LORD of Armies.
¹³ Here is another thing you do: You cover the LORD's altar with tears. You moan and groan because he no longer pays attention to your offerings or accepts them from you.
¹⁴ But you ask, "Why ˻aren't our offerings accepted˼?" It is because the LORD is a witness between you and the wife of your youth, to whom you have been unfaithful. Yet, she is your companion, the wife of your marriage vows. ¹⁵ Didn't ˻God˼ make you one? Your flesh and spirit belong to him. And what does the same ˻God˼ look for but godly descendants? So be careful not to be unfaithful to the wife of your youth.ᵇ
¹⁶ "I hate divorce," says the LORD God of Israel. "I hate the person who covers himself with violence," says the LORD of Armies. "Be careful not to be unfaithful."
¹⁷ You have tried the patience of the LORD with your words.
But you ask, "How have we tried his patience?"
When you say, "Everyone who does evil is considered good by the LORD. He is pleased with them," or "Where is the God of justice?"

The Coming of the Messenger of the Promise

3 ¹ "I'm going to send my messenger, and he will clear the way ahead of me. Then the Lord you are looking for will suddenly come to his temple. The messenger of the promiseᵃ will come. He is the one you want," says the LORD of Armies.
² But who will be able to endure the day he comes? Who will be able to survive on the day he appears? He is like a purifying fire and like a cleansing soap. ³ He will act like a refiner and a purifier of silver. He will purify Levi's sons and refine them like gold and silver. Then they will bring acceptable offerings to the LORD. ⁴ The offerings from Judah and Jerusalem will be pleasing to the LORD as in the past, as in years long ago.
⁵ "I will come to judge you. I will be quick to testify against sorcerers, adulterers, lying witnesses, and those who cheat workers out of their wages and oppress widows and orphans. I will also testify against those who deprive foreigners of their rights. None of them fear me," says the LORD of Armies.

The People Are Cheating God

⁶ "I, the LORD, never change. That is why you descendants of Jacob haven't been destroyed yet. ⁷ Since the time of your ancestors you have turned away from my laws and have not followed them. Return to me, and I will return to you," says the LORD of Armies.
"But you ask, 'How can we return?'
⁸ "Can a person cheat God? Yet, you are cheating me!
"But you ask, 'How are we cheating you?'
"When ˻you don't bring˼ a tenth of your income and other contributions. ⁹ So a curse is on you because the whole nation is cheating me!
¹⁰ "Bring one-tenth of your income into the storehouse so that there may be food in my house. Test me in this way," says the LORD of Armies. "See if I won't open the windows of heaven for you and flood you with blessings. ¹¹ Then, for your sake, I will stop insects from eating ˻your crops˼. They will not destroy the produce of your land. The vines in your fields will not lose their unripened grapes," says the LORD of Armies. ¹² "All nations will call you blessed because you will be a delightful land," says the LORD of Armies.
¹³ "You have used harsh words against me," says the LORD.
"You ask, 'How have we spoken against you?'
¹⁴ "You have said, 'It's pointless to serve God. What do we gain if we meet his standards or if we walk around feeling sorry for what we've done? ¹⁵ So now we call arrogant people blessed. Not only are evildoers encouraged, they even test God and get away with it.' "

ᵇ 2:15 Hebrew meaning of this verse uncertain.   ᵃ 3:1 Or "covenant."

¹⁶ Then those who feared the LORD spoke to one another, and the LORD paid attention and listened. A book was written in his presence to be a reminder to those who feared the LORD and respected his name.

¹⁷ "They will be mine," says the LORD of Armies. "On that day I will make them my special possession. I will spare them as a man spares his own son who serves him. ¹⁸ Then you will again see the difference between righteous people and wicked people, between the one who serves God and the one who doesn't serve him.

The Day of the LORD Brings Judgment

4 *ᵃ* ¹ "Certainly the day is coming! It will burn like a furnace. All arrogant people and all evildoers will be ˌlikeˌ straw. The day that is coming will burn them up completely," says the LORD of Armies. "It won't leave a single root or branch.

² "The Sun of Righteousness will rise with healing in his wings for you people who fear my name. You will go out and leap like calves let out of a stall. ³ You will trample on wicked people, because on the day I act they will be ashes under the soles of your feet," says the LORD of Armies.

Remember What God Has Done and Will Do

⁴ "Remember the teachings of my servant Moses, the rules and regulations that I gave to him at Horeb for all Israel.

⁵ "I'm going to send you the prophet Elijah before that very terrifying day of the LORD comes. ⁶ He will change parents' attitudes toward their children and children's attitudes toward their parents. If not, I will come and reclaim my land by destroying you."

ᵃ 4:1 Malachi 4:1–6 in English Bibles is Malachi 3:19–24 in the Hebrew Bible.

THE
NEW TESTAMENT

MATTHEW

The Family Line of Jesus Christ

1 ¹This is the list of ancestors of Jesus Christ, descendant of David and Abraham.

² **Abraham** was the father of Isaac,
Isaac the father of Jacob,
Jacob the father of Judah and his brothers.
³ **Judah** and **Tamar** were the father and mother of Perez and Zerah.
Perez was the father of Hezron,
Hezron the father of Ram,
⁴ **Ram** the father of Amminadab,
Amminadab the father of Nahshon,
Nahshon the father of Salmon.
⁵ **Salmon** and **Rahab** were the father and mother of Boaz.
Boaz and **Ruth** were the father and mother of Obed.
Obed was the father of Jesse,
⁶ **Jesse** the father of King David.
David and **Uriah's wife** ⌐Bathsheba⌐ were the father and mother of Solomon.
⁷ **Solomon** was the father of Rehoboam,
Rehoboam the father of Abijah,
Abijah the father of Asa,
⁸ **Asa** the father of Jehoshaphat,
Jehoshaphat the father of Joram,
Joram the father of Uzziah,
⁹ **Uzziah** the father of Jotham,
Jotham the father of Ahaz,
Ahaz the father of Hezekiah,
¹⁰ **Hezekiah** the father of Manasseh,
Manasseh the father of Amon,
Amon the father of Josiah.
¹¹ **Josiah** was the father of **Jechoniah** and his brothers.
They lived at the time when the people were exiled to Babylon.

¹²After the exile to Babylon,

Jechoniah became the father of Shealtiel.
Shealtiel was the father of Zerubbabel,
¹³ **Zerubbabel** the father of Abiud,
Abiud the father of Eliakim,
Eliakim the father of Azor,
¹⁴ **Azor** the father of Zadok,
Zadok the father of Achim,
Achim the father of Eliud,
¹⁵ **Eliud** the father of Eleazar,
Eleazar the father of Matthan,
Matthan the father of Jacob.
¹⁶ **Jacob** was the father of **Joseph,** who was the husband of Mary.
Mary was the mother of **Jesus,** who is called Christ.

¹⁷So there were

14 generations from Abraham to David,
14 generations from David until the exile to Babylon,
14 generations from the exile until the Messiah.

The Virgin Birth of Jesus

[18] The birth of Jesus Christ took place in this way. His mother Mary had been promised to Joseph in marriage. But before they were married, Mary realized that she was pregnant by the Holy Spirit. [19] Her husband Joseph was an honorable man and did not want to disgrace her publicly. So he decided to break the marriage agreement with her secretly.

[20] Joseph had this in mind when an angel of the Lord appeared to him in a dream. The angel said to him, "Joseph, descendant of David, don't be afraid to take Mary as your wife. She is pregnant by the Holy Spirit. [21] She will give birth to a son, and you will name him Jesus [He Saves], because he will save his people from their sins." [22] All this happened so that what the Lord had spoken through the prophet came true: [23] "The virgin will become pregnant and give birth to a son, and they will name him Immanuel," which means "God is with us."

[24] When Joseph woke up, he did what the angel of the Lord had commanded him to do. He took Mary to be his wife. [25] He did not have marital relations with her before she gave birth to a son. Joseph named the child Jesus.

The Wise Men Visit

2 [1] Jesus was born in Bethlehem in Judea when Herod was king. After Jesus' birth wise men[a] from the east arrived in Jerusalem. [2] They asked, "Where is the one who was born to be the king of the Jews? We saw his star rising and have come to worship him."

[3] When King Herod and all Jerusalem heard about this, they became disturbed. [4] He called together all the chief priests and scribes and tried to find out from them where the Messiah was supposed to be born.

[5] They told him, "In Bethlehem in Judea. The prophet wrote about this:

[6]   Bethlehem in the land of Judah,
        you are by no means least among the leaders of Judah.
            A leader will come from you.
            He will shepherd my people Israel."

[7] Then Herod secretly called the wise men and found out from them exactly when the star had appeared. [8] As he sent them to Bethlehem, he said, "Go and search carefully for the child. When you have found him, report to me so that I may go and worship him too."

[9] After they had heard the king, they started out. The star they had seen rising led them until it stopped over the place where the child was. [10] They were overwhelmed with joy to see the star. [11] When they entered the house, they saw the child with his mother Mary. So they bowed down and worshiped him. Then they opened their treasure chests and offered him gifts of gold, frankincense, and myrrh.[b]

[12] God warned them in a dream not to go back to Herod. So they left for their country by another road.

The Escape to Egypt

[13] After they had left, an angel of the Lord appeared to Joseph in a dream. The angel said to him, "Get up, take the child and his mother, and flee to Egypt. Stay there until I tell you, because Herod intends to search for the child and kill him."

[14] Joseph got up, took the child and his mother, and left for Egypt that night. [15] He stayed there until Herod died. What the Lord had spoken through the prophet came true: "I have called my son out of Egypt."

[16] When Herod saw that the wise men had tricked him, he became furious. He sent soldiers to kill all the boys two years old and younger in or near Bethlehem. This matched the exact time he had learned from the wise men. [17] Then the words spoken through the prophet Jeremiah came true:

[18]   "A sound was heard in Ramah,
            the sound of crying in bitter grief.
                Rachel was crying for her children.
                She refused to be comforted
                    because they were dead."

From Egypt to Nazareth

[19] After Herod was dead, an angel of the Lord appeared in a dream to Joseph in Egypt. [20] The angel said to him, "Get up, take the child and his mother, and go to Israel. Those who tried to kill the child are dead."

---

[a] 2:1 Or "astrologers."   [b] 2:11 Myrrh is a fragrant resin used for perfumes, embalming, and deodorizers.

²¹ Joseph got up, took the child and his mother, and went to Israel. ²² But when he heard that Archelaus had succeeded his father Herod as king of Judea, Joseph was afraid to go there. Warned in a dream, he left for Galilee ²³ and made his home in a city called Nazareth. So what the prophets had said came true: "He will be called a Nazarene."

John Prepares the Way—*Mark 1:1–8; Luke 3:1–18; John 1:19–28*

3 ¹ Later, John the Baptizer appeared in the desert of Judea. His message was, ² "Turn to God and change the way you think and act, because the kingdom of heaven is near." ³ Isaiah the prophet spoke about this man when he said,

> "A voice cries out in the desert:
>   'Prepare the way for the Lord!
>   Make his paths straight!' "

⁴ John wore clothes made from camel's hair and had a leather belt around his waist. His diet consisted of locusts and wild honey.

⁵ Jerusalem, all Judea, and the whole Jordan Valley went to him. ⁶ As they confessed their sins, he baptized them in the Jordan River.

⁷ But when he saw many Pharisees and Sadducees coming to be baptized, he said to them, "You poisonous snakes! Who showed you how to flee from God's coming anger? ⁸ Do those things that prove you have turned to God and have changed the way you think and act. ⁹ Don't think you can say, 'Abraham is our ancestor.' I can guarantee that God can raise up descendants for Abraham from these stones. ¹⁰ The ax is now ready to cut the roots of the trees. Any tree that doesn't produce good fruit will be cut down and thrown into a fire. ¹¹ I baptize you with water so that you will change the way you think and act. But the one who comes after me is more powerful than I. I am not worthy to remove his sandals. He will baptize you with the Holy Spirit and fire. ¹² His winnowing*ª* shovel is in his hand, and he will clean up his threshing floor.*ᵇ* He will gather his wheat into a barn, but he will burn the husks in a fire that can never be put out."

John Baptizes Jesus—*Mark 1:9–11; Luke 3:21–22*

¹³ Then Jesus appeared. He came from Galilee to the Jordan River to be baptized by John. ¹⁴ But John tried to stop him and said, "I need to be baptized by you. Why are you coming to me?"

¹⁵ Jesus answered him, "This is the way it has to be now. This is the proper way to do everything that God requires of us."

Then John gave in to him. ¹⁶ After Jesus was baptized, he immediately came up from the water. Suddenly, the heavens were opened, and he saw the Spirit of God coming down as a dove to him. ¹⁷ Then a voice from heaven said, "This is my Son, whom I love—my Son with whom I am pleased."

The Temptation of Jesus—*Mark 1:12–13; Luke 4:1–13*

4 ¹ Then the Spirit led Jesus into the desert to be tempted by the devil. ² Jesus did not eat anything for 40 days and 40 nights. At the end of that time, he was hungry.

³ The tempter came to him and said, "If you are the Son of God, tell these stones to become loaves of bread."

⁴ Jesus answered, "Scripture says, 'A person cannot live on bread alone but on every word that God speaks.' "

⁵ Then the devil took him into the holy city and had him stand on the highest part of the temple. ⁶ He said to Jesus, "If you are the Son of God, jump! Scripture says, 'He will put his angels in charge of you. They will carry you in their hands so that you never hit your foot against a rock.' "

⁷ Jesus said to him, "Again, Scripture says, 'Never tempt the Lord your God.' "*ª*

⁸ Once more the devil took him to a very high mountain and showed him all the kingdoms in the world and their glory. ⁹ The devil said to him, "I will give you all this if you will bow down and worship me."

¹⁰ Jesus said to him, "Go away, Satan! Scripture says, 'Worship the Lord your God and serve only him.' "

¹¹ Then the devil left him, and angels came to take care of him.

A Light Has Risen

¹² When Jesus heard that John had been put in prison, he went back to Galilee. ¹³ He left Nazareth and made his home in Capernaum on the shores of the Sea of Galilee. This was in the region of Zebulun and Naphtali. ¹⁴ So what the prophet Isaiah had said came true:

¹⁵   "Land of Zebulun and land of Naphtali,
         on the way to the sea,

ª 3:12 Winnowing is the process of separating husks from grain.   *ᵇ* 3:12 A threshing floor is an outdoor area where grain is separated from its husks.   *ª* 4:7 Or "Never put the Lord your God to any test."

across the Jordan River,
Galilee, where foreigners live!
[16] The people who lived in darkness
have seen a bright light.
A light has risen
for those who live in a land overshadowed by death."

[17] From then on, Jesus began to tell people, "Turn to God and change the way you think and act, because the kingdom of heaven is near!"

Calling of the First Disciples—*Mark 1:16–20; Luke 5:1–11*

[18] As he was walking along the Sea of Galilee, he saw two brothers, Simon (called Peter) and Andrew. They were throwing a net into the sea because they were fishermen. [19] Jesus said to them, "Come, follow me! I will teach you how to catch people instead of fish." [20] They immediately left their nets and followed him.

[21] As Jesus went on, he saw two other brothers, James and John, the sons of Zebedee. They were in a boat with their father Zebedee preparing their nets to go fishing. He called them, [22] and they immediately left the boat and their father and followed Jesus.

Spreading the Good News in Galilee—*Mark 1:35–39; Luke 4:42–44*

[23] Jesus went all over Galilee. He taught in the synagogues and spread the Good News of the kingdom. He also cured every disease and sickness among the people.

[24] The news about Jesus spread throughout Syria. People brought him everyone who was sick, those who suffered from any kind of disease or pain. They also brought epileptics, those who were paralyzed, and people possessed by demons, and he cured them all. [25] Large crowds followed him. They came from Galilee, the Ten Cities,[a] Jerusalem, Judea, and from across the Jordan River.

The Sermon on a Mountain:
The Beatitudes

5 [1] When Jesus saw the crowds, he went up a mountain and sat down. His disciples came to him, [2] and he began to teach them:

[3] "Blessed are those who recognize they are spiritually helpless.
The kingdom of heaven belongs to them.
[4] Blessed are those who mourn.
They will be comforted.
[5] Blessed are those who are gentle.
They will inherit the earth.
[6] Blessed are those who hunger and thirst for God's approval.
They will be satisfied.
[7] Blessed are those who show mercy.
They will be treated mercifully.
[8] Blessed are those whose thoughts are pure.
They will see God.
[9] Blessed are those who make peace.
They will be called God's children.
[10] Blessed are those who are persecuted for doing what God approves of.
The kingdom of heaven belongs to them.

[11] "Blessed are you when people insult you,
persecute you,
lie, and say all kinds of evil things about you because of me.
[12] Rejoice and be glad because you have a great reward in heaven!
The prophets who lived before you were persecuted in these ways.

God's People Make a Difference in the World—*Mark 4:21–23; Luke 11:33*

[13] "You are salt for the earth. But if salt loses its taste, how will it be made salty again? It is no longer good for anything except to be thrown out and trampled on by people.

[14] "You are light for the world. A city cannot be hidden when it is located on a hill. [15] No one lights a lamp and puts it under a basket. Instead, everyone who lights a lamp puts it on a lamp stand. Then its light shines on everyone in the house. [16] In the same way let your light shine in front of people. Then they will see the good that you do and praise your Father in heaven.

---

[a] 4:25 A federation of ten Greek city states east and west of the Jordan River.

Jesus Fulfills the Old Testament Scriptures

[17] "Don't ever think that I came to set aside Moses' Teachings or the Prophets. I didn't come to set them aside but to make them come true. [18] I can guarantee this truth: Until the earth and the heavens disappear, neither a period nor a comma will disappear from Moses' Teachings before everything has come true. [19] So whoever sets aside any command that seems unimportant and teaches others to do the same will be unimportant in the kingdom of heaven. But whoever does and teaches what the commands say will be called great in the kingdom of heaven. [20] I can guarantee that unless you live a life that has God's approval and do it more faithfully than the scribes and Pharisees, you will never enter the kingdom of heaven.

Jesus Talks About Anger

[21] "You have heard that it was said to your ancestors, 'Never murder. Whoever murders will answer for it in court.' [22] But I can guarantee that whoever is angry with another believer[a] will answer for it in court. Whoever calls another believer an insulting name will answer for it in the highest court. Whoever calls another believer a fool will answer for it in hellfire.

[23] "So if you are offering your gift at the altar and remember there that another believer has something against you, [24] leave your gift at the altar. First go away and make peace with that person. Then come back and offer your gift.

[25] "Make peace quickly with your opponent while you are on the way to court with him. Otherwise, he will hand you over to the judge. Then the judge will hand you over to an officer, who will throw you into prison. [26] I can guarantee this truth: You will never get out until you pay every penny of your fine.

About Sexual Sin

[27] "You have heard that it was said, 'Never commit adultery.' [28] But I can guarantee that whoever looks with lust at a woman has already committed adultery in his heart.

[29] "So if your right eye causes you to sin, tear it out and throw it away. It is better for you to lose a part of your body than to have all of it thrown into hell. [30] And if your right hand leads you to sin, cut it off and throw it away. It is better for you to lose a part of your body than to have all of it go into hell.

[31] "It has also been said, 'Whoever divorces his wife must give her a written notice.' [32] But I can guarantee that any man who divorces his wife for any reason other than unfaithfulness makes her look as though she has committed adultery. Whoever marries a woman divorced in this way makes himself look as though he has committed adultery.

About Oaths

[33] "You have heard that it was said to your ancestors, 'Never break your oath, but give to the Lord what you swore in an oath to give him.' [34] But I tell you don't swear an oath at all. Don't swear an oath by heaven, which is God's throne, [35] or by the earth, which is his footstool, or by Jerusalem, which is the city of the great King. [36] And don't swear an oath by your head. After all, you cannot make one hair black or white. [37] Simply say yes or no. Anything more than that comes from the evil one.

Love Your Enemies—Luke 6:27–36

[38] "You have heard that it was said, 'An eye for an eye and a tooth for a tooth.' [39] But I tell you not to oppose an evil person. If someone slaps you on your right cheek, turn your other cheek to him as well. [40] If someone wants to sue you in order to take your shirt, let him have your coat too. [41] If someone forces you to go one mile, go two miles with him. [42] Give to everyone who asks you for something. Don't turn anyone away who wants to borrow something from you.

[43] "You have heard that it was said, 'Love your neighbor, and hate your enemy.' [44] But I tell you this: Love your enemies, and pray for those who persecute you. [45] In this way you show that you are children of your Father in heaven. He makes his sun rise on people whether they are good or evil. He lets rain fall on them whether they are just or unjust. [46] If you love those who love you, do you deserve a reward? Even the tax collectors do that! [47] Are you doing anything remarkable if you welcome only your friends? Everyone does that! [48] That is why you must be perfect as your Father in heaven is perfect.

The Sermon on a Mountain Continues:
Don't Do Good Works to Be Praised by People

6 [1] "Be careful not to do your good works in public in order to attract attention. If you do, your Father in heaven will not reward you. [2] So when you give to the poor, don't announce it with trumpet fanfare. This is what hypocrites do in the synagogues and on the streets in

---

[a] 5:22 Some manuscripts and translations add "without a cause."

order to be praised by people. I can guarantee this truth: That will be their only reward. [3] When you give to the poor, don't let your left hand know what your right hand is doing. [4] Give your contributions privately. Your Father sees what you do in private. He will reward you.

The Lord's Prayer—Luke 11:1–4

[5] "When you pray, don't be like hypocrites. They like to stand in synagogues and on street corners to pray so that everyone can see them. I can guarantee this truth: That will be their only reward. [6] When you pray, go to your room and close the door. Pray privately to your Father who is with you. Your Father sees what you do in private. He will reward you.

[7] "When you pray, don't ramble like heathens who think they'll be heard if they talk a lot. [8] Don't be like them. Your Father knows what you need before you ask him.

[9] "This is how you should pray:

> Our Father in heaven,
> > let your name be kept holy.
> 10 Let your kingdom come.
> > Let your will be done on earth
> > > as it is done in heaven.
> 11 Give us our daily bread today.
> 12 Forgive us as we forgive others.
> 13 Don't allow us to be tempted.
> > Instead, rescue us from the evil one.[a]

[14] "If you forgive the failures of others, your heavenly Father will also forgive you. [15] But if you don't forgive others, your Father will not forgive your failures.

Fasting

[16] "When you fast, stop looking sad like hypocrites. They put on sad faces to make it obvious that they're fasting. I can guarantee this truth: That will be their only reward. [17] When you fast, wash your face and comb your hair. [18] Then your fasting won't be obvious. Instead, it will be obvious to your Father who is with you in private. Your Father sees what you do in private. He will reward you.

True Riches

[19] "Stop storing up treasures for yourselves on earth, where moths and rust destroy and thieves break in and steal. [20] Instead, store up treasures for yourselves in heaven, where moths and rust don't destroy and thieves don't break in and steal. [21] Your heart will be where your treasure is.

[22] "The eye is the lamp of the body. So if your eye is unclouded, your whole body will be full of light. [23] But if your eye is evil, your whole body will be full of darkness. If the light in you is darkness, how dark it will be!

[24] "No one can serve two masters. He will hate the first master and love the second, or he will be devoted to the first and despise the second. You cannot serve God and wealth.

Stop Worrying—Luke 12:22–34

[25] "So I tell you to stop worrying about what you will eat, drink, or wear. Isn't life more than food and the body more than clothes?

[26] "Look at the birds. They don't plant, harvest, or gather the harvest into barns. Yet, your heavenly Father feeds them. Aren't you worth more than they?

[27] "Can any of you add a single hour to your life by worrying?

[28] "And why worry about clothes? Notice how the flowers grow in the field. They never work or spin yarn for clothes. [29] But I say that not even Solomon in all his majesty was dressed like one of these flowers. [30] That's the way God clothes the grass in the field. Today it's alive, and tomorrow it's thrown into an incinerator. So how much more will he clothe you people who have so little faith?

[31] "Don't ever worry and say, 'What are we going to eat?' or 'What are we going to drink?' or 'What are we going to wear?' [32] Everyone is concerned about these things, and your heavenly Father certainly knows you need all of them. [33] But first, be concerned about his kingdom and what has his approval. Then all these things will be provided for you.

[34] "So don't ever worry about tomorrow. After all, tomorrow will worry about itself. Each day has enough trouble of its own.

---

[a] 6:13 Or "rescue us from evil."

The Sermon on a Mountain Continues:
Stop Judging—Luke 6:37–42

7 [1] "Stop judging so that you will not be judged. [2] Otherwise, you will be judged by the same standard you use to judge others. The standards you use for others will be applied to you. [3] So why do you see the piece of sawdust in another believer's eye and not notice the wooden beam in your own eye? [4] How can you say to another believer, 'Let me take the piece of sawdust out of your eye,' when you have a beam in your own eye? [5] You hypocrite! First remove the beam from your own eye. Then you will see clearly to remove the piece of sawdust from another believer's eye.

Don't Throw Pearls to Pigs

[6] "Don't give what is holy to dogs or throw your pearls to pigs. Otherwise, they will trample them and then tear you to pieces.

The Power of Prayer—Luke 11:5–13

[7] "Ask, and you will receive. Search, and you will find. Knock, and the door will be opened for you. [8] Everyone who asks will receive. The one who searches will find, and for the one who knocks, the door will be opened.

[9] "If your child asks you for bread, would any of you give him a stone? [10] Or if your child asks for a fish, would you give him a snake? [11] Even though you're evil, you know how to give good gifts to your children. So how much more will your Father in heaven give good things to those who ask him?

The Golden Rule—Luke 6:31

[12] "Always do for other people everything you want them to do for you. That is ˌthe meaning of, Moses' Teachings and the Prophets.

The Narrow Gate

[13] "Enter through the narrow gate because the gate and road that lead to destruction are wide. Many enter through the wide gate. [14] But the narrow gate and the road that lead to life are full of trouble. Only a few people find the narrow gate.

False Prophets—Luke 6:43–45

[15] "Beware of false prophets. They come to you disguised as sheep, but in their hearts they are vicious wolves. [16] You will know them by what they produce.

"People don't pick grapes from thornbushes or figs from thistles, do they? [17] In the same way every good tree produces good fruit, but a rotten tree produces bad fruit. [18] A good tree cannot produce bad fruit, and a rotten tree cannot produce good fruit. [19] Any tree that fails to produce good fruit is cut down and thrown into a fire. [20] So you will know them by what they produce.

[21] "Not everyone who says to me, 'Lord, Lord!' will enter the kingdom of heaven, but only the person who does what my Father in heaven wants. [22] Many will say to me on that day, 'Lord, Lord, didn't we prophesy in your name? Didn't we force out demons and do many miracles by the power and authority of your name?' [23] Then I will tell them publicly, 'I've never known you. Get away from me, you evil people.'

Build on the Rock—Luke 6:47–49

[24] "Therefore, everyone who hears what I say and obeys it will be like a wise person who built a house on rock. [25] Rain poured, and floods came. Winds blew and beat against that house. But it did not collapse, because its foundation was on rock.

[26] "Everyone who hears what I say but doesn't obey it will be like a foolish person who built a house on sand. [27] Rain poured, and floods came. Winds blew and struck that house. It collapsed, and the result was a total disaster."

[28] When Jesus finished this speech, the crowds were amazed at his teachings. [29] Unlike their scribes, he taught them with authority.

Jesus Cures a Man With a Skin Disease—Mark 1:40–45; Luke 5:12–16

8 [1] When Jesus came down from the mountain, large crowds followed him.
[2] A man with a serious skin disease came and bowed down in front of him. The man said to Jesus, "Sir, if you're willing, you can make me clean."[a]
[3] Jesus reached out, touched him, and said, "I'm willing. So be clean!" Immediately, his skin disease went away, and he was clean.
[4] Jesus said to him, "Don't tell anyone about this! Instead, show yourself to the priest. Then offer the sacrifice Moses commanded as proof to people that you are clean."

---

[a] 8:2 "Clean" refers to anything that Moses' Teachings say is presentable to God.

A Believing Army Officer—*Luke 7:1–10*

⁵ When Jesus went to Capernaum, a Roman army officer came to beg him for help. ⁶ The officer said, "Sir, my servant is lying at home paralyzed and in terrible pain."

⁷ Jesus said to him, "I'll come to heal him."

⁸ The officer responded, "Sir, I don't deserve to have you come into my house. But just give a command, and my servant will be healed. ⁹ As you know, I'm in a chain of command and have soldiers at my command. I tell one of them, 'Go!' and he goes, and another, 'Come!' and he comes. I tell my servant, 'Do this!' and he does it."

¹⁰ Jesus was amazed when he heard this. He said to those who were following him, "I can guarantee this truth: I haven't found faith as great as this in anyone in Israel. ¹¹ I can guarantee that many will come from all over the world. They will eat with Abraham, Isaac, and Jacob in the kingdom of heaven. ¹² The citizens of that kingdom will be thrown outside into the darkness. People will cry and be in extreme pain there.

¹³ Jesus told the officer, "Go! What you believed will be done for you." And at that moment the servant was healed.

Jesus Cures Peter's Mother-in-Law and Many Others—*Mark 1:29–34; Luke 4:38–41*

¹⁴ When Jesus went to Peter's house, he saw Peter's mother-in-law in bed with a fever. ¹⁵ Jesus touched her hand, and the fever went away. So she got up and prepared a meal for him.

¹⁶ In the evening the people brought him many who were possessed by demons. He forced the ˎevilˎ spirits out of people with a command and cured everyone who was sick. ¹⁷ So what the prophet Isaiah had said came true: "He took away our weaknesses and removed our diseases."

¹⁸ Now, when Jesus saw a crowd around him, he ordered ˎhis disciplesˎ to cross to the other side of the Sea of Galilee.

What It Takes to Be a Disciple—*Luke 9:57–62*

¹⁹ A scribe came to him and said, "Teacher, I'll follow you wherever you go."

²⁰ Jesus told him, "Foxes have holes, and birds have nests, but the Son of Man has nowhere to sleep."

²¹ Another disciple said to him, "Sir, first let me go to bury my father."

²² But Jesus told him, "Follow me, and let the dead bury their own dead."

Jesus Calms the Sea—*Mark 4:35–41; Luke 8:22–25*

²³ Jesus' disciples went with him as he left in a boat. ²⁴ Suddenly, a severe storm came across the sea. The waves were covering the boat. Yet, Jesus was sleeping.

²⁵ So they woke him up, saying, "Lord! Save us! We're going to die!"

²⁶ Jesus said to them, "Why do you cowards have so little faith?" Then he got up, gave an order to the wind and the sea, and the sea became very calm.

²⁷ The men were amazed and asked, "What kind of man is this? Even the wind and the sea obey him!"

Jesus Cures Two Demon-Possessed Men—*Mark 5:1–20; Luke 8:26–39*

²⁸ When he arrived in the territory of the Gadarenes on the other side ˎof the Sea of Galileeˎ, two men met him. They were possessed by demons and had come out of the tombs. No one could travel along that road because the men were so dangerous.

²⁹ They shouted, "Why are you bothering us now, Son of God? Did you come here to torture us before it is time?"

³⁰ A large herd of pigs was feeding in the distance. ³¹ The demons begged Jesus, "If you're going to force us out, send us into that herd of pigs."

³² Jesus said to them, "Go!" The demons came out and went into the pigs. Suddenly, the whole herd rushed down the cliff into the sea and died in the water. ³³ Those who took care of the pigs ran into the city. There they reported everything, especially about the men possessed by demons.

³⁴ Everyone from the city went to meet Jesus. When they saw him, they begged him to leave their territory.

Jesus Forgives Sins—*Mark 2:1–12; Luke 5:17–26*

9 ¹ Jesus got into a boat, crossed the sea, and came to his own city. ² Some people brought him a paralyzed man on a stretcher.

When Jesus saw their faith, he said to the man, "Cheer up, friend! Your sins are forgiven."

³ Then some of the scribes thought, "He's dishonoring God."

⁴ Jesus knew what they were thinking. He asked them, "Why are you thinking evil things? ⁵ Is it easier to say, 'Your sins are forgiven,' or to say, 'Get up and walk'? ⁶ I want you to know that the Son of Man has authority on earth to forgive sins." Then he said to the paralyzed man, "Get up, pick up your stretcher, and go home."

⁷ So the man got up and went home. ⁸ When the crowd saw this, they were filled with awe and praised God for giving such authority to humans.

Jesus Chooses Matthew to Be a Disciple—*Mark 2:13–17; Luke 5:27–32*

⁹ When Jesus was leaving that place, he saw a man sitting in a tax office. The man's name was Matthew. Jesus said to him, "Follow me!" So Matthew got up and followed him.

¹⁰ Later Jesus was having dinner at Matthew's house. Many tax collectors and sinners came to eat with Jesus and his disciples. ¹¹ The Pharisees saw this and asked his disciples, "Why does your teacher eat with tax collectors and sinners?"

¹² When Jesus heard that, he said, "Healthy people don't need a doctor; those who are sick do. ¹³ Learn what this means: 'I want mercy, not sacrifices.' I've come to call sinners, not people who think they have God's approval."

Jesus Is Questioned About Fasting—*Mark 2:18–22; Luke 5:33–39*

¹⁴ Then John's disciples came to Jesus. They said, "Why do we and the Pharisees fast often but your disciples never do?"

¹⁵ Jesus replied, "Can wedding guests be sad while the groom is still with them? The time will come when the groom will be taken away from them. Then they will fast.

¹⁶ "No one patches an old coat with a new piece of cloth that will shrink. When the patch shrinks, it will rip away from the coat, and the tear will become worse. ¹⁷ Nor do people pour new wine into old wineskins. If they do, the skins burst, the wine runs out, and the skins are ruined. Rather, people pour new wine into fresh skins, and both are saved."

A Synagogue Leader's Daughter and the Woman With Chronic Bleeding—*Mark 5:21–43; Luke 8:40–56*

¹⁸ A ⌞synagogue⌟ leader came to Jesus while he was talking to John's disciples. He bowed down in front of Jesus and said, "My daughter just died. Come, lay your hand on her, and she will live."

¹⁹ Jesus and his disciples got up and followed the man.

²⁰ Then a woman came up behind Jesus and touched the edge of his clothes. She had been suffering from chronic bleeding for twelve years. ²¹ She thought, "If I only touch his clothes, I'll get well."

²² When Jesus turned and saw her he said, "Cheer up, daughter! Your faith has made you well." At that very moment the woman became well.

²³ Jesus came to the ⌞synagogue⌟ leader's house. He saw flute players and a noisy crowd. ²⁴ He said to them, "Leave! The girl is not dead. She's sleeping." But they laughed at him. ²⁵ When the crowd had been put outside, Jesus went in, took her hand, and the girl came back to life.

²⁶ The news about this spread throughout that region.

Jesus Heals Two Blind Men

²⁷ When Jesus left that place, two blind men followed him. They shouted, "Have mercy on us, Son of David."

²⁸ Jesus went into a house, and the blind men followed him. He said to them, "Do you believe that I can do this?"

"Yes, Lord," they answered.

²⁹ He touched their eyes and said, "What you have believed will be done for you!" ³⁰ Then they could see.

He warned them, "Don't let anyone know about this!" ³¹ But they went out and spread the news about him throughout that region.

Jesus Forces a Demon out of a Man Who Couldn't Talk

³² As they were leaving, some people brought a man to Jesus. The man was unable to talk because he was possessed by a demon. ³³ But as soon as the demon was forced out, the man began to speak.

The crowds were amazed and said, "We have never seen anything like this in Israel!"

³⁴ But the Pharisees said, "He forces demons out of people with the help of the ruler of demons."

Jesus' Compassion for People

³⁵ Jesus went to all the towns and villages. He taught in the synagogues and spread the Good News of the kingdom. He also cured every disease and sickness.

³⁶ When he saw the crowds, he felt sorry for them. They were troubled and helpless like sheep without a shepherd. ³⁷ Then he said to his disciples, "The harvest is large, but the workers are few. ³⁸ So ask the Lord who gives this harvest to send workers to harvest his crops."

Jesus Appoints Twelve Apostles—*Mark 3:13–19; Luke 6:12–16*

10 [1] Jesus called his twelve disciples and gave them authority to force evil spirits out of people and to cure every disease and sickness.

[2] These are the names of the twelve apostles: first and foremost, Simon (who is called Peter) and his brother Andrew; James and his brother John, the sons of Zebedee; [3] Philip and Bartholomew; Thomas and Matthew the tax collector; James (son of Alphaeus), and Thaddaeus; [4] Simon the Zealot and Judas Iscariot, who later betrayed Jesus.

Jesus Sends Out the Twelve—*Mark 6:7–13; Luke 9:1–6*

[5] Jesus sent these twelve out with the following instructions: "Don't go among people who are not Jewish or into any Samaritan city. [6] Instead, go to the lost sheep of the nation of Israel. [7] As you go, spread this message: 'The kingdom of heaven is near.' [8] Cure the sick, bring the dead back to life, cleanse those with skin diseases, and force demons out of people. Give these things without charging, since you received them without paying.

[9] "Don't take any gold, silver, or even copper coins in your pockets. [10] Don't take a traveling bag for the trip, a change of clothes, sandals, or a walking stick. After all, the worker deserves to have his needs met.

[11] "When you go into a city or village, look for people who will listen to you there. Stay with them until you leave ˌthat placeˌ. [12] When you go into a house, greet the family. [13] If it is a family that listens to you, allow your greeting to stand. But if it is not receptive, take back your greeting. [14] If anyone doesn't welcome you or listen to what you say, leave that house or city, and shake its dust off your feet. [15] I can guarantee this truth: Judgment day will be better for Sodom and Gomorrah than for that city.

[16] "I'm sending you out like sheep among wolves. So be as cunning as snakes but as innocent as doves. [17] Watch out for people who will hand you over to the Jewish courts and whip you in their synagogues. [18] Because of me you will even be brought in front of governors and kings to testify to them and to everyone in the world. [19] When they hand you over ˌto the authoritiesˌ, don't worry about what to say or how to say it. When the time comes, you will be given what to say. [20] Indeed, you're not the ones who will be speaking. The Spirit of your Father will be speaking through you.

[21] "Brother will hand over brother to death; a father will hand over his child. Children will rebel against their parents and kill them. [22] Everyone will hate you because you are committed to me. But the person who patiently endures to the end will be saved. [23] So when they persecute you in one city, flee to another. I can guarantee this truth: Before you have gone through every city in Israel, the Son of Man will come.

[24] "A student is not better than his teacher. Nor is a slave better than his owner. [25] It is enough for a student to become like his teacher and a slave like his owner. If they have called the owner of the house Beelzebul,[a] they will certainly call the family members the same name. [26] So don't be afraid of them. Nothing has been covered that will not be exposed. Whatever is secret will be made known. [27] Tell in the daylight what I say to you in the dark. Shout from the housetops what you hear whispered. [28] Don't be afraid of those who kill the body but cannot kill the soul. Instead, fear the one who can destroy both body and soul in hell.

[29] "Aren't two sparrows sold for a penny? Not one of them will fall to the ground without your Father's permission. [30] Every hair on your head has been counted. [31] Don't be afraid! You are worth more than many sparrows.

[32] "So I will acknowledge in front of my Father in heaven that person who acknowledges me in front of others. [33] But I will tell my Father in heaven that I don't know the person who tells others that he doesn't know me.

[34] "Don't think that I came to bring peace to earth. I didn't come to bring peace but conflict. [35] I came to turn a man against his father, a daughter against her mother, a daughter-in-law against her mother-in-law. [36] A person's enemies will be the members of his own family.

[37] "The person who loves his father or mother more than me does not deserve to be my disciple. The person who loves a son or daughter more than me does not deserve to be my disciple. [38] Whoever doesn't take up his cross and follow me doesn't deserve to be my disciple. [39] The person who tries to preserve his life will lose it, but the person who loses his life for me will preserve it.

[40] "The person who welcomes you welcomes me, and the person who welcomes me welcomes the one who sent me. [41] The person who welcomes a prophet as a prophet will receive a prophet's reward. The person who welcomes a righteous person as a righteous person will receive a righteous person's reward. [42] I can guarantee this truth: Whoever gives any of my humble followers a cup of cold water because that person is my disciple will certainly never lose his reward."

---

[a] 10:25 *Beelzebul* is another name for the devil. See Matthew 12:24.

11 [1] After Jesus finished giving his twelve disciples these instructions, he moved on from there to teach his message in their cities.

John Sends Two Disciples—*Luke 7:18–23*

[2] When John was in prison, he heard about the things Christ had done. So he sent his disciples [3] to ask Jesus, "Are you the one who is coming, or should we look for someone else?"

[4] Jesus answered John's disciples, "Go back, and tell John what you hear and see: [5] Blind people see again, lame people are walking, those with skin diseases are made clean, deaf people hear again, dead people are brought back to life, and poor people hear the Good News. [6] Whoever doesn't lose his faith in me is indeed blessed."

Jesus Speaks About John—*Luke 7:24–35*

[7] As they were leaving, Jesus spoke to the crowds about John. "What did you go into the desert to see? Tall grass swaying in the wind? [8] Really, what did you go to see? A man dressed in fine clothes? Those who wear fine clothes are in royal palaces. [9] "Really, what did you go to see? A prophet? Let me tell you that he is far more than a prophet. [10] John is the one about whom Scripture says,

> 'I'm sending my messenger ahead of you
>   to prepare the way in front of you.'

[11] "I can guarantee this truth: Of all the people ever born, no one is greater than John the Baptizer. Yet, the least important person in the kingdom of heaven is greater than John. [12] From the time of John the Baptizer until now, the kingdom of heaven has been forcefully advancing, and forceful people have been seizing it. [13] All the Prophets and Moses' Teachings prophesied up to the time of John. [14] If you are willing to accept their message, John is the Elijah who was to come. [15] Let the person who has ears listen!

[16] "How can I describe the people who are living now? They are like children who sit in the marketplaces and shout to other children,

> [17]   'We played music for you,
>   but you didn't dance.
>   We sang a funeral song,
>   but you didn't show any sadness.'

[18] "John came neither eating nor drinking, and people say, 'There's a demon in him!' [19] The Son of Man came eating and drinking, and people say, 'Look at him! He's a glutton and a drunk, a friend of tax collectors and sinners!'

"Yet, wisdom is proved right by its actions."

Jesus Warns Chorazin, Bethsaida, and Capernaum

[20] Then Jesus denounced the cities where he had worked most of his miracles because they had not changed the way they thought and acted. [21] "How horrible it will be for you, Chorazin! How horrible it will be for you, Bethsaida! If the miracles worked in you had been worked in Tyre and Sidon, they would have changed the way they thought and acted long ago in sackcloth and ashes. [22] I can guarantee that judgment day will be better for Tyre and Sidon than for you. [23] And you, Capernaum, will you be lifted to heaven? No, you will go down to hell! If the miracles that had been worked in you had been worked in Sodom, it would still be there today. [24] I can guarantee that judgment day will be better for Sodom than for you."

Jesus Praises the Father and Invites Disciples to Come to Him

[25] At that time Jesus said, "I praise you, Father, Lord of heaven and earth, for hiding these things from wise and intelligent people and revealing them to little children. [26] Yes, Father, this is what pleased you.

[27] "My Father has turned everything over to me. Only the Father knows the Son. And no one knows the Father except the Son and those to whom the Son is willing to reveal him.

[28] "Come to me, all who are tired from carrying heavy loads, and I will give you rest. [29] Place my yoke[a] over your shoulders, and learn from me, because I am gentle and humble. Then you will find rest for yourselves [30] because my yoke is easy and my burden is light."

Jesus Has Authority Over the Day of Worship—*Mark 2:23–28; Luke 6:1–5*

12 [1] Then on a day of worship Jesus walked through the grainfields. His disciples were hungry and began to pick the heads of grain to eat.

---

[a] 11:29 A yoke is a wooden bar placed over the necks of work animals so that they can pull plows or carts.

[2] When the Pharisees saw this, they said to him, "Look! Your disciples are doing something that is not right to do on the day of worship." [3] Jesus asked them, "Haven't you read what David did when he and his men were hungry? [4] Haven't you read how he went into the house of God and ate[a] the bread of the presence? He and his men had no right to eat those loaves. Only the priests have that right. [5] Or haven't you read in Moses' Teachings that on the day of worship the priests in the temple do things they shouldn't on the day of worship yet remain innocent? [6] I can guarantee that something[b] greater than the temple is here. [7] If you had known what 'I want mercy, not sacrifices' means, you would not have condemned innocent people.

[8] "The Son of Man has authority over the day of worship."

Jesus Heals on the Day of Worship—Mark 3:1–6; Luke 6:6–11

[9] Jesus moved on from there and went into a synagogue. [10] A man with a paralyzed hand was there. The people asked Jesus whether it was right to heal on a day of worship so that they could accuse him of doing something wrong.

[11] Jesus said to them, "Suppose one of you has a sheep. If it falls into a pit on a day of worship, wouldn't you take hold of it and lift it out? [12] Certainly, a human is more valuable than a sheep! So it is right to do good on the day of worship."

[13] Then he said to the man, "Hold out your hand." The man held it out, and it became normal again, as healthy as the other.

[14] The Pharisees left and plotted to kill Jesus. [15] He knew about this, so he left that place.

Jesus Is God's Servant

Many people followed him, and he cured all of them. [16] He also ordered them not to tell people who he was. [17] So what the prophet Isaiah had said came true:

[18]   "Here is my servant
      whom I have chosen,
         whom I love,
            and in whom I delight.
   I will put my Spirit on him,
      and he will announce justice to the nations.
[19]   He will not quarrel or shout,
      and no one will hear his voice in the streets.
[20]   He will not break off a damaged cattail.
      He will not even put out a smoking wick
      — until he has made justice victorious.
[21]   The nations will have hope because of him."

Jesus Is Accused of Working With Beelzebul—Mark 3:20–30; Luke 11:14–23

[22] Then some people brought Jesus a man possessed by a demon. The demon made the man blind and unable to talk. Jesus cured him so that he could talk and see.

[23] The crowds were all amazed and said, "Can this man be the Son of David?" [24] When the Pharisees heard this, they said, "This man can force demons out of people only with the help of Beelzebul, the ruler of demons."

[25] Since Jesus knew what they were thinking, he said to them, "Every kingdom divided against itself is ruined. And every city or household divided against itself will not last. [26] If Satan forces Satan out, he is divided against himself. How, then, can his kingdom last? [27] If I force demons out of people with the help of Beelzebul, who helps your followers force them out? That's why they will be your judges. [28] But if I force demons out with the help of God's Spirit, then the kingdom of God has come to you. [29] How can anyone go into a strong man's house and steal his property? First he must tie up the strong man. Then he can go through his house and steal his property.

[30] "Whoever isn't with me is against me. Whoever doesn't gather with me scatters. [31] So I can guarantee that people will be forgiven for any sin or cursing. However, cursing the Spirit will not be forgiven. [32] Whoever speaks a word against the Son of Man will be forgiven. But whoever speaks against the Holy Spirit will not be forgiven in this world or the next.

[33] "Make a tree good, and then its fruit will be good. Or make a tree rotten, and then its fruit will be rotten. A person can recognize a tree by its fruit. [34] You poisonous snakes! How can you evil people say anything good? Your mouth says what comes from inside you. [35] Good people do the good things that are in them. But evil people do the evil things that are in them.

---

[a] 12:4 Some manuscripts and translations read "they ate."   [b] 12:6 Some manuscripts and translations read "someone."

³⁶ "I can guarantee that on judgment day people will have to give an account of every careless word they say. ³⁷ By your words you will be declared innocent, or by your words you will be declared guilty."

The Sign of Jonah—Luke 11:29–32, 24–26

³⁸ Then some scribes and Pharisees said, "Teacher, we want you to show us a miraculous sign." ³⁹ He responded, "The people of an evil and unfaithful era look for a miraculous sign. But the only sign they will get is the sign of the prophet Jonah. ⁴⁰ Just as Jonah was in the belly of a huge fish for three days and three nights, so the Son of Man will be in the heart of the earth for three days and three nights. ⁴¹ The men of Nineveh will stand up with you at the time of judgment and will condemn you, because they turned to God and changed the way they thought and acted when Jonah spoke his message. But look, someone greater than Jonah is here! ⁴² The queen from the south will stand up at the time of judgment with you. She will condemn you, because she came from the ends of the earth to hear Solomon's wisdom. But look, someone greater than Solomon is here!

⁴³ "When an evil spirit comes out of a person, it goes through dry places looking for a place to rest. But it doesn't find any. ⁴⁴ Then it says, 'I'll go back to the home I left.' When it arrives, it finds the house unoccupied, swept clean, and in order. ⁴⁵ Then it goes and brings along seven other spirits more evil than itself. They enter and take up permanent residence there. In the end the condition of that person is worse than it was before. That is what will happen to the evil people of this day."

The True Family of Jesus—Mark 3:31–35; Luke 8:19–21

⁴⁶ While Jesus was still talking to the crowds, his mother and brothers were standing outside. They wanted to talk to him. ⁴⁷ Someone told him, "Your mother and your brothers are standing outside. They want to talk to you." ⁴⁸ He replied to the man speaking to him, "Who is my mother, and who are my brothers?" ⁴⁹ Pointing with his hand at his disciples, he said, "Look, here are my mother and my brothers. ⁵⁰ Whoever does what my Father in heaven wants is my brother and sister and mother."

A Story About a Farmer—Mark 4:1–20; Luke 8:4–15

13 ¹ That same day Jesus left the house and sat down by the Sea of Galilee. ² The crowd that gathered around him was so large that he got into a boat. He sat in the boat while the entire crowd stood on the shore. ³ Then he used stories as illustrations to tell them many things.

He said, "Listen! A farmer went to plant seed. ⁴ Some seeds were planted along the road, and birds came and devoured them. ⁵ Other seeds were planted on rocky ground, where there was little soil. The plants sprouted quickly because the soil wasn't deep. ⁶ But when the sun came up, they were scorched. They withered because their roots weren't deep enough. ⁷ Other seeds were planted among thornbushes, and the thornbushes grew up and choked them. ⁸ But other seeds were planted on good ground and produced grain. They produced one hundred, sixty, or thirty times as much as was planted. ⁹ Let the person who has ears listen!"

¹⁰ The disciples asked him, "Why do you use stories as illustrations when you speak to people?" ¹¹ Jesus answered, "Knowledge about the mysteries of the kingdom of heaven has been given to you. But it has not been given to the crowd. ¹² Those who understand ˌthese mysteriesˌ will be given ˌmore knowledgeˌ, and they will excel ˌin understanding themˌ. However, some people don't understand ˌthese mysteriesˌ. Even what they understand will be taken away from them. ¹³ This is why I speak to them this way. They see, but they're blind. They hear, but they don't listen. They don't even try to understand. ¹⁴ So they make Isaiah's prophecy come true:

'You will hear clearly but never understand.
You will see clearly but never comprehend.
¹⁵   These people have become close-minded
         and hard of hearing.
            They have shut their eyes
            so that their eyes never see.
         Their ears never hear.
         Their minds never understand.
And they never return to me for healing!'

¹⁶ "Blessed are your eyes because they see and your ears because they hear. ¹⁷ I can guarantee this truth: Many prophets and many of God's people longed to see what you see but didn't see it, to hear what you hear but didn't hear it.

¹⁸ "Listen to what the story about the farmer means. ¹⁹ Someone hears the word about the kingdom but doesn't understand it. The evil one comes at once and snatches away what was planted in him. This is what the seed planted along the road illustrates. ²⁰ The seed planted on rocky ground ˏis the person whoˏ hears the word and accepts it at once with joy. ²¹ Since he doesn't have any root, he lasts only a little while. When suffering or persecution comes along because of the word, he immediately falls ˏfrom faithˏ. ²² The seed planted among thornbushes ˏis another person whoˏ hears the word. But the worries of life and the deceitful pleasures of riches choke the word so that it can't produce anything. ²³ But the seed planted on good ground ˏis the person whoˏ hears and understands the word. This type produces crops. They produce one hundred, sixty, or thirty times as much as was planted."

A Story About Weeds in the Wheat

²⁴ Jesus used another illustration. He said, "The kingdom of heaven is like a man who planted good seed in his field. ²⁵ But while people were asleep, his enemy planted weeds in the wheat field and went away. ²⁶ When the wheat came up and formed kernels, weeds appeared.

²⁷ "The owner's workers came to him and asked, 'Sir, didn't you plant good seed in your field? Where did the weeds come from?'

²⁸ "He told them, 'An enemy did this.'

"His workers asked him, 'Do you want us to pull out the weeds?'

²⁹ "He replied, 'No. If you pull out the weeds, you may pull out the wheat with them. ³⁰ Let both grow together until the harvest. When the grain is cut, I will tell the workers to gather the weeds first and tie them in bundles to be burned. But I'll have them bring the wheat into my barn.' "

Stories About a Mustard Seed and Yeast—Mark 4:30–34; Luke 13:18–21

³¹ Jesus used another illustration. He said, "The kingdom of heaven is like a mustard seed that someone planted in a field. ³² It's one of the smallest seeds. However, when it has grown, it is taller than the garden plants. It becomes a tree that is large enough for birds to nest in its branches."

³³ He used another illustration. "The kingdom of heaven is like yeast that a woman mixed into a large amount of flour until the yeast worked its way through all the dough."

³⁴ Jesus used illustrations to tell the crowds all these things. He did not tell them anything without illustrating it with a story. ³⁵ So what the prophet had said came true:

"I will open my mouth to illustrate points.
I will tell what has been hidden since the world was made."

The Meaning of the Weeds in the Wheat

³⁶ When Jesus had sent the people away, he went into the house. His disciples came to him and said, "Explain what the illustration of the weeds in the field means."

³⁷ He answered, "The one who plants the good seeds is the Son of Man. ³⁸ The field is the world. The good seeds are those who belong to the kingdom. The weeds are those who belong to the evil one. ³⁹ The enemy who planted them is the devil. The harvest is the end of the world. The workers are angels. ⁴⁰ Just as weeds are gathered and burned, so it will be at the end of time. ⁴¹ The Son of Man will send his angels. They will gather everything in his kingdom that causes people to sin and everyone who does evil. ⁴² The angels will throw them into a blazing furnace. People will cry and be in extreme pain there. ⁴³ Then the people who have God's approval will shine like the sun in their Father's kingdom. Let the person who has ears listen!

Stories About a Treasure, a Merchant, and a Net

⁴⁴ "The kingdom of heaven is like a treasure buried in a field. When a man discovered it, he buried it again. He was so delighted with it that he went away, sold everything he had, and bought that field.

⁴⁵ "Also, the kingdom of heaven is like a merchant who was searching for fine pearls. ⁴⁶ When he found a valuable pearl, he went away, sold everything he had, and bought it.

⁴⁷ "Also, the kingdom of heaven is like a net that was thrown into the sea. It gathered all kinds of fish. ⁴⁸ When it was full, they pulled it to the shore. Then they sat down, gathered the good fish into containers, and threw the bad ones away. ⁴⁹ The same thing will happen at the end of time. The angels will go out and separate the evil people from people who have God's approval. ⁵⁰ Then the angels will throw the evil people into a blazing furnace. They will cry and be in extreme pain there.

⁵¹ "Have you understood all of this?"

"Yes," they answered.

⁵² So Jesus said to them, "That is why every scribe who has become a disciple of the kingdom of heaven is like a home owner. He brings new and old things out of his treasure chest."

⁵³ When Jesus had finished these illustrations, he left that place.

Nazareth Rejects Jesus—Mark 6:1–6; Luke 4:14–30

⁵⁴ Jesus went to his hometown and taught the people in the synagogue in a way that amazed them. People were asking, "Where did this man get this wisdom and the power to do these miracles? ⁵⁵ Isn't this the carpenter's son? Isn't his mother's name Mary? Aren't his brothers' names James, Joseph, Simon, and Judas? ⁵⁶ And aren't all his sisters here with us? Where, then, did this man get all this?" ⁵⁷ So they took offense at him.

But Jesus said to them, "The only place a prophet isn't honored is in his hometown and in his own house."

⁵⁸ He didn't work many miracles there because of their lack of faith.

Recalling John's Death—Mark 6:14–29; Luke 9:7–9

14 ¹ At that time Herod, ruler of Galilee, heard the news about Jesus. ² He said to his officials, "This is John the Baptizer! He has come back to life. That's why he has the power to perform these miracles."

³ Herod had arrested John, tied him up, and put him in prison. Herod did this for Herodias, the wife of his brother Philip. ⁴ John had been telling Herod, "It's not right for you to be married to her." ⁵ So Herod wanted to kill John. However, he was afraid of the people because they thought John was a prophet.

⁶ When Herod celebrated his birthday, Herodias' daughter danced for his guests. Herod was so delighted with her that ⁷ he swore he would give her anything she wanted.

⁸ Urged by her mother, she said, "Give me the head of John the Baptizer on a platter."

⁹ The king regretted his promise. But because of his oath and his guests, he ordered that her wish be granted. ¹⁰ He had John's head cut off in prison. ¹¹ So the head was brought on a platter and given to the girl, who took it to her mother.

¹² John's disciples came for the body and buried it. Then they went to tell Jesus.

Jesus Feeds More Than Five Thousand—Mark 6:30–44; Luke 9:10–17; John 6:1–14

¹³ When Jesus heard about John, he left in a boat and went to a place where he could be alone. The crowds heard about this and followed him on foot from the cities. ¹⁴ When Jesus got out of the boat, he saw a large crowd. He felt sorry for them and cured their sick people.

¹⁵ In the evening the disciples came to him. They said, "No one lives around here, and it's already late. Send the crowds to the villages to buy food for themselves."

¹⁶ Jesus said to them, "They don't need to go away. You give them something to eat."

¹⁷ They told him, "All we have here are five loaves of bread and two fish."

¹⁸ Jesus said, "Bring them to me."

¹⁹ Then he ordered the people to sit down on the grass. After he took the five loaves and the two fish, he looked up to heaven and blessed the food. He broke the loaves apart, gave them to the disciples, and they gave them to the people. ²⁰ All of them ate as much as they wanted. When they picked up the leftover pieces, they filled twelve baskets.

²¹ About five thousand men had eaten. (This number does not include the women and children who had eaten.)

Jesus Walks on the Sea—Mark 6:45–56; John 6:15–21

²² Jesus quickly made his disciples get into a boat and cross to the other side ahead of him while he sent the people away. ²³ After sending the people away, he went up a mountain to pray by himself. When evening came, he was there alone.

²⁴ The boat, now hundreds of yards from shore, was being thrown around by the waves because it was going against the wind.

²⁵ Between three and six o'clock in the morning, he came to them. He was walking on the sea. ²⁶ When the disciples saw him walking on the sea, they were terrified. They said, "It's a ghost!" and began to scream because they were afraid.

²⁷ Immediately, Jesus said, "Calm down! It's me. Don't be afraid!"

²⁸ Peter answered, "Lord, if it is you, order me to come to you on the water."

²⁹ Jesus said, "Come!" So Peter got out of the boat and walked on the water toward Jesus. ³⁰ But when he noticed how strong the wind was, he became afraid and started to sink. He shouted, "Lord, save me!"

³¹ Immediately, Jesus reached out, caught hold of him, and said, "You have so little faith! Why did you doubt?"

³² When they got into the boat, the wind stopped blowing. ³³ The men in the boat bowed down in front of Jesus and said, "You are truly the Son of God."

³⁴ They crossed the sea and landed at Gennesaret. ³⁵ The men there recognized Jesus and sent messengers all around the countryside. The people brought him everyone who was sick. ³⁶ They begged him to let them touch just the edge of his clothes. Everyone who touched his clothes was made well.

Jesus Challenges the Pharisees' Traditions—Mark 7:1–23

15 [1] Then some Pharisees and scribes came from Jerusalem to Jesus. They asked, [2] "Why do your disciples break the traditions of our ancestors? They do not wash their hands before they eat."

[3] He answered them, "Why do you break the commandment of God because of your traditions? [4] For example, God said, 'Honor your father and your mother' and 'Whoever curses father or mother must be put to death.' [5] But you say that whoever tells his father or mother, 'I have given to God whatever support you might have received from me,' [6] does not have to honor his father. Because of your traditions you have destroyed the authority of God's word. [7] You hypocrites! Isaiah was right when he prophesied about you:

[8] 'These people honor me with their lips,
but their hearts are far from me.
[9] Their worship of me is pointless,
because their teachings are rules made by humans.' "

[10] Then he called the crowd and said to them, "Listen and try to understand! [11] What goes into a person's mouth doesn't make him unclean.[a] It's what comes out of the mouth that makes a person unclean."

[12] Then the disciples came and said to him, "Do you realize that when the Pharisees heard your statement they were offended?"

[13] He answered, "Any plant that my heavenly Father did not plant will be uprooted. [14] Leave them alone! They are blind leaders. When one blind person leads another, both will fall into the same pit."

[15] Peter said to him, "Explain this illustration to us."

[16] Jesus said, "Don't you understand yet? [17] Don't you know that whatever goes into the mouth goes into the stomach and then into a toilet? [18] But whatever goes out of the mouth comes from within, and that's what makes a person unclean. [19] Evil thoughts, murder, adultery, ˌother ˌ sexual sins, stealing, lying, and cursing come from within. [20] These are the things that make a person unclean. But eating without washing one's hands doesn't make a person unclean."

The Faith of a Canaanite Woman—Mark 7:24–30

[21] Jesus left that place and went to the region of Tyre and Sidon.

[22] A Canaanite woman from that territory came ˌto him ˌ and began to shout, "Have mercy on me, Lord, Son of David! My daughter is tormented by a demon."

[23] But he did not answer her at all. Then his disciples came to him and urged him, "Send her away. She keeps shouting behind us."

[24] Jesus responded, "I was sent only to the lost sheep of the nation of Israel."

[25] She came to him, bowed down, and said, "Lord, help me!"

[26] Jesus replied, "It's not right to take the children's food and throw it to the dogs."

[27] She said, "You're right, Lord. But even the dogs eat scraps that fall from their masters' tables."

[28] Then Jesus answered her, "Woman, you have strong faith! What you wanted will be done for you." At that moment her daughter was cured.

[29] Jesus moved on from there and went along the Sea of Galilee. Then he went up a mountain and sat there.

[30] A large crowd came to him, bringing with them the lame, blind, disabled, those unable to talk, and many others. They laid them at his feet, and he cured them. [31] The crowd was amazed to see mute people talking, the disabled cured, the lame walking, and the blind seeing. So they praised the God of Israel.

Jesus Feeds More Than Four Thousand—Mark 8:1–10

[32] Jesus called his disciples and said, "I feel sorry for the people. They have been with me three days now and have nothing to eat. I don't want to send them away hungry, or they may become exhausted on their way home."

[33] His disciples asked him, "Where could we get enough bread to feed such a crowd in this place where no one lives?"

[34] Jesus asked them, "How many loaves of bread do you have?"
They answered, "Seven, and a few small fish."

[35] He ordered the crowd to sit down on the ground. [36] He took the seven loaves and the fish and gave thanks to God. Then he broke the bread and gave it to the disciples, and they gave the bread and fish to the people.

---

[a] 15:11 "Unclean" refers to anything that Moses' Teachings say is not presentable to God.

[37] All of them ate as much as they wanted. The disciples picked up the leftover pieces and filled seven large baskets. [38] Four thousand men had eaten. (This number does not include the women and children who had eaten.)

[39] After he sent the people on their way, Jesus stepped into the boat and came to the territory of Magadan.

The Pharisees Ask For a Sign From Heaven—*Mark 8:11–13a*

16 [1] The Pharisees and Sadducees came to test Jesus. So they asked him to show them a miraculous sign from heaven.

[2] He responded to them, "In the evening you say that the weather will be fine because the sky is red. [3] And in the morning you say that there will be a storm today because the sky is red and overcast. You can forecast the weather by judging the appearance of the sky, but you cannot interpret the signs of the times.

[4] "Evil and unfaithful people look for a miraculous sign. But the only sign they will be given is that of Jonah."

Then he left them standing there and went away.

The Yeast of the Pharisees—*Mark 8:13b–21*

[5] The disciples had forgotten to take any bread along when they went to the other side of the Sea of Galilee.

[6] Jesus said to them, "Be careful! Watch out for the yeast of the Pharisees and Sadducees!"

[7] The disciples had been discussing among themselves that they had not taken any bread along.

[8] Jesus knew about their conversation and asked, "Why are you discussing among yourselves that you don't have any bread? You have so little faith! [9] Don't you understand yet? Don't you remember the five loaves for the five thousand and how many baskets you filled? [10] Don't you remember the seven loaves for the four thousand and how many large baskets you filled? [11] Why don't you understand that I wasn't talking to you about bread? Watch out for the yeast of the Pharisees and Sadducees!"

[12] Then they understood that he didn't say to watch out for the yeast in bread, but to watch out for the teachings of the Pharisees and Sadducees.

Peter Declares His Belief About Jesus—*Mark 8:27–30; Luke 9:18–21*

[13] When Jesus came to the region of Caesarea Philippi, he asked his disciples, "Who do people say the Son of Man is?"

[14] They answered, "Some say you are John the Baptizer, others Elijah, still others Jeremiah or one of the prophets."

[15] He asked them, "But who do you say I am?"

[16] Simon Peter answered, "You are the Messiah, the Son of the living God!"

[17] Jesus replied, "Simon, son of Jonah, you are blessed! No human revealed this to you, but my Father in heaven revealed it to you. [18] You are Peter, and I can guarantee that on this rock[a] I will build my church. And the gates of hell will not overpower it. [19] I will give you the keys of the kingdom of heaven. Whatever you imprison, God will imprison. And whatever you set free, God will set free."

[20] Then he strictly ordered the disciples not to tell anyone that he was the Messiah.

Jesus Foretells That He Will Die and Come Back to Life—*Mark 8:31–33; Luke 9:22*

[21] From that time on Jesus began to inform his disciples that he had to go to Jerusalem. There he would have to suffer a lot because of the leaders, chief priests, and scribes. He would be killed, but on the third day he would be brought back to life.

[22] Peter took him aside and objected to this. He said, "Heaven forbid, Lord! This must never happen to you!"

[23] But Jesus turned and said to Peter, "Get out of my way, Satan! You are tempting me to sin. You aren't thinking the way God thinks but the way humans think."

What It Means to Follow Jesus—*Mark 8:34–9:1; Luke 9:23–27*

[24] Then Jesus said to his disciples, "Those who want to come with me must say no to the things they want, pick up their crosses, and follow me. [25] Those who want to save their lives will lose them. But those who lose their lives for me will find them. [26] What good will it do for people to win the whole world and lose their lives? Or what will a person give in exchange for life? [27] The Son of Man will come with his angels in his Father's glory. Then he will pay back each person based on what that person has done. [28] I can guarantee this truth: Some people who are standing here will not die until they see the Son of Man coming in his kingdom."

---

[a] 16:18 In Greek there is a play on words between *petros* (Peter or pebble) and *petra* (rock).

Moses and Elijah Appear With Jesus—Mark 9:2–13; Luke 9:28–36

17 ¹ After six days Jesus took Peter, James, and John (the brother of James) and led them up a high mountain where they could be alone.

² Jesus' appearance changed in front of them. His face became as bright as the sun and his clothes as white as light. ³ Suddenly, Moses and Elijah appeared to them and were talking with Jesus.

⁴ Peter said to Jesus, "Lord, it's good that we're here. If you want, I'll put up three tents here—one for you, one for Moses, and one for Elijah."

⁵ He was still speaking when a bright cloud overshadowed them. Then a voice came out of the cloud and said, "This is my Son, whom I love and with whom I am pleased. Listen to him!"

⁶ The disciples were terrified when they heard this and fell facedown on the ground. ⁷ But Jesus touched them and said, "Get up, and don't be afraid!" ⁸ As they raised their heads, they saw no one but Jesus.

⁹ On their way down the mountain, Jesus ordered them, "Don't tell anyone what you have seen. Wait until the Son of Man has been brought back to life."

¹⁰ So the disciples asked him, "Why do the scribes say that Elijah must come first?"

¹¹ Jesus answered, "Elijah is coming and will put everything in order again. ¹² Actually, I can guarantee that Elijah has already come. Yet, people treated him as they pleased because they didn't recognize him. In the same way they're going to make the Son of Man suffer."

¹³ Then the disciples understood that he was talking about John the Baptizer.

Jesus Cures a Demon-Possessed Boy—Mark 9:14–29; Luke 9:37–43a

¹⁴ When they came to a crowd, a man came up to Jesus, knelt in front of him, ¹⁵ and said, "Sir, have mercy on my son. He suffers from seizures. Often he falls into fire or water. ¹⁶ I brought him to your disciples, but they couldn't cure him."

¹⁷ Jesus replied, "You unbelieving and corrupt generation! How long must I be with you? How long must I put up with you? Bring him here to me!"

¹⁸ Jesus ordered the demon to come out of the boy. At that moment the boy was cured.

¹⁹ Then the disciples came to Jesus privately and asked, "Why couldn't we force the demon out of the boy?"

²⁰ He told them, "Because you have so little faith. I can guarantee this truth: If your faith is the size of a mustard seed, you can say to this mountain, 'Move from here to there,' and it will move. Nothing will be impossible for you."ᵃ

Jesus Again Foretells That He Will Die and Come Back to Life—Mark 9:30–32; Luke 9:43b–45

²² While they were traveling together in Galilee, Jesus told them, "The Son of Man will be betrayed and handed over to people. ²³ They will kill him, but on the third day he will be brought back to life." Then the disciples became very sad.

Paying the Temple Tax

²⁴ When they came to Capernaum, the collectors of the temple tax came to Peter. They asked him, "Doesn't your teacher pay the temple tax?"

²⁵ "Certainly," he answered.

Peter went into the house. Before he could speak, Jesus asked him, "What do you think, Simon? From whom do the kings of the world collect fees or taxes? Is it from their family members or from other people?"

²⁶ "From other people," Peter answered.

Jesus said to him, "Then the family members are exempt. ²⁷ However, so that we don't create a scandal, go to the sea and throw in a hook. Take the first fish that you catch. Open its mouth, and you will find a coin. Give that coin to them for you and me."

Greatness in the Kingdom—Mark 9:33–37; Luke 9:46–48

18 ¹ At that time the disciples came to Jesus and asked, "Who is greatest in the kingdom of heaven?"

² He called a little child and had him stand among them. ³ Then he said to them, "I can guarantee this truth: Unless you change and become like little children, you will never enter the kingdom of heaven. ⁴ Whoever becomes like this little child is the greatest in the kingdom of heaven. ⁵ And whoever welcomes a child like this in my name welcomes me.

Causing Others to Lose Faith—Mark 9:42–50; Luke 17:1–4

⁶ "These little ones believe in me. It would be best for the person who causes one of them to lose faith to be drowned in the sea with a large stone hung around his neck. ⁷ How horrible

---

ᵃ 17:20 Some manuscripts and translations add verse 21: "However, this kind ⌐of demon⌐ goes away only by prayer and fasting."

it will be for the world because it causes people to lose their faith. Situations that cause people to lose their faith will arise. How horrible it will be for the person who causes someone to lose his faith!

⁸ "If your hand or your foot causes you to lose your faith, cut it off and throw it away. It is better for you to enter life disabled or injured than to have two hands or two feet and be thrown into everlasting fire. ⁹ If your eye causes you to lose your faith, tear it out and throw it away. It is better for you to enter life with one eye than to have two eyes and be thrown into hellfire.

¹⁰ "Be careful not to despise these little ones. I can guarantee that their angels in heaven always see the face of my Father, who is in heaven.ᵃ

The Lost Sheep—Luke 15:1–7

¹² "What do you think? Suppose a man has 100 sheep and one of them strays. Won't he leave the 99 sheep in the hills to look for the one that has strayed? ¹³ I can guarantee this truth: If he finds it, he is happier about it than about the 99 that have not strayed. ¹⁴ In the same way, your Father in heaven does not want one of these little ones to be lost.

Dealing With Believers When They Do Wrong

¹⁵ "If a believer does something wrong,ᵇ go, confront him when the two of you are alone. If he listens to you, you have won back that believer. ¹⁶ But if he does not listen, take one or two others with you so that every accusation may be verified by two or three witnesses. ¹⁷ If he ignores these witnesses, tell it to the community of believers. If he also ignores the community, deal with him as you would a heathen or a tax collector. ¹⁸ I can guarantee this truth: Whatever you imprison, God will imprison. And whatever you set free, God will set free.

¹⁹ "I can guarantee again that if two of you agree on anything here on earth, my Father in heaven will accept it. ²⁰ Where two or three have come together in my name, I am there among them."

Personally Forgiving Others

²¹ Then Peter came to Jesus and asked him, "Lord, how often do I have to forgive a believer who wrongs me? Seven times?"

²² Jesus answered him, "I tell you, not just seven times, but seventy times seven.

²³ "That is why the kingdom of heaven is like a king who wanted to settle accounts with his servants. ²⁴ When he began to do this, a servant who owed him millions of dollars was brought to him. ²⁵ Because he could not pay off the debt, the master ordered him, his wife, his children, and all that he had to be sold to pay off the account. ²⁶ Then the servant fell at his master's feet and said, 'Be patient with me, and I will repay everything!'

²⁷ "The master felt sorry for his servant, freed him, and canceled his debt. ²⁸ But when that servant went away, he found a servant who owed him hundreds of dollars. He grabbed the servant he found and began to choke him. 'Pay what you owe!' he said.

²⁹ "Then that other servant fell at his feet and begged him, 'Be patient with me, and I will repay you.' ³⁰ But he refused. Instead, he turned away and had that servant put into prison until he would repay what he owed.

³¹ "The other servants who worked with him saw what had happened and felt very sad. They told their master the whole story.

³² "Then his master sent for him and said to him, 'You evil servant! I canceled your entire debt, because you begged me. ³³ Shouldn't you have treated the other servant as mercifully as I treated you?'

³⁴ "His master was so angry that he handed him over to the torturers until he would repay everything that he owed. ³⁵ That is what my Father in heaven will do to you if each of you does not sincerely forgive other believers."

A Discussion About Divorce and Celibacy—Mark 10:1–12

19 ¹ When Jesus finished speaking, he left Galilee and traveled along the other side of the Jordan River to the territory of Judea. ² Large crowds followed him, and he healed them there.

³ Some Pharisees came to test him. They asked, "Can a man divorce his wife for any reason?"

⁴ Jesus answered, "Haven't you read that the Creator made them male and female in the beginning ⁵ and that he said, 'That's why a man will leave his father and mother and will remain united with his wife, and the two will be one'? ⁶ So they are no longer two but one. Therefore, don't let anyone separate what God has joined together."

ᵃ 18:10 Some manuscripts and translations add verse 11: "The Son of Man came to save the lost." ᵇ 18:15 Some manuscripts and translations add "against you."

⁷ The Pharisees asked him, "Why, then, did Moses order a man to give his wife a written notice to divorce her?"

⁸ Jesus answered them, "Moses allowed you to divorce your wives because you're heartless. It was never this way in the beginning. ⁹ I can guarantee that whoever divorces his wife for any reason other than her unfaithfulness is committing adultery if he marries another woman."

¹⁰ The disciples said to him, "If that is the only reason a man can use to divorce his wife, it's better not to get married."

¹¹ He answered them, "Not everyone can do what you suggest. Only those who have that gift can. ¹² For example, some men are celibate because they were born that way. Others are celibate because they were castrated. Still others have decided to be celibate because of the kingdom of heaven. If anyone can do what you've suggested, then he should do it."

Jesus Blesses Children—Mark 10:13–16; Luke 18:15–17

¹³ Then some people brought little children to Jesus to have him bless them and pray for them. But the disciples told the people not to do that.

¹⁴ Jesus said, "Don't stop children from coming to me! Children like these are part of the kingdom of God." ¹⁵ After Jesus blessed them, he went away from there.

Eternal Life in the Kingdom—Mark 10:17–31; Luke 18:18–30

¹⁶ Then a man came to Jesus and said, "Teacher, what good deed should I do to gain eternal life?"

¹⁷ Jesus said to him, "Why do you ask me about what is good? There is only one who is good. If you want to enter into life, obey the commandments."

¹⁸ "Which commandments?" the man asked.

Jesus said, "Never murder. Never commit adultery. Never steal. Never give false testimony. ¹⁹ Honor your father and mother. Love your neighbor as you love yourself."

²⁰ The young man replied, "I have obeyed all these commandments. What else do I need to do?"

²¹ Jesus said to him, "If you want to be perfect, sell what you own. Give the money to the poor, and you will have treasure in heaven. Then follow me!"

²² When the young man heard this, he went away sad because he owned a lot of property.

²³ Jesus said to his disciples, "I can guarantee this truth: It will be hard for a rich person to enter the kingdom of heaven. ²⁴ I can guarantee again that it is easier for a camel to go through the eye of a needle than for a rich person to enter the kingdom of God."

²⁵ He amazed his disciples more than ever when they heard this. "Then who can be saved?" they asked.

²⁶ Jesus looked at them and said, "It is impossible for people ⸤to save themselves⸥, but everything is possible for God."

²⁷ Then Peter replied to him, "Look, we've given up everything to follow you. What will we get out of it?"

²⁸ Jesus said to them, "I can guarantee this truth: When the Son of Man sits on his glorious throne in the world to come, you, my followers, will also sit on twelve thrones, judging the twelve tribes of Israel. ²⁹ And everyone who gave up homes, brothers or sisters, father, mother, children, or fields because of my name will receive a hundred times more and will inherit eternal life. ³⁰ However, many who are first will be last, and many who are last will be first.

A Story About Vineyard Workers

20 ¹ "The kingdom of heaven is like a landowner who went out at daybreak to hire workers for his vineyard. ² After agreeing to pay the workers the usual day's wages, he sent them to work in his vineyard. ³ About 9 a.m. he saw others standing in the marketplace without work. ⁴ He said to them, 'Work in my vineyard, and I'll give you whatever is right.' So they went.

⁵ "He went out again about noon and 3 p.m. and did the same thing. ⁶ About 5 p.m. he went out and found some others standing around. He said to them, 'Why are you standing here all day long without work?'

⁷ " 'No one has hired us,' they answered him.

"He said to them, 'Work in my vineyard.'

⁸ "When evening came, the owner of the vineyard told the supervisor, 'Call the workers, and give them their wages. Start with the last, and end with the first.'

⁹ "Those who started working about 5 p.m. came, and each received a day's wages. ¹⁰ When those who had been hired first came, they expected to receive more. But each of them received a day's wages. ¹¹ Although they took it, they began to protest to the owner. ¹² They said, 'These last workers have worked only one hour. Yet, you've treated us all the same, even though we worked hard all day under a blazing sun.'

¹³ "The owner said to one of them, 'Friend, I'm not treating you unfairly. Didn't you agree with me on a day's wages? ¹⁴ Take your money and go! I want to give this last worker as much as I gave you. ¹⁵ Can't I do what I want with my own money? Or do you resent my generosity towards others?'

¹⁶ "In this way the last will be first, and the first will be last."

For the Third Time Jesus Foretells That He Will Die and Come Back to Life—
Mark 10:32–34; Luke 18:31–34

¹⁷ When Jesus was on his way to Jerusalem, he took the twelve apostles aside and said to them privately, ¹⁸ "We're going to Jerusalem. There the Son of Man will be betrayed to the chief priests and scribes. They will condemn him to death ¹⁹ and hand him over to foreigners. They will make fun of him, whip him, and crucify him. But on the third day he will be brought back to life."

A Mother Makes a Request—*Mark 10:35–45*

²⁰ Then the mother of Zebedee's sons came to Jesus with her two sons. She bowed down in front of him to ask him for a favor.

²¹ "What do you want?" he asked her.

She said to him, "Promise that one of my sons will sit at your right and the other at your left in your kingdom."

²² Jesus replied, "You don't realize what you're asking. Can you drink the cup that I'm going to drink?"

"We can," they told him.

²³ Jesus said to them, "You will drink my cup. But I don't have the authority to grant you a seat at my right or left. My Father has already prepared these positions for certain people."

²⁴ When the other ten apostles heard about this, they were irritated with the two brothers. ²⁵ Jesus called the apostles and said, "You know that the rulers of nations have absolute power over people and their officials have absolute authority over people. ²⁶ But that's not the way it's going to be among you. Whoever wants to become great among you will be your servant. ²⁷ Whoever wants to be most important among you will be your slave. ²⁸ It's the same way with the Son of Man. He didn't come so that others could serve him. He came to serve and to give his life as a ransom for many people."

Jesus Gives Two Blind Men Their Sight—*Mark 10:46–52; Luke 18:35–43*

²⁹ As they were leaving Jericho, a large crowd followed Jesus. ³⁰ Two blind men were sitting by the road. When they heard that Jesus was passing by, they shouted, "Lord, Son of David, have mercy on us!"

³¹ The crowd told them to be quiet. But they shouted even louder, "Lord, Son of David, have mercy on us!"

³² Jesus stopped and called them. "What do you want me to do for you?" he asked.

³³ They told him, "Lord, we want you to give us our eyesight back."

³⁴ Jesus felt sorry for them, so he touched their eyes. Their sight was restored at once, and they followed him.

The King Comes to Jerusalem—*Mark 11:1–11; Luke 19:29–44; John 12:12–19*

21 ¹ When they came near Jerusalem and had reached Bethphage on the Mount of Olives, Jesus sent two disciples ahead of him. ² He said to them, "Go into the village ahead of you. You will find a donkey tied there and a colt with it. Untie them, and bring them to me. ³ If anyone says anything to you, tell him that the Lord needs them. That person will send them at once."

⁴ This happened so that what the prophet had said came true:

5   "Tell the people of Zion,
          'Your king is coming to you.
             He's gentle,
                riding on a donkey,
                   on a colt, a young pack animal.' "

⁶ The disciples did as Jesus had directed them. ⁷ They brought the donkey and the colt and put their coats on them for Jesus to sit on. ⁸ Most of the people spread their coats on the road. Others cut branches from the trees and spread them on the road. ⁹ The crowd that went ahead of him and that followed him was shouting,

          "Hosanna to the Son of David!
             Blessed is the one who comes in the name of the Lord!
          Hosanna in the highest heaven!"

¹⁰ When Jesus came into Jerusalem, the whole city was in an uproar. People were asking, "Who is this?"

¹¹ The crowd answered, "This is the prophet Jesus from Nazareth in Galilee."

Jesus Throws Out the Moneychangers—Mark 11:15–19; Luke 19:45–48

¹² Jesus went into the temple courtyard and threw out everyone who was buying and selling there. He overturned the moneychangers' tables and the chairs of those who sold pigeons. ¹³ He told them, "Scripture says, 'My house will be called a house of prayer,' but you're turning it into a gathering place for thieves!"

¹⁴ Blind and lame people came to him in the temple courtyard, and he healed them.

¹⁵ When the chief priests and the scribes saw the amazing miracles he performed and the children shouting in the temple courtyard, "Hosanna to the Son of David!" they were irritated. ¹⁶ They said to him, "Do you hear what these children are saying?"

Jesus replied, "Yes, I do. Have you never read, 'From the mouths of little children and infants, you have created praise'?"

¹⁷ He left them and went out of the city to Bethany and spent the night there.

Jesus Curses the Fig Tree—Mark 11:12–14, 20–25

¹⁸ In the morning, as Jesus returned to the city, he became hungry. ¹⁹ When he saw a fig tree by the road, he went up to the tree and found nothing on it but leaves. He said to the tree, "May fruit never grow on you again!" At once the fig tree dried up.

²⁰ The disciples were surprised to see this. They asked, "How did the fig tree dry up so quickly?"

²¹ Jesus answered them, "I can guarantee this truth: If you have faith and do not doubt, you will be able to do what I did to the fig tree. You could also say to this mountain, 'Be uprooted and thrown into the sea,' and it will happen. ²² Have faith that you will receive whatever you ask for in prayer."

Jesus' Authority Challenged—Mark 11:27–33; Luke 20:1–8

²³ Then Jesus went into the temple courtyard and began to teach. The chief priests and the leaders of the people came to him. They asked, "What gives you the right to do these things? Who told you that you could do this?"

²⁴ Jesus answered them, "I, too, have a question for you. If you answer it for me, I'll tell you why I have the right to do these things. ²⁵ Did John's right to baptize come from heaven or from humans?"

They discussed this among themselves. They said, "If we say, 'from heaven,' he will ask us, 'Then why didn't you believe him?' ²⁶ But if we say, 'from humans,' we're afraid of what the crowd might do. All those people think of John as a prophet." ²⁷ So they answered Jesus, "We don't know."

Jesus told them, "Then I won't tell you why I have the right to do these things.

A Story About Two Sons

²⁸ "What do you think about this? A man had two sons. He went to the first and said, 'Son, go to work in the vineyard today.'

²⁹ "His son replied, 'I don't want to!' But later he changed his mind and went.

³⁰ "The father went to the other son and told him the same thing. He replied, 'I will, sir,' but he didn't go.

³¹ "Which of the two sons did what the father wanted?"

"The first," they answered.

Jesus said to them, "I can guarantee this truth: Tax collectors and prostitutes are going into the kingdom of God ahead of you. ³² John came to you and showed you the way that God wants you to live, but you didn't believe him. The tax collectors and prostitutes believed him. But even after you had seen that, you didn't change your minds and believe him.

A Story About a Vineyard—Mark 12:1–12; Luke 20:9–19

³³ "Listen to another illustration. A landowner planted a vineyard. He put a wall around it, made a winepress, and built a watchtower. Then he leased it to vineyard workers and went on a trip.

³⁴ "When the grapes were getting ripe, he sent his servants to the workers to collect his share of the produce. ³⁵ The workers took his servants and beat one, killed another, and stoned a third to death. ³⁶ So the landowner sent more servants. But the workers treated them the same way.

³⁷ "Finally, he sent his son to them. He thought, 'They will respect my son.'

³⁸ "When the workers saw his son, they said to one another, 'This is the heir. Let's kill him and get his inheritance.' ³⁹ So they grabbed him, threw him out of the vineyard, and killed him.

⁴⁰ "Now, when the owner of the vineyard comes, what will he do to those workers?"

⁴¹ They answered, "He will destroy those evil people. Then he will lease the vineyard to other workers who will give him his share of the produce when it is ready."

⁴² Jesus asked them, "Have you never read in the Scriptures:

'The stone that the builders rejected
  has become the cornerstone.
The Lord is responsible for this,
  and it is amazing for us to see'?

⁴³ That is why I can guarantee that the kingdom of God will be taken away from you and given to a people who will produce what God wants. ⁴⁴ Anyone who falls on this stone will be broken. If the stone falls on anyone, it will crush that person."ᵃ

⁴⁵ When the chief priests and the Pharisees heard his illustrations, they knew that he was talking about them. ⁴⁶ They wanted to arrest him but were afraid of the crowds, who thought he was a prophet.

A Story About a Wedding Reception

22 ¹ Again Jesus used stories as illustrations when he spoke to them. He said, ² "The kingdom of heaven is like a king who planned a wedding for his son. ³ He sent his servants to those who had been invited to the wedding, but they refused to come. ⁴ He sent other servants to tell the people who had been invited, 'I've prepared dinner. My bulls and fattened calves have been butchered. Everything is ready. Come to the wedding!'

⁵ "But they paid no attention and went away. Some went to work in their own fields, and others went to their businesses. ⁶ The rest grabbed the king's servants, mistreated them, and then killed them.

⁷ "The king became angry. He sent his soldiers, killed those murderers, and burned their city.

⁸ "Then the king said to his servants, 'The wedding is ready, but those who were invited don't deserve the honor. ⁹ Go where the roads leave the city. Invite everyone you find to the wedding.' ¹⁰ The servants went into the streets and brought in all the good people and all the evil people they found. And the wedding hall was filled with guests.

¹¹ "When the king came to see the guests, he saw a person who was not dressed in the wedding clothes ˎprovided for the guestsˎ. ¹² He said to him, 'Friend, how did you get in here without proper wedding clothes?'

"The man had nothing to say. ¹³ Then the king told his servants, 'Tie his hands and feet, and throw him outside into the darkness. People will cry and be in extreme pain there.'

¹⁴ "Therefore, many are invited, but few of those are chosen to stay."

A Question About Taxes—Mark 12:13–17; Luke 20:20–26

¹⁵ Then the Pharisees went away and planned to trap Jesus into saying the wrong thing. ¹⁶ They sent their disciples to him along with Herod's followers. They said to him, "Teacher, we know that you tell the truth and that you teach the truth about the way of God. You don't favor individuals because of who they are. ¹⁷ So tell us what you think. Is it right to pay taxes to the emperor or not?"

¹⁸ Jesus recognized their evil plan, so he asked, "Why do you test me, you hypocrites? ¹⁹ Show me a coin used to pay taxes."

They brought him a coin. ²⁰ He said to them, "Whose face and name is this?"

²¹ They replied, "The emperor's."

Then he said to them, "Very well, give the emperor what belongs to the emperor, and give God what belongs to God."

²² They were surprised to hear this. Then they left him alone and went away.

The Dead Come Back to Life—Mark 12:18–27; Luke 20:27–40

²³ On that day some Sadducees, who say that people will never come back to life, came to Jesus. They asked him, ²⁴ "Teacher, Moses said, 'If a man dies childless, his brother should marry his widow and have children for his brother.' ²⁵ There were seven brothers among us. The first married and died. Since he had no children, he left his widow to his brother. ²⁶ The second brother also died, as well as the third, and the rest of the seven brothers. ²⁷ At last the woman died. ²⁸ Now, when the dead come back to life, whose wife will she be? All seven brothers had been married to her."

²⁹ Jesus answered, "You're mistaken because you don't know the Scriptures or God's power. ³⁰ When people come back to life, they don't marry. Rather, they are like the angels in heaven.

ᵃ 21:44 Some manuscripts and translations omit this verse.

[31] Haven't you read what God told you about the dead coming back to life? He said, [32] 'I am the God of Abraham, Isaac, and Jacob.' He's not the God of the dead but of the living."

[33] He amazed the crowds who heard his teaching.

Love God and Your Neighbor—*Mark 12:28–34*

[34] When the Pharisees heard that Jesus had silenced the Sadducees, they gathered together. [35] One of them, an expert in Moses' Teachings, tested Jesus by asking, [36] "Teacher, which commandment is the greatest in Moses' Teachings?"

[37] Jesus answered him, " 'Love the Lord your God with all your heart, with all your soul, and with all your mind.' [38] This is the greatest and most important commandment. [39] The second is like it: 'Love your neighbor as you love yourself.' [40] All of Moses' Teachings and the Prophets depend on these two commandments."

How Can David's Son Be David's Lord?—*Mark 12:35–37a; Luke 20:41–44*

[41] While the Pharisees were still gathered, Jesus asked them, [42] "What do you think about the Messiah? Whose son is he?"

They answered him, "David's."

[43] He said to them, "Then how can David, guided by the Spirit, call him Lord? David says,

[44]   'The Lord said to my Lord,
      "Take the highest position in heaven
         until I put your enemies under your control." '

[45] If David calls him Lord, how can he be his son?"

[46] No one could answer him, and from that time on no one dared to ask him another question.

Jesus Disapproves of the Example Set By Scribes and Pharisees—*Mark 12:37b–40; Luke 20:45–47*

23 [1] Then Jesus said to the crowds and to his disciples, [2] "The scribes and the Pharisees teach with Moses' authority. [3] So be careful to do everything they tell you. But don't follow their example, because they don't practice what they preach. [4] They make loads that are hard to carry and lay them on the shoulders of the people. However, they are not willing to lift a finger to move them.

[5] "They do everything to attract people's attention. They make their headbands large and the tassels on their shawls long. [6] They love the place of honor at dinners and the front seats in synagogues. [7] They love to be greeted in the marketplaces and to have people call them Rabbi. [8] But don't make others call you Rabbi, because you have only one teacher, and you are all followers. [9] And don't call anyone on earth your father, because you have only one Father, and he is in heaven. [10] Don't make others call you a leader, because you have only one leader, the Messiah. [11] The person who is greatest among you will be your servant. [12] Whoever honors himself will be humbled, and whoever humbles himself will be honored.

The Hypocrisy of the Scribes and Pharisees

[13] "How horrible it will be for you, scribes and Pharisees! You hypocrites! You lock people out of the kingdom of heaven. You don't enter it yourselves, and you don't permit others to enter when they try.[a]

[15] "How horrible it will be for you, scribes and Pharisees! You hypocrites! You cross land and sea to recruit a single follower, and when you do, you make that person twice as fit for hell as you are.

[16] "How horrible it will be for you, you blind guides! You say, 'To swear an oath by the temple doesn't mean a thing. But to swear an oath by the gold in the temple means a person must keep his oath.' [17] You blind fools! What is more important, the gold or the temple that made the gold holy? [18] Again you say, 'To swear an oath by the altar doesn't mean a thing. But to swear an oath by the gift on the altar means a person must keep his oath.' [19] You blind men! What is more important, the gift or the altar that makes the gift holy? [20] To swear an oath by the altar is to swear by it and by everything on it. [21] To swear an oath by the temple is to swear by it and by the one who lives there. [22] And to swear an oath by heaven is to swear by God's throne and the one who sits on it.

[23] "How horrible it will be for you, scribes and Pharisees! You hypocrites! You give ˻God˼ one-tenth of your mint, dill, and cumin. But you have neglected justice, mercy, and faithfulness. These are the most important things in Moses' Teachings. You should have done these things

---

[a] 23:13 Some manuscripts and translations add verse 14: "How horrible it will be for you, scribes and Pharisees! You hypocrites! You rob widows by taking their houses and then say long prayers to make yourselves look good. You will receive a most severe punishment." (See Mark 12:40 and Luke 20:47.)

without neglecting the others. ²⁴ You blind guides! You strain gnats ‚out of your wine‚, but you swallow camels.

²⁵ "How horrible it will be for you, scribes and Pharisees! You hypocrites! You clean the outside of cups and dishes. But inside they are full of greed and uncontrolled desires. ²⁶ You blind Pharisees! First clean the inside of the cups and dishes so that the outside may also be clean.

²⁷ "How horrible it will be for you, scribes and Pharisees! You hypocrites! You are like whitewashed graves that look beautiful on the outside but inside are full of dead people's bones and every kind of impurity. ²⁸ So on the outside you look as though you have God's approval, but inside you are full of hypocrisy and lawlessness.

²⁹ "How horrible it will be for you, scribes and Pharisees! You hypocrites! You build tombs for the prophets and decorate the monuments of those who had God's approval. ³⁰ Then you say, 'If we had lived at the time of our ancestors, we would not have helped to murder the prophets.' ³¹ So you testify against yourselves that you are the descendants of those who murdered the prophets. ³² Go ahead, finish what your ancestors started!

³³ "You snakes! You poisonous snakes! How can you escape being condemned to hell? ³⁴ I'm sending you prophets, wise men, and teachers of the Scriptures. You will kill and crucify some of them. Others you will whip in your synagogues and persecute from city to city. ³⁵ As a result, you will be held accountable for all the innocent blood of those murdered on earth, from the murder of righteous Abel to that of Zechariah, son of Barachiah, whom you murdered between the temple and the altar. ³⁶ I can guarantee this truth: The people living now will be held accountable for all these things.

³⁷ "Jerusalem, Jerusalem, you kill the prophets and stone to death those sent to you! How often I wanted to gather your children together the way a hen gathers her chicks under her wings! But you were not willing! ³⁸ Your house will be abandoned, deserted. ³⁹ I can guarantee that you will not see me again until you say, 'Blessed is the one who comes in the name of the Lord!' "

Jesus Teaches His Disciples on the Mount of Olives—Mark 13:1–31; Luke 21:5–33

24 ¹ As Jesus left the temple courtyard and was walking away, his disciples came to him. They proudly pointed out to him the temple buildings. ² Jesus said to them, "You see all these buildings, don't you? I can guarantee this truth: Not one of these stones will be left on top of another. Each one will be torn down."

³ As Jesus was sitting on the Mount of Olives, his disciples came to him privately and said, "Tell us, when will this happen? What will be the sign that you are coming again, and when will the world come to an end?"

⁴ Jesus answered them, "Be careful not to let anyone deceive you. ⁵ Many will come using my name. They will say, 'I am the Messiah,' and they will deceive many people.

⁶ "You will hear of wars and rumors of wars. Don't be alarmed! These things must happen, but they don't mean that the end has come. ⁷ Nation will fight against nation and kingdom against kingdom. There will be famines and earthquakes in various places. ⁸ All of these are only the beginning pains ‚of the end‚.

⁹ "Then they will hand you over to those who will torture and kill you. All nations will hate you because you are committed to me. ¹⁰ Then many will lose faith. They will betray and hate each other. ¹¹ Many false prophets will appear and deceive many people. ¹² And because there will be more and more lawlessness, most people's love will grow cold. ¹³ But the person who endures to the end will be saved.

¹⁴ "This Good News about the kingdom will be spread throughout the world as a testimony to all nations. Then the end will come.

¹⁵ "The prophet Daniel said that the disgusting thing that will cause destruction will stand in the holy place. When you see this (let the reader take note), ¹⁶ those of you in Judea should flee to the mountains. ¹⁷ Those who are on the roof should not come down to get anything out of their houses. ¹⁸ Those who are in the field should not turn back to get their coats.

¹⁹ "How horrible it will be for the women who are pregnant or who are nursing babies in those days. ²⁰ Pray that it will not be winter or a day of worship when you flee. ²¹ There will be a lot of misery at that time, a kind of misery that has not happened from the beginning of the world until now and will certainly never happen again. ²² If God does not reduce the number of those days, no one will be saved. But those days will be reduced because of those whom God has chosen.

²³ "At that time don't believe anyone who tells you, 'Here is the Messiah!' or 'There he is!' ²⁴ False messiahs and false prophets will appear. They will work spectacular, miraculous signs and do wonderful things to deceive, if possible, even those whom God has chosen. ²⁵ Listen! I've told you this before it happens. ²⁶ So if someone tells you, 'He's in the desert!' don't go out ‚looking for him‚. And don't believe anyone who says, 'He's in a secret place!' ²⁷ The Son of Man will come again just as lightning flashes from east to west. ²⁸ Vultures will gather wherever there is a dead body.

²⁹ "Immediately after the misery of those days, the sun will turn dark, the moon will not give light, the stars will fall from the sky, and the powers of the universe will be shaken. ³⁰ "Then the sign of the Son of Man will appear in the sky. All the people on earth will cry in agony when they see the Son of Man coming on the clouds in the sky with power and great glory. ³¹ He will send out his angels with a loud trumpet call, and from every direction under the sky, they will gather those whom God has chosen.

³² "Learn from the story of the fig tree. When its branch becomes tender and it sprouts leaves, you know that summer is near. ³³ In the same way, when you see all these things, you know that he is near, at the door.

³⁴ "I can guarantee this truth: This generation will not disappear until all these things take place. ³⁵ The earth and the heavens will disappear, but my words will never disappear.

No One Knows When the Son of Man Will Return

³⁶ "No one knows when that day or hour will come. Even the angels in heaven and the Son don't know. Only the Father knows.

³⁷ "When the Son of Man comes again, it will be exactly like the days of Noah. ³⁸ In the days before the flood, people were eating, drinking, and getting married until the day that Noah went into the ship. ³⁹ They were not aware of what was happening until the flood came and swept all of them away. That is how it will be when the Son of Man comes again.

⁴⁰ "At that time two men will be working in the field. One will be taken, and the other one will be left. ⁴¹ Two women will be working at a mill. One will be taken, and the other one will be left.

⁴² "Therefore, be alert, because you don't know on what day your Lord will return. ⁴³ You realize that if a homeowner had known at what time of the night a thief was coming, he would have stayed awake. He would not have let the thief break into his house. ⁴⁴ Therefore, you, too, must be ready because the Son of Man will return when you least expect him.

⁴⁵ "Who, then, is the faithful and wise servant? The master will put that person in charge of giving the other servants their food at the right time. ⁴⁶ That servant will be blessed if his master finds him doing this job when he comes. ⁴⁷ I can guarantee this truth: He will put that servant in charge of all his property. ⁴⁸ On the other hand, that servant, if he is wicked, may think that it will be a long time before his master comes. ⁴⁹ The servant may begin to beat the other servants and eat and drink with the drunks. ⁵⁰ His master will return unexpectedly. ⁵¹ Then his master will severely punish him and assign him a place with the hypocrites. People will cry and be in extreme pain there.

A Story About Ten Bridesmaids

25 ¹ "When the end comes, the kingdom of heaven will be like ten bridesmaids. They took their oil lamps and went to meet the groom. ² Five of them were foolish, and five were wise. ³ The foolish bridesmaids took their lamps, but they didn't take any extra oil. ⁴ The wise bridesmaids, however, took along extra oil for their lamps. ⁵ Since the groom was late, all the bridesmaids became drowsy and fell asleep.

⁶ "At midnight someone shouted, 'The groom is here! Come to meet him!' ⁷ Then all the bridesmaids woke up and got their lamps ready.

⁸ "The foolish ones said to the wise ones, 'Give us some of your oil. Our lamps are going out.'

⁹ "But the wise bridesmaids replied, 'We can't do that. There won't be enough for both of us. Go! Find someone to sell you some oil.'

¹⁰ "While they were buying oil, the groom arrived. The bridesmaids who were ready went with him into the wedding hall, and the door was shut.

¹¹ "Later the other bridesmaids arrived and said, 'Sir, sir, open the door for us!'

¹² "But he answered them, 'I don't even know who you are!'

¹³ "So stay awake, because you don't know the day or the hour.

A Story About Three Servants

¹⁴ "The kingdom of heaven is like a man going on a trip. He called his servants and entrusted some money to them. ¹⁵ He gave one man ten thousand dollars, another four thousand dollars, and another two thousand dollars. Each was given money based on his ability. Then the man went on his trip.

¹⁶ "The one who received ten thousand dollars invested the money at once and doubled his money. ¹⁷ The one who had four thousand dollars did the same and also doubled his money. ¹⁸ But the one who received two thousand dollars went off, dug a hole in the ground, and hid his master's money.

¹⁹ "After a long time the master of those servants returned and settled accounts with them. ²⁰ The one who received ten thousand dollars brought the additional ten thousand. He said, 'Sir, you gave me ten thousand dollars. I've doubled the amount.'

²¹ "His master replied, 'Good job! You're a good and faithful servant! You proved that you could be trusted with a small amount. I will put you in charge of a large amount. Come and share your master's happiness.'

²² "The one who received four thousand dollars came and said, 'Sir, you gave me four thousand dollars. I've doubled the amount.'

²³ "His master replied, 'Good job! You're a good and faithful servant! You proved that you could be trusted with a small amount. I will put you in charge of a large amount. Come and share your master's happiness.'

²⁴ "Then the one who received two thousand dollars came and said, 'Sir, I knew that you are a hard person to please. You harvest where you haven't planted and gather where you haven't scattered any seeds. ²⁵ I was afraid. So I hid your two thousand dollars in the ground. Here's your money!'

²⁶ "His master responded, 'You evil and lazy servant! If you knew that I harvest where I haven't planted and gather where I haven't scattered, ²⁷ then you should have invested my money with the bankers. When I returned, I would have received my money back with interest. ²⁸ Take the two thousand dollars away from him! Give it to the one who has the ten thousand! ²⁹ To all who have, more will be given, and they will have more than enough. But everything will be taken away from those who don't have much. ³⁰ Throw this useless servant outside into the darkness. People will cry and be in extreme pain there.'

Jesus Will Judge the World

³¹ "When the Son of Man comes in his glory and all his angels are with him, he will sit on his glorious throne. ³² The people of every nation will be gathered in front of him. He will separate them as a shepherd separates the sheep from the goats. ³³ He will put the sheep on his right but the goats on his left.

³⁴ "Then the king will say to those on his right, 'Come, my Father has blessed you! Inherit the kingdom prepared for you from the creation of the world. ³⁵ I was hungry, and you gave me something to eat. I was thirsty, and you gave me something to drink. I was a stranger, and you took me into your home. ³⁶ I needed clothes, and you gave me something to wear. I was sick, and you took care of me. I was in prison, and you visited me.'

³⁷ "Then the people who have God's approval will reply to him, 'Lord, when did we see you hungry and feed you or see you thirsty and give you something to drink? ³⁸ When did we see you as a stranger and take you into our homes or see you in need of clothes and give you something to wear? ³⁹ When did we see you sick or in prison and visit you?'

⁴⁰ "The king will answer them, 'I can guarantee this truth: Whatever you did for one of my brothers or sisters, no matter how unimportant ˛they seemed˛, you did for me.'

⁴¹ "Then the king will say to those on his left, 'Get away from me! God has cursed you! Go into everlasting fire that was prepared for the devil and his angels! ⁴² I was hungry, and you gave me nothing to eat. I was thirsty, and you gave me nothing to drink. ⁴³ I was a stranger, and you didn't take me into your homes. I needed clothes, and you didn't give me anything to wear. I was sick and in prison, and you didn't take care of me.'

⁴⁴ "They, too, will ask, 'Lord, when did we see you hungry or thirsty or as a stranger or in need of clothes or sick or in prison and didn't help you?'

⁴⁵ "He will answer them, 'I can guarantee this truth: Whatever you failed to do for one of my brothers or sisters, no matter how unimportant ˛they seemed˛, you failed to do for me.'

⁴⁶ "These people will go away into eternal punishment, but those with God's approval will go into eternal life."

The Plot to Kill Jesus—*Mark 14:1–2; Luke 22:1–6; John 11:45–57*

26 ¹ When Jesus finished saying all these things, he told his disciples, ² "You know that the Passover will take place in two days. At that time the Son of Man will be handed over to be crucified."

³ Then the chief priests and the leaders of the people gathered in the palace of the chief priest Caiaphas. ⁴ They made plans to arrest Jesus in an underhanded way and to kill him. ⁵ But they said, "We shouldn't arrest him during the festival, or else there may be a riot among the people."

A Woman Prepares Jesus' Body for the Tomb—*Mark 14:3–9; John 12:1–8*

⁶ Jesus was in Bethany in the home of Simon, a man who had suffered from a skin disease. ⁷ While Jesus was sitting there, a woman went to him with a bottle of very expensive perfume and poured it on his head.

⁸ The disciples were irritated when they saw this. They asked, "Why did she waste it like this? ⁹ It could have been sold for a high price, and the money could have been given to the poor."

[10] Since Jesus knew what was going on, he said to them, "Why are you bothering this woman? She has done a beautiful thing for me. [11] You will always have the poor with you, but you will not always have me with you. [12] She poured this perfume on my body before it is placed in a tomb. [13] I can guarantee this truth: Wherever this Good News is spoken in the world, what she has done will also be told in memory of her."

Judas Plans to Betray Jesus—Mark 14:10–11; Luke 22:3–6

[14] Then one of the twelve apostles, the one named Judas Iscariot, went to the chief priests. [15] He asked, "What will you pay me if I hand him over to you?"

They offered him 30 silver coins. [16] From then on, he looked for a chance to betray Jesus.

Preparations for the Passover—Mark 14:12–17; Luke 22:7–17

[17] On the first day of the Festival of Unleavened Bread, the disciples went to Jesus. They asked, "Where do you want us to prepare the Passover meal for you?"

[18] He said, "Go to a certain man in the city, and tell him that the teacher says, 'My time is near. I will celebrate the Passover with my disciples at your house.' "

[19] The disciples did as Jesus had directed them and prepared the Passover.

[20] When evening came, Jesus was at the table with the twelve apostles.

Jesus Knows Who Will Betray Him—Mark 14:18–21; Luke 22:21–23; John 13:21–30

[21] While they were eating, he said, "I can guarantee this truth: One of you is going to betray me." [22] Feeling deeply hurt, they asked him one by one, "You don't mean me, do you, Lord?" [23] Jesus answered, "Someone who has dipped his hand into the bowl with me will betray me. [24] The Son of Man is going to die as the Scriptures say he will. But how horrible it will be for that person who betrays the Son of Man. It would have been better for that person if he had never been born."

[25] Then Judas, who betrayed him, asked, "You don't mean me, do you, Rabbi?"

"Yes, I do," Jesus replied.

The Lord's Supper—Mark 14:22–26; Luke 22:19–20

[26] While they were eating, Jesus took bread and blessed it. He broke the bread, gave it to his disciples, and said, "Take this, and eat it. This is my body."

[27] Then he took a cup and spoke a prayer of thanksgiving. He gave it to them and said, "Drink from it, all of you. [28] This is my blood, the blood of the promise.[a] It is poured out for many people so that sins are forgiven.

[29] "I can guarantee that I won't drink this wine again until that day when I drink new wine with you in my Father's kingdom."

[30] After they sang a hymn, they went to the Mount of Olives.

Jesus Predicts Peter's Denial—Mark 14:27–31; Luke 22:31–34; John 13:36–38

[31] Then Jesus said to them, "All of you will abandon me tonight. Scripture says,

> 'I will strike the shepherd,
>   and the sheep in the flock will be scattered.'

[32] "But after I am brought back to life, I will go to Galilee ahead of you."

[33] Peter said to him, "Even if everyone else abandons you, I never will."

[34] Jesus replied to Peter, "I can guarantee this truth: Before a rooster crows tonight, you will say three times that you don't know me."

[35] Peter told him, "Even if I have to die with you, I'll never say that I don't know you!" All the other disciples said the same thing.

Jesus Prays in the Garden of Gethsemane—Mark 14:32–42; Luke 22:39–46

[36] Then Jesus went with the disciples to a place called Gethsemane. He said to them, "Stay here while I go over there and pray."

[37] He took Peter and Zebedee's two sons with him. He was beginning to feel deep anguish. [38] Then he said to them, "My anguish is so great that I feel as if I'm dying. Wait here, and stay awake with me."

[39] After walking a little farther, he quickly bowed with his face to the ground and prayed, "Father, if it's possible, let this cup ˏof sufferingˌ be taken away from me. But let your will be done rather than mine."

---

[a] 26:28 Or "testament," or "covenant."

⁴⁰ When he went back to the disciples; he found them asleep. He said to Peter, "Couldn't you stay awake with me for one hour? ⁴¹ Stay awake, and pray that you won't be tempted. You want to do what's right, but you're weak."

⁴² Then he went away a second time and prayed, "Father, if this cup cannot be taken away unless I drink it, let your will be done."

⁴³ He found them asleep again because they couldn't keep their eyes open.

⁴⁴ After leaving them again, he went away and prayed the same prayer a third time. ⁴⁵ Then he came back to the disciples and said to them, "You might as well sleep now. The time is near for the Son of Man to be handed over to sinners. ⁴⁶ Get up! Let's go! The one who is betraying me is near."

Jesus Is Arrested—*Mark 14:43–52; Luke 22:47–54a; John 18:1–14*

⁴⁷ Just then, while Jesus was still speaking, Judas, one of the twelve apostles, arrived. A large crowd carrying swords and clubs was with him. They were from the chief priests and leaders of the people. ⁴⁸ Now, the traitor had given them a signal. He said, "The one I kiss is the man you want. Arrest him!"

⁴⁹ Then Judas quickly stepped up to Jesus and said, "Hello, Rabbi!" and kissed him.

⁵⁰ Jesus said to him, "Friend, why are you here?"

Then some men came forward, took hold of Jesus, and arrested him. ⁵¹ Suddenly, one of the men with Jesus pulled out his sword and cut off the ear of the chief priest's servant. ⁵² Then Jesus said to him, "Put your sword away! All who use a sword will be killed by a sword. ⁵³ Don't you think that I could call on my Father to send more than twelve legions of angels to help me now? ⁵⁴ How, then, are the Scriptures to be fulfilled that say this must happen?"

⁵⁵ At that time Jesus said to the crowd, "Have you come out with swords and clubs to arrest me as if I were a criminal? I used to sit teaching in the temple courtyard every day. But you didn't arrest me then. ⁵⁶ All of this has happened so that what the prophets have written would come true."

Then all the disciples abandoned him and ran away.

The Trial in Front of the Jewish Council—*Mark 14:53–65; Luke 22:63–71*

⁵⁷ Those who had arrested Jesus took him to Caiaphas, the chief priest, where the scribes and the leaders had gathered together. ⁵⁸ Peter followed at a distance until he came to the chief priest's courtyard. He went inside and sat with the guards to see how this would turn out.

⁵⁹ The chief priests and the whole council were searching for false testimony to use against Jesus in order to execute him. ⁶⁰ But they did not find any, although many came forward with false testimony. At last two men came forward. ⁶¹ They stated, "This man said, 'I can tear down God's temple and rebuild it in three days.' "

⁶² The chief priest stood up and said to Jesus, "Don't you have any answer to what these men testify against you?"

⁶³ But Jesus was silent.

Then the chief priest said to him, "Swear an oath in front of the living God and tell us, are you the Messiah, the Son of God?"

⁶⁴ Jesus answered him, "Yes, I am. But I can guarantee that from now on you will see the Son of Man in the highest position in heaven. He will be coming on the clouds of heaven."

⁶⁵ Then the chief priest tore his robes in horror and said, "He has dishonored God! Why do we need any more witnesses? You've just heard him dishonor God! ⁶⁶ What's your verdict?"

They answered, "He deserves the death penalty!"

⁶⁷ Then they spit in his face, hit him with their fists, and some of them slapped him. ⁶⁸ They said, "You Christ, if you're a prophet, tell us who hit you."

Peter Denies Jesus—*Mark 14:66–72; Luke 22:54b–62; John 18:15–18, 25–27*

⁶⁹ Peter was sitting in the courtyard. A female servant came to him and said, "You, too, were with Jesus the Galilean."

⁷⁰ But Peter denied it in front of them all by saying, "I don't know what you're talking about."

⁷¹ As he went to the entrance, another female servant saw him. She told those who were there, "This man was with Jesus from Nazareth."

⁷² Again Peter denied it and swore with an oath, "I don't know the man!"

⁷³ After a little while the men standing there approached Peter and said, "It's obvious you're also one of them. Your accent gives you away!"

⁷⁴ Then Peter began to curse and swear with an oath, "I don't know the man!" Just then a rooster crowed. ⁷⁵ Peter remembered what Jesus had said: "Before a rooster crows, you will say three times that you don't know me." Then Peter went outside and cried bitterly.

The Death of Judas

27 ¹ Early in the morning all the chief priests and the leaders of the people decided to execute Jesus. ² They tied him up, led him away, and handed him over to Pilate, the governor.

³ Then Judas, who had betrayed Jesus, regretted what had happened when he saw that Jesus was condemned. He brought the 30 silver coins back to the chief priests and leaders. ⁴ He said, "I've sinned by betraying an innocent man."

They replied, "What do we care? That's your problem."

⁵ So he threw the money into the temple, went away, and hanged himself.

⁶ The chief priests took the money and said, "It's not right to put it into the temple treasury, because it's blood money." ⁷ So they decided to use it to buy a potter's field for the burial of strangers. ⁸ That's why that field has been called the Field of Blood ever since. ⁹ Then what the prophet Jeremiah had said came true, "They took the 30 silver coins, the price the people of Israel had placed on him, ¹⁰ and used the coins to buy a potter's field, as the Lord had directed me."

Pilate Questions Jesus—Mark 15:1–5; Luke 23:1–4; John 18:28–38

¹¹ Jesus stood in front of the governor, ⌊Pilate⌋. The governor asked him, "Are you the king of the Jews?"

"Yes, I am," Jesus answered.

¹² While the chief priests and leaders were accusing him, he said nothing. ¹³ Then Pilate asked him, "Don't you hear how many charges they're bringing against you?"

¹⁴ But Jesus said absolutely nothing to him in reply, so the governor was very surprised.

The Crowd Rejects Jesus—Mark 15:6–15; Luke 23:18–25; John 18:39, 40

¹⁵ At every Passover festival the governor would free one prisoner whom the crowd wanted. ¹⁶ At that time there was a well-known prisoner by the name of Barabbas. ¹⁷ So when the people gathered, Pilate asked them, "Which man do you want me to free for you? Do you want me to free Barabbas or Jesus, who is called Christ?" ¹⁸ Pilate knew that they had handed Jesus over to him because they were jealous.

¹⁹ While Pilate was judging the case, his wife sent him a message. It said, "Leave that innocent man alone. I've been very upset today because of a dream I had about him."

²⁰ But the chief priests and leaders persuaded the crowd to ask for the release of Barabbas and the execution of Jesus.

²¹ The governor asked them, "Which of the two do you want me to free for you?"

They said, "Barabbas."

²² Pilate asked them, "Then what should I do with Jesus, who is called Christ?"

"He should be crucified!" they all said.

²³ Pilate asked, "Why? What has he done wrong?"

But they began to shout loudly, "He should be crucified!"

²⁴ Pilate saw that he was not getting anywhere. Instead, a riot was breaking out. So Pilate took some water and washed his hands in front of the crowd. He said, "I won't be guilty of killing this man. Do what you want!"

²⁵ All the people answered, "The responsibility for killing him will rest on us and our children."

²⁶ Then Pilate freed Barabbas for the people. But he had Jesus whipped and handed over to be crucified.

The Soldiers Make Fun of Jesus—Mark 15:16–19; John 19:1–3

²⁷ Then the governor's soldiers took Jesus into the palace and gathered the whole troop around him. ²⁸ They took off his clothes and put a bright red cape on him. ²⁹ They twisted some thorns into a crown, placed it on his head, and put a stick in his right hand. They knelt in front of him and made fun of him by saying, "Long live the king of the Jews!" ³⁰ After they had spit on him, they took the stick and kept hitting him on the head with it.

The Crucifixion—Mark 15:20–32; Luke 23:33–38; John 19:16b–24

³¹ After the soldiers finished making fun of Jesus, they took off the cape and put his own clothes back on him. Then they led him away to crucify him.

³² On the way they found a man named Simon. He was from the city of Cyrene. The soldiers forced him to carry Jesus' cross.

³³ They came to a place called Golgotha (which means "the place of the skull"). ³⁴ They gave him a drink of wine mixed with a drug called gall. When he tasted it, he refused to drink it. ³⁵ After they had crucified him, they divided his clothes among themselves by throwing dice. ³⁶ Then they sat there and kept watch over him. ³⁷ They placed a written accusation above his head. It read, "This is Jesus, the king of the Jews."

³⁸ At that time they crucified two criminals with him, one on his right and the other on his left.

[39] Those who passed by insulted him. They shook their heads [40] and said, "You were going to tear down God's temple and build it again in three days. Save yourself! If you're the Son of God, come down from the cross." [41] The chief priests together with the scribes and the leaders made fun of him in the same way. They said, [42] "He saved others, but he can't save himself. So he's Israel's king! Let him come down from the cross now, and we'll believe him. [43] He trusted God. Let God rescue him now if he wants. After all, this man said, 'I am the Son of God.'" [44] Even the criminals crucified with him were insulting him the same way.

Jesus Dies on the Cross—Mark 15:33–41; Luke 23:44–49; John 19:28–30

[45] At noon darkness came over the whole land until three in the afternoon. [46] About three o'clock Jesus cried out in a loud voice, "Eli, Eli, lema sabachthani?" which means, "My God, my God, why have you abandoned me?" [47] When some of the people standing there heard him say that, they said, "He's calling Elijah." [48] One of the men ran at once, took a sponge, and soaked it in some vinegar. Then he put it on a stick and offered Jesus a drink. [49] The others said, "Leave him alone! Let's see if Elijah comes to save him."

[50] Then Jesus loudly cried out once again and gave up his life.

[51] Suddenly, the curtain in the temple was split in two from top to bottom. The earth shook, and the rocks were split open. [52] The tombs were opened, and the bodies of many holy people who had died came back to life. [53] They came out of the tombs after he had come back to life, and they went into the holy city where they appeared to many people.

[54] An army officer and those watching Jesus with him saw the earthquake and the other things happening. They were terrified and said, "Certainly, this was the Son of God!"

[55] Many women were there watching from a distance. They had followed Jesus from Galilee and had always supported him. [56] Among them were Mary from Magdala, Mary (the mother of James and Joseph), and the mother of Zebedee's sons.

Jesus Is Buried—Mark 15:42–47; Luke 23:50–56; John 19:38–42

[57] In the evening a rich man named Joseph arrived. He was from the city of Arimathea and had become a disciple of Jesus. [58] He went to Pilate and asked for the body of Jesus. Pilate ordered that it be given to him.

[59] Joseph took the body and wrapped it in a clean linen cloth. [60] Then he laid it in his own new tomb, which had been cut in a rock. After rolling a large stone against the door of the tomb, he went away. [61] Mary from Magdala and the other Mary were sitting there, facing the tomb.

The Chief Priests and Pharisees Secure Jesus' Tomb

[62] The next day, which was the day of worship, the chief priests and Pharisees gathered together and went to Pilate. [63] They said, "Sir, we remember how that deceiver said while he was still alive, 'After three days I will be brought back to life.' [64] Therefore, give the order to make the tomb secure until the third day. Otherwise, his disciples may steal him and say to the people, 'He has been brought back to life.' Then the last deception will be worse than the first."

[65] Pilate told them, "You have the soldiers you want for guard duty. Go and make the tomb as secure as you know how."

[66] So they went to secure the tomb. They placed a seal on the stone and posted the soldiers on guard duty.

Jesus Comes Back to Life—Mark 16:1–8; Luke 24:1–12; John 20:1–10

28 [1] After the day of worship, as the sun rose Sunday morning, Mary from Magdala and the other Mary went to look at the tomb.

[2] Suddenly, there was a powerful earthquake. An angel of the Lord had come down from heaven, rolled the stone away, and was sitting on it. [3] He was as bright as lightning, and his clothes were as white as snow. [4] The guards were so deathly afraid of him that they shook.

[5] The angel said to the women, "Don't be afraid! I know you're looking for Jesus, who was crucified. [6] He's not here. He has been brought back to life as he said. Come, see the place where he was lying. [7] Then go quickly, and tell his disciples that he has been brought back to life. He's going ahead of them into Galilee. There they will see him. Take note that I have told you."

[8] They hurried away from the tomb with fear and great joy and ran to tell his disciples.

[9] Suddenly, Jesus met them and greeted them. They went up to him, bowed down to worship him, and took hold of his feet.

[10] Then Jesus said to them, "Don't be afraid! Go, tell my followers to go to Galilee. There they will see me."

The Guards Report to the Chief Priests

[11] While the women were on their way, some of the guards went into the city. They told the chief priests everything that had happened.

¹² The chief priests gathered together with the leaders and agreed on a plan. They gave the soldiers a large amount of money ¹³ and told them to say that Jesus' disciples had come at night and had stolen his body while they were sleeping. ¹⁴ ⸤They added,⸥ "If the governor hears about it, we'll take care of it, and you'll have nothing to worry about."

¹⁵ The soldiers took the money and did as they were told. Their story has been spread among the Jewish people to this day.

Jesus Gives Instructions to the Disciples

¹⁶ The eleven disciples went to the mountain in Galilee where Jesus had told them to go. ¹⁷ When they saw him, they bowed down in worship, though some had doubts.

¹⁸ When Jesus came near, he spoke to them. He said, "All authority in heaven and on earth has been given to me. ¹⁹ So wherever you go, make disciples of all nations: Baptize them in the name of the Father, and of the Son, and of the Holy Spirit. ²⁰ Teach them to do everything I have commanded you.

"And remember that I am always with you until the end of time."

MARK

John Prepares the Way—*Matthew 3:1–12; Luke 3:1–18*

1 ¹ This is the beginning of the Good News about Jesus Christ, the Son of God. ² The prophet Isaiah wrote,

> "I am sending my messenger ahead of you
>   to prepare the way for you."
> ³ "A voice cries out in the desert:
>   'Prepare the way for the Lord!
>   Make his paths straight!' "

⁴ John the Baptizer was in the desert telling people about a baptism of repentance[a] for the forgiveness of sins. ⁵ All Judea and all the people of Jerusalem went to him. As they confessed their sins, he baptized them in the Jordan River.

⁶ John was dressed in clothes made from camel's hair. He wore a leather belt around his waist and ate locusts and wild honey.

⁷ He announced, "The one who comes after me is more powerful than I. I am not worthy to bend down and untie his sandal straps. ⁸ I have baptized you with water, but he will baptize you with the Holy Spirit."

John Baptizes Jesus—*Matthew 3:13–17; Luke 3:21–22*

⁹ At that time Jesus came from Nazareth in Galilee and was baptized by John in the Jordan River. ¹⁰ As Jesus came out of the water, he saw heaven split open and the Spirit coming down to him as a dove. ¹¹ A voice from heaven said, "You are my Son, whom I love. I am pleased with you."

Satan Tempts Jesus—*Matthew 4:1–11; Luke 4:1–13*

¹² At once the Spirit brought him into the desert, ¹³ where he was tempted by Satan for 40 days. He was there with the wild animals, and the angels took care of him.

Calling of the First Disciples—*Matthew 4:18–22; Luke 5:1–11*

¹⁴ After John had been put in prison, Jesus went to Galilee and told people the Good News of God. ¹⁵ He said, "The time has come, and the kingdom of God is near. Change the way you think and act, and believe the Good News."

¹⁶ As he was going along the Sea of Galilee, he saw Simon and his brother Andrew. They were throwing a net into the sea because they were fishermen. ¹⁷ Jesus said to them, "Come, follow me! I will teach you how to catch people instead of fish." ¹⁸ They immediately left their nets and followed him.

¹⁹ As Jesus went on a little farther, he saw James and John, the sons of Zebedee. They were in a boat preparing their nets ⸢to go fishing⸣. ²⁰ He immediately called them, and they left their father Zebedee and the hired men in the boat and followed Jesus.

Jesus Forces an Evil Spirit out of a Man—*Luke 4:31–37*

²¹ Then they went to Capernaum. On the next day of worship, Jesus went into the synagogue and began to teach. ²² The people were amazed at his teachings. Unlike their scribes, he taught them with authority.

²³ At that time there was a man in the synagogue who was controlled by an evil spirit. He shouted, ²⁴ "What do you want with us, Jesus from Nazareth? Have you come to destroy us? I know who you are—the Holy One of God!"

²⁵ Jesus ordered the spirit, "Keep quiet, and come out of him!" ²⁶ The evil spirit threw the man into convulsions and came out of him with a loud shriek.

²⁷ Everyone was stunned. They said to each other, "What is this? This is a new teaching that has authority behind it! He gives orders to evil spirits, and they obey him."

²⁸ The news about him spread quickly throughout the surrounding region of Galilee.

---

[a] 1:4 "Repentance" is turning to God with a complete change in the way a person thinks and acts.

Jesus Cures Simon's Mother-in-Law and Many Others—*Matthew 8:14–18; Luke 4:38–41*

²⁹ After they left the synagogue, they went directly to the house of Simon and Andrew. James and John went with them. ³⁰ Simon's mother-in-law was in bed with a fever. The first thing they did was to tell Jesus about her. ³¹ Jesus went to her, took her hand, and helped her get up. The fever went away, and she prepared a meal for them.

³² In the evening, when the sun had set, people brought to him everyone who was sick and those possessed by demons. ³³ The whole city had gathered at his door. ³⁴ He cured many who were sick with various diseases and forced many demons out of people. However, he would not allow the demons to speak. After all, they knew who he was.

Spreading the Good News in Galilee—*Matthew 4:23–25; Luke 4:42–44*

³⁵ In the morning, long before sunrise, Jesus went to a place where he could be alone to pray. ³⁶ Simon and his friends searched for him. ³⁷ When they found him, they told him, "Everyone is looking for you."

³⁸ Jesus said to them, "Let's go somewhere else, to the small towns that are nearby. I have to spread ˎthe Good Newsˏ in them also. This is why I have come."

³⁹ So he went to spread ˎthe Good Newsˏ in the synagogues all over Galilee, and he forced demons out of people.

Jesus Cures a Man With a Skin Disease—*Matthew 8:1–4; Luke 5:12–14*

⁴⁰ Then a man with a serious skin disease came to him. The man fell to his knees and begged Jesus, "If you're willing, you can make me clean."ᵇ

⁴¹ Jesus felt sorry for him, reached out, touched him, and said, "I'm willing. So be clean!"

⁴² Immediately, his skin disease went away, and he was clean.

⁴³ Jesus sent him away at once and warned him, ⁴⁴ "Don't tell anyone about this! Instead, show yourself to the priest. Then offer the sacrifices which Moses commanded as proof to people that you are clean."

⁴⁵ When the man left, he began to talk freely. He spread his story so widely that Jesus could no longer enter any city openly. Instead, he stayed in places where he could be alone. But people still kept coming to him from everywhere.

Jesus Forgives Sins—*Matthew 9:1–8; Luke 5:17–26*

2 ¹ Several days later Jesus came back to Capernaum. The report went out that he was home. ² Many people had gathered. There was no room left, even in front of the door. Jesus was speaking ˎGod'sˏ word to them.

³ Four men came to him carrying a paralyzed man. ⁴ Since they could not bring him to Jesus because of the crowd, they made an opening in the roof over the place where Jesus was. Then they lowered the cot on which the paralyzed man was lying.

⁵ When Jesus saw their faith, he said to the man, "Friend, your sins are forgiven."

⁶ Some scribes were sitting there. They thought, ⁷ "Why does he talk this way? He's dishonoring God. Who besides God can forgive sins?"

⁸ At once, Jesus knew inwardly what they were thinking. He asked them, "Why do you have these thoughts? ⁹ Is it easier to say to this paralyzed man, 'Your sins are forgiven,' or to say, 'Get up, pick up your cot, and walk'? ¹⁰ I want you to know that the Son of Man has authority on earth to forgive sins." Then he said to the paralyzed man, ¹¹ "I'm telling you to get up, pick up your cot, and go home!"

¹² The man got up, immediately picked up his cot, and walked away while everyone watched. Everyone was amazed and praised God, saying, "We have never seen anything like this."

Jesus Chooses Levi [Matthew] to Be a Disciple—*Matthew 9:9–13; Luke 5:27–32*

¹³ Jesus went to the seashore again. Large crowds came to him, and he taught them.

¹⁴ When Jesus was leaving, he saw Levi, son of Alphaeus, sitting in a tax office. Jesus said to him, "Follow me!" So Levi got up and followed him.

¹⁵ Later Jesus was having dinner at Levi's house. Many tax collectors and sinners who were followers of Jesus were eating with him and his disciples. ¹⁶ When the scribes who were Pharisees saw him eating with sinners and tax collectors, they asked his disciples, "Why does he eat with tax collectors and sinners?"

¹⁷ When Jesus heard that, he said to them, "Healthy people don't need a doctor; those who are sick do. I've come to call sinners, not people who think they have God's approval."

Jesus Is Questioned About Fasting—*Matthew 9:14–17; Luke 5:33–39*

¹⁸ John's disciples and the Pharisees were fasting. Some people came to Jesus and said to him, "Why do John's disciples and the Pharisees' disciples fast, but your disciples don't?"

ᵇ 1:40 "Clean" refers to anything that Moses' Teachings say is presentable to God.

[19] Jesus replied, "Can wedding guests fast while the groom is still with them? As long as they have the groom with them, they cannot fast. [20] But the time will come when the groom will be taken away from them. Then they will fast.

[21] "No one patches an old coat with a new piece of cloth that will shrink. Otherwise, the new patch will shrink and rip away some of the old cloth, and the tear will become worse. [22] People don't pour new wine into old wineskins. If they do, the wine will make the skins burst, and both the wine and the skins will be ruined. Rather, new wine is to be poured into fresh skins."

Jesus Has Authority Over the Day of Worship—*Matthew 12:1–8; Luke 6:1–5*

[23] Once on a day of worship Jesus was going through the grainfields. As the disciples walked along, they began to pick the heads of grain.

[24] The Pharisees asked him, "Look! Why are your disciples doing something that is not permitted on the day of worship?"

[25] Jesus asked them, "Haven't you ever read what David did when he and his men were in need and were hungry? [26] Haven't you ever read how he went into the house of God when Abiathar was chief priest and ate the bread of the presence? He had no right to eat those loaves. Only the priests have that right. Haven't you ever read how he also gave some of it to his men?"

[27] Then he added, "The day of worship was made for people, not people for the day of worship. [28] For this reason the Son of Man has authority over the day of worship."

Jesus Heals on the Day of Worship—*Matthew 12:9–15a; Luke 6:6–11*

3 [1] Jesus went into a synagogue again. A man who had a paralyzed hand was there. [2] The people were watching Jesus closely. They wanted to see whether he would heal the man on the day of worship so that they could accuse him of doing something wrong.

[3] So he told the man with the paralyzed hand, "Stand in the center ˻of the synagogue˼."
[4] Then he asked them, "Is it right to do good or to do evil on the day of worship, to give a person back his health or to let him die?"

But they were silent. [5] Jesus was angry as he looked around at them. He was deeply hurt because their minds were closed. Then he told the man, "Hold out your hand." The man held it out, and his hand became normal again.

[6] The Pharisees left, and with Herod's followers they immediately plotted to kill Jesus.

Many People Are Cured—*Luke 6:17–19*

[7] Jesus left with his disciples for the Sea of Galilee. A large crowd from Galilee, Judea, [8] Jerusalem, Idumea, and from across the Jordan River, and from around Tyre and Sidon followed him. They came to him because they had heard about everything he was doing. [9] Jesus told his disciples to have a boat ready so that the crowd would not crush him. [10] He had cured so many that everyone with a disease rushed up to him in order to touch him. [11] Whenever people with evil spirits saw him, they would fall down in front of him and shout, "You are the Son of God!" [12] He gave them orders not to tell people who he was.

Jesus Appoints Twelve Apostles—*Matthew 10:1–4; Luke 6:13–16*

[13] Jesus went up a mountain, called those whom he wanted, and they came to him. [14] He appointed twelve whom he called apostles.[a] They were to accompany him and to be sent out by him to spread ˻the Good News˼. [15] They also had the authority to force demons out of people.

[16] He appointed these twelve: Simon (whom Jesus named Peter), [17] James and his brother John (Zebedee's sons whom Jesus named Boanerges, which means "Thunderbolts"), [18] Andrew, Philip, Bartholomew, Matthew, Thomas, James (son of Alphaeus), Thaddaeus, Simon the Zealot, [19] and Judas Iscariot (who later betrayed Jesus).

Jesus Is Accused of Working With Beelzebul—*Matthew 12:22–32; Luke 11:14–23*

[20] Then Jesus went home. Another crowd gathered so that Jesus and his disciples could not even eat. [21] When his family heard about it, they went to get him. They said, "He's out of his mind!"

[22] The scribes who had come from Jerusalem said, "Beelzebul is in him," and "He forces demons out of people with the help of the ruler of demons."

[23] Jesus called them together and used this illustration: "How can Satan force out Satan? [24] If a kingdom is divided against itself, that kingdom cannot last. [25] And if a household is divided against itself, that household will not last. [26] So if Satan rebels against himself and is divided, he cannot last. That will be the end of him.

[27] "No one can go into a strong man's house and steal his property. First he must tie up the strong man. Then he can go through the strong man's house and steal his property.

---

[a] 3:14 Some manuscripts and translations omit "whom he called apostles."

²⁸ "I can guarantee this truth: People will be forgiven for any sin or curse. ²⁹ But whoever curses the Holy Spirit will never be forgiven. He is guilty of an everlasting sin." ³⁰ Jesus said this because the scribes had said that he had an evil spirit.

The True Family of Jesus—*Matthew 12:46–50; Luke 8:19–21*

³¹ Then his mother and his brothers arrived. They stood outside and sent someone to ask him to come out. ³² The crowd sitting around Jesus told him, "Your mother and your brothers are outside looking for you."

³³ He replied to them, "Who is my mother, and who are my brothers?" ³⁴ Then looking at those who sat in a circle around him, he said, "Look, here are my mother and my brothers. ³⁵ Whoever does what God wants is my brother and sister and mother."

A Story About a Farmer—*Matthew 13:1–23; Luke 8:4–15*

4 ¹ Jesus began to teach again by the Sea of Galilee. A very large crowd gathered around him, so he got into a boat and sat in it. The boat was in the water while the entire crowd lined the shore. ² He used stories as illustrations to teach them many things.

While he was teaching them, he said, ³ "Listen! A farmer went to plant seed. ⁴ Some seeds were planted along the road, and birds came and devoured them. ⁵ Other seeds were planted on rocky ground, where there wasn't much soil. The plants sprouted quickly because the soil wasn't deep. ⁶ When the sun came up, they were scorched. They didn't have any roots, so they withered. ⁷ Other seeds were planted among thornbushes. The thornbushes grew up and choked them, and they didn't produce anything. ⁸ But other seeds were planted on good ground, sprouted, and produced thirty, sixty, or one hundred times as much as was planted." ⁹ He added, "Let the person who has ears listen!"

¹⁰ When he was alone with his followers and the twelve apostles, they asked him about the stories.

¹¹ Jesus replied to them, "The mystery about the kingdom of God has been given ˪directly˺ to you. To those on the outside, it is given in stories:

¹²   'They see clearly but don't perceive.
      They hear clearly but don't understand.
      They never return to me
        and are never forgiven.' "

¹³ Jesus asked them, "Don't you understand this story? How, then, will you understand any of the stories I use as illustrations?

¹⁴ "The farmer plants the word. ¹⁵ Some people are like seeds that were planted along the road. Whenever they hear the word, Satan comes at once and takes away the word that was planted in them. ¹⁶ Other people are like seeds that were planted on rocky ground. Whenever they hear the word, they accept it at once with joy. ¹⁷ But they don't develop any roots. They last for a short time. When suffering or persecution comes along because of the word, they immediately fall ˪from faith˺. ¹⁸ Other people are like seeds planted among thornbushes. They hear the word, ¹⁹ but the worries of life, the deceitful pleasures of riches, and the desires for other things take over. They choke the word so that it can't produce anything. ²⁰ Others are like seeds planted on good ground. They hear the word, accept it, and produce crops—thirty, sixty, or one hundred times as much as was planted."

A Story About a Lamp

²¹ Jesus said to them, "Does anyone bring a lamp into a room to put it under a basket or under a bed? Isn't it put on a lamp stand? ²² There is nothing hidden that will not be revealed. There is nothing kept secret that will not come to light. ²³ Let the person who has ears listen!"

²⁴ He went on to say, "Pay attention to what you're listening to! ˪Knowledge˺ will be measured out to you by the measure ˪of attention˺ you give. This is the way knowledge increases. ²⁵ Those who understand ˪these mysteries˺ will be given ˪more knowledge˺. However, some people don't understand ˪these mysteries˺. Even what they understand will be taken away from them."

A Story About Seeds That Grow

²⁶ Jesus said, "The kingdom of God is like a man who scatters seeds on the ground. ²⁷ He sleeps at night and is awake during the day. The seeds sprout and grow, although the man doesn't know how. ²⁸ The ground produces grain by itself. First the green blade appears, then the head, then the head full of grain. ²⁹ As soon as the grain is ready, he cuts it with a sickle, because harvest time has come."

A Story About a Mustard Seed—Matthew 13:31–32; Luke 13:18–19

[30] Jesus asked, "How can we show what the kingdom of God is like? To what can we compare it? [31] It's like a mustard seed planted in the ground. The mustard seed is one of the smallest seeds on earth. [32] However, when planted, it comes up and becomes taller than all the garden plants. It grows such large branches that birds can nest in its shade."

[33] Jesus spoke ˌGod'sˌ word to them using many illustrations like these. In this way people could understand what he taught. [34] He did not speak to them without using an illustration. But when he was alone with his disciples, he explained everything to them.

Jesus Calms the Sea—Matthew 8:23–27; Luke 8:22–25

[35] That evening, Jesus said to his disciples, "Let's cross to the other side."

[36] Leaving the crowd, they took Jesus along in a boat just as he was. Other boats were with him.

[37] A violent windstorm came up. The waves were breaking into the boat so that it was quickly filling up. [38] But he was sleeping on a cushion in the back of the boat.

So they woke him up and said to him, "Teacher, don't you care that we're going to die?"

[39] Then he got up, ordered the wind to stop, and said to the sea, "Be still, absolutely still!" The wind stopped blowing, and the sea became very calm.

[40] He asked them, "Why are you such cowards? Don't you have any faith yet?"

[41] They were overcome with fear and asked each other, "Who is this man? Even the wind and the sea obey him!"

Jesus Cures a Demon-Possessed Man—Matthew 8:28–34; Luke 8:26–39

5 [1] They arrived in the territory of the Gerasenes on the other side of the Sea of Galilee. [2] As Jesus stepped out of the boat, a man came out of the tombs and met him. The man was controlled by an evil spirit [3] and lived among the tombs. No one could restrain him any longer, not even with a chain. [4] He had often been chained hand and foot. However, he snapped the chains off his hands and broke the chains from his feet. No one could control him. [5] Night and day he was among the tombs and on the mountainsides screaming and cutting himself with stones.

[6] The man saw Jesus at a distance. So he ran ˌto Jesusˌ, bowed down in front of him, [7] and shouted, "Why are you bothering me now, Jesus, Son of the Most High God? Swear to God that you won't torture me." [8] He shouted this because Jesus said, "You evil spirit, come out of the man."

[9] Jesus asked him, "What is your name?"

He told Jesus, "My name is Legion [Six Thousand], because there are many of us." [10] He begged Jesus not to send them out of the territory.

[11] A large herd of pigs was feeding on a mountainside nearby. [12] The demons begged him, "Send us into the pigs! Let us enter them!"

[13] Jesus let them do this. The evil spirits came out of the man and went into the pigs. The herd of about two thousand pigs rushed down the cliff into the sea and drowned.

[14] Those who took care of the pigs ran away. In the city and countryside they reported everything that had happened. So the people came to see what had happened. [15] They came to Jesus and saw the man who had been possessed by the legion of demons. The man was sitting there dressed and in his right mind. The people were frightened. [16] Those who saw this told what had happened to the demon-possessed man and the pigs. [17] Then the people began to beg Jesus to leave their territory.

[18] As Jesus stepped into the boat, the man who had been demon-possessed begged him, "Let me stay with you." [19] But Jesus would not allow it. Instead, he told the man, "Go home to your family, and tell them how much the Lord has done for you and how merciful he has been to you."

[20] So the man left. He began to tell how much Jesus had done for him in the Ten Cities.[a] Everyone was amazed.

Jairus' Daughter and a Woman With Chronic Bleeding—Matthew 9:18–26; Luke 8:40–56

[21] Jesus again crossed to the other side of the Sea of Galilee in a boat. A large crowd gathered around him by the seashore.

[22] A synagogue leader named Jairus also arrived. When he saw Jesus, he quickly bowed down in front of him. [23] He begged Jesus, "My little daughter is dying. Come, lay your hands on her so that she may get well and live."

[24] Jesus went with the man. A huge crowd followed Jesus and pressed him on every side.

[25] In the crowd was a woman who had been suffering from chronic bleeding for twelve years. [26] Although she had been under the care of many doctors and had spent all her money, she had

---

[a] 5:20 A federation of ten Greek city states east and west of the Jordan River.

not been helped at all. Actually, she had become worse. [27] Since she had heard about Jesus, she came from behind in the crowd and touched his clothes. [28] She said, "If I can just touch his clothes, I'll get well." [29] Her bleeding stopped immediately. She felt cured from her illness.

[30] At that moment Jesus felt power had gone out of him. He turned around in the crowd and asked, "Who touched my clothes?"

[31] His disciples said to him, "How can you ask, 'Who touched me,' when you see the crowd pressing you on all sides?"

[32] But he kept looking around to see the woman who had done this. [33] The woman trembled with fear. She knew what had happened to her. So she quickly bowed in front of him and told him the whole truth.

[34] Jesus told her, "Daughter, your faith has made you well. Go in peace! Be cured from your illness."

[35] While Jesus was still speaking to her, some people came from the synagogue leader's home. They told the synagogue leader, "Your daughter has died. Why bother the teacher anymore?"

[36] When Jesus overheard what they said, he told the synagogue leader, "Don't be afraid! Just believe."

[37] Jesus allowed no one to go with him except Peter and the two brothers James and John. [38] When they came to the home of the synagogue leader, Jesus saw a noisy crowd there. People were crying and sobbing loudly. [39] When he came into the house, he asked them, "Why are you making so much noise and crying? The child isn't dead. She's just sleeping."

[40] They laughed at him. So he made all of them go outside. Then he took the child's father, mother, and his three disciples and went to the child. [41] Jesus took the child's hand and said to her, "Talitha, koum!" which means, "Little girl, I'm telling you to get up!"

[42] The girl got up at once and started to walk. (She was twelve years old.) They were astonished.

[43] Jesus ordered them not to let anyone know about this. He also told them to give the little girl something to eat.

Nazareth Rejects Jesus—*Matthew 13:54–58; Luke 4:14–30*

6 [1] Jesus left that place and went to his hometown. His disciples followed him. [2] When the day of worship came, he began to teach in the synagogue. He amazed many who heard him. They asked, "Where did this man get these ideas? Who gave him this kind of wisdom and the ability to do such great miracles? [3] Isn't this the carpenter, the son of Mary, and the brother of James, Joseph, Judas, and Simon? Aren't his sisters here with us?" So they took offense at him.

[4] But Jesus told them, "The only place a prophet isn't honored is in his hometown, among his relatives, and in his own house." [5] He couldn't work any miracles there except to lay his hands on a few sick people and cure them. [6] Their unbelief amazed him.

Jesus Sends Out the Twelve—*Matthew 10:5–42; Luke 9:1–6*

Then Jesus went around to the villages and taught.

[7] He called the twelve apostles, sent them out two by two, and gave them authority over evil spirits. [8] He instructed them to take nothing along on the trip except a walking stick. They were not to take any food, a traveling bag, or money in their pockets. [9] They could wear sandals but could not take along a change of clothes.

[10] He told them, "Whenever you go into a home, stay there until you're ready to leave that place. [11] Wherever people don't welcome you or listen to you, leave and shake the dust from your feet as a warning to them."

[12] So the apostles went and told people that they should turn to God and change the way they think and act. [13] They also forced many demons out of people and poured oil on many who were sick to cure them.

Recalling John's Death—*Matthew 14:1–12; Luke 9:7–9*

[14] King Herod heard about Jesus, because Jesus' name had become well-known. Some people were saying, "John the Baptizer has come back to life. That's why he has the power to perform these miracles." [15] Others said, "He is Elijah." Still others said, "He is a prophet like one of the other prophets." [16] But when Herod heard about it, he said, "I had John's head cut off, and he has come back to life!"

[17] Herod had sent men who had arrested John, tied him up, and put him in prison. Herod did that for Herodias, whom he had married. (She used to be his brother Philip's wife.) [18] John had been telling Herod, "It's not right for you to be married to your brother's wife."

[19] So Herodias held a grudge against John and wanted to kill him. But she wasn't allowed to do it [20] because Herod was afraid of John. Herod knew that John was a fair and holy man, so

he protected him. When he listened to John, he would become very disturbed, and yet he liked to listen to him.

[21] An opportunity finally came on Herod's birthday. Herod gave a dinner for his top officials, army officers, and the most important people of Galilee. [22] His daughter, that is, Herodias' daughter, came in and danced. Herod and his guests were delighted with her. The king told the girl, "Ask me for anything you want, and I'll give it to you." [23] He swore an oath to her: "I'll give you anything you ask for, up to half of my kingdom."

[24] So she went out and asked her mother, "What should I ask for?"

Her mother said, "Ask for the head of John the Baptizer."

[25] So the girl hurried back to the king with her request. She said, "I want you to give me the head of John the Baptizer on a platter at once."

[26] The king deeply regretted his promise. But because of his oath and his guests, he didn't want to refuse her. [27] Immediately, the king sent a guard and ordered him to bring John's head. The guard cut off John's head in prison. [28] Then he brought the head on a platter and gave it to the girl, and the girl gave it to her mother.

[29] When John's disciples heard about this, they came for his body and laid it in a tomb.

Jesus Feeds Five Thousand—Matthew 14:13–21; Luke 9:10–17; John 6:1–14

[30] The apostles gathered around Jesus. They reported to him everything they had done and taught. [31] So he said to them, "Let's go to a place where we can be alone to rest for a while." Many people were coming and going, and Jesus and the apostles didn't even have a chance to eat.

[32] So they went away in a boat to a place where they could be alone. [33] But many people saw them leave and recognized them. The people ran from all the cities and arrived ahead of them. [34] When Jesus got out of the boat, he saw a large crowd and felt sorry for them. They were like sheep without a shepherd. So he spent a lot of time teaching them.

[35] When it was late, his disciples came to him. They said, "No one lives around here, and it's already late. [36] Send the people to the closest farms and villages to buy themselves something to eat."

[37] Jesus replied, "You give them something to eat."

They said to him, "Should we go and spend about a year's wages on bread to feed them?"

[38] He said to them, "How many loaves do you have? Go and see."

When they found out, they told him, "Five loaves of bread and two fish."

[39] Then he ordered all of them to sit down in groups on the green grass. [40] They sat down in groups of hundreds and fifties.

[41] After he took the five loaves and the two fish, he looked up to heaven and blessed the food. He broke the loaves apart and kept giving them to the disciples to give to the people. He also gave pieces of the two fish to everyone. [42] All of them ate as much as they wanted. [43] When they picked up the leftover pieces, they filled twelve baskets with bread and fish. [44] There were 5,000 men who had eaten the bread.

Jesus Walks on the Sea—Matthew 14:22–36; John 6:15–21

[45] Jesus quickly made his disciples get into a boat and cross to Bethsaida ahead of him while he sent the people away. [46] After saying goodbye to them, he went up a mountain to pray. [47] When evening came, the boat was in the middle of the sea, and he was alone on the land. [48] Jesus saw that they were in a lot of trouble as they rowed, because they were going against the wind. Between three and six o'clock in the morning, he came to them. He was walking on the sea. He wanted to pass by them. [49] When they saw him walking on the sea, they thought, "It's a ghost!" and they began to scream. [50] All of them saw him and were terrified.

Immediately, he said, "Calm down! It's me. Don't be afraid!" [51] He got into the boat with them, and the wind stopped blowing. The disciples were astounded. [52] (They didn't understand what had happened with the loaves of bread. Instead, their minds were closed.)

[53] They crossed the sea, came to shore at Gennesaret, and anchored there.

[54] As soon as they stepped out of the boat, the people recognized Jesus. [55] They ran all over the countryside and began to carry the sick on cots to any place where they heard he was. [56] Whenever he would go into villages, cities, or farms, people would put their sick in the marketplaces. They begged him to let them touch the edge of his clothes. Everyone who touched his clothes was made well.

Jesus Challenges the Pharisees' Traditions—Matthew 15:1–20

7 [1] The Pharisees and some scribes who had come from Jerusalem gathered around Jesus. [2] They saw that some of his disciples were unclean[a] because they ate without washing their hands.

---

[a] 7:2 "Unclean" refers to anything that Moses' Teachings say is not presentable to God.

³ (The Pharisees, like all other Jewish people, don't eat unless they have properly washed their hands. They follow the traditions of their ancestors. ⁴ When they come from the market-place, they don't eat unless they have washed first. They have been taught to follow many other rules. For example, they must also wash their cups, jars, brass pots, and dinner tables.ᵇ)

⁵ The Pharisees and the scribes asked Jesus, "Why don't your disciples follow the traditions taught by our ancestors? They are unclean because they don't wash their hands before they eat!"

⁶ Jesus told them, "Isaiah was right when he prophesied about you hypocrites in Scripture:

'These people honor me with their lips,
  but their hearts are far from me.
⁷   Their worship of me is pointless,
  because their teachings are rules made by humans.'

⁸ "You abandon the commandments of God to follow human traditions." ⁹ He added, "You have no trouble rejecting the commandments of God in order to keep your own traditions! ¹⁰ For example, Moses said, 'Honor your father and your mother' and 'Whoever curses father or mother must be put to death.' ¹¹ But you say, 'If a person tells his father or mother that what-ever he might have used to help them is *corban* (that is, an offering to God), ¹² he no longer has to do anything for his father or mother.' ¹³ Because of your traditions you have destroyed the authority of God's word. And you do many other things like that."

¹⁴ Then he called the crowd again and said to them, "Listen to me, all of you, and try to understand! ¹⁵ Nothing that goes into a person from the outside can make him unclean. It's what comes out of a person that makes him unclean. ¹⁶ Let the person who has ears listen!"ᶜ

¹⁷ When he had left the people and gone home, his disciples asked him about this illustration. ¹⁸ Jesus said to them, "Don't you understand? Don't you know that whatever goes into a per-son from the outside can't make him unclean? ¹⁹ It doesn't go into his thoughts but into his stomach and then into a toilet." (By saying this, Jesus declared all foods acceptable.) ²⁰ He con-tinued, "It's what comes out of a person that makes him unclean. ²¹ Evil thoughts, sexual sins, stealing, murder, ²² adultery, greed, wickedness, cheating, shameless lust, envy, cursing, arro-gance, and foolishness come from within a person. ²³ All these evils come from within and make a person unclean."

The Faith of a Greek Woman—*Matthew 15:21–31*

²⁴ Jesus left that place and went to the territory of Tyre. He didn't want anyone to know that he was staying in a house there. However, it couldn't be kept a secret.

²⁵ A woman whose little daughter had an evil spirit heard about Jesus. She went to him and bowed down. ²⁶ The woman happened to be Greek, born in Phoenicia in Syria. She asked him to force the demon out of her daughter.

²⁷ Jesus said to her, "First, let the children eat all they want. It's not right to take the chil-dren's food and throw it to the dogs."

²⁸ She answered him, "Lord, even the dogs under the table eat some of the children's scraps."

²⁹ Jesus said to her, "Because you have said this, go! The demon has left your daughter."

³⁰ The woman went home and found the little child lying on her bed, and the demon was gone.

Jesus Cures a Deaf Man

³¹ Jesus then left the neighborhood of Tyre. He went through Sidon and the territory of the Ten Citiesᵈ to the Sea of Galilee.

³² Some people brought to him a man who was deaf and who also had a speech defect. They begged Jesus to lay his hand on him. ³³ Jesus took him away from the crowd to be alone with him. He put his fingers into the man's ears, and after spitting, he touched the man's tongue. ³⁴ Then he looked up to heaven, sighed, and said to the man, "Ephphatha!" which means, "Be opened!" ³⁵ At once the man could hear and talk normally.

³⁶ Jesus ordered the people not to tell anyone. But the more he ordered them, the more they spread the news. ³⁷ Jesus completely amazed the people. They said, "He has done everything well. He makes the deaf hear and the mute talk."

Jesus Feeds Four Thousand—*Matthew 15:32–39*

8 ¹ About that time there was once again a large crowd with nothing to eat. Jesus called his disciples and said to them, ² "I feel sorry for the people. They have been with me three days now and have nothing to eat. ³ If I send them home before they've eaten, they will become exhausted on the road. Some of them have come a long distance."

ᵇ 7:4 Some manuscripts and translations omit "and dinner tables."   ᶜ 7:16 Some manuscripts and translations omit this verse.   ᵈ 7:31 A federation of ten Greek city states east and west of the Jordan River.

⁴ His disciples asked him, "Where could anyone get enough bread to feed these people in this place where no one lives?"

⁵ Jesus asked them, "How many loaves of bread do you have?"

They answered, "Seven."

⁶ He ordered the crowd to sit down on the ground. He took the seven loaves and gave thanks to God. Then he broke the bread and gave it to his disciples to serve to the people. ⁷ They also had a few small fish. He blessed them and said that the fish should also be served to the people. ⁸ The people ate as much as they wanted. The disciples picked up the leftover pieces and filled seven large baskets. ⁹ About four thousand people were there. Then he sent the people on their way.

¹⁰ After that, Jesus and his disciples got into a boat and went into the region of Dalmanutha.

The Pharisees Ask For a Sign From Heaven—Matthew 16:1–4

¹¹ The Pharisees went to Jesus and began to argue with him. They tested him by demanding that he perform a miraculous sign from heaven.

¹² With a deep sigh he asked, "Why do these people demand a sign? I can guarantee this truth: If these people are given a sign, it will be far different than what they want!"

¹³ Then he left them there.

The Yeast of the Pharisees—Matthew 16:5–12

He got into a boat again and crossed to the other side of the Sea of Galilee. ¹⁴ The disciples had forgotten to take any bread along and had only one loaf with them in the boat.

¹⁵ Jesus warned them, "Be careful! Watch out for the yeast of the Pharisees and the yeast of Herod!"

¹⁶ They had been discussing with one another that they didn't have any bread.

¹⁷ Jesus knew what they were saying and asked them, "Why are you discussing the fact that you don't have any bread? Don't you understand yet? Don't you catch on? Are your minds closed? ¹⁸ Are you blind and deaf? Don't you remember? ¹⁹ When I broke the five loaves for the five thousand, how many baskets did you fill with leftover pieces?"

They told him, "Twelve."

²⁰ "When I broke the seven loaves for the four thousand, how many large baskets did you fill with leftover pieces?"

They answered him, "Seven."

²¹ He asked them, "Don't you catch on yet?"

Jesus Gives Sight to a Blind Man

²² As they came to Bethsaida, some people brought a blind man to Jesus. They begged Jesus to touch him. ²³ Jesus took the blind man's hand and led him out of the village. He spit into the man's eyes and placed his hands on him. Jesus asked him, "Can you see anything?"

²⁴ The man looked up and said, "I see people. They look like trees walking around."

²⁵ Then Jesus placed his hands on the man's eyes a second time, and the man saw clearly. His sight was normal again. He could see everything clearly even at a distance. ²⁶ Jesus told him when he sent him home, "Don't go into the village."

Peter Declares His Belief About Jesus—Matthew 16:13–20; Luke 9:18–21

²⁷ Then Jesus and his disciples went to the villages around Caesarea Philippi. On the way he asked his disciples, "Who do people say I am?"

²⁸ They answered him, "Some say you are John the Baptizer, others Elijah, still others one of the prophets."

²⁹ He asked them, "But who do you say I am?"

Peter answered him, "You are the Messiah!"

³⁰ He ordered them not to tell anyone about him.

Jesus Foretells That He Will Die and Come Back to Life—Matthew 16:21–23; Luke 9:22

³¹ Then he began to teach them that the Son of Man would have to suffer a lot. He taught them that he would be rejected by the leaders, the chief priests, and the scribes. He would be killed, but after three days he would come back to life. ³² He told them very clearly what he meant.

Peter took him aside and objected to this. ³³ Jesus turned, looked at his disciples, and objected to what Peter said. Jesus said, "Get out of my way, Satan! You aren't thinking the way God thinks but the way humans think."

What It Means to Follow Jesus—Matthew 16:24–28; Luke 9:23–27

³⁴ Then Jesus called the crowd to himself along with his disciples. He said to them, "Those who want to follow me must say no to the things they want, pick up their crosses, and follow

me. [35] Those who want to save their lives will lose them. But those who lose their lives for me and for the Good News will save them. [36] What good does it do for people to win the whole world yet lose their lives? [37] Or what should a person give in exchange for life? [38] If people are ashamed of me and what I say in this unfaithful and sinful generation, the Son of Man will be ashamed of those people when he comes with the holy angels in his Father's glory."

9 [1] He said to them, "I can guarantee this truth: Some people who are standing here will not die until they see the kingdom of God arrive with power."

Moses and Elijah Appear With Jesus—*Matthew 17:1–8; Luke 9:28–36*

[2] After six days Jesus took only Peter, James, and John and led them up a high mountain where they could be alone.

Jesus' appearance changed in front of them. [3] His clothes became dazzling white, whiter than anyone on earth could bleach them. [4] Then Elijah and Moses appeared to them and were talking with Jesus.

[5] Peter said to Jesus, "Rabbi, it's good that we're here. Let's put up three tents—one for you, one for Moses, and one for Elijah." [6] (Peter didn't know how to respond. He and the others were terrified.)

[7] Then a cloud overshadowed them. A voice came out of the cloud and said, "This is my Son, whom I love. Listen to him!"

[8] Suddenly, as they looked around, they saw no one with them but Jesus.

[9] On their way down the mountain, Jesus ordered them not to tell anyone what they had seen. They were to wait until the Son of Man had come back to life. [10] They kept in mind what he said but argued among themselves what he meant by "come back to life." [11] So they asked him, "Don't the scribes say that Elijah must come first?"

[12] Jesus said to them, "Elijah is coming first and will put everything in order again. But in what sense was it written that the Son of Man must suffer a lot and be treated shamefully? [13] Indeed, I can guarantee that Elijah has come. Yet, people treated him as they pleased, as Scripture says about him."

Jesus Cures a Demon-Possessed Boy—*Matthew 17:14–20; Luke 9:37–43a*

[14] When they came to the other disciples, they saw a large crowd around them. Some scribes were arguing with them. [15] All the people were very surprised to see Jesus and ran to welcome him.

[16] Jesus asked the scribes, "What are you arguing about with them?"

[17] A man in the crowd answered, "Teacher, I brought you my son. He is possessed by a spirit that won't let him talk. [18] Whenever the spirit brings on a seizure, it throws him to the ground. Then he foams at the mouth, grinds his teeth, and becomes exhausted. I asked your disciples to force the spirit out, but they didn't have the power to do it."

[19] Jesus said to them, "You unbelieving generation! How long must I be with you? How long must I put up with you? Bring him to me!"

[20] They brought the boy to him. As soon as the spirit saw Jesus, it threw the boy into convulsions. He fell on the ground, rolled around, and foamed at the mouth.

[21] Jesus asked his father, "How long has he been like this?"

The father replied, "He has been this way since he was a child. [22] The demon has often thrown him into fire or into water to destroy him. If it's possible for you, put yourself in our place, and help us!"

[23] Jesus said to him, "As far as possibilities go, everything is possible for the person who believes."

[24] The child's father cried out at once, "I believe! Help my lack of faith."

[25] When Jesus saw that a crowd was running to the scene, he gave an order to the evil spirit. He said, "You spirit that won't let him talk, I command you to come out of him and never enter him again."

[26] The evil spirit screamed, shook the child violently, and came out. The boy looked as if he were dead, and everyone said, "He's dead!"

[27] Jesus took his hand and helped him to stand up.

[28] When Jesus went into a house, his disciples asked him privately, "Why couldn't we force the spirit out of the boy?"

[29] He told them, "This kind of spirit can be forced out only by prayer."[a]

Jesus Again Foretells That He Will Die and Come Back to Life—*Matthew 17:22–23; Luke 9:43b–45*

[30] They left that place and were passing through Galilee. Jesus did not want anyone to know where he was [31] because he was teaching his disciples. He taught them, "The Son of Man will

---

[a] 9:29 Some manuscripts and translations add "and fasting."

be betrayed and handed over to people. They will kill him, but on the third day he will come back to life."

³² The disciples didn't understand what he meant and were afraid to ask him.

Greatness in the Kingdom—*Matthew 18:1–5; Luke 9:46–48*

³³ Then they came to Capernaum. While Jesus was at home, he asked the disciples, "What were you arguing about on the road?" ³⁴ They were silent. On the road they had argued about who was the greatest.

³⁵ He sat down and called the twelve apostles. He told them, "Whoever wants to be the most important person must take the last place and be a servant to everyone else." ³⁶ Then he took a little child and had him stand among them. He put his arms around the child and said to them, ³⁷ "Whoever welcomes a child like this in my name welcomes me. Whoever welcomes me welcomes not me but the one who sent me."

Using the Name of Jesus—*Luke 9:49–50*

³⁸ John said to Jesus, "Teacher, we saw someone forcing demons out of a person by using the power and authority of your name. We tried to stop him because he was not one of us."

³⁹ Jesus said, "Don't stop him! No one who works a miracle in my name can turn around and speak evil of me. ⁴⁰ Whoever isn't against us is for us. ⁴¹ I can guarantee this truth: Whoever gives you a cup of water to drink because you belong to Christ will certainly not lose his reward."

Causing Others to Lose Faith—*Matthew 18:6–10; Luke 17:1–4*

⁴² "These little ones believe in me. It would be best for the person who causes one of them to lose faith to be thrown into the sea with a large stone hung around his neck.

⁴³ "So if your hand causes you to lose your faith, cut it off! It is better for you to enter life disabled than to have two hands and go to hell, to the fire that cannot be put out.^b ⁴⁵ If your foot causes you to lose your faith, cut it off! It is better for you to enter life lame than to have two feet and be thrown into hell. ⁴⁷ If your eye causes you to lose your faith, tear it out! It is better for you to enter the kingdom of God with one eye than to have two eyes and be thrown into hell. ⁴⁸ In hell worms that eat the body never die, and the fire is never put out. ⁴⁹ Everyone will be salted with fire. ⁵⁰ Salt is good. But if salt loses its taste, how will you restore its flavor? Have salt within you, and live in peace with one another."

A Discussion About Divorce—*Matthew 19:1–12*

10 ¹ Jesus left there and went into the territory of Judea along the other side of the Jordan River. Crowds gathered around him again, and he taught them as he usually did.

² Some Pharisees came to test him. They asked, "Can a husband divorce his wife?"

³ Jesus answered them, "What command did Moses give you?"

⁴ They said, "Moses allowed a man to give his wife a written notice to divorce her."

⁵ Jesus said to them, "He wrote this command for you because you're heartless. ⁶ But God made them male and female in the beginning, at creation. ⁷ That's why a man will leave his father and mother and will remain united with his wife, ⁸ and the two will be one. So they are no longer two but one. ⁹ Therefore, don't let anyone separate what God has joined together."

¹⁰ When they were in a house, the disciples asked him about this. ¹¹ He answered them, "Whoever divorces his wife and marries another woman is committing adultery. ¹² If a wife divorces her husband and marries another man, she is committing adultery."

Jesus Blesses Children—*Matthew 19:13–15; Luke 18:15–17*

¹³ Some people brought little children to Jesus to have him hold them. But the disciples told the people not to do that.

¹⁴ When Jesus saw this, he became irritated. He told them, "Don't stop the children from coming to me. Children like these are part of the kingdom of God. ¹⁵ I can guarantee this truth: Whoever doesn't receive the kingdom of God as a little child receives it will never enter it."

¹⁶ Jesus put his arms around the children and blessed them by placing his hands on them.

Eternal Life in the Kingdom—*Matthew 19:16–30; Luke 18:18–30*

¹⁷ As Jesus was coming out to the road, a man came running to him and knelt in front of him. He asked Jesus, "Good Teacher, what should I do to inherit eternal life?"

¹⁸ Jesus said to him, "Why do you call me good? No one is good except God alone. ¹⁹ You know the commandments: Never murder. Never commit adultery. Never steal. Never give false testimony. Never cheat. Honor your father and mother."

²⁰ The man replied, "Teacher, I've obeyed all these commandments since I was a boy."

---

^b 9:43 Some manuscripts and translations add verses 44 and 46, which both say: "In hell worms that eat the body never die, and the fire is never put out."

²¹ Jesus looked at him and loved him. He told him, "You're still missing one thing. Sell everything you have. Give the money to the poor, and you will have treasure in heaven. Then follow me!"

²² When the man heard that, he looked unhappy and went away sad, because he owned a lot of property.

²³ Jesus looked around and said to his disciples, "How hard it will be for rich people to enter the kingdom of God!"

²⁴ The disciples were stunned by his words. But Jesus said to them again, "Children, how hard it is to enter the kingdom of God! ²⁵ It is easier for a camel to go through the eye of a needle than for a rich person to enter the kingdom of God."

²⁶ This amazed his disciples more than ever. They asked each other, "Who, then, can be saved?"

²⁷ Jesus looked at them and said, "It's impossible for people ˌto save themselvesˌ, but it's not impossible for God to save them. Everything is possible for God."

²⁸ Then Peter spoke up, "We've given up everything to follow you."

²⁹ Jesus said, "I can guarantee this truth: Anyone who gave up his home, brothers, sisters, mother, father, children, or fields because of me and the Good News ³⁰ will certainly receive a hundred times as much here in this life. They will certainly receive homes, brothers, sisters, mothers, children and fields, along with persecutions. But in the world to come they will receive eternal life. ³¹ But many who are first will be last, and the last will be first."

For the Third Time Jesus Foretells That He Will Die and Come Back to Life—
Matthew 20:17–19; Luke 18:31–34

³² Jesus and his disciples were on their way to Jerusalem. Jesus was walking ahead of them. His disciples were shocked ˌthat he was going to Jerusalemˌ. The others who followed were afraid. Once again he took the twelve apostles aside. He began to tell them what was going to happen to him. ³³ "We're going to Jerusalem. There the Son of Man will be betrayed to the chief priests and the scribes. They will condemn him to death and hand him over to foreigners. ³⁴ They will make fun of him, spit on him, whip him, and kill him. But after three days he will come back to life."

James and John Make a Request—Matthew 20:20–28

³⁵ James and John, sons of Zebedee, went to Jesus. They said to him, "Teacher, we want you to do us a favor."

³⁶ "What do you want me to do for you?" he asked them.

³⁷ They said to him, "Let one of us sit at your right and the other at your left in your glory."

³⁸ Jesus said, "You don't realize what you're asking. Can you drink the cup that I'm going to drink? Can you be baptized with the baptism that I'm going to receive?"

³⁹ "We can," they told him.

Jesus told them, "You will drink the cup that I'm going to drink. You will be baptized with the baptism that I'm going to receive. ⁴⁰ But I don't have the authority to grant you a seat at my right or left. Those positions have already been prepared for certain people."

⁴¹ When the other ten apostles heard about it, they were irritated with James and John. ⁴² Jesus called the apostles and said, "You know that the acknowledged rulers of nations have absolute power over people and their officials have absolute authority over people. ⁴³ But that's not the way it's going to be among you. Whoever wants to become great among you will be your servant. ⁴⁴ Whoever wants to be most important among you will be a slave for everyone. ⁴⁵ It's the same way with the Son of Man. He didn't come so that others could serve him. He came to serve and to give his life as a ransom for many people."

Jesus Gives Sight to Bartimaeus—Matthew 20:29–34; Luke 18:35–43

⁴⁶ Then they came to Jericho. As Jesus, his disciples, and many people were leaving Jericho, a blind beggar named Bartimaeus, son of Timaeus, was sitting by the road. ⁴⁷ When he heard that Jesus from Nazareth ˌwas passing byˌ, he began to shout, "Jesus, Son of David, have mercy on me!"

⁴⁸ The people told him to be quiet. But he shouted even louder, "Son of David, have mercy on me!"

⁴⁹ Jesus stopped and said, "Call him!" They called the blind man and told him, "Cheer up! Get up! He's calling you." ⁵⁰ The blind man threw off his coat, jumped up, and went to Jesus.

⁵¹ Jesus asked him, "What do you want me to do for you?"

The blind man said, "Teacher, I want to see again."

⁵² Jesus told him, "Go, your faith has made you well."

At once he could see again, and he followed Jesus on the road.

The King Comes to Jerusalem—*Matthew 21:1–11; Luke 19:29–44; John 12:12–19*

11 ¹ When they came near Jerusalem, to Bethphage and Bethany, at the Mount of Olives, Jesus sent two of his disciples ahead of him. ² He said to them, "Go into the village ahead of you. As you enter it, you will find a young donkey tied there. No one has ever sat on it. Untie it, and bring it. ³ If anyone asks you what you are doing, say that the Lord needs it. That person will send it here at once."

⁴ The disciples found the young donkey in the street. It was tied to the door of a house. As they were untying it, ⁵ some men standing there asked them, "Why are you untying that donkey?" ⁶ The disciples answered them as Jesus had told them. So the men let them go.

⁷ They brought the donkey to Jesus, put their coats on it, and he sat on it. ⁸ Many spread their coats on the road. Others cut leafy branches in the fields and spread them on the road. ⁹ Those who went ahead and those who followed him were shouting,

> "Hosanna!
> Blessed is the one who comes in the name of the Lord!
> ¹⁰ Blessed is our ancestor David's kingdom that is coming!
> Hosanna in the highest heaven!"

¹¹ Jesus came into Jerusalem and went into the temple courtyard, where he looked around at everything. Since it was already late, he went out with the twelve apostles to Bethany.

Jesus Curses the Fig Tree—*Matthew 21:18–19*

¹² The next day, when they left Bethany, Jesus became hungry. ¹³ In the distance he saw a fig tree with leaves. He went to see if he could find any figs on it. When he came to it, he found nothing but leaves because it wasn't the season for figs. ¹⁴ Then he said to the tree, "No one will ever eat fruit from you again!" His disciples heard this.

Jesus Throws Out the Moneychangers—*Matthew 21:12–17; Luke 19:45–48*

¹⁵ When they came to Jerusalem, Jesus went into the temple courtyard and began to throw out those who were buying and selling there. He overturned the moneychangers' tables and the chairs of those who sold pigeons. ¹⁶ He would not let anyone carry anything across the temple courtyard.

¹⁷ Then he taught them by saying, "Scripture says, 'My house will be called a house of prayer for all nations,' but you have turned it into a gathering place for thieves."

¹⁸ When the chief priests and scribes heard him, they looked for a way to kill him. They were afraid of him because he amazed all the crowds with his teaching.

¹⁹ (Every evening Jesus and his disciples would leave the city.)

The Fig Tree Dries Up—*Matthew 21:20–22*

²⁰ While Jesus and his disciples were walking early in the morning, they saw that the fig tree had dried up. ²¹ Peter remembered ˌwhat Jesus had saidˌ, so he said to Jesus, "Rabbi, look! The fig tree you cursed has dried up."

²² Jesus said to them, "Have faith in God! ²³ I can guarantee this truth: This is what will be done for someone who doesn't doubt but believes what he says will happen: He can say to this mountain, 'Be uprooted and thrown into the sea,' and it will be done for him. ²⁴ That's why I tell you to have faith that you have already received whatever you pray for, and it will be yours. ²⁵ Whenever you pray, forgive anything you have against anyone. Then your Father in heaven will forgive your failures."^a

Jesus' Authority Challenged—*Matthew 21:23–27; Luke 20:1–8*

²⁷ Jesus and his disciples returned to Jerusalem. As he was walking in the temple courtyard, the chief priests, the scribes, and the leaders came to him. ²⁸ They asked him, "What gives you the right to do these things? Who told you that you could do this?"

²⁹ Jesus said to them, "I'll ask you a question. Answer me, and then I'll tell you why I have the right to do these things. ³⁰ Did John's right to baptize come from heaven or from humans? Answer me!"

³¹ They discussed this among themselves. They said, "If we say, 'from heaven,' he will ask, 'Then why didn't you believe him?' ³² But if we say, 'from humans,' ˌthen what will happenˌ?" They were afraid of the people. All the people thought of John as a true prophet. ³³ So they answered Jesus, "We don't know."

Jesus told them, "Then I won't tell you why I have the right to do these things."

---

^a 11:25 Some manuscripts and translations add verse 26: "But if you don't forgive, your Father in heaven will not forgive your failures."

A Story About a Vineyard—*Matthew 21:33–46; Luke 20:9–19*

12 ¹Then, using this illustration, Jesus spoke to them. He said, "A man planted a vineyard. He put a wall around it, made a vat for the winepress, and built a watchtower. Then he leased it to vineyard workers and went on a trip.

² "At the right time he sent a servant to the workers to collect from them a share of the grapes from the vineyard. ³ The workers took the servant, beat him, and sent him back with nothing. ⁴ So the man sent another servant to them. They hit the servant on the head and treated him shamefully. ⁵ The man sent another, and they killed that servant. Then he sent many other servants. Some of these they beat, and others they killed.

⁶ "He had one more person to send. That person was his son, whom he loved. Finally, he sent his son to them. He thought, 'They will respect my son.'

⁷ "But those workers said to one another, 'This is the heir. Let's kill him, and the inheritance will be ours.' ⁸ So they took him, killed him, and threw him out of the vineyard.

⁹ "What will the owner of the vineyard do? He will come and destroy the workers and give the vineyard to others. ¹⁰ Have you never read the Scripture passage:

> 'The stone that the builders rejected
> has become the cornerstone.
> ¹¹ The Lord has done this,
> and it is amazing for us to see'?"

¹² They wanted to arrest him but were afraid of the crowd. They knew that he had directed this illustration at them. So they left him alone and went away.

A Question About Taxes—*Matthew 22:15–22; Luke 20:20–26*

¹³ The leaders sent some of the Pharisees and some of Herod's followers to Jesus. They wanted to trap him into saying the wrong thing. ¹⁴ When they came to him, they said, "Teacher, we know that you tell the truth. You don't favor individuals because of who they are. Rather, you teach the way of God truthfully. Is it right to pay taxes to the emperor or not? Should we pay taxes or not?"

¹⁵ Jesus recognized their hypocrisy, so he asked them, "Why do you test me? Bring me a coin so that I can look at it."

¹⁶ They brought a coin. He said to them, "Whose face and name is this?"

They told him, "The emperor's."

¹⁷ Jesus said to them, "Give the emperor what belongs to the emperor, and give God what belongs to God."

They were surprised at his reply.

The Dead Come Back to Life—*Matthew 22:23–33; Luke 20:27–40*

¹⁸ Some Sadducees, who say that people will never come back to life, came to Jesus. They asked him, ¹⁹ "Teacher, Moses wrote for us, 'If a man dies and leaves a wife but no child, his brother should marry his widow and have children for his brother.' ²⁰ There were seven brothers. The first got married and died without having children. ²¹ The second married her and died without having children. So did the third. ²² None of the seven brothers had any children. Last of all, the woman died. ²³ When the dead come back to life, whose wife will she be? The seven brothers had married her."

²⁴ Jesus said to them, "Aren't you mistaken because you don't know the Scriptures or God's power? ²⁵ When the dead come back to life, they don't marry. Rather, they are like the angels in heaven. ²⁶ Haven't you read in the book of Moses that the dead come back to life? It's in the passage about the bush, where God said, 'I am the God of Abraham, Isaac, and Jacob.' ²⁷ He's not the God of the dead but of the living. You're badly mistaken!"

Love God and Your Neighbor—*Matthew 22:34–40*

²⁸ One of the scribes went to Jesus during the argument with the Sadducees. He saw how well Jesus answered them, so he asked him, "Which commandment is the most important of them all?"

²⁹ Jesus answered, "The most important is, 'Listen, Israel, the Lord our God is the only Lord. ³⁰ So love the Lord your God with all your heart, with all your soul, with all your mind, and with all your strength.' ³¹ The second most important commandment is this: 'Love your neighbor as you love yourself.' No other commandment is greater than these."

³² The scribe said to Jesus, "Teacher, that was well said! You've told the truth that there is only one God and no other besides him! ³³ To love him with all your heart, with all your understanding, with all your strength, and to love your neighbor as you love yourself is more important than all the burnt offerings and sacrifices."

³⁴ When Jesus heard how wisely the man answered, he told the man, "You're not too far from the kingdom of God."

After that, no one dared to ask him another question.

How Can David's Son Be David's Lord?—*Matthew 22:41–46; Luke 20:41–44*

³⁵ While Jesus was teaching in the temple courtyard, he asked, "How can the scribes say that the Messiah is David's son? ³⁶ David, guided by the Holy Spirit, said,

'The Lord said to my Lord:
"Take the highest position in heaven
· until I put your enemies under your control.' "

³⁷ David calls him Lord. So how can he be his son?"

Jesus Disapproves of the Example Set by Scribes—*Matthew 23:1–12; Luke 20:45–47*

The large crowd enjoyed listening to him. ³⁸ As he taught, he said, "Watch out for the scribes! They like to walk around in long robes, to be greeted in the marketplaces, ³⁹ and to have the front seats in synagogues and the places of honor at dinners. ⁴⁰ They rob widows by taking their houses and then say long prayers to make themselves look good. The scribes will receive the most severe punishment."

A Widow's Contribution—*Luke 21:1–4*

⁴¹ As Jesus sat facing the temple offering box, he watched how ⌐much⌐ money people put into it. Many rich people put in large amounts. ⁴² A poor widow dropped in two small coins, worth less than a cent.

⁴³ He called his disciples and said to them, "I can guarantee this truth: This poor widow has given more than all the others. ⁴⁴ All of them have given what they could spare. But she, in her poverty, has given everything she had to live on."

Jesus Teaches Disciples on the Mount of Olives—*Matthew 24:1–35; Luke 21:5–33*

13 ¹ As Jesus was going out of the temple courtyard, one of his disciples said to him, "Teacher, look at these huge stones and these beautiful buildings!"

² Jesus said to him, "Do you see these large buildings? Not one of these stones will be left on top of another. Each one will be torn down." ·

³ As Jesus was sitting on the Mount of Olives facing the temple buildings, Peter, James, John, and Andrew asked him privately, ⁴ "Tell us, when will this happen? What will be the sign when all this will come to an end?"

⁵ Jesus answered them, "Be careful not to let anyone deceive you. ⁶ Many will come using my name. They will say, 'I am he,' and they will deceive many people.

⁷ "When you hear of wars and rumors of wars, don't be alarmed! These things must happen, but they don't mean that the end has come. ⁸ Nation will fight against nation and kingdom against kingdom. There will be earthquakes and famines in various places. These are only the beginning pains ⌐of the end⌐.

⁹ "Be on your guard! People will hand you over to the Jewish courts and whip you in their synagogues. You will stand in front of governors and kings to testify to them because of me. ¹⁰ But first, the Good News must be spread to all nations. ¹¹ When they take you away to hand you over to the authorities, don't worry ahead of time about what you will say. Instead, say whatever is given to you to say when the time comes. Indeed, you are not the one who will be speaking, but the Holy Spirit will.

¹² "Brother will hand over brother to death; a father will hand over his child. Children will rebel against their parents and kill them. ¹³ Everyone will hate you because you are committed to me. But the person who endures to the end will be saved.

¹⁴ "When you see the disgusting thing that will cause destruction standing where it should not (let the reader take note), those of you in Judea should flee to the mountains. ¹⁵ Those who are on the roof should not come down to get anything out of their houses. ¹⁶ Those who are in the field should not turn back to get their coats.

¹⁷ "How horrible it will be for the women who are pregnant or who are nursing babies in those days. ¹⁸ Pray that it will not be in winter. ¹⁹ It will be a time of misery that has not happened from the beginning of God's creation until now, and will certainly never happen again. ²⁰ If the Lord does not reduce that time, no one will be saved. But those days will be reduced because of those whom God has chosen.

²¹ "At that time don't believe anyone who tells you, 'Here is the Messiah!' or 'There he is!' ²² False messiahs and false prophets will appear. They will work miraculous signs and do wonderful things to deceive, if possible, those whom God has chosen. ²³ Be on your guard! I have told you everything before it happens.

[24] "Now, after the misery of those days, the sun will turn dark, the moon will not give light, [25] the stars will fall from the sky, and the powers of the universe will be shaken.

[26] "Then people will see the Son of Man coming in clouds with great power and glory. [27] He will send out his angels, and from every direction under the sky, they will gather those whom God has chosen.

[28] "Learn from the story of the fig tree. When its branch becomes tender and it sprouts leaves, you know summer is near. [29] In the same way, when you see these things happen, you know that he is near, at the door.

[30] "I can guarantee this truth: This generation will not disappear until all these things take place. [31] The earth and the heavens will disappear, but my words will never disappear.

No One Knows When the Earth and the Heavens Will Disappear

[32] "No one knows when that day or hour will come. Even the angels in heaven and the Son don't know. Only the Father knows. [33] Be careful! Watch! You don't know the exact time. [34] It is like a man who went on a trip. As he left home, he put his servants in charge. He assigned work to each one and ordered the guard to be alert. [35] Therefore, be alert, because you don't know when the owner of the house will return. It could be in the evening or at midnight or at dawn or in the morning. [36] Make sure he doesn't come suddenly and find you asleep. [37] I'm telling everyone what I'm telling you: 'Be alert!' "

The Plot to Kill Jesus—Matthew 26:1–5; Luke 22:1–2; John 11:45–57

14 [1] It was two days before the Passover and the Festival of Unleavened Bread. The chief priests and the scribes were looking for some underhanded way to arrest Jesus and to kill him. [2] However, they said, "We shouldn't arrest him during the festival, or else there will be a riot among the people."

A Woman Prepares Jesus' Body for the Tomb—Matthew 26:6–13; John 12:1–8

[3] Jesus was in Bethany at the home of Simon, a man who had suffered from a skin disease. While Jesus was sitting there, a woman went to him. She had a bottle of very expensive perfume made from pure nard. She opened the bottle and poured the perfume on his head.

[4] Some who were there were irritated and said to one another, "Why was the perfume wasted like this? [5] This perfume could have been sold for a high price, and the money could have been given to the poor." So they said some very unkind things to her.

[6] Jesus said, "Leave her alone! Why are you bothering her? She has done a beautiful thing for me. [7] You will always have the poor with you and can help them whenever you want. But you will not always have me with you. [8] She did what she could. She came to pour perfume on my body before it is placed in a tomb. [9] I can guarantee this truth: Wherever the Good News is spoken in the world, what she has done will also be told in memory of her."

Judas Plans to Betray Jesus—Matthew 26:14–16; Luke 22:3–6

[10] Judas Iscariot, one of the twelve apostles, went to the chief priests to betray Jesus. [11] They were pleased to hear what Judas had to say and promised to give him money. So he kept looking for a chance to betray Jesus.

Preparations for the Passover—Matthew 26:17–20; Luke 22:7–17

[12] Killing the Passover lamb was customary on the first day of the Festival of Unleavened Bread. The disciples asked Jesus, "Where do you want us to prepare the Passover meal for you?"

[13] He sent two of his disciples and told them, "Go into the city. You will meet a man carrying a jug of water. Follow him. [14] When he goes into a house, tell the owner that the teacher asks, 'Where is my room where I can eat the Passover meal with my disciples?' [15] He will take you upstairs and show you a large room. The room will be completely furnished. Get everything ready for us there."

[16] The disciples left. They went into the city and found everything as Jesus had told them. So they prepared the Passover.

[17] When evening came, Jesus arrived with the twelve apostles.

Jesus Knows Who Will Betray Him—Matthew 26:21–25; Luke 22:21–23; John 13:21–30

[18] While they were at the table eating, Jesus said, "I can guarantee this truth: One of you is going to betray me, one who is eating with me!"

[19] Feeling hurt, they asked him one by one, "You don't mean me, do you?"

[20] He said to them, "It's one of you twelve, someone dipping his hand into the bowl with me. [21] The Son of Man is going to die as the Scriptures say he will. But how horrible it will be for that person who betrays the Son of Man! It would have been better for that person if he had never been born."

The Lord's Supper—*Matthew 26:26–30; Luke 22:19–20*

22 While they were eating, Jesus took bread and blessed it. He broke the bread, gave it to them, and said, "Take this. This is my body."

23 Then he took a cup, spoke a prayer of thanksgiving, and gave the cup to them. They all drank from it. **24** He said to them, "This is my blood, the blood of the promise.ª It is poured out for many people.

25 "I can guarantee this truth: I won't drink this wine again until that day when I drink new wine in the kingdom of God."

26 After they sang a hymn, they went to the Mount of Olives.

Jesus Predicts Peter's Denial—*Matthew 26:31–35; Luke 22:31–34; John 13:36–38*

27 Then Jesus said to them, "All of you will abandon me. Scripture says,

> 'I will strike the shepherd,
>   and the sheep will be scattered.'

28 "But after I am brought back to life, I will go to Galilee ahead of you."

29 Peter said to him, "Even if everyone else abandons you, I won't."

30 Jesus said to Peter, "I can guarantee this truth: Tonight, before a rooster crows twice, you will say three times that you don't know me."

31 But Peter said very strongly, "Even if I have to die with you, I will never say that I don't know you." All the other disciples said the same thing.

Jesus Prays in the Garden of Gethsemane—*Matthew 26:36–46; Luke 22:39–46*

32 Then they came to a place called Gethsemane. He said to his disciples, "Stay here while I pray."

33 He took Peter, James, and John with him and began to feel distressed and anguished. **34** He said to them, "My anguish is so great that I feel as if I'm dying. Wait here, and stay awake."

35 After walking a little farther, he fell to the ground and prayed that if it were possible he might not have to suffer what was ahead of him. **36** He said, "Abba!ᵇ Father! You can do anything. Take this cup ⌊of suffering⌋ away from me. But let your will be done rather than mine."

37 He went back and found them asleep. He said to Peter, "Simon, are you sleeping? Couldn't you stay awake for one hour? **38** Stay awake, and pray that you won't be tempted. You want to do what's right, but you're weak."

39 He went away again and prayed the same prayer as before. **40** He found them asleep because they couldn't keep their eyes open. They didn't even know what they should say to him.

41 He came back a third time and said to them, "You might as well sleep now. It's all over.ᶜ The time has come for the Son of Man to be handed over to sinners. **42** Get up! Let's go! The one who is betraying me is near."

Jesus Is Arrested—*Matthew 26:47–56; Luke 22:47–54a; John 18:1–14*

43 Just then, while Jesus was still speaking, Judas, one of the twelve apostles, arrived. A crowd carrying swords and clubs was with him. They were from the chief priests, scribes, and leaders of the people. **44** Now, the traitor had given them a signal. He said, "The one I kiss is the man you want. Arrest him, and guard him closely as you take him away."

45 Then Judas quickly stepped up to Jesus and said, "Rabbi!" and kissed him.

46 Some men took hold of Jesus and arrested him. **47** One of those standing there pulled out his sword and cut off the ear of the chief priest's servant.

48 Jesus asked them, "Have you come out with swords and clubs to arrest me as if I were a criminal? **49** I·used to teach in the temple courtyard every day. But you didn't arrest me then. But what the Scriptures say must come true."

50 Then all the disciples abandoned him and ran away.

51 A certain young man was following Jesus. He had nothing on but a linen sheet. They tried to arrest him, **52** but he left the linen sheet behind and ran away naked.

The Trial in Front of the Jewish Council—*Matthew 26:57–68; Luke 22:63–71*

53 The men took Jesus to the chief priest. All the chief priests, leaders, and scribes had gathered together. **54** Peter followed him at a distance and went into the chief priest's courtyard. He sat with the guards and warmed himself facing the glow of a fire.

55 The chief priests and the whole Jewish council were searching for some testimony against Jesus in order to execute him. But they couldn't find any. **56** Many gave false testimony against him, but their statements did not agree.

ª 14:24 Or "testament," or "covenant."   ᵇ 14:36 *Abba* is Aramaic for "father."   ᶜ 14:41 Greek meaning uncertain.

⁵⁷ Then some men stood up and gave false testimony against him. They said, ⁵⁸ "We heard him say, 'I'll tear down this temple made by humans, and in three days I'll build another temple, one not made by human hands.' " ⁵⁹ But their testimony did not agree even on this point.

⁶⁰ So the chief priest stood up in the center and asked Jesus, "Don't you have any answer to what these men testify against you?"

⁶¹ But he was silent.

The chief priest asked him again, "Are you the Messiah, the Son of the Blessed One?"

⁶² Jesus answered, "Yes, I am, and you will see the Son of Man in the highest position in heaven. He will be coming with the clouds of heaven."

⁶³ The chief priest tore his clothes in horror and said, "Why do we need any more witnesses? ⁶⁴ You've heard him dishonor God! What's your verdict?"

All of them condemned him with the death sentence. ⁶⁵ Some of them began to spit on him. They covered his face and hit him with their fists. They said to him, "Prophesy!" Even the guards took him and slapped him.

Peter Denies Jesus—*Matthew 26:69–75; Luke 22:54b–62; John 18:15–18, 25–27*

⁶⁶ Peter was in the courtyard. One of the chief priest's female servants ⁶⁷ saw Peter warming himself. She looked at him and said, "You, too, were with Jesus from Nazareth!"

⁶⁸ But Peter denied it by saying, "I don't know him, and I don't understand what you're talking about."

He went to the entrance. Then a rooster crowed.ᵈ

⁶⁹ The servant saw him. Once again she said to those who were standing around, "This man is one of them!" ⁷⁰ Peter again denied it.

After a little while the men standing there said to Peter again, "It's obvious you're one of them. You're a Galilean!"

⁷¹ Then Peter began to curse and swear with an oath, "I don't know this man you're talking about!" ⁷² Just then a rooster crowed a second time. Peter remembered that Jesus said to him, "Before a rooster crows twice, you will say three times that you don't know me." Then Peter began to cry very hard.

Pilate Questions Jesus—*Matthew 27:11–14; Luke 23:1–4; John 18:28–38*

15 ¹ Early in the morning the chief priests immediately came to a decision with the leaders and the scribes. The whole Jewish council decided to tie Jesus up, lead him away, and hand him over to Pilate.

² Pilate asked him, "Are you the king of the Jews?"

"Yes, I am," Jesus answered him.

³ The chief priests were accusing him of many things.

⁴ So Pilate asked him again, "Don't you have any answer? Look how many accusations they're bringing against you!"

⁵ But Jesus no longer answered anything, so Pilate was surprised.

The Crowd Rejects Jesus—*Matthew 27:15–26; Luke 23:18–25; John 18:39–40*

⁶ At every Passover festival, Pilate would free one prisoner whom the people asked for. ⁷ There was a man named Barabbas in prison. He was with some rebels who had committed murder during a riot. ⁸ The crowd asked Pilate to do for them what he always did. ⁹ Pilate answered them, "Do you want me to free the king of the Jews for you?" ¹⁰ Pilate knew that the chief priests had handed Jesus over to him because they were jealous.

¹¹ The chief priests stirred up the crowd so that Pilate would free Barabbas for them instead.

¹² So Pilate again asked them, "Then what should I do with the king of the Jews?"

¹³ "Crucify him!" they shouted back.

¹⁴ Pilate said to them, "Why? What has he done wrong?"

But they shouted even louder, "Crucify him!"

¹⁵ Pilate wanted to satisfy the people, so he freed Barabbas for them. But he had Jesus whipped and handed over to be crucified.

The Soldiers Make Fun of Jesus—*Matthew 27:27–30; John 19:1–3*

¹⁶ The soldiers led Jesus into the courtyard of the palace and called together the whole troop. ¹⁷ They dressed him in purple, twisted some thorns into a crown, and placed it on his head. ¹⁸ Then they began to greet him, "Long live the king of the Jews!" ¹⁹ They kept hitting him on the head with a stick, spitting on him, and kneeling in front of him with false humility.

ᵈ 14:68 Some manuscripts and translations omit this sentence.

The Crucifixion—*Matthew 27:31–44; Luke 23:33–38; John 19:16b–24*

20 After the soldiers finished making fun of Jesus, they took off the purple cape and put his own clothes back on him. Then they led him out to crucify him. **21** A man named Simon from the city of Cyrene was coming ˌinto Jerusalemˌ from his home in the country. He was the father of Alexander and Rufus. As he was about to pass by, the soldiers forced him to carry Jesus' cross. **22** They took Jesus to Golgotha (which means "the place of the skull"). **23** They tried to give him wine mixed with a drug called myrrh, but he wouldn't take it. **24** Next they crucified him. Then they divided his clothes among themselves by throwing dice to see what each one would get. **25** It was nine in the morning when they crucified him. **26** There was a written notice of the accusation against him. It read, "The king of the Jews." **27** They crucified two criminals with him, one on his right and the other on his left.*ª*

29 Those who passed by insulted him. They shook their heads and said, "What a joke! You were going to tear down God's temple and build it again in three days. **30** Come down from the cross, and save yourself!" **31** The chief priests and the scribes made fun of him among themselves in the same way. They said, "He saved others, but he can't save himself. **32** Let the Messiah, the king of Israel, come down from the cross now so that we may see and believe." Even those who were crucified with him were insulting him.

Jesus Dies on the Cross—*Matthew 27:45–56; Luke 23:44–49; John 19:28–30*

33 At noon darkness came over the whole land until three in the afternoon. **34** At three o'clock Jesus cried out in a loud voice, "Eloi, Eloi, lema sabachthani?" which means, "My God, my God, why have you abandoned me?"

35 When some of the people standing there heard him say that, they said, "Listen! He's calling Elijah." **36** Someone ran and soaked a sponge in vinegar. Then he put it on a stick and offered Jesus a drink. The man said, "Let's see if Elijah comes to take him down."

37 Then Jesus cried out in a loud voice and died. **38** The curtain in the temple was split in two from top to bottom.

39 When the officer who stood facing Jesus saw how he gave up his spirit, he said, "Certainly, this man was the Son of God!"

40 Some women were watching from a distance. Among them were Mary from Magdala, Mary (the mother of young James and Joseph), and Salome. **41** They had followed him and supported him while he was in Galilee. Many other women who had come to Jerusalem with him were there too.

Jesus Is Buried—*Matthew 27:57–61; Luke 23:50–56; John 19:38–42*

42 It was Friday evening, before the day of worship, **43** when Joseph arrived. He was from the city of Arimathea and was an important member of the Jewish council. He, too, was waiting for the kingdom of God. Joseph boldly went to Pilate's quarters to ask for the body of Jesus.

44 Pilate wondered if Jesus had already died. So he summoned the officer to ask him if Jesus was, in fact, dead. **45** When the officer had assured him that Jesus was dead, Pilate let Joseph have the corpse.

46 Joseph had purchased some linen cloth. He took the body down from the cross and wrapped it in the cloth. Then he laid the body in a tomb, which had been cut out of rock, and he rolled a stone against the door of the tomb. **47** Mary from Magdala and Mary (the mother of Joses) watched where Jesus was laid.

Jesus Comes Back to Life—*Matthew 28:1–10; Luke 24:1–12; John 20:1–10*

16 **1** When the day of worship was over, Mary from Magdala, Mary (the mother of James), and Salome bought spices to go and anoint Jesus.

2 On Sunday they were going to the tomb very early when the sun had just come up. **3** They said to one another, "Who will roll away the stone for us from the entrance to the tomb?" **4** When they looked up, they saw that the stone had been rolled away. It was a very large stone. **5** As they went into the tomb, they saw a young man. He was dressed in a white robe and sat on the right side. They were panic-stricken.

6 The young man said to them, "Don't panic! You're looking for Jesus from Nazareth, who was crucified. He has been brought back to life. He's not here. Look at the place where they laid him. **7** Go and tell his disciples and Peter that he's going ahead of them to Galilee. There they will see him, just as he told them."

8 They went out of the tomb and ran away. Shock and trembling had overwhelmed them. They didn't say a thing to anyone, because they were afraid.*ª*

ª 15:27 Some manuscripts and translations add verse 28: "And what the Scriptures said came true: 'He was counted with criminals.'"
ª 16:8 Some manuscripts and translations end Mark here; some add verses 9–20.

Jesus Appears to His Followers

⁹ After Jesus came back to life early on Sunday, he appeared first to Mary from Magdala, from whom he had forced out seven demons. ¹⁰ She went and told his friends, who were grieving and crying. ¹¹ They didn't believe her when they heard that he was alive and that she had seen him.

¹² Later Jesus appeared to two disciples as they were walking to their home in the country. He did not look as he usually did. ¹³ They went back and told the others, who did not believe them either. ¹⁴ Still later Jesus appeared to the eleven apostles while they were eating. He put them to shame for their unbelief and because they were too stubborn to believe those who had seen him alive.

¹⁵ Then Jesus said to them, "So wherever you go in the world, tell everyone the Good News. ¹⁶ Whoever believes and is baptized will be saved, but whoever does not believe will be condemned.

¹⁷ "These are the miraculous signs that will accompany believers: They will use the power and authority of my name to force demons out of people. They will speak new languages. ¹⁸ They will pick up snakes, and if they drink any deadly poison, it will not hurt them. They will place their hands on the sick and cure them."

¹⁹ After talking with the apostles, the Lord was taken to heaven, where God gave him the highest position.

²⁰ The disciples spread the Good News everywhere. The Lord worked with them. He confirmed his word by the miraculous signs that accompanied it.

LUKE

Luke Writes to Theophilus

1 ¹ Many have attempted to write about what had taken place among us. ² They received their information from those who had been eyewitnesses and servants of God's word from the beginning, and they passed it on to us. ³ I, too, have followed everything closely from the beginning. So I thought it would be a good idea to write an orderly account for Your Excellency, Theophilus. ⁴ In this way you will know that what you've been told is true.

The Angel Gabriel Appears to Zechariah

⁵ When Herod was king of Judea, there was a priest named Zechariah, who belonged to the division of priests named after Abijah. Zechariah's wife Elizabeth was a descendant of Aaron. ⁶ Zechariah and Elizabeth had God's approval. They followed all the Lord's commands and regulations perfectly. ⁷ Yet, they never had any children because Elizabeth couldn't become pregnant. Both of them were too old to have children.

⁸ Zechariah was on duty with his division of priests. As he served in God's presence, ⁹ he was chosen by priestly custom to go into the Lord's temple to burn incense. ¹⁰ All the people were praying outside while he was burning incense.

¹¹ Then, to the right of the incense altar, an angel of the Lord appeared to him. ¹² Zechariah was troubled and overcome with fear.

¹³ The angel said to him, "Don't be afraid, Zechariah! God has heard your prayer. Your wife Elizabeth will have a son, and you will name him John. ¹⁴ He will be your pride and joy, and many people will be glad that he was born. ¹⁵ As far as the Lord is concerned, he will be a great man. He will never drink wine or any other liquor. He will be filled with the Holy Spirit even before he is born. ¹⁶ He will bring many people in Israel back to the Lord their God. ¹⁷ He will go ahead of the Lord with the spirit and power that Elijah had. He will change parents' attitudes toward their children. He will change disobedient people so that they will accept the wisdom of those who have God's approval. In this way he will prepare the people for their Lord."

¹⁸ Zechariah said to the angel, "What proof is there for this? I'm an old man, and my wife is beyond her childbearing years."

¹⁹ The angel answered him, "I'm Gabriel! I stand in God's presence. God sent me to tell you this good news. ²⁰ But because you didn't believe what I said, you will be unable to talk until the day this happens. Everything will come true at the right time."

²¹ Meanwhile, the people were waiting for Zechariah. They were amazed that he was staying in the temple so long. ²² When he did come out, he was unable to speak to them. So they realized that he had seen a vision in the temple. He motioned to them but remained unable to talk.

²³ When the days of his service were over, he went home. ²⁴ Later, his wife Elizabeth became pregnant and didn't go out in public for five months. She said, ²⁵ "The Lord has done this for me now. He has removed my public disgrace."

The Angel Gabriel Comes to Mary

²⁶ Six months after Elizabeth had become pregnant, God sent the angel Gabriel to Nazareth, a city in Galilee. ²⁷ The angel went to a virgin promised in marriage to a descendant of David named Joseph. The virgin's name was Mary.

²⁸ When the angel entered her home, he greeted her and said, "You are favored by the Lord! The Lord is with you."

²⁹ She was startled by what the angel said and tried to figure out what this greeting meant. ³⁰ The angel told her,

"Don't be afraid, Mary. You have found favorᵃ with God.
³¹ You will become pregnant, give birth to a son,
    and name him Jesus.
³² He will be a great man
    and will be called the Son of the Most High.
The Lord God will give him

ᵃ 1:30 Or "grace."

the throne of his ancestor David.
33   Your son will be king of Jacob's people forever,
        and his kingdom will never end."

³⁴ Mary asked the angel, "How can this be? I've never had sexual intercourse."

³⁵ The angel answered her, "The Holy Spirit will come to you, and the power of the Most High will overshadow you. Therefore, the holy child developing inside you will be called the Son of God.

³⁶ "Elizabeth, your relative, is six months pregnant with a son in her old age. People said she couldn't have a child. ³⁷ But nothing is impossible for God."

³⁸ Mary answered, "I am the Lord's servant. Let everything you've said happen to me." Then the angel left her.

Mary Visits Elizabeth

³⁹ Soon afterward, Mary hurried to a city in the mountain region of Judah. ⁴⁰ She entered Zechariah's home and greeted Elizabeth.

⁴¹ When Elizabeth heard the greeting, she felt the baby kick. Elizabeth was filled with the Holy Spirit. ⁴² She said in a loud voice, "You are the most blessed of all women, and blessed is the child that you will have. ⁴³ I feel blessed that the mother of my Lord is visiting me. ⁴⁴ As soon as I heard your greeting, I felt the baby jump for joy. ⁴⁵ You are blessed for believing that the Lord would keep his promise to you."

Mary Praises God

⁴⁶ Mary said,

"My soul praises the Lord's greatness!
47   My spirit finds its joy in God, my Savior,
48   because he has looked favorably on me, his humble servant.

"From now on, all people will call me blessed
49   because the Almighty has done great things to me.
            His name is holy.
50   For those who fear him,
                his mercy lasts throughout every generation.

51   "He displayed his mighty power.
        He scattered those who think too highly of themselves.
52   He pulled strong rulers from their thrones.
                He honored humble people.
53   He fed hungry people with good food.
                    He sent rich people away with nothing.

54   "He remembered to help his servant Israel forever.
55   This is the promise he made to our ancestors,
            to Abraham and his descendants."

⁵⁶ Mary stayed with Elizabeth about three months and then went back home.

John Is Born

⁵⁷ When the time came for Elizabeth to have her child, she gave birth to a son. ⁵⁸ Her neighbors and relatives heard that the Lord had been very kind to her, and they shared her joy.

⁵⁹ When the child was eight days old, they went ˌto the templeˌ to circumcise him. They were going to name him Zechariah after his father. ⁶⁰ But his mother spoke up, "Absolutely not! His name will be John."

⁶¹ Their friends said to her, "But you don't have any relatives with that name."

⁶² So they motioned to the baby's father to see what he wanted to name the child. ⁶³ Zechariah asked for a writing tablet and wrote, "His name is John." Everyone was amazed. ⁶⁴ Suddenly, Zechariah was able to speak, and he began to praise God.

⁶⁵ All their neighbors were filled with awe. Throughout the mountain region of Judea, people talked about everything that had happened. ⁶⁶ Everyone who heard about it seriously thought it over and asked, "What does the future hold for this child?" It was clear that the Lord was with him.

⁶⁷ His father Zechariah was filled with the Holy Spirit and prophesied,

68   "Praise the Lord God of Israel!
        He has come to take care of his people
            and to set them free.
69   He has raised up a mighty Savior for us
            in the family of his servant David.

⁷⁰ He made this promise through his holy prophets long ago.
⁷¹ He promised to save us from our enemies
    and from the power of all who hate us.
⁷² He has shown his mercy to our ancestors
    and remembered his holy promise,^b
⁷³   the oath that he swore to our ancestor Abraham.
⁷⁴ He promised to rescue us from our enemies' power
    so that we could serve him without fear
⁷⁵   by being holy and honorable as long as we live.

⁷⁶ "You, child, will be called a prophet of the Most High.
    You will go ahead of the Lord to prepare his way.
⁷⁷ You will make his people know that they can be saved
    through the forgiveness of their sins.
⁷⁸   A new day will dawn on us from above
        because our God is loving and merciful.
⁷⁹ He will give light to those who live in the dark
    and in death's shadow.
    He will guide us into the way of peace."

⁸⁰ The child John grew and became spiritually strong. He lived in the desert until the day he appeared to the people of Israel.

Jesus Is Born

2 ¹ At that time the Emperor Augustus ordered a census of the Roman Empire. ² This was the first census taken while Quirinius was governor of Syria. ³ All the people went to register in the cities where their ancestors had lived.

⁴ So Joseph went from Nazareth, a city in Galilee, to a Judean city called Bethlehem. Joseph, a descendant of King David, went to Bethlehem because David had been born there. ⁵ Joseph went there to register with Mary. She had been promised to him in marriage and was pregnant.

⁶ While they were in Bethlehem, the time came for Mary to have her child. ⁷ She gave birth to her firstborn son. She wrapped him in strips of cloth and laid him in a manger because there wasn't any room for them in the inn.

Angels Announce the Birth of Jesus

⁸ Shepherds were in the fields near Bethlehem. They were taking turns watching their flock during the night. ⁹ An angel from the Lord suddenly appeared to them. The glory of the Lord filled the area with light, and they were terrified. ¹⁰ The angel said to them, "Don't be afraid! I have good news for you, a message that will fill everyone with joy. ¹¹ Today your Savior, Christ the Lord, was born in David's city. ¹² This is how you will recognize him: You will find an infant wrapped in strips of cloth and lying in a manger."

¹³ Suddenly, a large army of angels appeared with the angel. They were praising God by saying,

¹⁴   "Glory to God in the highest heaven,
        and on earth peace to those who have his good will!"

¹⁵ The angels left them and went back to heaven. The shepherds said to each other, "Let's go to Bethlehem and see what the Lord has told us about."

¹⁶ They went quickly and found Mary and Joseph with the baby, who was lying in a manger. ¹⁷ When they saw the child, they repeated what they had been told about him. ¹⁸ Everyone who heard the shepherds' story was amazed.

¹⁹ Mary treasured all these things in her heart and always thought about them.

²⁰ As the shepherds returned to their flock, they glorified and praised God for everything they had seen and heard. Everything happened the way the angel had told them.

Jesus' Parents Obey Moses' Teachings

²¹ Eight days after his birth, the child was circumcised and named Jesus. This was the name the angel had given him before his mother became pregnant.

²² After the days required by Moses' Teachings to make a mother clean^a had passed, Joseph and Mary went to Jerusalem. They took Jesus to present him to the Lord. ²³ They did exactly what was written in the Lord's Teachings: "Every firstborn boy is to be set apart as holy to the Lord." ²⁴ They also offered a sacrifice as required by the Lord's Teachings: "a pair of mourning doves or two young pigeons."

---

^b 1:72 Or "covenant."   ^a 2:22 "Clean" refers to anything that Moses' Teachings say is presentable to God.

Simeon's Prophecy

²⁵ A man named Simeon was in Jerusalem. He lived an honorable and devout life. He was waiting for the one who would comfort Israel. The Holy Spirit was with Simeon ²⁶ and had told him that he wouldn't die until he had seen the Messiah, whom the Lord would send.

²⁷ Moved by the Spirit, Simeon went into the temple courtyard. Mary and Joseph were bringing the child Jesus into the courtyard at the same time. They brought him so that they could do for him what Moses' Teachings required. ²⁸ Then Simeon took the child in his arms and praised God by saying,

²⁹   "Now, Lord, you are allowing your servant to leave in peace
        as you promised.
³⁰   My eyes have seen your salvation,
³¹   which you have prepared for all people to see.
³²   He is a light that will reveal ˏsalvationˏ to the nations
            and bring glory to your people Israel."

³³ Jesus' father and mother were amazed at what was said about him. ³⁴ Then Simeon blessed them and said to Mary, his mother, "This child is the reason that many people in Israel will be condemned and many others will be saved. He will be a sign that will expose ³⁵ the thoughts of those who reject him. And a sword will pierce your heart."

Anna's Prophecy

³⁶ Anna, a prophet, was also there. She was a descendant of Phanuel from the tribe of Asher. She was now very old. Her husband had died seven years after they were married, ³⁷ and she had been a widow for 84 years. Anna never left the temple courtyard but worshiped day and night by fasting and praying. ³⁸ At that moment she came up to Mary and Joseph and began to thank God. She spoke about Jesus to all who were waiting for Jerusalem to be set free.

³⁹ After doing everything the Lord's Teachings required, Joseph and Mary returned to their hometown of Nazareth in Galilee. ⁴⁰ The child grew and became strong. He was filled with wisdom, and God's favor⁰ was with him.

Mary and Joseph Find Jesus With the Teachers in the Temple Courtyard

⁴¹ Every year Jesus' parents would go to Jerusalem for the Passover festival. ⁴² When he was 12 years old, they went as usual.

⁴³ When the festival was over, they left for home. The boy Jesus stayed behind in Jerusalem, but his parents didn't know it. ⁴⁴ They thought that he was with the others who were traveling with them. After traveling for a day, they started to look for him among their relatives and friends. ⁴⁵ When they didn't find him, they went back to Jerusalem to look for him.

⁴⁶ Three days later, they found him in the temple courtyard. He was sitting among the teachers, listening to them, and asking them questions. ⁴⁷ His understanding and his answers stunned everyone who heard him.

⁴⁸ When his parents saw him, they were shocked. His mother asked him, "Son, why have you done this to us? Your father and I have been worried sick looking for you!"

⁴⁹ Jesus said to them, "Why were you looking for me? Didn't you realize that I had to be in my Father's house?" ⁵⁰ But they didn't understand what he meant.

⁵¹ Then he returned with them to Nazareth and was obedient to them.

His mother treasured all these things in her heart. ⁵² Jesus grew in wisdom and maturity. He gained favor from God and people.

John Prepares the Way—Matthew 3:1–12; Mark 1:1–8; John 1:19–28

3 ¹ It was the fifteenth year in the reign of the Emperor Tiberius. Pontius Pilate was governor of Judea. Herod ruled Galilee, and his brother Philip ruled Iturea and Trachonitis. Lysanias was the ruler of Abilene. ² It was at the time when Annas and Caiaphas were chief priests that God spoke to John, son of Zechariah, in the desert. ³ John traveled throughout the region around the Jordan River. He told people about a baptism of repentance⁰ for the forgiveness of sins. ⁴ As the prophet Isaiah wrote in his book,

    "A voice cries out in the desert:
        'Prepare the way for the Lord!
    Make his paths straight!
⁵   Every valley will be filled.
        Every mountain and hill will be leveled.
        The crooked ways will be made straight.

⁰ 2:40 Or "grace."   ⁰ 3:3 Repentance is turning to God with a complete change in the way a person thinks and acts.

The rough roads will be made smooth.

⁶   All people will see the salvation that God gives.' "

⁷ Crowds of people were coming to be baptized by John. He would say to them, "You poisonous snakes! Who showed you how to flee from God's coming anger? ⁸ Do those things that prove that you have turned to God and have changed the way you think and act. Don't say, 'Abraham is our ancestor.' I guarantee that God can raise up descendants for Abraham from these stones. ⁹ The ax is now ready to cut the roots of the trees. Any tree that doesn't produce good fruit will be cut down and thrown into a fire."

¹⁰ The crowds asked him, "What should we do?"

¹¹ He answered them, "Whoever has two shirts should share with the person who doesn't have any. Whoever has food should share it too."

¹² Some tax collectors came to be baptized. They asked him, "Teacher, what should we do?"

¹³ He told them, "Don't collect more money than you are ordered to collect."

¹⁴ Some soldiers asked him, "And what should we do?"

He told them, "Be satisfied with your pay, and never use threats or blackmail to get money from anyone."

¹⁵ People's hopes were rising as they all wondered whether John was the Messiah. ¹⁶ John replied to all of them, "I baptize you with water. But the one who is more powerful than I is coming. I am not worthy to untie his sandal straps. He will baptize you with the Holy Spirit and fire. ¹⁷ His winnowing*ᵇ* shovel is in his hand to clean up his threshing floor.ᶜ He will gather the wheat into his barn, but he will burn the husks in a fire that can never be put out."

¹⁸ With many other encouraging words, he told the Good News to the people.

¹⁹ John spoke out against the ruler Herod because Herod had married his own sister-in-law, Herodias. He also spoke out against Herod for all the evil things he had done. ²⁰ So Herod added one more evil to all the others; he locked John in prison.

The Baptism of Jesus—*Matthew 3:13–17; Mark 1:9–11*

²¹ When all the people were baptized, Jesus, too, was baptized. While he was praying, heaven opened, ²² and the Holy Spirit came down to him in the form of a dove. A voice from heaven said, "You are my Son, whom I love. I am pleased with you."

²³ Jesus was about 30 years old when he began ˏhis ministryˏ.

The Ancestors of Jesus

Jesus, so people thought, was the son of Joseph, son of Eli, ²⁴ son of Matthat, son of Levi, son of Melchi, son of Jannai, son of Joseph, ²⁵ son of Mattathias, son of Amos, son of Nahum, son of Esli, son of Naggai, ²⁶ son of Maath, son of Mattathias, son of Semein, son of Josech, son of Joda, ²⁷ son of Joanan, son of Rhesa, son of Zerubbabel, son of Shealtiel, son of Neri, ²⁸ son of Melchi, son of Addi, son of Cosam, son of Elmadam, son of Er, ²⁹ son of Joshua, son of Eliezer, son of Jorim, son of Matthat, son of Levi, ³⁰ son of Simeon, son of Judah, son of Joseph, son of Jonam, son of Eliakim, ³¹ son of Melea, son of Menna, son of Mattatha, son of Nathan, son of David, ³² son of Jesse, son of Obed, son of Boaz, son of Salmon, son of Nahshon, ³³ son of Amminadab, son of Admin, son of Arni, son of Hezron, son of Perez, son of Judah, ³⁴ son of Jacob, son of Isaac, son of Abraham, son of Terah, son of Nahor, ³⁵ son of Serug, son of Reu, son of Peleg, son of Eber, son of Shelah, ³⁶ son of Cainan, son of Arphaxad, son of Shem, son of Noah, son of Lamech, ³⁷ son of Methuselah, son of Enoch, son of Jared, son of Mahalaleel, son of Cainan, ³⁸ son of Enos, son of Seth, son of Adam, son of God.

The Devil Tempts Jesus—*Matthew 4:1–11; Mark 1:12–13*

4 ¹ Jesus was filled with the Holy Spirit as he left the Jordan River. The Spirit led him while he was in the desert, ² where he was tempted by the devil for 40 days. During those days Jesus ate nothing, so when they were over, he was hungry.

³ The devil said to him, "If you are the Son of God, tell this stone to become a loaf of bread."

⁴ Jesus answered him, "Scripture says, 'A person cannot live on bread alone.' "ᵃ

⁵ The devil took him to a high place and showed him all the kingdoms of the world in an instant. ⁶ The devil said to him, "I will give you all the power and glory of these kingdoms. All of it has been given to me, and I give it to anyone I please. ⁷ So if you will worship me, all this will be yours."

⁸ Jesus answered him, "Scripture says, 'Worship the Lord your God and serve only him.' "

⁹ Then the devil took him into Jerusalem and had him stand on the highest part of the temple. He said to Jesus, "If you are the Son of God, jump from here! ¹⁰ Scripture says, 'He will put

---

ᵇ 3:17 Winnowing is the process of separating husks from grain.   ᶜ 3:17 A threshing floor is an outdoor area where grain is separated from its husks.   ᵃ 4:4 Some manuscripts and translations add "but on every word of God."

his angels in charge of you to watch over you carefully. [11] They will carry you in their hands so that you never hit your foot against a rock.' "

[12] Jesus answered him, "It has been said, 'Never tempt the Lord your God.' "[b]

[13] After the devil had finished tempting Jesus in every possible way, the devil left him until another time.

Nazareth Rejects Jesus—Matthew 13:54–58; Mark 6:1–6

[14] Jesus returned to Galilee. The power of the Spirit was with him, and the news about him spread throughout the surrounding country. [15] He taught in the synagogues, and everyone praised him.

[16] Then Jesus came to Nazareth, where he had been brought up. As usual he went into the synagogue on the day of worship. He stood up to read the lesson. [17] The attendant gave him the book of the prophet Isaiah. He opened it and found the place where it read:

> [18]   "The Spirit of the Lord is with me.
>   He has anointed me
>   to tell the Good News to the poor.
>   He has sent me[c]
>   to announce forgiveness to the prisoners of sin
>   and the restoring of sight to the blind,
>   to forgive those who have been shattered by sin,
> [19]   to announce the year of the Lord's favor."

[20] Jesus closed the book, gave it back to the attendant, and sat down. Everyone in the synagogue watched him closely. [21] Then he said to them, "This passage came true today when you heard me read it."

[22] All the people spoke well of him. They were amazed to hear the gracious words flowing from his lips. They said, "Isn't this Joseph's son?"

[23] So he said to them, "You'll probably quote this proverb to me, 'Doctor, cure yourself!' and then say to me, 'Do all the things in your hometown that we've heard you've done in Capernaum.' " [24] Then Jesus added, "I can guarantee this truth: A prophet isn't accepted in his hometown.

[25] "I can guarantee this truth: There were many widows in Israel in Elijah's time. It had not rained for three-and-a-half years, and the famine was severe everywhere in the country. [26] But God didn't send Elijah to anyone except a widow at Zarephath in the territory of Sidon. [27] There were also many people with skin diseases in Israel in the prophet Elisha's time. But God cured no one except Naaman from Syria."

[28] Everyone in the synagogue became furious when they heard this. [29] Their city was built on a hill with a cliff. So they got up, forced Jesus out of the city, and led him to the cliff. They intended to throw him off of it. [30] But Jesus walked right by them and went away.

Jesus Forces an Evil Spirit out of a Man—Mark 1:21–28

[31] Jesus went to Capernaum, a city in Galilee, and taught them on a day of worship. [32] The people were amazed at his teachings because he spoke with authority.

[33] In the synagogue was a man possessed by a spirit, an evil demon. He shouted very loudly, [34] "Oh, no! What do you want with us, Jesus from Nazareth? Have you come to destroy us? I know who you are—the Holy One of God!"

[35] Jesus ordered the spirit, "Keep quiet, and come out of him!" The demon threw the man down in the middle of the synagogue and came out without hurting him.

[36] Everyone was stunned. They said to one another, "What kind of command is this? With authority and power he gives orders to evil spirits, and they come out."

[37] So news about him spread to every place throughout the surrounding region.

Jesus Cures Simon's Mother-in-Law and Many Others—Matthew 8:14–18; Mark 1:29–34

[38] Jesus left the synagogue and went to Simon's house. Simon's mother-in-law was sick with a high fever. They asked Jesus to help her. [39] He bent over her, ordered the fever to leave, and it went away. She got up immediately and prepared a meal for them.

[40] When the sun was setting, everyone who had friends suffering from various diseases brought them to him. He placed his hands on each of them and cured them. [41] Demons came out of many people, shouting, "You are the Son of God!" But Jesus ordered them not to speak. After all, they knew he was the Messiah.

---

[b] 4:12 Or "Never put the Lord your God to any test."   [c] 4:18 Some manuscripts and translations add "to heal those who are brokenhearted."

Spreading the Good News—*Matthew 4:23–25; Mark 1:35–39*

[42] In the morning he went to a place where he could be alone. The crowds searched for him. When they came to him, they tried to keep him from leaving. [43] But he said to them, "I have to tell the Good News about the kingdom of God in other cities also. That's what I was sent to do."

[44] So he spread his message in the synagogues of Judea.[d]

Calling of the First Disciples—*Matthew 4:18–22; Mark 1:14–20*

5 [1] One day Jesus was standing by the Sea of Galilee. The people crowded around him as they listened to God's word. [2] Jesus saw two boats on the shore. The fishermen had stepped out of them and were washing their nets. [3] So Jesus got into the boat that belonged to Simon and asked him to push off a little from the shore. Then Jesus sat down and taught the crowd from the boat.

[4] When he finished speaking, he told Simon, "Take the boat into deep water, and lower your nets to catch some fish."

[5] Simon answered, "Teacher, we worked hard all night and caught nothing. But if you say so, I'll lower the nets."

[6] After the men had done this, they caught such a large number of fish that their nets began to tear. [7] So they signaled to their partners in the other boat to come and help them. Their partners came and filled both boats until the boats nearly sank.

[8] When Simon Peter saw this, he knelt in front of Jesus and said, "Leave me, Lord! I'm a sinful person!" [9] Simon and everyone who was with him was amazed to see the large number of fish they had caught. [10] James and John, who were Zebedee's sons and Simon's partners, were also amazed.

Jesus told Simon, "Don't be afraid. From now on you will catch people instead of fish." [11] Simon and his partners brought the boats to shore, left everything, and followed Jesus.

Jesus Cures a Man With a Skin Disease—*Matthew 8:1–4; Mark 1:40–44*

[12] One day Jesus was in a city where there was a man covered with a serious skin disease. When the man saw Jesus, he bowed with his face to the ground. He begged Jesus, "Sir, if you want to, you can make me clean."[a]

[13] Jesus reached out, touched him, and said, "I want to. So be clean!" Immediately, his skin disease went away.

[14] Jesus ordered him, "Don't tell anyone. Instead, show yourself to the priest. Then offer the sacrifice as Moses commanded as proof to people that you are clean."

[15] The news about Jesus spread even more. Large crowds gathered to hear him and have their diseases cured. [16] But he would go away to places where he could be alone for prayer.

Jesus Forgives Sins—*Matthew 9:1–8; Mark 2:1–12*

[17] One day when Jesus was teaching, some Pharisees and experts in Moses' Teachings were present. They had come from every village in Galilee and Judea and from Jerusalem. Jesus had the power of the Lord to heal.

[18] Some men brought a paralyzed man on a stretcher. They tried to take him into the house and put him in front of Jesus. [19] But they could not find a way to get him into the house because of the crowd. So they went up on the roof. They made an opening in the tiles and let the man down on his stretcher among the people. (They lowered him in front of Jesus.)

[20] When Jesus saw their faith, he said, "Sir, your sins are forgiven." [21] The scribes and the Pharisees thought, "Who is this man? He's dishonoring God! Who besides God can forgive sins?"

[22] Jesus knew what they were thinking. So he said to them, "What are you thinking? [23] Is it easier to say, 'Your sins are forgiven,' or to say, 'Get up and walk'? [24] I want you to know that the Son of Man has authority on earth to forgive sins." Then he said to the paralyzed man, "Get up, pick up your stretcher, and go home."

[25] The man immediately stood up in front of them and picked up the stretcher he had been lying on. Praising God, he went home. [26] Everyone was amazed and praised God. They were filled with awe and said, "We've seen things today we can hardly believe!"

Jesus Chooses Levi [Matthew] to Be a Disciple—*Matthew 9:9–13; Mark 2:13–17*

[27] After that, Jesus left. He saw a tax collector named Levi sitting in a tax office. Jesus said to him, "Follow me!" [28] So Levi got up, left everything, and followed him.

[29] Levi held a large reception at his home for Jesus. A huge crowd of tax collectors and others were eating with them.

---

[d] 4:44 Some manuscripts read "in the synagogues of Galilee."   [a] 5:12 "Clean" refers to anything that Moses' Teachings say is presentable to God.

[30] The Pharisees and their scribes complained to Jesus' disciples. They asked, "Why do you eat and drink with tax collectors and sinners?"

[31] Jesus answered them, "Healthy people don't need a doctor; those who are sick do. [32] I've come to call sinners to change the way they think and act, not to call people who think they have God's approval."

Jesus Is Questioned About Fasting—Matthew 9:14–17; Mark 2:18–22

[33] They said to him, "John's disciples frequently fast and say prayers, and so do the disciples of the Pharisees. But your disciples eat and drink."

[34] Jesus asked them, "Can you force wedding guests to fast while the groom is still with them? [35] The time will come when the groom will be taken away from them. At that time they will fast."

[36] He also used these illustrations: "No one tears a piece of cloth from a new coat to patch an old coat. Otherwise, the new cloth will tear the old. Besides, the patch from the new will not match the old. [37] People don't pour new wine into old wineskins. If they do, the new wine will make the skins burst. The wine will run out, and the skins will be ruined. [38] Rather, new wine is to be poured into fresh skins.

[39] "No one who has been drinking old wine wants new wine. He says, 'The old wine is better!' "

Jesus Has Authority Over the Day of Worship—Matthew 12:1–8; Mark 2:23–28

6 [1] Once, on a day of worship, Jesus was walking through some grainfields. His disciples were picking the heads of grain, removing the husks, and eating the grain.

[2] Some of the Pharisees asked, "Why are your disciples doing something that is not right to do on the day of worship?"

[3] Jesus answered them, "Haven't you read what David did when he and his men were hungry? [4] Haven't you read how he went into the house of God, ate the bread of the presence, and gave some of it to the men who were with him? He had no right to eat those loaves. Only the priests have that right."

[5] Then he added, "The Son of Man has authority over the day of worship."

Jesus Heals on the Day of Worship—Matthew 12:9–15a; Mark 3:1–6

[6] On another day of worship, Jesus went into a synagogue to teach. A man whose right hand was paralyzed was there. [7] The scribes and the Pharisees were watching Jesus closely. They wanted to see whether he would heal the man on the day of worship so that they could find a way to accuse him of doing something wrong.

[8] But Jesus knew what they were thinking. So he told the man with the paralyzed hand, "Get up, and stand in the center ˌof the synagogue ˌ!" The man got up and stood there. [9] Then Jesus said to them, "I ask you—what is the right thing to do on a day of worship: to do good or evil, to give a person his health or to destroy it?" [10] He looked around at all of them and then said to the man, "Hold out your hand." The man did so, and his hand became normal again.

[11] The scribes and Pharisees were furious and began to discuss with each other what they could do to Jesus.

Jesus Appoints Twelve Apostles—Matthew 10:1–4; Mark 3:13–19

[12] At that time Jesus went to a mountain to pray. He spent the whole night in prayer to God.

[13] When it was day, he called his disciples. He chose twelve of them and called them apostles. [14] They were Simon (whom Jesus named Peter) and Simon's brother Andrew, James, John, Philip, Bartholomew, [15] Matthew, Thomas, James (son of Alphaeus), Simon (who was called the Zealot), [16] Judas (son of James), and Judas Iscariot (who became a traitor).

Many People Are Cured—Mark 3:7–12

[17] Jesus came down from the mountain with them and stood on a level place. A large crowd of his disciples and many other people were there. They had come from all over Judea, Jerusalem, and the seacoast of Tyre and Sidon. [18] They wanted to hear him and be cured of their diseases. Those who were tormented by evil spirits were cured. [19] The entire crowd was trying to touch him because power was coming from him and curing all of them.

Jesus Teaches His Disciples

[20] Jesus looked at his disciples and said,

"Blessed are those who are poor.
    The kingdom of God is theirs.
[21]   Blessed are those who are hungry.
    They will be satisfied.
Blessed are those who are crying.
    They will laugh.

²² Blessed are you when people hate you, avoid you,
indent insult you, and slander you
indent indent because you are committed to the Son of Man.
²³ indent indent Rejoice then, and be very happy!
indent indent indent You have a great reward in heaven.
indent indent indent indent That's the way their ancestors treated the prophets.

²⁴ "But how horrible it will be for those who are rich.
indent They have had their comfort.
²⁵ How horrible it will be for those who are well-fed.
indent They will be hungry.
How horrible it will be for those who are laughing.
indent They will mourn and cry.
²⁶ How horrible it will be for you
indent when everyone says nice things about you.
indent indent That's the way their ancestors treated the false prophets.

Love Your Enemies—*Matthew 5:38–48*

²⁷ "But I tell everyone who is listening: Love your enemies. Be kind to those who hate you.
²⁸ Bless those who curse you. Pray for those who insult you. ²⁹ If someone strikes you on the cheek, offer the other cheek as well. If someone takes your coat, don't stop him from taking your shirt. ³⁰ Give to everyone who asks you for something. If someone takes what is yours, don't insist on getting it back.

³¹ "Do for other people everything you want them to do for you.

³² "If you love those who love you, do you deserve any thanks for that? Even sinners love those who love them. ³³ If you help those who help you, do you deserve any thanks for that? Sinners do that too. ³⁴ If you lend anything to those from whom you expect to get something back, do you deserve any thanks for that? Sinners also lend to sinners to get back what they lend. ³⁵ Rather, love your enemies, help them, and lend to them without expecting to get anything back. Then you will have a great reward. You will be the children of the Most High God. After all, he is kind to unthankful and evil people. ³⁶ Be merciful as your Father is merciful.

Stop Judging—*Matthew 7:1–5*

³⁷ "Stop judging, and you will never be judged. Stop condemning, and you will never be condemned. Forgive, and you will be forgiven. ³⁸ Give, and you will receive. A large quantity, pressed together, shaken down, and running over will be put into your pocket. The standards you use for others will be applied to you."

³⁹ Jesus also gave them this illustration: "Can one blind person lead another? Won't both fall into the same pit? ⁴⁰ A student is no better than his teacher. But everyone who is well-trained will be like his teacher.

⁴¹ "Why do you see the piece of sawdust in another believer's eye and not notice the wooden beam in your own eye? ⁴² How can you say to another believer, 'Friend, let me take the piece of sawdust out of your eye,' when you don't see the beam in your own eye? You hypocrite! First remove the beam from your own eye. Then you will see clearly to remove the piece of sawdust from another believer's eye.

Evil People—*Matthew 7:15–23*

⁴³ "A good tree doesn't produce rotten fruit, and a rotten tree doesn't produce good fruit. ⁴⁴ Each tree is known by its fruit. You don't pick figs from thorny plants or grapes from a thornbush. ⁴⁵ Good people do the good that is in them. But evil people do the evil that is in them. The things people say come from inside them.

Build on the Rock—*Matthew 7:24–29*

⁴⁶ "Why do you call me Lord but don't do what I tell you?

⁴⁷ "I will show you what everyone who comes to me, hears what I say, and obeys it is like. ⁴⁸ He is like a person who dug down to bedrock to lay the foundation of his home. When a flood came, the floodwaters pushed against that house. But the house couldn't be washed away because it had a good foundation. ⁴⁹ The person who hears ˛what I say˛ but doesn't obey it is like someone who built a house on the ground without any foundation. The floodwaters pushed against it, and that house quickly collapsed and was destroyed."

A Believing Army Officer—*Matthew 8:5–13*

7 ¹ When Jesus had finished everything he wanted to say to the people, he went to Capernaum. ² There a Roman army officer's valuable slave was sick and near death. ³ The officer had heard about Jesus and sent some Jewish leaders to him. They were to ask Jesus to come and save the servant's life. [4] They came to Jesus and begged, "He deserves your help. [5] He loves our people and built our synagogue at his own expense."

[6] Jesus went with them. He was not far from the house when the officer sent friends to tell Jesus, "Sir, don't bother. I don't deserve to have you come into my house. [7] That's why I didn't come to you. But just give a command, and let my servant be cured. [8] As you know, I'm in a chain of command and have soldiers at my command. I tell one of them, 'Go!' and he goes, and another, 'Come!' and he comes. I tell my servant, 'Do this!' and he does it."

[9] Jesus was amazed at the officer when he heard these words. He turned to the crowd following him and said, "I can guarantee that I haven't found faith as great as this in Israel." [10] When the men who had been sent returned to the house, they found the servant healthy again.

Jesus Brings a Widow's Son Back to Life

[11] Soon afterward, Jesus went to a city called Nain. His disciples and a large crowd went with him. [12] As he came near the entrance to the city, he met a funeral procession. The dead man was a widow's only child. A large crowd from the city was with her. [13] When the Lord saw her, he felt sorry for her. He said to her, "Don't cry." [14] He went up to the open coffin, took hold of it, and the men who were carrying it stopped. He said, "Young man, I'm telling you to come back to life!" [15] The dead man sat up and began to talk, and Jesus gave him back to his mother.

[16] Everyone was struck with fear and praised God. They said, "A great prophet has appeared among us," and "God has taken care of his people." [17] This news about Jesus spread throughout Judea and the surrounding region.

John Sends Two Disciples—Matthew 11:2–6

[18] John's disciples told him about all these things. Then John called two of his disciples [19] and sent them to ask the Lord, "Are you the one who is coming, or should we look for someone else?"

[20] The men came to Jesus and said, "John the Baptizer sent us to ask you, 'Are you the one who is coming, or should we look for someone else?' "

[21] At that time Jesus was curing many people who had diseases, sicknesses, and evil spirits. Also, he was giving back sight to many who were blind.

[22] Jesus answered John's disciples, "Go back, and tell John what you have seen and heard: Blind people see again, lame people are walking, those with skin diseases are made clean,[a] deaf people hear again, dead people are brought back to life, and poor people hear the Good News. [23] Whoever doesn't lose his faith in me is indeed blessed."

Jesus Speaks About John—Matthew 11:7–19

[24] When John's messengers had left, Jesus spoke to the crowds about John. "What did you go into the desert to see? Tall grass swaying in the wind? [25] Really, what did you go to see? A man dressed in fine clothes? Those who wear splendid clothes and live in luxury are in royal palaces. [26] Really, what did you go to see? A prophet? Let me tell you that he is far more than a prophet. [27] John is the one about whom Scripture says,

> 'I am sending my messenger ahead of you
>   to prepare the way in front of you.'

[28] I can guarantee that of all the people ever born, no one is greater than John. Yet, the least important person in the kingdom of God is greater than John.

[29] "All the people, including tax collectors, heard John. They admitted that God was right by letting John baptize them. [30] But the Pharisees and the experts in Moses' Teachings rejected God's plan for them. They refused to be baptized.

[31] "How can I describe the people who are living now? What are they like? [32] They are like children who sit in the marketplace and shout to each other,

> 'We played music for you,
>   but you didn't dance.
> We sang a funeral song,
>   but you didn't cry.'

[33] John the Baptizer has come neither eating bread nor drinking wine, and you say, 'There's a demon in him!' [34] The Son of Man has come eating and drinking, and you say, 'Look at him! He's a glutton and a drunk, a friend of tax collectors and sinners!'

[35] "Yet, wisdom is proved right by all its results."

---

[a] 7:22 "Clean" refers to anything that Moses' Teachings say is presentable to God.

A Sinful Woman Receives Forgiveness

36 One of the Pharisees invited Jesus to eat with him. Jesus went to the Pharisee's house and was eating at the table.

37 A woman who lived a sinful life in that city found out that Jesus was eating at the Pharisee's house. So she took a bottle of perfume **38** and knelt at his feet. She was crying and washed his feet with her tears. Then she dried his feet with her hair, kissed them over and over again, and poured the perfume on them.

39 The Pharisee who had invited Jesus saw this and thought, "If this man really were a prophet, he would know what sort of woman is touching him. She's a sinner."

40 Jesus spoke up, "Simon, I have something to say to you."

Simon replied, "Teacher, you're free to speak."

41 ˏSo Jesus said,ˏ "Two men owed a moneylender some money. One owed him five hundred silver coins, and the other owed him fifty. **42** When they couldn't pay it back, he was kind enough to cancel their debts. Now, who do you think will love him the most?"

43 Simon answered, "I suppose the one who had the largest debt canceled."

Jesus said to him, "You're right!" **44** Then, turning to the woman, he said to Simon, "You see this woman, don't you? I came into your house. You didn't wash my feet. But she has washed my feet with her tears and dried them with her hair. **45** You didn't give me a kiss. But ever since I came in, she has not stopped kissing my feet. **46** You didn't put any olive oil on my head. But she has poured perfume on my feet. **47** That's why I'm telling you that her many sins have been forgiven. Her great love proves that. But whoever receives little forgiveness loves very little."

48 Then Jesus said to her, "Your sins have been forgiven." **49** The other guests thought, "Who is this man who even forgives sins?"

50 Jesus said to the woman, "Your faith has saved you. Go in peace!"

Women Who Supported Jesus

8 **1** After this, Jesus traveled from one city and village to another. He spread the Good News about God's kingdom. The twelve apostles were with him. **2** Also, some women were with him. They had been cured from evil spirits and various illnesses. These women were Mary, also called Magdalene, from whom seven demons had gone out; **3** Joanna, whose husband Chusa was Herod's administrator; Susanna; and many other women. They provided financial support for Jesus and his disciples.

A Story About a Farmer—Matthew 13:1–23; Mark 4:1–20

4 When a large crowd had gathered and people had come to Jesus from every city, he used this story as an illustration: **5** "A farmer went to plant his seeds. Some seeds were planted along the road, were trampled, and were devoured by birds. **6** Others were planted on rocky soil. When the plants came up, they withered because they had no moisture. **7** Others were planted among thornbushes. The thornbushes grew up with them and choked them. **8** Others were planted on good ground. When they came up, they produced a hundred times as much as was planted."

After he had said this, he called out, "Let the person who has ears listen!"

9 His disciples asked him what this story meant. **10** Jesus answered, "Knowledge about the mysteries of the kingdom of God has been given ˏdirectlyˏ to you. But it is given to others in stories. When they look, they don't see, and when they hear, they don't understand.

11 "This is what the story illustrates: The seed is God's word. **12** Some people are like seeds that were planted along the road. They hear the word, but then the devil comes. He takes the word away from them so that they don't believe and become saved. **13** Some people are like seeds on rocky soil. They welcome the word with joy whenever they hear it, but they don't develop any roots. They believe for a while, but when their faith is tested, they abandon it. **14** The seeds that were planted among thornbushes are people who hear the word, but as life goes on the worries, riches, and pleasures of life choke them. So they don't produce anything good. **15** The seeds that were planted on good ground are people who also hear the word. But they keep it in their good and honest hearts and produce what is good despite what life may bring.

16 "No one lights a lamp and hides it under a bowl or puts it under a bed. Instead, everyone who lights a lamp puts it on a lamp stand so that those who come in will see the light. **17** There is nothing hidden that will not be revealed. There is nothing kept secret that will not come to light.

18 "So pay attention to how you listen! Those who understand ˏthese mysteriesˏ will be given ˏmore knowledgeˏ. However, some people don't understand ˏthese mysteriesˏ. Even what they think they understand will be taken away from them."

The True Family of Jesus—Matthew 12:46–50; Mark 3:31–35

19 His mother and his brothers came to see him. But they couldn't meet with him because of the crowd. **20** Someone told Jesus, "Your mother and your brothers are standing outside. They want to see you."

²¹ He answered them, "My mother and my brothers are those who hear and do what God's word says."

Jesus Calms the Sea—*Matthew 8:23–27; Mark 4:35–41*

²² One day Jesus and his disciples got into a boat. He said to them, "Let's cross to the other side of the lake." So they started out. ²³ As they were sailing along, Jesus fell asleep.

A violent storm came across the lake. The boat was taking on water, and they were in danger. ²⁴ They went to him, woke him up, and said, "Master! Master! We're going to die!"

Then he got up and ordered the wind and the waves to stop. The wind stopped, and the sea became calm. ²⁵ He asked them, "Where is your faith?"

Frightened and amazed, they asked each other, "Who is this man? He gives orders to the wind and the water, and they obey him!"

Jesus Cures a Demon-Possessed Man—*Matthew 8:28–34; Mark 5:1–20*

²⁶ They landed in the region of the Gerasenes across from Galilee. ²⁷ When Jesus stepped out on the shore, a certain man from the city met him. The man was possessed by demons and had not worn clothes for a long time. He would not stay in a house but lived in the tombs. ²⁸ When he saw Jesus, he shouted, fell in front of him, and said in a loud voice, "Why are you bothering me, Jesus, Son of the Most High God? I beg you not to torture me!" ²⁹ Jesus ordered the evil spirit to come out of the man. (The evil spirit had controlled the man for a long time. People had kept him under guard. He was chained hand and foot. But he would break the chains. Then the demon would force him to go into the desert.)

³⁰ Jesus asked him, "What is your name?"

He answered, "Legion [Six Thousand]." (Many demons had entered him.) ³¹ The demons begged Jesus not to order them to go into the bottomless pit.

³² A large herd of pigs was feeding on a mountainside. The demons begged Jesus to let them enter those pigs. So he let them do this. ³³ The demons came out of the man and went into the pigs. Then the herd rushed down the cliff into the lake and drowned.

³⁴ When those who had taken care of the pigs saw what had happened, they ran away. They reported everything in the city and countryside. ³⁵ The people went to see what had happened. They came to Jesus and found the man from whom the demons had gone out. Dressed and in his right mind, he was sitting at Jesus' feet. The people were frightened. ³⁶ Those who had seen this told the people how Jesus had restored the demon-possessed man to health.

³⁷ Then all the people from the surrounding region of the Gerasenes asked Jesus to leave because they were terrified.

Jesus got into a boat and started back. ³⁸ The man from whom the demons had gone out begged him, "Let me go with you."

But Jesus sent the man away and told him, ³⁹ "Go home to your family, and tell them how much God has done for you." So the man left. He went through the whole city and told people how much Jesus had done for him.

Jairus' Daughter and a Woman With Chronic Bleeding—*Matthew 9:18–26; Mark 5:21–43*

⁴⁰ When Jesus came back, a crowd welcomed him. Everyone was expecting him.

⁴¹ A man named Jairus, a synagogue leader, arrived and quickly bowed down in front of Jesus. He begged Jesus to come to his home. ⁴² His only daughter, who was about twelve years old, was dying. As Jesus went, the people were crowding around him.

⁴³ A woman who had been suffering from chronic bleeding for twelve years was in the crowd. No one could cure her. ⁴⁴ She came up behind Jesus, touched the edge of his clothes, and her bleeding stopped at once.

⁴⁵ Jesus asked, "Who touched me?"

After everyone denied touching him, Peter said, "Teacher, the people are crowding you and pressing against you."

⁴⁶ Jesus said, "Someone touched me. I know power has gone out of me."

⁴⁷ The woman saw that she couldn't hide. Trembling, she quickly bowed in front of him. There, in front of all the people, she told why she touched him and how she was cured at once.

⁴⁸ Jesus told her, "Daughter, your faith has made you well. Go in peace!"

⁴⁹ While Jesus was still speaking to her, someone came from the synagogue leader's home. He said, "Your daughter is dead. Don't bother the teacher anymore."

⁵⁰ When Jesus heard this, he told the synagogue leader, "Don't be afraid! Just believe, and she will get well."

⁵¹ Jesus went into the house. He allowed no one to go with him except Peter, John, James, and the child's parents. ⁵² Everyone was crying and showing how sad they were. Jesus said, "Don't cry! She's not dead. She's just sleeping."

⁵³They laughed at him because they knew she was dead. ⁵⁴But Jesus took her hand and called out, "Child, get up!" ⁵⁵She came back to life and got up at once. He ordered her parents to give her something to eat. ⁵⁶They were amazed. Jesus ordered them not to tell anyone what had happened.

Jesus Sends Out the Twelve—*Matthew 10:5–42; Mark 6:7–13*

9 ¹Jesus called the twelve apostles together and gave them power and authority over every demon and power and authority to cure diseases. ²He sent them to spread the message about the kingdom of God and to cure the sick.

³He told them, "Don't take anything along on the trip. Don't take a walking stick, traveling bag, any food, money, or a change of clothes. ⁴When you go into a home, stay there until you're ready to leave. ⁵If people don't welcome you, leave that city, and shake its dust off your feet as a warning to them."

⁶The apostles went from village to village, told the Good News, and cured the sick everywhere.

Rumors About Jesus—*Matthew 14:1–12; Mark 6:14–29*

⁷Herod the ruler heard about everything that was happening. He didn't know what to make of it. Some people were saying that John had come back to life. ⁸Others said that Elijah had appeared, and still others said that one of the prophets from long ago had come back to life. ⁹Herod said, "I had John's head cut off. Who is this person I'm hearing so much about?" So Herod wanted to see Jesus.

Jesus Feeds Five Thousand—*Matthew 14:13–21; Mark 6:30–44; John 6:1–14*

¹⁰The apostles came back and told Jesus everything they had done. He took them with him to a city called Bethsaida so that they could be alone. ¹¹But the crowds found out about this and followed him. He welcomed them, talked to them about the kingdom of God, and cured those who were sick.

¹²Toward the end of the day, the twelve apostles came to him. They said to him, "Send the crowd to the closest villages and farms so that they can find some food and a place to stay. No one lives around here."

¹³Jesus replied, "You give them something to eat."

They said to him, "We have five loaves of bread and two fish. Unless we go to buy food for all these people, that's all we have." ¹⁴(There were about five thousand men.)

Then he told his disciples, "Have them sit in groups of about fifty." ¹⁵So they did this.

¹⁶Then he took the five loaves and the two fish, looked up to heaven, and blessed the food. He broke the loaves apart and kept giving them to the disciples to give to the crowd. ¹⁷All of them ate as much as they wanted. When they picked up the leftover pieces, they filled twelve baskets.

Peter Declares His Belief About Jesus—*Matthew 16:13–20; Mark 8:27–30*

¹⁸Once when Jesus was praying privately and his disciples were with him, he asked them, "Who do people say I am?"

¹⁹They answered, "Some say you are John the Baptizer, others Elijah, and still others say that one of the prophets from long ago has come back to life."

²⁰He asked them, "But who do you say I am?"

Peter answered, "You are the Messiah, whom God has sent."

²¹He ordered them not to tell this to anyone.

Jesus Foretells That He Will Die and Come Back to Life—*Matthew 16:21–23; Mark 8:31–33*

²²Jesus said that the Son of Man would have to suffer a lot. He would be rejected by the leaders, the chief priests, and the scribes. He would be killed, but on the third day he would come back to life.

What It Means to Follow Jesus—*Matthew 16:24–28; Mark 8:34–9:1*

²³He said to all of them, "Those who want to come with me must say no to the things they want, pick up their crosses every day, and follow me. ²⁴Those who want to save their lives will lose them. But those who lose their lives for me will save them. ²⁵What good does it do for people to win the whole world but lose their lives by destroying them? ²⁶If people are ashamed of me and what I say, the Son of Man will be ashamed of those people when he comes in the glory that he shares with the Father and the holy angels.

²⁷"I can guarantee this truth: Some people who are standing here will not die until they see the kingdom of God."

Moses and Elijah Appear With Jesus—*Matthew 17:1–8; Mark 9:2–13*

²⁸About eight days after he had said this, Jesus took Peter, John, and James with him and went up a mountain to pray. ²⁹While Jesus was praying, the appearance of his face changed,

and his clothes became dazzling white. ³⁰ Suddenly, both Moses and Elijah were talking with him. ³¹ They appeared in heavenly glory and were discussing Jesus' approaching death and what he was about to fulfill in Jerusalem.

³² Peter and the men with him were sleeping soundly. When they woke up, they saw Jesus' glory and the two men standing with him. ³³ As Moses and Elijah were leaving him, Peter said to Jesus, "Teacher, it's good that we're here. Let's put up three tents—one for you, one for Moses, and one for Elijah." Peter didn't know what he was saying.

³⁴ While he was saying this, a cloud overshadowed them. They were frightened as they went into the cloud. ³⁵ A voice came out of the cloud and said, "This is my Son, whom I have chosen. Listen to him!"

³⁶ After the voice had spoken, they saw that Jesus was alone. The disciples said nothing, and for some time they told no one about what they had seen.

Jesus Cures a Demon-Possessed Boy—*Matthew 17:14–20; Mark 9:14–29*

³⁷ The next day, when they had come down from the mountain, a large crowd met Jesus. ³⁸ A man in the crowd shouted, "Teacher, I beg you to look at my son. He's my only child. ³⁹ Whenever a spirit takes control of him, he shrieks, goes into convulsions, and foams at the mouth. After a struggle, the spirit goes away, leaving the child worn out. ⁴⁰ I begged your disciples to force the spirit out of him, but they couldn't do it."

⁴¹ Jesus answered, "You unbelieving and corrupt generation! How long must I be with you and put up with you? Bring your son here!"

⁴² While he was coming ˌto Jesusˌ, the demon knocked the boy to the ground and threw him into convulsions.

Jesus ordered the evil spirit to leave. He cured the boy and gave him back to his father. ⁴³ Everyone was amazed to see God's wonderful power.

The Son of Man Again Foretells His Betrayal—*Matthew 17:22–23; Mark 9:30–32*

Everyone was amazed at all the things that Jesus was doing. So he said to his disciples, ⁴⁴ "Listen carefully to what I say. The Son of Man will be betrayed and handed over to people." ⁴⁵ They didn't know what he meant. The meaning was hidden from them so that they didn't understand it. Besides, they were afraid to ask him about what he had said.

Greatness in the Kingdom—*Matthew 18:1–5; Mark 9:33–37*

⁴⁶ A discussion started among them about who would be the greatest. ⁴⁷ Jesus knew what they were thinking. So he took a little child and had him stand beside him. ⁴⁸ Then he said to them, "Whoever welcomes this little child in my name welcomes me. Whoever welcomes me welcomes the one who sent me. The one who is least among all of you is the one who is greatest."

Using the Name of Jesus—*Mark 9:38–41*

⁴⁹ John replied, "Master, we saw someone forcing demons out of a person by using the power and authority of your name. We tried to stop him because he was not one of us." ⁵⁰ Jesus said to him, "Don't stop him! Whoever isn't against you is for you."

People From a Samaritan Village Reject Jesus

⁵¹ The time was coming closer for Jesus to be taken to heaven. So he was determined to go to Jerusalem. ⁵² He sent messengers ahead of him. They went into a Samaritan village to arrange a place for him to stay. ⁵³ But the people didn't welcome him, because he was on his way to Jerusalem. ⁵⁴ James and John, his disciples, saw this. They asked, "Lord, do you want us to call down fire from heaven to burn them up?"

⁵⁵ But he turned and corrected them.ᵃ ⁵⁶ So they went to another village.

What It Takes to Be a Disciple—*Matthew 8:19–22*

⁵⁷ As they were walking along the road, a man said to Jesus, "I'll follow you wherever you go." ⁵⁸ Jesus told him, "Foxes have holes, and birds have nests, but the Son of Man has nowhere to sleep."

⁵⁹ He told another man, "Follow me!"

But the man said, "Sir, first let me go to bury my father."

⁶⁰ But Jesus told him, "Let the dead bury their own dead. You must go everywhere and tell about the kingdom of God."

⁶¹ Another said, "I'll follow you, sir, but first let me tell my family goodbye."

⁶² Jesus said to him, "Whoever starts to plow and looks back is not fit for the kingdom of God."

ᵃ 9:55 Some manuscripts and translations add " 'You don't know the kind of spirit that is influencing you. The Son of Man didn't come to destroy people's lives but to save them,' he said."

Jesus Sends Disciples to Do Mission Work

10 ¹ After this, the Lord appointed 70ᵃ other disciples to go ahead of him to every city and place that he intended to go. They were to travel in pairs.

² He told them, "The harvest is large, but the workers are few. So ask the Lord who gives this harvest to send workers to harvest his crops. ³ Go! I'm sending you out like lambs among wolves. ⁴ Don't carry a wallet, a traveling bag, or sandals, and don't stop to greet anyone on the way. ⁵ Whenever you go into a house, greet the family right away with the words, 'May there be peace in this house.' ⁶ If a peaceful person lives there, your greeting will be accepted. But if that's not the case, your greeting will be rejected. ⁷ Stay with the family that accepts you. Eat and drink whatever they offer you. After all, the worker deserves his pay. Do not move around from one house to another. ⁸ Whenever you go into a city and the people welcome you, eat whatever they serve you. ⁹ Heal the sick that are there, and tell the people, 'The kingdom of God is near you!'

¹⁰ "But whenever you go into a city and people don't welcome you, leave. Announce in its streets, ¹¹ 'We are wiping your city's dust from our feet in protest against you! But realize that the kingdom of God is near you!' ¹² I can guarantee that judgment day will be easier for Sodom than for that city.

¹³ "How horrible it will be for you, Chorazin! How horrible it will be for you, Bethsaida! If the miracles worked in your cities had been worked in Tyre and Sidon, they would have changed the way they thought and acted. Long ago they would have worn sackcloth and sat in ashes. ¹⁴ Judgment day will be better for Tyre and Sidon than for you. ¹⁵ And you, Capernaum, will you be lifted to heaven? No, you will go to hell!

¹⁶ "The person who hears you hears me, and the person who rejects you rejects me. The person who rejects me rejects the one who sent me."

¹⁷ The 70 disciples came back very happy. They said, "Lord, even demons obey us when we use the power and authority of your name!"

¹⁸ Jesus said to them, "I watched Satan fall from heaven like lightning. ¹⁹ I have given you the authority to trample snakes and scorpions and to destroy the enemy's power. Nothing will hurt you. ²⁰ However, don't be happy that evil spirits obey you. Be happy that your names are written in heaven."

²¹ In that hour the Holy Spirit filled Jesus with joy. Jesus said, "I praise you, Father, Lord of heaven and earth, for hiding these things from wise and intelligent people and revealing them to little children. Yes, Father, this is what pleased you.

²² "My Father has turned everything over to me. Only the Father knows who the Son is. And no one knows who the Father is except the Son and those to whom the Son is willing to reveal him."

²³ He turned to his disciples in private and said to them, "How blessed you are to see what you've seen. ²⁴ I can guarantee that many prophets and kings wanted to see and hear what you've seen and heard, but they didn't."

A Story About a Good Samaritan

²⁵ Then an expert in Moses' Teachings stood up to test Jesus. He asked, "Teacher, what must I do to inherit eternal life?"

²⁶ Jesus answered him, "What is written in Moses' Teachings? What do you read there?"

²⁷ He answered, " 'Love the Lord your God with all your heart, with all your soul, with all your strength, and with all your mind. And love your neighbor as you love yourself.' "

²⁸ Jesus told him, "You're right! Do this, and life will be yours."

²⁹ But the man wanted to justify his question. So he asked Jesus, "Who is my neighbor?"

³⁰ Jesus replied, "A man went from Jerusalem to Jericho. On the way robbers stripped him, beat him, and left him for dead.

³¹ "By chance, a priest was traveling along that road. When he saw the man, he went around him and continued on his way. ³² Then a Levite came to that place. When he saw the man, he, too, went around him and continued on his way.

³³ "But a Samaritan, as he was traveling along, came across the man. When the Samaritan saw him, he felt sorry for the man, ³⁴ went to him, and cleaned and bandaged his wounds. Then he put him on his own animal, brought him to an inn, and took care of him. ³⁵ The next day the Samaritan took out two silver coins and gave them to the innkeeper. He told the innkeeper, 'Take care of him. If you spend more than that, I'll pay you on my return trip.'

³⁶ "Of these three men, who do you think was a neighbor to the man who was attacked by robbers?"

³⁷ The expert said, "The one who was kind enough to help him."

Jesus told him, "Go and imitate his example!"

ᵃ 10:1 Some manuscripts have "72."

Mary Listens to Jesus

38 As they were traveling along, Jesus went into a village. A woman named Martha welcomed him into her home. **39** She had a sister named Mary. Mary sat at the Lord's feet and listened to him talk.

40 But Martha was upset about all the work she had to do. So she asked, "Lord, don't you care that my sister has left me to do the work all by myself? Tell her to help me."

41 The Lord answered her, "Martha, Martha! You worry and fuss about a lot of things. **42** There's only one thing you need.*b* Mary has made the right choice, and that one thing will not be taken away from her."

The Lord's Prayer—Matthew 6:9–13

11 **1** Once Jesus was praying in a certain place. When he stopped praying, one of his disciples said to him, "Lord, teach us to pray as John taught his disciples."

2 Jesus told them, "When you pray, say this:

> Father,
> > let your name be kept holy.
> > Let your kingdom come.
> **3**   Give us our bread day by day.
> **4**   Forgive us as we forgive everyone else.
> > Don't allow us to be tempted."

The Power of Prayer—Matthew 7:7–11

5 Jesus said to his disciples, "Suppose one of you has a friend. Suppose you go to him at midnight and say, 'Friend, let me borrow three loaves of bread. **6** A friend of mine on a trip has dropped in on me, and I don't have anything to serve him.' **7** Your friend might answer you from inside his house, 'Don't bother me! The door is already locked, and my children are in bed. I can't get up to give you anything.' **8** I can guarantee that although he doesn't want to get up to give you anything, he will get up and give you whatever you need because he is your friend and because you were so bold.

9 "So I tell you to ask, and you will receive. Search, and you will find. Knock, and the door will be opened for you. **10** Everyone who asks will receive. The one who searches will find, and for the person who knocks, the door will be opened.

11 "If your child asks you, his father, for a fish, would you give him a snake instead? **12** Or if your child asks you for an egg, would you give him a scorpion? **13** Even though you're evil, you know how to give good gifts to your children. So how much more will your Father in heaven give the Holy Spirit to those who ask him?"

Jesus Is Accused of Working With Beelzebul—Matthew 12:22–32, 43–45; Mark 3:20–30

14 Jesus was forcing a demon out of a man. The demon had made the man unable to talk. When the demon had gone out, the man began to talk.

The people were amazed. **15** But some of them said, "He can force demons out of people only with the help of Beelzebul, the ruler of demons." **16** Others wanted to test Jesus and demanded that he show them some miraculous sign from heaven.

17 Since Jesus knew what they were thinking, he said to them, "Every kingdom divided against itself is ruined. A house divided against itself falls. **18** Now, if Satan is divided against himself, how can his kingdom last? I say this because you say Beelzebul helps me force demons out of people. **19** If I force demons out with the help of Beelzebul, who helps your followers force them out? That's why they will be your judges. **20** But if I force out demons with the help of God's power, then the kingdom of God has come to you.

21 "When a strong man, fully armed, guards his own mansion, his property is safe. **22** But a stronger man than he may attack him and defeat him. Then the stronger man will take away all the weapons in which the strong man trusted and will divide the loot.

23 "Whoever isn't with me is against me. Whoever doesn't gather with me scatters.

24 "When an evil spirit comes out of a person, it goes through dry places looking for a place to rest. But it doesn't find any. Then it says, 'I'll go back to the home I left.' **25** When it comes, it finds the house swept clean and in order. **26** Then the spirit goes and brings along seven other spirits more evil than itself. They enter and take up permanent residence there. In the end the condition of that person is worse than it was before."

---

b 10:42 Some manuscripts and translations read, "But of the few things ˻worth worrying about˼, there is only one thing you need."

The Sign of Jonah—*Matthew 12:38–42*

²⁷ While Jesus was speaking, a woman in the crowd shouted, "How blessed is the mother who gave birth to you and the breasts that nursed you."

²⁸ Jesus replied, "Rather, how blessed are those who hear and obey God's word."

²⁹ As the people were gathering around him, Jesus said, "The people living today are evil. They look for a miraculous sign. But the only sign they will get is the sign of Jonah. ³⁰ Just as Jonah became a miraculous sign to the people of Nineveh, so the Son of Man will be a miraculous sign to the people living today. ³¹ The queen from the south will stand up at the time of judgment with the men who live today. She will condemn them, because she came from the ends of the earth to hear Solomon's wisdom. But look, someone greater than Solomon is here! ³² The men of Nineveh will stand up at the time of judgment with the people living today. Since the men of Nineveh turned to God and changed the way they thought and acted when Jonah spoke his message, they will condemn the people living today. But look, someone greater than Jonah is here!

Jesus Talks About Light

³³ "No one lights a lamp and hides it or puts it under a basket. Instead, everyone who lights a lamp puts it on a lamp stand so that those who come in will see its light.

³⁴ "Your eye is the lamp of your body. When your eye is unclouded, your whole body is full of light. But when your eye is evil, your body is full of darkness. ³⁵ So be careful that the light in you isn't darkness. ³⁶ If your whole body is full of light and not darkness, it will be as bright as a lamp shining on you."

Jesus Criticizes Some Jewish Leaders

³⁷ After Jesus spoke, a Pharisee invited him to have lunch at his house. So Jesus accepted the invitation. ³⁸ The Pharisee was surprised to see that Jesus didn't wash before the meal.

³⁹ The Lord said to him, "You Pharisees clean the outside of cups and dishes. But inside you are full of greed and evil. ⁴⁰ You fools! Didn't the one who made the outside make the inside too? ⁴¹ Give what is inside as a gift to the poor, and then everything will be clean*ᵃ* for you.

⁴² "How horrible it will be for you Pharisees! You give ˏGodˏ one-tenth of your mint, spices, and every garden herb. But you have ignored justice and the love of God. You should have done these things without ignoring the others.

⁴³ "How horrible it will be for you Pharisees! You love to sit in the front seats in the synagogues and to be greeted in the marketplaces. ⁴⁴ How horrible it will be for you! You are like unmarked graves. People walk on them without knowing what they are."

⁴⁵ One of the experts in Moses' Teachings said to him, "Teacher, when you talk this way, you insult us too."

⁴⁶ Jesus said, "How horrible it will be for you experts in Moses' Teachings! You burden people with loads that are hard to carry. But you won't lift a finger to carry any of these loads.

⁴⁷ "How horrible it will be for you! You build the monuments for the prophets. But it was your ancestors who murdered them. ⁴⁸ So you are witnesses and approve of what your ancestors did. They murdered the prophets for whom you build monuments. ⁴⁹ That's why the Wisdom of God said, 'I will send them prophets and apostles. They will murder some of those prophets and apostles and persecute others.' ⁵⁰ So the people living now will be charged with the murder of every prophet since the world was made. ⁵¹ This includes the murders from Abel to Zechariah, who was killed between the altar and the temple. Yes, I can guarantee this truth: The people living today will be held responsible for this.

⁵² "How horrible it will be for you experts in Moses' Teachings! You have taken away the key that unlocks knowledge. You haven't gained entrance into ˏknowledgeˏ yourselves, and you've kept out those who wanted to enter."

⁵³ When Jesus left, the scribes and the Pharisees held a terrible grudge against him. They questioned him about many things ⁵⁴ and watched him closely to trap him in something he might say.

Jesus Speaks to His Disciples

12 ¹ Meanwhile, thousands of people had gathered. They were so crowded that they stepped on each other. Jesus spoke to his disciples and said, "Watch out for the yeast of the Pharisees. I'm talking about their hypocrisy. ² Nothing has been covered that will not be exposed. Whatever is secret will be made known. ³ Whatever you have said in the dark will be heard in the daylight. Whatever you have whispered in private rooms will be shouted from the housetops.

ᵃ 11:41 "Clean" refers to anything that Moses' Teachings say is presentable to God.

⁴ "My friends, I can guarantee that you don't need to be afraid of those who kill the body. After that they can't do anything more. ⁵ I'll show you the one you should be afraid of. Be afraid of the one who has the power to throw you into hell after killing you. I'm warning you to be afraid of him.

⁶ "Aren't five sparrows sold for two cents? God doesn't forget any of them. ⁷ Even every hair on your head has been counted. Don't be afraid! You are worth more than many sparrows. ⁸ I can guarantee that the Son of Man will acknowledge in front of God's angels every person who acknowledges him in front of others. ⁹ But God's angels will be told that I don't know those people who tell others that they don't know me. ¹⁰ Everyone who says something against the Son of Man will be forgiven. But the person who dishonors the Holy Spirit will not be forgiven.

¹¹ "When you are put on trial in synagogues or in front of rulers and authorities, don't worry about how you will defend yourselves or what you will say. ¹² At that time the Holy Spirit will teach you what you must say."

A Story About Material Possessions

¹³ Someone in the crowd said to him, "Teacher, tell my brother to give me my share of the inheritance that our father left us."

¹⁴ Jesus said to him, "Who appointed me to be your judge or to divide ˌyour inheritanceˌ?" ¹⁵ He told the people, "Be careful to guard yourselves from every kind of greed. Life is not about having a lot of material possessions."

¹⁶ Then he used this illustration. He said, "A rich man had land that produced good crops. ¹⁷ He thought, 'What should I do? I don't have enough room to store my crops.' ¹⁸ He said, 'I know what I'll do. I'll tear down my barns and build bigger ones so that I can store all my grain and goods in them. ¹⁹ Then I'll say to myself, "You've stored up a lot of good things for years to come. Take life easy, eat, drink, and enjoy yourself." '

²⁰ "But God said to him, 'You fool! I will demand your life from you tonight! Now who will get what you've accumulated?' ²¹ That's how it is when a person has material riches but is not rich in his relationship with God."

Stop Worrying—Matthew 6:25–34

²² Then Jesus said to his disciples, "So I tell you to stop worrying about what you will eat or wear. ²³ Life is more than food, and the body is more than clothes. ²⁴ Consider the crows. They don't plant or harvest. They don't even have a storeroom or a barn. Yet, God feeds them. You are worth much more than birds.

²⁵ "Can any of you add an hour to your life by worrying? ²⁶ If you can't do a small thing like that, why worry about other things? ²⁷ Consider how the flowers grow. They never work or spin yarn for clothes. But I say that not even Solomon in all his majesty was dressed like one of these flowers. ²⁸ That's the way God clothes the grass in the field. Today it's alive, and tomorrow it's thrown into an incinerator. So how much more will he clothe you people who have so little faith?

²⁹ "Don't concern yourself about what you will eat or drink, and quit worrying about these things. ³⁰ Everyone in the world is concerned about these things, but your Father knows you need them. ³¹ Rather, be concerned about his kingdom. Then these things will be provided for you. ³² Don't be afraid, little flock. Your Father is pleased to give you the kingdom.

³³ "Sell your material possessions, and give the money to the poor. Make yourselves wallets that don't wear out! Make a treasure for yourselves in heaven that never loses its value! In heaven thieves and moths can't get close enough to destroy your treasure. ³⁴ Your heart will be where your treasure is.

The Son of Man Will Return When You Least Expect Him

³⁵ "Be ready for action, and have your lamps burning. ³⁶ Be like servants waiting to open the door at their master's knock when he returns from a wedding. ³⁷ Blessed are those servants whom the master finds awake when he comes. I can guarantee this truth: He will change his clothes, make them sit down at the table, and serve them. ³⁸ They will be blessed if he comes in the middle of the night or toward morning and finds them awake.

³⁹ "Of course, you realize that if the homeowner had known at what hour the thief was coming, he would not have let him break into his house. ⁴⁰ Be ready, because the Son of Man will return when you least expect him."

⁴¹ Peter asked, "Lord, did you use this illustration just for us or for everyone?"

⁴² The Lord asked, "Who, then, is the faithful, skilled manager that the master will put in charge of giving the other servants their share of food at the right time? ⁴³ That servant will be blessed if his master finds him doing this job when he comes. ⁴⁴ I can guarantee this truth: He will put that servant in charge of all his property. ⁴⁵ On the other hand, that servant may think

that his master is taking a long time to come home. The servant may begin to beat the other servants and to eat, drink, and get drunk. ⁴⁶ His master will return at an unexpected time. Then his master will punish him severely and assign him a place with unfaithful people.

⁴⁷ "The servant who knew what his master wanted but didn't get ready to do it will receive a hard beating. ⁴⁸ But the servant who didn't know ˎwhat his master wantedˌ and did things for which he deserved punishment will receive a light beating. A lot will be expected from everyone who has been given a lot. More will be demanded from everyone who has been entrusted with a lot.

Jesus Will Cause Conflict

⁴⁹ "I have come to throw fire on the earth. I wish that it had already started! ⁵⁰ I have a baptism to go through, and I will suffer until it is over.

⁵¹ "Do you think I came to bring peace to earth? No! I can guarantee that I came to bring nothing but division. ⁵² From now on a family of five will be divided. Three will be divided against two and two against three. ⁵³ A father will be against his son and a son against his father. A mother will be against her daughter and a daughter against her mother. A mother-in-law will be against her daughter-in-law and a daughter-in-law against her mother-in-law."

Use Good Judgment

⁵⁴ Jesus said to the crowds, "When you see a cloud coming up in the west, you immediately say, 'There's going to be a rainstorm,' and it happens. ⁵⁵ When you see a south wind blowing, you say, 'It's going to be hot,' and that's what happens. ⁵⁶ You hypocrites! You can forecast the weather by judging the appearance of earth and sky. But for some reason you don't know how to judge the time in which you're living. ⁵⁷ So why don't you judge for yourselves what is right? ⁵⁸ For instance, when an opponent brings you to court in front of a ruler, do your best to settle with him before you get there. Otherwise, he will drag you in front of a judge. The judge will hand you over to an officer who will throw you into prison. ⁵⁹ I can guarantee that you won't get out until you pay every penny of your fine."

Jesus Tells People to Turn to God and Change the Way They Think and Act

13 ¹ At that time some people reported to Jesus about some Galileans whom Pilate had executed while they were sacrificing animals. ² Jesus replied to them, "Do you think that this happened to them because they were more sinful than other people from Galilee? ³ No! I can guarantee that they weren't. But if you don't turn to God and change the way you think and act, then you, too, will all die. ⁴ What about those 18 people who died when the tower at Siloam fell on them? Do you think that they were more sinful than other people living in Jerusalem? ⁵ No! I can guarantee that they weren't. But if you don't turn to God and change the way you think and act, then you, too, will all die."

A Story About a Fruitless Tree

⁶ Then Jesus used this illustration: "A man had a fig tree growing in his vineyard. He went to look for fruit on the tree but didn't find any. ⁷ He said to the gardener, 'For the last three years I've come to look for figs on this fig tree but haven't found any. Cut it down! Why should it use up ˎgoodˌ soil?'

⁸ "The gardener replied, 'Sir, let it stand for one more year. I'll dig around it and fertilize it. ⁹ Maybe next year it'll have figs. But if not, then cut it down.' "

Jesus Heals a Disabled Woman

¹⁰ Jesus was teaching in a synagogue on the day of worship. ¹¹ A woman who was possessed by a spirit was there. The spirit had disabled her for 18 years. She was hunched over and couldn't stand up straight. ¹² When Jesus saw her, he called her to come to him and said, "Woman, you are free from your disability." ¹³ He placed his hands on her, and she immediately stood up straight and praised God.

¹⁴ The synagogue leader was irritated with Jesus for healing on the day of worship. The leader told the crowd, "There are six days when work can be done. So come on one of those days to be healed. Don't come on the day of worship."

¹⁵ The Lord said, "You hypocrites! Don't each of you free your ox or donkey on the day of worship? Don't you then take it out of its stall to give it some water to drink? ¹⁶ Now, here is a descendant of Abraham. Satan has kept her in this condition for 18 years. Isn't it right to free her on the day of worship?"

¹⁷ As he said this, everyone who opposed him felt ashamed. But the entire crowd was happy about the miraculous things he was doing.

Stories About a Mustard Seed and Yeast—*Matthew 13:31–33; Mark 4:30–32*

¹⁸ Jesus asked, "What is the kingdom of God like? What can I compare it to? ¹⁹ It's like a mustard seed that someone planted in a garden. It grew and became a tree, and the birds nested in its branches."

²⁰ He asked again, "What can I compare the kingdom of God to? ²¹ It's like yeast that a woman mixed into a large amount of flour until the yeast worked its way through all the dough."

The Narrow Door

²² Then Jesus traveled and taught in one city and village after another on his way to Jerusalem.

²³ Someone asked him, "Sir, are only a few people going to be saved?"

He answered, ²⁴ "Try hard to enter through the narrow door. I can guarantee that many will try to enter, but they won't succeed. ²⁵ After the homeowner gets up and closes the door, it's too late. You can stand outside, knock at the door, and say, 'Sir, open the door for us!' But he will answer you, 'I don't know who you are.' ²⁶ Then you will say, 'We ate and drank with you, and you taught in our streets.' ²⁷ But he will tell you, 'I don't know who you are. Get away from me, all you evil people.' ²⁸ Then you will cry and be in extreme pain. That's what you'll do when you see Abraham, Isaac, Jacob, and all the prophets. They'll be in the kingdom of God, but you'll be thrown out. ²⁹ People will come from all over the world and will eat in the kingdom of God. ³⁰ Some who are last will be first, and some who are first will be last."

Jesus Warns Jerusalem

³¹ At that time some Pharisees told Jesus, "Get out of here, and go somewhere else! Herod wants to kill you."

³² Jesus said to them, "Tell that fox that I will force demons out of people and heal people today and tomorrow. I will finish my work on the third day. ³³ But I must be on my way today, tomorrow, and the next day. It's not possible for a prophet to die outside Jerusalem.

³⁴ "Jerusalem, Jerusalem, you kill the prophets and stone to death those sent to you! How often I wanted to gather your children together the way a hen gathers her chicks under her wings! But you were not willing! ³⁵ Your house will be abandoned. I can guarantee that you will not see me again until you say, 'Blessed is the one who comes in the name of the Lord!' "

Jesus Attends a Banquet

14 ¹ On a day of worship Jesus went to eat at the home of a prominent Pharisee. The guests were watching Jesus very closely.

² A man whose body was swollen with fluid was there. ³ Jesus reacted by asking the Pharisees and the experts in Moses' Teachings, "Is it right to heal on the day of worship or not?" ⁴ But they didn't say a thing.

So Jesus took hold of the man, healed him, and sent him away. ⁵ Jesus asked them, "If your son or your ox falls into a well on a day of worship, wouldn't you pull him out immediately?" ⁶ They couldn't argue with him about this.

⁷ Then Jesus noticed how the guests always chose the places of honor. So he used this illustration when he spoke to them: ⁸ "When someone invites you to a wedding, don't take the place of honor. Maybe someone more important than you was invited. ⁹ Then your host would say to you, 'Give this person your place.' Embarrassed, you would have to take the place of least honor. ¹⁰ So when you're invited, take the place of least honor. Then, when your host comes, he will tell you, 'Friend, move to a more honorable place.' Then all the other guests will see how you are honored. ¹¹ Those who honor themselves will be humbled, but people who humble themselves will be honored."

¹² Then he told the man who had invited him, "When you invite people for lunch or dinner, don't invite only your friends, family, other relatives, or rich neighbors. Otherwise, they will return the favor. ¹³ Instead, when you give a banquet, invite the poor, the handicapped, the lame, and the blind. ¹⁴ Then you will be blessed because they don't have any way to pay you back. You will be paid back when those who have God's approval come back to life."

¹⁵ One of those eating with him heard this. So he said to Jesus, "The person who will be at the banquet in the kingdom of God is blessed."

¹⁶ Jesus said to him, "A man gave a large banquet and invited many people. ¹⁷ When it was time for the banquet, he sent his servant to tell those who were invited, 'Come! Everything is ready now.'

¹⁸ "Everyone asked to be excused. The first said to him, 'I bought a field, and I need to see it. Please excuse me.' ¹⁹ Another said, 'I bought five pairs of oxen, and I'm on my way to see how well they plow. Please excuse me.' ²⁰ Still another said, 'I recently got married, and that's why I can't come.'

²¹ "The servant went back to report this to his master. Then the master of the house became angry. He told his servant, 'Run to every street and alley in the city! Bring back the poor, the handicapped, the blind, and the lame.'

²² "The servant said, 'Sir, what you've ordered has been done. But there is still room for more people.'

²³ "Then the master told his servant, 'Go to the roads and paths! Urge the people to come to my house. I want it to be full. ²⁴ I can guarantee that none of those invited earlier will taste any food at my banquet.' "

The Cost of Being a Disciple

²⁵ Large crowds were traveling with Jesus. He turned to them and said, ²⁶ "If people come to me and are not ready to abandon their fathers, mothers, wives, children, brothers, and sisters, as well as their own lives, they cannot be my disciples. ²⁷ So those who do not carry their crosses and follow me cannot be my disciples.

²⁸ "Suppose you want to build a tower. You would first sit down and figure out what it costs. Then you would see if you have enough money to finish it. ²⁹ Otherwise, if you lay a foundation and can't finish the building, everyone who watches will make fun of you. ³⁰ They'll say, 'This person started to build but couldn't finish the job.'

³¹ "Or suppose a king is going to war against another king. He would first sit down and think things through. Can he and his 10,000 soldiers fight against a king with 20,000 soldiers? ³² If he can't, he'll send ambassadors to ask for terms of peace while the other king is still far away. ³³ In the same way, none of you can be my disciples unless you give up everything.

³⁴ "Salt is good. But if salt loses its taste, how will you restore its flavor? ³⁵ It's not any good for the ground or for the manure pile. People throw it away.

"Let the person who has ears listen!"

The Lost Sheep—*Matthew 18:12–14*

15 ¹ All the tax collectors and sinners came to listen to Jesus. ² But the Pharisees and the scribes complained, "This man welcomes sinners and eats with them."

³ Jesus spoke to them using this illustration: ⁴ "Suppose a man has 100 sheep and loses one of them. Doesn't he leave the 99 sheep grazing in the pasture and look for the lost sheep until he finds it? ⁵ When he finds it, he's happy. He puts that sheep on his shoulders and ⁶ goes home. Then he calls his friends and neighbors together and says to them, 'Let's celebrate! I've found my lost sheep!' ⁷ I can guarantee that there will be more happiness in heaven over one person who turns to God and changes the way he thinks and acts than over 99 people who already have turned to God and have his approval."

The Lost Coin

⁸ "Suppose a woman has ten coins and loses one. Doesn't she light a lamp, sweep the house, and look for the coin carefully until she finds it? ⁹ When she finds it, she calls her friends and neighbors together and says, 'Let's celebrate! I've found the coin that I lost.' ¹⁰ So I can guarantee that God's angels are happy about one person who turns to God and changes the way he thinks and acts."

The Lost Son

¹¹ Then Jesus said, "A man had two sons. ¹² The younger son said to his father, 'Father, give me my share of the property.' So the father divided his property between his two sons.

¹³ "After a few days, the younger son gathered his possessions and left for a country far away from home. There he wasted everything he had on a wild lifestyle. ¹⁴ He had nothing left when a severe famine spread throughout that country. He had nothing to live on. ¹⁵ So he got a job from someone in that country and was sent to feed pigs in the fields. ¹⁶ No one in the country would give him any food, and he was so hungry that he would have eaten what the pigs were eating.

¹⁷ "Finally, he came to his senses. He said, 'How many of my father's hired men have more food than they can eat, while I'm starving to death here? ¹⁸ I'll go at once to my father, and I'll say to him, "Father, I've sinned against heaven and you. ¹⁹ I don't deserve to be called your son anymore. Make me one of your hired men." '

²⁰ "So he went at once to his father. While he was still at a distance, his father saw him and felt sorry for him. He ran to his son, put his arms around him, and kissed him. ²¹ Then his son said to him, 'Father, I've sinned against heaven and you. I don't deserve to be called your son anymore.'ᵃ

ᵃ 15:21 Some manuscripts and translations add "Make me one of your hired hands."

²² "The father said to his servants, 'Hurry! Bring out the best robe, and put it on him. Put a ring on his finger and sandals on his feet. ²³ Bring the fattened calf, kill it, and let's celebrate with a feast. ²⁴ My son was dead and has come back to life. He was lost but has been found.' Then they began to celebrate.

²⁵ "His older son was in the field. As he was coming back to the house, he heard music and dancing. ²⁶ He called to one of the servants and asked what was happening.

²⁷ "The servant told him, 'Your brother has come home. So your father has killed the fattened calf to celebrate your brother's safe return.'

²⁸ "Then the older son became angry and wouldn't go into the house. His father came out and begged him to come in. ²⁹ But he answered his father, 'All these years I've worked like a slave for you. I've never disobeyed one of your commands. Yet, you've never given me so much as a little goat for a celebration with my friends. ³⁰ But this son of yours spent your money on prostitutes, and when he came home, you killed the fattened calf for him.'

³¹ "His father said to him, 'My child, you're always with me. Everything I have is yours. ³² But we have something to celebrate, something to be happy about. This brother of yours was dead but has come back to life. He was lost but has been found.' "

Jesus Speaks About Dishonesty

16 ¹ Then Jesus said to his disciples, "A rich man had a business manager. The manager was accused of wasting the rich man's property. ² So the rich man called for his manager and said to him, 'What's this I hear about you? Let me examine your books. It's obvious that you can't manage my property any longer.'

³ "The manager thought, 'What should I do? My master is taking my job away from me. I'm not strong enough to dig, and I'm ashamed to beg. ⁴ I know what I'll do so that people will welcome me into their homes when I've lost my job.'

⁵ "So the manager called for each one of his master's debtors. He said to the first, 'How much do you owe my master?'

⁶ "The debtor replied, 'Eight hundred gallons of olive oil.'

"The manager told him, 'Take my master's ledger. Quick! Sit down, and write "four hundred!" '

⁷ "Then he asked another debtor, 'How much do you owe?'

"The debtor replied, 'A thousand bushels of wheat.'

"The manager told him, 'Take the ledger, and write "eight hundred!" '

⁸ "The master praised the dishonest manager for being so clever. Worldly people are more clever than spiritually-minded people when it comes to dealing with others."

⁹ Jesus continued, "I'm telling you that although wealth is often used in dishonest ways, you should use it to make friends for yourselves. When life is over, you will be welcomed into an eternal home. ¹⁰ Whoever can be trusted with very little can also be trusted with a lot. Whoever is dishonest with very little is dishonest with a lot. ¹¹ Therefore, if you can't be trusted with wealth that is often used dishonestly, who will trust you with wealth that is real? ¹² If you can't be trusted with someone else's wealth, who will give you your own?

¹³ "A servant cannot serve two masters. He will hate the first master and love the second, or he will be devoted to the first and despise the second. You cannot serve God and wealth."

¹⁴ The Pharisees, who love money, heard all this and were making sarcastic remarks about him. ¹⁵ So Jesus said to them, "You try to justify your actions in front of people. But God knows what's in your hearts. What is important to humans is disgusting to God.

¹⁶ "Moses' Teachings and the Prophets were in force until the time of John. Since that time, people have been telling the Good News about the kingdom of God, and everyone is trying to force their way into it. ¹⁷ It is easier for the earth and the heavens to disappear than to drop a comma from Moses' Teachings.

¹⁸ "Any man who divorces his wife to marry another woman is committing adultery. The man who marries a woman divorced in this way is committing adultery.

A Rich Man and Lazarus

¹⁹ "There was a rich man who wore expensive clothes. Every day was like a party to him. ²⁰ There was also a beggar named Lazarus who was regularly brought to the gate of the rich man's house. ²¹ Lazarus would have eaten any scraps that fell from the rich man's table. Lazarus was covered with sores,ᵃ and dogs would lick them.

²² "One day the beggar died, and the angels carried him to be with Abraham. The rich man also died and was buried. ²³ He went to hell, where he was constantly tortured. As he looked up, in the distance he saw Abraham and Lazarus. ²⁴ He yelled, 'Father Abraham! Have mercy

---

ᵃ 16:21 The last sentence in verse 20 (in Greek) has been moved to verse 21 to express the complex Greek paragraph structure more clearly in English.

on me! Send Lazarus to dip the tip of his finger in water to cool off my tongue. I am suffering in this fire.'

²⁵ "Abraham replied, 'Remember, my child, that you had a life filled with good times, while Lazarus' life was filled with misery. Now he has peace here, while you suffer. ²⁶ Besides, a wide area separates us. People couldn't cross it in either direction even if they wanted to.'

²⁷ "The rich man responded, 'Then I ask you, Father, to send Lazarus back to my father's home. ²⁸ I have five brothers. He can warn them so that they won't end up in this place of torture.'

²⁹ "Abraham replied, 'They have Moses' ˌTeachingsˌ and the Prophets. Your brothers should listen to them!'

³⁰ "The rich man replied, 'No, Father Abraham! If someone comes back to them from the dead, they will turn to God and change the way they think and act.'

³¹ "Abraham answered him, 'If they won't listen to Moses' ˌTeachingsˌ and the Prophets, they won't be persuaded even if someone comes back to life.' "

Causing Others to Lose Faith—*Matthew 18:6–10; Mark 9:42–50*

17 ¹ Jesus told his disciples, "Situations that cause people to lose their faith are certain to arise. But how horrible it will be for the person who causes someone to lose his faith! ² It would be best for that person to be thrown into the sea with a large stone hung around his neck than for him to cause one of these little ones to lose his faith. ³ So watch yourselves!

"If a believer sins, correct him. If he changes the way he thinks and acts, forgive him. ⁴ Even if he wrongs you seven times in one day and comes back to you seven times and says that he is sorry, forgive him."

The Apostles Ask For More Faith

⁵ Then the apostles said to the Lord, "Give us more faith."

⁶ The Lord said, "If you have faith the size of a mustard seed, you could say to this mulberry tree, 'Pull yourself up by the roots, and plant yourself in the sea!' and it would obey you.

⁷ "Suppose someone has a servant who is plowing fields or watching sheep. Does he tell his servant when he comes from the field, 'Have something to eat'? ⁸ No. Instead, he tells his servant, 'Get dinner ready for me! After you serve me my dinner, you can eat yours.' ⁹ He doesn't thank the servant for following orders. ¹⁰ That's the way it is with you. When you've done everything you're ordered to do, say, 'We're worthless servants. We've only done our duty.' "

Ten Men With a Skin Disease Are Healed

¹¹ Jesus traveled along the border between Samaria and Galilee on his way to Jerusalem. ¹² As he went into a village, ten men with a skin disease met him. They stood at a distance ¹³ and shouted, "Jesus, Teacher, have mercy on us!"

¹⁴ When he saw them, he told them, "Show yourselves to the priests." As they went, they were made clean.ᵃ ¹⁵ When one of them saw that he was healed, he turned back and praised God in a loud voice. ¹⁶ He quickly bowed at Jesus' feet and thanked him. (The man was a Samaritan.)

¹⁷ Jesus asked, "Weren't ten men made clean? Where are the other nine? ¹⁸ Only this foreigner came back to praise God."

¹⁹ Jesus told the man, "Get up, and go home! Your faith has made you well."

The Pharisees Ask About the Kingdom of God

²⁰ The Pharisees asked Jesus when the kingdom of God would come.

He answered them, "People can't observe the coming of the kingdom of God. ²¹ They can't say, 'Here it is!' or 'There it is!' You see, the kingdom of God is withinᵇ you."

Jesus Teaches About the Time When He Will Come Again

²² Jesus said to his disciples, "The time will come when you will long to see one of the days of the Son of Man, but you will not see it. ²³ People will say, 'There he is!' or 'Here he is!' Don't run after those people. ²⁴ The day of the Son of Manᶜ will be like lightning that flashes from one end of the sky to the other. ²⁵ But first he must suffer a lot and be rejected by the people of his day.

²⁶ "When the Son of Man comes again, the situation will be like the time of Noah. ²⁷ People were eating, drinking, and getting married until the day that Noah went into the ship. Then the flood destroyed all of them.

²⁸ "The situation will also be like the time of Lot. People were eating, drinking, buying and selling, planting and building. ²⁹ But on the day that Lot left Sodom, fire and sulfur rained from the sky and destroyed all of them. ³⁰ The day when the Son of Man is revealed will be like that.

ᵃ 17:14 "Clean" refers to anything that Moses' Teachings say is presentable to God.   ᵇ 17:21 Or "among."   ᶜ 17:24 Some manuscripts and translations omit "The day of."

31 "On that day those who are on the roof shouldn't come down to get their belongings out of their houses. Those who are in the field shouldn't turn back. **32** Remember Lot's wife! **33** Those who try to save their lives will lose them, and those who lose their lives will save them. **34** "I can guarantee that on that night if two people are in one bed, one will be taken and the other one will be left. **35** Two women will be grinding grain together. One will be taken, and the other one will be left."*d*

37 They asked him, "Where, Lord?"

Jesus told them, "Vultures will gather wherever there is a dead body."

God Will Help His People

18 **1** Jesus used this illustration with his disciples to show them that they need to pray all the time and never give up. **2** He said, "In a city there was a judge who didn't fear God or respect people. **3** In that city there was also a widow who kept coming to him and saying, 'Give me justice.'

4 "For a while the judge refused to do anything. But then he thought, 'This widow really annoys me. Although I don't fear God or respect people, **5** I'll have to give her justice. Otherwise, she'll keep coming to me until she wears me out.'"

6 The Lord added, "Pay attention to what the dishonest judge thought. **7** Won't God give his chosen people justice when they cry out to him for help day and night? Is he slow to help them? **8** I can guarantee that he will give them justice quickly. But when the Son of Man comes, will he find faith on earth?"

A Pharisee and a Tax Collector

9 Jesus also used this illustration with some who were sure that God approved of them while they looked down on everyone else. **10** He said, "Two men went into the temple courtyard to pray. One was a Pharisee, and the other was a tax collector. **11** The Pharisee stood up and prayed, 'God, I thank you that I'm not like other people! I'm not a robber or a dishonest person. I haven't committed adultery. I'm not even like this tax collector. **12** I fast twice a week, and I give you a tenth of my entire income.'

13 "But the tax collector was standing at a distance. He wouldn't even look up to heaven. Instead, he became very upset, and he said, 'God, be merciful to me, a sinner!'

14 "I can guarantee that this tax collector went home with God's approval, but the Pharisee didn't. Everyone who honors himself will be humbled, but the person who humbles himself will be honored."

Jesus Blesses Children—*Matthew 19:13–15; Mark 10:13–16*

15 Some people brought infants to Jesus to have him hold them. When the disciples saw this, they told the people not to do that.

16 But Jesus called the infants to him and said, "Don't stop the children from coming to me! Children like these are part of the kingdom of God. **17** I can guarantee this truth: Whoever doesn't receive the kingdom of God as a little child receives it will never enter it."

Eternal Life in the Kingdom—*Matthew 19:16–30; Mark 10:17–31*

18 An official asked Jesus, "Good Teacher, what must I do to inherit eternal life?"

19 Jesus said to him, "Why do you call me good? No one is good except God. **20** You know the commandments: Never commit adultery. Never murder. Never steal. Never give false testimony. Honor your father and your mother."

21 The official replied, "I've obeyed all these commandments since I was a boy."

22 When Jesus heard this, he said to him, "You still need one thing. Sell everything you have. Distribute the money to the poor, and you will have treasure in heaven. Then follow me!"

23 When the official heard this, he became sad, because he was very rich. **24** Jesus watched him and said, "How hard it is for rich people to enter the kingdom of God! **25** Indeed, it is easier for a camel to go through the eye of a needle than for a rich person to enter the kingdom of God."

26 Those who heard him asked, "Who, then, can be saved?"

27 Jesus said, "The things that are impossible for people to do are possible for God to do."

28 Then Peter said, "We've left everything to follow you."

29 Jesus said to them, "I can guarantee this truth: Anyone who gave up his home, wife, brothers, parents, or children because of the kingdom of God **30** will certainly receive many times as much in this life and will receive eternal life in the world to come."

---

d 17:35 Some manuscripts and translations add verse 36: "Two will be in a field. One will be taken, and the other will be left." See Matthew 24:40.

For the Third Time Jesus Foretells That He Will Die and Come Back to Life—
Matthew 20:17–19; Mark 10:32–34

³¹ Jesus took the twelve apostles aside and said to them, "We're going to Jerusalem. Everything that the prophets wrote about the Son of Man will come true. ³² He will be handed over to foreigners. They will make fun of him, insult him, spit on him, ³³ whip him, and kill him. But on the third day he will come back to life."

³⁴ But they didn't understand any of this. What he said was a mystery to them, and they didn't know what he meant.

Jesus Gives Sight to a Blind Man—*Matthew 20:29–34; Mark 10:46–52*

³⁵ As Jesus came near Jericho, a blind man was sitting and begging by the road. ³⁶ When he heard the crowd going by, he tried to find out what was happening. ³⁷ The people told him that Jesus from Nazareth was passing by. ³⁸ Then the blind man shouted, "Jesus, Son of David, have mercy on me!" ³⁹ The people at the front of the crowd told the blind man to be quiet. But he shouted even louder, "Son of David, have mercy on me!"

⁴⁰ Jesus stopped and ordered them to bring the man to him. When the man came near, Jesus asked him, ⁴¹ "What do you want me to do for you?"

The blind man said, "Lord, I want to see again."

⁴² Jesus told him, "Receive your sight! Your faith has made you well." ⁴³ Immediately, he could see again. He followed Jesus and praised God. All the people saw this, and they, too, praised God.

Zacchaeus Meets Jesus

19 ¹ Jesus was passing through Jericho. ² A man named Zacchaeus was there. He was the director of tax collectors, and he was rich. ³ He tried to see who Jesus was. But Zacchaeus was a small man, and he couldn't see Jesus because of the crowd. ⁴ So Zacchaeus ran ahead and climbed a fig tree to see Jesus, who was coming that way.

⁵ When Jesus came to the tree, he looked up and said, "Zacchaeus, come down! I must stay at your house today."

⁶ Zacchaeus came down and was glad to welcome Jesus into his home. ⁷ But the people who saw this began to express disapproval. They said, "He went to be the guest of a sinner."

⁸ Later, at dinner, Zacchaeus stood up and said to the Lord, "Lord, I'll give half of my property to the poor. I'll pay four times as much as I owe to those I have cheated in any way."

⁹ Then Jesus said to Zacchaeus, "You and your family have been saved today. You've shown that you, too, are one of Abraham's descendants. ¹⁰ Indeed, the Son of Man has come to seek and to save people who are lost."

A Story About a King

¹¹ Jesus was getting closer to Jerusalem, and the people thought that the kingdom of God would appear suddenly. While Jesus had the people's attention, he used this illustration. ¹² He said, "A prince went to a distant country to be appointed king, and then he returned. ¹³ Before he left, he called ten of his servants and gave them ten coins. He said to his servants, 'Invest this money until I come back.'

¹⁴ "The citizens of his own country hated him. They sent representatives to follow him and say to the person who was going to appoint him, 'We don't want this man to be our king.'

¹⁵ "After he was appointed king, he came back. Then he said, 'Call those servants to whom I gave money. I want to know how much each one has made by investing.'

¹⁶ "The first servant said, 'Sir, the coin you gave me has earned ten times as much.'

¹⁷ "The king said to him, 'Good job! You're a good servant. You proved that you could be trusted with a little money. Take charge of ten cities.'

¹⁸ "The second servant said, 'The coin you gave me, sir, has made five times as much.'

¹⁹ "The king said to this servant, 'You take charge of five cities.'

²⁰ "Then the other servant said, 'Sir, look! Here's your coin. I've kept it in a cloth for safekeeping because ²¹ I was afraid of you. You're a tough person to get along with. You take what isn't yours and harvest grain you haven't planted.'

²² "The king said to him, 'I'll judge you by what you've said, you evil servant! You knew that I was a tough person to get along with. You knew that I take what isn't mine and harvest grain I haven't planted. ²³ Then why didn't you put my money in the bank? When I came back, I could have collected it with interest.' ²⁴ The king told his men, 'Take his coin away, and give it to the man who has ten.'

²⁵ "They replied, 'Sir, he already has ten coins.'

²⁶ " 'I can guarantee that everyone who has something will be given more. But everything will be taken away from those who don't have much. ²⁷ Bring my enemies, who didn't want me to be their king. Kill them in front of me.' "

The King Comes to Jerusalem—*Matthew 21:1–11; Mark 11:1–11; John 12:12–19*

[28] After Jesus had given this illustration, he continued on his way to Jerusalem.

[29] When he came near Bethphage and Bethany at the Mount of Olives (as it was called), Jesus sent two of his disciples ahead of him. [30] He said to them, "Go into the village ahead of you. As you enter, you will find a young donkey tied there. No one has ever sat on it. Untie it, and bring it. [31] If anyone asks you why you are untying it, say that the Lord needs it."

[32] The men Jesus sent found it as he had told them. [33] While they were untying the young donkey, its owners asked them, "Why are you untying the donkey?"

[34] The disciples answered, "The Lord needs it."

[35] They brought the donkey to Jesus, put their coats on it, and helped Jesus onto it. [36] As he was riding along, people spread their coats on the road. [37] By this time he was coming near the place where the road went down the Mount of Olives. Then the whole crowd of disciples began to praise God for all the miracles they had seen. [38] They shouted joyfully,

> "Blessed is the king who comes in the name of the Lord!
> Peace in heaven, and glory in the highest heaven."

[39] Some of the Pharisees in the crowd said to Jesus, "Teacher, tell your disciples to be quiet."

[40] Jesus replied, "I can guarantee that if they are quiet, the stones will cry out."

[41] When he came closer and saw the city, he began to cry. [42] He said, "If you had only known today what would bring you peace! But now it is hidden, so you cannot see it. [43] The time will come when enemy armies will build a wall to surround you and close you in on every side. [44] They will level you to the ground and kill your people. One stone will not be left on top of another, because you didn't recognize the time when God came to help you."

Jesus Throws Out the Moneychangers—*Matthew 21:12–17; Mark 11:15–19*

[45] Jesus went into the temple courtyard and began to throw out those who were selling things there. [46] He said to them, "Scripture says, 'My house will be a house of prayer,' but you have turned it into a gathering place for thieves."

[47] Jesus taught in the temple courtyard every day. The chief priests, the scribes, and the leaders of the people looked for a way to kill him. [48] But they could not find a way to do it, because all the people were eager to hear him.

Jesus' Authority Challenged—*Matthew 21:23–27; Mark 11:27–33*

20 [1] One day Jesus was teaching the people in the temple courtyard and telling them the Good News. The chief priests, scribes, and leaders came up to him. [2] They asked him, "Tell us, what gives you the right to do these things? Who told you that you could do this?"

[3] Jesus answered them, "I, too, have a question for you. Tell me, [4] did John's right to baptize come from heaven or from humans?"

[5] They talked about this among themselves. They said, "If we say, 'from heaven,' he will ask, 'Why didn't you believe him?' [6] But if we say, 'from humans,' everyone will stone us to death. They're convinced that John was a prophet." [7] So they answered that they didn't know who gave John the right to baptize.

[8] Jesus told them, "Then I won't tell you why I have the right to do these things."

A Story About a Vineyard—*Matthew 21:33–46; Mark 12:1–12*

[9] Then, using this illustration, Jesus spoke to the people: "A man planted a vineyard, leased it to vineyard workers, and went on a long trip.

[10] "At the right time he sent a servant to the workers to obtain from them a share of the grapes from the vineyard. But the workers beat the servant and sent him back with nothing. [11] So he sent a different servant. The workers beat him, treated him shamefully, and sent him back with nothing. [12] Then he sent a third servant. But they injured this one and threw him out ˌof the vineyardˌ.

[13] "Then the owner of the vineyard said, 'What should I do? I'll send my son, whom I love. They'll probably respect him.'

[14] "When the workers saw him, they talked it over among themselves. They said, 'This is the heir. Let's kill him so that the inheritance will be ours.' [15] So they threw him out of the vineyard and killed him.

"What will the owner of the vineyard do to them? [16] He will destroy these workers and give the vineyard to others."

Those who heard him said, "That's unthinkable!"

[17] Then Jesus looked straight at them and asked, "What, then, does this Scripture verse mean:

> 'The stone that the builders rejected
> has become the cornerstone'?

¹⁸ Everyone who falls on that stone will be broken. If that stone falls on anyone, it will crush that person."

¹⁹ The scribes and the chief priests wanted to arrest him right there, but they were afraid of the people. They knew that he had directed this illustration at them.

A Question About Taxes—*Matthew 22:15–22; Mark 12:13–17*

²⁰ So they watched for an opportunity to send out some spies. The spies were to act like sincere religious people. They wanted to catch him saying the wrong thing so that they could hand him over to the governor. ²¹ They asked him, "Teacher, we know that you're right in what you say and teach. Besides, you don't play favorites. Rather, you teach the way of God truthfully. ²² Is it right for us to pay taxes to the emperor or not?"

²³ He saw through their scheme, so he said to them, ²⁴ "Show me a coin. Whose face and name is this?"

They answered, "The emperor's."

²⁵ He said to them, "Well, then give the emperor what belongs to the emperor, and give God what belongs to God."

²⁶ They couldn't make him say anything wrong in front of the people. His answer surprised them, so they said no more.

The Dead Come Back to Life—*Matthew 22:23–33; Mark 12:18–27*

²⁷ Some Sadducees, who say that people will never come back to life, came to Jesus. They asked him, ²⁸ "Teacher, Moses wrote for us, 'If a married man dies and has no children, his brother should marry his widow and have children for his brother.' ²⁹ There were seven brothers. The first got married and died without having children. ³⁰ Then the second brother married the widow, ³¹ and so did the third. In the same way all seven brothers married the widow, died, and left no children. ³² Finally, the woman died. ³³ Now, when the dead come back to life, whose wife will she be? The seven brothers had married her."

³⁴ Jesus said to them, "In this world people get married. ³⁵ But people who are considered worthy to come back to life and live in the next world will neither marry ³⁶ nor die anymore. They are the same as the angels. They are God's children who have come back to life.

³⁷ "Even Moses showed in the passage about the bush that the dead come back to life. He says that the Lord is the God of Abraham, Isaac, and Jacob. ³⁸ He's not the God of the dead but of the living. In God's sight all people are living."

³⁹ Some scribes responded, "Teacher, that was well said." ⁴⁰ From that time on, no one dared to ask him another question.

How Can David's Son Be David's Lord?—*Matthew 22:41–46; Mark 12:35–37a*

⁴¹ Jesus said to them, "How can people say that the Messiah is David's son? ⁴² David says in the book of Psalms,

> 'The Lord said to my Lord,
> "Take the highest position in heaven
> ⁴³   until I make your enemies your footstool." '

⁴⁴ David calls him Lord. So how can he be his son?"

Jesus Disapproves of the Example Set By Scribes—*Matthew 23:1–12; Mark 12:37b–40*

⁴⁵ While all the people were listening, Jesus said to the disciples, ⁴⁶ "Beware of the scribes! They like to walk around in long robes and love to be greeted in the marketplaces, to have the front seats in the synagogues and the places of honor at dinners. ⁴⁷ They rob widows by taking their houses and then say long prayers to make themselves look good. The scribes will receive the most severe punishment."

A Widow's Contribution—*Mark 12:41–44*

21 ¹ Looking up, Jesus saw people, especially the rich, dropping their gifts into the temple offering box. ² He noticed a poor widow drop in two small coins. ³ He said, "I can guarantee this truth: This poor widow has given more than all the others. ⁴ All of these people have given what they could spare. But she, in her poverty, has given everything she had to live on."

Jesus Teaches His Disciples—*Matthew 24:1–35; Mark 13:1–31*

⁵ Some ⸢of the disciples⸣ were talking about the temple complex. They noted that it was built with fine stones and decorated with beautiful gifts. So Jesus said, ⁶ "About these buildings that you see—the time will come when not one of these stones will be left on top of another. Each one will be torn down."

⁷The disciples asked him, "Teacher, when will this happen? What will be the sign when all this will occur?"

⁸Jesus said, "Be careful that you are not deceived. Many will come using my name. They will say, 'I am he!' and 'The time is near.' Don't follow them!

⁹"When you hear of wars and revolutions, don't be terrified! These things must happen first, but the end will not come immediately."

¹⁰Then Jesus continued, "Nation will fight against nation and kingdom against kingdom. ¹¹There will be terrible earthquakes, famines, and dreadful diseases in various places. Terrifying sights and miraculous signs will come from the sky.

¹²"Before all these things happen, people will arrest and persecute you. They will hand you over to their synagogues and put you into their prisons. They will drag you in front of kings and governors because of my name. ¹³It will be your opportunity to testify to them. ¹⁴So make up your minds not to worry beforehand how you will defend yourselves. ¹⁵I will give you words and wisdom that none of your enemies will be able to oppose or prove wrong.

¹⁶"Even parents, brothers, relatives, and friends will betray you and kill some of you. ¹⁷Everyone will hate you because you are committed to me. ¹⁸But not a hair on your head will be lost. ¹⁹By your endurance you will save your life.

²⁰"When you see armies camped around Jerusalem, realize that the time is near for it to be destroyed. ²¹Then those of you in Judea should flee to the mountains. Those of you in Jerusalem should leave it. Those of you in the fields shouldn't go back into them. ²²This will be a time of vengeance. Everything that is written about it will come true.

²³"How horrible it will be for women who are pregnant or who are nursing babies in those days. Indeed, the land will suffer very hard times, and its people will be punished. ²⁴Swords will cut them down, and they will be carried off into all nations as prisoners. Nations will trample Jerusalem until the times allowed for the nations ˌto do this˛ are over.

²⁵"Miraculous signs will occur in the sun, moon, and stars. The nations of the earth will be deeply troubled and confused because of the roaring and tossing of the sea. ²⁶People will faint as they fearfully wait for what will happen to the world. Indeed, the powers of the universe will be shaken.

²⁷"Then people will see the Son of Man coming in a cloud with power and great glory.

²⁸"When these things begin to happen, stand with confidence! The time when you will be set free is near."

²⁹Then Jesus used this story as an illustration. "Look at the fig tree or any other tree. ³⁰As soon as leaves grow on them, you know without being told that summer is near. ³¹In the same way, when you see these things happen, you know that the kingdom of God is near.

³²"I can guarantee this truth: This generation will not disappear until all this takes place. ³³The earth and the heavens will disappear, but my words will never disappear.

No One Knows When the Earth and the Heavens Will Disappear

³⁴"Make sure that you don't become drunk, hung over, and worried about life. Then that day could suddenly catch you by surprise ³⁵like a trap that catches a bird. That day will surprise all people who live on the earth. ³⁶Be alert at all times. Pray so that you have the power to escape everything that is about to happen and to stand in front of the Son of Man."

³⁷During the day Jesus would teach in the temple courtyard. But at night he would go to the Mount of Olives (as it was called) and spend the night there. ³⁸All of the people would get up early to hear him speak in the temple courtyard.

The Plot to Kill Jesus—Matthew 26:1–5, 14–16; Mark 14:1–2, 10–11; John 11:45–57

22 ¹The Festival of Unleavened Bread, called Passover, was near. ²The chief priests and the scribes were looking for some way to kill Jesus. However, they were afraid of the people.

³Then Satan entered Judas Iscariot, one of the twelve apostles. ⁴Judas went to the chief priests and the temple guards and discussed with them how he could betray Jesus. ⁵They were pleased and agreed to give him some money. ⁶So Judas promised to do it. He kept looking for an opportunity to betray Jesus to them when there was no crowd.

The Passover—Matthew 26:17–20; Mark 14:12–17

⁷The day came during the Festival of Unleavened Bread when the Passover lamb had to be killed. ⁸Jesus sent Peter and John and told them, "Go, prepare the Passover lamb for us to eat."

⁹They asked him, "Where do you want us to prepare it?"

¹⁰He told them, "Go into the city, and you will meet a man carrying a jug of water. Follow him into the house he enters. ¹¹Tell the owner of the house that the teacher asks, 'Where is the room where I can eat the Passover meal with my disciples?' ¹²He will take you upstairs and show you a large furnished room. Get things ready there."

¹³ The disciples left. They found everything as Jesus had told them and prepared the Passover.

¹⁴ When it was time to eat the Passover meal, Jesus and the apostles were at the table. ¹⁵ Jesus said to them, "I've had a deep desire to eat this Passover with you before I suffer. ¹⁶ I can guarantee that I won't eat it again until it finds its fulfillment in the kingdom of God." ¹⁷ Then he took a cup and spoke a prayer of thanksgiving. He said, "Take this, and share it. ¹⁸ I can guarantee that from now on I won't drink this wine until the kingdom of God comes."

The Lord's Supper—*Matthew 26:26–30; Mark 14:22–26*

¹⁹ Then Jesus took bread and spoke a prayer of thanksgiving. He broke the bread, gave it to them, and said, "This is my body, which is given up for you. Do this to remember me." ²⁰ When supper was over, he did the same with the cup. He said, "This cup that is poured out for you is the new promiseᵃ made with my blood."

Jesus Knows Who Will Betray Him—*Matthew 26:21–25; Mark 14:18–21; John 13:21–30*

²¹ "The hand of the one who will betray me is with me on the table. ²² The Son of Man is going to die the way it has been planned for him. But how horrible it will be for that person who betrays him."

²³ So they began to discuss with each other who could do such a thing.

An Argument About Greatness

²⁴ Then a quarrel broke out among the disciples. They argued about who should be considered the greatest.

²⁵ Jesus said to them, "The kings of nations have power over their people, and those in authority call themselves friends of the people. ²⁶ But you're not going to be that way! Rather, the greatest among you must be like the youngest, and your leader must be like a servant. ²⁷ Who's the greatest, the person who sits at the table or the servant? Isn't it really the person who sits at the table? But I'm among you as a servant.

²⁸ "You have stood by me in the troubles that have tested me. ²⁹ So as my Father has given me a kingdom, I'm giving it to you. ³⁰ You will eat and drink at my table in my kingdom. You will also sit on thrones and judge the twelve tribes of Israel."

Jesus Predicts Peter's Denial—*Matthew 26:31–35; Mark 14:27–31; John 13:36–38*

³¹ ˻Then the Lord said,˺ "Simon, Simon, listen! Satan has demanded to have you apostles for himself. He wants to separate you from me as a farmer separates wheat from husks. ³² But I have prayed for you, Simon, that your faith will not fail. So when you recover, strengthen the other disciples."

³³ But Peter said to him, "Lord, I'm ready to go to prison with you and to die with you."

³⁴ Jesus replied, "Peter, I can guarantee that the rooster won't crow tonight until you say three times that you don't know me."

³⁵ Then Jesus said to them, "When I sent you out without a wallet, traveling bag, or sandals, you didn't lack anything, did you?"

"Not a thing!" they answered.

³⁶ Then he said to them, "But now, the person who has a wallet and a traveling bag should take them along. The person who doesn't have a sword should sell his coat and buy one. ³⁷ I can guarantee that the Scripture passage which says, 'He was counted with criminals,' must find its fulfillment in me. Indeed, whatever is written about me will come true."

³⁸ The disciples said, "Lord, look! Here are two swords!"

Then Jesus said to them, "That's enough!"

Jesus Prays in the Garden of Gethsemane—*Matthew 26:36–46; Mark 14:32–42*

³⁹ Jesus went out ˻of the city˺ to the Mount of Olives as he usually did. His disciples followed him. ⁴⁰ When he arrived, he said to them, "Pray that you won't be tempted."

⁴¹ Then he withdrew from them about a stone's throw, knelt down, and prayed, ⁴² "Father, if it is your will, take this cup ˻of suffering˺ away from me. However, your will must be done, not mine."

⁴³ Then an angel from heaven appeared to him and gave him strength. ⁴⁴ So he prayed very hard in anguish. His sweat became like drops of blood falling to the ground.ᵇ

⁴⁵ When Jesus ended his prayer, he got up and went to the disciples. He found them asleep and overcome with sadness. ⁴⁶ He said to them, "Why are you sleeping? Get up, and pray that you won't be tempted."

ᵃ 22:20 Or "testament," or "covenant."　　ᵇ 22:44 Some manuscripts and translations omit verses 43 and 44.

Jesus Is Arrested—*Matthew 26:47–56; Mark 14:43–52; John 18:1–14*

⁴⁷ While he was still speaking to the disciples, a crowd arrived. The man called Judas, one of the twelve apostles, was leading them. He came close to Jesus to kiss him.

⁴⁸ Jesus said to him, "Judas, do you intend to betray the Son of Man with a kiss?"

⁴⁹ The men who were with Jesus saw what was going to happen. So they asked him, "Lord, should we use our swords to fight?" ⁵⁰ One of the disciples cut off the right ear of the chief priest's servant.

⁵¹ But Jesus said, "Stop! That's enough of this." Then he touched the servant's ear and healed him.

⁵² Then Jesus said to the chief priests, temple guards, and leaders who had come for him, "Have you come out with swords and clubs as if I were a criminal? ⁵³ I was with you in the temple courtyard every day and you didn't try to arrest me. But this is your time, when darkness rules."

⁵⁴ So they arrested Jesus and led him away to the chief priest's house.

Peter Denies Jesus—*Matthew 26:69–75; Mark 14:66–72; John 18:15–18, 25–27*

Peter followed at a distance.

⁵⁵ Some men had lit a fire in the middle of the courtyard. As they sat together, Peter sat among them. ⁵⁶ A female servant saw him as he sat facing the glow of the fire. She stared at him and said, "This man was with Jesus."

⁵⁷ But Peter denied it by saying, "I don't know him, woman."

⁵⁸ A little later someone else saw Peter and said, "You are one of them."

But Peter said, "Not me!"

⁵⁹ About an hour later another person insisted, "It's obvious that this man was with him. He's a Galilean!"

⁶⁰ But Peter said, "I don't know what you're talking about!"

Just then, while he was still speaking, a rooster crowed. ⁶¹ Then the Lord turned and looked directly at Peter. Peter remembered what the Lord had said: "Before a rooster crows today, you will say three times that you don't know me." ⁶² Then Peter went outside and cried bitterly.

The Trial in Front of the Jewish Council—*Matthew 26:57–68; Mark 14:53–65*

⁶³ The men who were guarding Jesus made fun of him as they beat him. ⁶⁴ They blindfolded him and said to him, "Tell us who hit you." ⁶⁵ They also insulted him in many other ways.

⁶⁶ In the morning the council of the people's leaders, the chief priests and the scribes, gathered together. They brought Jesus in front of their highest court and asked him, ⁶⁷ "Tell us, are you the Messiah?"

Jesus said to them, "If I tell you, you won't believe me. ⁶⁸ And if I ask you, you won't answer. ⁶⁹ But from now on, the Son of Man will be in the highest position in heaven."

⁷⁰ Then all of them said, "So you're the Son of God?"

Jesus answered them, "You're right to say that I am."

⁷¹ Then they said, "Why do we need any more testimony? We've heard him say it ourselves."

Pilate Questions Jesus—*Matthew 27:11–14; Mark 15:1–5; John 18:28–38*

23 ¹ Then the entire assembly stood up and took him to Pilate.

² They began to accuse Jesus by saying, "We found that he stirs up trouble among our people: He keeps them from paying taxes to the emperor, and he says that he is Christ, a king."

³ Pilate asked him, "Are you the king of the Jews?"

"Yes, I am," Jesus answered.

⁴ Pilate said to the chief priests and the crowd, "I can't find this man guilty of any crime."

Pilate Sends Jesus to Herod

⁵ The priests and the crowd became more forceful. They said, "He stirs up the people throughout Judea with his teachings. He started in Galilee and has come here."

⁶ When Pilate heard that, he asked if the man was from Galilee. ⁷ When Pilate found out that he was, he sent Jesus to Herod. Herod ruled Galilee and was in Jerusalem at that time.

⁸ Herod was very pleased to see Jesus. For a long time he had wanted to see him. He had heard about Jesus and hoped to see him perform some kind of miracle. ⁹ Herod asked Jesus many questions, but Jesus wouldn't answer him. ¹⁰ Meanwhile, the chief priests and the scribes stood there and shouted their accusations against Jesus.

¹¹ Herod and his soldiers treated Jesus with contempt and made fun of him. They put a colorful robe on him and sent him back to Pilate. ¹² So Herod and Pilate became friends that day. They had been enemies before this.

¹³ Then Pilate called together the chief priests, the rulers, and the people. ¹⁴ He told them, "You brought me this man as someone who turns the people against the government. I've

questioned him in front of you and haven't found this man guilty of the crimes of which you accuse him. [15] Neither could Herod. So he sent this man back to us. This man hasn't done anything to deserve the death penalty. [16] So I'm going to have him whipped and set free."[a]

The Crowd Rejects Jesus—*Matthew 27:15–26; Mark 15:6–15; John 18:39–40*

[18] The whole crowd then shouted, "Take him away! Free Barabbas for us." [19] (Barabbas had been thrown into prison for his involvement in a riot that had taken place in the city and for murder.)

[20] But because Pilate wanted to free Jesus, he spoke to the people again.

[21] They began yelling, "Crucify him! Crucify him!"

[22] A third time Pilate spoke to them. He asked, "Why? What has he done wrong? I haven't found this man deserving of the death penalty. So I'm going to have him whipped and set free."

[23] But the crowd pressured Pilate. They shouted that Jesus had to be crucified, and they finally won. [24] Pilate decided to give in to their demand. [25] He freed Barabbas, who had been put in prison for rioting and murdering, because that's what they wanted. But he let them do what they wanted to Jesus.

Jesus Is Led Away to Be Crucified

[26] As the soldiers led Jesus away, they grabbed a man named Simon, who was from the city of Cyrene. Simon was coming into Jerusalem. They laid the cross on him and made him carry it behind Jesus.

[27] A large crowd followed Jesus. The women in the crowd cried and sang funeral songs for him. [28] Jesus turned to them and said, "You women of Jerusalem, don't cry for me! Rather, cry for yourselves and your children! [29] The time is coming when people will say, 'Blessed are the women who couldn't get pregnant, who couldn't give birth, and who couldn't nurse a child.' [30] Then people will say to the mountains, 'Fall on us!' and to the hills, 'Cover us!' [31] If people do this to a green tree, what will happen to a dry one?"

[32] Two others, who were criminals, were led away to be executed with him.

The Crucifixion—*Matthew 27:31–44; Mark 15:20–32; John 19:16b–24*

[33] When they came to the place called The Skull, they crucified him. The criminals were also crucified, one on his right and the other on his left.

[34] Then Jesus said, "Father, forgive them. They don't know what they're doing."[b]

Meanwhile, the soldiers divided his clothes among themselves by throwing dice.

[35] The people stood there watching. But the rulers were making sarcastic remarks. They said, "He saved others. If he's the Messiah that God has chosen, let him save himself!" [36] The soldiers also made fun of him. They would go up to him, offer him some vinegar, [37] and say, "If you're the king of the Jews, save yourself!"

[38] A written notice was placed above him. It said, "This is the king of the Jews."

Criminals Talk to Jesus

[39] One of the criminals hanging there insulted Jesus by saying, "So you're really the Messiah, are you? Well, save yourself and us!"

[40] But the other criminal scolded him: "Don't you fear God at all? Can't you see that you're condemned in the same way that he is? [41] Our punishment is fair. We're getting what we deserve. But this man hasn't done anything wrong."

[42] Then he said, "Jesus, remember me when you enter your kingdom."

[43] Jesus said to him, "I can guarantee this truth: Today you will be with me in paradise."

Jesus Dies on the Cross—*Matthew 27:45–56; Mark 15:33–41; John 19:28–30*

[44] Around noon darkness came over the entire land and lasted until three in the afternoon. [45] The sun had stopped shining. The curtain in the temple was split in two.

[46] Jesus cried out in a loud voice, "Father, into your hands I entrust my spirit." After he said this, he died.

[47] When an army officer saw what had happened, he praised God and said, "Certainly, this man was innocent!" [48] Crowds had gathered to see the sight. But when all of them saw what had happened, they cried and returned to the city. [49] All his friends, including the women who had followed him from Galilee, stood at a distance and watched everything.

---

[a] 23:16 Some manuscripts and translations add verse 17: "At every Passover festival the governor had to set someone free for them."   [b] 23:34 Some manuscripts and translations omit "Then . . . doing."

Jesus Is Buried—*Matthew 27:57–61; Mark 15:42–47; John 19:38–42*

⁵⁰ There was a good man who had God's approval. His name was Joseph. He was a member of the Jewish council, ⁵¹ but he had not agreed with what they had done. He was from the Jewish city of Arimathea, and he was waiting for the kingdom of God.

⁵² He went to Pilate and asked for the body of Jesus. ⁵³ After he took it down from the cross, he wrapped it in linen. Then he laid the body in a tomb cut in rock, a tomb in which no one had ever been buried. ⁵⁴ It was Friday, and the day of worship was just beginning.

⁵⁵ The women who had come with Jesus from Galilee followed closely behind Joseph. They observed the tomb and how his body was laid in it. ⁵⁶ Then they went back to the city and prepared spices and perfumes. But on the day of worship they rested according to the commandment.

Jesus Comes Back to Life—*Matthew 28:1–10; Mark 16:1–8; John 20:1–10*

24 ¹ Very early on Sunday morning the women went to the tomb. They were carrying the spices that they had prepared. ² They found that the stone had been rolled away from the tomb. ³ When they went in, they did not find the body of the Lord Jesus. ⁴ While they were puzzled about this, two men in clothes that were as bright as lightning suddenly stood beside them. ⁵ The women were terrified and bowed to the ground.

The men asked the women, "Why are you looking among the dead for the living one? ⁶ He's not here. He has been brought back to life! Remember what he told you while he was still in Galilee. ⁷ He said, 'The Son of Man must be handed over to sinful people, be crucified, and come back to life on the third day.' " ⁸ Then the women remembered what Jesus had told them.

⁹ The women left the tomb and went back to the city. They told everything to the eleven apostles and all the others. ¹⁰ The women were Mary from Magdala, Joanna, and Mary (the mother of James). There were also other women with them. They told the apostles everything.

¹¹ The apostles thought that the women's story didn't make any sense, and they didn't believe them.

¹² But Peter got up and ran to the tomb. He bent down to look inside and saw only the strips of linen. Then he went away, wondering what had happened.

Jesus Appears to Disciples on a Road to Emmaus

¹³ On the same day, two of Jesus' disciples were going to a village called Emmaus. It was about seven miles from Jerusalem. ¹⁴ They were talking to each other about everything that had happened.

¹⁵ While they were talking, Jesus approached them and began walking with them. ¹⁶ Although they saw him, they didn't recognize him.

¹⁷ He asked them, "What are you discussing?"

They stopped and looked very sad. ¹⁸ One of them, Cleopas, replied, "Are you the only one in Jerusalem who doesn't know what has happened recently?"

¹⁹ "What happened?" he asked.

They said to him, "We were discussing what happened to Jesus from Nazareth. He was a powerful prophet in what he did and said in the sight of God and all the people. ²⁰ Our chief priests and rulers had him condemned to death and crucified. ²¹ We were hoping that he was the one who would free Israel. What's more, this is now the third day since everything happened. ²² Some of the women from our group startled us. They went to the tomb early this morning ²³ and didn't find his body. They told us that they had seen angels who said that he's alive. ²⁴ Some of our men went to the tomb and found it empty, as the women had said, but they didn't see him."

²⁵ Then Jesus said to them, "How foolish you are! You're so slow to believe everything the prophets said! ²⁶ Didn't the Messiah have to suffer these things and enter into his glory?" ²⁷ Then he began with Moses' Teachings and the Prophets to explain to them what was said about him throughout the Scriptures.

²⁸ When they came near the village where they were going, Jesus acted as if he were going farther. ²⁹ They urged him, "Stay with us! It's getting late, and the day is almost over." So he went to stay with them.

³⁰ While he was at the table with them, he took bread and blessed it. He broke the bread and gave it to them. ³¹ Then their eyes were opened, and they recognized him. But he vanished from their sight.

³² They said to each other, "Weren't we excited when he talked with us on the road and opened up the meaning of the Scriptures for us?"

³³ That same hour they went back to Jerusalem. They found the eleven apostles and those who were with them gathered together. ³⁴ They were saying, "The Lord has really come back to life and has appeared to Simon."

[35] Then the two disciples told what had happened on the road and how they had recognized Jesus when he broke the bread.

Jesus Appears to the Apostles—*John 20:19–23*

[36] While they were talking about what had happened, Jesus stood among them. He said to them, "Peace be with you!" [37] They were terrified, and thought they were seeing a ghost. [38] He asked them, "Why are you afraid? Why do you have doubts? [39] Look at my hands and feet, and see that it's really me. Touch me, and see for yourselves. Ghosts don't have flesh and bones, but you can see that I do." [40] As he said this, he showed them his hands and feet.

[41] The disciples were overcome with joy and amazement because this seemed too good to be true. Then Jesus asked them, "Do you have anything to eat?" [42] They gave him a piece of broiled fish. [43] He took it and ate it while they watched him.

[44] Then he said to them, "These are the words I spoke to you while I was still with you. I told you that everything written about me in Moses' Teachings, the Prophets, and the Psalms had to come true." [45] Then he opened their minds to understand the Scriptures. [46] He said to them, "Scripture says that the Messiah would suffer and that he would come back to life on the third day. [47] Scripture also says that by the authority of Jesus people would be told to turn to God and change the way they think and act so that their sins will be forgiven. This would be told to people from all nations, beginning in the city of Jerusalem. [48] You are witnesses to these things.

[49] "I'm sending you what my Father promised. Wait here in the city until you receive power from heaven."

[50] Then Jesus took them to a place near Bethany. There he raised his hands and blessed them. [51] While he was blessing them, he left them and was taken to heaven.

[52] The disciples worshiped him and were overjoyed as they went back to Jerusalem. [53] They were always in the temple, where they praised God.

JOHN

The Word Becomes Human

1 ¹ In the beginning the Word already existed. The Word was with God, and the Word was God. ² He was already with God in the beginning.

³ Everything came into existence through him. Not one thing that exists was made without him.

⁴ He was the source of life, and that life was the light for humanity.

⁵ The light shines in the dark, and the dark has never extinguished it.ᵃ

⁶ God sent a man named John to be his messenger. ⁷ John came to declare the truth about the light so that everyone would become believers through his message. ⁸ John was not the light, but he came to declare the truth about the light.

⁹ The real light, which shines on everyone, was coming into the world. ¹⁰ He was in the world, and the world came into existence through him. Yet, the world didn't recognize him. ¹¹ He went to his own people, and his own people didn't accept him. ¹² However, he gave the right to become God's children to everyone who believed in him. ¹³ These people didn't become God's children in a physical way—from a human impulse or from a husband's desire ₜto have a childₛ. They were born from God.

¹⁴ The Word became human and lived among us. We saw his glory. It was the glory that the Father shares with his only Son, a glory full of kindnessᵇ and truth.

¹⁵ (John declared the truth about him when he said loudly, "This is the person about whom I said, 'The one who comes after me was before me because he existed before I did.' ")

¹⁶ Each of us has received one gift after another because of all that the Word is. ¹⁷ The Teachings were given through Moses, but kindness and truth came into existence through Jesus Christ. ¹⁸ No one has ever seen God. God's only Son, the one who is closest to the Father's heart, has made him known.

John Prepares the Way—*Matthew 3:1–12; Mark 1:1–8; Luke 3:1–18*

¹⁹ This was John's answer when the Jews sent priests and Levites from Jerusalem to ask him, "Who are you?" ²⁰ John didn't refuse to answer. He told them clearly, "I'm not the Messiah."

²¹ They asked him, "Well, are you Elijah?"

John answered, "No, I'm not."

Then they asked, "Are you the prophet?"

John replied, "No."

²² So they asked him, "Who are you? Tell us so that we can take an answer back to those who sent us. What do you say about yourself?"

²³ John said, "I'm a voice crying out in the desert, 'Make the way for the Lord straight,' as the prophet Isaiah said."

²⁴ Some of those who had been sent were Pharisees. ²⁵ They asked John, "Why do you baptize if you're not the Messiah or Elijah or the prophet?"

²⁶ John answered them, "I baptize with water. Someone you don't know is standing among you. ²⁷ He's the one who comes after me. I am not worthy to untie his sandal strap."

²⁸ This happened in Bethany on the east side of the Jordan River, where John was baptizing.

John Identifies Jesus as the Lamb of God

²⁹ John saw Jesus coming toward him the next day and said, "Look! This is the Lamb of God who takes away the sin of the world. ³⁰ He is the one I spoke about when I said, 'A man who comes after me was before me because he existed before I did.' ³¹ I didn't know who he was. However, I came to baptize with water to show him to the people of Israel."

³² John said, "I saw the Spirit come down as a dove from heaven and stay on him. ³³ I didn't know who he was. But God, who sent me to baptize with water, had told me, 'When you see the Spirit come down and stay on someone, you'll know that person is the one who baptizes with the Holy Spirit.' ³⁴ I have seen this and have declared that this is the Son of God."

ᵃ 1:5 English equivalent difficult.   ᵇ 1:14 Or "grace."

Calling of the First Disciples

[35] The next day John was standing with two of his disciples. [36] John saw Jesus walk by. John said, "Look! This is the Lamb of God." [37] When the two disciples heard John say this, they followed Jesus.

[38] Jesus turned around and saw them following him. He asked them, "What are you looking for?"

They said to him, "Rabbi" (which means "teacher"), "where are you staying?"

[39] Jesus told them, "Come, and you will see." So they went to see where he was staying and spent the rest of that day with him. It was about ten o'clock in the morning.

[40] Andrew, Simon Peter's brother, was one of the two disciples who heard John and followed Jesus. [41] Andrew at once found his brother Simon and told him, "We have found the Messiah" (which means "Christ"). [42] Andrew brought Simon to Jesus.

Jesus looked at Simon and said, "You are Simon, son of John. Your name will be Cephas" (which means "Peter").

[43] The next day Jesus wanted to go to Galilee. He found Philip and told him, "Follow me!" [44] (Philip was from Bethsaida, the hometown of Andrew and Peter.)

[45] Philip found Nathanael and told him, "We have found the man whom Moses wrote about in his teachings and whom the prophets wrote about. He is Jesus, son of Joseph, from the city of Nazareth."

[46] Nathanael said to Philip, "Can anything good come from Nazareth?"

Philip told him, "Come and see!"

[47] Jesus saw Nathanael coming toward him and remarked, "Here is a true Israelite who is sincere."

[48] Nathanael asked Jesus, "How do you know anything about me?"

Jesus answered him, "I saw you under the fig tree before Philip called you."

[49] Nathanael said to Jesus, "Rabbi, you are the Son of God! You are the king of Israel!"

[50] Jesus replied, "You believe because I told you that I saw you under the fig tree. You will see greater things than that." [51] Jesus said to Nathanael, "I can guarantee this truth: You will see the sky open and God's angels going up and coming down to the Son of Man."

Jesus Changes Water Into Wine

2 [1] Three days later a wedding took place in the city of Cana in Galilee. Jesus' mother was there. [2] Jesus and his disciples had been invited too.

[3] When the wine was gone, Jesus' mother said to him, "They're out of wine."

[4] Jesus said to her, "Why did you come to me? My time has not yet come."

[5] His mother told the servers, "Do whatever he tells you."

[6] Six stone water jars were there. They were used for Jewish purification rituals. Each jar held 18 to 27 gallons.

[7] Jesus told the servers, "Fill the jars with water." The servers filled the jars to the brim. [8] Jesus said to them, "Pour some, and take it to the person in charge." The servers did as they were told.

[9] The person in charge tasted the water that had become wine. He didn't know where it had come from, although the servers who had poured the water knew. The person in charge called the groom [10] and said to him, "Everyone serves the best wine first. When people are drunk, the host serves cheap wine. But you have saved the best wine for now."

[11] Cana in Galilee was the place where Jesus began to perform miracles. He made his glory public there, and his disciples believed in him.

[12] After this, Jesus, his mother, brothers, and disciples went to the city of Capernaum and stayed there for a few days.

Jesus Throws Merchants and Moneychangers Out of the Temple Courtyard

[13] The Jewish Passover was near, so Jesus went to Jerusalem. [14] He found those who were selling cattle, sheep, and pigeons in the temple courtyard. He also found moneychangers sitting there. [15] He made a whip from small ropes and threw everyone with their sheep and cattle out of the temple courtyard. He dumped the moneychangers' coins and knocked over their tables.

[16] He told those who sold pigeons, "Pick up this stuff, and get it out of here! Stop making my Father's house a marketplace!"

[17] His disciples remembered that Scripture said, "Devotion for your house will consume me."

[18] The Jews reacted by asking Jesus, "What miracle can you show us to justify what you're doing?"

[19] Jesus replied, "Tear down this temple, and I'll rebuild it in three days."

[20] The Jews said, "It took forty-six years to build this temple. Do you really think you're going to rebuild it in three days?"

²¹ But the temple Jesus spoke about was his own body. ²² After he came back to life, his disciples remembered that he had said this. So they believed the Scripture and this statement that Jesus had made.

²³ While Jesus was in Jerusalem at the Passover festival, many people believed in him because they saw the miracles that he performed. ²⁴ Jesus, however, was wary of these believers. He understood people ²⁵ and didn't need anyone to tell him about human nature. He knew what people were really like.

A Conversation With Nicodemus

3 ¹ Nicodemus was a Pharisee and a member of the Jewish council. ² He came to Jesus one night and said to him, "Rabbi, we know that God has sent you as a teacher. No one can perform the miracles you perform unless God is with him."

³ Jesus replied to Nicodemus, "I can guarantee this truth: No one can see the kingdom of God without being born from above."ᵃ

⁴ Nicodemus asked him, "How can anyone be born when he's an old man? He can't go back inside his mother a second time to be born, can he?"

⁵ Jesus answered Nicodemus, "I can guarantee this truth: No one can enter the kingdom of God without being born of water and the Spirit. ⁶ Flesh and blood give birth to flesh and blood, but the Spirit gives birth to things that are spiritual. ⁷ Don't be surprised when I tell you that all of you must be born from above. ⁸ The windᵇ blows wherever it pleases. You hear its sound, but you don't know where the wind comes from or where it's going. That's the way it is with everyone born of the Spirit."

⁹ Nicodemus replied, "How can that be?"

¹⁰ Jesus told Nicodemus, "You're a well-known teacher of Israel. Can't you understand this? ¹¹ I can guarantee this truth: We know what we're talking about, and we confirm what we've seen. Yet, you don't accept our message. ¹² If you don't believe me when I tell you about things on earth, how will you believe me when I tell you about things in heaven? ¹³ No one has gone to heaven except the Son of Man, who came from heaven.

¹⁴ "As Moses lifted up the snake ˏon a poleˏ in the desert, so the Son of Man must be lifted up. ¹⁵ Then everyone who believes in him will have eternal life."

¹⁶ God loved the world this way: He gave his only Son so that everyone who believes in him will not die but will have eternal life. ¹⁷ God sent his Son into the world, not to condemn the world, but to save the world. ¹⁸ Those who believe in him won't be condemned. But those who don't believe are already condemned because they don't believe in God's only Son.

¹⁹ This is why people are condemned: The light came into the world. Yet, people loved the dark rather than the light because their actions were evil. ²⁰ People who do what is wrong hate the light and don't come to the light. They don't want their actions to be exposed. ²¹ But people who do what is true come to the light so that the things they do for God may be clearly seen.

John the Baptizer Talks About Christ

²² Later, Jesus and his disciples went to the Judean countryside, where he spent some time with them and baptized people. ²³ John was baptizing in Aenon, near Salim. Water was plentiful there. (People came to John to be baptized, ²⁴ since John had not yet been put in prison.)

²⁵ Some of John's disciples had an argument with a Jew about purification ceremonies. ²⁶ So they went to John and asked him, "Rabbi, do you remember the man you spoke so favorably about when he was with you on the other side of the Jordan River? Well, he's baptizing, and everyone is going to him!"

²⁷ John answered, "People can't receive anything unless it has been given to them from heaven. ²⁸ You are witnesses that I said, 'I'm not the Messiah, but I've been sent ahead of him.'

²⁹ "The groom is the person to whom the bride belongs. The best man, who stands and listens to him, is overjoyed when the groom speaks. This is the joy that I feel. ³⁰ He must increase in importance, while I must decrease in importance.

³¹ "The person who comes from above is superior to everyone. I, a person from the earth, know nothing but what is on earth, and that's all I can talk about. The person who comes from heaven is superior to everyone ³² and tells what he has seen and heard. Yet, no one accepts what he says. ³³ I have accepted what that person said, and I have affirmed that God is truthful. ³⁴ The man whom God has sent speaks God's message. After all, God gives him the Spirit without limit. ³⁵ The Father loves his Son and has put everything in his power. ³⁶ Whoever believes in the Son has eternal life, but whoever rejects the Son will not see life. Instead, he will see God's constant anger."

ᵃ 3:3 Or "born again."   ᵇ 3:8 The Greek word for *wind* is the same as the Greek word for *Spirit*.

A Samaritan Woman Meets Jesus at a Well

4 ¹ Jesus knew that the Pharisees had heard that he was making and baptizing more disciples than John. ² (Actually, Jesus was not baptizing people. His disciples were.) ³ So he left the Judean countryside and went back to Galilee.

⁴ Jesus had to go through Samaria. ⁵ He arrived at a city in Samaria called Sychar. Sychar was near the piece of land that Jacob had given to his son Joseph. ⁶ Jacob's Well was there. Jesus sat down by the well because he was tired from traveling. The time was about six o'clock in the evening.

⁷ A Samaritan woman went to get some water. Jesus said to her, "Give me a drink of water." ⁸ (His disciples had gone into the city to buy some food.)

⁹ The Samaritan woman asked him, "How can a Jewish man like you ask a Samaritan woman like me for a drink of water?" (Jews, of course, don't associate with Samaritans.)

¹⁰ Jesus replied to her, "If you only knew what God's gift is and who is asking you for a drink, you would have asked him for a drink. He would have given you living water."

¹¹ The woman said to him, "Sir, you don't have anything to use to get water, and the well is deep. So where are you going to get this living water? ¹² You're not more important than our ancestor Jacob, are you? He gave us this well. He and his sons and his animals drank water from it."

¹³ Jesus answered her, "Everyone who drinks this water will become thirsty again. ¹⁴ But those who drink the water that I will give them will never become thirsty again. In fact, the water I will give them will become in them a spring that gushes up to eternal life."

¹⁵ The woman told Jesus, "Sir, give me this water! Then I won't get thirsty or have to come here to get water."

¹⁶ Jesus told her, "Go to your husband, and bring him here."

¹⁷ The woman replied, "I don't have a husband."

Jesus told her, "You're right when you say that you don't have a husband. ¹⁸ You've had five husbands, and the man you have now isn't your husband. You've told the truth."

¹⁹ The woman said to Jesus, "I see that you're a prophet! ²⁰ Our ancestors worshiped on this mountain. But you Jews say that people must worship in Jerusalem."

²¹ Jesus told her, "Believe me. A time is coming when you Samaritans won't be worshiping the Father on this mountain or in Jerusalem. ²² You don't know what you're worshiping. We Jews know what we're worshiping, because salvation comes from the Jews. ²³ Indeed, the time is coming, and it is now here, when the true worshipers will worship the Father in spirit and truth. The Father is looking for people like that to worship him. ²⁴ God is a spirit. Those who worship him must worship in spirit and truth."

²⁵ The woman said to him, "I know that the Messiah is coming. When he comes, he will tell us everything." (*Messiah* is the one called *Christ*.)

²⁶ Jesus told her, "I am he, and I am speaking to you now."

²⁷ At that time his disciples returned. They were surprised that he was talking to a woman. But none of them asked him, "What do you want from her?" or "Why are you talking to her?"

²⁸ Then the woman left her water jar and went back into the city. She told the people, ²⁹ "Come with me, and meet a man who told me everything I've ever done. Could he be the Messiah?" ³⁰ The people left the city and went to meet Jesus.

³¹ Meanwhile, the disciples were urging him, "Rabbi, have something to eat."

³² Jesus told them, "I have food to eat that you don't know about."

³³ The disciples asked each other, "Did someone bring him something to eat?"

³⁴ Jesus told them, "My food is to do what the one who sent me wants me to do and to finish the work he has given me.

³⁵ "Don't you say, 'In four more months the harvest will be here'? I'm telling you to look and see that the fields are ready to be harvested. ³⁶ The person who harvests the crop is already getting paid. He is gathering grain for eternal life. So the person who plants the grain and the person who harvests it are happy together. ³⁷ In this respect the saying is true: 'One person plants, and another person harvests.' ³⁸ I have sent you to harvest a crop you have not worked for. Other people have done the hard work, and you have followed them in their work."

³⁹ Many Samaritans in that city believed in Jesus because of the woman who said, "He told me everything I've ever done." ⁴⁰ So when the Samaritans went to Jesus, they asked him to stay with them. He stayed in Samaria for two days. ⁴¹ Many more Samaritans believed because of what Jesus said. ⁴² They told the woman, "Our faith is no longer based on what you've said. We have heard him ourselves, and we know that he really is the savior of the world."

A Believing Official—Matthew 8:5–13; Luke 7:1–10

⁴³ After spending two days in Samaria, Jesus left for Galilee. ⁴⁴ Jesus had said that a prophet is not honored in his own country. ⁴⁵ But when Jesus arrived in Galilee, the people of Galilee

welcomed him. They had seen everything he had done at the festival in Jerusalem, since they, too, had attended the festival.

[46] Jesus returned to the city of Cana in Galilee, where he had changed water into wine. A government official was in Cana. His son was sick in Capernaum. [47] The official heard that Jesus had returned from Judea to Galilee. So he went to Jesus and asked him to go to Capernaum with him to heal his son who was about to die.

[48] Jesus told the official, "If people don't see miracles and amazing things, they won't believe."

[49] The official said to him, "Sir, come with me before my little boy dies."

[50] Jesus told him, "Go home. Your son will live." The man believed what Jesus told him and left.

[51] While the official was on his way to Capernaum, his servants met him and told him that his boy was alive. [52] The official asked them at what time his son got better. His servants told him, "The fever left him yesterday evening at seven o'clock." [53] Then the boy's father realized that it was the same time that Jesus had told him, "Your son will live." So the official and his entire family became believers.

[54] This was the second miracle that Jesus performed after he had come back from Judea to Galilee.

Jesus Cures a Man at the Bethesda Pool

5 [1] Later, Jesus went to Jerusalem for a Jewish festival.

[2] Near Sheep Gate in Jerusalem was a pool called *Bethesda* in Hebrew. It had five porches. [3] Under these porches a large number of sick people—people who were blind, lame, or paralyzed—used to lie.[a] [5] One man, who had been sick for 38 years, was lying there. [6] Jesus saw the man lying there and knew that he had been sick for a long time. So Jesus asked the man, "Would you like to get well?"

[7] The sick man answered Jesus, "Sir, I don't have anyone to put me into the pool when the water is stirred. While I'm trying to get there, someone else steps into the pool ahead of me."

[8] Jesus told the man, "Get up, pick up your cot, and walk." [9] The man immediately became well, picked up his cot, and walked.

That happened on a day of worship. [10] So the Jews told the man who had been healed, "This is a day of worship. You're not allowed to carry your cot today."

[11] The man replied, "The man who made me well told me to pick up my cot and walk."

[12] The Jews asked him, "Who is the man who told you to pick it up and walk?" [13] But the man who had been healed didn't know who Jesus was. (Jesus had withdrawn from the crowd.)

[14] Later, Jesus met the man in the temple courtyard and told him, "You're well now. Stop sinning so that something worse doesn't happen to you."

[15] The man went back to the Jews and told them that Jesus was the man who had made him well.

The Son Is Equal to the Father

[16] The Jews began to persecute Jesus because he kept healing people on the day of worship. [17] Jesus replied to them, "My Father is working right now, and so am I."

[18] His reply made the Jews more intent on killing him. Not only did he break the laws about the day of worship, but also he made himself equal to God when he said repeatedly that God was his Father.

[19] Jesus said to the Jews, "I can guarantee this truth: The Son cannot do anything on his own. He can do only what he sees the Father doing. Indeed, the Son does exactly what the Father does. [20] The Father loves the Son and shows him everything he is doing. The Father will show him even greater things to do than these things so that you will be amazed. [21] In the same way that the Father brings back the dead and gives them life, the Son gives life to anyone he chooses.

[22] "The Father doesn't judge anyone. He has entrusted judgment entirely to the Son [23] so that everyone will honor the Son as they honor the Father. Whoever doesn't honor the Son doesn't honor the Father who sent him. [24] I can guarantee this truth: Those who listen to what I say and believe in the one who sent me will have eternal life. They won't be judged because they have already passed from death to life.

[25] "I can guarantee this truth: A time is coming (and is now here) when the dead will hear the voice of the Son of God and those who respond to it will live. [26] The Father is the source of life, and he has enabled the Son to be the source of life too.

---

[a] 5:3 Some manuscripts and translations add verses 3b–4: "They would wait for the water to move. People believed that at a certain time an angel from the Lord would go into the pool and stir up the water. The first person who would step into the water after it was stirred up would be cured from whatever disease he had."

[27] "He has also given the Son authority to pass judgment because he is the Son of Man.[b] [28] Don't be surprised at what I've just said. A time is coming when all the dead will hear his voice, [29] and they will come out of their tombs. Those who have done good will come back to life and live. But those who have done evil will come back to life and will be judged. [30] I can't do anything on my own. As I listen ˌto the Fatherˌ, I make my judgments. My judgments are right because I don't try to do what I want but what the one who sent me wants.

[31] "If I testify on my own behalf, what I say isn't true. [32] Someone else testifies on my behalf, and I know that what he says about me is true. [33] You sent people to John ˌthe Baptizerˌ, and he testified to the truth. [34] But I don't depend on human testimony. I'm telling you this to save you. [35] John was a lamp that gave off brilliant light. For a time you enjoyed the pleasure of his light. [36] But I have something that testifies more favorably on my behalf than John's testimony. The tasks that the Father gave me to carry out, these tasks which I perform, testify on my behalf. They prove that the Father has sent me. [37] The Father who sent me testifies on my behalf. You have never heard his voice, and you have never seen his form. [38] So you don't have the Father's message within you, because you don't believe in the person he has sent. [39] You study the Scriptures in detail because you think you have the source of eternal life in them. These Scriptures testify on my behalf. [40] Yet, you don't want to come to me to get ˌeternalˌ life.

[41] "I don't accept praise from humans. [42] But I know what kind of people you are. You don't have any love for God. [43] I have come with the authority my Father has given me, but you don't accept me. If someone else comes with his own authority, you will accept him. [44] How can you believe when you accept each other's praise and don't look for the praise that comes from the only God?

[45] "Don't think that I will accuse you in the presence of the Father. Moses, the one you trust, is already accusing you. [46] If you really believed Moses, you would believe me. Moses wrote about me. [47] If you don't believe what Moses wrote, how will you ever believe what I say?"

Jesus Feeds More Than Five Thousand—*Matthew 14:13–21; Mark 6:30–44; Luke 9:10–17*

6 [1] Jesus later crossed to the other side of the Sea of Galilee (or the Sea of Tiberias). [2] A large crowd followed him because they saw the miracles that he performed for the sick. [3] Jesus went up a mountain and sat with his disciples. [4] The time for the Jewish Passover festival was near.

[5] As Jesus saw a large crowd coming to him, he said to Philip, "Where can we buy bread for these people to eat?" [6] Jesus asked this question to test him. He already knew what he was going to do.

[7] Philip answered, "We would need about a year's wages to buy enough bread for each of them to have a piece."

[8] One of Jesus' disciples, Andrew, who was Simon Peter's brother, told him, [9] "A boy who has five loaves of barley bread and two small fish is here. But they won't go very far for so many people."

[10] Jesus said, "Have the people sit down."

The people had plenty of grass to sit on. (There were about 5,000 men in the crowd.) [11] Jesus took the loaves, gave thanks, and distributed them to the people who were sitting there. He did the same thing with the fish. All the people ate as much as they wanted.

[12] When the people were full, Jesus told his disciples, "Gather the leftover pieces so that nothing will be wasted." [13] The disciples gathered the leftover pieces of bread and filled twelve baskets.

[14] When the people saw the miracle Jesus performed, they said, "This man is certainly the prophet who is to come into the world." [15] Jesus realized that the people intended to take him by force and make him king. So he returned to the mountain by himself.

Jesus Walks on the Sea—*Matthew 14:22–33; Mark 6:45–52*

[16] When evening came, his disciples went to the sea. [17] They got into a boat and started to cross the sea to the city of Capernaum. By this time it was dark, and Jesus had not yet come to them. [18] A strong wind started to blow and stir up the sea.

[19] After they had rowed three or four miles, they saw Jesus walking on the sea. He was coming near the boat, and they became terrified.

[20] Jesus told them, "It's me. Don't be afraid!"

[21] So they were willing to help Jesus into the boat. Immediately, the boat reached the shore where they were going.

Jesus Is the Bread of Life

[22] On the next day the people were still on the other side of the sea. They noticed that only one boat was there and that Jesus had not stepped into that boat with his disciples. The disci-

---

[b] 5:27 "Son of Man" is a name Jesus called himself to show that he was not only God's Son but also human.

ples had gone away without him. ²³ Other boats from Tiberias arrived near the place where they had eaten the bread after the Lord gave thanks. ²⁴ When the people saw that neither Jesus nor his disciples were there, they got into these boats and went to the city of Capernaum to look for Jesus. ²⁵ When they found him on the other side of the sea, they asked him, "Rabbi, when did you get here?"

²⁶ Jesus replied to them, "I can guarantee this truth: You're not looking for me because you saw miracles. You are looking for me because you ate as much of those loaves as you wanted. ²⁷ Don't work for food that spoils. Instead, work for the food that lasts into eternal life. This is the food the Son of Man will give you. After all, the Father has placed his seal of approval on him."

²⁸ The people asked Jesus, "What does God want us to do?"

²⁹ Jesus replied to them, "God wants to do something for you so that you believe in the one whom he has sent."

³⁰ The people asked him, "What miracle are you going to perform so that we can see it and believe in you? What are you going to do? ³¹ Our ancestors ate the manna in the desert. Scripture says, 'He gave them bread from heaven to eat.' "

³² Jesus said to them, "I can guarantee this truth: Moses didn't give you bread from heaven, but my Father gives you the true bread from heaven. ³³ God's bread is the man who comes from heaven and gives life to the world."

³⁴ They said to him, "Sir, give us this bread all the time."

³⁵ Jesus told them, "I am the bread of life. Whoever comes to me will never become hungry, and whoever believes in me will never become thirsty. ³⁶ I've told you that you have seen me. However, you don't believe in me. ³⁷ Everyone whom the Father gives me will come to me. I will never turn away anyone who comes to me. ³⁸ I haven't come from heaven to do what I want to do. I've come to do what the one who sent me wants me to do. ³⁹ The one who sent me doesn't want me to lose any of those he gave me. He wants me to bring them back to life on the last day. ⁴⁰ My Father wants all those who see the Son and believe in him to have eternal life. He wants me to bring them back to life on the last day."

⁴¹ The Jews began to criticize Jesus for saying, "I am the bread that came from heaven." ⁴² They asked, "Isn't this man Jesus, Joseph's son? Don't we know his father and mother? How can he say now, 'I came from heaven'?"

⁴³ Jesus responded, "Stop criticizing me! ⁴⁴ People cannot come to me unless the Father who sent me brings them to me. I will bring these people back to life on the last day. ⁴⁵ The prophets wrote, 'God will teach everyone.' Those who do what they have learned from the Father come to me. ⁴⁶ I'm saying that no one has seen the Father. Only the one who is from God has seen the Father. ⁴⁷ I can guarantee this truth: Every believer has eternal life.

⁴⁸ "I am the bread of life. ⁴⁹ Your ancestors ate the manna in the desert and died. ⁵⁰ This is the bread that comes from heaven so that whoever eats it won't die. ⁵¹ I am the living bread that came from heaven. Whoever eats this bread will live forever. The bread I will give to bring life to the world is my flesh."

⁵² The Jews began to quarrel with each other. They said, "How can this man give us his flesh to eat?"

⁵³ Jesus told them, "I can guarantee this truth: If you don't eat the flesh of the Son of Man and drink his blood, you don't have the source of life in you. ⁵⁴ Those who eat my flesh and drink my blood have eternal life, and I will bring them back to life on the last day. ⁵⁵ My flesh is true food, and my blood is true drink. ⁵⁶ Those who eat my flesh and drink my blood live in me, and I live in them. ⁵⁷ The Father who has life sent me, and I live because of the Father. So those who feed on me will live because of me. ⁵⁸ This is the bread that came from heaven. It is not like the bread your ancestors ate. They eventually died. Those who eat this bread will live forever."

⁵⁹ Jesus said this while he was teaching in a synagogue in Capernaum. ⁶⁰ When many of Jesus' disciples heard him, they said, "What he says is hard to accept. Who wants to listen to him anymore?"

⁶¹ Jesus was aware that his disciples were criticizing his message. So Jesus asked them, "Did what I say make you lose faith? ⁶² What if you see the Son of Man go where he was before? ⁶³ Life is spiritual. Your physical existence doesn't contribute to that life. The words that I have spoken to you are spiritual. They are life. ⁶⁴ But some of you don't believe." Jesus knew from the beginning those who wouldn't believe and the one who would betray him. ⁶⁵ So he added, "That is why I told you that people cannot come to me unless the Father provides the way."

⁶⁶ Jesus' speech made many of his disciples go back to the lives they had led before they followed Jesus. ⁶⁷ So Jesus asked the twelve apostles, "Do you want to leave me too?"

⁶⁸ Simon Peter answered Jesus, "Lord, to what person could we go? Your words give eternal life. ⁶⁹ Besides, we believe and know that you are the Holy One of God."

⁷⁰ Jesus replied, "I chose all twelve of you. Yet, one of you is a devil." ⁷¹ Jesus meant Judas, son of Simon Iscariot. Judas, who was one of the twelve apostles, would later betray Jesus.

Jesus Goes to the Festival of Booths

7 ¹ Jesus later traveled throughout Galilee. He didn't want to travel in Judea because Jews there wanted to kill him.

² The time for the Jewish Festival of Booths was near. ³ So Jesus' brothers told him, "Leave this place, and go to Judea so that your disciples can see the things that you're doing. ⁴ No one does things secretly when he wants to be known publicly. If you do these things, you should let the world see you." ⁵ Even his brothers didn't believe in him.

⁶ Jesus told them, "Now is not the right time for me to go. Any time is right for you. ⁷ The world cannot hate you, but it hates me because I say that what everyone does is evil. ⁸ Go to the festival. I'm not going to this festival right now. Now is not the right time for me to go."

⁹ After saying this, Jesus stayed in Galilee. ¹⁰ But after his brothers had gone to the festival, Jesus went. He didn't go publicly but secretly.

¹¹ The Jews were looking for Jesus in the crowd at the festival. They kept asking, "Where is that man?" ¹² The crowds argued about Jesus. Some people said, "He's a good man," while others said, "No he isn't. He deceives the people." ¹³ Yet, no one would talk openly about him because they were afraid of the Jews.

¹⁴ When the festival was half over, Jesus went to the temple courtyard and began to teach. ¹⁵ The Jews were surprised and asked, "How can this man be so educated when he hasn't gone to school?"

¹⁶ Jesus responded to them, "What I teach doesn't come from me but from the one who sent me. ¹⁷ Those who want to follow the will of God will know if what I teach is from God or if I teach my own thoughts. ¹⁸ Those who speak their own thoughts are looking for their own glory. But the man who wants to bring glory to the one who sent him is a true teacher and doesn't have dishonest motives. ¹⁹ Didn't Moses give you his teachings? Yet, none of you does what Moses taught you. So why do you want to kill me?"

²⁰ The crowd answered, "You're possessed by a demon! Who wants to kill you?"

²¹ Jesus answered them, "I performed one miracle, and all of you are surprised by it. ²² Moses gave you the teaching about circumcision (although it didn't come from Moses but from our ancestors). So you circumcise a male on a day of worship. ²³ If you circumcise a male on the day of worship to follow Moses' Teachings, why are you angry with me because I made a man entirely well on the day of worship? ²⁴ Stop judging by outward appearance! Instead, judge correctly."

²⁵ Some of the people who lived in Jerusalem said, "Isn't this the man they want to kill? ²⁶ But look at this! He's speaking in public, and no one is saying anything to him! Can it be that the rulers really know that this man is the Messiah? ²⁷ However, we know where this man comes from. When the Christ comes, no one will know where he is from."

²⁸ Then, while Jesus was teaching in the temple courtyard, he said loudly, "You know me, and you know where I come from. I didn't decide to come on my own. The one who sent me is true. He's the one you don't know. ²⁹ I know him because I am from him and he sent me."

³⁰ The Jews tried to arrest him but couldn't because his time had not yet come.

³¹ However, many people in the crowd believed in him. They asked, "When the Messiah comes, will he perform more miracles than this man has?"

³² The Pharisees heard the crowd saying things like this about him. So the chief priests and the Pharisees sent temple guards to arrest Jesus.

³³ Jesus said, "I will still be with you for a little while. Then I'll go to the one who sent me. ³⁴ You will look for me, but you won't find me. You can't go where I'm going."

³⁵ The Jews said among themselves, "Where does this man intend to go so that we won't find him? Does he mean that he'll live with the Jews who are scattered among the Greeks and that he'll teach the Greeks? ³⁶ What does he mean when he says, 'You will look for me, but you won't find me,' and 'You can't go where I'm going'?"

³⁷ On the last and most important day of the festival, Jesus was standing in the temple courtyard. He said loudly, "Whoever is thirsty must come to me to drink. ³⁸ As Scripture says, 'Streams of living water will flow from deep within the person who believes in me.' " ³⁹ Jesus said this about the Spirit, whom his believers would receive. The Spirit was not yet evident, as it would be after Jesus had been glorified.

⁴⁰ After some of the crowd heard Jesus say these words, they said, "This man is certainly the prophet." ⁴¹ Other people said, "This man is the Messiah." Still other people asked, "How can the Messiah come from Galilee? ⁴² Doesn't Scripture say that the Messiah will come from the descendants of David and from the village of Bethlehem, where David lived?" ⁴³ So the people were divided because of Jesus. ⁴⁴ Some of them wanted to arrest him, but they couldn't.

⁴⁵ When the temple guards returned, the chief priests and Pharisees asked them, "Why didn't you bring Jesus?"

⁴⁶ The temple guards answered, "No human has ever spoken like this man."

⁴⁷ The Pharisees asked the temple guards, "Have you been deceived too? ⁴⁸ Has any ruler or any Pharisee believed in him? ⁴⁹ This crowd is cursed because it doesn't know Moses' Teachings."

⁵⁰ One of those Pharisees was Nicodemus, who had previously visited Jesus. Nicodemus asked them, ⁵¹ "Do Moses' Teachings enable us to judge a person without first hearing that person's side of the story? We can't judge a person without finding out what that person has done."

⁵² They asked Nicodemus, "Are you saying this because you're from Galilee? Study the Scriptures, and you'll see that no prophet comes from Galilee."ᵃ

⁵³ Then each of them went home.

A Woman Caught in Adultery

8 ¹ Jesus went to the Mount of Olives. ² Early the next morning he returned to the temple courtyard. All the people went to him, so he sat down and began to teach them.

³ The scribes and the Pharisees brought a woman who had been caught committing adultery. They made her stand in front of everyone ⁴ and asked Jesus, "Teacher, we caught this woman in the act of adultery. ⁵ In his teachings, Moses ordered us to stone women like this to death. What do you say?" ⁶ They asked this to test him. They wanted to find a reason to bring charges against him.

Jesus bent down and used his finger to write on the ground. ⁷ When they persisted in asking him questions, he straightened up and said, "The person who is sinless should be the first to throw a stone at her." ⁸ Then he bent down again and continued writing on the ground.

⁹ One by one, beginning with the older men, the scribes and Pharisees left. Jesus was left alone with the woman. ¹⁰ Then Jesus straightened up and asked her, "Where did they go? Has anyone condemned you?"

¹¹ The woman answered, "No one, sir."

Jesus said, "I don't condemn you either. Go! From now on don't sin."

Jesus Speaks With the Pharisees About His Father

¹² Jesus spoke to the Pharisees again. He said, "I am the light of the world. Whoever follows me will have a life filled with light and will never live in the dark."

¹³ The Pharisees said to him, "You testify on your own behalf, so your testimony isn't true."

¹⁴ Jesus replied to them, "Even if I testify on my own behalf, my testimony is true because I know where I came from and where I'm going. However, you don't know where I came from or where I'm going. ¹⁵ You judge the way humans do. I don't judge anyone. ¹⁶ Even if I do judge, my judgment is valid because I don't make it on my own. I make my judgment with the Father who sent me. ¹⁷ Your own teachings say that the testimony of two people is true. ¹⁸ I testify on my own behalf, and so does the Father who sent me."

¹⁹ The Pharisees asked him, "Where is your father?"

Jesus replied, "You don't know me or my Father. If you knew me, you would also know my Father."

²⁰ Jesus spoke these words while he was teaching in the treasury area of the temple courtyard. No one arrested him, because his time had not yet come.

²¹ Jesus spoke to the Pharisees again. He said, "I'm going away, and you'll look for me. But you will die because of your sin. You can't go where I'm going."

²² Then the Jews asked, "Is he going to kill himself? Is that what he means when he says, 'You can't go where I'm going'?"

²³ Jesus said to them, "You're from below. I'm from above. You're from this world. I'm not from this world. ²⁴ For this reason I told you that you'll die because of your sins. If you don't believe that I am the one, you'll die because of your sins."

²⁵ The Jews asked him, "Who did you say you are?"

Jesus told them, "I am who I said I was from the beginning. ²⁶ I have a lot I could say about you and a lot I could condemn you for. But the one who sent me is true. So I tell the world exactly what he has told me." ²⁷ (The Jews didn't know that he was talking to them about the Father.)

²⁸ So Jesus told them, "When you have lifted up the Son of Man, then you'll know that I am the one and that I can't do anything on my own. Instead, I speak as the Father taught me. ²⁹ Besides, the one who sent me is with me. He hasn't left me by myself. I always do what pleases him."

³⁰ As Jesus was saying this, many people believed in him. ³¹ So Jesus said to those Jews who believed in him, "If you live by what I say, you are truly my disciples. ³² You will know the truth, and the truth will set you free."

ᵃ 7:52 John 7:53–8:11 is not found in many manuscripts and some translations. Some manuscripts place these verses between 7:36 and 7:37. Other manuscripts place them between 7:44 and 7:45. Others place them after 21:25, and some place them between Luke 21:38 and 22:1.

³³ They replied to Jesus, "We are Abraham's descendants, and we've never been anyone's slaves. So how can you say that we will be set free?"

³⁴ Jesus answered them, "I can guarantee this truth: Whoever lives a sinful life is a slave to sin. ³⁵ A slave doesn't live in the home forever, but a son does. ³⁶ So if the Son sets you free, you will be absolutely free. ³⁷ I know that you're Abraham's descendants. However, you want to kill me because you don't like what I'm saying. ³⁸ What I'm saying is what I have seen in my Father's presence. But you do what you've heard from your father."

³⁹ The Jews replied to Jesus, "Abraham is our father."

Jesus told them, "If you were Abraham's children, you would do what Abraham did. ⁴⁰ I am a man who has told you the truth that I heard from God. But now you want to kill me. Abraham wouldn't have done that. ⁴¹ You're doing what your father does."

The Jews said to Jesus, "We're not illegitimate children. God is our only Father."

⁴² Jesus told them, "If God were your Father, you would love me. After all, I'm here, and I came from God. I didn't come on my own. Instead, God sent me. ⁴³ Why don't you understand the language I use? Is it because you can't understand the words I use? ⁴⁴ You come from your father, the devil, and you desire to do what your father wants you to do. The devil was a murderer from the beginning. He has never been truthful. He doesn't know what the truth is. Whenever he tells a lie, he's doing what comes naturally to him. He's a liar and the father of lies. ⁴⁵ So you don't believe me because I tell the truth. ⁴⁶ Can any of you convict me of committing a sin? If I'm telling the truth, why don't you believe me? ⁴⁷ The person who belongs to God understands what God says. You don't understand because you don't belong to God."

⁴⁸ The Jews replied to Jesus, "Aren't we right when we say that you're a Samaritan and that you're possessed by a demon?"

⁴⁹ Jesus answered, "I'm not possessed. I honor my Father, but you dishonor me. ⁵⁰ I don't want my own glory. But there is someone who wants it, and he is the judge. ⁵¹ I can guarantee this truth: Whoever obeys what I say will never see death."

⁵² The Jews told Jesus, "Now we know that you're possessed by a demon. Abraham died, and so did the prophets, but you say, 'Whoever does what I say will never taste death.' ⁵³ Are you greater than our father Abraham, who died? The prophets have also died. Who do you think you are?"

⁵⁴ Jesus said, "If I bring glory to myself, my glory is nothing. My Father is the one who gives me glory, and you say that he is your God. ⁵⁵ Yet, you haven't known him. However, I know him. If I would say that I didn't know him, I would be a liar like all of you. But I do know him, and I do what he says. ⁵⁶ Your father Abraham was pleased to see that my day was coming. He saw it and was happy."

⁵⁷ The Jews said to Jesus, "You're not even fifty years old. How could you have seen Abraham?"

⁵⁸ Jesus told them, "I can guarantee this truth: Before Abraham was ever born, I am."

⁵⁹ Then some of the Jews picked up stones to throw at Jesus. However, Jesus was concealed, and he left the temple courtyard.

Jesus Gives Sight to a Blind Man

9 ¹ As Jesus walked along, he saw a man who had been born blind. ² His disciples asked him, "Rabbi, why was this man born blind? Did he or his parents sin?"

³ Jesus answered, "Neither this man nor his parents sinned. Instead, he was born blind so that God could show what he can do for him. ⁴ We must do what the one who sent me wants us to do while it is day. The night when no one can do anything is coming. ⁵ As long as I'm in the world, I'm light for the world."

⁶ After Jesus said this, he spit on the ground and mixed the spit with dirt. Then he smeared it on the man's eyes ⁷ and told him, "Wash it off in the pool of Siloam." (*Siloam* means "sent.") The blind man washed it off and returned. He was able to see.

⁸ His neighbors and those who had previously seen him begging asked, "Isn't this the man who used to sit and beg?"

⁹ Some of them said, "He's the one." Others said, "No, he isn't, but he looks like him." But the man himself said, "I am the one."

¹⁰ So they asked him, "How did you receive your sight?"

¹¹ He replied, "The man people call Jesus mixed some spit with dirt, smeared it on my eyes, and told me, 'Go to Siloam, and wash it off.' So I went there, washed it off, and received my sight."

¹² They asked him, "Where is that man?"

The man answered, "I don't know."

¹³ Some people brought the man who had been blind to the Pharisees. ¹⁴ The day when Jesus mixed the spit and dirt and gave the man sight was a day of worship. ¹⁵ So the Pharisees asked the man again how he received his sight.

The man told the Pharisees, "He put a mixture of spit and dirt on my eyes. I washed it off, and now I can see."

[16] Some of the Pharisees said, "The man who did this is not from God because he doesn't follow the traditions for the day of worship." Other Pharisees asked, "How can a man who is a sinner perform miracles like these?" So the Pharisees were divided in their opinions.

[17] They asked the man who had been born blind another question: "What do you say about the man who gave you sight?"

The man answered, "He's a prophet."

[18] Until they talked to the man's parents, the Jews didn't believe that the man had been blind and had been given sight. [19] They asked his parents, "Is this your son, the one you say was born blind? Why can he see now?"

[20] His parents replied, "We know that he's our son and that he was born blind. [21] But we don't know how he got his sight or who gave it to him. You'll have to ask him. He's old enough to answer for himself." [22] (His parents said this because they were afraid of the Jews. The Jews had already agreed to put anyone who acknowledged that Jesus was the Christ out of the synagogue. [23] That's why his parents said, "You'll have to ask him. He's old enough.")

[24] So once again the Jews called the man who had been blind. They told him, "Give glory to God. We know that this man who gave you sight is a sinner."

[25] The man responded, "I don't know if he's a sinner or not. But I do know one thing. I used to be blind, but now I can see."

[26] The Jews asked him, "What did he do to you? How did he give you sight?"

[27] The man replied, "I've already told you, but you didn't listen. Why do you want to hear the story again? Do you want to become his disciples too?"

[28] The Jews yelled at him, "You're his disciple, but we're Moses' disciples. [29] We know that God spoke to Moses, but we don't know where this man came from."

[30] The man replied to them, "That's amazing! You don't know where he's from. Yet, he gave me sight. [31] We know that God doesn't listen to sinners. Instead, he listens to people who are devout and who do what he wants. [32] Since the beginning of time, no one has ever heard of anyone giving sight to a person born blind. [33] If this man were not from God, he couldn't do anything like that."

[34] The Jews answered him, "You were born full of sin. Do you think you can teach us?" Then they threw him out ˻of the synagogue˼.

[35] Jesus heard that the Jews had thrown the man out ˻of the synagogue˼. So when Jesus found the man, he asked him, "Do you believe in the Son of Man?"

[36] The man replied, "Sir, tell me who he is so that I can believe in him."

[37] Jesus told him, "You've seen him. He is the person who is now talking with you."

[38] The man bowed in front of Jesus and said, "I believe, Lord."

[39] Then Jesus said, "I have come into this world to judge: Blind people will be given sight, and those who can see will become blind."

[40] Some Pharisees who were with Jesus heard this. So they asked him, "Do you think we're blind?"

[41] Jesus told them, "If you were blind, you wouldn't be sinners. But now you say, 'We see,' so you continue to be sinners.

Jesus, the Good Shepherd

10 [1] "I can guarantee this truth: The person who doesn't enter the sheep pen through the gate but climbs in somewhere else is a thief or a robber. [2] But the one who enters through the gate is the shepherd. [3] The gatekeeper opens the gate for him, and the sheep respond to his voice. He calls his sheep by name and leads them out of the pen. [4] After he has brought out all his sheep, he walks ahead of them. The sheep follow him because they recognize his voice. [5] They won't follow a stranger. Instead, they will run away from a stranger because they don't recognize his voice." [6] Jesus used this illustration as he talked to the people, but they didn't understand what he meant.

[7] Jesus emphasized, "I can guarantee this truth: I am the gate for the sheep. [8] All who came before I did were thieves or robbers. However, the sheep didn't respond to them. [9] I am the gate. Those who enter the sheep pen through me will be saved. They will go in and out of the sheep pen and find food. [10] A thief comes to steal, kill, and destroy. But I came so that my sheep will have life and so that they will have everything they need.

[11] "I am the good shepherd. The good shepherd gives his life for the sheep. [12] A hired hand isn't a shepherd and doesn't own the sheep. When he sees a wolf coming, he abandons the sheep and quickly runs away. So the wolf drags the sheep away and scatters the flock. [13] The hired hand is concerned about what he's going to get paid and not about the sheep.

[14] "I am the good shepherd. I know my sheep as the Father knows me.[a] My sheep know me as I know the Father. [15] So I give my life for my sheep. [16] I also have other sheep that are not from this pen. I must lead them. They, too, will respond to my voice. So they will be one flock with one shepherd. [17] The Father loves me because I give my life in order to take it back again. [18] No one takes my life from me. I give my life of my own free will. I have the authority to give my life, and I have the authority to take my life back again. This is what my Father ordered me to do."

[19] The Jews were divided because of what Jesus said. [20] Many of them said, "He's possessed by a demon! He's crazy! Why do you listen to him?" [21] Others said, "No one talks like this if he's possessed by a demon. Can a demon give sight to the blind?"

The Jews Reject Jesus

[22] The Festival of the Dedication of the Temple took place in Jerusalem during the winter. [23] Jesus was walking on Solomon's porch in the temple courtyard.

[24] The Jews surrounded him. They asked him, "How long will you keep us in suspense? If you are the Messiah, tell us plainly."

[25] Jesus answered them, "I've told you, but you don't believe me. The things that I do in my Father's name testify on my behalf. [26] However, you don't believe because you're not my sheep. [27] My sheep respond to my voice, and I know who they are. They follow me, [28] and I give them eternal life. They will never be lost, and no one will tear them away from me. [29] My Father, who gave them to me, is greater than everyone else, and no one can tear them away from my Father. [30] The Father and I are one."

[31] The Jews had again brought some rocks to stone Jesus to death. [32] Jesus replied to them, "I've shown you many good things that come from the Father. For which of these good things do you want to stone me to death?"

[33] The Jews answered Jesus, "We're going to stone you to death, not for any good things you've done, but for dishonoring God. You claim to be God, although you're only a man."

[34] Jesus said to them, "Don't your Scriptures say, 'I said, "You are gods"'? [35] The Scriptures cannot be discredited. So if God calls people gods (and they are the people to whom he gave the Scriptures), [36] why do you say that I'm dishonoring God because I said, 'I'm the Son of God'? God set me apart for this holy purpose and has sent me into the world. [37] If I'm not doing the things my Father does, don't believe me. [38] But if I'm doing those things and you refuse to believe me, then at least believe the things that I'm doing. Then you will know and recognize that the Father is in me and that I am in the Father."

[39] The Jews tried to arrest Jesus again, but he got away from them. [40] He went back across the Jordan River and stayed in the place where John first baptized people.

[41] Many people went to Jesus. They said, "John didn't perform any miracles, but everything John said about this man is true." [42] Many people there believed in Jesus.

Jesus Brings Lazarus Back to Life

11 [1] Lazarus, who lived in Bethany, the village where Mary and her sister Martha lived, was sick. [2] (Mary was the woman who poured perfume on the Lord and wiped his feet with her hair. Her brother Lazarus was the one who was sick.)

[3] So the sisters sent a messenger to tell Jesus, "Lord, your close friend is sick."

[4] When Jesus heard the message, he said, "His sickness won't result in death. Instead, this sickness will bring glory to God so that the Son of God will receive glory through it."

[5] Jesus loved Martha, her sister, and Lazarus. [6] Yet, when Jesus heard that Lazarus was sick, he stayed where he was for two more days.

[7] Then, after the two days, Jesus said to his disciples, "Let's go back to Judea."

[8] The disciples said to him, "Rabbi, not long ago the Jews wanted to stone you to death. Do you really want to go back there?"

[9] Jesus answered, "Aren't there twelve hours of daylight? Those who walk during the day don't stumble, because they see the light of this world. [10] However, those who walk at night stumble because they have no light in themselves."

[11] After Jesus said this, he told his disciples, "Our friend Lazarus is sleeping, and I'm going to Bethany to wake him."

[12] His disciples said to him, "Lord, if he's sleeping, he'll get well."

[13] Jesus meant that Lazarus was dead, but the disciples thought Jesus meant that Lazarus was only sleeping. [14] Then Jesus told them plainly, "Lazarus has died, [15] but I'm glad that I wasn't there so that you can grow in faith. Let's go to Lazarus."

[16] Thomas, who was called Didymus, said to the rest of the disciples, "Let's go so that we, too, can die with Jesus."

---

[a] 10:14 The first part of verse 15 (in Greek) has been moved to verse 14 to express the complex Greek sentence structure more clearly in English.

¹⁷ When Jesus arrived, he found that Lazarus had been in the tomb for four days. ¹⁸ (Bethany was near Jerusalem, not quite two miles away.) ¹⁹ Many Jews had come to Martha and Mary to comfort them about their brother.

²⁰ When Martha heard that Jesus was coming, she went to meet him. Mary stayed at home. ²¹ Martha told Jesus, "Lord, if you had been here, my brother would not have died. ²² But even now I know that God will give you whatever you ask him."

²³ Jesus told Martha, "Your brother will come back to life."

²⁴ Martha answered Jesus, "I know that he'll come back to life on the last day, when everyone will come back to life."

²⁵ Jesus said to her, "I am the one who brings people back to life, and I am life itself. Those who believe in me will live even if they die. ²⁶ Everyone who lives and believes in me will never die. Do you believe that?"

²⁷ Martha said to him, "Yes, Lord, I believe that you are the Messiah, the Son of God, the one who was expected to come into the world."

²⁸ After Martha had said this, she went back home and whispered to her sister Mary, "The teacher is here, and he is calling for you."

²⁹ When Mary heard this, she got up quickly and went to Jesus. ³⁰ (Jesus had not yet come into the village but was still where Martha had met him.) ³¹ The Jews who were comforting Mary in the house saw her get up quickly and leave. So they followed her. They thought that she was going to the tomb to cry. ³² When Mary arrived where Jesus was and saw him, she knelt at his feet and said, "Lord, if you had been here, my brother would not have died."

³³ When Jesus saw her crying, and the Jews who were crying with her, he was deeply moved and troubled.

³⁴ So Jesus asked, "Where did you put Lazarus?"

They answered him, "Lord, come and see."

³⁵ Jesus cried. ³⁶ The Jews said, "See how much Jesus loved him." ³⁷ But some of the Jews asked, "Couldn't this man who gave a blind man sight keep Lazarus from dying?"

³⁸ Deeply moved again, Jesus went to the tomb. It was a cave with a stone covering the entrance. ³⁹ Jesus said, "Take the stone away."

Martha, the dead man's sister, told Jesus, "Lord, there must already be a stench. He's been dead for four days."

⁴⁰ Jesus said to her, "Didn't I tell you that if you believe, you would see God's glory?" ⁴¹ So the stone was moved away from the entrance of the tomb.

Jesus looked up and said, "Father, I thank you for hearing me. ⁴² I've known that you always hear me. However, I've said this so that the crowd standing around me will believe that you sent me." ⁴³ After Jesus had said this, he shouted as loudly as he could, "Lazarus, come out!"

⁴⁴ The dead man came out. Strips of cloth were wound around his feet and hands, and his face was wrapped with a handkerchief. Jesus told them, "Free Lazarus, and let him go."

The Jewish Council Plans to Kill Jesus

⁴⁵ Many Jews who had visited Mary and had seen what Jesus had done believed in him. ⁴⁶ But some of them went to the Pharisees and told them what Jesus had done. ⁴⁷ So the chief priests and the Pharisees called a meeting of the council. They asked, "What are we doing? This man is performing a lot of miracles. ⁴⁸ If we let him continue what he's doing, everyone will believe in him. Then the Romans will take away our position and our nation."

⁴⁹ One of them, Caiaphas, who was chief priest that year, told them, "You people don't know anything. ⁵⁰ You haven't even considered this: It is better for one man to die for the people than for the whole nation to be destroyed."

⁵¹ Caiaphas didn't say this on his own. As chief priest that year, he prophesied that Jesus would die for the Jewish nation. ⁵² He prophesied that Jesus wouldn't die merely for this nation, but that Jesus would die to bring God's scattered children together and make them one.

⁵³ From that day on, the Jewish council planned to kill Jesus. ⁵⁴ So Jesus no longer walked openly among the Jews. Instead, he left Bethany and went to the countryside near the desert, to a city called Ephraim, where he stayed with his disciples.

⁵⁵ The Jewish Passover was near. Many people came from the countryside to Jerusalem to purify themselves before the Passover. ⁵⁶ As they stood in the temple courtyard, they looked for Jesus and asked each other, "Do you think that he'll avoid coming to the festival?" ⁵⁷ (The chief priests and the Pharisees had given orders that whoever knew where Jesus was should tell them so that they could arrest him.)

Mary Prepares Jesus' Body for the Tomb—*Matthew 26:6–13; Mark 14:3–9*

12 ¹ Six days before Passover, Jesus arrived in Bethany. Lazarus, whom Jesus had brought back to life, lived there. ² Dinner was prepared for Jesus in Bethany. Martha served the dinner, and Lazarus was one of the people eating with Jesus.

³ Mary took a bottle of very expensive perfume made from pure nard and poured it on Jesus' feet. Then she dried his feet with her hair. The fragrance of the perfume filled the house.

⁴ One of his disciples, Judas Iscariot, who was going to betray him, asked, ⁵ "Why wasn't this perfume sold for a high price and the money given to the poor?" ⁶ (Judas didn't say this because he cared about the poor but because he was a thief. He was in charge of the money-bag and carried the contributions.) ⁷ Jesus said to Judas, "Leave her alone! She has done this to prepare me for the day I will be placed in a tomb. ⁸ You will always have the poor with you, but you will not always have me with you."

⁹ A large crowd of Jews found out that Jesus was in Bethany. So they went there not only to see Jesus but also to see Lazarus, whom Jesus had brought back to life. ¹⁰ The chief priests planned to kill Lazarus too. ¹¹ Lazarus was the reason why many people were leaving the Jews and believing in Jesus.

The King Comes to Jerusalem—*Matthew 21:1–11; Mark 11:1–11; Luke 19:29–44*

¹² On the next day the large crowd that had come to the Passover festival heard that Jesus was coming to Jerusalem. ¹³ So they took palm branches and went to meet him. They were shouting,

> "Hosanna!
> Blessed is the one who comes in the name of the Lord,
>   the king of Israel!"

¹⁴ Jesus obtained a donkey and sat on it, as Scripture says:

¹⁵   "Don't be afraid, people of Zion!
>   Your king is coming.
>   He is riding on a donkey's colt."

¹⁶ At first Jesus' disciples didn't know what these prophecies meant. However, when Jesus was glorified, the disciples remembered that these prophecies had been written about him. The disciples remembered that they had taken part in fulfilling the prophecies.

¹⁷ The people who had been with Jesus when he called Lazarus from the tomb and brought him back to life reported what they had seen. ¹⁸ Because the crowd heard that Jesus had performed this miracle, they came to meet him. ¹⁹ The Pharisees said to each other, "This is getting us nowhere. Look! The whole world is following him!"

Some Greeks Ask to See Jesus

²⁰ Some Greeks were among those who came to worship during the Passover festival. ²¹ They went to Philip (who was from Bethsaida in Galilee) and told him, "Sir, we would like to meet Jesus." ²² Philip told Andrew, and they told Jesus.

²³ Jesus replied to them, "The time has come for the Son of Man to be glorified. ²⁴ I can guarantee this truth: A single grain of wheat doesn't produce anything unless it is planted in the ground and dies. If it dies, it will produce a lot of grain. ²⁵ Those who love their lives will destroy them, and those who hate their lives in this world will guard them for everlasting life. ²⁶ Those who serve me must follow me. My servants will be with me wherever I will be. If people serve me, the Father will honor them.

²⁷ "I am too deeply troubled now to know how to express my feelings. Should I say, 'Father, save me from this time ˌof sufferingˌ'? No! I came for this time of suffering. ²⁸ Father, give glory to your name."

A voice from heaven said, "I have given it glory, and I will give it glory again."

²⁹ The crowd standing there heard the voice and said that it had thundered. Others in the crowd said that an angel had talked to him. ³⁰ Jesus replied, "That voice wasn't for my benefit but for yours.

³¹ "This world is being judged now. The ruler of this world will be thrown out now. ³² When I have been lifted up from the earth, I will draw all people toward me." ³³ By saying this, he indicated how he was going to die.

³⁴ The crowd responded to him, "We have heard from the Scriptures that the Messiah will remain here forever. So how can you say, 'The Son of Man must be lifted up from the earth'? Who is this 'Son of Man'?"

³⁵ Jesus answered the crowd, "The light will still be with you for a little while. Walk while you have light so that darkness won't defeat you. Those who walk in the dark don't know where they're going. ³⁶ While you have the light, believe in the light so that you will become people whose lives show the light."

After Jesus had said this, he was concealed as he left. [37] Although they had seen Jesus perform so many miracles, they wouldn't believe in him. [38] In this way the words of the prophet Isaiah came true:

"Lord, who has believed our message?
To whom has the Lord's power been revealed?"

[39] So the people couldn't believe because, as Isaiah also said,

[40] "God blinded them
and made them close-minded
so that their eyes don't see
and their minds don't understand.
And they never turn to me for healing!"

[41] Isaiah said this because he had seen Jesus' glory and had spoken about him. [42] Many rulers believed in Jesus. However, they wouldn't admit it publicly because the Pharisees would have thrown them out of the synagogue. [43] They were more concerned about what people thought of them than about what God thought of them.

[44] Then Jesus said loudly, "Whoever believes in me believes not only in me but also in the one who sent me. [45] Whoever sees me sees the one who sent me. [46] I am the light that has come into the world so that everyone who believes in me will not live in the dark. [47] If anyone hears my words and doesn't follow them, I don't condemn him. I didn't come to condemn the world but to save the world. [48] Those who reject me by not accepting what I say have a judge appointed for them. The words that I have spoken will judge them on the last day. [49] I have not spoken on my own. Instead, the Father who sent me told me what I should say and how I should say it. [50] I know that what he commands is eternal life. Whatever I say is what the Father told me to say."

Jesus Washes the Disciples' Feet

13 [1] Before the Passover festival, Jesus knew that the time had come for him to leave this world and go back to the Father. Jesus loved his own who were in the world, and he loved them to the end.

[2] While supper was taking place, the devil had already put the idea of betraying Jesus into the mind of Judas, son of Simon Iscariot. [3] The Father had put everything in Jesus' control. Jesus knew that. He also knew that he had come from God and was going back to God. [4] So he got up from the table, removed his outer clothes, took a towel, and tied it around his waist. [5] Then he poured water into a basin and began to wash the disciples' feet and dry them with the towel that he had tied around his waist.

[6] When Jesus came to Simon Peter, Peter asked him, "Lord, are you going to wash my feet?"

[7] Jesus answered Peter, "You don't know now what I'm doing. You will understand later."

[8] Peter told Jesus, "You will never wash my feet."

Jesus replied to Peter, "If I don't wash you, you don't belong to me."

[9] Simon Peter said to Jesus, "Lord, don't wash only my feet. Wash my hands and my head too!"

[10] Jesus told Peter, "People who have washed are completely clean. They need to have only their feet washed. All of you, except for one, are clean." [11] (Jesus knew who was going to betray him. That's why he said, "All of you, except for one, are clean.")

[12] After Jesus had washed their feet and put on his outer clothes, he took his place at the table again. Then he asked his disciples, "Do you understand what I've done for you? [13] You call me teacher and Lord, and you're right because that's what I am. [14] So if I, your Lord and teacher, have washed your feet, you must wash each other's feet. [15] I've given you an example that you should follow. [16] I can guarantee this truth: Slaves are not superior to their owners, and messengers are not superior to the people who send them. [17] If you understand all of this, you are blessed whenever you follow my example.

[18] "I'm not talking about all of you. I know the people I've chosen ˎto be apostlesˏ. However, I've made my choice so that Scripture will come true. It says, 'The one who eats my bread has turned against me.' [19] I'm telling you now before it happens. Then, when it happens, you will believe that I am the one.

[20] "I can guarantee this truth: Whoever accepts me accepts the one who sent me."

Jesus Knows Who Will Betray Him—*Matthew 26:21–25; Mark 14:18–21; Luke 22:21–23*

[21] After saying this, Jesus was deeply troubled. He declared, "I can guarantee this truth: One of you is going to betray me!"

[22] The disciples began looking at each other and wondering which one of them Jesus meant.

²³ One disciple, the one whom Jesus loved, was near him at the table. ²⁴ Simon Peter motioned to that disciple and said, "Ask Jesus whom he's talking about!"

²⁵ Leaning close to Jesus, that disciple asked, "Lord, who is it?"

²⁶ Jesus answered, "He's the one to whom I will give this piece of bread after I've dipped it in the sauce." So Jesus dipped the bread and gave it to Judas, son of Simon Iscariot.

²⁷ Then, after Judas took the piece of bread, Satan entered him. So Jesus told him, "Hurry! Do what you have to do." ²⁸ No one at the table knew why Jesus said this to him. ²⁹ Judas had the moneybag. So some thought that Jesus was telling him to buy what they needed for the festival or to give something to the poor.

³⁰ Judas took the piece of bread and immediately went outside. It was night.

³¹ When Judas was gone, Jesus said, "The Son of Man is now glorified, and because of him God is glorified. ³² If God is glorified because of the Son of Man, God will glorify the Son of Man because of himself, and he will glorify the Son of Man at once."

Jesus Predicts Peter's Denial—*Matthew 26:31–35; Mark 14:27–31; Luke 22:31–34*

³³ Jesus said, "Dear children, I will still be with you for a little while. I'm telling you what I told the Jews. You will look for me, but you can't go where I'm going.

³⁴ "I'm giving you a new commandment: Love each other in the same way that I have loved you. ³⁵ Everyone will know that you are my disciples because of your love for each other."

³⁶ Simon Peter asked him, "Lord, where are you going?"

Jesus answered him, "You can't follow me now to the place where I'm going. However, you will follow me later."

³⁷ Peter said to Jesus, "Lord, why can't I follow you now? I'll give my life for you."

³⁸ Jesus replied, "Will you give your life for me? I can guarantee this truth: No rooster will crow until you say three times that you don't know me.

Jesus Promises to Send the Holy Spirit

14 ¹ "Don't be troubled. Believe in God, and believe in me. ² My Father's house has many rooms. If that were not true, would I have told you that I'm going to prepare a place for you? ³ If I go to prepare a place for you, I will come again. Then I will bring you into my presence so that you will be where I am. ⁴ You know the way to the place where I am going."

⁵ Thomas said to him, "Lord, we don't know where you're going. So how can we know the way?"

⁶ Jesus answered him, "I am the way, the truth, and the life. No one goes to the Father except through me. ⁷ If you have known me, you will also know my Father. From now on you know him ˌthrough meˌ and have seen him ˌin meˌ."

⁸ Philip said to Jesus, "Lord, show us the Father, and that will satisfy us."

⁹ Jesus replied, "I have been with all of you for a long time. Don't you know me yet, Philip? The person who has seen me has seen the Father. So how can you say, 'Show us the Father'? ¹⁰ Don't you believe that I am in the Father and the Father is in me? What I'm telling you doesn't come from me. The Father, who lives in me, does what he wants. ¹¹ Believe me when I say that I am in the Father and that the Father is in me. Otherwise, believe me because of the things I do.

¹² "I can guarantee this truth: Those who believe in me will do the things that I am doing. They will do even greater things because I am going to the Father. ¹³ I will do anything you ask ˌthe Fatherˌ in my name so that the Father will be given glory because of the Son. ¹⁴ If you ask me to do something, I will do it.

¹⁵ "If you love me, you will obey my commandments. ¹⁶ I will ask the Father, and he will give you another helper who will be with you forever. ¹⁷ That helper is the Spirit of Truth. The world cannot accept him, because it doesn't see or know him. You know him, because he lives with you and will be in you.

¹⁸ "I will not leave you all alone. I will come back to you. ¹⁹ In a little while the world will no longer see me, but you will see me. You will live because I live. ²⁰ On that day you will know that I am in my Father and that you are in me and that I am in you. ²¹ Whoever knows and obeys my commandments is the person who loves me. Those who love me will have my Father's love, and I, too, will love them and show myself to them."

²² Judas (not Iscariot) asked Jesus, "Lord, what has happened that you are going to reveal yourself to us and not to the world?"

²³ Jesus answered him, "Those who love me will do what I say. My Father will love them, and we will go to them and make our home with them. ²⁴ A person who doesn't love me doesn't do what I say. I don't make up what you hear me say. What I say comes from the Father who sent me.

²⁵ "I have told you this while I'm still with you. ²⁶ However, the helper, the Holy Spirit, whom the Father will send in my name, will teach you everything. He will remind you of everything that I have ever told you.

²⁷ "I'm leaving you peace. I'm giving you my peace. I don't give you the kind of peace that the world gives. So don't be troubled or cowardly. ²⁸ You heard me tell you, 'I'm going away, but I'm coming back to you.' If you loved me, you would be glad that I'm going to the Father, because the Father is greater than I am.

²⁹ "I'm telling you this now before it happens. When it does happen, you will believe. ³⁰ The ruler of this world has no power over me. But he's coming, so I won't talk with you much longer. ³¹ However, I want the world to know that I love the Father and that I am doing exactly what the Father has commanded me to do. Get up! We have to leave."

Jesus, the True Vine

15 ¹ ⌐Then Jesus said,⌐ "I am the true vine, and my Father takes care of the vineyard. ² He removes every one of my branches that doesn't produce fruit. He also prunes every branch that does produce fruit to make it produce more fruit.

³ "You are already clean*ᵃ* because of what I have told you. ⁴ Live in me, and I will live in you. A branch cannot produce any fruit by itself. It has to stay attached to the vine. In the same way, you cannot produce fruit unless you live in me.

⁵ "I am the vine. You are the branches. Those who live in me while I live in them will produce a lot of fruit. But you can't produce anything without me. ⁶ Whoever doesn't live in me is thrown away like a branch and dries up. Branches like this are gathered, thrown into a fire, and burned. ⁷ If you live in me and what I say lives in you, then ask for anything you want, and it will be yours. ⁸ You give glory to my Father when you produce a lot of fruit and therefore show that you are my disciples.

⁹ "I have loved you the same way the Father has loved me. So live in my love. ¹⁰ If you obey my commandments, you will live in my love. I have obeyed my Father's commandments, and in that way I live in his love. ¹¹ I have told you this so that you will be as joyful as I am, and your joy will be complete. ¹² Love each other as I have loved you. This is what I'm commanding you to do. ¹³ The greatest love you can show is to give your life for your friends. ¹⁴ You are my friends if you obey my commandments. ¹⁵ I don't call you servants anymore, because a servant doesn't know what his master is doing. But I've called you friends because I've made known to you everything that I've heard from my Father. ¹⁶ You didn't choose me, but I chose you. I have appointed you to go, to produce fruit that will last, and to ask the Father in my name to give you whatever you ask for. ¹⁷ Love each other. This is what I'm commanding you to do.

¹⁸ "If the world hates you, realize that it hated me before it hated you. ¹⁹ If you had anything in common with the world, the world would love you as one of its own. But you don't have anything in common with the world. I chose you from the world, and that's why the world hates you. ²⁰ Remember what I told you: 'A servant isn't greater than his master.' If they persecuted me, they will also persecute you. If they did what I said, they will also do what you say. ²¹ Indeed, they will do all this to you because you are committed to me, since they don't know the one who sent me. ²² If I hadn't come and spoken to them, they wouldn't have any sin. But now they have no excuse for their sin. ²³ The person who hates me also hates my Father. ²⁴ If I hadn't done among them what no one else has done, they wouldn't have any sin. But now they have seen and hated both me and my Father. ²⁵ In this way what is written in their Scriptures has come true: 'They hate me for no reason.'

²⁶ "The helper whom I will send to you from the Father will come. This helper, the Spirit of Truth who comes from the Father, will declare the truth about me. ²⁷ You will declare the truth, too, because you have been with me from the beginning."

Sadness Will Turn to Joy

16 ¹ ⌐Jesus continued,⌐ "I have said these things to you so that you won't lose your faith. ² You will be thrown out of synagogues. Certainly, the time is coming when people who murder you will think that they are serving God. ³ They will do these things to you because they haven't known the Father or me. ⁴ But I've told you this so that when it happens you'll remember what I've told you. I didn't tell you this at first, because I was with you.

⁵ "Now I'm going to the one who sent me. Yet, none of you asks me where I'm going. ⁶ But because I've told you this, you're filled with sadness. ⁷ However, I am telling you the truth: It's good for you that I'm going away. If I don't go away, the helper won't come to you. But if I go, I will send him to you. ⁸ He will come to convict the world of sin, to show the world what has God's approval, and to convince the world that God judges it. ⁹ He will convict the world of sin, because people don't believe in me. ¹⁰ He will show the world what has God's approval, because I'm going to the Father and you won't see me anymore. ¹¹ He will convince the world that God judges it, because the ruler of this world has been judged.

ᵃ 15:3 "Clean" refers to anything that Moses' Teachings say is presentable to God.

¹² "I have a lot more to tell you, but that would be too much for you now. ¹³ When the Spirit of Truth comes, he will guide you into the full truth. He won't speak on his own. He will speak what he hears and will tell you about things to come. ¹⁴ He will give me glory, because he will tell you what I say. ¹⁵ Everything the Father says is also what I say. That is why I said, 'He will take what I say and tell it to you.'

¹⁶ "In a little while you won't see me anymore. Then in a little while you will see me again."

¹⁷ Some of his disciples said to each other, "What does he mean? He tells us that in a little while we won't see him. Then he tells us that in a little while we will see him again and that he's going to the Father." ¹⁸ So they were asking each other, "What does he mean when he says, 'In a little while'? We don't understand what he's talking about."

¹⁹ Jesus knew they wanted to ask him something. So he said to them, "Are you trying to figure out among yourselves what I meant when I said, 'In a little while you won't see me, and in a little while you will see me again'? ²⁰ I can guarantee this truth: You will cry because you are sad, but the world will be happy. You will feel pain, but your pain will turn to happiness. ²¹ A woman has pain when her time to give birth comes. But after the child is born, she doesn't remember the pain anymore because she's happy that a child has been brought into the world.

²² "Now you're in a painful situation. But I will see you again. Then you will be happy, and no one will take that happiness away from you. ²³ When that day comes, you won't ask me any more questions. I can guarantee this truth: If you ask the Father for anything in my name, he will give it to you. ²⁴ So far you haven't asked for anything in my name. Ask and you will receive so that you can be completely happy.

²⁵ "I have used examples to illustrate these things. The time is coming when I won't use examples to speak to you. Rather, I will speak to you about the Father in plain words. ²⁶ When that day comes, you will ask for what you want in my name. I'm telling you that I won't have to ask the Father for you. ²⁷ The Father loves you because you have loved me and have believed that I came from God. ²⁸ I left the Father and came into the world. Again, ⌐as I've said,⌐ I'm going to leave the world and go back to the Father."

²⁹ His disciples said, "Now you're talking in plain words and not using examples. ³⁰ Now we know that you know everything. You don't need to wait for questions to be asked. Because of this, we believe that you have come from God."

³¹ Jesus replied to them, "Now you believe. ³² The time is coming, and is already here, when all of you will be scattered. Each of you will go your own way and leave me all alone. Yet, I'm not all alone, because the Father is with me. ³³ I've told you this so that my peace will be with you. In the world you'll have trouble. But cheer up! I have overcome the world."

Jesus Prays for Himself, His Disciples, and His Church

17 ¹ After saying this, Jesus looked up to heaven and said, "Father, the time is here. Give your Son glory so that your Son can give you glory. ² After all, you've given him authority over all humanity so that he can give eternal life to all those you gave to him. ³ This is eternal life: to know you, the only true God, and Jesus Christ, whom you sent. ⁴ On earth I have given you glory by finishing the work you gave me to do. ⁵ Now, Father, give me glory in your presence with the glory I had with you before the world existed.

⁶ "I made your name known to the people you gave me. They are from this world. They belonged to you, and you gave them to me. They did what you told them. ⁷ Now they know that everything you gave me comes from you, ⁸ because I gave them the message that you gave me. They have accepted this message, and they know for sure that I came from you. They have believed that you sent me.

⁹ "I pray for them. I'm not praying for the world but for those you gave me, because they are yours. ¹⁰ Everything I have is yours, and everything you have is mine. I have been given glory by the people you have given me. ¹¹ I won't be in the world much longer, but they are in the world, and I'm coming back to you. Holy Father, keep them safe by the power of your name, the name that you gave me, so that their unity may be like ours. ¹² While I was with them, I kept them safe by the power of your name, the name that you gave me. I watched over them, and none of them, except one person, became lost. So Scripture came true.

¹³ "But now, ⌐Father,⌐ I'm coming back to you. I say these things while I'm still in the world so that they will have the same joy that I have. ¹⁴ I have given them your message. But the world has hated them because they don't belong to the world any more than I belong to the world. ¹⁵ I'm not asking you to take them out of the world but to protect them from the evil one. ¹⁶ They don't belong to the world any more than I belong to the world.

¹⁷ "Use the truth to make them holy. Your words are truth. ¹⁸ I have sent them into the world the same way you sent me into the world. ¹⁹ I'm dedicating myself to this holy work I'm doing for them so that they, too, will use the truth to be holy.

²⁰ "I'm not praying only for them. I'm also praying for those who will believe in me through their message. ²¹ I pray that all of these people continue to have unity in the way that you, Father, are in me and I am in you. I pray that they may be united with us so that the world may believe that you have sent me. ²² I have given them the glory that you gave me. I did this so that they are united in the same way we are. ²³ I am in them, and you are in me. So they are completely united. In this way the world knows that you have sent me and that you have loved them in the same way you have loved me.

²⁴ "Father, I want those you have given to me to be with me, to be where I am. I want them to see my glory, which you gave me because you loved me before the world was made. ²⁵ Righteous Father, the world didn't know you. Yet, I knew you, and these ˏdisciples˳ have known that you sent me. ²⁶ I have made your name known to them, and I will make it known so that the love you have for me will be in them and I will be in them."

Jesus Is Arrested—*Matthew 26:47–56; Mark 14:43–52; Luke 22:47–54a*

18 ¹ After Jesus finished his prayer, he went with his disciples to the other side of the Kidron Valley. They entered the garden that was there.

² Judas, who betrayed him, knew the place because Jesus and his disciples often gathered there. ³ So Judas took a troop of soldiers and the guards from the chief priests and Pharisees and went to the garden. They were carrying lanterns, torches, and weapons.

⁴ Jesus knew everything that was going to happen to him. So he went to meet them and asked, "Who are you looking for?"

⁵ They answered him, "Jesus from Nazareth."

Jesus told them, "I am he."

Judas, who betrayed him, was standing with the crowd. ⁶ When Jesus told them, "I am he," the crowd backed away and fell to the ground.

⁷ Jesus asked them again, "Who are you looking for?"

They said, "Jesus from Nazareth."

⁸ Jesus replied, "I told you that I am he. So if you are looking for me, let these other men go." ⁹ In this way what Jesus had said came true: "I lost none of those you gave me."

¹⁰ Simon Peter had a sword. He drew it, attacked the chief priest's servant, and cut off the servant's right ear. (The servant's name was Malchus.)

¹¹ Jesus told Peter, "Put your sword away. Shouldn't I drink the cup ˏof suffering˳ that my Father has given me?"

¹² Then the army officer and the Jewish guards arrested Jesus. They tied Jesus up ¹³ and took him first to Annas, the father-in-law of Caiaphas. Caiaphas, the chief priest that year, ¹⁴ was the person who had advised the Jews that it was better to have one man die for the people.

Peter Denies Jesus—*Matthew 26:69–75; Mark 14:66–72; Luke 22:54b–62*

¹⁵ Simon Peter and another disciple followed Jesus. The other disciple was well-known to the chief priest. So that disciple went with Jesus into the chief priest's courtyard. ¹⁶ Peter, however, was standing outside the gate. The other disciple talked to the woman who was the gatekeeper and brought Peter into the courtyard.

¹⁷ The gatekeeper asked Peter, "Aren't you one of this man's disciples too?"

Peter answered, "No, I'm not!"

¹⁸ The servants and the guards were standing around a fire they had built and were warming themselves because it was cold. Peter was standing there, too, and warming himself with the others.

The Chief Priest Questions Jesus

¹⁹ The chief priest questioned Jesus about his disciples and his teachings.

²⁰ Jesus answered him, "I have spoken publicly for everyone to hear. I have always taught in synagogues or in the temple courtyard, where all the Jews gather. I haven't said anything in secret. ²¹ Why do you question me? Question those who heard what I said to them. They know what I've said."

²² When Jesus said this, one of the guards standing near Jesus slapped his face and said, "Is that how you answer the chief priest?"

²³ Jesus replied to him, "If I've said anything wrong, tell me what it was. But if I've told the truth, why do you hit me?"

²⁴ Annas sent Jesus to Caiaphas, the chief priest. Jesus was still tied up.

Peter Denies Jesus Again—*Matthew 26:69–75; Mark 14:66–72; Luke 22:54b–62*

²⁵ Simon Peter continued to stand and warm himself by the fire. Some men asked him, "Aren't you, too, one of his disciples?"

Peter denied it by saying, "No, I'm not!"

26 One of the chief priest's servants, a relative of the man whose ear Peter had cut off, asked him, "Didn't I see you with Jesus in the garden?"

27 Peter again denied it, and just then a rooster crowed.

Pilate Questions Jesus—*Matthew 27:11–14; Mark 15:1–5; Luke 23:1–4*

28 Early in the morning, Jesus was taken from Caiaphas' house to the governor's palace.

The Jews wouldn't go into the palace. They didn't want to become unclean,[a] since they wanted to eat the Passover. 29 So Pilate came out to them and asked, "What accusation are you making against this man?"

30 The Jews answered Pilate, "If he weren't a criminal, we wouldn't have handed him over to you."

31 Pilate told the Jews, "Take him, and try him by your law."

The Jews answered him, "We're not allowed to execute anyone." 32 In this way what Jesus had predicted about how he would die came true.

33 Pilate went back into the palace, called for Jesus, and asked him, "Are you the king of the Jews?"

34 Jesus replied, "Did you think of that yourself, or did others tell you about me?"

35 Pilate answered, "Am I a Jew? Your own people and the chief priests handed you over to me. What have you done?"

36 Jesus answered, "My kingdom doesn't belong to this world. If my kingdom belonged to this world, my followers would fight to keep me from being handed over to the Jews. My kingdom doesn't have its origin on earth."

37 Pilate asked him, "So you are a king?"

Jesus replied, "You're correct in saying that I'm a king. I have been born and have come into the world for this reason: to testify to the truth. Everyone who belongs to the truth listens to me."

38 Pilate said to him, "What is truth?"

After Pilate said this, he went out to the Jews again and told them, "I don't find this man guilty of anything. 39 You have a custom that I should free one person for you at Passover. Would you like me to free the king of the Jews for you?"

40 The Jews shouted again, "Don't free this man! Free Barabbas!" (Barabbas was a political revolutionary.)

The Soldiers Make Fun of Jesus—*Matthew 27:27–30; Mark 15:16–19*

19 1 Then Pilate had Jesus taken away and whipped. 2 The soldiers twisted some thorny branches into a crown, placed it on his head, and put a purple cape on him. 3 They went up to him, said, "Long live the king of the Jews!" and slapped his face.

The People Want Jesus Crucified

4 Pilate went outside again and told the Jews, "I'm bringing him out to you to let you know that I don't find this man guilty of anything." 5 Jesus went outside. He was wearing the crown of thorns and the purple cape. Pilate said to them, "Look, here's the man!"

6 When the chief priests and the guards saw Jesus, they shouted, "Crucify him! Crucify him!"

Pilate told them, "You take him and crucify him. I don't find this man guilty of anything."

7 The Jews answered Pilate, "We have a law, and by that law he must die because he claimed to be the Son of God."

8 When Pilate heard them say that, he became more afraid than ever. 9 He went into the palace again and asked Jesus, "Where are you from?" But Jesus didn't answer him.

10 So Pilate said to Jesus, "Aren't you going to answer me? Don't you know that I have the authority to free you or to crucify you?"

11 Jesus answered Pilate, "You wouldn't have any authority over me if it hadn't been given to you from above. That's why the man who handed me over to you is guilty of a greater sin."

12 When Pilate heard what Jesus said, he wanted to free him. But the Jews shouted, "If you free this man, you're not a friend of the emperor. Anyone who claims to be a king is defying the emperor."

13 When Pilate heard what they said, he took Jesus outside and sat on the judge's seat in a place called Stone Pavement. (In Hebrew it is called *Gabbatha.*) 14 The time was about six o'clock in the morning on the Friday of the Passover festival.

Pilate said to the Jews, "Look, here's your king!"

15 Then the Jews shouted, "Kill him! Kill him! Crucify him!"

Pilate asked them, "Should I crucify your king?"

The chief priests responded, "The emperor is the only king we have!"

16 Then Pilate handed Jesus over to them to be crucified.

---

a 18:28 "Unclean" refers to anything that Moses' Teachings say is not presentable to God.

The Crucifixion—*Matthew 27:31–44; Mark 15:20–32; Luke 23:26–38*

So the soldiers took Jesus. [17] He carried his own cross and went out ˌof the cityˌ to a location called The Skull. (In Hebrew this place is called *Golgotha*.) [18] The soldiers crucified Jesus and two other men there. Jesus was in the middle.

[19] Pilate wrote a notice and put it on the cross. The notice read, "Jesus from Nazareth, the king of the Jews." [20] Many Jews read this notice, because the place where Jesus was crucified was near the city. The notice was written in Hebrew, Latin, and Greek.

[21] The chief priests of the Jewish people told Pilate, "Don't write, 'The king of the Jews!' Instead, write, 'He said that he is the king of the Jews.' "

[22] Pilate replied, "I have written what I've written."

[23] When the soldiers had crucified Jesus, they took his clothes and divided them four ways so that each soldier could have a share. His robe was left over. It didn't have a seam because it had been woven in one piece from top to bottom. [24] The soldiers said to each other, "Let's not rip it apart. Let's throw dice to see who will get it." In this way the Scripture came true: "They divided my clothes among themselves. They threw dice for my clothing." So that's what the soldiers did.

[25] Jesus' mother, her sister, Mary (the wife of Clopas), and Mary from Magdala were standing beside Jesus' cross. [26] Jesus saw his mother and the disciple whom he loved standing there. He said to his mother, "Look, here's your son!" [27] Then he said to the disciple, "Look, here's your mother!"

From that time on she lived with that disciple in his home.

Jesus Dies on the Cross—*Matthew 27:45–56; Mark 15:33–41; Luke 23:44–49*

[28] After this, when Jesus knew that everything had now been finished, he said, "I'm thirsty." He said this so that Scripture could finally be concluded.

[29] A jar filled with vinegar was there. So the soldiers put a sponge soaked in the vinegar on a hyssop stick and held it to his mouth.

[30] After Jesus had taken the vinegar, he said, "It is finished!"

Then he bowed his head and died.

[31] Since it was Friday and the next day was an especially important day of worship, the Jews didn't want the bodies to stay on the crosses. So they asked Pilate to have the men's legs broken and their bodies removed. [32] The soldiers broke the legs of the first man and then of the other man who had been crucified with Jesus.

[33] When the soldiers came to Jesus and saw that he was already dead, they didn't break his legs. [34] However, one of the soldiers stabbed Jesus' side with his spear, and blood and water immediately came out. [35] The one who saw this is an eyewitness. What he says is true, and he knows that he is telling the truth so that you, too, will believe.

[36] This happened so that the Scripture would come true: "None of his bones will be broken." [37] Another Scripture passage says, "They will look at the person whom they have stabbed."

Jesus Is Buried—*Matthew 27:57–61; Mark 15:42–47; Luke 23:50–56*

[38] Later Joseph from the city of Arimathea asked Pilate to let him remove Jesus' body. (Joseph was a disciple of Jesus but secretly because he was afraid of the Jews). Pilate gave him permission to remove Jesus' body. So Joseph removed it. [39] Nicodemus, the one who had first come to Jesus at night, went with Joseph and brought 75 pounds of a myrrh and aloe mixture. [40] These two men took the body of Jesus and bound it with strips of linen. They laced the strips with spices. This was the Jewish custom for burial.

[41] A garden was located in the place where Jesus was crucified. In that garden was a new tomb in which no one had yet been placed. [42] Joseph and Nicodemus put Jesus in that tomb, since that day was the Jewish day of preparation and since the tomb was nearby.

Jesus Comes Back to Life—*Matthew 28:1–10; Mark 16:1–8; Luke 24:1–12*

20 [1] Early on Sunday morning, while it was still dark, Mary from Magdala went to the tomb. She saw that the stone had been removed from the tomb's entrance. [2] So she ran to Simon Peter and the other disciple, whom Jesus loved. She told them, "They have removed the Lord from the tomb, and we don't know where they've put him."

[3] So Peter and the other disciple headed for the tomb. [4] The two were running side by side, but the other disciple ran faster than Peter and came to the tomb first. [5] He bent over and looked inside the tomb. He saw the strips of linen lying there but didn't go inside.

[6] Simon Peter arrived after him and went into the tomb. He saw the strips of linen lying there. [7] He also saw the cloth that had been on Jesus' head. It wasn't lying with the strips of linen but was rolled up separately. [8] Then the other disciple, who arrived at the tomb first, went inside. He saw and believed. [9] They didn't know yet what Scripture meant when it said that Jesus had to come back to life. [10] So the disciples went back home.

Jesus Appears to Mary From Magdala

11 Mary, however, stood there and cried as she looked at the tomb. As she cried, she bent over and looked inside. **12** She saw two angels in white clothes. They were sitting where the body of Jesus had been lying. One angel was where Jesus' head had been, and the other was where his feet had been. **13** The angels asked her why she was crying.

Mary told them, "They have removed my Lord, and I don't know where they've put him."

14 After she said this, she turned around and saw Jesus standing there. However, she didn't know that it was Jesus. **15** Jesus asked her, "Why are you crying? Who are you looking for?"

Mary thought it was the gardener speaking to her. So she said to him, "Sir, if you carried him away, tell me where you have put him, and I'll remove him."

16 Jesus said to her, "Mary!"

Mary turned around and said to him in Hebrew, "Rabboni!" (This word means "teacher.")

17 Jesus told her, "Don't hold on to me. I have not yet gone to the Father. But go to my brothers and sisters and tell them, 'I am going to my Father and your Father, to my God and your God.'"

18 Mary from Magdala went to the disciples and told them, "I have seen the Lord." She also told them what he had said to her.

Jesus Appears to the Disciples—Luke 24:36–48

19 That Sunday evening, the disciples were together behind locked doors because they were afraid of the Jews. Jesus stood among them and said to them, "Peace be with you!" **20** When he said this, he showed them his hands and his side. The disciples were glad to see the Lord.

21 Jesus said to them again, "Peace be with you! As the Father has sent me, so I am sending you." **22** After he had said this, he breathed on the disciples and said, "Receive the Holy Spirit. **23** Whenever you forgive sins, they are forgiven. Whenever you don't forgive them, they are not forgiven."

Jesus Appears to Thomas

24 Thomas, one of the twelve apostles, who was called Didymus, wasn't with them when Jesus came. **25** The other disciples told him, "We've seen the Lord."

Thomas told them, "I refuse to believe this unless I see the nail marks in his hands, put my fingers into them, and put my hand into his side."

26 A week later Jesus' disciples were again in the house, and Thomas was with them. Even though the doors were locked, Jesus stood among them and said, "Peace be with you!" **27** Then Jesus said to Thomas, "Put your finger here, and look at my hands. Take your hand, and put it into my side. Stop doubting, and believe."

28 Thomas responded to Jesus, "My Lord and my God!"

29 Jesus said to Thomas, "You believe because you've seen me. Blessed are those who haven't seen me but believe."

30 Jesus performed many other miracles that his disciples saw. Those miracles are not written in this book. **31** But these miracles have been written so that you will believe that Jesus is the Messiah, the Son of God, and so that you will have life by believing in him.

Jesus Appears to His Disciples Again

21 **1** Later, by the Sea of Tiberias, Jesus showed himself again to the disciples. This is what happened. **2** Simon Peter, Thomas (called Didymus), Nathanael from Cana in Galilee, Zebedee's sons, and two other disciples of Jesus were together. **3** Simon Peter said to the others, "I'm going fishing."

They told him, "We're going with you."

They went out in a boat but didn't catch a thing that night. **4** As the sun was rising, Jesus stood on the shore. The disciples didn't realize that it was Jesus.

5 Jesus asked them, "Friends, haven't you caught any fish?"

They answered him, "No, we haven't."

6 He told them, "Throw the net out on the right side of the boat, and you'll catch some." So they threw the net out and were unable to pull it in because so many fish were in it.

7 The disciple whom Jesus loved said to Peter, "It's the Lord." When Simon Peter heard that it was the Lord, he put back on the clothes that he had taken off and jumped into the sea. **8** The other disciples came with the boat and dragged the net full of fish. They weren't far from the shore, only about 100 yards.

9 When they went ashore, they saw a fire with a fish lying on the coals, and they saw a loaf of bread.

10 Jesus told them, "Bring some of the fish you've just caught." **11** Simon Peter got into the boat and pulled the net ashore. Though the net was filled with 153 large fish, it was not torn.

¹² Jesus told them, "Come, have breakfast." None of the disciples dared to ask him who he was. They knew he was the Lord. ¹³ Jesus took the bread, gave it to them, and did the same with the fish.

¹⁴ This was the third time that Jesus showed himself to the disciples after he had come back to life.

Jesus Speaks With Peter

¹⁵ After they had eaten breakfast, Jesus asked Simon Peter, "Simon, son of John, do you love me more than the other disciples do?"

Peter answered him, "Yes, Lord, you know that I love you."

Jesus told him, "Feed my lambs."

¹⁶ Jesus asked him again, a second time, "Simon, son of John, do you love me?"

Peter answered him, "Yes, Lord, you know that I love you."

Jesus told him, "Take care of my sheep."

¹⁷ Jesus asked him a third time, "Simon, son of John, do you love me?"

Peter felt sad because Jesus had asked him a third time, "Do you love me?" So Peter said to him, "Lord, you know everything. You know that I love you."

Jesus told him, "Feed my sheep. ¹⁸ I can guarantee this truth: When you were young, you would get ready to go where you wanted. But when you're old, you will stretch out your hands, and someone else will get you ready to take you where you don't want to go." ¹⁹ Jesus said this to show by what kind of death Peter would bring glory to God. After saying this, Jesus told Peter, "Follow me!"

²⁰ Peter turned around and saw the disciple whom Jesus loved. That disciple was following them. He was the one who leaned against Jesus' chest at the supper and asked, "Lord, who is going to betray you?" ²¹ When Peter saw him, he asked Jesus, "Lord, what about him?"

²² Jesus said to Peter, "If I want him to live until I come again, how does that concern you? Follow me!" ²³ So a rumor that that disciple wouldn't die spread among Jesus' followers. But Jesus didn't say that he wouldn't die. What Jesus said was, "If I want him to live until I come again, how does that concern you?"

²⁴ This disciple was an eyewitness of these things and wrote them down. We know that what he says is true.

²⁵ Jesus also did many other things. If every one of them were written down, I suppose the world wouldn't have enough room for the books that would be written.

ACTS

Introduction

1 [1] In my first book, Theophilus, I wrote about what Jesus began to do and teach. This included everything from the beginning of his life, [2] until the day he was taken to heaven. Before he was taken to heaven, he gave instructions through the Holy Spirit to the apostles, whom he had chosen.

Jesus Ascends to Heaven

[3] After his death Jesus showed the apostles a lot of convincing evidence that he was alive. For 40 days he appeared to them and talked with them about the kingdom of God.

[4] Once, while he was meeting with them, he ordered them not to leave Jerusalem but to wait there for what the Father had promised. Jesus said to them, "I've told you what the Father promises: [5] John baptized with water, but in a few days you will be baptized with the Holy Spirit."

[6] So when the apostles came together, they asked him, "Lord, is this the time when you're going to restore the kingdom to Israel?"

[7] Jesus told them, "You don't need to know about times or periods that the Father has determined by his own authority. [8] But you will receive power when the Holy Spirit comes to you. Then you will be my witnesses to testify about me in Jerusalem, throughout Judea and Samaria, and to the ends of the earth."

[9] After he had said this, he was taken to heaven. A cloud hid him so that they could no longer see him.

[10] They were staring into the sky as he departed. Suddenly, two men in white clothes stood near them. [11] They asked, "Why are you men from Galilee standing here looking at the sky? Jesus, who was taken from you to heaven, will come back in the same way that you saw him go to heaven."

A New Apostle Takes Judas' Place

[12] Then they returned to Jerusalem from the mountain called the Mount of Olives. It is near Jerusalem, about half a mile away.

[13] When they came into the city, Peter, John, James, Andrew, Philip, Thomas, Bartholomew, Matthew, James (son of Alphaeus), Simon the Zealot, and Judas (son of James) went to the second-story room where they were staying.

[14] The apostles had a single purpose as they devoted themselves to prayer. They were joined by some women, including Mary (the mother of Jesus), and they were joined by his brothers.

[15] At a time when about 120 disciples had gathered together, Peter got up and spoke to them. He said, [16] "Brothers, what the Holy Spirit predicted through David in Scripture about Judas had to come true. Judas led the men to arrest Jesus. [17] He had been one of us and had been given an active role in this ministry. [18] With the money he received from the wrong he had done, he bought a piece of land where he fell headfirst to his death. His body split open, and all his internal organs came out. [19] Everyone living in Jerusalem knows about this. They even call that piece of land *Akeldama,* which means 'Field of Blood' in their dialect. [20] You've read in Psalms, 'Let his home be deserted, and let no one live there,' and 'Let someone else take his position.' "

"Therefore, someone must be added to our number to serve with us as a witness that Jesus came back to life. [21] He must be one of the men who accompanied Jesus with us the entire time that the Lord Jesus was among us. [22] This person must have been with us from the time that John was baptizing people to the day that Jesus was taken from us."[a]

[23] The disciples determined that two men were qualified. These men were Joseph (who was called Barsabbas and was also known as Justus) and Matthias. [24] Then they prayed, "Lord, you know everyone's thoughts. Show us which of these two you have chosen. [25] Show us who is to take the place of Judas as an apostle, since Judas abandoned his position to go to the place where he belongs."

[26] They drew names to choose an apostle. Matthias was chosen and joined the eleven apostles.

---

[a] 1:22 Verses 21–22 have been rearranged to express the complex Greek sentence structure more clearly in English.

The Believers Are Filled With the Holy Spirit

2 ¹ When Pentecost, the fiftieth day after Passover, came, all the believers were together in one place. ² Suddenly, a sound like a violently blowing wind came from the sky and filled the whole house where they were staying. ³ Tongues that looked like fire appeared to them. The tongues arranged themselves so that one came to rest on each believer. ⁴ All the believers were filled with the Holy Spirit and began to speak in other languages as the Spirit gave them the ability to speak.

⁵ Devout Jewish men from every nation were living in Jerusalem. ⁶ They gathered when they heard the wind. Each person was startled to recognize his own dialect when the disciples spoke.

⁷ Stunned and amazed, the people in the crowd said, "All of these men who are speaking are Galileans. ⁸ Why do we hear them speaking in our native dialects? ⁹ We're Parthians, Medes, and Elamites. We're people from Mesopotamia, Judea, Cappadocia, Pontus, the province of Asia, ¹⁰ Phrygia, Pamphylia, Egypt, and the country near Cyrene in Libya. We're Jewish people, converts to Judaism, and visitors from Rome, ¹¹ Crete, and Arabia. We hear these men in our own languages as they tell about the miracles that God has done."

¹² All of these devout men were stunned and puzzled. They asked each other, "What can this mean?" ¹³ Others said jokingly, "They're drunk on sweet wine."

Peter Talks to the Crowd

¹⁴ Then Peter stood up with the eleven apostles. In a loud voice he said to them, "Men of Judea and everyone living in Jerusalem! You must understand this, so pay attention to what I say. ¹⁵ These men are not drunk as you suppose. It's only nine in the morning. ¹⁶ Rather, this is what the prophet Joel spoke about:

¹⁷   'In the last days, God says,
        I will pour my Spirit on everyone.
        Your sons and daughters will speak what God has revealed.
        Your young men will see visions.
        Your old men will dream dreams.
¹⁸   In those days
        I will pour my Spirit on my servants, on both men and women.
        They will speak what God has revealed.
¹⁹   I will work miracles in the sky and give signs on the earth:
        blood, fire, and clouds of smoke.
²⁰   The sun will become dark,
        and the moon will become as red as blood
            before the terrifying day of the Lord comes.
²¹   Then whoever calls on the name of the Lord will be saved.'

²² "Men of Israel, listen to what I say: Jesus from Nazareth was a man whom God brought to your attention. You know that through this man God worked miracles, did amazing things, and gave signs. ²³ By using men who don't acknowledge Moses' Teachings, you crucified Jesus, who was given over to death, by a plan that God had determined in advance. ²⁴ But God raised him from death to life and destroyed the pains of death, because death had no power to hold him. ²⁵ This is what David meant when he said about Jesus:

      'I always see the Lord in front of me.
        I cannot be moved because he is by my side.
²⁶   That is why my heart is glad and my tongue rejoices.
        My body also rests securely
²⁷   because you do not abandon my soul to the grave
            or allow your holy one to decay.
²⁸   You make the path of life known to me.
        In your presence there is complete joy.'

²⁹ "Brothers, I can tell you confidently that our ancestor David died and was buried and that his tomb is here to this day. ³⁰ David was a prophet and knew that God had promised with an oath that he would place one of David's descendants on his throne. ³¹ David knew that the Messiah would come back to life, and he spoke about that before it ever happened. He said that the Messiah wouldn't be left in the grave and that his body wouldn't decay.

³² "God brought this man Jesus back to life. We are all witnesses to that. ³³ God used his power to give Jesus the highest position. Jesus has also received and has poured out the Holy Spirit as the Father had promised, and this is what you're seeing and hearing. ³⁴ David didn't go up to heaven, but he said,

'The Lord said to my Lord,
"Take my highest position of power
35   until I put your enemies under your control." '

[36] "All the people of Israel should know beyond a doubt that God made Jesus, whom you crucified, both Lord and Christ."

[37] When the people heard this, they were deeply upset. They asked Peter and the other apostles, "Brothers, what should we do?"

[38] Peter answered them, "All of you must turn to God and change the way you think and act, and each of you must be baptized in the name of Jesus Christ so that your sins will be forgiven. Then you will receive the Holy Spirit as a gift. [39] This promise belongs to you and to your children and to everyone who is far away. It belongs to everyone who worships the Lord our God."

[40] Peter said much more to warn them. He urged, "Save yourselves from this corrupt generation." [41] Those who accepted what Peter said were baptized. That day about 3,000 people were added ˌto the groupˌ.

Life as a Christian

[42] The disciples were devoted to the teachings of the apostles, to fellowship, to the breaking of bread, and to prayer. [43] A feeling of fear came over everyone as many amazing things and miraculous signs happened through the apostles. [44] All the believers kept meeting together, and they shared everything with each other. [45] From time to time, they sold their property and other possessions and distributed the money to anyone who needed it. [46] The believers had a single purpose and went to the temple every day. They were joyful and humble as they ate at each other's homes and shared their food. [47] At the same time, they praised God and had the good will of all the people. Every day the Lord saved people, and they were added to the group.

A Lame Man Is Healed

3 [1] Peter and John were going to the temple courtyard for the three o'clock prayer. [2] At the same time, a man who had been lame from birth was being carried by some men. Every day these men would put the lame man at a gate in the temple courtyard. The gate was called Beautiful Gate. There he would beg for handouts from people going into the courtyard. [3] When the man saw that Peter and John were about to go into the courtyard, he asked them for a handout.

[4] Peter and John stared at him. "Look at us!" Peter said. [5] So the man watched them closely. He expected to receive something from them. [6] However, Peter said to him, "I don't have any money, but I'll give you what I do have. Through the power of Jesus Christ from Nazareth, walk!" [7] Peter took hold of the man's right hand and began to help him up. Immediately, the man's feet and ankles became strong. [8] Springing to his feet, he stood up and started to walk. He went with Peter and John into the temple courtyard. The man was walking, jumping, and praising God.

[9] All the people saw him walking and praising God. [10] They knew that he was the man who used to sit and beg at the temple's Beautiful Gate. The people were amazed and stunned to see what had happened to him. [11] They were excited, and everyone ran to see them at the place called Solomon's Porch. The man wouldn't let go of Peter and John.

[12] When Peter saw this, he said to the people, "Men of Israel, why are you amazed about this man? Why are you staring at us as though we have made him walk by our own power or godly life? [13] The God of our ancestors Abraham, Isaac, and Jacob has glorified his servant Jesus. You handed Jesus over to Pilate. You rejected him in Pilate's presence, even though Pilate had decided to let him go free. [14] You rejected the man who was holy and innocent. You asked to have a murderer given to you, [15] and you killed the source of life. But God brought him back to life, and we are witnesses to that. [16] We believe in the one named Jesus. Through his power alone this man, whom you know, was healed, as all of you saw.

[17] "And now, brothers, I know that like your rulers you didn't know what you were doing. [18] But in this way God made the sufferings of his Messiah come true. God had predicted these sufferings through all the prophets. [19] So change the way you think and act, and turn ˌto Godˌ to have your sins removed. [20] Then times will come when the Lord will refresh you. He will send you Jesus, whom he has appointed to be the Christ. [21] Heaven must receive Jesus until the time when everything will be restored as God promised through his holy prophets long ago.

[22] "Moses said, 'The Lord your God will send you a prophet, an Israelite like me. Listen to everything he tells you. [23] Those who won't listen to that prophet will be excluded from the people.' [24] Samuel and all the prophets who followed him spoke about these days. [25] You are the descendants of the prophets and the heirs of the promise[a] that God made to our ancestors when he said to Abraham, 'Through your descendant all people on earth will be blessed.'

---

[a] 3:25 Or "covenant."

26 God has brought his servant back to life and has sent him to you first. God did this to bless you by turning every one of you from your evil ways."

Peter and John's Trial in Front of the Jewish Council

4 **1** Some priests, the officer in charge of the temple guards, and some Sadducees approached Peter and John while they were speaking to the people. **2** These religious authorities were greatly annoyed. Peter and John were teaching the people and spreading the message that the dead will come back to life through Jesus. **3** So the temple guards arrested them. Since it was already evening, they put Peter and John in jail until the next day.

4 But many of those who had heard the message became believers, so the number of men who believed grew to about 5,000.

5 The next day the Jewish rulers, leaders, and scribes met in Jerusalem. **6** The chief priest Annas, Caiaphas, John, Alexander, and the rest of the chief priest's family were present. **7** They made Peter and John stand in front of them and then asked, "By what power or in whose name did you do this?"

8 Then Peter, because he was filled with the Holy Spirit, said to them, "Rulers and leaders of the people, **9** today you are cross-examining us about the good we did for a crippled man. You want to know how he was made well. **10** You and all the people of Israel must understand that this man stands in your presence with a healthy body because of the power of Jesus Christ from Nazareth. You crucified Jesus Christ, but God has brought him back to life. **11** He is the stone that the builders rejected, the stone that has become the cornerstone. **12** No one else can save us. Indeed, we can be saved only by the power of the one named Jesus and not by any other person."

13 After they found out that Peter and John had no education or special training, they were surprised to see how boldly they spoke. They realized that these men had been with Jesus. **14** When they saw the man who was healed standing with Peter and John, they couldn't say anything against the two apostles. **15** So they ordered Peter and John to leave the council room and began to discuss the matter among themselves. **16** They said, "What should we do to these men? Clearly, they've performed a miracle that everyone in Jerusalem knows about. We can't deny that. **17** So let's threaten them. Let's tell them that they must never speak to anyone about the one named Jesus. Then the news about the miracle that they have performed will not spread any further among the people."

18 They called Peter and John and ordered them never to teach about Jesus or even mention his name.

19 Peter and John answered them, "Decide for yourselves whether God wants people to listen to you rather than to him. **20** We cannot stop talking about what we've seen and heard."

21 The authorities threatened them even more and then let them go. Since all the people were praising God for what had happened, the authorities couldn't find any way to punish Peter and John. **22** (The man who was healed by this miracle was over 40 years old.)

The Apostles Pray for God's Help

23 When Peter and John were released, they went to the other apostles and told them everything the chief priests and leaders had said. **24** When the apostles heard this, they were united and loudly prayed to God, "Master, you made the sky, the land, the sea, and everything in them. **25** You said through the Holy Spirit, who spoke through your servant David (our ancestor),

> 'Why do the nations act arrogantly?
> Why do their people devise useless plots?
> **26**   Kings take their stand.
> Rulers make plans together
>   against the Lord and against his Messiah.'

27 "In this city Herod and Pontius Pilate made plans together with non-Jewish people and the people of Israel. They made their plans against your holy servant Jesus, whom you anointed. **28** Through your will and power, they did everything that you had already decided should be done.

29 "Lord, pay attention to their threats now, and allow us to speak your word boldly. **30** Show your power by healing, performing miracles, and doing amazing things through the power and the name of your holy servant Jesus."

31 When the apostles had finished praying, their meeting place shook. All of them were filled with the Holy Spirit and continued to speak the word of God boldly.

The Believers Share Their Property

32 The whole group of believers lived in harmony. No one called any of his possessions his own. Instead, they shared everything.

[33] With great power the apostles continued to testify that the Lord Jesus had come back to life. ˌGod'sˌ abundant good will[a] was with all of them. [34] None of them needed anything. From time to time, people sold land or houses and brought the money [35] to the apostles. Then the money was distributed to anyone who needed it.

[36] Joseph, a descendant of Levi, had been born on the island of Cyprus. The apostles called him Barnabas, which means "a person who encourages." [37] He had some land. He sold it and turned the money over to the apostles.

Ananias and Sapphira

5 [1] A man named Ananias and his wife Sapphira sold some property. [2] They agreed to hold back some of the money ˌthey had pledged ˌ and turned only part of it over to the apostles. [3] Peter asked, "Ananias, why did you let Satan fill you with the idea that you could deceive the Holy Spirit? You've held back some of the money you received for the land. [4] While you had the land, it was your own. After it was sold, you could have done as you pleased with the money. So how could you do a thing like this? You didn't lie to people but to God!"

[5] When Ananias heard Peter say this, he dropped dead. Everyone who heard about his death was terrified. [6] Some young men got up, wrapped his body in a sheet, carried him outside, and buried him.

[7] About three hours later Ananias' wife arrived. She didn't know what had happened. [8] So Peter asked her, "Tell me, did you sell the land for that price?"

She answered, "Yes, that was the price."

[9] Then Peter said to her, "How could you and your husband agree to test the Lord's Spirit? Those who buried your husband are standing at the door, and they will carry you outside for burial."

[10] Immediately, she dropped dead in front of Peter. When the young men came back, they found Sapphira dead. So they carried her outside and buried her next to her husband. [11] The whole church and everyone else who heard about what had happened were terrified.

The Apostles Perform Many Miracles

[12] The people saw the apostles perform many miracles and do amazing things. The believers had a common faith in Jesus as they met on Solomon's Porch. [13] None of the other people dared to join them, although everyone spoke highly of them. [14] More men and women than ever began to believe in the Lord. [15] As a result, people carried their sick into the streets. They placed them on stretchers and cots so that at least Peter's shadow might fall on some sick people as he went by. [16] Crowds from the cities around Jerusalem would gather. They would bring their sick and those who were troubled by evil spirits, and each person was cured.

The Apostles' Trial in Front of the Jewish Council

[17] The chief priest and the whole party of the Sadducees who were with him were extremely jealous. So they took action [18] by arresting the apostles and putting them in the city jail. [19] But at night an angel from the Lord opened the doors to their cell and led them out of the prison. [20] The angel told them, "Stand in the temple courtyard, and tell the people everything about life ˌin Christˌ."

[21] Early in the morning, after they had listened to the angel, the apostles went into the temple courtyard and began to teach.

The chief priest and those who were with him called together the Jewish council, that is, all the leaders of Israel. They also sent men to the prison to get the apostles. [22] When the temple guards arrived at the prison, they didn't find the apostles. The guards came back and reported, [23] "We found the prison securely locked and the guards standing at the doors. However, when we opened the doors, we found no one inside." [24] When the officer of the temple guards and the chief priests heard this, they were puzzled about what could have happened.

[25] Then someone told them, "The men you put in prison are standing in the temple courtyard. They're teaching the people."

[26] Then the officer of the temple guards went with some of his men to bring back the apostles without using force. After all, the officer and his guards were afraid that the people would stone them to death for using force. [27] When they brought back the apostles, they made them stand in front of the council. The chief priest questioned them. [28] He said, "We gave you strict orders not to mention Jesus' name when you teach. Yet, you've filled Jerusalem with your teachings. You want to take revenge on us for putting that man to death."

[29] Peter and the other apostles answered, "We must obey God rather than people. [30] You murdered Jesus by hanging him on a cross. But the God of our ancestors brought him back

---

[a] 4:33 Or "grace."

to life. [31] God used his power to give Jesus the highest position as leader and savior. He did this to lead the people of Israel to him, to change the way they think and act, and to forgive their sins. [32] We are witnesses to these things, and so is the Holy Spirit, whom God has given to those who obey him."

[33] When the men on the council heard this, they became furious and wanted to execute the apostles. [34] But a Pharisee named Gamaliel stood up. He was a highly respected expert in Moses' Teachings. He ordered that the apostles should be taken outside for a little while.

[35] Then he said to the council, "Men of Israel, consider carefully what you do with these men. [36] Some time ago Theudas appeared. He claimed that he was important, and about four hundred men joined him. He was killed, and all his followers were scattered. The whole movement was a failure.

[37] "After that man, at the time of the census, Judas from Galilee appeared and led people in a revolt. He, too, died, and all his followers were scattered.

[38] "We should keep away from these men for now. We should leave them alone. I can guarantee that if the plan they put into action is of human origin, it will fail. [39] However, if it's from God, you won't be able to stop them. You may even discover that you're fighting against God."

[40] The council took his advice. They called the apostles, beat them, ordered them not to speak about the one named Jesus, and let them go.

[41] The apostles left the council room. They were happy to have been considered worthy to suffer dishonor for speaking about Jesus. [42] Every day in the temple courtyard and from house to house, they refused to stop teaching and telling the Good News that Jesus is the Messiah.

The Disciples Choose Seven Men to Help the Apostles

6 [1] At that time, as the number of disciples grew, Greek-speaking Jews complained about the Hebrew-speaking Jews. The Greek-speaking Jews claimed that the widows among them were neglected every day when food and other assistance was distributed.

[2] The twelve apostles called all the disciples together and told them, "It's not right for us to give up God's word in order to distribute food. [3] So, brothers and sisters, choose seven men whom the people know are spiritually wise. We will put them in charge of this problem. [4] However, we will devote ourselves to praying and to serving in ways that are related to the word."

[5] The suggestion pleased the whole group. So they chose Stephen, who was a man full of faith and the Holy Spirit, and they chose Philip, Prochorus, Nicanor, Timon, Parmenas, and Nicolaus, who had converted to Judaism in the city of Antioch. [6] The disciples had these men stand in front of the apostles, who prayed and placed their hands on these seven men.

[7] The word of God continued to spread, and the number of disciples in Jerusalem grew very large. A large number of priests accepted the faith.

Stephen Is Arrested

[8] Stephen was a man filled with God's favor[a] and power. He did amazing things and performed miracles. [9] One day, some men from the cities of Cyrene and Alexandria and the provinces of Cilicia and Asia started an argument with Stephen. They belonged to a synagogue called Freedmen's Synagogue. [10] They couldn't argue with Stephen because he spoke with the wisdom that the Spirit had given him. [11] Then they bribed some men to lie.

These men said, "We heard him slander Moses and God." [12] The liars stirred up trouble among the people, the leaders, and the scribes. So they went to Stephen, took him by force, and brought him in front of the Jewish council. [13] Some witnesses stood up and lied about Stephen. They said, "This man never stops saying bad things about the holy place and Moses' Teachings. [14] We heard him say that Jesus from Nazareth will destroy the temple and change the customs that Moses gave us."

[15] Everyone who sat in the council stared at him and saw that his face looked like an angel's face.

Stephen Speaks in His Own Defense

7 [1] Then the chief priest asked Stephen, "Is this true?"

[2] Stephen answered, "Brothers and fathers, listen to me. The God who reveals his glory appeared to our ancestor Abraham in Mesopotamia. This happened before Abraham lived in Haran. [3] God told him, 'Leave your land and your relatives. Go to the land that I will show you.'

[4] "Then Abraham left the country of Chaldea and lived in the city of Haran. After his father died, God made him move from there to this land where we now live.

[5] "Yet, God didn't give Abraham anything in this land to call his own, not even a place to rest his feet. But God promised to give this land to him and to his descendants, even though

---

[a] 6:8 Or "grace."

Abraham didn't have a child. **⁶** God told Abraham that his descendants would be foreigners living in another country and that the people there would make them slaves and mistreat them for 400 years. **⁷** God also told him, 'I will punish the people whom they will serve. After that, they will leave that country and worship me here.'

⁸ "God gave Abraham circumcision to confirm his promise.ᵃ So when Abraham's son Isaac was born, Abraham circumcised him on the eighth day. Isaac did the same to his son Jacob, and Jacob did the same to his twelve sons (the ancestors of our tribes).

⁹ "Jacob's sons were jealous of their brother Joseph. They sold him into slavery, and he was taken to Egypt. But God was with Joseph **¹⁰** and rescued him from all his suffering. When Joseph stood in the presence of Pharaoh (the king of Egypt), God gave Joseph divine favorᵇ and wisdom so that he became ruler of Egypt and of Pharaoh's whole palace. **¹¹** Then a famine throughout Egypt and Canaan brought a lot of suffering. Our ancestors couldn't find any food. **¹²** When Jacob heard that Egypt had food, he sent our ancestors there. That was their first trip. **¹³** On the second trip, Joseph told his brothers who he was, and Pharaoh learned about Joseph's family. **¹⁴** Joseph sent for his father Jacob and his relatives, 75 people in all. **¹⁵** So Jacob went to Egypt, and he and our ancestors died there. **¹⁶** They were taken to Shechem for burial in the tomb that Abraham purchased in Shechem from Hamor's sons.

¹⁷ "When the time that God had promised to Abraham had almost come, the number of our people in Egypt had grown very large. **¹⁸** Then a different king, who knew nothing about Joseph, began to rule in Egypt. **¹⁹** This king was shrewd in the way he took advantage of our people. He mistreated our ancestors. He made them abandon their newborn babies outdoors, where they would die.

²⁰ "At that time Moses was born, and he was a very beautiful child. His parents took care of him for three months. **²¹** When Moses was abandoned outdoors, Pharaoh's daughter adopted him and raised him as her son. **²²** So Moses was educated in all the wisdom of the Egyptians and became a great man in what he said and did. **²³** When he was 40 years old, he decided to visit his own people, the Israelites. **²⁴** When he saw an Israelite man being treated unfairly by an Egyptian, he defended the Israelite. He took revenge by killing the Egyptian. **²⁵** Moses thought his own people would understand that God was going to use him to give them freedom. But they didn't understand. **²⁶** The next day Moses saw two Israelites fighting, and he tried to make peace between them. He said to them, 'Men, you are brothers. Why are you treating each other unfairly?'

²⁷ "But one of the men pushed Moses aside. He asked Moses, 'Who made you our ruler and judge? **²⁸** Do you want to kill me as you killed the Egyptian yesterday?' **²⁹** After he said that, Moses quickly left Egypt and lived in Midian as a foreigner. In Midian he fathered two sons.

³⁰ "Forty years later, a messenger appeared to him in the flames of a burning bush in the desert of Mount Sinai. **³¹** Moses was surprised when he saw this. As he went closer to look at the bush, the voice of the Lord said to him, **³²** 'I am the God of your ancestors—the God of Abraham, Isaac, and Jacob.' Moses began to tremble and didn't dare to look at the bush. **³³** The Lord told him, 'Take off your sandals. The place where you're standing is holy ground. **³⁴** I've seen how my people are mistreated in Egypt. I've heard their groaning and have come to rescue them. So now I'm sending you to Egypt.'

³⁵ "This is the Moses whom the Israelites rejected by saying, 'Who made you our ruler and judge?' This is the one God sent to free them and to rule them with the help of the messenger who appeared to him in the bush. **³⁶** This is the man who led our ancestors out of Egypt. He is the person who did amazing things and worked miracles in Egypt, at the Red Sea, and in the desert for 40 years. **³⁷** This is the same Moses who told the Israelites, 'God will send you a prophet, an Israelite like me.' **³⁸** This is the Moses who was in the assembly in the desert. Our ancestors and the messenger who spoke to him on Mount Sinai were there with him. Moses received life-giving messages to give to us, **³⁹** but our ancestors were not willing to obey him. Instead, they pushed him aside, and in their hearts they turned back to Egypt. **⁴⁰** They told Aaron, 'We don't know what has happened to this Moses, who led us out of Egypt. So make gods who will lead us.' **⁴¹** That was the time they made a calf. They offered a sacrifice to that false god and delighted in what they had made.

⁴² "So God turned away from them and let them worship the sun, moon, and stars. This is written in the book of the prophets: 'Did you bring me sacrifices and grain offerings in the desert for 40 years, nation of Israel? **⁴³** You carried along the shrine of Moloch, the star of the god Rephan, and the statues you made for yourselves to worship. I will send you into exile beyond the city of Babylon.'

⁴⁴ "In the desert our ancestors had the tent of God's promise. Moses built this tent exactly as God had told him. He used the model he had seen. **⁴⁵** After our ancestors received the tent,

---

ᵃ 7:8 Or "covenant."   ᵇ 7:10 Or "grace."

they brought it into this land. They did this with Joshua's help when they took possession of the land from the nations that God forced out of our ancestors' way. This tent remained here until the time of David, [46] who won God's favor. David asked that he might provide a permanent place for the family of Jacob.[c] [47] But Solomon was the one who built a house for God.

[48] "However, the Most High doesn't live in a house built by humans, as the prophet says:

[49]   'The Lord says,
         "Heaven is my throne.
         The earth is my footstool.
            What kind of house are you going to build for me?
            Where will I rest?
[50]   Didn't I make all these things?" '

[51] "How stubborn can you be? How can you be so heartless and disobedient? You're just like your ancestors. They always opposed the Holy Spirit, and so do you! [52] Was there ever a prophet your ancestors didn't persecute? They killed those who predicted that a man with God's approval would come. You have now become the people who betrayed and murdered that man. [53] You are the people who received Moses' Teachings, which were put into effect by angels. But you haven't obeyed those teachings."

Stephen Is Executed

[54] As council members listened to Stephen, they became noticeably furious. [55] But Stephen was full of the Holy Spirit. He looked into heaven, saw God's glory, and Jesus in the position of authority that God gives. [56] So Stephen said, "Look, I see heaven opened and the Son of Man in the position of authority that God has given him!"

[57] But the council members shouted and refused to listen. Then they rushed at Stephen with one purpose in mind, [58] and after they had thrown him out of the city, they began to stone him to death. The witnesses left their coats with a young man named Saul.

[59] While council members were executing Stephen, he called out, "Lord Jesus, welcome my spirit." [60] Then he knelt down and shouted, "Lord, don't hold this sin against them." After he had said this, he died.

8 [1] Saul approved of putting Stephen to death.
On that day widespread persecution broke out against the church in Jerusalem. Most believers, except the apostles, were scattered throughout Judea and Samaria.

[2] Devout men buried Stephen as they mourned loudly for him.

[3] Saul tried to destroy the church. He dragged men and women out of one home after another and threw them into prison.

Some Samaritans Become Believers

[4] The believers who were scattered went from place to place, where they spread the word. [5] Philip went to the city of Samaria and told people about the Messiah. [6] The crowds paid close attention to what Philip said. They listened to him and saw the miracles that he performed. [7] Evil spirits screamed as they came out of the many people they had possessed. Many paralyzed and lame people were cured. [8] As a result, that city was extremely happy.

[9] A man named Simon lived in that city. He amazed the people of Samaria with his practice of magic. He claimed that he was great. [10] Everyone from children to adults paid attention to him. They said, "This man is the power of God, and that power is called great." [11] They paid attention to Simon because he had amazed them for a long time with his practice of magic. [12] However, when Philip spread the Good News about the kingdom of God and the one named Jesus Christ, men and women believed him and were baptized. [13] Even Simon believed, and after he was baptized, he became devoted to Philip. Simon was amazed to see the miracles and impressive things that were happening.

[14] When the apostles in Jerusalem heard that the Samaritans had accepted the word of God, they sent Peter and John to them. [15] Peter and John went to Samaria and prayed that the Samaritans would receive the Holy Spirit. [16] (Before this the Holy Spirit had not come to any of the Samaritans. They had only been baptized in the name of the Lord Jesus.) [17] Then Peter and John placed their hands on them, and the Samaritans received the Holy Spirit.

[18] Simon saw that the Spirit was given to the Samaritans when the apostles placed their hands on them. So he offered Peter and John money [19] and said, "Give me this power so that anyone I place my hands on will receive the Holy Spirit."

[20] Peter told Simon, "May your money be destroyed with you because you thought you could buy God's gift. [21] You won't have any share in this because God can see how twisted your think-

---

[c] 7:46 Some manuscripts and translations read "God of Jacob."

ing is. ²² So change your wicked thoughts, and ask the Lord if he will forgive you for thinking like this. ²³ I can see that you are bitter with jealousy and wrapped up in your evil ways."

²⁴ Simon answered, "Pray to the Lord for me that none of the things you said will happen to me."

²⁵ After they had boldly spoken about the message of the Lord, they spread the Good News in many Samaritan villages on their way back to Jerusalem.

Philip Tells an Ethiopian About Jesus

²⁶ An angel from the Lord said to Philip, "Get up, and take the desert road that goes south from Jerusalem to Gaza." ²⁷ So Philip went.

An Ethiopian man who had come to Jerusalem to worship was on his way home. The man was a eunuch, a high-ranking official in charge of all the treasures of Queen Candace of Ethiopia. ²⁸ As the official rode along in his carriage, he was reading the prophet Isaiah out loud. ²⁹ The Spirit said to Philip, "Go to that carriage, and stay close to it."

³⁰ Philip ran to the carriage and could hear the official reading the prophet Isaiah out loud. Philip asked him, "Do you understand what you're reading?"

³¹ The official answered, "How can I understand unless someone guides me?" So he invited Philip to sit with him in his carriage.

³² This was the part of the Scriptures that the official was reading:

> "He was led like a lamb to the slaughter.
> He was like a sheep that is silent
>   when its wool is cut off.
>   He didn't open his mouth.
> ³³   When he humbled himself,
>   he was not judged fairly.
>   Who from his generation
>   will talk about his life on earth being cut short?"

³⁴ The official said to Philip, "I would like to know who the prophet is talking about. Is he talking about himself or someone else?" ³⁵ Then Philip spoke. Starting with that passage, Philip told the official the Good News about Jesus.

³⁶ As they were going along the road, they came to some water. The official said to Philip, "Look, there's some water. What can keep me from being baptized?"ᵃ ³⁸ The official ordered the carriage to stop. He and Philip stepped into the water, and Philip baptized him. ³⁹ When they had stepped out of the water, the Spirit of the Lord suddenly took Philip away. The official joyfully continued on his way and didn't see Philip again.

⁴⁰ Philip found himself in the city of Azotus. He traveled through all the cities and spread the Good News until he came to the city of Caesarea.

Saul Becomes a Follower of Jesus

9 ¹ Saul kept threatening to murder the Lord's disciples. He went to the chief priest ² and asked him to write letters of authorization to the synagogue leaders in the city of Damascus. Saul wanted to arrest any man or woman who followed the way ⸤of Christ⸥ and imprison them in Jerusalem.

³ As Saul was coming near the city of Damascus, a light from heaven suddenly flashed around him. ⁴ He fell to the ground and heard a voice say to him, "Saul! Saul! Why are you persecuting me?"

⁵ Saul asked, "Who are you, sir?"

The person replied, "I'm Jesus, the one you're persecuting. ⁶ Get up! Go into the city, and you'll be told what you should do."

⁷ Meanwhile, the men traveling with him were speechless. They heard the voice but didn't see anyone.

⁸ Saul was helped up from the ground. When he opened his eyes, he was blind. So his companions led him into Damascus. ⁹ For three days he couldn't see and didn't eat or drink.

¹⁰ A disciple named Ananias lived in the city of Damascus. The Lord said to him in a vision, "Ananias!"

Ananias answered, "Yes, Lord."

¹¹ The Lord told him, "Get up! Go to Judas' house on Straight Street, and ask for a man named Saul from the city of Tarsus. He's praying. ¹² In a vision he has seen a man named Ananias place his hands on him to restore his sight."

ᵃ 8:36 Some manuscripts and translations add verse 37: "Philip said to the official, 'If you believe with all your heart, you can be baptized.' The official answered, 'I believe Jesus Christ is the Son of God.'"

¹³ Ananias replied, "Lord, I've heard a lot of people tell about the many evil things this man has done to your people in Jerusalem. ¹⁴ Saul has come here to Damascus with authority from the chief priests to put anyone who calls on your name in prison."

¹⁵ The Lord told Ananias, "Go! I've chosen this man to bring my name to nations, to kings, and to the people of Israel. ¹⁶ I'll show him how much he has to suffer for the sake of my name."

¹⁷ Ananias left and entered Judas' house. After he placed his hands on Saul, Ananias said, "Brother Saul, the Lord Jesus, who appeared to you on your way to Damascus, sent me to you. He wants you to see again and to be filled with the Holy Spirit."

¹⁸ Immediately, something like fish scales fell from Saul's eyes, and he could see again. Then Saul stood up and was baptized. ¹⁹ After he had something to eat, his strength came back to him.

Saul was with the disciples in the city of Damascus for several days. ²⁰ He immediately began to spread the word in their synagogues that Jesus was the Son of God. ²¹ Everyone who heard him was amazed. They asked, "Isn't this the man who destroyed those who worshiped the one named Jesus in Jerusalem? Didn't he come here to take these worshipers as prisoners to the chief priests ⸤in Jerusalem⸥?"

²² Saul grew more powerful, and he confused the Jews living in Damascus by proving that Jesus was the Messiah. ²³ Later the Jews planned to murder Saul, ²⁴ but Saul was told about their plot. They were watching the city gates day and night in order to murder him. ²⁵ However, Saul's disciples lowered him in a large basket through an opening in the wall one night.

²⁶ After Saul arrived in Jerusalem, he tried to join the disciples. But everyone was afraid of him. They wouldn't believe that he was a disciple.

²⁷ Then Barnabas took an interest in Saul and brought him to the apostles. Barnabas told the apostles how Saul had seen the Lord on the road and that the Lord had spoken to him. Barnabas also told them how boldly Saul had spoken about the one named Jesus in the city of Damascus. ²⁸ Then Saul went throughout Jerusalem with the disciples. He spoke boldly with the power and authority of the Lord.

²⁹ He talked and argued with Greek-speaking Jews, but they tried to murder him. ³⁰ As soon as the disciples found out about this, they took Saul to Caesarea and sent him to Tarsus.

³¹ Then the church throughout Judea, Galilee, and Samaria had peace. The number of people increased as people lived in the fear of the Lord and the comfort of the Holy Spirit.

Peter Heals Aeneas

³² When Peter was going around to all of God's people, he came to those who lived in the city of Lydda. ³³ In Lydda Peter found a man named Aeneas who was paralyzed and confined to a cot for eight years.

³⁴ Peter said to him, "Aeneas, Jesus Christ makes you well. Get up, and pick up your cot." Aeneas immediately got up.

³⁵ Everyone who lived in the city of Lydda and the coastal region of Sharon saw what had happened to Aeneas and turned to the Lord in faith.

Peter Brings Tabitha Back to Life

³⁶ A disciple named Tabitha lived in the city of Joppa. Her Greek name was Dorcas. She always helped people and gave things to the poor. ³⁷ She became sick and died. Her body was prepared for burial and was laid in an upstairs room.

³⁸ Lydda is near the city of Joppa. When the disciples heard that Peter was in Lydda, they sent two men to him. They begged Peter, "Hurry to Joppa! We need your help!"

³⁹ So Peter went with them. When he arrived, he was taken upstairs. All the widows stood around him. They were crying and showing Peter the articles of clothing that Dorcas had made while she was still with them.

⁴⁰ Peter made everyone leave the room.

He knelt and prayed. Then he turned toward the body and said, "Tabitha, get up!"

Tabitha opened her eyes, saw Peter, and sat up. ⁴¹ Peter took her hand and helped her stand up. After he called the believers, especially the widows, he presented Tabitha to them. She was alive.

⁴² The news about this spread throughout the city of Joppa, and as a result, many people believed in the Lord.

⁴³ Peter stayed in Joppa for a number of days with Simon, a leatherworker.

Cornelius Has a Vision

10 ¹ A man named Cornelius lived in the city of Caesarea. He was a Roman army officer in the Italian Regiment. ² He and everyone in his home were devout and respected God. Cornelius gave many gifts to poor Jewish people and always prayed to God.

³ One day, about three in the afternoon, he had a vision. He clearly saw an angel from God come to him and say, "Cornelius!"

⁴ He stared at the angel and was terrified. Cornelius asked the angel, "What do you want, sir?"

The angel answered him, "God is aware of your prayers and your gifts to the poor, and he has remembered you. ⁵ Send messengers now to the city of Joppa, and summon a man whose name is Simon Peter. ⁶ He is a guest of Simon, a leatherworker, whose house is by the sea."

⁷ After saying this, the angel left. Cornelius called two of his household servants and a devout soldier, one of those who served him regularly. ⁸ Cornelius explained everything to them and sent them to Joppa.

Peter Has a Vision

⁹ Around noon the next day, while Cornelius' men were on their way and coming close to Joppa, Peter went on the roof to pray. ¹⁰ He became hungry and wanted to eat. While the food was being prepared, he fell into a trance. ¹¹ He saw the sky open and something like a large linen sheet being lowered by its four corners to the ground. ¹² In the sheet were all kinds of four-footed animals, reptiles, and birds.

¹³ A voice told him, "Get up, Peter! Kill these animals, and eat them."

¹⁴ Peter answered, "I can't do that, Lord! I've never eaten anything that is impure or unclean."ᵃ

¹⁵ A voice spoke to him a second time, "Don't say that the things which God has made cleanᵇ are impure."

¹⁶ This happened three times. Then the sheet was quickly taken into the sky.

¹⁷ While Peter was puzzled by the meaning of the vision, the men sent by Cornelius found Simon's house and went to the gate. ¹⁸ They asked if Simon Peter was staying there. ¹⁹ Peter was still thinking about the vision when the Spirit said to him, "Three men are looking for you. ²⁰ Get up, and go downstairs. Don't hesitate to go with these men. I have sent them."

²¹ So Peter went to the men. He said, "I'm the man you're looking for. Why are you here?"

²² The men replied, "Cornelius, a Roman army officer, sent us. He's a man who has God's approval and who respects God. Also, the Jewish people respect him. A holy angel told him to summon you to his home to hear what you have to say."

²³ Peter asked the men to come into the house and had them stay overnight.

Peter Speaks With Cornelius

The next day Peter left with them. Some disciples from Joppa went along. ²⁴ The following day they arrived in Caesarea. Cornelius was expecting them and had called his relatives and close friends together.

²⁵ When Peter was about to enter Cornelius' house, Cornelius met him, bowed down, and worshiped Peter. ²⁶ But Peter made him get up. He told him, "Stand up! I'm only a man."

²⁷ As Peter talked, he entered Cornelius' house and found that many people had gathered. ²⁸ He said to them, "You understand how wrong it is for a Jewish man to associate or visit with anyone of another race. But God has shown me that I should no longer call anyone impure or unclean. ²⁹ That is why I didn't object to coming here when you sent for me. I want to know why you sent for me."

³⁰ Cornelius answered, "Four days ago I was praying at home. It was at this same time, three o'clock in the afternoon. Suddenly, a man dressed in radiant clothes stood in front of me. ³¹ He said to me, 'Cornelius, God has heard your prayer and has remembered your gifts to the poor. ³² So send messengers to Joppa, and summon a man whose name is Simon Peter. He's a guest in the home of Simon, a leatherworker who lives by the sea.' ³³ So I sent for you immediately. Thank you for coming. All of us are here now in the presence of God to listen to everything the Lord has ordered you to say."

³⁴ Then Peter said, "Now I understand that God doesn't play favorites. ³⁵ Rather, whoever respects God and does what is right is acceptable to him in any nation. ³⁶ God sent his word to the people of Israel and brought them the Good News of peace through Jesus Christ. This Jesus Christ is everyone's Lord. ³⁷ You know what happened throughout Judea. Everything began in Galilee after John spread the news about baptism. ³⁸ You know that God anointed Jesus from Nazareth with the Holy Spirit and with power. Jesus went everywhere and did good things, such as healing everyone who was under the devil's power. Jesus did these things because God was with him. ³⁹ We can testify to everything Jesus did in the land of the Jews and in Jerusalem. People hung him on a cross and killed him, ⁴⁰ but God brought him back to life on the third day. God didn't show him ⁴¹ to all the people. He showed Jesus to witnesses, apostles he had already chosen. We apostles are those men who ate and drank with Jesus after he came back to life. ⁴² He ordered us to warn the people, 'God has appointed Jesus to judge the living and the dead.' ⁴³ In addition, all the prophets testify that people who believe in the one named Jesus receive forgiveness for their sins through him."

ᵃ 10:14 "Unclean" refers to anything that Moses' Teachings say is not presentable to God.   ᵇ 10:15 "Clean" refers to anything that Moses' Teachings say is presentable to God.

44 While Peter was still speaking, the Holy Spirit came to everyone who heard his message. **45** All the believers who were circumcised and who had come with Peter were amazed that the gift of the Holy Spirit had been poured on people who were not Jewish. **46** They heard these non-Jewish people speaking in other languages and praising God.

Then Peter said, **47** "No one can refuse to baptize these people with water. They have received the Holy Spirit in the same way that we did." **48** So Peter ordered that they should be baptized in the name of Jesus Christ.

Then they asked Peter to stay with them for several days.

Peter Reports That Non-Jewish People Can Belong to the Church

11 **1** The apostles and the believers throughout Judea heard that people who were not Jewish had accepted God's word. **2** However, when Peter went to Jerusalem, the believers who insisted on circumcision began to argue with him. **3** They said, "You went to visit men who were uncircumcised, and you even ate with them."

4 Then Peter began to explain to them point by point what had happened. He said, **5** "I was praying in the city of Joppa when I fell into a trance. I saw something like a large linen sheet being lowered by its four corners from the sky. The sheet came near me. **6** I looked into the sheet very closely and saw tame animals, wild animals, reptiles, and birds. **7** I also heard a voice telling me, 'Get up, Peter! Kill these animals, and eat them.'

8 "But I answered, 'I can't do that, Lord! I've never put anything impure or unclean*a* into my mouth.'

9 "A voice spoke from heaven a second time, 'Don't say that the things which God has made clean*b* are impure.' **10** This happened three times. Then everything was pulled back into the sky again.

11 "At that moment three men arrived at the house where we were staying. They had been sent from Caesarea to find me. **12** The Spirit told me to go with them without any hesitation. Six believers ˌfrom Joppaˌ went with me, and we visited Cornelius' home.

13 "He told us that he had seen an angel standing in his home. The angel told him, 'Send messengers to Joppa, and summon a man whose name is Simon Peter. **14** He will give you a message that will save you and everyone in your home.'

15 "When I began to speak, the Holy Spirit came to these people. This was the same thing that happened to us in the beginning. **16** I remembered that the Lord had said, 'John baptized with water, but you will be baptized by the Holy Spirit.' **17** When they believed, God gave them the same gift that he gave us when we believed in the Lord Jesus Christ. So who was I to interfere with God?"

18 When the others heard this, they had no further objections. They praised God by saying, "Then God has also led people who are not Jewish to turn to him so that they can change the way they think and act and have eternal life."

The New Church in Antioch

19 Some of the believers who were scattered by the trouble that broke out following Stephen's death went as far as Phoenicia, Cyprus, and the city of Antioch. They spoke God's word only to Jewish people. **20** But other believers, who were from Cyprus and Cyrene, arrived in Antioch. They started to spread the Good News about the Lord Jesus to Greeks. **21** The Lord's power was with his followers, and a large number of people believed and turned to the Lord.

22 After the news about Antioch reached the church in Jerusalem, Barnabas was sent to Antioch. **23** When he arrived there, he was pleased to see what God had done for them out of kindness.*c* So he encouraged all the people to remain solidly committed to the Lord. **24** Barnabas was a dependable man, and he was full of the Holy Spirit and faith. A large crowd believed in the Lord.

25 Then Barnabas left Antioch to go to the city of Tarsus to look for Saul. **26** After finding Saul, Barnabas brought him back to Antioch. Barnabas and Saul met with the church in Antioch for a whole year and taught a large group of people. The disciples were called Christians for the first time in the city of Antioch.

27 At that time some prophets came from Jerusalem to the city of Antioch. **28** One of them was named Agabus. Through the Spirit Agabus predicted that a severe famine would affect the entire world. This happened while Claudius was emperor. **29** All the disciples in Antioch decided to contribute whatever they could afford to help the believers living in Judea. **30** The disciples did this and sent their contribution with Barnabas and Saul to the leaders ˌin Jerusalemˌ.

---

a 11:8 "Unclean" refers to anything that Moses' Teachings say is not presentable to God.   *b* 11:9 "Clean" refers to anything that Moses' Teachings say is presentable to God.   *c* 11:23 Or "grace."

An Angel Frees Peter From Prison

12 [1] About that time King Herod devoted his attention to mistreating certain members of the church. [2] He had James, the brother of John, executed. [3] When he saw how this pleased the Jews, he arrested Peter too. This happened during the days of Unleavened Bread. [4] After capturing Peter, Herod had him thrown into prison with sixteen soldiers in squads of four to guard him. Herod wanted to bring Peter to trial in front of the people after Passover. [5] So Peter was kept in prison, but the church was praying very hard to God for him.

[6] The night before Herod was going to bring Peter to trial, Peter was sleeping between two soldiers. His hands were bound with two chains, and guards were in front of the door. They were watching the prison.

[7] Suddenly, an angel from the Lord stood near Peter, and his cell was filled with light. The angel nudged Peter's side, woke him up, and said, "Hurry! Get up!" At that moment the chains fell from Peter's hands.

[8] The angel told him, "Put your shoes on, and get ready to go!" Peter did this. Then the angel told him, "Put your coat on, and follow me."

[9] Peter followed the angel out of the cell. He didn't realize that what the angel was doing was actually happening. He thought he was seeing a vision. [10] They passed the first and second guardposts and came to the iron gate that led into the city. This gate opened by itself for them, so they went outside and up the street. The angel suddenly left Peter.

[11] When Peter came to his senses, he said, "Now I'm sure that the Lord sent his angel to rescue me from Herod and from everything the Jewish people are expecting to happen to me."

[12] When Peter realized what had happened, he went to the home of Mary, the mother of John Mark. Many people had gathered at her home and were praying. [13] Peter knocked on the door of the entryway, and a servant named Rhoda came to answer. [14] When she recognized Peter's voice, she was so happy that instead of opening the door, she ran back inside and reported, "Peter is standing at the door!"

[15] The people told her, "You're crazy!" But she insisted that Peter was at the door. They said, "It has to be his angel."

[16] But Peter kept knocking. When they opened the door, they were shocked to see him. [17] Peter motioned with his hand to quiet them down and told them how the Lord had taken him out of prison. He added, "Tell James and the other believers about this." Then he left and went somewhere else.

[18] In the morning the soldiers were in an uproar over what had happened to Peter. [19] Herod searched for Peter but couldn't find him. So he questioned the guards and gave orders to have them executed.

Herod's Death

Then Herod left Judea and went to Caesarea, where he stayed for a while.

[20] Herod was very angry with the people of Tyre and Sidon. They were going to meet with Herod. They had agreed on what they wanted to do: They enlisted the help of Blastus to ask Herod for terms of peace. This was because their cities depended on Herod for their food supply. (Blastus was in charge of the king's living quarters.)

[21] The appointed day came. Herod, wearing his royal clothes, sat on his throne and began making a speech to them. [22] The people started shouting, "The voice of a god and not of a man!"

[23] Immediately, an angel from the Lord killed Herod for not giving glory to God. Herod was eaten by maggots, and he died.

[24] But God's word continued to spread and win many followers.

Barnabas and Saul Travel to Cyprus

[25] After Barnabas and Saul delivered the contribution ˌto the leaders in Jerusalemˌ, they returned ˌto Antiochˌ from Jerusalem. They brought John Mark with them.

13 [1] Barnabas, Simeon (called the Black), Lucius (from Cyrene), Manaen (a close friend of Herod since childhood), and Saul were prophets and teachers in the church in Antioch. [2] While they were worshiping the Lord and fasting, the Holy Spirit said, "Set Barnabas and Saul apart for me. I want them to do the work for which I called them." [3] After fasting and praying, Simeon, Lucius, and Manaen placed their hands on Barnabas and Saul, and released them ˌfrom their work in Antiochˌ.

[4] After Barnabas and Saul were sent by the Holy Spirit, they went to the city of Seleucia and from there sailed to the island of Cyprus. [5] Arriving in the city of Salamis, they began to spread God's word in the synagogues. John Mark had gone along to help them. [6] They went through the whole island as far as the city of Paphos.

In Paphos they met a Jewish man named Barjesus. He was an astrologer who claimed to be a prophet. [7] He was associated with an intelligent man, Sergius Paulus, who was the governor of the island. The governor sent for Barnabas and Saul because he wanted to hear the word of God. [8] Elymas, whose name means *astrologer,* opposed them and tried to distort the meaning of the faith so that the governor wouldn't believe.

[9] But Saul, also known as Paul, was filled with the Holy Spirit. He stared at Elymas [10] and said, "You are full of dirty tricks and schemes, you son of the devil! You hate everything that has God's approval. Quit trying to distort the truth about the way the Lord wants people to live. [11] The Lord is against you now. For a while you will be blind, unable to see the light of day."

Suddenly, Elymas couldn't see a thing. He tried to find people to lead him. [12] When the governor saw what had happened, he believed. The Lord's teachings amazed him.

Paul and Barnabas Go to Antioch Near Pisidia

[13] Paul and his men took a ship from Paphos and arrived in Perga, a city in Pamphylia. John Mark deserted them there and went back to Jerusalem. [14] Paul and Barnabas left Perga and arrived in Antioch, a city near Pisidia. On the day of worship they went into the synagogue and sat down.

[15] After reading from Moses' Teachings and the Prophets, the synagogue leaders sent a message to Paul and Barnabas. The message said, "Brothers, if you have any words of encouragement for the people, feel free to speak."

[16] Then Paul stood up, motioned with his hand, and said, "Men of Israel and converts to Judaism, listen to me. [17] The God of the people of Israel chose our ancestors and made them a strong nation while they lived as foreigners in Egypt. He used his powerful arm to bring them out of Egypt, [18] and he put up with them for about forty years in the desert. [19] Then he destroyed seven nations in Canaan and gave their land to his people as an inheritance. [20] He did all this in about four hundred and fifty years.

"After that he gave his people judges until the time of the prophet Samuel.

[21] "Then the people demanded a king, so God gave them Saul, son of Kish, from the tribe of Benjamin. After forty years [22] God removed Saul and made David their king. God spoke favorably about David. He said, 'I have found that David, son of Jesse, is a man after my own heart. He will do everything I want him to do.'

[23] "God had the Savior, Jesus, come to Israel from David's descendants, as he had promised. [24] Before Jesus began his ministry, John the Baptizer told everyone in Israel about the baptism of repentance.[a] [25] When John was finishing his work, he said, 'Who do you think I am? I'm not the person you're looking for. He will come later. I'm not even good enough to untie his sandals.'

[26] "Brothers—descendants of Abraham and converts to Judaism—the message that God saves people was sent to us. [27] The people who live in Jerusalem and their rulers didn't know who Jesus was. They didn't understand the prophets' messages, which are read every day of worship. So they condemned Jesus and fulfilled what the prophets had said. [28] Although they couldn't find any good reason to kill him, they asked Pilate to have him executed. [29] When they had finished doing everything that was written about him, they took him down from the cross and placed him in a tomb. [30] But God brought him back to life, [31] and for many days he appeared to those who had come with him to Jerusalem from Galilee. These people are now witnesses and are testifying to the Jewish people about him. [32] We are telling you the Good News: What God promised our ancestors has happened. [33] God has fulfilled the promise for us, their descendants, by bringing Jesus back to life. This is what Scripture says in the second psalm:

'You are my Son.
    Today I have become your Father.'

[34] "God stated that he brought Jesus back to life and that Jesus' body never decayed. He said, 'I will give you the enduring love promised to David.' [35] Another psalm says, 'You will not allow your holy one to decay.' [36] After doing God's will by serving the people of his time, David died. He was laid to rest with his ancestors, but his body decayed. [37] However, the man God brought back to life had a body that didn't decay.

[38] "So, brothers, I'm telling you that through Jesus your sins can be forgiven. Sins kept you from receiving God's approval through Moses' Teachings. [39] However, everyone who believes in Jesus receives God's approval.

[40] "Be careful, or what the prophets said may happen to you.

[41]   'Look, you mockers!
        Be amazed and die!
        I am going to do something in your days
            that you would not believe even if it were reported to you!' "

---

[a] 13:24 "Repentance" is turning to God with a complete change in the way a person thinks and acts.

[42] As Paul and Barnabas were leaving the synagogue, the people invited them to speak on the same subject the next day of worship. [43] When the meeting of the synagogue broke up, many Jews and converts to Judaism followed Paul and Barnabas. Paul and Barnabas talked with them and were persuading them to continue trusting God's good will.[b]

[44] On the next day of worship, almost the whole city gathered to hear the Lord's word. [45] When the Jews saw the crowds, they became very jealous. They used insulting language to contradict whatever Paul said.

[46] Paul and Barnabas told them boldly, "We had to speak the word of God to you first. Since you reject the word and consider yourselves unworthy of everlasting life, we are now going to turn to people of other nations. [47] The Lord gave us the following order:

'I have made you a light for the nations
so that you would save people all over the world.' "

[48] The people who were not Jews were pleased with what they heard and praised the Lord's word. Everyone who had been prepared for everlasting life believed. [49] The word of the Lord spread throughout the whole region. [50] But Jews stirred up devout women of high social standing and the officials of the city. These people started to persecute Paul and Barnabas and threw them out of their territory.

[51] In protest against these people, Paul and Barnabas shook the dust off their feet and went to the city of Iconium. [52] Meanwhile, the disciples ˎin Antiochˎ continued to be full of joy and the Holy Spirit.

Paul and Barnabas in Iconium

14 [1] The same thing happened in the city of Iconium. Paul and Barnabas went into the synagogue and spoke in such a way that a large crowd of Jews and Greeks believed. [2] But the Jews who refused to believe stirred up some people who were not Jewish and poisoned their minds against the believers. [3] Paul and Barnabas stayed in the city of Iconium for a long time. They spoke boldly about the Lord, who confirmed their message about his good will[a] by having them perform miracles and do amazing things. [4] But the people of Iconium were divided. Some were for the Jews, while others were for the apostles.

[5] In the meantime, Paul and Barnabas found out that the non-Jewish people and the Jewish people with their rulers planned to attack them and stone them to death. [6] So they escaped to Lystra and Derbe, cities of Lycaonia, and to the surrounding territory. [7] They spread the Good News there.

Paul and Barnabas in Lystra

[8] A man who was born lame was in Lystra. He was always sitting because he had never been able to walk. [9] He listened to what Paul was saying. Paul observed him closely and saw that the man believed he could be made well. [10] So Paul said in a loud voice, "Stand up." The man jumped up and began to walk.

[11] The crowds who saw what Paul had done shouted in the Lycaonian language, "The gods have come to us, and they look human." [12] They addressed Barnabas as Zeus and Paul as Hermes because Paul did most of the talking. [13] Zeus' temple was at the entrance to the city. The priest of the god Zeus brought bulls with flowery wreaths around their necks to the temple gates. The priest and the crowd wanted to offer a sacrifice ˎto Paul and Barnabasˎ.

[14] When the apostles Barnabas and Paul heard what was happening, they were very upset. They rushed into the crowd [15] and said, "Men, what are you doing? We're human beings like you. We're spreading the Good News to you to turn you away from these worthless gods to the living God. The living God made the sky, the land, the sea, and everything in them. [16] In the past God allowed all people to live as they pleased. [17] Yet, by doing good, he has given evidence of his existence. He gives you rain from heaven and crops in their seasons. He fills you with food and your lives with happiness." [18] Although Paul and Barnabas said these things, they hardly kept the crowd from sacrificing to them.

[19] However, Jews from the cities of Antioch and Iconium arrived in Lystra and won the people over. They tried to stone Paul to death and dragged him out of the city when they thought that he was dead. [20] But when the disciples gathered around him, he got up and went back into the city.

Paul and Barnabas Return to Antioch in Syria

The next day Paul and Barnabas left for the city of Derbe. [21] They spread the Good News in that city and won many disciples. Then they went back to the cities of Lystra, Iconium, and Antioch (which is in Pisidia). [22] They strengthened the disciples in these cities and encouraged

---

[b] 13:43 Or "grace."   [a] 14:3 Or "grace."

the disciples to remain faithful. Paul and Barnabas told them, "We must suffer a lot to enter the kingdom of God." [23] They had the disciples in each church choose spiritual leaders,[b] and with prayer and fasting they entrusted the leaders to the Lord in whom they believed.

[24] After they had gone through Pisidia, they went to Pamphylia. [25] They spoke the message in the city of Perga and went to the city of Attalia. [26] From Attalia they took a boat and headed home to the city of Antioch ˎin Syriaˌ. (In Antioch they had been entrusted to God's care[c] for the work they had now finished.) [27] When they arrived, they called the members of the church together. They reported everything God had done through them, especially that he had given people who were not Jewish the opportunity to believe. [28] They stayed for a long time with these disciples.

Controversy About Moses' Teachings

15 [1] Some men came from Judea and started to teach believers that people can't be saved unless they are circumcised as Moses' Teachings require. [2] Paul and Barnabas had a fierce dispute with these men. So Paul and Barnabas and some of the others were sent to Jerusalem to see the apostles and spiritual leaders[a] about this claim.

[3] The church sent Paul and Barnabas ˎto Jerusalemˌ. As they were going through Phoenicia and Samaria, they told the whole story of how non-Jewish people were turning to God. This story brought great joy to all the believers.

[4] The church in Jerusalem, the apostles, and the spiritual leaders welcomed Paul and Barnabas when they arrived. Paul and Barnabas reported everything that God had done through them. [5] But some believers from the party of the Pharisees stood up and said, "People who are not Jewish must be circumcised and ordered to follow Moses' Teachings."

[6] The apostles and spiritual leaders met to consider this statement. [7] After a lot of debating, Peter stood up and said to them, "Brothers, you know what happened some time ago. God chose me so that people who aren't Jewish could hear the Good News and believe. [8] God, who knows everyone's thoughts, showed that he approved of people who aren't Jewish by giving them the Holy Spirit as he gave the Holy Spirit to us. [9] God doesn't discriminate between Jewish and non-Jewish people. He has cleansed non-Jewish people through faith as he has cleansed us Jews. [10] So why are you testing God? You're putting a burden on the disciples, a burden neither our ancestors nor we can carry. [11] We certainly believe that the Lord Jesus saves us the same way that he saves them—through his kindness."[b]

[12] The whole crowd was silent. They listened to Barnabas and Paul tell about all the miracles and amazing things that God had done through them among non-Jewish people.

[13] After they finished speaking, James responded, "Brothers, listen to me. [14] Simon has explained how God first showed his concern by taking from non-Jewish people those who would honor his name. [15] This agrees with what the prophets said. Scripture says,

[16]   'Afterwards, I will return.
          I will set up David's fallen tent again.
          I will restore its ruined places again.
          I will set it up again
[17]   so that the survivors and all the people who aren't Jewish
               over whom my name is spoken,
                  may search for the Lord, declares the Lord.
[18]   He is the one who will do these things that have always been known!'

[19] "So I've decided that we shouldn't trouble non-Jewish people who are turning to God. [20] Instead, we should write a letter telling them to keep away from things polluted by false gods, from sexual sins, from eating the meat of strangled animals, and from eating bloody meat. [21] After all, Moses' words have been spread to every city for generations. His teachings are read in synagogues on every day of worship."

[22] Then the apostles, the spiritual leaders, and the whole church decided to choose some of their men to send with Paul and Barnabas to the city of Antioch. They chose Judas (called Barsabbas) and Silas, who were leaders among the believers. [23] They wrote this letter for them to deliver:

From the apostles and the spiritual leaders, your brothers.
To their non-Jewish brothers and sisters in Antioch, Syria, and Cilicia.
Dear brothers and sisters,
[24] We have heard that some individuals who came from us have confused you with statements that disturb you. We did not authorize these men ˎto speakˌ. [25] So we have come to a unanimous decision that we should choose men and send them to you with

---

[b] 14:23 Or "pastors," or "elders."   [c] 14:26 Or "grace."   [a] 15:2 Or "pastors," or "elders."   [b] 15:11 Or "grace."

our dear Barnabas and Paul. [26] Barnabas and Paul have dedicated their lives to our Lord, the one named Jesus Christ. [27] We have sent Judas and Silas to report to you on our decision. [28] The Holy Spirit and we have agreed not to place any additional burdens on you. Do only what is necessary [29] by keeping away from food sacrificed to false gods, from eating bloody meat, from eating the meat of strangled animals, and from sexual sins. If you avoid these things, you will be doing what's right.
Farewell!

[30] So the men were sent on their way and arrived in the city of Antioch. They gathered the congregation together and delivered the letter. [31] When the people read the letter, they were pleased with the encouragement it brought them. [32] Judas and Silas, who were also prophets, spoke a long time to encourage and strengthen the believers.
[33] After Judas and Silas had stayed in Antioch for some time, the congregation sent them back to Jerusalem with friendly greetings to those who had sent them.[c] [35] Paul and Barnabas stayed in Antioch. They and many others taught people about the Lord's word and spread the Good News.

Paul and Barnabas Disagree

[36] After a while Paul said to Barnabas, "Let's go back to every city where we spread the Lord's word. We'll visit the believers to see how they're doing." [37] Barnabas wanted to take John Mark along. [38] However, Paul didn't think it was right to take a person like him along. John Mark had deserted them in Pamphylia and had not gone with them to work. [39] Paul and Barnabas disagreed so sharply that they parted ways. Barnabas took Mark with him and sailed to the island of Cyprus. [40] Paul chose Silas and left after the believers entrusted him to the Lord's care.[d]
[41] Paul went through the provinces of Syria and Cilicia and strengthened the churches.

Timothy Joins Paul in Lystra

16 [1] Paul arrived in the city of Derbe and then went to Lystra, where a disciple named Timothy lived. Timothy's mother was a Jewish believer, but his father was Greek. [2] The believers in Lystra and Iconium spoke well of Timothy. [3] Paul wanted Timothy to go with him. So he circumcised him because of the Jews who lived in those places and because he knew that Timothy's father was Greek.
[4] As they went through the cities, they told people about the decisions that the apostles and spiritual leaders[a] in Jerusalem had made for the people. [5] So the churches were strengthened in the faith and grew in numbers every day.

Paul Has a Vision

[6] Paul and Silas went through the regions of Phrygia and Galatia because the Holy Spirit kept them from speaking the word in the province of Asia. [7] They went to the province of Mysia and tried to enter Bithynia, but the Spirit of Jesus wouldn't allow this. [8] So they passed by Mysia and went to the city of Troas.
[9] During the night Paul had a vision of a man from Macedonia. The man urged Paul, "Come to Macedonia to help us."
[10] As soon as Paul had seen the vision, we immediately looked for a way to go to Macedonia. We concluded that God had called us to tell the people of Macedonia about the Good News.

Paul and Silas in Philippi

[11] So we took a ship from Troas and sailed straight to the island of Samothrace. The next day we sailed to the city of Neapolis, [12] and from there we went to the city of Philippi. Philippi is a leading city in that part of Macedonia, and it is a Roman colony. We were in this city for a number of days.
[13] On the day of worship we went out of the city to a place along the river where we thought Jewish people gathered for prayer. We sat down and began talking to the women who had gathered there. [14] A woman named Lydia was present. She was a convert to Judaism from the city of Thyatira and sold purple dye for a living. She was listening because the Lord made her willing to pay attention to what Paul said. [15] When Lydia and her family were baptized, she invited us to stay at her home. She said, "If you're convinced that I believe in the Lord, then stay at my home." She insisted. So we did.
[16] One day when we were going to the place of prayer, a female servant met us. She was possessed by an evil spirit that told fortunes. She made a lot of money for her owners by telling fortunes. [17] She used to follow Paul and shout, "These men are servants of the Most High God.

---

[c] 15:33 Some manuscripts and translations add verse 34: "But Silas decided to stay there, and Judas went back to Jerusalem alone."   [d] 15:40 Or "grace."   [a] 16:4 Or "pastors," or "elders."

They're telling you how you can be saved." [18] She kept doing this for many days. Paul became annoyed, turned to the evil spirit, and said, "I command you in the name of Jesus Christ to come out of her!"

As Paul said this, the evil spirit left her. [19] When her owners realized that their hope of making money was gone, they grabbed Paul and Silas and dragged them to the authorities in the public square. [20] In front of the Roman officials, they said, "These men are stirring up a lot of trouble in our city. They're Jews, [21] and they're advocating customs that we can't accept or practice as Roman citizens."

[22] The crowd joined in the attack against Paul and Silas. Then the officials tore the clothes off Paul and Silas and ordered the guards to beat them with sticks. [23] After they had hit Paul and Silas many times, they threw them in jail and ordered the jailer to keep them under tight security. [24] So the jailer followed these orders and put Paul and Silas into solitary confinement with their feet in leg irons.

[25] Around midnight Paul and Silas were praying and singing hymns of praise to God. The other prisoners were listening to them. [26] Suddenly, a violent earthquake shook the foundations of the jail. All the doors immediately flew open, and all the prisoners' chains came loose.

[27] The jailer woke up and saw the prison doors open. Thinking the prisoners had escaped, he drew his sword and was about to kill himself. [28] But Paul shouted as loudly as he could, "Don't hurt yourself! We're all here!"

[29] The jailer asked for torches and rushed into the jail. He was trembling as he knelt in front of Paul and Silas. [30] Then he took Paul and Silas outside and asked, "Sirs, what do I have to do to be saved?"

[31] They answered, "Believe in the Lord Jesus, and you and your family will be saved." [32] They spoke the Lord's word to the jailer and everyone in his home.

[33] At that hour of the night, the jailer washed Paul and Silas' wounds. The jailer and his entire family were baptized immediately. [34] He took Paul and Silas upstairs into his home and gave them something to eat. He and his family were thrilled to be believers in God.

[35] In the morning the Roman officials sent guards who told the jailer, "You can release those men now."

[36] The jailer reported this order to Paul by saying, "The officials have sent word to release you. So you can leave peacefully now."

[37] But Paul told the guards, "Roman officials have had us beaten publicly without a trial and have thrown us in jail, even though we're Roman citizens. Now are they going to throw us out secretly? There's no way they're going to get away with that! Have them escort us out!"

[38] The guards reported to the officials what Paul had said. When the Roman officials heard that Paul and Silas were Roman citizens, they were afraid. [39] So the officials went to the jail and apologized to Paul and Silas. As the officials escorted Paul and Silas out of the jail, they asked them to leave the city.

[40] After Paul and Silas left the jail, they went to Lydia's house. They met with the believers, encouraged them, and then left.

Paul and Silas in Thessalonica

17 [1] Paul and Silas traveled through the cities of Amphipolis and Apollonia and came to the city of Thessalonica, where there was a synagogue. [2] As usual, Paul went into the synagogue. On three consecutive days of worship, he had discussions about Scripture with the synagogue members. [3] He explained and showed them that the Messiah had to suffer, die, and come back to life, and that Jesus, the person he talked about, was this Messiah.

[4] Some of the Jews were persuaded to join Paul and Silas, especially a large group of Greeks who had converted to Judaism and the wives of many prominent men.

[5] Then the Jews became jealous. They took some low-class characters who hung around the public square, formed a mob, and started a riot in the city. They attacked Jason's home and searched it for Paul and Silas in order to bring them out to the crowd. [6] When they didn't find Paul and Silas, they dragged Jason and some other believers in front of the city officials. They shouted, "Those men who have made trouble all over the world are now here in Thessalonica, [7] and Jason has welcomed them as his guests. All of them oppose the emperor's decrees by saying that there is another king, whose name is Jesus."

[8] The crowd and the officials were upset when they heard this. [9] But after they had made Jason and the others post bond, they let them go.

[10] Immediately when night came, the believers sent Paul and Silas to the city of Berea.

Paul and Silas in Berea

When Paul and Silas arrived in the city of Berea, they entered the synagogue. [11] The people of Berea were more open-minded than the people of Thessalonica. They were very willing to receive God's message, and every day they carefully examined the Scriptures to see if what Paul said was true. [12] Many of them became believers, and quite a number of them were prominent Greek men and women.

[13] But when the Jews in Thessalonica found out that Paul was also spreading God's word in Berea, they went there to upset and confuse the people. [14] The believers immediately sent Paul to the seacoast, but Silas and Timothy stayed in Berea.

Paul in Athens

[15] The men who escorted Paul took him all the way to the city of Athens. When the men left Athens, they took instructions back to Silas and Timothy to join Paul as soon as possible.

[16] While Paul was waiting for Silas and Timothy in Athens, he saw that the city had statues of false gods everywhere. This upset him. [17] He held discussions in the synagogue with Jews and converts to Judaism. He also held discussions every day in the public square with anyone who happened to be there. [18] Some Epicurean and Stoic philosophers had discussions with him. Some asked, "What is this babbling fool trying to say?" Others said, "He seems to be speaking about foreign gods." The philosophers said these things because Paul was telling the Good News about Jesus and saying that people would come back to life.

[19] Then they brought Paul to the city court, the Areopagus, and asked, "Could you tell us these new ideas that you're teaching? [20] Some of the things you say sound strange to us. So we would like to know what they mean."

[21] Everyone who lived in Athens looked for opportunities to tell or hear something new and unusual.

[22] Paul stood in the middle of the court and said, "Men of Athens, I see that you are very religious. [23] As I was going through your city and looking closely at the objects you worship, I noticed an altar with this written on it: 'To an unknown god.' I'm telling you about the unknown god you worship. [24] The God who made the universe and everything in it is the Lord of heaven and earth. He doesn't live in shrines made by humans, [25] and he isn't served by humans as if he needed anything. He gives everyone life, breath, and everything they have. [26] From one man he has made every nation of humanity to live all over the earth. He has given them the seasons of the year and the boundaries within which to live. [27] He has done this so that they would look for God, somehow reach for him, and find him. In fact, he is never far from any one of us. [28] Certainly, we live, move, and exist because of him. As some of your poets have said, 'We are God's children.' [29] So if we are God's children, we shouldn't think that the divine being is like an image made from gold, silver, or stone, an image that is the product of human imagination and skill.

[30] "God overlooked the times when people didn't know any better. But now he commands everyone everywhere to turn to him and change the way they think and act. [31] He has set a day when he is going to judge the world with justice, and he will use a man he has appointed to do this. God has given proof to everyone that he will do this by bringing that man back to life."

[32] When the people of the court heard that a person had come back to life, some began joking about it, while others said, "We'll hear you talk about this some other time."

[33] With this response, Paul left the court. [34] Some men joined him and became believers. With them were Dionysius, who was a member of the court, and a woman named Damaris, and some other people.

Paul in Corinth

18 [1] After this, Paul left Athens and went to the city of Corinth. [2] In Corinth he met a Jewish man named Aquila and his wife Priscilla. Aquila had been born in Pontus, and they had recently come from Italy because Claudius had ordered all Jews to leave Rome. Paul went to visit them, [3] and because they made tents for a living as he did, he stayed with them and they worked together.

[4] On every day of worship, Paul would discuss ˌScriptureˌ in the synagogue. He tried to win over Jews and Greeks who had converted to Judaism. [5] But when Silas and Timothy arrived from Macedonia, Paul devoted all his time to teaching the word of God. He assured the Jews that Jesus is the Messiah. [6] But they opposed him and insulted him. So Paul shook the dust from his clothes and told them, "You're responsible for your own death. I'm innocent. From now on I'm going to people who are not Jewish."

[7] Then he left the synagogue and went to the home of a man named Titius Justus, who was a convert to Judaism. His house was next door to the synagogue. [8] The synagogue leader Crispus and his whole family believed in the Lord. Many Corinthians who heard Paul believed and were baptized.

[9] One night the Lord said to Paul in a vision, "Don't be afraid to speak out! Don't be silent! [10] I'm with you. No one will attack you or harm you. I have many people in this city." [11] Paul lived in Corinth for a year and a half and taught the word of God to them.

[12] While Gallio was governor of Greece, the Jews had one thought in mind. They attacked Paul and brought him to court. [13] They said, "This man is persuading people to worship God in ways that are against Moses' Teachings."

[14] Paul was about to answer when Gallio said to the Jews, "If there were some kind of misdemeanor or crime involved, reason would demand that I put up with you Jews. [15] But since you're disputing words, names, and your own teachings, you'll have to take care of that yourselves. I don't want to be a judge who gets involved in those things." [16] So Gallio had them forced out of his court.

[17] Then all ˌthe governor's officersˌ took Sosthenes, the synagogue leader, and beat him in front of the court. But Gallio couldn't have cared less.

Paul's Return Trip to Antioch

[18] After staying in Corinth quite a while longer, Paul left ˌfor Ephesusˌ. Priscilla and Aquila went with him. In the city of Cenchrea, Aquila had his hair cut, since he had taken a vow. From Cenchrea they took a boat headed for Syria [19] and arrived in the city of Ephesus, where Paul left Priscilla and Aquila. Paul went into the synagogue and had a discussion with the Jews. [20] The Jews asked him to stay longer, but he refused. [21] As he left, he told them, "I'll come back to visit you if God wants me to."

Paul took a boat from Ephesus [22] and arrived in the city of Caesarea. He went ˌto Jerusalemˌ, greeted the church, and went back to the city of Antioch.

[23] After spending some time in Antioch, Paul went through the regions of Galatia and Phrygia, where he strengthened ˌthe faith ofˌ all the disciples.

Apollos Tells Others About Jesus

[24] A Jew named Apollos, who had been born in Alexandria, arrived in the city of Ephesus. He was an eloquent speaker and knew how to use the Scriptures in a powerful way. [25] He had been instructed in the Lord's way and spoke enthusiastically. He accurately taught about Jesus but knew only about the baptism John performed. [26] He began to speak boldly in the synagogue. When Priscilla and Aquila heard him, they took him ˌhomeˌ with them and explained God's way to him more accurately.

[27] When Apollos wanted to travel to Greece, the believers ˌin Ephesusˌ encouraged him. They wrote to the disciples in Greece to tell them to welcome him. When he arrived in Greece, God's kindness[a] enabled him to help the believers a great deal. [28] In public Apollos helped them by clearly showing from the Scriptures that Jesus is the Messiah and that the Jews were wrong.

Paul in Ephesus

19 [1] While Apollos was in Corinth, Paul traveled through the interior provinces to get to the city of Ephesus. He met some disciples in Ephesus [2] and asked them, "Did you receive the Holy Spirit when you became believers?"

They answered him, "No, we've never even heard of the Holy Spirit."

[3] Paul asked them, "What kind of baptism did you have?"

They answered, "John's baptism."

[4] Paul said, "John's baptism was a baptism of repentance.[a] John told people to believe in Jesus, who was coming later."

[5] After they heard this, they were baptized in the name of the Lord Jesus. [6] When Paul placed his hands on them, the Holy Spirit came to them, and they began to talk in other languages and to speak what God had revealed. [7] About twelve men were in the group.

[8] For three months Paul would go into the synagogue and speak boldly. He had discussions with people to convince them about the kingdom of God. [9] But when some people became stubborn, refused to believe, and had nothing good to say in front of the crowd about the way ˌof Christˌ, he left them. He took his disciples and held daily discussions in the lecture hall of Tyrannus. [10] This continued for two years so that all the Jews and Greeks who lived in the province of Asia heard the word of the Lord.

[11] God worked unusual miracles through Paul. [12] People would take handkerchiefs and aprons that had touched Paul's skin to those who were sick. Their sicknesses would be cured, and evil spirits would leave them.

[13] Some Jews used to travel from place to place and force evil spirits out of people. They tried to use the name of the Lord Jesus to force evil spirits out of those who were possessed. These Jews would say, "I order you ˌto come outˌ in the name of Jesus, whom Paul talks about." [14] Seven sons of Sceva, a Jewish chief priest, were doing this.

---

[a] 18:27 Or "grace."   [a] 19:4 "Repentance" is turning to God with a complete change in the way a person thinks and acts.

¹⁵ But the evil spirit answered them, "I know Jesus, and I'm acquainted with Paul, but who are you?" ¹⁶ Then the man possessed by the evil spirit attacked them. He beat them up so badly that they ran out of that house naked and wounded.

¹⁷ All the Jews and Greeks living in the city of Ephesus heard about this. All of them were filled with awe for the name of the Lord Jesus and began to speak very highly about it. ¹⁸ Many believers openly admitted their involvement with magical spells and told all the details. ¹⁹ Many of those who were involved in the occult gathered their books and burned them in front of everyone. They added up the cost of these books and found that they were worth 50,000 silver coins. ²⁰ In this powerful way the word of the Lord was spreading and gaining strength.

²¹ After all these things had happened, Paul decided to go to Jerusalem by traveling through Macedonia and Greece. He said, "After I have been there, I must see Rome." ²² So he sent two of his helpers, Timothy and Erastus, to Macedonia, while he stayed longer in the province of Asia.

A Riot in Ephesus

²³ During that time a serious disturbance concerning the way ˻of Christ˼ broke out in the city of Ephesus.

²⁴ Demetrius, a silversmith, was in the business of making silver models of the temple of Artemis. His business brought a huge profit for the men who worked for him. ²⁵ He called a meeting of his workers and others who did similar work. Demetrius said, "Men, you know that we're earning a good income from this business, ²⁶ and you see and hear what this man Paul has done. He has won over a large crowd that follows him not only in Ephesus but also throughout the province of Asia. He tells people that gods made by humans are not gods. ²⁷ There's a danger that people will discredit our line of work, and there's a danger that people will think that the temple of the great goddess Artemis is nothing. Then she whom all Asia and the rest of the world worship will be robbed of her glory."

²⁸ When Demetrius' workers and the others heard this, they became furious and began shouting, "Artemis of the Ephesians is great!" ²⁹ The confusion spread throughout the city, and the people had one thought in mind as they rushed into the theater. They grabbed Gaius and Aristarchus, the Macedonians who traveled with Paul, and they dragged the two men into the theater with them.

³⁰ Paul wanted to go into the crowd, but his disciples wouldn't let him. ³¹ Even some officials who were from the province of Asia and who were Paul's friends sent messengers to urge him not to risk going into the theater.

³² Some people shouted one thing while others shouted something else. The crowd was confused. Most of the people didn't even know why they had come together. ³³ Some people concluded that Alexander was the cause, so the Jews pushed him to the front. Alexander motioned with his hand to quiet the people because he wanted to defend himself in front of them. ³⁴ But when they recognized that Alexander was a Jew, everyone started to shout in unison, "Artemis of the Ephesians is great!" They kept doing this for about two hours.

³⁵ The city clerk finally quieted the crowd. Then he said, "Citizens of Ephesus, everyone knows that this city of the Ephesians is the keeper of the temple of the great Artemis. Everyone knows that Ephesus is the keeper of the statue that fell down from Zeus. ³⁶ No one can deny this. So you have to be quiet and not do anything foolish. ³⁷ The men you brought here don't rob temples or insult our goddess. ³⁸ If Demetrius and the men who work for him have a legal complaint against anyone, we have special days and officials to hold court. That's where they should bring charges against each other. ³⁹ If you want anything else, you must settle the matter in a legal assembly. ⁴⁰ At this moment we run the risk of being accused of rioting today for no reason. We won't be able to explain this mob." ⁴¹ After saying this, he dismissed the assembly.^b

20 ¹ When the uproar was over, Paul sent for the disciples, encouraged them, said goodbye, and left for Macedonia. ² He went through that region and spoke many words of encouragement to the people. Then he went to Greece ³ and stayed there for three months.

Paul in Troas

When Paul was going to board a ship for Syria, he found out that the Jews were plotting to kill him. So he decided to go back through Macedonia. ⁴ Sopater (son of Pyrrhus) from Berea, Aristarchus and Secundus from Thessalonica, Gaius from Derbe, Timothy, and Tychicus and Trophimus from the province of Asia accompanied Paul. ⁵ All these men went ahead and were waiting for us in Troas. ⁶ After the Festival of Unleavened Bread, we boarded a ship at Philippi. Five days later we joined them in Troas and stayed there for seven days.

---

^b 19:41 Acts 19:41 in English Bibles is Acts 19:40b in the Greek Bible.

⁷ On Sunday we met to break bread. Paul was discussing ˌScriptureˌ with the people. Since he intended to leave the next day, he kept talking until midnight. ⁸ (Many lamps were lit in the upstairs room where we were meeting.)

⁹ A young man named Eutychus was sitting in a window. As Paul was talking on and on, Eutychus was gradually falling asleep. Finally, overcome by sleep, he fell from the third story and was dead when they picked him up. ¹⁰ Paul went to him, took him into his arms, and said, "Don't worry! He's alive!" ¹¹ Then Eutychus went upstairs again, broke the bread, and ate. Paul talked with the people for a long time, until sunrise, and then left.

¹² The people took the boy home. They were greatly relieved that he was alive.

Paul's Trip to Miletus

¹³ We went ahead to the ship and sailed for the city of Assos. At Assos, we were going to pick up Paul. He had made these arrangements, since he had planned to walk overland to Assos. ¹⁴ When Paul met us in Assos, we took him on board and went to the city of Mitylene. ¹⁵ We sailed from there. On the following day we approached the island of Chios. The next day we went by the island of Samos, and on the next day we arrived at the city of Miletus. ¹⁶ Paul had decided to sail past Ephesus to avoid spending time in the province of Asia. He was in a hurry to get to Jerusalem for the day of Pentecost, if that was possible.

Paul Meets With the Spiritual Leaders From Ephesus

¹⁷ From Miletus Paul sent messengers to the city of Ephesus and called the spiritual leaders[a] of the church to meet with him ˌin Miletusˌ. ¹⁸ When they were with him, he said to them, "You know how I spent all my time with you from the first day I arrived in the province of Asia. ¹⁹ I humbly served the Lord, often with tears in my eyes. I served the Lord during the difficult times I went through when the Jews plotted against me. ²⁰ I didn't avoid telling you anything that would help you, and I didn't avoid teaching you publicly and from house to house. ²¹ I warned Jews and Greeks to change the way they think and act and to believe in our Lord Jesus.

²² "I am determined to go to Jerusalem now. I don't know what will happen to me there. ²³ However, the Holy Spirit warns me in every city that imprisonment and suffering are waiting for me. ²⁴ But I don't place any value on my own life. I want to finish the race I'm running. I want to carry out the mission I received from the Lord Jesus—the mission of testifying to the Good News of God's kindness.[b]

²⁵ "Now I know that none of you whom I told about the kingdom ˌof Godˌ will see me again. ²⁶ Therefore, I declare to you today that I am not responsible for the ˌspiritualˌ death of any of you. ²⁷ I didn't avoid telling you the whole plan of God. ²⁸ Pay attention to yourselves and to the entire flock in which the Holy Spirit has placed you as bishops[c] to be shepherds for God's church which he acquired with his own blood. ²⁹ I know that fierce wolves will come to you after I leave, and they won't spare the flock. ³⁰ Some of your own men will come forward and say things that distort the truth. They will do this to lure disciples into following them. ³¹ So be alert! Remember that I instructed each of you for three years, day and night, at times with tears in my eyes.

³² "I am now entrusting you to God and to his message that tells how kind he is. That message can help you grow and can give you the inheritance that is shared by all of God's holy people.

³³ "I never wanted anyone's silver, gold, or clothes. ³⁴ You know that I worked to support myself and those who were with me. ³⁵ I have given you an example that by working hard like this we should help the weak. We should remember the words that the Lord Jesus said, 'Giving gifts is more satisfying than receiving them.' "

³⁶ When Paul had finished speaking, he knelt down and prayed with all of them. ³⁷ Everyone cried a lot as they put their arms around Paul and kissed him. ³⁸ The thought of not seeing Paul again hurt them most of all. Then they took Paul to the ship.

Paul in Tyre

21 ¹ When we finally left them, we sailed straight to the island of Cos. The next day we sailed to the island of Rhodes and from there to the city of Patara. ² In Patara, we found a ship that was going to Phoenicia, so we went aboard and sailed away. ³ We could see the island of Cyprus as we passed it on our left and sailed to Syria. We landed at the city of Tyre, where the ship was to unload its cargo.

⁴ In Tyre we searched for the disciples. After we found them, we stayed there for seven days. The Spirit had the disciples tell Paul not to go to Jerusalem. ⁵ When our time was up, we started on our way. All of them with their wives and children accompanied us out of the city. We knelt on the beach, prayed, ⁶ and said goodbye to each other. Then we went aboard the ship, and the disciples went back home.

---

^a 20:17 Or "pastors," or "elders."   ^b 20:24 Or "grace."   ^c 20:28 English equivalent difficult.

Paul in Caesarea

[7] Our sea travel ended when we sailed from Tyre to the city of Ptolemais. We greeted the believers in Ptolemais and spent the day with them. [8] The next day we went to Philip's home in Caesarea and stayed with him. He was a missionary and one of the seven men who helped the apostles. [9] Philip had four unmarried daughters who had the ability to speak what God had revealed.

[10] After we had been there for a number of days, a prophet named Agabus arrived from Judea. [11] During his visit he took Paul's belt and tied his own feet and hands with it. Then he said, "The Holy Spirit says, 'This is how the Jews in Jerusalem will tie up the man who owns this belt. Then they will hand him over to people who are not Jewish.' "

[12] When we heard this, we and the believers who lived there begged Paul not to go to Jerusalem.

[13] Then Paul replied, "Why are you crying like this and breaking my heart? I'm ready not only to be tied up in Jerusalem but also to die there for the sake of the Lord, the one named Jesus."

[14] When Paul could not be persuaded, we dropped the issue and said, "May the Lord's will be done."

Paul in Jerusalem

[15] After that, we got ready to go to Jerusalem. [16] Some of the disciples from Caesarea went with us. They took us to Mnason's home, where we would be staying. Mnason was from the island of Cyprus and was one of the first disciples. [17] When we arrived in Jerusalem, the believers welcomed us warmly.

[18] The next day Paul went with us to visit James. All the spiritual leaders[a] were present. [19] After greeting them, Paul related everything God had done through his work with non-Jewish people.

[20] When the spiritual leaders heard about everything, they praised God. They said to Paul, "You see, brother, how many thousands of Jews are now believers, and all of them are deeply committed to Moses' Teachings. [21] But they have been told that you teach all the Jews living among non-Jewish people to abandon Moses. They claim that you tell them not to circumcise their children or follow Jewish customs. [22] What should we do about this? They will certainly hear that you're in town. [23] So follow our advice. We have four men who have made a vow to God. [24] Take these men, go through the purification ceremony with them, and pay the expenses to shave their heads. Then everyone will know that what they've been told about you isn't true. Instead, they'll see that you carefully follow Moses' Teachings.

[25] " To clarify this matter, we have written non-Jewish believers a letter with our decision. We told them that they should not eat food sacrificed to false gods, bloody meat, or the meat of strangled animals. They also should not commit sexual sins."

[26] The next day, Paul took the men and went through the purification ceremony with them. Then he went into the temple courtyard to announce the time when the purification would be over and the sacrifice would be offered for each of them.

[27] When the seven days were almost over, the Jews from the province of Asia saw Paul in the temple courtyard. They stirred up the whole crowd and grabbed Paul. [28] Then they began shouting, "Men of Israel, help! This is the man who teaches everyone everywhere to turn against the Jewish people, Moses' Teachings, and this temple. He has even brought Greeks into the temple courtyard and has made this holy place unclean."[b] [29] They had seen Trophimus from Ephesus with him in the city earlier and thought Paul had taken him into the temple courtyard.

[30] The whole city was in chaos, and a mob formed. The mob grabbed Paul and dragged him out of the temple courtyard. The courtyard doors were immediately shut.

[31] As the people were trying to kill Paul, the officer in charge of the Roman soldiers received a report that all Jerusalem was rioting. [32] Immediately, he took some soldiers and officers and charged the crowd. When the crowd saw the officer and the soldiers, they stopped beating Paul. [33] Then the officer went to Paul, grabbed him, and ordered him to be tied up with two chains.

The officer asked who Paul was and what he had done. [34] Some of the crowd shouted one thing, while others shouted something else. The officer couldn't get any facts because of the noise and confusion, so he ordered Paul to be taken into the barracks. [35] When Paul came to the stairs of the barracks, the crowd was so violent that the soldiers had to carry him. [36] The mob was behind them shouting, "Kill him!"

Paul Speaks in His Own Defense

[37] As the soldiers were about to take Paul into the barracks, he asked the officer, "May I say something to you?"

---

[a] 21:18 Or "pastors," or "elders."   [b] 21:28 "Unclean" refers to anything that Moses' Teachings say is not presentable to God.

The officer replied to Paul, "Can you speak Greek? [38] Aren't you the Egyptian who started a revolution not long ago and led four thousand terrorists into the desert?"

[39] Paul answered, "I'm a Jew, a citizen from the well-known city of Tarsus in Cilicia. I'm asking you to let me talk to the people."

[40] The officer gave Paul permission to speak. So Paul stood on the stairs of the barracks and motioned with his hand for the people to be quiet. When the mob was silent, Paul spoke to them in the Hebrew language.

22 [1] "Brothers and fathers, listen as I now present my case to you."

[2] When the mob heard him speak to them in Hebrew, they became even more quiet. Then Paul continued, [3] "I'm a Jew. I was born and raised in the city of Tarsus in Cilicia and received my education from Gamaliel here in Jerusalem. My education was in the strict rules handed down by our ancestors. I was as devoted to God as all of you are today. [4] I persecuted people who followed the way ˌof Christˌ: I tied up men and women and put them into prison until they were executed. [5] The chief priest and the entire council of our leaders can prove that I did this. In fact, they even gave me letters to take to the Jewish community in the city of Damascus. I was going there to tie up believers and bring them back to Jerusalem to punish them.

[6] "But as I was on my way and approaching the city of Damascus about noon, a bright light from heaven suddenly flashed around me. [7] I fell to the ground and heard a voice asking me, 'Saul! Saul! Why are you persecuting me?'

[8] "I answered, 'Who are you, sir?'

"The person told me, 'I'm Jesus from Nazareth, the one you're persecuting.'

[9] "The men who were with me saw the light but didn't understand what the person who was speaking to me said.

[10] "Then I asked, 'What do you want me to do, Lord?'

"The Lord told me, 'Get up! Go into the city of Damascus, and you'll be told everything I've arranged for you to do.'

[11] "I was blind because the light had been so bright. So the men who were with me led me into the city of Damascus.

[12] "A man named Ananias lived in Damascus. He was a devout person who followed Moses' Teachings. All the Jews living in Damascus spoke highly of him. [13] He came to me, stood beside me, and said, 'Brother Saul, receive your sight!' At that moment my sight came back and I could see Ananias.

[14] "Ananias said, 'The God of our ancestors has chosen you to know his will, to see the one who has God's approval, and to hear him speak to you. [15] You will be his witness and will tell everyone what you have seen and heard. [16] What are you waiting for now? Get up! Be baptized, and have your sins washed away as you call on his name.'

[17] "After that, I returned to Jerusalem. While I was praying in the temple courtyard, I fell into a trance [18] and saw the Lord. He told me, 'Hurry! Get out of Jerusalem immediately. The people here won't accept your testimony about me.'

[19] "I said, 'Lord, people here know that I went from synagogue to synagogue to imprison and whip those who believe in you. [20] When Stephen, who witnessed about you, was being killed, I was standing there. I approved of his death and guarded the coats of those who were murdering him.'

[21] "But the Lord told me, 'Go! I'll send you on a mission. You'll go far away to people who aren't Jewish.' "

[22] Up to that point the mob listened. Then they began to shout, "Kill him! The world doesn't need a man like this. He shouldn't have been allowed to live this long!"

[23] The mob was yelling, taking off their coats, and throwing dirt into the air. [24] So the officer ordered the soldiers to take Paul into the barracks and told them to question Paul as they whipped him. The officer wanted to find out why the people were yelling at Paul like this. [25] But when the soldiers had Paul stretch out ˌto tie him to the whipping postˌ with the straps, Paul asked the sergeant who was standing there, "Is it legal for you to whip a Roman citizen who hasn't had a trial?"

[26] When the sergeant heard this, he reported it to his commanding officer. The sergeant asked him, "What are you doing? This man is a Roman citizen."

[27] The officer went to Paul and asked him, "Tell me, are you a Roman citizen?"

Paul answered, "Yes."

[28] The officer replied, "I paid a lot of money to become a Roman citizen."

Paul replied, "But I was born a Roman citizen."

[29] Immediately, the soldiers who were going to question Paul stepped away from him. The officer was afraid when he found out that he had tied up a Roman citizen.

Paul in Front of the Jewish Council

[30] The officer wanted to find out exactly what accusation the Jews had against Paul. So the officer released Paul the next day and ordered the chief priests and the entire Jewish council to meet. Then the officer brought Paul and had him stand in front of them.

23 [1] Paul stared at the Jewish council and said, "Brothers, my relationship with God has always given me a perfectly clear conscience."

[2] The chief priest Ananias ordered the men standing near Paul to strike him on the mouth. [3] Then Paul said to him, "God will strike you, you hypocrite! You sit there and judge me by Moses' Teachings and yet you break those teachings by ordering these men to strike me!"

[4] The men standing near Paul said to him, "You're insulting God's chief priest!"

[5] Paul answered, "Brothers, I didn't know that he is the chief priest. After all, Scripture says, 'Don't speak evil about a ruler of your people.' "

[6] When Paul saw that some of them were Sadducees and others were Pharisees, he shouted in the council, "Brothers, I'm a Pharisee and a descendant of Pharisees. I'm on trial because I expect that the dead will come back to life."

[7] After Paul said that, the Pharisees and Sadducees began to quarrel, and the men in the meeting were divided. [8] (The Sadducees say that the dead won't come back to life and that angels and spirits don't exist. The Pharisees believe in all these things.) [9] The shouting became very loud. Some of the scribes were Pharisees who argued their position forcefully. They said, "We don't find anything wrong with this man. Maybe a spirit or an angel actually spoke to him!"

[10] The quarrel was becoming violent, and the officer was afraid that they would tear Paul to pieces. So the officer ordered his soldiers to drag Paul back to the barracks.

[11] The Lord stood near Paul the next night and said to him, "Don't lose your courage! You've told the truth about me in Jerusalem. Now you must tell the truth about me in Rome."

Some Jews Plot to Kill Paul

[12] In the morning the Jews formed a conspiracy. They asked God to curse them if they ate or drank anything before they had killed Paul. [13] More than forty men took part in this plot.

[14] They went to the chief priests and leaders of the people, and said, "We've asked God to curse us if we taste any food before we've killed Paul. [15] Here's our plan: You and the council must go to the Roman officer on the pretext that you need more information from Paul. You have to make it look as though you want to get more accurate information about him. We'll be ready to kill him before he gets to you."

[16] But Paul's nephew heard about the ambush. He entered the barracks and told Paul. [17] Then Paul called one of the sergeants and told him, "Take this young man to the officer. He has something to tell him."

[18] The sergeant took the young man to the officer and said, "The prisoner Paul called me. He asked me to bring this young man to you because he has something to tell you."

[19] The officer took the young man by the arm, went where they could be alone, and asked him, "What do you have to tell me?"

[20] The young man answered, "The Jews have planned to ask you to bring Paul to the Jewish council tomorrow. They're going to make it look as though they want more accurate information about him. [21] Don't let them persuade you to do this. More than forty of them are planning to ambush him. They have asked God to curse them if they eat or drink anything before they have murdered him. They are ready now and are expecting you to promise that you will bring Paul."

[22] The officer dismissed the young man and ordered him not to tell this information to anyone else.

[23] Then the officer summoned two of his sergeants and told them, "I want 200 infantrymen, 70 soldiers on horseback, and 200 soldiers with spears. Have them ready to go to Caesarea at nine o'clock tonight. [24] Provide an animal for Paul to ride, and take him safely to Governor Felix." [25] The officer wrote a letter to the governor with the following message:

[26] Claudius Lysias sends greetings to Your Excellency, Governor Felix:

[27] The Jews had seized this man and were going to murder him. When I found out that he was a Roman citizen, I went with my soldiers to rescue him. [28] I wanted to know what they had against him. So I took him to their Jewish council [29] and found their accusations had to do with disputes about Jewish teachings. He wasn't accused of anything for which he deserved to die or to be put into prison. [30] Since I was informed that there was a plot against this man, I immediately sent him to you. I have also ordered his accusers to state their case against him in front of you.

[31] So the infantrymen did as they had been ordered. They took Paul to the city of Antipatris during the night. [32] They returned to their barracks the next day and let the soldiers on horse-

back travel with Paul. ³³ When the soldiers arrived in the city of Caesarea with Paul, they delivered the letter to the governor and handed Paul over to him.

³⁴ After the governor had read the letter, he asked Paul which province he was from. When he found out that Paul was from the province of Cilicia, ³⁵ he said, "I'll hear your case when your accusers arrive." Then the governor gave orders to keep Paul under guard in Herod's palace.

Paul Presents His Case to Felix

24 ¹ Five days later the chief priest Ananias went to the city of Caesarea with some leaders of the people and an attorney named Tertullus. They reported to the governor their charges against Paul.

² When Paul had been summoned, Tertullus began to accuse him. He said to Felix, "Your Excellency, through your wise leadership we have lasting peace and reforms that benefit the people. ³ We appreciate what you've done in every way and in every place, and we want to thank you very much. ⁴ I don't want to keep you too long. Please listen to us. We will be brief. ⁵ We have found this man to be a troublemaker. He starts quarrels among all Jews throughout the world. He's a ringleader of the Nazarene sect. ⁶ He also entered the temple courtyard in a way that violates our tradition. So we arrested him.ᵃ ⁸ When you cross-examine him, you'll be able to find out from him that our accusations are true."

⁹ The Jews supported Tertullus' accusations and asserted that everything Tertullus said was true.

¹⁰ The governor motioned for Paul to speak. Paul responded, "I know that you have been a judge over this nation for many years. So I'm pleased to present my case to you. ¹¹ You can verify for yourself that I went to Jerusalem to worship no more than twelve days ago. ¹² No one found me having a discussion with anyone in the temple courtyard or stirring up a crowd in the synagogues throughout the city. ¹³ These people cannot even prove their accusations to you. ¹⁴ But I'll admit to you that I'm a follower of the way ˏof Christˏ, which they call a sect. This means that I serve our ancestors' God and believe everything written in Moses' Teachings and the Prophets. ¹⁵ I hope for the same thing my accusers do, that people with God's approval and those without it will come back to life. ¹⁶ With this belief I always do my best to have a clear conscience in the sight of God and people. ¹⁷ After many years I have come back to my people and brought gifts for the poor and offerings ˏfor Godˏ. ¹⁸ My accusers found me in the temple courtyard doing these things after I had gone through the purification ceremony. No crowd or noisy mob was present. ¹⁹ But some Jews from the province of Asia were there. They should be here in front of you to accuse me if they have anything against me. ²⁰ Otherwise, these men who are accusing me should tell what I was charged with when I stood in front of their council. ²¹ They could accuse me of only one thing. As I stood among them, I shouted, 'I'm being tried in front of you because ˏI believe thatˏ the dead will come back to life.' "

²² Felix knew the way ˏof Christˏ rather well, so he adjourned the trial. He told them, "When the officer Lysias arrives, I'll decide your case." ²³ Felix ordered the sergeant to guard Paul but to let him have some freedom and to let his friends take care of his needs.

²⁴ Some days later Felix arrived with his wife Drusilla, who was Jewish. He sent for Paul and listened to him talk about faith in Christ Jesus. ²⁵ As Paul discussed the subjects of God's approval, self-control, and the coming judgment, Felix became afraid and said, "That's enough for now. You can go. When I find time, I'll send for you again." ²⁶ At the same time, Felix was hoping that Paul would give him some money. For that reason, Felix would send for Paul rather often to have friendly conversations with him.

²⁷ Two years passed. Then Porcius Festus took Felix's place. (Since Felix wanted to do the Jews a favor, he left Paul in prison.)

Paul Makes an Appeal

25 ¹ Three days after Festus took over his duties in the province of Judea, he went from the city of Caesarea to Jerusalem. ² The chief priests and the other important Jewish leaders informed Festus about their charges against Paul. They were urging ³ Festus to do them the favor of having Paul brought to Jerusalem. The Jews had a plan to ambush and kill Paul as he traveled to Jerusalem.

⁴ Festus replied that he would be returning to Caesarea soon and would keep Paul there. ⁵ He told them, "Have your authorities come to Caesarea with me and accuse him there if the man has done something wrong."

⁶ Festus stayed in Jerusalem for eight or ten days at the most and then returned to Caesarea. The next day Festus took his place in court and summoned Paul.

ᵃ 24:6 Some manuscripts and translations add verses 6b–8a: "We wanted to try him under our law. But the officer Lysias used force to take him from us. He ordered his accusers to come in front of you."

[7] When Paul entered the room, the Jews who had come from Jerusalem surrounded him. They made a lot of serious accusations that they couldn't prove. [8] Paul defended himself by saying, "I haven't broken any Jewish law or done anything against the temple or the emperor."

[9] But Festus wanted to do the Jews a favor. So he asked Paul, "Are you willing to go to Jerusalem to be tried there on these charges with me as your judge?"

[10] Paul said, "I am standing in the emperor's court where I must be tried. I haven't done anything wrong to the Jews, as you know very well. [11] If I am guilty and have done something wrong for which I deserve the death penalty, I don't reject the idea of dying. But if their accusations are untrue, no one can hand me over to them as a favor. I appeal my case to the emperor!"

[12] Festus discussed the appeal with his advisers and then replied to Paul, "You have appealed your case to the emperor, so you'll go to the emperor!"

King Agrippa Meets Paul

[13] Later King Agrippa and Bernice came to the city of Caesarea to welcome Festus. [14] Since they were staying there for a number of days, Festus told the king about Paul's case.

Festus said, "Felix left a man here in prison. [15] When I went to Jerusalem, the chief priests and the Jewish leaders brought me some information about him and asked me to condemn him.

[16] "I replied to them, 'That's not the Roman way of doing things. A person can't be sentenced as a favor. Before he is sentenced, he must face his accusers and have a chance to defend himself against their accusation.'

[17] "So the Jewish leaders came to Caesarea with me. The next day I immediately convened court and summoned the man. [18] When his accusers stood up, they didn't accuse him of the crimes I was expecting. [19] They were disputing with him about their own religion and about some man named Jesus who had died. But Paul claimed that Jesus is alive. [20] Their debate about these things left me puzzled. So I asked Paul if he would like to go to Jerusalem to have his case heard there. [21] But Paul appealed his case. He asked to be held in prison and to have His Majesty the Emperor decide his case. So I ordered him to be held in prison until I could send him to the emperor."

[22] Agrippa told Festus, "I would like to hear the man."

Festus replied, "You'll hear him tomorrow."

[23] The next day Agrippa and Bernice entered the auditorium with a lot of fanfare. Roman army officers and the most important men of the city entered the auditorium with them. Festus gave the order, and Paul was brought into the auditorium.

[24] Then Festus said, "King Agrippa and everyone who is present with us! All the Jews in Jerusalem and Caesarea have talked to me about this man you see in front of you. They shout that he must not be allowed to live any longer. [25] However, I don't think that he has done anything to deserve the death penalty. But since he made an appeal to His Majesty the Emperor, I have decided to send him to Rome. [26] But I don't have anything reliable to write our emperor about him. So I have brought him to all of you, and especially to you, King Agrippa. Then I'll have something to write after he is cross-examined. [27] I find it ridiculous to send a prisoner to Rome when I can't specify any charges against him."

26 [1] Agrippa said to Paul, "You're free to speak for yourself."

Paul acknowledged King Agrippa and then began his defense. [2] "King Agrippa, I think I'm fortunate today to stand in front of you and defend myself against every charge that the Jews brought against me. [3] I say this since you are especially familiar with every custom and controversy in Judaism. So I ask you to listen patiently to me.

[4] "All the Jews know how I lived the earliest days of my youth with my own people and in Jerusalem. [5] They've known me for a long time and can testify, if they're willing, that I followed the strictest party of our religion. They know that I lived my life as a Pharisee.

[6] "I'm on trial now because I expect God to keep the promise that he made to our ancestors. [7] Our twelve tribes expect this promise to be kept as they worship with intense devotion day and night. Your Majesty, the Jews are making accusations against me because I expect God to keep his promise. [8] Why do all of you refuse to believe that God can bring dead people back to life?

[9] "I used to think that I had to do a lot of things to oppose the one named Jesus of Nazareth. [10] That is what I did in Jerusalem. By the authority I received from the chief priests, I locked many Christians in prison. I voted to have them killed every time a vote was taken. [11] I even went to each synagogue, punished believers, and forced them to curse ˌthe name of Jesusˌ. In my furious rage against them, I hunted them down in cities outside ˌJerusalemˌ.

[12] "I was carrying out these activities when I went to the city of Damascus. I had the power and authority of the chief priests. [13] Your Majesty, at noon, while I was traveling, I saw a light

that was brighter than the sun. The light came from the sky and shined around me and those who were with me. [14] All of us fell to the ground, and I heard a voice asking me in Hebrew, 'Saul, Saul! Why are you persecuting me? It's hard for ⌊a mortal like⌋ you to resist God.'

[15] "I asked, 'Who are you, sir?'

"The Lord answered, 'I am Jesus, the one you're persecuting. [16] Stand up! I have appeared to you for a reason. I'm appointing you to be a servant and witness of what you have seen and of what I will show you. [17] I will rescue you from the Jewish people and from the non-Jewish people to whom I am sending you. [18] You will open their eyes and turn them from darkness to light and from Satan's control to God's. Then they will receive forgiveness for their sins and a share among God's people who are made holy by believing in me.'

[19] "At that point I did not disobey the vision I saw from heaven, King Agrippa. [20] Instead, I spread the message that I first told to the ⌊Jewish⌋ people in Damascus and Jerusalem and throughout the whole country of Judea. I spread the same message to non-Jewish people. Both groups were expected to change the way they thought and acted and to turn to God. I told them to do things that prove they had changed their lives. [21] For this reason the Jews took me prisoner in the temple courtyard and tried to murder me.

[22] "God has been helping me to this day so that I can stand and testify to important and unimportant people. I tell them only what the prophets and Moses said would happen. [23] They said that the Messiah would suffer and be the first to come back to life and would spread light to Jewish and non-Jewish people."

[24] As Paul was defending himself in this way, Festus shouted, "Paul, you're crazy! Too much education is driving you crazy!"

[25] Paul replied, "I'm not crazy, Your Excellency Festus. What I'm saying is true and sane. [26] I can easily speak to a king who knows about these things. I'm sure that none of these things has escaped his attention. None of this was done secretly. [27] King Agrippa, do you believe the prophets? I know you believe them!"

[28] Agrippa said to Paul, "Do you think you can quickly persuade me to become a Christian?"

[29] Paul replied, "I wish to God that you and everyone listening to me today would quickly and completely become as I am (except for being a prisoner)."

[30] The king, the governor, Bernice, and the people who were sitting with them got up. [31] As they were leaving, they said to each other, "This man isn't doing anything for which he deserves to die or be put in prison."

[32] Agrippa told Festus, "This man could have been set free if he hadn't appealed his case to the emperor."

Paul Sails for Rome

27 [1] When it was decided that we should sail to Italy, Paul and some other prisoners were turned over to an army officer. His name was Julius, and he belonged to the emperor's division. [2] We set sail on a ship from the city of Adramyttium. The ship was going to stop at ports on the coast of the province of Asia. Aristarchus, a Macedonian from the city of Thessalonica, went with us.

[3] The next day we arrived at the city of Sidon. Julius treated Paul kindly and allowed him to visit his friends and receive any care he needed. [4] Leaving Sidon, we sailed on the northern side of the island of Cyprus because we were traveling against the wind. [5] We sailed along the coast of the provinces of Cilicia and Pamphylia and arrived at the city of Myra in the province of Lycia. [6] In Myra the officer found a ship from Alexandria that was on its way to Italy and put us on it. [7] We were sailing slowly for a number of days. Our difficulties began along the coast of the city of Cnidus because the wind would not let us go further. So at Cape Salmone, we started to sail for the south side of the island of Crete. [8] We had difficulty sailing along the shore of Crete. We finally came to a port called Fair Harbors. The port was near the city of Lasea.

[9] We had lost so much time that the day of fasting had already past. Sailing was now dangerous, so Paul advised them, [10] "Men, we're going to face a disaster and heavy losses on this voyage. This disaster will cause damage to the cargo and the ship, and it will affect our lives." [11] However, the officer was persuaded by what the pilot and the owner of the ship said and not by what Paul said. [12] Since the harbor was not a good place to spend the winter, most of the men decided to sail from there. They hoped to reach the city of Phoenix somehow and spend the winter there. (Phoenix is a harbor that faces the southwest and northwest winds and is located on the island of Crete.)

[13] When a gentle breeze began to blow from the south, the men thought their plan would work. They raised the anchor and sailed close to the shore of Crete.

[14] Soon a powerful wind (called a northeaster) blew from the island. [15] The wind carried the ship away, and we couldn't sail against the wind. We couldn't do anything, so we were carried

along by the wind. **16** As we drifted to the sheltered side of a small island called Cauda, we barely got control of the ship's lifeboat. **17** The men pulled it up on deck. Then they passed ropes under the ship to reinforce it. Fearing that they would hit the large sandbank off the shores of Libya, they lowered the sail and were carried along by the wind. **18** We continued to be tossed so violently by the storm that the next day the men began to throw the cargo overboard. **19** On the third day they threw the ship's equipment overboard. **20** For a number of days we couldn't see the sun or the stars. The storm wouldn't let up. It was so severe that we finally began to lose any hope of coming out of it alive.

21 Since hardly anyone wanted to eat, Paul stood among them and said, "Men, you should have followed my advice not to sail from Crete. You would have avoided this disaster and loss. **22** Now I advise you to have courage. No one will lose his life. Only the ship will be destroyed. **23** I know this because an angel from the God to whom I belong and whom I serve stood by me last night. **24** The angel told me, 'Don't be afraid, Paul! You must present your case to the emperor. God has granted safety to everyone who is sailing with you.' **25** So have courage, men! I trust God that everything will turn out as he told me. **26** However, we will run aground on some island."

The Shipwreck

27 On the fourteenth night we were still drifting through the Mediterranean Sea. About midnight the sailors suspected that we were approaching land. **28** So they threw a line with a weight on it into the water. It sank 120 feet. They waited a little while and did the same thing again. This time the line sank 90 feet. **29** Fearing we might hit rocks, they dropped four anchors from the back of the ship and prayed for morning to come.

30 The sailors tried to escape from the ship. They let the lifeboat down into the sea and pretended they were going to lay out the anchors from the front of the ship. **31** Paul told the officer and the soldiers, "If these sailors don't stay on the ship, you have no hope of staying alive." **32** Then the soldiers cut the ropes that held the lifeboat and let it drift away.

33 Just before daybreak Paul was encouraging everyone to have something to eat. "This is the fourteenth day you have waited and have had nothing to eat. **34** So I'm encouraging you to eat something. Eating will help you survive, since not a hair from anyone's head will be lost." **35** After Paul said this, he took some bread, thanked God in front of everyone, broke it, and began to eat. **36** Everyone was encouraged and had something to eat. **37** (There were 276 of us on the ship.) **38** After the people had eaten all they wanted, they lightened the ship by dumping the wheat into the sea.

39 In the morning they couldn't recognize the land, but they could see a bay with a beach. So they decided to try to run the ship ashore. **40** They cut the anchors free and left them in the sea. At the same time they untied the ropes that held the steering oars. Then they raised the top sail to catch the wind and steered the ship to the shore. **41** They struck a sandbar in the water and ran the ship aground. The front of the ship stuck and couldn't be moved, while the back of the ship was broken to pieces by the force of the waves.

42 The soldiers had a plan to kill the prisoners to keep them from swimming away and escaping. **43** However, the officer wanted to save Paul, so he stopped the soldiers from carrying out their plan. He ordered those who could swim to jump overboard first and swim ashore. **44** Then he ordered the rest to follow on planks or some other pieces ⌊of wood⌋ from the ship. In this way everyone got to shore safely.

Paul on the Island of Malta

28 **1** When we were safely on shore, we found out that the island was called Malta. **2** The people who lived on the island were unusually kind to us. They made a fire and welcomed all of us around it because of the rain and the cold.

3 Paul gathered a bundle of brushwood and put it on the fire. The heat forced a poisonous snake out of the brushwood. The snake bit Paul's hand and wouldn't let go. **4** When the people who lived on the island saw the snake hanging from his hand, they said to each other, "This man must be a murderer! He may have escaped from the sea, but justice won't let him live." **5** Paul shook the snake into the fire and wasn't harmed. **6** The people were waiting for him to swell up or suddenly drop dead. But after they had waited a long time and saw nothing unusual happen to him, they changed their minds and said he was a god.

7 A man named Publius, who was the governor of the island, had property around the area. He welcomed us and treated us kindly, and for three days we were his guests. **8** His father happened to be sick in bed. He was suffering from fever and dysentery. Paul went to him, prayed, placed his hands on him, and made him well. **9** After that had happened, other sick people on the island went to Paul and were made well. **10** They showed respect for us in many ways, and when we were going to set sail, they put whatever we needed on board.

Paul Sails From Malta to Rome

[11] After three months we sailed on an Alexandrian ship that had spent the winter at the island. The ship had the gods Castor and Pollux carved on its front. [12] We stopped at the city of Syracuse and stayed there for three days. [13] We sailed from Syracuse and arrived at the city of Rhegium. The next day a south wind began to blow, and two days later we arrived at the city of Puteoli. [14] In Puteoli we discovered some believers who begged us to spend a week with them.

[15] Believers in Rome heard that we were coming, so they came as far as the cities of Appius' Market and Three Taverns to meet us. When Paul saw them, he thanked God and felt encouraged. So we finally arrived in the city of Rome.[a] [16] After our arrival, Paul was allowed to live by himself, but he had a soldier who guarded him.

Paul in Rome

[17] After three days Paul invited the most influential Jews in Rome to meet with him. When they assembled, he said to them, "Brothers, I haven't done anything against the Jewish people or violated the customs handed down by our ancestors. Yet, I'm a prisoner from Jerusalem, and I've been handed over to the Roman authorities. [18] The Roman authorities cross-examined me and wanted to let me go because I was accused of nothing for which I deserved to die. [19] But when the Jews objected, I was forced to appeal my case to the emperor. That doesn't mean I have any charges to bring against my own people. [20] That's why I asked to see you and speak with you. I'm wearing these chains because of what Israel hopes for."

[21] The Jewish leaders told Paul, "We haven't received any letters from Judea about you, and no Jewish person who has come to Rome has reported or mentioned anything bad about you. [22] However, we would like to hear what you think. We know that everywhere people are talking against this sect."

[23] On a designated day a larger number of influential Jews ˌthan expectedˌ went to the place where Paul was staying. From morning until evening, Paul was explaining the kingdom of God to them. He was trying to convince them about Jesus from Moses' Teachings and the Prophets. [24] Some of them were convinced by what he said, but others continued to disbelieve.

[25] The Jews, unable to agree among themselves, left after Paul had quoted this particular passage to them: "How well the Holy Spirit spoke to your ancestors through the prophet Isaiah! [26] The Spirit said: 'Go to these people and say,

> "You will hear clearly but never understand.
> You will see clearly but never comprehend.
> [27]   These people have become close-minded
>   and hard of hearing.
>   They have shut their eyes
>   so that their eyes never see.
>   Their ears never hear.
>   Their minds never understand.
> And they never turn to me for healing." '

[28] "You need to know that God has sent his salvation to people who are not Jews. They will listen."[b]

[30] Paul rented a place to live for two full years and welcomed everyone who came to him. [31] He spread the message about God's kingdom and taught very boldly about the Lord Jesus Christ. No one stopped him.

---

[a] 28:15 The last sentence in verse 14 has been placed in verse 15 to express the complex Greek sentence structure more clearly in English.   [b] 28:28 Some manuscripts and translations add verse 29: "After Paul said this, the Jews left. They argued intensely among themselves."

ROMANS

Greeting

1 ¹ From Paul, a servant of Jesus Christ, called to be an apostle and appointed to spread the Good News of God.

² (God had already promised this Good News through his prophets in the Holy Scriptures. ³ This Good News is about his Son, our Lord Jesus Christ.ᵃ In his human nature he was a descendant of David. ⁴ In his spiritual, holy nature he was declared the Son of God. This was shown in a powerful way when he came back to life. ⁵ Through him we have received God's kindnessᵇ and the privilege of being apostles who bring people from every nation to the obedience that is associated with faith. This is for the honor of his name. ⁶ You are among those who have been called to belong to Jesus Christ.)

⁷ To everyone in Rome whom God loves and has called to be his holy people.

Good willᵇ and peace from God our Father and the Lord Jesus Christ are yours!

Paul's Prayer and Desire to Visit Rome

⁸ First, I thank my God through Jesus Christ for every one of you because the news of your faith is spreading throughout the whole world. ⁹ I serve God by spreading the Good News about his Son. God is my witness that I always mention you ¹⁰ every time I pray. I ask that somehow God will now at last make it possible for me to visit you. ¹¹ I long to see you to share a spiritual blessing with you so that you will be strengthened. ¹² What I mean is that we may be encouraged by each other's faith.

¹³ I want you to know, brothers and sisters, that I often planned to visit you. However, until now I have been kept from doing so. What I want is to enjoy some of the results of working among you as I have also enjoyed the results of working among the rest of the nations. ¹⁴ I have an obligation to those who are civilized and those who aren't, to those who are wise and those who aren't. ¹⁵ That's why I'm eager to tell you who live in Rome the Good News also.

¹⁶ I'm not ashamed of the Good News. It is God's power to save everyone who believes, Jews first and Greeks as well. ¹⁷ God's approval is revealed in this Good News. This approval begins and ends with faith as Scripture says, "The person who has God's approval will live by faith."

God's Anger Against Sinful Humanity

¹⁸ God's anger is revealed from heaven against every ungodly and immoral thing people do as they try to suppress the truth by their immoral living. ¹⁹ What can be known about God is clear to them because he has made it clear to them. ²⁰ From the creation of the world, God's invisible qualities, his eternal power and divine nature, have been clearly observed in what he made. As a result, people have no excuse. ²¹ They knew God but did not praise and thank him for being God. Instead, their thoughts were pointless, and their misguided minds were plunged into darkness. ²² While claiming to be wise, they became fools. ²³ They exchanged the glory of the immortal God for statues that looked like mortal humans, birds, animals, and snakes.

²⁴ For this reason God allowed their lusts to control them. As a result, they dishonor their bodies by sexual perversion with each other. ²⁵ These people have exchanged God's truth for a lie. So they have become ungodly and serve what is created rather than the Creator, who is blessed forever. Amen!

²⁶ For this reason God allowed their shameful passions to control them. Their women have exchanged natural sexual relations for unnatural ones. ²⁷ Likewise, their men have given up natural sexual relations with women and burn with lust for each other. Men commit indecent acts with men, so they experience among themselves the punishment they deserve for their perversion.

²⁸ And because they thought it was worthless to acknowledge God, God allowed their own immoral minds to control them. So they do these indecent things. ²⁹ Their lives are filled with all kinds of sexual sins, wickedness, and greed. They are mean. They are filled with envy, murder, quarreling, deceit, and viciousness. They are gossips, ³⁰ slanderers, haters of God,

---

ᵃ 1:3 "Our Lord Jesus Christ" from verse 4 (in Greek) has been placed in verse 3 to express the complex Greek sentence structure more clearly in English.   ᵇ 1:5, 7 Or "grace."

haughty, arrogant, and boastful. They think up new ways to be cruel. They don't obey their parents, [31] don't have any sense, don't keep promises, and don't show love to their own families or mercy to others. [32] Although they know God's judgment that those who do such things deserve to die, they not only do these things but also approve of others who do them.

God Will Judge Everyone

2 [1] No matter who you are, if you judge anyone, you have no excuse. When you judge another person, you condemn yourself, since you, the judge, do the same things. [2] We know that God's judgment is right when he condemns people for doing these things. [3] When you judge people for doing these things but then do them yourself, do you think you will escape God's judgment? [4] Do you have contempt for God, who is very kind to you, puts up with you, and deals patiently with you? Don't you realize that it is God's kindness that is trying to lead you to him and change the way you think and act?

[5] Since you are stubborn and don't want to change the way you think and act, you are adding to the anger that God will have against you on that day when God vents his anger. At that time God will reveal that his decisions are fair. [6] He will pay all people back for what they have done. [7] He will give everlasting life to those who search for glory, honor, and immortality by persisting in doing what is good. But he will bring [8] anger and fury on those who, in selfish pride, refuse to believe the truth and who follow what is wrong. [9] There will be suffering and distress for every person who does evil, for Jews first and Greeks as well. [10] But there will be glory, honor, and peace for every person who does what is good, for Jews first and Greeks as well. [11] God does not play favorites.

[12] Here's the reason: Whoever sins without having laws from God will still be condemned to destruction. And whoever has laws from God and sins will still be judged by them. [13] People who merely listen to laws from God don't have God's approval. Rather, people who do what those laws demand will have God's approval.

God Will Judge People Who Are Not Jewish

[14] For example, whenever non-Jews who don't have laws from God do by nature the things that Moses' Teachings contain, they are a law to themselves even though they don't have any laws from God. [15] They show that some requirements found in Moses' Teachings are written in their hearts. Their consciences speak to them. Their thoughts accuse them on one occasion and defend them on another. [16] This happens as they face the day when God, through Christ Jesus, will judge people's secret thoughts. He will use the Good News that I am spreading to make that judgment.

God Will Judge Jewish People

[17] You call yourself a Jew, rely on the laws in Moses' Teachings, brag about your God, [18] know what he wants, and distinguish right from wrong because you have been taught Moses' Teachings. [19] You are confident that you are a guide for the blind, a light to those in the dark, [20] an instructor of ignorant people, and a teacher of children because you have the full content of knowledge and truth in Moses' Teachings. [21] As you teach others, are you failing to teach yourself? As you preach against stealing, are you stealing? [22] As you tell others not to commit adultery, are you committing adultery? As you treat idols with disgust, are you robbing temples? [23] As you brag about the laws in Moses' Teachings, are you dishonoring God by ignoring Moses' Teachings? [24] As Scripture says, "God's name is cursed among the nations because of you."

[25] For example, circumcision is valuable if you follow Moses' laws. If you don't follow those laws, your circumcision amounts to uncircumcision. [26] So if a man does what Moses' Teachings demand, won't he be considered circumcised even if he is uncircumcised? [27] The uncircumcised man who carries out what Moses' Teachings say will condemn you for not following them. He will condemn you in spite of the fact that you are circumcised and have Moses' Teachings in writing. [28] A person is not a Jew because of his appearance, nor is circumcision a matter of how the body looks. [29] Rather, a person is a Jew inwardly, and circumcision is something that happens in a person's heart. Circumcision is spiritual, not just a written rule. That person's praise will come from God, not from people.

Everyone Is a Sinner

3 [1] Is there any advantage, then, in being a Jew? Or is there any value in being circumcised? [2] There are all kinds of advantages. First of all, God entrusted them with his word.

[3] What if some of them were unfaithful? Can their unfaithfulness cancel God's faithfulness? [4] That would be unthinkable! God is honest, and everyone else is a liar, as Scripture says,

> "So you hand down justice when you speak,
>   and you win your case in court."

[5] But if what we do wrong shows that God is fair, what should we say? Is God unfair when he vents his anger on us? (I'm arguing the way humans would.) [6] That's unthinkable! Otherwise, how would God be able to judge the world? [7] If my lie increases the glory that God receives by showing that God is truthful, why am I still judged as a sinner? [8] Or can we say, "Let's do evil so that good will come from it"? Some slander us and claim that this is what we say. They are condemned, and that's what they deserve.

[9] What, then, is the situation? Do we have any advantage? Not at all. We have already accused everyone (both Jews and Greeks) of being under the power of sin, [10] as Scripture says,

"Not one person has God's approval.
[11]   No one understands.
        No one searches for God.
[12]   Everyone has turned away.
            Together they have become rotten to the core.
            No one does anything good,
                not even one person.
[13]   Their throats are open graves.
        Their tongues practice deception.
            Their lips hide the venom of poisonous snakes.
[14]   Their mouths are full of curses and bitter resentment.
[15]   They run quickly to murder people.
[16]   There is ruin and suffering wherever they go.
[17]   They have not learned to live in peace.
[18]   They are not terrified of God."

[19] We know that whatever is in Moses' Teachings applies to everyone under their influence, and no one can say a thing. The whole world is brought under the judgment of God. [20] Not one person can have God's approval by following Moses' Teachings. Moses' Teachings show what sin is.

God Gives Us His Approval as a Gift

[21] Now, the way to receive God's approval has been made plain in a way other than Moses' Teachings. Moses' Teachings and the Prophets tell us this. [22] Everyone who believes has God's approval through faith in Jesus Christ.

There is no difference between people. [23] Because all people have sinned, they have fallen short of God's glory. [24] They receive God's approval freely by an act of his kindness[a] through the price Christ Jesus paid to set us free ˏfrom sinˌ. [25] God showed that Christ is the throne of mercy where God's approval is given through faith in Christ's blood. In his patience God waited to deal with sins committed in the past. [26] He waited so that he could display his approval at the present time. This shows that he is a God of justice, a God who approves of people who believe in Jesus.

[27] So, do we have anything to brag about? Bragging has been eliminated. On what basis was it eliminated? On the basis of our own efforts? No, indeed! Rather, it is eliminated on the basis of faith. [28] We conclude that a person has God's approval by faith, not by his own efforts.

[29] Is God only the God of the Jews? Isn't he also the God of people who are not Jewish? Certainly, he is, [30] since it is the same God who approves circumcised people by faith and uncircumcised people through this same faith.

[31] Are we abolishing Moses' Teachings by this faith? That's unthinkable! Rather, we are supporting Moses' Teachings.

We Have God's Approval by Faith

4 [1] What can we say that we have discovered about our ancestor Abraham? [2] If Abraham had God's approval because of something he did, he would have had a reason to brag. But he could not brag to God about it. [3] What does Scripture say? "Abraham believed God, and that faith was regarded by God to be his approval of Abraham."

[4] When people work, their pay is not regarded as a gift but something they have earned. [5] However, when people don't work but believe God, the one who approves ungodly people, their faith is regarded as God's approval. [6] David says the same thing about those who are blessed: God approves of people without their earning it. David said,

[7]   "Blessed are those whose disobedience is forgiven
            and whose sins are pardoned.
[8]   Blessed is the person whom the Lord no longer considers sinful."

---

[a] 3:24 Or "grace."

[9] Are only the circumcised people blessed, or are uncircumcised people blessed as well? We say, "Abraham's faith was regarded as God's approval of him." [10] How was his faith regarded as God's approval? Was he circumcised or was he uncircumcised at that time? He had not been circumcised. [11] Abraham's faith was regarded as God's approval while he was still uncircumcised. The mark of circumcision is the seal of that approval. Therefore, he is the father of every believer who is not circumcised, and their faith, too, is regarded as God's approval of them. [12] He is also the father of those who not only are circumcised but also are following in the footsteps of his faith. Our father Abraham had that faith before he was circumcised.

[13] So it was not by obeying Moses' Teachings that Abraham or his descendants received the promise that he would inherit the world. Rather, it was through God's approval of his faith. [14] If those who obey Moses' Teachings are the heirs, then faith is useless and the promise is worthless. [15] The laws in Moses' Teachings bring about anger. But where laws don't exist, they can't be broken. [16] Therefore, the promise is based on faith so that it can be a gift.[a] Consequently, the promise is guaranteed for every descendant, not only for those who are descendants by obeying Moses' Teachings but also for those who are descendants by believing as Abraham did. He is the father of all of us, [17] as Scripture says: "I have made you a father of many things."

Abraham believed when he stood in the presence of the God who gives life to dead people and calls into existence nations that don't even exist. [18] When there was nothing left to hope for, Abraham still hoped and believed. As a result, he became a father of many nations, as he had been told: "That is how many descendants you will have." [19] Abraham didn't weaken. Through faith he regarded the facts: His body was already as good as dead now that he was about a hundred years old, and Sarah was unable to have children. [20] He didn't doubt God's promise out of a lack of faith. Instead, giving honor to God ˌfor the promiseˌ, he became strong because of faith [21] and was absolutely confident that God would do what he promised. [22] That is why his faith was regarded as God's approval of him.

[23] But the words "his faith was regarded as God's approval of him" were written not only for him [24] but also for us. Our faith will be regarded as God's approval of us who believe in the one who brought Jesus, our Lord, back to life. [25] Jesus, our Lord, was handed over to death because of our failures and was brought back to life so that we could receive God's approval.

We Are at Peace With God Because of Jesus

5 [1] Now that we have God's approval by faith, we have peace with God because of what our Lord Jesus Christ has done. [2] Through Christ we can approach God[a] and stand in his favor.[b] So we brag because of our confidence that we will receive glory from God. [3] But that's not all. We also brag when we are suffering. We know that suffering creates endurance, [4] endurance creates character, and character creates confidence. [5] We're not ashamed to have this confidence, because God's love has been poured into our hearts by the Holy Spirit, who has been given to us.

[6] Look at it this way: At the right time, while we were still helpless, Christ died for ungodly people. [7] Finding someone who would die for a godly person is rare. Maybe someone would have the courage to die for a good person. [8] Christ died for us while we were still sinners. This demonstrates God's love for us.

[9] Since Christ's blood has now given us God's approval, we are even more certain that Christ will save us from God's anger. [10] If the death of his Son restored our relationship with God while we were still his enemies, we are even more certain that, because of this restored relationship, the life of his Son will save us. [11] In addition, our Lord Jesus Christ lets us continue to brag about God. After all, it is through Christ that we now have this restored relationship with God.

A Comparison Between Adam and Christ

[12] Sin came into the world through one person, and death came through sin. So death spread to everyone, because everyone sinned. [13] Sin was in the world before there were any laws. But no record of sin can be kept when there are no laws. [14] Yet, death ruled from the time of Adam to the time of Moses, even over those who did not sin in the same way Adam did when he disobeyed. Adam is an image of the one who would come.

[15] There is no comparison between ˌGod'sˌ gift and ˌAdam'sˌ failure. If humanity died as the result of one person's failure, it is certainly true that God's kindness[b] and the gift given through the kindness of one person, Jesus Christ, have been showered on humanity.

[16] There is also no comparison between ˌGod'sˌ gift and the one who sinned. The verdict which followed one person's failure condemned everyone. But, even after many failures, the gift brought God's approval. [17] It is certain that death ruled because of one person's failure. It's

---

[a] 4:16 Or "grace."   [a] 5:2 Some manuscripts read "we can approach God through faith."   [b] 5:2, 15 Or "grace."

even more certain that those who receive God's overflowing kindness and the gift of his approval will rule in life because of one person, Jesus Christ. [18] Therefore, everyone was condemned through one failure, and everyone received God's life-giving approval through one verdict. [19] Clearly, through one person's disobedience humanity became sinful, and through one person's obedience humanity will receive God's approval. [20] Laws were added to increase the failure. But where sin increased, God's kindness increased even more. [21] As sin ruled by bringing death, God's kindness would rule by bringing us his approval. This results in our living forever because of Jesus Christ our Lord.

No Longer Slaves to Sin, but God's Servants

6 [1] What should we say then? Should we continue to sin so that God's kindness[a] will increase? [2] That's unthinkable! As far as sin is concerned, we have died. So how can we still live under sin's influence?

[3] Don't you know that all of us who were baptized into Christ Jesus were baptized into his death? [4] When we were baptized into his death, we were placed into the tomb with him. As Christ was brought back from death to life by the glorious power of the Father, so we, too, should live a new kind of life. [5] If we've become united with him in a death like his, certainly we will also be united with him when we come back to life as he did. [6] We know that the person we used to be was crucified with him to put an end to sin in our bodies. Because of this we are no longer slaves to sin. [7] The person who has died has been freed from sin.

[8] If we have died with Christ, we believe that we will also live with him. [9] We know that Christ, who was brought back to life, will never die again. Death no longer has any power over him. [10] When he died, he died once and for all to sin's power. But now he lives, and he lives for God. [11] So consider yourselves dead to sin's power but living for God in the power Christ Jesus gives you.

[12] Therefore, never let sin rule your physical body so that you obey its desires. [13] Never offer any part of your body to sin's power. No part of your body should ever be used to do any ungodly thing. Instead, offer yourselves to God as people who have come back from death and are now alive. Offer all the parts of your body to God. Use them to do everything that God approves of. [14] Certainly, sin shouldn't have power over you because you're not controlled by laws, but by God's favor.[a]

[15] Then what is the implication? Should we sin because we are not controlled by laws but by God's favor? That's unthinkable! [16] Don't you know that if you offer to be someone's slave, you must obey that master? Either your master is sin, or your master is obedience. Letting sin be your master leads to death. Letting obedience be your master leads to God's approval. [17] You were slaves to sin. But I thank God that you have become wholeheartedly obedient to the teachings which you were given. [18] Freed from sin, you were made slaves who do what God approves of.

[19] I'm speaking in a human way because of the weakness of your corrupt nature. Clearly, you once offered all the parts of your body as slaves to sexual perversion and disobedience. This led you to live disobedient lives. Now, in the same way, offer all the parts of your body as slaves that do what God approves of. This leads you to live holy lives. [20] When you were slaves to sin, you were free from doing what God approves of.

[21] What did you gain by doing those things? You're ashamed of what you used to do because it ended in death. [22] Now you have been freed from sin and have become God's slaves. This results in a holy life and, finally, in everlasting life. [23] The payment for sin is death, but the gift that God freely gives is everlasting life found in Christ Jesus our Lord.

7 [1] Don't you realize, brothers and sisters, that laws have power over people only as long as they are alive? (I'm speaking to people who are familiar with Moses' Teachings.) [2] For example, a married woman is bound by law to her husband as long as he is alive. But if her husband dies, that marriage law is no longer in effect for her. [3] So if she marries another man while her husband is still alive, she will be called an adulterer. But if her husband dies, she is free from this law, so she is not committing adultery if she marries another man.

[4] In the same way, brothers and sisters, you have died to the laws in Moses' Teachings through Christ's body. You belong to someone else, the one who was brought back to life.

As a result, we can do what God wants. [5] While we were living under the influence of our corrupt nature, sinful passions were at work throughout our bodies. Stirred up by Moses' laws, our sinful passions did things that result in death. [6] But now we have died to those laws that bound us. God has broken their effect on us so that we are serving in a new spiritual way, not in an old way dictated by written words.

---

[a] 6:1, 14 Or "grace."

Moses' Laws Show What Sin Is

⁷ What should we say, then? Are Moses' laws sinful? That's unthinkable! In fact, I wouldn't have recognized sin if those laws hadn't shown it to me. For example, I wouldn't have known that some desires are sinful if Moses' Teachings hadn't said, "Never have wrong desires." ⁸ But sin took the opportunity provided by this commandment and made me have all kinds of wrong desires. Clearly, without laws sin is dead. ⁹ At one time I was alive without any laws. But when this commandment came, sin became alive ¹⁰ and I died. I found that the commandment which was intended to bring me life actually brought me death. ¹¹ Sin, taking the opportunity provided by this commandment, deceived me and then killed me.

¹² So Moses' Teachings are holy, and the commandment is holy, right, and good. ¹³ Now, did something good cause my death? That's unthinkable! Rather, my death was caused by sin so that sin would be recognized for what it is. Through a commandment sin became more sinful than ever.

God's Standards Are at War With Sin's Standards

¹⁴ I know that God's standards are spiritual, but I have a corrupt nature, sold as a slave to sin. ¹⁵ I don't realize what I'm doing. I don't do what I want to do. Instead, I do what I hate. ¹⁶ I don't do what I want to do, but I agree that God's standards are good. ¹⁷ So I am no longer the one who is doing the things I hate, but sin that lives in me is doing them.

¹⁸ I know that nothing good lives in me; that is, nothing good lives in my corrupt nature. Although I have the desire to do what is right, I don't do it. ¹⁹ I don't do the good I want to do. Instead, I do the evil that I don't want to do. ²⁰ Now, when I do what I don't want to do, I am no longer the one who is doing it. Sin that lives in me is doing it.

²¹ So I've discovered this truth: Evil is present with me even when I want to do what God's standards say is good. ²² I take pleasure in God's standards in my inner being. ²³ However, I see a different standard ˎat workˌ throughout my body. It is at war with the standards my mind sets and tries to take me captive to sin's standards which still exist throughout my body. ²⁴ What a miserable person I am! Who will rescue me from my dying body? ²⁵ I thank God that our Lord Jesus Christ rescues me! So I am obedient to God's standards with my mind, but I am obedient to sin's standards with my corrupt nature.

God's Spirit Makes Us His Children

8 ¹ So those who are believers in Christ Jesus can no longer be condemned. ² The standards of the Spirit, who gives life through Christ Jesus, have set you free from the standards of sin and death. ³ It is impossible to do what God's standards demand because of the weakness our human nature has. But God sent his Son to have a human nature as sinners have and to pay for sin. That way God condemned sin in our corrupt nature. ⁴ Therefore, we, who do not live by our corrupt nature but by our spiritual nature, are able to meet God's standards.

⁵ Those who live by the corrupt nature have the corrupt nature's attitude. But those who live by the spiritual nature have the spiritual nature's attitude. ⁶ The corrupt nature's attitude leads to death. But the spiritual nature's attitude leads to life and peace. ⁷ This is so because the corrupt nature has a hostile attitude toward God. It refuses to place itself under the authority of God's standards because it can't. ⁸ Those who are under the control of the corrupt nature can't please God. ⁹ But if God's Spirit lives in you, you are under the control of your spiritual nature, not your corrupt nature.

Whoever doesn't have the Spirit of Christ doesn't belong to him. ¹⁰ However, if Christ lives in you, your bodies are dead because of sin, but your spirits are alive because you have God's approval. ¹¹ Does the Spirit of the one who brought Jesus back to life live in you? Then the one who brought Christ back to life will also make your mortal bodies alive by his Spirit who lives in you.

¹² So, brothers and sisters, we have no obligation to live the way our corrupt nature wants us to live. ¹³ If you live by your corrupt nature, you are going to die. But if you use your spiritual nature to put to death the evil activities of the body, you will live. ¹⁴ Certainly, all who are guided by God's Spirit are God's children. ¹⁵ You haven't received the spirit of slaves that leads you into fear again. Instead, you have received the spirit of God's adopted children by which we call out, "Abba!ᵃ Father!" ¹⁶ The Spirit himself testifies with our spirit that we are God's children. ¹⁷ If we are his children, we are also God's heirs. If we share in Christ's suffering in order to share his glory, we are heirs together with him.

God's Spirit Helps Us

¹⁸ I consider our present sufferings insignificant compared to the glory that will soon be revealed to us. ¹⁹ All creation is eagerly waiting for God to reveal who his children are.

ᵃ 8:15 *Abba* is Aramaic for "father."

[20] Creation was subjected to frustration but not by its own choice. The one who subjected it to frustration did so in the hope [21] that it would also be set free from slavery to decay in order to share the glorious freedom that the children of God will have. [22] We know that all creation has been groaning with the pains of childbirth up to the present time.

[23] However, not only creation groans. We, who have the Spirit as the first of God's gifts, also groan inwardly. We groan as we eagerly wait for our adoption, the freeing of our bodies ˌfrom sinˌ. [24] We were saved with this hope in mind. If we hope for something we already see, it's not really hope. Who hopes for what can be seen? [25] But if we hope for what we don't see, we eagerly wait for it with perseverance.

[26] At the same time the Spirit also helps us in our weakness, because we don't know how to pray for what we need. But the Spirit intercedes along with our groans that cannot be expressed in words. [27] The one who searches our hearts knows what the Spirit has in mind. The Spirit intercedes for God's people the way God wants him to.

Nothing Can Separate Us From God's Love

[28] We know that all things work together for the good of those who love God—those whom he has called according to his plan. [29] This is true because he already knew his people and had already appointed them to have the same form as the image of his Son. Therefore, his Son is the firstborn among many children. [30] He also called those whom he had already appointed. He approved of those whom he had called, and he gave glory to those whom he had approved of.

[31] What can we say about all of this? If God is for us, who can be against us? [32] God didn't spare his own Son but handed him over ˌto deathˌ for all of us. So he will also give us everything along with him. [33] Who will accuse those whom God has chosen? God has approved of them. [34] Who will condemn them? Christ has died, and more importantly, he was brought back to life. Christ has the highest position in heaven. Christ also intercedes for us. [35] What will separate us from the love Christ has for us? Can trouble, distress, persecution, hunger, nakedness, danger, or violent death separate us from his love? [36] As Scripture says:

> "We are being killed all day long because of you.
> We are thought of as sheep to be slaughtered."

[37] The one who loves us gives us an overwhelming victory in all these difficulties. [38] I am convinced that nothing can ever separate us from God's love which Christ Jesus our Lord shows us.[b] We can't be separated by death or life, by angels or rulers, by anything in the present or anything in the future, by forces [39] or powers in the world above or in the world below, or by anything else in creation.

Paul's Concern for the Jewish People

9 [1] As a Christian, I'm telling you the truth. I'm not lying. The Holy Spirit, along with my own thoughts, supports me in this. [2] I have deep sorrow and endless heartache. [3] I wish I could be condemned and cut off from Christ for the sake of others who, like me, are Jewish by birth. [4] They are Israelites, God's adopted children. They have the Lord's glory, the pledges,[a] Moses' Teachings, the true worship, and the promises. [5] The Messiah is descended from their ancestors according to his human nature. The Messiah is God over everything, forever blessed. Amen.

[6] Now it is not as though God's word has failed. Clearly, not everyone descended from Israel is part of Israel [7] or a descendant of Abraham. However, ˌas Scripture says,ˌ "Through Isaac your descendants will carry on your name." [8] This means that children born by natural descent ˌfrom Abrahamˌ are not necessarily God's children. Instead, children born by the promise are considered Abraham's descendants.

[9] For example, this is what the promise said, "I will come back at the right time, and Sarah will have a son." [10] The same thing happened to Rebekah. Rebekah became pregnant by our ancestor Isaac. [11] Before the children had been born or had done anything good or bad, Rebekah was told that the older child would serve the younger one. This was said to Rebekah so that God's plan would remain a matter of his choice, [12] a choice based on God's call and not on anything people do.[b] [13] The Scriptures say, "I loved Jacob, but I hated Esau."

[14] What can we say—that God is unfair? That's unthinkable! [15] For example, God said to Moses, "I will be kind to anyone I want to. I will be merciful to anyone I want to." [16] Therefore, God's choice does not depend on a person's desire or effort, but on God's mercy.

---

[b] 8:38 The last part of verse 39 (in Greek) has been moved to verse 38 to express the complex Greek sentence structure more clearly in English.   [a] 9:4 Or "covenants."   [b] 9:12 The last part of verse 12 (in Greek) has been placed in verse 11 to express the complex Greek sentence structure more clearly in English.

17 For example, Scripture says to Pharaoh, "I put you here for this reason: to demonstrate my power through you and to spread my name throughout the earth." **18** Therefore, if God wants to be kind to anyone, he will be. If he wants to make someone stubborn, he will.

19 You may ask me, "Why does God still find fault with anyone? Who can resist whatever God wants to do?"

20 Who do you think you are to talk back to God like that? Can an object that was made say to its maker, "Why did you make me like this?" **21** A potter has the right to do whatever he wants with his clay. He can make something for a special occasion or something for everyday use from the same lump of clay.

22 If God wants to demonstrate his anger and reveal his power, he can do it. But can't he be extremely patient with people who are objects of his anger because they are headed for destruction? **23** Can't God also reveal the riches of his glory to people who are objects of his mercy and who he had already prepared for glory? **24** This is what God did for us whom he called—whether we are Jews or not.

God Chose People Who Are Not Jewish

25 As God says in Hosea:

> "Those who are not my people
>   I will call my people.
> Those who are not loved
>   I will call my loved ones.
> **26**   Wherever they were told,
>   'You are not my people,'
>   they will be called children of the living God."

27 Isaiah also says about Israel:

> "Although the descendants of Israel are
>   as numerous as the grains of sand on the seashore,
>   only a few will be saved.
> **28**   The Lord will carry out his sentence on the land,
>   completely and decisively."

29 This is what Isaiah predicted:

> "If the Lord of Armies hadn't left us some descendants,
>   we would have been like Sodom and Gomorrah."

30 So what can we say? We can say that non-Jewish people who were not trying to gain God's approval won his approval, an approval based on faith. **31** The people of Israel tried to gain God's approval by obeying Moses' Teachings, but they did not reach their goal. **32** Why? They didn't rely on faith to gain God's approval, but they relied on their own efforts. They stumbled over the rock that trips people. **33** As Scripture says,

> "I am placing a rock in Zion that people trip over,
>   a large rock that people find offensive.
> Whoever believes in him will not be ashamed."

If You Believe You Will Be Saved

10 **1** Brothers and sisters, my heart's desire and prayer to God on behalf of the Jewish people is that they would be saved. **2** I can assure you that they are deeply devoted to God, but they are misguided. **3** They don't understand how to receive God's approval. So they try to set up their own way to get it, and they have not accepted God's way for receiving his approval. **4** Christ is the fulfillment of Moses' Teachings so that everyone who has faith may receive God's approval.

5 Moses writes about receiving God's approval by following his laws. He says, "The person who obeys laws will live because of the laws he obeys." **6** However, Scripture says about God's approval which is based on faith, "Don't ask yourself who will go up to heaven," (that is, to bring Christ down). **7** "Don't ask who will go down into the depths," (that is, to bring Christ back from the dead). **8** However, what else does it say? "This message is near you. It's in your mouth and in your heart." This is the message of faith that we spread. **9** If you declare that Jesus is Lord, and believe that God brought him back to life, you will be saved. **10** By believing you receive God's approval, and by declaring your faith you are saved. **11** Scripture says, "Whoever believes in him will not be ashamed."

12 There is no difference between Jews and Greeks. They all have the same Lord, who gives his riches to everyone who calls on him. **13** So then, "Whoever calls on the name of the Lord will be saved."

¹⁴ But how can people call on him if they have not believed in him? How can they believe in him if they have not heard his message? How can they hear if no one tells ˻the Good News˼? ¹⁵ How can people tell the Good News if no one sends them? As Scripture says, "How beautiful are the feet of the messengers who announce the Good News." ¹⁶ But not everyone has believed the Good News.

Isaiah asks, "Lord, who has believed our message?" ¹⁷ So faith comes from hearing the message, and the message that is heard is what Christ spoke.

¹⁸ But I ask, "Didn't they hear that message?" Certainly they did! "The voice of the messengers has gone out into the whole world and their words to the ends of the earth."

¹⁹ Again I ask, "Didn't Israel understand ˻that message˼?" Moses was the first to say, "I will make you jealous of people who are not a nation. I will make you angry about a nation that doesn't understand." ²⁰ Isaiah said very boldly, "I was found by those who weren't looking for me. I was revealed to those who weren't asking for me." ²¹ Then Isaiah said about Israel, "All day long I have stretched out my hands to disobedient and rebellious people."

God's Continuing Love for Jewish People

11 ¹ So I ask, "Has God rejected his people Israel?" That's unthinkable! Consider this. I'm an Israelite myself, a descendant of Abraham from the tribe of Benjamin. ² God has not rejected his people whom he knew long ago. Don't you know what Elijah says in the Scripture passage when he complains to God about Israel? He says, ³ "Lord, they've killed your prophets and torn down your altars. I'm the only one left, and they're trying to take my life." ⁴ But what was God's reply? God said, "I've kept 7,000 people for myself who have not knelt to worship Baal." ⁵ So, as there were then, there are now a few left that God has chosen by his kindness.ᵃ ⁶ If they were chosen by God's kindness, they weren't chosen because of anything they did. Otherwise, God's kindness wouldn't be kindness.

⁷ So what does all this mean? It means that Israel has never achieved what it has been striving for. However, those whom God has chosen have achieved it. The minds of the rest of Israel were closed, ⁸ as Scripture says,

> "To this day God has given them a spirit of deep sleep.
>   Their eyes don't see,
>   and their ears don't hear!"

⁹ And David says,

> "Let the table set for them become a trap and a net,
>   a snare and a punishment for them.
> ¹⁰   Let their vision become clouded so that they cannot see.
> Let them carry back-breaking burdens forever."

¹¹ So I ask, "Has Israel stumbled so badly that it can't get up again?" That's unthinkable! By Israel's failure, salvation has come to people who are not Jewish to make the Jewish people jealous. ¹² The fall of the Jewish people made the world spiritually rich. Their failure made people who are not Jewish spiritually rich. So the inclusion of Jewish people will make the world even richer.

¹³ Now, I speak to you who are not Jewish. As long as I am an apostle sent to people who are not Jewish, I bring honor to my ministry. ¹⁴ Perhaps I can make my people jealous and save some of them. ¹⁵ If Israel's rejection means that the world has been brought back to God, what does Israel's acceptance mean? It means that Israel has come back to life.

¹⁶ If the first handful of dough is holy, the whole batch of dough is holy. If the root is holy, the branches are holy. ¹⁷ But some of the olive branches have been broken off, and you, a wild olive branch, have been grafted in their place. You get your nourishment from the roots of the olive tree. ¹⁸ So don't brag about being better than the other branches. If you brag, remember that you don't support the root, the root supports you. ¹⁹ "Well," you say, "Branches were cut off so that I could be grafted onto the tree." ²⁰ That's right! They were broken off because they didn't believe, but you remain on the tree because you do believe. Don't feel arrogant, but be afraid. ²¹ If God didn't spare the natural branches, he won't spare you, either. ²² Look at how kind and how severe God can be. He is severe to those who fell, but kind to you if you continue to hold on to his kindness. Otherwise, you, too, will be cut off ˻from the tree˼.

²³ If Jewish people do not continue in their unbelief, they will be grafted onto the tree again, because God is able to do that. ²⁴ In spite of the fact that you have been cut from a wild olive tree, you have been grafted onto a cultivated one. So wouldn't it be easier for these natural branches to be grafted onto the olive tree they belong to?

ᵃ 11:5 Or "grace."

²⁵ Brothers and sisters, I want you to understand this mystery so that you won't become arrogant. The minds of some Israelites have become closed until all of God's non-Jewish people are included. ²⁶ In this way Israel as a whole will be saved, as Scripture says,

> "The Savior will come from Zion.
>   He will remove godlessness from Jacob.
> ²⁷ My promise^b to them will be fulfilled
>   when I take away their sins."

²⁸ The Good News made the Jewish people enemies because of you. But by God's choice they are loved because of their ancestors. ²⁹ God never changes his mind when he gives gifts or when he calls someone. ³⁰ In the past, you disobeyed God. But now God has been merciful to you because of the disobedience of the Jewish people. ³¹ In the same way, the Jewish people have also disobeyed so that God may be merciful to them as he was to you. ³² God has placed all people into the prison of their own disobedience so that he could be merciful to all people.

> ³³   God's riches, wisdom, and knowledge are so deep
>   that it is impossible to explain his decisions
>   or to understand his ways.
> ³⁴   "Who knows how the Lord thinks?
>   Who can become his adviser?"
> ³⁵   Who gave the Lord something
>   which the Lord must pay back?
> ³⁶   Everything is from him and by him and for him.
>   Glory belongs to him forever! Amen!

Dedicate Your Lives to God

12 ¹ Brothers and sisters, in view of all we have just shared about God's compassion, I encourage you to offer your bodies as living sacrifices, dedicated to God and pleasing to him. This kind of worship is appropriate for you. ² Don't become like the people of this world. Instead, change the way you think. Then you will always be able to determine what God really wants—what is good, pleasing, and perfect.

³ Because of the kindness^a that God has shown me, I ask you not to think of yourselves more highly than you should. Instead, your thoughts should lead you to use good judgment based on what God has given each of you as believers. ⁴ Our bodies have many parts, but these parts don't all do the same thing. ⁵ In the same way, even though we are many individuals, Christ makes us one body and individuals who are connected to each other. ⁶ God in his kindness gave each of us different gifts. If your gift is speaking God's word, make sure what you say agrees with the Christian faith. ⁷ If your gift is serving, then devote yourself to serving. If it is teaching, devote yourself to teaching. ⁸ If it is encouraging others, devote yourself to giving encouragement. If it is sharing, be generous. If it is leadership, lead enthusiastically. If it is helping people in need, help them cheerfully.

⁹ Love sincerely. Hate evil. Hold on to what is good. ¹⁰ Be devoted to each other like a loving family. Excel in showing respect for each other. ¹¹ Don't be lazy in showing your devotion. Use your energy to serve the Lord. ¹² Be happy in your confidence, be patient in trouble, and pray continually. ¹³ Share what you have with God's people who are in need. Be hospitable.

¹⁴ Bless those who persecute you. Bless them, and don't curse them. ¹⁵ Be happy with those who are happy. Be sad with those who are sad. ¹⁶ Live in harmony with each other. Don't be arrogant, but be friendly to humble people. Don't think that you are smarter than you really are.

¹⁷ Don't pay people back with evil for the evil they do to you. Focus your thoughts on those things that are considered noble. ¹⁸ As much as it is possible, live in peace with everyone. ¹⁹ Don't take revenge, dear friends. Instead, let God's anger take care of it. After all, Scripture says, "I alone have the right to take revenge. I will pay back, says the Lord." ²⁰ But,

> "If your enemy is hungry, feed him.
>   If he is thirsty, give him a drink.
>   If you do this, you will make him feel guilty and ashamed."

²¹ Don't let evil conquer you, but conquer evil with good.

Obey the Government

13 ¹ Every person should obey the government in power. No government would exist if it hadn't been established by God. The governments which exist have been put in place

---

^b 11:27 Or "covenant."   ^a 12:3 Or "grace."

by God. [2] Therefore, whoever resists the government opposes what God has established. Those who resist will bring punishment on themselves.

[3] People who do what is right don't have to be afraid of the government. But people who do what is wrong should be afraid of it. Would you like to live without being afraid of the government? Do what is right, and it will praise you. [4] The government is God's servant working for your good.

But if you do what is wrong, you should be afraid. The government has the right to carry out the death sentence. It is God's servant, an avenger to execute God's anger on anyone who does what is wrong. [5] Therefore, it is necessary for you to obey, not only because you're afraid of God's anger but also because of your own conscience.

[6] That is also why you pay your taxes. People in the government are God's servants while they do the work he has given them. [7] Pay everyone whatever you owe them. If you owe taxes, pay them. If you owe tolls, pay them. If you owe someone respect, respect that person. If you owe someone honor, honor that person.

Love One Another

[8] Pay your debts as they come due. However, one debt you can never finish paying is the debt of love that you owe each other. The one who loves another person has fulfilled Moses' Teachings. [9] The commandments, "Never commit adultery; never murder; never steal; never have wrong desires," and every other commandment are summed up in this statement: "Love your neighbor as you love yourself." [10] Love never does anything that is harmful to a neighbor. Therefore, love fulfills Moses' Teachings.

[11] You know the times ‿in which we are living‿. It's time for you to wake up. Our salvation is nearer now than when we first became believers. [12] The night is almost over, and the day is near. So we should get rid of the things that belong to the dark and take up the weapons that belong to the light. [13] We should live decently, as people who live in the light of day. Wild parties, drunkenness, sexual immorality, promiscuity, rivalry, and jealousy cannot be part of our lives. [14] Instead, live like the Lord Jesus Christ did, and forget about satisfying the desires of your sinful nature.

How to Treat Christians Who Are Weak in Faith

14 [1] Welcome people who are weak in faith, but don't get into an argument over differences of opinion. [2] Some people believe that they can eat all kinds of food. Other people with weak faith believe that they can eat only vegetables. [3] People who eat all foods should not despise people who eat only vegetables. In the same way, the vegetarians should not criticize people who eat all foods, because God has accepted those people. [4] Who are you to criticize someone else's servant? The Lord will determine whether his servant has been successful. The servant will be successful because the Lord makes him successful.

[5] One person decides that one day is holier than another. Another person decides that all days are the same. Every person must make his own decision. [6] When people observe a special day, they observe it to honor the Lord. When people eat all kinds of foods, they honor the Lord as they eat, since they give thanks to God. Vegetarians also honor the Lord when they eat, and they, too, give thanks to God. [7] It's clear that we don't live to honor ourselves, and we don't die to honor ourselves. [8] If we live, we honor the Lord, and if we die, we honor the Lord. So whether we live or die, we belong to the Lord. [9] For this reason Christ died and came back to life so that he would be the Lord of both the living and the dead.

[10] Why do you criticize or despise other Christians? Everyone will stand in front of God to be judged. [11] Scripture says,

> "As certainly as I live, says the Lord,
> 　everyone will worship me,
> 　　and everyone will praise God."

[12] All of us will have to give an account of ourselves to God.
[13] So let's stop criticizing each other. Instead, you should decide never to do anything that would make other Christians have doubts or lose their faith.

[14] The Lord Jesus has given me the knowledge and conviction that no food is unacceptable in and of itself. But it is unacceptable to a person who thinks it is. [15] So if what you eat hurts another Christian, you are no longer living by love. Don't destroy anyone by what you eat. Christ died for that person. [16] Don't allow anyone to say that what you consider good is evil.

[17] God's kingdom does not consist of what a person eats or drinks. Rather, God's kingdom consists of God's approval and peace, as well as the joy that the Holy Spirit gives. [18] The person who serves Christ with this in mind is pleasing to God and respected by people.

[19] So let's pursue those things which bring peace and which are good for each other. [20] Don't ruin God's work because of what you eat. All food is acceptable, but it's wrong for a person to eat something if it causes someone else to have doubts. [21] The right thing to do is to avoid

eating meat, drinking wine, or doing anything else that causes another Christian to have doubts. [22] So whatever you believe about these things, keep it between yourself and God. The person who does what he knows is right shouldn't feel guilty. He is blessed. [23] But if a person has doubts and still eats, he is condemned because he didn't act in faith. Anything that is not done in faith is sin.

15 [1] So those of us who have a strong ˌfaithˌ must be patient with the weaknesses of those whose ˌfaithˌ is not so strong. We must not think only of ourselves. [2] We should all be concerned about our neighbor and the good things that will build his faith. [3] Christ did not think only of himself. Rather, as Scripture says, "The insults of those who insult you have fallen on me."

God Gives Us Unity

[4] Everything written long ago was written to teach us so that we would have confidence through the endurance and encouragement which the Scriptures give us. [5] May God, who gives you this endurance and encouragement, allow you to live in harmony with each other by following the example of Christ Jesus. [6] Then, having the same goal, you will praise the God and Father of our Lord Jesus Christ.

[7] Therefore, accept each other in the same way that Christ accepted you. He did this to bring glory to God. [8] Let me explain. Christ became a servant for the Jewish people to reveal God's truth. As a result, he fulfilled God's promise to the ancestors of the Jewish people. [9] People who are not Jewish praise God for his mercy as well. This is what the Scriptures say,

> "That is why I will give thanks to you among the nations
>   and I will sing praises to your name."

[10] And Scripture says again,

> "You nations, be happy together with his people!"

[11] And again,

> "Praise the Lord, all you nations!
>   Praise him, all you people of the world!"

[12] Again, Isaiah says,

> "There will be a root from Jesse.
> He will rise to rule the nations,
>   and he will give the nations hope."

[13] May God, the source of hope, fill you with joy and peace through your faith in him. Then you will overflow with hope by the power of the Holy Spirit.

Paul's Desire to Tell the Good News to the World

[14] I'm convinced, brothers and sisters, that you, too, are filled with goodness. I'm also convinced that you have all the knowledge you need and that you are able to instruct each other. [15] However, I've written you a letter, parts of which are rather bold, as a reminder to you. I'm doing this because God gave me the gift [16] to be a servant of Christ Jesus to people who are not Jewish. I serve as a priest by spreading the Good News of God. I do this in order that I might bring the nations to God as an acceptable offering, made holy by the Holy Spirit. [17] So Christ Jesus gives me the right to brag about what I'm doing for God. [18] I'm bold enough to tell you only what Christ has done through me to bring people who are not Jewish to obedience. By what I have said and done, [19] by the power of miraculous and amazing signs, and by the power of God's Spirit, I have finished spreading the Good News about Christ from Jerusalem to Illyricum. [20] My goal was to spread the Good News where the name of Christ was not known. I didn't want to build on a foundation which others had laid. [21] As Scripture says,

> "Those who were never told about him will see,
>   and those who never heard will understand."

[22] This is what has so often kept me from visiting you. [23] But now I have no new opportunities for work in this region. For many years I have wanted to visit you. [24] Now I am on my way to Spain, so I hope to see you when I come your way. After I have enjoyed your company for a while, I hope that you will support my trip to Spain.

[25] Right now I'm going to Jerusalem to bring help to the Christians there. [26] Because the believers in Macedonia and Greece owe a debt to the Christians in Jerusalem, they have decided to take up a collection for the poor among the Christians in Jerusalem. [27] These Macedonians and Greeks have shared the spiritual wealth of the Christians in Jerusalem. So they are obligated to use their earthly wealth to help them.

[28] When the collection is completed and I have officially turned the money over to the Christians in Jerusalem, I will visit you on my way to Spain. [29] I know that when I come to you I will bring the full blessing of Christ.

[30] Brothers and sisters, I encourage you through our Lord Jesus Christ and by the love that the Spirit creates, to join me in my struggle. Pray to God for me [31] that I will be rescued from those people in Judea who refuse to believe. Pray that God's people in Jerusalem will accept the help I bring. [32] Also pray that by the will of God I may come to you with joy and be refreshed when I am with you.

[33] May the God of peace be with you all. Amen.

Farewell

16 [1] With this letter I'm introducing Phoebe to you. She is our sister in the Christian faith and a deacon[a] of the church in the city of Cenchrea. [2] Give her a Christian welcome that shows you are God's holy people. Provide her with anything she may need, because she has provided help to many people, including me.

[3] Greet Prisca and Aquila, my coworkers in the service of Christ Jesus. [4] They risked their lives to save me. I'm thankful to them and so are all the churches among the nations. [5] Also greet the church that meets in their house.

Greet my dear friend Epaenetus. He was the first person in the province of Asia to become a believer in Christ.

[6] Greet Mary, who has worked very hard for you.

[7] Greet Andronicus and Junia, who are Jewish by birth like me. They are prisoners like me and are prominent among the apostles. They also were Christians before I was.

[8] Greet Ampliatus my dear friend in the service of the Lord.

[9] Greet Urbanus our coworker in the service of Christ, and my dear friend Stachys.

[10] Greet Apelles, a true Christian.

Greet those who belong to the family of Aristobulus.

[11] Greet Herodion, who is Jewish by birth like me.

Greet those Christians who belong to the family of Narcissus.

[12] Greet Tryphaena and Tryphosa, who have worked hard for the Lord.

Greet dear Persis, who has worked very hard for the Lord.

[13] Greet Rufus, that outstanding Christian, and his mother, who has been a mother to me too.

[14] Greet Asyncritus, Phlegon, Hermes, Patrobas, Hermas, and the brothers and sisters who are with them.

[15] Greet Philologus and Julia, Nereus, and his sister, and Olympas, and all God's people who are with them.

[16] Greet each other with a holy kiss.

All the churches of Christ greet you.

[17] Brothers and sisters, I urge you to watch out for those people who create divisions and who make others fall away ˏfrom the Christian faithˏ by teaching doctrine that is not the same as you have learned. Stay away from them. [18] People like these are not serving Christ our Lord. They are serving their own desires. By their smooth talk and flattering words they deceive unsuspecting people.

[19] Everyone has heard about your obedience and this makes me happy for you. I want you to do what is good and to avoid what is evil. [20] The God of peace will quickly crush Satan under your feet. May the good will[b] of our Lord Jesus be with you!

[21] Timothy my coworker greets you; so do Lucius, Jason, and Sosipater, who are Jewish by birth like me.

[22] I, Tertius, who wrote this letter, send you Christian greetings.

[23] Gaius greets you. He is host to me and the whole church.

Erastus, the city treasurer, greets you.

Quartus, our brother in the Christian faith, greets you.[c]

[25] God can strengthen you by the Good News and the message I tell about Jesus Christ. He can strengthen you by revealing the mystery that was kept in silence for a very long time [26] but now is publicly known. The everlasting God ordered that what the prophets wrote must be shown to the people of every nation to bring them to the obedience that is associated with faith. [27] God alone is wise. Glory belongs to him through Jesus Christ forever! Amen.

---

[a] 16:1 English equivalent difficult.   [b] 16:20 Or "grace."   [c] 16:23 Some manuscripts and translations add verse 24: "May the good will of our Lord Jesus Christ be with all of you. Amen."

1 CORINTHIANS

Greeting

1 ¹ From Paul, called to be an apostle of Christ Jesus by the will of God, and from Sosthenes, our brother in the Christian faith.

² To God's church that was made holy by Christ Jesus and called to be God's holy people in the city of Corinth and to people everywhere who call on the name of our Lord Jesus Christ. ³ Good will[a] and peace from God our Father and the Lord Jesus Christ are yours!

⁴ I always thank God for you because Christ Jesus has shown you God's good will. ⁵ Through Christ Jesus you have become rich in every way—in speech and knowledge of every kind. ⁶ Our message about Christ has been verified among you. ⁷ Therefore, you don't lack any gift as you wait eagerly for our Lord Jesus Christ to be revealed. ⁸ He will continue to give you strength until the end so that no one can accuse you of anything on the day of our Lord Jesus Christ. ⁹ God faithfully keeps his promises. He called you to be partners with his Son Jesus Christ our Lord.

God's Wisdom Is Better Than the World's Wisdom

¹⁰ Brothers and sisters, I encourage all of you in the name of our Lord Jesus Christ to agree with each other and not to split into opposing groups. I want you to be united in your understanding and opinions. ¹¹ Brothers and sisters, some people from Chloe's family have made it clear to me that you are quarreling among yourselves. ¹² This is what I mean: Each of you is saying, "I follow Paul," or "I follow Apollos," or "I follow Cephas,"[b] or "I follow Christ." ¹³ Has Christ been divided? Was Paul crucified for you? Were you baptized in Paul's name? ¹⁴ I thank God that[c] I didn't baptize any of you except Crispus and Gaius ¹⁵ so that no one can say you were baptized in my name. ¹⁶ I also baptized Stephanas and his family. Beyond that, I'm not sure whether I baptized anyone else. ¹⁷ Christ didn't send me to baptize. Instead, he sent me to spread the Good News. I didn't use intellectual arguments. That would have made the cross of Christ lose its meaning.

¹⁸ The message about the cross is nonsense to those who are being destroyed, but it is God's power to us who are being saved. ¹⁹ Scripture says,

> "I will destroy the wisdom of the wise.
> I will reject the intelligence of intelligent people."

²⁰ Where is the wise person? Where is the scholar? Where is the persuasive speaker of our time? Hasn't God turned the wisdom of the world into nonsense? ²¹ The world with its wisdom was unable to recognize God in terms of his own wisdom. So God decided to use the nonsense of the Good News we speak to save those who believe. ²² Jews ask for miraculous signs, and Greeks look for wisdom, ²³ but our message is that Christ was crucified. This offends Jewish people and makes no sense to people who are not Jewish. ²⁴ But to those Jews and Greeks who are called, he is Christ, God's power and God's wisdom. ²⁵ God's nonsense is wiser than human wisdom, and God's weakness is stronger than human strength.

²⁶ Brothers and sisters, consider what you were when God called you to be Christians. Not many of you were wise from a human point of view. You were not in powerful positions or in the upper social classes. ²⁷ But God chose what the world considers nonsense to put wise people to shame. God chose what the world considers weak to put what is strong to shame. ²⁸ God chose what the world considers ordinary and what it despises—what it considers to be nothing—in order to destroy what it considers to be something. ²⁹ As a result, no one can brag in God's presence. ³⁰ You are partners with Christ Jesus because of God. Jesus has become our wisdom sent from God, our righteousness, our holiness, and our ransom from sin. ³¹ As Scripture says, "Whoever brags must brag about what the Lord has done."

2 ¹ Brothers and sisters, when I came to you, I didn't speak about God's mystery[a] as if it were some kind of brilliant message or wisdom. ² While I was with you, I decided to deal with only one subject—Jesus Christ, who was crucified. ³ When I came to you, I was weak. I was afraid and very nervous. ⁴ I didn't speak my message with persuasive intellectual arguments. I spoke

---

[a] 1:3 Or "Grace."   [b] 1:12 Cephas is the Aramaic name for the Apostle Peter.   [c] 1:14 A few of the older manuscripts read "I am thankful that."   [a] 2:1 Some manuscripts and translations read "testimony."

my message with a show of spiritual power [5] so that your faith would not be based on human wisdom but on God's power.

[6] However, we do use wisdom to speak to those who are mature. It is a wisdom that doesn't belong to this world or to the rulers of this world who are in power today and gone tomorrow. [7] We speak about the mystery of God's wisdom. It is a wisdom that has been hidden, which God had planned for our glory before the world began. [8] Not one of the rulers of this world has known it. If they had, they wouldn't have crucified the Lord of glory. [9] But as Scripture says:

> "No eye has seen,
>   no ear has heard,
>   and no mind has imagined
>   the things that God has prepared
>   for those who love him."

[10] God has revealed those things to us by his Spirit. The Spirit searches everything, especially the deep things of God. [11] After all, who knows everything about a person except that person's own spirit? In the same way, no one has known everything about God except God's Spirit. [12] Now, we didn't receive the spirit that belongs to the world. Instead, we received the Spirit who comes from God so that we could know the things which God has freely given us. [13] We don't speak about these things using teachings that are based on intellectual arguments like people do. Instead, we use the Spirit's teachings. We explain spiritual things to those who have the Spirit.[b]

[14] A person who isn't spiritual doesn't accept the teachings of God's Spirit. He thinks they're nonsense. He can't understand them because a person must be spiritual to evaluate them. [15] Spiritual people evaluate everything but are subject to no one's evaluation.

[16]   "Who has known the mind of the Lord
>   so that he can teach him?"

However, we have the mind of Christ.

You Belong to Christ

3 [1] Brothers and sisters, I couldn't talk to you as spiritual people but as people still influenced by your corrupt nature. You were infants in your faith in Christ. [2] I gave you milk to drink. I didn't give you solid food because you weren't ready for it. Even now you aren't ready for it [3] because you're still influenced by your corrupt nature.

When you are jealous and quarrel among yourselves, aren't you influenced by your corrupt nature and living by human standards? [4] When some of you say, "I follow Paul" and others say, "I follow Apollos," aren't you acting like ˌsinfulˌ humans? [5] Who is Apollos? Who is Paul? They are servants who helped you come to faith. Each did what the Lord gave him to do. [6] I planted, and Apollos watered, but God made it grow. [7] So neither the one who plants nor the one who waters is important because ˌonlyˌ God makes it grow. [8] The one who plants and the one who waters have the same goal, and each will receive a reward for his own work. [9] We are God's coworkers. You are God's field.

You are God's building. [10] As a skilled and experienced builder, I used the gift[a] that God gave me to lay the foundation ˌfor that buildingˌ. However, someone else is building on it. Each person must be careful how he builds on it. [11] After all, no one can lay any other foundation than the one that is already laid, and that foundation is Jesus Christ. [12] People may build on this foundation with gold, silver, precious stones, wood, hay, or straw. [13] The day will make what each one does clearly visible because fire will reveal it. That fire will determine what kind of work each person has done. [14] If what a person has built survives, he will receive a reward. [15] If his work is burned up, he will suffer ˌthe lossˌ. However, he will be saved, though it will be like going through a fire.

[16] Don't you know that you are God's temple and that God's Spirit lives in you? [17] If anyone destroys God's temple, God will destroy him because God's temple is holy. You are that holy temple!

[18] Don't deceive yourselves. If any of you think you are wise in the ways of this world, you should give up that wisdom in order to become really wise. [19] The wisdom of this world is nonsense in God's sight. That's why Scripture says, "God catches the wise in their cleverness." [20] Again Scripture says, "The Lord knows that the thoughts of the wise are pointless."

[21] So don't brag about people. Everything belongs to you. [22] Whether it is Paul, Apollos, Cephas, the world, life or death, present or future things, everything belongs to you. [23] You belong to Christ, and Christ belongs to God.

---

[b] 2:13 Or "We explain spiritual things in spiritual words."   [a] 3:10 Or "grace."

The Work of the Apostles

4 [1] People should think of us as servants of Christ and managers who are entrusted with God's mysteries. [2] Managers are required to be trustworthy.

[3] It means very little to me that you or any human court should cross-examine me. I don't even ask myself questions. [4] I have a clear conscience, but that doesn't mean I have God's approval. It is the Lord who cross-examines me. [5] Therefore, don't judge anything before the appointed time. Wait until the Lord comes. He will also bring to light what is hidden in the dark and reveal people's motives. Then each person will receive praise from God.

[6] Brothers and sisters, I have applied this to Apollos and myself for your sake. You should learn from us not to go beyond what is written in Scripture. Then you won't arrogantly place one of us in opposition to the other.

[7] Who says that you are any better than other people? What do you have that wasn't given to you? If you were given what you have, why are you bragging as if it weren't a gift?

[8] You already have what you want! You've already become rich! You've become kings without us! I wish you really were kings so that we could be kings with you.

[9] As I see it, God has placed us apostles last in line, like people condemned to die. We have become a spectacle for people and angels to look at. [10] We have given up our wisdom for Christ, but you have insight because of Christ. We are weak, but you are strong. You are honored, but we are dishonored. [11] To this moment, we are hungry, thirsty, poorly dressed, roughly treated, and homeless. [12] We wear ourselves out doing physical labor. When people verbally abuse us, we bless them. When people persecute us, we endure it. [13] When our reputations are attacked, we remain courteous. Right now we have become garbage in the eyes of the world and trash in the sight of all people.

[14] I'm not writing this to make you feel ashamed but to instruct you as my dear children. [15] You may have countless Christian guardians, but you don't have many ˌspiritualˌ fathers. I became your father in the Christian life by telling you the Good News about Christ Jesus. [16] So I encourage you to imitate me. [17] That's why I've sent Timothy to you to help you remember my Christian way of life as I teach it everywhere in every church. Timothy is my dear child, and he faithfully does the Lord's work.

[18] Some of you have become arrogant because you think I won't pay you a visit. [19] If it's the Lord's will, I'll visit you soon. Then I'll know what these arrogant people are saying and what power they have. [20] God's kingdom is not just talk, it is power.

[21] When I come to visit you, would you prefer that I punish you or show you love and a gentle spirit?

How to Treat Christians Who Live Like Non-Christians

5 [1] Your own members are aware that there is sexual sin going on among them. This kind of sin is not even heard of among unbelievers—a man is actually married to his father's wife. [2] You're being arrogant when you should have been more upset about this. If you had been upset, the man who did this would have been removed from among you. [3] Although I'm not physically present with you, I am with you in spirit. I have already judged the man who did this as though I were present with you. [4] When you have gathered together, I am with you in spirit. Then, in the name of our Lord Jesus, and with his power, [5] hand such a person over to Satan to destroy his corrupt nature so that his spiritual nature may be saved on the day of the Lord.

[6] It's not good for you to brag. Don't you know that a little yeast spreads through the whole batch of dough? [7] Remove the old yeast ˌof sinˌ so that you may be a new batch of dough, since you don't actually have the yeast ˌof sinˌ.

Christ, our Passover lamb, has been sacrificed. [8] So we must not celebrate our festival with the old yeast ˌof sinˌ or with the yeast of vice and wickedness. Instead, we must celebrate it with the bread of purity and truth that has no yeast.

[9] In my letter to you I told you not to associate with people who continue to commit sexual sins. [10] I didn't tell you that you could not have any contact with unbelievers who commit sexual sins, are greedy, are dishonest, or worship false gods. If that were the case, you would have to leave this world. [11] Now, what I meant was that you should not associate with people who call themselves brothers or sisters in the Christian faith but live in sexual sin, are greedy, worship false gods, use abusive language, get drunk, or are dishonest. Don't eat with such people.

[12] After all, do I have any business judging those who are outside ˌthe Christian faithˌ? Isn't it your business to judge those who are inside? [13] God will judge those who are outside. Remove that wicked man from among you.

Settling Disagreements Between Christians

6 [1] When one of you has a complaint against another, how dare you go to court to settle the matter in front of wicked people. Why don't you settle it in front of God's holy people?

[2] Don't you know that God's people will judge the world? So if you're going to judge the world, aren't you capable of judging insignificant cases? [3] Don't you know that we will judge angels, not to mention things in this life? [4] When you have cases dealing with this life, why do you allow people whom the church has a low opinion of to be your judges? [5] You should be ashamed of yourselves! Don't you have at least one wise person who is able to settle disagreements between believers? [6] Instead, one believer goes to court against another believer, and this happens in front of unbelievers.

[7] You are already totally defeated because you have lawsuits against each other. Why don't you accept the fact that you have been wronged? Why don't you accept that you have been cheated? [8] Instead, you do wrong and cheat, and you do this to other believers.

[9] Don't you know that wicked people won't inherit the kingdom of God? Stop deceiving yourselves! People who continue to commit sexual sins, who worship false gods, those who commit adultery, homosexuals, [10] or thieves, those who are greedy or drunk, who use abusive language, or who rob people will not inherit the kingdom of God. [11] That's what some of you were! But you have been washed and made holy, and you have received God's approval in the name of the Lord Jesus Christ and in the Spirit of our God.

Stay Away From Sexual Sins

[12] Someone may say, "I'm allowed to do anything," but not everything is helpful. I'm allowed to do anything, but I won't allow anything to gain control over my life. [13] Food is for the stomach, and the stomach is for food, but God will put an end to both of them. However, the body is not for sexual sin but for the Lord, and the Lord is for the body. [14] God raised the Lord, and by his power God will also raise us.

[15] Don't you realize that your bodies are parts of Christ's body? Should I take the parts of Christ's body and make them parts of a prostitute's body? That's unthinkable! [16] Don't you realize that the person who unites himself with a prostitute becomes one body with her? God says, "The two will be one." [17] However, the person who unites himself with the Lord becomes one spirit with him.

[18] Stay away from sexual sins. Other sins that people commit don't affect their bodies the same way sexual sins do. People who sin sexually sin against their own bodies. [19] Don't you know that your body is a temple that belongs to the Holy Spirit? The Holy Spirit, whom you received from God, lives in you. You don't belong to yourselves. [20] You were bought for a price. So bring glory to God in the way you use your body.

Advice About Marriage

7 [1] Now, concerning the things that you wrote about: It's good for men not to get married. [2] But in order to avoid sexual sins, each man should have his own wife, and each woman should have her own husband.

[3] Husbands and wives should satisfy each other's ˌsexualˌ needs. [4] A wife doesn't have authority over her own body, but her husband does. In the same way, a husband doesn't have authority over his own body, but his wife does.

[5] Don't withhold yourselves from each other unless you agree to do so for a set time to devote yourselves to prayer. Then you should get back together so that Satan doesn't use your lack of self-control to tempt you. [6] What I have just said is not meant as a command but as a suggestion. [7] I would like everyone to be like me. However, each person has a special gift from God, and these gifts vary from person to person.

[8] I say to those who are not married, especially to widows: It is good for you to stay single like me. [9] However, if you cannot control your desires, you should get married. It is better for you to marry than to burn ˌwith sexual desireˌ.

[10] I pass this command along (not really I, but the Lord): A wife shouldn't leave her husband. [11] If she does, she should stay single or make up with her husband. Likewise, a husband should not divorce his wife.

[12] I (not the Lord) say to the rest of you: If any Christian man is married to a woman who is an unbeliever, and she is willing to live with him, he should not divorce her. [13] If any Christian woman is married to a man who is an unbeliever, and he is willing to live with her, she should not divorce her husband. [14] Actually, the unbelieving husband is made holy because of his wife, and an unbelieving wife is made holy because of her husband. Otherwise, their children would be unacceptable ˌto Godˌ, but now they are acceptable to him. [15] But if the unbelieving partners leave, let them go. Under these circumstances a Christian man or Christian woman is not bound ˌby a marriage vowˌ. God has called you to live in peace. [16] How do you as a wife know whether you will save your husband? How do you as a husband know whether you will save your wife?

[17] Everyone should live the life that the Lord gave him when God called him. This is the guideline I use in every church.

¹⁸ Any man who was already circumcised when he was called to be a Christian shouldn't undo his circumcision. Any man who was uncircumcised when he was called to be a Christian shouldn't get circumcised. ¹⁹ Circumcision is nothing, and the lack of it is nothing. But keeping what God commands is everything. ²⁰ All people should stay as they were when they were called. ²¹ Were you a slave when you were called? That shouldn't bother you. However, if you have a chance to become free, take it. ²² If the Lord called you when you were a slave, you are the Lord's free person. In the same way, if you were free when you were called, you are Christ's slave. ²³ You were bought for a price. Don't become anyone's slaves. ²⁴ Brothers and sisters, you should remain in whatever circumstances you were in when God called you. God is with you in those circumstances.

²⁵ Concerning virgins: Even though I don't have any command from the Lord, I'll give you my opinion. I'm a person to whom the Lord has shown mercy, so I can be trusted. ²⁶ Because of the present crisis I believe it is good for people to remain as they are. ²⁷ Do you have a wife? Don't seek a divorce. Are you divorced from your wife? Don't look for another one. ²⁸ But if you do get married, you have not sinned. If a virgin gets married, she has not sinned. However, these people will have trouble, and I would like to spare them from that.

²⁹ This is what I mean, brothers and sisters: The time has been shortened. While it lasts, those who are married should live as though they were not. ³⁰ Those who have eyes filled with tears should live as though they have no sorrow. Those who are happy should live as though there was nothing to be happy about. Those who buy something should live as though they didn't own it. ³¹ Those who use the things in this world should do so but not depend on them. It is clear that this world in its present form is passing away.

³² So I don't want you to have any concerns. An unmarried man is concerned about the things of the Lord, ⌐that is,⌐ about how he can please the Lord. ³³ But the married man is concerned about earthly things, ⌐that is,⌐ about how he can please his wife. ³⁴ His attention is divided.

An unmarried woman or a virgin is concerned about the Lord's things so that she may be holy in body and in spirit. But the married woman is concerned about earthly things, ⌐that is,⌐ about how she can please her husband. ³⁵ I'm saying this for your benefit, not to restrict you. I'm showing you how to live a noble life of devotion to the Lord without being distracted by other things.

³⁶ No father would want to do the wrong thing when his virgin daughter is old enough to get married. If she wants to get married, he isn't sinning by letting her get married. ³⁷ However, a father may have come to a decision about his daughter. If his decision is to keep her ⌐at home⌐ because she doesn't want to get married, that's fine. ³⁸ So it's fine for a father to give his daughter in marriage, but the father who doesn't give his daughter in marriage does even better.

³⁹ A married woman must remain with her husband as long as he lives. If her husband dies, she is free to marry anyone she wishes, but only if the man is a Christian.ᵃ ⁴⁰ However, she will be more blessed if she stays as she is. That is my opinion, and I think that I, too, have God's Spirit.

Advice About Food Offered to False Gods

8 ¹ Now, concerning food offered to false gods: We know that we all have knowledge. Knowledge makes people arrogant, but love builds them up. ² Those who think they know something still have a lot to learn. ³ But if they love God, they are known by God.

⁴ Now about eating food that was offered to false gods: We know that the false gods in this world don't really exist and that no god exists except the one God. ⁵ People may say that there are gods in heaven and on earth—many gods and many lords, as they would call them. ⁶ But for us,

> "There is only one God, the Father.
>   Everything came from him, and we live for him.
> There is only one Lord, Jesus Christ.
>   Everything came into being through him,
>   and we live because of him."

⁷ But not everyone knows this. Some people are so used to worshiping false gods that they believe they are eating food offered to a false god. So they feel guilty because their conscience is weak.

⁸ Food will not affect our relationship with God. We are no worse off if we eat ⌐that food⌐ and no better off if we don't. ⁹ But be careful that by using your freedom you don't somehow make a believer who is weak in faith fall into sin. ¹⁰ For example, suppose someone with a weak conscience sees you, who have this knowledge, eating in the temple of a false god. Won't you be encouraging that person to eat food offered to a false god? ¹¹ In that case, your knowledge is

---

ᵃ 7:39 Or "only as the Lord guides her."

ruining a believer whose faith is weak, a believer for whom Christ died. [12] When you sin against other believers in this way and harm their weak consciences, you are sinning against Christ. [13] Therefore, if eating food ⌐offered to false gods⌐ causes other believers to lose their faith, I will never eat that kind of food so that I won't make other believers lose their faith.

Paul's Right to Be Paid for His Work as an Apostle

9 [1] Don't you agree that I'm a free man? Don't you agree that I'm an apostle? Haven't I seen Jesus our Lord? Aren't you the result of my work for the Lord? [2] If I'm not an apostle to other people, at least I'm an apostle to you. You are the seal which proves that I am the Lord's apostle. [3] This is how I defend myself to those who cross-examine me. [4] Don't we have the right to eat and drink? [5] Don't we have the right to take our wives along with us like the other apostles, the Lord's brothers, and Cephas[a] do? [6] Or is it only Barnabas and I who don't have any rights, except to find work to support ourselves?

[7] Does a soldier ever serve in the army at his own expense? Does anyone plant a vineyard and not eat the grapes? Does anyone take care of a flock and not drink milk from the sheep? [8] Am I merely stating some human rule? Don't Moses' Teachings say the same thing? [9] Moses' Teachings say, "Never muzzle an ox when it is threshing[b] grain." God's concern isn't for oxen. [10] Isn't he speaking entirely for our benefit? This was written for our benefit so that the person who plows or threshes should expect to receive a share of the crop. [11] If we have planted the spiritual seed that has been of benefit to you, is it too much if we receive part of the harvest from your earthly goods? [12] If others have the right to expect this from you, don't we deserve even more? But we haven't used our rights. Instead, we would put up with anything in order not to hinder the Good News of Christ in any way.

[13] Don't you realize that those who work at the temple get their food from the temple? Don't those who help at the altar get a share of what is on the altar? [14] In the same way, the Lord has commanded that those who spread the Good News should earn their living from the Good News.

[15] I haven't used any of these rights, and I haven't written this in order to use them now. I would rather die than have anyone turn my bragging into meaningless words. [16] If I spread the Good News, I have nothing to brag about because I have an obligation to do this. How horrible it will be for me if I don't spread the Good News! [17] If I spread the Good News willingly, I'll have a reward. But if I spread the Good News unwillingly, I'm ⌐only⌐ doing what I've been entrusted to do. [18] So what is my reward? It is to spread the Good News free of charge. In that way I won't use the rights that belong to those who spread the Good News.

Paul's Work as an Apostle

[19] Although I'm free from all people, I have made myself a slave for all people to win more of them. [20] I became Jewish for Jewish people. I became subject to Moses' Teachings for those who are subject to those laws. I did this to win them even though I'm not subject to Moses' Teachings. [21] I became like a person who does not have Moses' Teachings for those who don't have those teachings. I did this to win them even though I have God's teachings. I'm really subject to Christ's teachings. [22] I became like a person weak in faith to win those who are weak in faith. I have become everything to everyone in order to save at least some of them. [23] I do all this for the sake of the Good News in order to share what it offers.

[24] Don't you realize that everyone who runs in a race runs to win, but only one runner gets the prize? Run like them, so that you can win. [25] Everyone who enters an athletic contest goes into strict training. They do it to win a temporary crown, but we do it to win one that will be permanent. [26] So I run—but not without a clear goal ahead of me. So I box—but not as if I were just shadow boxing. [27] Rather, I toughen my body with punches and make it my slave so that I will not be disqualified after I have spread the Good News to others.

Learn From What Happened in the Time of Moses

10 [1] I want you to know, brothers and sisters, that all our ancestors ⌐who left Egypt⌐ were under the cloud, and they all went through the sea. [2] They were all united with Moses by baptism in the cloud and in the sea. [3] All of them ate the same spiritual food, [4] and all of them drank the same spiritual drink. They drank from the spiritual rock that went with them, and that rock was Christ. [5] Yet, God was not pleased with most of them, so their dead bodies were scattered over the desert.

[6] These things have become examples for us so that we won't desire what is evil, as they did. [7] So don't worship false gods as some of them did, as Scripture says, "The people sat down

---

[a] 9:5 Cephas is the Aramaic name for the Apostle Peter.   [b] 9:9 Threshing is the process of beating stalks to separate them from the grain.

to a feast which turned into an orgy." [8] We shouldn't sin sexually as some of them did. Twenty-three thousand of them died on one day. [9] We shouldn't put the Lord[a] to the test as some of them did. They were killed by snakes. [10] Don't complain as some of them did. The angel of death destroyed them. [11] These things happened to make them an example for others. These things were written down as a warning for us who are living in the closing days of history. [12] So, people who think they are standing firmly should be careful that they don't fall.

[13] There isn't any temptation that you have experienced which is unusual for humans. God, who faithfully keeps his promises, will not allow you to be tempted beyond your power to resist. But when you are tempted, he will also give you the ability to endure the temptation as your way of escape.

Stay Away From Worshiping False Gods

[14] Therefore, my dear friends, get as far away from the worship of false gods as you can. [15] I'm talking to intelligent people. Judge for yourselves what I'm saying. [16] When we bless the cup of blessing aren't we sharing in the blood of Christ? When we break the bread aren't we sharing in the body of Christ? [17] Because there is one loaf, we are one body, although we are many individuals. All of us share one loaf.

[18] Look at the people of Israel from a human point of view. Don't those who eat the sacrifices share what is on the altar? [19] Do I mean that an offering made to a false god is anything, or that a false god itself is anything? [20] Hardly! What I am saying is that these sacrifices which people make are made to demons and not to God. I don't want you to be partners with demons. [21] You cannot drink the Lord's cup and the cup of demons. You cannot participate at the table of the Lord and at the table of demons. [22] Are we trying to make the Lord jealous? Are we stronger than he is?

[23] Someone may say, "I'm allowed to do anything," but not everything is helpful. I'm allowed to do anything, but not everything encourages growth. [24] People should be concerned about others and not just about themselves. [25] Eat anything that is sold in the market without letting your conscience trouble you. [26] Certainly, "The earth is the Lord's and everything it contains is his." [27] If an unbeliever invites you ⸢to his house for dinner⸥, and you wish to go, eat anything he serves you without letting your conscience trouble you. [28] However, if someone says to you, "This was sacrificed to a god," don't eat it because of the one who informed you and because of conscience. [29] I'm not talking about your conscience but the other person's conscience. Why should my freedom be judged by someone else's conscience? [30] If I give thanks to God for the food I eat, why am I condemned for that? [31] So, whether you eat or drink, or whatever you do, do everything to the glory of God. [32] Don't cause others to stumble, whether they are Jewish, Greek, or members of God's church. [33] I try to please everyone in every way. I don't think about what would be good for me but about what would be good for many people so that they might be saved.

11

[1] Imitate me as I imitate Christ.

Advice About Worship

[2] I praise you for always thinking about me and for carefully following the traditions that I handed down to you.

[3] However, I want you to realize that Christ has authority over every man, a husband has authority over his wife, and God has authority over Christ. [4] Every man who covers his head when he prays or speaks what God has revealed dishonors the one who has authority over him. [5] Every woman who prays or speaks what God has revealed and has her head uncovered while she speaks dishonors the one who has authority over her. She is like the woman who has her head shaved. [6] So if a woman doesn't cover her head, she should cut off her hair. If it's a disgrace for a woman to cut off her hair or shave her head, she should cover her head. [7] A man should not cover his head. He is God's image and glory. The woman, however, is man's glory. [8] Clearly, man wasn't made from woman but woman from man. [9] Man wasn't created for woman but woman for man. [10] Therefore, a woman should wear something on her head to show she is under ⸢someone's⸥ authority, out of respect for the angels.

[11] Yet, as believers in the Lord, women couldn't exist without men and men couldn't exist without women. [12] As a woman came into existence from a man, so men come into existence by women, but everything comes from God.

[13] Judge your own situation. Is it proper for a woman to pray to God with her head uncovered? [14] Doesn't nature itself teach you that it is disgraceful for a man to have long hair? [15] Doesn't it teach you that it is a woman's pride to wear her hair long? Her hair is given to her

---

[a] 10:9 Some manuscripts and translations; other manuscripts and translations "Christ."

in place of a covering. [16] If anyone wants to argue about this ˌthey can't, becauseˌ we don't have any custom like this—nor do any of the churches of God.

[17] I have no praise for you as I instruct you in the following matter: When you gather, it results in more harm than good. [18] In the first place, I hear that when you gather as a church you split up into opposing groups. I believe some of what I hear. [19] Factions have to exist in order to make it clear who the genuine believers among you are.

[20] When you gather in the same place, you can't possibly be eating the Lord's Supper. [21] Each of you eats his own supper ˌwithout waiting for each otherˌ. So one person goes hungry and another gets drunk. [22] Don't you have homes in which to eat and drink? Do you despise God's church and embarrass people who don't have anything to eat? What can I say to you? Should I praise you? I won't praise you for this. [23] After all, I passed on to you what I had received from the Lord.

On the night he was betrayed, the Lord Jesus took bread [24] and spoke a prayer of thanksgiving. He broke the bread and said, "This is my body, which is given for you. Do this to remember me." [25] When supper was over, he did the same with the cup. He said, "This cup is the new promiseª made with my blood. Every time you drink from it, do it to remember me." [26] Every time you eat this bread and drink from this cup, you tell about the Lord's death until he comes.

[27] Therefore, whoever eats the bread or drinks from the Lord's cup in an improper way will be held responsible for the Lord's body and blood. [28] With this in mind, individuals must determine whether what they are doing is proper when they eat the bread and drink from the cup. [29] Anyone who eats and drinks is eating and drinking a judgment against himself when he doesn't recognize the Lord's body.

[30] This is the reason why many of you are weak and sick and quite a number ˌof youˌ have died. [31] If we were judging ourselves correctly, we would not be judged. [32] But when the Lord judges us, he disciplines us so that we won't be condemned along with the rest of the world.

[33] Therefore, brothers and sisters, when you gather to eat, wait for each other. [34] Whoever is hungry should eat at home so that you don't have a gathering that brings judgment on you.

I will give directions concerning the other matters when I come.

Spiritual Gifts

12 [1] Brothers and sisters, I don't want there to be any misunderstanding concerning spiritual gifts. [2] You know that when you were unbelievers, every time you were led to worship false gods you were worshiping gods who couldn't even speak. [3] So I want you to know that no one speaking by God's Spirit says, "Jesus is cursed." No one can say, "Jesus is Lord," except by the Holy Spirit.

[4] There are different spiritual gifts, but the same Spirit gives them. [5] There are different ways of serving, and yet the same Lord is served. [6] There are different types of work to do, but the same God produces every gift in every person.

[7] The evidence of the Spirit's presence is given to each person for the common good of everyone. [8] The Spirit gives one person the ability to speak with wisdom. The same Spirit gives another person the ability to speak with knowledge. [9] To another person the same Spirit gives ˌcourageousˌ faith. To another person the same Spirit gives the ability to heal. [10] Another can work miracles. Another can speak what God has revealed. Another can tell the difference between spirits. Another can speak in different kinds of languages. Another can interpret languages. [11] There is only one Spirit who does all these things by giving what God wants to give to each person.

[12] For example, the body is one unit and yet has many parts. As all the parts form one body, so it is with Christ. [13] By one Spirit we were all baptized into one body. Whether we are Jewish or Greek, slave or free, God gave all of us one Spirit to drink.

[14] As you know, the human body is not made up of only one part, but of many parts. [15] Suppose a foot says, "I'm not a hand, so I'm not part of the body!" Would that mean it's no longer part of the body? [16] Or suppose an ear says, "I'm not an eye, so I'm not a part of the body!" Would that mean it's no longer part of the body? [17] If the whole body were an eye, how could it hear? If the whole body were an ear, how could it smell? [18] So God put each and every part of the body together as he wanted it. [19] How could it be a body if it only had one part? [20] So there are many parts but one body.

[21] An eye can't say to a hand, "I don't need you!" Or again, the head can't say to the feet, "I don't need you!" [22] The opposite is true. The parts of the body that we think are weaker are the ones we really need. [23] The parts of the body that we think are less honorable are the ones we give special honor. So our unpresentable parts are made more presentable. [24] However, our presentable parts don't need this kind of treatment. God has put the body together and given special honor to the part that doesn't have it. [25] God's purpose was that the body should not be

---

ª 11:25 Or "testament," or "covenant."

divided but rather that all of its parts should feel the same concern for each other. **26** If one part of the body suffers, all the other parts share its suffering. If one part is praised, all the others share in its happiness.

27 You are Christ's body and each of you is an individual part of it. **28** In the church God has appointed first apostles, next prophets, third teachers, then those who perform miracles, then those who have the gift of healing, then those who help others, those who are managers, and those who can speak in a number of languages. **29** Not all believers are apostles, are they? Are all of them prophets? Do all of them teach? Do all of them perform miracles **30** or have gifts of healing? Can all of them speak in other languages or interpret languages?

31 You ˏonlyˎ want the better gifts, but I will show you the best thing to do.ᵃ

Love

13 **1** I may speak in the languages of humans and of angels. But if I don't have love, I am a loud gong or a clashing cymbal. **2** I may have the gift to speak what God has revealed, and I may understand all mysteries and have all knowledge. I may even have enough faith to move mountains. But if I don't have love, I am nothing. **3** I may even give away all that I have and give up my body to be burned.ᵃ But if I don't have love, none of these things will help me.

4 Love is patient. Love is kind. Love isn't jealous. It doesn't sing its own praises. It isn't arrogant. **5** It isn't rude. It doesn't think about itself. It isn't irritable. It doesn't keep track of wrongs. **6** It isn't happy when injustice is done, but it is happy with the truth. **7** Love never stops being patient, never stops believing, never stops hoping, never gives up.

8 Love never comes to an end. There is the gift of speaking what God has revealed, but it will no longer be used. There is the gift of speaking in other languages, but it will stop by itself. There is the gift of knowledge, but it will no longer be used. **9** Our knowledge is incomplete and our ability to speak what God has revealed is incomplete. **10** But when what is complete comes, then what is incomplete will no longer be used. **11** When I was a child, I spoke like a child, thought like a child, and reasoned like a child. When I became an adult, I no longer used childish ways. **12** Now we see a blurred image in a mirror. Then we will see very clearly. Now my knowledge is incomplete. Then I will have complete knowledge as God has complete knowledge of me.

13 So these three things remain: faith, hope, and love. But the best one of these is love.

Speak in Ways That Can Be Understood

14 **1** Pursue love, and desire spiritual gifts, but especially the gift of speaking what God has revealed. **2** When a person speaks in another language, he doesn't speak to people but to God. No one understands him. His spirit is speaking mysteries. **3** But when a person speaks what God has revealed, he speaks to people to help them grow, to encourage them, and to comfort them. **4** When a person speaks in another language, he helps himself grow. But when a person speaks what God has revealed, he helps the church grow. **5** I wish that all of you could speak in other languages, but especially that you could speak what God has revealed. The person who speaks what God has revealed is more important than the person who speaks in other languages. This is true unless he can interpret what he says to help the church grow. **6** Brothers and sisters, it wouldn't do you any good if I came to you speaking in other languages, unless I explained revelation, knowledge, prophecy, or doctrine to you.

7 Musical instruments like the flute or harp produce sounds. If there is no difference in the notes, how can a person tell what tune is being played? **8** For example, if the trumpet doesn't sound a clear call, who will get ready for battle? **9** In the same way, if you don't speak in a way that can be understood, how will anyone know what you're saying? You will be talking into thin air.

10 No matter how many different languages there are in the world, not one of them is without meaning. **11** If I don't know what a language means, I will be a foreigner to the person who speaks it and that person will be a foreigner to me. **12** In the same way, since you're eager to have spiritual gifts, try to excel in them so that you help the church grow. **13** So the person who speaks in another language should pray for an interpretation of what he says.

14 If I pray in another language, my spirit prays, but my mind is not productive. **15** So what does this mean? It means that I will pray with my spirit, and I will pray with my mind. I will sing psalms with my spirit, and I will sing psalms with my mind. **16** Otherwise, if you praise God only with your spirit, how can outsiders say "Amen!" to your prayer of thanksgiving? They don't know what you're saying. **17** Your prayer of thanksgiving may be very good, but it doesn't help other people grow. **18** I thank God that I speak in other languages more than any of you. **19** Yet, in order to teach others in church, I would rather say five words that can be understood than ten thousand words in another language.

ᵃ 12:31 Or "Desire the better gifts, and I will show you the best thing to do."   ᵃ 13:3 Some manuscripts read "give up my body so that I may brag."

[20] Brothers and sisters, don't think like children. When it comes to evil, be like babies, but think like mature people. [21] God's word says,

> "Through people who speak foreign languages
>   and through the mouths of foreigners
>   I will speak to these people,
>   but even then they will not listen to me,
>   says the Lord."

[22] So the gift of speaking in other languages is a sign for unbelievers, not for believers. The gift of speaking what God had revealed is a sign for believers, not for unbelievers. [23] Suppose the whole congregation gathers in the same place and you speak in other languages. When outsiders or unbelievers come in, won't they say that you're out of your mind? [24] Now suppose you speak what God has revealed. When unbelievers or outsiders come in you will show them where they are wrong and convince them that they are sinners. [25] The secrets in their hearts will become known, and in this way they will quickly bow with their faces touching the ground, worship God, and confess that God is truly among you.

Maintain Order in Your Worship Services

[26] So what does this mean, brothers and sisters? When you gather, each person has a psalm, doctrine, revelation, another language, or an interpretation. Everything must be done to help each other grow. [27] If people speak in other languages, only two or three at the most should speak. They should do it one at a time, and someone must interpret what each person says. [28] But if an interpreter isn't present, those people should remain silent in church. They should only speak to themselves and to God.

[29] Two or three people should speak what God has revealed. Everyone else should decide whether what each person said is right or wrong. [30] If God reveals something to another person who is seated, the first speaker should be silent. [31] All of you can take your turns speaking what God has revealed. In that way, everyone will learn and be encouraged. [32] People who speak what God has revealed must control themselves. [33] God is not a God of disorder but a God of peace.

As in all the churches of God's holy people, [34] the women must keep silent. They don't have the right to speak. They must take their place as Moses' Teachings say. [35] If they want to know anything they should ask their husbands at home. It's shameful for a woman to speak in church. [36] Did God's word originate with you? Are you the only ones it has reached?

[37] Whoever thinks that he speaks for God or that he is spiritually gifted must acknowledge that what I write to you is what the Lord commands. [38] But whoever ignores what I write should be ignored.

[39] So, brothers and sisters, desire to speak what God has revealed, and don't keep anyone from speaking in other languages. [40] Everything must be done in a proper and orderly way.

Jesus Came Back to Life

15 [1] Brothers and sisters, I'm making known to you the Good News which I already told you, which you received, and on which your faith is based. [2] In addition, you are saved by this Good News if you hold on to the doctrine I taught you, unless you believed it without thinking it over. [3] I passed on to you the most important points of doctrine that I had received:
Christ died to take away our sins as the Scriptures predicted.
[4] He was placed in a tomb.
He was brought back to life on the third day as the Scriptures predicted.
[5] He appeared to Cephas.[a] Next he appeared to the twelve apostles. [6] Then he appeared to more than 500 believers at one time. (Most of these people are still living, but some have died.) [7] Next he appeared to James. Then he appeared to all the apostles. [8] Last of all, he also appeared to me.
I'm like an aborted fetus ˌwho was given lifeˌ. [9] I'm the least of the apostles. I'm not even fit to be called an apostle because I persecuted God's church. [10] But God's kindness[b] made me what I am, and that kindness was not wasted on me. Instead, I worked harder than all the others. It was not I who did it, but God's kindness was with me. [11] So, whether it was I or someone else, this is the message we brought you, and this is what you believed.

We Will Come Back to Life

[12] If we have told you that Christ has been brought back to life, how can some of you say that coming back from the dead is impossible? [13] If the dead can't be brought back to life, then Christ hasn't come back to life. [14] If Christ hasn't come back to life, our message has no mean-

---

[a] 15:5 Cephas is the Aramaic name for the Apostle Peter.   [b] 15:10 Or "grace."

ing and your faith also has no meaning. ¹⁵ In addition, we are obviously witnesses who lied about God because we testified that he brought Christ back to life. But if it's true that the dead don't come back to life, then God didn't bring Christ back to life. ¹⁶ Certainly, if the dead don't come back to life, then Christ hasn't come back to life either. ¹⁷ If Christ hasn't come back to life, your faith is worthless and sin still has you in its power. ¹⁸ Then those who have died as believers in Christ no longer exist. ¹⁹ If Christ is our hope in this life only, we deserve more pity than any other people.

²⁰ But now Christ has come back from the dead. He is the very first person of those who have died to come back to life. ²¹ Since a man brought death, a man also brought life back from death. ²² As everyone dies because of Adam, so also everyone will be made alive because of Christ. ²³ This will happen to each person in his own turn. Christ is the first, then at his coming, those who belong to him ˌwill be made aliveˌ. ²⁴ Then the end will come. Christ will hand over the kingdom to God the Father as he destroys every ruler, authority, and power.

²⁵ Christ must rule until God has put every enemy under his control. ²⁶ The last enemy he will destroy is death. ²⁷ Clearly, God has put everything under Christ's authority. When God says that everything has been put under Christ's authority, this clearly excludes God, since God has put everything under Christ's authority. ²⁸ But when God puts everything under Christ's authority, the Son will put himself under God's authority, since God had put everything under the Son's authority. Then God will be in control of everything.

²⁹ However, people are baptized because the dead ˌwill come back to lifeˌ. What will they do? If the dead can't come back to life, why do people get baptized as if they can ˌcome back to lifeˌ?

³⁰ Why are we constantly putting ourselves in danger? ³¹ Brothers and sisters, I swear to you on my pride in you which Christ Jesus our Lord has given me: I face death every day. ³² If I have fought with wild animals in Ephesus, what have I gained according to the way people look at things? If the dead are not raised, "Let's eat and drink because tomorrow we're going to die!" ³³ Don't let anyone deceive you. Associating with bad people will ruin decent people. ³⁴ Come back to the right point of view, and stop sinning. Some people don't know anything about God. You should be ashamed of yourselves.

We Will Have Bodies That Will Not Decay

³⁵ But someone will ask, "How do the dead come back to life? With what kind of body will they come back?"

³⁶ You fool! The seed you plant doesn't come to life unless it dies first. ³⁷ What you plant, whether it's wheat or something else, is only a seed. It doesn't have the form that the plant will have. ³⁸ God gives the plant the form he wants it to have. Each kind of seed grows into its own form. ³⁹ Not all flesh is the same. Humans have one kind of flesh, animals have another, birds have another, and fish have still another. ⁴⁰ There are heavenly bodies and earthly bodies. Heavenly bodies don't all have the same splendor, neither do earthly bodies. ⁴¹ The sun has one kind of splendor, the moon has another kind of splendor, and the stars have still another kind of splendor. Even one star differs in splendor from another star.

⁴² That is how it will be when the dead come back to life. When the body is planted, it decays. When it comes back to life, it cannot decay. ⁴³ When the body is planted, it doesn't have any splendor and is weak. When it comes back to life, it has splendor and is strong. ⁴⁴ It is planted as a physical body. It comes back to life as a spiritual body. As there is a physical body, so there is also a spiritual body.

⁴⁵ This is what Scripture says: "The first man, Adam, became a living being." The last Adam became a life-giving spirit. ⁴⁶ The spiritual does not come first, but the physical and then the spiritual. ⁴⁷ The first man was made from the dust of the earth. He came from the earth. The second man came from heaven. ⁴⁸ The people on earth are like the man who was made from the dust of the earth. The people in heaven are like the man who came from heaven. ⁴⁹ As we have worn the likeness of the man who was made from the dust of the earth, we will also wear the likeness of the man who came from heaven. ⁵⁰ Brothers and sisters, this is what I mean: Flesh and blood cannot inherit the kingdom of God. What decays cannot inherit what doesn't decay.

⁵¹ I'm telling you a mystery. Not all of us will die, but we will all be changed. ⁵² It will happen in an instant, in a split second at the sound of the last trumpet. Indeed, that trumpet will sound, and then the dead will come back to life. They will be changed so that they can live forever. ⁵³ This body that decays must be changed into a body that cannot decay. This mortal body must be changed into a body that will live forever. ⁵⁴ When this body that decays is changed into a body that cannot decay, and this mortal body is changed into a body that will live forever, then the teaching of Scripture will come true:

"Death is turned into victory!
55　　Death, where is your victory?
　　　　Death, where is your sting?"

56 Sin gives death its sting, and God's standards give sin its power. **57** Thank God that he gives us the victory through our Lord Jesus Christ.

58 So, then, brothers and sisters, don't let anyone move you off the foundation ˻of your faith˼. Always excel in the work you do for the Lord. You know that the hard work you do for the Lord is not pointless.

The Collection for the People in Jerusalem

16 **1** Now, concerning the money to be collected for God's people ˻in Jerusalem˼: I want you to do as I directed the churches in Galatia. **2** Every Sunday each of you should set aside some of your money and save it. Then money won't have to be collected when I come. **3** When I come, I will give letters of introduction to the people whom you choose. You can send your gift to Jerusalem with them. **4** If I think it's worthwhile for me to go, they can go with me.

Paul's Plans

5 After I go through the province of Macedonia, I'll visit you. (I will be going through Macedonia.) **6** I'll probably stay with you. I might even spend the winter. Then you can give me your support as I travel, wherever I decide to go. **7** Right now all I could do is visit you briefly, but if the Lord lets me, I hope to spend some time with you. **8** I will be staying here in Ephesus until Pentecost. **9** I have a great opportunity to do effective work here, although there are many people who oppose me.

News About Timothy, Apollos, and Others

10 If Timothy comes, make sure that he doesn't have anything to be afraid of while he is with you. He's doing the Lord's work as I am, **11** so no one should treat him with contempt. Without quarreling, give him your support for his trip so that he may come to me. I'm expecting him to arrive with the other Christians.

12 Concerning Apollos, our brother in the Christian faith: I tried hard to get him to visit you with the other Christians. He didn't want to at this time. However, he will visit you when he has an opportunity.

13 Be alert. Be firm in the Christian faith. Be courageous and strong. **14** Do everything with love.

15 You know that the family of Stephanas was the first family to be won ˻for Christ˼ in Greece. This family has devoted itself to serving God's people. So I encourage you, brothers and sisters, **16** to follow the example of people like these and anyone else who shares their labor and hard work. **17** I am glad that Stephanas, Fortunatus, and Achaicus came here. They have made up for your absence. **18** They have comforted me, and they have comforted you. Therefore, show people like these your appreciation.

Greetings

19 The churches in the province of Asia greet you. Aquila and Prisca and the church that meets in their house send their warmest Christian greetings. **20** All the brothers and sisters ˻here˼ greet you. Greet each other with a holy kiss. **21** I, Paul, am writing this greeting with my own hand.

22 If anyone doesn't love the Lord, let him be cursed! Our Lord, come!

23 May the good will*ª* of the Lord Jesus be with you. **24** Through Christ Jesus my love is with all of you.

ª 16:23 Or "grace."

2 CORINTHIANS

Greeting

1 ¹ From Paul, an apostle of Christ Jesus by the will of God, and from Timothy our brother.

To God's church in the city of Corinth and to all God's holy people everywhere in Greece. ² Good will[a] and peace from God our Father and the Lord Jesus Christ are yours!

God Comforts Paul and the Corinthians

³ Praise the God and Father of our Lord Jesus Christ! He is the Father who is compassionate and the God who gives comfort. ⁴ He comforts us whenever we suffer. That is why whenever other people suffer, we are able to comfort them by using the same comfort we have received from God. ⁵ Because Christ suffered so much for us, we can receive so much comfort from him. ⁶ Besides, if we suffer, it brings you comfort and salvation. If we are comforted, we can effectively comfort you when you endure the same sufferings that we endure. ⁷ We have confidence in you. We know that as you share our sufferings, you also share our comfort.

God Rescued Paul When He Was Suffering

⁸ Brothers and sisters, we don't want you to be ignorant about the suffering we experienced in the province of Asia. It was so extreme that it was beyond our ability to endure. We even wondered if we could go on living. ⁹ In fact, we still feel as if we're under a death sentence. But we suffered so that we would stop trusting ourselves and learn to trust God, who brings the dead back to life. ¹⁰ He has rescued us from a terrible death, and he will rescue us in the future. We are confident that he will continue to rescue us, ¹¹ since you are also joining to help us when you pray for us. Then many people will thank God for the favor he will show us because many people prayed for us.

Paul's Reason for Being Proud

¹² We are proud that our conscience is clear. We are proud of the way that we have lived in this world. We have lived with a God-given holiness[b] and sincerity, especially toward you. It was not by human wisdom that we have lived but by God's kindness.[a] ¹³ We are only writing you what you already knew before you read this. I hope you will understand this as long as you live, ¹⁴ even though you now understand it only partially. We are your reason to be proud, as you will be our reason to be proud on the day of our Lord Jesus.

Why Paul Changed His Plans

¹⁵ Confident of this, I had previously wanted to visit you so that you could benefit twice. ¹⁶ My plans had been to go from the city of Corinth to the province of Macedonia. Then from Macedonia I had planned to return to you again in Corinth and have you support my trip to Judea.

¹⁷ You don't think that I made these plans lightly, do you? Do you think that when I make plans, I make them in a sinful way? Why would I say that something is true when it isn't? ¹⁸ You can depend on God. Our message to you isn't false; it's true. ¹⁹ God's Son, Jesus Christ, whom I, Silvanus, and Timothy told you about, was true not false. Because of him our message was always true. ²⁰ Certainly, Christ made God's many promises come true. For that reason, because of our message, people also honor God by saying, "Amen!"

²¹ God establishes us, together with you, in a relationship with Christ. He has also anointed us. ²² In addition, he has put his seal ⌐of ownership⌐ on us and has given us the Spirit as his guarantee.

²³ I appeal to God as a witness on my behalf, that I stayed away from Corinth because I wanted to spare you. ²⁴ It isn't that we want to have control over your Christian faith. Rather, we want to work with you so that you will be happy. Certainly, you are firmly established in the Christian faith.

2 ¹ I decided not to visit you again while I was distressed. ² After all, if I had made you uncomfortable, how could you have cheered me up when you were uncomfortable?

---

[a] 1:2; 12 Or "grace." [b] 1:12 Some manuscripts and translations read "God-given openness."

³This is the very reason I wrote to you. I didn't want to visit you and be distressed by those who should make me happy. I'm confident about all of you that whatever makes me happy also makes you happy. ⁴I was deeply troubled and anguished. In fact, I had tears in my eyes when I wrote to you. I didn't write to make you uncomfortable but to let you know how much I love you.

Forgive the Person Who Sinned

⁵If someone caused distress, I'm not the one really affected. To some extent—although I don't want to emphasize this too much—it has affected all of you. ⁶The majority of you have imposed a severe enough punishment on that person. ⁷So now forgive and comfort him. Such distress could overwhelm someone like that if he's not forgiven and comforted. ⁸That is why I urge you to assure him that you love him. ⁹I had also written to you to test you. I wanted to see if you would be obedient in every way.

¹⁰If you forgive someone, so do I. Indeed, what I have forgiven, if I have forgiven anything, I did in the presence of Christ for your benefit. ¹¹I don't want Satan to outwit us. After all, we are not ignorant about Satan's scheming.

Paul's Mission as Christ's Spokesman

¹²When I went to the city of Troas, the Lord gave me an opportunity to spread the Good News about Christ. ¹³But I didn't have any peace of mind, because I couldn't find Titus, our brother, there. So I said goodbye to the people in Troas and went to the province of Macedonia. ¹⁴But I thank God, who always leads us in victory because of Christ. Wherever we go, God uses us to make clear what it means to know Christ. It's like a fragrance that fills the air. ¹⁵To God we are the aroma of Christ among those who are saved and among those who are dying. ¹⁶To some people we are a deadly fragrance, while to others we are a life-giving fragrance.

Who is qualified to tell about Christ? ¹⁷At least we don't go around selling an impure word of God like many others. The opposite is true. As Christ's spokesmen and in God's presence, we speak the pure message that comes from God.

The Ministry That Comes From Christ Is Greater Than Moses' Ministry

3 ¹Do we have to show you our qualifications again? Do we, like some people, need letters that recommend us to you or letters from you that recommend us to others? ²You're our letter of recommendation written in our hearts that everyone knows and reads. ³It's clear that you are Christ's letter, written as a result of our ministry. You are a letter written not with ink but with the Spirit of the living God, a letter written not on tablets of stone but on tablets of human hearts.

⁴Christ gives us confidence about you in God's presence. ⁵By ourselves we are not qualified in any way to claim that we can do anything. Rather, God makes us qualified. ⁶He has also qualified us to be ministers of a new promise,ᵃ a spiritual promise, not a written one. Clearly, what was written brings death, but the Spirit brings life.

⁷The ministry that brought death was inscribed on stone. Yet, it came with such glory that the people of Israel couldn't look at Moses' face. His face was shining with glory, even though that glory was fading. ⁸Won't the ministry that brings the Spirit have even more glory? ⁹If the ministry that brings punishment has glory, then the ministry that brings God's approval has an overwhelming glory. ¹⁰In fact, the ministry that brings punishment lost its glory because of the superior glory of the other ministry. ¹¹If that former ministry faded away despite its glory, how much more does that ministry which remains continue to be glorious?

¹²Since we have confidence in the new promise, we speak very boldly. ¹³We are not like Moses. He kept covering his face with a veil. He didn't want the people of Israel to see the glory fading away. ¹⁴However, their minds became closed. In fact, to this day the same veil is still there when they read the Old Testament. It isn't removed, because only Christ can remove it. ¹⁵Yet, even today, when they read the books of Moses, a veil covers their minds. ¹⁶But whenever a person turns to the Lord, the veil is taken away.

¹⁷This Lord is the Spirit. Wherever the Lord's Spirit is, there is freedom. ¹⁸As all of us reflect the Lord's glory with faces that are not covered with veils, we are being changed into his image with ever-increasing glory. This comes from the Lord, who is the Spirit.

Paul Is Never Discouraged

4 ¹We don't become discouraged, since God has given us this ministry through his mercy. ²Instead, we have refused to use secret and shameful ways. We don't use tricks, and we don't distort God's word. As God watches, we clearly reveal the truth to everyone. This is our ⸤letter of⸥ recommendation.

ᵃ 3:6 Or "covenant."

³ So if the Good News that we tell others is covered with a veil, it is hidden from those who are dying. ⁴ The god of this world has blinded the minds of those who don't believe. As a result, they don't see the light of the Good News about Christ's glory. It is Christ who is God's image.

⁵ Our message is not about ourselves. It is about Jesus Christ as the Lord. We are your servants for his sake. ⁶ We are his servants because the same God who said that light should shine out of darkness has given us light. For that reason we bring to light the knowledge about God's glory which shines from Christ's face.

⁷ Our bodies are made of clay, yet we have the treasure of the Good News in them. This shows that the superior power of this treasure belongs to God and doesn't come from us. ⁸ In every way we're troubled, but we aren't crushed by our troubles. We're frustrated, but we don't give up. ⁹ We're persecuted, but we're not abandoned. We're captured, but we're not killed. ¹⁰ We always carry around the death of Jesus in our bodies so that the life of Jesus is also shown in our bodies. ¹¹ While we are alive, we are constantly handed over to death for Jesus' sake so that the life of Jesus is also shown in our mortal nature. ¹² Death is at work in us, but life is at work in you.

¹³ The following is written, "I believed; therefore, I spoke." We have that same spirit of faith. We also believe; therefore, we also speak. ¹⁴ We know that the one who brought the Lord Jesus back to life will also bring us back to life through Jesus. He will present us to God together with you.

¹⁵ All this is for your sake so that, as God's kindness[a] overflows in the lives of many people, it will produce even more thanksgiving to the glory of God. ¹⁶ That is why we are not discouraged. Though outwardly we are wearing out, inwardly we are renewed day by day. ¹⁷ Our suffering is light and temporary and is producing for us an eternal glory that is greater than anything we can imagine. ¹⁸ We don't look for things that can be seen but for things that can't be seen. Things that can be seen are only temporary. But things that can't be seen last forever.

Faith Guides Our Lives

5 ¹ We know that if the life we live here on earth is ever taken down like a tent, we still have a building from God. It is an eternal house in heaven that isn't made by human hands. ² In our present tent-like existence we sigh, since we long to put on the house we will have in heaven. ³ After we have put it on,[a] we won't be naked. ⁴ While we are in this tent, we sigh. We feel distressed because we don't want to take off the tent, but we do want to put on the eternal house. Then ˻eternal˼ life will put an end to our mortal existence. ⁵ God has prepared us for this and has given us his Spirit to guarantee it.

⁶ So we are always confident. We know that as long as we are living in these bodies, we are living away from the Lord. ⁷ Indeed, our lives are guided by faith, not by sight. ⁸ We are confident and prefer to live away from this body and to live with the Lord. ⁹ Whether we live in the body or move out of it, our goal is to be pleasing to him. ¹⁰ All of us must appear in front of Christ's judgment seat. Then all people will receive what they deserve for the good or evil they have done while living in their bodies.

Christ's Love Guides Us

¹¹ As people who know what it means to fear the Lord, we try to persuade others. God already knows what we are, and I hope that you also know what we are. ¹² We are not trying to show you our qualifications again, but we are giving you an opportunity to be proud of us. Then you can answer those who are proud of their appearance rather than their character. ¹³ So if we were crazy, it was for God. If we are sane, it is for you. ¹⁴ Clearly, Christ's love guides us. We are convinced of the fact that one man has died for all people. Therefore, all people have died. ¹⁵ He died for all people so that those who live should no longer live for themselves but for the man who died and was brought back to life for them.

¹⁶ So from now on we don't think of anyone from a human point of view. If we did think of Christ from a human point of view, we don't anymore. ¹⁷ Whoever is a believer in Christ is a new creation. The old way of living has disappeared. A new way of living has come into existence. ¹⁸ God has done all this. He has restored our relationship with him through Christ, and has given us this ministry of restoring relationships. ¹⁹ In other words, God was using Christ to restore his relationship with humanity. He didn't hold people's faults against them, and he has given us this message of restored relationships to tell others. ²⁰ Therefore, we are Christ's representatives, and through us God is calling you. We beg you on behalf of Christ to become reunited with God. ²¹ God had Christ, who was sinless, take our sin so that we might receive God's approval through him.

ᵃ 4:15 Or "grace."   ᵃ 5:3 Some manuscripts and translations read "taken it off."

6 ¹ Since we are God's coworkers, we urge you not to let God's kindness*ᵃ* be wasted on you. ² God says,

> "At the right time I heard you.
> On the day of salvation I helped you."

Listen, now is God's acceptable time! Now is the day of salvation!

Our Lives Demonstrate That We Are God's Servants

³ We don't give people any opportunity to find fault with how we serve. ⁴ Instead, our lives demonstrate that we are God's servants. We have endured many things: suffering, distress, anxiety, ⁵ beatings, imprisonments, riots, hard work, sleepless nights, and lack of food. ⁶ ⌞People can see⌟ our purity, knowledge, patience, kindness, the Holy Spirit's presence ⌞in our lives⌟, our sincere love, ⁷ truthfulness, and the presence of God's power. We demonstrate that we are God's servants ⁸ as we are praised and dishonored, as we are slandered and honored, and as we use what is right to attack what is wrong and to defend the truth.*ᵇ* We are treated as dishonest although we are honest, ⁹ as unknown although we are well-known, as dying although, as you see, we go on living. We are punished, but we are not killed. ¹⁰ People think we are sad although we're always glad, that we're beggars although we make many people spiritually rich, that we have nothing although we possess everything.

¹¹ We have been very open in speaking to you Corinthians. We have a place for you in our hearts. ¹² We haven't cut you off. Your own emotions have cut you off ⌞from us⌟. ¹³ I'm talking to you as I would talk to children. Treat us the same way we've treated you. Make a place for us in your hearts too.

Christians and Their Relationships With Unbelievers

¹⁴ Stop forming inappropriate relationships with unbelievers. Can right and wrong be partners? Can light have anything in common with darkness? ¹⁵ Can Christ agree with the devil? Can a believer share life with an unbeliever? ¹⁶ Can God's temple contain false gods? Clearly, we are the temple of the living God. As God said,

> "I will live and walk among them.
> I will be their God,
>   and they will be my people."

¹⁷   The Lord says, "Get away from unbelievers.
>   Separate yourselves from them.
>   Have nothing to do with anything unclean.*ᶜ*
>   Then I will welcome you."

¹⁸   The Lord Almighty says, "I will be your Father,
>   and you will be my sons and daughters."

7 ¹ Since we have these promises, dear friends, we need to cleanse ourselves from everything that contaminates body and spirit and live a holy life in the fear of God.

Paul Was Comforted by What the Corinthians Did

² Open your hearts to us. We haven't treated anyone unjustly, ruined anyone, or cheated anyone. ³ I'm not saying this to condemn you. I've already told you that you are in our hearts so that we will live and die together. ⁴ I have great confidence in you, and I have a lot of reasons to be proud of you. Even as we suffer, I'm encouraged and feel very happy.

⁵ Ever since we arrived in the province of Macedonia, we've had no rest. Instead, we suffer in a number of ways. Outwardly we have conflicts, and inwardly we have fears. ⁶ Yet God, who comforts those who are dejected, comforted us when Titus arrived. ⁷ We were comforted not only by his arrival but also by learning about the comfort he had received while he was with you. He told us how you wanted to see me, how sorry you are for what you've done, and how concerned you are about me. This made me even happier.

⁸ If my letter made you uncomfortable, I'm not sorry. But since my letter did make you uncomfortable for a while, I was sorry. ⁹ But I'm happy now, not because I made you uncomfortable, but because the distress I caused you has led you to change the way you think and act. You were distressed in a godly way, so we haven't done you any harm. ¹⁰ In fact, to be distressed in a godly way causes people to change the way they think and act and leads them to be saved. No one can regret that. But the distress that the world causes brings only death.

¹¹ When you became distressed in a godly way, look at how much devotion it caused you to have. You were ready to clear yourselves of the charges against you. You were disgusted with

---

ᵃ 6:1 Or "grace."   *ᵇ* 6:8 The last part of verse 7 (in Greek) has been moved to verse 8 to express the complex Greek sentence structure more clearly in English.   *ᶜ* 6:17 "Unclean" refers to anything that Moses' Teachings say is not presentable to God.

the wrong that had been done. You were afraid. You wanted to see us. You wanted to show your concern for us. You were ready to punish the wrong that had been done. In every way you have demonstrated that you are people who are innocent in this matter. [12] So, when I wrote to you, I didn't write because of the man who did the wrong or the man who was hurt by it. Rather, I wrote because I wanted you to show your devotion to us in God's sight. [13] This is what has comforted us.

In addition to being comforted, we were especially pleased to see how happy Titus was. All of you had put his mind at ease. [14] I didn't have to be ashamed of anything I had said to him when I bragged about you. Since everything we told you was true, our bragging to Titus has also proved to be true. [15] His deepest feelings go out to you even more as he remembers how obedient all of you were, and how you welcomed him with fear and trembling. [16] I'm pleased that I can be confident about you in every way.

The Collection for Christians in Jerusalem

8 [1] Brothers and sisters, we want you to know how God showed his kindness[a] to the churches in the province of Macedonia. [2] While they were being severely tested by suffering, their overflowing joy, along with their extreme poverty, has made them even more generous. [3] I assure you that by their own free will they have given all they could, even more than they could afford. [4] They made an appeal to us, begging us to let them participate in the ministry of God's kindness to his holy people ˎin Jerusalemˎ. [5] They did more than we had expected. First, they gave themselves to the Lord and to us, since this was God's will. [6] This led us to urge Titus to finish his work of God's kindness among you in the same way as he had already started it.

[7] Indeed, the more your faith, your ability to speak, your knowledge, your dedication, and your love for us increase, the more we want you to participate in this work of God's kindness.

[8] I'm not commanding you, but I'm testing how genuine your love is by pointing out the dedication of others. [9] You know about the kindness of our Lord Jesus Christ. He was rich, yet for your sake he became poor in order to make you rich through his poverty.

[10] I'm giving you my opinion because it will be helpful to you. Last year you were not only willing ˎto take a collectionˎ, but had already started to do it. [11] So finish what you began to do. Then your willingness will be matched by what you accomplish [12] with whatever contributions you have. Since you are willing to do this, ˎrememberˎ that people are accepted if they give what they are able to give. God doesn't ask for what they don't have.

[13] I don't mean that others should have relief while you have hardship. Rather, it's a matter of striking a balance. [14] At the present time, your surplus fills their need so that their surplus may fill your need. In this way things balance out. [15] This is what Scripture says: "Those who had gathered a lot didn't have too much, and those who gathered a little didn't have too little."

[16] I thank God for making Titus as dedicated to you as I am. [17] He accepted my request and eagerly went to visit you by his own free will.

[18] With him we have sent our Christian brother whom all the churches praise for the way he tells the Good News. [19] More than that, the churches elected him to travel with us and bring this gift of God's kindness. We are administering it in a way that brings glory to the Lord and shows that we are doing it willingly. [20] We don't want anyone to find fault with the way we are administering this generous gift. [21] We intend to do what is right, not only in the sight of the Lord, but also in the sight of people.

[22] We have also sent with them our Christian brother whom we have often tested in many ways and found to be a dedicated worker. We find that he is much more dedicated now than ever because he has so much confidence in you.

[23] If any questions are raised, remember that Titus is my partner and coworker to help you. The other men are representatives of the churches and bring glory to Christ. [24] So give these men a demonstration of your love. Show their congregations that we were right to be proud of you.

The Reason to Give to the Christians in Jerusalem

9 [1] I don't need to write anything further to you about helping the Christians ˎin Jerusalemˎ. [2] I know how willing you are to help, and I brag about you to the believers in the province of Macedonia. I tell them, "The people of Greece have been ready ˎto send their collectionˎ since last year," and your enthusiasm has moved most of them ˎto actˎ. [3] I've sent my coworkers so that when we brag that you're ready, we can back it up. [4] Otherwise, if any Macedonians come with me, they might find out that you're not ready after all. This would embarrass us for feeling so confident as much as it would embarrass you. [5] So I thought that I should encourage our coworkers to visit you before I do and make arrange-

---

[a] 8:1 Or "grace."

ments for this gift that you had already promised to give. Then it will be the blessing it was intended to be, and it won't be something you're forced to do. ⁶ Remember this: The farmer who plants a few seeds will have a very small harvest. But the farmer who plants because he has received God's blessings will receive a harvest of God's blessings in return. ⁷ Each of you should give whatever you have decided. You shouldn't be sorry that you gave or feel forced to give, since God loves a cheerful giver. ⁸ Besides, God will give you his constantly overflowing kindness.ᵃ Then, when you always have everything you need, you can do more and more good things. ⁹ Scripture says,

> "The righteous person gives freely to the poor.
>   His righteousness continues forever."

¹⁰ God gives seed to the farmer and food to those who need to eat. God will also give you seed and multiply it. In your lives he will increase the things you do that have his approval. ¹¹ God will make you rich enough so that you can always be generous. Your generosity will produce thanksgiving to God because of us. ¹² What you do to serve others not only provides for the needs of God's people, but also produces more and more prayers of thanksgiving to God. ¹³ You will honor God through this genuine act of service because of your commitment to spread the Good News of Christ and because of your generosity in sharing with them and everyone else. ¹⁴ With deep affection they will pray for you because of the extreme kindness that God has shown you. ¹⁵ I thank God for his gift that words cannot describe.

Paul's Authority to Speak Forcefully

10 ¹ I, Paul, make my appeal to you with the gentleness and kindness of Christ. I'm the one who is humble when I'm with you but forceful toward you when I'm not with you. ² I beg you that when I am with you I won't have to deal forcefully with you. I expect I will have to because some people think that we are only guided by human motives. ³ Of course we are human, but we don't fight like humans. ⁴ The weapons we use in our fight are not made by humans. Rather, they are powerful weapons from God. With them we destroy people's defenses, that is, their arguments ⁵ and all their intellectual arrogance that oppose the knowledge of God. We take every thought captive so that it is obedient to Christ. ⁶ We are ready to punish every act of disobedience when you have become completely obedient.

⁷ Look at the plain facts! If anyone is confident he belongs to Christ, he should take note that we also belong to Christ. ⁸ So, if I brag a little too much about the authority which the Lord gave us, I'm not ashamed. The Lord gave us this authority to help you, not to hurt you. ⁹ I don't want you to think that I'm trying to frighten you with my letters. ¹⁰ I know that someone is saying that my letters are powerful and strong, but that I'm a weakling and a terrible speaker. ¹¹ The person who is saying those things should take note of this fact: When we are with you we will do the things that we wrote about in our letters when we weren't with you.

Paul's Reason for Bragging

¹² We wouldn't put ourselves in the same class with or compare ourselves to those who are bold enough to make their own recommendations. Certainly, when they measure themselves by themselves and compare themselves to themselves, they show how foolish they are. ¹³ How can we brag about things that no one can evaluate? Instead, we will only brag about what God has given us to do—coming to ˌthe city of Corinthˌ where you live. ¹⁴ It's not as though we hadn't already been to Corinth. We're not overstating the facts. The fact is that we were the first to arrive in Corinth with the Good News about Christ. ¹⁵ How can we brag about things done by others that can't be evaluated?

We have confidence that as your faith grows, you will think enough of us to give us the help we need to carry out our assignment— ¹⁶ spreading the Good News in the regions far beyond you. We won't brag about things already accomplished by someone else. ¹⁷ "Whoever brags should brag about what the Lord has done." ¹⁸ It isn't the person who makes his own recommendation who receives approval, but the person whom the Lord recommends.

Paul Contrasts Himself With False Apostles

11 ¹ I want you to put up with a little foolishness from me. I'm sure that you will. ² I'm as protective of you as God is. After all, you're a virgin whom I promised in marriage to one man—Christ. ³ However, I'm afraid that as the snake deceived Eve by its tricks, so your minds may somehow be lured away from your sincere and pure devotion to Christ. ⁴ When someone comes to you telling about another Jesus whom we didn't tell you about, you're will-

---

ᵃ 9:8 Or "grace."

ing to put up with it. When you receive a spirit that is different from the Spirit you received earlier, you're also willing to put up with that. When someone tells you good news that is different from the Good News you already accepted, you're willing to put up with that too.

[5] I don't think I'm inferior in any way to your super-apostles. [6] Even though I'm not good with words, I know what I'm talking about. Timothy and I have made this clear to you in every possible way.

[7] Did I commit a sin when I humbled myself by telling you the Good News of God free of charge so that you could become important? [8] I robbed other churches by taking pay from them to serve you. [9] When I was with you and needed something, I didn't bother any of you for help. My friends from the province of Macedonia supplied everything I needed. I kept myself from being a financial burden to you in any way, and I will continue to do that.

[10] As surely as I have Christ's truth, my bragging will not be silenced anywhere in Greece. [11] Why? Because I don't love you? God knows that I do love you. [12] But I'll go on doing what I'm doing. This will take away the opportunity of those people who want to brag because they think they're like us. [13] People who brag like this are false apostles. They are dishonest workers, since they disguise themselves as Christ's apostles. [14] And no wonder, even Satan disguises himself as an angel of light. [15] So it's not surprising if his servants also disguise themselves as servants who have God's approval. In the end they will get what they deserve.

More Reasons for Paul to Brag

[16] Again I say that no one should think that I'm a fool. But if you do, then take me for a fool so that I can also brag a little. [17] What I say as I start bragging is foolishness. It's not something I would say if I were speaking for the Lord. [18] Since it's common for people to brag, I'll do it too. [19] You're wise, so you'll gladly put up with fools. [20] When someone makes you slaves, consumes your wealth, seizes your property, orders you around, or slaps your faces, you put up with it. [21] I'm ashamed to admit it, but Timothy and I don't have the strength to do those things to you.

Whatever other people dare to brag about, I, like a fool, can also brag about. [22] Are they Hebrews? So am I. Are they Israelites? So am I. Are they Abraham's descendants? So am I. [23] Are they Christ's servants? It's insane to say it, but I'm a far better one. I've done much more work, been in prison many more times, been beaten more severely, and have faced death more often. [24] Five times the Jewish leaders had me beaten with 39 lashes; [25] three times Roman officials had me beaten with clubs. Once people tried to stone me to death; three times I was shipwrecked, and I drifted on the sea for a night and a day. [26] Because I've traveled a lot, I've faced dangers from raging rivers, from robbers, from my own people, and from other people. I've faced dangers in the city, in the open country, on the sea, and from believers who turned out to be false friends. [27] Because I've had to work so hard, I've often gone without sleep, been hungry and thirsty, and gone without food and without proper clothes during cold weather. [28] Besides these external matters, I have the daily pressure of my anxiety about all the churches. [29] When anyone is weak, I'm weak too. When anyone is caught in a trap, I'm also harmed.

[30] If I must brag, I will brag about the things that show how weak I am. [31] The God and Father of the Lord Jesus, who is praised forever, knows that I'm not lying. [32] The governor under King Aretas put guards around the city of Damascus to catch me. [33] So I was let down in a basket through an opening in the wall and escaped from him.

Paul's Visions and Revelations From the Lord

12 [1] I must brag, although it doesn't do any good. I'll go on to visions and revelations from the Lord. [2] I know a follower of Christ who was snatched away to the third heaven fourteen years ago. I don't know whether this happened to him physically or spiritually. Only God knows. [3] I know that this person [4] was snatched away to paradise where he heard things that can't be expressed in words, things that humans cannot put into words. I don't know whether this happened to him physically or spiritually. Only God knows.[a] [5] I'll brag about this person, but I won't brag about myself unless it's about my weaknesses.

[6] If I ever wanted to brag, I wouldn't be a fool. Instead, I would be telling the truth. But I'm going to spare you so that no one may think more of me than what he sees or hears about me, [7] especially because of the excessive number of revelations that I've had.

Therefore, to keep me from becoming conceited, I am forced to deal with a recurring problem. That problem, Satan's messenger, torments me to keep me from being conceited. [8] I begged the Lord three times to take it away from me. [9] But he told me: "My kindness[b] is all you need. My power is strongest when you are weak." So I will brag even more about my weak-

---

[a] 12:4 The last two sentences of verse 3 (in Greek) have been moved to verse 4 to express the complex Greek sentence structure more clearly in English.   [b] 12:9 Or "grace."

nesses in order that Christ's power will live in me. **¹⁰** Therefore, I accept weakness, mistreatment, hardship, persecution, and difficulties suffered for Christ. It's clear that when I'm weak, I'm strong.

Paul Was Not a Burden to the Corinthians

¹¹ I have become a fool. You forced me to be one. You should have recommended me to others. Even if I'm nothing, I wasn't inferior in any way to your super-apostles. **¹²** While I was among you I patiently did the signs, wonders, and miracles which prove that I'm an apostle. **¹³** How were you treated worse than the other churches, except that I didn't bother you for help? Forgive me for this wrong!

¹⁴ I'm ready to visit you for a third time, and I won't bother you for help. I don't want your possessions. Instead, I want you. Children shouldn't have to provide for their parents, but parents should provide for their children. **¹⁵** I will be very glad to spend whatever I have. I'll even give myself for you. Do you love me less because I love you so much?

¹⁶ You agree, then, that I haven't been a burden to you. Was I a clever person who trapped you by some trick? **¹⁷** Did I take advantage of you through any of the men I sent you? **¹⁸** I encouraged Titus to visit you, and I sent my friend with him. Did Titus take advantage of you? Didn't we have the same motives and do things the same way?

¹⁹ Have you been thinking all along that we're trying to defend ourselves to you? We speak as Christ's people in God's sight. Everything we do, dear friends, is for your benefit.

Paul's Concern About the Corinthians' Way of Life

²⁰ I'm afraid that I may come and find you different from what I want you to be, and that you may find me different from what you want me to be. I'm afraid that there may be rivalry, jealousy, hot tempers, selfish ambition, slander, gossip, arrogance, and disorderly conduct. **²¹** I'm afraid that when I come to you again, my God may humble me. I may have to grieve over many who formerly led sinful lives and have not changed the way they think and act about the perversion, sexual sins, and promiscuity in which they have been involved.

Paul Tells the Corinthians to Prepare for His Visit

13 **¹** This is the third time that I'll be visiting you. Every accusation must be verified by two or three witnesses. **²** I already warned you when I was with you the second time, and even though I'm not there now, I'm warning you again. When I visit you again, I won't spare you. That goes for all those who formerly led sinful lives as well as for all the others. **³** Since you want proof that Christ is speaking through me, that's what you'll get. Christ isn't weak in dealing with you. Instead, he makes his power felt among you. **⁴** He was weak when he was crucified, but by God's power he lives. We are weak with him, but by God's power we will live for you with his help.

⁵ Examine yourselves to see whether you are still in the Christian faith. Test yourselves! Don't you recognize that you are people in whom Jesus Christ lives? Could it be that you're failing the test? **⁶** I hope that you will realize that we haven't failed the test. **⁷** We pray to God that you won't do anything wrong. It's not that we want to prove that we've passed the test. Rather, we want you to do whatever is right, even if we seem to have failed. **⁸** We can't do anything against the truth but only to help the truth. **⁹** We're glad when we are weak and you are strong. We are also praying for your improvement.

¹⁰ That's why I'm writing this letter while I'm not with you. When I am with you I don't want to be harsh by using the authority that the Lord gave me. The Lord gave us this authority to help you, not to hurt you.

Farewell

¹¹ With that, brothers and sisters, I must say goodbye. Make sure that you improve. Accept my encouragement. Share the same attitude and live in peace. The God of love and peace will be with you. **¹²** Greet one another with a holy kiss. All of God's holy people greet you.[a]

¹³ May the Lord Jesus Christ's good will,[b] God's love, and the Holy Spirit's presence be with all of you!

---

[a] 13:12 Some English Bibles count the last sentence of verse 12 as verse 13. Verse 13 is then counted as verse 14.
[b] 13:13 Or "grace."

GALATIANS

Greeting

1 ¹ From Paul—an apostle ˪chosen˪ not by any group or individual but by Jesus Christ and God the Father who brought him back to life— ² and all the believers who are with me. To the churches in Galatia.

³ Good will[a] and peace are yours from God the Father and our Lord Jesus Christ! ⁴ In order to free us from this present evil world, Christ took the punishment for our sins, because that was what our God and Father wanted. ⁵ Glory belongs to our God and Father forever! Amen.

Follow the Good News We Gave You

⁶ I'm surprised that you're so quickly deserting Christ, who called you in his kindness,[a] to follow a different kind of good news. ⁷ But what some people are calling good news is not really good news at all. They are confusing you. They want to distort the Good News about Christ. ⁸ Whoever tells you good news that is different from the Good News we gave you should be condemned to hell, even if he is one of us or an angel from heaven. ⁹ I'm now telling you again what we've told you in the past: If anyone tells you good news that is different from the Good News you received, that person should be condemned to hell.

¹⁰ Am I saying this now to win the approval of people or God? Am I trying to please people? If I were still trying to please people, I would not be Christ's servant.

Jesus Alone Gave Paul the Good News He Spreads

¹¹ I want you to know, brothers and sisters, that the Good News I have spread is not a human message. ¹² I didn't receive it from any person. I wasn't taught it, but Jesus Christ revealed it to me.

¹³ You heard about the way I once lived when I followed the Jewish religion. You heard how I violently persecuted God's church and tried to destroy it. ¹⁴ You also heard how I was far ahead of other Jews in my age group in following the Jewish religion. I had become that fanatical for the traditions of my ancestors.

¹⁵ But God, who appointed me before I was born and who called me by his kindness, was pleased ¹⁶ to show me his Son. He did this so that I would tell people who are not Jewish that his Son is the Good News. When this happened, I didn't talk it over with any other person. ¹⁷ I didn't even go to Jerusalem to see those who were apostles before I was. Instead, I went to Arabia and then came back to Damascus.

¹⁸ Then, three years later I went to Jerusalem to become personally acquainted with Cephas.[b] I stayed with him for fifteen days. ¹⁹ I didn't see any other apostle. I only saw James, the Lord's brother. ²⁰ (God is my witness that what I'm writing is not a lie.) ²¹ Then I went to the regions of Syria and Cilicia. ²² The churches of Christ in Judea didn't know me personally. ²³ The only thing they had heard was this: "The man who persecuted us is now spreading the faith that he once tried to destroy." ²⁴ So they praised God for what had happened to me.

Paul Was Accepted as an Apostle by the Leaders in Jerusalem

2 ¹ Then 14 years later I went to Jerusalem again with Barnabas. I also took Titus along. ² I went in response to a revelation ˪from God˪. I showed them the way I spread the Good News among people who are not Jewish. I did this in a private meeting with those recognized as important people to see whether all my efforts had been wasted.

³ Titus was with me, and although he is Greek, no one forced him to be circumcised.

⁴ False Christians were brought in. They slipped in as spies to learn about the freedom Christ Jesus gives us. They hoped to find a way to control us. ⁵ But we did not give in to them for a moment, so that the truth of the Good News would always be yours.

⁶ Those who were recognized as important people didn't add a single thing to my message. (What sort of people they were makes no difference to me, since God doesn't play favorites.) ⁷ In fact, they saw that I had been entrusted with telling the Good News to people who are not

---

^a 1:3, 6 Or "Grace."   ^b 1:18 Cephas is the Aramaic name for the apostle Peter.

circumcised as Peter had been entrusted to tell it to those who are circumcised. [8] The one who made Peter an apostle to Jewish people also made me an apostle to people who are not Jewish. [9] James, Cephas, and John (who were recognized as the most important people) acknowledged that God had given me this special gift.[a] So they shook hands with Barnabas and me, agreeing to be our partners. It was understood that we would work among the people who are not Jewish and they would work among Jewish people. [10] The only thing they asked us to do was to remember the poor, the very thing which I was eager to do.

Paul Shows How Cephas Was Wrong

[11] When Cephas came to Antioch, I had to openly oppose him because he was completely wrong. [12] He ate with people who were not Jewish until some men James had sent ˌfrom Jerusalemˌ arrived. Then Cephas drew back and would not associate with people who were not Jewish. He was afraid of those who insisted that circumcision was necessary. [13] The other Jewish Christians also joined him in this hypocrisy. Even Barnabas was swept along with them.

[14] But I saw that they were not properly following the truth of the Good News. So I told Cephas in front of everyone, "You're Jewish, but you live like a person who is not Jewish. So how can you insist that people who are not Jewish must live like Jews?"

[15] We are Jewish by birth, not sinners from other nations. [16] Yet, we know that people don't receive God's approval because of their own efforts to live according to a set of standards, but only by believing in Jesus Christ. So we also believed in Jesus Christ in order to receive God's approval by faith in Christ and not because of our own efforts. People won't receive God's approval because of their own efforts to live according to a set of standards.

[17] If we, the same people who are searching for God's approval in Christ, are still sinners, does that mean that Christ encourages us to sin? That's unthinkable! [18] If I rebuild something that I've torn down, I admit that I was wrong to tear it down. [19] When I tried to obey the law's standards, those laws killed me. As a result, I live in a relationship with God. I have been crucified with Christ. [20] I no longer live, but Christ lives in me. The life I now live I live by believing in God's Son, who loved me and took the punishment for my sins. [21] I don't reject God's kindness.[b] If we receive God's approval by obeying laws, then Christ's death was pointless.

God Approves of Those Who Believe

3 [1] You stupid people of Galatia! Who put you under an evil spell? Wasn't Christ Jesus' crucifixion clearly described to you? [2] I want to learn only one thing from you. Did you receive the Spirit by your own efforts to live according to a set of standards or by believing what you heard? [3] Are you that stupid? Did you begin in a spiritual way only to end up doing things in a human way? [4] Did you suffer so much for nothing? ˌI doubtˌ that it was for nothing! [5] Does God supply you with the Spirit and work miracles among you through your own efforts or through believing what you heard?

[6] Abraham serves as an example. He believed God, and that faith was regarded by God to be his approval of Abraham. [7] You must understand that people who have faith are Abraham's descendants. [8] Scripture saw ahead of time that God would give his approval to non-Jewish people who have faith. So Scripture announced the Good News to Abraham ahead of time when it said, "Through you all the people of the world will be blessed." [9] So people who believe are blessed together with Abraham, the man of faith.

[10] Certainly, there is a curse on all who rely on their own efforts to live according to a set of standards because Scripture says, "Whoever doesn't obey everything that is written in Moses' Teachings is cursed." [11] No one receives God's approval by obeying the law's standards since, "The person who has God's approval will live by faith." [12] Laws have nothing to do with faith, but, "Whoever obeys laws will live because of the laws he obeys."

[13] Christ paid the price to free us from the curse that God's laws bring by becoming cursed instead of us. Scripture says, "Everyone who is hung on a tree is cursed." [14] ˌChrist paid the priceˌ so that the blessing promised to Abraham would come to all the people of the world through Jesus Christ and we would receive the promised Spirit through faith.

The Relationship Between Law and Promise

[15] Brothers and sisters, let me use an example from everyday life. No one can cancel a person's will or add conditions to it once that will is put into effect. [16] The promises were spoken to Abraham and to his descendant. Scripture doesn't say, "descendants," referring to many, but "your descendant," referring to one. That descendant is Christ. [17] This is what I mean: The laws ˌgiven to Mosesˌ 430 years after God had already put his promise ˌto Abrahamˌ into effect didn't cancel the promise ˌto Abrahamˌ. [18] If we have to gain the inheritance by follow-

---

ing those laws, then it no longer comes to us because of the promise. However, God freely gave the inheritance to Abraham through a promise.

[19] What, then, is the purpose of the laws given to Moses? They were added to identify what wrongdoing is. Moses' laws did this until the descendant to whom the promise was given came.[a] It was put into effect through angels, using a mediator. [20] A mediator is not used when there is only one person involved, and God has acted on his own.

[21] Does this mean, then, that the laws given to Moses contradict God's promises? That's unthinkable! If those laws could give us life, then certainly we would receive God's approval because we obeyed them. [22] But Scripture states that the whole world is controlled by the power of sin. Therefore, a promise based on faith in Jesus Christ could be given to those who believe.

[23] We were kept under control by Moses' laws until this faith came. We were under their control until this faith which was about to come would be revealed.

[24] Before Christ came, Moses' laws served as our guardian. Christ came so that we could receive God's approval by faith. [25] But now that this faith has come, we are no longer under the control of a guardian. [26] You are all God's children by believing in Christ Jesus. [27] Clearly, all of you who were baptized in Christ's name have clothed yourselves with Christ. [28] There are neither Jews nor Greeks, slaves nor free people, males nor females. You are all the same in Christ Jesus. [29] If you belong to Christ, then you are Abraham's descendants and heirs, as God promised.

You Are God's Children

4 [1] Let me explain further. As long as an heir is a child, he is no better off than a slave, even though he owns everything. [2] He is placed under the control of guardians and trustees until the time set by his father. [3] It was the same way with us. When we were children, we were slaves to the principles of this world. [4] But when the right time came, God sent his Son into the world. A woman gave birth to him, and he came under the control of God's laws. [5] God sent him to pay for the freedom of those who were controlled by these laws so that we would be adopted as his children. [6] Because you are God's children, God has sent the Spirit of his Son into us to call out, "Abba![a] Father!" [7] So you are no longer slaves but God's children. Since you are God's children, God has also made you heirs.

[8] When you didn't know God, you were slaves to things which are really not gods at all. [9] But now you know God, or rather, God knows you. So how can you turn back again to the powerless and bankrupt principles of this world? Why do you want to become their slaves all over again? [10] You religiously observe days, months, seasons, and years! [11] I'm afraid for you. Maybe the hard work I spent on you has been wasted.

What Happened to Your Positive Attitude?

[12] Brothers and sisters, I beg you to become like me. After all, I became like you were.

You didn't do anything wrong to me. [13] You know that the first time I brought you the Good News I was ill. [14] Even though my illness was difficult for you, you didn't despise or reject me. Instead, you welcomed me as if I were God's messenger[b] or Christ Jesus himself. [15] What happened to your positive attitude? It's a fact that if it had been possible, you would have torn out your eyes and given them to me. [16] Can it be that I have become your enemy for telling you the truth?

[17] These people who distort the Good News are devoted to you, but not in a good way. They don't want you to associate with me so that you will be devoted only to them. [18] (Devotion to a good cause is always good, even when I'm not with you.)

[19] My children, I am suffering birth pains for you again until Christ is formed in you. [20] I wish I were with you right now so that I could change the tone of my voice. I'm completely puzzled by what you've done!

You Are Children of the Promise

[21] Those who want to be controlled by Moses' laws should tell me something. Are you really listening to what Moses' Teachings say? [22] Scripture says that Abraham had two sons, one by a woman who was a slave and the other by a free woman. [23] Now, the son of the slave woman was conceived in a natural way, but the son of the free woman was conceived through a promise made to Abraham. [24] I'm going to use these historical events as an illustration. The women illustrate two arrangements.[c] The one woman, Hagar, is the arrangement made on Mount Sinai. Her children are born into slavery. [25] Hagar is Mount Sinai in Arabia. She is like Jerusalem today because she and her children are slaves. [26] But the Jerusalem that is above is free, and she is our mother. [27] Scripture says:

---

[a] 3:19 Or "Moses' laws did this until the descendant referred to in the promise to Abraham came."   [a] 4:6 Abba is Aramaic for "father."   [b] 4:14 Or "an angel of God."   [c] 4:24 Or "covenants."

"Rejoice, women who cannot get pregnant,
   who cannot give birth to any children!
Break into shouting, those who feel no pains of childbirth!
   Because the deserted woman will have more children
     than the woman who has a husband."

[28] Now you, brothers and sisters, are children of the promise like Isaac.
[29] Furthermore, at that time the son who was conceived in a natural way persecuted the son conceived in a spiritual way. That's exactly what's happening now. [30] But what does Scripture say? "Get rid of the slave woman and her son, because the son of the slave woman must never share the inheritance with the son of the free woman." [31] Brothers and sisters, we are not children of a slave woman but of the free woman.

Live in the Freedom That Christ Gives You

5 [1] Christ has freed us so that we may enjoy the benefits of freedom. Therefore, be firm ˌin this freedomˌ, and don't become slaves again.
[2] I, Paul, can guarantee that if you allow yourselves to be circumcised, Christ will be of no benefit to you. [3] Again, I insist that everyone who allows himself to be circumcised must realize that he obligates himself to do everything Moses' Teachings demand. [4] Those of you who try to earn God's approval by obeying his laws have been cut off from Christ. You have fallen out of God's favor.[a] [5] However, in our spiritual nature, faith causes us to wait eagerly for the confidence that comes with God's approval. [6] As far as our relationship to Christ Jesus is concerned, it doesn't matter whether we are circumcised or not. But what matters is a faith that expresses itself through love.

[7] You were doing so well. Who stopped you from being influenced by the truth? [8] The arguments of the person who is influencing you do not come from the one who is calling you. [9] A little yeast spreads through the whole batch of dough. [10] The Lord gives me confidence that you will not disagree with this. However, the one who is confusing you will suffer God's judgment regardless of who he is. [11] Brothers and sisters, if I am still preaching that circumcision is necessary, why am I still being persecuted? In that case the cross wouldn't be offensive anymore. [12] I wish those troublemakers would castrate themselves.

[13] You were indeed called to be free, brothers and sisters. Don't turn this freedom into an excuse for your corrupt nature to express itself. Rather, serve each other through love. [14] All of Moses' Teachings are summarized in a single statement, "Love your neighbor as you love yourself." [15] But if you criticize and attack each other, be careful that you don't destroy each other.

[16] Let me explain further. Live your life as your spiritual nature directs you. Then you will never follow through on what your corrupt nature wants. [17] What your corrupt nature wants is contrary to what your spiritual nature wants, and what your spiritual nature wants is contrary to what your corrupt nature wants. They are opposed to each other. As a result, you don't always do what you intend to do. [18] If your spiritual nature is your guide, you are not subject to Moses' laws.

[19] Now, the effects of the corrupt nature are obvious: illicit sex, perversion, promiscuity, [20] idolatry, drug use, hatred, rivalry, jealousy, angry outbursts, selfish ambition, conflict, factions, [21] envy, drunkenness, wild partying, and similar things. I've told you in the past and I'm telling you again that people who do these kinds of things will not inherit the kingdom of God.

[22] But the spiritual nature produces love, joy, peace, patience, kindness, goodness, faithfulness, [23] gentleness, and self-control. There are no laws against things like that. [24] Those who belong to Christ Jesus have crucified their corrupt nature along with its passions and desires. [25] If we live by our spiritual nature, then our lives need to conform to our spiritual nature. [26] We can't allow ourselves to act arrogantly and to provoke or envy each other.

Help Carry Each Other's Burdens

6 [1] Brothers and sisters, if a person gets trapped by wrongdoing, those of you who are spiritual should help that person turn away from doing wrong. Do it in a gentle way. At the same time watch yourself so that you also are not tempted. [2] Help carry each other's burdens. In this way you will follow Christ's teachings. [3] So if any one of you thinks you're important when you're really not, you're only fooling yourself. [4] Each of you must examine your own actions. Then you can be proud of your own accomplishments without comparing yourself to others. [5] Assume your own responsibility.

We Will Harvest What We Plant

[6] The person who is taught God's word should share all good things with his teacher. [7] Make no mistake about this: You can never make a fool out of God. Whatever you plant is what you'll harvest. [8] If you plant in ˌthe soil ofˌ your corrupt nature, you will harvest destruc-

tion. But if you plant in ˌthe soil ofˌ your spiritual nature, you will harvest everlasting life. [9] We can't allow ourselves to get tired of living the right way. Certainly, each of us will receive ˌever-lasting lifeˌ at the proper time, if we don't give up. [10] Whenever we have the opportunity, we have to do what is good for everyone, especially for the family of believers.

Paul Summarizes His Teachings About Circumcision

[11] Look at how large the letters ˌin these wordsˌ are because I'm writing this myself.

[12] These people who want to make a big deal out of a physical thing are trying to force you to be circumcised. Their only aim is to avoid persecution because of the cross of Christ. [13] It's clear that not even those who had themselves circumcised did this to follow Jewish laws. Yet, they want you to be circumcised so that they can brag about what was done to your body. [14] But it's unthinkable that I could ever brag about anything except the cross of our Lord Jesus Christ. By his cross my relationship to the world and its relationship to me have been cruci-fied. [15] Certainly, it doesn't matter whether a person is circumcised or not. Rather, what mat-ters is being a new creation. [16] Peace and mercy will come to rest on all those who conform to this principle. They are the Israel of God.[a]

[17] From now on, don't make any trouble for me! After all, I carry the scars of Jesus on my body.

[18] May the good will[b] of our Lord Jesus Christ be with your spirit, brothers and sisters! Amen.

---

[a] 6:16 Or "Peace and mercy will come to rest on them and on the Israel of God."   [b] 6:18 Or "grace."

EPHESIANS

Greeting

1 ¹ From Paul, an apostle of Christ Jesus by God's will.
To God's holy and faithful people who are united with Christ in the city of Ephesus.ª
² Good willᵇ and peace from God our Father and the Lord Jesus Christ are yours!

God Chose Us Through Christ

³ Praise the God and Father of our Lord Jesus Christ! Through Christ, God has blessed us with every spiritual blessing that heaven has to offer. ⁴ Before the creation of the world, he chose us through Christ to be holy and perfect in his presence. ⁵ Because of his love he had already decided to adopt us through Jesus Christ. He freely chose to do this ⁶ so that the kindnessᵇ he had given us in his dear Son would be praised and given glory.

⁷ Through the blood of his Son, we are set free from our sins. God forgives our failures because of his overflowing kindness. ⁸ He poured out his kindness by giving us every kind of wisdom and insight ⁹ when he revealed the mystery of his plan to us. He had decided to do this through Christ. ¹⁰ He planned to bring all of history to its goal in Christ. Then Christ would be the head of everything in heaven and on earth. ¹¹ God also decided ahead of time to choose us through Christ according to his plan, which makes everything work the way he intends. ¹² He planned all of this so that we who had already focused our hope on Christ would praise him and give him glory.

¹³ You heard and believed the message of truth, the Good News that he has saved you. In him you were sealed with the Holy Spirit whom he promised. ¹⁴ This Holy Spirit is the guarantee that we will receive our inheritance. We have this guarantee until we are set free to belong to him. God receives praise and glory for this.

Paul's Prayer for the Ephesians

¹⁵ I, too, have heard about your faith in the Lord Jesus and your love for all of God's people. For this reason ¹⁶ I never stop thanking God for you. I always remember you in my prayers. ¹⁷ I pray that the glorious Father, the God of our Lord Jesus Christ, would give you a spirit of wisdom and revelation as you come to know Christ better. ¹⁸ Then you will have deeper insight. You will know the confidence that he calls you to have and the glorious wealth that God's people will inherit. ¹⁹ You will also know the unlimited greatness of his power as it works with might and strength for us, the believers. ²⁰ He worked with that same power in Christ when he brought him back to life and gave him the highest position in heaven. ²¹ He is far above all rulers, authorities, powers, lords, and all other names that can be named, not only in this present world but also in the world to come. ²² God has put everything under the control of Christ. He has made Christ the head of everything for the good of the church. ²³ The church is Christ's body and completes him as he fills everything in every way.

God Saved Us Because of His Great Love for Us

2 ¹ You were once dead because of your failures and sins. ² You followed the ways of this present world and its spiritual ruler. This ruler continues to work in people who refuse to obey God. ³ All of us once lived among these people, and followed the desires of our corrupt nature. We did what our corrupt desires and thoughts wanted us to do. So, because of our nature, we deserved God's anger just like everyone else.

⁴ But God is rich in mercy because of his great love for us. ⁵ We were dead because of our failures, but he made us alive together with Christ. (It is God's kindnessª that saved you.) ⁶ God has brought us back to life together with Christ Jesus and has given us a position in heaven with him. ⁷ He did this through Christ Jesus out of his generosity to us in order to show his extremely rich kindness in the world to come. ⁸ God saved you through faith as an act of kindness. You had nothing to do with it. Being saved is a gift from God. ⁹ It's not the result of anything you've done, so no one can brag about it. ¹⁰ God has made us what we are. He has created us in Christ Jesus to live lives filled with good works that he has prepared for us to do.

ª 1:1 Some early manuscripts omit "in the city of Ephesus." ᵇ 1:2, 6 Or "Grace." ª 2:5 Or "grace."

God Has United Jewish and Non-Jewish People

¹¹ Remember that once you were not Jewish physically. Those who called themselves "the circumcised" because of what they had done to their bodies called you "the uncircumcised." ¹² Also, at that time you were without Christ. You were excluded from citizenship in Israel, and the pledges[b] ⌞God made in his⌟ promise were foreign to you. You had no hope and were in the world without God.

¹³ But now through Christ Jesus you, who were once far away, have been brought near by the blood of Christ. ¹⁴ So he is our peace. In his body he has made Jewish and non-Jewish people one by breaking down the wall of hostility that kept them apart. ¹⁵ He brought an end to the commandments and demands found in Moses' Teachings so that he could take Jewish and non-Jewish people and create one new humanity in himself. So he made peace. ¹⁶ He also brought them back to God in one body by his cross, on which he killed the hostility. ¹⁷ He came with the Good News of peace for you who were far away and for those who were near. ¹⁸ So Jewish and non-Jewish people can go to the Father in one Spirit.

¹⁹ That is why you are no longer foreigners and outsiders but citizens together with God's people and members of God's family. ²⁰ You are built on the foundation of the apostles and prophets. Christ Jesus himself is the cornerstone. ²¹ In him all the parts of the building fit together and grow into a holy temple in the Lord. ²² Through him you, also, are being built in the Spirit together with others into a place where God lives.

Paul's Work of Spreading the Good News

3 ¹ This is the reason I, Paul, am the prisoner of Christ Jesus[a] for those of you who are not Jewish.

² Certainly, you have heard how God gave me the responsibility of bringing his kindness[b] to you. ³ You have heard that he let me know this mystery through a revelation. I've already written to you about this briefly. ⁴ When you read this, you'll see that I understand the mystery about Christ. ⁵ In the past, this mystery was not known by people as it is now. The Spirit has now revealed it to his holy apostles and prophets. ⁶ This mystery is the Good News that people who are not Jewish have the same inheritance as Jewish people do. They belong to the same body and share the same promise that God made in Christ Jesus. ⁷ I became a servant of this Good News through God's kindness freely given to me when his power worked ⌞in me⌟.

⁸ I am the least of all God's people. Yet, God showed me his kindness by allowing me to spread the Good News of the immeasurable wealth of Christ to people who are not Jewish. ⁹ He allowed me to explain the way this mystery works. God, who created all things, kept it hidden in the past. ¹⁰ He did this so that now, through the church, he could let the rulers and authorities in heaven know his infinite wisdom. ¹¹ This was God's plan for all of history which he carried out through Christ Jesus our Lord. ¹² We can go to God with bold confidence through faith in Christ. ¹³ So then, I ask you not to become discouraged by the troubles I suffer for you. In fact, my troubles bring you glory.

Paul Prays That God Would Strengthen Christians

¹⁴ This is the reason I kneel in the presence of the Father ¹⁵ from whom all the family in heaven and on earth receives its name. ¹⁶ I'm asking God to give you a gift from the wealth of his glory. I pray that he would give you inner strength and power through his Spirit. ¹⁷ Then Christ will live in you through faith. I also pray that love may be the ground into which you sink your roots and on which you have your foundation. ¹⁸ This way, with all of God's people you will be able to understand how wide, long, high, and deep his love is. ¹⁹ You will know Christ's love, which goes far beyond any knowledge. I am praying this so that you may be completely filled with God.

²⁰ Glory belongs to God, whose power is at work in us. By this power he can do infinitely more than we can ask or imagine. ²¹ Glory belongs to God in the church and in Christ Jesus for all time and eternity! Amen.

Christ's Gifts to the Church

4 ¹ I, a prisoner in the Lord, encourage you to live the kind of life which proves that God has called you. ² Be humble and gentle in every way. Be patient with each other and lovingly accept each other. ³ Through the peace that ties you together, do your best to maintain the unity that the Spirit gives. ⁴ There is one body and one Spirit. In the same way you were called to share one hope. ⁵ There is one Lord, one faith, one baptism, ⁶ one God and Father of all, who is over everything, through everything, and in everything.

⁷ God's favor[a] has been given to each of us. It was measured out to us by Christ who gave it. ⁸ That's why the Scriptures say:

ᵇ 2:12 Or "covenants."   ᵃ 3:1 Some manuscripts omit "Jesus."   ᵇ 3:2 Or "grace."   ᵃ 4:7 Or "grace."

"When he went to the highest place,
　　he took captive those who had captured us
　　　　and gave gifts to people."

⁹ Now what does it mean that he went up except that he also had gone down to the lowest parts of the earth? ¹⁰ The one who had gone down also went up above all the heavens so that he fills everything. ¹¹ He also gave apostles, prophets, missionaries, as well as pastors and teachers as gifts ⌊to his church⌋. ¹² Their purpose is to prepare God's people to serve and to build up the body of Christ. ¹³ This is to continue until all of us are united in our faith and in our knowledge about God's Son, until we become mature, until we measure up to Christ, who is the standard. ¹⁴ Then we will no longer be little children, tossed and carried about by all kinds of teachings that change like the wind. We will no longer be influenced by people who use cunning and clever strategies to lead us astray. ¹⁵ Instead, as we lovingly speak the truth, we will grow up completely in our relationship to Christ, who is the head. ¹⁶ He makes the whole body fit together and unites it through the support of every joint. As each and every part does its job, he makes the body grow so that it builds itself up in love.

Live as God's People

¹⁷ So I tell you and encourage you in the Lord's name not to live any longer like other people in the world. Their minds are set on worthless things. ¹⁸ They can't understand because they are in the dark. They are excluded from the life that God approves of because of their ignorance and stubbornness. ¹⁹ Since they no longer have any sense of shame, they have become promiscuous. They practice every kind of sexual perversion with a constant desire for more.

²⁰ But that is not what you learned from Christ's teachings. ²¹ You have certainly heard his message and have been taught his ways. The truth is in Jesus. ²² You were taught to change the way you were living. The person you used to be will ruin you through desires that deceive you. ²³ However, you were taught to have a new attitude. ²⁴ You were also taught to become a new person created to be like God, truly righteous and holy.

²⁵ So then, get rid of lies. Speak the truth to each other, because we are all members of the same body.

²⁶ Be angry without sinning. Don't go to bed angry. ²⁷ Don't give the devil any opportunity ⌊to work⌋.

²⁸ Thieves must quit stealing and, instead, they must work hard. They should do something good with their hands so that they'll have something to share with those in need.

²⁹ Don't say anything that would hurt ⌊another person⌋. Instead, speak only what is good so that you can give help wherever it is needed. That way, what you say will help those who hear you. ³⁰ Don't give God's Holy Spirit any reason to be upset with you. He has put his seal on you for the day you will be set free ⌊from the world of sin⌋.

³¹ Get rid of your bitterness, hot tempers, anger, loud quarreling, cursing, and hatred. ³² Be kind to each other, sympathetic, forgiving each other as God has forgiven you through Christ.

Imitate God

5 ¹ Imitate God, since you are the children he loves. ² Live in love as Christ also loved us. He gave his life for us as an offering and sacrifice, a soothing aroma to God.

³ Don't let sexual sin, perversion of any kind, or greed even be mentioned among you. This is not appropriate behavior for God's holy people. ⁴ It's not right that dirty stories, foolish talk, or obscene jokes should be mentioned among you either. Instead, give thanks ⌊to God⌋. ⁵ You know very well that no person who is involved in sexual sin, perversion, or greed (which means worshiping wealth) can have any inheritance in the kingdom of Christ and of God. ⁶ Don't let anyone deceive you with meaningless words. It is because of sins like these that God's anger comes to those who refuse to obey him. ⁷ Don't be partners with them.

⁸ Once you lived in the dark, but now the Lord has filled you with light. Live as children who have light. ⁹ Light produces everything that is good, that has God's approval, and that is true. ¹⁰ Determine which things please the Lord. ¹¹ Have nothing to do with the useless works that darkness produces. Instead, expose them for what they are. ¹² It is shameful to talk about what some people do in secret. ¹³ Light exposes the true character of everything ¹⁴ because light makes everything easy to see. That's why it says:

"Wake up, sleeper!
　　Rise from the dead,
　　　　and Christ will shine on you."[a]

---

[a] 5:14 Or "and you will shine with Christ's light."

¹⁵ So then, be very careful how you live. Don't live like foolish people but like wise people. ¹⁶ Make the most of your opportunities because these are evil days. ¹⁷ So don't be foolish, but understand what the Lord wants. ¹⁸ Don't get drunk on wine, which leads to wild living. Instead, be filled with the Spirit*ᵇ* ¹⁹ by reciting psalms, hymns, and spiritual songs for your own good. Sing and make music to the Lord with your hearts. ²⁰ Always thank God the Father for everything in the name of our Lord Jesus Christ.

Advice to Wives and Husbands

²¹ Place yourselves under each other's authority out of respect for Christ.

²² Wives, place yourselves under your husbands' authority as you have placed yourselves under the Lord's authority.*ᶜ* ²³ The husband is the head of his wife as Christ is the head of the church. It is his body, and he is its Savior. ²⁴ As the church is under Christ's authority, so wives are under their husbands' authority in everything.

²⁵ Husbands, love your wives as Christ loved the church and gave his life for it. ²⁶ He did this to make the church holy by cleansing it, washing it using water along with spoken words. ²⁷ Then he could present it to himself as a glorious church, without any kind of stain or wrinkle— holy and without faults. ²⁸ So husbands must love their wives as they love their own bodies. A man who loves his wife loves himself. ²⁹ No one ever hated his own body. Instead, he feeds and takes care of it, as Christ takes care of the church. ³⁰ We are parts of his body. ³¹ That's why a man will leave his father and mother and be united with his wife, and the two will be one. ³² This is a great mystery. (I'm talking about Christ's relationship to the church.) ³³ But every husband must love his wife as he loves himself, and wives should respect their husbands.

Advice to Children and Parents

6 ¹ Children, obey your parents because you are Christians.*ᵃ* This is the right thing to do. ² "Honor your father and mother ³ that everything may go well for you, and you may have a long life on earth." This is an important commandment with a promise.*ᵇ*

⁴ Fathers, don't make your children bitter about life. Instead, bring them up in Christian discipline and instruction.

Advice to Slaves and Masters

⁵ Slaves, obey your earthly masters with proper respect. Be as sincere as you are when you obey Christ. ⁶ Don't obey them only while you're being watched, as if you merely wanted to please people. But obey like slaves who belong to Christ, who have a deep desire to do what God wants them to do. ⁷ Serve eagerly as if you were serving your heavenly master and not merely serving human masters. ⁸ You know that your heavenly master will reward all of us for whatever good we do, whether we're slaves or free people.

⁹ Masters, treat your slaves with respect. Don't threaten a slave. You know that there is one master in heaven who has authority over both of you, and he doesn't play favorites.

Put On All the Armor That God Supplies

¹⁰ Finally, receive your power from the Lord and from his mighty strength. ¹¹ Put on all the armor that God supplies. In this way you can take a stand against the devil's strategies. ¹² This is not a wrestling match against a human opponent. We are wrestling with rulers, authorities, the powers who govern this world of darkness, and spiritual forces that control evil in the heavenly world. ¹³ For this reason, take up all the armor that God supplies. Then you will be able to take a stand during these evil days.*ᶜ* Once you have overcome all obstacles, you will be able to stand your ground.

¹⁴ So then, take your stand! Fasten truth around your waist like a belt. Put on God's approval as your breastplate. ¹⁵ Put on your shoes so that you are ready to spread the Good News that gives peace. ¹⁶ In addition to all these, take the Christian faith as your shield. With it you can put out all the flaming arrows of the evil one. ¹⁷ Also take salvation as your helmet and the word of God as the sword that the Spirit supplies.

¹⁸ Pray in the Spirit*ᵈ* in every situation. Use every kind of prayer and request there is. For the same reason be alert. Use every kind of effort and make every kind of request for all of God's people. ¹⁹ Also pray that God will give me the right words to say. Then I will speak boldly when I reveal the mystery of the Good News. ²⁰ Because I have already been doing this as Christ's representative, I am in prison. So pray that I speak about this Good News as boldly as I have to.

ᵇ 5:18 Or "in ˌyourˌ spirit."   *ᶜ* 5:22 English equivalent difficult.   *ᵃ* 6:1 Some manuscripts and translations omit "because you are Christians."   *ᵇ* 6:3 The first part of verse 2 (in Greek) has been placed at the end of verse 3 to express the complex Greek sentence structure more clearly in English.   *ᶜ* 6:13 Or "when the evil day comes."   *ᵈ* 6:18 Or "in ˌyourˌ spirit."

Greetings From Paul

²¹ I'm sending Tychicus to you. He is our dear brother and a faithful deacon*e* in the Lord's work. He will tell you everything that is happening to me so that you will know how I'm getting along. ²² That's why I'm sending him to you so that you may know how we're doing and that he may encourage you.

²³ May God the Father and the Lord Jesus Christ give our brothers and sisters peace and love along with faith. ²⁴ His favor*f* is with everyone who has an undying love for our Lord Jesus Christ.

PHILIPPIANS

Greeting

1 [1] From Paul and Timothy, servants of Christ Jesus.
To God's people in the city of Philippi and their bishops[a] and deacons[a]—to everyone who
is united with Christ Jesus.
2 Good will[b] and peace from God our Father and the Lord Jesus Christ are yours!

Paul's Prayer for the Philippians

3 I thank my God for all the memories I have of you. 4 Every time I pray for all of you, I do it
with joy. 5 I can do this because of the partnership we've had with you in the Good News from the
first day ⌞you believed⌟ until now. 6 I'm convinced that God, who began this good work in you, will
carry it through to completion on the day of Christ Jesus. 7 You have a special place in my heart.
So it's right for me to think this way about all of you. All of you are my partners. Together we share
God's favor,[b] whether I'm in prison or defending and confirming the truth of the Good News. 8 God
is my witness that, with all the compassion of Christ Jesus, I long ⌞to see⌟ every one of you.
9 I pray that your love will keep on growing because of your knowledge and insight. 10 That
way you will be able to determine what is best and be pure and blameless until the day of
Christ. 11 Jesus Christ will fill your lives with everything that God's approval produces. Your
lives will then bring glory and praise to God.

Nothing Matters Except That People Are Told About Christ

12 I want you to know, brothers and sisters, that what happened to me has helped to spread
the Good News. 13 As a result, it has become clear to all the soldiers who guard the emperor
and to everyone else that I am in prison because of Christ. 14 So through my being in prison,
the Lord has given most of our brothers and sisters confidence to speak God's word more
boldly and fearlessly than ever.
15 Some people tell the message about Christ because of their jealousy and envy. Others tell
the message about him because of their good will. 16 Those who tell the message about Christ
out of love know that God has put me here to defend the Good News. 17 But the others are
insincere. They tell the message about Christ out of selfish ambition in order to stir up trouble for me while I'm in prison. 18 But what does it matter? Nothing matters except that, in one
way or another, people are told the message about Christ, whether with honest or dishonest
motives, and I'm happy about that.

Paul Honors Christ Whether He Lives or Dies

Yes, I will continue to be happy 19 for another reason. I know that I will be set free through
your prayers and through the help that comes from the Spirit of Jesus Christ. 20 I eagerly expect
and hope that I will have nothing to be ashamed of. I will speak very boldly and honor Christ in
my body, now as always, whether I live or die. 21 Christ means everything to me in this life, and
when I die I'll have even more. 22 If I continue to live in this life, my work will produce more
results. I don't know which I would prefer. 23 I find it hard to choose between the two. I would
like to leave this life and be with Christ. That's by far the better choice. 24 But for your sake it's
better that I remain in this life. 25 Since I'm convinced of this, I know that I will continue to live
and be with all of you. This will help you to grow and be joyful in your faith. 26 So by coming to
you again, I want to give you even more reason to have pride in Christ Jesus with me.

Fighting for the Faith

27 Live as citizens who reflect the Good News about Christ. Then, whether I come to see you or
whether I stay away, I'll hear all about you. I'll hear that you are firmly united in spirit, united in
fighting for the faith that the Good News brings. 28 So don't let your opponents intimidate you in
any way. This is God's way of showing them that they will be destroyed and that you will be saved.
29 God has given you the privilege not only to believe in Christ but also to suffer for him. 30 You are
involved in the same struggle that you saw me having. Now you hear that I'm still involved in it.

---

[a] 1:1 English equivalent difficult. [b] 1:2, 7 Or "Grace."

Have the Same Attitude as Christ

2 ¹ So then, as Christians, do you have any encouragement? Do you have any comfort from love? Do you have any spiritual relationships? Do you have any sympathy and compassion? ² Then fill me with joy by having the same attitude and the same love, living in harmony, and keeping one purpose in mind. ³ Don't act out of selfish ambition or be conceited. Instead, humbly think of others as being better than yourselves. ⁴ Don't be concerned only about your own interests, but also be concerned about the interests of others. ⁵ Have the same attitude that Christ Jesus had.

⁶ Although he was in the form of God and equal with God,
　　he did not take advantage of this equality.
⁷ Instead, he emptied himself by taking on the form of a servant,
　　by becoming like other humans,
　　by having a human appearance.
⁸ He humbled himself by becoming obedient to the point of death,
　　death on a cross.
⁹ This is why God has given him an exceptional honor—
　　the name honored above all other names—
¹⁰ 　　so that at the name of Jesus everyone in heaven, on earth,
　　　and in the world below will kneel
¹¹ 　　　and confess that Jesus Christ is Lord
　　　　to the glory of God the Father.

¹² My dear friends, you have always obeyed, not only when I was with you but even more now that I'm absent. In the same way continue to work out your salvation with fear and trembling. ¹³ It is God who produces in you the desires and actions that please him.

¹⁴ Do everything without complaining or arguing. ¹⁵ Then you will be blameless and innocent. You will be God's children without any faults among people who are crooked and corrupt. You will shine like stars among them in the world ¹⁶ as you hold firmly to the word of life. Then I can brag on the day of Christ that my effort was not wasted and that my work produced results. ¹⁷ My life is being poured out as a part of the sacrifice and service ˌI offer to Godˌ for your faith. Yet, I am filled with joy, and I share that joy with all of you. ¹⁸ For this same reason you also should be filled with joy and share that joy with me.

Paul Will Send Timothy and Epaphroditus

¹⁹ I hope that the Lord Jesus will allow me to send Timothy to you soon so that I can receive some encouraging news about you. ²⁰ I don't have anyone else like Timothy. He takes a genuine interest in your welfare. ²¹ Everyone else looks after his own interests, not after those of Jesus Christ. ²² But you know what kind of person Timothy proved to be. Like a father and son we worked hard together to spread the Good News. ²³ I hope to send him as soon as I see how things are going to turn out for me. ²⁴ But the Lord gives me confidence that I will come ˌto visit youˌ soon.

²⁵ I feel that I must send Epaphroditus—my brother, coworker, and fellow soldier—back to you. You sent him as your personal representative to help me in my need. ²⁶ He has been longing to see all of you and is troubled because you heard that he was sick. ²⁷ Indeed, he was so sick that he almost died. But God had mercy not only on him but also on me and kept me from having one sorrow on top of another. ²⁸ So I'm especially eager to send him to you. In this way you will have the joy of seeing him again and I will feel relieved. ²⁹ Give him a joyful Christian welcome. Make sure you honor people like Epaphroditus highly. ³⁰ He risked his life and almost died for the work of Christ in order to make up for the help you couldn't give me.

Run Straight Toward the Goal

3 ¹ Now then, brothers and sisters, be joyful in the Lord. It's no trouble for me to write the same things to you, and it's for your safety. ² Beware of dogs! Beware of those who do evil things. Beware of those who insist on circumcision. ³ We are the ˌtrueˌ circumcised people ˌofˌ Godˌ because we serve God's Spirit and take pride in Christ Jesus. We don't place any confidence in physical things, ⁴ although I could have confidence in my physical qualifications. If anyone else thinks that he can trust in something physical, I can claim even more. ⁵ I was circumcised on the eighth day. I'm a descendant of Israel. I'm from the tribe of Benjamin. I'm a pure-blooded Hebrew. When it comes to living up to standards, I was a Pharisee. ⁶ When it comes to being enthusiastic, I was a persecutor of the church. When it comes to winning God's approval by keeping Jewish laws, I was perfect.

⁷ These things that I once considered valuable, I now consider worthless for Christ. ⁸ It's far more than that! I consider everything else worthless because I'm much better off knowing Christ Jesus my Lord. It's because of him that I think of everything as worthless. I threw it all

away in order to gain Christ [9] and to have a relationship with him. This means that I didn't receive God's approval by obeying his laws. The opposite is true! I have God's approval through faith in Christ. This is the approval that comes from God and is based on faith [10] that knows Christ. Faith knows the power that his coming back to life gives and what it means to share his suffering. In this way I'm becoming like him in his death, [11] with the confidence that I'll come back to life from the dead.

[12] It's not that I've already reached the goal or have already completed the course. But I run to win that which Jesus Christ has already won for me. [13] Brothers and sisters, I can't consider myself a winner yet. This is what I do: I don't look back, I lengthen my stride, and [14] I run straight toward the goal to win the prize that God's heavenly call offers in Christ Jesus.

[15] Whoever has a mature faith should think this way. And if you think differently, God will show you how to think. [16] However, we should be guided by what we have learned so far.

Imitate Me

[17] Brothers and sisters, imitate me, and pay attention to those who live by the example we have given you. [18] I have often told you, and now tell you with tears in my eyes, that many live as the enemies of the cross of Christ. [19] In the end they will be destroyed. Their own emotions are their god, and they take pride in the shameful things they do. Their minds are set on worldly things. [20] We, however, are citizens of heaven. We look forward to the Lord Jesus Christ coming from heaven as our Savior. [21] Through his power to bring everything under his authority, he will change our humble bodies and make them like his glorified body.

Paul's Advice

4 [1] So, brothers and sisters, I love you and miss you. You are my joy and my crown. Therefore, dear friends, keep your relationship with the Lord firm!

[2] I encourage both Euodia and Syntyche to have the attitude the Lord wants them to have. [3] Yes, I also ask you, Syzugus, my true partner, to help these women. They fought beside me to spread the Good News along with Clement and the rest of my coworkers, whose names are in the Book of Life.

Always Be Joyful

[4] Always be joyful in the Lord! I'll say it again: Be joyful! [5] Let everyone know how considerate you are. The Lord is near. [6] Never worry about anything. But in every situation let God know what you need in prayers and requests while giving thanks. [7] Then God's peace, which goes beyond anything we can imagine, will guard your thoughts and emotions through Christ Jesus.

[8] Finally, brothers and sisters, keep your thoughts on whatever is right or deserves praise: things that are true, honorable, fair, pure, acceptable, or commendable. [9] Practice what you've learned and received from me, what you heard and saw me do. Then the God who gives this peace will be with you.

Thanks for Your Gifts

[10] The Lord has filled me with joy because you again showed interest in me. You were interested but did not have an opportunity to show it. [11] I'm not saying this because I'm in any need. I've learned to be content in whatever situation I'm in. [12] I know how to live in poverty or prosperity. No matter what the situation, I've learned the secret of how to live when I'm full or when I'm hungry, when I have too much or when I have too little. [13] I can do everything through Christ who strengthens me. [14] Nevertheless, it was kind of you to share my troubles.

[15] You Philippians also know that in the early days, when I left the province of Macedonia to spread the Good News, you were the only church to share your money with me. You gave me what I needed, and you received what I gave you. [16] Even while I was in Thessalonica, you provided for my needs twice. [17] It's not that I'm looking for a gift. The opposite is true. I'm looking for your resources to increase. [18] You have paid me in full, and I have more than enough. Now that Epaphroditus has brought me your gifts, you have filled my needs. Your gifts are a soothing aroma, a sacrifice that God accepts and with which he is pleased. [19] My God will richly fill your every need in a glorious way through Christ Jesus. [20] Glory belongs to our God and Father forever! Amen.

[21] Greet everyone who believes in Christ Jesus. The brothers and sisters who are with me send greetings to you. [22] All God's people here, especially those in the emperor's palace, greet you. [23] May the good will[a] of our Lord Jesus Christ be with you.

---

[a] 4:23 Or "grace."

COLOSSIANS

Greeting

1 ¹ From Paul, an apostle of Christ Jesus by God's will, and from our brother Timothy. ² To God's holy and faithful people, our brothers and sisters who are united with Christ in the city of Colossae.

Good will[a] and peace from God our Father are yours!

Paul's Prayer for the Colossians

³ We always thank God, the Father of our Lord Jesus Christ, in our prayers for you. ⁴ We thank God because we have heard about your faith in Christ Jesus and your love for all of God's people. ⁵ You have these because of the hope which is kept safe for you in heaven. Some time ago you heard about this hope in the Good News which is the message of truth. ⁶ This Good News is present with you now. It is producing results and spreading all over the world as it did among you from the first day you heard it. At that time you came to know what God's kindness[a] truly means. ⁷ You learned about this Good News from Epaphras, our dear fellow servant. He is taking your place here as a trustworthy deacon[b] for Christ ⁸ and has told us about the love that the Spirit has given you.

⁹ For this reason we have not stopped praying for you since the day we heard about you. We ask ˌGodˌ to fill you with the knowledge of his will through every kind of spiritual wisdom and insight. ¹⁰ We ask this so that you will live the kind of lives that prove you belong to the Lord. Then you will want to please him in every way as you grow in producing every kind of good work by this knowledge about God. ¹¹ We ask him to strengthen you by his glorious might with all the power you need to patiently endure everything with joy. ¹² You will also thank the Father, who has made you able to share the light, which is what God's people inherit.

What God Has Done Through Christ

¹³ God has rescued us from the power of darkness and has brought us into the kingdom of his Son, whom he loves. ¹⁴ His Son paid the price to free us, which means that our sins are forgiven.

¹⁵ He is the image of the invisible God,
   the firstborn of all creation.
¹⁶ He created all things in heaven and on earth,
   visible and invisible.
      Whether they are kings or lords,
         rulers or powers—
            everything has been created through him and for him.
¹⁷ He existed before everything
   and holds everything together.
¹⁸ He is also the head of the church, which is his body.
   He is the beginning,
      the first to come back to life
         so that he would have first place in everything.

¹⁹ God was pleased to have all of himself live in Christ. ²⁰ God was also pleased to bring everything on earth and in heaven back to himself through Christ. He did this by making peace through Christ's blood sacrificed on the cross.

²¹ Once you were separated from God. The evil things you did showed your hostile attitude. ²² But now Christ has brought you back to God by dying in his physical body. He did this so that you could come into God's presence without sin, fault, or blame. ²³ This is on the condition that you continue in faith without being moved from the solid foundation of the hope that the Good News contains. You've heard this Good News of which I, Paul, became a servant. It has been spread throughout all creation under heaven.

---

[a] 1:2, 6 Or "Grace."   [b] 1:7 English equivalent difficult.

Paul Describes His Work

[24] I am happy to suffer for you now. In my body I am completing whatever remains of Christ's sufferings. I am doing this on behalf of his body, the church. [25] I became a servant of the church when God gave me the work of telling you his entire message. [26] In the past God hid this mystery, but now he has revealed it to his people. [27] God wanted his people throughout the world to know the glorious riches of this mystery—which is Christ living in you, giving you the hope of glory.

[28] We spread the message about Christ as we instruct and teach everyone with all the wisdom there is. We want to present everyone as mature Christian people. [29] I work hard and struggle to do this while his mighty power works in me.

2 [1] I want you to know how hard I work for you, for the people of Laodicea, and for people I have never met. [2] Because they are united in love, I work so that they may be encouraged by all the riches that come from a complete understanding of Christ. He is the mystery of God. [3] God has hidden all the treasures of wisdom and knowledge in Christ. [4] I say this so that no one will mislead you with arguments that merely sound good. [5] Although I'm absent from you physically, I'm with you in spirit. I'm happy to see how orderly you are and how firm your faith in Christ is.

[6] You received Christ Jesus the Lord, so continue to live as Christ's people. [7] Sink your roots in him and build on him. Be strengthened by the faith that you were taught, and overflow with thanksgiving.

Beware of Requirements Invented by Humans

[8] Be careful not to let anyone rob you ˌof this faithˌ through a shallow and misleading philosophy. Such a person follows human traditions and the world's way of doing things rather than following Christ.

[9] All of God lives in Christ's body, [10] and God has made you complete in Christ. Christ is in charge of every ruler and authority. [11] In him you were also circumcised. It was not a circumcision performed by human hands. But it was a removal of the corrupt nature in the circumcision performed by Christ. [12] This happened when you were placed in the tomb with Christ through baptism. In baptism you were also brought back to life with Christ through faith in the power of God,[a] who brought him back to life.

[13] You were once dead because of your failures and your uncircumcised corrupt nature. But God made you alive with Christ when he forgave all our failures. [14] He did this by erasing the charges that were brought against us by the written laws God had established. He took the charges away by nailing them to the cross. [15] He stripped the rulers and authorities ˌof their powerˌ and made a public spectacle of them as he celebrated his victory in Christ.

[16] Therefore, let no one judge you because of what you eat or drink or about the observance of annual holy days, New Moon Festivals, or weekly worship days. [17] These are a shadow of the things to come, but the body ˌthat casts the shadowˌ belongs to Christ.

[18] Let no one who delights in ˌfalseˌ humility and the worship of angels tell you that you don't deserve a prize. Such a person, whose sinful mind fills him with arrogance, gives endless details of the visions he has seen. [19] He doesn't hold on to ˌChrist,ˌ the head. Christ makes the whole body grow as God wants it to, through support and unity given by the joints and ligaments.

[20] If you have died with Christ to the world's way of doing things, why do you let others tell you how to live? It's as though you were still under the world's influence. [21] People will tell you, "Don't handle this! Don't taste or touch that!" [22] All of these things deal with objects that are only used up anyway. [23] These things look like wisdom with their self-imposed worship, ˌfalseˌ humility, and harsh treatment of the body. But they have no value for holding back the constant desires of your corrupt nature.

Live as God's People

3 [1] Since you were brought back to life with Christ, focus on the things that are above— where Christ holds the highest position. [2] Keep your mind on things above, not on worldly things. [3] You have died, and your life is hidden with Christ in God. [4] Christ is your life. When he appears, then you, too, will appear with him in glory.

[5] Therefore, put to death whatever is worldly in you: your sexual sin, perversion, passion, lust, and greed (which is the same thing as worshiping wealth). [6] It is because of these sins that God's anger comes on those who refuse to obey him.[a] [7] You used to live that kind of sinful life. [8] Also get rid of your anger, hot tempers, hatred, cursing, obscene language, and all similar sins. [9] Don't lie to each other. You've gotten rid of the person you used to be and the life you used to live, [10] and you've become a new person. This new person is continually

---

[a] 2:12 Or "through faith produced by God."   [a] 3:6 Some manuscripts and translations omit "on those who refuse to obey him."

renewed in knowledge to be like its Creator. **11** Where this happens, there is no Greek or Jew, circumcised or uncircumcised, barbarian, uncivilized person, slave, or free person. Instead, Christ is everything and in everything.

12 As holy people whom God has chosen and loved, be sympathetic, kind, humble, gentle, and patient. **13** Put up with each other, and forgive each other if anyone has a complaint. Forgive as the Lord forgave you. **14** Above all, be loving. This ties everything together perfectly. **15** Also, let Christ's peace control you. God has called you into this peace by bringing you into one body. Be thankful. **16** Let Christ's word with all its wisdom and richness live in you. Use psalms, hymns, and spiritual songs to teach and instruct yourselves about ˴God's˴ kindness.ᵇ Sing to God in your hearts. **17** Everything you say or do should be done in the name of the Lord Jesus, giving thanks to God the Father through him.

Advice for Wives and Husbands, Parents and Children, Slaves and Masters

18 Wives, place yourselves under your husbands' authority.ᶜ This is appropriate behavior for the Lord's people. **19** Husbands, love your wives, and don't be harsh with them.

20 Children, always obey your parents. This is pleasing to the Lord. **21** Fathers, don't make your children resentful, or they will become discouraged.

22 Slaves, always obey your earthly masters. Don't obey them only while you're being watched, as if you merely wanted to please people. Be sincere in your motives out of respect for your real master. **23** Whatever you do, do it wholeheartedly as though you were working for your real master and not merely for humans. **24** You know that your real master will give you an inheritance as your reward. It is Christ, your real master, whom you are serving. **25** The person who does wrong will be paid back for the wrong he has done. God does not play favorites.

4 **1** Masters, be just and fair to your slaves because you know that you also have a master in heaven.

Advice for All Christians

2 Keep praying. Pay attention when you offer prayers of thanksgiving. **3** At the same time also pray for us. Pray that God will give us an opportunity to speak the word so that we may tell the mystery about Christ. It is because of this mystery that I am a prisoner. **4** Pray that I may make this mystery as clear as possible. This is what I have to do.

5 Be wise in the way you act toward those who are outside ˴the Christian faith˴. Make the most of your opportunities.

6 Everything you say should be kind and well thought out so that you know how to answer everyone.

Greetings From Paul and His Coworkers

7 I'm sending Tychicus to you. He is our dear brother, trustworthy deacon,ᵃ and partner in the Lord's work. He will tell you everything that is happening to me. **8** I'm sending him to you so that you may know how we are doing and so that he may encourage you. **9** I'm sending Onesimus with him. Onesimus is from your city and is our faithful and dear brother. They will tell you about everything that's happening here.

10 Aristarchus, who is a prisoner like me, sends greetings. So does Mark, the cousin of Barnabas. You have received instructions about Mark. If he comes to you, welcome him. **11** Jesus, called Justus, also greets you. They are the only converts from the Jewish religion who are working with me for God's kingdom. They have provided me with comfort. **12** Epaphras, a servant of Christ Jesus from your city, greets you. He always prays intensely for you. He prays that you will continue to be mature and completely convinced of everything that God wants. **13** I assure you that he works hard for you and the people in Laodicea and Hierapolis. **14** My dear friend Luke, the physician, and Demas greet you. **15** Greet our brothers and sisters in Laodicea, especially Nympha and the church that meets in her house.

16 After you have read this letter, read it in the church at Laodicea. Make sure that you also read the letter from Laodicea.

17 Tell Archippus to complete all the work that he started as the Lord's servant.

18 I, Paul, am writing this greeting with my own hand. Remember that I'm a prisoner. God's good willᵇ be with you.

ᵇ 3:16 Or "grace."   ᶜ 3:18 English equivalent difficult.   ᵃ 4:7 English equivalent difficult.   ᵇ 4:18 Or "grace."

1 THESSALONIANS

Greeting

1 ¹ From Paul, Silas, and Timothy.
To the church at Thessalonica united with God the Father and the Lord Jesus Christ. Good will[a] and peace are yours!

Paul's Prayer for the Thessalonians

² We always thank God for all of you as we remember you in our prayers. ³ In the presence of our God and Father, we never forget that your faith is active, your love is working hard, and your confidence in our Lord Jesus Christ is enduring. ⁴ Brothers and sisters, we never forget this because we know that God loves you and has chosen you. ⁵ We know this because from the Good News we brought came to you not only with words but also with power, with the Holy Spirit, and with complete certainty. In the same way you know what kind of people we were while we were with you and the good things we did for you.

⁶ You imitated us and the Lord. In spite of a lot of suffering, you welcomed God's word with the kind of joy that the Holy Spirit gives. ⁷ This way, you became a model for all the believers in the province of Macedonia and Greece. ⁸ From you the Lord's word has spread out not only through the province of Macedonia and Greece but also to people everywhere who have heard about your faith in God. We don't need to say a thing about it. ⁹ They talk about how you welcomed us when we arrived. They even report how you turned away from false gods to serve the real, living God ¹⁰ and to wait for his Son to come from heaven. His Son is Jesus, whom he brought back to life. Jesus is the one who rescues us from ˎGod'sˎ coming anger.

Paul Remembers When He Was With the Thessalonians

2 ¹ You know, brothers and sisters, that our time with you was not wasted. ² As you know, we suffered rough and insulting treatment in Philippi. But our God gave us the courage to tell you his Good News in spite of strong opposition.

³ When we encouraged you, we didn't use unethical schemes, corrupt practices, or deception. ⁴ Rather, we are always spreading the Good News. God trusts us to do this because we passed his test. We don't try to please people but God, who tests our motives. ⁵ As you know, we never used flattery or schemes to make money. God is our witness! ⁶ We didn't seek praise from people, from you or from anyone else, ⁷ although as apostles of Christ we had the right to do this.

Instead, we were gentle when we were with you, like a mother taking care of her children. ⁸ We felt so strongly about you that we were determined to share with you not only the Good News of God but also our lives. That's how dear you were to us! ⁹ You remember, brothers and sisters, our work and what we did to earn a living. We worked night and day so that we could bring you the Good News of God without being a burden to any of you. ¹⁰ You and God are witnesses of how pure, honest, and blameless we were in our dealings with you believers. ¹¹ You know very well that we treated each of you the way a father treats his children. We comforted you and encouraged you. Yet, we insisted that ¹² you should live in a way that proves you belong to the God who calls you into his kingdom and glory.

Paul Remembers How the Thessalonians Received the Word of God

¹³ Here is another reason why we never stop thanking God: When you received God's word from us, you realized it wasn't the word of humans. Instead, you accepted it for what it really is—the word of God. This word is at work in you believers.

¹⁴ You, brothers and sisters, were like the churches of God in Judea that are united with Christ Jesus. You suffered the same persecutions from the people of your own country as those churches did from the Jews ¹⁵ who killed the Lord Jesus and the prophets and who have persecuted us severely. They are displeasing to God. They are enemies of the whole human race ¹⁶ because they try to keep us from telling people who are not Jewish how they can be saved. The result is that those Jews always commit as many sins as possible. So at last they are receiving ˎGod'sˎ anger.

ᵃ 1:1 Or "Grace."

[17] Brothers and sisters, we have been separated from you for a little while. Although we may not be able to see you, you're always in our thoughts. We have made every possible effort to fulfill our desire to see you. [18] We wanted to visit you. I, Paul, wanted to visit you twice already, but Satan made that impossible.

[19] Who is our hope, joy, or prize that we can brag about in the presence of our Lord Jesus when he comes? Isn't it you? [20] You are our glory and joy!

Timothy's Report to Paul

3 [1] We thought it best to remain in Athens by ourselves. But, because we couldn't wait any longer ˏfor news about youˏ, [2] we sent our brother Timothy to you. He serves God by spreading the Good News about Christ. His mission was to strengthen and encourage you in your faith [3] so that these troubles don't disturb any of you. You know that we're destined to suffer persecution. [4] In fact, when we were with you, we told you ahead of time that we were going to suffer persecution. And as you know, that's what happened. [5] But when I couldn't wait any longer, I sent ˏTimothyˏ to find out about your faith. I wanted to see whether the tempter had in some way tempted you, making our work meaningless.

[6] But Timothy has just now come back to us from you and has told us the good news about your faith and love. He also told us that you always have fond memories of us and want to see us, as we want to see you. [7] So brothers and sisters, your faith has encouraged us in all our distress and trouble. [8] Now we can go on living as long as you keep your relationship with the Lord firm.

[9] We can never thank God enough for all the joy you give us as we rejoice in God's presence. [10] We pray very hard night and day that we may see you again so that we can supply whatever you still need for your faith. [11] We pray that God our Father and the Lord Jesus will guide us to you. [12] We also pray that the Lord will greatly increase your love for each other and for everyone else, just as we love you. [13] Then he will strengthen you to be holy. Then you will be blameless in the presence of our God and Father when our Lord Jesus comes with all God's holy people.

Instructions on the Way Christians Should Live

4 [1] Now then, brothers and sisters, because of the Lord Jesus we ask and encourage you to excel in living a God-pleasing life even more than you already do. Do this the way we taught you. [2] You know what orders we gave you through the Lord Jesus. [3] It is God's will that you keep away from sexual sin as a mark of your devotion to him. [4] Each of you should know that finding a husband or wife for yourself is to be done in a holy and honorable way, [5] not in the passionate, lustful way of people who don't know God. [6] No one should take advantage of or exploit other believers that way. The Lord is the one who punishes people for all these things. We've already told you and warned you about this. [7] God didn't call us to be sexually immoral but to be holy. [8] Therefore, whoever rejects this ˏorderˏ is not rejecting human authority but God, who gives you his Holy Spirit.

[9] You don't need anyone to write to you about the way Christians should love each other. God has taught you to love each other. [10] In fact, you are showing love to all the Christians throughout the province of Macedonia. We encourage you as believers to excel in love even more. [11] Also, make it your goal to live quietly, do your work, and earn your own living, as we ordered you. [12] Then your way of life will win respect from those outside ˏthe churchˏ, and you won't have to depend on anyone else for what you need.

Comfort About Christians Who Have Died

[13] Brothers and sisters, we don't want you to be ignorant about those who have died. We don't want you to grieve like other people who have no hope. [14] We believe that Jesus died and came back to life. We also believe that, through Jesus, God will bring back those who have died. They will come back with Jesus. [15] We are telling you what the Lord taught. We who are still alive when the Lord comes will not go ˏinto his kingdomˏ ahead of those who have already died. [16] The Lord will come from heaven with a command, with the voice of the archangel, and with the trumpet ˏcallˏ of God. First, the dead who believed in Christ will come back to life. [17] Then, together with them, we who are still alive will be taken in the clouds to meet the Lord in the air. In this way we will always be with the Lord. [18] So then, comfort each other with these words!

Be Ready for the Day of the Lord

5 [1] Brothers and sisters, you don't need anyone to write to you about times and dates. [2] You know very well that the day of the Lord will come like a thief in the night. [3] When people say, "Everything is safe and sound!" destruction will suddenly strike them. It will be as sudden as labor pains come to a pregnant woman. They won't be able to escape. [4] But, brothers and sisters, you don't live in the dark. That day won't take you by surprise as a thief would. [5] You belong to the day and the light not to the night and the dark. [6] Therefore, we must not fall

asleep like other people, but we must stay awake and be sober. [7] People who sleep, sleep at night; people who get drunk, get drunk at night. [8] Since we belong to the day, we must be sober. We must put on faith and love as a breastplate and the hope of salvation as a helmet. [9] It was not God's intention that we experience his anger but that we obtain salvation through our Lord Jesus Christ. [10] He died for us so that, whether we are awake in this life or asleep in death, we will live together with him. [11] Therefore, encourage each other and strengthen one another as you are doing.

Paul Encourages the Thessalonians

[12] Brothers and sisters, we ask you to show your appreciation for those leaders who work among you and instruct you. [13] We ask you to love them and think very highly of them because of the work they are doing. Live in peace with each other.

[14] We encourage you, brothers and sisters, to instruct those who are not living right, cheer up those who are discouraged, help the weak, and be patient with everyone. [15] Make sure that no one ever pays back one wrong with another wrong. Instead, always try to do what is good for each other and everyone else.

[16] Always be joyful. [17] Never stop praying. [18] Whatever happens, give thanks, because it is God's will in Christ Jesus that you do this.

[19] Don't put out the Spirit's fire. [20] Don't despise what God has revealed. [21] Instead, test everything. Hold on to what is good. [22] Keep away from every kind of evil.

Farewell

[23] May the God who gives peace make you holy in every way. May he keep your whole being—spirit, soul, and body—blameless when our Lord Jesus Christ comes. [24] The one who calls you is faithful, and he will do this.

[25] Brothers and sisters, pray for us.

[26] Greet all the brothers and sisters with a holy kiss.

[27] In the Lord's name, I order you to read this letter to all the brothers and sisters.

[28] The good will[a] of our Lord Jesus Christ be with you.

---

[a] 5:28 Or "grace."

2 THESSALONIANS

Greeting

1 ¹ From Paul, Silas, and Timothy.
To the church at Thessalonica united with God our Father and the Lord Jesus Christ.
² Good will[a] and peace from God our Father and the Lord Jesus Christ are yours!

Paul's Prayer for the Thessalonians

³ We always have to thank God for you, brothers and sisters. It's right to do this because your faith is showing remarkable growth and your love for each other is increasing. ⁴ That's why we brag in God's churches about your endurance and faith in all the persecutions and suffering you are experiencing. ⁵ Your suffering proves that God's judgment is right and that you are considered worthy of his kingdom.

⁶ Certainly, it is right for God to give suffering to those who cause you to suffer. ⁷ It is also right for God to give all of us relief from our suffering. He will do this when the Lord Jesus is revealed, ˪coming˩ from heaven with his mighty angels in a blazing fire. ⁸ He will take revenge on those who refuse to acknowledge God and on those who refuse to respond to the Good News about our Lord Jesus. ⁹ They will pay the penalty by being destroyed forever, by being separated from the Lord's presence and from his glorious power. ¹⁰ ˪This will happen˩ on that day when he comes to be honored among all his holy people and admired by all who have believed in him. This includes you because you believed the testimony we gave you.

¹¹ With this in mind, we always pray that our God will make you worthy of his call. We also pray that through ˪his˩ power he will help you accomplish every good desire and help you do everything your faith produces. ¹² That way the name of our Lord Jesus will be honored among you. Then, because of the good will of Jesus Christ, our God and Lord, you will be honored by him.

Don't Be Deceived About the Day of the Lord

2 ¹ Brothers and sisters, we have this request to make of you about our Lord Jesus Christ's coming and our gathering to meet him. ² Don't get upset right away or alarmed when someone claims that we said through some spirit, conversation, or letter that the day of the Lord has already come. ³ Don't let anyone deceive you about this in any way. ˪That day cannot come unless˩ a revolt takes place first, and the man of sin, the man of destruction, is revealed. ⁴ He opposes every so-called god or anything that is worshiped and places himself above them, sitting in God's temple and claiming to be God.

⁵ Don't you remember that I told you about these things when I was still with you? ⁶ You know what it is that now holds him back, so that he will be revealed when his time comes. ⁷ The mystery of this sin is already at work. But it cannot work effectively until the person now holding it back gets out of the way. ⁸ Then the man of sin will be revealed and the Lord Jesus will destroy him by what he says. When the Lord Jesus comes, his appearance will put an end to this man.

⁹ The man of sin will come with the power of Satan. He will use every kind of power, including miraculous and wonderful signs. But they will be lies. ¹⁰ He will use everything that God disapproves of to deceive those who are dying, those who refused to love the truth that would save them. ¹¹ That's why God will send them a powerful delusion so that they will believe a lie. ¹² Then everyone who did not believe the truth, but was delighted with what God disapproves of, will be condemned.

Paul Encourages the Thessalonians

¹³ We always have to thank God for you, brothers and sisters. You are loved by the Lord and we thank God that in the beginning he chose you to be saved through a life of spiritual devotion and faith in the truth. ¹⁴ With this in mind he called you by the Good News which we told you so that you would obtain the glory of our Lord Jesus Christ.

¹⁵ Then, brothers and sisters, firmly hold on to the traditions we taught you either when we spoke to you or in our letter.

---

a 1:2 Or "Grace."

[16] God our Father loved us and by his kindness[a] gave us everlasting encouragement and good hope. Together with our Lord Jesus Christ, [17] may he encourage and strengthen you to do and say everything that is good.

Paul's Final Instructions for the Thessalonians

3 [1] Finally, brothers and sisters, pray that we spread the Lord's word rapidly and that it will be honored the way it was among you. [2] Also pray that we may be rescued from worthless and evil people, since not everyone shares our faith. [3] But the Lord is faithful and will strengthen you and protect you against the evil one.

[4] The Lord gives us confidence that you are doing and will continue to do what we ordered you to do. [5] May the Lord direct your lives as you show God's love and Christ's endurance.

[6] Brothers and sisters, in the name of our Lord Jesus Christ we order you not to associate with any believer who doesn't live a disciplined life and doesn't follow the tradition you received from us. [7] You know what you must do to imitate us. We lived a disciplined life among you. [8] We didn't eat anyone's food without paying for it. Instead, we worked hard and struggled night and day in order not to be a burden to any of you. [9] It's not as though we didn't have a right to receive support. Rather, we wanted to set an example for you to follow. [10] While we were with you, we gave you the order: "Whoever doesn't want to work shouldn't be allowed to eat."

[11] We hear that some of you are not living disciplined lives. You're not working, so you go around interfering in other people's lives. [12] We order and encourage such people by the Lord Jesus Christ to pay attention to their own work so they can support themselves. [13] Brothers and sisters, we can't allow ourselves to get tired of doing what is right.

[14] It may be that some people will not listen to what we say in this letter. Take note of them and don't associate with them so that they will feel ashamed. [15] Yet, don't treat them like enemies, but instruct them like brothers and sisters.

Farewell

[16] May the Lord of peace give you his peace at all times and in every way. The Lord be with all of you.

[17] I, Paul, am writing this greeting with my own hand. In every letter that I send, this is proof that I wrote it.

[18] The good will[a] of our Lord Jesus Christ be with all of you.

---

[a] 2:16; 3:18 Or "grace."

1 TIMOTHY

Greeting

1 [1] From Paul, an apostle of Christ Jesus by the command of God our Savior and Christ Jesus our confidence.

[2] To Timothy, a genuine child in faith.

Good will,[a] mercy, and peace from God the Father and Christ Jesus our Lord are yours!

A Warning About False Teachers

[3] When I was going to the province of Macedonia, I encouraged you to stay in the city of Ephesus. That way you could order certain people to stop teaching false doctrine [4] and occupying themselves with myths and endless genealogies. These myths and genealogies raise a lot of questions rather than promoting God's plan, which centers in faith.

[5] My goal in giving you this order is for love to flow from a pure heart, from a clear conscience, and from a sincere faith. [6] Some people have left these qualities behind and have turned to useless discussions. [7] They want to be experts in Moses' Teachings. However, they don't understand what they're talking about or the things about which they speak so confidently.

[8] We know that Moses' Teachings are good if they are used as they were intended to be used. [9] For example, a person must realize that laws are not intended for people who have God's approval. Laws are intended for lawbreakers and rebels, for ungodly people and sinners, for those who think nothing is holy or sacred, for those who kill their fathers, their mothers, or other people. [10] Laws are intended for people involved in sexual sins, for homosexuals, for kidnappers, for liars, for those who lie when they take an oath, and for whatever else is against accurate teachings. [11] Moses' Teachings were intended to be used in agreement with the Good News that contains the glory of the blessed God. I was entrusted with that Good News.

God's Mercy to Paul

[12] I thank Christ Jesus our Lord that he has trusted me and has appointed me to do his work with the strength he has given me. [13] In the past I cursed him, persecuted him, and acted arrogantly toward him. However, I was treated with mercy because I acted ignorantly in my unbelief. [14] Our Lord was very kind[b] to me. Through his kindness he brought me to faith and gave me the love that Christ Jesus shows people.

[15] This is a statement that can be trusted and deserves complete acceptance: Christ Jesus came into the world to save sinners, and I am the foremost sinner. [16] However, I was treated with mercy so that Christ Jesus could use me, the foremost sinner, to demonstrate his patience. This patience serves as an example for those who would believe in him and live forever. [17] Worship and glory belong forever to the eternal king, the immortal, invisible, and only God. Amen.

Guidelines for the Church

[18] Timothy, my child, I'm giving you this order about the prophecies that are still coming to you: Use these prophecies in faith and with a clear conscience to fight this noble war. [19] Some have refused to let their faith guide their conscience and their faith has been destroyed like a wrecked ship.[c] [20] Among these people are Hymenaeus and Alexander, whom I have handed over to Satan in order to teach them not to dishonor God.

2 [1] First of all, I encourage you to make petitions, prayers, intercessions, and prayers of thanks for all people, [2] for rulers, and for everyone who has authority over us. Pray for these people so that we can have a quiet and peaceful life always lived in a godly and reverent way. [3] This is good and pleases God our Savior. [4] He wants all people to be saved and to learn the truth. [5] There is one God. There is also one mediator between God and humans—a human, Christ Jesus. [6] He sacrificed himself for all people to free them from their sins.

This message is valid for every era. [7] I was appointed to spread this Good News and to be an apostle to teach people who are not Jewish about faith and truth. I'm telling you the truth. I'm not lying.

---

[8] I want men to offer prayers everywhere. They should raise their hands in prayer after putting aside their anger and any quarrels they have with anyone.

[9] I want women to show their beauty by dressing in appropriate clothes that are modest and respectable. Their beauty will be shown by what they do,[a] not by their hair styles or the gold jewelry, pearls, or expensive clothes they wear. [10] This is what is proper for women who claim to have reverence for God.

[11] A woman must learn in silence, in keeping with her position. [12] I don't allow a woman to teach or to have authority over a man. Instead, she should be quiet. [13] After all, Adam was formed first, then Eve. [14] Besides that, Adam was not deceived. It was the woman who was deceived and sinned. [15] However, she and all women will be saved through the birth of the child,[b] if they lead respectable lives in faith, love, and holiness.

Guidelines for Leaders in the Church

3 [1] This is a statement that can be trusted: If anyone sets his heart on being a bishop,[a] he desires something excellent. [2] A bishop must have a good reputation. He must have only one wife, be sober, use good judgment, be respectable, be hospitable, and be able to teach. [3] He must not drink excessively or be a violent person, but he must be gentle. He must not be quarrelsome or love money. [4] He must manage his own family well. His children should respectfully obey him. [5] (If a man doesn't know how to manage his own family, how can he take care of God's church?) [6] He must not be a new Christian, or he might become arrogant like the devil and be condemned. [7] People who are not Christians must speak well of him, or he might become the victim of disgraceful insults that the devil sets as traps for him.

[8] Deacons[a] must also be of good character. They must not be two-faced or addicted to alcohol. They must not use shameful ways to make money. [9] They must have clear consciences about possessing the mystery of the Christian faith. [10] First, a person must be evaluated. Then, if he has a good reputation, he may become a deacon.

[11] Their wives must also be of good character. They must not be gossips, but they must control their tempers and be trustworthy in every way.

[12] A deacon must have only one wife. Deacons must manage their children and their families well. [13] Those deacons who serve well gain an excellent reputation and will have confidence as a result of their faith in Christ Jesus.

[14] I hope to visit you soon. However, I'm writing this to you [15] in case I'm delayed. I want you to know how people who are members of God's family must live. God's family is the church of the living God, the pillar and foundation of the truth.

[16] The mystery that gives us our reverence for God is acknowledged to be great:

> He[b] appeared in his human nature,
>   was approved by the Spirit,
>   was seen by angels,
>   was announced throughout the nations,
>   was believed in the world,
>   and was taken to heaven in glory.

A Prophecy About the Last Times

4 [1] The Spirit says clearly that in later times some believers will desert the Christian faith. They will follow spirits that deceive, and they will believe the teachings of demons. [2] These people will speak lies disguised as truth. Their consciences have been scarred as if branded by a red-hot iron. [3] They will try to stop others from getting married and from eating certain foods. God created food to be received with prayers of thanks by those who believe and know the truth. [4] Everything God created is good. Nothing should be rejected if it is received with prayers of thanks. [5] The word of God and prayer set it apart as holy.

Guidelines for Serving Christ

[6] You are a good servant of Christ Jesus when you point these things out to our brothers and sisters. Then you will be nourished by the words of the Christian faith and the excellent teachings which you have followed closely. [7] Don't have anything to do with godless myths that old women like to tell. Rather, train yourself to live a godly life. [8] Training the body helps a little, but godly living helps in every way. Godly living has the promise of life now and in the world to come. [9] This is a statement that can be trusted and deserves complete acceptance.

---

[a] 2:9 The first part of verse 10 (in Greek) has been moved to verse 9 to express the complex Greek sentence structure more clearly in English.   [b] 2:15 Taken to refer to Jesus. Or "will be saved by having children," or "will be kept safe as they have children."   [a] 3:1, 8 English equivalent difficult.   [b] 3:16 Some manuscripts read "God."

[10] Certainly, we work hard and struggle to live a godly life, because we place our confidence in the living God. He is the Savior of all people, especially of those who believe.

[11] Insist on these things and teach them. [12] Don't let anyone look down on you for being young. Instead, make your speech, behavior, love, faith, and purity an example for other believers. [13] Until I get there, concentrate on reading ˌScriptureˌ in worship, giving encouraging messages, and teaching people. [14] Don't neglect the gift which you received through prophecy when the spiritual leaders[a] placed their hands on you ˌto ordain youˌ. [15] Practice these things. Devote your life to them so that everyone can see your progress. [16] Focus on your life and your teaching. Continue to do what I've told you. If you do this, you will save yourself and those who hear you.

Guidelines for Dealing With Other Christians

5 [1] Never use harsh words when you correct an older man, but talk to him as if he were your father. Talk to younger men as if they were your brothers, [2] older women as if they were your mothers, and younger women as if they were your sisters, while keeping yourself morally pure.

[3] Honor widows who have no families. [4] The children or grandchildren of a widow must first learn to respect their own family by repaying their parents. This is pleasing in God's sight. [5] A widow who has no family has placed her confidence in God by praying and asking for his help night and day. [6] But the widow who lives for pleasure is dead although she is still alive. [7] Insist on these things so that widows will have good reputations. [8] If anyone doesn't take care of his own relatives, especially his immediate family, he has denied the Christian faith and is worse than an unbeliever.

[9] Any widow who had only one husband and is at least 60 years old should be put on your list ˌof widowsˌ. [10] People should tell about the good things she has done: raising children, being hospitable, taking care of believers' needs, helping the suffering, or always doing good things.

[11] Don't include younger widows ˌon your listˌ. Whenever their natural desires become stronger than their devotion to Christ, they'll want to marry. [12] They condemn themselves by rejecting the Christian faith, the faith they first accepted. [13] At the same time, they learn to go around from house to house since they have nothing else to do. Not only this, but they also gossip and get involved in other people's business, saying things they shouldn't say.

[14] So I want younger widows to marry, have children, manage their homes, and not give the enemy any chance to ridicule them. [15] Some of them have already turned away to follow Satan. [16] If any woman is a believer and has relatives who are widows, she should help them. In this way the church is not burdened and can help widows who have no families.

[17] Give double honor to spiritual leaders[a] who handle their duties well. This is especially true if they work hard at teaching the word ˌof Godˌ. [18] After all, Scripture says, "Never muzzle an ox when it is threshing[b] grain," and "The worker deserves his pay."

[19] Don't pay attention to an accusation against a spiritual leader unless it is supported by two or three witnesses. [20] Reprimand those leaders who sin. Do it in front of everyone so that the other leaders will also be afraid.

[21] I solemnly call on you in the sight of God, Christ Jesus, and the chosen angels to be impartial when you follow what I've told you. Never play favorites.

[22] Don't be in a hurry to place your hands on anyone ˌto ordain himˌ. Don't participate in the sins of others. Keep yourself morally pure.

[23] Stop drinking only water. Instead, drink a little wine for your stomach because you are frequently sick.

[24] The sins of some people are obvious, going ahead of them to judgment. The sins of others follow them there. [25] In the same way, the good things that people do are obvious, and those that aren't obvious can't remain hidden.

6 [1] All slaves who believe must give complete respect to their own masters. In this way no one will speak evil of God's name and what we teach. [2] Slaves whose masters also believe should respect their masters even though their masters are also believers. As a result, believers who are slaves should serve their masters even better because those who receive the benefit of their work are believers whom they love.

Guidelines for Living a Godly Life

Teach and encourage people to do these things. [3] Whoever teaches false doctrine and doesn't agree with the accurate words of our Lord Jesus Christ and godly teachings [4] is a conceited person. He shows that he doesn't understand anything. Rather, he has an unhealthy desire to argue and quarrel about words. This produces jealousy, rivalry, cursing, suspicion, [5] and conflict between people whose corrupt minds have been robbed of the truth. They think that a godly life is a way to make a profit.

---

[a] 4:14, 5:17 Or "pastors," or "elders." [b] 5:18 Threshing is the process of beating stalks to separate them from the grain.

[6] A godly life brings huge profits to people who are content with what they have. [7] We didn't bring anything into the world, and we can't take anything out of it. [8] As long as we have food and clothes, we should be satisfied.

[9] But people who want to get rich keep falling into temptation. They are trapped by many stupid and harmful desires which drown them in destruction and ruin. [10] Certainly, the love of money is the root of all kinds of evil. Some people who have set their hearts on getting rich have wandered away from the Christian faith and have caused themselves a lot of grief.

[11] But you, man of God, must avoid these things. Pursue what God approves of: a godly life, faith, love, endurance, and gentleness. [12] Fight the good fight for the Christian faith. Take hold of everlasting life to which you were called and about which you made a good testimony in front of many witnesses.

[13] In the sight of God, who gives life to everything, and in the sight of Christ Jesus, who gave a good testimony in front of Pontius Pilate, [14] I insist that, until our Lord Jesus Christ appears, you obey this command completely. Then you cannot be blamed for doing anything wrong. [15] At the right time God will make this known. God is the blessed and only ruler. He is the King of kings and Lord of lords. [16] He is the only one who cannot die. He lives in light that no one can come near. No one has seen him, nor can they see him. Honor and power belong to him forever! Amen.

[17] Tell those who have the riches of this world not to be arrogant and not to place their confidence in anything as uncertain as riches. Instead, they should place their confidence in God who richly provides us with everything to enjoy. [18] Tell them to do good, to do a lot of good things, to be generous, and to share. [19] By doing this they store up a treasure for themselves which is a good foundation for the future. In this way they take hold of what life really is.

[20] Timothy, guard the Good News which has been entrusted to you. Turn away from pointless discussions and the claims of false knowledge that people use to oppose ˌthe Christian faithˌ. [21] Although some claim to have knowledge, they have abandoned the faith.

God's good will[a] be with all of you.

---

2 TIMOTHY

Greeting

1 [1] From Paul, an apostle of Christ Jesus by God's will—a will that contains Christ Jesus' promise of life. [2] To Timothy, my dear child.

Good will,[a] mercy, and peace from God the Father and Christ Jesus our Lord.

[3] I constantly remember you in my prayers night and day when I thank God, whom I serve with a clear conscience as my ancestors did. [4] I remember your tears and want to see you so that I can be filled with happiness. [5] I'm reminded of how sincere your faith is. That faith first lived in your grandmother Lois and your mother Eunice. I'm convinced that it also lives in you.

Paul's Advice for Timothy

[6] You received a gift from God when I placed my hands on you ˎto ordain youˏ. Now I'm reminding you to fan that gift into flames. [7] God didn't give us a cowardly spirit but a spirit of power, love, and good judgment. [8] So never be ashamed to tell others about our Lord or be ashamed of me, his prisoner. Instead, by God's power, join me in suffering for the sake of the Good News. [9] God saved us and called us to be holy, not because of what we had done, but because of his own plan and kindness.[a] Before the world began, God planned that Christ Jesus would show us God's kindness. [10] Now with the coming of our Savior Christ Jesus, he has revealed it. Christ has destroyed death, and through the Good News he has brought eternal life into full view. [11] I was appointed to be a messenger of this Good News, an apostle, and a teacher.

[12] For this reason I suffer as I do. However, I'm not ashamed. I know whom I trust. I'm convinced that he is able to protect what he had entrusted to me until that day.

[13] With faith and love for Christ Jesus, consider what you heard me say to be the pattern of accurate teachings. [14] With the help of the Holy Spirit who lives in us, protect the Good News that has been entrusted to you.

News About Paul's Coworkers

[15] You know that everyone in the province of Asia has deserted me, including Phygelus and Hermogenes.

[16] May the Lord be merciful to the family of Onesiphorus. He often took care of my needs and wasn't ashamed that I was a prisoner. [17] When he arrived in Rome, he searched hard for me and found me. [18] May the Lord grant that Onesiphorus finds mercy when that day comes. You know very well that he did everything possible to help me in Ephesus.

Remain Focused on Jesus

2 [1] My child, find your source of strength in the kindness[a] of Christ Jesus. [2] You've heard my message, and it's been confirmed by many witnesses. Entrust this message to faithful individuals who will be competent to teach others.

[3] Join me in suffering like a good soldier of Christ Jesus. [4] Whoever serves in the military doesn't get mixed up in non-military activities. This pleases his commanding officer. [5] Whoever enters an athletic competition wins the prize only when playing by the rules. [6] A hard-working farmer should have the first share of the crops. [7] Understand what I'm saying. The Lord will help you understand all these things.

[8] Always think about Jesus Christ. He was brought back to life and is a descendant of David. This is the Good News that I tell others. [9] I'm suffering disgrace for spreading this Good News. I have even been put into prison like a criminal. However, God's word is not imprisoned. [10] For that reason, I endure everything for the sake of those who have been chosen so that they, too, may receive salvation from Christ Jesus with glory that lasts forever. [11] This is a statement that can be trusted:

If we have died with him, we will live with him.
[12] If we endure, we will rule with him.
If we disown him, he will disown us.

---

[a] 1:2, 9; 2:1 Or "Grace."

¹³ If we are unfaithful, he remains faithful
　　·because he cannot be untrue to himself.

¹⁴ Remind believers about these things, and warn them in the sight of God not to quarrel over words. Quarreling doesn't do any good but only destroys those who are listening. ¹⁵ Do your best to present yourself to God as a tried-and-true worker who isn't ashamed to teach the word of truth correctly. ¹⁶ Avoid pointless discussions. People who ˏpay attention to these pointless discussionsˏ will become more ungodly, ¹⁷ and what they say will spread like cancer. Hymenaeus and Philetus are like that. ¹⁸ They have abandoned the truth. They are destroying the faith of others by saying that people who have died have already come back to life.

¹⁹ In spite of all that, God's ˏpeopleˏ have a solid foundation. These words are engraved on it: "The Lord knows those who belong to him," and "Whoever worships the Lord must give up doing wrong."

²⁰ In a large house there are not only objects made of gold and silver, but also those made of wood and clay. Some objects are honored when they are used; others aren't. ²¹ Those who stop associating with dishonorable people will be honored. They will be set apart for the master's use, prepared to do good things.

²² Stay away from lusts which tempt young people. Pursue what has God's approval. Pursue faith, love, and peace together with those who worship the Lord with a pure heart. ²³ Don't have anything to do with foolish and stupid arguments. You know they cause quarrels. ²⁴ A servant of the Lord must not quarrel. Instead, he must be kind to everyone. He must be a good teacher. He must be willing to suffer wrong. ²⁵ He must be gentle in correcting those who oppose the Good News. Maybe God will allow them to change the way they think and act and lead them to know the truth. ²⁶ Then they might come back to their senses and God will free them from the devil's snare so that they can do his will.

Watch Out for Sinful People

3 ¹ You must understand this: In the last days there will be violent periods of time. ² People will be selfish and love money. They will brag, be arrogant, and use abusive language. They will curse their parents, show no gratitude, have no respect for what is holy, ³ and lack normal affection for their families. They will refuse to make peace with anyone. They will be slanderous, lack self-control, be brutal, and have no love for what is good. ⁴ They will be traitors. They will be reckless and conceited. They will love pleasure rather than God. ⁵ They will appear to have a godly life, but they will not let its power change them. Stay away from such people.

⁶ Some of these men go into homes and mislead weak-minded women who are burdened with sins and led by all kinds of desires. ⁷ These women are always studying but are never able to recognize the truth.

⁸ As Jannes and Jambres opposed Moses, so these men oppose the truth. Their minds are corrupt, and the faith they teach is counterfeit. ⁹ Certainly, they won't get very far. Like the stupidity of Jannes and Jambres, their stupidity will be plain to everyone.

Teach the Truth

¹⁰ But you know all about my teachings, my way of life, my purpose, my faith, my patience, my love, and my endurance. ¹¹ You also know about the kind of persecutions and sufferings which happened to me in the cities of Antioch, Iconium, and Lystra. I endured those persecutions, and the Lord rescued me from all of them. ¹² Those who try to live a godly life because they believe in Christ Jesus will be persecuted. ¹³ But evil people and phony preachers will go from bad to worse as they mislead people and are themselves misled.

¹⁴ However, continue in what you have learned and found to be true. You know who your teachers were. ¹⁵ From infancy you have known the Holy Scriptures. They have the power to give you wisdom so that you can be saved through faith in Christ Jesus. ¹⁶ Every Scripture passage is inspired by God. All of them are useful for teaching, pointing out errors, correcting people, and training them for a life that has God's approval. ¹⁷ They equip God's servants so that they are completely prepared to do good things.

Continue to Do Your Work

4 ¹ I solemnly call on you in the presence of God and Christ Jesus, who is going to judge those who are living and those who are dead. I do this because Christ Jesus will come to rule ˏthe worldˏ. ² Be ready to spread the word whether or not the time is right. Point out errors, warn people, and encourage them. Be very patient when you teach.

³ A time will come when people will not listen to accurate teachings. Instead, they will follow their own desires and surround themselves with teachers who tell them what they want to hear. ⁴ People will refuse to listen to the truth and turn to myths.

⁵ But you must keep a clear head in everything. Endure suffering. Do the work of a missionary. Devote yourself completely to your work.

⁶ My life is coming to an end, and it is now time for me to be poured out as a sacrifice to God. ⁷ I have fought the good fight. I have completed the race. I have kept the faith. ⁸ The prize that shows I have God's approval is now waiting for me. The Lord, who is a fair judge, will give me that prize on that day. He will give it not only to me but also to everyone who is eagerly waiting for him to come again.

Paul's Final Instructions to Timothy

⁹ Hurry to visit me soon. ¹⁰ Demas has abandoned me. He fell in love with this present world and went to the city of Thessalonica. Crescens went to the province of Galatia, and Titus went to the province of Dalmatia. ¹¹ Only Luke is with me. Get Mark and bring him with you. He is useful to me in my work. ¹² I'm sending Tychicus to the city of Ephesus as my representative.

¹³ When you come, bring the warm coat I left with Carpus in the city of Troas. Also bring the scrolls and especially the parchments.ᵃ

¹⁴ Alexander the metalworker did me a great deal of harm. The Lord will pay him back for what he did. ¹⁵ Watch out for him. He violently opposed what we said. ¹⁶ At my first hearing no one stood up in my defense. Everyone abandoned me. I pray that it won't be held against them. ¹⁷ However, the Lord stood by me and gave me strength so that I could finish spreading the Good News for all the nations to hear. I was snatched out of a lion's mouth. ¹⁸ The Lord will rescue me from all harm and will take me safely to his heavenly kingdom. Glory belongs to him forever! Amen.

Final Greetings

¹⁹ Give my greetings to Prisca and Aquila and the family of Onesiphorus. ²⁰ Erastus stayed in the city of Corinth and I left Trophimus in the city of Miletus because he was sick. ²¹ Hurry to visit me before winter comes. Eubulus, Pudens, Linus, Claudia and all the brothers and sisters send you greetings.

²² The Lord be with you. His good willᵇ be with all of you.

ᵃ 4:13 Parchments are writing materials made from animal skins.   ᵇ 4:22 Or "grace."

TITUS

Greeting

1 ¹ From Paul, a servant of God and an apostle of Jesus Christ. I was sent to lead God's chosen people to faith and to the knowledge of the truth that leads to a godly life. ² My message is based on the confidence of eternal life. God, who never lies, promised this eternal life before the world began. ³ God has revealed this in every era by spreading his word. I was entrusted with this word by the command of God our Savior.

⁴ To Titus, a genuine child in the faith we share.

Good will*ᵃ* and peace from God the Father and from Christ Jesus our Savior are yours!

Guidelines for Leaders in the Church

⁵ I left you in Crete to do what still needed to be done—appointing spiritual leaders*ᵇ* in every city as I directed you. ⁶ A spiritual leader must have a good reputation. He must have only one wife and have children who are believers. His children shouldn't be known for having wild lifestyles or being rebellious. ⁷ Because a bishop*ᶜ* is a supervisor appointed by God, he must have a good reputation. He must not be a stubborn or irritable person. He must not drink too much or be a violent person. He must not use shameful ways to make money. ⁸ Instead, he must be hospitable, love what is good, use good judgment, be fair and moral, and have self-control. ⁹ He must be devoted to the trustworthy message we teach. Then he can use these accurate teachings to encourage people and correct those who oppose the word.

Correct Whoever Teaches What Is Wrong

¹⁰ There are many believers, especially converts from Judaism, who are rebellious. They speak nonsense and deceive people. ¹¹ They must be silenced because they are ruining whole families by teaching what they shouldn't teach. This is the shameful way they make money. ¹² Even one of their own prophets said, "Cretans are always liars, savage animals, and lazy gluttons." ¹³ That statement is true. For this reason, sharply correct believers so that they continue to have faith that is alive and well. ¹⁴ They shouldn't pay attention to Jewish myths or commands given by people who are always rejecting the truth. ¹⁵ Everything is clean*ᵈ* to those who are clean. But nothing is clean to corrupt unbelievers. Indeed, their minds and their consciences are corrupted. ¹⁶ They claim to know God, but they deny him by what they do. They are detestable, disobedient, and unfit to do anything good.

Guidelines for Christian Living

2 ¹ Tell believers to live the kind of life that goes along with accurate teachings. ² Tell older men to be sober. Tell them to be men of good character, to use good judgment, and to be well-grounded in faith, love, and endurance.

³ Tell older women to live their lives in a way that shows they are dedicated to God. Tell them not to be gossips or addicted to alcohol, but to be examples of virtue. ⁴ In this way they will teach young women to show love to their husbands and children, ⁵ to use good judgment, and to be morally pure. Also, tell them to teach young women to be homemakers, to be kind, and to place themselves under their husbands' authority. Then no one can speak evil of God's word.

⁶ Encourage young men to use good judgment. ⁷ Always set an example by doing good things. When you teach, be an example of moral purity and dignity. ⁸ Speak an accurate message that cannot be condemned. Then those who oppose us will be ashamed because they cannot say anything bad about us.

⁹ Tell slaves who are believers to place themselves under their masters' authority in everything they do. Tell them to please their masters, not to argue with them ¹⁰ or steal from them. Instead, tell slaves to show their masters how good and completely loyal they can be. Then they will show the beauty of the teachings about God our Savior in everything they do.

¹¹ After all, God's saving kindness*ᵃ* has appeared for the benefit of all people. ¹² It trains us to avoid ungodly lives filled with worldly desires so that we can live self-controlled, moral, and

---

ᵃ 1:4; 2:11 Or "Grace."   *ᵇ* 1:5 Or "pastors," or "elders."   *ᶜ* 1:7 English equivalent difficult.   *ᵈ* 1:15 "Clean" refers to anything that Moses' Teachings say is presentable to God.

godly lives in this present world. [13] At the same time we can expect what we hope for—the appearance of the glory of our great God and Savior, Jesus Christ. [14] He gave himself for us to set us free from every sin and to cleanse us so that we can be his special people who are enthusiastic about doing good things.

[15] Tell these things to the believers. Encourage and correct them, using your full authority. Don't let anyone ignore you.

3 [1] Remind believers to willingly place themselves under the authority of government officials. Believers should obey them and be ready to help them with every good thing they do. [2] Believers shouldn't curse anyone or be quarrelsome, but they should be gentle and show courtesy to everyone.

What God Did for Us

[3] Indeed, we, too, were once stupid, disobedient, and misled. We were slaves to many kinds of lusts and pleasures. We were mean and jealous. We were hated, and we hated each other. [4] However, when God our Savior made his kindness and love for humanity appear, [5] he saved us, but not because of anything we had done to gain his approval. Instead, because of his mercy he saved us through the washing in which the Holy Spirit gives us new birth and renewal. [6] God poured a generous amount of the Spirit on us through Jesus Christ our Savior. [7] As a result, God in his kindness[a] has given us his approval and we have become heirs who have the confidence that we have everlasting life. [8] This is a statement that can be trusted. I want you to insist on these things so that those who believe in God can concentrate on setting an example by doing good things. This is good and helps other people.

Advice for Titus

[9] Avoid foolish controversies, arguments about genealogies, quarrels, and fights about Moses' Teachings. This is useless and worthless. [10] Have nothing to do with people who continue to teach false doctrine after you have warned them once or twice. [11] You know that people like this are corrupt. They are sinners condemned by their own actions.

Farewell

[12] When I send Artemas or Tychicus to you, hurry to visit me in the city of Nicopolis. I have decided to spend the winter there. [13] Give Zenas the lawyer and Apollos your best support for their trip so that they will have everything they need.

[14] Our people should also learn how to set an example by doing good things when urgent needs arise so that they can live productive lives.

[15] Everyone with me sends you greetings. Greet our faithful friends.

God's good will[a] be with all of you.

---

[a] 3:7, 15 Or "grace."

PHILEMON

Greeting

¹ From Paul, who is a prisoner for Christ Jesus, and our brother Timothy.

To our dear coworker Philemon, ² our sister Apphia, our fellow soldier Archippus, and the church that meets in your house.

³ Good will[a] and peace from God our Father and the Lord Jesus Christ are yours!

Paul's Prayer for Philemon

⁴ ⌊Philemon,⌋ I always thank my God when I mention you in my prayers because ⁵ I hear about your faithfulness to the Lord Jesus and your love for all of God's people. ⁶ As you share the faith you have in common with others, I pray that you may come to have a complete knowledge of every blessing we have in Christ. ⁷ Your love ⌊for God's people⌋ gives me a lot of joy and encouragement. You, brother, have comforted God's people.

Paul's Advice About Onesimus

⁸ Christ makes me bold enough to order you to do the right thing. ⁹ However, I would prefer to make an appeal on the basis of love. I, Paul, as an old man and now a prisoner for Christ Jesus, ¹⁰ appeal to you for my child Onesimus [Useful]. I became his spiritual father here in prison. ¹¹ Once he was useless to you, but now he is very useful to both of us.

¹² I am sending him back to you. This is like sending you a part of myself. ¹³ I wanted to keep him here with me. Then he could have served me in your place while I am in prison for spreading the Good News. ¹⁴ Yet, I didn't want to do anything without your consent. I want you to do this favor for me out of your own free will without feeling forced to do it.

¹⁵ Maybe Onesimus was gone for a while so that you could have him back forever— ¹⁶ no longer as a slave but better than a slave—as a dear brother. He is especially dear to me, but even more so to you, both as a person and as a Christian.

¹⁷ If you think of me as your partner, welcome him as you would welcome me. ¹⁸ If he wronged you in any way or owes you anything, charge it to me. ¹⁹ I, Paul, promise to pay it back. I'm writing this with my own hand. I won't even mention that you owe me your life. ²⁰ So, because we're brothers in the Lord, do something for me. Give me some comfort because of Christ. ²¹ I am confident as I write to you that you will do this. And I know that you will do even more than I ask.

²² One more thing—have a guest room ready for me. I hope that, because of your prayers, God will give me back to you.

Greetings From Paul's Coworkers

²³ Epaphras, who is a prisoner because of Christ Jesus like I am, ²⁴ and my coworkers Mark, Aristarchus, Demas, and Luke send you greetings.

²⁵ The good will of our Lord Jesus Christ be yours.

ᵃ 3 Or "Grace."

HEBREWS

God Has Spoken to Us Through His Son

1 [1] In the past God spoke to our ancestors at many different times and in many different ways through the prophets. [2] In these last days he has spoken to us through his Son. God made his Son responsible for everything. His Son is the one through whom God made the universe. [3] His Son is the reflection of God's glory and the exact likeness of God's being. He holds everything together through his powerful words. After he had cleansed people from their sins, he received the highest position, the one next to the Father in heaven.

God's Son Is Superior to the Angels

[4] The Son has become greater than the angels since he has been given a name that is superior to theirs. [5] God never said to any of his angels,

"You are my Son.
    Today I have become your Father."

And God never said to any of his angels,

"I will be his Father,
    and he will be my Son."

[6] When God was about to send his firstborn Son into the world, he said,

"All of God's angels must worship him."

[7] God said about the angels,

"He makes his messengers winds.
    He makes his servants flames of fire."

[8] But God said about his Son,

"Your throne, O God, is forever and ever.
    The scepter in your kingdom is a scepter for justice.
[9] You have loved what is right and hated what is wrong.
    That is why God, your God,
        anointed you, rather than your companions, with the oil of joy."

[10] God also said,

"Lord, in the beginning you laid the foundation of the earth.
    With your own hands you made the heavens.
[11] They will come to an end, but you will live forever.
    They will all wear out like clothes.
[12] They will be taken off like a coat.
        You will change them like clothes.
            But you remain the same, and your life will never end."

[13] But God never said to any of the angels,

"Sit in the highest position in heaven
    until I make your enemies your footstool."

[14] What are all the angels? They are spirits sent to serve those who are going to receive salvation.

Everything Is Under Jesus' Control

2 [1] For this reason we must pay closer attention to what we have heard. Then we won't drift away from the truth. [2] After all, the message that the angels brought was reliable, and every violation and act of disobedience was properly punished. [3] So how will we escape punishment if we reject the important message, the message that God saved us? First, the Lord told this saving message. Then those who heard him confirmed that message. [4] God verified

what they said through miraculous signs, amazing things, other powerful acts, and with other gifts from the Holy Spirit as he wanted.

[5] He didn't put the world that will come (about which we are talking) under the angels' control. [6] Instead, someone has declared this somewhere in Scripture:

> "What is a mortal that you should remember him,
>   or the Son of Man[a] that you take care of him?
> [7] You made him a little lower than the angels.
>   You crowned him with glory and honor.
> [8] You put everything under his control."

When God put everything under his Son's control, nothing was left out.

However, at the present time we still don't see everything under his Son's control. [9] Jesus was made a little lower than the angels, but we see him crowned with glory and honor because he suffered death. Through God's kindness[b] he died on behalf of everyone. [10] God is the one for whom and through whom everything exists. Therefore, while God was bringing many sons and daughters to glory, it was the right time to bring Jesus, the source of their salvation, to the end of his work through suffering.

Jesus Became One of Us to Help Us

[11] Jesus, who makes people holy, and all those who are made holy have the same Father. That is why Jesus isn't ashamed to call them brothers and sisters. [12] He says,

> "I will tell my people about your name.
> I will praise you within the congregation."

[13] In addition, Jesus says,

> "I will trust him."

And Jesus says,

> "I am here with the sons and daughters God has given me."

[14] Since all of these sons and daughters have flesh and blood, Jesus took on flesh and blood to be like them. He did this so that by dying he would destroy the one who had power over death (that is, the devil). [15] In this way he would free those who were slaves all their lives because they were afraid of dying. [16] So Jesus helps Abraham's descendants rather than helping angels. [17] Therefore, he had to become like his brothers and sisters so that he could be merciful. He became like them so that he could serve as a faithful chief priest in God's presence and make peace with God for their sins. [18] Because Jesus experienced temptation when he suffered, he is able to help others when they are tempted.

Christs Is Superior to Moses

3 [1] Brothers and sisters, you are holy partners in a heavenly calling. So look carefully at Jesus, the apostle and chief priest about whom we make our declaration of faith. [2] Jesus is faithful to God, who appointed him, in the same way that Moses was faithful when he served in God's house. [3] Jesus deserves more praise than Moses in the same way that the builder of a house is praised more than the house. [4] After all, every house has a builder, but the builder of everything is God. [5] Moses was a faithful servant in God's household. He told the people what God would say in the future. [6] But Christ is a faithful son in charge of God's household. We are his household if we continue to have courage and to be proud of the confidence we have.

[7] As the Holy Spirit says,

> "If you hear God speak today, don't be stubborn.
> [8] Don't be stubborn like those who rebelled
>   and tested me in the desert.
> [9]   That is where your ancestors tested me,
> [10]   although they had seen what I had done for 40 years.
> That is why I was angry with those people. So I said,
> 'Their hearts continue to stray,
>   and they have not learned my ways.'
> [11] So I angrily took a solemn oath
>   that they would never enter my place of rest."

---

[a] 2:6 "Son of Man" is a name for Jesus. It shows that he was not only God's Son but also human. Some believe "son of man" here refers to humans in general.   [b] 2:9 Or "grace."

¹² Be careful, brothers and sisters, that none of you ever develop a wicked, unbelieving heart that turns away from the living God. ¹³ Encourage each other every day while you have the opportunity. If you do this, none of you will be deceived by sin and become stubborn. ¹⁴ After all, we will remain Christ's partners only if we continue to hold on to our original confidence until the end.

¹⁵ Scripture says,

> "If you hear God speak today, don't be stubborn.
>   Don't be stubborn like those who rebelled."

¹⁶ Who heard God and rebelled? All those whom Moses led out of Egypt rebelled. ¹⁷ With whom was God angry for 40 years? He was angry with those who sinned and died in the desert. ¹⁸ Who did God swear would never enter his place of rest? He was talking about those who didn't obey him. ¹⁹ So we see that they couldn't enter his place of rest because they didn't believe.

We Will Enter God's Place of Rest

4 ¹ God's promise that we may enter his place of rest still stands. We are afraid that some of you think you won't enter his place of rest. ² We have heard the same Good News that your ancestors heard. But the message didn't help those who heard it in the past because they didn't believe.

³ We who believe are entering that place of rest. As God said, "So I angrily took a solemn oath that they would never enter my place of rest." God said this even though he had finished his work when he created the world. ⁴ Somewhere in Scripture God has said this about the seventh day: "On the seventh day God rested from all his work."

⁵ God also said in the same passage, "They will never enter my place of rest." ⁶ However, some people enter that place of rest. Those who heard the Good News in the past did not enter God's place of rest because they did not obey God. ⁷ So God set another day. That day is today. Many years after your ancestors failed to enter that place of rest, God spoke about it through David in the passage already quoted: "If you hear God speak today, don't be stubborn." ⁸ If Joshua had given the people rest, God would not have spoken about another day. ⁹ Therefore, a time of rest and worship exists for God's people. ¹⁰ Those who entered his place of rest also rested from their work as God did from his.

¹¹ So we must make every effort to enter that place of rest. Then no one will be lost by following the example of those who refused to obey.

¹² God's word is living and active. It is sharper than any two-edged sword and cuts as deep as the place where soul and spirit meet, the place where joints and marrow meet. God's word judges a person's thoughts and intentions. ¹³ No creature can hide from God. Everything is uncovered and exposed for him to see. We must answer to him.

Christ Is Superior to Other Chief Priests

¹⁴ We need to hold on to our declaration of faith: We have a superior chief priest who has gone through the heavens. That person is Jesus, the Son of God. ¹⁵ We have a chief priest who is able to sympathize with our weaknesses. He was tempted in every way that we are, but he didn't sin. ¹⁶ So we can go confidently to the throne of God's kindness[a] to receive mercy and find kindness, which will help us at the right time.

5 ¹ Every chief priest is chosen from humans to represent them in front of God, that is, to offer gifts and sacrifices for sin. ² The chief priest can be gentle with people who are ignorant and easily deceived, because he also has weaknesses. ³ Because he has weaknesses, he has to offer sacrifices for his own sins in the same way that he does for the sins of his people.

⁴ No one takes this honor for himself. Instead, God calls him as he called Aaron. ⁵ So Christ did not take the glory of being a chief priest for himself. Instead, the glory was given to him by God, who said,

> "You are my Son.
>   Today I have become your Father."

⁶ In another place in Scripture, God said,

> "You are a priest forever,
>   in the way Melchizedek was a priest."

⁷ During his life on earth, Jesus prayed to God, who could save him from death. He prayed and pleaded with loud crying and tears, and he was heard because of his devotion to God. ⁸ Although Jesus was the Son of God, he learned to be obedient through his sufferings.

ᵃ 4:16 Or "grace."

[9] After he had finished his work, he became the source of eternal salvation for everyone who obeys him. [10] God appointed him chief priest in the way Melchizedek was a priest.

You Need Someone to Teach You

[11] We have a lot to explain about this. But since you have become too lazy to pay attention, explaining it to you is hard. [12] By now you should be teachers. Instead, you still need someone to teach you the elementary truths of God's word. You need milk, not solid food. [13] All those who live on milk lack the experience to talk about what is right. They are still babies. [14] However, solid food is for mature people, whose minds are trained by practice to know the difference between good and evil.

6 [1] With this in mind, we should stop going over the elementary truths about Christ and move on to topics for more mature people. We shouldn't repeat the basics about turning away from the useless things we did and the basics about faith in God. [2] We shouldn't repeat the basic teachings about such things as baptisms, setting people apart for holy tasks, dead people coming back to life, and eternal judgment. [3] If God permits, we will do this.

[4] Some people once had God's light. They experienced the heavenly gift and shared in the Holy Spirit. [5] They experienced the goodness of God's word and the powers of the world to come. [6] Yet, they have deserted ⌞Christ⌟. They are crucifying the Son of God again and publicly disgracing him. Therefore, they cannot be led a second time to God.

[7] God blesses the earth. So rain often falls on it, and it produces useful crops for farmers. [8] However, if the earth produces thorns and thistles, it is worthless and in danger of being cursed. In the end it will be burned.

God Will Not Forget You

[9] Dear friends, even though we say these things, we are still convinced that better things are in store for you and that they will save you. [10] God is fair. He won't forget what you've done or the love you've shown for him. You helped his holy people, and you continue to help them. [11] We want each of you to prove that you're working hard so that you will remain confident until the end. [12] Then, instead of being lazy, you will imitate those who are receiving the promises through faith and patience.

[13] God made a promise to Abraham. Since he had no one greater on whom to base his oath, he based it on himself. [14] He said, "I will certainly bless you and give you many descendants." [15] So Abraham received what God promised because he waited patiently for it.

[16] When people take oaths, they base their oaths on someone greater than themselves. Their oaths guarantee what they say and end all arguments. [17] God wouldn't change his plan. He wanted to make this perfectly clear to those who would receive his promise, so he took an oath. [18] God did this so that we would be encouraged. God cannot lie when he takes an oath or makes a promise. These two things can never be changed. Those of us who have taken refuge in him hold on to the confidence we have been given. [19] We have this confidence as a sure and strong anchor for our lives. This confidence goes into the ⌞holy⌟ place behind the curtain [20] where Jesus went before us on our behalf. He has become the chief priest forever in the way Melchizedek was a priest.

Christ Is Superior to Melchizedek

7 [1] Melchizedek was king of Salem and priest of the Most High God. He met Abraham and blessed him when Abraham was returning from defeating the kings. [2] Abraham gave Melchizedek a tenth of everything he had captured.

In the first place, Melchizedek's name means king of righteousness. He is also called king of Salem (which means king of peace). [3] No one knows anything about Melchizedek's father, mother, or ancestors. No one knows when he was born or when he died. Like the Son of God, Melchizedek continues to be a priest forever.

[4] You can see how important Melchizedek was. Abraham gave him a tenth of what he had captured, even though Abraham was the father of the chosen people. [5] Moses' Teachings say that members of the tribe of Levi who become priests must receive a tenth of everything from the people. The priests collect it from their own people, Abraham's descendants. [6] Although Melchizedek was not from the tribe of Levi, he received a tenth of everything from Abraham. Then Melchizedek blessed Abraham, who had God's promises. [7] No one can deny that the more important person blesses the less important person.

[8] Priests receive a tenth of everything, but they die. Melchizedek received a tenth of everything, but we are told that he lives. [9] We could even say that when Abraham gave Melchizedek a tenth of everything, Levi was giving a tenth of everything. Levi gave, although later his descendants would receive a tenth of everything. [10] Even though Levi had not yet been born, he was in the body of Abraham when Melchizedek met him.

¹¹ The people established the Levitical priesthood based on instructions they received. If the work of the Levitical priests had been perfect, we wouldn't need to speak about another kind of priest. However, we speak about another kind of priest, a priest like Melchizedek, not a Levitical priest like Aaron.

¹² When a different kind of priesthood is established, the regulations for those priests are different. ¹³ The priest whom we are talking about was a member of a different tribe. No one from that tribe ever served as a priest at the altar. ¹⁴ Everyone knows that our Lord came from the tribe of Judah. Moses never said anything about priests coming from that tribe. ¹⁵ The regulations were different. This became clear when a different priest who is like Melchizedek appeared. ¹⁶ That person is a priest, not because he met human requirements, but because he has power that comes from a life that cannot be destroyed. ¹⁷ The Scriptures say the following about him: "You are a priest forever, in the way Melchizedek was a priest." ¹⁸ The former requirements are rejected because they are weak and useless. ¹⁹ Moses' Teachings couldn't accomplish everything that God required. But we have something else that gives us greater confidence and allows us to approach God.

²⁰ None of this happened without an oath. The men from the tribe of Levi may have become priests without an oath, ²¹ but Jesus became a priest when God took an oath. God said about him, "The Lord has taken an oath and will not change his mind. You are a priest forever." ²² In this way Jesus has become the guarantee of a better promise.ᵃ

²³ There was a long succession of priests because when a priest died he could no longer serve. ²⁴ But Jesus lives forever, so he serves as a priest forever. ²⁵ That is why he is always able to save those who come to God through him. He can do this because he always lives and intercedes for them.

²⁶ We need a chief priest who is holy, innocent, pure, set apart from sinners, and who has the highest position in heaven. ²⁷ We need a priest who doesn't have to bring daily sacrifices as those chief priests did. First they brought sacrifices for their own sins, and then they brought sacrifices for the sins of the people. Jesus brought the sacrifice for the sins of the people once and for all when he sacrificed himself. ²⁸ Moses' Teachings designated mortals as chief priests even though they had weaknesses. But God's promise, which came after Moses' Teachings, designated the Son who forever accomplished everything that God required.

Jesus' Priestly Work Is Superior to Other Priests' Work

8 ¹ The main point we want to make is this: We do have this kind of chief priest. This chief priest has received the highest position, the throne of majesty in heaven. ² He serves as priest of the holy place and of the true tent set up by the Lord and not by any human.

³ Every chief priest is appointed to offer gifts and sacrifices. Therefore, this chief priest had to offer something. ⁴ If he were on earth, he would not even be a priest. On earth ⌐other⌐ priests offer gifts by following the instructions that Moses gave. ⁵ They serve at a place that is a pattern, a shadow, of what is in heaven. When Moses was about to make the tent, God warned him, "Be sure to make everything based on the plan I showed you on the mountain."

⁶ Jesus has been given a priestly work that is superior to the Levitical priests' work. He also brings a better promiseᵃ from God that is based on better guarantees. ⁷ If nothing had been wrong with the first promise, no one would look for another one. ⁸ But God found something wrong with his people and said to them,

> "The days are coming, says the Lord, when I will make a new promise to Israel and Judah. ⁹ It will not be like the promise that I made to their ancestors when I took them by the hand and brought them out of Egypt. They rejected that promise, so I ignored them, says the Lord. ¹⁰ But this is the promise that I will make to Israel after those days, says the Lord: I will put my teachings inside them, and I will write those teachings on their hearts. I will be their God, and they will be my people. ¹¹ No longer will each person teach his neighbors or his relatives by saying, 'Know the Lord.' All of them from the least important to the most important will all know me ¹² because I will forgive their wickedness and I will no longer hold their sins against them."

¹³ God made this new promise and showed that the first promise was outdated. What is outdated and aging will soon disappear.

Christ Offered a Superior Sacrifice

9 ¹ The first promise had rules for the priests' service. It also had a holy place on earth. ² A tent was set up. The first part of this tent was called the holy place. The lamp stand, the table, and the bread of the presence were in this part of the tent. ³ Behind the second curtain was the part of the tent called the most holy place. ⁴ It contained the gold incense burner and

the ark of the Lord's promise. The ark was completely covered with gold. In the ark were the gold jar filled with manna, Aaron's staff that had blossomed, and the tablets on which the promise[a] was written. [5] Above the ark were the angels[b] of glory with their wings overshadowing the throne of mercy. (Discussing these things in detail isn't possible now.)

[6] That is how these two parts of the tent were set up. The priests always went into the first part of the tent to perform their duties. [7] But only the chief priest went into the second part of the tent. Once a year he entered and brought blood that he offered for himself and for the things that the people did wrong unintentionally. [8] The Holy Spirit used this to show that the way into the most holy place was not open while the tent was still in use.

[9] The first part of the tent is an example for the present time. The gifts and sacrifices that were brought there could not give the worshiper a clear conscience. [10] These gifts and sacrifices were meant to be food, drink, and items used in various purification ceremonies. These ceremonies were required for the body until God would establish a new way of doing things.

[11] But Christ came as a chief priest of the good things that are now here. Christ went through a better, more perfect tent that was not made by human hands and that is not part of this created world. [12] He used his own blood, not the blood of goats and bulls, for the sacrifice. He went into the most holy place and offered this sacrifice once and for all to free us forever.

[13] The blood of goats and bulls and the ashes of cows sprinkled on unclean[c] people made their bodies holy and clean. [14] The blood of Christ, who had no defect, does even more. Through the eternal Spirit he offered himself to God and cleansed our consciences from the useless things we had done. Now we can serve the living God.

[15] Because Christ offered himself to God, he is able to bring a new promise from God. Through his death he paid the price to set people free from the sins they committed under the first promise. He did this so that those who are called can be guaranteed an inheritance that will last forever.

[16] In order for a will to take effect, it must be shown that the one who made it has died. [17] A will is used only after a person is dead because it goes into effect only when a person dies.

[18] That is why even the first promise was made with blood. [19] As Moses' Teachings tell us, Moses told all the people every commandment. Then he took the blood of calves and goats together with some water, red yarn, and hyssop and sprinkled the scroll and all the people. [20] He said, "Here is the blood that seals the promise God has made to you." [21] In the same way, Moses sprinkled blood on the tent and on everything used in worship. [22] As Moses' Teachings tell us, blood was used to cleanse almost everything, because if no blood is shed, no sins can be forgiven.

[23] The copies of the things in heaven had to be cleansed by these sacrifices. But the heavenly things themselves had to be cleansed by better sacrifices. [24] Christ didn't go into a holy place made by human hands. He didn't go into a model of the real thing. Instead, he went into heaven to appear in God's presence on our behalf. [25] Every year the chief priest went into the holy place to make a sacrifice with blood that isn't his own. However, Christ didn't go into heaven to sacrifice himself again and again. [26] Otherwise, he would have had to suffer many times since the world was created. But now, at the end of the ages, he has appeared once to remove sin by his sacrifice. [27] People die once, and after that they are judged. [28] Likewise, Christ was sacrificed once to take away the sins of humanity, and after that he will appear a second time. This time he will not deal with sin, but he will save those who eagerly wait for him.

We Can Enter the Most Holy Place Because of Christ's Superior Work

10 [1] Moses' Teachings with their yearly cycle of sacrifices are only a shadow of the good things in the future. They aren't an exact likeness of those things. They can never make those who worship perfect. [2] If these sacrifices could have made the worshipers perfect, the sacrifices would have stopped long ago. Those who worship would have been cleansed once and for all. Their consciences would have been free from sin. [3] Instead, this yearly cycle of sacrifices reminded people of their sins. [4] (The blood of bulls and goats cannot take away sins.)

[5] For this reason, when Christ came into the world, he said,

" 'You did not want sacrifices and offerings,
    but you prepared a body for me.
[6]   You did not approve of burnt offerings and sacrifices for sin.'
[7]   Then I said, 'I have come!
    (It is written about me in the scroll of the book.)
    I have come to do what you want, my God.' "

[8] In this passage Christ first said, "You did not want sacrifices, offerings, burnt offerings, and sacrifices for sin. You did not approve of them." (These are the sacrifices that Moses' Teachings

---

[a] 9:4 Or "covenant."   [b] 9:5 Or "cherubim."   [c] 9:13 "Unclean" refers to anything that Moses' Teachings say is not presentable to God.

require people to offer.) ⁹Then Christ says, "I have come to do what you want." He did away with sacrifices in order to establish the obedience that God wants. ¹⁰We have been set apart as holy because Jesus Christ did what God wanted him to do by sacrificing his body once and for all.

¹¹Every day each priest performed his religious duty. He offered the same type of sacrifice again and again. Yet, these sacrifices could never take away sins. ¹²However, this chief priest made one sacrifice for sins, and this sacrifice lasts forever. Then he received the highest position in heaven. ¹³Since that time, he has been waiting for his enemies to be made his footstool. ¹⁴With one sacrifice he accomplished the work of setting them apart for God forever.

¹⁵The Holy Spirit tells us the same thing: ¹⁶"This is the promise* that I will make to them after those days, says the Lord: 'I will put my teachings in their hearts and write them in their minds.' "

¹⁷Then he adds, "I will no longer hold their sins and their disobedience against them."

¹⁸When sins are forgiven, there is no longer any need to sacrifice for sins.

¹⁹Brothers and sisters, because of the blood of Jesus we can now confidently go into the holy place. ²⁰Jesus has opened a new and living way for us to go through the curtain. (The curtain is his own body.) ²¹We have a superior priest in charge of God's house. ²²We have been sprinkled ˌwith his bloodˌ to free us from a guilty conscience, and our bodies have been washed with clean water. So we must continue to come ˌto himˌ with a sincere heart and strong faith. ²³We must continue to hold firmly to our declaration of faith. The one who made the promise is faithful.

Encourage Each Other

²⁴We must also consider how to encourage each other to show love and to do good things. ²⁵We should not stop gathering together with other believers, as some of you are doing. Instead, we must continue to encourage each other even more as we see the day of the Lord coming.

²⁶If we go on sinning after we have learned the truth, no sacrifice can take away our sins. ²⁷All that is left is a terrifying wait for judgment and a raging fire that will consume God's enemies. ²⁸If two or three witnesses accused someone of rejecting Moses' Teachings, that person was shown no mercy as he was executed. ²⁹What do you think a person who shows no respect for the Son of God deserves? That person looks at the blood of the promise (the blood that made him holy) as no different from other people's blood, and he insults the Spirit that God gave us out of his kindness.ᵇ He deserves a much worse punishment. ³⁰We know the God who said,

> "I alone have the right to take revenge.
> I will pay back."

God also said,

> "The Lord will judge his people."

³¹Falling into the hands of the living God is a terrifying thing.

³²Remember the past, when you first learned the truth. You endured a lot of hardship and pain. ³³At times you were publicly insulted and mistreated. At times you associated with people who were treated this way. ³⁴You suffered with prisoners. You were cheerful even though your possessions were stolen, since you know that you have a better and more permanent possession.ᶜ

³⁵So don't lose your confidence. It will bring you a great reward. ³⁶You need endurance so that after you have done what God wants you to do, you can receive what he has promised.

> ³⁷ "Yet, the one who is coming will come soon. He will not delay.
> ³⁸ The person who has God's approval will live by faith.
> But if he turns back, I will not be pleased with him."

³⁹We don't belong with those who turn back and are destroyed. Instead, we belong with those who have faith and are saved.

Faith Directed People's Lives

11 ¹Faith assures us of things we expect and convinces us of the existence of things we cannot see. ²God accepted our ancestors because of their faith.

³Faith convinces us that God created the world through his word. This means what can be seen was made by something that could not be seen.

⁴Faith led Abel to offer God a better sacrifice than Cain's sacrifice. Through his faith Abel received God's approval, since God accepted his sacrifices. Through his faith Abel still speaks, even though he is dead.

⁵Faith enabled Enoch to be taken instead of dying. No one could find him, because God had taken him. Scripture states that before Enoch was taken, God was pleased with him. ⁶No

---

ᵃ 10:16 Or "covenant." *ᵇ* 10:29 Or "grace."   *ᶜ* 10:34 Some manuscripts and translations add "in heaven."

one can please God without faith. Whoever goes to God must believe that God exists and that he rewards those who seek him.

⁷ Faith led Noah to listen when God warned him about the things in the future that he could not see. He obeyed God and built a ship to save his family. Through faith Noah condemned the world and received God's approval that comes through faith.

⁸ Faith led Abraham to obey when God called him to go to a place that he would receive as an inheritance. Abraham left his own country without knowing where he was going.

⁹ Faith led Abraham to live as a foreigner in the country that God had promised him. He lived in tents, as did Isaac and Jacob, who received the same promise from God. ¹⁰ Abraham was waiting for the city that God had designed and built, the city with permanent foundations.

¹¹ Faith enabled Abraham to become a father, even though he was old and Sarah had never been able to have children. Abraham trusted that God would keep his promise. ¹² Abraham was as good as dead. Yet, from this man came descendants as numerous as the stars in the sky and as countless as the grains of sand on the seashore.

¹³ All these people died having faith. They didn't receive the things that God had promised them, but they saw these things coming in the distant future and rejoiced. They acknowledged that they were living as strangers with no permanent home on earth. ¹⁴ Those who say such things make it clear that they are looking for their own country. ¹⁵ If they had been thinking about the country that they had left, they could have found a way to go back. ¹⁶ Instead, these men were longing for a better country—a heavenly country. That is why God is not ashamed to be called their God. He has prepared a city for them.

¹⁷ When God tested Abraham, faith led him to offer his son Isaac. Abraham, the one who received the promises from God, was willing to offer his only son as a sacrifice. ¹⁸ God had said to him, "Through Isaac your descendants will carry on your name." ¹⁹ Abraham believed that God could bring Isaac back from the dead. Abraham did receive Isaac back from the dead in a figurative sense.

²⁰ Faith led Isaac to bless Jacob and Esau.

²¹ While Jacob was dying, faith led him to bless each of Joseph's sons. He leaned on the top of his staff and worshiped God.

²² While Joseph was dying, faith led him to speak about the Israelites leaving Egypt and give them instructions about burying his bones.

²³ Faith led Moses' parents to hide him for three months after he was born. They did this because they saw that Moses was a beautiful baby and they were not afraid to disobey the king's order.

²⁴ When Moses grew up, faith led him to refuse to be known as a son of Pharaoh's daughter. ²⁵ He chose to suffer with God's people rather than to enjoy the pleasures of sin for a little while. ²⁶ He thought that being insulted for Christ would be better than having the treasures of Egypt. He was looking ahead to his reward.

²⁷ Faith led Moses to leave Egypt without being afraid of the king's anger. Moses didn't give up but continued as if he could actually see the invisible God.

²⁸ Faith led Moses to establish the Passover and spread the blood ˏon the doorposts، so that the destroying angel would not kill the firstborn sons.

²⁹ Faith caused the people to go through the Red Sea as if it were dry land. The Egyptians also tried this, but they drowned.

³⁰ Faith caused the walls of Jericho to fall after the Israelites marched around them for seven days.

³¹ Faith led the prostitute Rahab to welcome the spies as friends. She was not killed with those who refused to obey God.

³² What more should I say? I don't have enough time to tell you about Gideon, Barak, Samson, Jephthah, David, Samuel, and the prophets. ³³ Through faith they conquered kingdoms, did what God approved, and received what God had promised. They shut the mouths of lions, ³⁴ put out raging fires, and escaped death. They found strength when they were weak. They were powerful in battle and defeated other armies. ³⁵ Women received their loved ones back from the dead. Other believers were brutally tortured but refused to be released so that they might gain eternal life. ³⁶ Some were made fun of and whipped, and some were chained and put in prison. ³⁷ Some were stoned to death, sawed in half, and killed with swords. Some wore the skins of sheep and goats. Some were poor, abused, and mistreated. ³⁸ The world didn't deserve these good people. Some wandered around in deserts and mountains and lived in caves and holes in the ground.

³⁹ All these people were known for their faith, but none of them received what God had promised. ⁴⁰ God planned to give us something very special so that we would gain eternal life with them.

Faith Directs Our Lives

12 [1] Since we are surrounded by so many examples ˌof faithˌ, we must get rid of everything that slows us down, especially sin that distracts us. We must run the race that lies ahead of us and never give up. [2] We must focus on Jesus, the source and goal of our faith. He saw the joy ahead of him, so he endured death on the cross and ignored the disgrace it brought him. Then he received the highest position in heaven, the one next to the throne of God. [3] Think about Jesus, who endured opposition from sinners, so that you don't become tired and give up.

[4] You struggle against sin, but your struggles haven't killed you. [5] You have forgotten the encouraging words that God speaks to you as his children:

"My child, pay attention when the Lord disciplines you.
Don't give up when he corrects you.
[6]   The Lord disciplines everyone he loves.
He severely disciplines everyone he accepts as his child."

[7] Endure your discipline. God corrects you as a father corrects his children. All children are disciplined by their fathers. [8] If you aren't disciplined like the other children, you aren't part of the family. [9] On earth we have fathers who disciplined us, and we respect them. Shouldn't we place ourselves under the authority of God, the father of spirits, so that we will live? [10] For a short time our fathers disciplined us as they thought best. Yet, God disciplines us for our own good so that we can become holy like him. [11] We don't enjoy being disciplined. It always seems to cause more pain than joy. But later on, those who learn from that discipline have peace that comes from doing what is right.

[12] Strengthen your tired arms and weak knees. [13] Keep walking along straight paths so that your injured leg won't get worse. Instead, let it heal.

[14] Try to live peacefully with everyone, and try to live holy lives, because if you don't, you will not see the Lord. [15] Make sure that everyone has kindness[a] from God so that bitterness doesn't take root and grow up to cause trouble that corrupts many of you. [16] Make sure that no one commits sexual sin or is as concerned about earthly things as Esau was. He sold his rights as the firstborn son for a single meal. [17] You know that afterwards, when he wanted to receive the blessing that the firstborn son was to receive, he was rejected. Even though he begged and cried for the blessing, he couldn't do anything to change what had happened.

[18] You have not come to something that you can feel, to a blazing fire, to darkness, to gloom, to a storm, [19] to a trumpet's blast, and to a voice. When your ancestors heard that voice, they begged not to hear it say another word. [20] They couldn't obey the command that was given, "If even an animal touches the mountain, it must be stoned to death." [21] The sight was so terrifying that even Moses said he was trembling and afraid.

[22] Instead, you have come to Mount Zion, to the city of the living God, to the heavenly Jerusalem. You have come to tens of thousands of angels joyfully gathered together [23] and to the assembly of God's firstborn children (whose names are written in heaven). You have come to a judge (the God of all people) and to the spirits of people who have God's approval and have gained eternal life. [24] You have come to Jesus, who brings the new promise[b] from God, and to the sprinkled blood that speaks a better message than Abel's.

[25] Be careful that you do not refuse to listen when God speaks. Your ancestors didn't escape when they refused to listen to God, who warned them on earth. We certainly won't escape if we turn away from God, who warns us from heaven. [26] When God spoke to your ancestors, his voice shook the earth. But now he has promised, "Once more I will shake not only the earth but also the sky."

[27] The words *once more* show clearly that God will change what he has made. These are the things that can be shaken. Then only the things that cannot be shaken will remain. [28] Therefore, we must be thankful that we have a kingdom that cannot be shaken. Because we are thankful, we must serve God with fear and awe in a way that pleases him. [29] After all, our God is a destructive fire.

13 [1] Continue to love each other. [2] Don't forget to show hospitality to believers you don't know. By doing this some believers have shown hospitality to angels without being aware of it. [3] Remember those in prison as if you were in prison with them. Remember those who are mistreated as if you were being mistreated.

[4] Marriage is honorable in every way, so husbands and wives should be faithful to each other. God will judge those who commit sexual sins, especially those who commit adultery.

[5] Don't love money. Be happy with what you have because God has said, "I will never abandon you or leave you." [6] So we can confidently say,

---

[a] 12:15 Or "grace."   [b] 12:24 Or "covenant."

> "The Lord is my helper.
>> I will not be afraid.
>>> What can mortals do to me?"

[7] Remember your leaders who have spoken God's word to you. Think about how their lives turned out, and imitate their faith.

[8] Jesus Christ is the same yesterday, today, and forever.

[9] Don't get carried away by all kinds of unfamiliar teachings. Gaining inner strength from God's kindness[a] is good for us. This strength does not come from following rules about food, rules that don't help those who follow them. [10] Those who serve at the tent have no right to eat what is sacrificed at our altar.

[11] The chief priest brings the blood of animals into the holy place as an offering for sin. But the bodies of those animals were burned outside the Israelite camp. [12] That is why Jesus suffered outside the gates of Jerusalem. He suffered to make the people holy with his own blood. [13] So we must go to him outside the camp and endure the insults he endured. [14] We don't have a permanent city here on earth, but we are looking for the city that we will have in the future. [15] Through Jesus we should always bring God a sacrifice of praise, that is, words that acknowledge him. [16] Don't forget to do good things for others and to share what you have with them. These are the kinds of sacrifices that please God.

[17] Obey your leaders, and accept their authority. They take care of you because they are responsible for you. Obey them so that they may do this work joyfully and not complain about you. (Causing them to complain would not be to your advantage.)

[18] Pray for us. We are sure that our consciences are clear because we want to live honorably in every way. [19] I especially ask for your prayers so that I may come back to you soon.

[20] The God of peace brought the great shepherd of the sheep, our Lord Jesus, back to life through the blood of an eternal promise.[b] [21] May this God of peace prepare you to do every good thing he wants. May he work in us through Jesus Christ to do what is pleasing to him. Glory belongs to Jesus Christ forever. Amen.

Farewell

[22] I urge you, brothers and sisters, to listen patiently to my encouraging words. I have written you a short letter. [23] You know that Timothy, our brother, has been freed. If he comes here soon, both of us will visit you.

[24] Greet all your leaders and all God's holy people. Those who are with us from Italy greet you.
[25] May God's good will[a] be with all of you!

---

[a] 13:9, 25 Or "grace."   [b] 13:20 Or "covenant."

JAMES

Greeting

1 ¹ From James, a servant of God and of the Lord Jesus Christ. To God's faithful people*a* who have been scattered. Greetings.

When You Are Tested, Turn to God

² My brothers and sisters, be very happy when you are tested in different ways. ³ You know that such testing of your faith produces endurance. ⁴ Endure until your testing is over. Then you will be mature and complete, and you won't need anything.

⁵ If any of you needs wisdom to know what you should do, you should ask God, and he will give it to you. God is generous to everyone and doesn't find fault with them. ⁶ When you ask for something, don't have any doubts. A person who has doubts is like a wave that is blown by the wind and tossed by the sea. ⁷ A person who has doubts shouldn't expect to receive anything from the Lord. ⁸ A person who has doubts is thinking about two different things at the same time and can't make up his mind about anything.

⁹ Humble believers should be proud because being humble makes them important. ¹⁰ Rich believers should be proud because being rich should make them humble. Rich people will wither like flowers. ¹¹ The sun rises with its scorching heat and dries up plants. The flowers drop off, and the beauty is gone. The same thing will happen to rich people. While they are busy, they will die.

¹² Blessed are those who endure when they are tested. When they pass the test, they will receive the crown of life that God has promised to those who love him. ¹³ When someone is tempted, he shouldn't say that God is tempting him. God can't be tempted by evil, and God doesn't tempt anyone. ¹⁴ Everyone is tempted by his own desires as they lure him away and trap him. ¹⁵ Then desire becomes pregnant and gives birth to sin. When sin grows up, it gives birth to death.

¹⁶ My dear brothers and sisters, don't be fooled. ¹⁷ Every good present and every perfect gift comes from above, from the Father who made the sun, moon, and stars. The Father doesn't change like the shifting shadows produced by the sun and the moon.

¹⁸ God decided to give us life through the word of truth to make us his most important creatures.

¹⁹ Remember this, my dear brothers and sisters: Everyone should be quick to listen, slow to speak, and should not get angry easily. ²⁰ An angry person doesn't do what God approves of. ²¹ So get rid of all immoral behavior and all the wicked things you do. Humbly accept the word that God has placed in you. This word can save you.

²² Do what God's word says. Don't merely listen to it, or you will fool yourselves. ²³ If someone listens to God's word but doesn't do what it says, he is like a person who looks at his face in a mirror, ²⁴ studies his features, goes away, and immediately forgets what he looks like. ²⁵ However, the person who continues to study God's perfect teachings that make people free and who remains committed to them will be blessed. People like that don't merely listen and forget; they actually do what God's teachings say.

²⁶ If a person thinks that he is religious but can't control his tongue, he is fooling himself. That person's religion is worthless. ²⁷ Pure, unstained religion, according to God our Father, is to take care of orphans and widows when they suffer and to remain uncorrupted by this world.

Don't Favor Rich People Over Poor People

2 ¹ My brothers and sisters, practice your faith in our glorious Lord Jesus Christ by not favoring one person over another. ² For example, two men come to your worship service. One man is wearing gold rings and fine clothes; the other man, who is poor, is wearing shabby clothes. ³ Suppose you give special attention to the man wearing fine clothes and say to him, "Please have a seat." But you say to the poor man, "Stand over there," or "Sit on the floor at my feet." ⁴ Aren't you discriminating against people and using a corrupt standard to make judgments?

---

a 1:1 Or "to the twelve tribes."

⁵ Listen, my dear brothers and sisters! Didn't God choose poor people in the world to become rich in faith and to receive the kingdom that he promised to those who love him? ⁶ Yet, you show no respect to poor people. Don't rich people oppress you and drag you into court? ⁷ Don't they curse the good name ˌof Jesusˌ, the name that was used to bless you?

⁸ You are doing right if you obey this law from the highest authority: "Love your neighbor as you love yourself." ⁹ If you favor one person over another, you're sinning, and this law convicts you of being disobedient. ¹⁰ If someone obeys all of God's laws except one, that person is guilty of breaking all of them. ¹¹ After all, the one who said, "Never commit adultery," is the same one who said, "Never murder." If you do not commit adultery but you murder, you become a person who disobeys God's laws.

¹² Talk and act as people who are going to be judged by laws that bring freedom. ¹³ No mercy will be shown to those who show no mercy to others. Mercy triumphs over judgment.

We Show Our Faith by What We Do

¹⁴ My brothers and sisters, what good does it do if someone claims to have faith but doesn't do any good things? Can this kind of faith save him? ¹⁵ Suppose a believer, whether a man or a woman, needs clothes or food ¹⁶ and one of you tells that person, "God be with you! Stay warm, and make sure you eat enough." If you don't provide for that person's physical needs, what good does it do? ¹⁷ In the same way, faith by itself is dead if it doesn't cause you to do any good things.

¹⁸ Another person might say, "You have faith, but I do good things." Show me your faith apart from the good things you do. I will show you my faith by the good things I do. ¹⁹ You believe that there is one God. That's fine! The demons also believe that, and they tremble with fear.

²⁰ You fool! Do you have to be shown that faith which does nothing is useless? ²¹ Didn't our ancestor Abraham receive God's approval as a result of what he did when he offered his son Isaac as a sacrifice on the altar? ²² You see that Abraham's faith and what he did worked together. His faith was shown to be genuine by what he did. ²³ The Scripture passage came true. It says, "Abraham believed God, and that faith was regarded by God to be his approval of Abraham." So Abraham was called God's friend. ²⁴ You see that a person receives God's approval because of what he does, not only because of what he believes. ²⁵ The same is true of the prostitute Rahab who welcomed the spies and sent them away on another road. She received God's approval because of what she did.

²⁶ A body that doesn't breatheᵃ is dead. In the same way faith that does nothing is dead.

Speak Wisely

3 ¹ Brothers and sisters, not many of you should become teachers. You know that we who teach will be judged more severely.

² All of us make a lot of mistakes. If someone doesn't make any mistakes when he speaks, he would be perfect. He would be able to control everything he does. ³ We put bits in the mouths of horses to make them obey us, and we have control over everything they do. ⁴ The same thing is true for ships. They are very big and are driven by strong winds. Yet, by using small rudders, pilots steer ships wherever they want them to go. ⁵ In the same way the tongue is a small part of the body, but it can brag about doing important things.

A large forest can be set on fire by a little flame. ⁶ The tongue is that kind of flame. It is a world of evil among the parts of our bodies, and it completely contaminates our bodies. The tongue sets our lives on fire, and is itself set on fire from hell. ⁷ People have tamed all kinds of animals, birds, reptiles, and sea creatures. ⁸ Yet, no one can tame the tongue. It is an uncontrollable evil filled with deadly poison.

⁹ With our tongues we praise our Lord and Father. Yet, with the same tongues we curse people, who were created in God's likeness. ¹⁰ Praise and curses come from the same mouth. My brothers and sisters, this should not happen! ¹¹ Do clean and polluted water flow out of the same spring? ¹² My brothers and sisters, can a fig tree produce olives? Can a grapevine produce figs? In the same way, a pool of salt water can't produce fresh water.

Live Wisely

¹³ Do any of you have wisdom and insight? Show this by living the right way with the humility that comes from wisdom. ¹⁴ But if you are bitterly jealous and filled with self-centered ambition, don't brag. Don't say that you are wise when it isn't true. ¹⁵ That kind of wisdom doesn't come from above. It belongs to this world. It is self-centered and demonic. ¹⁶ Wherever there is jealousy and rivalry, there is disorder and every kind of evil.

¹⁷ However, the wisdom that comes from above is first of all pure. Then it is peaceful, gentle, obedient, filled with mercy and good deeds, impartial, and sincere. ¹⁸ A harvest that has God's approval comes from the peace planted by peacemakers.

ᵃ 2:26 Or "A body without a spirit."

Stop Fighting With Each Other

4 [1] What causes fights and quarrels among you? Aren't they caused by the selfish desires that fight to control you? [2] You want what you don't have, so you commit murder. You're determined to have things, but you can't get what you want. You quarrel and fight. You don't have the things you want, because you don't pray for them. [3] When you pray for things, you don't get them because you want them for the wrong reason—for your own pleasure.

[4] You unfaithful people! Don't you know that love for this ˛evil˛ world is hatred toward God? Whoever wants to be a friend of this world is an enemy of God. [5] Do you think this passage means nothing? It says, "The Spirit that lives in us wants us to be his own."

[6] But God shows us even more˛kindness.[a] Scripture says,

> "God opposes arrogant people,
>   but he is kind to humble people."

[7] So place yourselves under God's authority. Resist the devil, and he will run away from you. [8] Come close to God, and he will come close to you. Clean up your lives, you sinners, and clear your minds, you doubters. [9] Be miserable, mourn, and cry. Turn your laughter into mourning and your joy into gloom. [10] Humble yourselves in the Lord's presence. Then he will give you a high position.

Stop Slandering Each Other

[11] Brothers and sisters, stop slandering each other. Those who slander and judge other believers slander and judge God's teachings. If you judge God's teachings, you are no longer following them. Instead, you are judging them. [12] There is only one teacher and judge. He is able to save or destroy you. So who are you to judge your neighbor?

Don't Brag About Your Plans for the Future

[13] Pay attention to this! You're saying, "Today or tomorrow we will go into some city, stay there a year, conduct business, and make money." [14] You don't know what will happen tomorrow. What is life? You are a mist that is seen for a moment and then disappears. [15] Instead, you should say, "If the Lord wants us to, we will live and carry out our plans." [16] However, you brag because you're arrogant. All such bragging is evil.

[17] Whoever knows what is right but doesn't do it is sinning.

Advice to Rich People

5 [1] Pay attention to this if you're rich. Cry and moan about the misery that is coming to you. [2] Your riches have decayed, and your clothes have been eaten by moths. [3] Your gold and silver are corroded, and their corrosion will be used as evidence against you. Like fire, it will destroy your body.

You have stored up riches in these last days. [4] The wages you refused to pay the people who harvested your fields shout ˛to God˛ against you. The Lord of Armies has heard the cries of those who gather the crops. [5] You have lived in luxury and pleasure here on earth. You have fattened yourselves for the day of slaughter. [6] You have condemned and murdered people who have God's approval, even though they didn't resist you.

Be Patient

[7] Brothers and sisters, be patient until the Lord comes again. See how farmers wait for their precious crops to grow. They wait patiently for fall and spring rains. [8] You, too, must be patient. Don't give up hope. The Lord will soon be here. [9] Brothers and sisters, stop complaining about each other, or you will be condemned. Realize that the judge is standing at the door.

[10] Brothers and sisters, follow the example of the prophets who spoke in the name of the Lord. They were patient when they suffered unjustly. [11] We consider those who endure to be blessed. You have heard about Job's endurance. You saw that the Lord ended Job's suffering because the Lord is compassionate and merciful.

Don't Take Oaths

[12] Above all things, my brothers and sisters, do not take an oath on anything in heaven or on earth. Do not take any oath. If you mean yes, say yes. If you mean no, say no. Do this so that you won't be condemned.

Prayer Is Powerful

[13] If any of you are having trouble, pray. If you are happy, sing psalms. [14] If you are sick, call for the church leaders. Have them pray for you and anoint you with olive oil[a] in the name of

---

[a] 4:6 Or "grace."   [a] 5:14 People in ancient times used olive oil for healing.

the Lord. [15] (Prayers offered in faith will save those who are sick, and the Lord will cure them.) If you have sinned, you will be forgiven. [16] So admit your sins to each other, and pray for each other so that you will be healed.

Prayers offered by those who have God's approval are effective. [17] Elijah was human like us. Yet, when he prayed that it wouldn't rain, no rain fell on the ground for three-and-a-half years. [18] Then he prayed again. It rained, and the ground produced crops.

Help Those Who Have Wandered Away From the Truth

[19] My brothers and sisters, if one of you wanders from the truth, someone can bring that person back. [20] Realize that whoever brings a sinner back from the error of his ways will save him from death, and many sins will be forgiven.

1 PETER

Greeting

1 ¹ From Peter, an apostle of Jesus Christ.

To God's chosen people who are temporary residents ˏin the worldˏ and are scattered throughout the provinces of Pontus, Galatia, Cappadocia, Asia, and Bithynia. ² God the Father knew you long ago and chose you to live holy lives with the Spirit's help so that you are obedient to Jesus Christ and are sprinkled with his blood.

May good will[a] and peace fill your lives!

Faith in Christ Brings You Joy

³ Praise the God and Father of our Lord Jesus Christ! God has given us a new birth because of his great mercy. We have been born into a new life that has a confidence which is alive because Jesus Christ has come back to life. ⁴ We have been born into a new life which has an inheritance that can't be destroyed or corrupted and can't fade away. That inheritance is kept in heaven for you, ⁵ since you are guarded by God's power through faith for a salvation that is ready to be revealed at the end of time.

⁶ You are extremely happy about these things, even though you have to suffer different kinds of trouble for a little while now. ⁷ The purpose of these troubles is to test your faith as fire tests how genuine gold is. Your faith is more precious than gold, and by passing the test, it gives praise, glory, and honor to God. This will happen when Jesus Christ appears again.

⁸ Although you have never seen Christ, you love him. You don't see him now, but you believe in him. You are extremely happy with joy and praise that can hardly be expressed in words ⁹ as you obtain the salvation that is the goal of your faith.

¹⁰ The prophets carefully researched and investigated this salvation. Long ago they spoke about God's kindness[a] that would come to you. ¹¹ So they tried to find out what time or situation the Spirit of Christ kept referring to whenever he predicted Christ's sufferings and the glory that would follow. ¹² God revealed to the prophets that the things they had spoken were not for their own benefit but for yours. What the prophets had spoken, the Holy Spirit, who was sent from heaven, has now made known to you by those who spread the Good News among you. These are things that even the angels want to look into.

Live Holy Lives

¹³ Therefore, your minds must be clear and ready for action. Place your confidence completely in what God's kindness will bring you when Jesus Christ appears again. ¹⁴ Because you are children who obey God, don't live the kind of lives you once lived. Once you lived to satisfy your desires because you didn't know any better. ¹⁵ But because the God who called you is holy you must be holy in every aspect of your life. ¹⁶ Scripture says, "Be holy, because I am holy." ¹⁷ So if you call God your Father, live your time as temporary residents on earth in fear. He is the God who judges all people by what they have done, and he doesn't play favorites. ¹⁸ Realize that you weren't set free from the worthless life handed down to you from your ancestors by a payment of silver or gold which can be destroyed. ¹⁹ Rather, the payment that freed you was the precious blood of Christ, the lamb with no defects or imperfections. ²⁰ He is the lamb who was known long ago before the world existed, but for your good he became publicly known in the last period of time. ²¹ Through him you believe in God who brought Christ back to life and gave him glory. So your faith and confidence are in God.

Love Each Other

²² Love each other with a warm love that comes from the heart. After all, you have purified yourselves by obeying the truth. As a result you have a sincere love for each other. ²³ You have been born again, not from a seed that can be destroyed, but through God's everlasting word that can't be destroyed. That's why ˏScripture saysˏ,

²⁴   "All people are like grass,
        and all their beauty is like a flower of the field.

---

[a] 1:2, 10 Or "grace."

The grass dries up and the flower drops off,
25   but the word of the Lord lasts forever."

This word is the Good News that was told to you.

Live as God's Chosen People

2 ¹ So get rid of every kind of evil, every kind of deception, hypocrisy, jealousy, and every kind of slander. ² Desire God's pure word as newborn babies desire milk. Then you will grow in your salvation. ³ Certainly you have tasted that the Lord is good!

⁴ You are coming to Christ, the living stone who was rejected by humans but was chosen as precious by God. ⁵ You come to him as living stones, a spiritual house that is being built into a holy priesthood. So offer spiritual sacrifices that God accepts through Jesus Christ. ⁶ That is why Scripture says,

"I am laying a chosen and precious cornerstone in Zion,
    and the person who believes in him
        will never be ashamed."

⁷ This honor belongs to those who believe. But to those who don't believe:

"The stone that the builders rejected
    has become the cornerstone,
8   a stone that people trip over,
            a large rock that people find offensive."

The people tripped over the word because they refused to believe it. Therefore, this is how they ended up.

⁹ However, you are chosen people, a royal priesthood, a holy nation, people who belong to God. You were chosen to tell about the excellent qualities of God, who called you out of darkness into his marvelous light. ¹⁰ Once you were not God's people, but now you are. Once you were not shown mercy, but now you have been shown mercy.

¹¹ Dear friends, since you are foreigners and temporary residents ˌin the worldˌ, I'm encouraging you to keep away from the desires of your corrupt nature. These desires constantly attack you. ¹² Live decent lives among unbelievers. Then, although they ridicule you as if you were doing wrong while they are watching you do good things, they will praise God on the day he comes to help you.

Respect the Authority of Others

¹³ Place yourselves under the authority of human governments to please the Lord. Obey the emperor. He holds the highest position of authority. ¹⁴ Also obey governors. They are people the emperor has sent to punish those who do wrong and to praise those who do right. ¹⁵ God wants you to silence the ignorance of foolish people by doing what is right. ¹⁶ Live as free people, but don't hide behind your freedom when you do evil. Instead, use your freedom to serve God. ¹⁷ Honor everyone. Love your brothers and sisters in the faith. Fear God. Honor the emperor.

¹⁸ Slaves, place yourselves under the authority of your owners and show them complete respect. Obey not only those owners who are good and kind, but also those who are unfair. ¹⁹ God is pleased if a person is aware of him while enduring the pains of unjust suffering. ²⁰ What credit do you deserve if you endure a beating for doing something wrong? But if you endure suffering for doing something good, God is pleased with you.

²¹ God called you to endure suffering because Christ suffered for you. He left you an example so that you could follow in his footsteps. ²² Christ never committed any sin. He never spoke deceitfully. ²³ Christ never verbally abused those who verbally abused him. When he suffered, he didn't make any threats but left everything to the one who judges fairly. ²⁴ Christ carried our sins in his body on the cross so that freed from our sins, we could live a life that has God's approval. His wounds have healed you. ²⁵ You were like lost sheep. Now you have come back to the shepherd and bishopᵃ of your lives.

3 ¹ Wives, in a similar way, place yourselves under your husbands' authority. Some husbands may not obey God's word. Their wives could win these men ˌfor Christˌ by the way they live without saying anything. ² Their husbands would see how pure and reverent their lives are.

³ Wives must not let their beauty be something external. Beauty doesn't come from hairstyles, gold jewelry, or clothes. ⁴ Rather, beauty is something internal that can't be destroyed. Beauty expresses itself in a gentle and quiet attitude which God considers precious. ⁵ After all, this is how holy women who had confidence in God expressed their beauty in the past. They placed themselves under their husbands' authority ⁶ as Sarah did. Sarah obeyed Abraham and

---

ᵃ 2:25 English equivalent difficult.

spoke to him respectfully. You became Sarah's daughters by not letting anything make you afraid to do good.

[7] Husbands, in a similar way, live with your wives with understanding since they are weaker than you are. Honor your wives as those who share God's life-giving kindness[a] so that nothing will interfere with your prayers.

Dedicate Your Lives to Jesus

[8] Finally, everyone must live in harmony, be sympathetic, love each other, have compassion, and be humble. [9] Don't pay people back with evil for the evil they do to you, or ridicule those who ridicule you. Instead, bless them, because you were called to inherit a blessing.

[10]   "People who want to live a full life and enjoy good days
       must keep their tongues from saying evil things,
       and their lips from speaking deceitful things.
[11]   They must turn away from evil and do good.
       They must seek peace and pursue it.
[12]   The Lord's eyes are on those who do what he approves.
       His ears hear their prayer.
       The Lord confronts those who do evil."

[13] Who will harm you if you are devoted to doing what is good? [14] But even if you suffer for doing what God approves, you are blessed. Don't be afraid of those who want to harm you. Don't get upset. [15] But dedicate your lives to Christ as Lord. Always be ready to defend your confidence ⌊in God⌋ when anyone asks you to explain it. However, make your defense with gentleness and respect. [16] Keep your conscience clear. Then those who treat the good Christian life you live with contempt will feel ashamed that they have ridiculed you. [17] After all, if it is God's will, it's better to suffer for doing good than for doing wrong.

[18] This is true because Christ suffered for our sins once. He was an innocent person, but he suffered for guilty people so that he could bring you to God. His body was put to death, but he was brought to life through his spirit. [19] In it he also went to proclaim his victory to the spirits kept in prison. [20] They are like those who disobeyed long ago in the days of Noah when God waited patiently while Noah built the ship. In this ship a few people—eight in all—were saved by water. [21] Baptism, which is like that water, now saves you. Baptism doesn't save by removing dirt from the body. Rather, baptism is a request to God for a clear conscience. It saves you through Jesus Christ, who came back from death to life. [22] Christ has gone to heaven where he has the highest position that God gives. Angels, rulers, and powers have been placed under his authority.

4 [1] Since Christ has suffered physically, take the same attitude that he had. (A person who has suffered physically no longer sins.) [2] That way you won't be guided by sinful human desires as you live the rest of your lives on earth. Instead, you will be guided by what God wants you to do. [3] You spent enough time in the past doing what unbelievers like to do. You were promiscuous, had sinful desires, got drunk, went to wild parties, and took part in the forbidden worship of false gods. [4] Unbelievers insult you now because they are surprised that you no longer join them in the same excesses of wild living. [5] They will give an account to the one who is ready to judge the living and the dead. [6] After all, the Good News was told to people like that, although they are now dead. It was told to them so that they could be judged like humans in their earthly lives and live like God in their spiritual lives.

[7] The end of everything is near. Therefore, practice self-control, and keep your minds clear so that you can pray. [8] Above all, love each other warmly, because love covers many sins. [9] Welcome each other as guests without complaining. [10] Each of you as a good manager must use the gift that God has given you to serve others. [11] Whoever speaks must speak God's words. Whoever serves must serve with the strength God supplies so that in every way God receives glory through Jesus Christ. Glory and power belong to Jesus Christ forever and ever! Amen.

Share Christ's Sufferings

[12] Dear friends, don't be surprised by the fiery troubles that are coming in order to test you. Don't feel as though something strange is happening to you, [13] but be happy as you share Christ's sufferings. Then you will also be full of joy when he appears again in his glory. [14] If you are insulted because of the name of Christ, you are blessed because the Spirit of glory—the Spirit of God—is resting on you.

[15] If you suffer, you shouldn't suffer for being a murderer, thief, criminal, or troublemaker. [16] If you suffer for being a Christian, don't feel ashamed, but praise God for being called that name. [17] The time has come for the judgment to begin, and it will begin with God's family. If it

---

[a] 3:7 Or "grace."

starts with us, what will be the end for those who refuse to obey the Good News of God? [18] If it's hard for the person who has God's approval to be saved, what will happen to the godless sinner? [19] Those who suffer because that is God's will for them must entrust themselves to a faithful creator and continue to do what is good.

Instructions for Spiritual Leaders

5 [1] I appeal to your spiritual leaders.[a] I make this appeal as a spiritual leader who also witnessed Christ's sufferings and will share in the glory that will be revealed. [2] Be shepherds over the flock God has entrusted to you. Watch over it as God does: Don't do this because you have to, but because you want to. Don't do it out of greed, but out of a desire to serve. [3] Don't be rulers over the people entrusted to you, but be examples for the flock to follow. [4] Then, when the chief shepherd appears, you will receive the crown of glory that will never fade away.

Instructions for Christians

[5] Young people, in a similar way, place yourselves under the authority of spiritual leaders.

Furthermore, all of you must serve each other with humility, because God opposes the arrogant but favors the humble. [6] Be humbled by God's power so that when the right time comes he will honor you.

[7] Turn all your anxiety over to God because he cares for you. [8] Keep your mind clear, and be alert. Your opponent the devil is prowling around like a roaring lion as he looks for someone to devour. [9] Be firm in the faith and resist him, knowing that other believers throughout the world are going through the same kind of suffering. [10] God, who shows you his kindness[b] and who has called you through Christ Jesus to his eternal glory, will restore you, strengthen you, make you strong, and support you as you suffer for a little while. [11] Power belongs to him forever. Amen.

Farewell

[12] I've written this short letter to you and I'm sending it by Silvanus, whom I regard as a faithful brother. I've written to encourage you and to testify that this is God's genuine good will.[b] Remain firmly established in it!

[13] Your sister church in Babylon, chosen by God, and my son Mark send you greetings. [14] Greet each other with a kiss of love. Peace to all of you who are in Christ.

---

[a] 5:1 Or "pastors," or "elders."　　[b] 5:10, 12 Or "grace."

2 PETER

Greeting

1 ¹ From Simon Peter, a servant and apostle of Jesus Christ.

To those who have obtained a faith that is as valuable as ours, a faith based on the approval that comes from our God and Savior, Jesus Christ.

² May good will*ᵃ* and peace fill your lives through your knowledge about Jesus, our God and Lord!

God's Power Gives Us the Ability to Live Godly Lives

³ God's divine power has given us everything we need for life and for godliness. This power was given to us through knowledge of the one who called us by his own glory and integrity. ⁴ Through his glory and integrity he has given us his promises that are of the highest value. Through these promises you will share in the divine nature because you have escaped the corruption that sinful desires cause in the world.

⁵ Because of this, make every effort to add integrity to your faith; and to integrity add knowledge; ⁶ to knowledge add self-control; to self-control add endurance; to endurance add godliness; ⁷ to godliness add Christian affection; and to Christian affection add love. ⁸ If you have these qualities and they are increasing, it demonstrates that your knowledge about our Lord Jesus Christ is living and productive. ⁹ If these qualities aren't present in your life, you're shortsighted and have forgotten that you were cleansed from your past sins. ¹⁰ Therefore, brothers and sisters, use more effort to make God's calling and choosing of you secure.

If you keep doing this, you will never fall away. ¹¹ Then you will also be given the wealth of entering into the eternal kingdom of our Lord and Savior Jesus Christ.

¹² Therefore, I will always remind you about these qualities, although you already know about them and are well-grounded in the truth that you now have. ¹³ As long as I'm still alive, I think it's right to refresh your memory. ¹⁴ I know that I will die soon. Our Lord Jesus Christ has made that clear to me. ¹⁵ So I will make every effort to see that you remember these things after I die.

Pay Attention to God's Words

¹⁶ When we apostles told you about the powerful coming of our Lord Jesus Christ, we didn't base our message on clever myths that we made up. Rather, we witnessed his majesty with our own eyes. ¹⁷ For example, we were eyewitnesses when he received honor and glory from God the Father and when the voice of our majestic God spoke these words to him: "This is my Son, whom I love and in whom I delight." ¹⁸ We heard that voice speak to him from heaven when we were with him on the holy mountain. ¹⁹ So we regard the words of the prophets as confirmed beyond all doubt. You're doing well by paying attention to their words. Continue to pay attention as you would to a light that shines in a dark place as you wait for day to come and the morning star to rise in your hearts. ²⁰ First, you must understand this: No prophecy in Scripture is a matter of one's own interpretation. ²¹ No prophecy ever originated from humans. Instead, it was given by the Holy Spirit as humans spoke under God's direction.

Warnings About False Teachers

2 ¹ False prophets were among God's people ⌊in the past⌋, as false teachers will be among you. They will secretly bring in their own destructive teachings. They will deny the Lord, who has bought them, and they will bring themselves swift destruction. ² Many people will follow them in their sexual freedom and will cause others to dishonor the way of truth. ³ In their greed they will use good-sounding arguments to exploit you. The verdict against them from long ago is still in force, and their destruction is not asleep.

⁴ God didn't spare angels who sinned. He threw them into hell, where he has secured them with chains of darkness and is holding them for judgment.

⁵ God didn't spare the ancient world either. He brought the flood on the world of ungodly people, but he protected Noah and seven other people. Noah was his messenger who told people about the kind of life that has God's approval.

ᵃ 1:2 Or "grace."

⁶ God condemned the cities of Sodom and Gomorrah and destroyed them by burning them to ashes. He made those cities an example to ungodly people of what is going to happen to them. ⁷ Yet, God rescued Lot, a man who had his approval. Lot was distressed by the lifestyle of people who had no principles and lived in sexual freedom. ⁸ Although he was a man who had God's approval, he lived among the people of Sodom and Gomorrah. Each day was like torture to him as he saw and heard the immoral things that people did.

⁹ Since the Lord did all this, he knows how to rescue godly people when they are tested. He also knows how to hold immoral people for punishment on the day of judgment. ¹⁰ This is especially true of those who follow their corrupt nature along the path of impure desires and who despise the Lord's authority.

These false teachers are bold and arrogant. They aren't afraid to insult the ₌Lord's₌ glory. ¹¹ Angels, who have more strength and power than these teachers, don't bring an insulting judgment against them from the Lord. ¹² These false teachers insult what they don't understand. They are like animals, which are creatures of instinct that are born to be caught and killed. So they will be destroyed like animals ¹³ and lose what their wrongdoing earned them.

These false teachers are stains and blemishes. They take pleasure in holding wild parties in broad daylight. They especially enjoy deceiving you while they eat with you. ¹⁴ They're always looking for an adulterous woman. They can't stop looking for sin as they seduce people who aren't sure of what they believe. Their minds are focused on their greed. They are cursed.

¹⁵ These false teachers have left the straight path and wandered off to follow the path of Balaam, son of Beor. Balaam loved what his wrongdoing earned him. ¹⁶ But he was convicted for his evil. A donkey, which normally can't talk, spoke with a human voice and wouldn't allow the prophet to continue his insanity.

¹⁷ These false teachers are dried-up springs. They are a mist blown around by a storm. Gloomy darkness has been kept for them. ¹⁸ They arrogantly use nonsense to seduce people by appealing to their sexual desires, especially to sexual freedom. They seduce people who have just escaped from those who live in error. ¹⁹ They promise these people freedom, but they themselves are slaves to corruption. A person is a slave to whatever he gives in to.

²⁰ People can know our Lord and Savior Jesus Christ and escape the world's filth. But if they get involved in this filth again and give in to it, they are worse off than they were before. ²¹ It would have been better for them never to have known the way of life that God approves of than to know it and turn their backs on the holy life God told them to live. ²² These proverbs have come true for them: "A dog goes back to its vomit," and "A sow that has been washed goes back to roll around in the mud."

Be Ready for the Day of the Lord

3 ¹ Dear friends, this is the second letter I'm writing to you. In both letters I'm trying to refresh your memory. ² I want you to remember the words spoken in the past by the holy prophets and what the Lord and Savior commanded you through your apostles.

³ First, you must understand this: In the last days people who follow their own desires will appear. These disrespectful people will ridicule ₌God's promise₌ ⁴ by saying, "What's happened to his promise to return? Ever since our ancestors died, everything continues as it did from the beginning of the world."

⁵ They are deliberately ignoring one fact: Because of God's word, heaven and earth existed a long time ago. The earth ₌appeared₌ out of water and was kept alive by water. ⁶ Water also flooded and destroyed that world. ⁷ By God's word, the present heaven and earth are designated to be burned. They are being kept until the day ungodly people will be judged and destroyed.

⁸ Dear friends, don't ignore this fact: One day with the Lord is like a thousand years, and a thousand years are like one day. ⁹ The Lord isn't slow to do what he promised, as some people think. Rather, he is patient for your sake. He doesn't want to destroy anyone but wants all people to have an opportunity to turn to him and change the way they think and act.

¹⁰ The day of the Lord will come like a thief. On that day heaven will pass away with a roaring sound. Everything that makes up the universe will burn and be destroyed. The earth and everything that people have done on it will be exposed.[a]

¹¹ All these things will be destroyed in this way. So think of the kind of holy and godly lives you must live ¹² as you look forward to the day of God and eagerly wait for it to come. When that day comes, heaven will be on fire and will be destroyed. Everything that makes up the universe will burn and melt. ¹³ But we look forward to what God has promised—a new heaven and a new earth—a place where everything that has God's approval lives.

¹⁴ Therefore, dear friends, with this to look forward to, make every effort to have him find you at peace, without ₌spiritual₌ stains or blemishes. ¹⁵ Think of our Lord's patience as an

---

[a] 3:10 Some manuscripts and translations read "will be burned up."

opportunity ˻for us˼ to be saved. This is what our dear brother Paul wrote to you about, using the wisdom God gave him. [16] He talks about this subject in all his letters. Some things in his letters are hard to understand. Ignorant people and people who aren't sure of what they believe distort what Paul says in his letters the same way they distort the rest of the Scriptures. These people will be destroyed.

[17] Dear friends, you already know these things. So be on your guard not to be carried away by the deception of people who have no principles. Then you won't fall from your firm position. [18] But grow in the good will[b] and knowledge of our Lord and Savior Jesus Christ. Glory belongs to him now and for that eternal day! Amen.

---

[b] 3:18 Or "grace."

1 JOHN

John's Reason for Writing

1 ¹ The Word of life existed from the beginning. We have heard it. We have seen it. We observed and touched it. ² This life was revealed to us. We have seen it, and we testify about it. We are reporting to you about this eternal life that was in the presence of the Father and was revealed to us. ³ This is the life we have seen and heard. We are reporting about it to you also so that you, too, can have a relationship with us. Our relationship is with the Father and with his Son Jesus Christ. ⁴ We are writing this so that we can be completely filled with joy.

Through Jesus We Have a Relationship With God

⁵ This is the message we heard from Christ and are reporting to you: God is light, and there isn't any darkness in him. ⁶ If we say, "We have a relationship with God" and yet live in the dark, we're lying. We aren't being truthful.

⁷ But if we live in the light in the same way that God is in the light, we have a relationship with each other. And the blood of his Son Jesus cleanses us from every sin. ⁸ If we say, "We aren't sinful" we are deceiving ourselves, and the truth is not in us. ⁹ God is faithful and reliable. If we confess our sins, he forgives them and cleanses us from everything we've done wrong. ¹⁰ If we say, "We have never sinned," we turn God into a liar and his Word is not in us.

2 ¹ My dear children, I'm writing this to you so that you will not sin. Yet, if anyone does sin, we have Jesus Christ, who has God's full approval. He speaks on our behalf when we come into the presence of the Father. ² He is the payment for our sins, and not only for our sins, but also for the sins of the whole world.

Those Who Know Christ Obey His Commandments

³ We are sure that we know Christ if we obey his commandments. ⁴ The person who says, "I know him," but doesn't obey his commandments is a liar. The truth isn't in that person. ⁵ But whoever obeys what Christ says is the kind of person in whom God's love is perfected. That's how we know we are in Christ. ⁶ Those who say that they live in him must live the same way he lived.

⁷ Dear friends, it's not as though I'm writing to give you a new commandment. Rather, I'm giving you an old commandment that you've had from the beginning. It's the old commandment you've already heard. ⁸ On the other hand, I'm writing to give you a new commandment. It's a truth that exists in Christ and in you: The darkness is fading, and the true light is already shining.

⁹ Those who say that they are in the light but hate other believers are still in the dark. ¹⁰ Those who love other believers live in the light. Nothing will destroy the faith of those who live in the light. ¹¹ Those who hate other believers are in the dark and live in the dark. They don't know where they're going, because they can't see in the dark.

Don't Love the World

¹² I'm writing to you, dear children, because your sins are forgiven through Christ.

¹³ I'm writing to you, fathers, because you know Christ who has existed from the beginning.
I'm writing to you, young people, because you have won the victory over the evil one.

¹⁴ I've written to you, children, because you know the Father.
I've written to you, fathers, because you know Christ, who has existed from the beginning.
I've written to you, young people, because you are strong and God's word lives in you.
You have won the victory over the evil one.

¹⁵ Don't love the world and what it offers. Those who love the world don't have the Father's love in them. ¹⁶ Not everything that the world offers—physical gratification, greed, and extravagant lifestyles—comes from the Father. It comes from the world, and ¹⁷ the world and its evil desires are passing away. But the person who does what God wants lives forever.

Live in Christ

¹⁸ Children, it's the end of time. You've heard that an antichrist is coming. Certainly, many antichrists are already here. That's how we know it's the end of time. ¹⁹ They left us. However,

they were never really part of us. If they had been, they would have stayed with us. But by leaving they made it clear that none of them were part of us.

²⁰ The Holy One has anointed you, so all of you have knowledge. ²¹ I'm writing to you because you know the truth, not because you don't know the truth. You know that no lie ever comes from the truth.

²² Who is a liar? Who else but the person who rejects Jesus as the Messiah? The person who rejects the Father and the Son is an antichrist. ²³ Everyone who rejects the Son doesn't have the Father either. The person who acknowledges the Son also has the Father. ²⁴ Make sure that the message you heard from the beginning lives in you. If that message lives in you, you will also live in the Son and in the Father. ²⁵ Christ has given us the promise of eternal life.

²⁶ I'm writing to you about those who are trying to deceive you. ²⁷ The anointing you received from Christ lives in you. You don't need anyone to teach you something else. Instead, Christ's anointing teaches you about everything. His anointing is true and contains no lie. So live in Christ as he taught you to do.

We Are God's Children

²⁸ Now, dear children, live in Christ. Then, when he appears we will have confidence, and when he comes we won't turn from him in shame. ²⁹ If you know that Christ has God's approval, you also know that everyone who does what God approves of has been born from God.

3 ¹ Consider this: The Father has given us his love. He loves us so much that we are actually called God's dear children. And that's what we are. For this reason the world doesn't recognize us, and it didn't recognize him either. ² Dear friends, now we are God's children. What we will be isn't completely clear yet. We do know that when Christ appears we will be like him because we will see him as he is. ³ So all people who have this confidence in Christ keep themselves pure, as Christ is pure.

⁴ Those who live sinful lives are disobeying God. Sin is disobedience. ⁵ You know that Christ appeared in order to take away our sins. He isn't sinful. ⁶ Those who live in Christ don't go on sinning. Those who go on sinning haven't seen or known Christ.

⁷ Dear children, don't let anyone deceive you. Whoever does what God approves of has God's approval as Christ has God's approval. ⁸ The person who lives a sinful life belongs to the devil, because the devil has been committing sin since the beginning. The reason that the Son of God appeared was to destroy what the devil does. ⁹ Those who have been born from God don't live sinful lives. What God has said lives in them, and they can't live sinful lives. They have been born from God. ¹⁰ This is the way God's children are distinguished from the devil's children. Everyone who doesn't do what is right or love other believers isn't God's child.

Love One Another

¹¹ The message that you have heard from the beginning is to love each other. ¹² Don't be like Cain. He was a child of the evil one and murdered his brother. And why did Cain murder his brother? Because the things Cain did were evil and the things his brother did had God's approval. ¹³ Brothers and sisters, don't be surprised if the world hates you.

¹⁴ We know that we have passed from death to life, because we love other believers. The person who doesn't grow in love remains in death. ¹⁵ Everyone who hates another believer is a murderer, and you know that a murderer doesn't have eternal life.

¹⁶ We understand what love is when we realize that Christ gave his life for us. That means we must give our lives for other believers. ¹⁷ Now, suppose a person has enough to live on and notices another believer in need. How can God's love be in that person if he doesn't bother to help the other believer? ¹⁸ Dear children, we must show love through actions that are sincere, not through empty words.

¹⁹ This is how we will know that we belong to the truth and how we will be reassured in his presence. ²⁰ Whenever our conscience condemns us, we will be reassured that God is greater than our conscience and knows everything. ²¹ Dear friends, if our conscience doesn't condemn us, we can boldly look to God ²² and receive from him anything we ask. We receive it because we obey his commandments and do what pleases him. ²³ This is his commandment: to believe in his Son, the one named Jesus Christ, and to love each other as he commanded us. ²⁴ Those who obey Christ's commandments live in God, and God lives in them. We know that he lives in us because he has given us the Spirit.

Test People Who Say They Have God's Spirit

4 ¹ Dear friends, don't believe all people who say that they have the Spirit. Instead, test them. See whether the spirit they have is from God, because there are many false prophets in the world. ² This is how you can recognize God's Spirit: Every person who declares that Jesus Christ has come as a human has the Spirit that is from God. ³ But every person who doesn't declare that Jesus Christ has come as a human has a spirit that isn't from God. This is the spirit of the antichrist that you have heard is coming. That spirit is already in the world. **⁴** Dear children, you belong to God. So you have won the victory over these people, because the one who is in you is greater than the one who is in the world. **⁵** These people belong to the world. That's why they speak the thoughts of the world, and the world listens to them. **⁶** We belong to God. The person who knows God listens to us. Whoever doesn't belong to God doesn't listen to us. That's how we can tell the Spirit of truth from the spirit of lies.

God's Love Lives in His People

⁷ Dear friends, we must love each other because love comes from God. Everyone who loves has been born from God and knows God. **⁸** The person who doesn't love doesn't know God, because God is love. **⁹** God has shown us his love by sending his only Son into the world so that we could have life through him. **¹⁰** This is love: not that we have loved God, but that he loved us and sent his Son to be the payment for our sins. **¹¹** Dear friends, if this is the way God loved us, we must also love each other. **¹²** No one has ever seen God. If we love each other, God lives in us, and his love is perfected in us. **¹³** We know that we live in him and he lives in us because he has given us his Spirit.

¹⁴ We have seen and testify to the fact that the Father sent his Son as the Savior of the world. **¹⁵** God lives in those who declare that Jesus is the Son of God, and they live in God. **¹⁶** We have known and believed that God loves us. God is love. Those who live in God's love live in God, and God lives in them.

¹⁷ God's love has reached its goal in us. So we look ahead with confidence to the day of judgment. While we are in this world, we are exactly like him ˌwith regard to loveˌ. **¹⁸** No fear exists where his love is. Rather, perfect love gets rid of fear, because fear involves punishment. The person who lives in fear doesn't have perfect love.

¹⁹ We love because God loved us first. **²⁰** Whoever says, "I love God," but hates another believer is a liar. People who don't love other believers, whom they have seen, can't love God, whom they have not seen. **²¹** Christ has given us this commandment: The person who loves God must also love other believers.

Those Who Believe in Jesus Are God's Children

5 **¹** Everyone who believes that Jesus is the Messiah has been born from God. Everyone who loves the Father also loves his children. **²** We know that we love God's children when we love God by obeying his commandments. **³** To love God means that we obey his commandments. Obeying his commandments isn't difficult **⁴** because everyone who has been born from God has won the victory over the world. Our faith is what wins the victory over the world. **⁵** Who wins the victory over the world? Isn't it the person who believes that Jesus is the Son of God?

⁶ This Son of God is Jesus Christ, who came by water and blood. He didn't come with water only, but with water and with blood. The Spirit is the one who verifies this, because the Spirit is the truth. **⁷** There are three witnesses:ᵃ **⁸** the Spirit, the water, and the blood. These three witnesses agree.

⁹ We accept human testimony. God's testimony is greater because it is the testimony that he has given about his Son. **¹⁰** Those who believe in the Son of God have the testimony of God in them. Those who don't believe God have made God a liar. They haven't believed the testimony that God has given about his Son.

¹¹ This is the testimony: God has given us eternal life, and this life is found in his Son. **¹²** The person who has the Son has this life. The person who doesn't have the Son of God doesn't have this life.

Conclusion

¹³ I've written this to those who believe in the Son of God so that they will know that they have eternal life.

¹⁴ We are confident that God listens to us if we ask for anything that has his approval. **¹⁵** We know that he listens to our requests. So we know that we already have what we ask him for.

¹⁶ If you see another believer committing a sin that doesn't lead to death, you should pray that God would give that person life. This is true for those who commit sins that don't lead to death. There is a sin that leads to death. I'm not telling you to pray about that. **¹⁷** Every kind of wrongdoing is sin, yet there are sins that don't lead to death.

¹⁸ We know that those who have been born from God don't go on sinning. Rather, the Son of God protects them, and the evil one can't harm them.

ᵃ 5:7 Four very late manuscripts add verses 7b–8a: "in heaven: the Father, the Word, and the Holy Spirit. These three witnesses agree. And there are three witnesses on earth:"

[19] We know that we are from God, and that the whole world is under the control of the evil one.

[20] We know that the Son of God has come and has given us understanding so that we know the real God. We are in the one who is real, his Son Jesus Christ. This Jesus Christ is the real God and eternal life.

[21] Dear children, guard yourselves from false gods.

2 JOHN

Greeting

¹ From the church leader.[a]

To the chosen lady and her children, whom I love because we share the truth. I'm not the only one who loves you. Everyone who knows the truth also loves you. ² We love you because of the truth which lives in us and will be with us forever.

³ Good will,[b] mercy, and peace will be with us. They come from God the Father and from Jesus Christ, who in truth and love is the Father's Son.

Living in the Truth

⁴ I was very happy to find some of your children living in the truth as the Father has commanded us. ⁵ Dear lady, I'm now requesting that we continue to love each other. It's not as though I'm writing to give you a new commandment. Rather, from the beginning we were commanded to love each other. ⁶ Love means that we live by doing what he commands. We were commanded to live in love, and you have heard this from the beginning.

Reject Teachers Who Don't Teach What Christ Taught

⁷ Many people who deceive others have gone into the world. They refuse to declare that Jesus Christ came in flesh and blood. This is the mark of a deceiver and an antichrist. ⁸ Be careful that you don't destroy what we've worked for, but that you receive your full reward.

⁹ Everyone who doesn't continue to teach what Christ taught doesn't have God. The person who continues to teach what Christ taught has both the Father and the Son. ¹⁰ If anyone comes to you and doesn't bring these teachings, don't take him into your home or even greet him. ¹¹ Whoever greets him shares the evil things he's doing.

Farewell

¹² I have a lot to write to you. I would prefer not to write a letter. Instead, I hope to visit and talk things over with you personally. Then we will be completely filled with joy.

¹³ The children of your chosen sister greet you.

---

[a] 1 Or "pastor," or "elder."   [b] 3 Or "Grace."

3 JOHN

Greeting

¹ From the church leader.[a]
To my dear friend Gaius, whom I love because we share the truth.

Encouragement for Gaius

² Dear friend, I know that you are spiritually well. I pray that you're doing well in every other way and that you're healthy. ³ I was very happy when some believers came and told us that you are living according to the truth. ⁴ Nothing makes me happier than to hear that my children are living according to the truth.

⁵ Dear friend, you are showing your faith in whatever you do for other believers, especially when they're your guests. ⁶ These believers have told the congregation about your love. You will do well to support them on their trip in a way that proves you belong to God. ⁷ After all, they went on their trip to serve the one named Christ, and they didn't accept any help from the people to whom they went. ⁸ We must support believers who go on trips like this so that we can work together with them in spreading the truth.

Criticism of Diotrephes

⁹ I wrote a letter to the congregation. But Diotrephes, who loves to be in charge, won't accept us. ¹⁰ For this reason, when I come I will bring up what he's doing. He's not satisfied with saying malicious things about us. He also refuses to accept the believers ˌwe sendˌ as guests. He even tries to stop others who want to accept them and attempts to throw those people out of the congregation.

Praise for Demetrius

¹¹ Dear friend, never imitate evil, but imitate good. The person who does good is from God. The person who does evil has never seen God.

¹² Everyone, including the truth itself, says good things about Demetrius. We also say good things about him, and you know that what we say is true.

Farewell

¹³ I have a lot to write to you. However, I would rather not write. ¹⁴ I hope to visit you very soon. Then we can talk things over personally.

¹⁵ Peace be with you! Your friends here send you their greetings. Greet each of our friends by name.

---

a 1 Or "pastor," or "elder."

JUDE

Greeting

¹ From Jude, a servant of Jesus Christ and brother of James.

To those who have been called, who are loved by God the Father, and who are kept safe for Jesus Christ.

² May mercy, peace, and love fill your lives!

Warnings About False Teachers

³ Dear friends, I had intended to write to you about the salvation we share. But something has come up. It demands that I write to you and encourage you to continue your fight for the Christian faith that was entrusted to God's holy people once for all time. ⁴ Some people have slipped in among you unnoticed. Not long ago they were condemned in writing for the following reason: They are people to whom God means nothing. They use God's kindnessᵃ as an excuse for sexual freedom and deny our only Master and Lord, Jesus Christ. ⁵ I want to remind you about what you already know: The Lord once saved his people from Egypt. But on another occasion he destroyed those who didn't believe. ⁶ He held angels for judgment on the great day. They were held in darkness, bound by eternal chains. These are the angels who didn't keep their position of authority but abandoned their assigned place. ⁷ What happened to Sodom and Gomorrah and the cities near them is an example for us of the punishment of eternal fire. The people of these cities suffered the same fate that God's people and the angels did, because they committed sexual sins and engaged in homosexual activities.

⁸ Yet, in a similar way, the people who slipped in among you are dreamers. They contaminate their bodies with sin, reject the Lord's authority, and insult his glory. ⁹ When the archangel Michael argued with the devil, they were arguing over the body of Moses. But Michael didn't dare to hand down a judgment against the devil. Instead, Michael said, "May the Lord reprimand you!" ¹⁰ Whatever these people don't understand, they insult. Like animals, which are creatures of instinct, they use whatever they know to destroy themselves. ¹¹ How horrible it will be for them! They have followed the path of Cain. They have rushed into Balaam's error to make a profit. They have rebelled like Korah and destroyed themselves. ¹² These people are a disgrace at the special meals you share with other believers. They eat with you and don't feel ashamed. They are shepherds who care ˻only˼ for themselves. They are dry clouds blown around by the winds. They are withered, uprooted trees without any fruit. As a result, they have died twice. ¹³ Their shame is like the foam on the wild waves of the sea. They are wandering stars for whom gloomy darkness is kept forever.

¹⁴ Furthermore, Enoch, from the seventh generation after Adam, prophesied about them. He said, "The Lord has come with countless thousands of his holy angels. ¹⁵ He has come to judge all these people. He has come to convict all these ungodly sinners for all the ungodly things they have done and all the harsh things they have said about him." ¹⁶ These people complain, find fault, follow their own desires, say arrogant things, and flatter people in order to take advantage of them.

¹⁷ Dear friends, remember what the apostles of our Lord Jesus Christ told you to expect: ¹⁸ "In the last times people who ridicule ˻God˼ will appear. They will follow their own ungodly desires." ¹⁹ These are the people who cause divisions. They are concerned about physical things, not spiritual things.

Final Advice

²⁰ Dear friends, use your most holy faith to grow. Pray with the Holy Spirit's help. ²¹ Remain in God's love as you look for the mercy of our Lord Jesus Christ to give you eternal life. ²² Show mercy to those who have doubts. ²³ Save others by snatching them from the fire ˻of hell˼. Show mercy to others, even though you are afraid that you might be stained by their sinful lives.

ᵃ 4 Or "grace."

[24] God can guard you so that you don't fall and so that you can be full of joy as you stand in his glorious presence without fault. [25] Before time began, now, and for eternity glory, majesty, power, and authority belong to the only God, our Savior, through Jesus Christ our Lord. Amen.

REVELATION

The Revelation of Jesus Christ to the Seven Churches

1 [1] This is the revelation of Jesus Christ. God gave it to him to show his servants the things that must happen soon. He sent this revelation through his angel to his servant John. [2] John testified about what he saw: God's word and the testimony about Jesus Christ. [3] Blessed is the one who reads, as well as those who hear the words of this prophecy and pay attention to what is written in it because the time is near.

[4] From John to the seven churches in the province of Asia. Good will[a] and peace to you from the one who is, the one who was, and the one who is coming, from the seven spirits who are in front of his throne, [5] and from Jesus Christ, the witness, the trustworthy one, the first to come back to life, and the ruler over the kings of the earth. Glory and power forever and ever[b] belong to the one who loves us and has freed us from our sins by his blood [6] and has made us a kingdom, priests for God his Father. Amen.

[7]   Look! He is coming in the clouds.
        Every eye will see him,
            even those who pierced him.
        Every tribe on earth will mourn because of him.
            This is true. Amen.

[8] "I am the A and the Z,"[c] says the Lord God, the one who is, the one who was, and the one who is coming, the Almighty.

[9] I am John, your brother. I share your suffering, ruling, and endurance because of Jesus. I was ˻exiled˼ on the island of Patmos because of God's word and the testimony about Jesus. [10] I came under the Spirit's power on the Lord's day. I heard a loud voice behind me like a trumpet, [11] saying, "Write on a scroll what you see, and send it to the seven churches: Ephesus, Smyrna, Pergamum, Thyatira, Sardis, Philadelphia, and Laodicea."

[12] I turned toward the voice which was talking to me, and when I turned, I saw seven gold lamp stands. [13] There was someone like the Son of Man among the lamp stands. He was wearing a robe that reached his feet. He wore a gold belt around his waist. [14] His head and his hair were white like wool—like snow. His eyes were like flames of fire. [15] His feet were like glowing bronze refined in a furnace. His voice was like the sound of raging waters. [16] In his right hand he held seven stars, and out of his mouth came a sharp, two-edged sword. His face was like the sun when it shines in all its brightness.

[17] When I saw him, I fell down at his feet like a dead man. Then he laid his right hand on me and said, "Don't be afraid! I am the first and the last, [18] the living one. I was dead, but now I am alive forever. I have the keys of death and hell. [19] Therefore, write down what you have seen, what is, and what is going to happen after these things. [20] The hidden meaning of the seven stars that you saw in my right hand and the seven gold lamp stands is this: The seven stars are the messengers of the seven churches, and the seven lamp stands are the seven churches.

A Letter to the Church in Ephesus

2 [1] "To the messenger of the church in Ephesus, write:

The one who holds the seven stars in his right hand, the one who walks among the seven gold lamp stands, says: [2] I know what you have done—how hard you have worked and how you have endured. I also know that you cannot tolerate wicked people. You have tested those who call themselves apostles but are not apostles. You have discovered that they are liars. [3] You have endured, suffered trouble because of my name, and have not grown weary. [4] However, I have this against you: The love you had at first is gone. [5] Remember how far you have fallen. Return to me and change the way you think and act, and do what you did at first. I will come to you and take your lamp stand from its place if you don't change. [6] But you have this in your favor—you hate what the Nicolaitans are doing. I also hate what they're doing.

---

[a] 1:4 Or "Grace."   [b] 1:5 The last part of verse 6 (in Greek) has been moved to verse 5 to express the complex Greek sentence structure more clearly in English.   [c] 1:8 Or "the Alpha and the Omega."

⁷ "Let the person who has ears listen to what the Spirit says to the churches. I will give the privilege of eating from the tree of life, which stands in the paradise of God, to everyone who wins the victory.

A Letter to the Church in Smyrna

⁸ "To the messenger of the church in Smyrna, write:

The first and the last, who was dead and became alive, says: ⁹ I know how you are suffering, how poor you are—but you are rich. I also know that those who claim to be Jews slander you. They are the synagogue of Satan. ¹⁰ Don't be afraid of what you are going to suffer. The devil is going to throw some of you into prison so that you may be tested. Your suffering will go on for ten days. Be faithful until death, and I will give you the crown of life.

¹¹ Let the person who has ears listen to what the Spirit says to the churches. Everyone who wins the victory will never be hurt by the second death.

A Letter to the Church in Pergamum

¹² "To the messenger of the church in Pergamum, write:

The one who holds the sharp two-edged sword says: ¹³ I know where you live. Satan's throne is there. You hold on to my name and have not denied your belief in me, even in the days of Antipas. He was my faithful witness who was killed in your presence, where Satan lives. ¹⁴ But I have a few things against you: You have among you those who follow what Balaam taught Balak. Balak trapped the people of Israel by ˌencouragingˌ them to eat food sacrificed to idols and to sin sexually. ¹⁵ You also have some who follow what the Nicolaitans teach. ¹⁶ So return to me and change the way you think and act, or I will come to you quickly and wage war against them with the sword from my mouth.

¹⁷ Let the person who has ears listen to what the Spirit says to the churches. I will give some of the hidden manna to everyone who wins the victory. I will also give each person a white stone with a new name written on it, a name that is known only to the person who receives it.

A Letter to the Church in Thyatira

¹⁸ "To the messenger of the church in Thyatira, write:

The Son of God, whose eyes are like flames of fire and whose feet are like glowing bronze, says: ¹⁹ I know what you do. I know your love, faith, service, and endurance. I also know that what you are doing now is greater than what you did at first. ²⁰ But I have something against you: You tolerate that woman Jezebel, who calls herself a prophet. She teaches and misleads my servants to sin sexually and to eat food sacrificed to idols. ²¹ I gave her time to turn to me and change the way she thinks and acts, but she refuses to turn away from her sexual sins. ²² Watch me! I'm going to throw her into a sickbed. Those who commit sexual sins with her will also suffer a lot, unless they turn away from what she is doing. ²³ I will kill her children. Then all the churches will know that I am the one who searches hearts and minds. I will reward each of you for what you have done. ²⁴ But the rest of you in Thyatira—all who don't hold on to Jezebel's teaching, who haven't learned what are called the deep things of Satan—I won't burden you with anything else. ²⁵ Just hold on to what you have until I come.

²⁶ I have received authority from my Father.^a I will give authority over the nations to everyone who wins the victory and continues to do what I want until the end. ²⁷ Those people will rule the nations with iron scepters and shatter them like pottery. ²⁸ I will also give them the morning star. ²⁹ Let the person who has ears listen to what the Spirit says to the churches.

A Letter to the Church in Sardis

3 ¹ "To the messenger of the church in Sardis, write:

The one who has God's seven spirits and the seven stars says: I know what you have done. You are known for being alive, but you are dead. ² Be alert, and strengthen the things that are left which are about to die. I have found that what you are doing has not been completed in the sight of my God. ³ So remember what you received and heard. Obey, and change the way you think and act. If you're not alert, I'll come like a thief. You don't know when I will come. ⁴ But you have a few people in Sardis who have kept their clothes clean. They will walk with me in white clothes because they deserve it.

---

^a 2:26 The first part of verse 28 (in Greek) has been moved to the beginning of verse 26 to express the complex Greek sentence structure more clearly in English.

⁵Everyone who wins the victory this way will wear white clothes. I will never erase their names from the Book of Life. I will acknowledge them in the presence of my Father and his angels. ⁶Let the person who has ears listen to what the Spirit says to the churches.

A Letter to the Church in Philadelphia

⁷"To the messenger of the church in Philadelphia, write:

The one who is holy, who is true, who has the key of David, who opens ˌa doorˌ that no one can shut, and who shuts ˌa doorˌ that no one can open, says: ⁸I know what you have done. See, I have opened a door in front of you that no one can shut. You only have a little strength, but you have paid attention to my word and have not denied my name. ⁹I will make those who are in Satan's synagogue come and bow at your feet and realize that I have loved you. They claim that they are Jewish, but they are lying. ¹⁰Because you have obeyed my command to endure, I will keep you safe during the time of testing which is coming to the whole world to test those living on earth. ¹¹I am coming soon! Hold on to what you have so that no one takes your crown.

¹²I will make everyone who wins the victory a pillar in the temple of my God. They will never leave it again. I will write on them the name of my God, the name of the city of my God (the New Jerusalem coming down out of heaven from my God), and my new name. ¹³Let the person who has ears listen to what the Spirit says to the churches.

A Letter to the Church in Laodicea

¹⁴"To the messenger of the church in Laodicea, write:

The amen, the witness who is faithful and true, the source of God's creation, says: ¹⁵I know what you have done, that you are neither cold nor hot. I wish you were cold or hot. ¹⁶But since you are lukewarm and not hot or cold, I'm going to spit you out of my mouth. ¹⁷You say, 'I'm rich. I'm wealthy. I don't need anything.' Yet, you do not realize that you are miserable, pitiful, poor, blind, and naked. ¹⁸I advise you: Buy gold purified in fire from me so that you may be rich. Buy white clothes from me. Wear them so that you may keep your shameful, naked body from showing. Buy ointment to put on your eyes so that you may see. ¹⁹I correct and discipline everyone I love. Take this seriously, and change the way you think and act. ²⁰Look, I'm standing at the door and knocking. If anyone listens to my voice and opens the door, I'll come in and we'll eat together.

²¹I will allow everyone who wins the victory to sit with me on my throne, as I have won the victory and have sat down with my Father on his throne. ²²Let the person who has ears listen to what the Spirit says to the churches."

A Vision of God's Throne in Heaven

4 ¹After these things I saw a door standing open in heaven. I heard the first voice like a trumpet speaking to me. It said, "Come up here, and I will show you what must happen after this." ²Instantly, I came under the Spirit's power. I saw a throne in heaven, and someone was sitting on it. ³The one sitting there looked like gray quartz and red quartz. There was a rainbow around the throne which looked like an emerald.

⁴Around that throne were 24 other thrones, and on these thrones sat 24 leaders wearing white clothes. They had gold crowns on their heads. ⁵Lightning, noise, and thunder came from the throne. Seven flaming torches were burning in front of the throne. These are the seven spirits of God.

⁶In front of the throne, there was something like a sea of glass as clear as crystal. In the center near the throne and around the throne were four living creatures covered with eyes in front and in back. ⁷The first living creature was like a lion, the second was like a young bull, the third had a face like a human, and the fourth was like a flying eagle. ⁸Each of the four living creatures had six wings and were covered with eyes, inside and out. Without stopping day or night they were singing,

"Holy, holy, holy is the Lord God Almighty,
    who was, who is, and who is coming."

⁹Whenever the living creatures give glory, honor, and thanks to the one who sits on the throne, to the one who lives forever and ever, ¹⁰the 24 leaders bow in front of the one who sits on the throne and worship the one who lives forever and ever. They place their crowns in front of the throne and say,

¹¹   "Our Lord and God, you deserve to receive glory, honor, and power
        because you created everything.
    Everything came into existence and was created because of your will."

The Lamb Takes the Scroll That Has Seven Seals

5 ¹ I saw a scroll in the right hand of the one who sits on the throne. It had writing both on the inside and on the outside. It was sealed with seven seals. ² I saw a powerful angel calling out in a loud voice, "Who deserves to open the scroll and break the seals on it?" ³ No one in heaven, on earth, or under the earth could open the scroll or look inside it. ⁴ I cried bitterly because no one was found who deserved to open the scroll or look inside it.

⁵ Then one of the leaders said to me, "Stop crying! The Lion from the tribe of Judah, the Root of David, has won the victory. He can open the scroll and the seven seals on it."

⁶ I saw a lamb standing in the center near the throne with the four living creatures and the leaders. The lamb looked like he had been slaughtered. He had seven horns and seven eyes, which are the seven spirits of God sent all over the world. ⁷ He took the scroll from the right hand of the one who sits on the throne.

⁸ When the lamb had taken the scroll, the four living creatures and the 24 leaders bowed in front of him. Each held a harp and a gold bowl full of incense, the prayers of God's holy people. ⁹ Then they sang a new song,

> "You deserve to take the scroll and open the seals on it,
>   because you were slaughtered.
> You bought people with your blood to be God's own.
>   They are from every tribe, language, people, and nation.
> 10 You made them a kingdom and priests for our God.
>   They will rule as kings on the earth."

¹¹ Then I heard the voices of many angels, the four living creatures, and the leaders surrounding the throne. They numbered ten thousand times ten thousand and thousands times thousands. ¹² In a loud voice they were singing,

> "The lamb who was slain deserves to receive
>   power, wealth, wisdom, strength, honor, glory, and praise."

¹³ I heard every creature in heaven, on earth, under the earth, and on the sea. Every creature in those places was singing,

> "To the one who sits on the throne and to the lamb
>   be praise, honor, glory, and power forever and ever."

¹⁴ The four living creatures said, "Amen!" Then the leaders bowed and worshiped.

The Lamb Opens the First Six Seals

6 ¹ I watched as the lamb opened the first of the seven seals. I heard one of the four living creatures say with a voice like thunder, "Go!" ² Then I looked, and there was a white horse, and its rider had a bow. He was given a crown and rode off as a warrior to win battles.

³ When the lamb opened the second seal, I heard the second living creature say, "Go!" ⁴ A second horse went out. It was fiery red. Its rider was given the power to take peace away from the earth and to make people slaughter one another. So he was given a large sword.

⁵ When the lamb opened the third seal, I heard the third living creature say, "Go!" I looked, and there was a black horse, and its rider held a scale. ⁶ I heard what sounded like a voice from among the four living creatures, saying, "A quart of wheat for a day's pay or three quarts of barley for a day's pay. But do not damage the olive oil and the wine."

⁷ When the lamb opened the fourth seal, I heard the voice of the fourth living creature say, "Go!" ⁸ I looked, and there was a pale horse, and its rider's name was Death. Hell followed him. They were given power over one-fourth of the earth to kill people using wars, famines, plagues, and the wild animals on the earth.

⁹ When the lamb opened the fifth seal, I saw under the altar the souls of those who had been slaughtered because of God's word and the testimony they had given about him. ¹⁰ They cried out in a loud voice, "Holy and true Master, how long before you judge and take revenge on those living on earth who shed our blood?" ¹¹ Each of the souls was given a white robe. They were told to rest a little longer until all their coworkers, the other Christians, would be killed as they had been killed.

¹² I watched as the lamb opened the sixth seal. A powerful earthquake struck. The sun turned as black as sackcloth made of hair. The full moon turned as red as blood. ¹³ The stars fell from the sky to the earth like figs dropping from a fig tree when it is shaken by a strong wind. ¹⁴ The sky vanished like a scroll being rolled up. Every mountain and island was moved from its place. ¹⁵ Then the kings of the earth, the important people, the generals, the rich, the powerful, and all the slaves and free people hid themselves in caves and among the rocks in the mountains. ¹⁶ They said to the mountains and rocks, "Fall on us, and hide us from the face

of the one who sits on the throne and from the anger of the lamb, [17] because the frightening day of their anger has come, and who is able to endure it?"

144,000 People Are Sealed

7 [1] After this I saw four angels standing at the four corners of the earth. They were holding back the four winds of the earth to keep them from blowing on the land, the sea, or any tree. [2] I saw another angel coming from the east with the seal of the living God. He cried out in a loud voice to the four angels who had been allowed to harm the land and sea, [3] "Don't harm the land, the sea, or the trees until we have put the seal on the foreheads of the servants of our God." [4] I heard how many were sealed: 144,000. Those who were sealed were from every tribe of the people of Israel:

[5]   12,000 from the tribe of Judah were sealed,
       12,000 from the tribe of Reuben,
       12,000 from the tribe of Gad,
[6]   12,000 from the tribe of Asher,
       12,000 from the tribe of Naphtali,
       12,000 from the tribe of Manasseh,
[7]   12,000 from the tribe of Simeon,
       12,000 from the tribe of Levi,
       12,000 from the tribe of Issachar,
[8]   12,000 from the tribe of Zebulun,
       12,000 from the tribe of Joseph,
       12,000 from the tribe of Benjamin were sealed.

God's People Around His Throne in Heaven

[9] After these things I saw a large crowd from every nation, tribe, people, and language. No one was able to count how many people there were. They were standing in front of the throne and the lamb. They were wearing white robes, holding palm branches in their hands, [10] and crying out in a loud voice, "Salvation belongs to our God, who sits on the throne, and to the lamb!" [11] All the angels stood around the throne with the leaders and the four living creatures. They bowed in front of the throne with their faces touching the ground, worshiped God, [12] and said,

"Amen! Praise, glory, wisdom, thanks, honor, power, and strength
    be to our God forever and ever! Amen!"

[13] One of the leaders asked me, "Who are these people wearing white robes, and where did they come from?"
[14] I answered him, "Sir, you know."
Then he told me,

"These are the people who are coming out of the terrible suffering.
    They have washed their robes
       and made them white in the blood of the lamb.
[15]   That is why they are in front of the throne of God.
    They serve him day and night in his temple.
    The one who sits on the throne will spread his tent over them.
[16]   They will never be hungry or thirsty again.
    Neither the sun nor any burning heat will ever overcome them.
[17]   The lamb in the center near the throne will be their shepherd.
    He will lead them to springs filled with the water of life,
       and God will wipe every tear from their eyes."

The Lamb Opens the Seventh Seal

8 [1] When he opened the seventh seal, there was silence in heaven for about half an hour.

Seven Angels With Seven Trumpets

[2] Then I saw the seven angels who stand in God's presence, and they were given seven trumpets. [3] Another angel came with a gold incense burner and stood at the altar. He was given a lot of incense to offer on the gold altar in front of the throne. He offered it with the prayers of all of God's people. [4] The smoke from the incense went up from the angel's hand to God along with the prayers of God's people. [5] The angel took the incense burner, filled it with fire from the altar, and threw it on the earth. Then there was thunder, noise, lightning, and an earthquake.
[6] The seven angels who had the seven trumpets got ready to blow them.

The First Four Angels Blow Their Trumpets

7 When the first angel blew his trumpet, hail and fire were mixed with blood, and were thrown on the earth. One-third of the earth was burned up, one-third of the trees were burned up, and all the green grass was burned up.

8 When the second angel blew his trumpet, something like a huge mountain burning with fire was thrown into the sea. One-third of the sea turned into blood, **9** one-third of the creatures that were living in the sea died, and one-third of the ships were destroyed.

10 When the third angel blew his trumpet, a huge star flaming like a torch fell from the sky. It fell on one-third of the rivers and on the springs. **11** That star was named Wormwood. One-third of the water turned into wormwood, and many people died from this water because it had turned bitter.

12 When the fourth angel blew his trumpet, one-third of the sun, one-third of the moon, and one-third of the stars were struck so that one-third of them turned dark. There was no light for one-third of the day and one-third of the night.

13 I saw an eagle flying overhead, and I heard it say in a loud voice, "Catastrophe, catastrophe, catastrophe for those living on earth, because of the remaining trumpet blasts which the three angels are about to blow."

The Fifth and Sixth Angels Blow Their Trumpets

9 **1** When the fifth angel blew his trumpet, I saw a star that had fallen to earth from the sky. The star was given the key to the shaft of the bottomless pit. **2** It opened the shaft of the bottomless pit, and smoke came out of the shaft like the smoke from a large furnace. The smoke darkened the sun and the air. **3** Locusts came out of the smoke onto the earth, and they were given power like the power of earthly scorpions. **4** They were told not to harm any grass, green plant, or tree on the earth. They could harm only the people who do not have the seal of God on their foreheads. **5** They were not allowed to kill them. They were only allowed to torture them for five months. Their torture was like the pain of a scorpion's sting. **6** At that time people will look for death and never find it. They will long to die, but death will escape them.

7 The locusts looked like horses prepared for battle. They seemed to have crowns that looked like gold on their heads. Their faces were like human faces. **8** They had hair like women's hair and teeth like lions' teeth. **9** They had breastplates like iron. The noise from their wings was like the roar of chariots with many horses rushing into battle. **10** They had tails and stingers like scorpions. They had the power to hurt people with their tails for five months. **11** The king who ruled them was the angel from the bottomless pit. In Hebrew he is called Abaddon, and in Greek he is called Apollyon.

12 The first catastrophe is over. After these things there are two more catastrophes yet to come. **13** When the sixth angel blew his trumpet, I heard a voice from the four horns of the gold altar in front of God. **14** The voice said to the sixth angel who had the trumpet, "Release the four angels who are held at the great Euphrates River." **15** The four angels who were ready for that hour, day, month, and year were released to kill one-third of humanity. **16** The soldiers on horses numbered 20,000 times 10,000. I heard how many there were.

17 In the vision that I had, the horses and their riders looked like this: The riders had breastplates that were fiery red, pale blue, and yellow. The horses had heads like lions. Fire, smoke, and sulfur came out of their mouths. **18** These three plagues—the fire, smoke, and sulfur which came out of their mouths—killed one-third of humanity. **19** The power of these horses is in their mouths and their tails. (Their tails have heads like snakes which they use to hurt people.)

20 The people who survived these plagues still did not turn to me and change the way they were thinking and acting. If they had, they would have stopped worshiping demons and idols made of gold, silver, bronze, stone, and wood, which cannot see, hear, or walk. **21** They did not turn away from committing murder, practicing witchcraft, sinning sexually, or stealing.

John Eats a Small Scroll

10 **1** I saw another powerful angel come down from heaven. He was dressed in a cloud, and there was a rainbow over his head. His face was like the sun, and his feet were like columns of fire. **2** He held a small, opened scroll in his hand. He set his right foot on the sea and his left on the land. **3** Then he shouted in a loud voice as a lion roars. When he shouted, the seven thunders spoke with voices of their own. **4** When the seven thunders spoke, I was going to write it down. I heard a voice from heaven say, "Seal up what the seven thunders have said, and don't write it down."

5 The angel whom I saw standing on the sea and on the land raised his right hand to heaven. **6** He swore an oath by the one who lives forever and ever, who created heaven and everything in it, the earth and everything in it, and the sea and everything in it. He said, "There will be no more delay. **7** In the days when the seventh angel is ready to blow his trumpet, the mystery of God will be completed, as he had made this Good News known to his servants, the prophets." [8] The voice which I had heard from heaven spoke to me again. It said, "Take the opened scroll from the hand of the angel who is standing on the sea and on the land." [9] I went to the angel and asked him to give me the small scroll. He said to me, "Take it and eat it. It will be bitter in your stomach, but it will be as sweet as honey in your mouth."

[10] I took the small scroll from the angel's hand and ate it. It was as sweet as honey in my mouth, but when I had eaten it, it was bitter in my stomach. [11] The seven thunders told me, "Again you must speak what God has revealed in front of many people, nations, languages, and kings."

God's Two Witnesses

11 [1] Then I was given a stick like a measuring stick. I was told, "Stand up and measure the temple of God and the altar. Count those who worship there. [2] But do not measure the temple courtyard. Leave that out, because it is given to the nations, and they will trample the holy city for 42 months. [3] I will allow my two witnesses who wear sackcloth to speak what God has revealed. They will speak for 1,260 days."

[4] These witnesses are the two olive trees and the two lamp stands standing in the presence of the Lord of the earth. [5] If anyone wants to hurt them, fire comes out of the witnesses' mouths and burns up their enemies. If anyone wants to hurt them, he must be killed the same way. [6] These witnesses have authority to shut the sky in order to keep rain from falling during the time they speak what God has revealed. They have authority to turn water into blood and to strike the earth with any plague as often as they want.

[7] When the witnesses finish their testimony, the beast which comes from the bottomless pit will fight them, conquer them, and kill them. [8] Their dead bodies will lie on the street of the important city where their Lord was crucified. The spiritual names of that city are Sodom and Egypt. [9] For 3½ days some members of the people, tribes, languages, and nations will look at the witnesses' dead bodies and will not allow anyone to bury them. [10] Those living on earth will gloat over the witnesses' death. They will celebrate and send gifts to each other because these two prophets had tormented those living on earth.

[11] After 3½ days the breath of life from God entered the two witnesses, and they stood on their feet. Great fear fell on those who watched them. [12] The witnesses heard a loud voice from heaven calling to them, "Come up here." They went up to heaven in a cloud, and their enemies watched them. [13] At that moment a powerful earthquake struck. One-tenth of the city collapsed, 7,000 people were killed by the earthquake, and the rest were terrified. They gave glory to the God of heaven.

[14] The second catastrophe is over. The third catastrophe will soon be here.

[15] When the seventh angel blew his trumpet, there were loud voices in heaven, saying,

> "The kingdom of the world has become
>   the kingdom of our Lord and of his Messiah,
>   and he will rule as king forever and ever."

[16] Then the 24 leaders, who were sitting on their thrones in God's presence, immediately bowed, worshiped God, [17] and said,

> "We give thanks to you, Lord God Almighty,
>   who is and who was,
>   because you have taken your great power
>   and have begun ruling as king.
> [18]   The nations were angry, but your anger has come.
> The time has come for the dead to be judged:
>   to reward your servants, the prophets,
>   your holy people,
>   and those who fear your name,
>   no matter if they are important or unimportant,
>   and to destroy those who destroy the earth."

[19] God's temple in heaven was opened, and the ark of his promise was seen inside his temple. There was lightning, noise, thunder, an earthquake, and heavy hail.

Two Signs

12 [1] A spectacular sign appeared in the sky: There was a woman who was dressed in the sun, who had the moon under her feet and a crown of 12 stars on her head. [2] She was pregnant. She cried out from labor pains and the agony of giving birth.

[3] Another sign appeared in the sky: a huge fiery red serpent with seven heads, ten horns, and seven crowns on its heads. [4] Its tail swept away one-third of the stars in the sky and threw

them down to earth. The serpent stood in front of the woman who was going to give birth so that it could devour her child when it was born. **5** She gave birth to a son, a boy, who is to rule all the nations with an iron scepter. Her child was snatched away and taken to God and to his throne. **6** Then the woman fled into the wilderness where God had prepared a place for her so that she might be taken care of for 1,260 days.

7 Then a war broke out in heaven. Michael and his angels had to fight a war with the serpent. The serpent and its angels fought. **8** But it was not strong enough, and there was no longer any place for them in heaven. **9** The huge serpent was thrown down. That ancient snake, named Devil and Satan, the deceiver of the whole world, was thrown down to earth. Its angels were thrown down with it.

10 Then I heard a loud voice in heaven, saying,

"Now the salvation, power, kingdom of our God,
and the authority of his Messiah have come.
The one accusing our brothers and sisters,
the one accusing them day and night in the presence of our God,
has been thrown out.
11 They won the victory over him because of the blood of the lamb
and the word of their testimony.
They didn't love their life so much that they refused to give it up.
12 Be glad for this reason, heavens and those who live in them.
How horrible it is for the earth and the sea
because the Devil has come down to them with fierce anger,
knowing that he has little time left."

13 When the serpent saw that it had been thrown down to earth, it persecuted the woman who had given birth to the boy. **14** The woman was given the two wings of the large eagle in order to fly away from the snake to her place in the wilderness, where she could be taken care of for a time, times, and half a time. **15** The snake's mouth poured out a river of water behind the woman in order to sweep her away. **16** The earth helped the woman by opening its mouth and swallowing the river which had poured out of the serpent's mouth. **17** The serpent became angry with the woman. So it went away to fight with her other children, the ones who keep God's commands and hold on to the testimony of Jesus.

18 The serpent stood on the sandy shore of the sea.*a*

The Beast From the Sea

13 **1** I saw a beast coming out of the sea. It had ten horns, seven heads, and ten crowns on its horns. There were insulting names on its heads. **2** The beast that I saw was like a leopard. Its feet were like bear's feet. Its mouth was like a lion's mouth. The serpent gave its power, kingdom, and far-reaching authority to the beast. **3** One of the beast's heads looked like it had a fatal wound, but its fatal wound was healed.

All the people of the world were amazed and followed the beast. **4** They worshiped the serpent because it had given authority to the beast. They also worshiped the beast and said, "Who is like the beast? Who can fight a war with it?" **5** The beast was allowed to speak arrogant and insulting things. It was given authority to act for 42 months. **6** It opened its mouth to insult God, to insult his name and his tent—those who are living in heaven. **7** It was allowed to wage war against God's holy people and to conquer them. It was also given authority over every tribe, people, language, and nation. **8** Everyone living on earth will worship it, everyone whose name is not written in the Book of Life. That book belongs to the lamb who was slaughtered before the creation of the world.

9 If anyone has ears, let him listen:

10 If anyone is taken prisoner, he must go to prison.
If anyone is killed with a sword, with a sword he must be killed.

In this situation God's holy people need endurance and confidence.

The Beast From the Earth

11 I saw another beast come from the earth, and it had two horns like a lamb. It talked like a serpent. **12** The second beast uses all the authority of the first beast in its presence. The second beast makes the earth and those living on it worship the first beast, whose fatal wound was healed. **13** The second beast performs spectacular signs. It even makes fire come down from heaven to earth in front of people. **14** It deceives those living on earth with the signs that it is allowed to do in front of the ˌfirstˌ beast. It tells those living on earth to make a statue for the beast who was wounded by a sword and yet lived.

---

a 12:18 Some translations include this verse at the beginning of 13:1.

¹⁵ The second beast was allowed to put breath into the statue of the ˻first˼ beast. Then the statue of the ˻first˼ beast could talk and put to death whoever would not worship it. ¹⁶ The second beast forces all people—important and unimportant people, rich and poor people, free people and slaves—to be branded on their right hands or on their foreheads. ¹⁷ It does this so that no one may buy or sell unless he has the brand, which is the beast's name or the number of its name.

¹⁸ In this situation wisdom is needed. Let the person who has insight figure out the number of the beast, because it is a human number.[a] The beast's number is 666.

The New Song on Mount Zion

14 ¹ I looked, and the lamb was standing on Mount Zion. There were 144,000 people with him who had his name and his Father's name written on their foreheads. ² Then I heard a sound from heaven like the noise of raging water and the noise of loud thunder. The sound I heard was like the music played by harpists. ³ They were singing a new song in front of the throne, the four living creatures, and the leaders. Only the 144,000 people who had been bought on earth could learn the song.

⁴ These 144,000 virgins are pure. They follow the lamb wherever he goes. They were bought from among humanity as the first ones offered to God and to the lamb. ⁵ They've never told a lie. They are blameless.

The Harvest of the Earth

⁶ I saw another angel flying overhead with the everlasting Good News to spread to those who live on earth—to every nation, tribe, language, and people. ⁷ The angel said in a loud voice, "Fear God and give him glory, because the time has come for him to judge. Worship the one who made heaven and earth, the sea and springs."

⁸ Another angel, a second one, followed him, and said, "Fallen! Babylon the Great has fallen! She has made all the nations drink the wine of her passionate sexual sins."

⁹ Another angel, a third one, followed them, and said in a loud voice, "Whoever worships the beast or its statue, whoever is branded on his forehead or his hand, ¹⁰ will drink the wine of God's fury, which has been poured unmixed into the cup of God's anger. Then he will be tortured by fiery sulfur in the presence of the holy angels and the lamb. ¹¹ The smoke from their torture will go up forever and ever. There will be no rest day or night for those who worship the beast or its statue, or for anyone branded with its name." ¹² In this situation God's holy people, who obey his commands and keep their faith in Jesus, need endurance.

¹³ I heard a voice from heaven saying, "Write this: From now on those who die believing in the Lord are blessed."

"Yes," says the Spirit. "Let them rest from their hard work. What they have done goes with them."

¹⁴ Then I looked, and there was a white cloud, and on the cloud sat someone who was like the Son of Man. He had a gold crown on his head and a sharp sickle in his hand. ¹⁵ Another angel came out of the temple. He cried out in a loud voice to the one who sat on the cloud, "Swing your sickle, and gather the harvest. The time has come to gather it, because the harvest on the earth is overripe."

¹⁶ The one who sat on the cloud swung his sickle over the earth, and the harvesting of the earth was completed.

¹⁷ Another angel came out of the temple in heaven. He, too, had a sharp sickle. ¹⁸ Yet another angel came from the altar with authority over fire. This angel called out in a loud voice to the angel with the sharp sickle, "Swing your sickle, and gather the bunches of grapes from the vine of the earth, because those grapes are ripe." ¹⁹ The angel swung his sickle on the earth and gathered the grapes from the vine of the earth. He threw them into the winepress of God's anger. ²⁰ The grapes were trampled in the winepress outside the city. Blood flowed out of the winepress as high as a horse's bridle for 1,600 stadia.[a]

Seven Angels With Seven Plagues

15 ¹ I saw another sign in heaven. It was spectacular and amazing. There were seven angels with the last seven plagues which are the final expression of God's anger.

² Then I saw what looked like a sea of glass mixed with fire. Those who had won the victory over the beast, its statue, and the number of its name were standing on the glassy sea. They were holding God's harps ³ and singing the song of God's servant Moses and the song of the lamb. They sang,

> "The things you do are spectacular and amazing, Lord God Almighty.
> The way you do them is fair and true, King of the Nations.

---

[a] 13:18 Or "it is the number of a human."   [a] 14:20 One stadion is equivalent to 607 feet.

4   Lord, who won't fear and praise your name?
          You are the only holy one,
             and all the nations will come to worship you
                because they know about your fair judgments."

[5] After these things I looked, and I saw that the temple of the tent containing the words of God's promise was open in heaven. [6] The seven angels with the seven plagues came out of the temple wearing clean, shining linen with gold belts around their waists. [7] One of the four living creatures gave seven gold bowls full of the anger of God, who lives forever and ever, to the seven angels. [8] The temple was filled with smoke from the glory of God and his power. No one could enter the temple until the seven plagues of the seven angels came to an end.

The Seven Angels Pour Out Their Bowls

16 [1] I heard a loud voice from the temple saying to the seven angels, "Pour the seven bowls of God's anger over the earth."

[2] The first angel poured his bowl over the earth. Horrible, painful sores appeared on the people who had the brand of the beast and worshiped its statue.

[3] The second angel poured his bowl over the sea. The sea turned into blood like the blood of a dead man, and every living thing in the sea died.

[4] The third angel poured his bowl over the rivers and the springs. They turned into blood. [5] Then I heard the angel of the water say,

      "You are fair.
      You are the one who is and the one who was, the holy one,
         because you have judged these things.
6   You have given them blood to drink
         because they have poured out
            the blood of God's people and prophets.
               This is what they deserve."

[7] Then I heard the altar answer,

      "Yes, Lord God Almighty, your judgments are true and fair."

[8] The fourth angel poured his bowl on the sun. The sun was allowed to burn people with fire. [9] They were severely burned. They cursed the name of God, who has the authority over these plagues. They would not change the way they think and act and give him glory.

[10] The fifth angel poured his bowl on the throne of the beast. Its kingdom turned dark. People gnawed on their tongues in anguish [11] and cursed the God of heaven for their pains and their sores. However, they would not stop what they were doing.

[12] The sixth angel poured his bowl on the great Euphrates River. The water in the river dried up to make a road for the kings from the east. [13] Then I saw three evil spirits like frogs come out of the mouths of the serpent, the beast, and the false prophet. [14] They are spirits of demons that do miracles. These spirits go to the kings of the whole world and gather them for the war on the frightening day of God Almighty.

[15] "See, I am coming like a thief. Blessed is the one who remains alert and doesn't lose his clothes. He will not have to go naked and let others see his shame."

[16] The spirits gathered the kings at the place which is called Armageddon in Hebrew.

[17] The seventh angel poured his bowl into the air. A loud voice came from the throne in the temple, and said, "It has happened!" [18] There was lightning, noise, thunder, and a powerful earthquake. There has never been such a powerful earthquake since humans have been on earth. [19] The important city split into three parts, and the cities of the nations fell. God remembered to give Babylon the Great the cup of wine from his fierce anger. [20] Every island vanished, and the mountains could no longer be seen. [21] Large, heavy hailstones fell from the sky on people. The people cursed God because the plague of hail was such a terrible plague.

Babylon the Great

17 [1] One of the seven angels who held the seven bowls came and said to me, "Come, I will show you the judgment of that notorious prostitute who sits on raging waters. [2] The kings of the earth had sex with her, and those living on earth became drunk on the wine of her sexual sins." [3] Then the angel carried me by his power into the wilderness.

I saw a woman sitting on a bright red beast covered with insulting names. It had seven heads and ten horns. [4] The woman wore purple clothes, bright red clothes, gold jewelry, gems, and pearls. In her hand she was holding a gold cup filled with detestable and evil things from her sexual sins. [5] A name was written on her forehead. The name was Mystery: Babylon the

Great, the Mother of Prostitutes and Detestable Things of the Earth. [6] I saw that the woman was drunk with the blood of God's holy people and of those who testify about Jesus. I was very surprised when I saw her.

[7] The angel asked me, "Why are you surprised? I will tell you the mystery of the woman and the beast with the seven heads and the ten horns that carries her.

[8] "You saw the beast which once was, is no longer, and will come from the bottomless pit and go to its destruction. Those living on earth, whose names were not written in the Book of Life when the world was created, will be surprised when they see the beast because it was, is no longer, and will come again.

[9] "In this situation a wise mind is needed. The seven heads are seven mountains on which the woman is sitting. [10] They are also seven kings. Five of them have fallen, one is ruling now, and the other has not yet come. When he comes, he must remain for a little while. [11] The beast that was and is no longer is the eighth king. It belongs with the seven kings and goes to its destruction.

[12] "The ten horns that you saw are ten kings who have not yet started to rule. They will receive authority to rule as kings with the beast for one hour. [13] They have one purpose—to give their power and authority to the beast. [14] They will go to war against the lamb. The lamb will conquer them because he is Lord of lords and King of kings. Those who are called, chosen, and faithful are with him."

[15] The angel also said to me, "The waters you saw, on which the prostitute is sitting, are people, crowds, nations, and languages. [16] The ten horns and the beast you saw will hate the prostitute. They will leave her abandoned and naked. They will eat her flesh and burn her up in a fire. [17] God has made them do what he wants them to do. So they will give their kingdom to the beast until God's words are carried out. [18] The woman you saw is the important city which dominates the kings of the earth."

Babylon's Fall

18 [1] After these things I saw another angel come from heaven. He had tremendous power, and his glory lit up the earth. [2] He cried out in a powerful voice, "Fallen! Babylon the Great has fallen! She has become a home for demons. She is a prison for every evil spirit, every unclean[a] bird, and every unclean and hated beast. [3] All the nations fell because of the wine of her sexual sins. The kings of the earth had sex with her. Her luxurious wealth has made the merchants of the earth rich."

[4] I heard another voice from heaven saying, "Come out of Babylon, my people, so that you do not participate in her sins and suffer from any of her plagues. [5] Her sins are piled as high as heaven, and God has remembered her crimes. [6] Do to her what she has done. Give her twice as much as she gave. Serve her a drink in her own cup twice as large as the drink she served others. [7] She gave herself glory and luxury. Now give her just as much torture and misery. She says to herself, 'I'm a queen on a throne, not a widow. I'll never be miserable.' [8] For this reason her plagues of death, misery, and starvation will come in a single day. She will be burned up in a fire, because the Lord God, who judges her, is powerful.

[9] "The kings of the earth who had sex with her and lived in luxury with her will cry and mourn over her when they see the smoke rise from her raging fire. [10] Frightened by her torture, they will stand far away and say,

> 'How horrible, how horrible it is for that important city,
>   the powerful city Babylon!
> In one moment judgment has come to it!'

[11] "The merchants of the earth cry and mourn over her, because no one buys their cargo anymore. [12] No one buys their cargo of gold, silver, gems, pearls, fine linen, purple cloth, silk, bright red cloth, all kinds of citron wood, articles made of ivory and very costly wood, bronze, iron, marble, [13] cinnamon, spices, incense, perfume, frankincense, wine, olive oil, flour, wheat, cattle, sheep, horses, wagons, slaves (that is, humans).

[14]   'The fruit you craved is gone.
>   All your luxuries and your splendor have disappeared.
>   No one will ever find them again.'

[15] "Frightened by her torture, the merchants who had become rich by selling these things will stand far away. They will cry and mourn, [16] saying,

> 'How horrible, how horrible for that important city
>   which was wearing fine linen, purple clothes,

---

bright red clothes, gold jewelry, gems, and pearls.
¹⁷ In one moment all this wealth has been destroyed!'

Every ship's captain, everyone who traveled by ship, sailors, and everyone who made their living from the sea stood far away. ¹⁸ When they saw the smoke rise from her raging fire, they repeatedly cried out, 'Was there ever a city as important as this?' ¹⁹ Then they threw dust on their heads and shouted while crying and mourning,

'How horrible, how horrible for that important city.
Everyone who had a ship at sea
grew rich because of that city's high prices.
In one moment it has been destroyed!'

²⁰ "Gloat over it, heaven, God's people, apostles, and prophets.
God has condemned it for you."

²¹ Then a powerful angel picked up a stone that was like a large millstone. He threw it into the sea and said,

"The important city Babylon will be thrown down with the same force.
It will never be found again.
²² The sound of harpists, musicians, flutists, and trumpeters
will never be heard in it again.
Skilled craftsman
will never be found in it again.
The sound of a millstone
will never be heard in it again.
²³ Light from lamps
will never shine in it again.
Voices of brides and grooms
will never be heard in it again.
Its merchants were the important people of the world,
because all the nations were deceived by its witchcraft.

²⁴ "The blood of prophets, God's people, and everyone who had been murdered on earth was found in it."

The Lamb's Wedding

19 ¹ After these things I heard what sounded like the loud noise from a large crowd in heaven, saying,

"Hallelujah!
Salvation, glory, and power belong to our God.
² His judgments are true and fair.
He has condemned the notorious prostitute
who corrupted the world with her sexual sins.
He has taken revenge on her for the blood of his servants."

³ A second time they said, "Hallelujah! The smoke goes up from her forever and ever." ⁴ The 24 leaders and the 4 living creatures bowed and worshiped God, who was sitting on the throne. They said, "Amen! Hallelujah!" ⁵ A voice came from the throne. It said, "Praise our God, all who serve and fear him, no matter who you are."

⁶ I heard what sounded like the noise from a large crowd, like the noise of raging waters, like the noise of loud thunder, saying,

"Hallelujah! The Lord our God, the Almighty, has become king.
⁷ Let us rejoice, be happy, and give him glory
because it's time for the marriage of the lamb.
His bride has made herself ready.
⁸ She has been given the privilege of wearing
dazzling, pure linen."

This fine linen represents the things that God's holy people do that have his approval.
⁹ Then the angel said to me, "Write this: 'Blessed are those who are invited to the lamb's wedding banquet.'" He also told me, "These are the true words of God." ¹⁰ I bowed at his feet to worship him. But he told me, "Don't do that! I am your coworker and a coworker of the Christians who hold on to the testimony of Jesus. Worship God, because the testimony of Jesus is the spirit of prophecy!"

The Great Banquet of God

[11] I saw heaven standing open. There was a white horse, and its rider is named Faithful and True. With integrity he judges and wages war. [12] His eyes are flames of fire. On his head are many crowns. He has a name written on him, but only he knows what it is. [13] He wears clothes dipped in blood, and his name is the Word of God.

[14] The armies of heaven, wearing pure, white linen, follow him on white horses. [15] A sharp sword comes out of his mouth to defeat the nations. He will rule them with an iron scepter and tread the winepress of the fierce anger of God Almighty. [16] On his clothes and his thigh he has a name written: King of kings and Lord of lords.

[17] I saw an angel standing in the sun. He cried out in a loud voice to all the birds flying overhead, "Come! Gather for the great banquet of God. [18] Eat the flesh of kings, generals, warriors, horses and their riders, and all free people and slaves, both important or insignificant people."

[19] I saw the beast, the kings of the earth, and their armies gathered to wage war against the rider on the horse and his army. [20] The beast and the false prophet who had done miracles for the beast were captured. By these miracles the false prophet had deceived those who had the brand of the beast and worshiped its statue. Both of them were thrown alive into the fiery lake of burning sulfur. [21] The rider on the horse killed the rest with the sword that came out of his mouth. All the birds gorged themselves on the flesh of those who had been killed.

An Angel Overpowers the Devil

20 [1] I saw an angel coming down from heaven, holding the key to the bottomless pit and a large chain in his hand. [2] He overpowered the serpent, that ancient snake, named Devil and Satan. The angel chained up the serpent for 1,000 years. [3] He threw it into the bottomless pit. The angel shut and sealed the pit over the serpent to keep it from deceiving the nations anymore until the 1,000 years were over. After that it must be set free for a little while.

[4] I saw thrones, and those who sat on them were allowed to judge. Then I saw the souls of those whose heads had been cut off because of their testimony about Jesus and because of the word of God. They had not worshiped the beast or its statue and were not branded on their foreheads or hands. They lived and ruled with Christ for 1,000 years. [5] The rest of the dead did not live until the 1,000 years ended.

This is the first time that people come back to life. [6] Blessed and holy are those who are included the first time that people come back to life. The second death has no power over them. They will continue to be priests of God and Christ. They will rule with him for 1,000 years.

The Final Judgment

[7] When 1,000 years are over, Satan will be freed from his prison. [8] He will go out to deceive Gog and Magog, the nations in the four corners of the earth, and gather them for war. They will be as numerous as the grains of sand on the seashore. [9] I saw that, they spread over the broad expanse of the earth and surrounded the camp of God's holy people and the beloved city. Fire came from heaven and burned them up. [10] The devil, who deceived them, was thrown into the fiery lake of sulfur, where the beast and the false prophet were also thrown. They will be tortured day and night forever and ever.

[11] I saw a large, white throne and the one who was sitting on it. The earth and the sky fled from his presence, but no place was found for them. [12] I saw the dead, both important and unimportant people, standing in front of the throne. Books were opened, including the Book of Life. The dead were judged on the basis of what they had done, as recorded in the books. [13] The sea gave up its dead. Death and hell gave up their dead. People were judged based on what they had done. [14] Death and hell were thrown into the fiery lake. (The fiery lake is the second death.) [15] Those whose names were not found in the Book of Life were thrown into the fiery lake.

A New Heaven and a New Earth

21 [1] I saw a new heaven and a new earth, because the first heaven and earth had disappeared, and the sea was gone. [2] Then I saw the holy city, New Jerusalem, coming down from God out of heaven, dressed like a bride ready for her husband. [3] I heard a loud voice from the throne say, "God lives with humans! God will make his home with them, and they will be his people. God himself will be with them and be their God. [4] He will wipe every tear from their eyes. There won't be any more death. There won't be any grief, crying, or pain, because the first things have disappeared."

[5] The one sitting on the throne said, "I am making everything new." He said, "Write this: 'These words are faithful and true.' " [6] He said to me, "It has happened! I am the A and the Z,ᵃ the beginning and the end. I will give a drink from the fountain filled with the water of life to anyone who is thirsty. It won't cost anything. [7] Everyone who wins the victory will inherit these

ᵃ 21:6 Or "the Alpha and the Omega."

things. I will be their God, and they will be my children. [8] But cowardly, unfaithful, and detestable people, murderers, sexual sinners, sorcerers, idolaters, and all liars will find themselves in the fiery lake of burning sulfur. This is the second death."

A New Jerusalem

[9] One of the seven angels who had the seven bowls full of the last seven plagues came to me and said, "Come! I will show you the bride, the wife of the lamb." [10] He carried me by his power away to a large, high mountain. He showed me the holy city, Jerusalem, coming down from God out of heaven. [11] It had the glory of God. Its light was like a valuable gem, like gray quartz, as clear as crystal. [12] It had a large, high wall with 12 gates. Twelve angels were at the gates. The names of the 12 tribes of Israel were written on the gates. [13] There were three gates on the east, three gates on the north, three gates on the south, and three gates on the west. [14] The wall of the city had 12 foundations. The 12 names of the 12 apostles of the lamb were written on them. [15] The angel who was talking to me had a gold measuring stick to measure the city, its gates, and its wall. [16] The city was square. It was as wide as it was long. He measured the city with the stick. It was 12,000 stadia[b] long. Its length, width, and height were the same. [17] He measured its wall. According to human measurement, which the angel was using, it was 144 cubits.[c] [18] Its wall was made of gray quartz. The city was made of pure gold, as clear as glass. [19] The foundations of the city wall were beautifully decorated with all kinds of gems: The first foundation was gray quartz, the second sapphire, the third agate, the fourth emerald, [20] the fifth onyx, the sixth red quartz, the seventh yellow quartz, the eighth beryl, the ninth topaz, the tenth green quartz, the eleventh jacinth, and the twelfth amethyst. [21] The 12 gates were 12 pearls. Each gate was made of one pearl. The street of the city was made of pure gold, as clear as glass.

[22] I did not see any temple in it, because the Lord God Almighty and the lamb are its temple. [23] The city doesn't need any sun or moon to give it light because the glory of God gave it light. The lamb was its lamp. [24] The nations will walk in its light, and the kings of the earth will bring their glory into it. [25] Its gates will be open all day. They will never close because there won't be any night there. [26] They will bring the glory and wealth of the nations into the holy city. [27] Nothing unclean,[d] no one who does anything detestable, and no liars will ever enter it. Only those whose names are written in the lamb's Book of Life will enter it.

22 [1] The angel showed me a river filled with the water of life, as clear as crystal. It was flowing from the throne of God and the lamb. [2] Between the street of the city and the river there was a tree of life visible from both sides. It produced 12 kinds of fruit. Each month had its own fruit. The leaves of the tree will heal the nations. [3] There will no longer be any curse. The throne of God and the lamb will be in the city. His servants will worship him [4] and see his face. His name will be on their foreheads. [5] There will be no more night, and they will not need any light from lamps or the sun because the Lord God will shine on them. They will rule as kings forever and ever.

Jesus Says: I'm Coming Soon

[6] He said to me, "These words are trustworthy and true. The Lord God of the spirits of the prophets has sent his angel to show his servants the things that must happen soon. [7] I'm coming soon! Blessed is the one who follows the words of the prophecy in this book."

[8] I, John, heard and saw these things. When I had heard and seen them, I bowed to worship at the feet of the angel who had been showing me these things. [9] He told me, "Don't do that! I am your coworker. I work with other Christians, the prophets, and those who follow the words in this book. Worship God!"

[10] Then the angel said to me, "Don't seal up the words of the prophecy in this book because the time is near. [11] Let those who don't have God's approval go without it, and let filthy people continue to be filthy. Let those who have God's approval continue to have it, and let holy people continue to be holy."

[12] "I'm coming soon! I will bring my reward with me to pay all people based on what they have done. [13] I am the A and the Z,[a] the first and the last, the beginning and the end.

[14] "Blessed are those who wash their robes so that they may have the right to the tree of life and may go through the gates into the city. [15] Outside are dogs, sorcerers, sexual sinners, murderers, idolaters, and all who lie in what they say and what they do.

[16] "I, Jesus, have sent my angel to give this testimony to you for the churches. I am the root and descendant of David. I am the bright morning star."

[17] The Spirit and the bride say, "Come!" Let those who hear this say, "Come!" Let those who are thirsty come! Let those who want the water of life take it as a gift.

---

[b] 21:16 One stadion is equivalent to 607 feet.   [c] 21:17 One cubit is equivalent to 21 inches.   [d] 21:27 "Unclean" refers to anything that Moses' Teachings say is not presentable to God.   [a] 22:13 Or "the Alpha and the Omega."

18 I warn everyone who hears the words of the prophecy in this book: If anyone adds anything to this, God will strike him with the plagues that are written in this book. **19** If anyone takes away any words from this book of prophecy, God will take away his portion of the tree of life and the holy city that are described in this book.

20 The one who is testifying to these things says, "Yes, I'm coming soon!"
    Amen! Come, Lord Jesus!

21 The good will[b] of the Lord Jesus be with all of you. Amen!

---

b 22:21 Or "grace."

BIBLE STUDY
HELPS

THE TEACHINGS OF JESUS

Counting Cost
Cost of being a disciple. Luke 14:25–33

Cross
Carry your cross and follow Jesus. Matthew 10:38; Luke 14:27

Crucifixion
Jesus' prediction. John 8:28
People being drawn toward Jesus on the cross. John 12:32

David
Jesus, David's son. Matthew 22:42–45

Day of worship
Christ defending his disciples. Matthew 12:1–5
Do good. Matthew 12:12
The day of worship for people. Mark 2:27

Days of Noah
As when the Son of Man returns. Matthew 24:37

Death
Dividing of body and soul. Matthew 10:28
Life of the soul after death. Luke 16:22–31
How to never see death. John 8:51

Debtor
The compassionate creditor. Matthew 18:27
The cruel debtor. Matthew 18:28–30
Love according to amount forgiven. Luke 7:41–43

Disciple
How to be a disciple. Matthew 16:24
Salt and light. Matthew 5:13,14
Jesus' instructions. Matthew 28:19

Division
Divided tribe and kingdom. Matthew 12:25

Divorce
A written notice. Matthew 5:31; Mark 10:4,5
Reason for divorce. Matthew 5:32

Doctor
Needed by the sick. Matthew 9:12

Doctrine
Teaching human rules. Matthew 15:9

Dollars
Different amounts according to ability, the responsibility the same. Matthew 25:14
Faithful use of dollars. Matthew 25:16,17
The buried dollars. Matthew 25:25

Door
Christ the gate. John 10:9
The shut door. Matthew 25:10,11

Doubt
Effect of lack of faith on miracles. Matthew 13:58
Thomas' doubt. John 20:25,27

Drunkenness
Don't become drunk. Luke 21:34

Duty
To God and neighbors. Luke 10:27
To others. Matthew 25:35–45

Endurance
Leads to being saved. Matthew 10:22

Enemy
Love your enemies. Matthew 5:44,45

Eternal life
With God's approval. Matthew 25:46
Peace and suffering. Luke 16:25

Excuses
The lost blessing. Luke 14:18–20

Faith
Too little faith. Matthew 16:8; Mark 4:40
Faith in Jesus is faith in God. John 12:44
A reason for faith. John 14:11

Faith that saves and heals. Luke 7:50; 18:42; John 3:15
Believing what the prophets said. Luke 24:25
In receiving what you pray for. Mark 11:24
Results of faith in Jesus. John 11:25,26

Faithful
The servant of the master. Matthew 24:45
Rewarding a faithful servant. Matthew 25:21

Faithful servant
Responsibility for what is entrusted. Matthew 25:15
The unfaithful servant. Matthew 25:25
Reward for a good and faithful servant. Matthew 25:23

False prophets
Saying and not doing. Matthew 7:21

False testimony
Obey the commandments. Matthew 19:18

Fasting
Hypocritical fasting. Matthew 6:16

Father—God
His Father in heaven. Matthew 18:35
Sent Jesus. John 14:24
Seen in the Son. John 14:9
Given glory because of the Son. John 14:13
Love for the world. John 3:16
Our Father in heaven. Matthew 6:9

Fear
The one to fear. Luke 12:5
Don't be afraid. Luke 12:32

Food
Christ's food to do what the Father wants. John 4:34
From the Son of Man. John 6:27

Forgiveness
Forgiving others. Matthew 18:21–27,35
If a person changes the way he thinks and acts. Luke 17:3
Jesus forgiving. Luke 7:47,48
Christ's prayer. Luke 23:34

Friendship
Obey the commandments. John 15:14
Showing the greatest love. John 15:13

Fruitfulness
The fruitless life. Luke 13:6
Be fruitful by living in Christ. John 15:4
The pruned branch. John 15:2

Generosity
Give to all who ask. Luke 6:30
The golden rule. Luke 6:31
Give and you will receive. Luke 6:38

Gentleness
Blessed are the gentle. Matthew 5:5
Gentleness of Christ. Matthew 11:29

Gift
The acceptable gift. Matthew 5:23,24
Gifts without charge. Matthew 10:8
God's gift of living water. John 4:10

Glorified
God glorified in Christ. John 17:1
Christ glorified by people. John 17:10
Believers given glory. John 17:22

God's approval
Needed to enter the kingdom of Heaven. Matthew 5:20
Be concerned about his kingdom. Matthew 6:33
Mary's choice. Luke 10:42

God's house
Many rooms. John 14:2

Golden Rule
Moses' Teachings and the Prophets. Matthew 7:12

Gratitude
An unusual case. Luke 17:18
Christ praising God. Luke 10:21

Greed
The source. Mark 7:22,23
Warning against. Luke 12:15

Happiness
Eternal when you see Jesus. John 16:22
Happiness about the faithful. Matthew 25:21
Names written in heaven. Luke 10:20
Happiness in heaven. Luke 15:7

Harvest
A large harvest but few workers. Luke 10:2; John 4:35
Gather grain for eternal life. John 4:36

Healing
Because of faith. Luke 8:48

Heaven
The Father's house. John 14:2
God's angels. Luke 15:10
Happiness. Luke 15:7
Treasure. Luke 12:33

Heavenly care
The heavenly Father will provide. Matthew 6:25–34

Hell
A place of judging. Matthew 5:22
A place of torture. Luke 16:23

Helping
Thanks for helping others. Luke 6:33

Holy Spirit/Spirit of Truth
Sent by the Father. John 14:26
Will teach. John 14:26
Will convict and convince. John 16:8–11
Cursing the Spirit. Matthew 12:31

Honesty
The seed in a good and honest heart. Luke 8:15

Honor yourself
When humbled. Luke 14:9,11

Hospitality
Inviting the needy. Luke 14:12,13

House
Built on a rock. Matthew 7:24
The divided house. Luke 11:17

Humility
Becoming like a child. Matthew 18:4
Humbleness and honor. Matthew 23:12
Wash each other's feet. John 13:14

Hunger
Blessed are those who hunger. Matthew 5:6

Hypocrisy
In giving. Matthew 23:23,27
The praying hypocrite. Matthew 6:5
The fasting hypocrite. Matthew 6:16
Prophesied by Isaiah. Matthew 15:7,8
The beam in the hypocrite's eye. Luke 6:42

Ignorance
The blind leaders. Matthew 15:14

Intercession
Christ's prayer. John 17:9–26
On the cross. Luke 23:34

Invited
Many invited but few chosen. Matthew 22:14

Isaac—Jacob
Abraham, Isaac, and Jacob in the kingdom of Heaven. Matthew 8:11

Jerusalem
Killing and stoning. Matthew 23:37
Telling of its destruction. Matthew 24:2

John the Baptizer
More than a prophet. Prepares the way for Jesus. Luke 7:26–28

Jonah
The sign of Jonah. Matthew 12:40
Jonah's message. Matthew 12:41

Joy
Christ's joy. John 15:11

Judging
Hypocritical judging. Luke 6:42
Standards for you and others. Matthew 7:2
Stop judging. Matthew 7:1

Judgment
Separating the nations. Matthew 25:31,32
Of those who did good and those who did evil. John 5:28,29
Reward of those having God's approval. Luke 14:14

Justice
God will help his people. Luke 18:3–8
The wasteful business manager. Luke 16:1,2
The widow's justice. Luke 18:2–5

Kingdom of Heaven
Do and teach the commandments. Matthew 5:19
Stories about its people. Matthew 13
Like a king settling accounts. Matthew 18:23

Lazarus
A sick beggar. Luke 16:19–21
At peace after death. Luke 16:22,25

Lending
Reasons for lending. Luke 6:34,35

Life
Christ is the life. John 14:6
Christ brings people back to life and is life itself. John 11:25
Losing and preserving life. Matthew 10:39

Light
The light of the world. John 8:12
Light for the world. Matthew 5:14
Clouded by evil. Luke 11:34,35

Lord's Supper
His body and blood. Luke 22:19,20; Matthew 26:28

Love
God's love for the world. John 3:16
Christ's love. John 15:9,13
Love for Christ. Matthew 10:37; John 15:10
Love each other. John 15:12
Love your enemies. Matthew 5:44

Lust
Chokes the word. Mark 4:19

Make unclean
Comes from within a person. Matthew 15:19

Marriage
What God has joined together. Matthew 19:6

Mary's choice
Only one thing needed. Luke 10:42

Mercy
Blessed are those who show mercy. Matthew 5:7
The sinner's prayer. Luke 18:13; 16:24

Mind
Place of evil thoughts. Matthew 15:19

Where good and evil things are. Matthew 12:35
Slowness to believe. Luke 24:25
Love with all your mind. Luke 10:27

Minister
A servant. Matthew 20:26
Christ's life as a ransom. Matthew 20:28

Miracles
With the help of God's Spirit. Matthew 12:28
In Jesus' name. Mark 9:39
Jesus' proof. Luke 7:22

Missionary Work
Make disciples of all nations. Matthew 28:19

Money
Money of unrighteousness. Luke 16:9
Serving two masters. Matthew 6:24

Moneychangers
His house a gathering place for thieves. Mark 11:17

Moses' Teachings and the Prophets
Not set aside, but made to come true. Matthew 5:17
Teach with Moses' authority. Matthew 23:2
Refusing to listen to them. Luke 16:31
Not following Moses' teachings. John 7:19

Mourning
They are blessed and comforted. Matthew 5:4

Narrow Gate
The road to life. Matthew 7:14

Neighbor
Found in the good Samaritan. Luke 10:29

New Birth
Needed to enter the kingdom of God. John 3:5
Born of the Spirit. John 3:8

Obedience
Obedient like the foundation on bedrock. Luke 6:47,48

Overcoming
The triumphant Lord. John 16:33

Paradise
Guarantee to crucified criminal. Luke 23:43

Parents
Honor them. Matthew 15:4

Payment for sin
A ransom for sinners. Matthew 20:28
The gift of love. John 3:16
To give life. John 12:24

Peace
Given by Christ. John 14:27
In a troubled world. John 16:33
Blessed are those who make peace. Matthew 5:9

Pearls
Don't throw to pigs. Matthew 7:6

Perfection
How to be perfect. Matthew 19:21
Father in heaven. Matthew 5:48

Persecution
Falling from faith. Mark 4:17
Testify for Christ. Matthew 10:18
Rewards in heaven. Matthew 5:12

Poor
Invite them to a banquet. Luke 14:12

Prayer
Don't pray like hypocrites. Matthew 6:5
Power of prayer. Mark 9:29
Pray for persecutors. Matthew 5:44
Ask and you will receive. Matthew 7:7,8
The Lord's Prayer. Matthew 6:9–13

Prophecy
Fulfilled in Christ. Luke 18:31; 24:27
Predictions of Christ. Matthew 24:3–39

Prophet
Not accepted in his hometown. Luke 4:24
False prophets will appear. Matthew 24:11

Prostitutes
Going into the kingdom of God. Matthew 21:31

Punishment
Thrown out from the kingdom of God. Luke 13:28

Pureness
Blessed are those with pure thoughts. Matthew 5:8

Rabbi
In the marketplace. Matthew 23:7

Ransom
The Son of Man's ransom for many people. Matthew 20:28

Rejection of Christ
By the leaders. Luke 9:22
By those who love the dark. John 3:19
By rich people. Matthew 19:22–24

Responsibility
Based on ability. Matthew 25:15

Rest
Given by Christ. Matthew 11:28

Revenge
Pray for persecutors. Matthew 5:44

Reward
Based on what the person has done. Matthew 16:27
When those who have God's approval come back to life.
Luke 14:14
A great reward in heaven. Matthew 5:12

Riches
Deceitful pleasures of riches. Mark 4:19
A rich person entering the kingdom of God. Matthew 19:24
Treasures in heaven. Matthew 6:19,20

Sadness
Suffering in the fire. Luke 16:24,25
Thrown out of the kingdom of God. Luke 13:28

Salt
People as salt. Matthew 5:13

Salvation
Salvation comes from the Jews. John 4:22
Faith saved you. Luke 7:50
Salvation of Zacchaeus. Luke 19:9

Satan
Fallen from heaven. Luke 10:18
The ruler of demons. Matthew 12:24
His temptation of Christ. Matthew 4:3–9
Dealing with Satan. Matthew 4:10

Sawdust and Beam
An illustration of hypocrisy. Luke 6:41,42

Scriptures
The word of God. Matthew 4:4; 21:42
Christ in the Scriptures. Luke 24:27
The words are truth. John 17:17

Seed
The kingdom of heaven illustrated by stories.
Matthew 13:1–25
The seed is the word. Matthew 13:19; Mark 4:14
The Son of Man is the sower. Matthew 13:37

Seek
Christ seeking people who are lost. Luke 19:10

Self-blame
The lost son's confession. Luke 15:18,19

Self-Denial
In following Christ. Matthew 16:24
To be perfect, sell what you own. Matthew 19:21,22

Servant
Taking the slave's place. Matthew 20:27
The awake servant. Luke 12:37

Set apart
Truth makes holy. John 17:17
Christ set apart by God. John 10:36

Shepherd
Christ the good shepherd. John 10:11
The one flock. John 10:16
The lost sheep. Luke 15:4–7
The nations separated. Matthew 25:31–33

Sin
A slave to sin. John 8:34
Convict the world of sin. John 16:8
Die because of sins. John 8:24
Sin will be forgiven. Mark 3:28
Christ's promise. John 6:37

Slander God
Cursing the Spirit. Matthew 12:31

Snake
Lifted on a pole. John 3:14,15
Description of the Pharisees. Matthew 23:33

Solomon
Someone greater than Solomon. Luke 11:31

Soul
Separate from the body. Matthew 10:28
Satisfying the soul. Luke 12:19
Demanded by God. Luke 12:20
The soul after death. Luke 16:22,23

Stay alert
Blessed are those awake when he comes. Luke 12:37
Why you should stay alert. Luke 12:38–40

Submission
Christ's submission to His Father's will. Matthew 26:42

Suffering
Necessity of Christ's suffering. Luke 24:26; Matthew 26:38
Love your enemies. Luke 6:27–31

Surrender
Jesus' prayer. Matthew 26:38,39

Taxation
Give to Rome, give to God. Matthew 22:19–21

Teaching
The Holy Spirit will teach. Luke 12:12

Tell the Good News
Sent to announce forgiveness. Luke 4:18

Temptation
Jesus' power challenged. Matthew 4:3,6
What Scripture asks. Matthew 4:4,7,10
Ways to avoid temptation. Matthew 26:41

Treasure
Don't store treasures on earth. Matthew 6:19
Store treasures in heaven. Matthew 6:20

Tree
Fruit according to the tree. Matthew 7:16–20

Time of misery
Trouble in the world. John 16:33
The coming time of misery. Matthew 24:21,22

Trust
God will provide. Matthew 6:25–31
Don't worry. Matthew 6:34

Truth
Christ the truth. John 14:6
The Spirit of Truth. John 14:17
Words are truth. John 17:17

Unity
In the kingdom of heaven. Matthew 8:11
Unity with Christ. John 17:21
Unity of people in Christ and God. John 17:21

Vine
The vine, the worker, the branches. John 15:1,5
The vine is the life of the branch. John 15:4

Vineyard
The evil workers. Matthew 21:34–39
Lease it to others. Matthew 21:41

Wanting to do good
Sincerity in giving. Matthew 6:3
Helping the needy. Luke 14:13

War
Wars will happen. Matthew 24:6,7

Weeds
What they mean. Matthew 13:38
Planted by the devil. Matthew 13:39
The harvest. Matthew 13:30,39

Wheat
The good seed. What it means. Matthew 13:37,38
The separation and gathering. Matthew 13:30

Widow
Her contribution. Mark 12:43,44

Wisdom
Not new with old. Matthew 10:16
A story of Christ's wisdom. Matthew 22:18–22

Work
Work and wages. Matthew 20:1–16
Few workers but a large harvest. Luke 10:2

Worker
Have needs met. Matthew 10:10
The evil workers. Matthew 21:35
The true vine. John 15:1

Worldliness
Profit and loss. Matthew 16:26

Worship
On the mountain or in Jerusalem. John 4:20,21
The spirit and truth. John 4:23,24

Yeast
Teachings of the Pharisees. Matthew 16:11,12

APPLICATION INDEX

DICTIONARY/CONCORDANCE

A

Aaron the older brother of Moses (Exo 6:20; 7:7). He helped Moses free the Israelites from slavery in Egypt (Exo 12:31) and served as first chief priest (Exo 28:1). His male descendants became priests of Israel (Exo 29).

Abaddon in the Old Testament, the place of the dead (Job 31:12; Pro 15:11). In the New Testament, this is the name of the angel from the bottomless pit (Rev 9:11).

Abba the word for "father" in the Aramaic language (Mar 14:36; Rom 8:15; Gal 4:6).

Abel the second son of Adam, who was murdered by his older brother, Cain (Gen 4:8). Jesus called him "righteous" (Mat 23:35). The book of Hebrews lists him as one of the Old Testament people who was guided by faith (11:4).

Abiathar son of Ahimelech, the chief priest at Nob. He was the only survivor when King Saul killed the priests at Nob for helping David (1Sm 22:20). He later became King David's priest and advisor. After David's death he was exiled to Anathoth by Solomon for supporting Adonijah's claim to the throne.

Abib see *calendar*.

Abigail wife of Nabal, a rich man of Carmel, whose flocks David and his men protected. She saved her husband from David's anger when Nabal refused to repay David for his protection (1Sm 25:14–35). After the death of Nabal, she became David's wife (1Sm 25:39–42).

Abijah the son of Rehoboam and king of Judah, who reigned 913–910 B.C. (1Ki 15:1–8; 2Ch 13).

Abimelech son of Gideon (Jdg 8:31) who became king of Shechem by killing seventy of his brothers (Jdg 9).

Abishai David's nephew, and brother of Joab and Asahel (1Ch 2:16). A loyal companion of David and a great warrior (1Sm 26:1–12; 2Sm 16:9–12; 21:16–17), He became commander of David's "mighty men," called "the thirty" (2Sm 23:1–19).

Abner commander of King Saul's army. He made Saul's son, Ishbosheth, king of the northern tribes of Israel (2Sm 2:8–10). After a quarrel with Ishbosheth, Abner gave his support to David, who then became king of all Israel (2Sm 3:6–19). David sang a funeral song in his honor (2Sm 3:22–37).

abolish to do away with or destroy (Psa 119:126; Rom 3:31).

Abraham father of the Jewish people. He was told by God to leave his home and family and to go on a journey. He had faith in God and so he went. God promised to bless him with descendants beyond number and to give them the land of Canaan. To seal the promise, God changed his name from Abram to Abraham, which means "father of many." Abraham's story begins at Gen 11:26 and ends at Gen 25:11. In the New Testament, he is the main example of faith (Rom 4; Gal 3:6–18; Heb 11:8–19).

Absalom third son of David. His mother was Maacah (2Sm 3:3). He killed his half brother Amnon. Absalom led a rebellion against David, which ended in his death. Absalom's sad story is told in 2Sm 13–18.

abundant plentiful, more than enough (Psa 49:6; Act 4:33).

acacia a tree still common in the desert south of Israel. The wood of the acacia was used to build the ark of the Lord's promise, the altar, and the tent of meeting in which the ark was kept (Exo 25:10–13; 26:15–37).

account 1. a history or record of events (Gen 2:4; 5:1; 11:27); 2. to cause or provide explanation (1Sm 23:10; 2Ki 22:7; Rom 14:12); 3. to consider a thing's worth or importance (Lev 25:15, 50); 4. to punish or judge wrongdoing (Ecc 3:15; Isa 10:3).

Accuser a name given to Satan, the evil enemy of God and humanity (Job 1:3; 2:1; Zech. 3:1).

Achan a man who kept some of the loot captured at Jericho, for which he was put to death (Jos 7).

Achish king of Gath. David twice fled to him to escape from Saul (1Sm 21:10–15; 27:1–12; 28:1–12; 29:1–11).

acknowledge 1. to recognize or admit as true (Dtr 33:9; Psa 68:34); 2. to recognize the authority or standing of another (1Sm 11:14; Isa 48:1; Jer 9:6; Rom 1:28; 2Th 1:8).

Adam the first man created by God. The name means "man" or "mankind." Adam and his wife Eve disobeyed God and were thrown out of the Garden of Eden. Adam's sin caused all human beings to be cursed, and brought about a separation between God and humankind (Gen 1–5; Rom 5:14; 1Co 15:22).

Adar see *calendar*.

Adonijah fourth son of David; his mother was Haggith (2Sm 3:4). When David grew old, Adonijah plotted to make himself king, but his plan was foiled by the prophet Nathan and Bathsheba, mother of Solomon (1Ki 1–2).

adultery having sexual relations with anyone other than one's husband or wife (Exo 20:14; Dtr 5:18; Mat 5:32; 19:9).

Ahab son of Omri and one of Israel's most wicked kings (874–853 B.C.). He married Jezebel, daughter of a Phoenician king, who led the northern kingdom of Israel to worship Baal instead of God. Elijah the prophet spoke out against Ahab and Baal worship. The struggle between King Ahab and Elijah is recorded in I Kings 16:29–22:40.

Ahaz evil king of Judah (735–715 B.C.), who burned his son as a human sacrifice (2Ki 16; 2Ch 28). As the prophet Isaiah predicted, Ahaz brought ruin on Judah by putting his trust in the Assyrians rather than in God (Isa 7).

Ahaziah 1. ninth king of Israel (853–852 B.C.), who followed in the footsteps of his wicked parents, Ahab and Jezebel (1Ki 22:48–53; 2Ki 1); 2. a king of Judah who ruled for only one year (841 B.C.). He was wounded by Jehu's men while visiting King Joram of Israel, and died (2Ki 8:25–29; 9:14–28).

Ahijah a prophet of Shiloh who foretold that Jeroboam would become king of the northern tribes of Israel (1Ki 11:29–40; 14:1–18).

Ahimelech a priest of Nob, who aided David in his escape from King Saul. In anger, Saul ordered the execution of all the priests of Nob and their families. Only Abiathar, son of Ahimelech, escaped being killed (1Sm 21:1–9; 22:11–23).

Ai a small city near Bethel, at which Joshua and his troops first met defeat because of the sin of Achan (Jos 7–8).

Almighty a name used to describe God, meaning "all powerful" (Gen 17:1; Psa 71:16; Luk 1:49; Rev 1:8).

almond a common tree in Bible lands, its pink blossoms bloomed early before its leaves appeared.

aloe a fragrant wood, probably eaglewood, which comes from a tree in India. It was used in incense and perfumes (Psa 45:8; Pro 7:17). Jesus' body was prepared for burial with a mixture of myrrh and aloe (Jhn 19:39).

altar a raised platform on which a priest offered sacrifices. Altars were made of earth, stone, metal, or wood covered with metal (Gen 8:20; Exo 27:1–4; 1Ki 18:26–38). The altar of sacrifice used by Israel had horn-like projections at each corner, which were called the "horns of the altar" (1Ki 1:50–51).

Amalekites a wandering desert tribe descended from Esau's grandson, Amalek (Gen 36:12). They ranged the wasteland south and southeast of Canaan and were constant enemies of Israel (Exo 17:8–16; 1Sm 15:6–20).

Amaziah the son of King Jehoash and eighth king of Judah (796–767 B.C.). He began well but then turned away from God. He was murdered at Lachish by members of his own court (2Ki 14; 2Ch 25).

amen means "let it be true." It is spoken at the end of a prayer or pronouncement (Dtr 27:15–26; Rom 9:5; 1Pe 4:11; Rev 22:20–21).

Ammonites people descended from Abraham's nephew Lot (Gen 19:38). The territory of the Ammonites lay east of the Jordan River Valley between the Jabbok and Arnon Rivers. The Ammonites frequently warred with Israel (Dtr 23:3–5; Jdg 11:4–33; 2Sm 10; 2Ch 27:5).

Amon king of Judah, 642–640 B.C. Amon followed in the sins of his father Manasseh, but his son Josiah became one of Judah's most godly kings (2Ki 21:19–26).

Amorites people who lived in Canaan in the time of Abraham (Gen 15:16–21). Many Amorite kings were defeated by the Israelites under the leadership of Moses and Joshua (Num 21; Jos 10:1–13). Only a few Amorites remained by the time of David (2Sm 21:2).

Amos a prophet, herdsman, and tender of fig trees in Tekoa, south of Bethlehem. He bravely spoke out against the wasteful and cold-hearted ways of the wealthy people in Samaria, capital of the northern kingdom of Israel. The book of Amos records several of his sermons and visions.

Anak a man whose descendants terrified the Israelites because they were so tall and strong. Joshua defeated them (Num 13:17–33; Jos 11:21–22).

Ananias 1. an early Christian in Jerusalem. He and his wife Sapphira were struck dead for lying to God (Act 5:1–11); 2. a Christian in Damascus who healed Paul's blindness (Act 9:1–18); 3. a chief priest in Jerusalem before whom Paul was tried (Act 22:30–24:1).

Ancient One a name referring to God, "who has lived for endless years" (Dan 7:9,13, 22).

Andrew one of the twelve disciples and the brother of Peter (Mat 4:18; Jhn 1:35–52; Act 1:13).

angel a heavenly being who acts as God's messenger (Gen 22:11; Exo 3:2) or servant (Gen 48:16; Mal 2:13; 28:2–3).

anoint to pour oil or ointment on a person or an object. Anointing was used to prepare objects for religious use (Exo 29:36; 40:10) or to prepare people to serve the Lord (Exo 29:7; 1Ki 19:16). Kings were also anointed to show they had been chosen by God (1Sm 10:1; 2Ki 9:6).

antichrist one who is against Christ (1Jn 2:18–22; 2Jn 1:7). The Bible speaks of one antichrist who will appear at history's end to turn people against God, but he will finally be defeated when Christ returns.

Antioch 1. capital city of Syria, where Jesus' followers first became known as Christians (Act 11:19–29; 13:1–3); 2. a city in Phrygia near Pisidia, where Paul and Barnabas preached the Good News (Act 13:14–52).

Apollos a Jew from Alexandria who knew the Scriptures well. He became a Christian and a teacher in the church at Corinth (Act 18:24–28; 1Co 1:12; 3:4–6,22).

apostle means "a person sent out," a chosen messenger. Jesus chose twelve men to be his apostles during his ministry on earth (Mat 10:1–2; Mar 9:35). Paul was made an apostle by the Lord after he had risen from the dead (Rom 1:1; 1Co 9:1–2).

Aquila husband of Priscilla; like Paul, he was a tentmaker. With his wife, he led Apollos to the Lord (Act 18; Rom 16:3).

Aramaic a language closely related to Hebrew. Only the Jewish officials understood Aramaic in the time of Hezekiah (2Ki 18:26–28). By Jesus' time, Aramaic had become the common language of the people (Mat 26:73).

Arameans people descended from the fifth son of Shem (Gen 10:22–23). The Arameans formed a powerful kingdom northeast of Israel, with Damascus as its chief city. This Aramean nation became a lasting enemy of the kings of Israel (2Sm 8:5–12; 10; 1Ki 15:18–20; 20; 2Ki 16:5–9).

ark of the promise a box made of wood covered with gold that the Lord told Moses to make (Exo 25:10). The box contained the two stone tablets on which the ten commandments were written (Dtr 10:2–5). Also kept inside the ark was a jar of manna and Aaron's staff (Exo 16:33–34; Num 17:10). The ark was the most holy object in the worship of God (Exo 25:22; 1Sm 4:4; Psa 99:5).

Armageddon the place where the armies under Satan are destroyed by God at the end of history (Rev 16:16).

armor clothing worn to protect the body against weapons (Psa 91:4). Paul refers to armor from God in Eph 6:11–17 which symbolically describes Christian character qualities which protect one from Satan's schemes.

armorbearer servant who carried armor and weapons for a great warrior or leader (1Sm 14:1–17; 31:4–6).

aroma a pleasing scent (Lev 1:9, 13, 17; 2Co 2:15; Php 4:18).

arrogant proud; conceited (2Ki 14:10; Pro 16:18–19; Isa 2:11–17; 1Pe 5:5).

arrow a pointed shaft shot from a bow. Famous arrows were those shot by Johnathan (1Sm 20:36) and the one which killed King Ahab (1Ki 22:34).

Asa godly third king of Judah, who ruled from 910–869 B.C. (1Ki 15; 2Ch 14–16).

Asher one of the twelve tribes of Israel, descended from the second son of Jacob and Zilpah (Gen 35:26; Num 1:40–41; 1Ch 7:30–40). The land given to the tribe of Asher was in northwest Canaan along the Meditteranean Sea (Jos 19:24–34; Jdg 1:31–32).

Asherah a Canaanite goddess, in myth the mother of Baal and many other gods. Asherah poles were placed at sites where the goddess was worshipped (Dtr 16:21; 1Ki 16:33; 18:19; 2Ki 13:6).

assembly a gathering of people. The Israelites formed assemblies for worship of the Lord (Lev 23; 2Ch 1:3–5), to go to war (Jos 8:10; 1Sm 13:5), and to crown a new king (1Ki 12:20). Sometimes the entire Israelite people were referred to as the "assembly of Israel" (Jos 8:35; 1Ki 8:55).

Assyria an ancient and warlike nation in northern Mesopotamia; its main cities were Asshur, Calah, and Nineveh, all located along the Tigris River. The powerful Assyrians conquered Samaria in 722 B.C. and carried away the people of Israel, bringing to an end the northern kingdom of Israel (2Ki 17). Babylon defeated the Assyrian army in 609 B.C. and the Assyrians disappeared from history (2Ki 18–19).

Athaliah evil daughter of Ahab and Jezebel and wife of King Jehoram of Judah. She murdered her own grandchildren and became queen (841–835 B.C.) Her grandson Joash was hidden away, and when Athaliah was executed, he became king at the age of seven (2Ki 8:18, 26; 11:1–20).

authority the right or power to give orders and be obeyed (Heb 13:17; 1Pe 2:13). Human authorities include rulers, judges, and military leaders. God is the highest authority and rules over the whole universe (Job 25:2; Jud 1:25). "All authority in heaven and on earth" was given to Christ by the Father (Mat 28:18).

avenge to punish someone who has done wrong or caused harm (Dtr 19:6; Isa 1:24).

B

Baal the name means "lord" or "master," and refers to a number of Canaanite gods. During Israel's history in Canaan, the people often turned away from God to the worship of false gods such as the Baals (Jdg 2:11–13; 6:25–32; 2Ki 21:3). Under King Ahab and Queen Jezebel, the worship of Baal became the state religion of Israel, and the worship of the Lord was outlawed (1Ki 16:29–32). In a contest on Mount Carmel, Elijah the prophet stood up against the prophets of Baal and proved that the Lord was the one true God (1Ki 18).

Baasha Son of Hanani who murdered King Nadab and became third king of Israel (908–886 B.C.). He warred with Judah (1Ki 15:16–22, 27–28; 16:1–7).

Babel, Tower of a great building begun by descendants of Adam. God caused the people there to speak different languages, so they could not understand each other. Unable to work together, the people scattered over the earth as God intended (Gen 11:1–9).

Babylon ancient capital city of Babylonia, located between the Tigris and Euphrates rivers (Gen 10:10). Babylon was a large and powerful city from the eighteenth to

the sixth centuries B.C. In 609 B.C., Babylonian forces defeated the Assyrian army, and Babylon became the center of the most powerful empire in the world (Isa 39). King Nebuchadnezzar II (605–562 B.C.) became Babylon's greatest king during Bible times. He captured Jerusalem in 602 B.C. and took many of the leading Israelites into captivity (2Ki 24). The Babylonian Empire came to an end as foretold in prophecy when Cyrus the Persian took the city of Babylon (Isa 13–14; 47–48; Jer 25; 50–51). In the book of Revelation, Babylon is used as a symbol to represent the center of human society that is hostile to God (Rev 17–18).

Balaam son of Beor. A seer hired by Barak, king of Moab, to put a curse on the Israelites on their way to the promised land (Num 22–24). Balaam was forced to bless rather than curse Israel, but he later caused Israelites to worship the Moabite god, Baal of Peor, and for this he was put to death (Num 31:8; 2Pe 2:15).

banish to send a person away by force (2Sm 14:13–14; 1Ch 12:1).

baptize religious ceremony in which one is dipped below water as a sign or symbol (Mat 3:11; 28:19; Act 10:47). Some churches today baptize by sprinkling or pouring water over a person.

Barabbas a prisoner the Jews requested Pilate to release rather than Jesus. He was called a robber in one book of the Bible (Jhn 18:40), a murderer and leader of revolt in two others (Mar 15:7; Luk 23:19).

Barak the general who, under Deborah the judge, defeated the Canaanite army of King Jabin (Jdg 4:1–16).

barley a grain widely grown in Canaan, but of less value than wheat. It was harvested in March or April (2Ki 7:1; Jhn 6:9).

Barnabas an apostle of the early church and missionary co-worker with Paul (Act 4:36; 13–14). Later they separated over whether Mark should go with them (Col 4:10).

Bartholomew one of the twelve disciples of Jesus (Mat 10:3; Act 1:13). He may have been the same as Nathanael in John 1:45–51.

barren 1. a woman who is unable to have children (Pro 30:16); 2. land that is unable to produce plantlife (Eze 33:28–29; Joe 2:3, 20).

Baruch friend and secretary of Jeremiah the prophet. He wrote down and publicly read Jeremiah's prophecies of the destruction of Jerusalem (Jer 32:12–16; 36; 45).

Bathsheba a married woman with whom King David committed adultery. David later married Bathsheba, and they had four sons together, including Solomon (2Sm 11–12; 1Ki 1).

Beelzebul the ruler of demons; Satan (Mat 10:25; 12:24–29).

Beersheba the chief city in southern Judah. The expression "from Dan to Beersheba" means the whole nation of Israel from north to south (2Sm 17:11). God appeared to Isaac and Jacob here (Gen 21:25–31; 26:23–25; 46:1–5).

Behemoth a large beast, possibly the hippopotamus (Job 40:15–19).

believe to accept as true, to trust, or to have faith (Exo 4:1–9; Psa 119:66; Mat 21:25,32). The Bible teaches that to believe in Jesus means to accept Jesus as Lord and to trust in him for the forgiveness of sins. Those who believe in Jesus receive eternal life (Jhn 1:12; 3:16; 11:25–27).

Benjamin 1. twelfth and youngest son of Jacob. His mother was Rachel (Gen 42–45); 2. one of the twelve tribes of Israel, descended from Jacob's son, Benjamin (1Sm 9:21). The land given to this tribe lay just north of Jerusalem (Jos 18:11–20).

Bethany a village about two miles from Jerusalem. Jesus stayed at the home of Lazarus, Mary, and Martha in Bethany (Jhn 11:1–44; 12:1–11).

Bethel a city about fourteen miles north of Jerusalem (Gen 28:19). Bethel was located on the border between Judah and the northern kingdom of Israel after the kingdom was divided. Jeroboam I set up an idol at Bethel, which remained until it was destroyed by Josiah (1Ki 12:29–33; 13:1–10; 2Ki 23:15).

Bethlehem the birthplace of Jesus, located in Judea (Mat 2:1–12). Micah foretold that the Messiah would come from this city (Mic 5:2).

bishop a church leader; an overseer of church affairs (Act 20:28; 1Ti 3:1–7).

blemish a flaw or mark that makes a thing less than perfect (2Sm 14:25; 2Pe 3:14).

bless to say or do something good for another (Gen 12:2–3; Rom 12:14). In the Old Testament, God promised to bless the Israelites when they were obedient to his law (Dtr 11:26–28; Psa 119:1–2). In his sermon on a mountain, Jesus taught that people are blessed by anything that draws them closer to God (Mat 5:3–12).

blight any disease that causes plants to wither and die (Amo 4:9; Hag 2:17).

blood fluid in the veins and arteries of humans and animals. In the Bible, blood represented the life of a creature (Lev 17:11–14). Jews were forbidden to drink blood or use it in foods (Dtr 12:23). The blood of animal sacrifices was sprinkled on the altar to cover the sins of the Israelites (Lev 7:2; Heb 9:22). Christ shed his blood on the cross to pay for all the sins of people (Mat 26:28; Rom 3:23–25; 5:6–9).

boast to brag or speak with pride about something (1Sm 2:3; Psa 34:2; Rom 1:30).

Booths, Festival of see *festivals*.

boundary the limits of a piece of land. Stones called "boundary markers" were often set up to mark off the limits of each Israelite family's fields (Exo 19:21–24; Dtr 19:14; Hos 5:10).

branch the limb of a tree or shrub. In the Old Testament, "branch" was used as a symbol of the Messiah, who would come from David's family tree (Isa 4:2; Jer 33:15). Jesus called himself the "vine" and his disciples the "branches" because they depended on a close relationship with Christ to produce "fruit," which are good works (Jhn 15:5–6).

bread food made of barley meal or wheat flour, usually baked daily for that day's needs. Ceremonial bread and the bread of wealthy people was made from wheat, but the poor ate the cheaper and coarser bread made from barley (Gen 18:6; Exo 29:2; Jhn 6:9). *Unleavened bread* is made without yeast, so it does not rise (Exo 34:13). *Bread* is sometimes used in Scripture to refer to all food (Dtr 8:3; Mat 6:11; Jhn 6:31–58).

breastplate 1. a piece of armor made of leather or metal, worn over the chest of a soldier (1Ki 22:34; Eph 6:14); 2. the colorful linen covering worn by the chief priest fastened to its surface were twelve gems representing the twelve tribes of Israel (Exo 28:15–30).

bronze a metal that was a mixture of copper and tin. People in Bible times used bronze to make tools, weapons, pots, utensils, and jewelry (1Sm 17:5–6; 1Ki 7:45–47; 2Ch 4:17).

burnt offering a sacrifice in which an animal was burned on the altar as a sign of commitment to God (Exo 29:38–42; Psa 51:16–17).

C

Caesarea Roman capital of Judea in New Testament times. Herod the Great built this beautiful port city on the shore of the Mediterranean Sea. At Caesarea, Cornelius and his family became the first Gentiles to be saved (Act 10:24). Paul was later imprisoned in the city for two years while waiting to stand trial (Act 24–25).

Caiaphas chief priest at the trial of Jesus (Jhn 11:49–50; 18:24).

Cain firstborn son of Adam and Eve. He murdered his brother, Abel (Gen 4:1–16).

Caleb one of the twelve spies sent by Moses to explore the Promised Land (Num 13:1, 6,17–33). Only he and Joshua showed faith in God's promise to give the land to Israel (Num 13:30–14:24). For his loyalty to the Lord, Caleb and his descendants were given the religion of Hebron in southern Judah (Jos 14:6–14; 15:13–20).

calendar the Hebrew calendar was based on a lunar month. A month ran from one new moon to the next (29 days). This made the Hebrew year only 354 days long instead of 365 days, requiring a second month of Adar about every three years to keep the seasons regular. Four of the months have alternate Canaanite names which appear in the Old Testament. The month names begin with Nisan (Abib) in March–April, followed by Lyyar (Ziv), Sivan, Tammuz, Ab, Elul, Tishri (Ethanim), Heshvan (Bul), Chislev, Tebeth, Shebat, and Adar.

camel an animal used to serve people. The camel known in Bible lands had only one hump. They were used to carry people on journeys and goods from one country to another (Gen 12:16; 24:10–63; 2Ki 8:9; Mat 19:24; 23:24).

Cana a village near Nazareth where Jesus performed his first miracle (Jhn 2:1–11; 4:46–54).

Canaan ancient name of the land promised by God to Abraham and his descendants (Gen 12:5–7; Num 34:1–12).

Canaanites occupants of the land of Canaan, lying between the Jordan and the Mediterranean from Egypt to Syria. When the Israelites led by Moses arrived at Canaan, they found the Canaanites living in the land with many powerful walled cities. The Canaanites worshiped many gods, and their religion was known for its immorality (Gen 10:19; Exo 13:5; Jdg 1).

Capernaum a town on the north shore of the Sea of Galilee. It was a fishing harbor and the center of Christ's ministry (Mat 4:13; Mar 2:1).

carpenter someone who builds things of wood (Isa 44:13). Jesus was a carpenter (Mar 6:3).

census a counting of people. Moses held a census on two occasions to count the Israelites (Num 1:2–3; 26:1–2). Due to a Roman census, Joseph and Mary were required to travel to Bethlehem, where Jesus was born (Luk 2:1–3).

centurion a Roman officer in charge of 100 soldiers (Mar 15:39; Luk 7:1–10; Act 27:43), Cornelius was a Roman Centurion who became a Christian (Act 10). See *legion.*

chariot a two-wheeled vehicle pulled by horses, often used in war. A chariot carried two men: a driver and a warrior. Joseph was assigned a royal chariot (Gen 41:43). The Egyptians pursued the Israelites in chariots (Exo 14:28). Solomon built stables for his horses and chariots (1Ki 9:17–19).

chief priest leader of the priests (Num 35:25; Jhn 18:10–24; Act 4:6; Heb 4:14–16). One time each year the chief priest entered the holy place and offered a sacrifice for the sins of the people (Lev 16; Heb 9:25).

Chislev a month in the Jewish calendar, during which heavy rains fell (Neh 1:1; Zec 7:1). See *calendar.*

Christ a Greek word that means "anointed one." It refers to the person the Old Testament prophets said would come to save God's people. It is the same as the Hebrew word *Messiah.* Jesus was called "Christ" by those who believed he was the Son of God (Jhn 4:25; 9:22; Act 2:36–38).

Christian a believer or follower of Christ Jesus (Act 11:26; 26:10,28).

church a gathering of Christians who meet together regularly (Act 8:1; Rom 16:5; Rev 2–3). *Church* is sometimes used in the Bible to refer to all Christians around the world (Eph 5:23; Col 1:24).

circumcision the cutting off of the male foreskin at the end of the penis. Circumcision was the outward sign of dedication to the Lord (Gen 17:10–14; Lev 12:3; Rom 2:25–29; 4:11).

cistern a pit dug in rocky ground to collect rainwater (2Ki 18:31; Jer 2:13), usually bottle-shaped, 10 to 25 feet wide, 20 feet deep, and covered by one or more large stones. Both Joseph and Jeremiah were kept as prisoners in large cisterns (Gen 37:22–29; Jer 38:6–13).

cities of refuge God told Moses to set aside six cities to be places of safety for anyone who accidentally killed another person (Num 35:9–15; Jos 20:7–8).

City of David a name for Jerusalem, which David captured and made his capital city (2Sm 5:6–9).

clean and unclean the people of Israel were allowed to eat clean animals, but unclean animals could not be eaten (Lev 11:47). Persons with certain diseases were unclean, as were dead bodies, and could not be touched. Special rules for cleansing were needed to make an unclean person or thing clean again (Lev 14:49; Num 19:13,16–19).

commandment an order given by God. God carved the ten commandments on two stone tablets and gave them to Moses for everyone in Israel to obey (Exo 31:18). Jesus gave a new commandment to his followers, telling them to "love each other in the same way that I have loved you" (Jhn 13:34).

compassion sympathy or concern for another (Psa 51:1; Mat 9:36; 1Pe 3:8).

conceive 1. to become pregnant (Psa 51:5); 2. to form an idea; to imagine (Psa 7:14; Isa 59:13).

concubine in Old Testament times, a woman who became the property of a man, but who did not have the full rights of a wife (2Sm 5:13; 1Ki 11:1–13; 1Chr 1:32).

condemn to declare guilty and deserving of punishment (1Ki 8:32; Luk 6:37; Jhn 3:17).

confess 1. to admit sins (Neh 9:2–3; 1Jn 1:9); 2. to tell what one believes (Php 2:11).

congregation a group of people meeting together, often to worship God (Neh 5:13; Act 15:30–33).

conscience a sense of right and wrong (Rom 2:15; 1Jn 3:20–21).

consume to eat, use up, or destroy (Dtr 5:25; Zep 1:18).

contempt to ignore, disrespect, or look down on something or someone (Gen 25:34; Rom 2:4).

content to be satisfied (Php 4:11; 1Ti 6:6).

convert one who has changed his or her beliefs (Act 13:26, 43; 16:14).

convulsion violent shaking of the body (Mar 1:26; 9:20).

Corinth a large Greek seaport and important trade city. The Apostle Paul made only one visit there, staying with Aquila and Priscilla (Act 18:1–18). The books of I Corinthians and II Corinthians were two letters Paul wrote to the church in Corinth (1Co 1:2; 2Co 1:1, 23).

Cornelius a Roman centurion who lived in Caesarea. He and his family were the first Gentiles to be saved (Act 10).

cornerstone the most important stone used in constructing a building, needed to support the whole structure. Jesus is called the "cornerstone" because the whole church is built upon him (Act 4:11; Eph 2:21).

corpse a dead body (Isa 26:19; Hag 2:13; Mar 15:45).

corrupt 1. to make a person or thing bad (Pro 17:23; Heb 12:15); 2. a thing which has turned bad or a person who does evil (Gen 6:11–12; Mat 17:17; Rom 8:3–13).

Creator one who creates. God is the Creator who made the world and everything in it (Gen 1:1; Ecc 12:1–6; Col 3:10).

cross a raised wooden post used by the Romans to put criminals to death. Jesus died on a cross (Mat 10:38; 27:32–42; Php 2:8). After Jesus' death, the cross became a symbol of the Christian faith (Gal 6:14; Php 3:18).

crucify to put to death by binding or nailing a person to a wooden cross (Mar 15:13–20; 1Co 1:23; Gal 2:19).

cupbearer an important official who served wine to the king (Gen 40:1; Neh 1:4).

curse to ask God to send evil or injury down on some person or thing (Num 22:6; Mar 11:21; Luk 6:28; Jas 3:9). It is the opposite of *blessing* (Dtr 28).

Cyrus Persian king, called Cyrus the Great. In 538 B.C., he conquered Babylonia as Isaiah the prophet had foretold (Ezr 1:1–4; Isa 44:28; Dan 6:28).

D

Damascus important trade city and capital of Syria to the north of Israel. It became the center of an Aramean kingdom that warred with the Israelites (1Ki 11:24–25; 2Ch 16:2–4). Assyria conquered it in 732 B.C. (2Ki 16:9), bringing the destruction described by the prophets Isaiah (8:4; 17:1) and Amos (1:3). Christ appeared to Paul on the road to Damascus (Act 9:1–9).

Dan 1. fifth son of Jacob, his mother was Bilhah (Gen 30:1); 2. one of the twelve tribes of Israel. They were unable to drive the Canaanites from the land given to them (Jos 19:40–48; Jdg 1:23), so they traveled to Laish, a city in northern Palestine. They captured Laish and renamed it Dan (Jdg 18).

Daniel a young Jewish captive taken to Babylon. Daniel was a prophet and became an important official in the empire. An angel of God protected Daniel after he was thrown into a lions' den for praying (Dan 6). The book of Daniel tells of his life and prophecies.

dates sweet fruit that grows on the date palm tree. Jericho was famous for its dates. Dates were eaten fresh or pressed into cakes to eat later (2Sm 6:19).

David second and greatest king of Israel. His story begins at I Samuel 16 and ends at II Kings. As a youth, he killed Goliath the Philistine giant with only a sling (1Sm 17). When David became king, he brought all the tribes of Israel together under his rule (2Sm 5:1–5). Jesus was a descendant of David (Mat 1).

David, City of see *City of David.*

deacon a church leader who helps care for the poor and needy (Rom 16:1; 1Ti 3:12–13). The word is Greek for "servant."

Deborah a judge who led the tribes of Israel to a great victory against the Canaanites (Jdg 4). She chose Barak as her general to lead the Israelite army. The Song of Deborah in Judges 5 is a poem that tells her story.

debt something that a person owes another, usually money (Dtr 15:2–3; Mat 18:25–32; Rom 13:8).

deceive to mislead or fool someone (Lev 19:11; Mat 24:4–13; 1Co 3:18).

decree an order or law made by a ruler (Ezr 6:6–12; Pro 8:15; Dan 6:7–16, 25–27).

dedicate to set apart as holy, acceptable for the service of God (Exo 16:23–25; 40:9–13; Dtr 15:19; 1Sm 1:28).

defect a flaw or blemish (Lev 21:17–23; Heb 9:14).

defy to openly resist; to refuse to obey (Dtr 17:13; 2Ki 19:16, 23).

demon an evil spirit. Demons are the enemies of God and humans. A demon-possessed person is inhabited by an evil spirit, causing pain, disease, and even madness (Mat 12:22; 15:22; Mar 5:2–20). Jesus drove demons out of many people during his time on earth (Mar 1:34; Luk 4:35).

deport to take away to another land. In 722 B.C., the people in the northern kingdom of Israel were deported by the Assyrians, never to return. The people of Judah were later deported by the Babylonians, but returned to Judah after seventy years (Ezr 5:12).

despise to look down on or treat with contempt (Pro 1:7; Mic 3:9; Rom 14:3,10).

destiny God's plan for a person's future (Psa 16:5; Jer 13:25; 1Th 3:3).

destitute without food or means to support oneself; extremely poor (Lam 4:5).

detestable disgusting; something to be hated (2Ch 15:8; Eze 7:3–9; Rev 21:8, 27).

Deuteronomy name given to the fifth book of the Old Testament which means "Second Law."

devil a name for Satan, meaning "accuser." The devil is a powerful angel who rebelled against God and has become the greatest enemy of God and humans (Luk 4:2–13; Eph 4:27; Jas 4:7; 1Pe 5:8; Rev 12:9).

devout devoted to one's religion (Jhn 9:31; Act 2:5, 12; 22:12).

disciple from a Greek word meaning "learner," a devoted student or follower of a teacher or movement. Followers of Jesus were called his disciples (Mat 10:37–42; Mat 28:19; Jhn 13:35).

discipline to teach through punishment or correction (Pro 1:8–9; Dtr 8:5). The Lord "disciplines everyone he loves" (Heb 12:6–10).

discriminate to unfairly see some people as better or worse than others, or to unfairly treat certain people better or worse than others (Act 15:9; Jas 2:4).

disgrace to bring dishonor or shame on a person (Gen 30:23; 2Ti 2:9; Heb 12:2).

dispute an argument or disagreement (Pro 26:21; Act 15:2).

distress great pain or desperate need (2Sm 22:7; Isa 25:4; Rom 2:9).

divine from God or of God (Hab 1:1; Rom 1:20; 2Pe 1:3–4).

divorce legal ending of a marriage. Although the Bible says God hates divorce (Mal 2:16), Old Testament Law did permit divorce (Dtr 24:1). Jesus said that marital unfaithfulness was the only acceptable reason to divorce (Mat 19:3–10).

doctrine a basic teaching or belief, usually about God (Rom 16:17; 1Co 15:2–8).

doubt to be uncertain or undecided; to not believe (Mat 14:31; 21:21; Jas 1:6–8).

drought a long period without rain. Drought can cause food shortage because crops do not grow. While Ahab was king, Elijah the prophet foretold a terrible drought in Israel that lasted three years (1Ki 17:1–7; 18:1).

dye materials used to color clothing. Lydia was a seller of purple dye (Act 16:14).

dynasty a series of rulers from the same family (1 Ki 9:5; 11:38; Psa 89:3–4).

E

earthly of this world, rather than of heaven. Things which are earthly are imperfect, limited, and do not last (Isa 40:23; 1Co 7:33–34; 15:40; Heb 12:16).

Eden area in Mesopotamia where God created a garden and placed Adam and Eve. They were thrown out of the Garden of Eden after sinning (Gen 2:8, 15, 23–24).

Edomites people who lived in the nation of Edom, south of the Dead Sea. They were descended from Jacob's brother, Esau, so the Edomites were distant relatives of the Israelites (Gen 36; Num 20:14–21). However, the Edomites became enemies of Israel. Many of the prophets announced that God would punish the Edomites for their hatred of Israel (Jer 49:7–22; Amo 9:12; Obadiah).

Egypt an ancient country lying at the southeast corner of the Mediterranean Sea along the Nile River. In Egypt, Joseph rose from being a slave to second only to Pharaoh, the king of Egypt (Gen 39–50). The Israelites spent 400 years in Egypt, where they became slaves (Exo 1). God sent Moses to lead the people out of Egypt to the promised land of Canaan (Exo 2–14).

Eli chief priest of Israel who raised Samuel. The sins of Eli's sons resulted in the loss of the ark of the Lord's promise (1Sm 1:9–4:18).

Elijah a great prophet of the Lord during the reign of Ahab (874–853 B.C.). He predicted a terrible drought as God's punishment when Queen Jezebel made Baal worship Israel's religion. He won a contest against the priests of Baal to prove that the Lord was the only true God. His struggle against evil Queen Jezebel and her Phoenician priests of Baal is told in 1Ki 17–19 and 21. He was taken up to heaven without dying (2Ki 2).

Elisha prophet chosen by God to take Elijah's place (1 Ki 19:19–21). Elisha asked for and received a "double share" of Elijah's spirit. The Bible records fourteen miracles that Elisha performed, twice as many as the seven performed by Elijah (2Ki 2–9; 13:14–20).

Elizabeth mother of John the Baptizer and relative of Mary, the mother of Jesus (Luk 1:5–58).

Elul a hot, dry month in the Hebrew calendar (Neh 6:15). See *calendar.*

embalm treatment of a dead body to preserve it from decay (Gen 50:2–3).

endure to continue, to suffer patiently, or to keep on through hardship (Psa 136; Mat 24:13; 1Pe 2:20–21).

engrave to cut letters or images into a surface (1Ki 7:36; 2Ti 2:19). The gems on the chief priest's ephod and breastplate were engraved with the names of the Israelite tribes (Exo 28:9–21).

envy to want what belongs to another (Pro 23:17–18; 1Co 13:4; Gal 5:21).

Ephesus a large and important trade city on the west coast of Asia Minor. Paul spent over two years in the city preaching the Good News. His message had such a powerful effect that his enemies started a riot (Act 19). Paul wrote the book of Ephesians, a letter to the church in Ephesus.

ephod a sleeveless vest worn over a priest's robe (1Sm 22:18; 1Ch 15:27). The chief priest's ephod was made with red, blue, and purple cloth, woven with gold (Exo 39:2–7).

Ephraim 1. a son of Joseph (Gen 41:52); 2. the tribe of Ephraim, whose territory lay northwest of the Dead Sea (Jos 16:5–10); 3. a name for the northern kingdom of Israel after the tribes were divided. It became a name for the nation because Ephraim was the northern kingdom's leading tribe (Isa 7:2–9).

epileptic a disorder which causes uncontrollable shaking, called seizures. Epileptics were among the people brought to Jesus for healing (Mat 4:24).

Esau firstborn son of Isaac and twin brother of Jacob. He sold his birthright to Jacob for a pot of food (Gen 25). Jacob tricked Isaac into giving him Esau's blessing, then fled when Esau planned to kill him in revenge (Gen 27). When they were old, Esau and Jacob made peace with each other (Gen 33).

Esther a Jewish woman who lived in Persia. She was chosen as the queen of Xerxes, and her actions ended Haman's plot to wipe out the entire Jewish people. Her story is told in the book of Esther.

eternal without end; lasting forever. God is eternal (Jer 10:10). Eternal life is given to those who put their faith in Jesus (Jhn 3:16; 1Jn 5:11–13).

eunuch a male servant, usually one whose sex organs have been removed so he cannot father children. Many of these men were important officials (2Ki 9:32; Est 1:10–15; Act 8:26–38).

Eve the first woman created by God. Eve was deceived by Satan and disobeyed God (Gen 2–3).

everlasting continuing on without end; lasting forever (Gen 9:16; Isa 9:6; 55:3; Jer 31:3; 1Pe 1:23).

evil wicked; immoral; causing harm; acts that God has declared are wrong (Dtr 4:25; Rom 12:9,17; 1Ti 6:10). Evil is a consequence of sin's corrupting influence in human nature (Gen 2:17; 6:5). God's holy nature requires that evil be punished (Isa 13:11; 1Pe 3:10–12).

exile to take a person by force away from his or her home country; a person who has been taken from his or her home or country. The people of Judah were taken into exile by the Babylonians after the fall of Jerusalem in 587 B.C. (Isa 5:13; Eze 1:2).

Exodus name of the second book of the Bible, which means "a going out." The book of Exodus tells the story of the Israelites' release from slavery in Egypt.

extortion getting something from a person through the use of force (Psa 62:10; Isa 33:15).

Ezekiel a prophet among the people of Judah who were taken away to Babylon. The book of Ezekiel tells about his many visions and acts of prophecy.

Ezra a devout Jewish priest during the reign of Artaxerxes (Ezr 7:1). The book of Ezra tells how he led a group of Jews in Babylon back to Jerusalem and helped to restore temple worship.

F

faith firm belief and trust. Often people put their faith in God (Gen 15:6; Mat 17:20; Rom 1:17; Heb 11; Jas 2:14–26).Salvation comes through faith in Jesus Christ (Luk 7:50; Rom 3:22).

faithful reliable, trustworthy (Mat 25:21; Psa 51:10; 1Co 10:13; 1Jn 1:9). The Lord "is a faithful God, who always keeps his promise" (Dtr 7:9).

false prophet, false teacher a person who claims to speak for God but does not (Dtr 13:1–5; Isa 44:25; 2Pe 2; Jud). At history's end, a false prophet will deceive many with miracles (Rev 16:13–14; 19:20; 20:10).

famine a lack of food which causes great hunger (Gen 41; Rut 1:1; 2Ki 8:1; Luk 4:25–26). Famines in Bible lands were caused by drought, war, insect plagues, and other disasters.

fasts, fasting going without food and sometimes without water, especially as a religious duty. Some important fasts by individuals are found in Exodus 34:28; II Samuel 12:16; I Kings 19:8; 21:27; Nehemiah 1:4; Matthew 4:2; Acts 9:9. There were also fasts that were undertaken by the whole community (1Sm 31:13; Est 4:16; Act 13:3).

fatal causing death (Nah 3:19; Rev 13:3, 12).

fate certain future; destiny (Job 12:5; Isa 17:14; Jud 1:7).

father 1. a male parent (Gen 2:24; Exo 20:12); 2. ancestor (Gen 17:5; Jhn 8:39); 3. a name for God, showing his relationship with his Son, Jesus, and all believers, who become his adopted children (Mat 6:9; Luk 23:34; Jhn 14:6; Rom 8:15).

fear 1. to be afraid of (Psa 23:4; 55:5; 1Jn 4:18); 2. to greatly respect; to be in awe of. To fear God is to show deep respect for him, which leads to love and obedience (Exo 18:21; Dtr 6:13; Pro 1:7).

feasts see *festivals*.

fellowship friendship; a close and sharing relationship (Lev 3:1; Act 2:42).

fertile productive; fruitful; producing plenty (Gen 1:22; Isa 29:17; 32:15–16).

festivals joyful feasts that were an important part of the religious life of the Jewish people. In the time of Jesus the main festivals were Passover, Festival of Weeks, and Festival of Booths. Jews traveled from all over the world to attend these festivals in Jerusalem. Passover, held in the Hebrew month of Nisan (March–April), celebrates the Israelite's rescue from Egypt (Exo 12; Lev 23:5).
Festival of Unleavened Bread was celebrated about the same time and lasted for a week (Lev 23:6–14). This feast also recalled the Israelite's departure form Egypt. Festival of Weeks held in May, fifty days after Passover (Exo 34:22; Lev 23:15–21). It celebrated the end of the wheat harvest, and God's giving of the Teachings to Moses. On this same day, fifty days after the death of Jesus Christ, the Holy Spirit came upon Jesus' disciples. For this reason, Pentecost (which means "fiftieth") became a Christian holy day. See *Pentecost*.
Festival of Booths is a week long festival celebrated in late September and early October. The festival is held to celebrate the end of the harvest season and to remember Israel's forty years of wandering in the wilderness (Lev 23:33–43; Num 29:12–40). During the seven days, the Jewish people lived in "booths," small huts made of tree branches, that they built around Jerusalem.

fetus an unborn baby still in the mother's womb (Psa 139:16; 1Co 15:8).

figs a valued fruit of a tree common to Bible lands. Dried figs were pressed into cakes. Fig trees were valued for the shade they provided as well (Gen 3:7; 1 Ki 4:25; Isa 38:21). Jesus cursed a fig tree that failed to produce fruit (Mar 11:13–21).

firstborn the oldest male child. The firstborn son had special value in Hebrew families, for he would be the next head of the family, and he would be responsible for the family's welfare (Exo 13:1, 11–15; Num 18:15–16; Col 1:15).

flask a small bottle (1Sm 10:1; 2Ki 9:1–3).

flax a long-stemmed plant grown in Bible lands (Exo 9:31). Fibers of the flax plant were used to make linen cloth. The Israelite spies in Jericho hid under a pile of drying flax plants on Rahab's roof (Jos 2:6).

fleeting brief, quickly passing (Job 8:9; Pro 23:5).

flock a group of animals herded together, usually sheep or goats (SOS 1:7; 4:2; Mat 26:31). Believers are called God's flock, and Jesus is presented as their shepherd (Luk 12:32; 1Pe 5:2–3). See *shepherd*.

flood a great flowing of water over land (Nah 1:8; Mat 24:38–39; Luk 6:48). When God saw how evil humans had become, He sent a great flood to destroy them. God told Noah to build a boat and fill it with every kind of animal. As a result, Noah and his family were saved from the flood (Gen 6–8).

foolish unwise; lacking judgment (1Sm 25:25; Pro 10:1; Mat 25:2–8; Eph 5:15–17).

foreman workman in charge of a group of workers (Exo 5:6, 14–19; 1Sm 21:7).

forgive to pardon, to give up resentment, to no longer blame a person for what he or she has done (Mic 7:18; Mat 6:12–15; Luk 23:34; Col 3:13). When we confess our sins to God, "he forgives them and cleanses us from everything we've done wrong" (1Jn 1:9).

fortified strengthened against attack. A fortified city is protected with a stone wall, gates, and other defenses to protect its people against an enemy (Dtr 3:5; Lam 2:2; Jer 1:18). Joshua and the Israelites captured many large fortified cities in Canaan.

fortuneteller a person who claims to predict the future (2Ki 21:6; Zec 10:2). Old Testament law forbade the people of Israel to consult fortunetellers (Lev 19:26).

frankincense an incense that smelled sweet when burned. It was also used in perfume (Exo 30:34–38; SOS 3:6). The wise men from the east brought frankincense as a gift for the baby Jesus (Mat 2:11).

fulfill to finish or complete; to make a promise or prediction come true (1Ki 2:3; Mat 26:54; Act 13:27, 33; Rom 13:8).

G

Gabriel one of two angels named in the Bible. He appeared to Daniel to explain his visions of the future (Dan 8:16; 9:21). The angel Gabriel later appeared to announce the births of John the Baptizer and Jesus (Luk 1:11–20; 26–38).

Gad one of the twelve tribes of Israel, descended from the seventh son of Jacob (Gen 30:11; 46:16). The territory given to the tribe of Gad lay east of the Jordan River, between the Dead Sea and the Sea of Galilee (Num 32:20–36; Jos 13:24–28).

Galilee a region in northern Palestine, west of the Jordan River. It had a large Gentile population, so many Jews looked down on people from Galilee. Jesus grew up in Galilee and centered his ministry there. Twenty-five of his thirty-three recorded miracles were performed in Galilee (Mat 4:23–25; 28:16; Jhn 1:46; 7:41–42).

Galilee, Sea of a large fresh-water lake in northern Palestine, known for its plentiful fish and violent storms (Mat 14:22–36; Luk 5:1–11). Jesus calmed a storm on the Sea of Galilee (Mar 4:35–41).

gate entryway through a wall or fence (Mat 7:13–14). Jesus called himself "the gate" because he was the only way to be saved and enter heaven (Jhn 10:1–10).

genealogy a family tree; a list of a person's ancestors and descendants. The promised Messiah was to be a descendant of David. Jesus' genealogies show David was his ancestor (Mat 1:1–17; Luk 3:23–38).

generation all people born in the same period of time; generally the time between the birth of a man and his firstborn son, about thirty years (Num 32:13; Psa 145:13; Mat 1:17; 17:17).

Genesis the first book of the Bible, named after the first word in the book (in the Greek translation), which in English is translated, "In the beginning."

Gideon a judge of the tribe of Manasseh. With an army of just 300 men, he led Israel to victory against the Midianites, ending their cruel treatment of the Israelites (Jdg 6–8).

gift 1. something given as a sign of love or respect (Act 2:38; Rom 5:15–17; 6:23); 2. a spiritual gift; a special ability given to a believer by the Holy Spirit to better serve others (1Co 12:4–11; 13:2, 8).

glory 1. honor; praise (1 Ch 16:9; Luk 2:14); 2. a visible sign of greatness (Exo 24:16–17; 2Ch 5:14; Psa 19:1; Mat 25:31); 3. a source of great pride (1Co 10:31; Eph 3:13).

glutton a person who eats too much (Pro 23:20–21; Mat 11:19).

God creator and ruler of the universe (Gen 1:1; Psa 115:3; Isa 45:18). There is only one true God (Dtr 6:4; 1Ki 18:24–39). The Bible is God's word, describing his actions in human history, his will for human beings, and his plan for saving people through Jesus Christ (Exo 20:1–17; Dtr 6:5; Jhn 3:16; 1Jn 4:14–16).

godless 1. a wicked action (Dtr 22:21; Jdg 19:23); 2. a person who rejects or disobeys God, living as though God does not exist (Job 20:23–25; Psa 14:1; 1Pe 4:18).

godly holy; a person who lives in a way that God approves (Psa 37:28; 1Ti 4:7–10).

Goliath a Philistine giant who was killed in battle by young David (1Sm 17).

Good News the message that Jesus is the Messiah, who has come to save us from our sins (Mat 4:23; Act 5:42; Rom 1:16–17; Gal 1:11; Eph 1:13; Rev 14:6).

gossip 1. to spread rumors or unkind stories about another person (Lev 19:16; 2Co 12:20; 1Ti 5:13); 2. a person who spreads rumors (Pro 16:28; 26:20, 22; 1Ti 3:11).

grief pain and sadness at a great loss, such as loss of a loved one (Gen 37:33–35; Mat 2:18; Rev 21:4).

guilty 1. to have done something wrong; to have broken the law or God's commandments (Exo 34:7; 1Ki 8:32; Jhn 18:38); 2. the feeling of having done something wrong (Pro 25:22; 1Co 8:7; Heb 10:22).

gullible easily fooled (Psa 19:7; Pro 1:22; 14:15).

H

Habakkuk a Levite whose prophecies are recorded in the book of Habakkuk.

Hagar an Egyptian servant of Sarah who became a secondary wife of Abraham. The mother of Ishmael (Gen 16; 21:8–21; Gal 4:21–31).

Haggai a prophet who encouraged the Jews struggling to rebuild the temple in Jerusalem. (Ezr 5:1; Haggai).

hallelujah means "praise the Lord!" It is a joyful call to worship God (Psa 106:1; Rev 19:1–6).

Hannah an Israelite woman who could not have children. She prayed for a son, and God gave her Samuel, who became Israel's last judge (1Sm 1:1–2:11).

harvest 1. the gathering of a crop (Lev 2:14; Jhn 4:35–38; Gal 6:8); 2. the time of year when a crop is gathered (Jdg 15:1; Pro 6:8).

heart the center of a person's thoughts, desires, and emotions (Dtr 6:5; 1Sm 16:7; Psa 37:4; 51:10; Pro 3:5; Eze 36:26; Mat 6:21; 2Ti 2:22).

heathen a person who is unaware of or disrespectful of God (Mat 6:7; 18:17).

heaven the spiritual home of God. Believers who die go to spend eternal life in heaven with God (Gen 1:1; 2Ki 2:11; Psa 11:4; Mat 6:10; 18:1–4; 2Co 5:1–2; Rev 21:1).

Hebrew 1. the language of the Jewish people. The Old Testament was written in Hebrew (Jhn 19:13–20; Act 26:14; Rev 16:16); 2. an Israelite; anyone descended from Abraham (Exo 1:15–22; 7:16; Jhn 1:9; 2Co 11:22).

heir a person who receives the wealth or property of another who has died (Gen 15:3–4; 1Ki 2:4; Rom 8:17; Gal 4:7).

hell the place of punishment "prepared for the devil and his angels" (Mat 25:41). Those who do not turn to Christ to be saved will be sentenced to hell on judgment day (Mat 23:33; Luk 16:23; Rev 20:10–15).

Herod 1. Herod the Great, evil king of Judea who killed the children of Bethlehem in an attempt to take Jesus' life (Mat 2; Luk 1:5); 2. Herod Antipas, son of Herod the Great, who ruled over Galilee in Jesus' time. He put John the Baptizer to death (Mat 14:1–11; Luk 23:6–15); 3. Herod Agrippa I, grandson of Herod the Great. As king of Judea, he put James to death and threw Peter into prison (Act 12:1–4, 19–23); 4. Herod Agrippa II, son of Herod Agrippa I. He was present at Paul's trial before Festus (Act 23:35; 25:13–26:32).

Hezekiah godly king of Judah who destroyed Judah's idols and restored the temple in Jerusalem (2Ki 18–20; 2Ch 29–32; Isa 36–39).

holy 1. pure; godly (Lev 11:44–45; 1Sm 2:2; Rev 4:8); 2. sacred; set apart for God, to be used for serving or worshipping God (Exo 3:5; 20:8; Heb 10:19).

Holy Spirit third person of the Trinity with God the Father and God the Son. Those who accept Jesus Christ as their savior are given the Holy Spirit, who lives in their hearts (Rom 5:5; 2Co 3:3). The Holy Spirit helps believers to know God's will and to live holy lives (Jhn 14:26; 2Co 6:6).

homosexual someone who has sexual relations with a person of the same sex (Lev 18:22; Jud 1:7).

honor 1. a show of respect or a special favor given to a person (Rom 14:6–8; Eph 6:2); 2. highly regarded; worthy of respect (1Ti 5:17; 1Pe 2:17).

hope to eagerly look forward to; to rely on (1 Co 13:13). Those who put their hope in God believe in his promises and trust God for the future (Psa 31:24; Act 24:15; Rom 8:24–25; 15:13).

Hosanna a Hebrew shout of praise, meaning "save" (Mat 21:9; Mar 11:9).

Hosea a prophet to the northern kingdom of Israel during the reign of Jeroboam II. In the book of Hosea, the prophet uses his unfaithful wife, Gomer, as an example of how Israel has been unfaithful to God.

hospitality gladly welcoming others into one's home, and giving them food and drink. All Christians are to practice hospitality (Gen 18; Rom 12:13; Heb 13:2).

hostile very unfriendly; acting like an enemy (Jer 4:16; Col 1:21).

house arrest punishment that a person must stay in his house and not leave (Neh 6:10).

humble 1. to be made humble; to be reduced in importance (Php 2:7–8); 2. not proud or pretending to be important (Mic 6:8). Christians are to be humble with each other and toward God, depending on God rather than their own power (Php 2:3–4; Jas 3:13; 4:6; 1Pe 3:8; 5:5).

humiliate to make humble or reduce in importance; to shame (Pro 29:23; Dan 4:37).

hymn a song sung in praise of God and used in worship (Psa 26:7; Mar 4:26).

hypocrite a person who pretends to be what he or she is not (Mat 6:5). Those who pretend to love God but do evil things are hypocrites (Mat 7:5; 23:13; Luk 13:15).

I

I Am Who I Am   name God called himself when he spoke to Moses out of the burning bush. The Hebrew word is *Yahweh*, LORD (Exo 3:14; Jhn 8:58).

idol   a false god made in the image of a human or animal and used as an object of worship (Psa 106:19; Isa 44:9–20).

idolatry   1. the worship of idols (Dtr 4:15–16; Eze 23:49); 2. anything that takes the place of God in a person's life (Gal 5:19–20).

ignorant   lacking knowledge; failing to respond to the truth (1Th 4:13).

Immanuel   a name used in Isaiah's prophecy to refer to Jesus, meaning "God with us" (Isa 7:14; Mat 1:23).

immortal   one who will never die (Rom 1:23; 1Ti 1:17).

impure   1. not pure or clean (Act 10:14); 2. unholy or spiritually unclean (2Co 2:17).

incense   spices that are burned to produce a sweet-smelling smoke (Exo 30:1–10; Psa 141:2; Rev 5:8).

inheritance   property or possessions given to a person after the owner dies (Jdg 18:1; Eze 46:18). In Old Testament times, sons received an inheritance of the family property after their father died (Gen 21:10; Rut 4:5–6). The firstborn son received a double share (Dtr 21:16–17). See *heir*.

injustice   unfairness; a violation of a person's rights (Job 6:29; 1Co 13:6).

inscribe   to cut or write letters on a surface so they will last (Exo 31:18; Isa 30:8).

insight   wisdom or understanding (1Ki 4:29; 1Co 4:10; Col 1:9).

inspired   influenced, shaped, or guided by God (Hag 1:14; 2Ti 3:16).

integrity   having an honest and moral character; guided by good motives. Abraham, David, and Job were called people of integrity (Gen 6:9; Job 1:1; 2Pe 1:5).

intercede   to plead for another in need of help (Isa 53:12; Rom 8:27).

intermarry   to marry a person who is not of your race or religion. Old Testament law did not allow the Jewish people to intermarry with non-Jews (Dtr 7:3; Ezr 9:14; 1Ki 11:2).

intimidate   to frighten; to force another to do something out of fear (Isa 41:23; Php 1:28).

Isaac   son God promised to Abraham, born when he was 100 years old. Sarah was his mother (Gen 21:3–5). God told Abraham to sacrifice Isaac, but stopped him as Isaac lay on the altar. Isaac married Rebekah. Esau and Jacob were his sons (Gen 22:2–14; Gen 24).

Isaiah   prophet called by God to preach to the people of Judah (2Ki 19; Isa 6). His ministry lasted for over 40 years. He warned Judah to rely on God, not other nations. In his prophecies, Isaiah spoke of the fall of Jerusalem, the defeat of Assyria by Cyrus, and the coming of the Messiah (Isa 53). His words are recorded in the book of Isaiah.

Ishmael   son of Abraham and Hagar, Sarah's servant given to Abraham as a secondary wife (Gen 16:15–16).

Israel   1. name God gave to Jacob (Gen 32:28); 2. the nation of Israel, made up of the descendants of the twelve sons of Jacob (Exo 1:1; Jdg 19:1; 1Ki 9:5); 3. the northern kingdom of Israel, made up of ten of Israel's twelve tribes after the nation was divided. The remaining two tribes, Judah and Benjamin, formed the southern nation of Judah (1Ki 11:31; 1Ki 12:20–21).

Israelites   the people of Israel, members of the twelve tribes descended from Jacob's sons (Gen 49; Exo 1:9; 14:22).

Issachar   one of the twelve tribes of Israel, descended from the son of Jacob and Leah (Gen 30:14–18; Jos 19:17–23).

J

Jacob   son of Isaac and Rebekah, younger twin brother of Esau (Gen 25:12). He bought Esau's birthright for a pot of food (Gen 25:29–34). He later tricked Isaac into giving him Esau's blessing (Gen 27:18–30). He had two wives, Rachel and Leah. His twelve sons were the ancestors of the twelve tribes of Israel (Gen 28:13). Jacob wrestled with God and was given the name Israel (Gen 32:22–32; 35:9–15).

James   1. son of Zebedee and brother of John (Mat 4:21). He was one of the twelve apostles. Herod Agrippa I put him to death, fulfilling Jesus' prophecy about him (Mar 10:39; Act 12:2); 2. son of Alphaeus and one of the twelve apostles (Mat 10:3); 3. the brother of Jesus (Mar 6:3). He became a believer and a leader of the church in Jerusalem (Act 15:13–21; Gal 1:19; 2:9). He wrote the book of James.

jealousy   1. desire for what someone else has (Gal 5:20); 2. distrust; fear of losing someone's love (Gen 30:1); 3. careful to protect or defend (Zec 1:14); 4. expecting total commitment. God is "a jealous God" who desires that we remain faithful and not turn away from him (Exo 20:5–6).

Jehoshaphat   godly fourth king of Judah (872–848 B.C.). His father was King Asa. His son Jehoram became king after him (1Ki 22; 2Ch 17:6).

Jehu   army commander anointed to be king of Israel. He put Queen Jezebel to death and ended Baal worship in Israel (2Ki 9–10). Although Jehu claimed to be devoted to God (2Ki 10:16), he "didn't wholeheartedly obey the teachings of the Lord" (2Ki 10:31).

Jephthah   a judge of Isreal who rescued his people from the Ammonites (Jdg 10:6–12:7).

Jeremiah   a prophet called by God to warn Judah that the nation would soon be destroyed (Jer 4). His people rejected him, and members of his own family threatened his life (Jer 12:6). Once he was thrown into a cistern to die (Jer 38). The terrible fate of his people brought Jeremiah much sadness, and he is often called "the weeping prophet." His words are recorded in the books of Jeremiah and Lamentations.

Jericho   an ancient city near the Dead Sea. When Joshua's army shouted and blew their horns, its great walls collapsed (Dtr 34:3; Jos 6). They captured and destroyed the city, but it was later rebuilt. Jesus healed a blind beggar in Jericho (Mar 10:46–52).

Jeroboam   an official of Solomon told by a prophet that God would give him ten of Israel's tribes to rule (1Ki 11:26–14:20). He rebelled against Rehoboam, Solomon's son, and became king of the northern kingdom of Israel. He built golden calves in Bethel and Dan, and "worshiping them became Israel's sin" (1Ki 12:30).

Jerusalem   city that David made capital and religious center of Israel (2Sm 5:6–10). Solomon built the temple there, which was to be the only place to worship God

(1Ki 5–6). After the kingdom was divided, Jerusalem remained the capital of the nation of Judah. It was later destroyed by the Babylonians in 586 B.C. (2Ki 25). The temple and city wall were rebuilt in the time of Ezra and Nehemiah (Ezr 3:10–13; Neh 3). Jesus spent the last week of his life in Jerusalem and was crucified outside its walls (Mat 21:10). See *City of David; Zion.*

Jesus the Son of God in the flesh. He was born in Bethlehem to a virgin named Mary and raised in Nazareth. He was about thirty when he was baptized by John the Baptizer (Mar 1:9–11), and began a ministry of preaching and healing. He promised eternal life to those who believed in him (Jhn 3:14–19). Four books of the Bible—Matthew, Mark, Luke, and John—report the story of his life, death on the cross, and resurrection. See *Christ, Messiah.*

Jew an Israelite, a descendant of Abraham through Jacob (Est 2:5; Dan 3:8). The term came from the name of the southern Israelite kingdom, Judah.

Jezebel evil Phoenician wife of King Ahab. She was responsible for replacing the worship of the Lord with the worship of Baal in the northern kingdom of Israel (1Ki 16:29–33; 21:25). She killed many of the Lord's prophets, and tried but failed to end the prophet Elijah's life (1Ki 18:4,13; 19:1–2). As Elijah foretold in prophecy; she was eaten by dogs (1Ki 21:23; 2Ki 9:30–37).

Joab cruel leader of David's army. He murdered Abner and Amasa (2Sm 3:26–27; 20:9–10). He killed David's son Absalom, ending Absalom's rebellion against his father (2Sm 18:14–15).

Joash ninth king of Judah, crowned when he was only seven years old. He repaired the temple under the guidance of Jehoiada the priest (2Ki 12). Sadly, when Jehoiada died, King Joash turned away from God (2Ch 24:15–27).

Job a rich man who "feared God, and stayed away from evil". (Job 1:1). God allowed him to suffer many disasters as a test of his righteousness. Through all he suffered, Job remained faithful to God. In the end, God ended his suffering and gave him "twice as much as he had before" (Job 42:10). His story is told in the book of Job.

Joel a prophet who described a great army that would attack Israel at the end of history. He foretold the coming of the Holy Spirit at Pentecost (Act 2:16–21). His words are recorded in the book of Joel.

John 1. John the Baptizer, son of Zechariah and Elizabeth (Luk 1:5–6). He "prepared the way" for Jesus, preaching in the desert about the need to repent (Luk 3:16–18). He baptized Jesus in the Jordan River (Mar 1:9–11). Herod Antipas arrested him and later put him to death (Mar 6:17–28); 2. one of the twelve apostles, the brother of James. He wrote the book of John, the letters of I John, II John, and III John, and the book of Revelation; 3. John Mark, see *Mark, John.*

Jonah a prophet called by God to preach to the people of Nineveh (Jon 1:1–3). He disobeyed God's command and fled. Thrown overboard during a storm, he was swallowed by a great fish and spent three days in its belly (Jon 1:15–17). Finally, he submitted to God and went to the city of Nineveh, where his preaching led the people to repent (Jon 3:3–4).

Jonathan son of King Saul and loyal friend of David (1Sm 13:16; 18:1). A daring warrior, he was killed in battle against the Philistines (1Sm 31:2).

Jordan a river that flows from the north of Palestine into the Sea of Galilee and then south to the Dead Sea (Num 13:29; Mat 3:5). God dried up the Jordan River so that

Joshua and the Israelites could enter the Promised Land (Jos 3:9–17). John the Baptizer baptized Jesus in its waters (Mat 3:13).

Joseph 1. son of Jacob who was sold into slavery by his jealous brothers (Gen 37); 2. the husband of Mary. He was Jesus' earthly father. He was a carpenter who lived in Nazareth (Mat 1:16–25; 2:21–23).

Joshua righteous son of Nun who was chosen to lead Israel after Moses died (Dtr 31). The book of Joshua tells the story of the Israelite conquest of Canaan under his command. Famous battles he won included the attack on Jericho (Jos 6), and the defeat of five Amorite kings on the day the sun stood still (Jos 10).

Josiah godly seventeenth king of Judah. After the Book of the Teachings was found in the temple, he led Judah to renewed dedication to the Lord (2Ki 22–23).

Jubilee, Year of every fiftieth year. No crops were to be planted and all family lands that were sold were returned to the original owner (Lev 25:8–55; Num 36:4).

Judah 1. one of the twelve tribes of Israel, whose members were descended from Jacob's fourth son (Gen 29:35; Jos 15:1–12). David and Jesus belonged to the tribe of Judah; 2. a name for the southern kingdom after the tribes of Judah and Benjamin separated from the northern ten tribes (1Ki 12:17–24).

Judaism the religious teachings and way of life of the Jewish people (Act 6:5; Tit 1:10).

Judas 1. one of the twelve apostles, possibly the same as Thaddeus (Act 1:13); 2. a brother of Jesus and author of the book of Jude (Mat 13:54–55); 3. Judas Iscariot, one of the twelve apostles. He betrayed Jesus for thirty pieces of silver, and then took his own life (Mat 26:14–25, 47–50; 27:3–10).

Judea in New Testament times, the name for the Jewish district around Jerusalem (Act 1:8; 2:9). It was part of the Roman Empire.

judge 1. to decide an issue of law or morality (Exo 18:13–26; 1Ch 23:4); 2. to punish or condemn (Rom 3:6; Heb 10:30); 3. leaders of the Israelites before the time of Israel's kings were called "judges." They were chosen by God to save the people from their enemies. The stories of the judges are told in the book of Judges.

judgment day the time at the end of history when God will judge people (Mat 10:15; 11:22–23). Those who believe God will be rewarded with eternal life in heaven. All others will be judged for their sins and sentenced to hell.

just fair; morally right (Isa 58:2; Mat 5:45).

justice fairness; righteousness (Exo 23:6; Psa 37:28; Heb 1:8).

K

kingdom of God, kingdom of heaven the reign of God over the earth and the lives of believers. By choosing to give God rulership of their lives, all who believe in Christ become part of this kingdom (Mat 5:3; 13).

Korah a Levite who led a rebellion against Moses and Aaron. The earth opened up and swallowed Korah and his followers (Num 16).

L

Laban brother of Rebekah and uncle of Jacob (Gen 24:29). He was the father of Leah and Rachel, Jacob's two wives (Gen 29:16). He was greedy and dishonest with Jacob, who served him for twenty years (Gen 29–31).

Lamb of God a name given to Jesus. In the Old Testament, a lamb was sacrificed on Passover for the sins of the people. Like a sacrificial lamb, Jesus gave his life on Passover to save people from their sins (Isa 53:7; Jhn 1:29).

lame unable to walk (Pro 26:7; Luk 5:17–26). Jesus healed many people who were lame.

law 1. God's rules and commandments to show people right from wrong (Gen 26:5; Rom 2:12); 2. the first five books of the Old Testament written by Moses (Rom 4:15).

Lazarus 1. brother of Martha and Mary who Jesus raised from the dead in Bethany (Jhn 11–12); 2. the poor man in a parable of Jesus (Luk 16:19–31).

Leah daughter of Laban and older sister of Rachel. She became Jacob's first wife after Laban tricked Jacob into marrying her (Gen 29–31).

legion a unit of 6,000 soldiers in the Roman army. The word is often used to mean any great number of people or things (Mat 26:53). The evil spirits Jesus cast out of one man called themselves *Legion* because there were so many of them (Mar 5:15).

Levi one of the twelve tribes of Israel, whose members were descended from the third son of Jacob and Leah (Gen 29:34; Num 3:6).

Leviathan a powerful sea monster used as a symbol of evil (Psa 74:14; Isa 27:1).

Levites members of the tribe of Levi. The Levites were set apart to serve God and care for the temple (Num 3:39–51). Levites descended from Aaron became priests of Israel (Num 18:1–7).

Life, Book of God's list of those who put their faith in Jesus. Only those whose names are written in the Book of Life will enter heaven (Rev 20:12; 21:27).

light that which makes things visible; the opposite of darkness. In the Bible, light is often used as a symbol for the goodness and truth of God. Jesus called himself "the light of the world" because he showed people the way to God (Jhn 8:12).

linen cloth made from the fibers of the flax plant (Jos 2:6; 1Ch 4:21).

locust a kind of grasshopper. In Bible lands, large swarms of locusts sometimes covered the land, destroying crops and causing famine (Exo 10:12–20; Joe 1).

lord 1. master, owner. A term of respect (Gen 45:8); 2. LORD—in Hebrew, *Yahweh*, the personal name of God, revealed when God spoke to Moses from the burning bush (Exo 3:15). The name means "I Am Who I Am."

Lot nephew of Abraham. He unwisely chose to settle in the wealthy but corrupt city of Sodom (Gen 13). After his capture by raiders, he was rescued by Abraham (Gen 14). Later, he was warned by two angels to leave Sodom just before the city was destroyed by God (Gen 19).

lots small stones or objects used to make choices, similar to drawing straws or throwing dice. In Bible times, they were sometimes used to find out God's will (Pro 16:33). Lots were used to divide up the land of Canaan among the tribes of Israel (Num 26:55; Jos 18:10).

love 1. deep affection (Jdg 16:4; 2Sm 13:4); 2. compassion, commitment, or devotion (Mat 5:44; Rom 13:10; 1Jn 3:11–23; 4:16). God's love for us is so great that he gave his only Son to die on the cross for our sins (Jhn 3:16).

Luke a doctor who worked as a missionary with Paul (Col 4:14; 2Ti 4:11; Phm 24). He wrote the books of Luke and Acts.

lunatic a person who is insane (2Ki 9:20; Jer 29:26).

lust a strong desire or intense longing (Eze 6:9; Mar 7:22).

lyre a stringed musical instrument similar to a small harp (1Sm 10:5). It was used in temple worship (1Ch 23:5; Psa 147:7).

M

majestic displaying the dignity or greatness of a king (Dtr 33:17, 26; 1Sm 26:17).

Malachi prophet who wrote the book of Malachi. He encouraged the Jews who returned to Judah from Babylon to remain loyal to God.

malice hatred; evil desire to see harm come to another (Lam 3:60).

Manasseh 1. one of the twelve tribes of Israel whose members were descended from the firstborn son of Joseph (Gen 48; Num 26:28–34). The tribe was given territory in northern Israel on both sides of the Jordan River (Jos 17:1–13); 2. evil fourteenth king of Judah, who sacrificed his son and practiced black magic (2Ch 33:1–9). After he was taken captive by the Assyrians, Manasseh repented and changed his ways (2Ch 33:10–20).

mandrake a plant related to the potato. It produced a small, yellow fruit that was thought to help a woman conceive a child (Gen 30:14–16).

manger an open box or trough in a stable used for feeding animals (Luk 2:16).

manna the food God provided for the Israelites in the wilderness after they left Egypt (Exo 16:31–35; Jhn 6:31). The sweet, white seed-like manna appeared every morning with the dew. The name the surprised Israelites gave the food means "what is it?"

Mark John Mark, the young cousin of Barnabas (Col 4:10). He went with Paul and Barnabas on their first missionary journey, but left them at Perga (Act 12:25). Later, Paul and Barnabas parted company over an argument about him (Act 15:37–39). Mark wrote the book of Mark, the story of Jesus' life as told to him by Peter.

marriage the joining together of a man and woman in a love relationship for life (Heb 13:4).

Martha sister of Mary and Lazarus (Luk 10:38–42; Jhn 11:1–44). They lived in Bethany and were close friends of Jesus.

Mary 1. the virgin who became the mother of Jesus (Mat 1–2; Luk 1–3; Jhn 19:25–27). She married Joseph and lived in Nazareth; 2. sister of Martha and Lazarus, the man Jesus raised from the dead (Jhn 11:1–44; 12:1–3); 3. Mary Magdalene. Jesus cast a demon out of her, and she became one of his disciples. Jesus appeared to her first after his resurrection from the dead (Mat 27:56, 61; Luk 8:2; Jhn 20:1, 11–18).

Matthew one of the twelve apostles, also known as Levi (Mar 2:13–14; Luk 5:27–28). He was a tax collector before Jesus called him to be an apostle (Mat 9:9–13; 10:3). He is believed to be the author of the book of Matthew.

mature grown up. A mature Christian is one who is spiritually grown up (Eph 4:13; Php 3:10–15; Jas 1:4). Christian maturity is shown by living a wise and godly life (Heb 5:14).

mediator one who settles a disagreement or restores a relationship between two people or groups. Jesus is the mediator between God and people (Job 9:33; 1Ti 2:5).

meditate to think about; to go over carefully in one's mind (Gen 24:63; 1Ch 16:9).

medium a person who claims to be able to talk to the spirits of the dead (Lev 20:6; Isa 8:19).

mercy undeserved love and kindness; help given out of love (Psa 106:1; Eph 2:4).

Messiah a Hebrew word meaning "anointed one." The title was given to the leader that Old Testament prophets said would come to save God's people (Mat 16:16; Jhn 4:25–26). See *Christ*.

Micah a prophet in the time of Isaiah who warned the people of Israel and Judah that God would judge their sins. He foretold that the Messiah would come from Bethlehem (Mic 5:1–5). His words are recorded in the book of Micah.

midwife a woman who helps with the birth of a baby (Gen 38:27–29; Exo 1:19–20).

millstone either of a pair of large flat stones between which grain was ground into flour (Isa 47:2). The lower stone was usually much larger. The upper stone was pushed back and forth with the hands.

ministry service offered to God or to other people; the use of spiritual gifts to serve others (Luk 3:23; 2Co 3:3–11).

miracle an amazing act or happening done through the power of God (Mar 9:39; Act 2:11, 19, 22).

Miriam a prophetess, the sister of Moses and Aaron (Exo 2; Num 12). She led the Israelites in praise after God parted the Red Sea (Exo 15).

missionary a Christian sent out to tell about Jesus to people in distant lands (Act 21:8). Christ called his disciples to be missionaries and to "make disciples of all nations" (Mat 28:19).

missions sending out of believers to share their faith in Jesus with people in other lands (Act 20:24).

mock to make fun of; to treat with contempt (Pro 9:12; Isa 28:11).

moneychanger a businessman who traded in different kinds of money. In Jesus' time, moneychangers in the temple exchanged many kinds of money for a type of coin used to pay temple taxes and buy animals to sacrifice. The moneychangers often cheated their customers. Jesus chased the moneychangers out of the temple because they turned God's house "into a gathering place for thieves" (Mat 21:13).

Mordecai cousin of Esther, who warned King Xerxes of a plot to take his life. The story of how Mordecai and Esther stopped Haman's plot to wipe out the Jewish people is told in the book of Esther.

mortal anything that must someday die (Psa 89:48; Rom 8:11; 1Co 15:53–54).

Moses humble hero of Israel, called by God to lead the Israelites out of Egypt to the promised land. God gave him the ten commandments at Mount Sinai (Exo 19–20). He instructed the people in the worship of the Lord (Lev 1–27). He was allowed to see Canaan but died without entering it (Dtr 34). Moses is believed to be the author of the first five books of the Bible.

mourn to openly show sorrow or grief following the loss of a loved one or time of disaster (Jer 6:26; 16:4–7; Mat 5:4).

myrrh the sap of a plant that was used to make perfume and incense (Mat 2:11; Jhn 19:39).

N

Nahum a prophet who predicted the destruction of Nineveh, capital of Assyria. His words are recorded in the book of Nahum.

Naomi Jewish mother-in-law of Ruth. When her husband and two sons died, she returned home from Moab. The story of how she guided Ruth into a marriage with a relative named Boaz is told in the book of Ruth.

Naphtali one of the twelve tribes of Israel whose members were descended from the sixth son of Jacob (Gen 30:8). The territory given to the tribe lay in northern Palestine, west of the Jordan River and Sea of Galilee (Jos 19:32–39; 1Ki 15:20).

Nathan a prophet who announced God's judgment on David for his sin with Bathsheba (2Sm 7, 12; 1Ki 1).

Nathanael one of the twelve disciples. Jesus called him a "true Israelite who is sincere" (Jhn 1:45–51). He is probably the same as Bartholomew (Mat 10:3).

Nazarene a person from the town of Nazareth. It became one of the names for the early Christians because Christ came from Nazareth (Act 24:5).

Nazirite a person who has taken a special vow of dedication to the Lord (Num 6:1–21). They were not allowed to cut their hair, drink wine, or go near a dead body. Samson is the Bible's most famous Nazirite (Jdg 13:1–5).

Nehemiah Jewish cupbearer to Artaxerxes who became governor of Jerusalem. He led the Jews in rebuilding the walls of Jerusalem after returning from exile. His words are recorded in the book of Nehemiah.

neighbor someone who lives nearby. The Old Testament law commanded the Israelites to "love your neighbor as yourself" (Lev 19:18). A neighbor was understood to mean any fellow Israelite. Jesus told the story of the Good Samaritan to show that all people should be treated as neighbors (Luk 10:25–37).

nettles thorny plants (Isa 34:13).

Nicodemus a Pharisee who spoke in secret with Jesus (Jhn 3; 7:50–52; 19:38–42). He became a disciple of Jesus and helped prepare Jesus' body for burial.

Nineveh chief city of Assyria, located on the bank of the Tigris River. Jonah the prophet announced God's judgment in the city, leading its people to repent (Jon 3). In 612 B.C., about a hundred years and fifty years after Jonah's time, the city was destroyed by the Babylonians and Medes. As foretold by Old Testament prophets, the city was left in ruins, never to be rebuilt (Nah 2:10, 13; Zep 2:13–15).

Noah son of Lamech (Gen 5:29–32). He was told by God to build a boat and fill it with every kind of animal. He obeyed God and saved his family from a flood that covered the earth (Gen 6–9). In the New Testament, he is one of the heroes of faith (Heb 11:7; 2Pe 2:5).

O

oasis a place that has water and plant life in the middle of a desert (Num 20:13, 24).

oath an unbreakable promise taken in the name of God (Num 30:2; Dtr 6:13; Heb 6:16–18).

Obadiah a prophet who foretold the destruction of Edom. His words are recorded in the book of Obadiah.

obey to do what you are told to do; to follow the commands or will of another (1Sm 15:22; Jhn 14:21–23). Christians owe obedience to parents (Eph 6:1), the government (Rom 13:1–2), and most of all to God (Act 5:29; 1Jn 2:3–5).

obligation a duty; something one is expected to do (Neh 10:32; Rom 1:14).

observe 1. to see, to watch (Psa 17:2; Luk 23:55); 2. to honor, to celebrate (Exo 12:25; Lev 19:3; Rom 14:6).

offense 1. a sin or crime (Dtr 19:15; Job 31:11); 2. something done that causes anger or hurt feelings (Mat 13:57).

offering 1. something given to God as an act of worship (Act 24:17); 2. the killing of an animal offered as a sacrifice to God (Num 29:16; Mar 12:33). See *sacrifice*.

offspring 1. a child or children; 2. the young born to an animal (Dtr 24:8). In the Bible, it often means a descendant (Isa 44:3).

omen a sign or happening believed to reveal what will occur in the future (Isa 20:3; Eze 21:21–22).

oppress to keep people down by cruel or unfair use of power (2Sm 7:10; Psa 9:9; Zec 7:10).

ordain, ordination to set apart to serve God in a specific way; to appoint as a religious leader (Exo 29:9, 29; 1Ti 4:14).

ordinance a law or command given by one in power (2Ch 33:8).

ox a bull. Oxen were often used in pairs for plowing, threshing grain, and pulling wagons (Num 7:3; 2Sm 24:24; 1Ki 19:19).

P

pagan a person who does not believe in God; an idol worshipper (2Ki 23:5; Zep 1:4).

papyrus a reedlike plant that grows in marshes. As a baby, Moses was put in a basket made from papyrus stems (Exo 2:3–5).

parable stories using nature, history, and everyday life. Jesus often spoke in parables. Often a person had to interpret a deeper meaning in order for the parable to make sense (Mat 13:18–23; 21:28–32; Luk 15:2–3).

paradise a beautiful, perfect place. Heaven is a paradise (Luk 23:43; 2Co 12:4; Rev 2:7).

paralyzed unable to move part or all of one's body. Jesus healed many who were paralyzed (Mat 9:2; Mar 2:3–10).

parched dried up or very thirsty (Psa 63:1; Isa 5:13).

pardon to forgive; to free a guilty person from punishment (Psa 32:1; Hos 11:7).

passions strong emotions or desires (Rom 1:26; Gal 5:24).

Passover see *festivals*.

patient willing to wait; able to remain calm and self-controlled at times of difficulty (Rom 12:12). God is patient with unbelievers and gives people time to turn to him for forgiveness (Rom 2:4; 1Ti 1:16; 2Pe 3:15). The Holy Spirit helps believers to be patient (Gal 5:22; Col 1:11).

Paul apostle who preached the Good News to non-Jews. Also known as Saul, he was a Pharisee and an enemy of the early Christians until he met Jesus on the road to Damascus. His amazing conversion story is told in Acts 9:4–28 and Acts 26:12–18. Acts 13–28 tells about his exciting missionary journeys, his arrest in Jerusalem, and his trip to Rome to stand trial. Paul's letters make up about one fourth of the New Testament.

Phoenician a person born in Phoenicia (Mar 7:26). Phoenicia was located near the Mediterranean Sea mostly where Lebanon is today.

peace 1. freedom from war or trouble between people (Rom 5:1; Heb 12:14); 2. an inner calm given by God (Jhn 14:27; Col 3:12–15; Php 4:7).

Pentecost a Jewish festival held fifty days after Passover (the word *Pentecost* is Greek for "fiftieth"). The Holy Spirit came upon Christ's followers on the day of Pentecost (Act 2:1–4). See *festivals*.

perfect 1. complete and without flaw (Eph 1:4; Jas 3:2); 2. completely mature (Mat 5:48).

persecute to continually mistreat and show hatred for a person or a group (Hos 8:3). The early Christians were persecuted for their belief in Jesus (Mat 5:11; Rom 12:14).

pervert to use something in a way it was not meant to be used; to turn away from what is right or good (Dtr 16:19; Jdg 20:6; Hab1:4).

perversion immoral and unnatural sexual behavior (Rom 1:24–27; Eph 4:19).

pestilence widespread disease; a plague (Dtr 32:24).

Peter fisherman who became one of the twelve apostles (Mat 4:18–20), also known as Simon. His brother Andrew was also an apostle. He denied Jesus three times, as Jesus said he would (Mat 26:69–75). After the resurrection, Jesus forgave him (Jhn 21:15–25). He became a bold leader of the church in Jerusalem (Act 2). Acts 10 tells the story of a vision he received from God telling him to share the Good News with a non-Jew named Cornelius. This event showed that God had accepted non-Jews as believers (Act 11:18). He is the author of 1 and 2 Peter.

Pharaoh title of the rulers of Egypt (Gen 45:16–17).

Pharisees a small group of religious Jews who were very careful to follow the laws of God. They also followed many laws that they had made (Mar 7:1–13). Many Pharisees became enemies of Jesus and plotted his death (Mat 12:12–14). After Jesus rose from the dead, some Pharisees became Christians (Act 15:5).

Philip 1. one of the twelve apostles. He came from the same town as Peter and Andrew (Jhn 1:43–48); 2. one of the seven deacons of the Jerusalem church (Act 6:5). He became an important missionary to the Samaritans and non-Jews (Act 8:4–13, 26–40; 21:8–9).

Philistines sea people who settled along the coast of Canaan. They were Israel's chief enemy in the time of Samson (Jdg 3:31). As a boy, David defeated a Philistine giant named Goliath (1Sm 17). As king, David conquered the Philistines (1Ch 18:1–17).

Pilate Roman governor of Juda from A.D. 26–36. He gave in to the Jewish leaders and sentenced Jesus to die on the cross (Mat 27; Luk 23; Jhn 18:29–19:38).

plague terrible and widespread disease or disaster (Rev 6:8). God sent ten plagues against Egypt to free the Israelites from slavery (Exo 7:14–12:36).